ALGEBRA

Exponents and Radicals

$x^a x^b = x^{a+b}$ $\quad \dfrac{x^a}{x^b} = x^{a-b}$ $\quad x^{-a} = \dfrac{1}{x^a}$ $\quad (x^a)^b = x^{ab}$ $\quad \left(\dfrac{x}{y}\right)^a = \dfrac{x^a}{y^a}$

$x^{1/n} = \sqrt[n]{x}$ $\quad x^{m/n} = \sqrt[n]{x^m} = \left(\sqrt[n]{x}\right)^m$ $\quad \sqrt[n]{xy} = \sqrt[n]{x}\sqrt[n]{y}$ $\quad \sqrt[n]{x/y} = \sqrt[n]{x}/\sqrt[n]{y}$

Factoring Formulas

$a^2 - b^2 = (a - b)(a + b)$ $\qquad a^2 + b^2$ does not factor over real numbers

$a^3 - b^3 = (a - b)(a^2 + ab + b^2)$ $\qquad a^3 + b^3 = (a + b)(a^2 - ab + b^2)$

$a^n - b^n = (a - b)(a^{n-1} + a^{n-2}b + a^{n-3}b^2 + \cdots + ab^{n-2} + b^{n-1})$

Binomials

$(a \pm b)^2 = a^2 \pm 2ab + b^2$ $\qquad (a \pm b)^3 = a^3 \pm 3a^2b + 3ab^2 \pm b^3$

Binomial Theorem

$$(a + b)^n = a^n + \binom{n}{1}a^{n-1}b + \binom{n}{2}a^{n-2}b^2 + \cdots + \binom{n}{n-1}ab^{n-1} + b^n,$$

where $\displaystyle\binom{n}{k} = \frac{n(n-1)(n-2)\cdots(n-k+1)}{k(k-1)(k-2)\cdots 3\cdot 2\cdot 1} = \frac{n!}{k!(n-k)!}$

Quadratic Formula

The solutions of $ax^2 + bx + c = 0$ are $x = \dfrac{-b \pm \sqrt{b^2 - 4ac}}{2a}$

GEOMETRY

Parallelogram

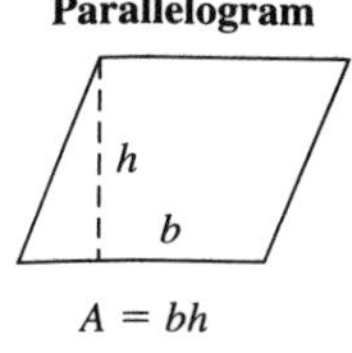

$A = bh$

Triangle

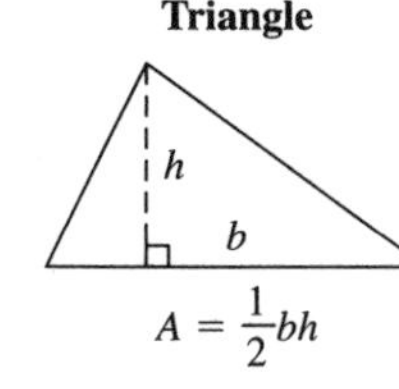

$A = \frac{1}{2}bh$

Trapezoid

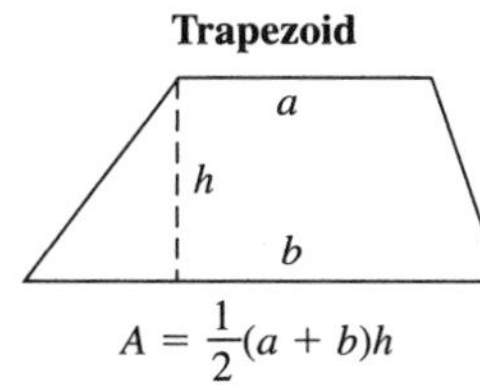

$A = \frac{1}{2}(a + b)h$

Circle

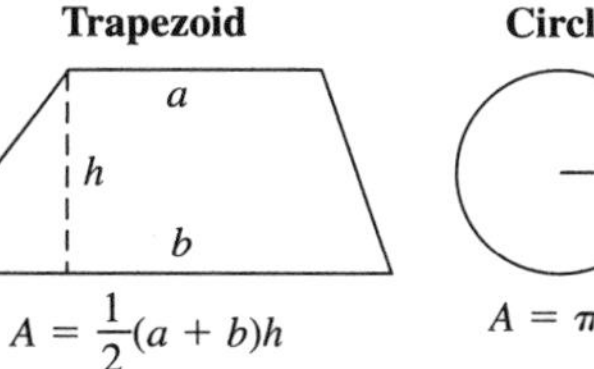

$A = \pi r^2$

$C = 2\pi r$

Sector

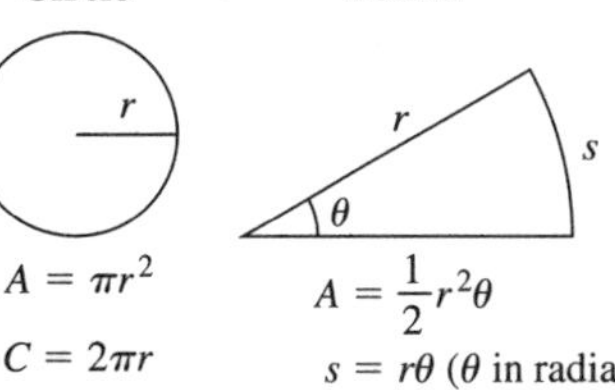

$A = \frac{1}{2}r^2\theta$

$s = r\theta$ (θ in radians)

Cylinder

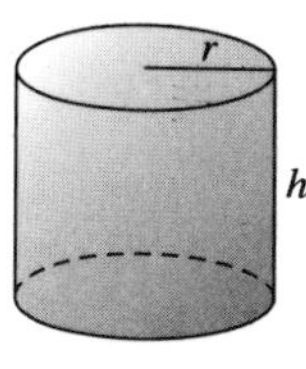

$V = \pi r^2 h$

$S = 2\pi rh$

(lateral surface area)

Cone

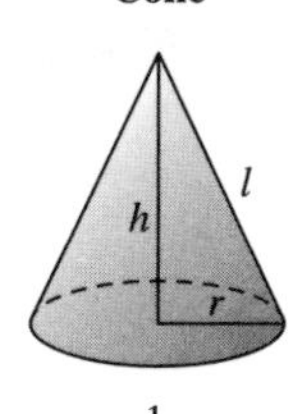

$V = \frac{1}{3}\pi r^2 h$

$S = \pi rl$

(lateral surface area)

Sphere

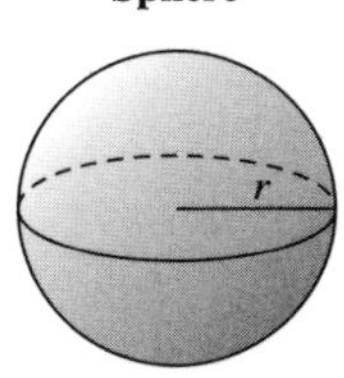

$V = \frac{4}{3}\pi r^3$

$S = 4\pi r^2$

Equations of Lines and Circles

$m = \dfrac{y_2 - y_1}{x_2 - x_1}$	slope of line through (x_1, y_1) and (x_2, y_2)
$y - y_1 = m(x - x_1)$	point-slope form of line through (x_1, y_1) with slope m
$y = mx + b$	slope-intercept form of line with slope m and y-intercept $(0, b)$
$(x - h)^2 + (y - k)^2 = r^2$	circle of radius r with center (h, k)

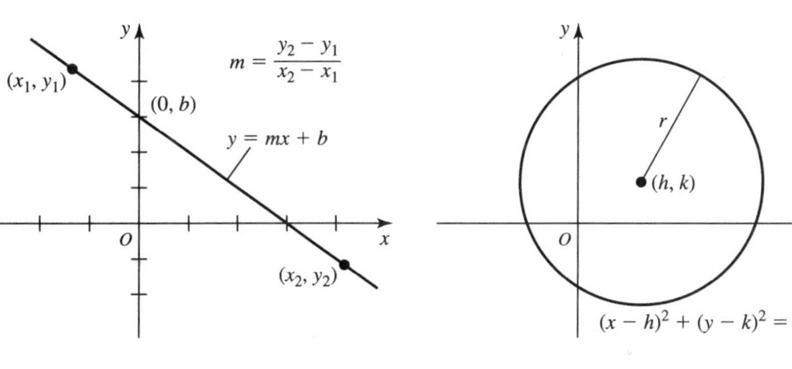

TRIGONOMETRY

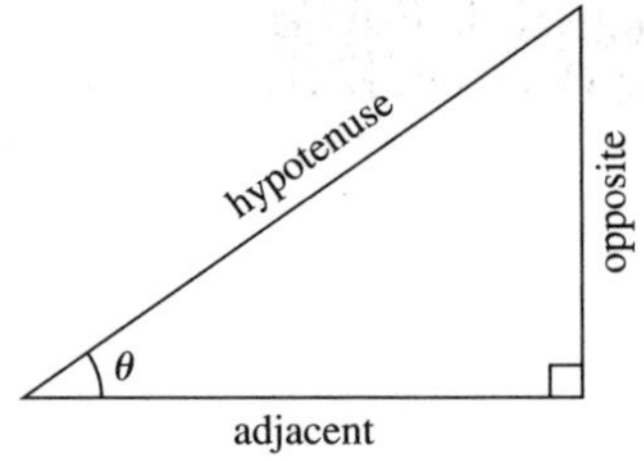

$$\cos\theta = \frac{\text{adj}}{\text{hyp}} \quad \sin\theta = \frac{\text{opp}}{\text{hyp}} \quad \tan\theta = \frac{\text{opp}}{\text{adj}}$$

$$\sec\theta = \frac{\text{hyp}}{\text{adj}} \quad \csc\theta = \frac{\text{hyp}}{\text{opp}} \quad \cot\theta = \frac{\text{adj}}{\text{opp}}$$

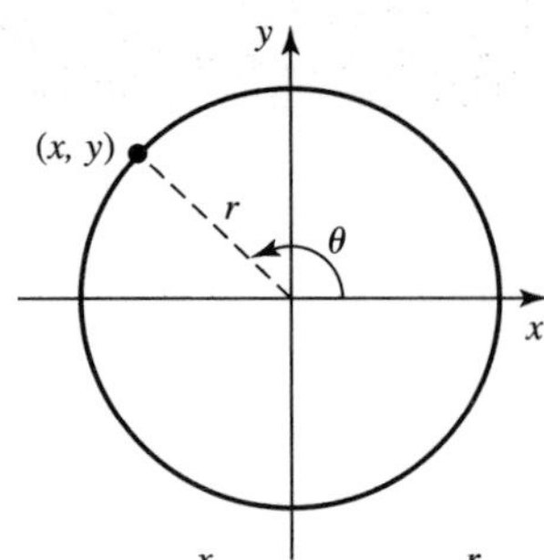

$$\cos\theta = \frac{x}{r} \quad \sec\theta = \frac{r}{x}$$

$$\sin\theta = \frac{y}{r} \quad \csc\theta = \frac{r}{y}$$

$$\tan\theta = \frac{y}{x} \quad \cot\theta = \frac{x}{y}$$

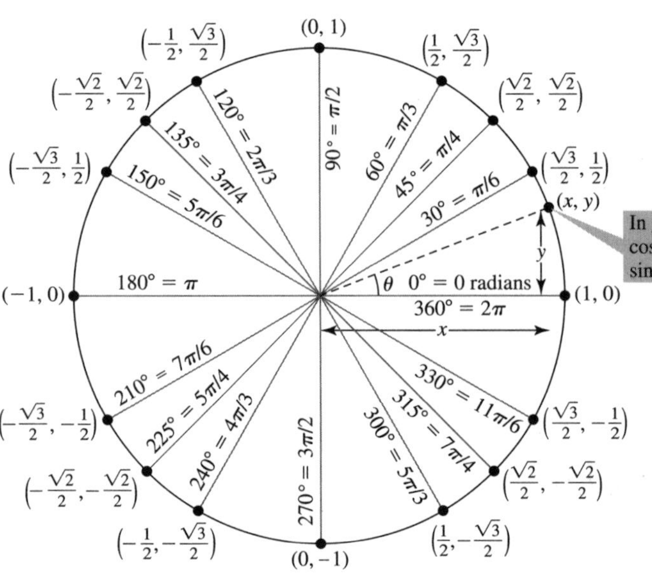

Reciprocal Identities

$$\tan\theta = \frac{\sin\theta}{\cos\theta} \quad \cot\theta = \frac{\cos\theta}{\sin\theta} \quad \sec\theta = \frac{1}{\cos\theta} \quad \csc\theta = \frac{1}{\sin\theta}$$

Pythagorean Identities

$$\sin^2\theta + \cos^2\theta = 1 \quad \tan^2\theta + 1 = \sec^2\theta \quad 1 + \cot^2\theta = \csc^2\theta$$

Sign Identities

$$\sin(-\theta) = -\sin\theta \quad \cos(-\theta) = \cos\theta \quad \tan(-\theta) = -\tan\theta$$

$$\csc(-\theta) = -\csc\theta \quad \sec(-\theta) = \sec\theta \quad \cot(-\theta) = -\cot\theta$$

Addition Formulas

$$\sin(\alpha + \beta) = \sin\alpha\cos\beta + \cos\alpha\sin\beta \qquad \sin(\alpha - \beta) = \sin\alpha\cos\beta - \cos\alpha\sin\beta$$

$$\cos(\alpha + \beta) = \cos\alpha\cos\beta - \sin\alpha\sin\beta \qquad \cos(\alpha - \beta) = \cos\alpha\cos\beta + \sin\alpha\sin\beta$$

$$\tan(\alpha + \beta) = \frac{\tan\alpha + \tan\beta}{1 - \tan\alpha\tan\beta} \qquad \tan(\alpha - \beta) = \frac{\tan\alpha - \tan\beta}{1 + \tan\alpha\tan\beta}$$

Double-Angle Identities

$$\sin 2\theta = 2\sin\theta\cos\theta \qquad \cos 2\theta = \cos^2\theta - \sin^2\theta$$

$$= 2\cos^2\theta - 1$$

$$\tan 2\theta = \frac{2\tan\theta}{1 - \tan^2\theta} \qquad = 1 - 2\sin^2\theta$$

Half-Angle Formulas

$$\cos^2\theta = \frac{1 + \cos 2\theta}{2} \qquad \sin^2\theta = \frac{1 - \cos 2\theta}{2}$$

Graphs of Trigonometric Functions and Their Inverses

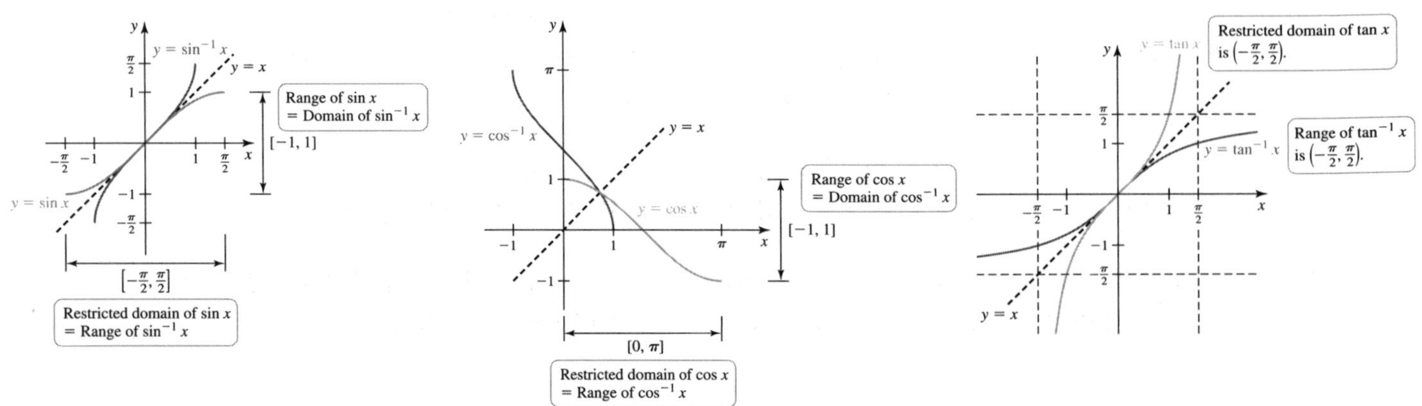

PEARSON ALWAYS LEARNING

Calculus

Fifth Custom Edition

Taken from:
Calculus
by William Briggs and Lyle Cochran

Thomas' Calculus, Twelfth Edition
by George B. Thomas, Jr., Maurice D. Weir, and Joel Hass

Thomas' Calculus, Media Upgrade Eleventh Edition
by George B. Thomas, Jr., Maurice D. Weir, Joel Hass, and Frank R. Giordano

Technical Calculus, Fifth Edition
by Dale Ewen, Joan S. Gary, and James E. Trefzger

Student Solutions Manual to Accompany Technical Calculus, Fifth Edition
by Dale Ewen, Joan S. Gary, and James E. Trefzger

Taken from:

Calculus
by William Briggs and Lyle Cochran
Copyright © 2011 by Pearson Education, Inc.
Published by Addison-Wesley
Boston, Massachusetts 02116

Thomas' Calculus, Twelfth Edition
by George B. Thomas, Jr., Maurice D. Weir, and Joel Hass
Copyright © 2010, 2005, 2001 by Pearson Education, Inc.
Published by Addison-Wesley

Thomas' Calculus, Media Upgrade, Eleventh Edition
by George B. Thomas, Jr., Maurice D. Weir, Joel Hass, and Frank R. Giordano
Copyright © 2008 by Pearson Education, Inc.
Published by Addison-Wesley

Technical Calculus, Fifth Edition
by Dale Ewen, Joan S. Gary, and James E. Trefzger
Copyright 2005, 2002, 1998, 1986, 1977 by Pearson Education, Inc.
Published by Pearson, Prentice Hall
Upper Saddle River, New Jersey 07458

Student Solutions Manual to Accompany Technical Calculus, Fifth Edition
by Dale Ewen, Joan S. Gary, and James E. Trefzger
Copyright 2005, 2002, 1998, 1986, 1977 by Pearson Education, Inc.
Published by Pearson, Prentice Hall
Upper Saddle River, New Jersey 07458

This special edition published in cooperation with Pearson Learning Solutions.

Pearson Learning Solutions, 501 Boylston Street, Suite 900, Boston, MA 02116
A Pearson Education Company
www.pearsoned.com

Printed in the United States of America

1 2 3 4 5 6 7 8 9 10 V357 18 17 16 15 14 13

000200010271749907

CW/OP

ISBN 10: 1-269-14649-1
ISBN 13: 978-1-269-14649-4

Contents

9 Sequences and Infinite Series 515

10 Power Series 578

11 Parametric and Polar Curves 623

12 Vectors and Vector-Valued Functions 669

13 Functions of Several Variables 763

Preface

This textbook supports a three-semester or four-quarter calculus sequence typically taken by students in mathematics, engineering, and the natural sciences. Our approach is based on many years of teaching calculus at diverse institutions using the best teaching practices we know.

Throughout the book, a concise and lively narrative motivates the ideas of calculus. Reviewers and class testers have consistently told us that the book mirrors the course they teach. Equally important, we believe that students will actually read the book. Topics are introduced through concrete examples, applications, and analogies rather than through abstract arguments. We appeal to students' intuition and geometric instincts to make calculus natural and believable. Once this intuitive foundation is established, generalizations and abstractions follow. We include informative proofs in the text, but less transparent proofs appear at the end of the sections or in Appendix B.

Pedagogical Features

Exercises

The exercises at the end of each section are one of the strongest features of the text. They are graded, varied, and original. In addition, they are labeled and carefully organized into groups.

- Each exercise set begins with *Review Questions* that check students' conceptual understanding of the essential ideas from the section.
- *Basic Skills* exercises are confidence-building problems that provide a solid foundation for the more challenging exercises to follow. Each example in the narrative is linked directly to a block of *Basic Skills* exercises via *Related Exercises* references at the end of the example solution.
- *Further Explorations* exercises expand on the *Basic Skills* exercises by challenging students to think creatively and to generalize newly acquired skills.
- *Applications* exercises connect skills developed in previous exercises to applications and modeling problems that demonstrate the power and utility of calculus.
- *Additional Exercises* are generally the most difficult and challenging problems; they include proofs of results cited in the narrative.

Each chapter concludes with a comprehensive set of *Review Exercises*.

Figures

Given the power of graphics software and the ease with which many students assimilate visual images, we devoted considerable time and deliberation to the figures in this book. Whenever possible, we let the figures communicate essential ideas using annotations

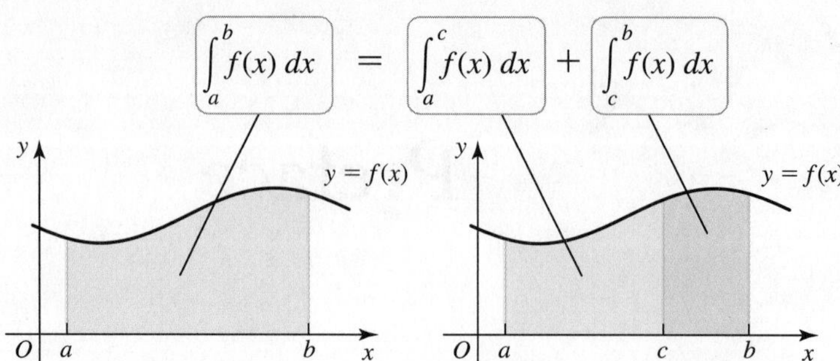

FIGURE 5.29

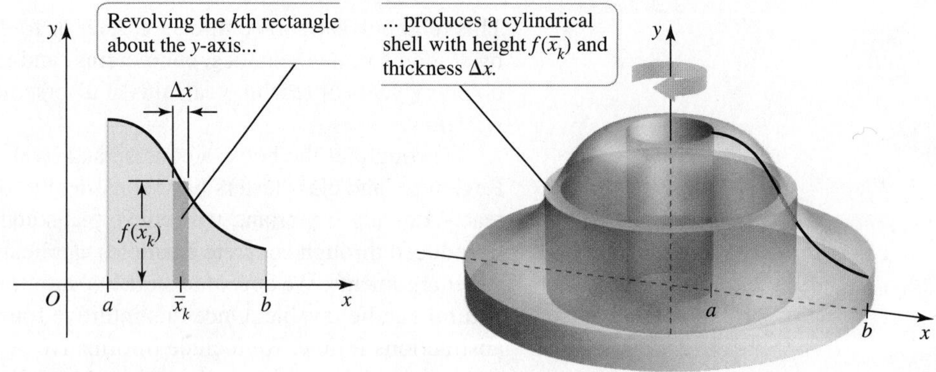

FIGURE 6.37

reminiscent of an instructor's voice at the board. Readers will quickly find that the figures facilitate learning in new ways.

Quick Check and *Margin Notes*

The narrative is interspersed with *Quick Check* questions that encourage students to read with pencil in hand and that resemble the kinds of questions instructors pose in class. Answers to the *Quick Check* questions are found at the end of the section in which they occur. *Margin Notes* offer reminders, provide insight, and clarify technical points.

Guided Projects

The *Instructor's Resource Guide and Test Bank* contains 78 *Guided Projects*. These projects allow students to work in a directed, step-by-step fashion, with various objectives: to carry out extended calculations, to derive physical models, to explore related theoretical topics, or to investigate new applications of calculus. The *Guided Projects* vividly demonstrate the breadth of calculus and provide a wealth of mathematical excursions that go beyond the typical classroom experience. A list of suggested *Guided Projects* is included at the end of each chapter.

Technology

We believe that a calculus text should help students strengthen their analytical skills *and* demonstrate how technology can extend (not replace) those skills. The exercises and examples in this text emphasize this balance. Calculators and graphing utilities are additional tools in the kit, and students must learn when and when not to use them. Our goal is to accommodate the different policies about technology that various instructors may use.

Throughout the book, exercises marked with T indicate that the use of technology—ranging from plotting a function with a graphing utility to carrying out a calculation using a computer algebra system—may be needed.

Interactive Figures

The textbook is supported by a groundbreaking electronic book, created by Eric Schulz of Walla Walla Community College. This "live book" contains the complete text of the print book plus interactive animated versions of approximately 700 figures. Instructors can use these animations in the classroom to illustrate the important ideas of calculus, and students can explore the interactive animations while they are reading the textbook. In each case, these animations will help build students' geometric intuition of calculus. Available only within MyMathLab, the eBook provides instructors with powerful new teaching tools that expand and enrich the learning experience for students.

Content Highlights

In writing this text, we identified content in the calculus curriculum that consistently presents challenges to our students. We made organizational changes to the standard presentation of these topics or slowed the pace of the narrative to facilitate students' comprehension of material that is traditionally difficult. Two noteworthy modifications appear in the material for Calculus II and Calculus III, as outlined below.

Often appearing near the end of the term, the topics of sequences and series are the most challenging in Calculus II. By splitting this material into two chapters, we have given these topics a more deliberate pace and made them more accessible without adding significantly to the length of the narrative.

There *is* a clear and logical path through multivariate calculus, which is not apparent in many textbooks. We have carefully separated functions of several variables from vector-valued functions, so that these ideas are distinct in the minds of students. The book culminates when these two threads are joined in the last chapter, which is devoted to vector calculus.

Accuracy Assurance

One of the challenges we face with a first edition is ensuring the book meets the high standards of accuracy that instructors expect. More than 200 mathematicians reviewed the manuscript for accuracy, level of difficulty, and effective pedagogy. Additionally, nearly 1000 students participated in class-testing this book before publication. A team of mathematicians carefully examined each example, exercise, and figure in multiple rounds of editing, proofreading, and accuracy checking. From the beginning and throughout development, our goal has been to craft a textbook that is mathematically precise and pedagogically sound.

Text Versions

Calculus

Complete (Chapters 1–15) ISBN 0-321-33611-9 | 978-0-321-33611-8
Single Variable Calculus (Chapters 1–11) ISBN 0-321-66407-8 | 978-0-321-66407-5
Multivariable Calculus (Chapters 9–15) ISBN 0-321-66415-9 | 978-0-321-66415-0

Calculus: Early Transcendentals

Complete (Chapters 1–14) ISBN 0-321-57056-1 | 978-0-321-57056-7
Single Variable Calculus (Chapters 1–10) ISBN 0-321-66414-0 | 978-0-321-66414-3
Multivariable Calculus (Chapters 8–14) ISBN 0-321-66415-9 | 978-0-321-66415-0

Print Supplements

Instructor's Resource Guide and Test Bank

0-321-66526-0 | 978-0-321-66526-3
Bernard Gillett, University of Colorado at Boulder
Anthony Tongen, James Madison University

This guide represents significant contributions by the textbook authors and contains a variety of classroom support materials for instructors.

- Seventy-eight *Guided Projects*, correlated to specific chapters of the text, can be assigned to students for individual or group work. The *Guided Projects* vividly demonstrate the breadth of calculus and provide a wealth of mathematical excursions that go beyond the typical classroom experience.
- *Lecture Support Notes* give an *Overview* of the material to be taught in each section of the text, helpful classroom *Teaching Tips*, and a list of the *Interactive Figures* from the eBook. *Connections* among various sections of the text are also pointed out, and *Additional Activities* are provided.
- *Quick Quizzes* for each section in the text consist of multiple-choice questions that can be used as in-class quiz material or as Active Learning Questions.
- *Chapter Reviews* provide a list of key concepts from each chapter, followed by a set of chapter review questions.
- *Chapter Test Banks* consist of between 25 and 30 questions that can be used for in-class exams, take-home exams, or additional review material.
- *Student Study Cards*, consisting of key concepts for both single variable and multivariable Calculus, are included for instructors to photocopy and distribute to their students as convenient study tools.
- *Answers* are provided at the back of the manual for all exercises in the manual, including the *Guided Projects*.

Instructor's Solutions Manuals

Mark Woodard, Furman University
Single Variable Calculus (Chapters 1–11) ISBN 0-321-65400-5 | 978-0-321-65400-7
Multivariable Calculus (Chapters 9–15) ISBN 0-321-66405-1 | 978-0-321-66405-1

The *Instructor's Solutions Manual* contains complete solutions to all the exercises in the text.

Student's Solutions Manuals

Mark Woodard, Furman University
Single Variable Calculus (Chapters 1–11) ISBN 0-321-66521-X | 978-0-321-66521-8
Multivariable Calculus (Chapters 9–15) ISBN 0-321-66411-6 | 978-0-321-66411-2

The *Student's Solutions Manual* is designed for the student and contains complete solutions to all the odd-numbered exercises in the text.

Just-in-Time Algebra and Trigonometry for Calculus, Third Edition

ISBN 0-321-26943-8 | 978-0-321-26943-0
Guntram Mueller and Ronald I. Brent, University of Massachusetts—Lowell

Sharp algebra and trigonometry skills are critical to mastering calculus, and *Just-in-Time Algebra and Trigonometry for Calculus* is designed to bolster these skills while students study calculus. As students make their way through calculus, this text is with them every step of the way, showing them the necessary algebra or trigonometry topics and pointing out potential problem spots. The easy-to-use table of contents has algebra and trigonometry topics arranged in the order in which students will need them as they study calculus.

Media and Online Supplements

Technology Resource Manuals

Maple Manual by James Stapleton, North Carolina State University
Mathematica Manual by Marie Vanisko, Carroll College
TI-Graphing Calculator Manual by Elaine McDonald-Newman, Sonoma State University, and Luz De Alba, Drake University

These manuals cover Maple™ 13, Mathematica® 7, and the TI-83 Plus/TI-84 Plus and TI-89, respectively. Each manual provides detailed guidance for integrating a specific software package or graphing calculator throughout the course, including syntax and commands. These manuals are available to instructors and students through the Pearson Math and Stats Resources page, **www.pearsonhighered.com/mathstatsresources**, and MyMathLab®.

MyMathLab® Online Course (access code required)

MyMathLab is a text-specific, easily customizable online course that integrates interactive multimedia instruction with textbook content. MyMathLab gives you the tools you need to deliver all or a portion of your course online, whether your students are in a lab setting or working from home.

- **eBook featuring Interactive Figures** that can be manipulated to illuminate difficult-to-convey concepts. Instructors can use these animations in the classroom to illustrate the important ideas of calculus, and students can try out the interactive animations while they are using MyMathLab. In each case, these animations help build geometric intuition of calculus.
- **Interactive homework exercises,** correlated to your textbook at the objective level, are algorithmically generated for unlimited practice and mastery. Most exercises are free response and provide guided solutions, sample problems, and tutorial learning aids for extra help.
- **"Getting Ready" chapter** includes hundreds of exercises that address prerequisite skills in algebra and trigonometry. Each student can receive remediation for those skills with which he or she needs help.
- **Personalized Study Plan,** generated when students complete a test or quiz, indicates which topics have been mastered and links to tutorial exercises for topics students have not mastered. You can customize the Study Plan so that the topics available match your course content, or so that students' homework results also determine mastery.
- **Multimedia learning aids,** such as video lectures, Java applets, animations, and a complete interactive eBook, help students independently improve their understanding and performance. You can assign these multimedia learning aids as homework to help your students grasp the concepts.
- **Homework and Test Manager** lets you assign homework, quizzes, and tests that are automatically graded. Select just the right mix of questions from the MyMathLab exercise bank, instructor-created custom exercises, and/or TestGen® test items.
- **Gradebook,** designed specifically for mathematics and statistics, automatically tracks students' results, lets instructors stay on top of student performance, and gives them

control over how to calculate final grades. You can also add offline (paper-and-pencil) grades to the gradebook.

- **MathXL® Exercise Builder** allows you to create static and algorithmic exercises for your online assignments. You can use the library of sample exercises as an easy starting point, or you can edit any course-related exercise.
- **Pearson Tutor Center (www.pearsontutorservices.com)** access is automatically included with MyMathLab. The Tutor Center is staffed by qualified math instructors who provide textbook-specific tutoring for students via toll-free phone, fax, email, and interactive Web sessions.

Students do their assignments in the Flash®-based MathXL Player, which is compatible with almost any browser (Firefox®, Safari™, or Internet Explorer®) on almost any platform (Macintosh® or Windows®). MyMathLab is powered by CourseCompass™, Pearson Education's online teaching and learning environment, and by MathXL, our online homework, tutorial, and assessment system. MyMathLab is available to qualified adopters. For more information, visit **www.mymathlab.com** or contact your Pearson representative.

MathXL® Online Course (access code required)

MathXL is an online homework, tutorial, and assessment system that accompanies Pearson's textbooks in mathematics or statistics.

- **Interactive homework exercises,** correlated to your textbook at the objective level, are algorithmically generated for unlimited practice and mastery. Most exercises are free response and provide guided solutions, sample problems, and learning aids for extra help.
- **"Getting Ready" chapter** includes hundreds of exercises that address prerequisite skills in algebra and trigonometry. Each student can receive remediation for those skills with which he or she needs help.
- **Personalized Study Plan,** generated when students complete a test, quiz, or homework, indicates which topics have been mastered and links to tutorial exercises for topics students have not mastered. Instructors can customize the available topics in the study plan to match their course concepts.
- **Multimedia learning aids,** such as video lectures, Java applets, and animations, help students independently improve their understanding and performance. These are assignable as homework, to further encourage their use.
- **Gradebook,** designed specifically for mathematics and statistics, automatically tracks students' results, lets you stay on top of student performance, and gives you control over how to calculate final grades.
- **MathXL Exercise Builder** allows you to create static and algorithmic exercises for your online assignments. You can use the library of sample exercises as an easy starting point or use the Exercise Builder to edit any of the course-related exercises.
- **Homework and Test Manager** lets you create online homework, quizzes, and tests that are automatically graded. Select just the right mix of questions from the MathXL exercise bank, instructor-created custom exercises, and/or TestGen test items.

The new, Flash®-based MathXL Player is compatible with almost any browser (Firefox®, Safari™, or Internet Explorer®) on almost any platform (Macintosh® or Windows®). MathXL is available to qualified adopters. For more information, visit our website at **www.mathxl.com**, or contact your Pearson representative.

TestGen®

TestGen (**www.pearsoned.com/testgen**) enables instructors to build, edit, print, and administer tests using a computerized bank of questions developed to cover all the objectives of the text. TestGen is algorithmically based, allowing instructors to create multiple but equivalent versions of the same question or test with the click of a button. Instructors can also modify test bank questions or add new questions.The software and test bank are available for download from Pearson Education's online catalog.

Video Lectures With Optional Captioning

The Video Lectures With Optional Captioning feature an engaging team of mathematics instructors who present comprehensive coverage of topics in the text. The lecturers' presentations include illustrative examples and exercises and support an approach that emphasizes visualization and problem solving. Available only through MyMathLab and MathXL.

PowerPoint® Lecture Slides

These PowerPoint slides contain key concepts, definitions, figures, and tables from the textbook. These files are available to qualified instructors through the Pearson Instructor Resource Center, **www.pearsonhighered/irc**, and MyMathLab.

Acknowledgments

We would like to express our thanks to the people who made many valuable contributions to this edition as it evolved through its many stages:

Development Editors

Elka Block
David Chelton
Roberta Lewis
Frank Purcell

Accuracy Checkers

Greg Friedman
Robert Pierce
Thomas Polaski
John Sammons
Joan Saniuk
Marie Vanisko
Diana Watson
Thomas Wegleitner
Roman Zadov

Reviewers, Class Testers, Focus Group Participants

Mary Kay Abbey, *Montgomery College*
J. Michael Albanese, *Central Piedmont Community College*
Michael R. Allen, *Tennessee Technological University*
Dale Alspach, *Oklahoma State University*
Alvina J. Atkinson, *Georgia Gwinnett College*
Richard Avery, *Dakota State University*
Rebecca L. Baranowski, *Estrella Mountain Community College*
Cathy Bonan-Hamada, *Mesa State College*
Michael J. Bonanno, *Suffolk County Community College*
Lynette Boos, *Trinity College*
Nathan A. Borchelt, *Clayton State University*
Mario B. Borha, *Moraine Valley Community College*
Michael R. Brewer, *California University of Pennsylvania*
Paul W. Britt, *Louisiana State University*
Tim Britt, *Jackson State Community College*
David E. Brown, *Utah State University*
Kirby Bunas, *Santa Rosa Junior College*

Chris K. Caldwell, *University of Tennessee at Martin*

Elizabeth Carrico, *Illinois Central College*

Tim Chappell, *Penn Valley Community College*

Karin Chess, *Owensboro Community & Technical College*

Ray E. Collings, *Georgia Perimeter College*

Carlos C. Corona, *San Antonio College*

Kyle Costello, *Salt Lake Community College*

Robert D. Crise, Jr., *Crafton Hills College*

Randall Crist, *Creighton University*

Joseph W. Crowley, *Community College of Rhode Island*

Patrick Cureton, *Hillsborough Community College*

Alberto L. Delgado, *Bradley University*

Amy Del Medico, *Waubonsee Community College*

Alicia Serfaty deMarkus, *Miami Dade College*

Joseph Dennin, *Fairfield University*

Emmett C. Dennis, *Southern Connecticut State University*

Andrzej Derdzinski, *Ohio State University*

Nirmal Devi, *Embry Riddle Aeronautical University*

Gary DeYoung, *Dordt College*

David E. Dobbs, *University of Tennessee*

Dr. Alvio Dominguez, *Miami-Dade College (Wolfson Campus)*

Christopher Donnelly, *Macomb Community College*

Anne M. Dougherty, *University of Colorado, Boulder*

Paul Drelles, *West Shore Community College*

Jerrett Dumouchel, *Florida State College at Jacksonville*

Sean Ellermeyer, *Kennesaw State University*

Dr. Amy H. Erickson, *Georgia Gwinnett College*

Robert Farinelli, *College of Southern Maryland*

Judith H. Fethe, *Pellissippi State Technical Community College*

Elaine B. Fitt, *Bucks County Community College*

Walden Freedman, *Humboldt State University*

Greg Friedman, *Texas Christian University*

Randy Gallaher, *Lewis & Clark Community College*

Javier Garza, *Tarleton State University*

Jürgen Gerlach, *Radford University*

Homa Ghaussi-Mujtaba, *Lansing Community College*

Tilmann Glimm, *Western Washington University*

Marvin Glover, *Milligan College*

Belarmino Gonzalez, *Miami-Dade College (Wolfson Campus)*

David Gove, *California State University, Bakersfield*

Phil Gustafson, *Mesa State College*

Aliakbar Montazer Haghighi, *Prairie View A&M University*

Mike Hall, *Arkansas State University*

Donnie Hallstone, *Green River Community College*

Sami Hamid, *University of North Florida*

Don L. Hancock, *Pepperdine University*

Keven Hansen, *Southwestern Illinois College*

David Hartenstine, *Western Washington University*

Kevin Hartshorn, *Moravian College*

Robert H. Hoar, *University of Wisconsin—LaCrosse*

Richard Hobbs, *Mission College*

Leslie Bolinger Horton, *Quinsigamond Community College*

Costel Ionita, *Dixie State College*

Stanislav Jabuka, *University of Nevada, Reno*

Mic Jackson, *Earlham College*

Tony Jenkins, *Northwestern Michigan College*

Jennifer Johnson-Leung, *University of Idaho*

Jack Keating, *Massasoit Community College*

Robert Keller, *Loras College*

Dan Kemp, *South Dakota State University*

Leonid Khazanov, *Borough of Manhattan Community College*

Gretchen Koch, *Goucher College*

Nicole Lang, *North Hennepin Community College*

Mary Margarita Legner, *Riverside City College*

Aihua Li, *Montclair State University*

John B. Little, *College of the Holy Cross*

Jean-Marie Magnier, *Springfield Technical Community College*

Shawna L. Mahan, *Pikes Peak Community College*

Tsun Zee Mai, *University of Alabama*

Nachimuthu Manickam, *DePauw University*

Tammi Marshall, *Cuyamaca College*

Lois Martin, *Massasoit Community College*

Chris Masters, *Doane College*

April Allen Materowski, *Baruch College*

Daniel Maxin, *Valparaiso University*

Mike McAsey, *Bradley University*

Stephen McDowall, *Western Washington University*

Mike McGrath, *Louisiana School for Math, Science, and the Arts*

Ken Mead, *Genesee Community College*

Jack Mealy, *Austin College*

Richard Mercer, *Wright State University*

Elaine Merrill, *Brigham Young University—Hawaii*

Juan Molina, *Austin Community College*

Kathleen Morris, *University of Arkansas*

Carrie Muir, *University of Colorado, Boulder*

Keith A. Nabb, *Moraine Valley Community College*

Paul O'Heron, *Broome Community College*

Michael Oppedisano, *Onondaga Community College*

Leticia M. Oropesa, *University of Miami*

Altay Ozgener, *Manatee Community College*

Shahrokh Parvini, *San Diego Mesa College*

Fred Peskoff, *Borough of Manhattan Community College*

Debra Pharo, *Northwestern Michigan College*

Philip Pickering, *Genesee Community College*

Jeffrey L. Poet, *Missiouri Western State University*

Tammy Potter, *Gadsden State Community College*

Jason Pozen, *Moraine Valley Community College*

Elaine A. Previte, *Bristol Community College*

Stephen Proietti, *Northern Essex Community College*

Suman Sanyal, *Clarkson University*

Brooke P. Quinlan, *Hillsborough Community College*

Douglas Quinney, *Keele University*

Traci M. Reed, *St. Johns River Community College*

Libbie H. Reeves, *Mitchell Community College*

Linda Reist, *Macomb Community College*

Harriette Markos Roadman, *New River Community College*

Kenneth Roblee, *Troy University*

Andrea Ronaldi, *College of Southern Maryland*

William T. Ross, *University of Richmond*

Behnaz Rouhani, *Georgia Perimeter College*

Eric Rowley, *Utah State University*

Ned W. Schillow, *Lehigh Carbon Community College*

Friedhelm Schwarz, *University of Toledo*

Randy Scott, *Santiago Canyon College*

Carl R. Seaquist, *Texas Tech University*

Deepthika Senaratne, *Fayetteville State University*

Dan Shagena, *New Hampshire Technical Institute*

Luz V. Shin, *Los Angeles Valley College*

Nándor Sieben, *Northern Arizona University*

Mark A. Smith, *Miami University*

Shing So, *University of Central Missouri*

Cindy Soderstrom, *Salt Lake Community College*

David St. John, *Malcolm X College*

Zina Stilman, *Community College of Denver*

Eleanor Storey, *Front Range Community College*

Jennifer Strehler, *Oakton Community College*

Linda Sturges, *SUNY—Maritime College*

Richard Sullivan, *Georgetown Unversity*

Donna M. Szott, *Community College of Allegheny County—South Campus*

Elena Toneva, *Eastern Washington University*

Anthony Tongen, *James Madison University*

Michael Tran, *Antelope Valley College*

John Travis, *Mississippi College*

Amitabha Tripathi, *SUNY at Oswego*

Preety N. Tripathi, *SUNY at Oswego*

Ruth Trygstad, *Salt Lake Community College*

David Tseng, *Miami Dade College—Kendall Campus*

Enefiok Umana, *Georgia Perimeter College*

Alexander Vaninsky, *Hostos Community College*

Linda D. VanNiewaal, *Coe College*

Anthony J. Vavra, *West Virginia Northern Community College*

Somasundaram Velummylum, *Claflin University*

Jim Voss, *Front Range Community College*

Yajni Warnapala-Yehiya, *Roger Williams University*

Leben Wee, *Montgomery College*

William Wells, *University of Nevada at Las Vegas*

Darren White, *Kennedy King College*

Bruno Wichnoski, *University of North Carolina—Charlotte*

Dana P. Williams, *Dartmouth College*

David B. Williams, *Clayton State University*

G. Brock Williams, *Texas Tech University*

Nicholas J. Willis, *George Fox University*

Mark R. Woodard, *Furman University*

Kenneth Word, *Central Texas College*

Zhanbo Yang, *University of the Incarnate Word*

Taeil Yi, *University of Texas at Brownsville*

David Zeigler, *California State University, Sacramento*

Hong Zhang, *University of Wisconsin, Oshkosh*

Credits

Note to Students

We offer several practical suggestions about how to gain the most from this book and from your calculus course.

1. Our experience in teaching calculus over many years tells us that the greatest obstacle to learning calculus is not the new ideas of calculus, which are often easily understood. Rather, students find a greater struggle with prerequisite skills—most notably algebra and trigonometry. Your progress with calculus will be far less difficult if you have a solid understanding of algebra and trigonometry before you begin Chapter 2. Take advantage of the material in Chapter 1 and Appendix A, as well as the review that your instructor may provide, so that your prerequisite skills are strong *before* you embark on the study of calculus.
2. An old saying is worth repeating: *Mathematics is not a spectator sport.* No one can expect to learn calculus merely by reading the book and listening to lectures. Your participation and engagement are essential. Read the book actively with a pencil and paper nearby. Use the margins for your notes, answer the Quick Check questions as you go, and work as many exercises as possible. Working exercises will accelerate your learning of calculus more than anything else you do.
3. The use of graphing calculators and computer software is a major issue in teaching and learning calculus. Instructors differ in their emphasis on technology, so it is important to understand your instructor's approach to the use of technology and to become proficient with the required technology as quickly as possible. You should strive for a balance between the use of technology and the use of what are called *analytical*, or pencil-and-paper, methods. Technology should be used to extend and check your analytical skills but never to replace them.

With these thoughts in mind, it is time to begin the calculus journey. We hope it is as exciting for you as it is for us every time we teach calculus.

William Briggs

Lyle Cochran

Bernard Gillett

1

Functions

Chapter Preview The goal of this chapter is to ensure that you begin your calculus journey fully equipped with the tools you will need. In this chapter, you will see many of the functions used in calculus: polynomials, rational functions, algebraic functions, and the trigonometric functions. (Logarithmic and exponential functions are introduced in Chapter 7.) It is imperative that you work hard to master the ideas in this chapter and refer to it when questions arise.

1.1 Review of Functions

Mathematics is a language with an alphabet, a vocabulary, and many rules. If you are unfamiliar with set notation, intervals on the real number line, absolute value, the Cartesian coordinate system, or equations of lines and circles, please refer to Appendix A. Our starting point in this book is the fundamental concept of a function.

Everywhere around us we see relationships among quantities, or **variables**. For example, the consumer price index changes in time and the temperature of the ocean varies with latitude. These relationships can often be expressed by mathematical objects called **functions**. Calculus is the study of functions, and because we use functions to describe the world around us, calculus is a universal language for human inquiry.

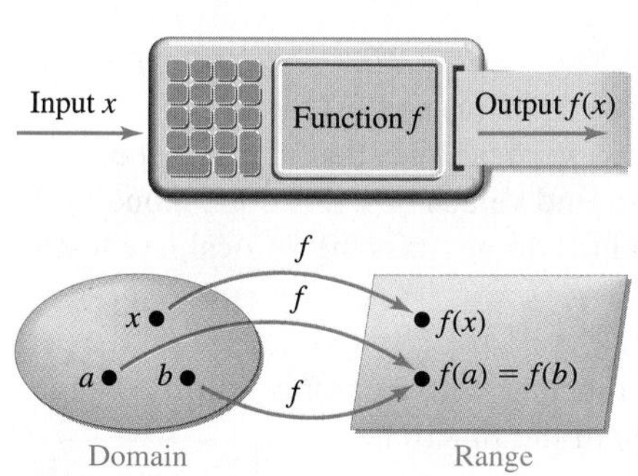

FIGURE 1.1

> **DEFINITION Function**
>
> A **function** f is a rule that assigns to each value x in a set D a *unique* value denoted $f(x)$. The set D is the **domain** of the function. The **range** is the set of all values of $f(x)$ produced as x varies over the domain (Figure 1.1).

➤ If the domain is not specified, we take it to be the set of all values of x for which f is defined. We will see shortly that the domain and range of a function may be restricted by the context of the problem.

The **independent variable** is the variable associated with the domain; the **dependent variable** belongs to the range. The **graph** of a function f is the set of all points (x, y) in the xy-plane that satisfy the equation $y = f(x)$. The **argument** of a function is the expression on which the function works. For example, x is the argument when we write $f(x)$. Similarly, 2 is the argument in $f(2)$ and $x^2 + 4$ is the argument in $f(x^2 + 4)$.

QUICK CHECK 1 If $f(x) = x^2 - 2x$, find $f(-1)$, $f(x^2)$, $f(t)$, and $f(p - 1)$. ◄

The requirement that a function must assign a *unique* value of the dependent variable to each value in the domain is expressed in the vertical line test (Figure 1.2).

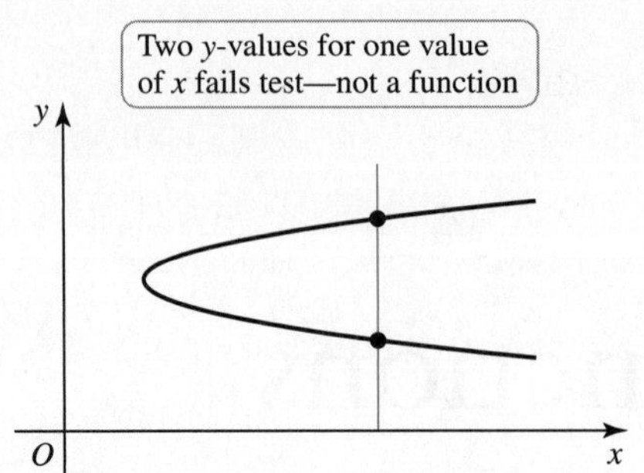

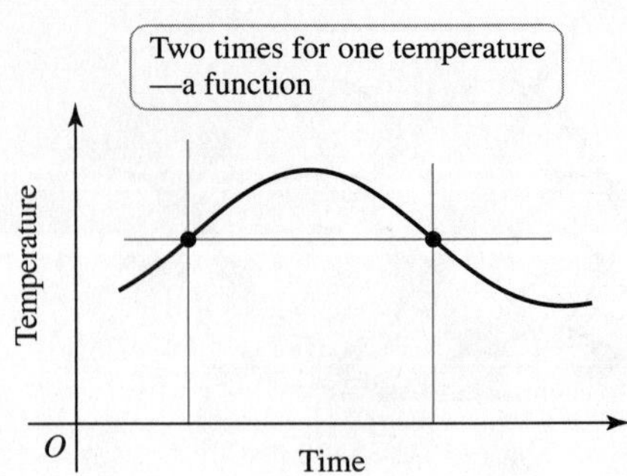

FIGURE 1.2

Vertical Line Test

A graph represents a function if and only if it passes the **vertical line test**: Every vertical line intersects the graph at most once. A graph that fails this test does not represent a function.

➤ A set of points or a graph that does *not* correspond to a function represents a **relation** between the variables. All functions are relations, but not all relations are functions.

EXAMPLE 1 **Identifying functions** State whether each graph in Figure 1.3 corresponds to a function.

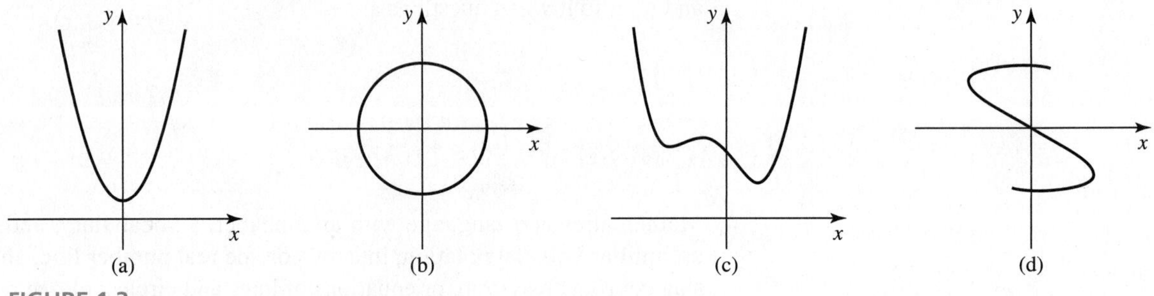

FIGURE 1.3

SOLUTION The vertical line test indicates that only graphs (a) and (c) represent functions. In graphs (b) and (d), it is possible to draw vertical lines that intersect the graph more than once. Equivalently, it is possible to find values of x that correspond to more than one value of y. Therefore, graphs (b) and (d) do not pass the vertical line test and do not represent functions. *Related Exercises 11–12* ◀

➤ A graphing window of $[a, b] \times [c, d]$ means $a \le x \le b$ and $c \le y \le d$.

EXAMPLE 2 **Domain and range** Graph each function with a graphing utility using the given window. Then state the domain and range of the function.

a. $y = f(x) = x^2 + 1$; $[-3, 3] \times [-1, 5]$

b. $z = g(t) = \sqrt{4 - t^2}$; $[-3, 3] \times [-1, 3]$

c. $w = h(u) = \dfrac{1}{u - 1}$; $[-3, 5] \times [-4, 4]$

SOLUTION

a. Figure 1.4 shows the graph of $f(x) = x^2 + 1$. Because f is defined for all values of x, its domain is the set of all real numbers, or $(-\infty, \infty)$, or $\mathbf{R}$. Because $x^2 \ge 0$ for all x, it follows that $x^2 + 1 \ge 1$ and the range of f is $[1, \infty)$.

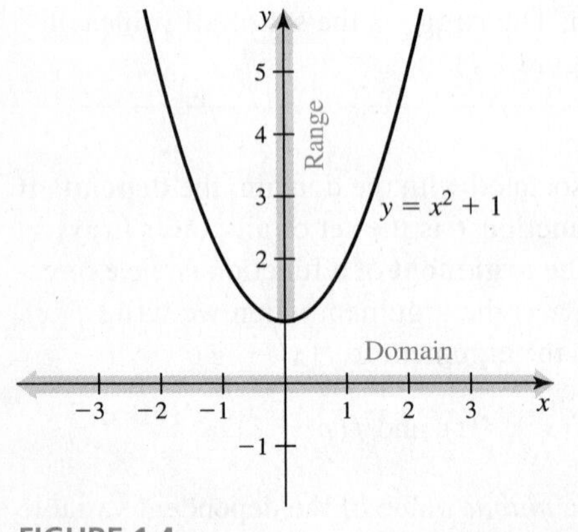

FIGURE 1.4

b. When n is even, functions involving nth roots are defined provided the quantity under the root is nonnegative. In this case, the function g is defined provided $4 - t^2 \ge 0$, which means $t^2 \le 4$, or $-2 \le t \le 2$. Therefore, the domain of g is $[-2, 2]$. By the

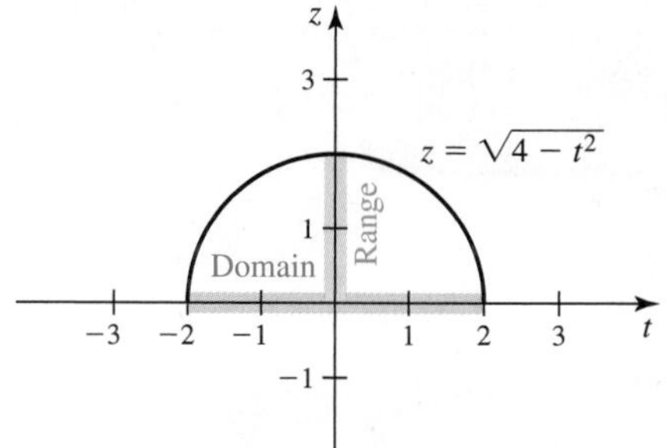

FIGURE 1.5

definition of the square root, the range consists only of nonnegative numbers. When $t = 0$, z reaches its maximum value of $g(0) = \sqrt{4} = 2$, and when $t = \pm 2$, z attains its minimum value of $g(\pm 2) = 0$. Therefore, the range of g is $[0, 2]$ (Figure 1.5).

c. The function h is undefined at $u = 1$, so its domain is $\{u: u \neq 1\}$ and the graph does not have a point corresponding to $u = 1$. We see that w takes on all values except 0; therefore, the range is $\{w: w \neq 0\}$. A graphing utility does *not* represent this function accurately if it shows the vertical line $u = 1$ as part of the graph (Figure 1.6).

Related Exercises 13–18

➤ The dashed vertical line $u = 1$ in Figure 1.6 indicates that the graph of $w = h(u)$ approaches a *vertical asymptote* as u approaches 1 and that w becomes large in magnitude for u near 1. Vertical and horizontal asymptotes are discussed in detail in Chapter 2.

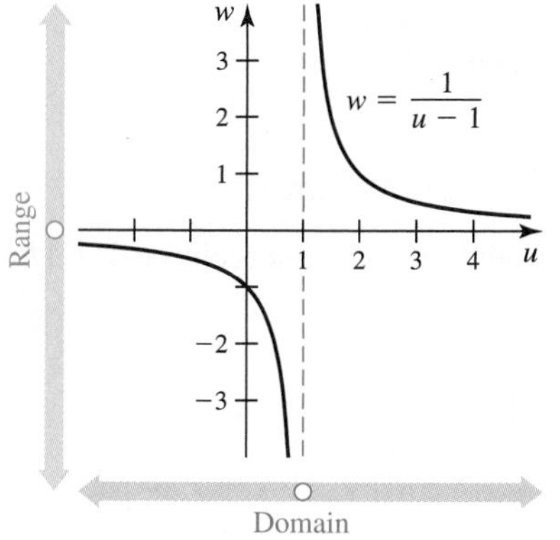

FIGURE 1.6

EXAMPLE 3 Domain and range in context At time $t = 0$ a stone is thrown vertically upward from the ground at a speed of 30 m/s. Its height above the ground in meters (neglecting air resistance) is approximated by the function $h = f(t) = 30t - 5t^2$. Find the domain and range of this function as they apply to this particular problem.

SOLUTION Although f is defined for all values of t, the only relevant times are between the time the stone is thrown ($t = 0$) and the time it strikes the ground. Solving the equation $h = 30t - 5t^2 = 0$, we find that

$$
\begin{aligned}
30t - 5t^2 &= 0 \\
5t(6 - t) &= 0 && \text{Factor.} \\
5t = 0 \quad &\text{or} \quad 6 - t = 0 && \text{Set each factor equal to 0.} \\
t = 0 \quad &\text{or} \quad t = 6. && \text{Solve.}
\end{aligned}
$$

Therefore, the stone leaves the ground at $t = 0$ and returns to the ground at $t = 6$. An appropriate domain that fits the context of this problem is $\{t: 0 \leq t \leq 6\}$. The range consists of all values of $h = 30t - 5t^2$ as t varies over $[0, 6]$. The largest value of h occurs when the stone reaches its highest point at $t = 3$ s, which is $h = f(3) = 45$ m. Therefore, the range is $[0, 45]$. These observations are confirmed by the graph of the height function (Figure 1.7). Note that this graph is *not* the trajectory of the stone; the stone moves vertically.

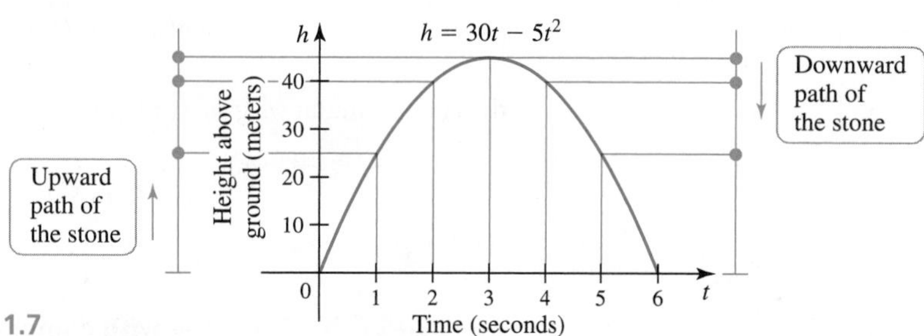

FIGURE 1.7

Related Exercises 19–20

QUICK CHECK 2 What are the domain and range of $f(x) = (x^2 + 1)^{-1}$?

Composite Functions

Functions may be combined using sums $(f + g)$, differences $(f - g)$, products (fg), or quotients (f/g). The process called *composition* also produces new functions.

➤ In the composition $y = f(g(x))$, f is called the *outer function* and g is the *inner function.*

DEFINITION Composite Functions

Given two functions f and g, the composite function $f \circ g$ is defined by $(f \circ g)(x) = f(g(x))$. It is evaluated in two steps: $y = f(u)$, where $u = g(x)$. The domain of $f \circ g$ consists of all x in the domain of g such that $u = g(x)$ is in the domain of f (Figure 1.8).

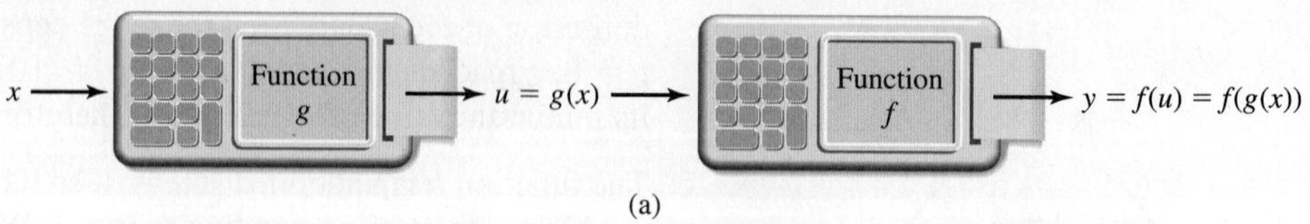

(a)

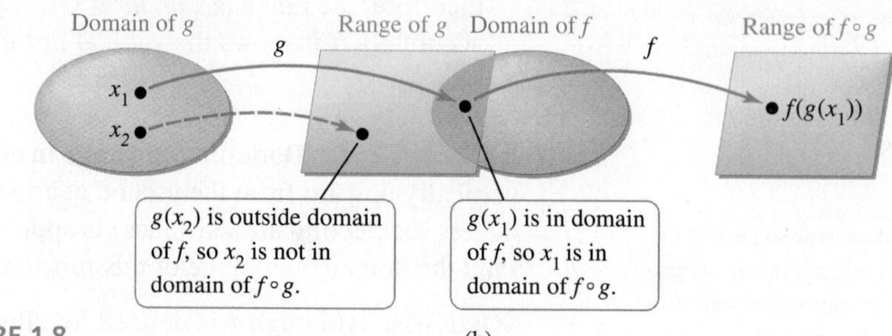

(b)

FIGURE 1.8

EXAMPLE 4 **Composite functions and notation** Let $f(x) = 3x^2 - x$ and $g(x) = 1/x$. Simplify the following expressions.

a. $f(5p + 1)$ **b.** $g(1/x)$ **c.** $f(g(x))$ **d.** $g(f(x))$

SOLUTION In each case, the functions work on their arguments.

a. The argument of f is $5p + 1$, so

$$f(5p + 1) = 3(5p + 1)^2 - (5p + 1) = 75p^2 + 25p + 2.$$

b. Because g requires taking the reciprocal of the argument, we take the reciprocal of $1/x$ and find that $g(1/x) = 1/(1/x) = x$.

c. The argument of f is $g(x)$, so

$$f(g(x)) = f\left(\frac{1}{x}\right) = 3\left(\frac{1}{x}\right)^2 - \left(\frac{1}{x}\right) = \frac{3 - x}{x^2}.$$

d. The argument of g is $f(x)$, so

$$g(f(x)) = g(3x^2 - x) = \frac{1}{3x^2 - x}.$$

Related Exercises 21–30 ◀

EXAMPLE 5 **Working with composite functions** Identify possible choices for the inner and outer functions in the following composite functions. Give the domain of the composite function.

a. $h(x) = \sqrt{9x - x^2}$ **b.** $h(x) = \dfrac{2}{(x^2 - 1)^3}$

SOLUTION

a. An obvious outer function is $f(x) = \sqrt{x}$, which works on the inner function $g(x) = 9x - x^2$. Therefore, h can be expressed as $h = f \circ g$ or $h(x) = f(g(x))$. The domain of $f \circ g$ consists of all values of x such that $9x - x^2 \geq 0$. Solving this inequality gives $\{x: 0 \leq x \leq 9\}$ as the domain of $f \circ g$.

b. One choice for an outer function is $f(x) = 2/x^3 = 2x^{-3}$, which works on the inner function $g(x) = x^2 - 1$. Therefore, h can be expressed as $h = f \circ g$ or $h(x) = f(g(x))$. The domain of $f \circ g$ consists of all values of $g(x)$ such that $g(x) \neq 0$, which is $\{x: x \neq \pm 1\}$.

Related Exercises 31–34 ◀

EXAMPLE 6 More composite functions Given $f(x) = \sqrt[3]{x}$ and $g(x) = x^2 - x - 6$, find **(a)** $g \circ f$ and **(b)** $g \circ g$, and their domains.

SOLUTION

a. We have

$$(g \circ f)(x) = g(f(x)) = (\underbrace{\sqrt[3]{x}}_{f(x)})^2 - \underbrace{\sqrt[3]{x}}_{f(x)} - 6 = x^{2/3} - x^{1/3} - 6.$$

Because the domains of f and g are $(-\infty, \infty)$, the domain of $f \circ g$ is also $(-\infty, \infty)$.

b. In this case, we have the composition of two polynomials:

$$\begin{aligned}(g \circ g)(x) &= g(g(x)) \\ &= g(x^2 - x - 6) \\ &= \underbrace{(x^2 - x - 6)^2}_{g(x)} - \underbrace{(x^2 - x - 6)}_{g(x)} - 6 \\ &= x^4 - 2x^3 - 12x^2 + 13x + 36\end{aligned}$$

The domain of the composition of two polynomials is $(-\infty, \infty)$.

Related Exercises 35–44

QUICK CHECK 3 If $f(x) = x^2 + 1$ and $g(x) = x^2$, find $f \circ g$ and $g \circ f$.

EXAMPLE 7 Using graphs to evaluate composite functions Use the graphs of f and g in Figure 1.9 to find the following values.

a. $f(g(5))$ **b.** $f(g(3))$ **c.** $g(f(3))$ **d.** $f(f(4))$

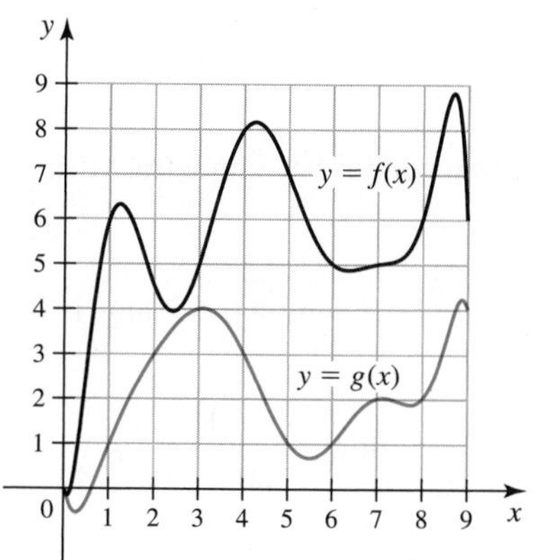

FIGURE 1.9

SOLUTION

a. According to the graphs, $g(5) = 1$ and $f(1) = 6$; it follows that $f(g(5)) = f(1) = 6$.

b. The graphs indicate that $g(3) = 4$ and $f(4) = 8$, so $f(g(3)) = f(4) = 8$.

c. We see that $g(f(3)) = g(5) = 1$. Observe that $f(g(3)) \neq g(f(3))$.

d. In this case, $f(\underbrace{f(4)}_{8}) = f(8) = 6$.

Related Exercises 45–46

Symmetry

The word *symmetry* has many meanings in mathematics. Here we consider symmetries of graphs and the relations they represent. Taking advantage of symmetry often saves time and leads to insights.

> **DEFINITION Symmetry in Graphs**
>
> A graph is **symmetric with respect to the y-axis** if whenever the point (x, y) is on the graph, the point $(-x, y)$ is also on the graph. This property means that the graph is unchanged when reflected about the y-axis (Figure 1.10a).
>
> A graph is **symmetric with respect to the x-axis** if whenever the point (x, y) is on the graph, the point $(x, -y)$ is also on the graph. This property means that the graph is unchanged when reflected about the x-axis (Figure 1.10b).
>
> A graph is **symmetric with respect to the origin** if whenever the point (x, y) is on the graph, the point $(-x, -y)$ is also on the graph (Figure 1.10c). Symmetry about both the x- and y-axes implies symmetry about the origin, but not vice versa.

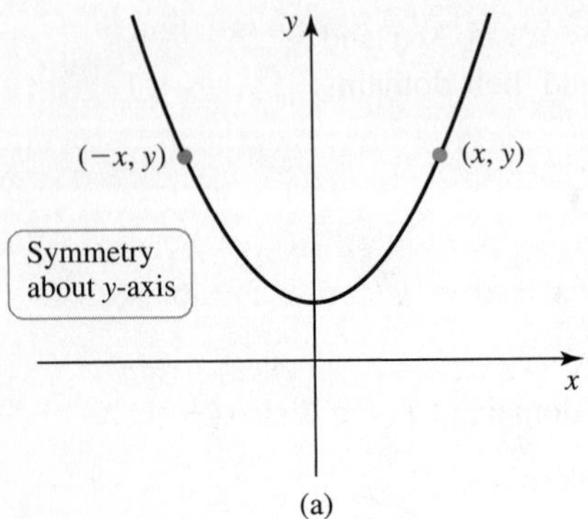

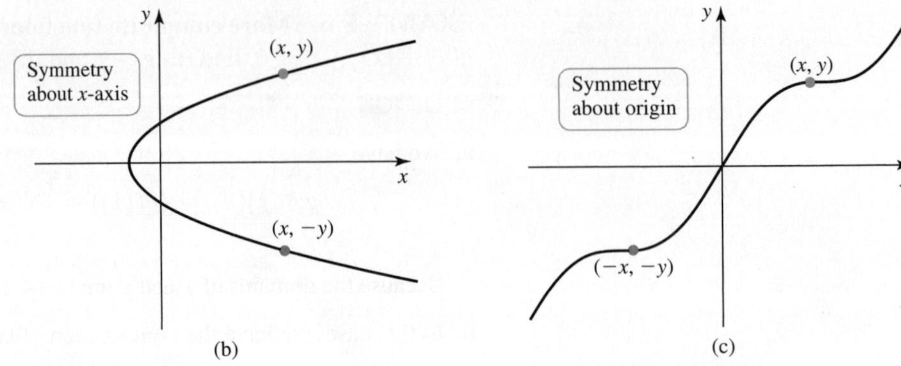

FIGURE 1.10

DEFINITION Symmetry in Functions

An **even function** f has the property that $f(-x) = f(x)$ for all x in the domain. The graph of an even function is symmetric about the y-axis. Polynomials consisting of only even powers of the variable (of the form x^{2n}, where n is a nonnegative integer) are even functions.

An **odd function** f has the property that $f(-x) = -f(x)$ for all x in the domain. The graph of an odd function is symmetric about the origin. Polynomials consisting of only odd powers of the variable (of the form x^{2n+1}, where n is a nonnegative integer) are odd functions.

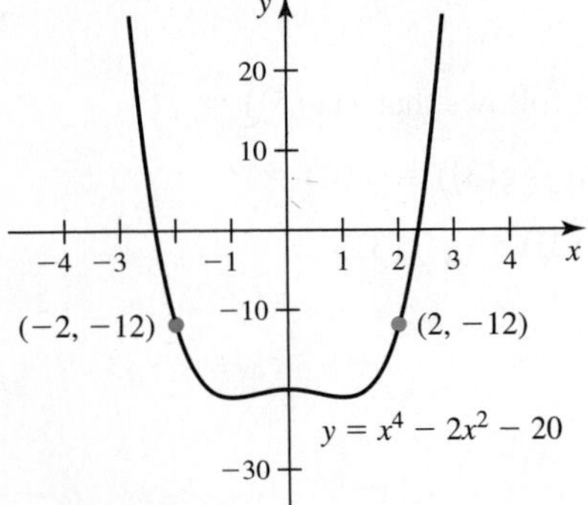

FIGURE 1.11

QUICK CHECK 4 Explain why the graph of a nonzero function cannot be symmetric with respect to the x-axis.

EXAMPLE 8 Identifying symmetry in functions Identify the symmetry, if any, in the following functions.

a. $f(x) = x^4 - 2x^2 - 20$ **b.** $g(x) = x^3 - 3x + 1$ **c.** $h(x) = \dfrac{1}{x^3 - x}$

SOLUTION

a. The function f consists of only even powers of x (where $20 = 20 \cdot 1 = 20x^0$ and x^0 is considered an even power). Therefore, f is an even function (Figure 1.11). This fact is verified by showing that $f(-x) = f(x)$:

$$f(-x) = (-x)^4 - 2(-x)^2 - 20 = x^4 - 2x^2 - 20 = f(x)$$

b. The function g consists of two odd powers and one even power (again, $1 = x^0$ is considered an even power). Therefore, we expect that the function has no symmetry about the y-axis or the origin (Figure 1.12). Note that

$$g(-x) = (-x)^3 - 3(-x) + 1 = -x^3 + 3x + 1,$$

so $g(-x)$ equals neither $g(x)$ nor $-g(x)$, and the function has no symmetry.

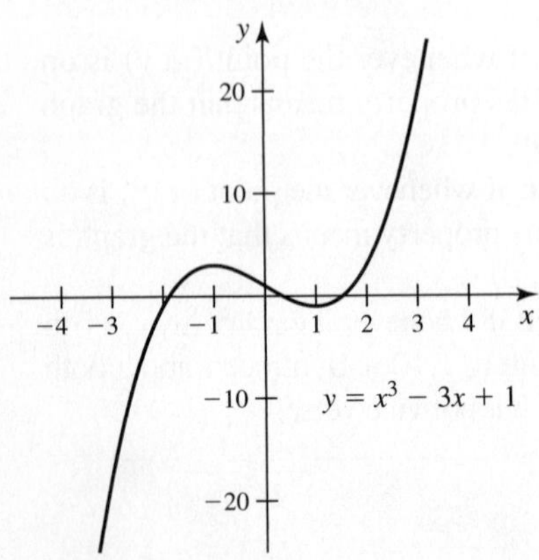

FIGURE 1.12

> The symmetry of compositions of even and odd functions is considered in Exercises 65–71.

c. In this case, h is a composition of an odd function $f(x) = 1/x$ with an odd function $g(x) = x^3 - x$. Note that

$$h(-x) = \frac{1}{(-x)^3 - (-x)} = -\frac{1}{x^3 - x} = -h(x).$$

Because $h(-x) = -h(x)$, h is an odd function (Figure 1.13).

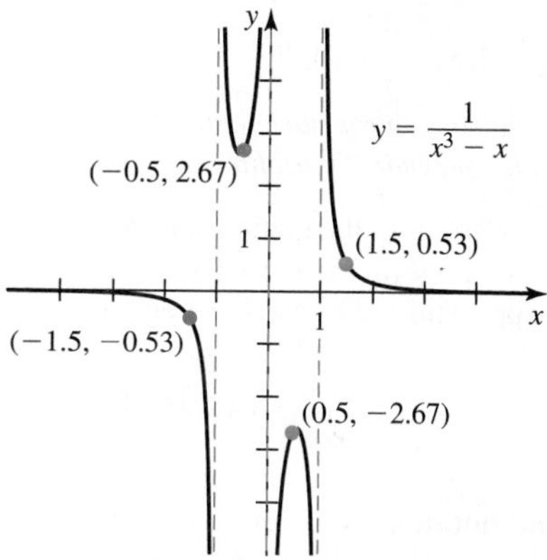

FIGURE 1.13

Related Exercises 47–54 ◀

SECTION 1.1 EXERCISES

Review Questions

1. Use the terms *domain, range, independent variable,* and *dependent variable* to explain how a function relates one variable to another variable.

2. Does the independent variable of a function belong to the domain or range? Does the dependent variable belong to the domain or range?

3. Explain how the vertical line test is used to detect functions.

4. If $f(x) = 1/(x^3 + 1)$, what is $f(2)$? What is $f(y^2)$?

5. Which statement about a function is true? (i) For each value of x in the domain, there corresponds one value of y; (ii) for each value of y in the range, there corresponds one value of x. Explain.

6. If $f(x) = \sqrt{x}$ and $g(x) = x^3 - 2$, find the compositions $f \circ g, g \circ f, f \circ f$, and $g \circ g$.

7. If $f(\pm 2) = 2$ and $g(\pm 2) = -2$, evaluate $f(g(2))$ and $g(f(-2))$.

8. Explain how to find the domain of $f \circ g$ if you know the domain and range of f and g.

9. Sketch a graph of an even function and give the function's defining property.

10. Sketch a graph of an odd function and give the function's defining property.

Basic Skills

11–12. Vertical line test *Decide whether graph A, graph B, or both graphs represent functions.*

11.

12.

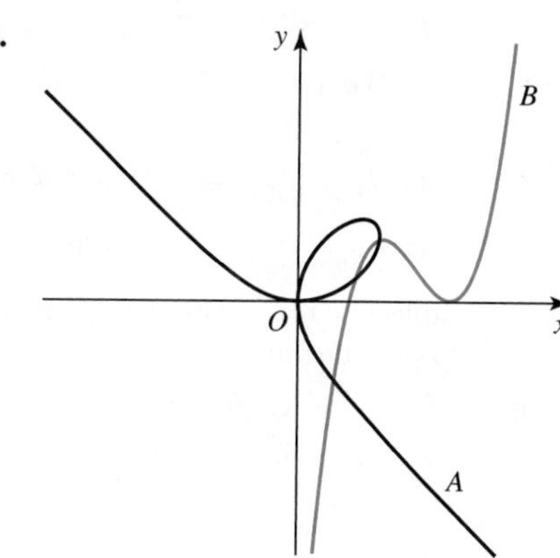

13–18. Domain and range *Graph each function with a graphing utility using the given window. Then state the domain and range of the function.*

13. $f(x) = 3x^4 - 10;\quad [-2, 2] \times [-10, 15]$

14. $g(y) = \dfrac{y + 1}{y^2 - y - 6};\quad [-4, 6] \times [-3, 3]$

15. $f(x) = \sqrt{4 - x^2};\quad [-4, 4] \times [-4, 4]$

16. $F(w) = \sqrt[4]{2 - w};\quad [-3, 2] \times [0, 2]$

17. $h(u) = \sqrt[3]{u - 1};\quad [-7, 9] \times [-2, 2]$

18. $g(x) = (x^2 - 4)\sqrt{x + 5};\quad [-5, 5] \times [-10, 50]$

19–20. Domain in context *Determine an appropriate domain of each function. Identify the independent and dependent variables.*

19. A stone is thrown vertically upward from the ground at a speed of 40 m/s at time $t = 0$. Its distance d (in m) above the ground (neglecting air resistance) is approximated by the function $f(t) = 40t - 5t^2$.

20. The average production cost for a company to make n bicycles is given by the function $c(n) = 120 - 0.25n$.

21–30. Composite functions and notation *Let $f(x) = x^2 - 4$, $g(x) = x^3$, and $F(x) = 1/(x - 3)$. Simplify or evaluate the following expressions.*

21. $f(10)$ 22. $f(p^2)$ 23. $g(1/z)$ 24. $F(y^4)$

25. $F(g(y))$ 26. $f(g(w))$ 27. $g(f(u))$ 28. $\dfrac{f(2 + h) - f(2)}{h}$

29. $F(F(x))$ 30. $g(F(f(x)))$

31–34. Working with composite functions *Find possible choices for outer and inner functions f and g such that the given function h equals $f \circ g$. Give the domain of h.*

31. $h(x) = (x^3 - 5)^{10}$ 32. $h(x) = 2/(x^6 + x^2 + 1)^2$

33. $h(x) = \sqrt{x^4 + 2}$ 34. $h(x) = \dfrac{1}{\sqrt{x^3 - 1}}$

35–40. More composite functions *Let $f(x) = |x|$, $g(x) = x^2 - 4$, $F(x) = \sqrt{x}$, and $G(x) = 1/(x - 2)$. Determine the following composite functions and give their domains.*

35. $f \circ g$ 36. $g \circ f$ 37. $f \circ G$

38. $f \circ g \circ G$ 39. $G \circ g \circ f$ 40. $F \circ g \circ g$

41–44. Missing piece *Let $g(x) = x^2 + 3$ and find a function f that produces the given composition.*

41. $(f \circ g)(x) = x^4 + 6x^2 + 9$ 42. $(f \circ g)(x) = x^4 + 6x^2 + 20$

43. $(g \circ f)(x) = x^4 + 3$ 44. $(g \circ f)(x) = x^{2/3} + 3$

45. **Composite functions from graphs** Use the graphs of f and g in the figure to determine the following function values.

a. $f(g(2))$ b. $g(f(2))$ c. $f(g(4))$
d. $g(f(5))$ e. $f(g(7))$ f. $f(f(8))$

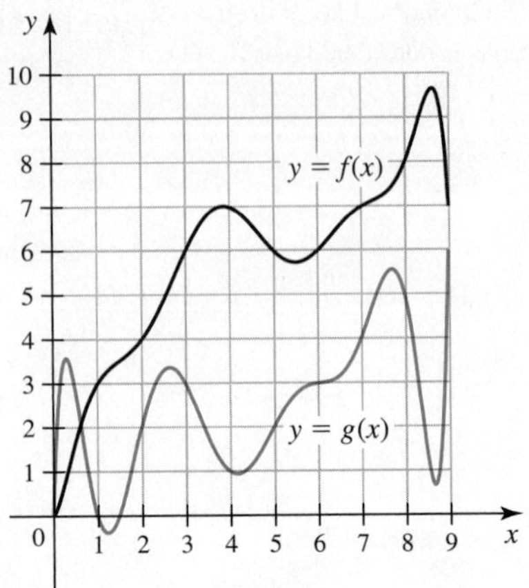

46. **Composite functions from tables** Use the table to evaluate the given compositions.

x	-1	0	1	2	3	4
$f(x)$	3	1	0	-1	-3	-1
$g(x)$	-1	0	2	3	4	5
$h(x)$	0	-1	0	3	0	4

a. $h(g(0))$ b. $g(f(4))$ c. $h(h(0))$
d. $g(h(f(4)))$ e. $f(f(f(1)))$ f. $h(h(h(0)))$
g. $f(h(g(2)))$ h. $g(f(h(4)))$ i. $g(g(g(1)))$
j. $f(f(h(3)))$

47–52. Symmetry *Determine whether the graphs of the following equations and functions have symmetry about the x-axis, the y-axis, or the origin. Check your work by graphing.*

47. $f(x) = x^4 + 5x^2 - 12$ 48. $f(x) = 3x^5 + 2x^3 - x$

49. $f(x) = x^5 - x^3 - 2$ 50. $f(x) = 2|x|$

51. $x^{2/3} + y^{2/3} = 1$ 52. $x^3 - y^5 = 0$

53. **Symmetry in graphs** State whether the functions represented by graphs A, B, and C in the figure are even, odd, or neither.

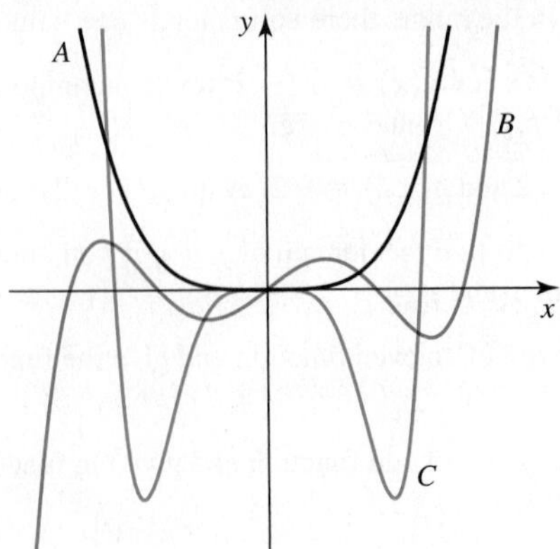

54. Symmetry in graphs State whether the functions represented by graphs A, B, and C in the figure are even, odd, or neither.

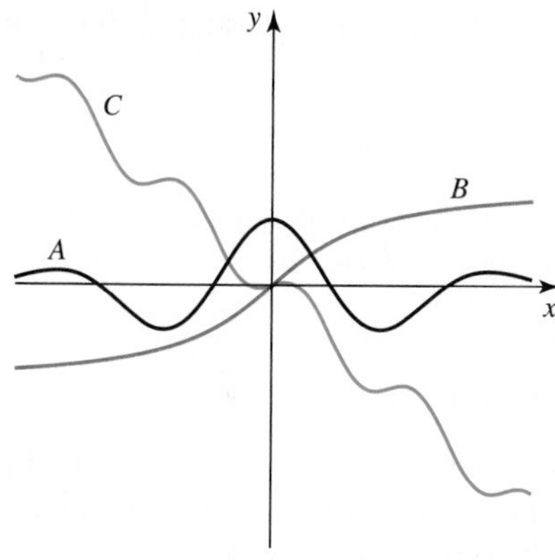

Further Explorations

55. Explain why or why not Determine whether the following statements are true and give an explanation or counterexample.

a. The range of $f(x) = 2x - 38$ is all real numbers.

b. The relation $f(x) = x^6 + 1$ is *not* a function because $f(1) = f(-1) = 2$.

c. If $f(x) = x^{-1}$, then $f(1/x) = 1/f(x)$.

d. In general, $f(f(x)) = (f(x))^2$.

e. In general, $f(g(x)) = g(f(x))$.

f. In general, $f(g(x)) = (f \circ g)(x)$.

g. If $f(x)$ is an even function, then $cf(ax)$ is an even function, where a and c are real numbers.

h. If $f(x)$ is an odd function, then $f(x) + d$ is an odd function, where d is a real number.

i. If f is both even *and* odd, then $f(x) = 0$ for all x.

56. Range of power functions Using words and figures, explain why the range of $f(x) = x^n$, where n is a positive odd integer, is all real numbers. Explain why the range of $g(x) = x^n$, where n is a positive even integer, is all nonnegative real numbers.

57. Absolute value graphs Use the definition of absolute value to graph the equation $|x| - |y| = 1$. Use a graphing utility only to check your work.

58. Even and odd at the origin

a. If $f(0)$ is defined and f is an even function, is it necessarily true that $f(0) = 0$? Explain.

b. If $f(0)$ is defined and f is an odd function, is it necessarily true that $f(0) = 0$? Explain.

T **59–62. Polynomial composition** *Determine a polynomial f that satisfies the following properties. (Hint: Determine the degree of f; then substitute a polynomial of that degree and solve for its coefficients.)*

59. $f(f(x)) = 9x - 8$ **60.** $(f(x))^2 = 9x^2 - 12x + 4$

61. $f(f(x)) = x^4 - 12x^2 + 30$ **62.** $(f(x))^2 = x^4 - 12x^2 + 36$

Applications

T **63. Launching a rocket** A small rocket is launched vertically upward from the edge of a cliff 80 ft off the ground at a speed of 96 ft/s. Its height above the ground is given by the function $h(t) = -16t^2 + 96t + 80$, where t represents time measured in seconds.

a. Assuming the rocket is launched at $t = 0$, what is an appropriate domain for h?

b. Graph h and determine the time at which the rocket reaches its highest point. What is the height at that time?

64. Draining a tank (Torricelli's law) A cylindrical tank with a cross-sectional area of 100 cm^2 is filled to a depth of 100 cm with water. At $t = 0$, a drain in the bottom of the tank with an area of 10 cm^2 is opened allowing water to flow out of the tank. The depth of water in the tank at time $t \geq 0$ is $d(t) = (10 - 2.2t)^2$.

a. Check that $d(0) = 100$, as specified.

b. What is an appropriate domain for d?

c. At what time is the tank first empty?

Additional Exercises

65–71. Combining even and odd functions *Let E be an even function and O be an odd function. Determine the symmetry, if any, of the following functions.*

65. $E + O$ **66.** $E \cdot O$ **67.** E/O **68.** $E \circ O$

69. $E \circ E$ **70.** $O \circ O$ **71.** $O \circ E$

72–75. Working with function notation *Consider the following functions and simplify the expressions* $\dfrac{f(x) - f(a)}{x - a}$ *and* $\dfrac{f(x + h) - f(x)}{h}$.

72. $f(x) = 3 - 2x$ **73.** $f(x) = 4x - 3$

74. $f(x) = 4x^2 - 1$ **75.** $f(x) = 1/(2x)$

QUICK CHECK ANSWERS

1. $3, x^4 - 2x^2, t^2 - 2t, p^2 - 4p + 3$
2. Domain is all real numbers; range is $\{y: 0 < y \leq 1\}$
3. $(f \circ g)(x) = x^4 + 1$ and $(g \circ f)(x) = (x^2 + 1)^2$.
4. If the graph were symmetric with respect to the x-axis, it would not pass the vertical line test. ◄

1.2 Representing Functions

We consider four different approaches to defining and representing functions: formulas, graphs, tables, and words.

Using Formulas

The following list is a brief catalog of the families of functions that are studied systematically throughout this book; they are all defined by *formulas*.

1. **Polynomials** are functions of the form

$$f(x) = a_n x^n + a_{n-1} x^{n-1} + \cdots + a_1 x + a_0,$$

where the **coefficients** $a_0, a_1, \ldots, a_n$ are real numbers with $a_n \neq 0$ and the nonnegative integer n is the **degree** of the polynomial. The domain of any polynomial is the set of all real numbers. An nth-degree polynomial can have as many as n real **zeros** or **roots**—values of x at which $f(x) = 0$, which correspond to points at which the graph of f intersects the x-axis.

➤ One version of the Fundamental Theorem of Algebra states that a nonconstant polynomial of degree n has exactly n roots, counting each root up to its multiplicity.

2. **Rational functions** are ratios of the form $f(x) = p(x)/q(x)$, where p and q are polynomials. Because division by zero is prohibited, the domain of a rational function is the set of all real numbers except those for which the denominator is zero.

3. **Algebraic functions** are constructed using the operations of algebra: addition, subtraction, multiplication, division, and roots. Examples of algebraic functions are $f(x) = \sqrt{2x^3 + 4}$ and $f(x) = x^{1/4}(x^3 + 2)$. In general, if an even root (square root, fourth root, and so forth) appears, then the domain does not contain points at which the quantity under the root is negative (and perhaps other points).

4. **Exponential functions** have the form $f(x) = b^x$, where the base $b \neq 1$ is a positive real number. Closely associated with exponential functions are **logarithmic functions** of the form $f(x) = \log_b x$, where $b > 0$ and $b \neq 1$. An exponential function has a domain consisting of all real numbers. Logarithmic functions are defined for positive real numbers.

   The most important exponential function is the **natural exponential function** $f(x) = e^x$, with base $b = e$, where $e \approx 2.71828\ldots$ is one of the fundamental constants of mathematics. Associated with the natural exponential function is the **natural logarithm function** $f(x) = \ln x$, which also has the base $b = e$.

➤ Exponential and logarithmic functions, along with inverse trigonometric functions, are introduced in Chapter 7.

5. The **trigonometric functions** are $\sin x$, $\cos x$, $\tan x$, $\cot x$, $\sec x$, and $\csc x$; they are fundamental to mathematics and many areas of application. Also important are their relatives, the **inverse trigonometric functions**.

6. Trigonometric, exponential, and logarithmic functions are a few examples of a large family called **transcendental functions**. Figure 1.14 shows the organization of these functions, all of which are explored in detail in upcoming chapters.

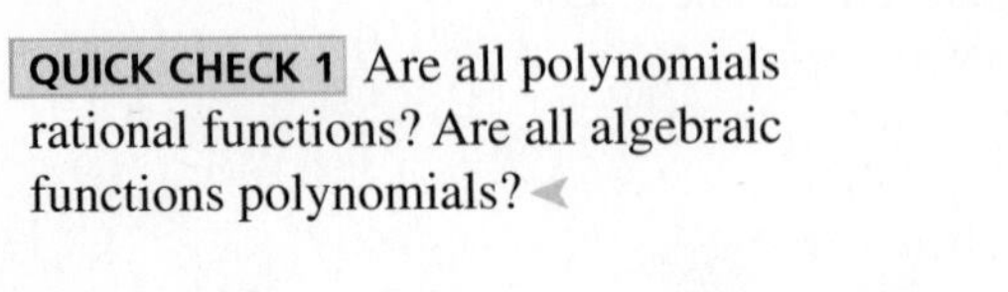
QUICK CHECK 1 Are all polynomials rational functions? Are all algebraic functions polynomials? ◄

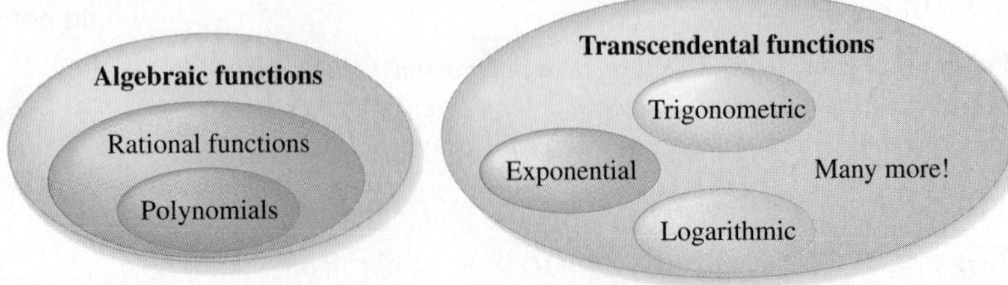

FIGURE 1.14

Using Graphs

Although formulas are the most compact way to represent many functions, graphs often provide the most illuminating representations. Two of countless examples of functions and their graphs are shown in Figure 1.15. Much of this book is devoted to creating and analyzing graphs of functions.

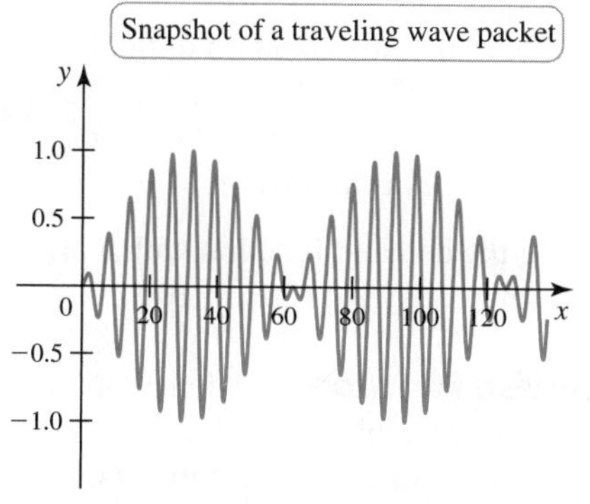

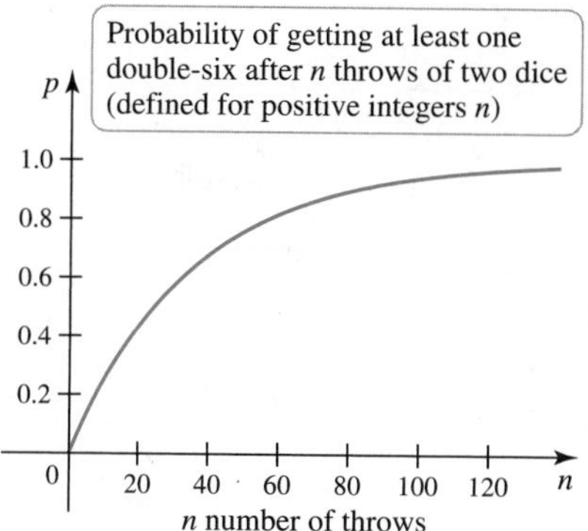

FIGURE 1.15

There are two approaches to graphing functions.

- Graphing calculators and software are powerful and easy to use. Such **technology** easily produces graphs of most functions encountered in this book. We assume you know how to use a graphing utility.
- Graphing calculators, however, are not infallible. Therefore, you should also strive to master **analytical methods** (pencil-and-paper methods) in order to analyze functions and make accurate graphs by hand. Analytical methods rely heavily on calculus and are presented throughout this book.

The important message is this: Both technology and analytical methods are essential and must be used together in an integrated way to produce accurate graphs.

Linear Functions One form of the equation of a line (see Appendix A) is $y = mx + b$, where the slope m and the y-intercept b are constants. Therefore, the function $f(x) = mx + b$ has a straight-line graph and is called a **linear function**.

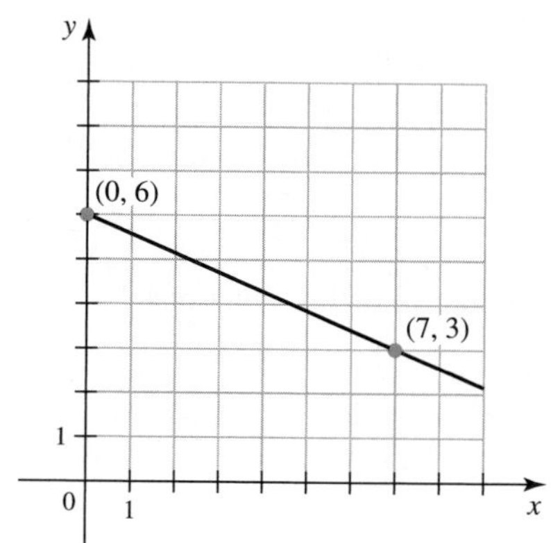

FIGURE 1.16

EXAMPLE 1 **Linear functions and their graphs** Determine the function represented by the line in Figure 1.16.

SOLUTION From the graph, we see that the y-intercept is $(0, 6)$. Using the points $(0, 6)$ and $(7, 3)$, the slope of the line is

$$m = \frac{3 - 6}{7 - 0} = -\frac{3}{7}.$$

Therefore, the line is described by the function $f(x) = -3x/7 + 6$.

Related Exercises 11–12 ◀

EXAMPLE 2 **Demand function for CDs** After studying sales for several months, the owner of a large CD retail outlet knows that the number of new CDs sold in a day (called the *demand*) decreases as the retail price increases. Specifically, her data indicate that at a price of \$14 per CD an average of 400 CDs are sold per day, while at a price of \$17 per CD an average of 250 CDs are sold per day. Assume that the demand d is a *linear* function of the price p.

a. Find and graph the demand function $d = f(p) = mp + b$.

b. According to this model, how many CDs (on average) are sold at a price of \$20?

SOLUTION

a. Two points on the graph of the demand function are given: $(p, d) = (14, 400)$ and $(17, 250)$. Therefore, the slope of the demand line is

> The units of the slope have meaning: For every dollar that the price is reduced, 50 more CDs can be sold.

$$m = \frac{400 - 250}{14 - 17} = -50 \text{ CDs per dollar.}$$

It follows that the equation of the linear demand function is

$$d - 250 = -50(p - 17).$$

Expressing d as a function of p, we have $d = f(p) = -50p + 1100$ (Figure 1.17).

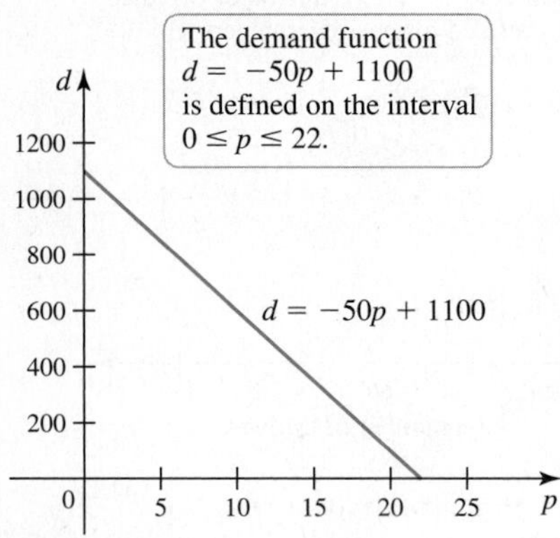

FIGURE 1.17

b. Using the demand function with a price of \$20, the average number of CDs that could be sold per day is $f(20) = 100$. *Related Exercises 13–14*

Piecewise Functions A function may have different definitions on different parts of its domain. For example, income tax is levied in tax brackets that have different tax rates. Functions that have different definitions on different parts of the domain are called **piecewise functions**. If all of the pieces are linear, the function is **piecewise linear**. Here are some examples.

EXAMPLE 3 **Defining a piecewise function** The graph of a piecewise linear function g is shown in Figure 1.18. Find a formula for the function.

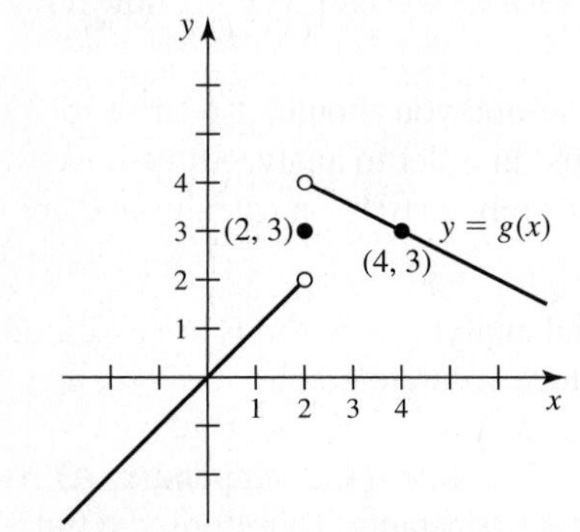

FIGURE 1.18

SOLUTION For $x < 2$, the graph is linear with a slope of 1 and a y-intercept of $(0, 0)$; its equation is $y = x$. For $x > 2$, the slope of the line is $-\frac{1}{2}$ and it passes through $(4, 3)$, so an equation of this piece of the function is

$$y - 3 = -\frac{1}{2}(x - 4) \quad \text{or} \quad y = -\frac{1}{2}x + 5.$$

For $x = 2$, we have $f(2) = 3$. Therefore,

$$g(x) = \begin{cases} x & \text{for } x < 2 \\ 3 & \text{for } x = 2 \\ -\dfrac{1}{2}x + 5 & \text{for } x > 2 \end{cases}.$$

Related Exercises 15–16

EXAMPLE 4 **Graphing piecewise functions** Graph the following functions.

a. $f(x) = \begin{cases} \dfrac{x^2 - 5x + 6}{x - 2} & \text{for } x \neq 2 \\ 1 & \text{for } x = 2 \end{cases}$

b. $f(x) = |x|$, the absolute value function

SOLUTION

a. The function f is simplified by factoring and then canceling $x - 2$, assuming $x \neq 2$:

$$\frac{x^2 - 5x + 6}{x - 2} = \frac{(x - 2)(x - 3)}{x - 2} = x - 3$$

Therefore, the graph of f is identical to the graph of the line $y = x - 3$ when $x \neq 2$. We are given that $f(2) = 1$ (Figure 1.19).

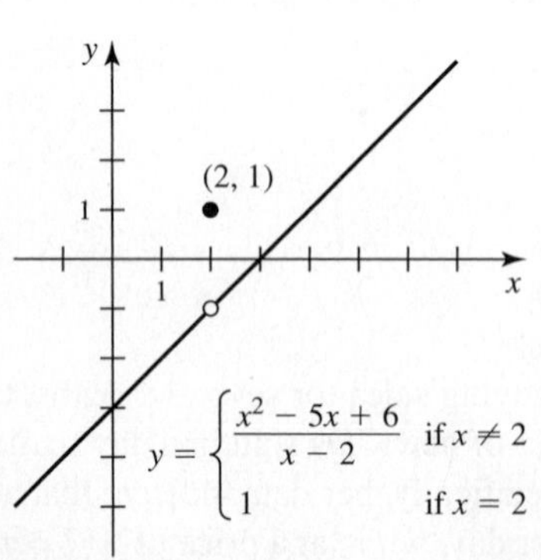

FIGURE 1.19

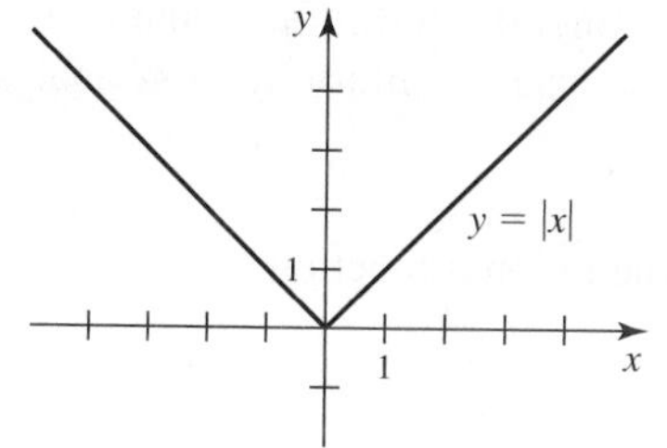

FIGURE 1.20

b. The absolute value of a real number is defined as

$$f(x) = |x| = \begin{cases} x & \text{for } x \geq 0 \\ -x & \text{for } x < 0 \end{cases}.$$

Graphing $y = -x$ for $x < 0$ and $y = x$ for $x \geq 0$ produces the graph in Figure 1.20.

Related Exercises 17–20

Power and Root Functions

1. **Power functions** are a special case of polynomials; they have the form $f(x) = x^n$, where n is a positive integer. When n is an even integer, the function values are nonnegative and the graph passes through the origin, opening upward (Figure 1.21). For odd integers, the power function $f(x) = x^n$ has values that are positive when x is positive and negative when x is negative (Figure 1.22).

QUICK CHECK 2 What is the range of $f(x) = x^7$? What is the range of $f(x) = x^8$?

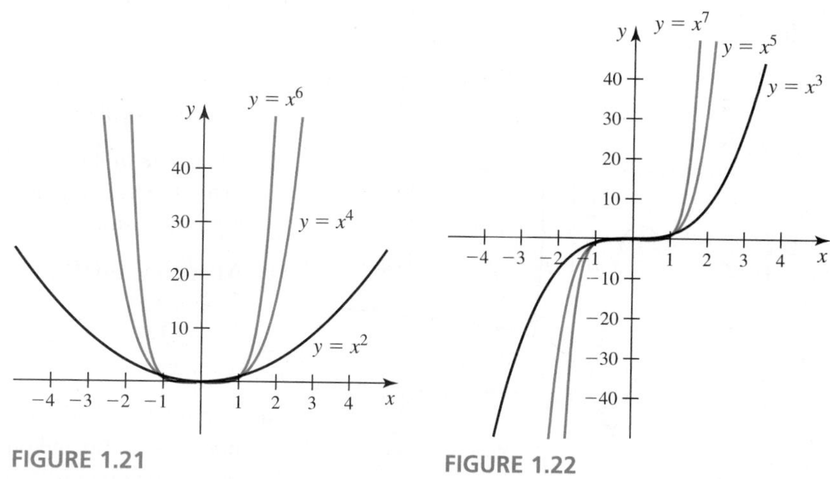

FIGURE 1.21

FIGURE 1.22

> Recall that if n is a positive integer, then $x^{1/n}$ is the nth root of x; that is, $f(x) = x^{1/n} = \sqrt[n]{x}$.

2. **Root functions** are a special case of algebraic functions; they have the form $f(x) = x^{1/n}$, where $n > 1$ is a positive integer. Notice that when n is even (square roots, fourth roots, and so forth), the domain and range consist of nonnegative numbers. Their graphs begin steeply at the origin and then flatten out as x increases (Figure 1.23).

   By contrast, the odd root functions (cube roots, fifth roots, and so forth) are defined for all real values of x; their range also consists of all real numbers. Their graphs pass through the origin, open upward for $x < 0$ and downward for $x > 0$, and flatten out as x increases in magnitude (Figure 1.24).

QUICK CHECK 3 What are the domain and range of $f(x) = x^{1/7}$? What are the domain and range of $f(x) = x^{1/10}$?

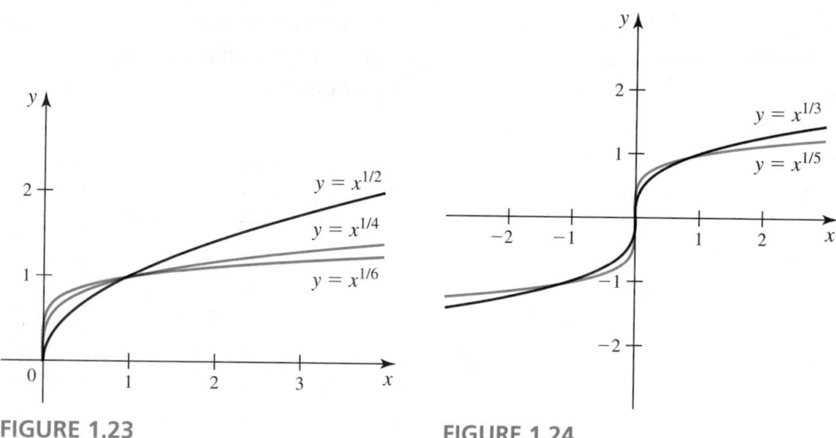

FIGURE 1.23

FIGURE 1.24

Rational Functions Rational functions figure prominently in this book and much is said later about graphing rational functions. The following example illustrates how analysis and technology work together.

EXAMPLE 5 **Technology and analysis** Consider the rational function

$$f(x) = \frac{3x^3 - x - 1}{x^3 + 2x^2 - 6}.$$

a. What is the domain of f?

b. Find the roots (zeros) of f.

c. Graph the function using a graphing utility.

d. At what points does the function have peaks and valleys?

e. How does f behave as x grows large in magnitude?

SOLUTION

a. The domain consists of all real numbers except those at which the denominator is zero. A computer algebra system shows that the denominator has one real zero at $x \approx 1.34$.

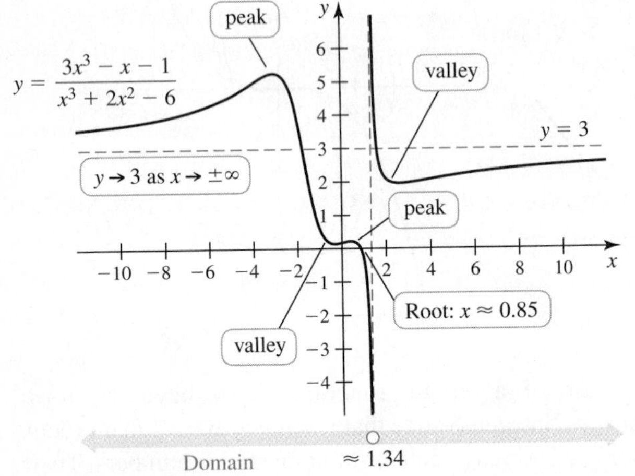

FIGURE 1.25

b. The roots of a rational function are the roots of the numerator, provided they are not also roots of the denominator. Using a computer algebra system, the only real root of the numerator is $x \approx 0.85$.

c. After experimenting with the graphing window, a reasonable graph of f is obtained (Figure 1.25). At the point where the denominator is zero, $x \approx 1.34$, the function becomes large in magnitude and f has a *vertical asymptote*.

d. The function has two peaks (soon to be called *local maxima*); one occurs near $x = -3.0$ and one occurs near $x = 0.4$. The function also has two valleys (soon to be called *local minima*); one occurs near $x = -0.3$ and one occurs near $x = 2.6$.

e. By zooming out, it appears that as x increases in the positive direction, the graph approaches the *horizontal asymptote* $y = 3$ from below, and as x becomes large and negative, the graph approaches $y = 3$ from above.

Related Exercises 21–24 ◀

Using Tables

Sometimes functions do not originate as formulas or graphs; they may start as numbers or data. For example, suppose you do an experiment in which a marble is dropped into a cylinder filled with heavy oil and is allowed to fall freely. You measure the total distance d, in cm, that the marble falls at times $t = 0, 1, 2, 3, 4, 5, 6,$ and 7 seconds after it is dropped (Table 1.1). The first step might be to plot the data points (Figure 1.26).

Table 1.1

t (s)	d (cm)
0	0
1	2
2	6
3	14
4	24
5	34
6	44
7	54

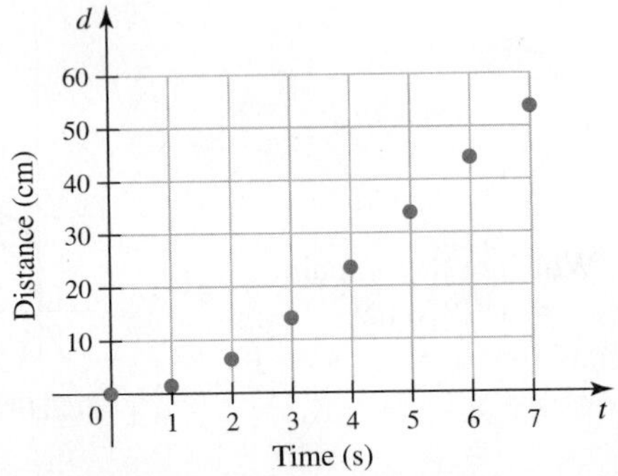

FIGURE 1.26

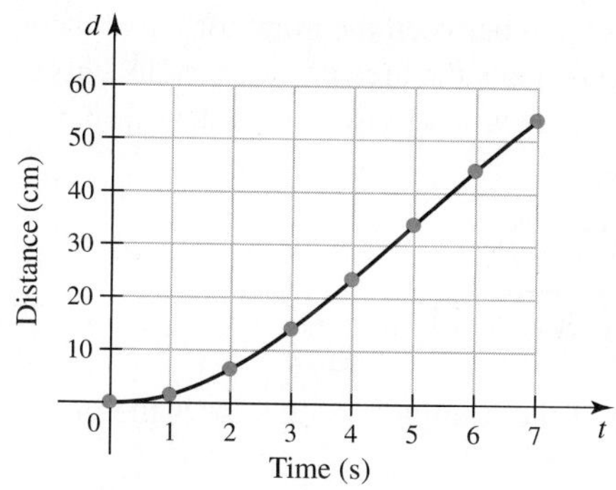

FIGURE 1.27

The data points suggest that there is a function $d = f(t)$ that gives the distance that the marble falls at *all* times of interest. Because the marble falls through the oil without abrupt changes, a smooth graph passing near the data points (Figure 1.27) is reasonable. Finding the best function that fits the data is a more difficult problem, which we discuss later in the text.

Using Words

Using words may be the least mathematical way to define functions, but it is often the way in which functions originate. Once a function is defined in words, it can often be tabulated, graphed, or expressed as a formula.

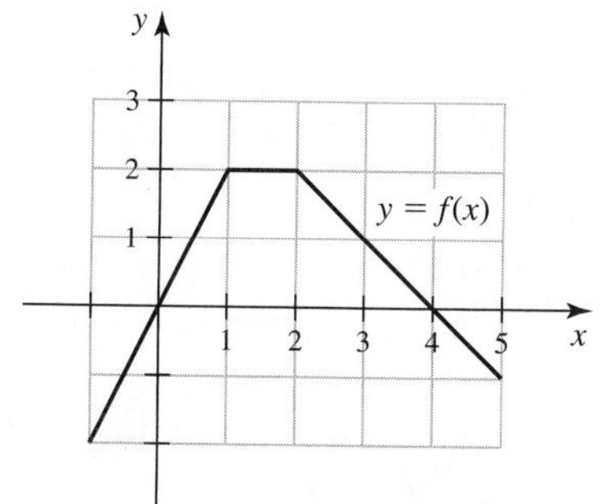

FIGURE 1.28

EXAMPLE 6 **A slope function** Let g be the **slope function** for a given function f. In words, this means that $g(x)$ is the slope of the curve $y = f(x)$ at the point $(x, f(x))$. Find and graph the slope function for the function f in Figure 1.28.

SOLUTION For $x < 1$, the slope of $y = f(x)$ is 2. The slope is 0 for $1 < x < 2$, and the slope is -1 for $x > 2$. At $x = 1$ and $x = 2$ the graph of f has a corner, so the slope is undefined at these points. Therefore, the domain of g is the set of all real numbers except $x = 1$ and $x = 2$, and the slope function is defined by the piecewise function (Figure 1.29)

$$g(x) = \begin{cases} 2 & \text{for } x < 1 \\ 0 & \text{for } 1 < x < 2. \\ -1 & \text{for } x > 2 \end{cases}$$

Related Exercises 25–26 ◀

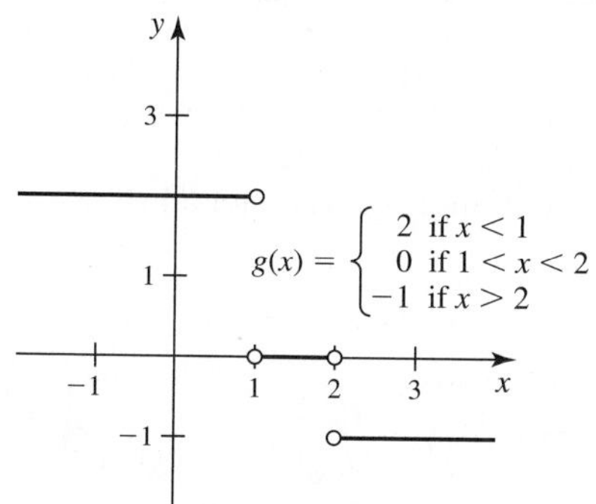

FIGURE 1.29

EXAMPLE 7 **An area function** Let A be an **area function** for a positive function f. In words, this means that $A(x)$ is the area of the region between the graph of f and the t-axis from $t = 0$ to $t = x$. Consider the function (Figure 1.30)

$$f(t) = \begin{cases} 2t & \text{for } 0 \le t \le 3 \\ 6 & \text{for } t > 3 \end{cases}.$$

a. Find $A(2)$ and $A(5)$.

b. Find a piecewise formula for the area function for f.

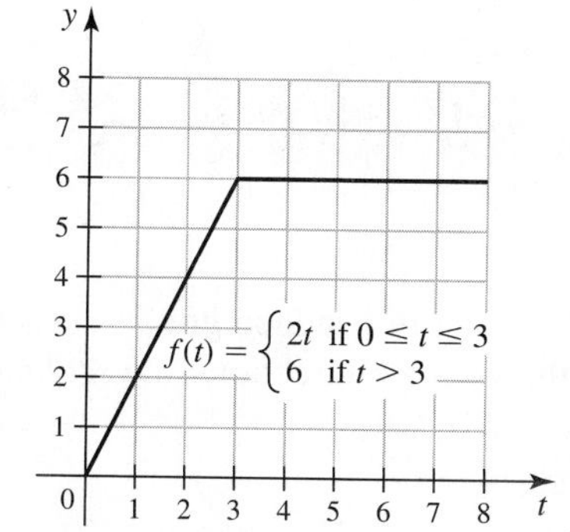

FIGURE 1.30

SOLUTION

a. The value of $A(2)$ is the area of the shaded region between the graph of f and the t-axis from $t = 0$ to $t = 2$ (Figure 1.31a). Using the formula for the area of a triangle,

$$A(2) = \frac{1}{2}(2)(4) = 4.$$

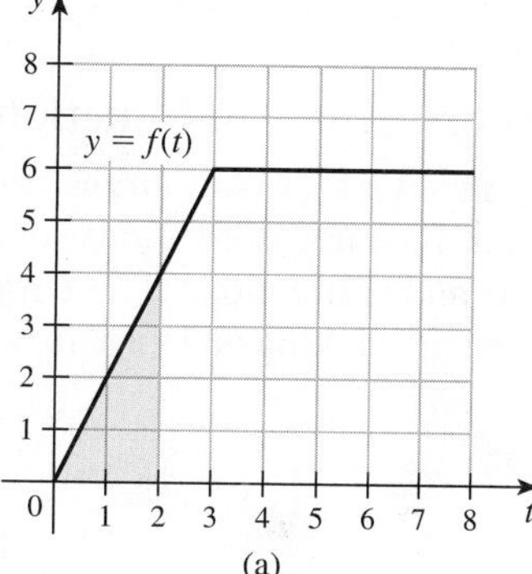

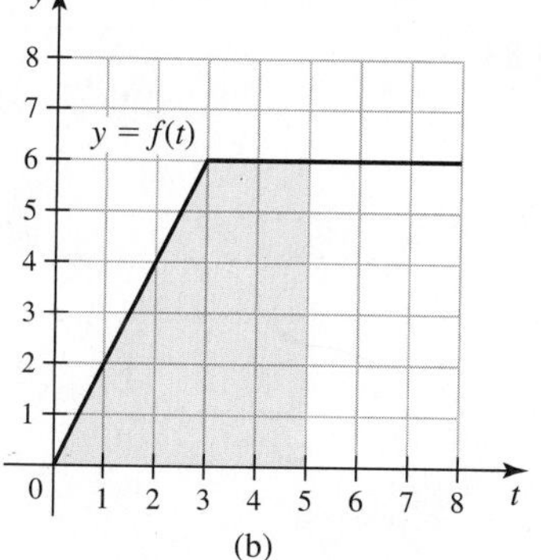

FIGURE 1.31

The value of $A(5)$ is the area of the shaded region between the graph of f and the t-axis from $t = 0$ to $t = 5$ (Figure 1.31b). This area equals the area of the triangle whose base is the interval $[0, 3]$ plus the area of the rectangle whose base is the interval $[3, 6]$:

$$A(5) = \underbrace{\frac{1}{2}(3)(6)}_{\text{area of the triangle}} + \underbrace{(2)(6)}_{\text{area of the rectangle}} = 21$$

b. For $0 \le x \le 3$ (Figure 1.32a), $A(x)$ is the area of the triangle whose base is the interval $[0, x]$. Because the height of the triangle at $t = x$ is $f(x)$,

$$A(x) = \frac{1}{2}xf(x) = \frac{1}{2}x\underbrace{(2x)}_{f(x)} = x^2.$$

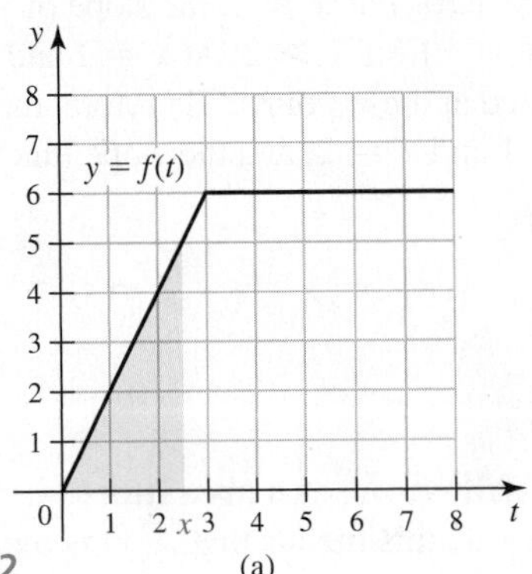

(a)

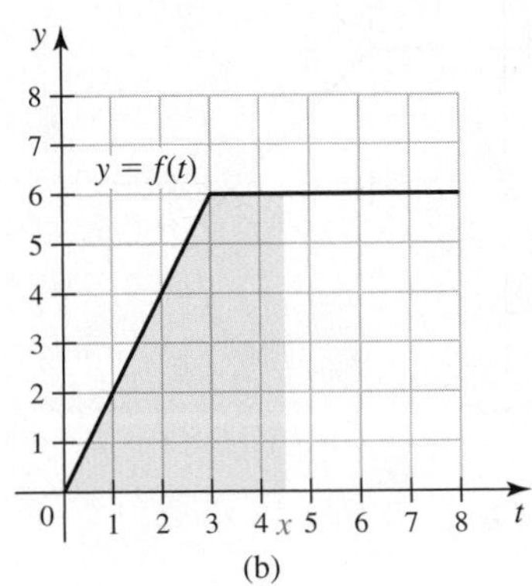

(b)

FIGURE 1.32

For $x > 3$ (Figure 1.32b), $A(x)$ is the area of the triangle on the interval $[0, 3]$ plus the area of the rectangle on the interval $[3, x]$:

$$A(x) = \underbrace{\frac{1}{2}(3)(6)}_{\text{area of the triangle}} + \underbrace{(x - 3)(6)}_{\text{area of the rectangle}} = 6x - 9$$

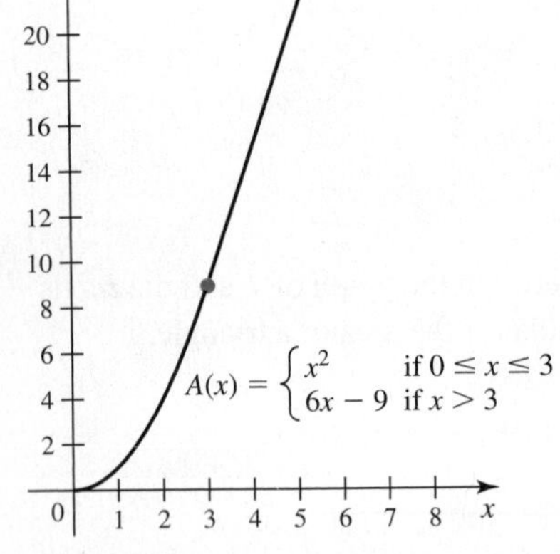

FIGURE 1.33

Therefore, the area function A (Figure 1.33) has the piecewise definition

$$y = A(x) = \begin{cases} x^2 & \text{for } 0 \le x \le 3 \\ 6x - 9 & \text{for } x > 3 \end{cases}.$$

Related Exercises 27–28 ◄

Transformations of Functions and Graphs

There are several ways to transform the graph of a function to produce graphs of new functions. Four transformations are common: *shifts* in the x- and y-directions and *scalings* in the x- and y-directions. These transformations, summarized in Figures 1.34–1.39, can save time in graphing and visualizing functions.

The graph of $y = f(x) + d$ is the graph of $y = f(x)$ shifted vertically by d units (up if $d > 0$ and down if $d < 0$).

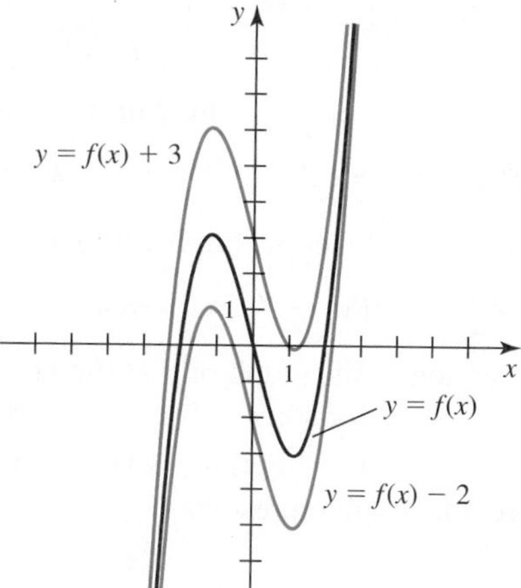

FIGURE 1.34

The graph of $y = f(x - b)$ is the graph of $y = f(x)$ shifted horizontally by b units (right if $b > 0$ and left if $b < 0$).

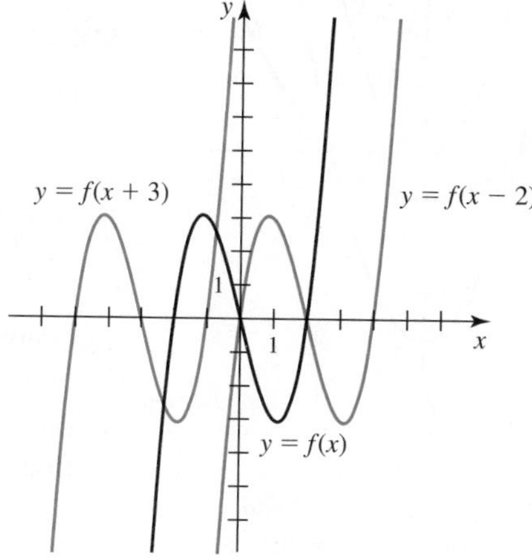

FIGURE 1.35

For $c > 0$, the graph of $y = cf(x)$ is the graph of $y = f(x)$ scaled vertically by a factor of c (broadened if $0 < c < 1$ and steepened if $c > 1$).

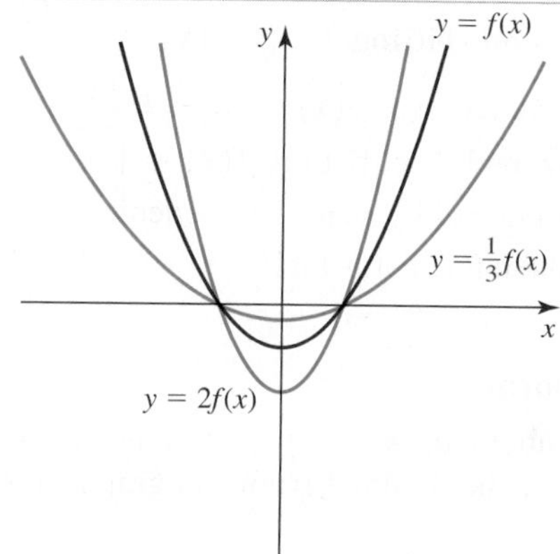

FIGURE 1.36

For $c < 0$, the graph of $y = cf(x)$ is the graph of $y = f(x)$ scaled vertically by a factor of $|c|$ and reflected across the x-axis (broadened if $-1 < c < 0$ and steepened if $c < -1$).

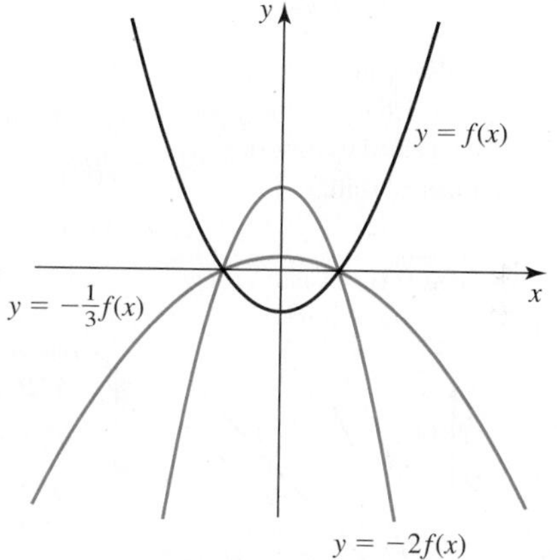

FIGURE 1.37

For $a > 0$, the graph of $y = f(ax)$ is the graph of $y = f(x)$ scaled horizontally by a factor of a (broadened if $0 < a < 1$ and steepened if $a > 1$).

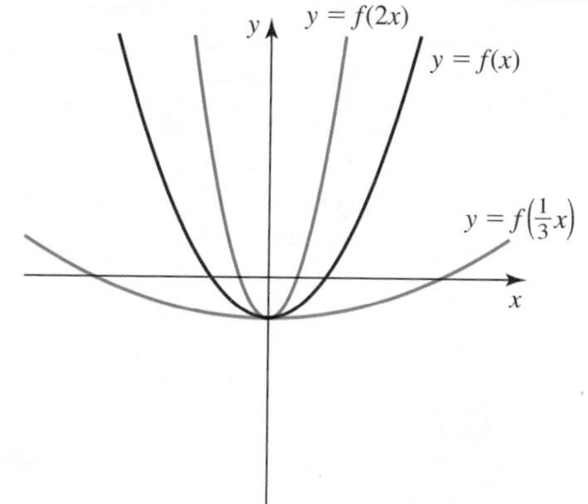

FIGURE 1.38

For $a < 0$, the graph of $y = f(ax)$ is the graph of $y = f(x)$ scaled horizontally by a factor of $|a|$ and reflected about the y-axis (broadened if $-1 < a < 0$ and steepened if $a < -1$).

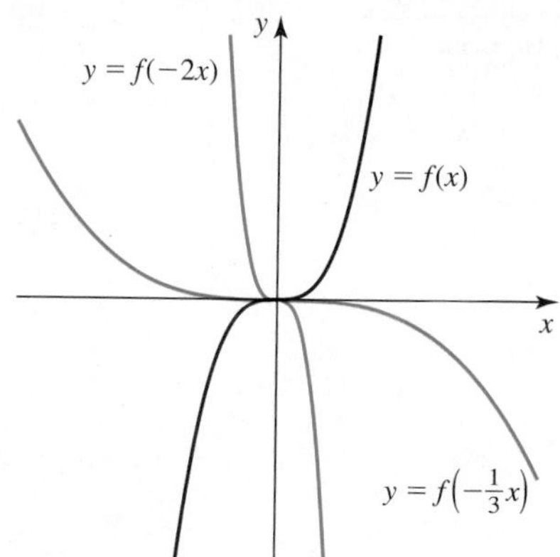

FIGURE 1.39

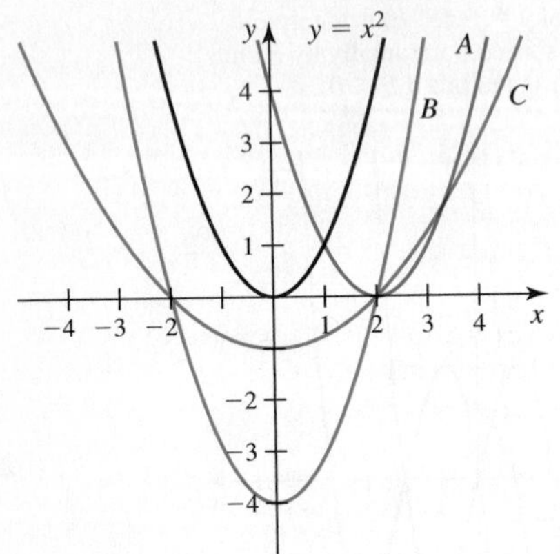

FIGURE 1.40

➤ You should verify that curve C also corresponds to a horizontal scaling and a vertical shift. It has the equation $y = f(ax) - 1$, where $a = \frac{1}{2}$.

EXAMPLE 8 Shifting parabolas The graphs A, B, and C in Figure 1.40 are obtained from the graph of $f(x) = x^2$ using shifts and scalings. Find the function that describes each graph.

SOLUTION

a. Graph A is the graph of f shifted to the right by 2 units. It represents the function

$$f(x - 2) = (x - 2)^2 = x^2 - 4x + 4.$$

b. Graph B is the graph of f shifted down by 4 units. It represents the function

$$f(x) - 4 = x^2 - 4.$$

c. Graph C is a broadened version of the graph of f shifted down by 1 unit. Therefore, it represents $cf(x) - 1 = cx^2 - 1$, for some value of c, with $0 < c < 1$ (because the graph is broadened). Using the fact that graph C passes through the points $(\pm 2, 0)$, we find that $c = \frac{1}{4}$. Therefore, the graph represents

$$y = \frac{1}{4}f(x) - 1 = \frac{1}{4}x^2 - 1.$$

Related Exercises 29–38 ◄

QUICK CHECK 4 How do you modify the graph of $f(x) = 1/x$ to produce the graph of $g(x) = 1/(x + 4)$? ◄

➤ Note that we can also write $g(x) = 2\left|x + \frac{1}{2}\right|$, which means the graph of g may also be obtained by a vertical scaling and a horizontal shift.

EXAMPLE 9 Scaling and shifting Graph $g(x) = |2x + 1|$.

SOLUTION We write the function as $g(x) = \left|2\left(x + \frac{1}{2}\right)\right|$ so it can be interpreted as a horizontal scaling and a horizontal shift. Letting $f(x) = |x|$, we have $g(x) = f\left(2\left(x + \frac{1}{2}\right)\right)$. Thus, the graph of g is obtained by scaling (steepening) the graph of f horizontally and shifting it $\frac{1}{2}$-unit to the left (Figure 1.41).

Related Exercises 29–38 ◄

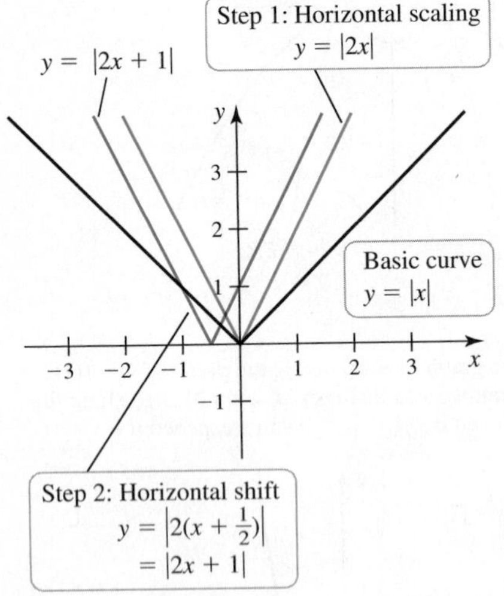

FIGURE 1.41

SUMMARY Transformations

Given the real numbers a, b, c, and d, and the function f, the graph of $y = cf(a(x - b)) + d$ is obtained from the graph of $y = f(x)$ in the following steps.

$y = f(x)$ —*horizontal scaling by a factor of $|a|$*→ $y = f(ax)$

—*horizontal shift by b units*→ $y = f(a(x - b))$

—*vertical scaling by a factor of $|c|$*→ $y = cf(a(x - b))$

—*vertical shift by d units*→ $y = cf(a(x - b)) + d$

SECTION 1.2 EXERCISES

Review Questions

1. Give four ways that functions may be defined and represented.
2. What is the domain of a polynomial?
3. What is the domain of a rational function?
4. Describe what is meant by a piecewise linear function.
5. Sketch a graph of $y = x^5$.
6. Sketch a graph of $y = x^{1/5}$.
7. If you have the graph of $y = f(x)$, how do you obtain the graph of $y = f(x + 2)$?
8. If you have the graph of $y = f(x)$, how do you obtain the graph of $y = -3f(x)$?
9. If you have the graph of $y = f(x)$, how do you obtain the graph of $y = f(3x)$?
10. Given the graph of $y = x^2$, how do you obtain the graph of $y = 4(x + 3)^2 + 6$?

Basic Skills

11–12. Graphs of functions *Find the linear functions that correspond to the following graphs.*

11.

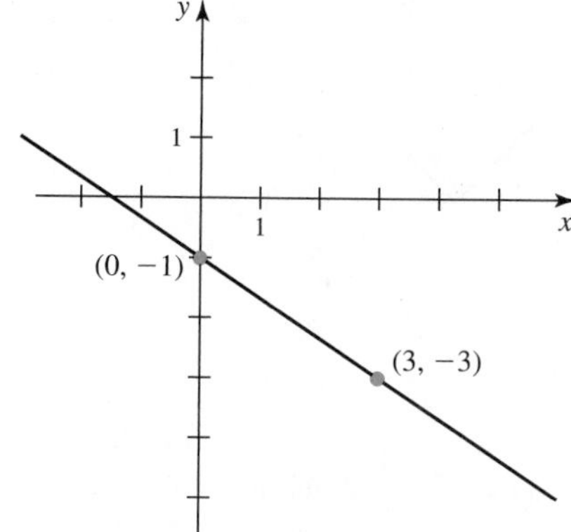

12.

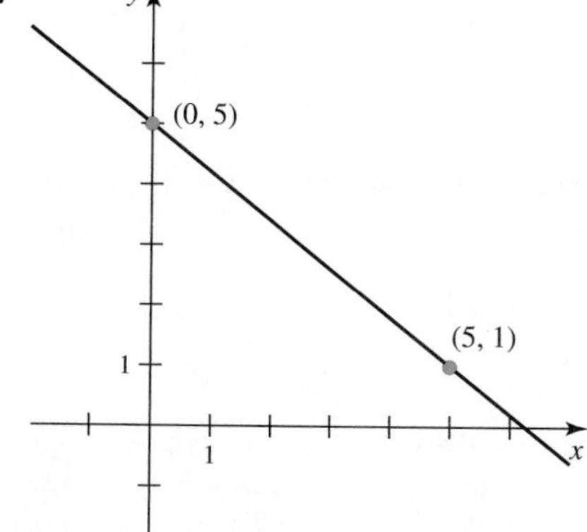

13. Demand function Sales records indicate that if DVD players are priced at \$250, then a large store sells an average of 12 units per day. If they are priced at \$200, then the store sells an average of 15 units per day. Find and graph the linear demand function for DVD sales. For what prices is the demand function defined?

14. Fundraiser The Biology Club plans to have a fundraiser for which \$8 tickets will be sold. The cost of room rental and refreshments is \$175. Find and graph the function $p = f(n)$ that gives the profit from the fundraiser when n tickets are sold. Notice that $f(0) = -\$175$; that is, the cost of room rental and refreshments must be paid regardless of how many tickets are sold. How many tickets must be sold to break even (zero profit)?

15–16. Graphs of piecewise functions *Write a definition of the functions whose graphs are given.*

15.

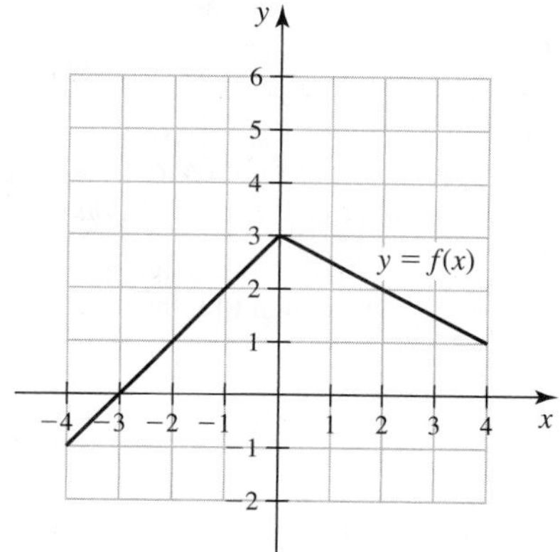

16.

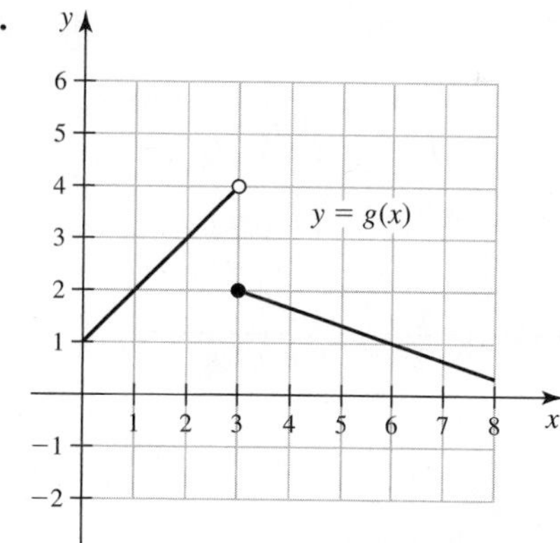

17–20. Piecewise linear functions *Graph the following functions.*

17. $f(x) = \begin{cases} 3x - 1 & \text{for } x \leq 0 \\ -2x + 1 & \text{for } x > 0 \end{cases}$

18. $f(x) = \begin{cases} 3x - 1 & \text{for } x < 1 \\ x + 1 & \text{for } x \geq 1 \end{cases}$

19. $f(x) = \begin{cases} -2x - 1 & \text{for } x < -1 \\ 1 & \text{for } -1 \leq x \leq 1 \\ 2x - 1 & \text{for } x > 1 \end{cases}$

20. $f(x) = \begin{cases} 2x + 2 & \text{for } x < 0 \\ x + 2 & \text{for } 0 \leq x \leq 2 \\ 3 - x/2 & \text{for } x > 2 \end{cases}$

21–24. Graphs of functions

a. *Use a graphing utility to produce a graph of the given function. Experiment with your choice of plot windows to see how the graph changes on different scales.*

b. *Classify the function and give its domain.*

c. *Discuss the interesting features of the function such as peaks, valleys, and intercepts (as in Example 5).*

21. $f(x) = x^3 - 2x^2 + 6$

22. $f(x) = \sqrt[3]{2x^2 - 8}$

23. $g(x) = \left|\dfrac{x^2 - 4}{x + 3}\right|$

24. $f(x) = \dfrac{\sqrt{3x^2 - 12}}{x + 1}$

25–26. Slope functions *Determine the slope function for the following functions.*

25. Use the figure for Exercise 15.

26. Use the figure for Exercise 16.

27–28. Area functions *Let $A(x)$ be the area of the region bounded by the t-axis and the graph of $y = f(t)$ from $t = 0$ to $t = x$. Consider the following functions and graphs.*

a. Find $A(2)$ **b.** Find $A(6)$ **c.** Find a formula for $A(x)$

27. $f(t) = 6$ (see figure)

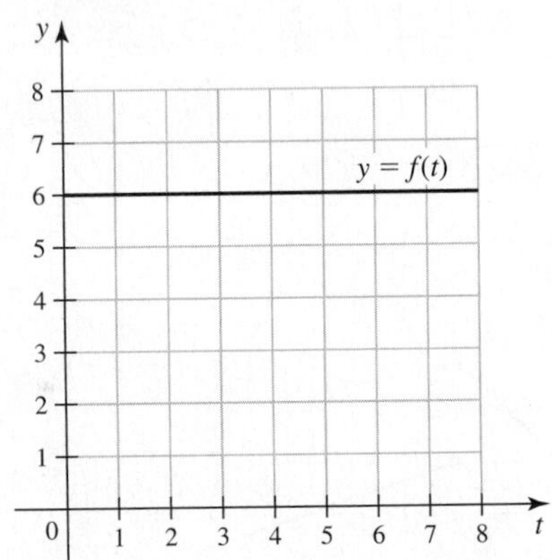

28. $y = f(t) = \begin{cases} -t + 2 & \text{for } t \le 2 \\ 2t - 4 & \text{for } 2 < t < 4 \\ -\frac{1}{2}t + 6 & \text{for } t \ge 4 \end{cases}$ (see figure)

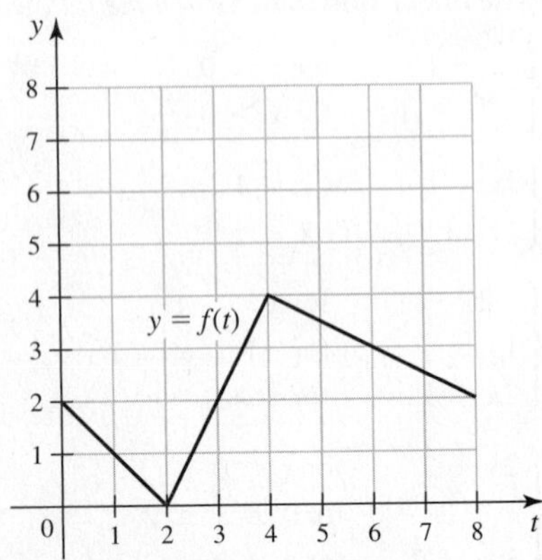

29. Transformations of $y = |x|$ The functions f and g in the figure were obtained by vertical and horizontal shifts and scalings of $y = |x|$. Find formulas for f and g. Verify your answers with a graphing utility.

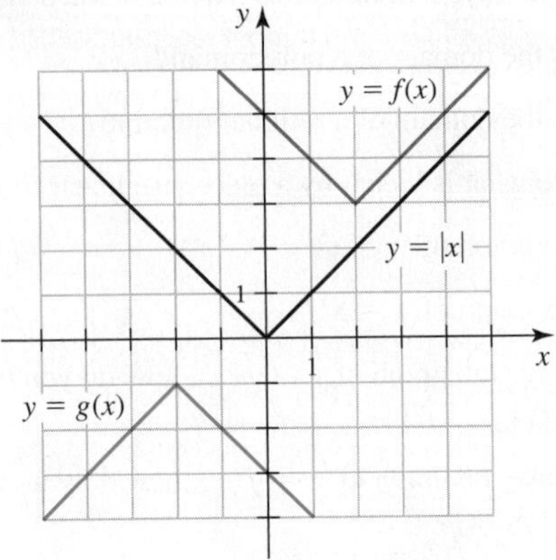

30. Transformations Use the graph of f in the figure to plot the following functions.

a. $y = -f(x)$ **b.** $y = f(x + 2)$ **c.** $y = f(x - 2)$

d. $y = f(2x)$ **e.** $y = f(x - 1) + 2$ **f.** $y = 2f(x)$

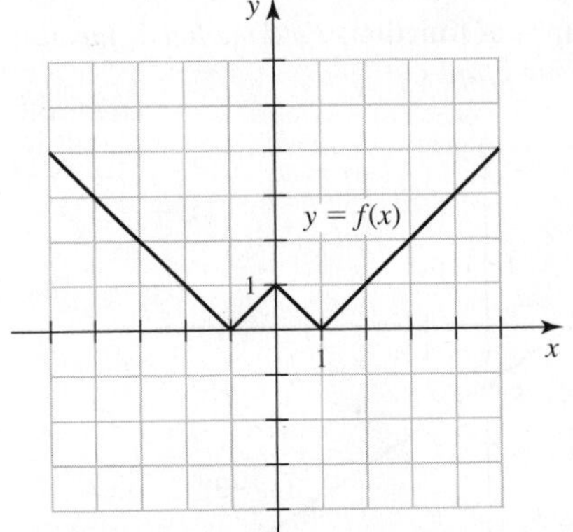

31. Transformations of $f(x) = x^2$ Use shifts and scalings to transform the graph of $f(x) = x^2$ into the graph of g. Use a graphing utility only to check your work.

a. $g(x) = f(x - 3)$ **b.** $g(x) = f(2x - 4)$

c. $g(x) = -3f(x - 2) + 4$ **d.** $g(x) = 6f\left(\dfrac{x - 2}{3}\right) + 1$

32. Transformations of $f(x) = \sqrt{x}$ Use shifts and scalings to transform the graph of $f(x) = \sqrt{x}$ into the graph of g. Use a graphing utility only to check your work.

a. $g(x) = f(x + 4)$ **b.** $g(x) = 2f(2x - 1)$

c. $g(x) = \sqrt{x - 1}$ **d.** $g(x) = 3\sqrt{x - 1} - 5$

33–38. Shifting and scaling *Use shifts and scalings to graph the given functions. Then check your work with a graphing utility. Be sure to identify an original function on which the shifts and scalings are performed.*

33. $g(x) = -3x^2$

34. $g(x) = 2x^3 - 1$

35. $g(x) = 2(x + 3)^2$

36. $p(x) = x^2 + 3x - 5$

37. $h(x) = -4x^2 - 4x + 12$

38. $h(x) = |3x - 6| + 1$

Further Explorations

39. Explain why or why not Determine whether the following statements are true and give an explanation or a counterexample.

a. All polynomials are rational functions, but not all rational functions are polynomials.
b. If f is a linear polynomial, then $f \circ f$ is a quadratic polynomial.
c. If f and g are polynomials, then the degrees of $f \circ g$ and $g \circ f$ are equal.
d. To graph $g(x) = f(x + 2)$, shift the graph of f two units to the right.

40–41. Intersection problems *Use analytical methods to find the following points of intersection. Use a graphing utility only to check your work.*

40. Find the point(s) of intersection between the parabola $y = x^2 + 2$ and the line $y = x + 4$.

41. Find the point(s) of intersection between the parabolas $y = x^2$ and $y = -x^2 + 8x$.

42–43. Functions from tables *Find a simple function that fits the data in the tables.*

42.

x	y
−1	0
0	1
1	2
2	3
3	4

43.

x	y
0	−1
1	0
4	1
9	2
16	3

T **44–47. Functions from words** *Find a formula for a function describing the given situation. Graph the function and give a domain that makes sense for the problem. Recall that with constant speed, distance = speed · time elapsed or $d = vt$.*

44. A function $y = f(x)$ such that y is 1 less than the cube of x.

45. A function $y = f(x)$ such that if you run at a constant rate of 5 mi/hr for x hours, then you run y miles.

46. A function $y = f(x)$ such that if you ride a bike for 50 mi at x miles per hour, you arrive at your destination in y hours.

47. A function $y = f(x)$ such that if your car gets 32 mi/gal and gasoline costs $\$x$/gallon, then \$100 is the cost of taking a y-mile trip.

48. Floor function The floor function, or greatest integer function, $f(x) = \lfloor x \rfloor$, gives the greatest integer less than or equal to x. Graph the floor function for $-3 \leq x \leq 3$.

49. Ceiling function The ceiling function, or smallest integer function, $f(x) = \lceil x \rceil$, gives the smallest integer greater than or equal to x. Graph the ceiling function for $-3 \leq x \leq 3$.

50. Sawtooth wave Graph the sawtooth wave defined by

$$f(x) = \begin{cases} \vdots & \vdots \\ x + 1 & \text{for } -1 \leq x < 0 \\ x & \text{for } 0 \leq x < 1 \\ x - 1 & \text{for } 1 \leq x < 2 \\ x - 2 & \text{for } 2 \leq x < 3 \\ \vdots & \vdots \end{cases}$$

51. Square wave Graph the square wave defined by

$$f(x) = \begin{cases} 0 & \text{for } x < 0 \\ 1 & \text{for } 0 \leq x < 1 \\ 0 & \text{for } 1 \leq x < 2 \\ 1 & \text{for } 2 \leq x < 3 \\ & \vdots \end{cases}$$

52–54. Roots and powers *Make a rough sketch of the given pairs of functions. Be sure to draw the graphs accurately relative to each other.*

52. $y = x^4$ and $y = x^6$

53. $y = x^3$ and $y = x^7$

54. $y = x^{1/3}$ and $y = x^{1/5}$

Applications

55. Bald eagle population Since DDT was banned and the Endangered Species Act was passed in 1973, the number of bald eagles in the United States has increased dramatically (see figure). In the lower 48 states, the number of breeding pairs of bald eagles increased at a nearly linear rate from 1875 pairs in 1986 to 6471 pairs in the year 2000.

a. Find a linear function $p(t)$ that models the number of breeding pairs from 1986 to 2000 $(0 \leq t \leq 14)$.
b. Using the function in part (a), approximately how many breeding pairs were in the lower 48 states in 1995?

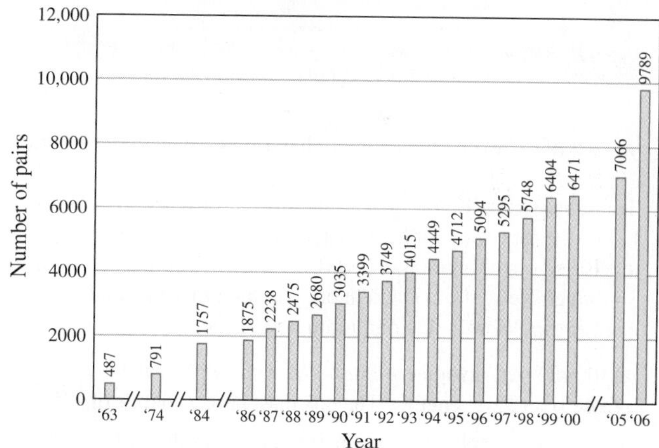

Source: U.S. Fish and Wildlife Service

56. Temperature scales

a. Find the linear function $C = f(F)$ that gives the reading on the Celsius temperature scale corresponding to a reading on the Fahrenheit scale. Use the facts that $C = 0$ when $F = 32$ (freezing point) and $C = 100$ when $F = 212$ (boiling point).
b. At what temperature are the Celsius and Fahrenheit readings equal?

57. Automobile lease vs. buy A car dealer offers a purchase option and a lease option on all new cars. Suppose you are interested in a car that can be bought outright for \$25,000 or leased for a start-up fee of \$1200 plus monthly payments of \$350.

a. Find the linear function $y = f(m)$ that gives the total amount you have paid on the lease option after m months.

b. With the lease option, after a 48-month (4-year) term, the car has a residual value of \$10,000, which is the amount that you could pay to purchase the car. Assuming no other costs, should you lease or buy?

58–59. Functions from geometry

58. The surface area of a sphere of radius r is $S = 4\pi r^2$. Solve for r in terms of S and graph the radius function for $S \geq 0$.

T 59. A single slice through a sphere of radius r produces a *cap* of the sphere. If the thickness of the cap is h, then its volume is $V = \frac{1}{3}\pi h^2(3r - h)$. Graph the volume as a function of h for a sphere of radius 1. For what values of h does this function make sense?

T 60. Walking and rowing Kelly has finished a picnic on an island that is 200 m off shore (see figure). She wants to return to a beach house that is 600 m from the point P on the shore closest to the island. She plans to row a boat to a point on shore x meters from P and then jog along the (straight) shore to the house.

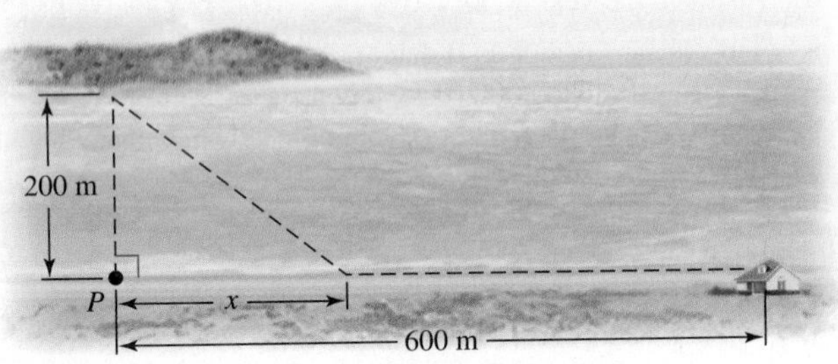

a. Let $d(x)$ be the total length of her trip as a function of x. Graph this function.

b. Suppose that Kelly can row at 2 m/s and jog at 4 m/s. Let $T(x)$ be the total time for her trip as a function of x. Graph $y = T(x)$.

c. Based on your graph in part (b), estimate the point on the shore at which Kelly should land in order to minimize the total time of her trip. What is that minimum time?

T 61. Optimal boxes Imagine a lidless box with height h and a square base whose sides have length x. The box must have a volume of 125 ft^3.

a. Find and graph the function $S(x)$ that gives the surface area of the box for all values of $x > 0$.

b. Based on your graph in part (a), estimate the value of x that produces the box with a minimum surface area.

Additional Exercises

62. Composition of polynomials Let f be an nth-degree polynomial and let g be an mth-degree polynomial. What is the degree of the following polynomials?

a. $f \cdot f$ **b.** $f \circ f$ **c.** $f \cdot g$ **d.** $f \circ g$

63. Parabola vertex property Prove that if a parabola crosses the x-axis twice, the x-coordinate of the vertex of the parabola is halfway between the x-intercepts.

64. Parabola properties Consider the general quadratic function $f(x) = ax^2 + bx + c$, with $a \neq 0$.

a. Find the coordinates of the vertex in terms of a, b, and c.

b. Find the conditions on a, b, and c that guarantee that the graph of f crosses the x-axis twice.

65. Factorial function The factorial function is defined for positive integers as $n! = n(n - 1)(n - 2)\cdots 3 \cdot 2 \cdot 1$.

a. Make a table of the factorial function for $n = 1, 2, 3, 4, 5$.

b. Graph these data points and then connect them with a smooth curve.

c. What is the least value of n for which $n! > 10^6$?

66. Sum of integers Let $S(n) = 1 + 2 + \cdots + n$, where n is a positive integer. It can be shown that $S(n) = n(n + 1)/2$.

a. Make a table of $S(n)$ for $n = 1, 2, \ldots, 10$.

b. How would you describe the domain of this function?

c. What is the least value of n for which $S(n) > 1000$?

67. Sum of squared integers Let $T(n) = 1^2 + 2^2 + \cdots + n^2$, where n is a positive integer. It can be shown that $T(n) = n(n + 1)(2n + 1)/6$.

a. Make a table of $T(n)$ for $n = 1, 2, \ldots, 10$.

b. How would you describe the domain of this function?

c. What is the least value of n for which $T(n) > 1000$?

QUICK CHECK ANSWERS

1. Yes; no **2.** $(-\infty, \infty), [0, \infty)$ **3.** Domain and range are $(-\infty, \infty)$. Domain and range are $[0, \infty)$. **4.** Shift the graph of f horizontally 4 units to the left. ◄

1.3 Trigonometric Functions

This section is a review of what you need to know in order to study the calculus of trigonometric functions.

Radian Measure

Calculus typically requires that angles be measured in **radians** (rad). Working with a circle of radius r, the radian measure of an angle θ is the length of the arc associated with θ, denoted s, divided by the radius of the circle r (Figure 1.42a). Working on a unit circle

Degrees	Radians
0	0
30	$\pi/6$
45	$\pi/4$
60	$\pi/3$
90	$\pi/2$
120	$2\pi/3$
135	$3\pi/4$
150	$5\pi/6$
180	π

$(r = 1)$, the radian measure of an angle is simply the length of the arc s associated with θ (Figure 1.42b). For example, the length of a full unit circle is 2π; therefore, an angle with a radian measure of π corresponds to a half circle ($\theta = 180°$) and an angle with a radian measure of $\pi/2$ corresponds to a quarter circle ($\theta = 90°$).

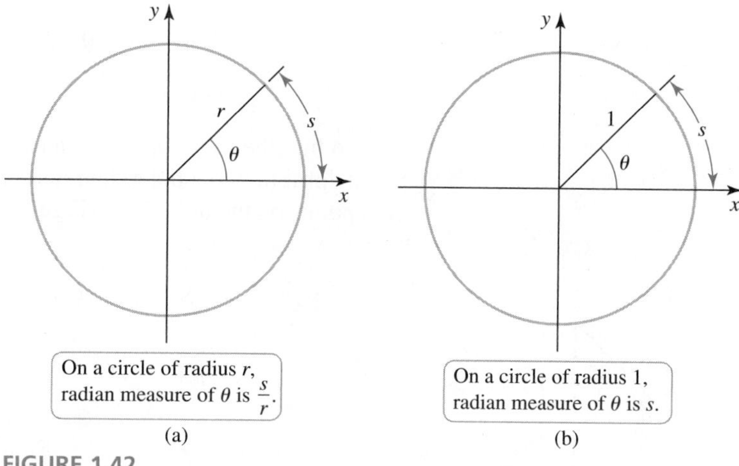

FIGURE 1.42

QUICK CHECK 1 What is the radian measure of a 270° angle? What is the degree measure of a $5\pi/4$-rad angle?

Trigonometric Functions

For acute angles, the trigonometric functions are defined as ratios of the sides of a right triangle (Figure 1.43). To extend these definitions to include all angles, we work in an xy-coordinate system with a circle of radius r centered at the origin. Suppose that $P(x, y)$ is a point on the circle. An angle θ is in **standard position** if its initial side is on the positive x-axis and its terminal side is the line segment OP between the origin and P. An angle is positive if it is obtained by a counterclockwise rotation from the positive x-axis (Figure 1.44). When the right-triangle definitions of Figure 1.43 are used with the right triangle in Figure 1.44, the trigonometric functions may be expressed in terms of x, y, and the radius of the circle, $r = \sqrt{x^2 + y^2}$.

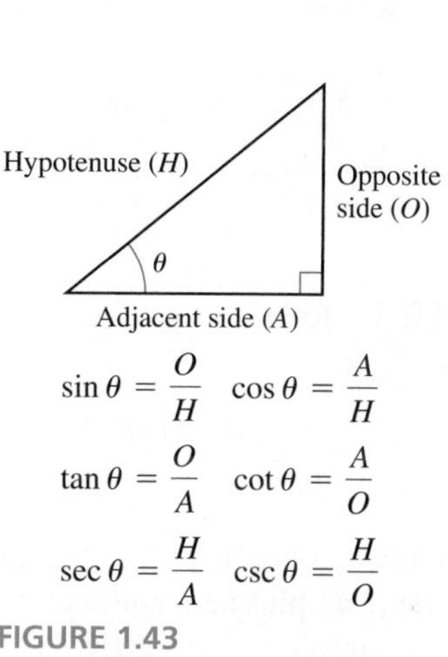

$$\sin\theta = \frac{O}{H} \quad \cos\theta = \frac{A}{H}$$

$$\tan\theta = \frac{O}{A} \quad \cot\theta = \frac{A}{O}$$

$$\sec\theta = \frac{H}{A} \quad \csc\theta = \frac{H}{O}$$

FIGURE 1.43

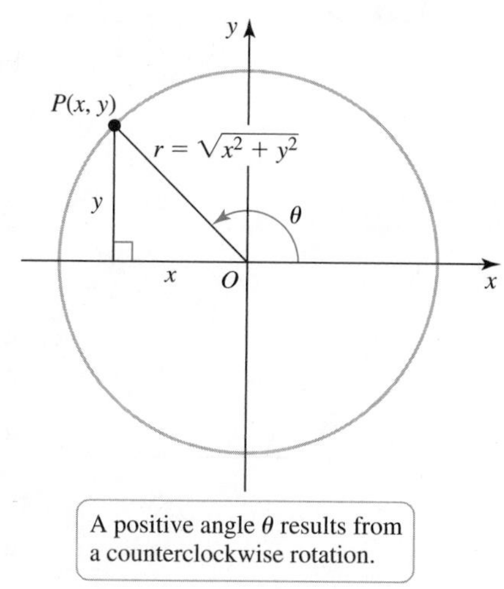

FIGURE 1.44

➤ When working on a unit circle ($r = 1$), these definitions become

$$\sin\theta = y \qquad \cos\theta = x$$

$$\tan\theta = \frac{y}{x} \qquad \cot\theta = \frac{x}{y}$$

$$\sec\theta = \frac{1}{x} \qquad \csc\theta = \frac{1}{y}$$

DEFINITION Trigonometric Functions

Let $P(x, y)$ be a point on a circle of radius r associated with the angle θ. Then

$$\sin\theta = \frac{y}{r} \qquad \cos\theta = \frac{x}{r} \qquad \tan\theta = \frac{y}{x}$$

$$\cot\theta = \frac{x}{y} \qquad \sec\theta = \frac{r}{x} \qquad \csc\theta = \frac{r}{y}$$

To find the trigonometric functions of the standard angles (multiples of 30° and 45°), it is helpful to know the radian measure of those angles and the coordinates of the associated points on the unit circle (Figure 1.45).

➤ Standard Triangles

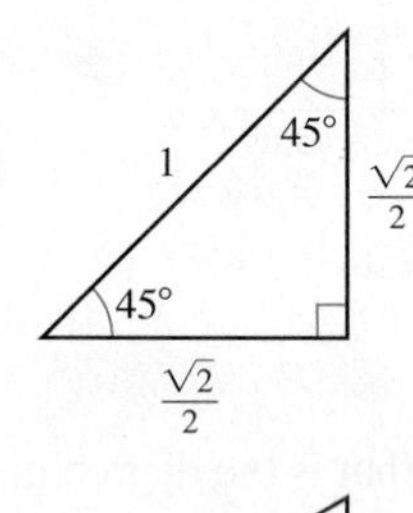

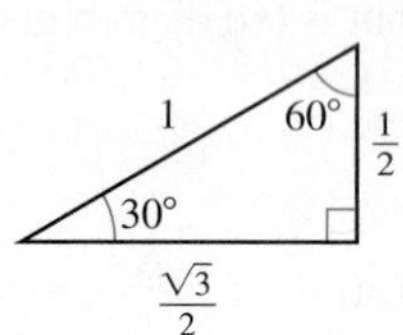

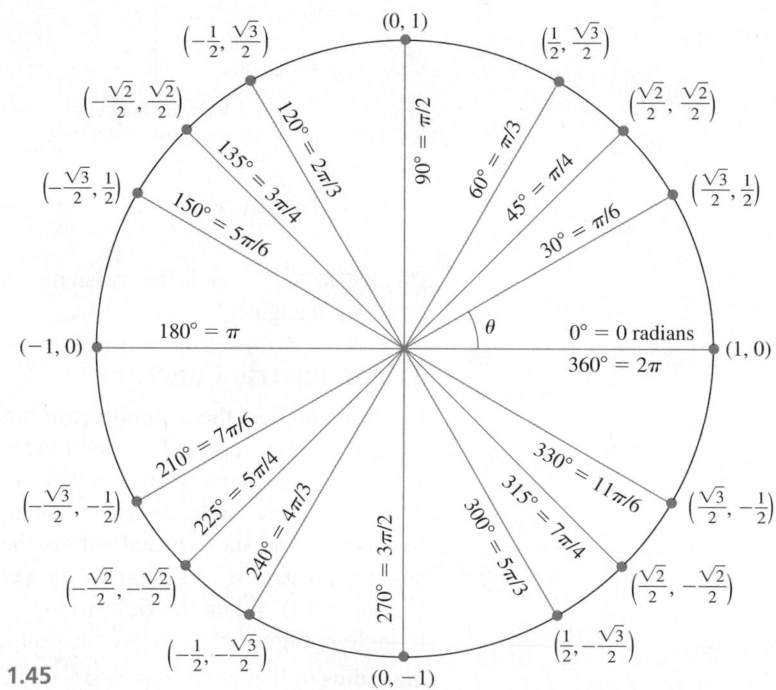

FIGURE 1.45

Combining the definitions of the trigonometric functions with the coordinates shown in Figure 1.45, we may evaluate these functions at any standard angle. For example,

$$\sin\frac{2\pi}{3} = \frac{\sqrt{3}}{2} \qquad \cos\frac{5\pi}{6} = -\frac{\sqrt{3}}{2} \qquad \tan\frac{7\pi}{6} = \frac{1}{\sqrt{3}}$$

$$\cot\frac{5\pi}{3} = -\frac{1}{\sqrt{3}} \qquad \sec\frac{7\pi}{4} = \sqrt{2} \qquad \csc\frac{3\pi}{2} = -1$$

EXAMPLE 1 Evaluating trigonometric functions Evaluate the following expressions.

a. $\sin(8\pi/3)$ **b.** $\csc(-11\pi/3)$

SOLUTION

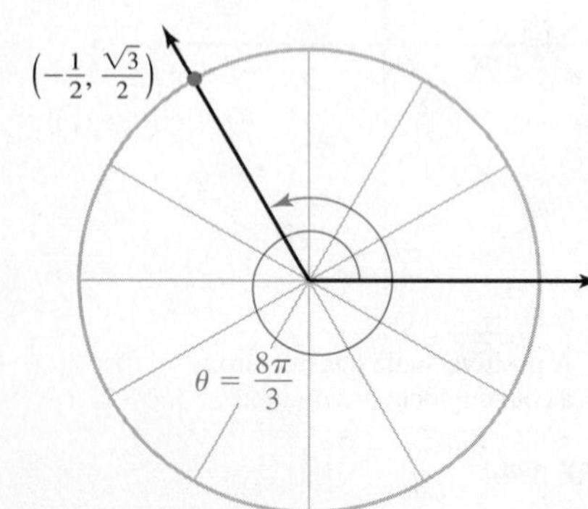

FIGURE 1.46

a. The angle $8\pi/3 = 2\pi + 2\pi/3$ corresponds to a *counterclockwise* revolution of one full circle (2π) plus an additional $2\pi/3$ rad (Figure 1.46). Therefore, this angle has the same terminal side as the angle $2\pi/3$, and the corresponding point on the unit circle is $(-1/2, \sqrt{3}/2)$. It follows that $\sin(8\pi/3) = y = \sqrt{3}/2$.

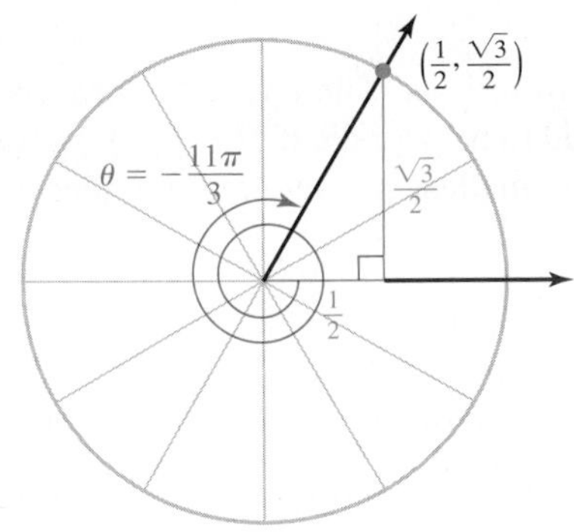

FIGURE 1.47

b. The angle $\theta = -11\pi/3 = -2\pi - 5\pi/3$ corresponds to a *clockwise* revolution of one full circle (2π) plus an additional $5\pi/3$ rad (Figure 1.47). Therefore, this angle has the same terminal side as the angle $\pi/3$. The coordinates of the corresponding point on the unit circle are $(1/2, \sqrt{3}/2)$, so $\csc(-11\pi/3) = 1/y = 2/\sqrt{3}$.

Related Exercises 9–16 ◀

QUICK CHECK 2 Evaluate $\cos(11\pi/6)$ and $\sin(5\pi/4)$. ◀

Trigonometric Identities

Trigonometric functions have a variety of properties, called **identities**, that are true for all angles in the domain. Here is a list of some commonly used identities.

Trigonometric Identities

Reciprocal Identities

$$\tan\theta = \frac{\sin\theta}{\cos\theta} \qquad \cot\theta = \frac{1}{\tan\theta} = \frac{\cos\theta}{\sin\theta}$$

$$\csc\theta = \frac{1}{\sin\theta} \qquad \sec\theta = \frac{1}{\cos\theta}$$

Pythagorean Identities

$$\sin^2\theta + \cos^2\theta = 1 \qquad 1 + \cot^2\theta = \csc^2\theta \qquad \tan^2\theta + 1 = \sec^2\theta$$

Double- and Half-Angle Formulas

$$\sin 2\theta = 2\sin\theta\cos\theta \qquad \cos 2\theta = \cos^2\theta - \sin^2\theta$$

$$\cos^2\theta = \frac{1 + \cos 2\theta}{2} \qquad \sin^2\theta = \frac{1 - \cos 2\theta}{2}$$

QUICK CHECK 3 Prove that $1 + \cot^2\theta = \csc^2\theta$. ◀

EXAMPLE 2 **Solving trigonometric equations** Solve the following equations.

a. $\sqrt{2}\sin x + 1 = 0$ **b.** $\cos 2x = \sin 2x$ where $0 \le x < 2\pi$

SOLUTION

a. First, we solve for $\sin x$ to obtain $\sin x = -1/\sqrt{2} = -\sqrt{2}/2$. From the unit circle (Figure 1.45), we find that $\sin x = -\sqrt{2}/2$ if $x = 5\pi/4$ or $x = 7\pi/4$. Adding integer multiples of 2π produces additional solutions. Therefore, the set of all solutions is

$$x = \frac{5\pi}{4} + 2n\pi \quad \text{and} \quad x = \frac{7\pi}{4} + 2n\pi, \qquad n = 0, \pm1, \pm2, \pm3, \ldots.$$

➤ By rationalizing the denominator, observe that $\frac{1}{\sqrt{2}} = \frac{1}{\sqrt{2}} \cdot \frac{\sqrt{2}}{\sqrt{2}} = \frac{\sqrt{2}}{2}$.

b. Dividing both sides of the equation by $\cos 2x$ (assuming $\cos 2x \neq 0$), we obtain $\tan 2x = 1$. Letting $\theta = 2x$ gives us the equivalent equation $\tan\theta = 1$. This equation is satisfied by

$$\theta = \frac{\pi}{4}, \frac{5\pi}{4}, \frac{9\pi}{4}, \frac{13\pi}{4}, \frac{17\pi}{4}, \ldots.$$

Dividing by two and using the restriction $0 \le x < 2\pi$ gives the solutions

$$x = \frac{\theta}{2} = \frac{\pi}{8}, \frac{5\pi}{8}, \frac{9\pi}{8}, \text{ and } \frac{13\pi}{8}.$$

Related Exercises 17–28 ◀

➤ Notice that the assumption $\cos 2x \neq 0$ is valid for these values of x.

Graphs of the Trigonometric Functions

Trigonometric functions are examples of **periodic functions**: Their values repeat over every interval of some fixed length. A function f is said to be periodic if $f(x + P) = f(x)$ for all x in the domain, where the **period** P is the smallest positive real number that has this property.

> **Period of Trigonometric Functions**
>
> The functions $\sin\theta$, $\cos\theta$, $\sec\theta$, and $\csc\theta$ have a period of 2π:
>
> $$\sin(\theta + 2\pi) = \sin\theta \qquad \cos(\theta + 2\pi) = \cos\theta$$
> $$\sec(\theta + 2\pi) = \sec\theta \qquad \csc(\theta + 2\pi) = \csc\theta$$
>
> for all θ in the domain.
>
> The functions $\tan\theta$ and $\cot\theta$ have a period of π:
>
> $$\tan(\theta + \pi) = \tan\theta \qquad \cot(\theta + \pi) = \cot\theta$$
>
> for all θ in the domain.

The graph of $y = \sin\theta$ is shown in Figure 1.48a. Because $\csc\theta = 1/\sin\theta$, these two functions have the same sign, but $y = \csc\theta$ is undefined with vertical asymptotes at $\theta = 0, \pm\pi, \pm 2\pi, \ldots$. The functions $\cos\theta$ and $\sec\theta$ have a similar relationship (Figure 1.48b).

The graphs of $y = \sin\theta$ and its reciprocal, $y = \csc\theta$

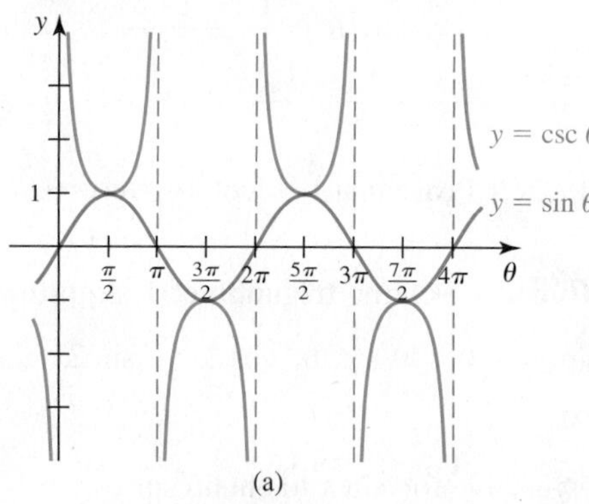

(a)

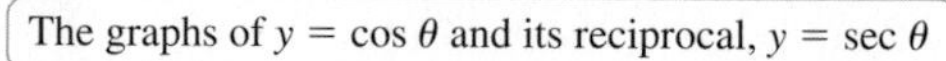

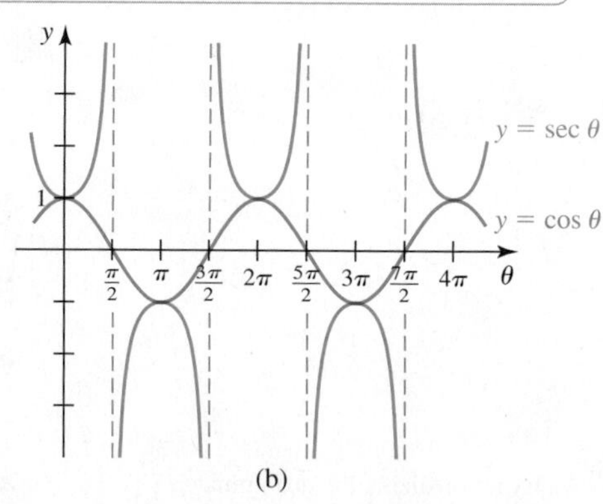

(b)

FIGURE 1.48

The graphs of $\tan\theta$ and $\cot\theta$ are shown in Figure 1.49. Each function has points, separated by π units, at which it is undefined.

The graph of $y = \tan\theta$ has period π.

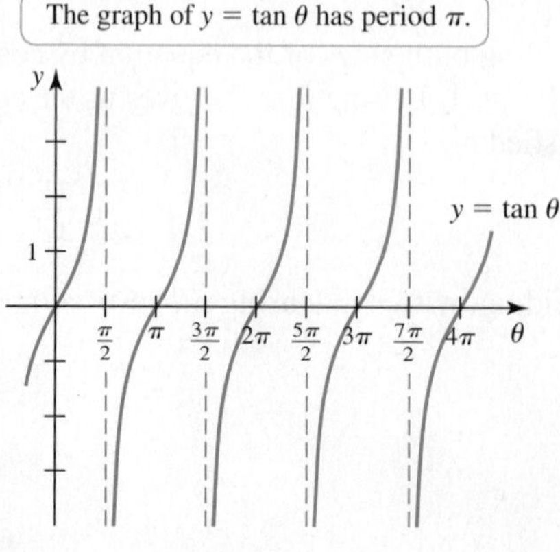

The graph of $y = \cot\theta$ has period π.

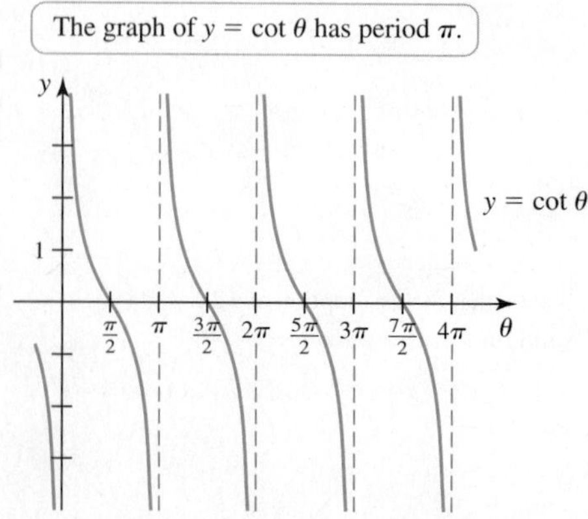

FIGURE 1.49

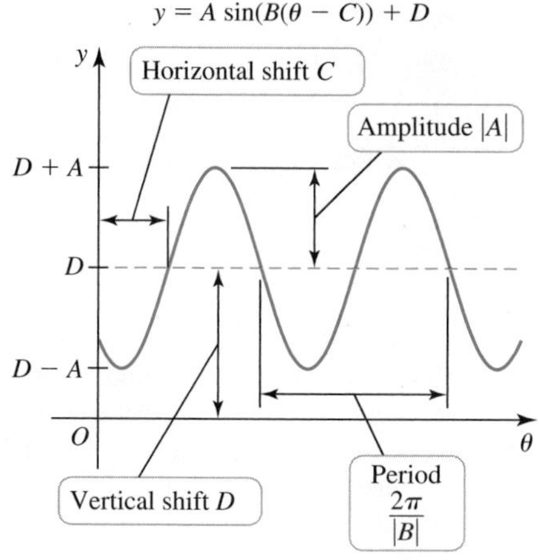

FIGURE 1.50

Transforming Graphs

Many physical phenomena, such as the motion of waves or the rising and setting of the sun, can be modeled using trigonometric functions; the sine and cosine functions are especially useful. With the transformation methods introduced in Section 1.2, we can show that the functions

$$y = A\sin(B(\theta - C)) + D \quad \text{and} \quad y = A\cos(B(\theta - C)) + D,$$

when compared to the graphs of $y = \sin\theta$ and $y = \cos\theta$, have a vertical stretch (or **amplitude**) of $|A|$, a **period** of $2\pi/|B|$, a horizontal shift (or **phase shift**) of C, and a **vertical shift** of D (Figure 1.50).

For example, at latitude 40° north (Beijing, Madrid, Philadelphia) there are 12 hr of daylight on the equinoxes (approximately March 21 and September 21), with a maximum of 14.8 hr of daylight on the summer solstice (approximately June 21) and a minimum of 9.2 hr of daylight on the winter solstice (approximately December 21). Using this information, it can be shown that the function

$$D(t) = 2.8\sin\left(\frac{2\pi}{365}(t - 81)\right) + 12 \quad \text{(Figure 1.51)}$$

models the number of daylight hours t days after January 1 (Exercise 44). Notice that the graph of this function is obtained from the graph of $y = \sin t$ by (1) a horizontal scaling by a factor of $2\pi/365$, (2) a horizontal shift of 81, (3) a vertical scaling by a factor of 2.8, and (4) a vertical shift of 12.

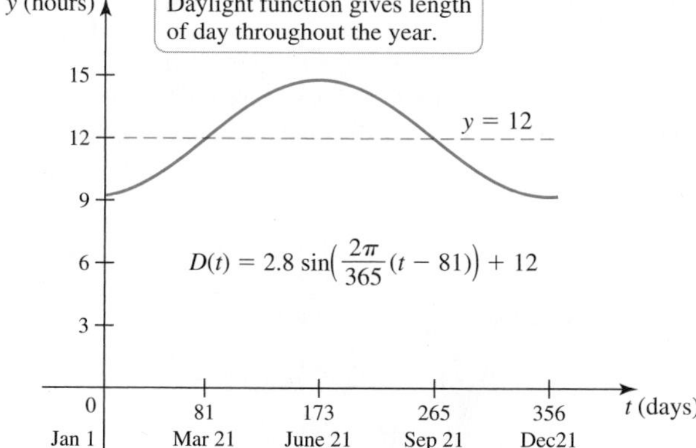

FIGURE 1.51

SECTION 1.3 EXERCISES

Review Questions

1. Define the six trigonometric functions in terms of the sides of a right triangle.
2. Explain how a point $P(x, y)$ on a circle of radius r determines an angle θ and the values of the six trigonometric functions at θ.
3. Explain how the radian measure of an angle is determined.
4. Explain what is meant by the period of a trigonometric function. What are the periods of the six trigonometric functions?
5. What are the three Pythagorean identities for the trigonometric functions?
6. How are the sine and cosine functions used to define the other four trigonometric functions?
7. Where is the tangent function undefined?
8. What is the domain of the secant function?

Basic Skills

9–16. Evaluating trigonometric functions *Evaluate the following expressions by drawing the unit circle and the appropriate right triangle. Use a calculator only to check your work. All angles are in radians.*

9. $\cos(2\pi/3)$ **10.** $\sin(2\pi/3)$ **11.** $\tan(-3\pi/4)$

12. $\tan(15\pi/4)$ **13.** $\cot(-13\pi/3)$ **14.** $\sec(7\pi/6)$

15. $\cot(-17\pi/3)$ **16.** $\sin(16\pi/3)$

17–22. Trigonometric identities

17. Prove that $\tan^2\theta + 1 = \sec^2\theta$.

18. Prove that $\dfrac{\sin\theta}{\csc\theta} + \dfrac{\cos\theta}{\sec\theta} = 1$.

19. Prove that $\sec(\pi/2 - \theta) = \csc\theta$.

20. Prove that $\sec(x + \pi) = -\sec x$.

21. Find the exact value of $\cos(\pi/12)$.

22. Find the exact value of $\tan(3\pi/8)$.

23–28. Solving trigonometric equations *Solve the following equations.*

23. $\tan x = 1$ **24.** $2\theta\cos\theta + \theta = 0$

25. $\sqrt{2}\sin x - 1 = 0$ **26.** $\sin 3x = \sqrt{2}/2,\ 0 \le x < 2\pi$

27. $\cos 3x = \sin 3x,\ 0 \le x < 2\pi$

28. $\sin^2\theta - 1 = 0$

Further Explorations

29. Explain why or why not Determine whether the following statements are true and give an explanation or counterexample.

a. $\sin(a + b) = \sin a + \sin b$

b. The equation $\cos\theta = 2$ has multiple solutions.

c. The equation $\sin\theta = \frac{1}{2}$ has exactly one solution.

d. The function $\sin(\pi x/12)$ has a period of 12.

e. Of the six basic trigonometric functions, only tangent and cotangent have a range of $(-\infty, \infty)$.

30–33. One function gives all six *Given the following information about one trigonometric function, evaluate the other five functions.*

30. $\sin\theta = -\frac{4}{5}$ and $\pi < \theta < 3\pi/2$ (Find $\cos\theta$, $\tan\theta$, $\cot\theta$, $\sec\theta$, and $\csc\theta$.)

31. $\cos\theta = \frac{5}{13}$ and $0 < \theta < \pi/2$

32. $\sec\theta = \frac{5}{3}$ and $3\pi/2 < \theta < 2\pi$

33. $\csc\theta = \frac{13}{12}$ and $0 < \theta < \pi/2$

34–37. Amplitude and period *Identify the amplitude and period of the following functions.*

34. $f(\theta) = 2\sin 2\theta$

35. $g(\theta) = 3\cos(\theta/3)$

36. $p(t) = 2.5\sin\left(\frac{1}{2}(t - 3)\right)$

37. $q(x) = 3.6\cos(\pi x/24)$

38–41. Graphing sine and cosine functions *Beginning with the graphs of $y = \sin x$ or $y = \cos x$, use shifting and scaling transformations to sketch the graph of the following functions. Use a graphing utility only to check your work.*

38. $f(x) = 3\sin 2x$

39. $g(x) = -2\cos(x/3)$

40. $p(x) = 3\sin(2x - \pi/3) + 1$

41. $q(x) = 3.6\cos(\pi x/24) + 2$

42–43. Designer functions *Design a sine function with the given properties.*

42. It has a period of 12 hr with a minimum value of -4 at $t = 0$ hr and a maximum value of 4 at $t = 6$ hr.

43. It has a period of 24 hr with a minimum value of 10 at $t = 3$ hr and a maximum value of 16 at $t = 15$ hr.

Applications

44. Daylight function for 40° N Verify that the function

$$D(t) = 2.8\sin\left(\frac{2\pi}{365}(t - 81)\right) + 12$$

has the following properties, where t is measured in days and D is measured in hours.

a. It has a period of 365 days.

b. Its maximum and minimum values are 14.8 hr and 9.2 hr, respectively, which occur approximately at $t = 172$ and $t = 355$, respectively (corresponding to the solstices).

c. $D(81) = D(264) = 12$ (corresponding to the equinoxes).

45. Block on a spring A light block hangs at rest from the end of a spring when it is pulled down 10 cm and released. Assume the block oscillates with an amplitude of 10 cm on either side of its initial position, and with a period of 1.5 s. Find a function $d(t)$ that gives the displacement of the block t seconds after it is released, where $d(t) > 0$ represents downward displacement.

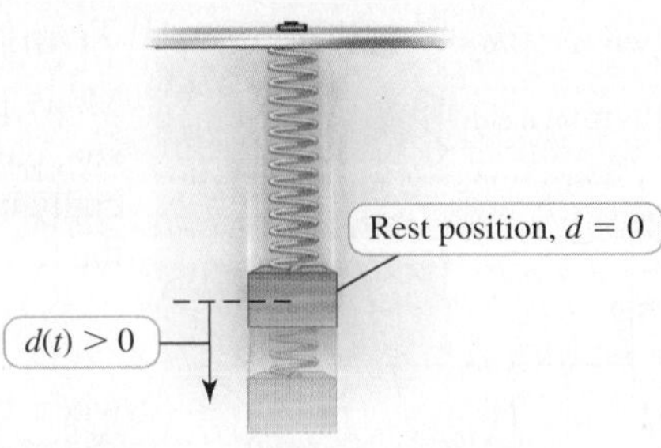

46. Approaching a lighthouse A boat approaches a 50-ft-high lighthouse whose base is at sea level. Let d be the distance between the boat and the base of the lighthouse. Let L be the distance between the boat and the top of the lighthouse. Let θ be the angle of elevation between the boat and the top of the lighthouse.

a. Express d as a function of θ.

b. Express L as a function of θ.

47. Ladders Two ladders of length a lean against opposite walls of an alley with their feet touching (see figure). One ladder extends h feet up the wall and makes a 75° angle with the ground. The other ladder extends k feet up the opposite wall and makes a 45° angle with the ground. Find the width of the alley in terms of a, h, and/or k. Assume the ground is horizontal and perpendicular to both walls.

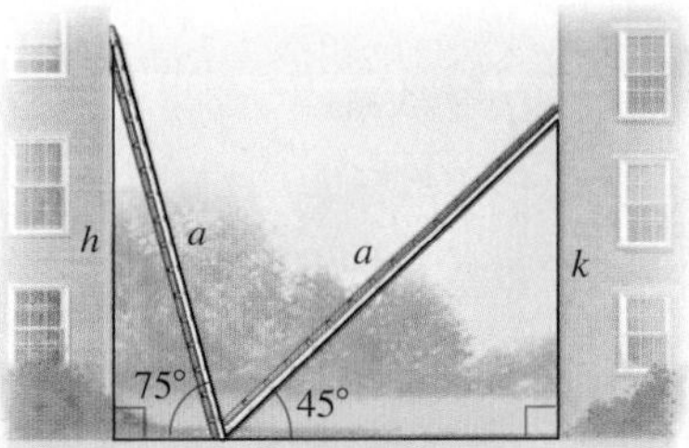

48. Pole in a corner A pole of length L is carried horizontally around a corner where a 3-ft-wide hallway meets a 4-ft-wide hallway. For $0 < \theta < \pi/2$, find the relationship between L and θ at the moment when the pole simultaneously touches both walls and the corner P. Estimate θ when $L = 10$ ft.

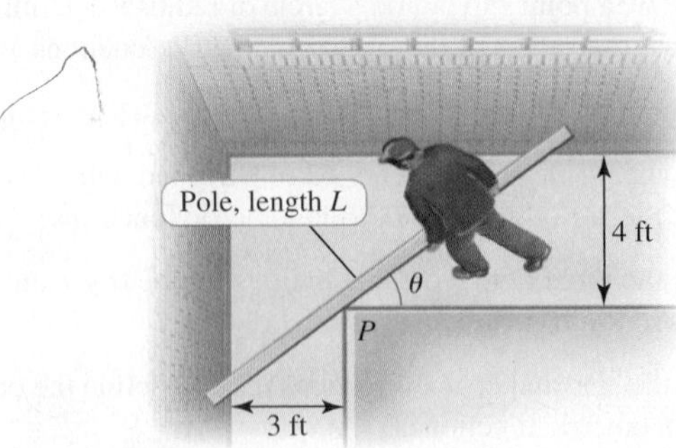

49. Little-known fact The shortest day of the year occurs on the winter solstice (near December 21) and the longest day of the year occurs on the summer solstice (near June 21). However, the latest sunrise and the earliest sunset do not occur on the winter solstice, and the earliest sunrise and the latest sunset do not occur on the summer solstice. At latitude 40° north, the latest sunrise occurs on January 4 at 7:25 A.M. (14 days after the solstice), and the earliest sunset occurs on December 7 at 4:37 P.M. (14 days before the solstice). Similarly, the earliest sunrise occurs on July 2 at 4:30 A.M. (14 days after the solstice) and the latest sunset occurs on June 7 at 7:32 P.M. (14 days before the solstice). Using sine functions, devise a function $s(t)$ that gives the time of sunrise t days after January 1 and a function $S(t)$ that gives the time of sunset t days after January 1. Assume that s and S are measured in minutes and $s = 0$ and $S = 0$ correspond to 4:00 A.M. Graph the functions. Then graph the length of the day function $D(t) = S(t) - s(t)$ and show that the longest and shortest days occur on the solstices.

Additional Exercises

50. Area of a circular sector Prove that the area of a sector of a circle of radius r associated with a central angle θ (measured in rad) is $A = \frac{1}{2}r^2\theta$.

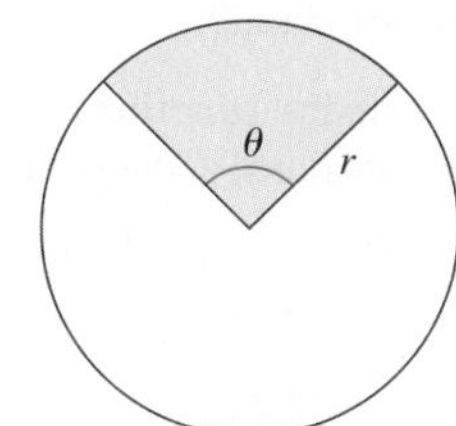

51. Law of cosines Use the figure to prove the law of cosines (which is a generalization of the Pythagorean theorem): $c^2 = a^2 + b^2 - 2ab\cos\theta$.

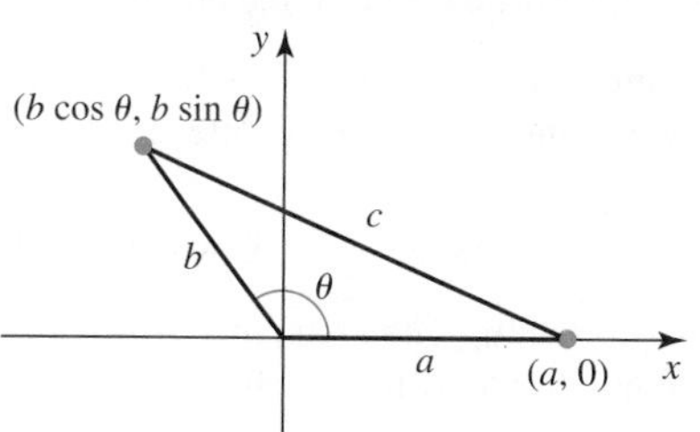

QUICK CHECK ANSWERS

1. $3\pi/2, 225°$ **2.** $\sqrt{3}/2; -\sqrt{2}/2$ **3.** Divide both sides of $\sin^2\theta + \cos^2\theta = 1$ by $\sin^2\theta$.

CHAPTER 1 REVIEW EXERCISES

1. **Explain why or why not** Determine whether the following statements are true and give an explanation or counterexample.
   a. A function could have the property that $f(x) = f(-x)$ for all x.
   b. $\cos(a + b) = \cos a + \cos b$ for all a and b in $[0, 2\pi]$.
   c. If f is a linear function of the form $f(x) = mx + b$, then $f(u + v) = f(u) + f(v)$ for all u and v.
   d. The function $f(x) = 1 - x$ has the property that $f(f(x)) = x$.
   e. The set $\{x: |x + 3| > 4\}$ can be drawn on the number line without lifting your pencil.

2. **Domain and range** Find the domain and range of the following functions.
   a. $f(x) = x^5 + \sqrt{x}$ b. $g(y) = \dfrac{1}{y - 2}$
   c. $h(z) = \sqrt{z^2 - 2z - 3}$

3. **Equations of lines** Find an equation of the lines with the following properties. Graph the lines.
   a. The line passing through the points $(2, -3)$ and $(4, 2)$
   b. The line with slope $\frac{3}{4}$ and x-intercept $(-4, 0)$
   c. The line with intercepts $(4, 0)$ and $(0, -2)$

4. **Piecewise linear functions** The parking costs in a city garage are \$2.00 for the first half hour and \$1.00 for each additional half hour. Graph the function $C = f(t)$ that gives the cost of parking for t hours, where $0 \le t \le 3$.

5. **Graphing absolute value** Consider the function $f(x) = 2(x - |x|)$. Express the function in two pieces without using the absolute value. Then graph the function by hand. Use a graphing utility only to check your work.

6. **Function from words** Suppose you plan to take a 500-mi trip in a car that gets 35 mi/gal. Find the function $C = f(p)$ that gives the cost of gasoline for the trip when gasoline costs \$$p$ per gallon.

7. **Graphing equations** Graph the following equations. Use a graphing utility only to check your work.
   a. $2x - 3y + 10 = 0$
   b. $y = x^2 + 2x - 3$
   c. $x^2 + 2x + y^2 + 4y + 1 = 0$
   d. $x^2 - 2x + y^2 - 8y + 5 = 0$

8. **Root functions** Graph the functions $f(x) = x^{1/3}$ and $g(x) = x^{1/4}$. Find all points where the two graphs intersect. For $x > 1$, is $f(x) > g(x)$ or is $g(x) > f(x)$?

9. **Root functions** Find the domain and range of the functions $f(x) = x^{1/7}$ and $g(x) = x^{1/4}$.

10. **Intersection points** Graph the equations $y = x^2$ and $x^2 + y^2 - 7y + 8 = 0$. At what point(s) do the curves intersect?

11. **Boiling-point function** Water boils at 212° F at sea level and at 200° F at an elevation of 6000 ft. Assume that the boiling point B varies linearly with altitude a. Find the function $B = f(a)$ that describes the dependence. Comment on whether a linear function gives a realistic model.

12. **Publishing costs** A small publisher plans to spend \$1000 for advertising a paperback book and estimates the printing cost is \$2.50 per book. The publisher will receive \$7 for each book sold.
    a. Find the function $C = f(x)$ that gives the cost of producing x books.

b. Find the function $R = g(x)$ that gives the revenue from selling x books.

c. Graph the cost and revenue functions and find the number of books that must be sold for the publisher to break even.

13. Shifting and scaling Starting with the graph of $f(x) = x^2$, graph the following functions. Use a graphing calculator only to check your work.

a. $f(x + 3)$ **b.** $2f(x - 4)$ **c.** $-f(3x)$ **d.** $f(2(x - 3))$

14. Shifting and scaling The graph of $y = f(x)$ is shown in the figure. Graph the following functions.

a. $f(x + 1)$ **b.** $2f(x - 1)$ **c.** $-f(x/2)$ **d.** $f(2(x - 1))$

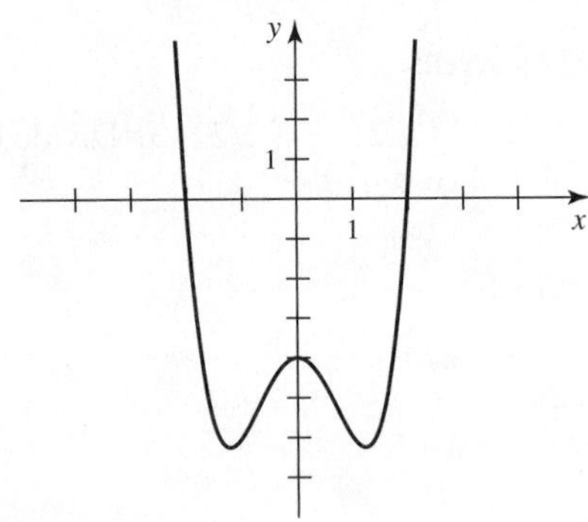

15. Composite functions Let $f(x) = x^3$, $g(x) = \sin x$, and $h(x) = \sqrt{x}$.

a. Evaluate $h(g(\pi/2))$. **b.** Find $h(f(x))$.
c. Find $f(g(h(x)))$. **d.** Find the domain of $g \circ f$.

16. Composite functions Find functions f and g such that $h = f \circ g$.

a. $h(x) = \sin (x^2 + 1)$ **b.** $h(x) = (x^2 - 4)^{-3}$

17. Symmetry Identify the symmetry in the graphs of the following equations.

a. $y = \cos 3x$ **b.** $y = 3x^4 - 3x^2 + 1$ **c.** $y^2 - 4x^2 = 4$

T **18. Comparing areas** Consider the region in the first quadrant bounded by the unit circle. Let R_1 be the triangle OPQ and let R_2 be the sector ORQ with the triangle OPQ removed (see figure).

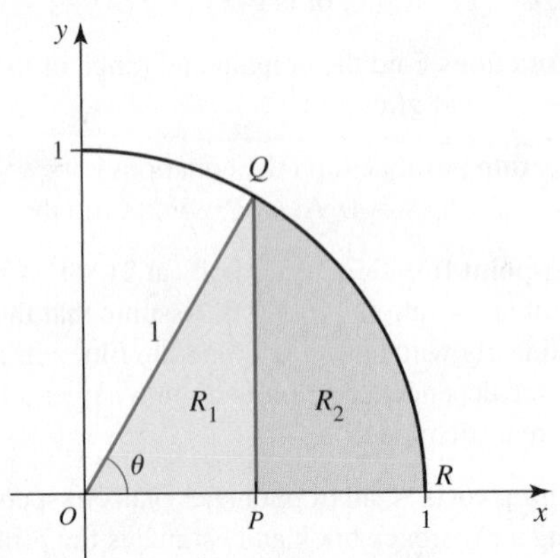

a. Find the area of R_1 as a function of θ; call it $A_1(\theta)$, where $0 \leq \theta \leq \pi/2$.

b. Graph the function A_1.

c. For what value of θ in the interval $0 \leq \theta \leq \pi/2$ does A_1 have it maximum value?

d. Find the area of R_2 as a function of θ; call it $A_2(\theta)$. Use the fact that the area of the sector ORQ is $\theta/2$, where θ is measured in radians.

e. Graph the function A_2.

f. For what value of θ in the interval $0 \leq \theta \leq \pi/2$ does A_2 have its maximum value?

g. For approximately what value of θ in the interval $0 \leq \theta \leq \pi/2$ are the areas of R_1 and R_2 equal?

19. Degrees and radians

a. What is the radian measure of a 135° angle?

b. What is the degree measure of a $4\pi/5$-rad angle?

c. What is the length of the arc of a circle of radius 10 associated with an angle of $4\pi/3$ rad?

20. Graphing sine and cosine functions Use shifts and scalings to graph the following functions, and identify the amplitude and period.

a. $f(x) = 4 \cos (x/2)$ **b.** $g(\theta) = 2 \sin (2\pi\theta/3)$
c. $h(\theta) = -\cos (2(\theta - \pi/4))$

21. Designing functions Find a trigonometric function f that satisfies each set of properties. Answers are not unique.

a. It has a period of 6 hr with a minimum value of -2 at $t = 0$ hr and a maximum value of 2 at $t = 3$ hr.

b. It has a period of 24 hr with a maximum value of 20 at $t = 6$ hr and a minimum value of 10 at $t = 18$ hr.

22. Graph to function Find a trigonometric function f represented by the graph in the figure.

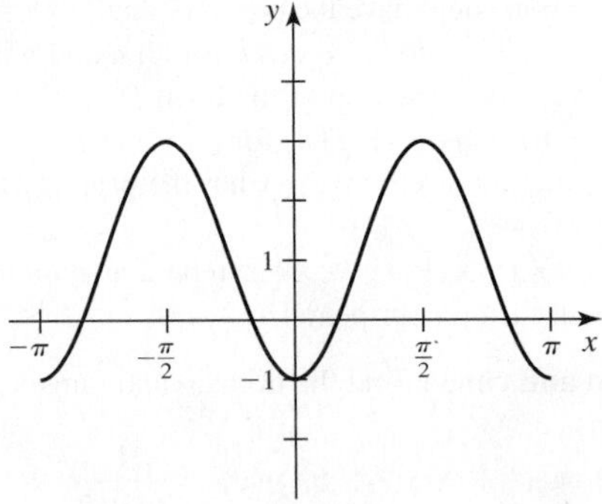

23. Matching Match each function with the corresponding graphs A–F.

a. $f(x) = -\sin x$ **b.** $f(x) = \cos 2x$ **c.** $f(x) = \tan (x/2)$
d. $f(x) = -\sec x$ **e.** $f(x) = \cot 2x$ **f.** $f(x) = \sin^2 x$

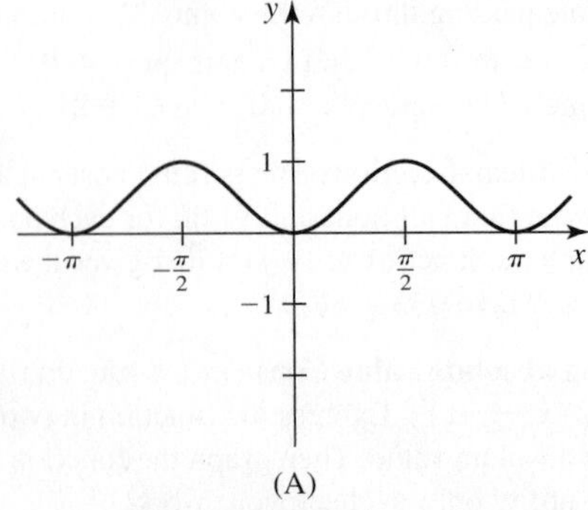

(A)

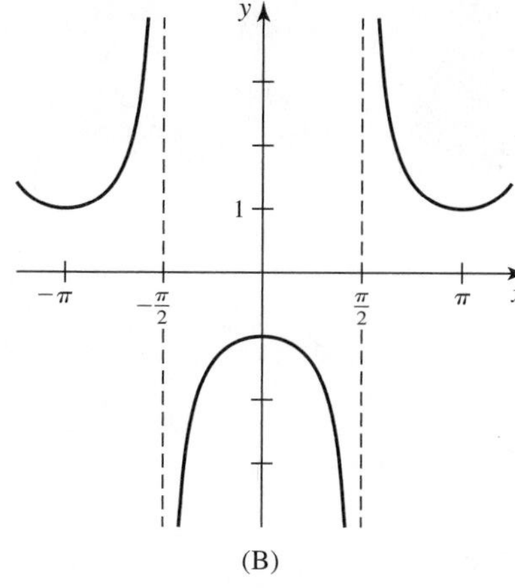
(B)

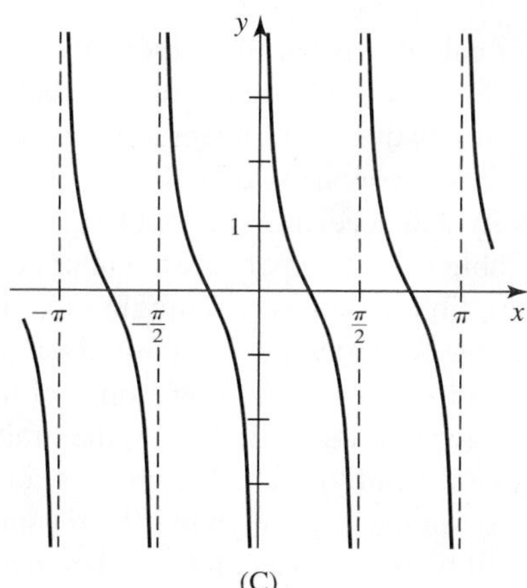
(C)

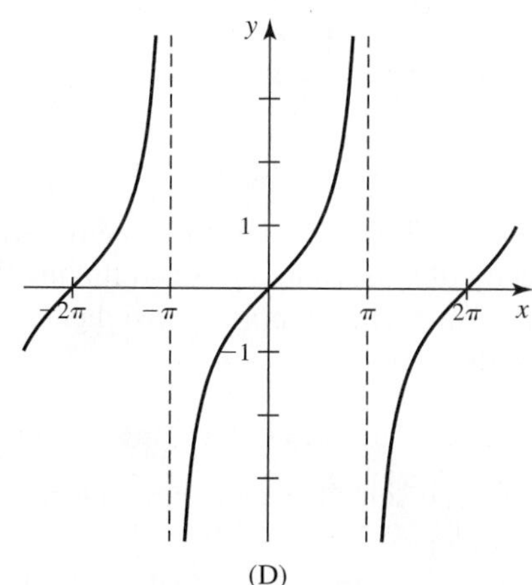
(D)

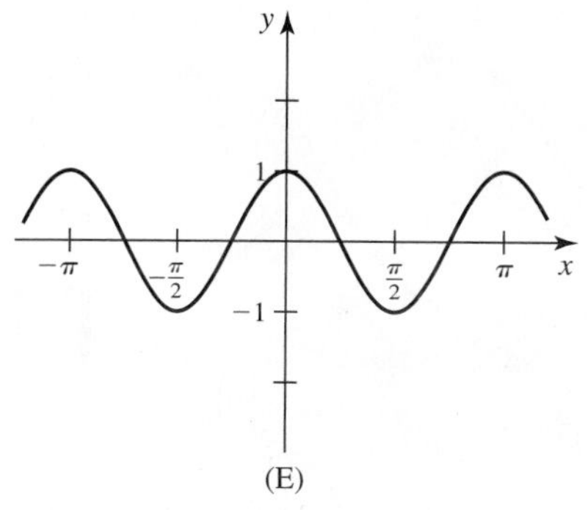
(E)

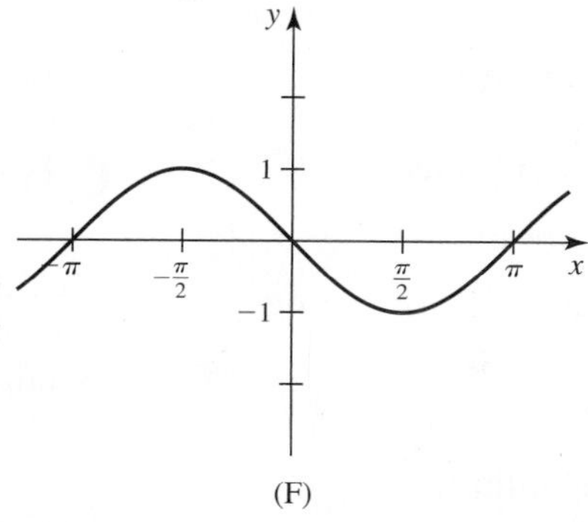
(F)

24. Stereographic projections A common way of displaying a sphere (such as Earth) on a plane (such as a map) is to use a *stereographic projection.* Here is the two-dimensional version of the method, which maps a circle to a line. Let P be a point on the right half of a circle of radius R identified by the angle φ. Find the function $x = F(\varphi)$ that gives the x-coordinate ($x \geq 0$) corresponding to φ for $0 < \varphi \leq \pi$.

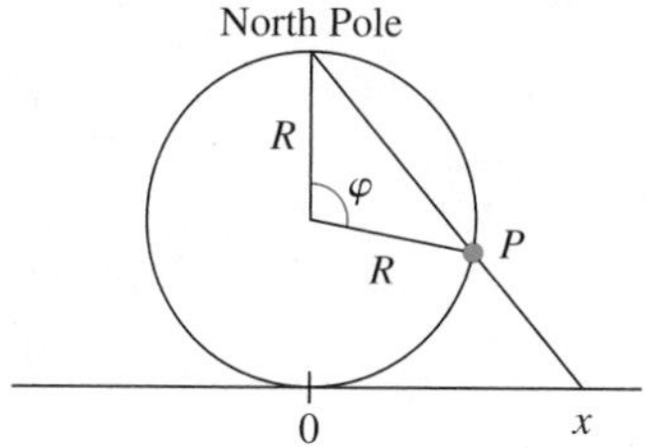

Chapter 1 Guided Projects

Applications of the material in this chapter and related topics can be found in the following Guided Projects. For additional information, see the Preface.

- Problem-solving skills
- Functions in action I
- Functions in action II
- Constant-rate problems
- Supply and demand
- Phase and amplitude

2

Limits

Chapter Preview All of calculus is based on the idea of a *limit*. Not only are limits important in their own right, but they underlie the two fundamental operations of calculus: differentiation (calculating derivatives) and integration (evaluating integrals). Derivatives enable us to talk about the instantaneous rate of change of a function, which, in turn, leads to concepts such as velocity and acceleration, population growth rates, marginal cost, and flow rates. Integrals enable us to compute areas under curves, surface areas, and volumes. Because of the incredible reach of this single idea, it is essential to develop a solid understanding of limits. We first present limits intuitively by showing how they arise in computing instantaneous velocities and finding slopes of tangent lines. As the chapter progresses, we build more rigor into the definition of the limit, and we examine the different ways in which limits exist or fail to exist. The chapter concludes by introducing the important property called *continuity* and by giving the formal definition of a limit. By the end of the chapter, you will be ready to use limits when needed throughout the remainder of the book.

2.1 The Idea of Limits

This brief opening section illustrates how limits arise in two seemingly unrelated problems: finding the instantaneous velocity of a moving object and finding the slope of a line tangent to a curve. These two problems provide important insights into limits, and they reappear in various forms throughout the book.

Average Velocity

Suppose you want to calculate your average velocity as you travel along a straight highway. If you pass milepost 100 at noon and milepost 130 at 12:30 P.M., you travel 30 mi in a half hour, so your **average velocity** over this time interval is $(30\text{ mi})/(0.5\text{ hr}) = 60\text{ mi/hr}$. By contrast, even though your average velocity may be 60 mi/hr, it's almost certain that your **instantaneous velocity**, the speed indicated by the speedometer, varies from one moment to the next.

EXAMPLE 1 **Average velocity** A rock is launched vertically upward from the ground with a speed of 96 ft/s. Neglecting air resistance, a well-known formula from physics states that the position of the rock after t seconds is given by the function

$$s(t) = -16t^2 + 96t.$$

The position s is measured in feet with $s = 0$ corresponding to the ground. Find the average velocity of the rock between each pair of times.

a. $t = 1$ s and $t = 3$ s **b.** $t = 1$ s and $t = 2$ s

SOLUTION Figure 2.1 shows the position of the rock on the time interval $0 \le t \le 3$.

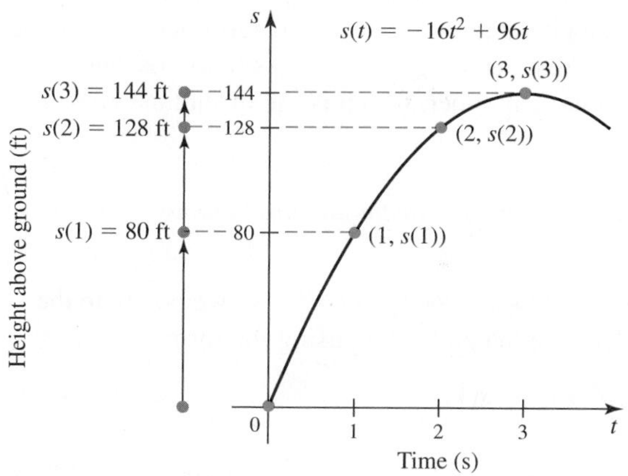

FIGURE 2.1

a. The average velocity of the rock over any time interval $[t_0, t_1]$ is the change in position divided by the elapsed time:

$$v_{av} = \frac{s(t_1) - s(t_0)}{t_1 - t_0}.$$

Therefore, the average velocity over the interval $[1, 3]$ is

$$v_{av} = \frac{s(3) - s(1)}{3 - 1} = \frac{144 \text{ ft} - 80 \text{ ft}}{3 \text{ s} - 1 \text{ s}} = \frac{64 \text{ ft}}{2 \text{ s}} = 32 \text{ ft/s}.$$

Here is an important observation: As shown in Figure 2.2a, the average velocity is the slope of the line joining the points $(1, s(1))$ and $(3, s(3))$ on the graph of the position function.

b. The average velocity of the rock over the interval $[1, 2]$ is

$$v_{av} = \frac{s(2) - s(1)}{2 - 1} = \frac{128 \text{ ft} - 80 \text{ ft}}{2 \text{ s} - 1 \text{ s}} = \frac{48 \text{ ft}}{1 \text{ s}} = 48 \text{ ft/s}.$$

Again, the average velocity is the slope of the line joining the points $(1, s(1))$ and $(2, s(2))$ on the graph of the position function (Figure 2.2b).

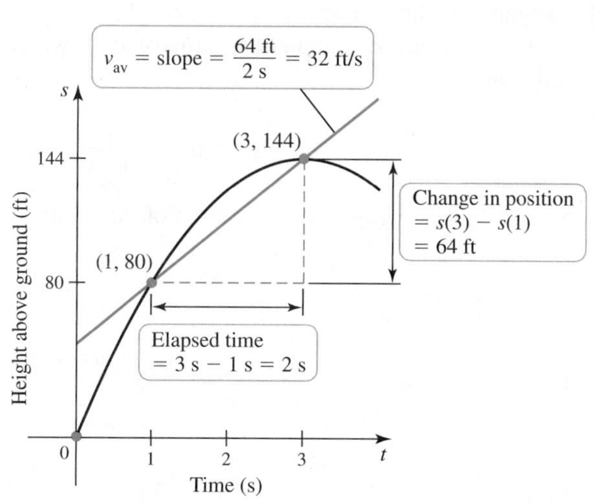

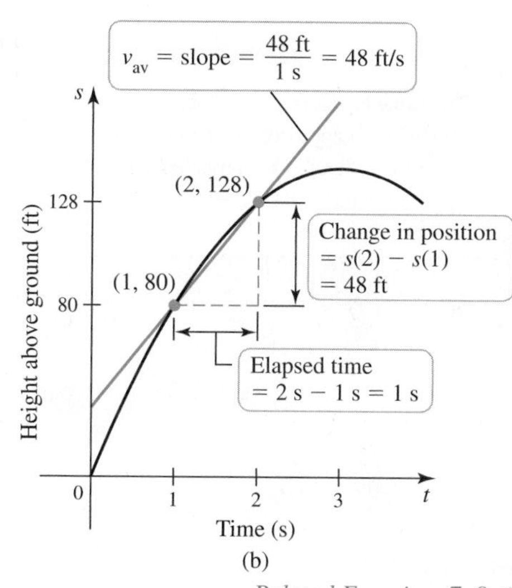

FIGURE 2.2

Related Exercises 7–8◀

A line joining two points on a curve is called a **secant line**. The slope of the secant line, denoted m_{sec}, for the position function in Example 1 on the interval $[t_0, t_1]$ is

$$m_{sec} = \frac{s(t_1) - s(t_0)}{t_1 - t_0}.$$

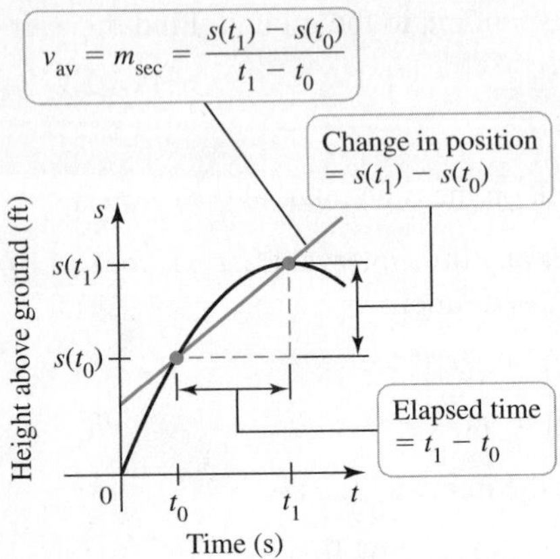

FIGURE 2.3

Example 1 demonstrates that the average velocity is the slope of a secant line on the graph of the position function; that is, $v_{av} = m_{sec}$ (Figure 2.3).

Instantaneous Velocity

To compute the average velocity, we use the position of the object at *two* distinct points in time. How do we compute the instantaneous velocity at a *single* point in time? As illustrated in Example 2, the instantaneous velocity at a point $t = t_0$ is determined by computing average velocities over intervals $[t_0, t_1]$ that decrease in length. As t_1 approaches t_0, the average velocities typically approach a unique number, which is the instantaneous velocity. This single number is called a **limit**.

EXAMPLE 2 **Instantaneous velocity** Estimate the *instantaneous velocity* of the rock in Example 1 at the *single* point $t = 1$.

SOLUTION We are interested in the instantaneous velocity at $t = 1$, so we compute the average velocity over smaller and smaller time intervals $[1, t]$ using the formula

$$v_{av} = \frac{s(t) - s(1)}{t - 1}.$$

Table 2.1

Time interval	Average velocity
$[1, 2]$	48 ft/s
$[1, 1.5]$	56 ft/s
$[1, 1.1]$	62.4 ft/s
$[1, 1.01]$	63.84 ft/s
$[1, 1.001]$	63.984 ft/s
$[1, 1.0001]$	63.9984 ft/s

Notice that these average velocities are also slopes of secant lines, several of which are shown in Table 2.1. We see that as t approaches 1, the average velocities appear to approach 64 ft/s. In fact, we could make the average velocity as close to 64 ft/s as we like by taking t sufficiently close to 1. Therefore, 64 ft/s is a reasonable estimate of the instantaneous velocity at $t = 1$.

Related Exercises 9–12 ◄

In language to be introduced in Section 2.2, we say that the limit of v_{av} as t approaches 1 equals the instantaneous velocity v_{inst}, which is 64 ft/s. This statement is written compactly as

$$v_{inst} = \lim_{t \to 1} v_{av} = \lim_{t \to 1} \frac{s(t) - s(1)}{t - 1} = 64 \text{ ft/s}.$$

➤ The same instantaneous velocity is obtained as t approaches 1 from the left (with $t < 1$) and as t approaches 1 from the right (with $t > 1$).

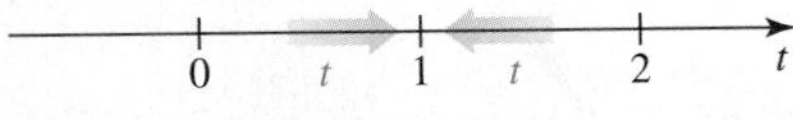

Figure 2.4 gives a graphical illustration of this limit.

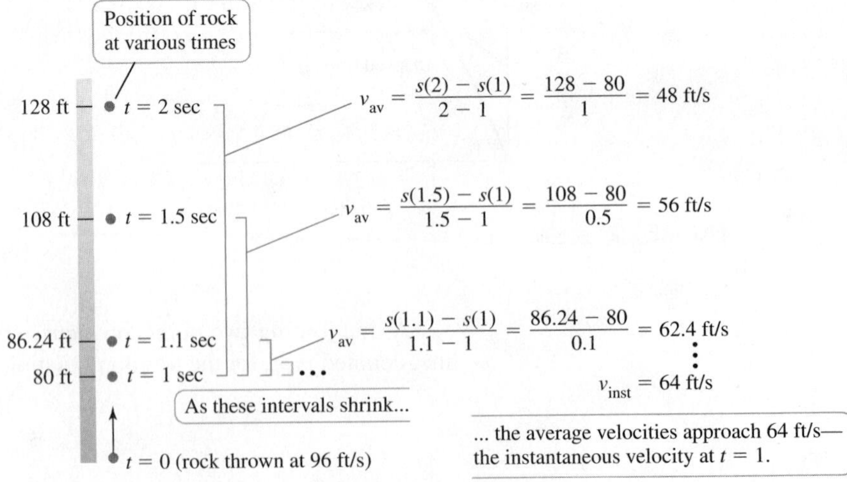

FIGURE 2.4

Slope of the Tangent Line

Several important conclusions follow from Examples 1 and 2. Each average velocity in Table 2.1 corresponds to the slope of a secant line on the graph of the position function (Figure 2.5). Just as the average velocities approach a limit as t approaches 1, the slopes of the secant lines approach the same limit as t approaches 1. Specifically, as t approaches 1, two things happen:

1. The secant lines approach a unique line called the **tangent line**.
2. The slopes of the secant lines m_{sec} approach the slope of the tangent line m_{tan} at the point $(1, s(1))$. Therefore, the slope of the tangent line is also expressed as a limit:

$$m_{\tan} = \lim_{t \to 1} m_{\text{sec}} = \lim_{t \to 1} \frac{s(t) - s(1)}{t - 1} = 64.$$

➤ We define tangent lines carefully in Section 3.1. For the moment, imagine zooming in on a point P on a smooth curve. As you zoom in, the curve appears more and more like a line passing through P. This line is the *tangent line* at P.

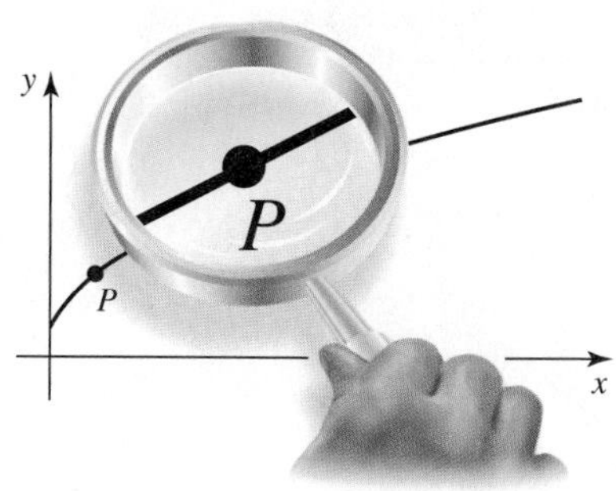

Because this limit is the same limit that defines the instantaneous velocity, the instantaneous velocity at $t = 1$ is the slope of the line tangent to the position curve at $t = 1$.

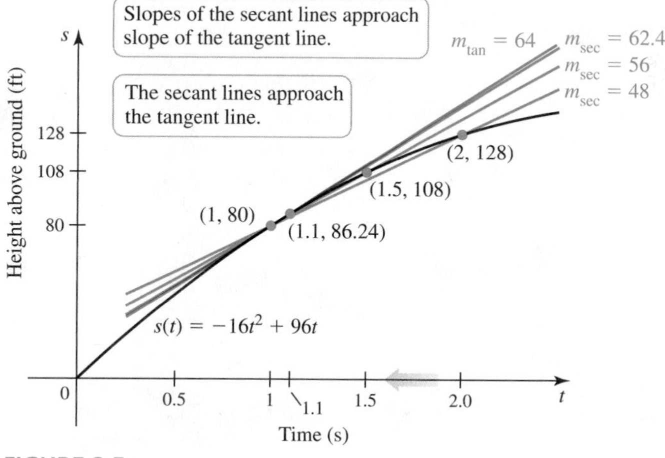

FIGURE 2.5

The parallels between average and instantaneous velocities, on one hand, and between slopes of secant lines and tangent lines, on the other, illuminate the power behind the idea of a limit. As $t \to 1$, slopes of secant lines approach the slope of a tangent line. And as $t \to 1$, average velocities approach an instantaneous velocity. Figure 2.6 summarizes these two parallel limit processes. These ideas lie at the foundation of what follows in the coming chapters.

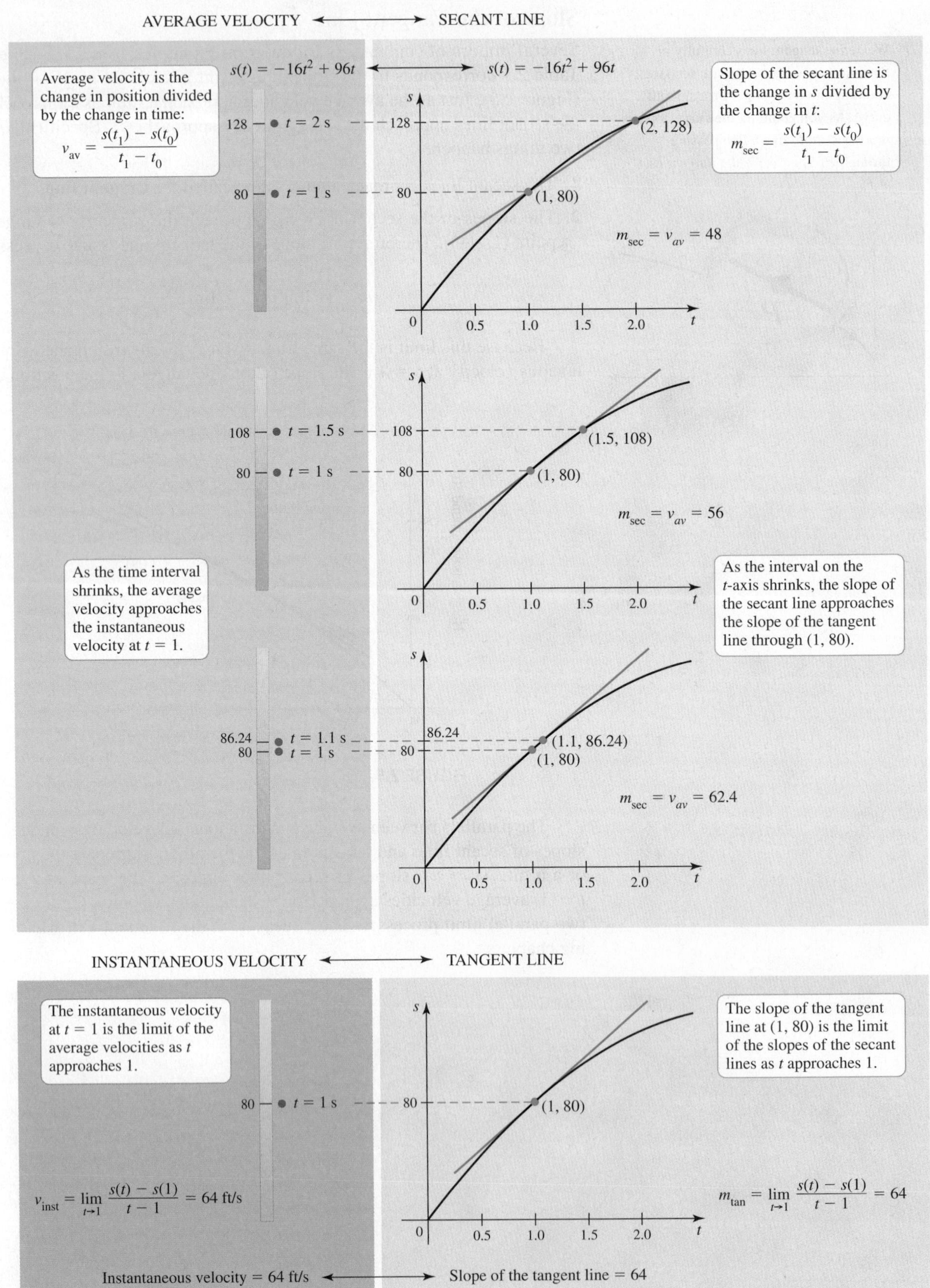
AVERAGE VELOCITY ⟷ SECANT LINE
$s(t) = -16t^2 + 96t$ ⟷ $s(t) = -16t^2 + 96t$
Average velocity is the change in position divided by the change in time:
$v_{av} = \frac{s(t_1) - s(t_0)}{t_1 - t_0}$
Slope of the secant line is the change in s divided by the change in t:
$m_{sec} = \frac{s(t_1) - s(t_0)}{t_1 - t_0}$
128 — t = 2 s
80 — t = 1 s
(2, 128)
(1, 80)
$m_{sec} = v_{av} = 48$
108 — t = 1.5 s
80 — t = 1 s
(1.5, 108)
(1, 80)
$m_{sec} = v_{av} = 56$
As the time interval shrinks, the average velocity approaches the instantaneous velocity at t = 1.
As the interval on the t-axis shrinks, the slope of the secant line approaches the slope of the tangent line through (1, 80).
86.24 — t = 1.1 s
80 — t = 1 s
(1.1, 86.24)
(1, 80)
$m_{sec} = v_{av} = 62.4$
INSTANTANEOUS VELOCITY ⟷ TANGENT LINE
The instantaneous velocity at t = 1 is the limit of the average velocities as t approaches 1.
The slope of the tangent line at (1, 80) is the limit of the slopes of the secant lines as t approaches 1.
80 — t = 1 s
(1, 80)
$v_{inst} = \lim_{t \to 1} \frac{s(t) - s(1)}{t - 1} = 64$ ft/s
$m_{tan} = \lim_{t \to 1} \frac{s(t) - s(1)}{t - 1} = 64$
Instantaneous velocity = 64 ft/s ⟷ Slope of the tangent line = 64

FIGURE 2.6

SECTION 2.1 EXERCISES

Review Questions

1. Suppose $s(t)$ is the position of an object moving along a line at time $t \geq 0$. What is the average velocity between the times $t = a$ and $t = b$?

2. Suppose $s(t)$ is the position of an object moving along a line at time t. Describe a process for finding the instantaneous velocity at $t = a$.

3. What is the slope of the secant line between the points $(a, f(a))$ and $(b, f(b))$ on the graph of f?

4. Describe a process for finding the slope of the line tangent to the graph of f at $(a, f(a))$.

5. Describe the parallels between finding the instantaneous velocity of an object at a point in time and finding the slope of the line tangent to the graph of a function at a point.

6. Graph the parabola $f(x) = x^2$. Explain why the secant lines between the points $(-a, f(-a))$ and $(a, f(a))$ have slope zero. What is the slope of the tangent line at $x = 0$?

Basic Skills

7. **Average velocity** The position of an object moving along a line is given by the function $s(t) = -16t^2 + 128t$. Find the average velocity of the object over the following intervals.

   a. $[1, 4]$ b. $[1, 3]$
   c. $[1, 2]$ d. $[1, 1 + h]$, where $h > 0$ is a real number

8. **Average velocity** The position of an object moving along a line is given by the function $s(t) = -4.9t^2 + 30t + 20$. Find the average velocity of the object over the following intervals.

   a. $[0, 3]$ b. $[0, 2]$
   c. $[0, 1]$ d. $[0, h]$, where $h > 0$ is a real number

T 9. **Instantaneous velocity** Consider the position function $s(t) = -16t^2 + 128t$ (Exercise 7). Complete the following table with the appropriate average velocities. Then make a conjecture about the value of the instantaneous velocity at $t = 1$.

Time interval	$[1, 2]$	$[1, 1.5]$	$[1, 1.1]$	$[1, 1.01]$	$[1, 1.001]$
Average velocity					

T 10. **Instantaneous velocity** Consider the position function $s(t) = -4.9t^2 + 30t + 20$ (Exercise 8). Complete the following table with the appropriate average velocities. Then make a conjecture about the value of the instantaneous velocity at $t = 2$.

Time interval	$[2, 3]$	$[2, 2.5]$	$[2, 2.1]$	$[2, 2.01]$	$[2, 2.001]$
Average velocity					

T 11. **Instantaneous velocity** Consider the position function $s(t) = -16t^2 + 100t$. Complete the following table with the appropriate average velocities. Then make a conjecture about the value of the instantaneous velocity at $t = 3$.

Time interval	Average velocity
$[2, 3]$	
$[2.9, 3]$	
$[2.99, 3]$	
$[2.999, 3]$	
$[2.9999, 3]$	

T 12. **Instantaneous velocity** Consider the position function $s(t) = 3 \sin t$ that describes a block bouncing vertically on a spring. Complete the following table with the appropriate average velocities. Then make a conjecture about the value of the instantaneous velocity at $t = \pi/2$.

Time interval	Average velocity
$[\pi/2, \pi]$	
$[\pi/2, \pi/2 + 0.1]$	
$[\pi/2, \pi/2 + 0.01]$	
$[\pi/2, \pi/2 + 0.001]$	
$[\pi/2, \pi/2 + 0.0001]$	

Further Explorations

T 13–16. **Instantaneous velocity** *For the following position functions, make a table of average velocities similar to those in Exercises 9–12 and make a conjecture about the instantaneous velocity at the indicated time.*

13. $s(t) = -16t^2 + 80t + 60$ at $t = 3$

14. $s(t) = 20 \cos t$ at $t = \pi/2$

15. $s(t) = 40 \sin 2t$ at $t = 0$

16. $s(t) = 20/(t + 1)$ at $t = 0$

T 17–20. **Slopes of tangent lines** *For the following functions, make a table of slopes of secant lines and make a conjecture about the slope of the tangent line at the indicated point.*

17. $f(x) = 2x^2$ at $x = 2$

18. $f(x) = 3 \cos x$ at $x = \pi/2$

19. $f(x) = 4 - x^2$ at $x = 1$

20. $f(x) = x^3 - x$ at $x = 1$

T 21. **Tangent lines with zero slope**

   a. Graph the function $f(x) = x^2 - 4x + 3$.
   b. Identify the point $(a, f(a))$ at which the function has a tangent line with zero slope.
   c. Confirm your answer to part (b) by making a table of slopes of secant lines to approximate the slope of the tangent line at this point.

22. Tangent lines with zero slope

a. Graph the function $f(x) = 4 - x^2$.

b. Identify the point $(a, f(a))$ at which the function has a tangent line with zero slope.

c. Consider the point $(a, f(a))$ found in part (b). Is it true that the secant line between $(a - h, f(a - h))$ and $(a + h, f(a + h))$ has slope zero for any value of $h \neq 0$?

23. Zero velocity A projectile is fired vertically upward and has a position given by $s(t) = -16t^2 + 128t + 192$, for $0 \leq t \leq 9$.

a. Graph the position function, for $0 \leq t \leq 9$.

b. From the graph of the position function, identify the time at which the projectile has an instantaneous velocity of zero; call this time $t = a$.

c. Confirm your answer to part (b) by making a table of average velocities to approximate the instantaneous velocity at $t = a$.

d. For what values of t on the interval $[0, 9]$ is the instantaneous velocity positive (the projectile moves upward)?

e. For what values of t on the interval $[0, 9]$ is the instantaneous velocity negative (the projectile moves downward)?

24. Impact speed A rock is dropped off the edge of a cliff and its distance s (in feet) from the top of the cliff after t seconds is $s(t) = 16t^2$. Assume the distance from the top of the cliff to the water below is 96 ft.

a. When will the rock strike the water?

b. Make a table of average velocities and approximate the velocity at which the rock strikes the water.

25. Slope of tangent line Given the function $f(x) = 1 - \cos x$ and the points $A(\pi/2, f(\pi/2))$, $B(\pi/2 + 0.05, f(\pi/2 + 0.05))$, $C(\pi/2 + 0.5, f(\pi/2 + 0.5))$, and $D(\pi, f(\pi))$ (see figure), find the slopes of the secant lines through A and D, A and C, and A and B. Use your calculations to make a conjecture about the slope of the line tangent to the graph of f at $x = \pi/2$.

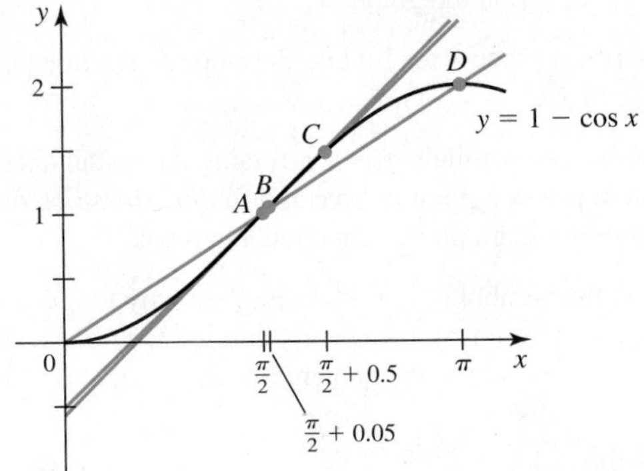

2.2 Definitions of Limits

Computing tangent lines and instantaneous velocities are just two of many important calculus problems that rely on limits. We now put these two problems aside until Chapter 3 and begin with a preliminary definition of the limit of a function.

➤ The terms *arbitrarily close* and *sufficiently close* will be made precise when rigorous definitions of limits are given in Section 2.7.

> DEFINITION **Limit of a Function (Preliminary)**
>
> Suppose the function f is defined for all x near a except possibly at a. If $f(x)$ is arbitrarily close to L (as close to L as we like) for all x sufficiently close (but not equal) to a, we write
>
> $$\lim_{x \to a} f(x) = L$$
>
> and say the limit of $f(x)$ as x approaches a equals L.

Informally, we say that $\lim_{x \to a} f(x) = L$ if $f(x)$ gets closer and closer to L as x gets closer and closer to a from both sides of a. The value of $\lim_{x \to a} f(x)$ (if it exists) depends upon the values of f near a, but it does not depend on the value of $f(a)$. In some cases, the limit $\lim_{x \to a} f(x)$ equals $f(a)$. In other instances, $\lim_{x \to a} f(x)$ and $f(a)$ differ, or $f(a)$ may not even be defined.

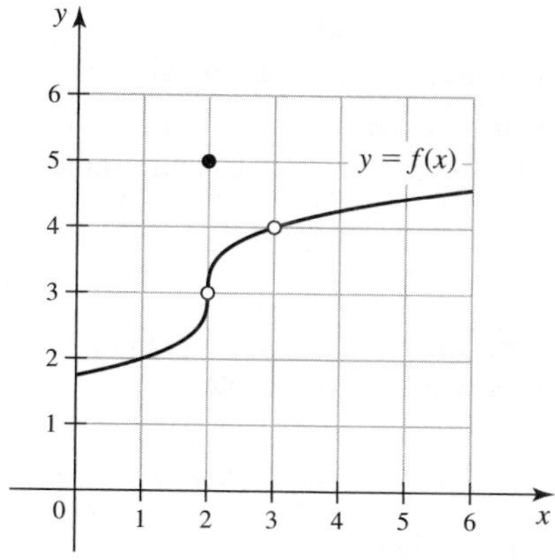

FIGURE 2.7

EXAMPLE 1 Finding limits from a graph Use the graph of f (Figure 2.7) to determine the following values, if possible.

a. $f(1)$ and $\lim_{x\to 1} f(x)$ **b.** $f(2)$ and $\lim_{x\to 2} f(x)$ **c.** $f(3)$ and $\lim_{x\to 3} f(x)$

SOLUTION

a. We see that $f(1) = 2$. As x approaches 1 from either side, the values of $f(x)$ approach 2 (Figure 2.8). Therefore, $\lim_{x\to 1} f(x) = 2$.

b. We see that $f(2) = 5$. However, as x approaches 2 from either side, $f(x)$ approaches 3 because the points on the graph of f approach the open circle at $(2, 3)$ (Figure 2.9). Therefore, $\lim_{x\to 2} f(x) = 3$ even though $f(2) = 5$.

c. In this case, $f(3)$ is undefined. We see that $f(x)$ approaches 4 as x approaches 3 from either side (Figure 2.10). Therefore, $\lim_{x\to 3} f(x) = 4$ even though $f(3)$ does not exist.

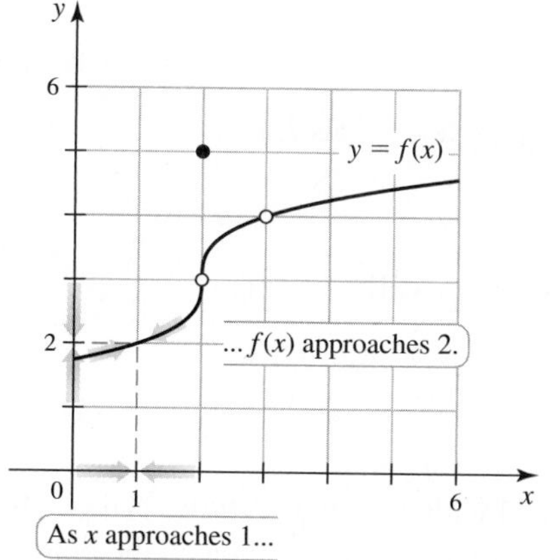

FIGURE 2.8

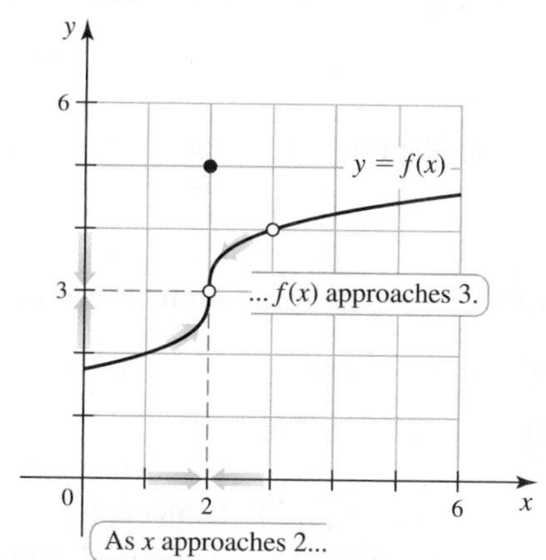

FIGURE 2.9

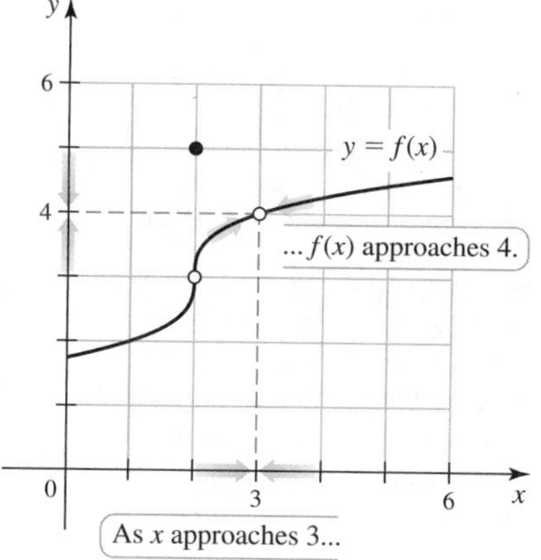

FIGURE 2.10

Related Exercises 7–10

QUICK CHECK 1 In Example 1, suppose we redefine the function at one point so that $f(1) = 1$. Does this change the value of $\lim_{x\to 1} f(x)$?

EXAMPLE 2 Finding limits from a table Create a table of values of $f(x) = \dfrac{\sqrt{x} - 1}{x - 1}$ corresponding to values of x near 1. Then make a conjecture about the value of $\lim_{x\to 1} f(x)$.

SOLUTION Table 2.2 lists values of f corresponding to values of x approaching 1 from both sides. The numerical evidence suggests that $f(x)$ approaches 0.5 as x approaches 1. Therefore, we make the conjecture that $\lim_{x\to 1} f(x) = 0.5$.

➤ In Example 2, we have not stated with certainty that $\lim_{x\to 1} f(x) = 0.5$. But this is our best guess based upon the numerical evidence. Methods for calculating limits precisely are introduced in Section 2.3.

Table 2.2

	⟶				1	⟵		
x	0.9	0.99	0.999	0.9999	1.0001	1.001	1.01	1.1
$f(x) = \dfrac{\sqrt{x} - 1}{x - 1}$	0.5131670	0.5012563	0.5001251	0.5000125	0.4999875	0.4998750	0.4987562	0.4880885

Related Exercises 11–14

One-Sided Limits

The limit $\lim_{x \to a} f(x) = L$ is referred to as a *two-sided* limit because $f(x)$ approaches L as x approaches a for values of x less than a *and* for values of x greater than a. For some functions, it makes sense to examine *one-sided* limits called left-hand and right-hand limits.

> As with two-sided limits, the value of a one-sided limit (if it exists) depends on the values of $f(x)$ near $x = a$ but not on the value of $f(a)$.

DEFINITION One-Sided Limits

1. **Right-hand limit** Suppose f is defined for all x near a with $x > a$. If $f(x)$ is arbitrarily close to L for all x sufficiently close to a with $x > a$, we write

$$\lim_{x \to a^+} f(x) = L$$

and say the limit of $f(x)$ as x approaches a from the right equals L.

2. **Left-hand limit** Suppose f is defined for all x near a with $x < a$. If $f(x)$ is arbitrarily close to L for all x sufficiently close to a with $x < a$, we write

$$\lim_{x \to a^-} f(x) = L$$

and say the limit of $f(x)$ as x approaches a from the left equals L.

> Computer-generated graphs and tables help us understand the idea of a limit. Keep in mind, however, that computers are not infallible and they may produce incorrect results, even for simple functions (see Example 5 and Exercises 37–38).

EXAMPLE 3 Examining limits graphically and numerically Let $f(x) = \dfrac{x^3 - 8}{4(x - 2)}$. Use tables and graphs to make a conjecture about the values of $\lim_{x \to 2^+} f(x)$, $\lim_{x \to 2^-} f(x)$, and $\lim_{x \to 2} f(x)$, if they exist.

SOLUTION Figure 2.11a shows the graph of f obtained with a graphing utility. The graph is misleading because $f(2)$ is undefined, which means there should be a hole in the graph at $(2, 3)$ (Figure 2.11b).

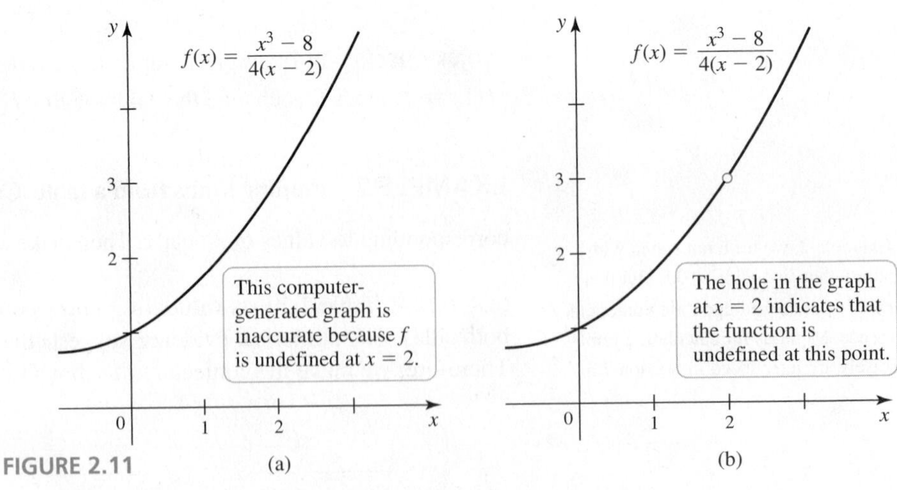

FIGURE 2.11

The graph in Figure 2.12a and the function values in Table 2.3 suggest that $f(x)$ approaches 3 as x approaches 2 from the right. Therefore, we write

$$\lim_{x \to 2^+} f(x) = 3,$$

which says the limit of $f(x)$ as x approaches 2 from the right equals 3.

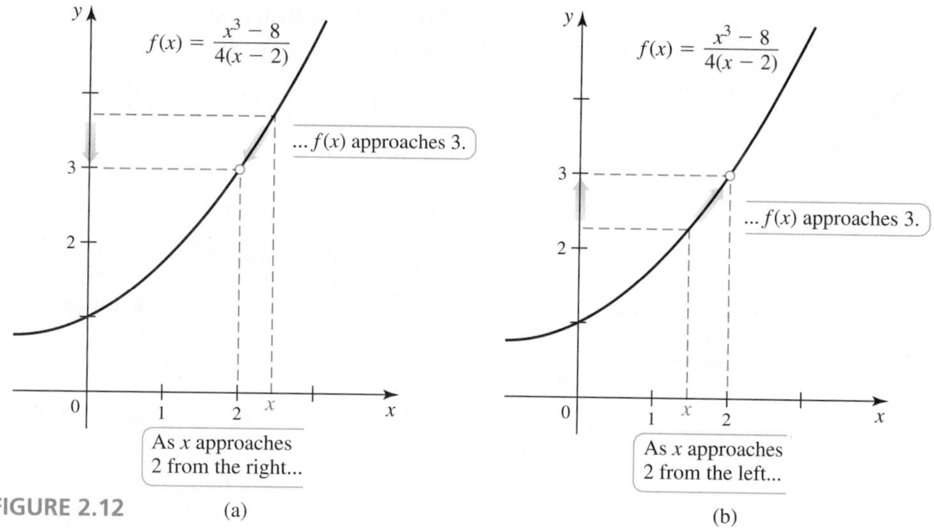

FIGURE 2.12 (a) (b)

Remember that the value of the limit does not depend upon the value of $f(2)$. In this case, $\lim_{x\to 2} f(x) = 3$ despite the fact that $f(2)$ is undefined.

Similarly, Figure 2.12b and Table 2.3 suggest that as x approaches 2 from the left, $f(x)$ approaches 3. So, we write

$$\lim_{x\to 2^-} f(x) = 3,$$

which says the limit of $f(x)$ as x approaches 2 from the left equals 3. Because $f(x)$ approaches 3 as x approaches 2 from either side, we write $\lim_{x\to 2} f(x) = 3$.

Table 2.3

	→ 2 ←							
x	1.9	1.99	1.999	1.9999	2.0001	2.001	2.01	2.1
$f(x) = \frac{x^3 - 8}{4(x - 2)}$	2.8525	2.985025	2.99850025	2.99985000	3.00015000	3.00150025	3.015025	3.1525

Related Exercises 15–16◀

Based upon the previous example, you might wonder whether the limits $\lim_{x\to a^-} f(x)$, $\lim_{x\to a^+} f(x)$, and $\lim_{x\to a} f(x)$ always exist and are equal. The remaining examples demonstrate that these limits sometimes have different values and in other cases, some or all of these limits do not exist. The following result is useful when comparing one-sided and two-sided limits.

Recall that we write P *if and only if* Q when P implies Q *and* Q implies P.

THEOREM 2.1 Relationship Between One-Sided and Two-Sided Limits
Assume f is defined for all x near a except possibly at a. Then $\lim_{x\to a} f(x) = L$ if and only if $\lim_{x\to a^+} f(x) = \lim_{x\to a^-} f(x) = L$.

A proof of Theorem 2.1 is outlined in Exercise 44 of Section 2.7. Using this theorem, it follows that $\lim_{x\to a} f(x) \neq L$ if either $\lim_{x\to a^+} f(x) \neq L$ or $\lim_{x\to a^-} f(x) \neq L$ (or both). Furthermore, if either $\lim_{x\to a^+} f(x)$ or $\lim_{x\to a^-} f(x)$ does not exist, then $\lim_{x\to a} f(x)$ does not exist. We put these ideas to work in the next two examples.

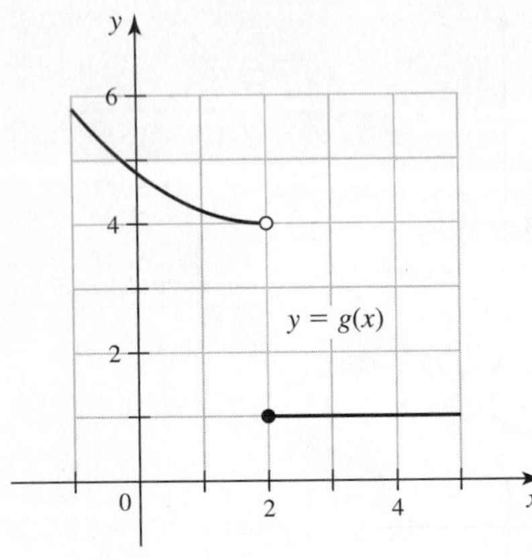

FIGURE 2.13

EXAMPLE 4 **A function with a jump** Given the graph of g in Figure 2.13, find the following limits, if they exist.

a. $\lim_{x \to 2^-} g(x)$ **b.** $\lim_{x \to 2^+} g(x)$ **c.** $\lim_{x \to 2} g(x)$

SOLUTION

a. As x approaches 2 from the left, $g(x)$ approaches 4. Therefore, $\lim_{x \to 2^-} g(x) = 4$.

b. Because $g(x) = 1$ for all $x \geq 2$, $\lim_{x \to 2^+} g(x) = 1$.

c. By Theorem 2.1, $\lim_{x \to 2} g(x)$ does not exist because $\lim_{x \to 2^-} g(x) \neq \lim_{x \to 2^+} g(x)$.

Related Exercises 17–20 ◀

EXAMPLE 5 **Some strange behavior** Examine $\lim_{x \to 0} \cos(1/x)$.

SOLUTION From the first three values of $\cos(1/x)$ in Table 2.4, it is tempting to conclude that $\lim_{x \to 0^+} \cos(1/x) = -1$. But this conclusion is not confirmed when we evaluate $\cos(1/x)$ for values of x closer to 0.

Table 2.4

x	$\cos(1/x)$
0.001	0.56238
0.0001	−0.95216
0.00001	−0.99936
0.000001	0.93675
0.0000001	−0.90727
0.00000001	−0.36338

We might *incorrectly* conclude that $\cos(1/x)$ approaches -1 as x approaches 0 from the right.

The behavior of $\cos(1/x)$ near $x = 0$ is better understood by letting $x = 1/(n\pi)$, where n is a positive integer. In this case,

$$\cos\left(\frac{1}{x}\right) = \cos n\pi = \begin{cases} 1 & \text{if } n \text{ is even} \\ -1 & \text{if } n \text{ is odd} \end{cases}.$$

As n increases, the values of $x = 1/(n\pi)$ approach zero, while the values of $\cos(1/x)$ oscillate between -1 and 1 (Figure 2.14). Therefore, $\cos(1/x)$ does not approach one single number as x approaches 0 from the right. We conclude that $\lim_{x \to 0^+} \cos(1/x)$ does *not* exist, which implies that $\lim_{x \to 0} \cos(1/x)$ does not exist.

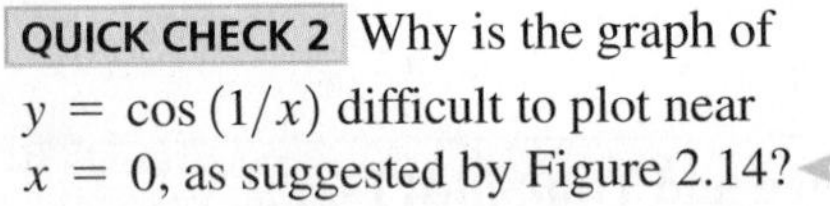

QUICK CHECK 2 Why is the graph of $y = \cos(1/x)$ difficult to plot near $x = 0$, as suggested by Figure 2.14? ◀

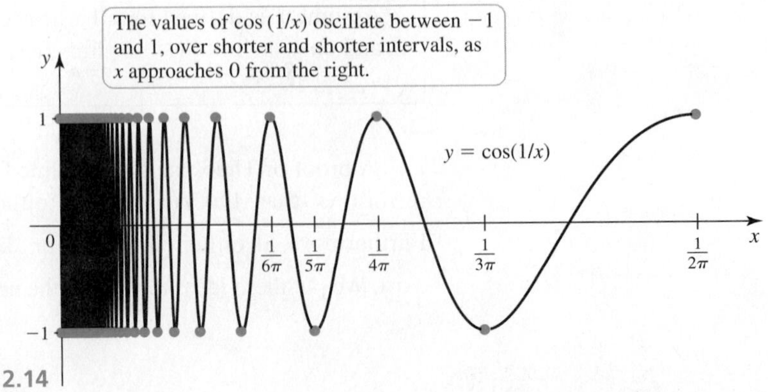

FIGURE 2.14

Related Exercises 21–22 ◀

Using tables and graphs to make conjectures for the values of limits worked well until Example 5. The limitation of technology in this example is not an isolated incident. For this reason, analytical techniques (paper-and-pencil methods) for finding limits are developed in the next section.

SECTION 2.2 EXERCISES

Review Questions

1. Explain in words the meaning of $\lim_{x \to a} f(x) = L$.
2. True or false: When $\lim_{x \to a} f(x)$ exists, it equals $f(a)$. Explain.
3. Explain the meaning of $\lim_{x \to a^+} f(x) = L$.
4. Explain the meaning of $\lim_{x \to a^-} f(x) = L$.
5. If $\lim_{x \to a^-} f(x) = L$ and $\lim_{x \to a^+} f(x) = M$, where L and M are finite real numbers, then what must be true about L and M in order for $\lim_{x \to a} f(x)$ to exist?
6. What are the potential problems of using a graphing utility to determine $\lim_{x \to a} f(x)$?

Basic Skills

7. **Finding limits from a graph** Use the graph of h in the figure to find the following values, if they exist.

   a. $h(2)$ **b.** $\lim_{x \to 2} h(x)$ **c.** $h(4)$ **d.** $\lim_{x \to 4} h(x)$ **e.** $\lim_{x \to 5} h(x)$

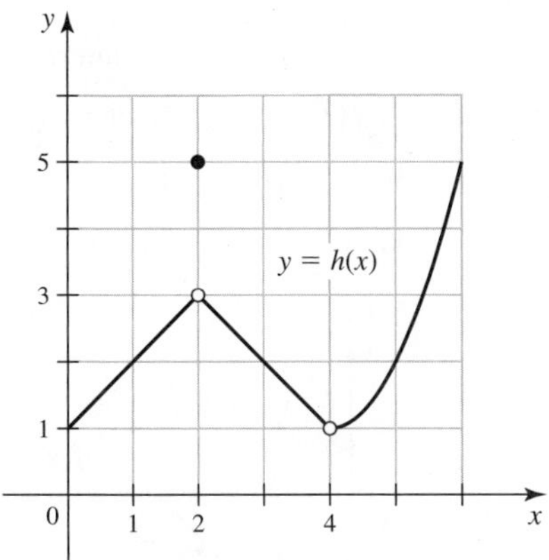

8. **Finding limits from a graph** Use the graph of g in the figure to find the following values, if they exist.

   a. $g(0)$ **b.** $\lim_{x \to 0} g(x)$ **c.** $g(1)$ **d.** $\lim_{x \to 1} g(x)$

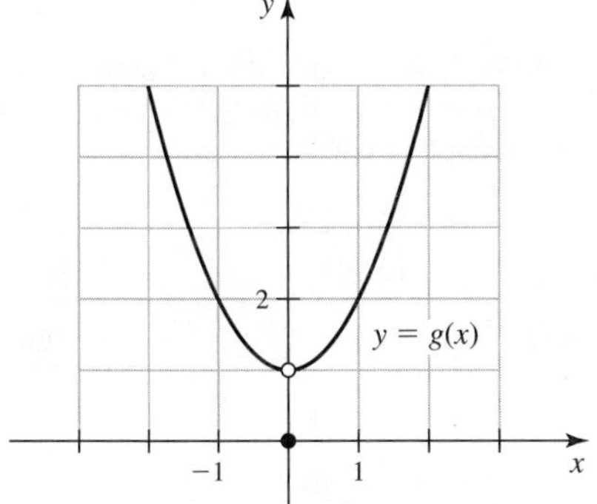

9. **Finding limits from a graph** Use the graph of f in the figure to find the following values, if they exist.

   a. $f(1)$ **b.** $\lim_{x \to 1} f(x)$ **c.** $f(0)$ **d.** $\lim_{x \to 0} f(x)$

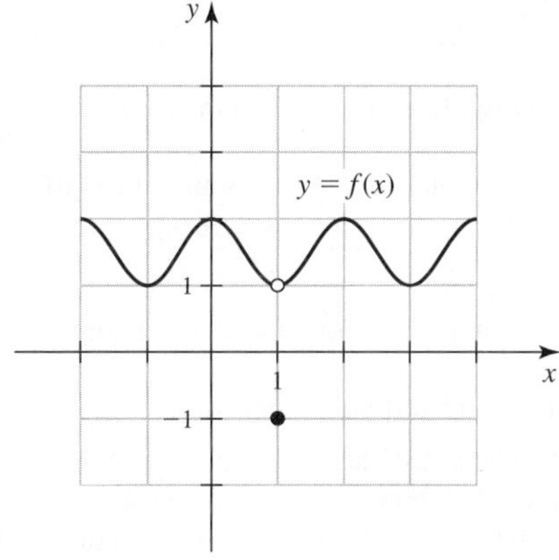

10. **Finding limits from a graph** Use the graph of f in the figure to find the following values, if they exist.

   a. $f(2)$ **b.** $\lim_{x \to 2} f(x)$ **c.** $\lim_{x \to 4} f(x)$ **d.** $\lim_{x \to 5} f(x)$

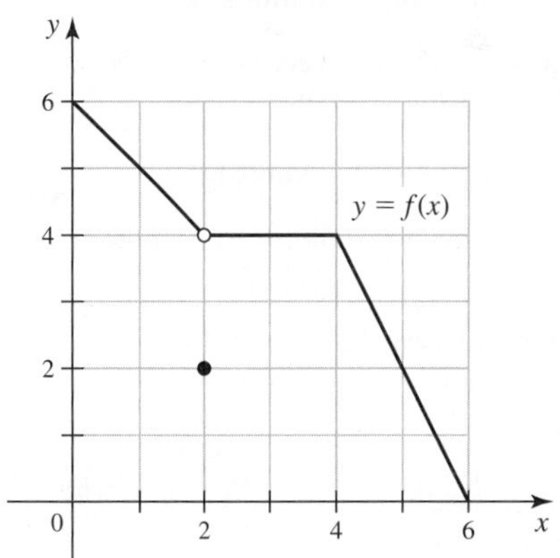

T 11. **Estimating a limit from tables** Let $f(x) = \dfrac{x^2 - 4}{x - 2}$.

   a. Calculate $f(x)$ for each value of x in the following table.

   b. Make a conjecture about the value of $\lim_{x \to 2} \dfrac{x^2 - 4}{x - 2}$.

x	1.9	1.99	1.999	1.9999
$f(x) = \dfrac{x^2 - 4}{x - 2}$				
x	2.1	2.01	2.001	2.0001
$f(x) = \dfrac{x^2 - 4}{x - 2}$				

12. Estimating a limit from tables Let $f(x) = \dfrac{x^3 - 1}{x - 1}$.

a. Calculate $f(x)$ for each value of x in the following table.

b. Make a conjecture about the value of $\lim\limits_{x \to 1} \dfrac{x^3 - 1}{x - 1}$.

x	0.9	0.99	0.999	0.9999
$f(x) = \dfrac{x^3 - 1}{x - 1}$				
x	1.1	1.01	1.001	1.0001
$f(x) = \dfrac{x^3 - 1}{x - 1}$				

13. Estimating the limit of a function Let $g(t) = \dfrac{t - 9}{\sqrt{t} - 3}$.

a. Make two tables, one showing the values of g for $t = 8.9, 8.99$, and 8.999 and one showing values of g for $t = 9.1, 9.01$, and 9.001.

b. Make a conjecture about the value of $\lim\limits_{t \to 9} \dfrac{t - 9}{\sqrt{t} - 3}$.

14. Estimating the limit of a function Let $f(x) = (1 + x)^{1/x}$.

a. Make two tables, one showing the values of f for $x = 0.01$, 0.001, 0.0001, and 0.00001 and one showing values of f for $x = -0.01, -0.001, -0.0001$, and -0.00001. Round your answers to five digits.

b. Estimate the value of $\lim\limits_{x \to 0} (1 + x)^{1/x}$.

c. What mathematical constant does $\lim\limits_{x \to 0} (1 + x)^{1/x}$ appear to equal?

15. One-sided and two-sided limits Let $f(x) = \dfrac{x^2 - 25}{x - 5}$. Use tables and graphs to make a conjecture about the values of $\lim\limits_{x \to 5^+} f(x)$, $\lim\limits_{x \to 5^-} f(x)$, and $\lim\limits_{x \to 5} f(x)$, if they exist.

16. One-sided and two-sided limits Let $g(x) = \dfrac{x - 100}{\sqrt{x} - 10}$. Use tables and graphs to make a conjecture about the values of $\lim\limits_{x \to 100^+} g(x)$, $\lim\limits_{x \to 100^-} g(x)$, and $\lim\limits_{x \to 100} g(x)$, if they exist.

17. One-sided and two-sided limits Use the graph of f in the figure to find the following values, if they exist. If a limit does not exist, explain why.

a. $f(1)$ **b.** $\lim\limits_{x \to 1^-} f(x)$ **c.** $\lim\limits_{x \to 1^+} f(x)$ **d.** $\lim\limits_{x \to 1} f(x)$

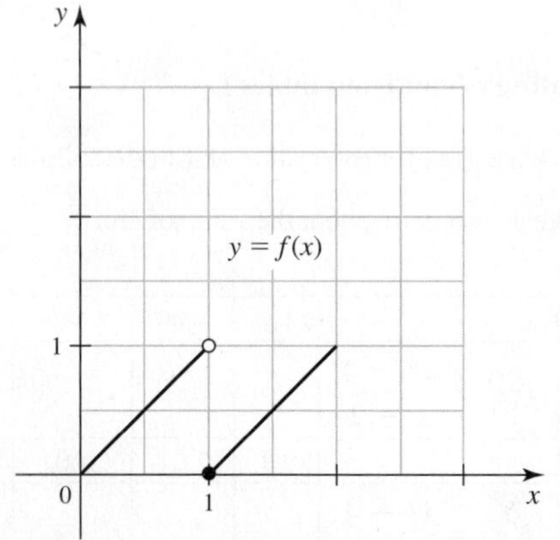

18. One-sided and two-sided limits Use the graph of g in the figure to find the following values, if they exist. If a limit does not exist, explain why.

a. $g(2)$ **b.** $\lim\limits_{x \to 2^-} g(x)$ **c.** $\lim\limits_{x \to 2^+} g(x)$

d. $\lim\limits_{x \to 2} g(x)$ **e.** $g(3)$ **f.** $\lim\limits_{x \to 3^-} g(x)$

g. $\lim\limits_{x \to 3^+} g(x)$ **h.** $g(4)$ **i.** $\lim\limits_{x \to 4} g(x)$

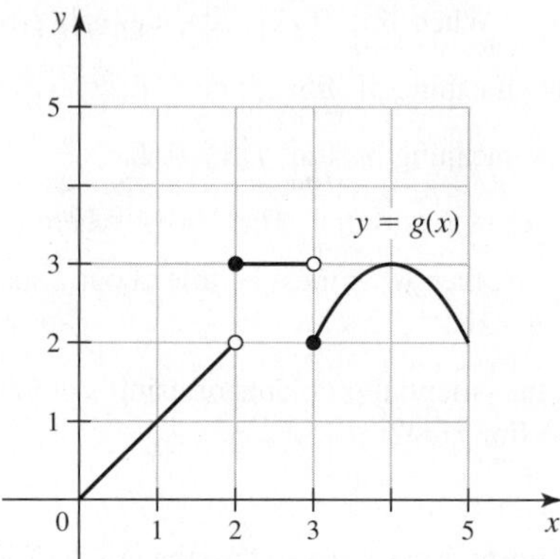

19. Finding limits from a graph Use the graph of f in the figure to find the following values, if they exist. If a limit does not exist, explain why.

a. $f(1)$ **b.** $\lim\limits_{x \to 1^-} f(x)$ **c.** $\lim\limits_{x \to 1^+} f(x)$

d. $\lim\limits_{x \to 1} f(x)$ **e.** $f(3)$ **f.** $\lim\limits_{x \to 3^-} f(x)$

g. $\lim\limits_{x \to 3^+} f(x)$ **h.** $\lim\limits_{x \to 3} f(x)$ **i.** $f(2)$

j. $\lim\limits_{x \to 2^-} f(x)$ **k.** $\lim\limits_{x \to 2^+} f(x)$ **l.** $\lim\limits_{x \to 2} f(x)$

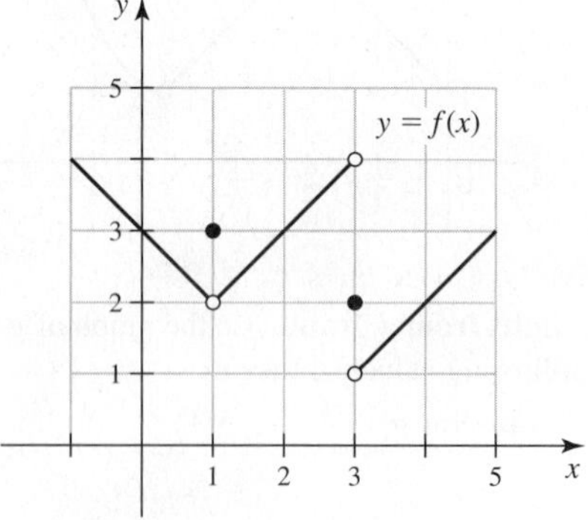

20. Finding limits from a graph Use the graph of g in the figure on the next page to find the following values, if they exist. If a limit does not exist, explain why.

a. $g(-1)$ **b.** $\lim\limits_{x \to -1^-} g(x)$ **c.** $\lim\limits_{x \to -1^+} g(x)$

d. $\lim\limits_{x \to -1} g(x)$ **e.** $g(1)$ **f.** $\lim\limits_{x \to 1} g(x)$

g. $\lim\limits_{x \to 3} g(x)$ **h.** $g(5)$ **i.** $\lim\limits_{x \to 5^-} g(x)$

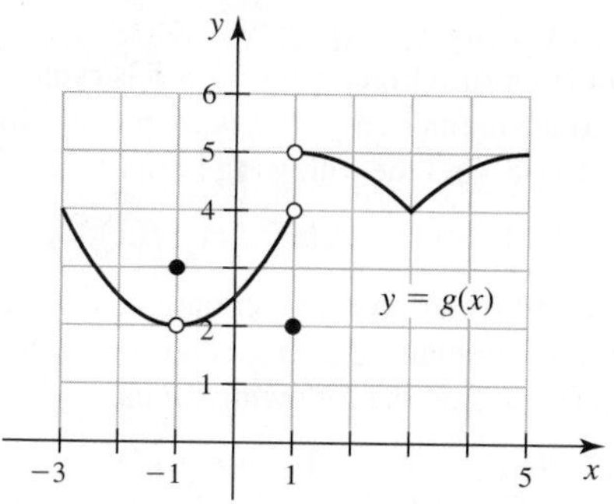

21. Strange behavior near $x = 0$

a. Create a table of values of $\sin\left(\frac{1}{x}\right)$ for $x = \frac{2}{\pi}, \frac{2}{3\pi}, \frac{2}{5\pi}, \frac{2}{7\pi}, \frac{2}{9\pi}$, and $\frac{2}{11\pi}$. Describe the pattern of values you observe.

b. Why does a graphing utility have difficulty plotting the graph of $y = \sin(1/x)$ near $x = 0$ (see figure)?

c. What do you conclude about $\lim_{x\to 0} \sin(1/x)$?

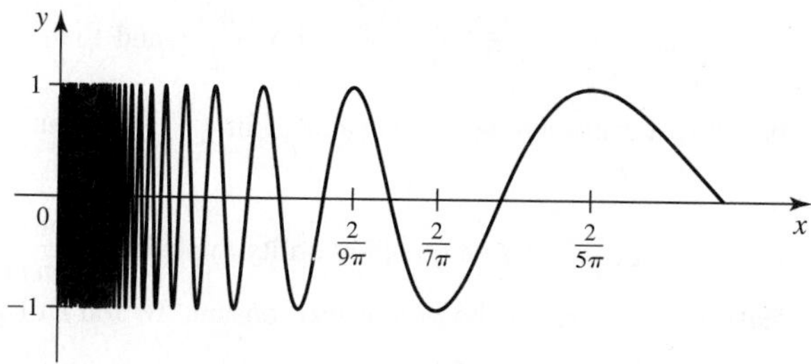

22. Strange behavior near $x = 0$

a. Create a table of values of $\tan(3/x)$ for $x = 1, 0.1, 0.01, 0.001, 0.0001$, and 0.00001. Describe the general pattern in the values you observe.

b. Use a graphing utility to graph $y = \tan(3/x)$. Why does a graphing utility have difficulty plotting the graph near $x = 0$?

c. What do you conclude about $\lim_{x\to 0} \tan(3/x)$?

Further Explorations

23. Explain why or why not Determine whether the following statements are true and give an explanation or counterexample.

a. The value of $\lim_{x\to 3} \frac{x^2 - 9}{x - 3}$ does not exist.

b. The value of $\lim_{x\to a} f(x)$ can always be found by computing $f(a)$.

c. The value of $\lim_{x\to a} f(x)$ does not exist if $f(a)$ is undefined.

24–25. Sketching graphs of functions *Sketch the graph of a function with the given properties. You do not need to find a formula for the function.*

24. $f(1) = 0, f(2) = 4, f(3) = 6, \lim_{x\to 2^-} f(x) = -3, \lim_{x\to 2^+} f(x) = 5$

25. $g(1) = 0, g(2) = 1, g(3) = -2, \lim_{x\to 2} g(x) = 0, \lim_{x\to 3^-} g(x) = -1, \lim_{x\to 3^+} g(x) = -2$

26–29. Calculator limits *Estimate the value of the following limits by creating a table of function values for $h = 0.01, 0.001$, and 0.0001, and $h = -0.01, -0.001$, and -0.0001.*

26. $\lim_{h\to 0} \frac{\sin h}{h}$

27. $\lim_{h\to 0} \frac{\tan 3h}{h}$

28. $\lim_{h\to 0} \frac{\sqrt{h + 4} - 2}{h}$

29. $\lim_{h\to 0} \frac{1 - \cos h}{h}$

30. A step function Let $f(x) = \frac{|x|}{x}$, for $x \neq 0$.

a. Sketch a graph of f on the interval $[-2, 2]$.

b. Does $\lim_{x\to 0} f(x)$ exist? Explain your reasoning after first examining $\lim_{x\to 0^-} f(x)$ and $\lim_{x\to 0^+} f(x)$.

31. The floor function For any real number x, the *floor function* (or *greatest integer function*), $\lfloor x \rfloor$, is defined to be the greatest integer less than or equal to x (see figure).

a. Compute $\lim_{x\to -1^-} \lfloor x \rfloor$, $\lim_{x\to -1^+} \lfloor x \rfloor$, $\lim_{x\to 2^-} \lfloor x \rfloor$, and $\lim_{x\to 2^+} \lfloor x \rfloor$.

b. Compute $\lim_{x\to 2.3^-} \lfloor x \rfloor$, $\lim_{x\to 2.3^+} \lfloor x \rfloor$, and $\lim_{x\to 2.3} \lfloor x \rfloor$.

c. In general, for an integer a, state the values of $\lim_{x\to a^-} \lfloor x \rfloor$ and $\lim_{x\to a^+} \lfloor x \rfloor$.

d. In general, if a is not an integer, state the values of $\lim_{x\to a^-} \lfloor x \rfloor$ and $\lim_{x\to a^+} \lfloor x \rfloor$.

e. For what values of a does $\lim_{x\to a} \lfloor x \rfloor$ exist? Explain.

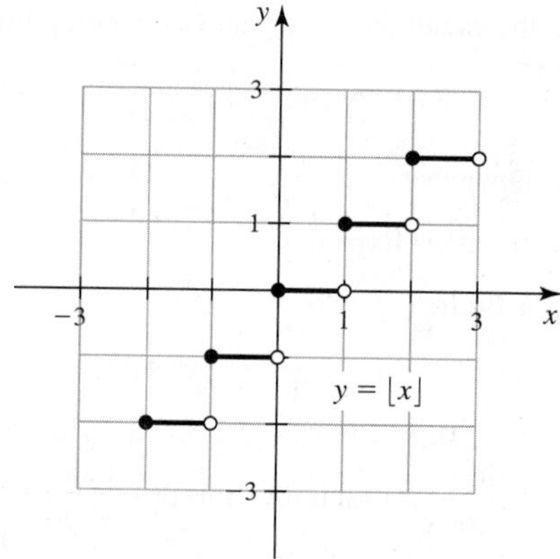

32. The ceiling function For any real number x, the *ceiling function*, $\lceil x \rceil$, is defined to be the least integer greater than or equal to x.

a. Graph the ceiling function $y = \lceil x \rceil$, for $-2 \le x \le 3$.

b. Evaluate $\lim_{x\to 2^-} \lceil x \rceil$, $\lim_{x\to 1^+} \lceil x \rceil$, and $\lim_{x\to 1.5} \lceil x \rceil$.

c. For what values of a does $\lim_{x\to a} \lceil x \rceil$ exist? Explain.

33. Limit by graphing Use the zoom and trace features of a graphing utility to approximate $\lim_{x\to 1} \frac{\sqrt{2x - x^4} - \sqrt[3]{x}}{1 - x^{3/4}}$.

34. Limit by graphing Use the zoom and trace features of a graphing utility to approximate $\lim_{x\to 3} \frac{x^4 - 7x^3 + 15x^2 - 9x}{x - 3}$.

Applications

35. Postage rates Assume that postage for sending a first-class letter in the United States is \$0.44 for the first ounce (up to and including 1 oz) plus \$0.17 for each additional ounce (up to and including each additional ounce).

a. Graph the function $p = f(w)$ that gives the postage p for sending a letter that weighs w ounces, for $0 < w \le 5$.

b. Evaluate $\lim_{w \to 3.3} f(w)$.

c. Interpret the limits $\lim_{w \to 1^+} f(w)$ and $\lim_{w \to 1^-} f(w)$.

d. Does $\lim_{w \to 4} f(w)$ exist? Explain.

36. The Heaviside function The Heaviside function is used in engineering applications to model flipping a switch. It is defined as

$$H(x) = \begin{cases} 0 & \text{if } x < 0 \\ 1 & \text{if } x \ge 0 \end{cases}$$

a. Sketch a graph of H on the interval $[-1, 2]$.

b. Does $\lim_{x \to 0} H(x)$ exist? Explain your reasoning after first examining $\lim_{x \to 0^-} H(x)$ and $\lim_{x \to 0^+} H(x)$.

T **37–38. Pitfalls of using a calculator** *Suppose you want to estimate* $\lim_{x \to a} \frac{f(x)}{g(x)}$. *If $g(x)$ is nearly equal to 0 when x is close to a, then a calculator utility may round the value of $g(x)$ to 0.*

T **37. Calculator limit** Evaluate $\frac{\sin x^{20}}{x^{20}}$, for $x = 0.1, 0.01, \ldots, 0.00001$. Based on the values given by your calculator, propose a value for $\lim_{x \to 0^+} \frac{\sin x^{20}}{x^{20}}$. Using limit techniques introduced later in the text, it can be shown that $\lim_{x \to 0^+} \frac{\sin x^{20}}{x^{20}} = 1$. Does your proposed value for the limit agree? Explain.

T **38. Calculator limit**

a. Graph the function $y = \frac{x \sin x}{1 - \cos x}$ with the window $[-1, 1] \times [0, 3]$. Based on this graph, estimate the value of $\lim_{x \to 0} \frac{x \sin x}{1 - \cos x}$. What is the value of $\frac{x \sin x}{1 - \cos x}$ at $x = 0$?

b. Values of $\frac{x \sin x}{1 - \cos x}$ near 0, computed with a computer algebra system, are shown in the accompanying table. It appears that $\lim_{x \to 0} \frac{x \sin x}{1 - \cos x}$ does not exist. Using limit techniques introduced later in the text, it can be shown that $\lim_{x \to 0} \frac{x \sin x}{1 - \cos x} = 2$.

What do you think happened, and why?

x	$\pm 10^{-6}$	$\pm 10^{-7}$	$\pm 10^{-8}$	$\pm 10^{-9}$	$\pm 10^{-10}$
$\frac{x \sin x}{1 - \cos x}$	2	1	undefined	undefined	undefined

Additional Exercises

39. Limits of even functions A function f is even if $f(-x) = f(x)$ for all x in the domain of f. If f is even, with $\lim_{x \to 2^+} f(x) = 5$ and $\lim_{x \to 2^-} f(x) = 8$, find the following limits.

a. $\lim_{x \to -2^+} f(x)$ **b.** $\lim_{x \to -2^-} f(x)$

40. Limits of odd functions A function g is odd if $g(-x) = -g(x)$ for all x in the domain of g. If g is odd, with $\lim_{x \to 2^+} g(x) = 5$ and $\lim_{x \to 2^-} g(x) = 8$, find the following limits.

a. $\lim_{x \to -2^+} g(x)$ **b.** $\lim_{x \to -2^-} g(x)$

T **41. Limits by graphs**

a. Use a graphing utility to estimate $\lim_{x \to 0} \frac{\tan 2x}{\sin x}$, $\lim_{x \to 0} \frac{\tan 3x}{\sin x}$, and $\lim_{x \to 0} \frac{\tan 4x}{\sin x}$.

b. Make a conjecture about the value of $\lim_{x \to 0} \frac{\tan nx}{\sin x}$ for any real constant n.

T **42. Limits by graphs** Graph $f(x) = \frac{\sin nx}{x}$, for $n = 1, 2, 3$, and 4 (four graphs). Use the window $[-1, 1] \times [0, 5]$.

a. Estimate $\lim_{x \to 0} \frac{\sin x}{x}$, $\lim_{x \to 0} \frac{\sin 2x}{x}$, $\lim_{x \to 0} \frac{\sin 3x}{x}$, and $\lim_{x \to 0} \frac{\sin 4x}{x}$.

b. Make a conjecture about the value of $\lim_{x \to 0} \frac{\sin nx}{x}$ for any real constant n.

T **43. Limits by graphs** Use a graphing utility to plot $y = \frac{\sin nx}{\sin mx}$ for at least three different pairs of nonzero constants m and n of your choice. Estimate $\lim_{x \to 0} \frac{\sin nx}{\sin mx}$ in each case. Then use your work to make a conjecture about the value of $\lim_{x \to 0} \frac{\sin nx}{\sin mx}$ for any nonzero values of m and n.

QUICK CHECK ANSWERS

1. The value of $\lim_{x \to 1} f(x)$ depends only on the values of f *near* 1, not at 1. Therefore, changing the value of $f(1)$ will not change $\lim_{x \to 1} f(x)$. **2.** A graphing device has difficulty plotting $y = \cos(1/x)$ near 0 because values of the function vary between −1 and 1 over shorter and shorter intervals as x approaches 0. ◀

2.3 Techniques for Computing Limits

Graphical and numerical techniques for estimating limits, like those presented in the previous section, provide intuition about limits. These techniques, however, occasionally lead to incorrect results. Therefore, we turn our attention to analytical methods for evaluating limits precisely.

Limits of Linear Functions

The graph of $f(x) = mx + b$ is a line with slope m and y-intercept b. From Figure 2.15, we see that for any value of a, $f(x)$ approaches $f(a)$ as x approaches a. Therefore, if f is a linear function we have $\lim_{x \to a} f(x) = f(a)$. It follows that for linear functions, $\lim_{x \to a} f(x)$ is found by direct substitution of $x = a$ into $f(x)$. This observation leads to the following theorem, which is proved in Exercise 28 of Section 2.7.

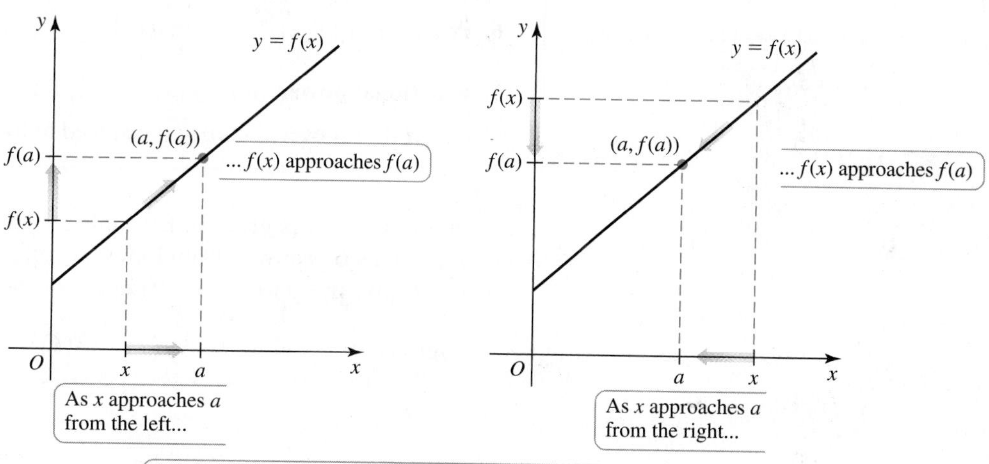

FIGURE 2.15

> **THEOREM 2.2 Limits of Linear Functions**
> Let a, b, and m be real numbers. For linear functions $f(x) = mx + b$,
> $$\lim_{x \to a} f(x) = f(a) = ma + b.$$

EXAMPLE 1 Limits of linear functions Evaluate the following limits.

a. $\lim_{x \to 3} f(x)$, where $f(x) = \frac{1}{2}x - 7$ **b.** $\lim_{x \to 2} g(x)$, where $g(x) = 6$

SOLUTION

a. $\lim_{x \to 3} f(x) = \lim_{x \to 3} \left(\frac{1}{2}x - 7\right) = f(3) = -\frac{11}{2}$. **b.** $\lim_{x \to 2} g(x) = \lim_{x \to 2} 6 = g(2) = 6$.

Related Exercises 11–16 ◀

Limit Laws

The following limit laws greatly simplify the evaluation of many limits.

THEOREM 2.3 Limit Laws

Assume $\lim_{x \to a} f(x)$ and $\lim_{x \to a} g(x)$ exist. The following properties hold, where c is a real number and $m > 0$ and $n > 0$ are integers.

1. **Sum** $\lim_{x \to a} [f(x) + g(x)] = \lim_{x \to a} f(x) + \lim_{x \to a} g(x)$
2. **Difference** $\lim_{x \to a} [f(x) - g(x)] = \lim_{x \to a} f(x) - \lim_{x \to a} g(x)$
3. **Constant multiple** $\lim_{x \to a} [cf(x)] = c \lim_{x \to a} f(x)$
4. **Product** $\lim_{x \to a} [f(x)g(x)] = \left[\lim_{x \to a} f(x)\right]\left[\lim_{x \to a} g(x)\right]$
5. **Quotient** $\lim_{x \to a} \left[\frac{f(x)}{g(x)}\right] = \frac{\lim_{x \to a} f(x)}{\lim_{x \to a} g(x)}$, provided $\lim_{x \to a} g(x) \neq 0$
6. **Power** $\lim_{x \to a} [f(x)]^n = \left[\lim_{x \to a} f(x)\right]^n$
7. **Fractional power** $\lim_{x \to a} [f(x)]^{n/m} = \left[\lim_{x \to a} f(x)\right]^{n/m}$, provided $f(x) \geq 0$ for x near a if m is even and n/m is reduced to lowest terms

➤ Law 6 is a special case of Law 7. Letting $m = 1$ in Law 7 gives Law 6.

A proof of Law 1 is given in Example 5 of Section 2.7. Laws 2–5 are proved in the Appendix B. Law 6 is proved from Law 4 as follows.

For a positive integer n, if $\lim_{x \to a} f(x)$ exists, then

$$\lim_{x \to a} [f(x)]^n = \lim_{x \to a} [\underbrace{f(x) f(x) \cdots f(x)}_{n \text{ factors of } f(x)}]$$

$$= \underbrace{\left[\lim_{x \to a} f(x)\right]\left[\lim_{x \to a} f(x)\right] \cdots \left[\lim_{x \to a} f(x)\right]}_{n \text{ factors of } \lim_{x \to a} f(x)} \quad \text{Repeated use of Law 4}$$

$$= \left[\lim_{x \to a} f(x)\right]^n.$$

➤ Recall that to take even roots of a number (for example, square roots or fourth roots), the number must be nonnegative if the result is to be real.

In Law 7, the limit of $[f(x)]^{n/m}$ involves the mth root of $f(x)$ when x is near a. If the fraction n/m is in lowest terms and m is even, this root is undefined unless $f(x)$ is nonnegative for all x near $x = a$, which explains the restrictions shown.

EXAMPLE 2 Evaluating limits Suppose $\lim_{x \to 2} f(x) = 4$, $\lim_{x \to 2} g(x) = 5$, and $\lim_{x \to 2} h(x) = 8$. Use the limit laws in Theorem 2.3 to compute each limit.

a. $\lim_{x \to 2} \frac{f(x) - g(x)}{h(x)}$ **b.** $\lim_{x \to 2} [6f(x)g(x) + h(x)]$ **c.** $\lim_{x \to 2} [g(x)]^3$

SOLUTION

a.

$$\lim_{x \to 2} \frac{f(x) - g(x)}{h(x)} = \frac{\lim_{x \to 2} [f(x) - g(x)]}{\lim_{x \to 2} h(x)} \quad \text{Law 5}$$

$$= \frac{\lim_{x \to 2} f(x) - \lim_{x \to 2} g(x)}{\lim_{x \to 2} h(x)} \quad \text{Law 2}$$

$$= \frac{4 - 5}{8} = -\frac{1}{8}$$

b. $\lim_{x\to 2}[6f(x)g(x) + h(x)] = \lim_{x\to 2}[6f(x)g(x)] + \lim_{x\to 2} h(x)$ Law 1

$= 6\cdot \lim_{x\to 2}[f(x)g(x)] + \lim_{x\to 2} h(x)$ Law 3

$= 6\cdot\left[\lim_{x\to 2} f(x)\right]\cdot\left[\lim_{x\to 2} g(x)\right] + \lim_{x\to 2} h(x)$ Law 4

$= 6\cdot 4\cdot 5 + 8 = 128$

c. $\lim_{x\to 2}[g(x)]^3 = \left[\lim_{x\to 2} g(x)\right]^3 = 5^3 = 125$ Law 6

Related Exercises 17–22 ◀

Limits of Polynomial and Rational Functions

The limit laws are now used to find the limits of polynomial and rational functions. For example, to evaluate the limit of the polynomial $p(x) = 7x^3 + 3x^2 + 4x + 2$ at an arbitrary point a, we proceed as follows:

$$\lim_{x\to a} p(x) = \lim_{x\to a}(7x^3 + 3x^2 + 4x + 2)$$

$$= \lim_{x\to a}(7x^3) + \lim_{x\to a}(3x^2) + \lim_{x\to a}(4x + 2) \quad \text{Law 1}$$

$$= 7\lim_{x\to a}(x^3) + 3\lim_{x\to a}(x^2) + \lim_{x\to a}(4x + 2) \quad \text{Law 3}$$

$$= 7\underbrace{\left(\lim_{x\to a} x\right)}_{a}{}^3 + 3\underbrace{\left(\lim_{x\to a} x\right)}_{a}{}^2 + \underbrace{\lim_{x\to a}(4x + 2)}_{4a+2} \quad \text{Law 6}$$

$$= 7a^3 + 3a^2 + 4a + 2 = p(a) \quad \text{Theorem 2.2}$$

As in the case of linear functions, the limit of a polynomial is found by direct substitution; that is, $\lim_{x\to a} p(x) = p(a)$ (Exercise 85).

It is now a short step to evaluating limits of rational functions of the form $f(x) = p(x)/q(x)$, where p and q are polynomials. Applying Law 5, we have

$$\lim_{x\to a}\frac{p(x)}{q(x)} = \frac{\lim_{x\to a} p(x)}{\lim_{x\to a} q(x)} = \frac{p(a)}{q(a)}, \quad \text{provided } q(a) \neq 0,$$

which shows that limits of rational functions are also evaluated by direct substitution.

➤ The conditions under which direct substitution $\left(\lim_{x\to a} f(x) = f(a)\right)$ can be used to evaluate a limit become clear in Section 2.6, when the important property of *continuity* is discussed.

> **THEOREM 2.4 Limits of Polynomial and Rational Functions**
> Assume p and q are polynomials and a is a constant.
>
> **a.** Polynomial functions: $\lim_{x\to a} p(x) = p(a)$
>
> **b.** Rational functions: $\lim_{x\to a}\frac{p(x)}{q(x)} = \frac{p(a)}{q(a)}$, provided $q(a) \neq 0$

QUICK CHECK 1 Evaluate $\lim_{x\to 2}(2x^4 - 8x - 16)$ and $\lim_{x\to -1}\frac{x - 1}{x}$. ◀

EXAMPLE 3 Limit of a rational function Evaluate $\lim_{x\to 2}\frac{3x^2 - 4x}{5x^3 - 36}$.

SOLUTION Notice that the denominator of this function is nonzero at $x = 2$. Using Theorem 2.4b,

$$\lim_{x\to 2}\frac{3x^2 - 4x}{5x^3 - 36} = \frac{3(2^2) - 4(2)}{5(2^3) - 36} = 1.$$

Related Exercises 23–25 ◀

QUICK CHECK 2 Use Theorem 2.4b to compute $\lim_{x\to 1}\frac{5x^4 - 3x^2 + 8x - 6}{x + 1}$. ◀

EXAMPLE 4 **An algebraic function** Evaluate $\lim_{x\to 2} \dfrac{\sqrt{2x^3 + 9} + 3x - 1}{4x + 1}$.

SOLUTION Using Theorems 2.3 and 2.4, we have

$$\lim_{x\to 2} \frac{\sqrt{2x^3 + 9} + 3x - 1}{4x + 1} = \frac{\lim_{x\to 2}\left(\sqrt{2x^3 + 9} + 3x - 1\right)}{\lim_{x\to 2}(4x + 1)} \qquad \text{Law 5}$$

$$= \frac{\sqrt{\lim_{x\to 2}(2x^3 + 9)} + \lim_{x\to 2}(3x - 1)}{\lim_{x\to 2}(4x + 1)} \qquad \text{Laws 1 and 7}$$

$$= \frac{\sqrt{(2(2)^3 + 9)} + (3(2) - 1)}{(4(2) + 1)} \qquad \text{Theorem 2.4}$$

$$= \frac{\sqrt{25} + 5}{9} = \frac{10}{9}.$$

Notice that the limit at $x = 2$ equals the value of the function at $x = 2$.

Related Exercises 26–30 ◀

One-Sided Limits

Theorem 2.2, limit laws 1–6, and Theorem 2.4 also hold for left-sided and right-sided limits. In other words, these laws remain valid if we replace $\lim_{x\to a}$ by $\lim_{x\to a^+}$ or $\lim_{x\to a^-}$. Law 7 must be modified slightly for one-sided limits, as shown below.

> **THEOREM 2.3 (CONTINUED)** **Limit Laws for One-Sided Limits**
> Laws 1–6 hold with $\lim_{x\to a}$ replaced by $\lim_{x\to a^+}$ or $\lim_{x\to a^-}$. Law 7 is modified as follows.
> Assume $m > 0$ and $n > 0$ are integers.
>
> **7. Fractional Power**
>
> **a.** $\lim_{x\to a^+} [f(x)]^{n/m} = \left[\lim_{x\to a^+} f(x)\right]^{n/m}$ provided $f(x) \ge 0$ for x near a with $x > a$, if m is even and n/m is reduced to lowest terms
>
> **b.** $\lim_{x\to a^-} [f(x)]^{n/m} = \left[\lim_{x\to a^-} f(x)\right]^{n/m}$ provided $f(x) \ge 0$ for x near a with $x < a$, if m is even and n/m is reduced to lowest terms

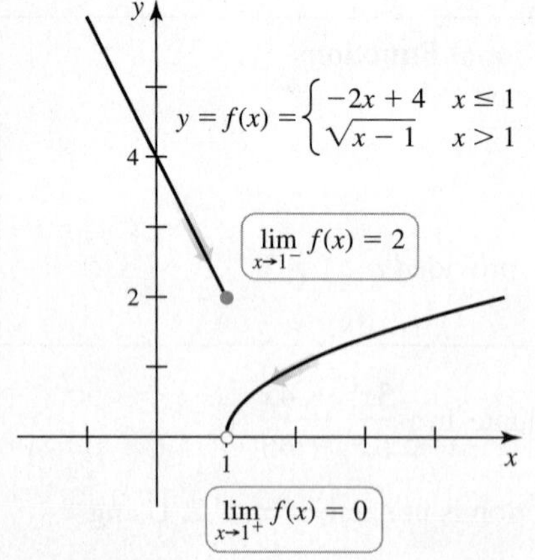

FIGURE 2.16

EXAMPLE 5 **Calculating left- and right-sided limits** Let

$$f(x) = \begin{cases} -2x + 4 & \text{if } x \le 1 \\ \sqrt{x - 1} & \text{if } x > 1 \end{cases}.$$

Find the values of $\lim_{x\to 1^-} f(x)$, $\lim_{x\to 1^+} f(x)$, and $\lim_{x\to 1} f(x)$, or state that they do not exist.

SOLUTION The graph of f (Figure 2.16) suggests that $\lim_{x\to 1^-} f(x) = 2$ and $\lim_{x\to 1^+} f(x) = 0$. We verify this observation analytically by applying the limit laws. For $x \le 1$, $f(x) = -2x + 4$; therefore,

$$\lim_{x\to 1^-} f(x) = \lim_{x\to 1^-} (-2x + 4) = 2. \qquad \text{Theorem 2.2}$$

For $x > 1$, note that $x - 1 > 0$; it follows that

$$\lim_{x \to 1^+} f(x) = \lim_{x \to 1^+} (\sqrt{x} - 1) = 0. \quad \text{Law 7}$$

Because $\lim_{x \to 1^-} f(x) = 2$ and $\lim_{x \to 1^+} f(x) = 0$, $\lim_{x \to 1} f(x)$ does not exist by Theorem 2.1.

Related Exercises 31–36 ◀

Other Techniques

So far, we have evaluated limits by direct substitution. A more challenging problem is finding $\lim_{x \to a} f(x)$ when the limit exists, but $\lim_{x \to a} f(x) \neq f(a)$. Two typical cases are shown in Figure 2.17. In the first case, $f(a)$ is defined, but it is not equal to $\lim_{x \to a} f(x)$; in the second case, $f(a)$ is not defined at all.

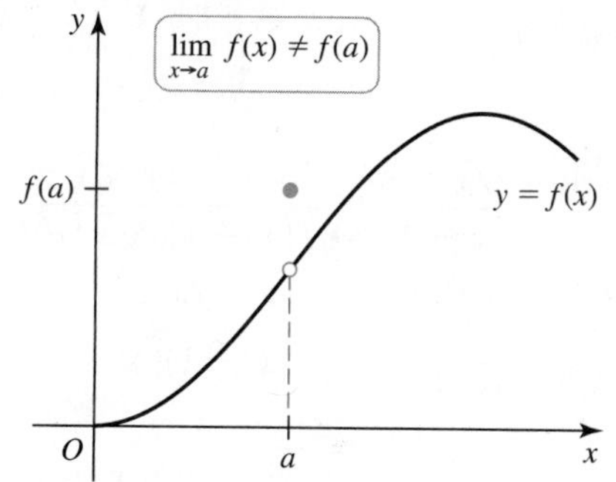

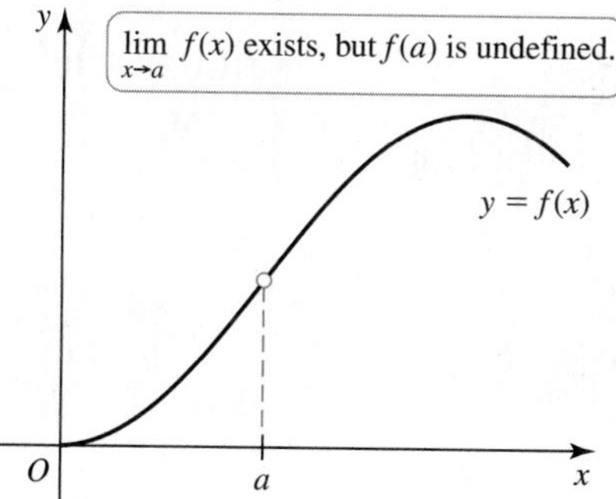

FIGURE 2.17

EXAMPLE 6 **Other techniques** Evaluate the following limits.

a. $\lim_{x \to 2} \frac{x^2 - 6x + 8}{x^2 - 4}$ **b.** $\lim_{x \to 1} \frac{\sqrt{x} - 1}{x - 1}$

SOLUTION

a. This limit cannot be found by direct substitution because the denominator is zero when $x = 2$. Instead, the numerator and denominator are factored; then, assuming $x \neq 2$, we cancel like factors:

$$\frac{x^2 - 6x + 8}{x^2 - 4} = \frac{(x - 2)(x - 4)}{(x - 2)(x + 2)} = \frac{x - 4}{x + 2}.$$

➤ The argument used in this example is common. In the limit process, x approaches 2, but $x \neq 2$. Therefore, we may cancel like factors.

Because $\frac{x^2 - 6x + 8}{x^2 - 4} = \frac{x - 4}{x + 2}$ whenever $x \neq 2$, the two functions have the same limit as x approaches 2 (Figure 2.18). Therefore,

$$\lim_{x \to 2} \frac{x^2 - 6x + 8}{x^2 - 4} = \lim_{x \to 2} \frac{x - 4}{x + 2} = \frac{2 - 4}{2 + 2} = -\frac{1}{2}.$$

b. This limit was approximated numerically in Example 2 of Section 2.2; we conjectured that the value of the limit is $\frac{1}{2}$. Direct substitution fails in this case because the denominator is zero at $x = 1$. Instead, we first simplify the function by multiplying the numerator and denominator by the *algebraic conjugate* of the numerator. The conjugate of $\sqrt{x} - 1$ is $\sqrt{x} + 1$; therefore,

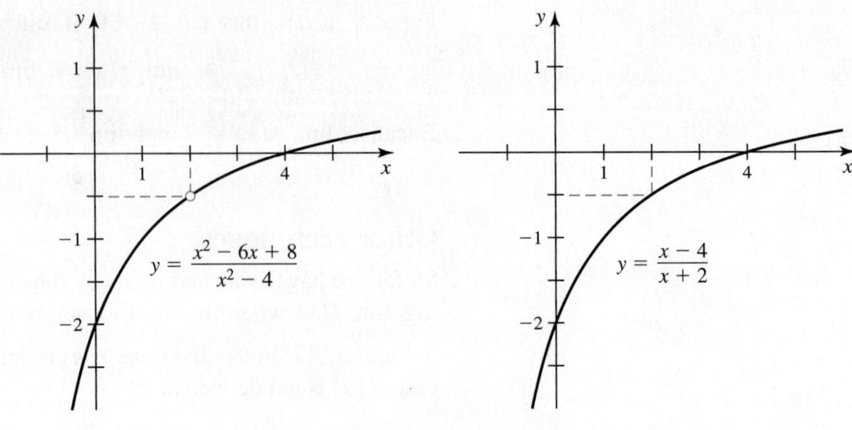

FIGURE 2.18

$$\frac{\sqrt{x} - 1}{x - 1} = \frac{(\sqrt{x} - 1)(\sqrt{x} + 1)}{(x - 1)(\sqrt{x} + 1)} \quad \text{Rationalize the numerator.}$$

$$= \frac{x + \sqrt{x} - \sqrt{x} - 1}{(x - 1)(\sqrt{x} + 1)} \quad \text{Expand the numerator.}$$

$$= \frac{x - 1}{(x - 1)(\sqrt{x} + 1)} \quad \text{Simplify.}$$

$$= \frac{1}{\sqrt{x} + 1}. \quad \text{Cancel like factors when } x \neq 1.$$

The limit can now be evaluated:

$$\lim_{x \to 1} \frac{\sqrt{x} - 1}{x - 1} = \lim_{x \to 1} \frac{1}{\sqrt{x} + 1} = \frac{1}{1 + 1} = \frac{1}{2}$$

Related Exercises 37–48 ◀

QUICK CHECK 3 Evaluate $\lim_{x \to 5} \frac{x^2 - 7x + 10}{x - 5}$. ◀

➤ The Squeeze Theorem is also called the Pinching Theorem or the Sandwich Theorem.

The Squeeze Theorem

The *Squeeze Theorem* provides another useful method for calculating limits. Suppose the functions f and h have the same limit L at a and assume the function g is trapped between f and h (Figure 2.19). The Squeeze Theorem says that g must also have the limit L at a. A proof of this theorem is outlined in Exercise 54 of Section 2.7.

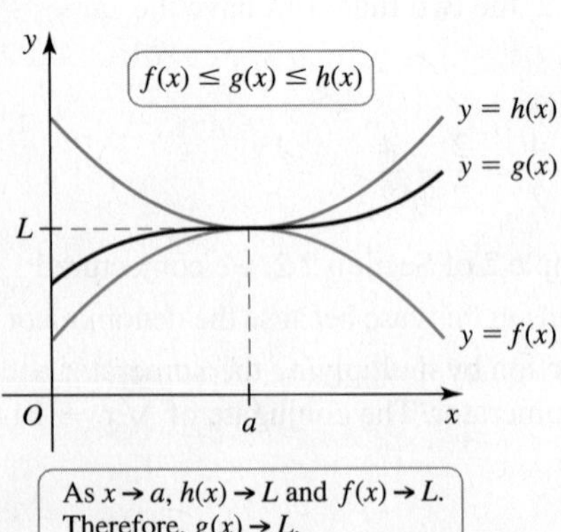

FIGURE 2.19

> **THEOREM 2.5 The Squeeze Theorem**
> Assume the functions f, g, and h satisfy $f(x) \leq g(x) \leq h(x)$ for values of x near a, except possibly at a. If $\lim_{x \to a} f(x) = \lim_{x \to a} h(x) = L$, then $\lim_{x \to a} g(x) = L$.

EXAMPLE 7 Sine and cosine limits A geometric argument (Exercise 84) may be used to show that for $-\pi/2 < x < \pi/2$,

$$-|x| \leq \sin x \leq |x| \quad \text{and} \quad 0 \leq 1 - \cos x \leq |x|.$$

Use the Squeeze Theorem to confirm the following limits:

a. $\lim_{x \to 0} \sin x = 0$ **b.** $\lim_{x \to 0} \cos x = 1$

The two limits in Example 7 play a crucial role in establishing fundamental properties of the trigonometric functions. They reappear in Section 2.6.

SOLUTION

a. Letting $f(x) = -|x|$, $g(x) = \sin x$, and $h(x) = |x|$, we see that g is trapped between f and h on $-\pi/2 < x < \pi/2$ (Figure 2.20a). Because $\lim_{x \to 0} f(x) = \lim_{x \to 0} h(x) = 0$ (Exercise 35), the Squeeze Theorem implies that $\lim_{x \to 0} g(x) = \lim_{x \to 0} \sin x = 0$.

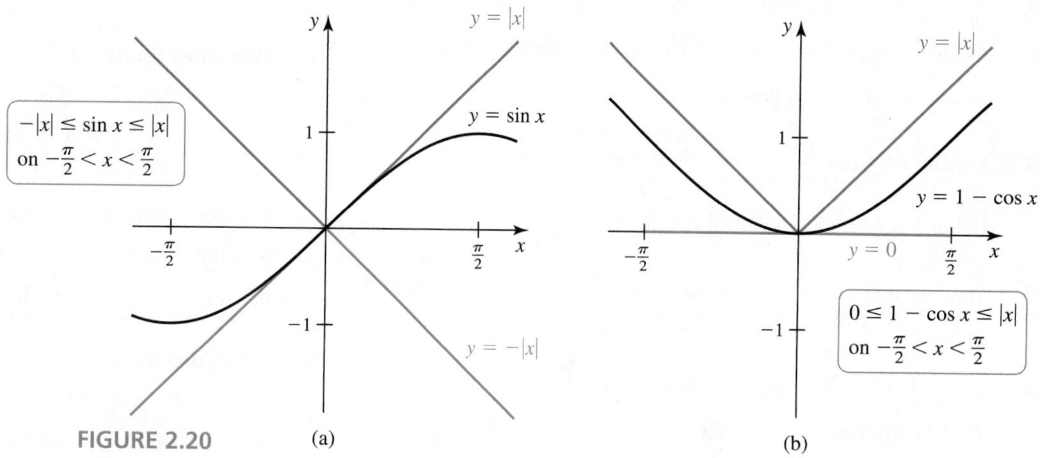

FIGURE 2.20

b. In this case, we let $f(x) = 0$, $g(x) = 1 - \cos x$, and $h(x) = |x|$ (Figure 2.20b). Because $\lim_{x \to 0} f(x) = \lim_{x \to 0} h(x) = 0$, the Squeeze Theorem implies that $\lim_{x \to 0} g(x) = \lim_{x \to 0} (1 - \cos x) = 0$. By the limit laws, it follows that $\lim_{x \to 0} 1 - \lim_{x \to 0} \cos x = 0$, or $\lim_{x \to 0} \cos x = 1$.

Related Exercises 49–52 ◄

EXAMPLE 8 Applying the Squeeze Theorem Use the Squeeze Theorem to verify that $\lim_{x \to 0} x^2 \sin(1/x) = 0$.

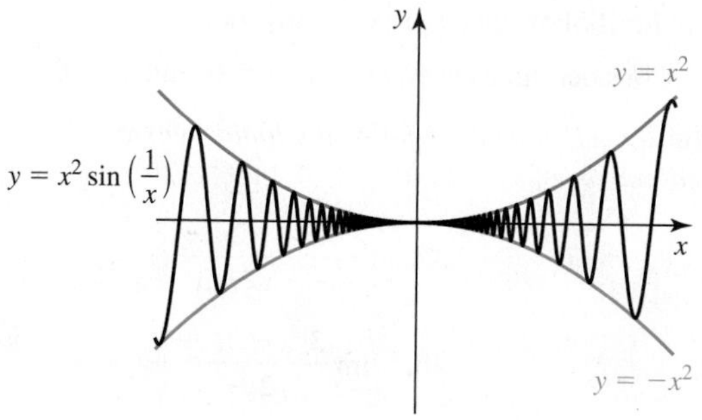

SOLUTION For any real number θ, $-1 \le \sin \theta \le 1$. Letting $\theta = 1/x$ for $x \ne 0$, it follows that

$$-1 \le \sin\left(\frac{1}{x}\right) \le 1.$$

Noting that $x^2 > 0$ for $x \ne 0$, each term in this inequality is multiplied by x^2:

$$-x^2 \le x^2 \sin\left(\frac{1}{x}\right) \le x^2.$$

These inequalities are illustrated in Figure 2.21. Because $\lim_{x \to 0} x^2 = \lim_{x \to 0} (-x^2) = 0$, the Squeeze Theorem implies that $\lim_{x \to 0} x^2 \sin(1/x) = 0$.

FIGURE 2.21

Related Exercises 49–52 ◄

QUICK CHECK 4 Suppose f satisfies $1 \le f(x) \le 1 + \frac{x^2}{6}$ for all values of x near zero. Find $\lim_{x \to 0} f(x)$, if possible. ◄

SECTION 2.3 EXERCISES

Review Questions

1. How is $\lim_{x\to a} f(x)$ calculated if f is a polynomial function?

2. How are $\lim_{x\to a^-} f(x)$ and $\lim_{x\to a^+} f(x)$ calculated if f is a polynomial function?

3. For what values of a does $\lim_{x\to a} r(x) = r(a)$ if r is a rational function?

4. Assume $\lim_{x\to 3} g(x) = 4$ and $f(x) = g(x)$ whenever $x \neq 3$. Evaluate $\lim_{x\to 3} f(x)$, if possible.

5. Explain why $\lim_{x\to 3} \frac{x^2 - 7x + 12}{x - 3} = \lim_{x\to 3} (x - 4)$.

6. If $\lim_{x\to 2} f(x) = -8$, find $\lim_{x\to 2} [f(x)]^{2/3}$.

7. Suppose p and q are polynomials. If $\lim_{x\to 0} \frac{p(x)}{q(x)} = 10$ and $q(0) = 2$, find $p(0)$.

8. If $\lim_{x\to 2} f(x) = \lim_{x\to 2} h(x) = 5$, find $\lim_{x\to 2} g(x)$ when $f(x) \le g(x) \le h(x)$ for all x.

9. Evaluate $\lim_{x\to 5} \sqrt{x^2 - 9}$.

10. Suppose

$$f(x) = \begin{cases} 4 & \text{if } x \le 3 \\ x + 2 & \text{if } x > 3 \end{cases}$$

Compute $\lim_{x\to 3^-} f(x)$ and $\lim_{x\to 3^+} f(x)$.

Basic Skills

11–16. Limits of linear functions *Evaluate the following limits.*

11. $\lim_{x\to 4} (3x - 7)$
12. $\lim_{x\to 1} (-2x + 5)$
13. $\lim_{x\to -9} (5x)$
14. $\lim_{x\to 2} (-3x)$
15. $\lim_{x\to 6} (4)$
16. $\lim_{x\to -5} (\pi)$

17–22. Applying limit laws *Assume* $\lim_{x\to 1} f(x) = 8$, $\lim_{x\to 1} g(x) = 3$, *and* $\lim_{x\to 1} h(x) = 2$. *Compute the following limits and state the limit laws used to justify your computations.*

17. $\lim_{x\to 1} [4f(x)]$
18. $\lim_{x\to 1} \left[\frac{f(x)}{h(x)}\right]$
19. $\lim_{x\to 1} \left[\frac{f(x)g(x)}{h(x)}\right]$
20. $\lim_{x\to 1} \left[\frac{f(x)}{g(x) - h(x)}\right]$
21. $\lim_{x\to 1} [h(x)]^5$
22. $\lim_{x\to 1} \sqrt[3]{f(x)g(x) + 3}$

23–30. Evaluating limits *Evaluate the following limits.*

23. $\lim_{x\to 1} (2x^3 - 3x^2 + 4x + 5)$
24. $\lim_{t\to -2} (t^2 + 5t + 7)$
25. $\lim_{x\to 1} \frac{5x^2 + 6x + 1}{8x - 4}$
26. $\lim_{t\to 3} \sqrt[3]{t^2 - 10}$
27. $\lim_{b\to 2} \frac{3b}{\sqrt{4b + 1} - 1}$
28. $\lim_{x\to 2} (x^2 - x)^5$
29. $\lim_{x\to 3} \frac{-5x}{\sqrt{4x - 3}}$
30. $\lim_{h\to 0} \frac{3}{\sqrt{16 + 3h} + 4}$

31. **One-sided limits** Let

$$f(x) = \begin{cases} x^2 + 1 & \text{if } x < -1 \\ \sqrt{x + 1} & \text{if } x \ge -1 \end{cases}$$

Compute the following limits or state that they do not exist.

a. $\lim_{x\to -1^-} f(x)$ **b.** $\lim_{x\to -1^+} f(x)$ **c.** $\lim_{x\to -1} f(x)$

32. **One-sided limits** Let

$$f(x) = \begin{cases} 0 & \text{if } x \le -5 \\ \sqrt{25 - x^2} & \text{if } -5 < x < 5 \\ 3x & \text{if } x \ge 5 \end{cases}$$

Compute the following limits or state that they do not exist.

a. $\lim_{x\to -5^-} f(x)$ **b.** $\lim_{x\to -5^+} f(x)$ **c.** $\lim_{x\to -5} f(x)$
d. $\lim_{x\to 5^-} f(x)$ **e.** $\lim_{x\to 5^+} f(x)$ **f.** $\lim_{x\to 5} f(x)$

33. **One-sided limits**

a. Evaluate $\lim_{x\to 2^+} \sqrt{x - 2}$.

b. Why don't we consider evaluating $\lim_{x\to 2^-} \sqrt{x - 2}$?

34. **One-sided limits**

a. Evaluate $\lim_{x\to 3^-} \sqrt{\frac{x - 3}{2 - x}}$.

b. Why don't we consider evaluating $\lim_{x\to 3^+} \sqrt{\frac{x - 3}{2 - x}}$?

35. **Absolute value limit** Show that $\lim_{x\to 0} |x| = 0$ by first evaluating $\lim_{x\to 0^-} |x|$ and $\lim_{x\to 0^+} |x|$. Recall that

$$|x| = \begin{cases} -x & \text{if } x < 0 \\ x & \text{if } x \ge 0 \end{cases}.$$

36. **Absolute value limit** Show that $\lim_{x\to a} |x| = |a|$ for any real number. (*Hint:* Consider three cases, $a < 0$, $a = 0$, and $a > 0$.)

37–48. Other techniques *Evaluate the following limits, where a and b are fixed real numbers.*

37. $\lim_{x\to 1} \frac{x^2 - 1}{x - 1}$
38. $\lim_{x\to 3} \frac{x^2 - 2x - 3}{x - 3}$
39. $\lim_{x\to 4} \frac{x^2 - 16}{4 - x}$
40. $\lim_{t\to 2} \frac{3t^2 - 7t + 2}{2 - t}$
41. $\lim_{x\to b} \frac{(x - b)^{50} - x + b}{x - b}$
42. $\lim_{x\to -b} \frac{(x + b)^7 + (x + b)^{10}}{4(x + b)}$
43. $\lim_{x\to -1} \frac{(2x - 1)^2 - 9}{x + 1}$
44. $\lim_{h\to 0} \frac{\frac{1}{5 + h} - \frac{1}{5}}{h}$
45. $\lim_{x\to 9} \frac{\sqrt{x} - 3}{x - 9}$
46. $\lim_{t\to a} \frac{\sqrt{3t + 1} - \sqrt{3a + 1}}{t - a}$
47. $\lim_{h\to 0} \frac{\sqrt{16 + h} - 4}{h}$
48. $\lim_{x\to 0} \frac{a - \sqrt{a^2 - x^2}}{x^2}$

49. Applying the Squeeze Theorem

a. Show that $-|x| \le x \sin\left(\frac{1}{x}\right) \le |x|$ for all $x \neq 0$.

b. Illustrate the inequalities in part (a) with a graph.

c. Use the Squeeze Theorem to show that $\lim_{x\to 0} x \sin\left(\frac{1}{x}\right) = 0$.

50. A cosine limit by the Squeeze Theorem It can be shown that $1 - x^2/2 \le \cos x \le 1$ for x near 0.

a. Illustrate these inequalities with a graph.

b. Use these inequalities to find $\lim_{x\to 0} \cos x$.

51. A sine limit by the Squeeze Theorem It can be shown that $1 - \frac{x^2}{6} \le \frac{\sin x}{x} \le 1$ for x near 0.

a. Illustrate these inequalities with a graph.

b. Use these inequalities to find $\lim_{x\to 0} \frac{\sin x}{x}$.

52. A secant limit by the Squeeze Theorem

a. Draw a graph to verify that $0 \le x^2 \sec x^2 \le x^4 + x^2$ for x near 0.

b. Use the Squeeze Theorem to determine $\lim_{x\to 0} x^2 \sec x^2$.

Further Explorations

53. Explain why or why not Determine whether the following statements are true and give an explanation or counterexample. Assume a and L are finite numbers.

a. If $\lim_{x\to a} f(x) = L$, then $f(a) = L$.

b. If $\lim_{x\to a^-} f(x) = L$, then $\lim_{x\to a^+} f(x) = L$.

c. If $\lim_{x\to a} f(x) = L$ and $\lim_{x\to a} g(x) = L$, then $f(a) = g(a)$.

d. The limit $\lim_{x\to a} \frac{f(x)}{g(x)}$ does not exist if $g(a) = 0$.

e. If $\lim_{x\to 1^+} \sqrt{f(x)} = \sqrt{\lim_{x\to 1^+} f(x)}$, it follows that $\lim_{x\to 1} \sqrt{f(x)} = \sqrt{\lim_{x\to 1} f(x)}$.

54–61. Evaluating limits *Evaluate the following limits, where c and k are constants.*

54. $\lim_{h\to 0} \frac{100}{(10h - 1)^{11} + 2}$

55. $\lim_{x\to 2} (5x - 6)^{3/2}$

56. $\lim_{x\to 5} (3x - 16)^{3/7}$

57. $\lim_{x\to 1} \frac{\sqrt{10x - 9} - 1}{x - 1}$

58. $\lim_{x\to 2} \left(\frac{1}{x - 2} - \frac{2}{x^2 - 2x}\right)$

59. $\lim_{h\to 0} \frac{(5 + h)^2 - 25}{h}$

60. $\lim_{x\to c} \frac{x^2 - 2cx + c^2}{x - c}$

61. $\lim_{w\to -k} \frac{w^2 + 5kw + 4k^2}{w^2 + kw}$

62. Finding a constant Suppose

$$f(x) = \begin{cases} 3x + b & \text{if } x \le 2 \\ x - 2 & \text{if } x > 2 \end{cases}.$$

Determine a value of the constant b for which $\lim_{x\to 2} f(x)$ exists and state the value of the limit, if possible.

63. Finding a constant Suppose

$$g(x) = \begin{cases} x^2 - 5x & \text{if } x \le -1 \\ ax^3 - 7 & \text{if } x > -1 \end{cases}.$$

Determine a value of the constant a for which $\lim_{x\to -1} g(x)$ exists and state the value of the limit, if possible.

64–70. Useful factorization formula *Calculate the following limits using the factorization formula*

$$x^n - a^n = (x - a)(x^{n-1} + x^{n-2}a + x^{n-3}a^2 + \cdots + xa^{n-2} + a^{n-1}),$$

where n is a positive integer and a is a real number.

64. $\lim_{x\to 2} \frac{x^5 - 32}{x - 2}$

65. $\lim_{x\to 1} \frac{x^6 - 1}{x - 1}$

66. $\lim_{x\to -1} \frac{x^7 + 1}{x + 1}$ (*Hint:* Use the formula for $x^7 - a^7$ with $a = -1$.)

67. $\lim_{x\to a} \frac{x^5 - a^5}{x - a}$

68. $\lim_{x\to a} \frac{x^n - a^n}{x - a}$, for any positive integer n

69. $\lim_{x\to 1} \frac{\sqrt[3]{x} - 1}{x - 1}$ $\left(\textit{Hint: } x - 1 = \left(\sqrt[3]{x}\right)^3 - (1)^3\right)$

70. $\lim_{x\to 16} \frac{\sqrt[4]{x} - 2}{x - 16}$

71–74. Limits involving conjugates *Evaluate the following limits.*

71. $\lim_{x\to 1} \frac{x - 1}{\sqrt{x} - 1}$

72. $\lim_{x\to 1} \frac{x - 1}{\sqrt{4x + 5} - 3}$

73. $\lim_{x\to 4} \frac{3(x - 4)\sqrt{x + 5}}{3 - \sqrt{x + 5}}$

74. $\lim_{x\to 0} \frac{x}{\sqrt{cx + 1} - 1}$, where c is a constant

75. Creating functions satisfying given limit conditions Give examples of functions f and g such that $\lim_{x\to 1} f(x) = 0$ and $\lim_{x\to 1} (f(x) \cdot g(x)) = 5$.

76. Creating functions satisfying given limit conditions Give an example of a function f satisfying $\lim_{x\to 1} \left(\frac{f(x)}{x - 1}\right) = 2$.

77. Finding constants Find constants b and c in the polynomial $p(x) = x^2 + bx + c$ such that $\lim_{x\to 2} \frac{p(x)}{x - 2} = 6$. Are the constants unique?

Applications

78. A problem from relativity theory Suppose a spaceship of length L_0 is traveling at a high rate of speed v relative to an observer. To the observer, the ship appears to have a smaller length given by the *Lorentz contraction formula*

$$L = L_0\sqrt{1 - \frac{v^2}{c^2}},$$

where c is the speed of light.

a. What is the observed length L of the ship if it is traveling at 50% of the speed of light?

b. What is the observed length L of the ship if it is traveling at 75% of the speed of light?

c. In parts (a) and (b), what happens to L as the speed of the ship increases?

d. Find $\lim_{v \to c^-} L_0\sqrt{1 - \frac{v^2}{c^2}}$ and explain the significance of this limit.

79. Limit of the radius of a cylinder A right circular cylinder with a height of 10 cm and a surface area of S cm^2 has a radius given by

$$r(S) = \frac{1}{2}\left(\sqrt{100 + \frac{2S}{\pi}} - 10\right).$$

Find $\lim_{S \to 0^+} r(S)$ and interpret your result.

80. Torricelli's Law A cylindrical tank is filled with water to a depth of 9 m. At $t = 0$, a drain in the bottom of the tank is opened and water flows out of the tank. The depth of water in the tank (measured from the bottom of the tank) t seconds after the drain is opened is approximated by

$$d(t) = (3 - 0.015t)^2, \text{ for } 0 \le t \le 200.$$

Evaluate and interpret $\lim_{t \to 200^-} d(t)$.

T **81. Electric field** The magnitude of the electric field at a point x meters from the midpoint of a 0.1-m line of charge is given by

$$E(x) = \frac{4.35}{x\sqrt{x^2 + 0.01}} \text{ (in units of newtons per coulomb, N/C).}$$

Evaluate $\lim_{x \to 10} E(x)$.

Additional Exercises

82–83. Limits of composite functions

82. If $\lim_{x \to 1} f(x) = 4$, find $\lim_{x \to -1} f(x^2)$.

83. Suppose $g(x) = f(1 - x)$ for all x, $\lim_{x \to 1^+} f(x) = 4$, and $\lim_{x \to 1^-} f(x) = 6$. Find $\lim_{x \to 0^+} g(x)$ and $\lim_{x \to 0^-} g(x)$.

84. Two trigonometric inequalities Consider the angle θ in standard position in a unit circle where $0 \le \theta < \pi/2$ or $-\pi/2 < \theta \le 0$ (use both figures).

a. Show that $|AC| = |\sin \theta|$, for $-\pi/2 < \theta < \pi/2$. (*Hint:* Consider the cases $0 < \theta < \pi/2$ and $-\pi/2 < \theta < 0$ separately.)

b. Show that $|\sin \theta| < |\theta|$, for $-\pi/2 < \theta < \pi/2$. (*Hint:* The length of arc AB is θ if $0 < \theta < \pi/2$ and $-\theta$ if $-\pi/2 < \theta < 0$.)

c. Conclude that $-|\theta| \le \sin \theta \le |\theta|$, for $-\pi/2 < \theta < \pi/2$.

d. Show that $0 \le 1 - \cos \theta \le |\theta|$, for $-\pi/2 < \theta < \pi/2$.

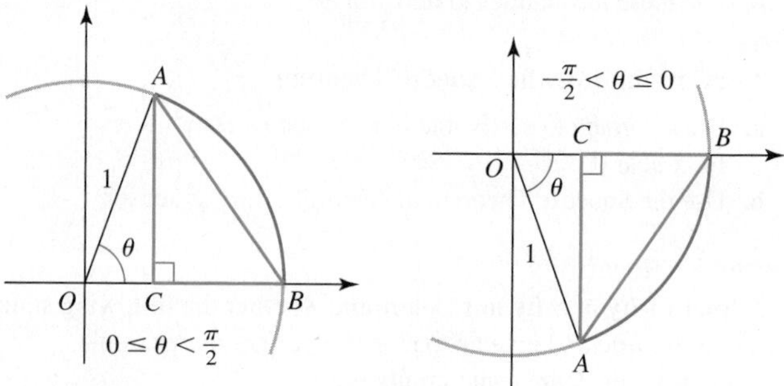

85. Theorem 2.4a Given the polynomial

$$p(x) = b_n x^n + b_{n-1}x^{n-1} + \cdots + b_1 x + b_0,$$

prove that $\lim_{x \to a} p(x) = p(a)$ for any value of a.

QUICK CHECK ANSWERS

1. 0, 2 **2.** 2 **3.** 3 **4.** 1 ◀

2.4 Infinite Limits

Two more limit scenarios are frequently encountered in calculus and are discussed in this and the following sections. An *infinite limit* occurs when function values increase or decrease without bound near a point. The other type of limit, known as a *limit at infinity,* occurs when the independent variable x increases or decreases without bound. The ideas behind infinite limits and limits at infinity are quite different. Therefore, it is important to distinguish these limits and the methods used to calculate them.

Table 2.5

x	$f(x) = 1/x^2$
± 0.1	100
± 0.01	10,000
± 0.001	1,000,000
$\downarrow$	$\downarrow$
0	∞

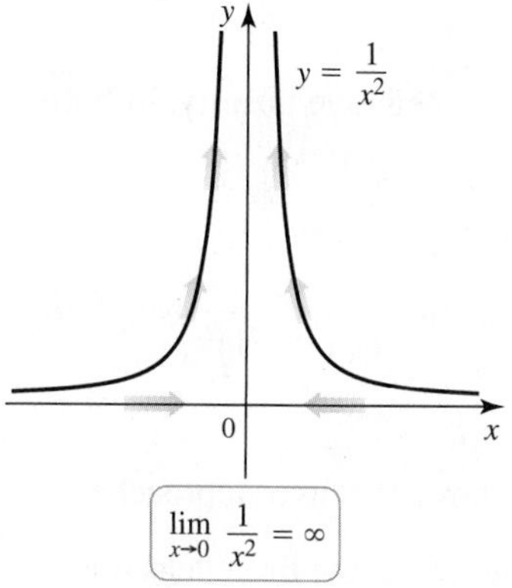

An Overview

To illustrate the differences between limits at infinity and infinite limits, consider the values of $f(x) = 1/x^2$ in Table 2.5. As x approaches 0 from either side, $f(x)$ grows larger and larger. Because $f(x)$ does not approach a finite number as x approaches 0, $\lim_{x \to 0} f(x)$ does not exist. Nevertheless, we use limit notation and write $\lim_{x \to 0} f(x) = \infty$. The infinity symbol indicates that $f(x)$ grows arbitrarily large as x approaches 0. This is an example of an **infinite limit**; in general, the *dependent variable* becomes arbitrarily large in magnitude as the *independent variable* approaches a finite number.

With **limits at infinity**, the opposite occurs: The *dependent variable* approaches a finite number as the *independent variable* becomes arbitrarily large. In Table 2.6 we see that $f(x) = 1/x^2$ approaches 0 as x becomes arbitrarily large. In this case we write $\lim_{x \to \infty} f(x) = 0$.

Table 2.6

x	$f(x) = 1/x^2$
10	0.01
100	0.0001
1000	0.000001
$\downarrow$	$\downarrow$
∞	0

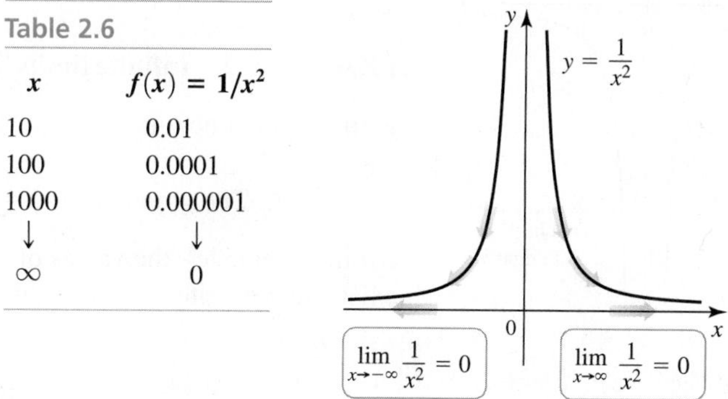

A general picture of these two limit scenarios is shown in Figure 2.22.

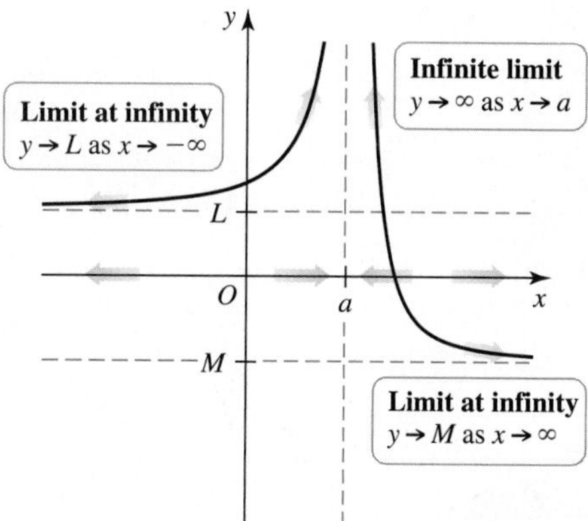

FIGURE 2.22

Infinite Limits

The following definition of infinite limits is informal, but it is adequate for most functions encountered in this book. A precise definition is given in Section 2.7.

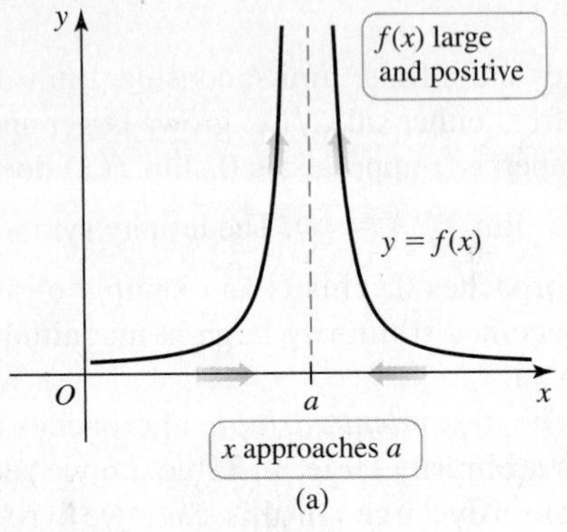

(a)

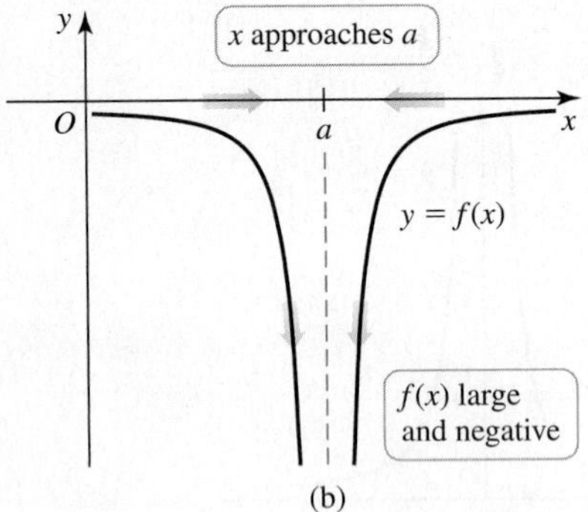

(b)

FIGURE 2.23

DEFINITION Infinite Limits

Suppose f is defined for all x near a. If $f(x)$ grows arbitrarily large for all x sufficiently close (but not equal) to a (Figure 2.23a), we write

$$\lim_{x \to a} f(x) = \infty.$$

We say the limit of $f(x)$ as x approaches a is infinity.

If $f(x)$ is negative and grows arbitrarily large in magnitude for all x sufficiently close (but not equal) to a (Figure 2.23b), we write

$$\lim_{x \to a} f(x) = -\infty.$$

In this case, we say the limit of $f(x)$ as x approaches a is negative infinity. In both cases, the limit does not exist.

EXAMPLE 1 Infinite limits Evaluate $\lim_{x \to 1} \dfrac{x}{(x^2 - 1)^2}$ and $\lim_{x \to -1} \dfrac{x}{(x^2 - 1)^2}$ using the graph of the function.

SOLUTION The graph of $f(x) = \dfrac{x}{(x^2 - 1)^2}$ (Figure 2.24) shows that as x approaches 1 (from either side), the values of f grow arbitrarily large. Therefore, the limit does not exist and we write

$$\lim_{x \to 1} \frac{x}{(x^2 - 1)^2} = \infty.$$

As x approaches -1, the values of f are negative and grow arbitrarily large in magnitude; therefore,

$$\lim_{x \to -1} \frac{x}{(x^2 - 1)^2} = -\infty.$$

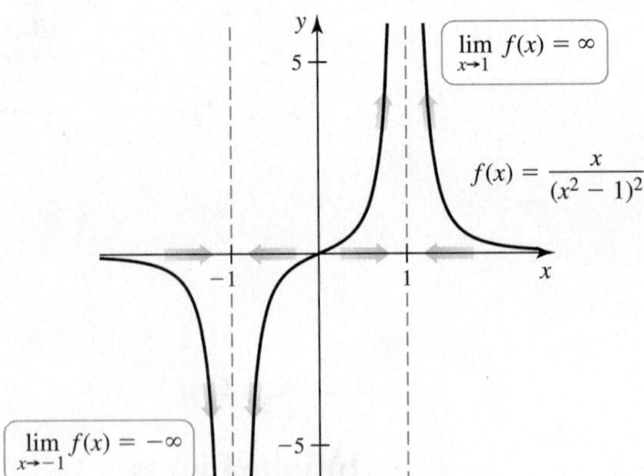

FIGURE 2.24

Related Exercises 7–8 ◀

Example 1 illustrates *two-sided* infinite limits. As with finite limits, we also need to work with right-hand and left-hand infinite limits, which are both *one-sided*.

> **DEFINITION One-sided Infinite Limits**
>
> Suppose f is defined for all x near a with $x > a$. If $f(x)$ becomes arbitrarily large for all x sufficiently close to a with $x > a$, we write $\lim_{x \to a^+} f(x) = \infty$ (Figure 2.25a). The one-sided infinite limits $\lim_{x \to a^+} f(x) = -\infty$ (Figure 2.25b), $\lim_{x \to a^-} f(x) = \infty$ (Figure 2.25c), and $\lim_{x \to a^-} f(x) = -\infty$ (Figure 2.25d) are defined analogously.

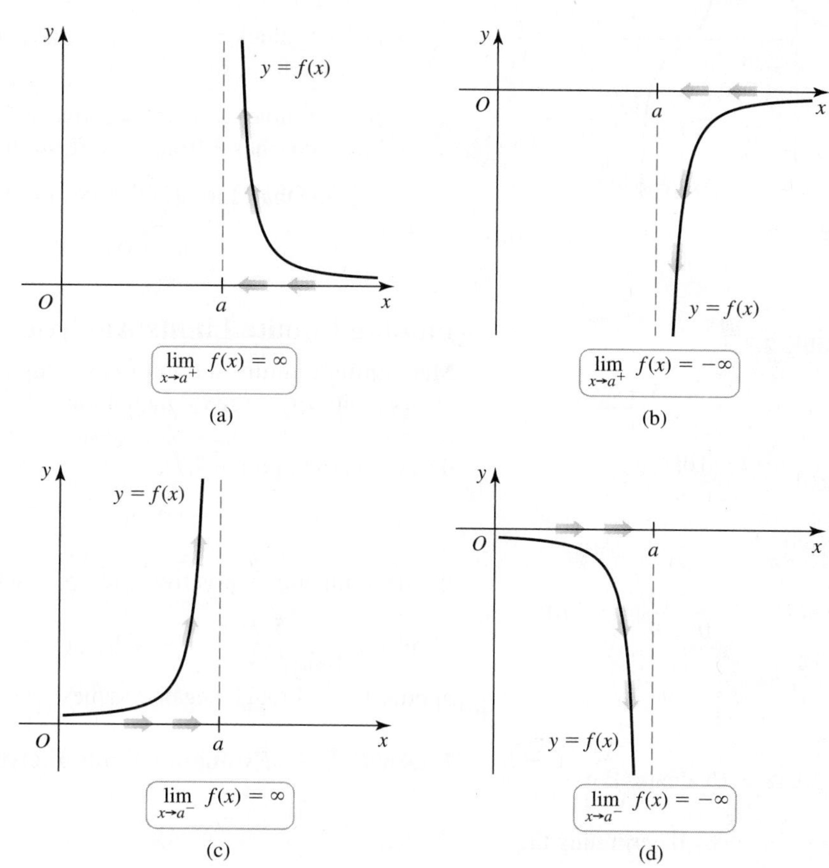

FIGURE 2.25

In all the infinite limits illustrated in Figure 2.25, the line $x = a$ is called a *vertical asymptote*, a vertical line that is approached by the graph of f as x approaches a.

> **DEFINITION Vertical Asymptote**
>
> If $\lim_{x \to a} f(x) = \pm\infty$, $\lim_{x \to a^+} f(x) = \pm\infty$, or $\lim_{x \to a^-} f(x) = \pm\infty$, the line $x = a$ is called a **vertical asymptote** of f.

➤ The shorthand notation $\pm\infty$ means either $+\infty$ or $-\infty$.

QUICK CHECK 1 Sketch the graph of a function and its vertical asymptote that satisfies the conditions $\lim_{x \to 2^+} f(x) = -\infty$ and $\lim_{x \to 2^-} f(x) = \infty$. ◄

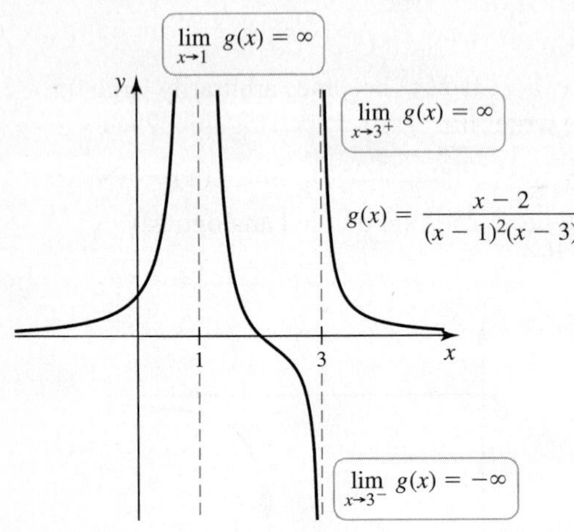

FIGURE 2.26

EXAMPLE 2 **Determining limits graphically** The vertical lines $x = 1$ and $x = 3$ are vertical asymptotes of the function $g(x) = \frac{x-2}{(x-1)^2(x-3)}$. Use Figure 2.26 to determine the following limits, if possible.

a. $\lim_{x\to1} g(x)$ **b.** $\lim_{x\to3^-} g(x)$ **c.** $\lim_{x\to3} g(x)$

SOLUTION

a. The values of g grow arbitrarily large as x approaches 1 from either side. Therefore, $\lim_{x\to1} g(x) = \infty$.

b. The values of g are negative and grow arbitrarily large in magnitude as x approaches 3 from the left, so $\lim_{x\to3^-} g(x) = -\infty$.

c. Note that $\lim_{x\to3^+} g(x) = \infty$. Because the one-sided limits at $x = 3$ are not equal, $\lim_{x\to3} g(x)$ does not exist.

Related Exercises 9–16 ◀

Finding Infinite Limits Analytically

Table 2.7

x	$\frac{5+x}{x}$
0.01	$\frac{5.01}{0.01} = 501$
0.001	$\frac{5.001}{0.001} = 5001$
0.0001	$\frac{5.0001}{0.0001} = 50{,}001$
↓	↓
0^+	∞

Many infinite limits are analyzed using a simple arithmetic property: The fraction a/b grows arbitrarily large in magnitude if b approaches 0 while a remains nonzero and relatively constant. For example, consider the fraction $(5 + x)/x$ for values of x approaching 0 from the right (Table 2.7).

We see that $\frac{5+x}{x} \to \infty$ as $x \to 0^+$ because the numerator $5 + x$ approaches 5 while the denominator is positive and approaches 0. Therefore, we write $\lim_{x\to0^+} \frac{5+x}{x} = \infty$. Similarly, $\lim_{x\to0^-} \frac{5+x}{x} = -\infty$ because the numerator approaches 5 while the denominator approaches 0 through negative values.

QUICK CHECK 2 Evaluate $\lim_{x\to0^+} \frac{x-5}{x}$ and $\lim_{x\to0^-} \frac{x-5}{x}$ by determining the sign of the numerator and denominator. ◀

EXAMPLE 3 **Evaluating limits analytically** Evaluate the following limits.

a. $\lim_{x\to3^+} \frac{2-5x}{x-3}$ **b.** $\lim_{x\to3^-} \frac{2-5x}{x-3}$

SOLUTION

a. As $x \to 3^+$, the numerator $2 - 5x$ approaches $2 - 5(3) = -13$ while the denominator $x - 3$ is positive and approaches 0. Therefore,

$$\lim_{x\to3^+} \frac{\overbrace{2-5x}^{\text{approaches } -13}}{\underbrace{x-3}_{\text{positive and approaches } 0}} = -\infty.$$

b. As $x \to 3^-$, $2 - 5x$ approaches $2 - 5(3) = -13$ while $x - 3$ is negative and approaches 0. Therefore,

$$\lim_{x\to3^-} \frac{\overbrace{2-5x}^{\text{approaches } -13}}{\underbrace{x-3}_{\text{negative and approaches } 0}} = \infty.$$

These limits imply that the given function has a vertical asymptote at $x = 3$.

Related Exercises 17–22 ◀

EXAMPLE 4 **Evaluating limits analytically** Evaluate $\lim_{x\to-4^+} \dfrac{-x^3 + 5x^2 - 6x}{-x^3 - 4x^2}$.

> We can assume that $x \neq 0$ because in this limit we are considering function values near $x = -4$.

SOLUTION First we factor and simplify, assuming $x \neq 0$:

$$\frac{-x^3 + 5x^2 - 6x}{-x^3 - 4x^2} = \frac{-x(x-2)(x-3)}{-x^2(x+4)} = \frac{(x-2)(x-3)}{x(x+4)}.$$

As $x \to -4^+$, we find that

$$\lim_{x\to-4^+} \frac{-x^3 + 5x^2 - 6x}{-x^3 - 4x^2} = \lim_{x\to-4^+} \frac{\overbrace{(x-2)(x-3)}^{\text{approaches } 42}}{\underbrace{x(x+4)}_{\text{negative and approaches } 0}} = -\infty.$$

This limit implies that the given function has a vertical asymptote at $x = -4$.

Related Exercises 17–22 ◀

QUICK CHECK 3 Verify that $x(x + 4) \to 0$ through negative values as $x \to -4^+$. ◀

EXAMPLE 5 **Location of vertical asymptotes** Let $f(x) = \dfrac{x^2 - 4x + 3}{x^2 - 1}$. Evaluate the following limits and find the vertical asymptotes of f. Verify your work with a graphing utility.

> Example 5 illustrates that $f(x)/g(x)$ might not grow arbitrarily large in magnitude if *both* $f(x)$ and $g(x)$ approach 0. Such limits are called *indeterminate forms* and are examined in detail in Section 4.7.

a. $\lim_{x\to1} f(x)$ **b.** $\lim_{x\to-1^-} f(x)$ **c.** $\lim_{x\to-1^+} f(x)$

SOLUTION

a. Notice that as $x \to 1$, both the numerator and denominator of f approach 0, and the function is undefined at $x = 1$. To compute $\lim_{x\to1} f(x)$, we first factor:

> It is permissible to cancel the $x - 1$ factors in $\lim_{x\to1} \dfrac{(x-1)(x-3)}{(x-1)(x+1)}$ because x approaches 1, but is not equal to 1. Therefore, $x - 1 \neq 0$.

$$\begin{aligned}
\lim_{x\to1} f(x) &= \lim_{x\to1} \frac{x^2 - 4x + 3}{x^2 - 1} \\
&= \lim_{x\to1} \frac{(x-1)(x-3)}{(x-1)(x+1)} && \text{Factor.} \\
&= \lim_{x\to1} \frac{(x-3)}{(x+1)} && \text{Cancel like factors, } x \neq 1. \\
&= \frac{1-3}{1+1} = -1 && \text{Substitute } x = 1.
\end{aligned}$$

Therefore, $\lim_{x\to1} f(x) = -1$ (even though $f(1)$ is undefined). The line $x = 1$ is *not* a vertical asymptote of f.

b. In part (a) we showed that

$$f(x) = \frac{x^2 - 4x + 3}{x^2 - 1} = \frac{x-3}{x+1}, \quad \text{provided } x \neq 1.$$

We use this fact again. As x approaches -1 from the left, the one-sided limit is

$$\lim_{x\to-1^-} f(x) = \lim_{x\to-1^-} \frac{\overbrace{x-3}^{\text{approaches } -4}}{\underbrace{x+1}_{\text{negative and approaches } 0}} = \infty.$$

c. As x approaches -1 from the right, the one-sided limit is

$$\lim_{x \to -1^+} f(x) = \lim_{x \to -1^+} \overbrace{\frac{x-3}{\underbrace{x+1}_{\substack{\text{positive and} \\ \text{approaches } 0}}}}^{\text{approaches } -4} = -\infty.$$

The infinite limits $\lim_{x \to -1^+} f(x) = -\infty$ and $\lim_{x \to -1^-} f(x) = \infty$ each imply that the line $x = -1$ is a vertical asymptote of f. The graph of f generated by a graphing utility *may* appear as shown in Figure 2.27a. If so, two corrections must be made. A hole should appear in the graph at $(1, -1)$ because $\lim_{x \to 1} f(x) = -1$, but $f(1)$ is undefined. It is also a good idea to replace the solid vertical line with a dashed line to emphasize that the vertical asymptote is not a part of the graph of f (Figure 2.27b).

➤ Graphing utilities vary in how they display vertical asymptotes. The errors shown in Figure 2.27 do not occur on all graphing utilities.

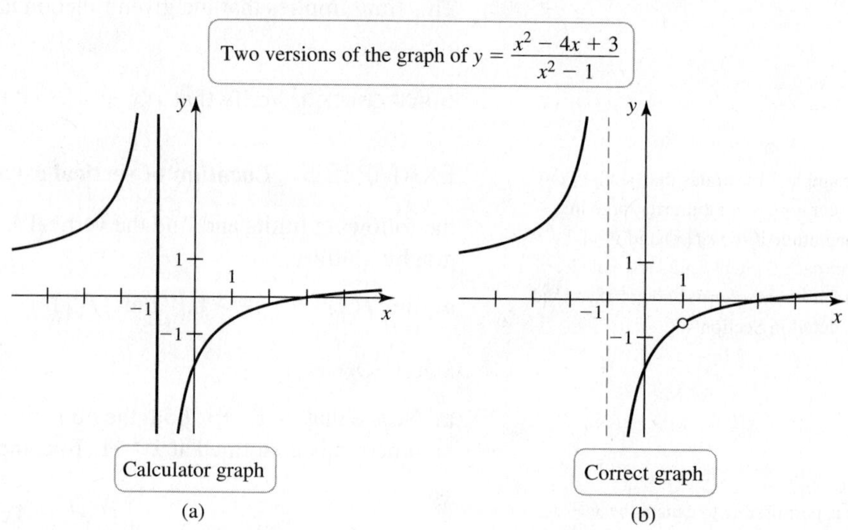

FIGURE 2.27

Related Exercises 23–26 ◀

QUICK CHECK 4 The line $x = 2$ is not a vertical asymptote of $y = \frac{(x-1)(x-2)}{x-2}$. Why not? ◀

EXAMPLE 6 Limits of trigonometric functions

Evaluate the following limits.

a. $\lim_{\theta \to 0^+} \cot \theta$ **b.** $\lim_{\theta \to 0^-} \cot \theta$

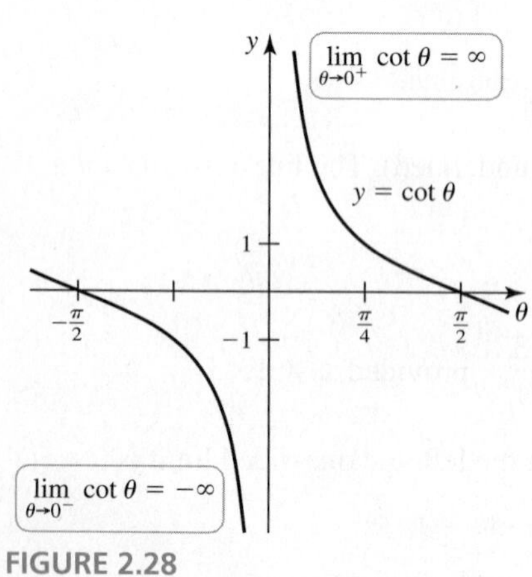

FIGURE 2.28

SOLUTION

a. Recall that $\cot \theta = \cos \theta / \sin \theta$. Furthermore (Example 7, Section 2.3), $\lim_{\theta \to 0^+} \cos \theta = 1$, and $\sin \theta$ is positive and approaches 0 as $\theta \to 0^+$. Therefore, as $\theta \to 0^+$, $\cot \theta$ becomes arbitrarily large and positive, which means $\lim_{\theta \to 0^+} \cot \theta = \infty$. This limit is confirmed by the graph of $\cot \theta$ (Figure 2.28), which has a vertical asymptote at $\theta = 0$.

b. In this case, $\lim_{\theta \to 0^-} \cos \theta = 1$ and as $\theta \to 0^-$, $\sin \theta \to 0$ with $\sin \theta < 0$. Therefore, as $\theta \to 0^-$, $\cot \theta$ is negative and becomes arbitrarily large in magnitude. It follows that $\lim_{\theta \to 0^-} \cot \theta = -\infty$, as confirmed by the graph of $\cot \theta$. *Related Exercises 27–32* ◀

SECTION 2.4 EXERCISES

Review Questions

1. Use a graph to explain the meaning of $\lim_{x \to a^+} f(x) = -\infty$.

2. Use a graph to explain the meaning of $\lim_{x \to a} f(x) = \infty$.

3. What is a vertical asymptote?

4. Consider the function $F(x) = f(x)/g(x)$ with $g(a) = 0$. Does F necessarily have a vertical asymptote at $x = a$? Explain your reasoning.

5. Suppose $f(x) \to 100$ and $g(x) \to 0$ with $g(x) < 0$ as $x \to 2$. Determine $\lim_{x \to 2} \frac{f(x)}{g(x)}$.

6. Evaluate $\lim_{x \to 3^-} \frac{1}{x - 3}$ and $\lim_{x \to 3^+} \frac{1}{x - 3}$.

Basic Skills

T 7. **Finding infinite limits numerically** Compute the values of $f(x) = \frac{x + 1}{(x - 1)^2}$ in the following table and use them to determine $\lim_{x \to 1} f(x)$.

x	$\frac{x+1}{(x-1)^2}$	x	$\frac{x+1}{(x-1)^2}$
1.1		0.9	
1.01		0.99	
1.001		0.999	
1.0001		0.9999	

8. **Finding infinite limits graphically** Use the graph of $f(x) = \frac{x}{(x^2 - 2x - 3)^2}$ to determine $\lim_{x \to -1} f(x)$ and $\lim_{x \to 3} f(x)$.

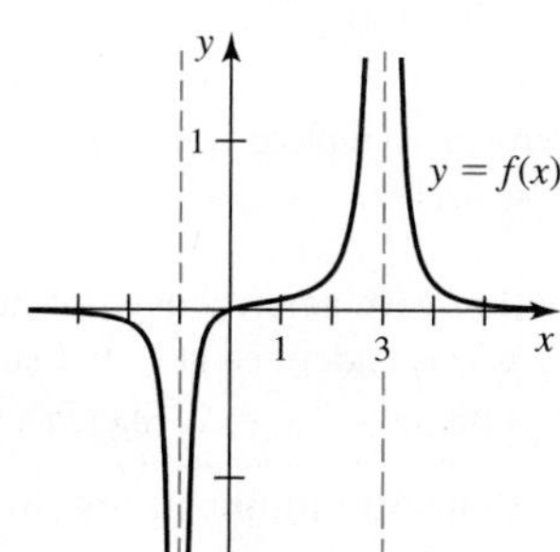

9. **Finding infinite limits graphically** The graph of f in the figure has vertical asymptotes at $x = 1$ and $x = 2$. Find the following limits, if possible.

a. $\lim_{x \to 1^-} f(x)$ b. $\lim_{x \to 1^+} f(x)$ c. $\lim_{x \to 1} f(x)$
d. $\lim_{x \to 2^-} f(x)$ e. $\lim_{x \to 2^+} f(x)$ f. $\lim_{x \to 2} f(x)$

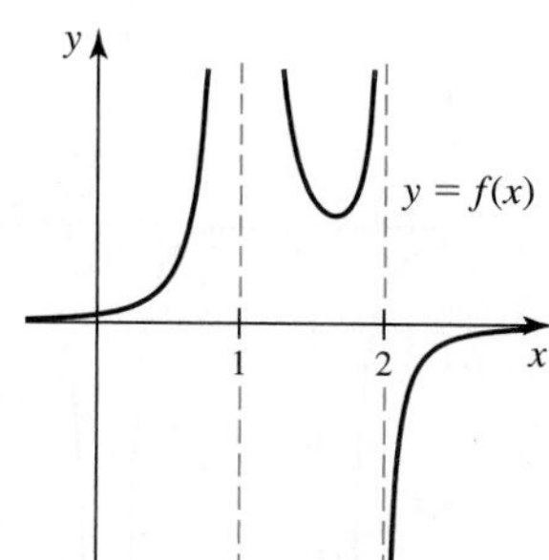

10. **Finding infinite limits graphically** The graph of g in the figure has vertical asymptotes at $x = 2$ and $x = 4$. Find the following limits, if possible.

a. $\lim_{x \to 2^-} g(x)$ b. $\lim_{x \to 2^+} g(x)$ c. $\lim_{x \to 2} g(x)$
d. $\lim_{x \to 4^-} g(x)$ e. $\lim_{x \to 4^+} g(x)$ f. $\lim_{x \to 4} g(x)$

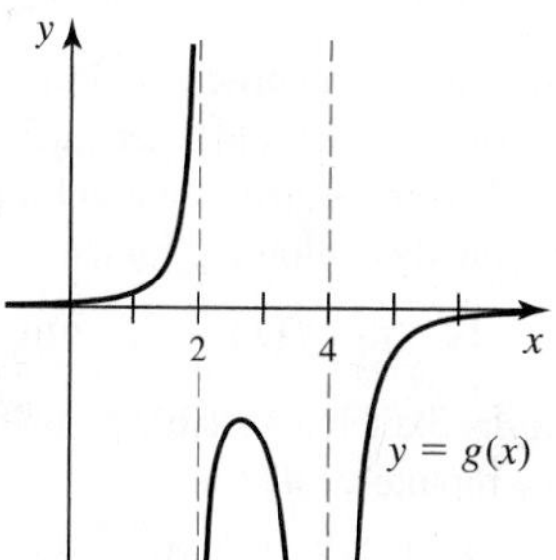

11. **Finding infinite limits graphically** The graph of h in the figure has vertical asymptotes at $x = -2$ and $x = 3$. Find the following limits, if possible.

a. $\lim_{x \to -2^-} h(x)$ b. $\lim_{x \to -2^+} h(x)$ c. $\lim_{x \to -2} h(x)$
d. $\lim_{x \to 3^-} h(x)$ e. $\lim_{x \to 3^+} h(x)$ f. $\lim_{x \to 3} h(x)$

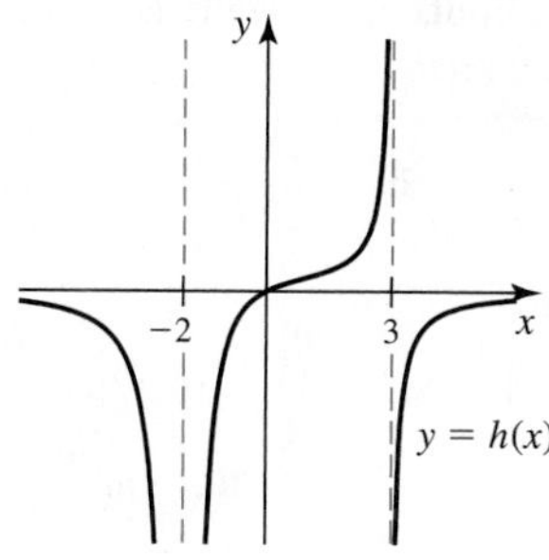

12. Finding infinite limits graphically The graph of p in the figure has vertical asymptotes at $x = -2$ and $x = 3$. Find the following limits, if possible.

a. $\lim_{x\to -2^-} p(x)$ b. $\lim_{x\to -2^+} p(x)$ c. $\lim_{x\to -2} p(x)$
d. $\lim_{x\to 3^-} p(x)$ e. $\lim_{x\to 3^+} p(x)$ f. $\lim_{x\to 3} p(x)$

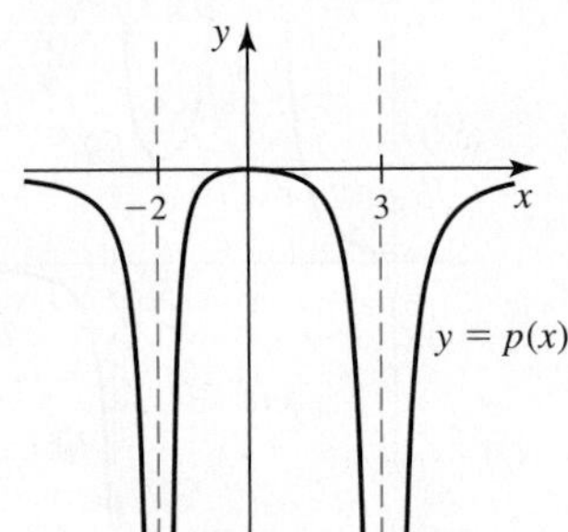

13. Finding infinite limits graphically Graph the function $f(x) = \dfrac{1}{x^2 - x}$ using a graphing utility with the window $[-1, 2] \times [-10, 10]$. Use the graph to determine the following limits.

a. $\lim_{x\to 0^-} f(x)$ b. $\lim_{x\to 0^+} f(x)$ c. $\lim_{x\to 1^-} f(x)$ d. $\lim_{x\to 1^+} f(x)$

14. Finding infinite limits graphically Graph the function $f(x) = x \cot x$ on the interval $[0, 2\pi]$ using a graphing utility. (Experiment with your choice of a graphing window.) Use the graph to determine the following limits.

a. $\lim_{x\to \pi^+} f(x)$ b. $\lim_{x\to \pi^-} f(x)$ c. $\lim_{x\to 2\pi^-} f(x)$ d. $\lim_{x\to 0^+} f(x)$

15. Sketching graphs Sketch a possible graph of a function f, together with vertical asymptotes, satisfying all of the following conditions.

$f(1) = 0$ $f(3)$ is undefined $\lim_{x\to 3} f(x) = 1$

$\lim_{x\to 0^+} f(x) = -\infty$ $\lim_{x\to 2} f(x) = \infty$ $\lim_{x\to 4^-} f(x) = \infty$

16. Sketching graphs Sketch a possible graph of a function g, together with vertical asymptotes, satisfying all of the following conditions.

$g(2) = 1$ $g(5) = -1$ $\lim_{x\to 4} g(x) = -\infty$

$\lim_{x\to 7^-} g(x) = \infty$ $\lim_{x\to 7^+} g(x) = -\infty$

17–22. Evaluating limits analytically *Evaluate the following limits or state that they do not exist.*

17. a. $\lim_{x\to 2^+} \dfrac{1}{x - 2}$ b. $\lim_{x\to 2^-} \dfrac{1}{x - 2}$ c. $\lim_{x\to 2} \dfrac{1}{x - 2}$

18. a. $\lim_{x\to 3^+} \dfrac{2}{(x - 3)^3}$ b. $\lim_{x\to 3^-} \dfrac{2}{(x - 3)^3}$ c. $\lim_{x\to 3} \dfrac{2}{(x - 3)^3}$

19. $\lim_{x\to 0} \dfrac{x^3 - 5x^2}{x^2}$

20. $\lim_{t\to 5} \dfrac{4t^2 - 100}{t - 5}$

21. $\lim_{x\to 1^+} \dfrac{x^2 - 5x + 6}{x - 1}$

22. $\lim_{z\to 4} \dfrac{z - 5}{(z^2 - 10z + 24)^2}$

23–26. Finding vertical asymptotes *Find all vertical asymptotes, $x = a$, of the following functions. For each value of a, evaluate $\lim_{x\to a^+} f(x)$, $\lim_{x\to a^-} f(x)$, and $\lim_{x\to a} f(x)$.*

23. $f(x) = \dfrac{x^2 - 9x + 14}{x^2 - 5x + 6}$

24. $f(x) = \dfrac{\cos x}{x^2 + 2x}$

25. $f(x) = \dfrac{x + 1}{x^3 - 4x^2 + 4x}$

26. $f(x) = \dfrac{x^3 - 10x^2 + 16x}{x^2 - 8x}$

27–30. Trigonometric limits *Evaluate the following limits.*

27. $\lim_{\theta\to 0^+} \csc \theta$

28. $\lim_{x\to 0^-} \csc x$

29. $\lim_{x\to 0^+} (-10 \cot x)$

30. $\lim_{\theta\to \pi/2^+} \dfrac{1}{3} \tan \theta$

31. Finding infinite limits graphically Graph the function $y = \tan x$ with the window $[-\pi, \pi] \times [-10, 10]$. Use the graph to determine the following limits.

a. $\lim_{x\to \pi/2^+} \tan x$ b. $\lim_{x\to \pi/2^-} \tan x$
c. $\lim_{x\to -\pi/2^+} \tan x$ d. $\lim_{x\to -\pi/2^-} \tan x$

32. Finding infinite limits graphically Graph the function $y = \sec x \tan x$ with the window $[-\pi, \pi] \times [-10, 10]$. Use the graph to determine the following limits.

a. $\lim_{x\to \pi/2^+} \sec x \tan x$ b. $\lim_{x\to \pi/2^-} \sec x \tan x$
c. $\lim_{x\to -\pi/2^+} \sec x \tan x$ d. $\lim_{x\to -\pi/2^-} \sec x \tan x$

Further Explorations

33. Explain why or why not Determine whether the following statements are true and give an explanation or counterexample.

a. The line $x = 1$ is a vertical asymptote of the function $f(x) = \dfrac{x^2 - 7x + 6}{x^2 - 1}$.

b. The line $x = -1$ is a vertical asymptote of the function $f(x) = \dfrac{x^2 - 7x + 6}{x^2 - 1}$.

c. If g has a vertical asymptote at $x = 1$ and $\lim_{x\to 1^+} g(x) = \infty$, then $\lim_{x\to 1^-} g(x) = \infty$.

34. Finding a function with vertical asymptotes Find polynomials p and q such that p/q is undefined at $x = 1$ and $x = 2$, but p/q has a vertical asymptote only at $x = 2$. Sketch a graph of your function.

35. Finding a function with infinite limits Give a formula for a function f that satisfies $\lim_{x\to 6^+} f(x) = \infty$ and $\lim_{x\to 6^-} f(x) = -\infty$.

36. Matching Match functions a–f with graphs A–F in the figure without using a graphing utility.

a. $f(x) = \dfrac{x}{x^2 + 1}$ b. $f(x) = \dfrac{x}{x^2 - 1}$

c. $f(x) = \dfrac{1}{x^2 - 1}$ d. $f(x) = \dfrac{x}{(x - 1)^2}$

e. $f(x) = \dfrac{1}{(x - 1)^2}$ f. $f(x) = \dfrac{x}{x + 1}$

A.

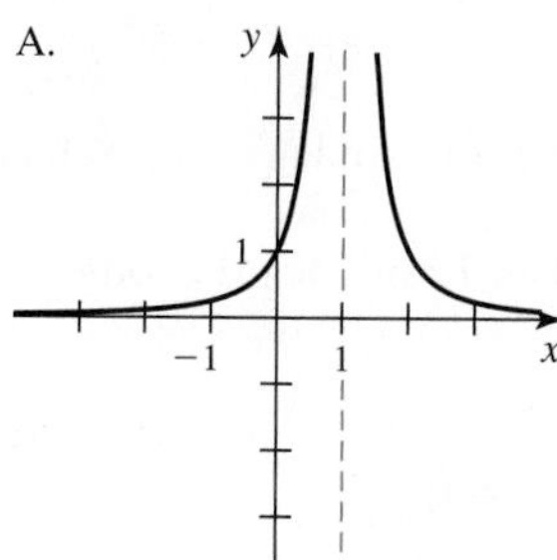

B.

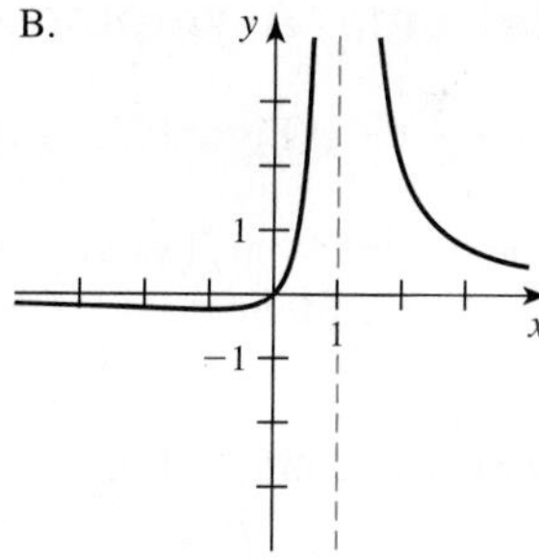

C.

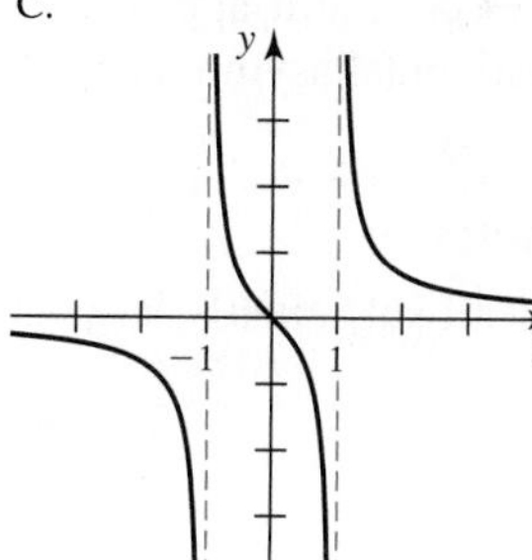

D.

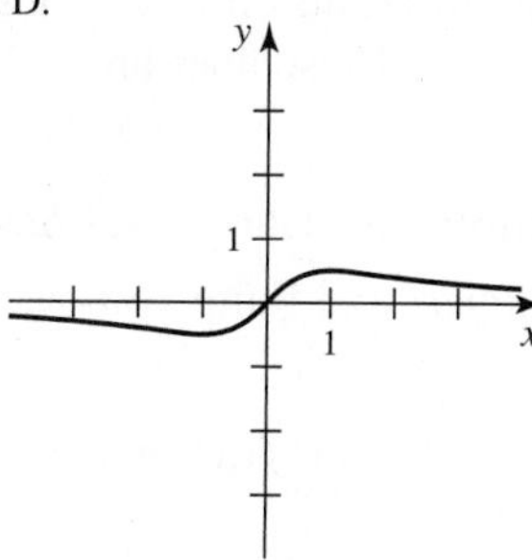

E.

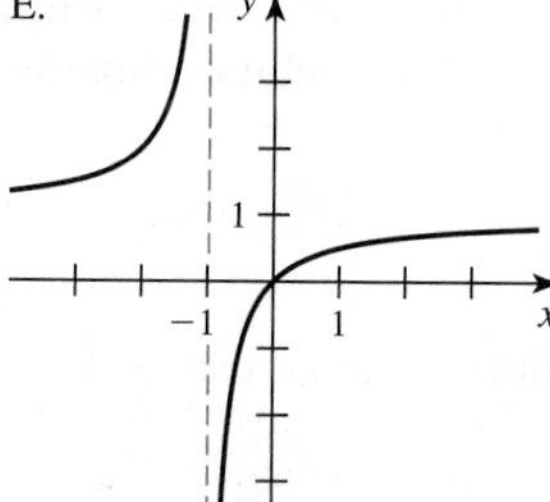

F.

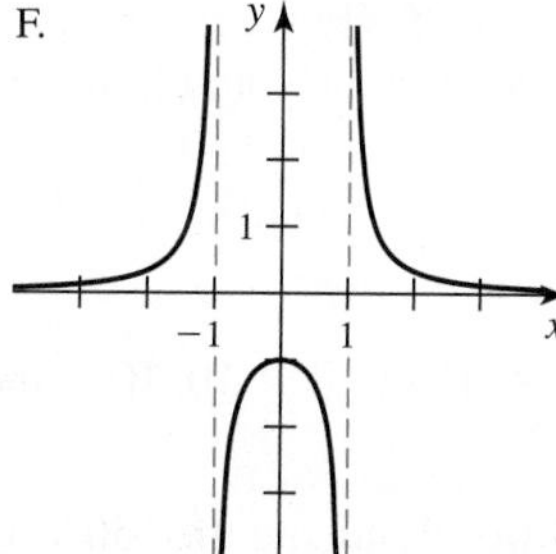

37–44. Asymptotes *Use analytical methods and/or a graphing utility to identify the vertical asymptotes (if any) of the following functions.*

37. $f(x) = \dfrac{x^2 - 3x + 2}{x^{10} - x^9}$

38. $g(x) = \cot\left(x - \dfrac{\pi}{2}\right), |x| \le \pi$

39. $h(x) = \dfrac{\cos x}{(x + 1)^3}$

40. $p(x) = \sec\left(\dfrac{\pi x}{2}\right), |x| < 2$

41. $g(\theta) = \tan\left(\dfrac{\pi\theta}{10}\right)$

42. $q(s) = \dfrac{\pi}{s - \sin s}$

43. $f(x) = \dfrac{1}{\sqrt{x} \sec x}$

44. $g(x) = \dfrac{1}{\sqrt{x(x^2 - 1)}}$

Additional Exercises

45. Limits with a parameter Let $f(x) = \dfrac{x^2 - 7x + 12}{x - a}$.

a. For what values of a, if any, does $\lim_{x \to a^+} f(x)$ equal a finite number?

b. For what values of a, if any, does $\lim_{x \to a^+} f(x) = \infty$?

c. For what values of a, if any, does $\lim_{x \to a^+} f(x) = -\infty$?

46–47. Steep secant lines

a. *Given the graph of f in the following figures, find the slope of the secant line that passes through $(0, 0)$ and $(h, f(h))$ in terms of h for $h > 0$ and $h < 0$.*

b. *Calculate the limit of the slope of the secant line found in part (a) as $h \to 0^+$ and $h \to 0^-$. What does this tell you about the tangent line to the curve at $(0, 0)$?*

46. $f(x) = x^{1/3}$

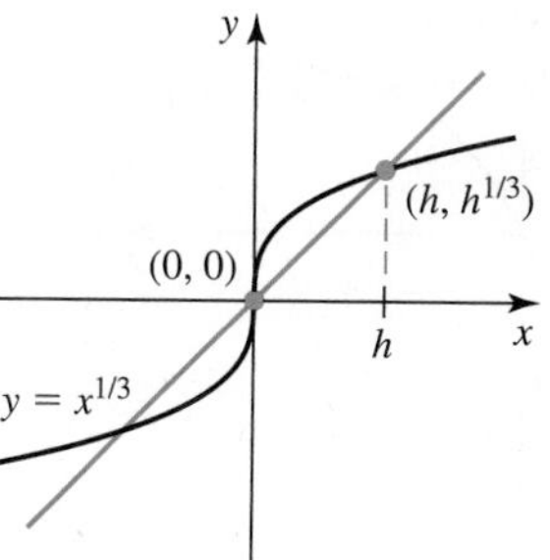

47. $f(x) = x^{2/3}$

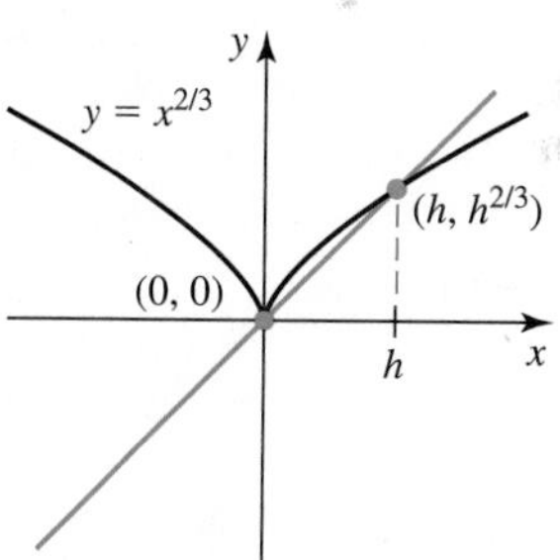

QUICK CHECK ANSWERS

1. Answers will vary, but all graphs should have a vertical asymptote at $x = 2$. **2.** $-\infty; \infty$ **3.** As $x \to -4^+$, $x < 0$ and $(x + 4) > 0$, so $x(x + 4) \to 0$ through negative values. **4.** $\lim_{x \to 2} \dfrac{(x - 1)(x - 2)}{x - 2} = \lim_{x \to 2} (x - 1) = 1$, which is not an infinite limit, so $x = 2$ is not a vertical asymptote.

2.5 Limits at Infinity

Limits at infinity—as opposed to infinite limits—occur when the independent variable becomes large in magnitude. For this reason, limits at infinity determine what is called the *end behavior* of a function. An application of these limits is to determine whether a system that evolves in time (such as an ecosystem or a large oscillating structure) reaches a steady state.

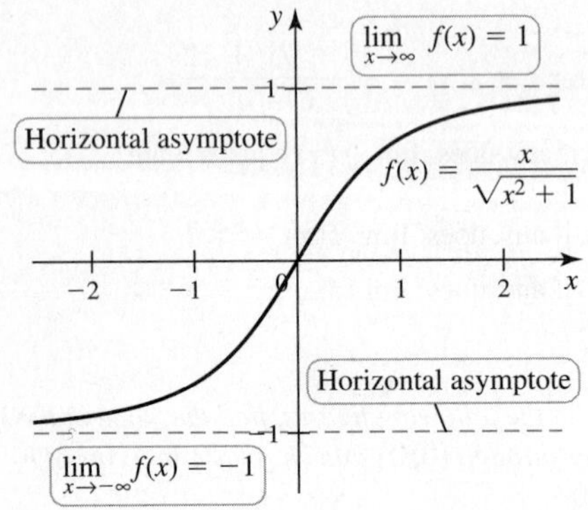

FIGURE 2.29

Limits at Infinity and Horizontal Asymptotes

Consider the function $f(x) = \dfrac{x}{\sqrt{x^2 + 1}}$, (Figure 2.29) whose domain is $(-\infty, \infty)$. As x becomes arbitrarily large (denoted $x \to \infty$), $f(x)$ approaches 1, and as x becomes arbitrarily large in magnitude and negative (denoted $x \to -\infty$), $f(x)$ approaches -1. These limits are expressed as

$$\lim_{x\to\infty} f(x) = 1 \quad \text{and} \quad \lim_{x\to-\infty} f(x) = -1.$$

The graph of f approaches the horizontal line $y = 1$ as $x \to \infty$ and it approaches the horizontal line $y = -1$ as $x \to -\infty$. These lines are called horizontal asymptotes.

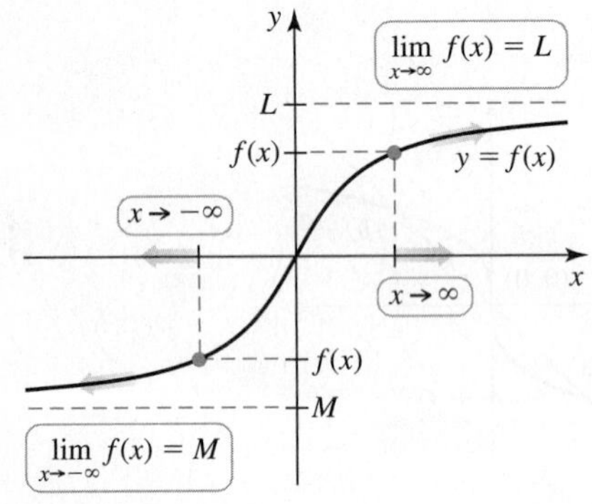

FIGURE 2.30

DEFINITION Limits at Infinity and Horizontal Asymptotes

If $f(x)$ becomes arbitrarily close to a finite number L for all sufficiently large and positive x, then we write

$$\lim_{x\to\infty} f(x) = L.$$

We say the limit of $f(x)$ as x approaches infinity is L. In this case the line $y = L$ is a **horizontal asymptote** of f (Figure 2.30). The limit at negative infinity, $\lim_{x\to-\infty} f(x) = M$, is defined analogously and in this case the horizontal asymptote is $y = M$.

QUICK CHECK 1 Evaluate $x/(x + 1)$ for $x = 10, 100$, and 1000. What is $\lim_{x\to\infty} \dfrac{x}{x+1}$?

EXAMPLE 1 Limits at infinity Evaluate the following limits.

a. $\lim_{x\to-\infty} \left(2 + \dfrac{10}{x^2}\right)$ **b.** $\lim_{x\to\infty} \left(5 + \dfrac{\sin x}{\sqrt{x}}\right)$

SOLUTION

a. As x becomes large and negative, x^2 becomes large and positive; in turn, $10/x^2$ approaches 0. By the limit laws of Theorem 2.3,

$$\lim_{x\to-\infty} \left(2 + \frac{10}{x^2}\right) = \underbrace{\lim_{x\to-\infty} 2}_{\text{equals } 2} + \underbrace{\lim_{x\to-\infty} \left(\frac{10}{x^2}\right)}_{\text{equals } 0} = 2 + 0 = 2.$$

> The limit laws of Theorem 2.3 and the Squeeze Theorem apply if $x \to a$ is replaced with $x \to \infty$ or $x \to -\infty$.

Notice that $\lim_{x\to\infty} \left(2 + \dfrac{10}{x^2}\right)$ is also equal to 2. Therefore, the graph of $y = 2 + 10/x^2$ approaches the horizontal asymptote $y = 2$ as $x \to \infty$ and as $x \to -\infty$ (Figure 2.31).

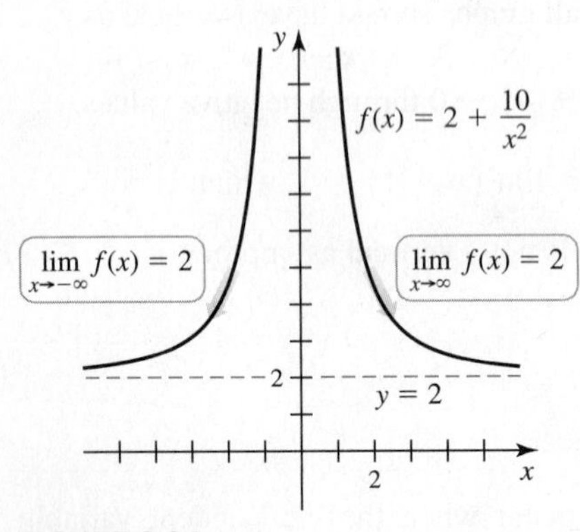

FIGURE 2.31

b. The numerator of $\sin x/\sqrt{x}$ is bounded between -1 and 1; therefore, for $x > 0$

$$-\frac{1}{\sqrt{x}} \le \frac{\sin x}{\sqrt{x}} \le \frac{1}{\sqrt{x}}.$$

As $x \to \infty$, $\sqrt{x}$ becomes arbitrarily large, which means that

$$\lim_{x\to\infty} \frac{-1}{\sqrt{x}} = \lim_{x\to\infty} \frac{1}{\sqrt{x}} = 0.$$

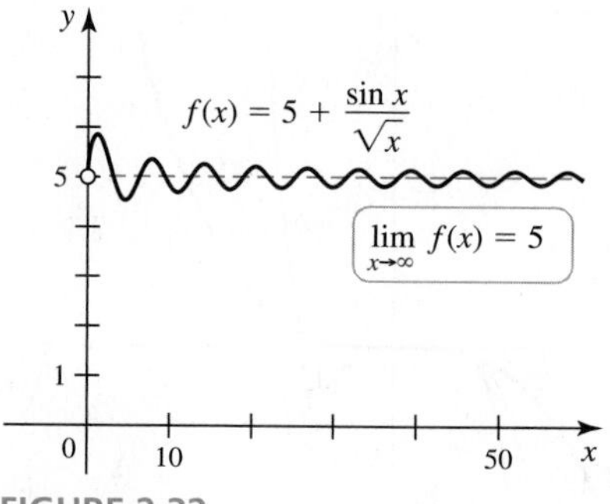

FIGURE 2.32

It follows by the Squeeze Theorem (Theorem 2.5) that $\lim_{x\to\infty} \frac{\sin x}{\sqrt{x}} = 0$.

Using the limit laws of Theorem 2.3,

$$\lim_{x\to\infty}\left(5 + \frac{\sin x}{\sqrt{x}}\right) = \underbrace{\lim_{x\to\infty} 5}_{\text{equals } 5} + \underbrace{\lim_{x\to\infty}\left(\frac{\sin x}{\sqrt{x}}\right)}_{\text{equals } 0} = 5.$$

The graph of $y = 5 + \frac{\sin x}{\sqrt{x}}$ approaches the horizontal asymptote $y = 5$ as x becomes large (Figure 2.32). Note that the curve intersects its asymptote infinitely many times.

Related Exercises 9–14 ◀

Infinite Limits at Infinity

It is possible for a limit to be *both* an infinite limit and a limit at infinity. This type of limit occurs if $f(x)$ becomes arbitrarily large in magnitude as x becomes arbitrarily large in magnitude. Such a limit is called an **infinite limit at infinity** and is illustrated by the function $f(x) = x^3$ (Figure 2.33).

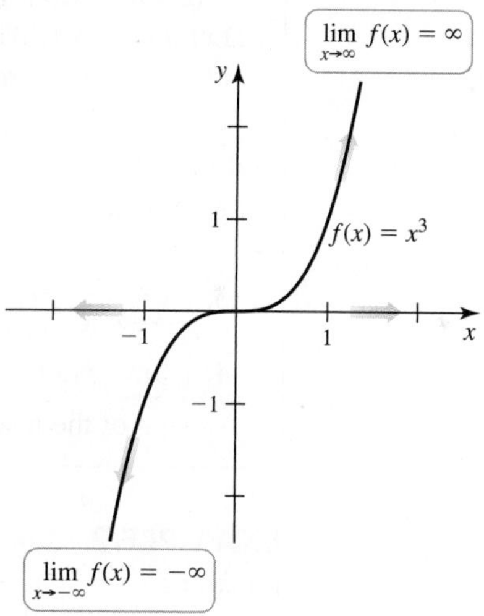

FIGURE 2.33

> **DEFINITION Infinite Limits at Infinity**
>
> If $f(x)$ becomes arbitrarily large as x becomes arbitrarily large, then we write
>
> $$\lim_{x\to\infty} f(x) = \infty.$$
>
> The limits $\lim_{x\to\infty} f(x) = -\infty$, $\lim_{x\to-\infty} f(x) = \infty$, and $\lim_{x\to-\infty} f(x) = -\infty$ are defined similarly.

Infinite limits at infinity tell us about the behavior of polynomials for large-magnitude values of x. First, consider power functions $f(x) = x^n$, where n is a positive integer. Figure 2.34 shows that when n is even, $\lim_{x\to\pm\infty} x^n = \infty$, and when n is odd, $\lim_{x\to\infty} x^n = \infty$ and $\lim_{x\to-\infty} x^n = -\infty$.

It follows that reciprocals of power functions, $f(x) = 1/x^n = x^{-n}$, where n is a positive integer, behave as follows:

$$\lim_{x\to\infty} \frac{1}{x^n} = \lim_{x\to\infty} x^{-n} = 0 \quad \text{and} \quad \lim_{x\to-\infty} \frac{1}{x^n} = \lim_{x\to-\infty} x^{-n} = 0.$$

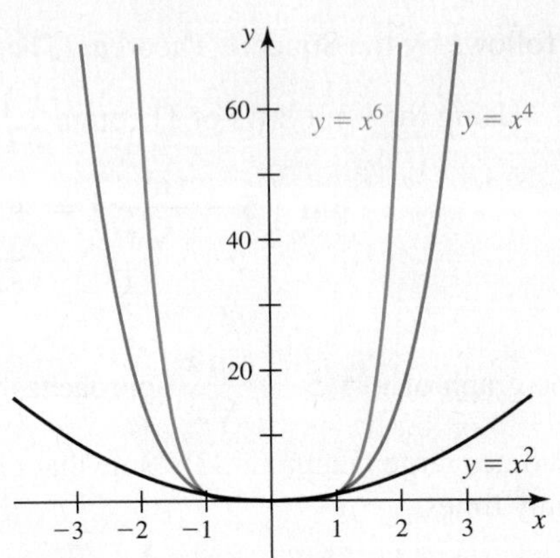

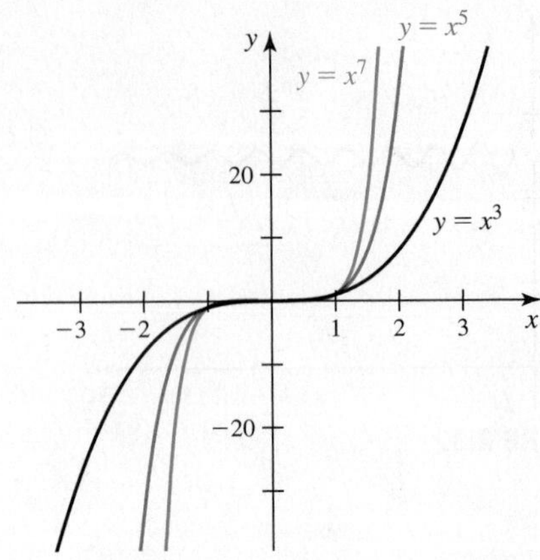

FIGURE 2.34

QUICK CHECK 2 Describe the behavior of $p(x) = -3x^3$ as $x \to \infty$ and as $x \to -\infty$. ◀

From here, it is a short step to finding the behavior of any polynomial as $x \to \pm\infty$. Let $p(x) = a_n x^n + a_{n-1}x^{n-1} + \cdots + a_2x^2 + a_1x + a_0$. Notice that as $x \to \pm\infty$, the behavior of p is determined by the term $a_n x^n$ with the highest power of x.

THEOREM 2.6 Limits at Infinity of Powers and Polynomials
Let n be a positive integer and let p be the polynomial $p(x) = a_n x^n + a_{n-1}x^{n-1} + \cdots + a_2x^2 + a_1x + a_0$, where $a_n \neq 0$.

1. $\lim_{x \to \pm\infty} x^n = \infty$ when n is even
2. $\lim_{x \to \infty} x^n = \infty$ and $\lim_{x \to -\infty} x^n = -\infty$ when n is odd
3. $\lim_{x \to \pm\infty} \frac{1}{x^n} = \lim_{x \to \pm\infty} x^{-n} = 0$
4. $\lim_{x \to \pm\infty} p(x) = \infty$ or $-\infty$, depending on the degree of the polynomial and the sign of the leading coefficient a_n.

EXAMPLE 2 Limits at infinity Evaluate the limits as $x \to \pm\infty$ of the following functions.

a. $p(x) = 3x^4 - 6x^2 + x - 10$ **b.** $q(x) = -2x^3 + 3x^2 - 12$

SOLUTION

a. We use the fact that the limit is determined by the behavior of the leading term:

$$\lim_{x \to \infty} (3x^4 - 6x^2 + x - 10) = \lim_{x \to \infty} 3\underbrace{x^4}_{\to\infty} = \infty.$$

Similarly,

$$\lim_{x \to -\infty} (3x^4 - 6x^2 + x - 10) = \lim_{x \to -\infty} 3\underbrace{x^4}_{\to\infty} = \infty.$$

b. Noting that the leading coefficient is negative, we have

$$\lim_{x \to \infty} (-2x^3 + 3x^2 - 12) = \lim_{x \to \infty} (-2\underbrace{x^3}_{\to\infty}) = -\infty$$

$$\lim_{x \to -\infty} (-2x^3 + 3x^2 - 12) = \lim_{x \to -\infty} (-2\underbrace{x^3}_{\to-\infty}) = \infty.$$

Related Exercises 15–20 ◀

End Behavior

The behavior of polynomials as $x \to \pm\infty$ is an example of what is often called *end behavior*. Having treated polynomials, we now turn to the end behavior of rational and algebraic functions.

EXAMPLE 3 **End behavior of rational functions** Determine the end behavior for the following rational functions and use a graph to confirm the results.

a. $f(x) = \dfrac{3x + 2}{x^2 - 1}$ **b.** $g(x) = \dfrac{40x^4 + 4x^2 - 1}{10x^4 + 8x^2 + 1}$ **c.** $h(x) = \dfrac{2x^2 + 6x - 2}{x + 1}$

SOLUTION

a. An effective approach for evaluating limits of rational functions at infinity is to divide both the numerator and denominator by x^n, where n is the largest power appearing in the denominator. This strategy forces the terms corresponding to lower powers of x to approach 0 in the limit. In this case, we divide by x^2:

$$\lim_{x\to\infty} \frac{3x+2}{x^2-1} = \lim_{x\to\infty} \frac{\dfrac{3x+2}{x^2}}{\dfrac{x^2-1}{x^2}} = \lim_{x\to\infty} \frac{\overbrace{\dfrac{3}{x} + \dfrac{2}{x^2}}^{\text{approaches } 0}}{1 - \underbrace{\dfrac{1}{x^2}}_{\text{approaches } 0}} = \frac{0}{1} = 0$$

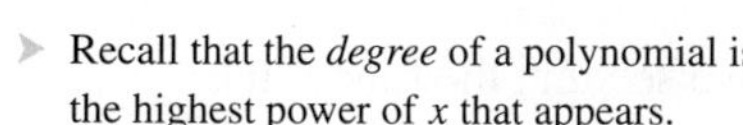

Recall that the *degree* of a polynomial is the highest power of x that appears.

A similar calculation gives $\displaystyle\lim_{x\to-\infty} \frac{3x+2}{x^2-1} = 0$, and thus the graph of f has the horizontal asymptote $y = 0$. You should confirm that the zeros of the denominator are $x = -1$ and $x = 1$, which correspond to vertical asymptotes (Figure 2.35). In this example, the degree of the polynomial in the numerator is *less than* the degree of the polynomial in the denominator.

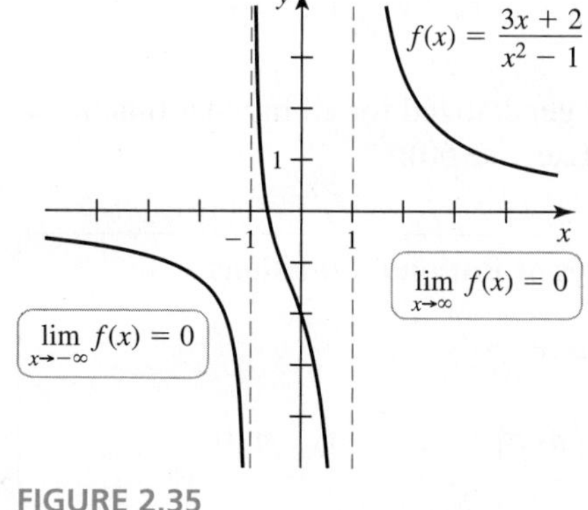

FIGURE 2.35

b. Again we divide both the numerator and denominator by the largest power appearing in the denominator, which is x^4:

$$\lim_{x\to\infty} \frac{40x^4 + 4x^2 - 1}{10x^4 + 8x^2 + 1} = \lim_{x\to\infty} \frac{\dfrac{40x^4}{x^4} + \dfrac{4x^2}{x^4} - \dfrac{1}{x^4}}{\dfrac{10x^4}{x^4} + \dfrac{8x^2}{x^4} + \dfrac{1}{x^4}} \qquad \text{Divide the numerator and denominator by } x^4.$$

$$= \lim_{x\to\infty} \frac{40 + \overbrace{\dfrac{4}{x^2}}^{\text{approaches } 0} - \overbrace{\dfrac{1}{x^4}}^{\text{approaches } 0}}{10 + \underbrace{\dfrac{8}{x^2}}_{\text{approaches } 0} + \underbrace{\dfrac{1}{x^4}}_{\text{approaches } 0}} \qquad \text{Simplify.}$$

$$= \frac{40 + 0 + 0}{10 + 0 + 0} = 4 \qquad \text{Evaluate limits.}$$

Using the same steps (dividing each term by x^4), it can be shown that $\displaystyle\lim_{x\to-\infty} \frac{40x^4 + 4x^2 - 1}{10x^4 + 8x^2 + 1} = 4$. This function has the horizontal asymptote $y = 4$ (Figure 2.36). In this example, the degree of the polynomial in the numerator *equals* the degree of the polynomial in the denominator.

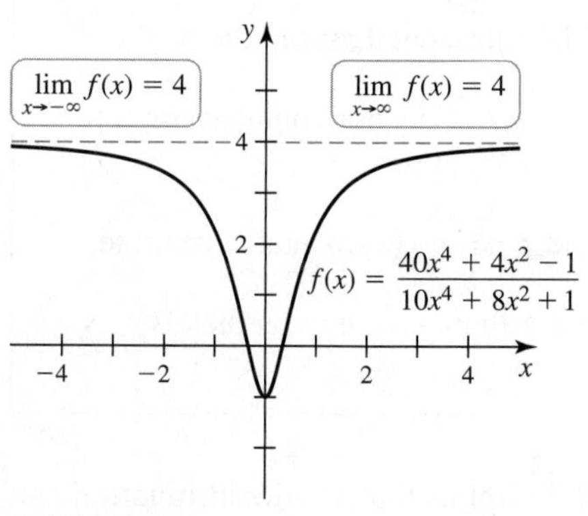

FIGURE 2.36

c. We first divide the numerator and denominator by the largest power of x appearing in the denominator, which is x:

$$\lim_{x\to\infty}\frac{2x^2+6x-2}{x+1}=\lim_{x\to\infty}\frac{\frac{2x^2}{x}+\frac{6x}{x}-\frac{2}{x}}{\frac{x}{x}+\frac{1}{x}}$$ Divide the numerator and denominator by x.

$$=\lim_{x\to\infty}\frac{\overbrace{2x}^{\text{arbitrarily large}}+\overbrace{6}^{\text{constant}}-\overbrace{\frac{2}{x}}^{\text{approaches 0}}}{\underbrace{1}_{\text{constant}}+\underbrace{\frac{1}{x}}_{\text{approaches 0}}}$$ Simplify.

$$=\infty$$ Take limits.

A similar analysis shows that $\lim_{x\to-\infty}\frac{2x^2+6x-2}{x+1}=-\infty$. Because these limits are not finite, there are no horizontal asymptotes. In this case, the degree of the polynomial in the numerator is *greater than* the degree of the polynomial in the denominator.

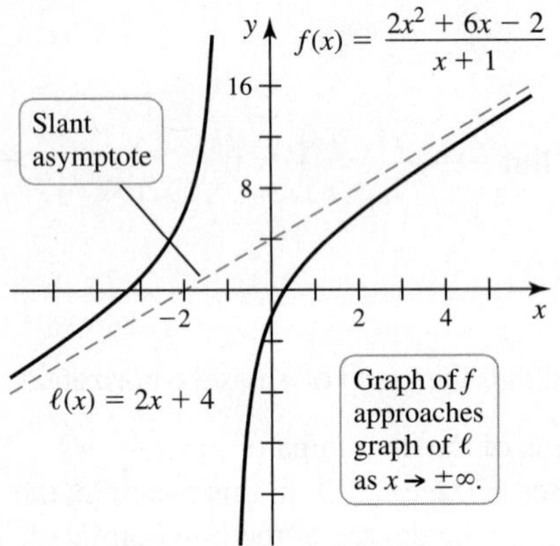

FIGURE 2.37

There is more to be learned about the end behavior of this function. Using long division, the function h is written

$$h(x)=\frac{2x^2+6x-2}{x+1}=2x+4-\underbrace{\frac{6}{x+1}}_{\text{approaches 0 as } x\to\infty}.$$

As $x\to\infty$, the term $6/(x+1)$ approaches 0, and we see that the function h behaves like the linear function $\ell(x)=2x+4$. For this reason, the graphs of h and ℓ approach each other as $x\to\infty$ (Figure 2.37). A similar argument shows that the graphs of h and ℓ approach each other as $x\to-\infty$. The line described by ℓ is called a **slant**, or **oblique, asymptote** (Exercises 54–59). *Related Exercises 21–26* ◀

The conclusions reached in Example 3 can be generalized for all rational functions. These results are summarized in Theorem 2.7 (see Exercise 60).

THEOREM 2.7 End Behavior and Asymptotes of Rational Functions

Suppose $f(x)=\frac{p(x)}{q(x)}$ is a rational function, where

$$p(x)=a_mx^m+a_{m-1}x^{m-1}+\cdots+a_2x^2+a_1x+a_0 \quad \text{and}$$
$$q(x)=b_nx^n+b_{n-1}x^{n-1}+\cdots+b_2x^2+b_1x+b_0$$

with $a_m\neq 0$ and $b_n\neq 0$.

a. If $m<n$, then $\lim_{x\to\pm\infty}f(x)=0$, and $y=0$ is a horizontal asymptote of f.

b. If $m=n$, then $\lim_{x\to\pm\infty}f(x)=a_m/b_n$, and $y=a_m/b_n$ is a horizontal asymptote of f.

c. If $m>n$, then $\lim_{x\to\pm\infty}f(x)=\infty$ or $-\infty$, and f has no horizontal asymptote.

d. Assuming that $f(x)$ is in reduced form (p and q share no common factors), vertical asymptotes occur at the zeros of q.

QUICK CHECK 3 Use Theorem 2.7 to find the vertical and horizontal asymptotes of $y=\frac{10x}{3x-1}$. ◀

Although it isn't stated explicitly, Theorem 2.7 implies that a rational function can have at most one horizontal asymptote, and whenever a horizontal asymptote exists,

$\lim_{x\to\infty} \frac{p(x)}{q(x)} = \lim_{x\to-\infty} \frac{p(x)}{q(x)}$. The same cannot be said of other functions, as shown in the next example.

EXAMPLE 4 **End behavior of an algebraic function** Examine the end behavior of $f(x) = \frac{10x^3 - 3x^2 + 8}{\sqrt{25x^6 + x^4 + 2}}$.

SOLUTION The square root in the denominator forces us to revise the strategy used with rational functions. First, consider the limit as $x \to \infty$. The highest power of the polynomial in the denominator is 6. The polynomial is under a square root, so we divide the numerator and denominator by $\sqrt{x^6} = x^3$ for $x \geq 0$. The limit is evaluated as follows:

$$\lim_{x\to\infty} \frac{10x^3 - 3x^2 + 8}{\sqrt{25x^6 + x^4 + 2}} = \lim_{x\to\infty} \frac{\frac{10x^3}{x^3} - \frac{3x^2}{x^3} + \frac{8}{x^3}}{\sqrt{\frac{25x^6}{x^6} + \frac{x^4}{x^6} + \frac{2}{x^6}}} \qquad \text{Divide by } \sqrt{x^6} = x^3.$$

$$= \lim_{x\to\infty} \frac{10 - \overbrace{\frac{3}{x}}^{\text{approaches 0}} + \overbrace{\frac{8}{x^3}}^{\text{approaches 0}}}{\sqrt{25 + \underbrace{\frac{1}{x^2}}_{\text{approaches 0}} + \underbrace{\frac{2}{x^6}}_{\text{approaches 0}}}} \qquad \text{Simplify.}$$

$$= \frac{10}{\sqrt{25}} = 2 \qquad \text{Evaluate limits.}$$

➤ Recall that

$$\sqrt{x^2} = |x| = \begin{cases} x & \text{if } x \geq 0 \\ -x & \text{if } x < 0 \end{cases}$$

Therefore,

$$\sqrt{x^6} = |x^3| = \begin{cases} x^3 & \text{if } x \geq 0 \\ -x^3 & \text{if } x < 0 \end{cases}$$

Because x is negative as $x \to -\infty$, we have $\sqrt{x^6} = -x^3$.

As $x \to -\infty$, x^3 is negative, so we divide numerator and denominator by $\sqrt{x^6} = -x^3$ (which is positive):

$$\lim_{x\to-\infty} \frac{10x^3 - 3x^2 + 8}{\sqrt{25x^6 + x^4 + 2}} = \lim_{x\to-\infty} \frac{\frac{10x^3}{-x^3} - \frac{3x^2}{-x^3} + \frac{8}{-x^3}}{\sqrt{\frac{25x^6}{x^6} + \frac{x^4}{x^6} + \frac{2}{x^6}}} \qquad \text{Divide by } \sqrt{x^6} = -x^3 > 0.$$

$$= \lim_{x\to-\infty} \frac{-10 + \overbrace{\frac{3}{x}}^{\text{approaches 0}} - \overbrace{\frac{8}{x^3}}^{\text{approaches 0}}}{\sqrt{25 + \underbrace{\frac{1}{x^2}}_{\text{approaches 0}} + \underbrace{\frac{2}{x^6}}_{\text{approaches 0}}}} \qquad \text{Simplify.}$$

$$= \frac{-10}{\sqrt{25}} = -2 \qquad \text{Evaluate limits.}$$

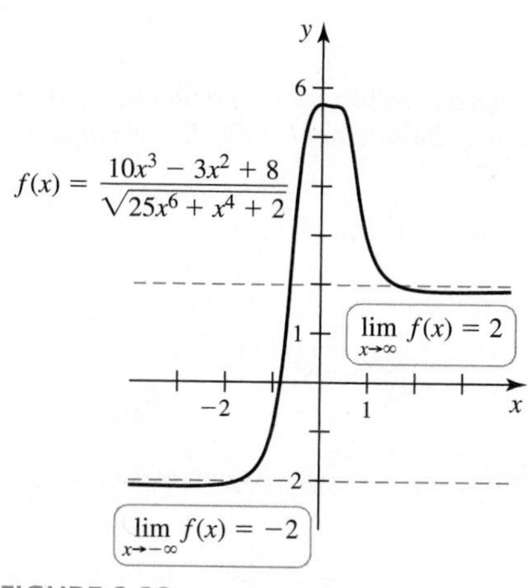

FIGURE 2.38

The limits reveal two horizontal asymptotes, $y = 2$ and $y = -2$. Observe that the graph crosses both horizontal asymptotes (Figure 2.38). *Related Exercises 27–30* ◀

End Behavior of sin *x* and cos *x*

Our future work requires knowing about the end behavior of $\sin x$ and $\cos x$. The values of both functions oscillate between -1 and 1 as x increases in magnitude. Therefore, $\lim_{x\to\pm\infty} \sin x$ and $\lim_{x\to\pm\infty} \cos x$ do not exist. However, both functions are bounded as $x \to \pm\infty$; that is, $|\sin x| \leq 1$ and $|\cos x| \leq 1$ for all x.

SECTION 2.5 EXERCISES

Review Questions

1. Explain the meaning of $\lim_{x\to-\infty} f(x) = 10$.

2. What is a horizontal asymptote?

3. Determine $\lim_{x\to\infty} \frac{f(x)}{g(x)}$ if $f(x) \to 100{,}000$ and $g(x) \to \infty$ as $x \to \infty$.

4. Describe the end behavior of $g(x) = (\sin x)/x$.

5. Describe the end behavior of $f(x) = -2x^3$.

6. Three cases arise when examining the end behavior of a rational function $f(x) = p(x)/q(x)$. State each case, and describe the associated end behavior.

7. Evaluate $\lim_{x\to\infty} \frac{1-x}{2x}$, $\lim_{x\to-\infty} \frac{1-x}{x^2}$, and $\lim_{x\to\infty} \frac{1-x^2}{2x}$.

8. Describe with a sketch the end behavior of $f(x) = \cos x$.

Basic Skills

9–14. Limits at infinity *Evaluate the following limits.*

9. $\lim_{x\to\infty} \left(3 + \frac{10}{x^2}\right)$

10. $\lim_{x\to\infty} \left(5 + \frac{1}{x} + \frac{10}{x^2}\right)$

11. $\lim_{\theta\to\infty} \frac{\cos\theta}{\theta^2}$

12. $\lim_{x\to\infty} \frac{3 + 2x + 4x^2}{x^2}$

13. $\lim_{x\to-\infty} \frac{\cos x^5}{x}$

14. $\lim_{x\to-\infty} \left(5 + \frac{100}{x} + \frac{\sin^4 x^3}{x^2}\right)$

15–20. Infinite limits at infinity *Determine the following limits.*

15. $\lim_{x\to\infty} (3x^{12} - 9x^7)$

16. $\lim_{x\to-\infty} (3x^7 + x^2)$

17. $\lim_{x\to-\infty} (-3x^{16} + 2)$

18. $\lim_{x\to-\infty} 2x^{-8}$

19. $\lim_{x\to\infty} (-12x^{-5})$

20. $\lim_{x\to-\infty} (2x^{-8} + 4x^3)$

21–26. Rational functions *Evaluate $\lim_{x\to\infty} f(x)$ and $\lim_{x\to-\infty} f(x)$ for the following rational functions. Then give the horizontal asymptote of f (if any).*

21. $f(x) = \frac{6x^2 - 9x + 8}{3x^2 + 2}$

22. $f(x) = \frac{4x^2 - 7}{8x^2 + 5x + 2}$

23. $f(x) = \frac{2x + 1}{3x^4 - 2}$

24. $f(x) = \frac{12x^8 - 3}{3x^8 - 2x^7}$

25. $f(x) = \frac{40x^5 + x^2}{16x^4 - 2x}$

26. $f(x) = \frac{-x^3 + 1}{2x + 8}$

27–30. Algebraic functions *Evaluate $\lim_{x\to\infty} f(x)$ and $\lim_{x\to-\infty} f(x)$ for the following functions. Then give the horizontal asymptote(s) of f (if any).*

27. $f(x) = \frac{4x^3 + 1}{2x^3 + \sqrt{16x^6 + 1}}$

28. $f(x) = \frac{4x^3}{2x^3 + \sqrt{9x^6 + 15x^4}}$

29. $f(x) = \frac{\sqrt[3]{x^6 + 8}}{4x^2 + \sqrt{3x^4 + 1}}$

30. $f(x) = 4x\left(3x - \sqrt{9x^2 + 1}\right)$

Further Explorations

31. **Explain why or why not** Determine whether the following statements are true and give an explanation or counterexample.
    a. The graph of a function can never cross one of its horizontal asymptotes.
    b. A rational function f can have both $\lim_{x\to\infty} f(x) = L$ and $\lim_{x\to-\infty} f(x) = \infty$.
    c. The graph of any function can have at most two horizontal asymptotes.

32–41. Horizontal and vertical asymptotes

a. *Evaluate $\lim_{x\to\infty} f(x)$ and $\lim_{x\to-\infty} f(x)$, and then identify any horizontal asymptotes.*

b. *Find the vertical asymptotes. For each vertical asymptote $x = a$, evaluate $\lim_{x\to a^-} f(x)$ and $\lim_{x\to a^+} f(x)$.*

32. $f(x) = \frac{x^2 - 4x + 3}{x - 1}$

33. $f(x) = \frac{2x^3 + 10x^2 + 12x}{x^3 + 2x^2}$

34. $f(x) = \frac{\sqrt{16x^4 + 64x^2} + x^2}{2x^2 - 4}$

35. $f(x) = \frac{3x^4 + 3x^3 - 36x^2}{x^4 - 25x^2 + 144}$

36. $f(x) = 16x^2\left(4x^2 - \sqrt{16x^4 + 1}\right)$

37. $f(x) = \frac{x^2 - 9}{x(x - 3)}$

38. $f(x) = \frac{x - 1}{x^{2/3} - 1}$

39. $f(x) = \frac{\sqrt{x^2 + 2x + 6} - 3}{x - 1}$

40. $f(x) = \frac{|1 - x^2|}{x(x + 1)}$

41. $f(x) = \sqrt{|x|} - \sqrt{|x - 1|}$

42–43. Sketching graphs *Sketch a possible graph of a function f that satisfies all of the given conditions. Be sure to identify all vertical and horizontal asymptotes.*

42. $f(-1) = -2$, $f(1) = 2$, $f(0) = 0$, $\lim_{x\to\infty} f(x) = 1$, $\lim_{x\to-\infty} f(x) = -1$

43. $\lim_{x\to0^+} f(x) = \infty$, $\lim_{x\to0^-} f(x) = -\infty$, $\lim_{x\to\infty} f(x) = 1$, $\lim_{x\to-\infty} f(x) = -2$

44. **Asymptotes** Find the vertical and horizontal asymptotes of $f(x) = \frac{2x}{\sqrt{x^2 - x - 2}}$.

45. **Asymptotes** Find the vertical and horizontal asymptotes of $f(x) = \frac{\cos x + 2\sqrt{x}}{\sqrt{x}}$.

Applications

46–49. Steady states *If a function f represents a system that varies in time, the existence of* $\lim_{t\to\infty} f(t)$ *means that the system reaches a steady state (or equilibrium). For the following systems, determine if a steady state exists and give the steady-state value.*

46. The population of a bacteria culture is given by $p(t) = \dfrac{2500}{t+1}$.

47. The population of a culture of tumor cells is given by $p(t) = \dfrac{3500t}{t+1}$.

48. The population of a colony of squirrels is given by $p(t) = \dfrac{1500t^2}{2t^2+3}$.

49. The amplitude of an oscillator is given by $a(t) = 2\left(\dfrac{t + \sin t}{t}\right)$.

50–53. Looking ahead to sequences *A sequence is an infinite ordered list of numbers that is often defined by a function. For example, the sequence* $\{2, 4, 6, 8, \ldots\}$ *is defined by the function* $f(n) = 2n$, *where* $n = 1, 2, 3, \ldots$. *The limit of such a sequence is* $\lim_{n\to\infty} f(n)$, *provided the limit exists. All the limit laws for limits at infinity may be applied to limits of sequences. Find the limit of the following sequences, or state that the limit does not exist.*

50. $\left\{4, 2, \frac{4}{3}, 1, \frac{4}{5}, \frac{2}{3}, \ldots\right\}$, which is defined by $f(n) = \dfrac{4}{n}$, for $n = 1, 2, 3, \ldots$

51. $\left\{0, \frac{1}{2}, \frac{2}{3}, \frac{3}{4}, \ldots\right\}$, which is defined by $f(n) = \dfrac{n-1}{n}$, for $n = 1, 2, 3, \ldots$

52. $\left\{\frac{1}{2}, \frac{4}{3}, \frac{9}{4}, \frac{16}{5}, \ldots\right\}$, which is defined by $f(n) = \dfrac{n^2}{n+1}$, for $n = 1, 2, 3, \ldots$

53. $\left\{2, \frac{3}{4}, \frac{4}{9}, \frac{5}{16}, \ldots\right\}$, which is defined by $f(n) = \dfrac{n+1}{n^2}$, for $n = 1, 2, 3, \ldots$

Additional Exercises

T **54–59. Oblique (slant) asymptotes** *Suppose p/q is a rational function where the degree of p is 1 greater than the degree of q. Using polynomial long division, p/q can be written as*

$$\frac{p(x)}{q(x)} = mx + b + \frac{r(x)}{s(x)}$$

where r/s is a rational function with the property $r(x)/s(x) \to 0$ *as* $x \to \pm\infty$. *This fact implies that* $\dfrac{p(x)}{q(x)} \approx mx + b$ *when x is large. The line* $y = mx + b$ *is an* oblique *(or* slant*)* asymptote *of p/q. Complete the following steps for the given functions.*

a. *Use polynomial long division to find the oblique asymptote of f.*
b. *Find the vertical asymptotes of f.*
c. *Graph f and all of its asymptotes with a graphing utility. Then sketch a graph of the function by hand, correcting any errors appearing in the computer-generated graph.*

54. $f(x) = \dfrac{x^2 - 1}{x + 2}$

55. $f(x) = \dfrac{x^2 - 3}{x + 6}$

56. $f(x) = \dfrac{3x^2 - 2x + 7}{2x - 5}$

57. $f(x) = \dfrac{x^2 - 2x + 5}{3x - 2}$

58. $f(x) = \dfrac{3x^2 - 2x + 5}{3x + 4}$

59. $f(x) = \dfrac{4x^3 + 4x^2 + 7x + 4}{1 + x^2}$

60. End behavior of rational functions Suppose $f(x) = \dfrac{p(x)}{q(x)}$ is a rational function, where
$p(x) = a_m x^m + a_{m-1}x^{m-1} + \cdots + a_2x^2 + a_1x + a_0$,
$q(x) = b_n x^n + b_{n-1}x^{n-1} + \cdots + b_2x^2 + b_1x + b_0$, $a_m \neq 0$, and $b_n \neq 0$.

a. Prove that if $m = n$, then $\lim_{x\to\pm\infty} f(x) = \dfrac{a_m}{b_n}$.
b. Prove that if $m < n$, then $\lim_{x\to\pm\infty} f(x) = 0$.

QUICK CHECK ANSWERS

1. 10/11, 100/101, 1000/1001, 1 **2.** $p(x) \to -\infty$ as $x \to \infty$ and $p(x) \to \infty$ as $x \to -\infty$ **3.** Horizontal asymptote is $y = \frac{10}{3}$; vertical asymptote is $x = \frac{1}{3}$ ◀

2.6 Continuity

The graphs of many functions encountered in this text contain no holes, jumps, or breaks. For example, if $L = f(t)$ represents the length of a fish t years after it is hatched, then the length of the fish changes gradually as t increases. Consequently, the graph of $L = f(t)$ contains no breaks (Figure 2.39a). Some functions, however, do contain abrupt changes in their values. Consider a parking meter that accepts only quarters and each quarter buys 15 min of parking. Letting $c(t)$ be the cost (in dollars) of parking for t min, the graph of c has breaks at integer multiples of 15 min (Figure 2.39b).

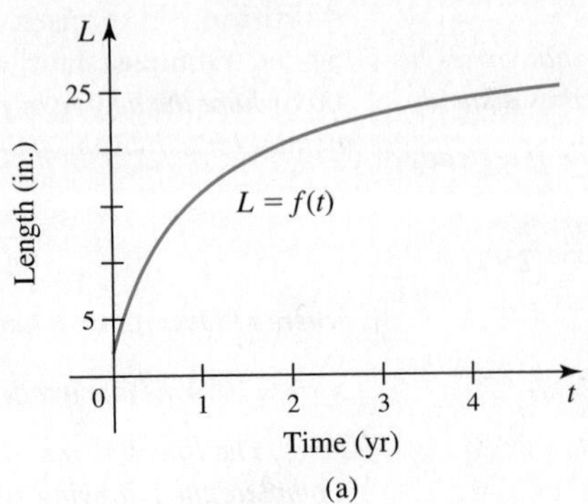

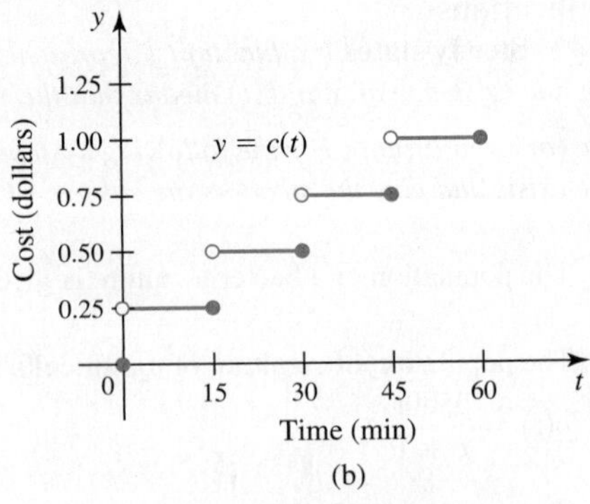

FIGURE 2.39

QUICK CHECK 1 For what values of t in $(0, 60)$ does the graph of $y = c(t)$ in Figure 2.39b have discontinuities?

Informally, we say that a function f is *continuous* at $x = a$ if the graph of f contains no holes or breaks at $x = a$ (if the graph near $x = a$ can be drawn without lifting the pencil). If a function is not continuous at $x = a$, then a is a point of discontinuity.

Continuity at a Point

This informal description of continuity is sufficient for determining the continuity of simple functions, but it is not precise enough to deal with more complicated functions such as

$$h(x) = \begin{cases} x \sin \dfrac{1}{x} & \text{if } x \neq 0 \\ 0 & \text{if } x = 0 \end{cases}.$$

It is difficult to determine whether the graph of h has a break at $x = 0$ because it oscillates rapidly as x approaches 0 (Figure 2.40). We need a better definition.

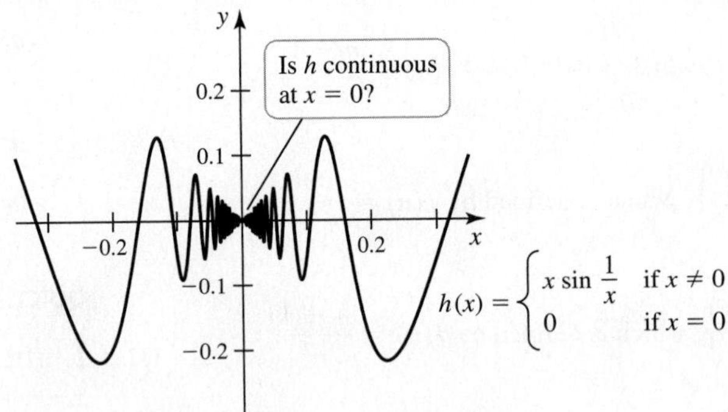

FIGURE 2.40

> **DEFINITION Continuity at a Point**
>
> A function f is **continuous** at a if $\lim_{x \to a} f(x) = f(a)$. If f is not continuous at a, then a is a point of discontinuity.

There is more to this definition than first appears. If $\lim_{x \to a} f(x) = f(a)$, then $f(a)$ and $\lim_{x \to a} f(x)$ must both exist, and they must be equal. The following checklist is helpful in determining whether a function is continuous at a.

> **Continuity Checklist**
>
> In order for f to be continuous at a, the following three conditions must hold:
>
> **1.** $f(a)$ is defined (a is in the domain of f).
>
> **2.** $\lim_{x \to a} f(x)$ exists.
>
> **3.** $\lim_{x \to a} f(x) = f(a)$ (the value of f equals the limit of f at a).

If *any* item in the continuity checklist fails to hold, the function fails to be continuous at a. From this definition, we see that continuity has an important practical consequence:

If f is continuous at a, then $\lim_{x \to a} f(x) = f(a)$, and direct substitution may be used to evaluate $\lim_{x \to a} f(x)$.

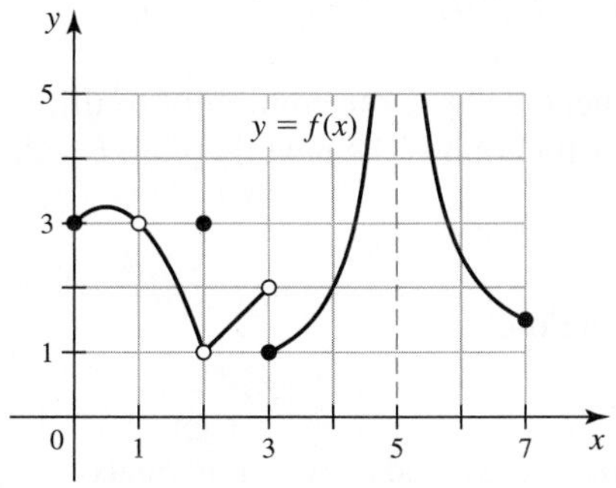

FIGURE 2.41

EXAMPLE 1 Points of discontinuity Use the graph of f in Figure 2.41 to identify values of x on the interval $(0, 7)$ at which f is not continuous.

SOLUTION The function f has discontinuities at $x = 1, 2, 3$, and 5 because the graph contains holes or breaks at each of these locations. These claims are verified using the continuity checklist.

- $f(1)$ is not defined.
- $f(2) = 3$ and $\lim_{x \to 2} f(x) = 1$. Therefore, $f(2)$ and $\lim_{x \to 2} f(x)$ exist but are not equal.
- $\lim_{x \to 3} f(x)$ does not exist because the left-hand limit $\lim_{x \to 3^-} f(x) = 2$ differs from the right-hand limit $\lim_{x \to 3^+} f(x) = 1$.
- Neither $\lim_{x \to 5} f(x)$ nor $f(5)$ exists.

Related Exercises 9–12 ◀

➤ In Example 1, the discontinuities at $x = 1$ and $x = 2$ are called **removable discontinuities** because they can be removed by defining or redefining the function at these points (in this case $f(1) = 3$ and $f(2) = 1$). The discontinuity at $x = 3$ is called a **jump discontinuity**. The discontinuity at $x = 5$ is called an **infinite discontinuity**. These terms are discussed in Exercises 79–85.

EXAMPLE 2 Identifying discontinuities Determine whether the following functions are continuous at a. Justify each answer using the continuity checklist.

a. $f(x) = \dfrac{3x^2 + 2x + 1}{x - 1}; \quad a = 1$

b. $g(x) = \dfrac{3x^2 + 2x + 1}{x - 1}; \quad a = 2$

c. $h(x) = \begin{cases} x \sin\left(\dfrac{1}{x}\right) & \text{if } x \neq 0 \\ 0 & \text{if } x = 0 \end{cases}; \; a = 0$

SOLUTION

a. The function f is not continuous at $x = 1$ because $f(1)$ is undefined.

b. Because g is a rational function and the denominator is nonzero at $x = 2$, it follows by Theorem 2.3 that $\lim_{x \to 2} g(x) = g(2) = 17$. Therefore, g is continuous at 2.

c. By definition, $h(0) = 0$. In Exercise 49 of Section 2.3, we used the Squeeze Theorem to show that $\lim_{x \to 0} x \sin\left(\dfrac{1}{x}\right) = 0$. Therefore, $\lim_{x \to 0} h(x) = h(0)$, which implies that h is continuous at 0.

Related Exercises 13–18 ◀

The following theorems make it easier to test various combinations of functions for continuity at a point.

THEOREM 2.8 Continuity Rules
If f and g are continuous at a, then the following functions are also continuous at a. Assume c is a constant and $n > 0$ is an integer.

a. $f + g$
b. $f - g$
c. cf
d. fg
e. f/g, provided $g(a) \neq 0$
f. f^n

To prove the first result, note that if f and g are continuous at a, then $\lim_{x \to a} f(x) = f(a)$ and $\lim_{x \to a} g(x) = g(a)$. From the limit laws of Theorem 2.3, it follows that

$$\lim_{x \to a} [f(x) + g(x)] = f(a) + g(a).$$

Therefore, $f + g$ is continuous at a. Similar arguments lead to the continuity of differences, products, quotients, and powers of continuous functions. The next theorem is a direct consequence of Theorem 2.8.

THEOREM 2.9 Polynomials and Rational Functions

a. A polynomial function is continuous for all x.

b. A rational function (a function of the form p/q, where p and q are polynomials) is continuous for all x for which $q(x) \neq 0$.

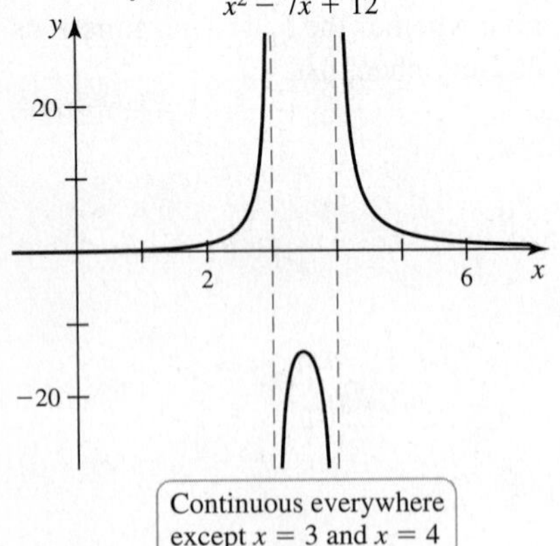

FIGURE 2.42

EXAMPLE 3 Applying the continuity theorems For what values of x is the function $f(x) = \dfrac{x}{x^2 - 7x + 12}$ continuous?

SOLUTION

a. Because f is rational, Theorem 2.9b implies it is continuous for all x at which the denominator is nonzero. The denominator factors as $(x - 3)(x - 4)$, so it is zero at $x = 3$ and $x = 4$. Therefore, f is continuous for all x except $x = 3$ and $x = 4$ (Figure 2.42).

Related Exercises 19–24 ◀

The following theorem allows us to determine when a composition of two functions is continuous at a point. Its proof is informative and is outlined in Exercise 86.

THEOREM 2.10 Continuity of Composite Functions at a Point
If g is continuous at a and f is continuous at $g(a)$, then the composite function $f \circ g$ is continuous at a.

The theorem says that under the stated conditions on f and g, the limit of their composition is evaluated by direct substitution; that is,

$$\lim_{x \to a} f(g(x)) = f(g(a)).$$

QUICK CHECK 2 Evaluate $\lim_{x \to 4} \sqrt{x^2 + 9}$ and $\sqrt{\lim_{x \to 4} (x^2 + 9)}$. How do these results illustrate that the order of a function evaluation and a limit may be switched for continuous functions? ◀

This result can be stated in another instructive way. Because g is continuous at a, we have $\lim_{x \to a} g(x) = g(a)$. Therefore,

$$\lim_{x \to a} f(g(x)) = f(\underbrace{g(a)}_{\lim_{x \to a} g(x)}) = f\left(\lim_{x \to a} g(x)\right).$$

In other words, the order of a function evaluation and a limit may be switched for continuous functions.

EXAMPLE 4 **Limit of a composition** Evaluate $\lim_{x \to 0} \left(\frac{x^4 - 2x + 2}{x^6 + 2x^4 + 1} \right)^{10}$.

SOLUTION The rational function $\frac{x^4 - 2x + 2}{x^6 + 2x^4 + 1}$ is continuous for all x because its denominator is always positive (Theorem 2.9b). Therefore, $\left(\frac{x^4 - 2x + 2}{x^6 + 2x^4 + 1} \right)^{10}$, which is the composition of the continuous function $f(x) = x^{10}$ and a continuous rational function, is continuous for all x by Theorem 2.10. By direct substitution,

$$\lim_{x \to 0} \left(\frac{x^4 - 2x + 2}{x^6 + 2x^4 + 1} \right)^{10} = \left(\frac{0^4 - 2 \cdot 0 + 2}{0^6 + 2 \cdot 0^4 + 1} \right)^{10} = 2^{10} = 1024.$$

Related Exercises 25–28 ◀

Continuity on an Interval

A function is *continuous on an interval* if it is continuous at every point in that interval. Consider the functions f and g whose graphs are shown in Figure 2.43. Both these functions are continuous for all x in (a, b), but what about the endpoints? To answer this question, we introduce the ideas of *left-continuity* and *right-continuity*.

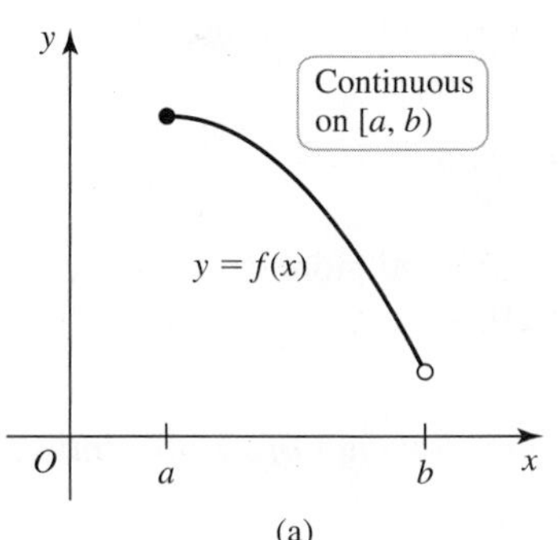

(a)

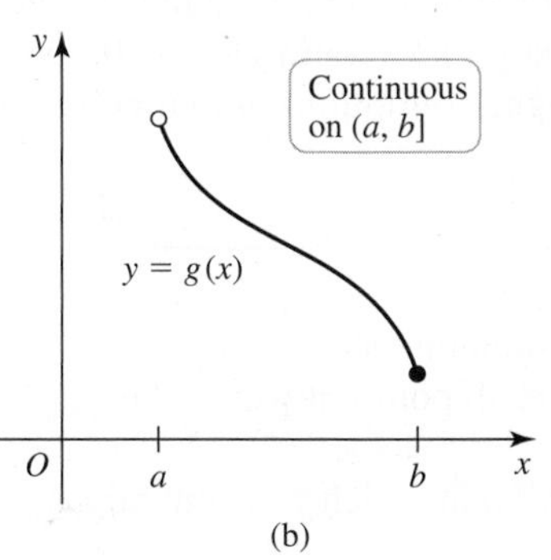

(b)

FIGURE 2.43

DEFINITION **Continuity at Endpoints**

A function f is **continuous from the left** (or **left-continuous**) at a if $\lim_{x \to a^-} f(x) = f(a)$ and f is **continuous from the right** (or **right-continuous**) at a if $\lim_{x \to a^+} f(x) = f(a)$.

Combining the definitions of left-continuous and right-continuous with the definition of continuity at a point, we define what it means for a function to be continuous on an interval.

DEFINITION **Continuity on an Interval**

A function f is **continuous on an interval *I*** if it is continuous at all points of I. If I contains its endpoints, continuity on I means continuous from the right or left at the endpoints.

To illustrate these definitions, consider again the functions in Figure 2.43. In Figure 2.43a, f is continuous from the right at a because $\lim_{x \to a^+} f(x) = f(a)$; but it is not continuous from the left at b because $f(b)$ is not defined. Therefore, f is continuous on the interval $[a, b)$. The behavior of the function g in Figure 2.43b is the opposite: It is continuous from the left at b, but it is not continuous from the right at a. Therefore, g is continuous on $(a, b]$.

QUICK CHECK 3 Modify the graphs of the functions f and g in Figure 2.43 to obtain functions that are continuous on $[a, b]$. ◀

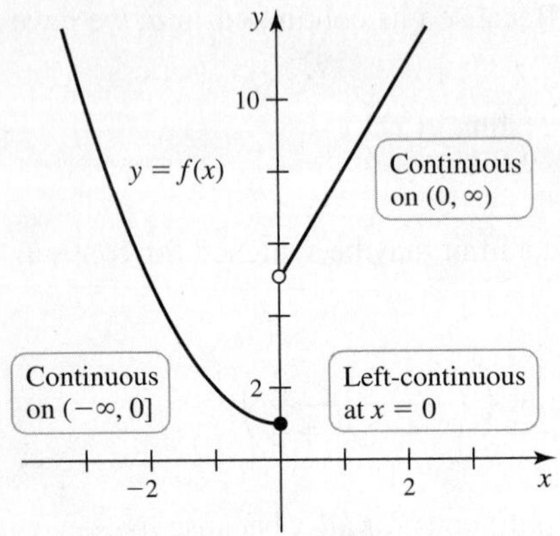

FIGURE 2.44

EXAMPLE 5 **Intervals of continuity** Determine the intervals of continuity for

$$f(x) = \begin{cases} x^2 + 1 & \text{if } x \le 0 \\ 3x + 5 & \text{if } x > 0 \end{cases}.$$

SOLUTION This piecewise function consists of two polynomials that describe a parabola and a line (Figure 2.44). By Theorem 2.9, f is continuous for all $x \neq 0$. From its graph, it appears that f is left-continuous at $x = 0$. This observation is verified by noting that

$$\lim_{x\to 0^-} f(x) = \lim_{x\to 0^-} (x^2 + 1) = 1,$$

which means that $\lim_{x\to 0^-} f(x) = f(0)$. However, because

$$\lim_{x\to 0^+} f(x) = \lim_{x\to 0^+} (3x + 5) = 5 \neq f(0),$$

we see that f is not right-continuous at $x = 0$. Therefore, f is continuous on $(-\infty, 0]$, and it is continuous on $(0, \infty)$.

Related Exercises 29–34 ◄

Functions Involving Roots

Recall that Limit Law 7 of Theorem 2.3 states

$$\lim_{x\to a} [f(x)]^{n/m} = \left[\lim_{x\to a} f(x)\right]^{n/m},$$

provided $f(x) \ge 0$ for x near a if m is even and n/m is reduced. Therefore, if m is odd and f is continuous at a, then $[f(x)]^{n/m}$ is continuous at a, because

$$\lim_{x\to a} [f(x)]^{n/m} = \left[\lim_{x\to a} f(x)\right]^{n/m} = [f(a)]^{n/m}.$$

When m is even, the continuity of $[f(x)]^{n/m}$ must be handled more carefully because this function is defined only when $f(x) \ge 0$. Exercise 59 of Section 2.7 establishes an important fact:

If f is continuous at a and $f(a) > 0$, then f is positive for all values of x sufficiently close to a.

Combining this fact with Theorem 2.10 (the continuity of composite functions), it follows that $[f(x)]^{n/m}$ is continuous at a provided $f(a) > 0$. At points where $f(a) = 0$, the behavior of $[f(x)]^{n/m}$ varies: $[f(x)]^{n/m}$ may be left- or right-continuous at that point, or it may be continuous from both sides.

THEOREM 2.11 **Continuity of Functions with Roots**
Assume that m and n are positive integers with no common factors.
If m is an odd integer, then $[f(x)]^{n/m}$ is continuous at all points at which f is continuous.
If m is even, then $[f(x)]^{n/m}$ is continuous at all points a at which f is continuous and $f(a) > 0$.

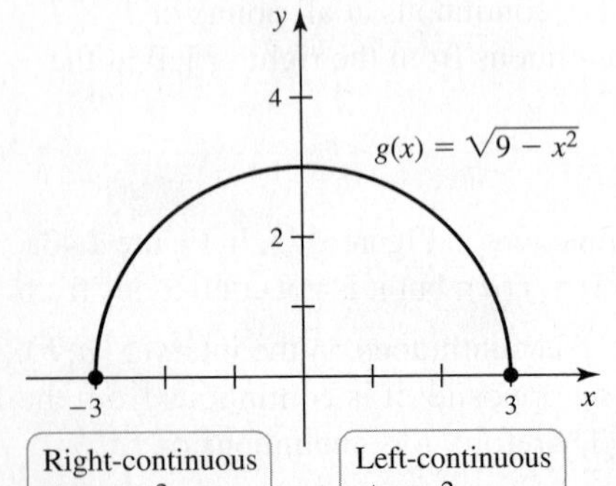

FIGURE 2.45

EXAMPLE 6 **Continuity with roots** For what values of x are the following functions continuous?

a. $g(x) = \sqrt{9 - x^2}$ **b.** $f(x) = (x^2 - 2x + 4)^{2/3}$

SOLUTION

a. The graph of g is the upper half of the circle $x^2 + y^2 = 9$ (which can be verified by solving $x^2 + y^2 = 9$ for y). From Figure 2.45, it appears that g is continuous on

$[-3, 3]$. To verify this fact, note that g involves an even root ($m = 2, n = 1$ in Theorem 2.11). If $-3 < x < 3$, then $9 - x^2 > 0$ and by Theorem 2.11, g is continuous for all x on $(-3, 3)$.

At the right endpoint, $\lim_{x \to 3^-} \sqrt{9 - x^2} = 0 = g(3)$ by Limit Law 7, which implies that g is left-continuous at 3. Similarly, g is right-continuous at -3 because $\lim_{x \to -3^+} \sqrt{9 - x^2} = 0 = g(-3)$. Therefore, g is continuous on $[-3, 3]$.

QUICK CHECK 4 On what interval is $f(x) = x^{1/4}$ continuous? On what interval is $f(x) = x^{2/5}$ continuous?

b. The polynomial $x^2 - 2x + 4$ is continuous for all x by Theorem 2.9a. Because f involves an odd root ($m = 3, n = 2$ in Theorem 2.11), f is continuous for all x.

Related Exercises 35–44

Continuity of Trigonometric Functions

In Example 7 of Section 2.3, we used the Squeeze Theorem to show that $\lim_{x \to 0} \sin x = 0$ and $\lim_{x \to 0} \cos x = 1$. Because $\sin 0 = 0$ and $\cos 0 = 1$, these limits imply that $\sin x$ and $\cos x$ are continuous at 0. The graph of $y = \sin x$ (Figure 2.46) suggests that $\lim_{x \to a} \sin x = \sin a$ for any value of a, which means that $\sin x$ is continuous everywhere. The graph of $y = \cos x$ also indicates that $\cos x$ is continuous for all x. Exercise 89 outlines a proof of these results.

With these facts in hand, we appeal to Theorem 2.8e to discover that the remaining trigonometric functions are continuous on their domains. For example, because $\sec x = 1/\cos x$, the secant function is continuous for all x for which $\cos x \neq 0$ (for all x except odd multiples of $\pi/2$) (Figure 2.47). Likewise, the tangent, cotangent, and cosecant functions are continuous at all points of their domains.

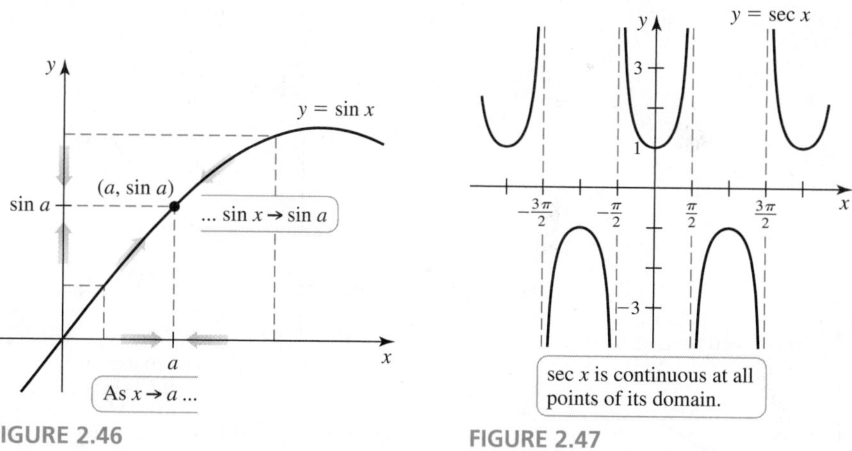

FIGURE 2.46

FIGURE 2.47

> **THEOREM 2.12 Continuity of Trigonometric Functions**
> The functions $\sin x$, $\cos x$, $\tan x$, $\cot x$, $\sec x$, and $\csc x$ are continuous at all points of their domains.

For each function listed in Theorem 2.12, we have $\lim_{x \to a} f(x) = f(a)$, provided a is in the domain of the function. This means that limits involving these functions may be evaluated by direct substitution at points in the domain.

EXAMPLE 7 Limits involving trigonometric functions Evaluate

$$\lim_{x \to 0} \frac{\cos^2 x - 1}{\cos x - 1}.$$

➤ Limits like the one in Example 7 are denoted $0/0$ and are known as *indeterminate forms*, to be studied further in Section 4.7.

SOLUTION Both $\cos^2 x - 1$ and $\cos x - 1$ are continuous for all x by Theorems 2.8 and 2.12. However, the ratio of these functions is not continuous when $\cos x - 1 = 0$, which corresponds to all integer multiples of 2π. Note that both the numerator and denominator of $\dfrac{\cos^2 x - 1}{\cos x - 1}$ approach 0 as $x \to 0$. To evaluate the limit, we factor and simplify:

$$\lim_{x\to 0} \frac{\cos^2 x - 1}{\cos x - 1} = \lim_{x\to 0} \frac{(\cos x - 1)(\cos x + 1)}{\cos x - 1} = \lim_{x\to 0} (\cos x + 1)$$

(where $\cos x - 1$ may be canceled because it is nonzero as x approaches 0). The limit on the right is now evaluated using direct substitution:

$$\lim_{x\to 0} (\cos x + 1) = \cos 0 + 1 = 2$$

Related Exercises 45–48 ◀

The Intermediate Value Theorem

A common problem in mathematics is finding solutions to equations of the form $f(x) = L$. Before attempting to find values of x satisfying this equation, it is worthwhile to determine whether a solution exists.

The existence of solutions is often established using a result known as the **Intermediate Value Theorem**. Given a function f and a constant L, we assume L lies between $f(a)$ and $f(b)$. The Intermediate Value Theorem says that if f is continuous on $[a, b]$, then the graph of $y = f(x)$ must cross the horizontal line $y = L$ at least once (Figure 2.48). Although this theorem is easily illustrated, its proof goes beyond the scope of this text.

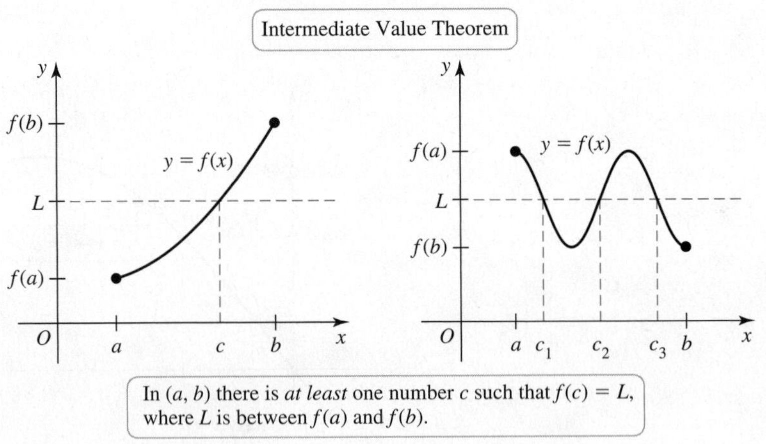
Intermediate Value Theorem
y
f(b)
y = f(x)
L
f(a)
O
a
c
b
x
y
f(a)
y = f(x)
L
f(b)
O
a c1 c2 c3 b
x
In (a, b) there is at least one number c such that f(c) = L, where L is between f(a) and f(b).

FIGURE 2.48

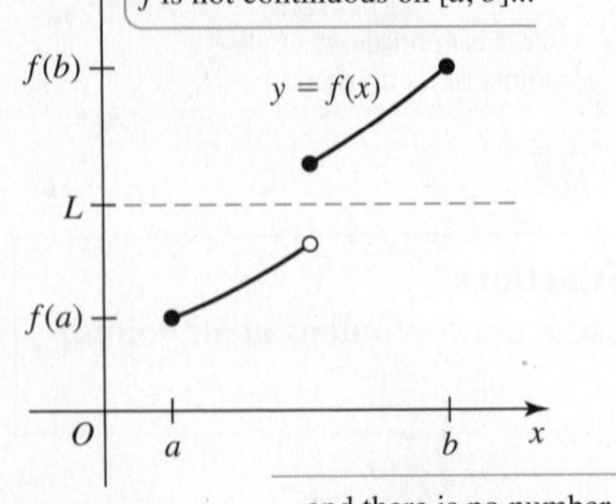
y
f is not continuous on [a, b]...
f(b)
y = f(x)
L
f(a)
O
a
b
x
... and there is no number c in (a, b) such that f(c) = L.

FIGURE 2.49

> **THEOREM 2.13 The Intermediate Value Theorem**
> Suppose f is continuous on the interval $[a, b]$ and L is a number between $f(a)$ and $f(b)$. Then there is at least one number c in (a, b) satisfying $f(c) = L$.

The importance of continuity in Theorem 2.13 is illustrated in Figure 2.49, where we see a function f that is not continuous on $[a, b]$. For the value of L shown in the figure, there is no value of c in (a, b) satisfying $f(c) = L$.

EXAMPLE 8 Finding an interest rate Suppose you invest \$1000 in a special 5-year savings account with a fixed annual interest rate r and with monthly compounding. The amount of money A in the account after 5 years (60 months) is $A(r) = 1000\left(1 + \dfrac{r}{12}\right)^{60}$. Your goal is to have \$1400 in the account after 5 years.

QUICK CHECK 5 Does the equation $f(x) = x^3 + x + 1 = 0$ have a solution on the interval $[-1, 1]$? Explain.

a. Use the Intermediate Value Theorem to show there is a value of r in $(0, 0.08)$—that is, an interest rate between 0% and 8%—for which $A(r) = 1400$.

b. Use a graphing utility to illustrate your explanation in part (a), and then estimate the interest rate required to reach your goal.

SOLUTION

a. As a polynomial in r (of degree 60), $A(r) = 1000\left(1 + \frac{r}{12}\right)^{60}$ is continuous for all r. Evaluating $A(r)$ at the endpoints of the interval $[0, 0.08]$, we have $A(0) = 1000$ and $A(0.08) = 1489.85$. Therefore,

$$A(0) < 1400 < A(0.08)$$

and it follows, by the Intermediate Value Theorem, that there is a value of r in $(0, 0.08)$ for which $A(r) = 1400$.

b. The graphs of $y = A(r)$ and the horizontal line $y = 1400$ are shown in Figure 2.50; it is evident that they intersect between $r = 0$ and $r = 0.08$. Solving $A(r) = 1400$ algebraically or using a root finder reveals that the curve and line intersect at $r \approx 0.0675$. Therefore, an interest rate of approximately 6.75% is required for the investment to be worth \$1400 after 5 years.

Related Exercises 49–54

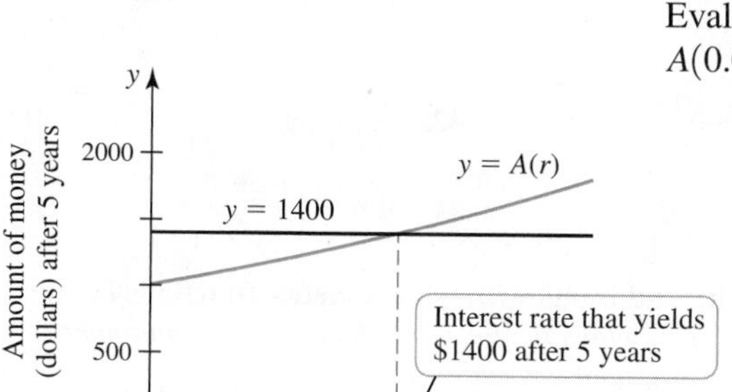

FIGURE 2.50

SECTION 2.6 EXERCISES

Review Questions

1. Which of the following functions are continuous for all values in their domain? Justify your answers.
   a. $a(t)$ = altitude of a skydiver t seconds after jumping from a plane
   b. $n(t)$ = number of quarters needed to park in a metered parking space for t minutes
   c. $T(t)$ = temperature t minutes after midnight in Chicago on January 1
   d. $p(t)$ = number of points scored by a basketball player after t minutes of a basketball game
2. Give the three conditions that must be satisfied by a function to be continuous at a point.
3. What does it mean for a function to be continuous on an interval?
4. We informally described a function f to be continuous at a if its graph contains no holes or breaks at a. Explain why this is not an adequate definition of continuity.
5. Complete the following sentences.
   a. A function is continuous from the left at a if ________.
   b. A function is continuous from the right at a if ________.
6. Describe the points (if any) at which a rational function fails to be continuous.
7. What is the domain of $f(x) = \sqrt{1 - x^2}$ and where is f continuous?
8. Explain in words and pictures what the Intermediate Value Theorem says.

Basic Skills

9–12. Discontinuities from a graph *Determine the points at which the following functions f have discontinuities. For each point state the conditions in the continuity checklist that are violated.*

9.

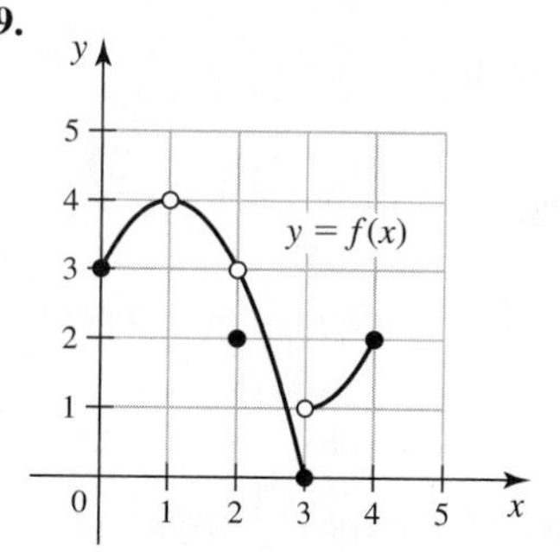

10.

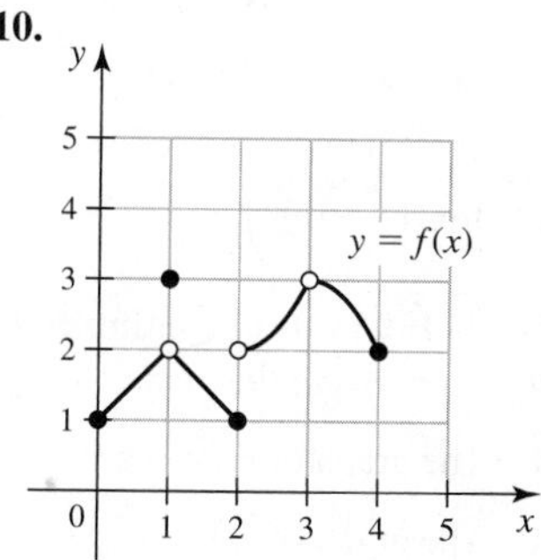

11.

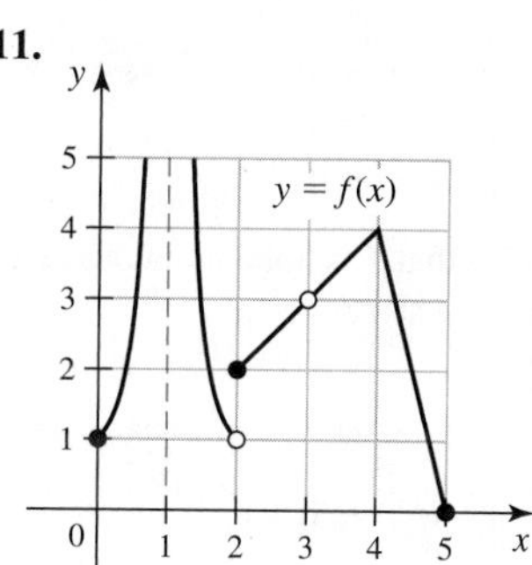

12.

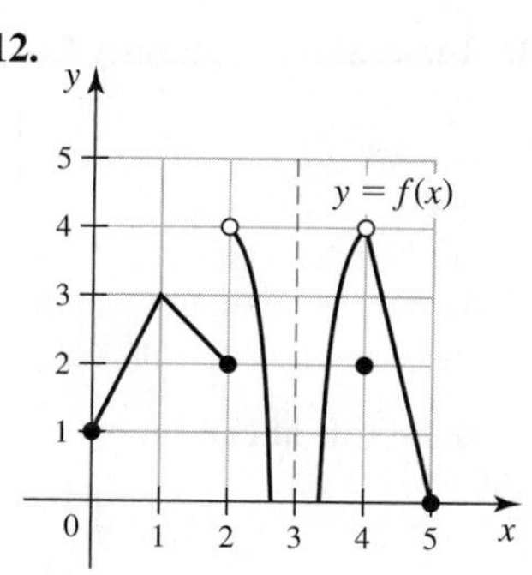

13–18. Continuity at a point *Determine whether the following functions are continuous at a. Use the continuity checklist to justify your answer.*

13. $f(x) = \sqrt{x - 2};\ a = 1$

14. $g(x) = \dfrac{1}{x - 3};\ a = 3$

15. $f(x) = \begin{cases} \dfrac{x^2 - 1}{x - 1} & \text{if } x \neq 1 \\ 3 & \text{if } x = 1 \end{cases};\ a = 1$

16. $f(x) = \begin{cases} \dfrac{x^2 - 4x + 3}{x - 3} & \text{if } x \neq 3 \\ 2 & \text{if } x = 3 \end{cases};\ a = 3$

17. $f(x) = \dfrac{5x - 2}{x^2 - 9x + 20};\ a = 4$

18. $f(x) = \begin{cases} \dfrac{x^2 - x}{x + 1} & \text{if } x \neq -1 \\ 0 & \text{if } x = -1 \end{cases};\ a = -1$

19–24. Continuity on intervals *Use Theorem 2.9 to determine the intervals on which the following functions are continuous.*

19. $p(x) = 4x^5 - 3x^2 + 1$

20. $g(x) = \dfrac{3x^2 - 6x + 7}{x^2 + x + 1}$

21. $f(x) = \dfrac{x^5 + 6x + 17}{x^2 - 9}$

22. $s(x) = \dfrac{x^2 - 4x + 3}{x^2 - 1}$

23. $f(x) = \dfrac{1}{x^2 - 4}$

24. $f(t) = \dfrac{t + 2}{t^2 - 4}$

25–28. Limits of compositions *Evaluate the following limits and justify your answers.*

25. $\lim_{x \to 0} (x^8 - 3x^6 - 1)^{40}$

26. $\lim_{x \to 2} \left(\dfrac{3}{2x^5 - 4x^2 - 50}\right)^4$

27. $\lim_{x \to 1} \left(\dfrac{x + 5}{x + 2}\right)^4$

28. $\lim_{x \to \infty} \left(\dfrac{2x + 1}{x}\right)^3$

29–32. Intervals of continuity *Determine the intervals of continuity for the following functions.*

29. The graph of Exercise 9

30. The graph of Exercise 10

31. The graph of Exercise 11

32. The graph of Exercise 12

33. Intervals of continuity Let

$$f(x) = \begin{cases} x^2 + 3x & \text{if } x \geq 1 \\ 2x & \text{if } x < 1 \end{cases}$$

a. Use the continuity checklist to show that f is not continuous at 1.
b. Is f continuous from the left or right at 1?
c. State the interval(s) of continuity.

34. Intervals of continuity Let

$$f(x) = \begin{cases} x^3 + 4x + 1 & \text{if } x \leq 0 \\ 2x^3 & \text{if } x > 0 \end{cases}$$

a. Use the continuity checklist to show that f is not continuous at 0.
b. Is f continuous from the left or right at 0?
c. State the interval(s) of continuity.

35–40. Functions with roots *Determine the interval(s) on which the following functions are continuous. Be sure to consider right- and left-continuity at the endpoints.*

35. $f(x) = \sqrt{2x^2 - 16}$

36. $g(x) = \sqrt{x^4 - 1}$

37. $f(x) = \sqrt[3]{x^2 - 2x - 3}$

38. $f(t) = (t^2 - 1)^{3/2}$

39. $f(x) = (2x - 3)^{2/3}$

40. $f(z) = (z - 1)^{3/4}$

41–44. Limits with roots *Determine the following limits and justify your answers.*

41. $\lim_{x \to 2} \sqrt{\dfrac{4x + 10}{2x - 2}}$

42. $\lim_{x \to -1} \left(x^2 - 4 + \sqrt[3]{x^2 - 9}\right)$

43. $\lim_{x \to 3} \left(\sqrt{x^2 + 7}\right)$

44. $\lim_{t \to 2} \dfrac{t^2 + 5}{1 + \sqrt{t^2 + 5}}$

45–48. Continuity and limits with trigonometric functions *Determine the interval(s) on which the following functions are continuous; then evaluate the given limits.*

45. $f(x) = \csc x;\quad \lim_{x \to \pi/4} f(x);\quad \lim_{x \to 2\pi^-} f(x)$

46. $f(x) = \sqrt{\sin x};\quad \lim_{x \to \pi/2} f(x);\quad \lim_{x \to 0^+} f(x)$

47. $f(x) = \dfrac{1 + \sin x}{\cos x};\quad \lim_{x \to \pi/2^-} f(x);\quad \lim_{x \to 4\pi/3} f(x)$

48. $f(x) = \dfrac{1}{2\cos x - 1};\quad \lim_{x \to \pi/6} f(x)$

T **49. Intermediate Value Theorem and interest rates** Suppose \$5000 is invested in a savings account for 10 years (120 months), with an annual interest rate of r, compounded monthly. The amount of money in the account after 10 years is $A(r) = 5000(1 + r/12)^{120}$.

a. Use the Intermediate Value Theorem to show there is a value of r in (0, 0.08)—an interest rate between 0% and 8%—that allows you to reach your savings goal of \$7000 in 10 years.
b. Use a graph to illustrate your explanation in part (a); then, approximate the interest rate required to reach your goal.

T **50. Intermediate Value Theorem and mortgage payments** You are shopping for a \$150,000, 30-year (360-month) loan to buy a house. The monthly payment is

$$m(r) = \frac{150{,}000(r/12)}{1 - (1 + r/12)^{-360}},$$

where r is the annual interest rate. Suppose banks are currently offering interest rates between 6% and 8%.

a. Use the Intermediate Value Theorem to show there is a value of r in (0.06, 0.08)—an interest rate between 6% and 8%—that allows you to make monthly payments of \$1000 per month.
b. Use a graph to illustrate your explanation to part (a). Then determine the interest rate you need for monthly payments of \$1000.

T **51–54. Applying the Intermediate Value Theorem**

a. *Use the Intermediate Value Theorem to show that the following equations have a solution on the given interval.*
b. *Use a graphing utility to find all the solutions to the equation on the given interval.*
c. *Illustrate your answers with an appropriate graph.*

51. $2x^3 + x - 2 = 0$; $(-1, 1)$

52. $\sqrt{x^4 + 25x^3 + 10} = 5$; $(0, 1)$

53. $x^3 - 5x^2 + 2x = -1$; $(-1, 5)$

54. $-x^5 - 4x^2 + 2\sqrt{x} + 5 = 0$; $(0, 3)$

Further Explorations

55. **Explain why or why not** Determine whether the following statements are true and give an explanation or counterexample.

a. If a function is left-continuous and right-continuous at a, then it is continuous at a.

b. If a function is continuous at a, then it is left-continuous and right-continuous at a.

c. If $a < b$ and $f(a) \leq L \leq f(b)$, then there is some value of c between a and b for which $f(c) = L$.

d. Suppose f is continuous on $[a, b]$. Then there is a point c in (a, b) such that $f(c) = (f(a) + f(b))/2$.

56. **Continuity of the absolute value function** Prove that the absolute value function $|x|$ is continuous for all values of x. (*Hint:* Using the definition of the absolute value function, compute $\lim_{x \to 0^-} |x|$ and $\lim_{x \to 0^+} |x|$.)

57–60. Continuity of functions with absolute values *Use the continuity of the absolute value function (Exercise 56) to determine the interval(s) on which the following functions are continuous.*

57. $f(x) = |x^2 + 3x - 18|$

58. $g(x) = \left|\dfrac{x + 4}{x^2 - 4}\right|$

59. $h(x) = \left|\dfrac{1}{\sqrt{x} - 4}\right|$

60. $h(x) = |x^2 + 2x + 5| + \sqrt{x}$

61–70. Miscellaneous limits *Evaluate the following limits.*

61. $\lim_{x \to \pi} \dfrac{\cos^2 x + 3\cos x + 2}{\cos x + 1}$

62. $\lim_{x \to 5\pi/2} \dfrac{\sin^2 x + 6\sin x + 5}{\sin^2 x - 1}$

63. $\lim_{x \to \pi/2} \dfrac{\sin x - 1}{\sqrt{\sin x} - 1}$

64. $\lim_{\theta \to 0} \dfrac{\dfrac{1}{2 + \sin\theta} - \dfrac{1}{2}}{\sin\theta}$

65. $\lim_{x \to 0} \dfrac{\cos x - 1}{\sin^2 x}$

66. $\lim_{x \to 0^+} \cot x$

67. **Pitfalls using technology** The graph of the *sawtooth function* $y = x - \lfloor x \rfloor$, where $\lfloor x \rfloor$ is the greatest integer function or floor function (Exercise 31, Section 2.2), was obtained using a graphing utility (see figure). Identify any inaccuracies appearing in the graph and then plot an accurate graph by hand.

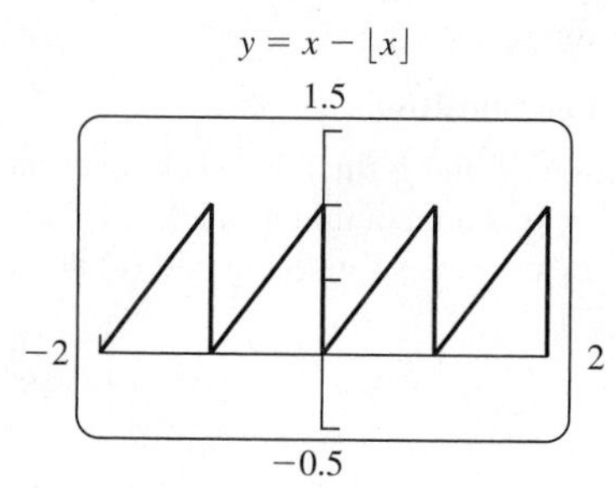

T 68. **Pitfalls using technology** Graph the function $f(x) = \dfrac{\sin x}{x}$ using a graphing window of $[-\pi, \pi] \times [0, 2]$.

a. Sketch a copy of the graph obtained with your graphing device and describe any inaccuracies appearing in the graph.

b. Sketch an accurate graph of the function. Is f continuous at 0?

69. **Sketching functions**

a. Sketch the graph of a function that is not continuous at 1, but is defined at 1.

b. Sketch the graph of a function that is not continuous at 1, but has a limit at 1.

70. **An unknown constant** Determine the value of the constant a for which the function

$$f(x) = \begin{cases} \dfrac{x^2 + 3x + 2}{x + 1} & \text{if } x \neq -1 \\ a & \text{if } x = -1 \end{cases}$$

is continuous at -1.

71. **An unknown constant** Let

$$g(x) = \begin{cases} x^2 + x & \text{if } x < 1 \\ a & \text{if } x = 1 \\ 3x + 5 & \text{if } x > 1 \end{cases}$$

a. Determine the value of a for which g is continuous from the left at 1.

b. Determine the value of a for which g is continuous from the right at 1.

c. Is there a value of a for which g is continuous at 1? Explain.

T **72–73. Applying the Intermediate Value Theorem** *Use the Intermediate Value Theorem to verify that the following equations have three solutions on the given interval. Use a graphing utility to find the approximate roots.*

72. $x^3 + 10x^2 - 100x + 50 = 0$; $(-20, 10)$

73. $70x^3 - 87x^2 + 32x - 3 = 0$; $(0, 1)$

Applications

74. **Parking costs** Determine the intervals of continuity for the parking cost function c introduced at the outset of this section (see figure). Consider $0 \leq t \leq 60$.

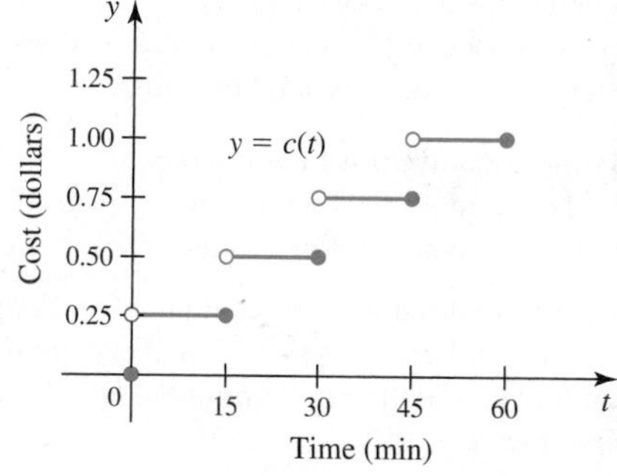

75. **Investment problem** Assume you invest \$250 at the end of each year for 10 years at an annual interest rate of r. The amount of money in your account after 10 years is $A = \frac{250[(1 + r)^{10} - 1]}{r}$. Assume your goal is to have \$3500 in your account after 10 years.
   a. Use the Intermediate Value Theorem to show that there is an interest rate r in the interval (0.01, 0.10)—between 1% and 10%—that allows you to reach your financial goal.
   b. Use a calculator to estimate the interest rate required to reach your financial goal.

76. **Applying the Intermediate Value Theorem** Suppose you park your car at a trailhead in a national park and begin a 2-hr hike to a lake at 7 A.M. on a Friday morning. On Sunday morning, you leave the lake at 7 A.M. and start the 2-hr hike back to your car. Assume the lake is 3 mi from your car. Let $f(t)$ be your distance from the car t hours after 7 A.M. on Friday morning and let $g(t)$ be your distance from the car t hours after 7 A.M. on Sunday morning.
   a. Evaluate $f(0)$, $f(2)$, $g(0)$, and $g(2)$.
   b. Let $h(t) = f(t) - g(t)$. Find $h(0)$ and $h(2)$.
   c. Use the Intermediate Value Theorem to show that there is some point along the trail that you will pass at exactly the same time of morning on both days.

77. **The monk and the mountain** A monk set out from a monastery in the valley at dawn. He walked all day up a winding path, stopping for lunch and taking a nap along the way. At dusk, he arrived at a temple on the mountaintop. The next day, the monk made the return walk to the valley, leaving the temple at dawn, walking the same path for the entire day, and arriving at the monastery in the evening. Must there be one point along the path that the monk occupied at the same time of day on both the ascent and descent? (*Hint:* The question can be answered without the Intermediate Value Theorem.) (*Source:* Arthur Koestler, *The Act of Creation.*)

Additional Exercises

78. **Does continuity of $|f|$ imply continuity of f?** Let
$$g(x) = \begin{cases} 1 & \text{if } x \ge 0 \\ -1 & \text{if } x < 0 \end{cases}$$
   a. Write a formula for $|g(x)|$.
   b. Is g continuous at $x = 0$? Explain.
   c. Is $|g|$ continuous at $x = 0$? Explain.
   d. For any function f, if $|f|$ is continuous at a, does it necessarily follow that f is continuous at a? Explain.

79–80. Classifying discontinuities *The discontinuities in graphs (a) and (b) are* removable discontinuities *because they disappear if we define or redefine f at a so that $f(a) = \lim_{x \to a} f(x)$. The function in graph (c) has a* jump discontinuity *because left and right limits exist at a but are unequal. The discontinuity in graph (d) is an* infinite discontinuity *because the function has a vertical asymptote at a.*

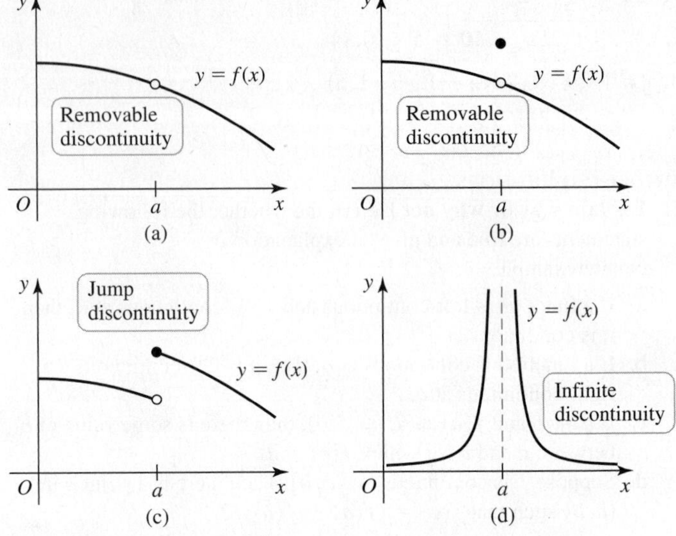

79. Is the discontinuity at a in graph (c) removable? Explain.

80. Is the discontinuity at a in graph (d) removable? Explain.

81–82. Removable discontinuities *Show that the following functions have a removable discontinuity at the given point.*

81. $f(x) = \frac{x^2 - 7x + 10}{x - 2}$; $x = 2$

82. $g(x) = \begin{cases} \frac{x^2 - 1}{1 - x} & \text{if } x \ne 1 \\ 3 & \text{if } x = 1 \end{cases}$; $x = 1$

83. **Do removable discontinuities exist?**
   a. Does the function $f(x) = x \sin(1/x)$ have a removable discontinuity at $x = 0$?
   b. Does the function $g(x) = \sin(1/x)$ have a removable discontinuity at $x = 0$?

T **84–85. Classifying discontinuities** *Classify the discontinuities in the following functions at the given points.*

84. $f(x) = \frac{|x - 2|}{x - 2}$; $x = 2$

85. $h(x) = \frac{x^3 - 4x^2 + 4x}{x(x - 1)}$; $x = 0$ and $x = 1$

86. **Continuity of composite functions** Prove Theorem 2.10: If g is continuous at a and f is continuous at $g(a)$, then the composition $f \circ g$ is continuous at a. (*Hint:* Write the definition of continuity for f and g separately; then, combine them to form the definition of continuity for $f \circ g$.)

87. **Continuity of compositions**
   a. Find functions f and g such that each function is continuous at 0, but $f \circ g$ is not continuous at 0.
   b. Explain why examples satisfying part (a) do not contradict Theorem 2.10.

88. Violation of the Intermediate Value Theorem? Let $f(x) = \frac{|x|}{x}$. Then $f(-2) = -1$ and $f(2) = 1$. Therefore, $f(-2) < 0 < f(2)$, but there is no value of c between -2 and 2 for which $f(c) = 0$. Does this fact violate the Intermediate Value Theorem? Explain.

89. Continuity of $\sin x$ and $\cos x$

a. Use the identity $\sin(a + h) = \sin a \cos h + \cos a \sin h$ with the fact that $\lim_{x\to 0} \sin x = 0$ to prove that $\lim_{x\to a} \sin x = \sin a$, thereby establishing that $\sin x$ is continuous for all x. (*Hint:* Let $h = x - a$ so that $x = a + h$ and note that $h \to 0$ as $x \to a$.)

b. Use the identity $\cos(a + h) = \cos a \cos h - \sin a \sin h$ with the fact that $\lim_{x\to 0} \cos x = 1$ to prove that $\lim_{x\to a} \cos x = \cos a$.

QUICK CHECK ANSWERS

1. $t = 15, 30, 45$ **2.** Both expressions have a value of 5, showing that $\lim_{x\to a} f(g(x)) = f\left(\lim_{x\to a} g(x)\right)$. **3.** Fill in the endpoints. **4.** $[0, \infty); (-\infty, \infty)$ **5.** The equation has a solution on the interval $[-1, 1]$ because f is continuous on $[-1, 1]$ and $f(-1) < 0 < f(1)$. ◄

2.7 Precise Definitions of Limits

The limit definitions already encountered in this chapter are adequate for most elementary limits. However some of the terminology used, such as *sufficiently close* and *arbitrarily large*, needs clarification. The goal of this section is to give limits a solid mathematical foundation by transforming the previous limit definitions into precise mathematical statements.

Moving Toward a Precise Definition

Assume the function f is defined for all x near a, except possibly at a. Recall that $\lim_{x\to a} f(x) = L$ means that $f(x)$ is arbitrarily close to L for all x sufficiently close (but not equal) to a. This limit definition is made precise by observing that the distance between $f(x)$ and L is $|f(x) - L|$ and that the distance between x and a is $|x - a|$. Therefore, we write $\lim_{x\to a} f(x) = L$ if we can make $|f(x) - L|$ arbitrarily small for any x, distinct from a, with $|x - a|$ sufficiently small. For instance, if we want $|f(x) - L|$ to be less than 0.1, then we must find a number $\delta > 0$ such that

$$|f(x) - L| < 0.1 \quad \text{whenever} \quad |x - a| < \delta \quad \text{and} \quad x \neq a.$$

➤ The phrase *for all x near a* means for all x in an open interval containing a.

➤ The two conditions $|x - a| < \delta$ and $x \neq a$ are written concisely as $0 < |x - a| < \delta$.

If, instead, we want $|f(x) - L|$ to be less than 0.001, then we must find *another* number $\delta > 0$ such that

$$|f(x) - L| < 0.001 \quad \text{whenever} \quad 0 < |x - a| < \delta.$$

➤ The Greek letters δ (delta) and ε (epsilon) represent small positive numbers when discussing limits.

For the limit to exist, it must be true that for *any* $\varepsilon > 0$, we can always find a $\delta > 0$ such that

$$|f(x) - L| < \varepsilon \quad \text{whenever} \quad 0 < |x - a| < \delta.$$

EXAMPLE 1 Determining values of δ from a graph Figure 2.51 shows the graph of a linear function f with $\lim_{x\to 3} f(x) = 5$. For each value of $\varepsilon > 0$, determine a value of $\delta > 0$ satisfying the statement

$$|f(x) - 5| < \varepsilon \quad \text{whenever} \quad 0 < |x - 3| < \delta.$$

a. $\varepsilon = 1$ **b.** $\varepsilon = \frac{1}{2}$

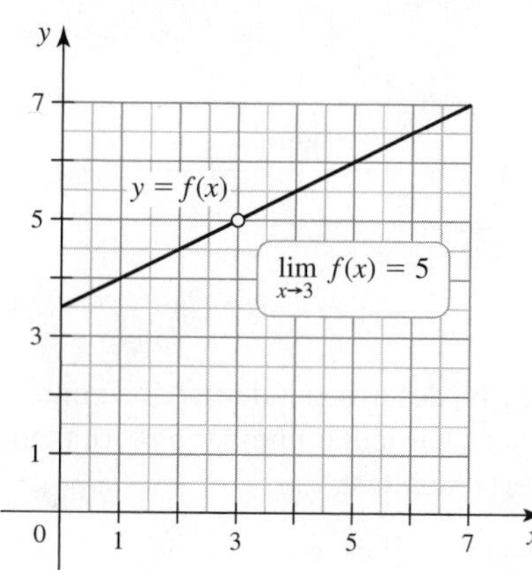

FIGURE 2.51

➤ The founders of calculus, Isaac Newton (1642–1727) and Gottfried Leibniz (1646–1716), developed the core ideas of calculus without using a precise definition of a limit. It was not until the 19th century that a rigorous definition was introduced by Louis Cauchy (1789–1857) and later refined by Karl Weierstrass (1815–1897).

SOLUTION

a. With $\varepsilon = 1$, we want $f(x)$ to be less than 1 unit from 5, which means $f(x)$ is between 4 and 6. To determine a corresponding value of δ, draw the horizontal lines $y = 4$ and $y = 6$ (Figure 2.52a). Then sketch vertical lines passing through the points where the horizontal lines and the graph of f intersect (Figure 2.52b). We see that the vertical lines intersect the x-axis at $x = 1$ and $x = 5$. Note that $f(x)$ is less than 1 unit from 5 on the y-axis if x is within 2 units of 3 on the x-axis. So, for $\varepsilon = 1$, we let $\delta = 2$ or any smaller positive value.

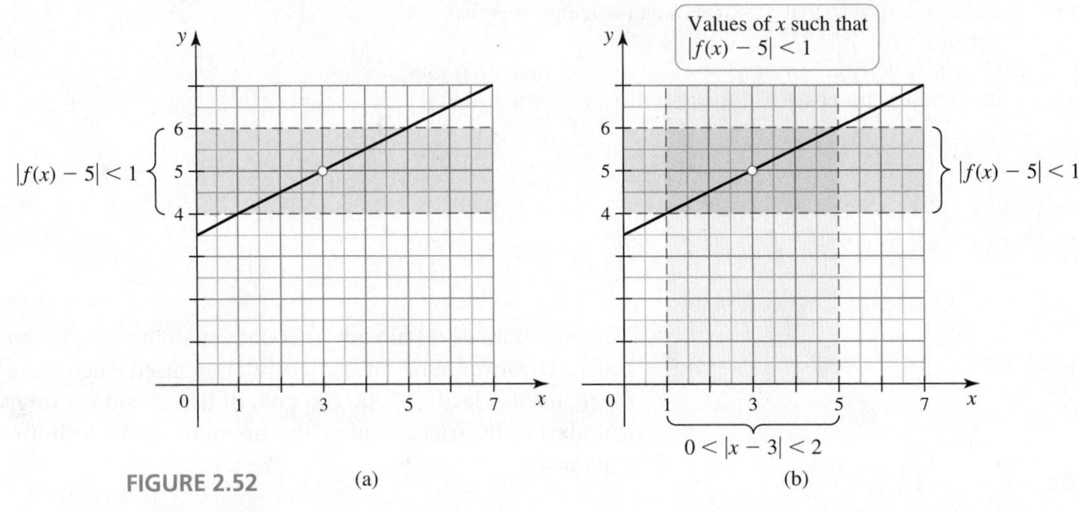

FIGURE 2.52

➤ Once an acceptable value of δ is found satisfying the statement

$$|f(x) - L| < \varepsilon \quad \text{whenever} \quad 0 < |x - a| < \delta,$$

any smaller positive value of δ also works.

b. With $\varepsilon = \frac{1}{2}$, we want $f(x)$ to lie within a half-unit of 5 or, equivalently, $f(x)$ must lie between 4.5 and 5.5. Proceeding as in part (a), we see that $f(x)$ is within a half-unit of 5 on the y-axis if x is less than 1 unit from 3 (Figure 2.53). So for $\varepsilon = \frac{1}{2}$, we let $\delta = 1$ or any smaller positive number.

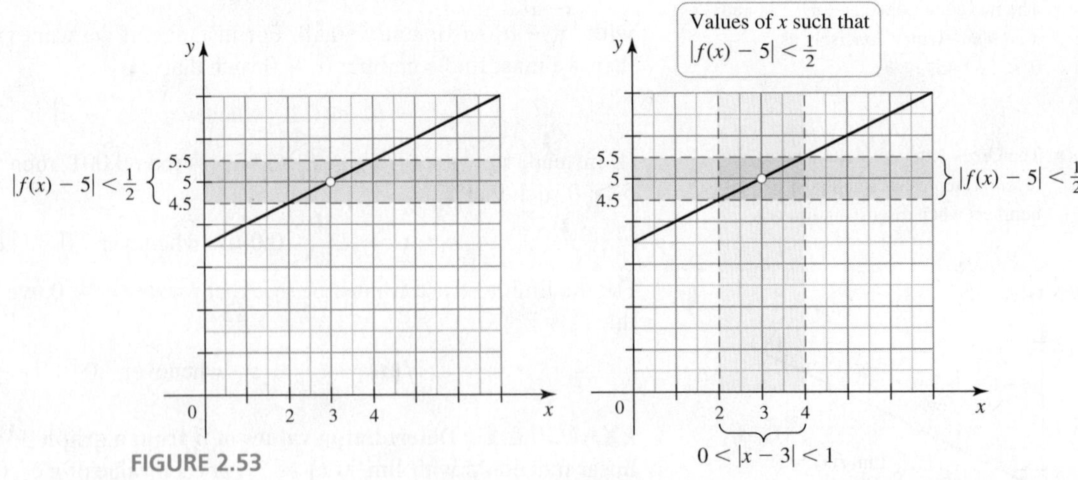

FIGURE 2.53

Related Exercises 9–12 ◀

The idea of a limit, as illustrated in Example 1, may be described in terms of a contest between two people named Epp and Del. First, Epp picks a particular number $\varepsilon > 0$; then, he challenges Del to find a corresponding value of $\delta > 0$ such that

$$|f(x) - 5| < \varepsilon \quad \text{whenever} \quad 0 < |x - 3| < \delta. \tag{1}$$

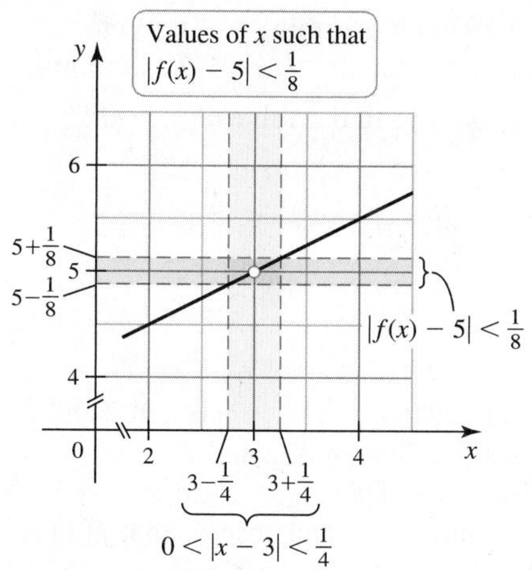

FIGURE 2.54

To illustrate, suppose Epp chooses $\varepsilon = 1$. From Example 1, we know that Del will satisfy (1) by choosing $0 < \delta \leq 2$. If Epp chooses $\varepsilon = \frac{1}{2}$, then (by Example 1) Del responds by letting $0 < \delta \leq 1$. If Epp lets $\varepsilon = \frac{1}{8}$, then Del chooses $0 < \delta \leq \frac{1}{4}$ (Figure 2.54). In fact, there is a pattern: For *any* $\varepsilon > 0$ that Epp chooses, no matter how small, Del will satisfy (1) by choosing a positive value of δ satisfying $0 < \delta \leq 2\varepsilon$. Del has discovered a mathematical relationship: If $0 < \delta \leq 2\varepsilon$ and $0 < |x - 3| < \delta$, then $|f(x) - 5| < \varepsilon$ for *any* $\varepsilon > 0$. This conversation illustrates the general procedure for proving that $\lim_{x \to a} f(x) = L$.

QUICK CHECK 1 In Example 1, find a positive number δ satisfying the statement

$$|f(x) - 5| < \frac{1}{100} \quad \text{whenever} \quad 0 < |x - 3| < \delta.$$

A Precise Definition

Example 1 dealt with a linear function, but it points the way to a precise definition of a limit for any function. As shown in Figure 2.55, $\lim_{x \to a} f(x) = L$ means that for *any* positive number ε, there is another positive number δ such that

$$|f(x) - L| < \varepsilon \quad \text{whenever} \quad 0 < |x - a| < \delta.$$

In all limit proofs, the goal is to find a relationship between ε and δ that gives an admissible value of δ, in terms of ε only. This relationship must work for any positive value of ε.

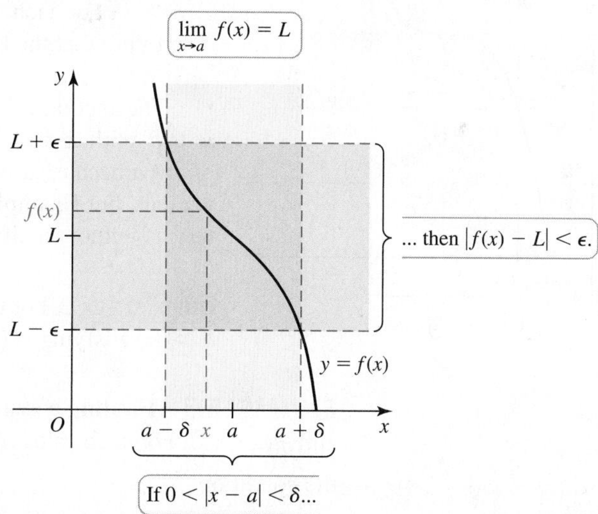

FIGURE 2.55

> The value of δ in the precise definition of a limit depends only on ε.

> Definitions of the one-sided limits $\lim_{x \to a^+} f(x) = L$ and $\lim_{x \to a^-} f(x) = L$ are discussed in Exercises 39–43.

DEFINITION Limit of a Function

Assume that $f(x)$ exists for all x in some open interval containing a, except possibly at a. We say that the **limit of $f(x)$ as x approaches a is L**, written

$$\lim_{x \to a} f(x) = L,$$

if for *any* number $\varepsilon > 0$ there is a corresponding number $\delta > 0$ such that

$$|f(x) - L| < \varepsilon \quad \text{whenever} \quad 0 < |x - a| < \delta.$$

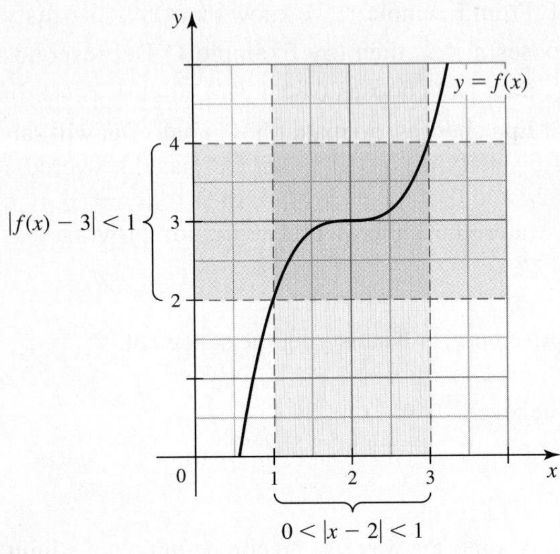

FIGURE 2.56

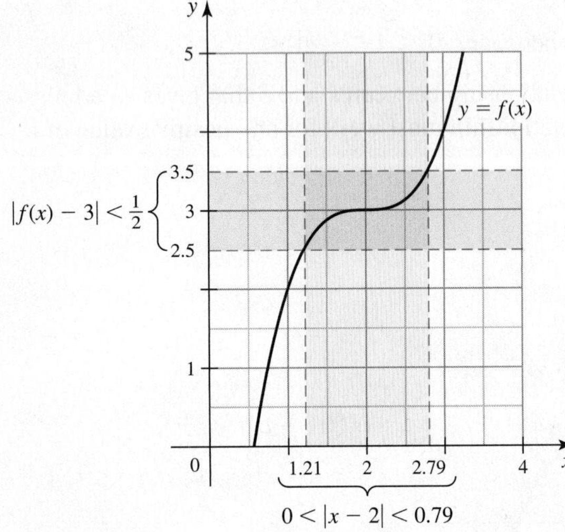

FIGURE 2.57

EXAMPLE 2 Finding δ for a given ε using a graphing utility Let $f(x) = x^3 - 6x^2 + 12x - 5$ and demonstrate that $\lim_{x\to 2} f(x) = 3$ as follows. For the given values of ε, use a graphing utility to find a value of $\delta > 0$ such that

$$|f(x) - 3| < \varepsilon \quad \text{whenever} \quad 0 < |x - 2| < \delta.$$

a. $\varepsilon = 1$ **b.** $\varepsilon = \frac{1}{2}$

SOLUTION

a. The condition $|f(x) - 3| < \varepsilon = 1$ implies that $f(x)$ lies between 2 and 4. Using a graphing utility, we graph f and the lines $y = 2$ and $y = 4$ (Figure 2.56). These lines intersect the graph of f at $x = 1$ and at $x = 3$. We now sketch the vertical lines $x = 1$ and $x = 3$ and observe that $f(x)$ is within 1 unit of 3 whenever x is within 1 unit of 2 on the x-axis (Figure 2.56). Therefore, with $\varepsilon = 1$, we choose δ such that $0 < \delta \le 1$.

b. The condition $|f(x) - 3| < \varepsilon = \frac{1}{2}$ implies that $f(x)$ lies between 2.5 and 3.5 on the y-axis. We now find that the lines $y = 2.5$ and $y = 3.5$ intersect the graph of f at $x \approx 1.21$ and $x \approx 2.79$ (Figure 2.57). Observe that if x is less than 0.79 units from 2 on the x-axis, then $f(x)$ is less than a half-unit from 3 on the y-axis. Therefore with $\varepsilon = \frac{1}{2}$ we let $0 < \delta \le 0.79$.

This procedure could be repeated for smaller and smaller values of $\varepsilon > 0$. For each value of ε, there exists a corresponding value of δ, proving that the limit exists. *Related Exercises 13–14* ◀

The inequality $0 < |x - a| < \delta$ means that x lies between $a - \delta$ and $a + \delta$ with $x \ne a$. We say that the interval $(a - \delta, a + \delta)$ is **symmetric about *a*** because a is the midpoint of the interval. Symmetric intervals are convenient, but Example 3 demonstrates that we don't always get symmetric intervals without a bit of extra work.

QUICK CHECK 2 For the function f given in Example 2, estimate a value of $\delta > 0$ satisfying $|f(x) - 3| < 0.25$ whenever $0 < |x - 2| < \delta$. ◀

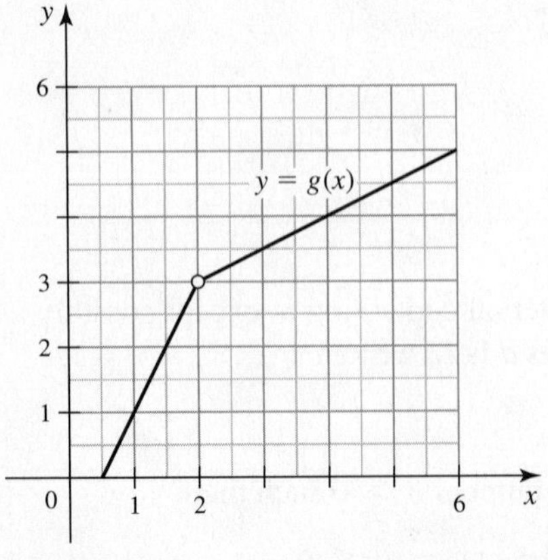

FIGURE 2.58

EXAMPLE 3 Finding a symmetric interval Figure 2.58 shows the graph of g with $\lim_{x\to 2} g(x) = 3$. For each value of ε, find the corresponding values of $\delta > 0$ that satisfy the condition

$$|g(x) - 3| < \varepsilon \quad \text{whenever} \quad 0 < |x - 2| < \delta.$$

a. $\varepsilon = 2$ **b.** $\varepsilon = 1$

c. For any $\varepsilon > 0$, make a conjecture about the corresponding values of δ that satisfy the limit condition.

SOLUTION

a. With $\varepsilon = 2$, we need a value of $\delta > 0$ such that $g(x)$ is within 2 units of 3, which means between 1 and 5, whenever x is less than δ units from 2. The horizontal lines $y = 1$ and $y = 5$ intersect the graph of g at $x = 1$ and $x = 6$. Therefore, $|g(x) - 3| < 2$ if x lies in the interval $(1, 6)$ with $x \ne 2$ (Figure 2.59a). However, we want x to lie in an interval that is *symmetric* about 2. We can guarantee that $|g(x) - 3| < 2$ only if x is less than 1 unit away from 2, on either side of 2 (Figure 2.59b). Therefore, with $\varepsilon = 2$ we take $\delta = 1$ or any smaller positive number.

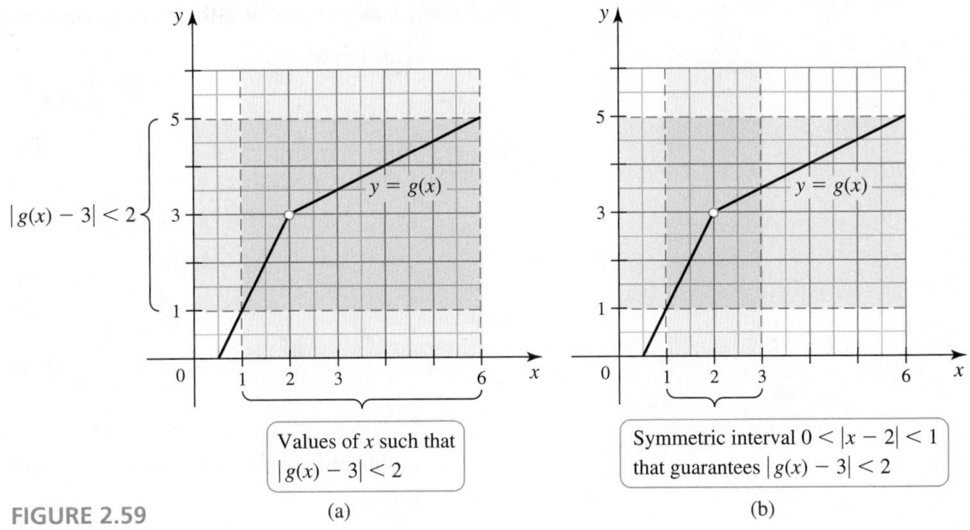

FIGURE 2.59 (a) (b)

b. With $\varepsilon = 1$, $g(x)$ must lie between 2 and 4 (Figure 2.60a). This implies that x must be within a half-unit to the left of 2 and within 2 units to the right of 2. Therefore, $|g(x) - 3| < 1$ provided x lies in the interval $(1.5, 4)$. To obtain a symmetric interval about 2, we take $\delta = \frac{1}{2}$ or any smaller positive number. Then we are guaranteed that $|g(x) - 3| < 1$ when $0 < |x - 2| < \frac{1}{2}$ (Figure 2.60b).

c. From parts (a) and (b), it appears that if we choose $\delta \le \varepsilon/2$, the limit condition is satisfied for any $\varepsilon > 0$.

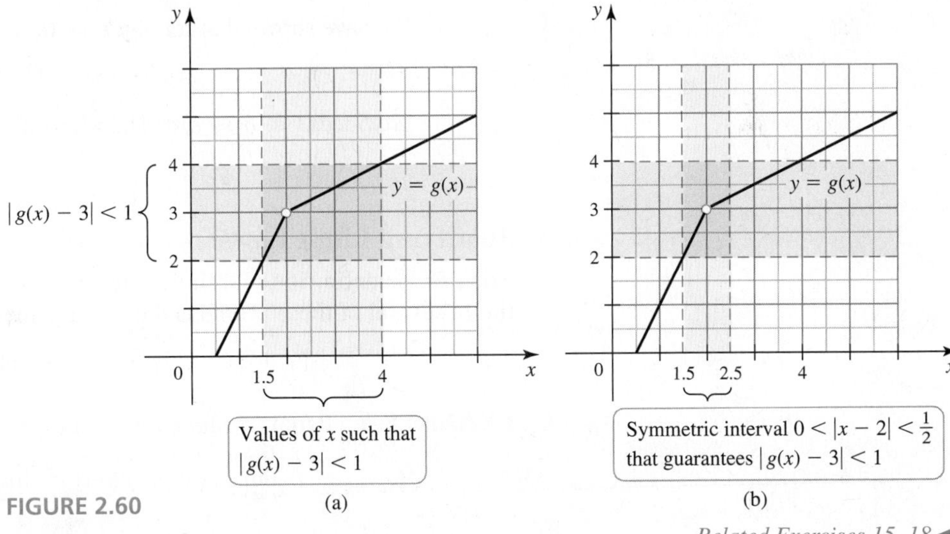

FIGURE 2.60 (a) (b)

Related Exercises 15–18 ◀

Limit Proofs

We use the following two-step process to prove that $\lim_{x \to a} f(x) = L$.

> The first step of the limit-proving process is the preliminary work of finding a candidate for δ. The second step verifies that the δ found in the first step actually works.

Steps for proving that $\lim_{x \to a} f(x) = L$

1. **Find δ.** Let ε be an arbitrary positive number. Use the inequality $|f(x) - L| < \varepsilon$ to find a condition of the form $|x - a| < \delta$, where δ depends only on the value of ε.

2. **Write a proof.** For any $\varepsilon > 0$, assume $0 < |x - a| < \delta$ and use the relationship between ε and δ found in Step 1 to prove that $|f(x) - L| < \varepsilon$.

EXAMPLE 4 **Limit of a linear function** Prove that $\lim_{x\to 4} (4x - 15) = 1$ using the precise definition of a limit.

SOLUTION

Step 1: *Find* δ. In this case, $a = 4$ and $L = 1$. Assuming $\varepsilon > 0$ is given, we use $|f(x) - L| = |(4x - 15) - 1| < \varepsilon$ to find an inequality of the form $|x - 4| < \delta$. If $|(4x - 15) - 1| < \varepsilon$, then

$$|4x - 16| < \varepsilon$$

$$4|x - 4| < \varepsilon \quad \text{Factor } 4x - 16.$$

$$|x - 4| < \frac{\varepsilon}{4}. \quad \text{Divide by 4 and identify } \delta = \varepsilon/4.$$

We have shown that $|(4x - 15) - 1| < \varepsilon$ implies $|x - 4| < \varepsilon/4$. Therefore, a plausible relationship between δ and ε is $\delta = \varepsilon/4$. We now write the actual proof.

Step 2: *Write a proof.* Let $\varepsilon > 0$ be given and assume $0 < |x - 4| < \delta$ where $\delta = \varepsilon/4$. The aim is to show that $|(4x - 15) - 1| < \varepsilon$ for all x such that $0 < |x - 4| < \delta$. We simplify $|(4x - 15) - 1|$ and isolate the $|x - 4|$ term:

$$|(4x - 15) - 1| = |4x - 16| = 4\underbrace{|x - 4|}_{\text{less than } \delta = \varepsilon/4} < 4\left(\frac{\varepsilon}{4}\right) = \varepsilon$$

We have shown that for any $\varepsilon > 0$,

$$|f(x) - L| = |(4x - 15) - 1| < \varepsilon \quad \text{whenever} \quad 0 < |x - 4| < \delta,$$

provided $0 < \delta \le \varepsilon/4$. Therefore, $\lim_{x\to 4} (4x - 15) = 1$.

Related Exercises 19–24 ◀

Justifying Limit Laws

The precise definition of a limit is used to prove the limit laws in Theorem 2.3. Essential in several of these proofs is the triangle inequality, which states that

$$|x + y| \le |x| + |y| \quad \text{for all real numbers } x \text{ and } y.$$

EXAMPLE 5 **Proof of Limit Law 1** Prove that if $\lim_{x\to a} f(x)$ and $\lim_{x\to a} g(x)$ exist, then

$$\lim_{x\to a} [f(x) + g(x)] = \lim_{x\to a} f(x) + \lim_{x\to a} g(x).$$

SOLUTION Assume that $\varepsilon > 0$ is given. Let $\lim_{x\to a} f(x) = L$, which implies that there exists a $\delta_1 > 0$ such that

$$|f(x) - L| < \frac{\varepsilon}{2} \quad \text{whenever} \quad 0 < |x - a| < \delta_1.$$

Similarly, let $\lim_{x\to a} g(x) = M$, which implies there exists a $\delta_2 > 0$ such that

$$|g(x) - M| < \frac{\varepsilon}{2} \quad \text{whenever} \quad 0 < |x - a| < \delta_2.$$

> The minimum value of a and b is denoted $\min\{a, b\}$. If $x = \min\{a, b\}$, then x is the smaller of a and b. If $a = b$, then x equals the common value of a and b. In either case, $x \le a$ and $x \le b$.

Let $\delta = \min\{\delta_1, \delta_2\}$ and suppose $0 < |x - a| < \delta$. Because $\delta \le \delta_1$, it follows that $0 < |x - a| < \delta_1$ and $|f(x) - L| < \varepsilon/2$. Similarly, because $\delta \le \delta_2$, it follows that $0 < |x - a| < \delta_2$ and $|g(x) - M| < \varepsilon/2$. Therefore,

$$\begin{aligned} |[f(x) + g(x)] - (L + M)| &= |(f(x) - L) + (g(x) - M)| && \text{Rearrange terms.} \\ &\le |f(x) - L| + |g(x) - M| && \text{Triangle inequality} \\ &< \frac{\varepsilon}{2} + \frac{\varepsilon}{2} = \varepsilon. \end{aligned}$$

> Proofs of other limit laws are outlined in Exercises 25–26.

We have shown that given any $\varepsilon > 0$, if $0 < |x - a| < \delta$ then $|[f(x) + g(x)] - (L + M)| < \varepsilon$, which implies that

$$\lim_{x\to a} [f(x) + g(x)] = L + M = \lim_{x\to a} f(x) + \lim_{x\to a} g(x).$$

Related Exercises 25–28◀

Infinite Limits

> Notice that for infinite limits, N plays the role that ε plays for ordinary limits. It sets a tolerance or bound for the function values $f(x)$.

In Section 2.4, we stated that $\lim_{x\to a} f(x) = \infty$ if $f(x)$ grows *arbitrarily large* as x approaches a. More precisely, this means that for any positive number N (no matter how large), $f(x)$ is larger than N if x is sufficiently close to a but not equal to a.

DEFINITION Two-Sided Infinite Limit

The **infinite limit** $\lim_{x\to a} f(x) = \infty$ means that for any positive number N there exists a corresponding $\delta > 0$ such that

$$f(x) > N \quad \text{whenever} \quad 0 < |x - a| < \delta.$$

As shown in Figure 2.61, to prove that $\lim_{x\to a} f(x) = \infty$, we let N represent *any* positive number. Then we find a value of $\delta > 0$, depending only on N, such that

$$f(x) > N \quad \text{whenever} \quad 0 < |x - a| < \delta.$$

This process is similar to the two-step process for finite limits.

> Precise definitions for $\lim_{x\to a} f(x) = -\infty$, $\lim_{x\to a^+} f(x) = -\infty$, $\lim_{x\to a^+} f(x) = \infty$, $\lim_{x\to a^-} f(x) = -\infty$, and $\lim_{x\to a^-} f(x) = \infty$ are discussed in Exercises 45–49.

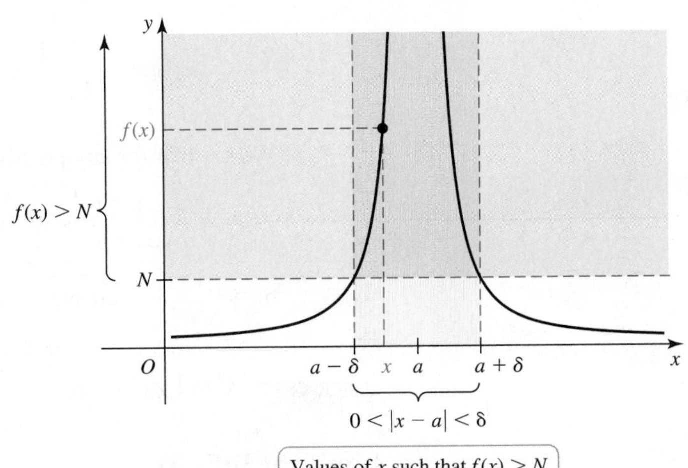

FIGURE 2.61

Steps for proving that $\lim_{x \to a} f(x) = \infty$

1. **Find δ.** Let N be an arbitrary positive number. Use the statement $f(x) > N$ to find an inequality of the form $|x - a| < \delta$, where δ depends only on N.
2. **Write a proof.** For any $N > 0$, assume $0 < |x - a| < \delta$ and use the relationship between N and δ found in Step 1 to prove that $f(x) > N$.

EXAMPLE 6 **An Infinite Limit Proof** Let $f(x) = \dfrac{1}{(x-2)^2}$. Prove that $\lim_{x \to 2} f(x) = \infty$.

SOLUTION

Step 1: *Find $\delta > 0$.* Assuming $N > 0$, we use the inequality $\dfrac{1}{(x-2)^2} > N$ to find δ, where δ depends only on N. Taking reciprocals of this inequality, it follows that

$$(x-2)^2 < \frac{1}{N}$$

$$|x - 2| < \frac{1}{\sqrt{N}}. \quad \text{Take the square root of both sides.}$$

➤ Recall that $\sqrt{x^2} = |x|$.

The inequality $|x - 2| < \dfrac{1}{\sqrt{N}}$ has the form $|x - 2| < \delta$ if we let $\delta = \dfrac{1}{\sqrt{N}}$. We now write a proof based on this relationship between δ and N.

Step 2: *Write a proof.* Suppose $N > 0$ is given. Let $\delta = \dfrac{1}{\sqrt{N}}$ and assume $0 < |x - 2| < \delta = \dfrac{1}{\sqrt{N}}$. Squaring both sides of the inequality $|x - 2| < \dfrac{1}{\sqrt{N}}$ and taking reciprocals, we have

$$(x-2)^2 < \frac{1}{N} \quad \text{Square both sides.}$$

$$\frac{1}{(x-2)^2} > N. \quad \text{Take reciprocals of both sides.}$$

We see that for any positive N, if $0 < |x - 2| < \delta = \dfrac{1}{\sqrt{N}}$, then $f(x) = \dfrac{1}{(x-2)^2} > N$. It follows that $\lim_{x \to 2} \dfrac{1}{(x-2)^2} = \infty$. Note that because $\delta = \dfrac{1}{\sqrt{N}}$, δ decreases as N increases.

Related Exercises 29–32 ◀

QUICK CHECK 3 In Example 6, if N is increased by a factor of 100, how must δ change? ◀

Limits at Infinity

Precise definitions can also be written for the limits at infinity $\lim_{x \to \infty} f(x) = L$ and $\lim_{x \to -\infty} f(x) = L$. For discussion and examples, see Exercises 50–53.

SECTION 2.7 EXERCISES

Review Questions

1. Suppose x lies in the interval $(1, 3)$ with $x \neq 2$. Find the smallest positive value of δ such that the inequality $0 < |x - 2| < \delta$ is true.

2. Suppose $f(x)$ lies in the interval $(2, 6)$. What is the smallest value of ε such that $|f(x) - 4| < \varepsilon$?

3. Which one of the following intervals is not symmetric about $x = 5$?

   a. $(1, 9)$ **b.** $(4, 6)$ **c.** $(3, 8)$ **d.** $(4.5, 5.5)$

4. Does the set $\{x: 0 < |x - a| < \delta\}$ include the point $x = a$? Explain.

5. State the precise definition of $\lim_{x \to a} f(x) = L$.

6. Interpret $|f(x) - L| < \varepsilon$ in words.

7. Suppose $|f(x) - 5| < 0.1$ whenever $0 < x < 5$. Find all values of $\delta > 0$ such that $|f(x) - 5| < 0.1$ whenever $0 < |x - 2| < \delta$.

8. Give the definition of $\lim_{x \to a} f(x) = \infty$ and interpret it using pictures.

Basic Skills

9. **Determining values of δ from a graph** The function f in the figure satisfies $\lim_{x \to 2} f(x) = 5$. Determine the largest value of $\delta > 0$ satisfying each statement.

   a. If $0 < |x - 2| < \delta$, then $|f(x) - 5| < 2$.

   b. If $0 < |x - 2| < \delta$, then $|f(x) - 5| < 1$.

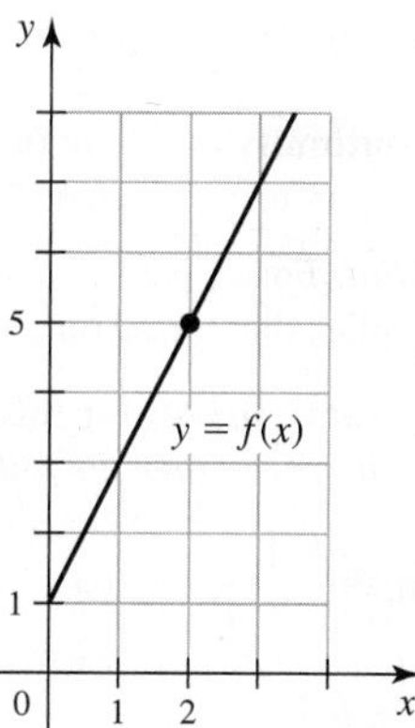

10. **Determining values of δ from a graph** The function f in the figure satisfies $\lim_{x \to 2} f(x) = 4$. Determine the largest value of $\delta > 0$ satisfying each statement.

    a. If $0 < |x - 2| < \delta$, then $|f(x) - 4| < 1$.

    b. If $0 < |x - 2| < \delta$, then $|f(x) - 4| < 1/2$.

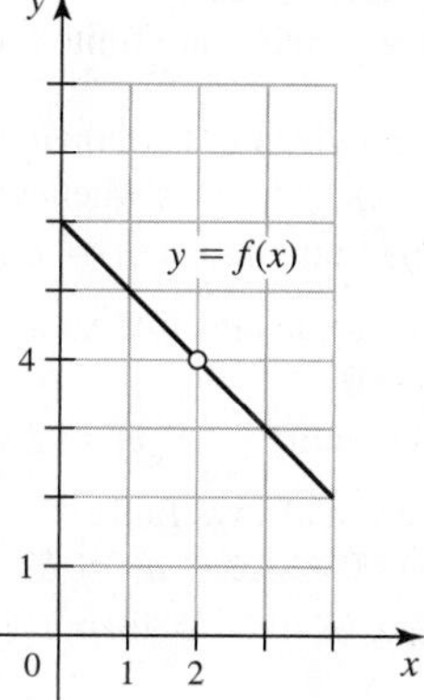

11. **Determining values of δ from a graph** The function f in the figure satisfies $\lim_{x \to 3} f(x) = 6$. Determine the largest value of $\delta > 0$ satisfying each statement.

    a. If $0 < |x - 3| < \delta$, then $|f(x) - 6| < 3$.

    b. If $0 < |x - 3| < \delta$, then $|f(x) - 6| < 1$.

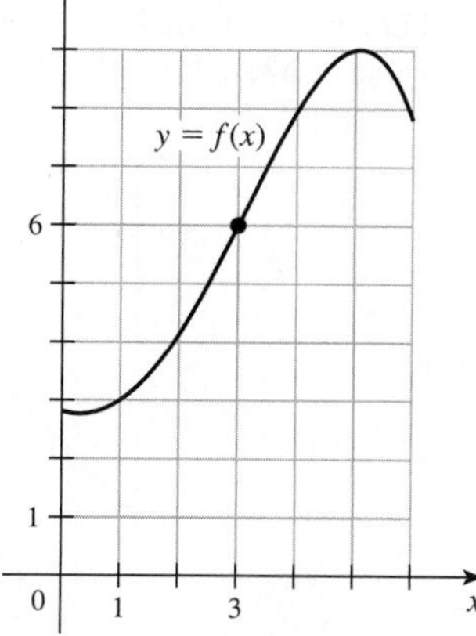

12. **Determining values of δ from a graph** The function f in the figure satisfies $\lim_{x \to 4} f(x) = 5$. Determine the largest value of $\delta > 0$ satisfying each statement.

    a. If $0 < |x - 4| < \delta$, then $|f(x) - 5| < 1$.

    b. If $0 < |x - 4| < \delta$, then $|f(x) - 5| < 0.5$.

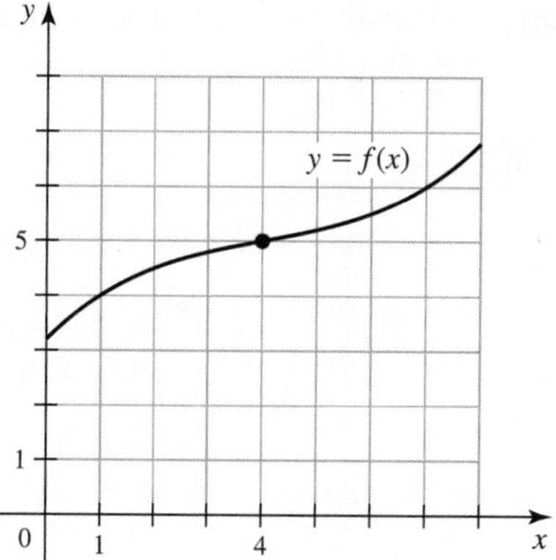

T 13. **Finding δ for a given ε using a graph** Let $f(x) = x^3 + 3$ and note that $\lim_{x \to 0} f(x) = 3$. For each value of ε, use a graphing utility to find a value of $\delta > 0$ such that $|f(x) - 3| < \varepsilon$ whenever $0 < |x - 0| < \delta$. Sketch graphs illustrating your work.

   a. $\varepsilon = 1$ **b.** $\varepsilon = 0.5$

T 14. **Finding δ for a given ε using a graph** Let $g(x) = 2x^3 - 12x^2 + 26x + 4$ and note that $\lim_{x \to 2} g(x) = 24$. For each value of ε, use a graphing utility to find a value of $\delta > 0$ such that $|g(x) - 24| < \varepsilon$ whenever $0 < |x - 2| < \delta$. Sketch graphs illustrating your work.

   a. $\varepsilon = 1$ **b.** $\varepsilon = 0.5$

15. Finding a symmetric interval The function f in the figure satisfies $\lim_{x \to 2} f(x) = 3$. For each value of ε, find a value of $\delta > 0$ such that

$$|f(x) - 3| < \varepsilon \quad \text{whenever} \quad 0 < |x - 2| < \delta. \qquad (2)$$

a. $\varepsilon = 1$ **b.** $\varepsilon = \frac{1}{2}$

c. For any $\varepsilon > 0$, make a conjecture about the corresponding value of δ satisfying (2).

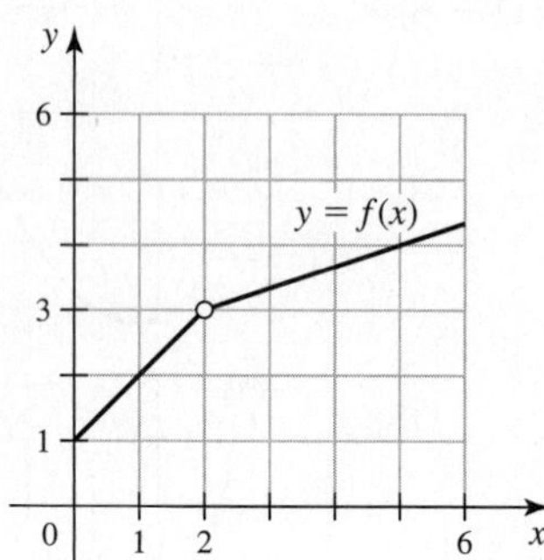

16. Finding a symmetric interval The function f in the figure satisfies $\lim_{x \to 3} f(x) = 4$. For each value of ε, find a value of $\delta > 0$ such that

$$|f(x) - 4| < \varepsilon \quad \text{whenever} \quad 0 < |x - 3| < \delta. \qquad (3)$$

a. $\varepsilon = 2$ **b.** $\varepsilon = \frac{1}{2}$

c. For any $\varepsilon > 0$, make a conjecture about the corresponding value of δ satisfying (3).

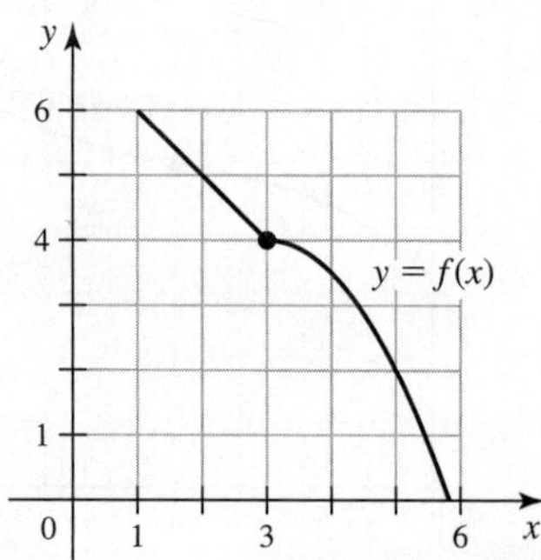

T **17. Finding a symmetric interval** Let $f(x) = x^2$ and note that $\lim_{x \to 2} f(x) = 4$. For each value of ε, use a graphing utility to find a value of $\delta > 0$ such that $|f(x) - 4| < \varepsilon$ whenever $0 < |x - 2| < \delta$.

a. $\varepsilon = 1$ **b.** $\varepsilon = 0.5$

c. For any $\varepsilon > 0$, make a conjecture about the value of δ that satisfies the preceding inequality.

T **18. Finding a symmetric interval** Let $f(x) = \dfrac{x^3 - 1}{x - 1}$ and note that $\lim_{x \to 1} f(x) = 3$. For each value of ε, use a graphing utility to find a value of $\delta > 0$ such that $|f(x) - 3| < \varepsilon$ whenever $0 < |x - 1| < \delta$.

a. $\varepsilon = 1.5$ **b.** $\varepsilon = 0.75$

c. For any $\varepsilon > 0$, make a conjecture about the value of δ that satisfies the preceding inequality.

19–24. Limit proofs *Use the precise definition of a limit to prove the following limits.*

19. $\lim_{x \to 1} (8x + 5) = 13$ **20.** $\lim_{x \to 3} (-2x + 8) = 2$

21. $\lim_{x \to 4} \dfrac{x^2 - 16}{x - 4} = 8$ (*Hint:* Factor and simplify.)

22. $\lim_{x \to 3} \dfrac{x^2 - 7x + 12}{x - 3} = -1$

23. $\lim_{x \to 0} x^2 = 0$ (*Hint:* Use the identity $\sqrt{x^2} = |x|$.)

24. $\lim_{x \to 3} (x - 3)^2 = 0$ (*Hint:* Use the identity $\sqrt{x^2} = |x|$.)

25. Proof of Limit Law 2 Suppose $\lim_{x \to a} f(x) = L$ and $\lim_{x \to a} g(x) = M$. Prove that $\lim_{x \to a} [f(x) - g(x)] = L - M$.

26. Proof of Limit Law 3 Suppose $\lim_{x \to a} f(x) = L$. Prove that $\lim_{x \to a} [cf(x)] = cL$, where c is a constant.

27. Limit of a constant function and $f(x) = x$ Give proofs of the following theorems.

a. $\lim_{x \to a} c = c$ for any constant c

b. $\lim_{x \to a} x = a$ for any constant a

28. Continuity of linear functions Prove Theorem 2.2: If $f(x) = mx + b$, then $\lim_{x \to a} f(x) = ma + b$ for constants m and b. (*Hint:* For a given $\varepsilon > 0$, let $\delta = \varepsilon/|m|$.) Explain why this result implies that linear functions are continuous.

29–32. Limit proofs for infinite limits *Use the precise definition of infinite limits to prove the following limits.*

29. $\lim_{x \to 4} \dfrac{1}{(x - 4)^2} = \infty$ **30.** $\lim_{x \to -1} \dfrac{1}{(x + 1)^4} = \infty$

31. $\lim_{x \to 0} \left(\dfrac{1}{x^2} + 1\right) = \infty$ **32.** $\lim_{x \to 0} \left(\dfrac{1}{x^4} - \sin x\right) = \infty$

Further Explorations

33. Explain why or why not Determine whether the following statements are true and give an explanation or counterexample. Assume a and L are finite numbers and assume $\lim_{x \to a} f(x) = L$.

a. For a given $\varepsilon > 0$, there is one value of $\delta > 0$ for which $|f(x) - L| < \varepsilon$ whenever $0 < |x - a| < \delta$.

b. The limit $\lim_{x \to a} f(x) = L$ means that given an arbitrary $\delta > 0$, we can always find an $\varepsilon > 0$ such that $|f(x) - L| < \varepsilon$ whenever $0 < |x - a| < \delta$.

c. The limit $\lim_{x \to a} f(x) = L$ means that for any arbitrary $\varepsilon > 0$, we can always find a $\delta > 0$ such that $|f(x) - L| < \varepsilon$ whenever $0 < |x - a| < \delta$.

d. If $|x - a| < \delta$, then $a - \delta < x < a + \delta$.

34. Finding δ algebraically Let $f(x) = x^2 - 2x + 3$.

a. For $\varepsilon = 0.25$, find a corresponding value of $\delta > 0$ satisfying the statement

$$|f(x) - 2| < \varepsilon \quad \text{whenever} \quad 0 < |x - 1| < \delta.$$

b. Verify that $\lim_{x \to 1} f(x) = 2$ as follows. For any $\varepsilon > 0$, find a corresponding value of $\delta > 0$ satisfying the statement

$$|f(x) - 2| < \varepsilon \quad \text{whenever} \quad 0 < |x - 1| < \delta.$$

35–38. Challenging limit proofs *Use the definition of a limit to prove the following results.*

35. $\lim_{x \to 3} \frac{1}{x} = \frac{1}{3}$ (*Hint:* As $x \to 3$, eventually the distance between x and 3 will be less than 1. Start by assuming $|x - 3| < 1$ and show $\frac{1}{|x|} < \frac{1}{2}$.)

36. $\lim_{x \to 4} \frac{x - 4}{\sqrt{x} - 2} = 4$ (*Hint:* Multiply the numerator and denominator by $\sqrt{x} + 2$.)

37. $\lim_{x \to 1/10} \frac{1}{x} = 10$ (*Hint:* To find δ, you will need to bound x away from 0. So let $\left| x - \frac{1}{10} \right| < \frac{1}{20}$.)

38. $\lim_{x \to 5} \frac{1}{x^2} = \frac{1}{25}$

39–43. Precise definitions for left- and right-hand limits *Use the following definitions.*

*Assume f exists for all x near a with x > a. We say that the **limit of f(x) as x approaches a from the right of a is L** and write* $\lim_{x \to a^+} f(x) = L$, *if for any* $\varepsilon > 0$ *there exists* $\delta > 0$ *such that*

$$|f(x) - L| < \varepsilon \text{ whenever } 0 < x - a < \delta.$$

*Assume f exists for all values of x near a with x < a. We say that the **limit of f(x) as x approaches a from the left of a is L** and write* $\lim_{x \to a^-} f(x) = L$, *if for any* $\varepsilon > 0$ *there exists* $\delta > 0$ *such that*

$$|f(x) - L| < \varepsilon \text{ whenever } 0 < a - x < \delta.$$

39. Comparing definitions Why is the last inequality in the definition of $\lim_{x \to a} f(x) = L$, namely, $0 < |x - a| < \delta$, replaced with $0 < x - a < \delta$ in the definition of $\lim_{x \to a^+} f(x) = L$?

40. Comparing definitions Why is the last inequality in the definition of $\lim_{x \to a} f(x) = L$, namely, $0 < |x - a| < \delta$, replaced with $0 < a - x < \delta$ in the definition of $\lim_{x \to a^-} f(x) = L$?

41. One-sided limit proofs Prove the following limits for

$$f(x) = \begin{cases} 3x - 4 & \text{if } x < 0 \\ 2x - 4 & \text{if } x \geq 0 \end{cases}$$

a. $\lim_{x \to 0^+} f(x) = -4$ b. $\lim_{x \to 0^-} f(x) = -4$

c. $\lim_{x \to 0} f(x) = -4$

42. Determining values of δ from a graph The function f in the figure satisfies $\lim_{x \to 2^+} f(x) = 0$ and $\lim_{x \to 2^-} f(x) = 1$. Determine a value of $\delta > 0$ satisfying each statement.

a. $|f(x) - 0| < 2$ whenever $0 < x - 2 < \delta$
b. $|f(x) - 0| < 1$ whenever $0 < x - 2 < \delta$
c. $|f(x) - 1| < 2$ whenever $0 < 2 - x < \delta$
d. $|f(x) - 1| < 1$ whenever $0 < 2 - x < \delta$

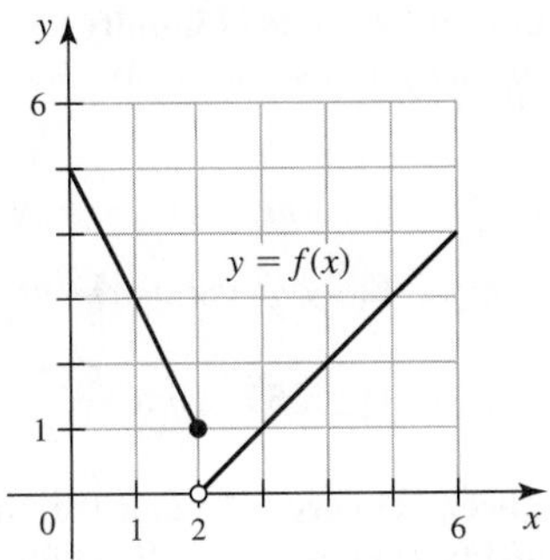

43. One-sided limit proof Prove that $\lim_{x \to 0^+} \sqrt{x} = 0$.

Additional Exercises

44. The relationship between one-sided and two-sided infinite limits Prove the following statements to establish the fact that $\lim_{x \to a} f(x) = L$ if and only if $\lim_{x \to a^-} f(x) = L$ and $\lim_{x \to a^+} f(x) = L$.

a. If $\lim_{x \to a^-} f(x) = L$ and $\lim_{x \to a^+} f(x) = L$, then $\lim_{x \to a} f(x) = L$.

b. If $\lim_{x \to a} f(x) = L$, then $\lim_{x \to a^-} f(x) = L$ and $\lim_{x \to a^+} f(x) = L$.

45. Definition of one-sided infinite limits We say that $\lim_{x \to a^+} f(x) = -\infty$ if for each negative number N, there exists $\delta > 0$ such that

$$f(x) < N \quad \text{whenever} \quad a < x < a + \delta.$$

a. Write an analogous formal definition for $\lim_{x \to a^+} f(x) = \infty$.

b. Write an analogous formal definition for $\lim_{x \to a^-} f(x) = -\infty$.

c. Write an analogous formal definition for $\lim_{x \to a^-} f(x) = \infty$.

46–47. One-sided infinite limits *Use the definitions given in Exercise 45 to prove the following infinite limits.*

46. $\lim_{x \to 1^+} \frac{1}{1 - x} = -\infty$ **47.** $\lim_{x \to 1^-} \frac{1}{1 - x} = \infty$

48–49. Definition of an infinite limit *We write* $\lim_{x \to a} f(x) = -\infty$ *if for any negative number M there exists a* $\delta > 0$ *such that*

$$f(x) < M \quad \textit{whenever} \quad 0 < |x - a| < \delta.$$

Use this definition to prove the following statements.

48. $\lim_{x \to 1} \frac{-2}{(x - 1)^2} = -\infty$ **49.** $\lim_{x \to -2} \frac{-10}{(x + 2)^4} = -\infty$

50–51. Definition of a limit at infinity *The limit at infinity* $\lim_{x\to\infty} f(x) = L$ *means that for any* $\varepsilon > 0$, *there exists* $N > 0$ *such that*

$$|f(x) - L| < \varepsilon \quad \textit{whenever} \quad x > N.$$

Use this definition to prove the following statements.

50. $\lim_{x\to\infty} \frac{10}{x} = 0$

51. $\lim_{x\to\infty} \frac{2x+1}{x} = 2$

52–53. Definition of infinite limits at infinity *We say that* $\lim_{x\to\infty} f(x) = \infty$ *if for each positive number M, there is a corresponding* $N > 0$ *such that*

$$f(x) > M \quad \textit{whenever} \quad x > N.$$

Use this definition to prove the following statements.

52. $\lim_{x\to\infty} \frac{x}{100} = \infty$

53. $\lim_{x\to\infty} \frac{x^2+x}{x} = \infty$

54. Proof of the Squeeze Theorem Assume the functions f, g, and h satisfy the inequality $f(x) \le g(x) \le h(x)$ for all values of x near a, except possibly at a. Prove that if $\lim_{x\to a} f(x) = \lim_{x\to a} h(x) = L$, then $\lim_{x\to a} g(x) = L$.

55. Limit proof Suppose f is defined for all values of x near a, except possibly at a. Assume for every integer $N > 0$ there is another integer $M > 0$ such that $|f(x) - L| < 1/N$ whenever $|x - a| < 1/M$. Prove that $\lim_{x\to a} f(x) = L$ using the precise definition of a limit.

56–58. Proving that $\lim_{x\to a} f(x) \ne L$ *Use the following definition for the nonexistence of a limit. Assume f is defined for all values of x near a, except possibly at a. We say that* $\lim_{x\to a} f(x) \ne L$ *if for some* $\varepsilon > 0$ *there is no value of* $\delta > 0$ *satisfying the condition*

$$|f(x) - L| < \varepsilon \quad \textit{whenever} \quad 0 < |x - a| < \delta.$$

56. For the following function, note that $\lim_{x\to 2} f(x) \ne 3$. Find a value of $\varepsilon > 0$ for which the preceding condition for nonexistence is satisfied.

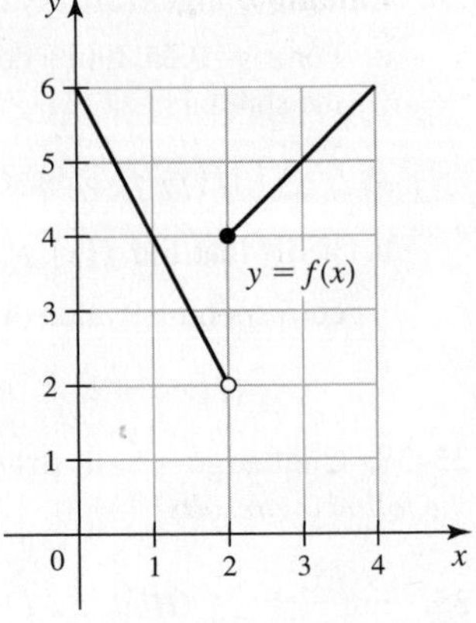

57. Prove that $\lim_{x\to 0} \frac{|x|}{x}$ does not exist.

58. Let

$$f(x) = \begin{cases} 0 & \text{if } x \text{ is rational} \\ 1 & \text{if } x \text{ is irrational} \end{cases}$$

Prove that $\lim_{x\to a} f(x)$ does not exist for any value of a. (*Hint:* Assume $\lim_{x\to a} f(x) = L$ for some values of a and L and let $\varepsilon = \frac{1}{2}$.)

59. A continuity proof Suppose f is continuous at a and assume $f(a) > 0$. Show that there is a positive number $\delta > 0$ for which $f(x) > 0$ for all values of x in $(a - \delta, a + \delta)$. (In other words, f is positive for all values of x sufficiently close to a.)

QUICK CHECK ANSWERS

1. $\delta = \frac{1}{50}$ or smaller **2.** $\delta = 0.62$ or smaller **3.** δ must decrease by a factor of $\sqrt{100} = 10$ (at least).

CHAPTER 2 REVIEW EXERCISES

1. Explain why or why not Determine whether the following statements are true and give an explanation or counterexample.

a. The rational function $\frac{x-1}{x^2-1}$ has vertical asymptotes at $x = -1$ and $x = 1$.

b. Numerical or graphical methods always produce good estimates of $\lim_{x\to a} f(x)$.

c. The value of $\lim_{x\to a} f(x)$, if it exists, is found by calculating $f(a)$.

d. If $\lim_{x\to a} f(x) = \infty$ or $\lim_{x\to a} f(x) = -\infty$, then $\lim_{x\to a} f(x)$ does not exist.

e. If $\lim_{x\to a} f(x)$ does not exist, then either $\lim_{x\to a} f(x) = \infty$ or $\lim_{x\to a} f(x) = -\infty$.

f. If a function is continuous on the intervals (a, b) and $[b, c)$, where $a < b < c$, then the function is also continuous on (a, c).

g. If $\lim_{x\to a} f(x)$ can be calculated by direct substitution, then f is continuous at $x = a$.

2. **Estimating limits graphically** Use the graph of f in the figure to find the following values, if possible.

a. $f(-1)$ b. $\lim_{x\to-1^-} f(x)$ c. $\lim_{x\to-1^+} f(x)$ d. $\lim_{x\to-1} f(x)$
e. $f(1)$ f. $\lim_{x\to1} f(x)$ g. $\lim_{x\to2} f(x)$ h. $\lim_{x\to3^-} f(x)$
i. $\lim_{x\to3^+} f(x)$ j. $\lim_{x\to3} f(x)$

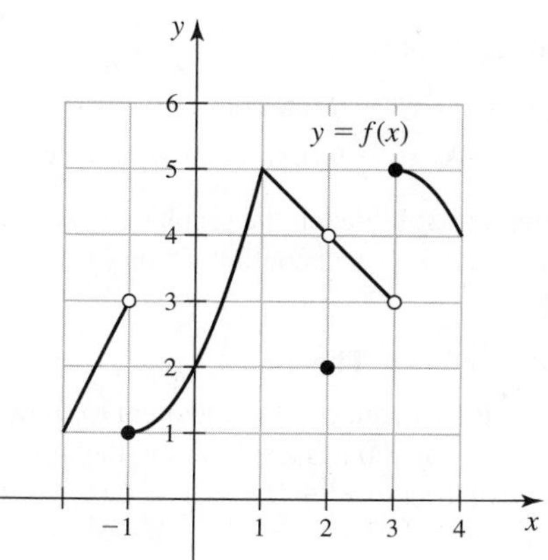

3. **Points of discontinuity** Use the graph of f in the figure to determine the values of x in the interval $(-3, 5)$ at which f fails to be continuous. Justify your answers using the continuity checklist.

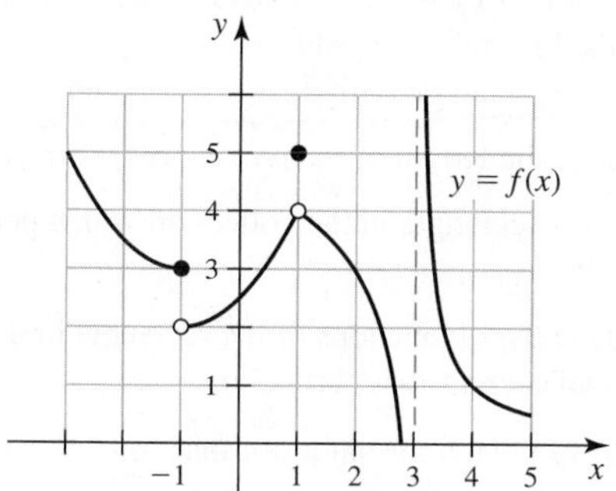

T 4. **Computing a limit graphically and analytically**

a. Graph $y = \dfrac{\sin 2\theta}{\sin\theta}$. Comment on any inaccuracies in the graph and then sketch an accurate graph of the function.

b. Estimate $\lim_{\theta\to0} \dfrac{\sin 2\theta}{\sin\theta}$ using the graph in part (a).

c. Verify your answer to part (b) by finding the value of $\lim_{\theta\to0} \dfrac{\sin 2\theta}{\sin\theta}$ analytically using the trigonometric identity $\sin 2\theta = 2\sin\theta\cos\theta$.

T 5. **Computing a limit numerically and analytically**

a. Estimate $\lim_{x\to\pi/4} \dfrac{\cos 2x}{\cos x - \sin x}$ by making a table of values of $\dfrac{\cos 2x}{\cos x - \sin x}$ for values of x approaching $\pi/4$. Round your estimate to four digits.

b. Use analytic methods to find the value of $\lim_{x\to\pi/4} \dfrac{\cos 2x}{\cos x - \sin x}$.

6. **Long-distance phone calls** Suppose a long-distance phone call costs \$0.75 for the first min (or any part of the first minute), plus \$0.10 for each additional min (or any part of a minute).

a. Graph the function $c = f(t)$ that gives the cost for talking on the phone for t minutes for $0 \le t \le 5$.

b. Evaluate $\lim_{t\to2.9} f(t)$.

c. Evaluate $\lim_{t\to3^-} f(t)$ and $\lim_{t\to3^+} f(t)$.

d. Interpret the meaning of the limits in part (c).

e. For what values of t is f continuous? Explain.

7. **Sketching a graph** Sketch the graph of a function f with all the following properties.

$$\lim_{x\to-2^-} f(x) = \infty \qquad \lim_{x\to-2^+} f(x) = -\infty \qquad \lim_{x\to0} f(x) = \infty$$
$$\lim_{x\to3^-} f(x) = 2 \qquad \lim_{x\to3^+} f(x) = 4 \qquad f(3) = 1$$

8–21. Calculating limits *Calculate the following limits analytically.*

8. $\lim_{x\to1000} 18\pi^2$

9. $\lim_{x\to1} \sqrt{5x + 6}$

10. $\lim_{h\to0} \dfrac{\sqrt{5x + 5h} - \sqrt{5x}}{h}$, where x is constant

11. $\lim_{x\to1} \dfrac{x^3 - 7x^2 + 12x}{4 - x}$

12. $\lim_{x\to4} \dfrac{x^3 - 7x^2 + 12x}{4 - x}$

13. $\lim_{x\to1} \dfrac{1 - x^2}{x^2 - 8x + 7}$

14. $\lim_{x\to3} \dfrac{\sqrt{3x + 16} - 5}{x - 3}$

15. $\lim_{x\to3} \dfrac{1}{x - 3}\left(\dfrac{1}{\sqrt{x + 1}} - \dfrac{1}{2}\right)$

16. $\lim_{t\to1/3} \dfrac{t - 1/3}{(3t - 1)^2}$

17. $\lim_{x\to3} \dfrac{x^4 - 81}{x - 3}$

18. $\lim_{p\to1} \dfrac{p^5 - 1}{p - 1}$

19. $\lim_{x\to81} \dfrac{\sqrt[4]{x} - 3}{x - 81}$

20. $\lim_{\theta\to\pi/4} \dfrac{\sin^2\theta - \cos^2\theta}{\sin\theta - \cos\theta}$

21. $\lim_{x\to\pi/2} \dfrac{\dfrac{1}{\sqrt{\sin x}} - 1}{x + \pi/2}$

22. **One-sided limits** Evaluate $\lim_{x\to1^+} \sqrt{\dfrac{x - 1}{x - 3}}$ and $\lim_{x\to1^-} \sqrt{\dfrac{x - 1}{x - 3}}$.

T 23. **Applying the Squeeze Theorem**

a. Use a graphing utility to illustrate the inequalities

$$\cos x \le \frac{\sin x}{x} \le \frac{1}{\cos x}$$

on $[-1, 1]$.

b. Use part (a) and the Squeeze Theorem to explain why $\lim_{x\to0} \dfrac{\sin x}{x} = 1$.

24. **Applying the Squeeze Theorem** Assume the function g satisfies the inequality $1 \le g(x) \le \sin^2 x + 1$ for x near 0. Use the Squeeze Theorem to find $\lim_{x\to0} g(x)$.

25–29. Finding infinite limits *Evaluate the following infinite limits or state that they do not exist.*

25. $\lim_{x\to5} \dfrac{x - 7}{x(x - 5)^2}$

26. $\lim_{x\to-5^+} \dfrac{x - 5}{x + 5}$

27. $\lim_{x\to3^-} \dfrac{x - 4}{x^2 - 3x}$

28. $\lim_{u\to0^+} \dfrac{u - 1}{\sin u}$

29. $\lim_{x\to0^-} \dfrac{2}{\tan x}$

30. Finding vertical asymptotes Let $f(x) = \dfrac{x^2 - 5x + 6}{x^2 - 2x}$.

a. Calculate $\lim_{x\to 0^-} f(x)$, $\lim_{x\to 0^+} f(x)$, $\lim_{x\to 2^-} f(x)$, and $\lim_{x\to 2^+} f(x)$.

b. Does the graph of f have any vertical asymptotes? Explain.

c. Graph f and then sketch the graph with paper and pencil, correcting any errors obtained with the graphing utility.

31–36. Limits at infinity *Evaluate the following limits or state that they do not exist.*

31. $\lim_{x\to\infty} \dfrac{2x - 3}{4x + 10}$

32. $\lim_{x\to\infty} \dfrac{x^4 - 1}{x^5 + 2}$

33. $\lim_{x\to-\infty} (-3x^3 + 5)$

34. $\lim_{x\to\infty} \dfrac{x}{\sqrt{4x^2 + 1}}$

35. $\lim_{x\to\infty} \dfrac{\sqrt{25x^2 + 8}}{x + 2}$

36. $\lim_{r\to\infty} \dfrac{1}{\cos r + 1}$

37–40. End behavior *Determine the end behavior of the following functions.*

37. $f(x) = \dfrac{4x^3 + 1}{1 - x^3}$

38. $f(x) = \dfrac{x + 1}{\sqrt{9x^2 + x}}$

39. $f(x) = \dfrac{12x^2}{\sqrt{16x^4 + 7}}$

40. $f(x) = \sqrt[3]{\dfrac{8x + 1}{x - 3}}$

41–42. Vertical and horizontal asymptotes *Find all vertical and horizontal asymptotes of the following functions.*

41. $f(x) = \dfrac{x^2 - x}{x^2 - 1}$

42. $f(x) = \dfrac{2x^2 + 6}{2x^2 + 3x - 2}$

43–46. Continuity at a point *Determine whether the following functions are continuous at $x = a$ using the continuity checklist to justify your answers.*

43. $f(x) = \dfrac{1}{x - 5}$; $a = 5$

44. $g(x) = \begin{cases} \dfrac{x^2 - 16}{x - 4} & \text{if } x \neq 4 \\ 9 & \text{if } x = 4 \end{cases}$; $a = 4$

45. $h(x) = \sqrt{x^2 - 9}$; $a = 3$

46. $g(x) = \begin{cases} \dfrac{x^2 - 16}{x - 4} & \text{if } x \neq 4 \\ 8 & \text{if } x = 4 \end{cases}$; $a = 4$

47–50. Continuity on intervals *Find the intervals on which the following functions are continuous. Specify right or left continuity at the endpoints.*

47. $f(x) = \sqrt{x^2 - 5}$

48. $g(x) = \sqrt{x^2 - 5x + 6}$

49. $h(x) = \dfrac{2x}{x^3 - 25x}$

50. $g(x) = \cos\sqrt{x}$

51. Determining unknown constants Let

$$g(x) = \begin{cases} 5x - 2 & \text{if } x < 1 \\ a & \text{if } x = 1 \\ ax^2 + bx & \text{if } x > 1 \end{cases}$$

Determine values of the constants a and b for which g is continuous at $x = 1$.

52. Left and right continuity

a. Is $h(x) = \sqrt{x^2 - 9}$ left-continuous at $x = 3$? Explain.

b. Is $h(x) = \sqrt{x^2 - 9}$ right-continuous at $x = 3$? Explain.

53. Sketching a graph Sketch the graph of a function that is continuous on $(0, 1]$ and continuous on $(1, 2)$ but is not continuous on $(0, 2)$.

54. Intermediate Value Theorem

a. Use the Intermediate Value Theorem to show that the equation $x^5 + 7x + 5 = 0$ has a solution in the interval $(-1, 0)$.

b. Find a solution to $x^5 + 7x + 5 = 0$ in $(-1, 0)$ using a root finder.

55. Variable rectangles Imagine the collection of rectangles with length x and width y, such that their area is $xy = 100$.

a. Show that the rectangle in this collection with length x has perimeter $P(x) = 2x + 200/x$, where $x > 0$.

b. Use the Intermediate Value Theorem to show that there is at least one rectangle with $2 \le x \le 30$ and perimeter 50.

c. Estimate the length of the rectangle(s) with perimeter 50.

d. Is there a rectangle in the collection with a perimeter of 30? Explain.

e. Estimate the dimensions of the rectangle in the collection with the smallest possible perimeter.

56. Limit proof Give a formal proof that $\lim_{x\to 1} (5x - 2) = 3$.

57. Limit proof Give a formal proof that $\lim_{x\to 5} \dfrac{x^2 - 25}{x - 5} = 10$.

58. Limit proofs

a. Assume $|f(x)| \le L$ for all x near a and $\lim_{x\to a} g(x) = 0$. Give a formal proof that $\lim_{x\to a} [f(x)g(x)] = 0$.

b. Find a function f for which $\lim_{x\to 2} [f(x)(x - 2)] \neq 0$. Why doesn't this violate the result stated in (a)?

c. The Heaviside function is defined as

$$H(x) = \begin{cases} 0 & \text{if } x < 0 \\ 1 & \text{if } x \ge 0 \end{cases}$$

Explain why $\lim_{x\to 0} [xH(x)] = 0$.

59. Infinite limit proof Give a formal proof that $\lim_{x\to 2} \dfrac{1}{(x - 2)^4} = \infty$.

Chapter 2 Guided Projects

Applications of the material in this chapter and related topics can be found in the following Guided Projects. For additional information, see the Preface.

- Fixed-point iteration
- Local linearity

3

Derivatives

Chapter Preview Now that you are familiar with limits, the door to calculus stands open. The first task is to introduce the fundamental concept of the *derivative*. Suppose a function f represents a quantity of interest, say the variable cost of manufacturing an item, the population of a country, or the position of an orbiting-satellite. The derivative of f is another function, denoted f', which gives the changing slope of the curve $y = f(x)$. Equivalently, the derivative of f gives the *instantaneous rate of change* of f at points in the domain. We use limits not only to define the derivative, but also to develop efficient rules for finding derivatives. The applications of the derivative—which we introduce along the way—are endless because almost everything around us is in a state of change, and derivatives describe change.

3.1 Introducing the Derivative

In this section we return to the problem of finding the slope of a line tangent to a curve, introduced at the beginning of Chapter 2. This concept is important for several reasons.

- We identify the slope of the tangent line with the *instantaneous rate of change* of a function (Figure 3.1).
- The slopes of the tangent lines as they change along a curve are the values of a new function called the *derivative*.
- If a curve represents the trajectory of a moving object, the line tangent to the curve at a point gives the direction of motion at that point (Figure 3.2).

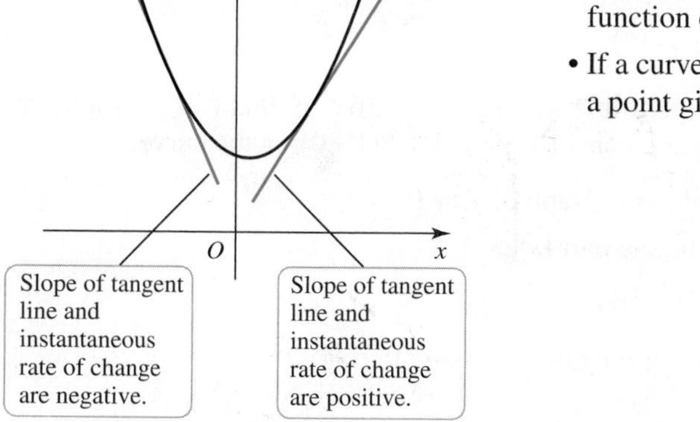

FIGURE 3.1

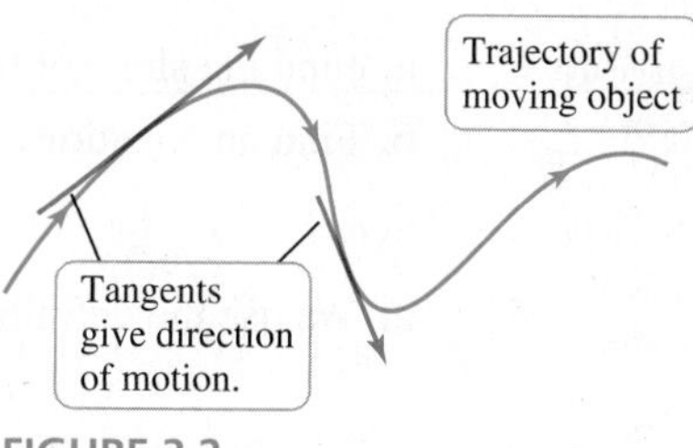

FIGURE 3.2

In Section 2.1 we gave an intuitive definition of a tangent line and used numerical evidence to estimate its slope. We now make these ideas precise.

Tangent Lines and Rates of Change

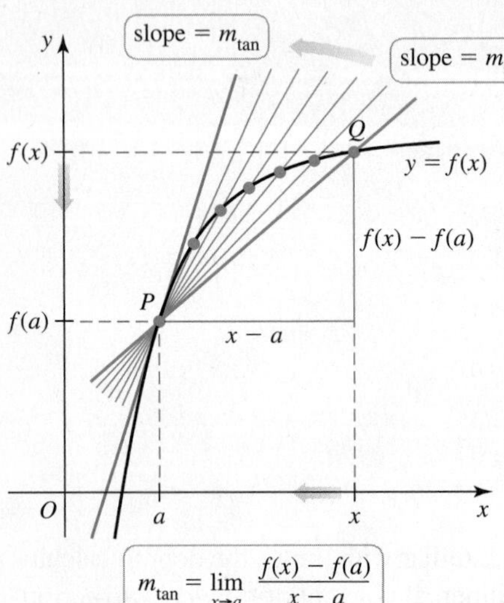

FIGURE 3.3

➤ Figure 3.3 assumes $x > a$. Analogous pictures and arguments can be made for $x < a$.

Consider the curve $y = f(x)$ and a secant line intersecting the curve at the points $P(a, f(a))$ and $Q(x, f(x))$ (Figure 3.3). The difference $f(x) - f(a)$ is the change in the value of f on the interval $[a, x]$, while $x - a$ is the change in x. As discussed in Chapter 2, the slope of the secant line $\overleftrightarrow{PQ}$ is

$$m_{\sec} = \frac{f(x) - f(a)}{x - a},$$

and it gives the *average rate of change* of f on the interval $[a, x]$.

Figure 3.3 also shows what happens as the variable point x approaches the fixed point a. Under suitable conditions on f, the slopes $m_{\sec}$ of the secant lines approach a unique number $m_{\tan}$ that we call the *slope of the tangent line*; that is,

$$m_{\tan} = \lim_{x\to a} \frac{f(x) - f(a)}{x - a}.$$

The secant lines themselves approach a unique line that intersects the curve at P with slope $m_{\tan}$; this line is the *tangent line at a*. The slope of the tangent line is also referred to as the *instantaneous rate of change* of f at a because it measures how quickly f changes at a. We summarize these observations as follows.

DEFINITION Rates of Change and the Tangent Line

The **average rate of change** in f on the interval $[a, x]$ is the slope of the corresponding secant line:

$$m_{\sec} = \frac{f(x) - f(a)}{x - a}.$$

The **instantaneous rate of change** in f at a is

$$m_{\tan} = \lim_{x\to a} \frac{f(x) - f(a)}{x - a}, \qquad (1)$$

which is also the **slope of the tangent line** at a, provided this limit exists. The **tangent line** at a is the unique line through $(a, f(a))$ with slope $m_{\tan}$. Its equation is

$$y - f(a) = m_{\tan}(x - a).$$

QUICK CHECK 1 Sketch the graph of a function f near a point a. As in Figure 3.3, draw a secant line that passes through $(a, f(a))$ and a neighboring point $(x, f(x))$ with $x < a$. Show how the secant lines approach the tangent line as x approaches a. ◄

EXAMPLE 1 Equation of a tangent line Let $f(x) = -16x^2 + 96x$ (the position function considered in Section 2.1) and consider the point $P(1, 80)$ on the curve.

a. Find the slope of the line tangent to the graph of f at P.

b. Find an equation of the tangent line in part (a).

➤ If x and y have physical units, then the average and instantaneous rates of change have units of (units of y)/(units of x). For example, if y has units of meters and x has units of seconds, the units of the rates of change are m/s.

SOLUTION

a. We use the definition of the slope of the tangent line with $a = 1$:

$$
\begin{aligned}
m_{\tan} &= \lim_{x\to 1} \frac{f(x) - f(1)}{x - 1} && \text{Definition of slope of tangent line}\\
&= \lim_{x\to 1} \frac{(-16x^2 + 96x) - 80}{x - 1} && f(x) = -16x^2 + 96x;\ f(1) = 80\\
&= \lim_{x\to 1} \frac{-16(x - 5)(x - 1)}{x - 1} && \text{Factor the numerator.}\\
&= -16 \underbrace{\lim_{x\to 1} (x - 5)}_{-4} = 64 && \text{Cancel factors } (x \neq 1) \text{ and evaluate the limit.}
\end{aligned}
$$

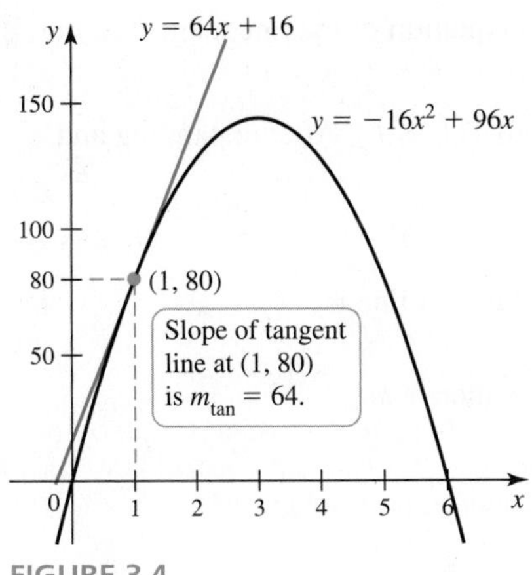

FIGURE 3.4

We have confirmed the conjecture made in Section 2.1 that the slope of the line tangent to the graph of $f(x) = -16x^2 + 96x$ at $(1, 80)$ is 64.

b. An equation of the line passing through $(1, 80)$ with slope $m_{\tan} = 64$ is $y - 80 = 64(x - 1)$ or $y = 64x + 16$. The graph of f and the tangent line at $(1, 80)$ are shown in Figure 3.4. *Related Exercises 11–16*

QUICK CHECK 2 In Example 1, is the slope of the tangent line at $(2, 128)$ greater than or less than the slope at $(1, 80)$?

An alternative formula for the slope of the tangent line is helpful for future work. We now let $(a, f(a))$ and $(a + h, f(a + h))$ be the coordinates of P and Q, respectively (Figure 3.5). The difference in the x-coordinates of P and Q is $(a + h) - a = h$. Note that Q is located to the right of P if $h > 0$ and to the left of P if $h < 0$.

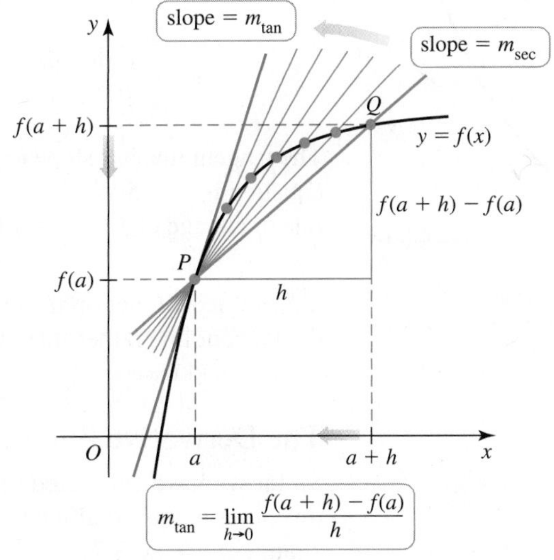

FIGURE 3.5

The slope of the secant line $\overleftrightarrow{PQ}$ using the new notation is $m_{\sec} = \dfrac{f(a + h) - f(a)}{h}$.

As h approaches 0, the variable point Q approaches P and the slopes of the secant lines approach the slope of the tangent line. Therefore, the slope of the tangent line at $(a, f(a))$, which is also the instantaneous rate of change of f at a, is

$$m_{\tan} = \lim_{h \to 0} \frac{f(a + h) - f(a)}{h}.$$

ALTERNATIVE DEFINITION Rates of Change and the Tangent Line

The **average rate of change** in f on the interval $[a, a + h]$ is the slope of the corresponding secant line:

$$m_{\sec} = \frac{f(a + h) - f(a)}{h}$$

The **instantaneous rate of change** in f at a is

$$m_{\tan} = \lim_{h \to 0} \frac{f(a + h) - f(a)}{h}, \qquad (2)$$

which is also the **slope of the tangent line** at $(a, f(a))$, provided this limit exists.

EXAMPLE 2 **Equation of a tangent line** Find an equation of the line tangent to the graph of $f(x) = x^3 + 4x$ at $x = 1$.

SOLUTION We let $a = 1$ in definition (2) and first find $f(1 + h)$. After expanding and collecting terms, we have

$$f(1 + h) = (1 + h)^3 + 4(1 + h) = h^3 + 3h^2 + 7h + 5.$$

➤ In this limit, notice that h approaches 0 but $h \neq 0$. Therefore, it is permissible to cancel h from the numerator and denominator of $\frac{h(h^2 + 3h + 7)}{h}$.

Substituting $f(1 + h)$ and $f(1) = 5$, the slope of the tangent line is

$$m_{\tan} = \lim_{h \to 0} \frac{f(1 + h) - f(1)}{h} \quad \text{Definition of } m_{\tan}$$

$$= \lim_{h \to 0} \frac{(h^3 + 3h^2 + 7h + 5) - 5}{h} \quad \text{Substitute } f(1 + h) \text{ and } f(1) = 5.$$

$$= \lim_{h \to 0} \frac{h(h^2 + 3h + 7)}{h} \quad \text{Simplify.}$$

$$= \lim_{h \to 0} (h^2 + 3h + 7) \quad \text{Cancel } h, \text{ noting } h \neq 0.$$

$$= 7. \quad \text{Evaluate the limit.}$$

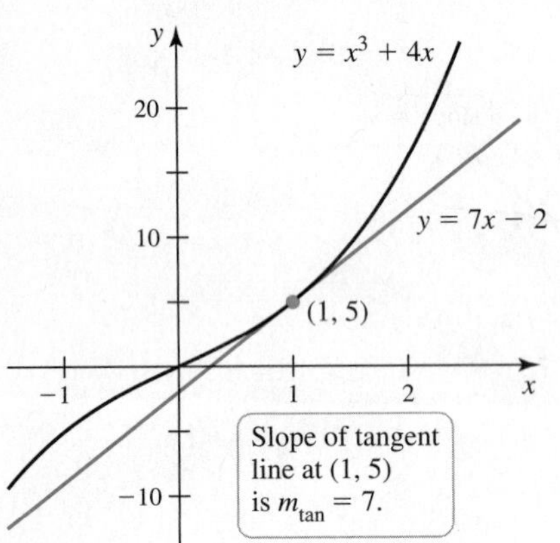

FIGURE 3.6

The tangent line has slope $m_{\tan} = 7$ and passes through the point (1, 5) (Figure 3.6); its equation is $y - 5 = 7(x - 1)$ or $y = 7x - 2$. We could also say that the instantaneous rate of change of f at $x = 1$ is 7.
Related Exercises 17–22 ➤

QUICK CHECK 3 Set up the calculation in Example 2 using definition (1) for the slope of the tangent line rather than definition (2). Does the calculation appear more difficult using definition (1)? ➤

The Derivative Function

So far we have computed the slope of the tangent line at one fixed point on the curve. If this point is moved along the curve, the tangent line also moves, and, in general, its slope changes (Figure 3.7). For this reason, the slope of the tangent line for the function f is itself a function of x, called the *derivative* of f.

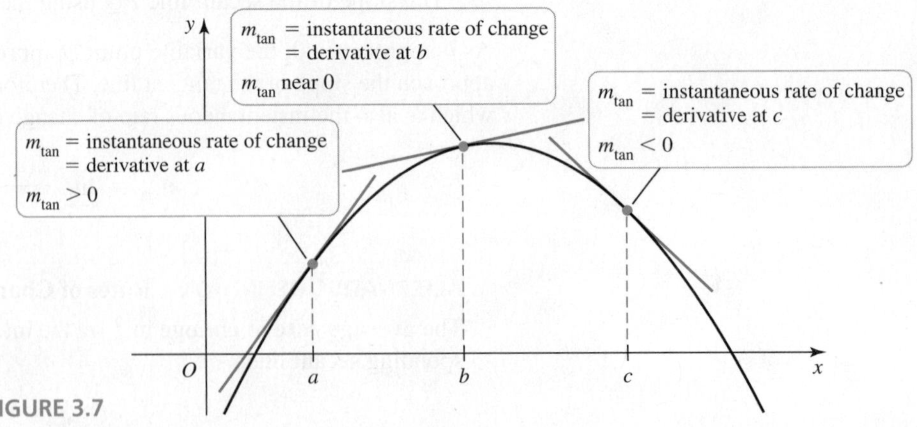

FIGURE 3.7

We let f' (read *f prime*) denote the derivative function for f, which means that $f'(a)$, when it exists, is the slope of the line tangent to the graph of f at $(a, f(a))$. Using definition (2) for the slope of the tangent line, we have

$$f'(a) = \lim_{h \to 0} \frac{f(a + h) - f(a)}{h}.$$

More generally, $f'(x)$, when it exists, is the slope of the tangent line (and the instantaneous rate of change) at the variable point $(x, f(x))$. Replacing a by the variable x in the expression for $f'(a)$ gives the definition of the *derivative function.*

> The process of finding f' is called *differentiation*, and to *differentiate* f means to find f'.

DEFINITION The Derivative

The **derivative** of f is the function

$$f'(x) = \lim_{h \to 0} \frac{f(x + h) - f(x)}{h},$$

provided the limit exists. If $f'(x)$ exists, we say f is **differentiable** at x. If f is differentiable at every point of an open interval I, we say that f is differentiable on I.

> Just as we have two definitions for the slope of a tangent line, we also have the following definition for the derivative of f at a:
>
> $$f'(a) = \lim_{x \to a} \frac{f(x) - f(a)}{x - a},$$
>
> provided the limit exists.

EXAMPLE 3 The slope of a curve Consider once again the function $f(x) = -16x^2 + 96x$ (Example 1) and find its derivative.

SOLUTION

$$f'(x) = \lim_{h \to 0} \frac{f(x + h) - f(x)}{h} \quad \text{Definition of } f'(x)$$

$$= \lim_{h \to 0} \frac{\overbrace{-16(x + h)^2 + 96(x + h)}^{f(x+h)} - \overbrace{(-16x^2 + 96x)}^{f(x)}}{h} \quad \text{Substitute.}$$

$$= \lim_{h \to 0} \frac{-16(x^2 + 2xh + h^2) + 96x + 96h + 16x^2 - 96x}{h} \quad \text{Expand the numerator.}$$

$$= \lim_{h \to 0} \frac{h(-32x + 96 - 16h)}{h} \quad \text{Simplify and factor out } h.$$

$$= \lim_{h \to 0} (-32x + 96 - 16h) = -32x + 96 \quad \text{Cancel } h \neq 0 \text{ and evaluate the limit.}$$

> Notice that this argument applies for $h > 0$ and for $h < 0$; that is, the limit as $h \to 0^+$ and the limit as $h \to 0^-$ are equal.

The derivative is $f'(x) = -32x + 96$, which gives the slope of the tangent line (equivalently, the instantaneous rate of change) at *any* point on the curve. For example, at the point $(1, 80)$, the slope of the tangent line is $f'(1) = -32(1) + 96 = 64$, confirming the calculation in Example 1. The slope of the tangent line at $(3, 144)$ is $f'(3) = -32(3) + 96 = 0$, which means the tangent line is horizontal at that point (Figure 3.8).

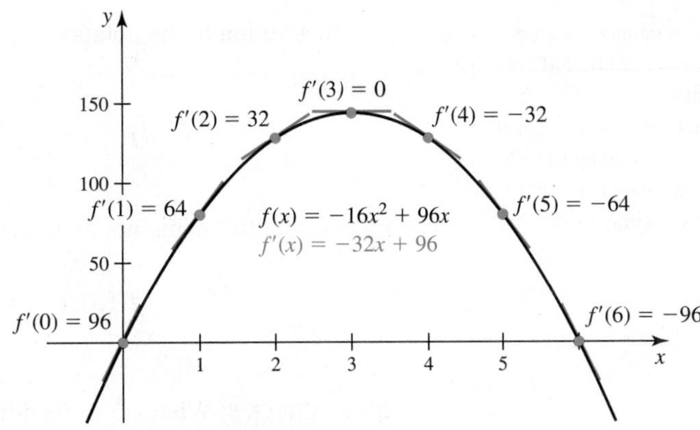

FIGURE 3.8

Related Exercises 23–32

QUICK CHECK 4 In Example 3, determine the slope of the tangent line at $x = 2$.

Derivative Notation

For historical and practical reasons, several notations for the derivative are used. To see the origin of one notation, recall that the slope of the secant line $\overleftrightarrow{PQ}$ between two points $P(x, f(x))$ and $Q(x + h, f(x + h))$ on the curve $y = f(x)$ is $\frac{f(x + h) - f(x)}{h}$. The quantity h is the *change* in the x-coordinates in moving from P to Q. A standard notation for change is the symbol Δ (uppercase Greek letter delta). So, we replace h by Δx to represent the change in x. Similarly, $f(x + h) - f(x)$ is the change in y, denoted Δy (Figure 3.9). Therefore, the slope of $\overleftrightarrow{PQ}$ is

$$\frac{f(x + \Delta x) - f(x)}{\Delta x} = \frac{\Delta y}{\Delta x}.$$

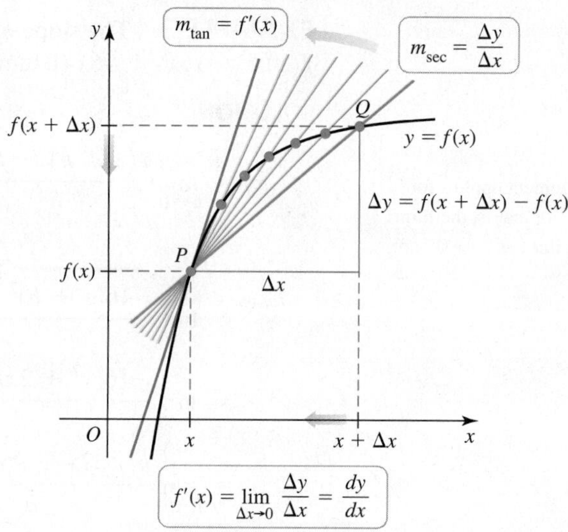

FIGURE 3.9

By letting $\Delta x \to 0$, the slope of the tangent line at $(x, f(x))$ is

$$f'(x) = \lim_{\Delta x \to 0} \frac{f(x + \Delta x) - f(x)}{\Delta x} = \lim_{\Delta x \to 0} \frac{\Delta y}{\Delta x} = \frac{dy}{dx}.$$

➤ The notation $\frac{dy}{dx}$ is read *the derivative of y with respect to x* or *dy dx*. It does not mean dy divided by dx, but it is a reminder of the limit of $\Delta y/\Delta x$.

The new notation for the derivative is $\frac{dy}{dx}$; it reminds us that $f'(x)$ is the limit of $\frac{\Delta y}{\Delta x}$ as $\Delta x \to 0$.

➤ The derivative notation dy/dx was introduced by Leibniz (1646–1716), one of the coinventors of calculus. His notation is used today in its original form. The notation used by Isaac Newton (1642–1727), the other coinventor of calculus, has fallen into disuse.

In addition to the notation $f'(x)$ and $\frac{dy}{dx}$, other common ways of writing the derivative include

$$\frac{df}{dx}, \quad \frac{d}{dx}(f(x)), \quad D_x(f(x)), \quad \text{and} \quad y'(x).$$

Each of the following notations represents the derivative of f evaluated at a.

$$f'(a), \quad y'(a), \quad \left.\frac{df}{dx}\right|_{x=a}, \quad \text{and} \quad \left.\frac{dy}{dx}\right|_{x=a}$$

QUICK CHECK 5 What are some other ways to write $f'(3)$, where $y = f(x)$? ◄

EXAMPLE 4 **A derivative calculation** Let $y = f(x) = \sqrt{x}$.

a. Compute $\dfrac{dy}{dx}$.

b. Find an equation of the line tangent to the graph of f at $(4, 2)$.

➤ Example 4 gives the first of many derivative formulas to be presented in the text:

$$\frac{d}{dx}(\sqrt{x}) = \frac{1}{2\sqrt{x}}.$$

SOLUTION

$$\textbf{a.}\ \frac{dy}{dx} = \lim_{h\to 0}\frac{f(x+h)-f(x)}{h} \qquad \text{Definition of } \frac{dy}{dx} = f'(x)$$

$$= \lim_{h\to 0}\frac{\sqrt{x+h}-\sqrt{x}}{h} \qquad \text{Substitute } f(x) = \sqrt{x}.$$

$$= \lim_{h\to 0}\frac{\left(\sqrt{x+h}-\sqrt{x}\right)}{h}\frac{\left(\sqrt{x+h}+\sqrt{x}\right)}{\left(\sqrt{x+h}+\sqrt{x}\right)} \qquad \text{Multiply the numerator and denominator by } \sqrt{x+h}+\sqrt{x}.$$

$$= \lim_{h\to 0}\frac{1}{\sqrt{x+h}+\sqrt{x}} = \frac{1}{2\sqrt{x}} \qquad \text{Simplify and evaluate the limit.}$$

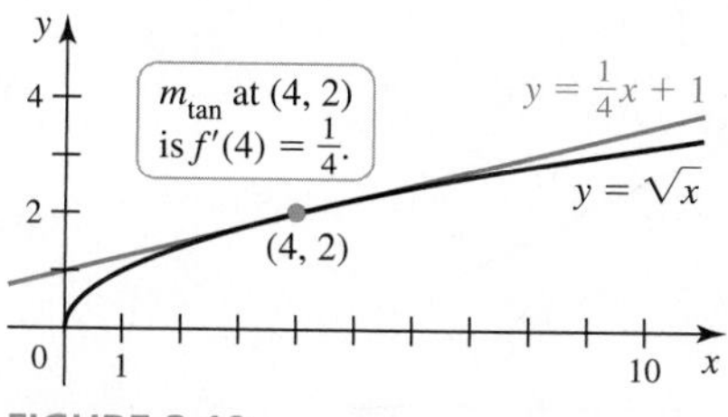

FIGURE 3.10

b. The slope of the tangent line at $x = 4$ is

$$\left.\frac{dy}{dx}\right|_{x=4} = \frac{1}{2\sqrt{4}} = \frac{1}{4}.$$

The tangent line at $(4, 2)$ has slope $m = \frac{1}{4}$ (Figure 3.10), so an equation is

$$y - 2 = \frac{1}{4}(x - 4) \text{ or } y = \frac{1}{4}x + 1.$$

Related Exercises 33–34 ◀

QUICK CHECK 6 In Example 4, do the slopes of the tangent lines increase or decrease as x increases? Explain. ◀

If a function is given in terms of variables other than x and y, we make an adjustment to the derivative definition. For example, if $y = g(t)$, we replace f by g and x by t to obtain the *derivative of g with respect to t*:

$$g'(t) = \lim_{h\to 0}\frac{g(t+h)-g(t)}{h}.$$

QUICK CHECK 7 Express the derivative of $p = q(r)$ in three ways. ◀

Other notation for $g'(t)$ includes $\dfrac{dg}{dt}$, $\dfrac{d}{dt}(g(t))$, $D_t(g(t))$, and $y'(t)$.

EXAMPLE 5 **Another derivative calculation** Let $g(t) = 1/t^2$ and compute $g'(t)$.

SOLUTION

$$g'(t) = \lim_{h\to 0}\frac{g(t+h)-g(t)}{h} \qquad \text{Definition of } g'$$

$$= \lim_{h\to 0}\frac{1}{h}\left[\frac{1}{(t+h)^2} - \frac{1}{t^2}\right] \qquad \text{Substitute } g(t) = 1/t^2.$$

$$= \lim_{h\to 0}\frac{1}{h}\left[\frac{t^2-(t+h)^2}{t^2(t+h)^2}\right] \qquad \text{Common denominator}$$

$$= \lim_{h\to 0}\frac{1}{h}\left[\frac{-2ht-h^2}{t^2(t+h)^2}\right] \qquad \text{Expand the numerator and simplify.}$$

$$= \lim_{h\to 0}\left[\frac{-2t-h}{t^2(t+h)^2}\right] \qquad \text{Cancel } h \neq 0.$$

$$= -\frac{2}{t^3} \qquad \text{Evaluate the limit.}$$

Related Exercises 35–38 ◀

Graphs of Derivatives

The function f' is called the derivative of f because it is *derived* from f. The following examples illustrate how to *derive* the graph of f' from the graph of f.

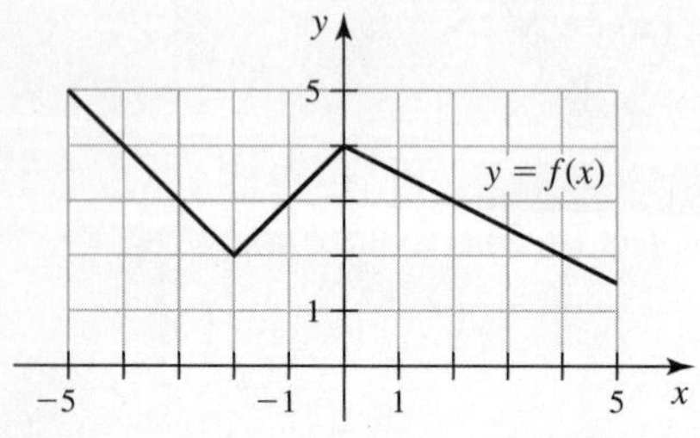

FIGURE 3.11

EXAMPLE 6 **Graph of the derivative** Sketch the graph of f' from the graph of f (Figure 3.11).

SOLUTION The graph of f consists of line segments, which are their own tangent lines. Therefore, the slope of the curve $y = f(x)$ for $x < -2$ is -1; that is, $f'(x) = -1$ for $x < -2$. Similarly, $f'(x) = 1$ for $-2 < x < 0$ and $f'(x) = -\frac{1}{2}$ for $x > 0$ (Figure 3.12).

➤ In terms of limits at $x = -2$, we can write $\lim_{h \to 0^-} \frac{f(-2 + h) - f(-2)}{h} = -1$ and $\lim_{h \to 0^+} \frac{f(-2 + h) - f(-2)}{h} = 1$. Because the one-sided limits are not equal, $f'(-2)$ does not exist. The analogous one-sided limits at $x = 0$ are also unequal.

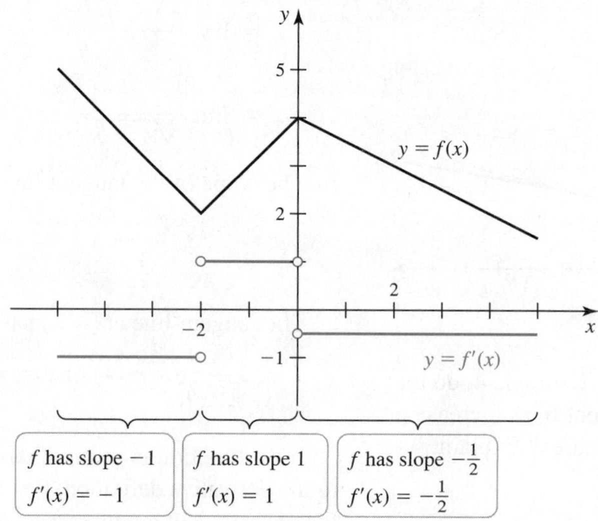

FIGURE 3.12

QUICK CHECK 8 In Example 6, why is the graph of f' not continuous at $x = -2$ and at $x = 0$? ◄

Notice that the slopes of the tangent lines change abruptly at $x = -2$ and $x = 0$. As a result, $f'(-2)$ and $f'(0)$ are undefined and the graph of the derivative is discontinuous at these points. *Related Exercises 39–44* ◄

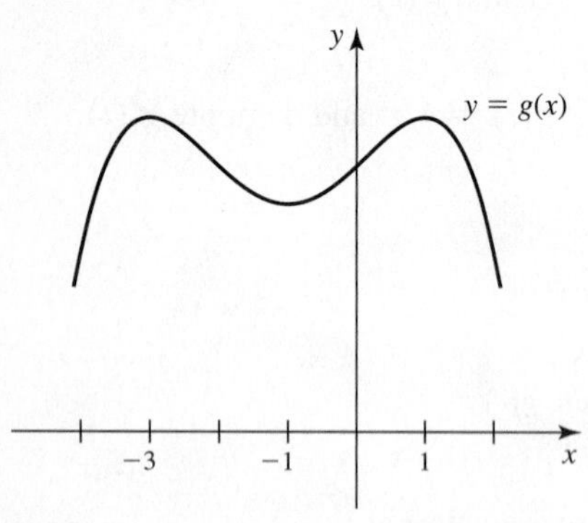

FIGURE 3.13

EXAMPLE 7 **Graph of the derivative** Sketch the graph of g' using the graph of g (Figure 3.13).

SOLUTION Without an equation for g, the best we can do is to find the general shape of the graph of g'. Here are the key observations.

1. First note that the lines tangent to the graph of g at $x = -3, -1$, and 1 have a slope of 0. Therefore,
$$g'(-3) = g'(-1) = g'(1) = 0,$$
which means the graph of g' has x-intercepts at these points (Figure 3.14).
2. For $x < -3$, the slopes of the tangent lines are positive and decrease to 0 as x approaches -3 from the left. Therefore, $g'(x)$ is positive for $x < -3$ and decreases to 0 as x approaches -3.
3. For $-3 < x < -1$, $g'(x)$ is negative; it initially decreases as x increases and then increases to 0 at $x = -1$. For $-1 < x < 1$, $g'(x)$ is positive; it initially increases as x increases and then returns to 0 at $x = 1$.

4. Finally, $g'(x)$ is negative and decreasing for $x > 1$. Because the slope of g changes gradually, the graph of g' is continuous with no jumps or breaks.

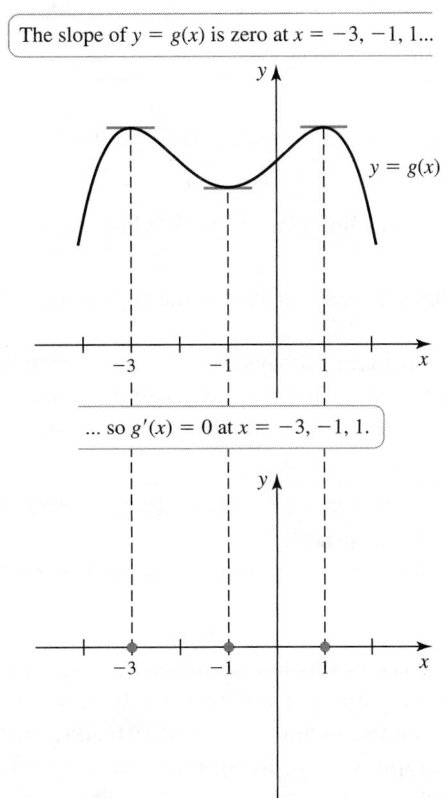

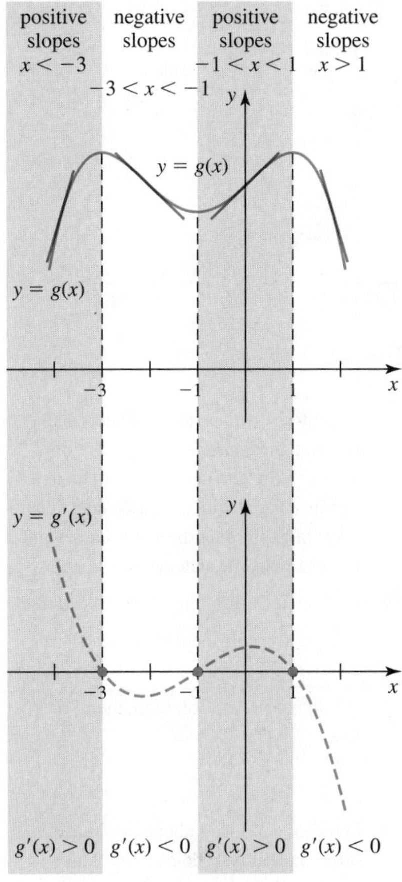

FIGURE 3.14

Related Exercises 39–44

Continuity

We now return to the discussion of continuity (Section 2.6) and investigate the relationship between continuity and differentiability. Specifically, we show that if a function is differentiable at a point, then it is also continuous at that point.

> **THEOREM 3.1 Differentiable Implies Continuous**
> If f is differentiable at a, then f is continuous at a.

Proof Assume f is differentiable at a point a, which implies that

$$f'(a) = \lim_{x \to a} \frac{f(x) - f(a)}{x - a}$$

exists. To show that f is continuous at a, we must show that $\lim_{x \to a} f(x) = f(a)$. The key is the identity

> Expression (3) is an identity because it holds for all values of $x \neq a$, which can be seen by canceling $x - a$ and simplifying.

$$f(x) = \frac{f(x) - f(a)}{x - a}(x - a) + f(a), \qquad x \neq a. \qquad (3)$$

Taking the limit as x approaches a on both sides of (3) and simplifying, we have

$$\begin{aligned}\lim_{x\to a} f(x) &= \lim_{x\to a}\left[\frac{f(x)-f(a)}{x-a}(x-a)+f(a)\right] && \text{Use identity.}\\ &= \underbrace{\lim_{x\to a}\left(\frac{f(x)-f(a)}{x-a}\right)}_{f'(a)}\underbrace{\lim_{x\to a}(x-a)}_{0}+\underbrace{\lim_{x\to a} f(a)}_{f(a)} && \text{Theorem 2.3}\\ &= f'(a)\cdot 0+f(a) && \text{Evaluate limits.}\\ &= f(a). && \text{Simplify.}\end{aligned}$$

Therefore, $\lim_{x\to a} f(x) = f(a)$, which means that f is continuous at a.

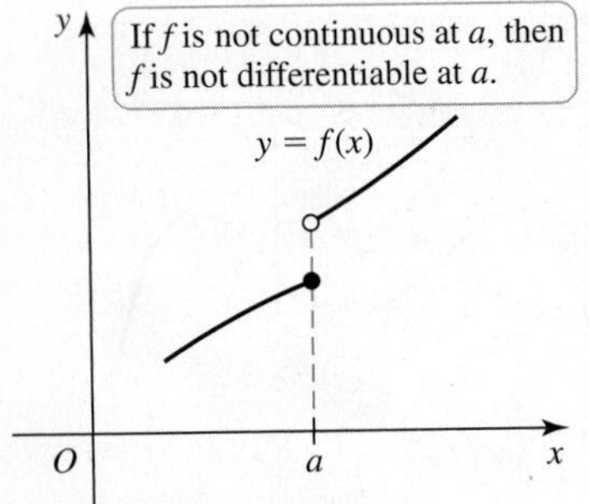

FIGURE 3.15

QUICK CHECK 9 Verify that the right-hand side of (3) equals $f(x)$ if $x \neq a$.

Theorem 3.1 says that if f is differentiable at a point, then it is necessarily continuous at that point. Therefore, if f is *not* continuous at a point, then f is *not* differentiable there (Figure 3.15). So, Theorem 3.1 can be stated in another way.

> The alternative version of Theorem 3.1 is called the *contrapositive* of the first statement of Theorem 3.1. A statement and its contrapositive are two equivalent ways of expressing the same statement. For example, the statement
>
> If I live in Denver, then I live in Colorado
>
> is logically equivalent to its contrapositive:
>
> If I do not live in Colorado, then I do not live in Denver.

THEOREM 3.1 (ALTERNATIVE VERSION) Not Continuous Implies Not Differentiable
If f is not continuous at a, then f is not differentiable at a.

It is tempting to read more into Theorem 3.1 than what it actually states. If f is continuous at a point, f is *not* necessarily differentiable at that point. For example, consider the continuous function in Figure 3.16 and note the **corner point** at a. Ignoring the portion of the graph for $x > a$, we might be tempted to conclude that ℓ_1 is the line tangent to the curve at a. Ignoring the part of the graph for $x < a$, we might incorrectly conclude that ℓ_2 is the line tangent to the curve at a. The slopes of ℓ_1 and ℓ_2 are not equal. Because of the abrupt change in the slope of the curve at a, f is not differentiable at a: The limit that defines f' does not exist at a.

> To avoid confusion about continuity and differentiability, it helps to think about the function $f(x) = |x|$: It is continuous everywhere but not differentiable at 0.

> Continuity requires that $\lim_{x\to a}(f(x) - f(a)) = 0$.
> Differentiability requires more: $\lim_{x\to a}\frac{f(x)-f(a)}{x-a}$ must exist.

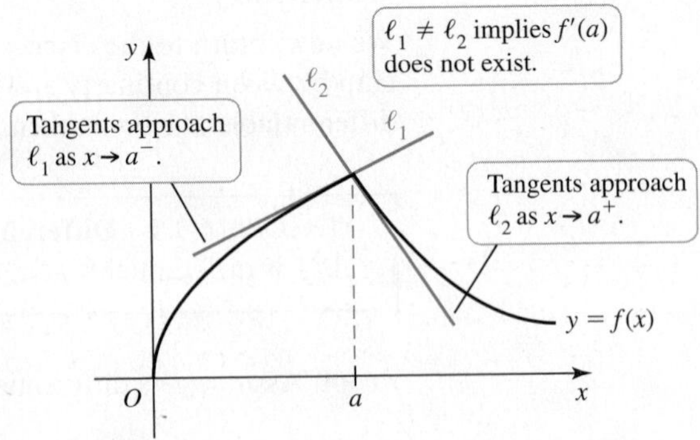

FIGURE 3.16

> See Exercises 61–64 for a formal definition of a vertical tangent line.

Another common situation occurs when the graph of a function f has a vertical tangent line at a. In this case, $f'(a)$ is undefined because the slope of a vertical line is undefined. A vertical tangent line may occur at a sharp point on the curve called a **cusp** (for example, the function $f(x) = \sqrt{|x|}$ in Figure 3.17a). In other cases, a vertical tangent line may occur without a cusp (for example, the function $f(x) = \sqrt[3]{x}$ in Figure 3.17b).

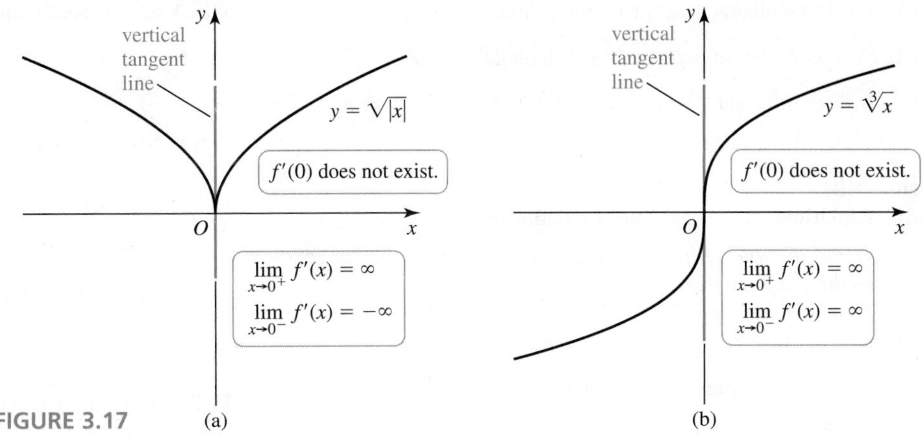

FIGURE 3.17

When Is a Function Not Differentiable at a Point?

A function f is *not* differentiable at a if at least one of the following conditions holds.

a. f is not continuous at a (Figure 3.15).

b. f has a corner at a (Figure 3.16).

c. f has a vertical tangent at a (Figure 3.17).

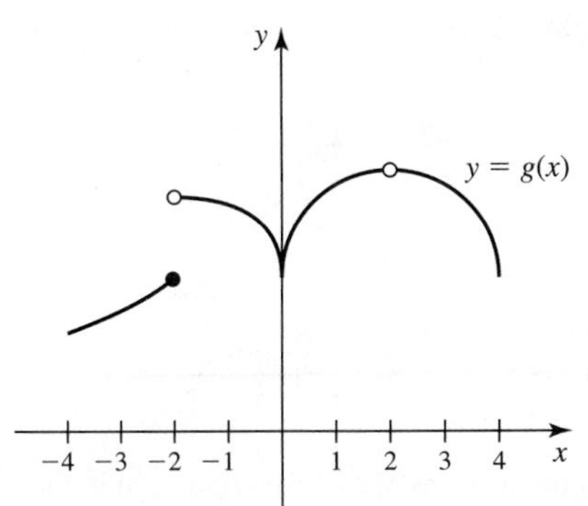

FIGURE 3.18

EXAMPLE 8 **Continuous and differentiable** Consider the graph of g in Figure 3.18.

a. Find the values of x in the interval $(-4, 4)$ at which g is not continuous.

b. Find the values of x in the interval $(-4, 4)$ at which g is not differentiable.

c. Sketch a graph of the derivative of g.

SOLUTION

a. The function g fails to be continuous at $x = -2$ (where the one-sided limits are not equal) and at $x = 2$ (where g is not defined).

b. Because it is not continuous at $x = \pm 2$, g is not differentiable at those points. Furthermore, g is not differentiable at $x = 0$, because the graph has a cusp at that point.

c. A rough sketch of the derivative (Figure 3.19) has the following features:

- $g'(x) > 0$, for $-4 < x < -2$ and $0 < x < 2$.
- $g'(x) < 0$, for $-2 < x < 0$ and $2 < x < 4$.
- $g'(x)$ approaches $-\infty$ as $x \to 0^-$ and $g'(x)$ approaches ∞ as $x \to 0^+$.
- $g'(x)$ approaches 0 as $x \to 2$ from either side, although $g'(2)$ does not exist.

Related Exercises 45–46 ◀

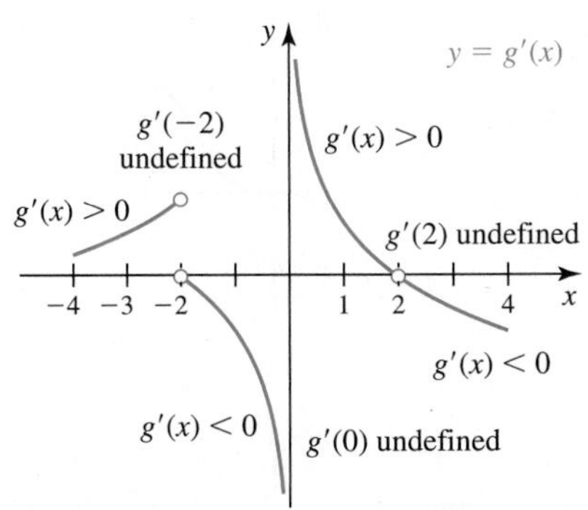

FIGURE 3.19

SECTION 3.1 EXERCISES

Review Questions

1. Use definition (1) for the slope of a tangent line to explain how slopes of secant lines approach the slope of the tangent line at a point.

2. Explain why the slope of a secant line can be interpreted as an average rate of change.

3. Explain why the slope of the tangent line can be interpreted as an instantaneous rate of change.

4. Given the function f, what does f' represent?

5. Given a function f and a point a in its domain, what does $f'(a)$ represent?

6. Explain the relationships among the slope of a tangent line, the instantaneous rate of change, and the value of the derivative at a point.

7. Why is the notation $\dfrac{dy}{dx}$ used to represent the derivative?

8. If f is differentiable at a, must f be continuous at a?

9. If f is continuous at a, must f be differentiable at a?

10. Give three different notations for the derivative of f with respect to x.

Basic Skills

11–16. Equations of tangent lines by definition (1)

a. *Use definition (1) (p. 100) to find the slope of the line tangent to the graph of f at P.*
b. *Determine an equation of the tangent line at P.*
c. *Plot the graph of f and the tangent line at P.*

11. $f(x) = x^2 - 5;\ P(3, 4)$

12. $f(x) = -3x^2 - 5x + 1;\ P(1, -7)$

13. $f(x) = -5x + 1;\ P(1, -4)$ **14.** $f(x) = 5;\ P(1, 5)$

15. $f(x) = \frac{1}{x};\ P(-1, -1)$ **16.** $f(x) = \frac{4}{x^2};\ P(-1, 4)$

17–22. Equations of tangent lines by definition (2)

a. *Use definition (2) (p. 101) to find the slope of the line tangent to the graph of f at P.*
b. *Determine an equation of the tangent line at P.*

17. $f(x) = 2x + 1;\ P(0, 1)$ **18.** $f(x) = 3x^2 - 4x;\ P(1, -1)$

19. $f(x) = x^4;\ P(-1, 1)$ **20.** $f(x) = \frac{1}{2x + 1};\ P(0, 1)$

21. $f(x) = \frac{1}{3 - 2x};\ P\left(-1, \frac{1}{5}\right)$ **22.** $f(x) = \sqrt{x - 1};\ P(2, 1)$

23–28. Derivatives and tangent lines

a. *For the following functions and points, find $f'(a)$.*
b. *Determine an equation of the line tangent to the graph of f at $(a, f(a))$ for the given value of a.*

23. $f(x) = 8x;\ a = -3$ **24.** $f(x) = x^2;\ a = 3$

25. $f(x) = 4x^2 + 2x;\ a = -2$ **26.** $f(x) = 2x^3;\ a = 10$

27. $f(x) = \frac{1}{\sqrt{x}};\ a = 1/4$ **28.** $f(x) = \frac{1}{x^2};\ a = 1$

29–32. Lines tangent to parabolas

a. *Find the derivative function f' for the following functions f.*
b. *Find an equation of the line tangent to the graph of f at $(a, f(a))$ for the given value of a.*
c. *Graph f and the tangent line.*

29. $f(x) = 3x^2 + 2x - 10;\ a = 1$ **30.** $f(x) = 3x^2;\ a = 0$

31. $f(x) = 5x^2 - 6x + 1;\ a = 2$ **32.** $f(x) = 1 - x^2;\ a = -1$

33. A derivative formula

a. Use the definition of the derivative to determine $\frac{d}{dx}(ax^2 + bx + c)$, where a, b, and c are constants.
b. Use the result of part (a) to find $\frac{d}{dx}(4x^2 - 3x + 10)$.

34. A derivative formula

a. Use the definition of the derivative to determine $\frac{d}{dx}(\sqrt{ax + b})$, where a and b are constants.
b. Use the result of part (a) to find $\frac{d}{dx}(\sqrt{5x + 9})$.

35–38. Derivative calculations *Evaluate the derivative of the following functions at the given point.*

35. $y = 1/(t + 1);\ t = 1$ **36.** $y = t - t^2;\ t = 2$

37. $c = 2\sqrt{s} - 1;\ s = 25$ **38.** $A = \pi r^2;\ r = 3$

39–40. Derivatives from graphs *Use the graph of f to sketch a graph of f'.*

39.

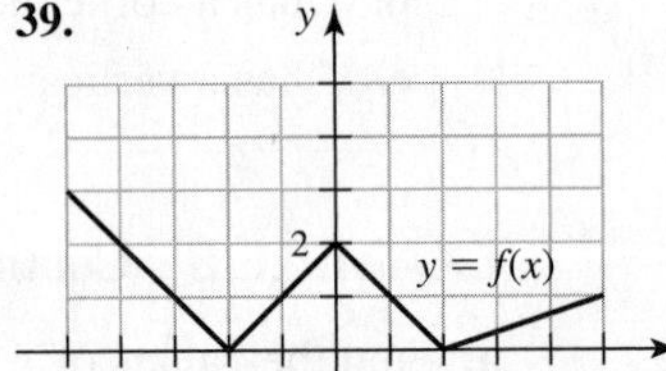

40.

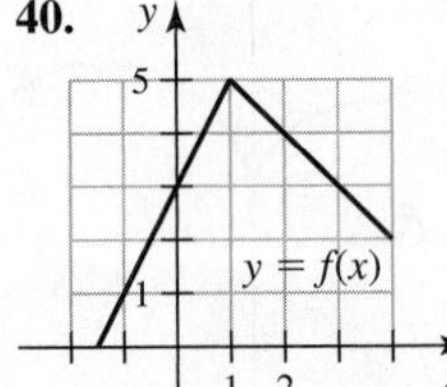

41. Matching functions with derivatives Match functions a–d in the first set of figures with derivative functions A–D in the next set of figures.

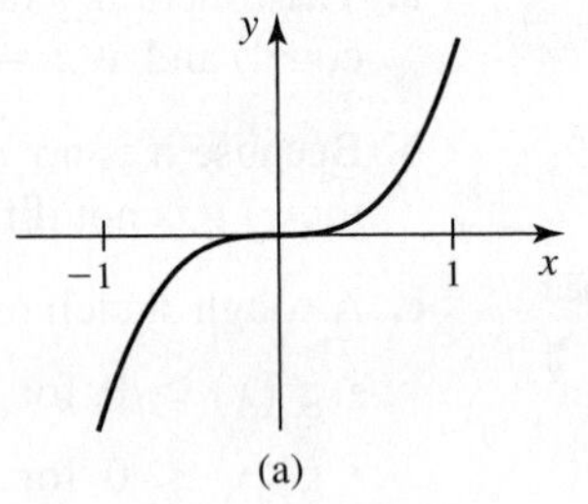

(a)

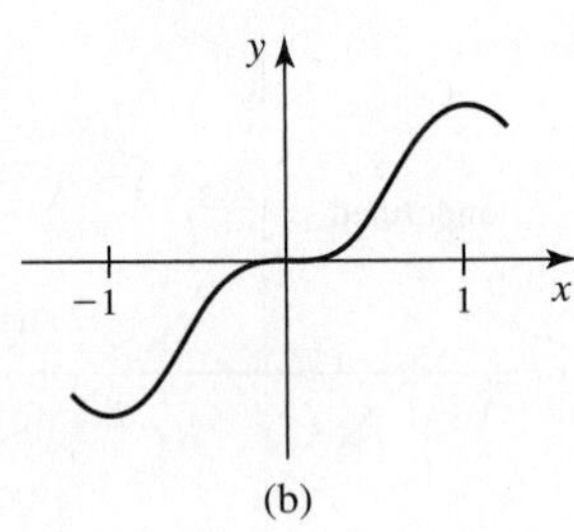

(b)

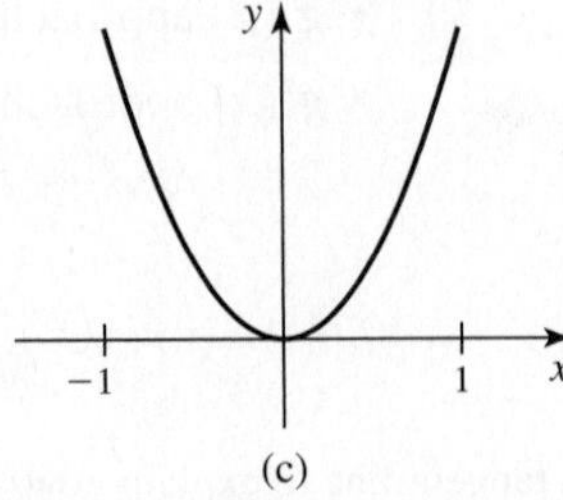

(c)

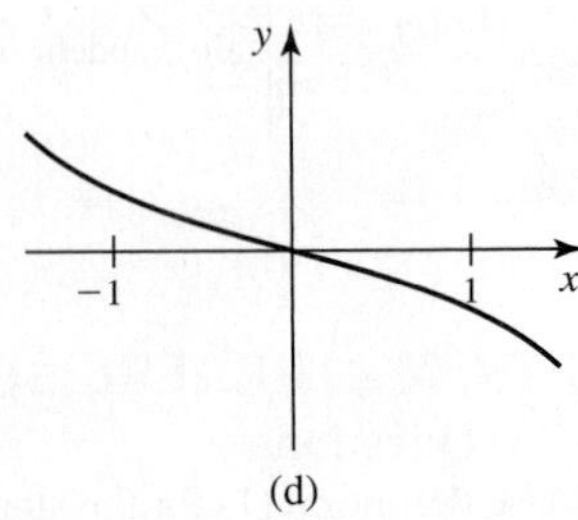

(d)

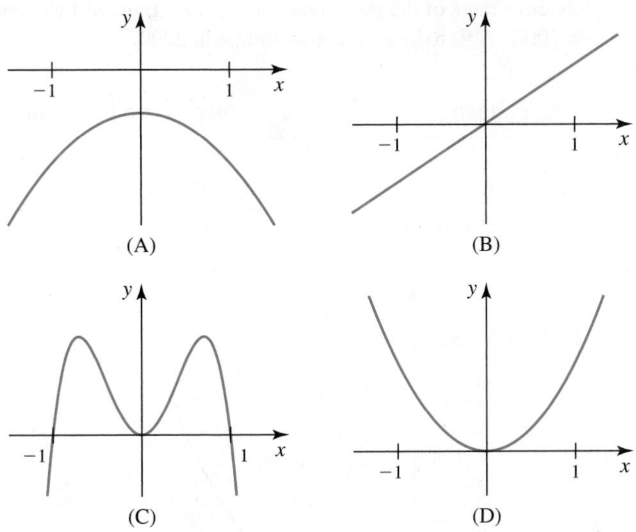

42–44. Sketching derivatives *Reproduce the graph of f and then sketch a graph of f' on the same axes.*

42.

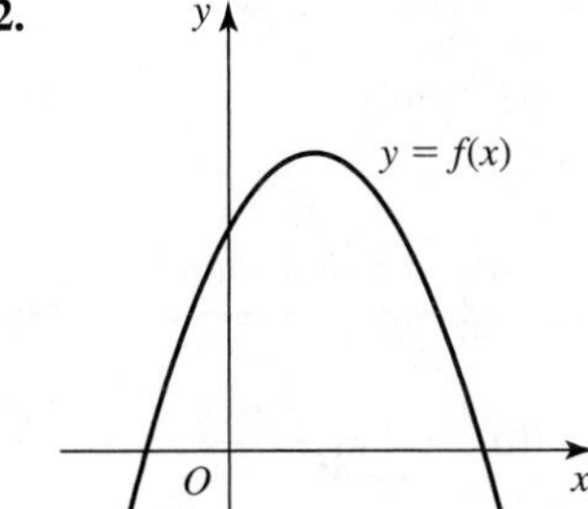

43.

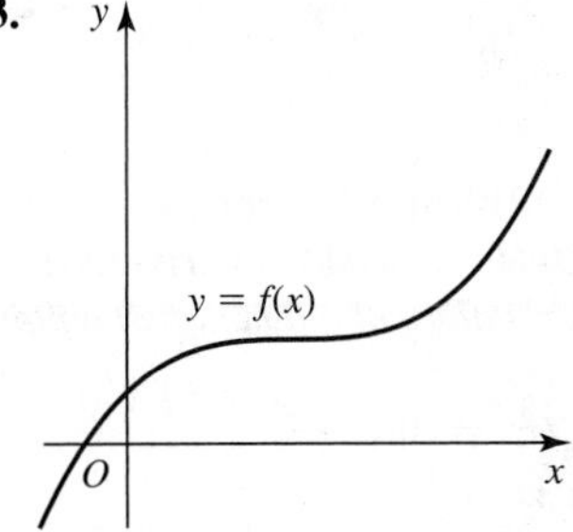

44.

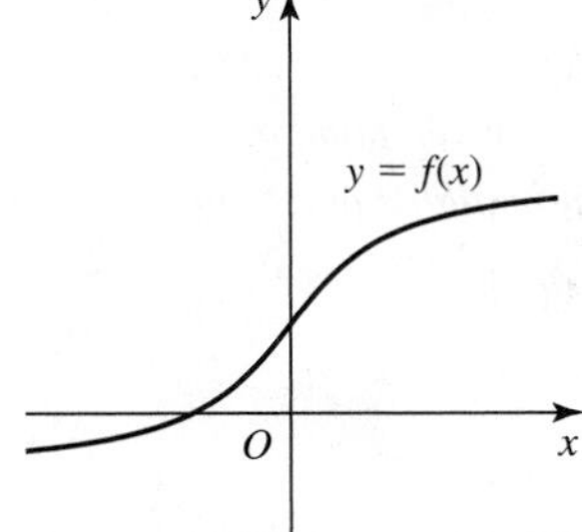

45. Where is the function continuous? Differentiable? Use the graph of f in the figure to do the following.

a. Find the values of x in $(0, 3)$ at which f is not continuous.
b. Find the values of x in $(0, 3)$ at which f is not differentiable.
c. Sketch a graph of f'.

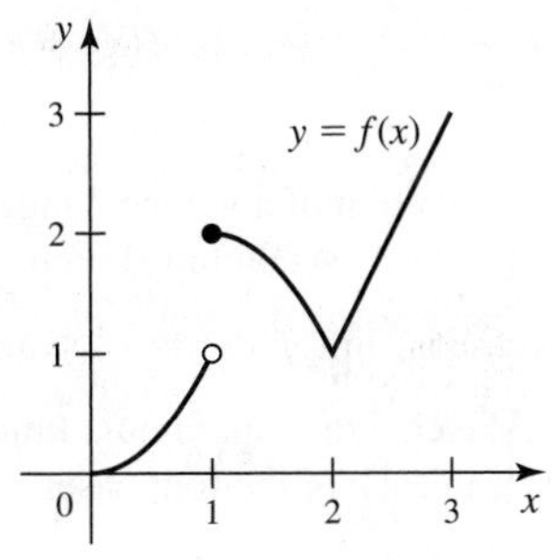

46. Where is the function continuous? Differentiable? Use the graph of g in the figure to do the following.

a. Find the values of x in $(0, 4)$ at which g is not continuous.
b. Find the values of x in $(0, 4)$ at which g is not differentiable.
c. Sketch a graph of g'.

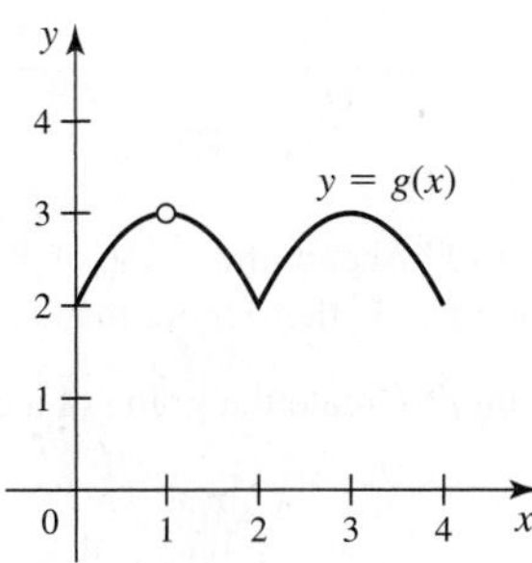

Further Explorations

47. Explain why or why not Determine whether the following statements are true and give an explanation or counterexample.

a. For linear functions, the slope of any secant line always equals the slope of any tangent line.
b. The slope of the secant line passing through the points P and Q is less than the slope of the tangent line at P.
c. Consider the graph of the parabola $f(x) = x^2$. For $x > 0$ and $h > 0$, the secant line through $(x, f(x))$ and $(x + h, f(x + h))$ always has a greater slope than the tangent line at $(x, f(x))$.
d. If the function f is differentiable for all values of x, then f is continuous for all values of x.

48. Slope of a line Consider the line $f(x) = mx + b$, where m and b are constants. Show that $f'(x) = m$ for all x. Interpret this result.

49–52. Calculating derivatives

a. For the following functions, find f' using the definition.
b. Determine an equation of the line tangent to the graph of f at $(a, f(a))$ for the given value of a.

49. $f(x) = \sqrt{3x + 1};\ a = 8$

50. $f(x) = \sqrt{x + 2};\ a = 7$

51. $f(x) = \dfrac{2}{3x + 1};\ a = -1$

52. $f(x) = \dfrac{1}{x};\ a = -5$

53–54. Analyzing slopes *Use the points A, B, C, D, and E in the following graphs to answer these questions.*

a. At which point(s) is the slope of the curve negative?
b. At which point(s) is the slope of the curve positive?
c. Using A–E, list the slopes in decreasing order.

53.

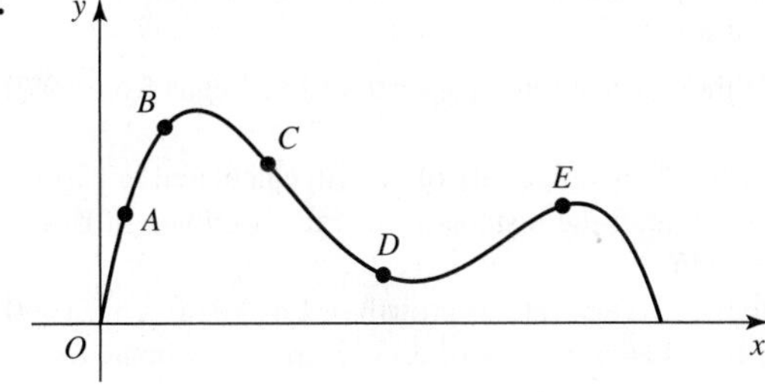

54.

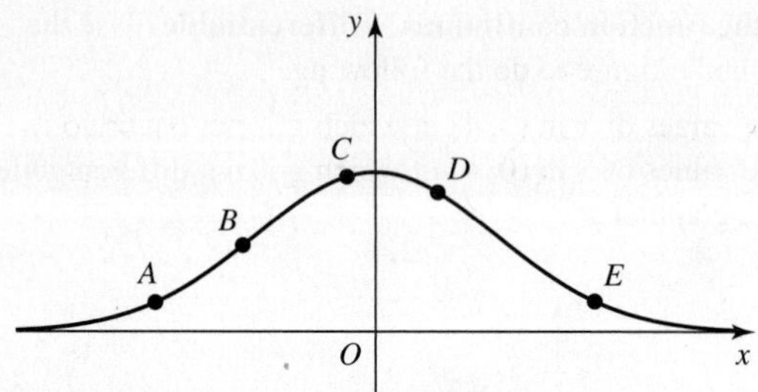

55. **Finding f from f'** Sketch the graph of $f'(x) = x$. Then, sketch a possible graph of f. Is there more than one possible graph?

56. **Finding f from f'** Create the graph of a continuous function f such that

$$f'(x) = \begin{cases} 1 & \text{if } x < 0 \\ 0 & \text{if } 0 < x < 1 \\ -1 & \text{if } x > 1 \end{cases}$$

Is there more than one possible graph?

Applications

57. **Power and energy** Energy is the capacity to do work and power is the rate at which energy is used or consumed. Therefore, if $E(t)$ is the energy function for a system, then $P(t) = E'(t)$ is the power function. A unit of energy is the kilowatt-hour (1 kWh is the amount of energy needed to light ten 100-W light bulbs for an hour); the corresponding units for power are kW. The following figure shows the energy consumed by a small community over a 25-hr period.

   a. Estimate the power at $t = 10$ and $t = 20$. Be sure to include units in your calculation.
   b. At what times on the interval $[0, 25]$ is the power zero?
   c. At what times on the interval $[0, 25]$ is the power a maximum?

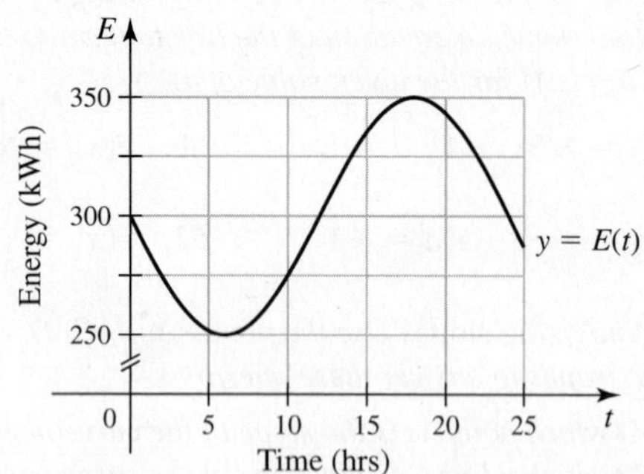

58. **Population of Las Vegas** Let $p(t)$ represent the population of the Las Vegas metropolitan area t years after 1950, as shown in the table and figure.

   a. Compute the average rate of growth of Las Vegas from 1970 to 1980.
   b. Explain why the average rate of growth calculated in part (a) is a good estimate of the instantaneous rate of growth of Las Vegas in 1975.
   c. Compute the average rate of growth of Las Vegas from 1990 to 2000. Is this average rate of growth an overestimate or underestimate of the instantaneous rate of growth of Las Vegas in 2000? Approximate the growth rate in 2000.

Year	1950	1960	1970	1980	1990	2000
t	0	10	20	30	40	50
$p(t)$	59,900	139,126	304,744	528,000	852,737	1,563,282

Source: U.S. Bureau of Census

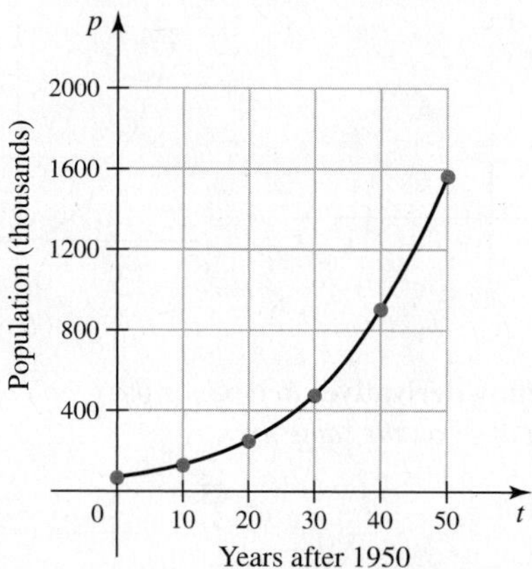

Additional Exercises

59–60. One-sided derivatives *The* ***left-hand*** *and* ***right-hand derivatives*** *of a function at a point a are given by*

$$f'_+(a) = \lim_{h\to 0^+} \frac{f(a+h) - f(a)}{h} \quad \text{and} \quad f'_-(a) = \lim_{h\to 0^-} \frac{f(a+h) - f(a)}{h}$$

provided these limits exist. The derivative $f'(a)$ exists if and only if $f'_+(a) = f'_-(a)$.

   a. Sketch the following functions.
   b. Compute $f'_+(a)$ and $f'_-(a)$ at the given point a.
   c. Is f continuous at a? Is f differentiable at a?

59. $f(x) = |x - 2|;\ a = 2$

60. $f(x) = \begin{cases} 4 - x^2 & \text{if } x \le 1 \\ 2x + 1 & \text{if } x > 1 \end{cases};\ a = 1$

61–64. Vertical tangent lines *If a function f is continuous at a and $\lim_{x\to a} |f'(x)| = \infty$, then the curve $y = f(x)$ has a vertical tangent line at a and the equation of the tangent line is $x = a$. If a is an endpoint of a domain, then the appropriate one-sided derivative (Exercises 59–60) is used. Use this definition to answer the following questions.*

61. Graph the following functions and determine the location of the vertical tangent lines.

   a. $f(x) = (x - 2)^{1/3}$
   b. $f(x) = (x + 1)^{2/3}$
   c. $f(x) = \sqrt{|x - 4|}$
   d. $f(x) = x^{5/3} - 2x^{1/3}$

62. The preceding definition of a vertical tangent line includes four cases: $\lim_{x\to a^+} f'(x) = \pm\infty$ combined with $\lim_{x\to a^-} f'(x) = \pm\infty$ (for example, one case is $\lim_{x\to a^+} f'(x) = -\infty$ and $\lim_{x\to a^-} f'(x) = \infty$). Make a rough sketch of a (continuous) function that has a vertical tangent line at a in each of the four cases.

63. Verify that $f(x) = x^{1/3}$ has a vertical tangent line at $x = 0$.

64. Graph the following curves and determine the location of any vertical tangent lines.

a. $x^2 + y^2 = 9$ b. $x^2 + y^2 + 2x = 0$

65–68. **Find the function** *The following limits represent the slope of a curve $y = f(x)$ at the point $(a, f(a))$. Determine a function f and a number a; then, calculate the limit.*

65. $\lim_{x\to 2} \dfrac{\frac{1}{x+1} - \frac{1}{3}}{x - 2}$

66. $\lim_{h\to 0} \dfrac{\sqrt{2+h} - \sqrt{2}}{h}$

67. $\lim_{h\to 0} \dfrac{(2+h)^4 - 16}{h}$

68. $\lim_{x\to 1} \dfrac{3x^2 + 4x - 7}{x - 1}$

69. **Is it differentiable?** Is $f(x) = \dfrac{x^2 - 5x + 6}{x - 2}$ differentiable at $x = 2$? Justify your answer.

70. **Looking ahead: Derivative of x^n** Use the symbolic capabilities of a calculator to calculate $f'(x)$ using the definition $\lim_{h\to 0} \dfrac{f(x+h) - f(x)}{h}$ for the following functions.

a. $f(x) = x^2$ b. $f(x) = x^3$ c. $f(x) = x^4$

d. Based upon your answers to parts (a)–(c), propose a formula for $f'(x)$ if $f(x) = x^n$ where n is a positive integer.

71. **Determining the unknown constant** Let

$$f(x) = \begin{cases} 2x^2 & \text{if } x \le 1 \\ ax - 2 & \text{if } x > 1 \end{cases}$$

Determine a value of a (if possible) for which $f'(1)$ exists.

72. **Graph of the derivative of the sine curve**

a. Use the graph of $y = \sin x$ (see figure) to sketch the graph of the derivative of the sine function.

b. Based upon your graph in part (a), what function equals $\dfrac{d}{dx}(\sin x)$?

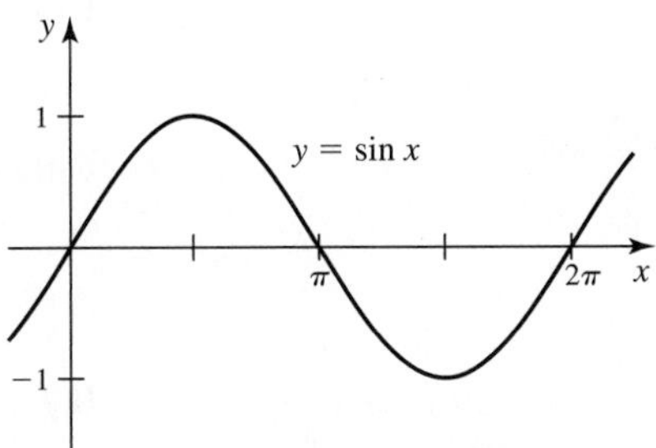

QUICK CHECK ANSWERS

2. Less 3. Definition (1) requires factoring the numerator or long division in order to cancel $(x - 1)$. 4. 32 5. $\left.\dfrac{df}{dx}\right|_{x=3}, \left.\dfrac{dy}{dx}\right|_{x=3}, y'(3)$ 6. The slopes of tangent lines decrease as x increases. The values of $f'(x) = \dfrac{1}{2\sqrt{x}}$ also decrease as x increases. 7. $\dfrac{dq}{dr}, \dfrac{dp}{dr}, D_r(q(r)), q'(r), p'(r)$ 8. The slopes of the tangent lines change abruptly at $x = -2$ and 0.

3.2 Rules of Differentiation

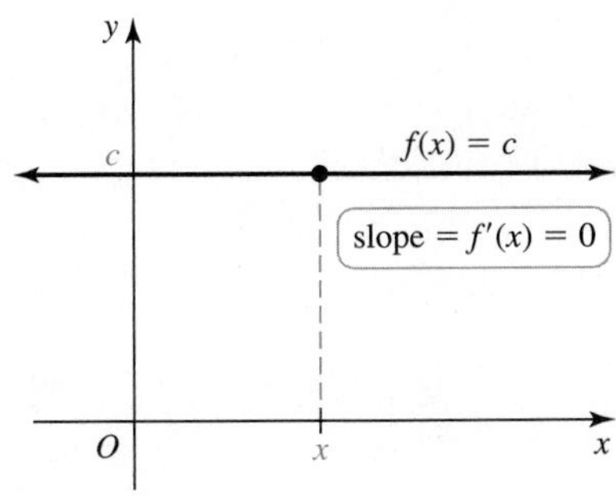

FIGURE 3.20

➤ We expect the derivative of a constant function to be 0 at every point because the values of a constant function do not change. This means the instantaneous rate of change is 0 at every point.

If you always had to use limits to evaluate derivatives, as we did in Section 3.1, calculus would be a tedious affair. The goal of this section is to establish rules and formulas for quickly evaluating derivatives—not just for individual functions but for entire families of functions.

The Constant and Power Rules for Derivatives

The graph of the **constant function** $f(x) = c$ is a horizontal line with a slope of 0 at every point (Figure 3.20). It follows that $f'(x) = 0$ or, equivalently, $\dfrac{d}{dx}(c) = 0$ (Exercise 64).

> **THEOREM 3.2 Constant Rule**
>
> If c is a real number, then $\dfrac{d}{dx}(c) = 0$.

QUICK CHECK 1 Find the values of $\frac{d}{dx}(5)$ and $\frac{d}{dx}(\pi)$. ◀

Next, consider power functions of the form $f(x) = x^n$, where n is a positive integer. If you completed Exercise 70 in Section 3.1, you found that

$$\frac{d}{dx}(x^2) = 2x, \quad \frac{d}{dx}(x^3) = 3x^2, \quad \text{and} \quad \frac{d}{dx}(x^4) = 4x^3.$$

In each case, the derivative of x^n appears to be evaluated by placing the exponent n in front of x as a coefficient and decreasing the exponent by 1; in other words, for positive integers n, $\frac{d}{dx}(x^n) = nx^{n-1}$. To verify this conjecture, we use the definition of the derivative in the form

$$f'(a) = \lim_{x \to a} \frac{f(x) - f(a)}{x - a}.$$

➤ Note that this formula agrees with familiar factoring formulas for differences of perfect squares and cubes:

$$x^2 - a^2 = (x - a)(x + a)$$

$$x^3 - a^3 = (x - a)(x^2 + ax + a^2)$$

If $f(x) = x^n$, then $f(x) - f(a) = x^n - a^n$. A factoring formula gives

$$x^n - a^n = (x - a)(x^{n-1} + x^{n-2}a + \cdots + xa^{n-2} + a^{n-1}).$$

Therefore,

$$\begin{aligned} f'(a) &= \lim_{x \to a} \frac{x^n - a^n}{x - a} && \text{Definition of } f'(a) \\ &= \lim_{x \to a} \frac{(x - a)(x^{n-1} + x^{n-2}a + \cdots + xa^{n-2} + a^{n-1})}{x - a} && \text{Factor } x^n - a^n. \\ &= \lim_{x \to a} (x^{n-1} + x^{n-2}a + \cdots + xa^{n-2} + a^{n-1}) && \text{Cancel common factors.} \\ &= \underbrace{a^{n-1} + a^{n-2}\cdot a + \cdots + a \cdot a^{n-2} + a^{n-1}}_{n \text{ times } a^{n-1}} = na^{n-1}. && \text{Evaluate the limit.} \end{aligned}$$

Replacing a by the variable x in $f'(a) = na^{n-1}$, we obtain the following result, known as the *Power Rule.*

➤ The $n = 0$ case of the Power Rule is the Constant Rule. You will see several versions of the Power Rule as we progress. It is extended first to integer powers, both positive and negative, then to rational powers, and, finally, to real powers.

THEOREM 3.3 Power Rule

If n is a positive integer, then $\frac{d}{dx}(x^n) = nx^{n-1}$.

EXAMPLE 1 Derivatives of power and constant functions Evaluate the following derivatives.

a. $\frac{d}{dx}(x^9)$ **b.** $\frac{d}{dx}(x)$ **c.** $\frac{d}{dx}(2^8)$

SOLUTION

a. $\frac{d}{dx}(x^9) = 9x^{9-1} = 9x^8$ Power Rule

b. $\frac{d}{dx}(x) = \frac{d}{dx}(x^1) = 1x^0 = 1$ Power Rule

c. You might be tempted to use the Power Rule here, but $2^8 = 256$ is a constant. So, by the Constant Rule, $\frac{d}{dx}(2^8) = 0$.

Related Exercises 7–12 ◀

QUICK CHECK 2 Use the graph of $y = x$ to give a geometric explanation of why $\frac{d}{dx}(x) = 1$. ◀

Constant Multiple Rule

Consider the problem of finding the derivative of a constant c multiplied by a function f (assuming that f' exists). We apply the definition of the derivative in the form

$$f'(x) = \lim_{h \to 0} \frac{f(x + h) - f(x)}{h}$$

to the function cf:

$$\begin{aligned}\frac{d}{dx}[cf(x)] &= \lim_{h \to 0} \frac{cf(x + h) - cf(x)}{h} && \text{Definition of the derivative of } cf \\ &= \lim_{h \to 0} \frac{c[f(x + h) - f(x)]}{h} && \text{Factor out } c. \\ &= c \lim_{h \to 0} \frac{f(x + h) - f(x)}{h} && \text{Theorem 2.3} \\ &= cf'(x) && \text{Definition of } f'(x)\end{aligned}$$

THEOREM 3.4 Constant Multiple Rule
If f is differentiable at x and c is a constant, then

$$\frac{d}{dx}[cf(x)] = cf'(x).$$

➤ Theorem 3.4 says that the derivative of a constant multiplied by a function is the constant multiplied by the derivative of the function.

EXAMPLE 2 Derivatives of constant multiples of functions Evaluate the following derivatives.

a. $\frac{d}{dx}\left(-\frac{7x^{11}}{8}\right)$ **b.** $\frac{d}{dt}\left(\frac{3}{8}\sqrt{t}\right)$

SOLUTION

a.

$$\begin{aligned}\frac{d}{dx}\left(-\frac{7x^{11}}{8}\right) &= -\frac{7}{8} \cdot \frac{d}{dx}(x^{11}) && \text{Constant Multiple Rule} \\ &= -\frac{7}{8} \cdot 11x^{10} && \text{Power Rule} \\ &= -\frac{77}{8}x^{10} && \text{Simplify.}\end{aligned}$$

b.

$$\begin{aligned}\frac{d}{dt}\left(\frac{3}{8}\sqrt{t}\right) &= \frac{3}{8} \cdot \frac{d}{dt}(\sqrt{t}) && \text{Constant Multiple Rule} \\ &= \frac{3}{8} \cdot \frac{1}{2\sqrt{t}} && \text{Replace } \frac{d}{dt}(\sqrt{t}) \text{ by } \frac{1}{2\sqrt{t}}. \\ &= \frac{3}{16\sqrt{t}}\end{aligned}$$

➤ Recall from Example 4 of Section 3.1 that $\frac{d}{dt}(\sqrt{t}) = \frac{1}{2\sqrt{t}}$.

Related Exercises 13–18 ◄

Sum Rule

Many functions are sums of simpler functions. Therefore, it is useful to establish a rule for calculating the derivative of the sum of two or more functions.

> In words, Theorem 3.5 states that the derivative of a sum is the sum of the derivatives.

THEOREM 3.5 Sum Rule
If f and g are differentiable at x, then

$$\frac{d}{dx}[f(x) + g(x)] = f'(x) + g'(x).$$

Proof Let $F = f + g$, where f and g are differentiable at x and use the definition of the derivative:

$$\begin{aligned}
\frac{d}{dx}[f(x) + g(x)] &= F'(x) \\
&= \lim_{h\to 0}\frac{F(x+h) - F(x)}{h} && \text{Definition of derivative} \\
&= \lim_{h\to 0}\frac{[f(x+h) + g(x+h)] - [f(x) + g(x)]}{h} && \text{Replace } F \text{ with } f + g. \\
&= \lim_{h\to 0}\left[\frac{f(x+h) - f(x)}{h} + \frac{g(x+h) - g(x)}{h}\right] && \text{Regroup.} \\
&= \lim_{h\to 0}\frac{f(x+h) - f(x)}{h} + \lim_{h\to 0}\frac{g(x+h) - g(x)}{h} && \text{Theorem 2.3} \\
&= f'(x) + g'(x) && \text{Definition of } f' \text{ and } g'
\end{aligned}$$

QUICK CHECK 3 If $f(x) = x^2$ and $g(x) = 2x$, what is the derivative of $f(x) + g(x)$?

The Sum Rule can be extended to three or more differentiable functions, $f_1, f_2, \ldots, f_n$, to obtain the **Generalized Sum Rule**:

$$\frac{d}{dx}[f_1(x) + f_2(x) + \cdots + f_n(x)] = f_1'(x) + f_2'(x) + \cdots + f_n'(x)$$

The difference of two functions $f - g$ can be rewritten as the sum $f + (-g)$. By combining the Sum Rule with the Constant Multiple Rule, the **Difference Rule** is established:

$$\frac{d}{dx}[f(x) - g(x)] = f'(x) - g'(x)$$

EXAMPLE 3 Derivative of a polynomial Determine $\frac{d}{dw}(2w^3 + 9w^2 - 6w + 4)$.

SOLUTION

$$\begin{aligned}
&\frac{d}{dw}(2w^3 + 9w^2 - 6w + 4) \\
&= \frac{d}{dw}(2w^3) + \frac{d}{dw}(9w^2) - \frac{d}{dw}(6w) + \frac{d}{dw}(4) && \text{Generalized Sum Rule and Difference Rule} \\
&= 2\frac{d}{dw}(w^3) + 9\frac{d}{dw}(w^2) - 6\frac{d}{dw}(w) + \frac{d}{dw}(4) && \text{Constant Multiple Rule} \\
&= 2\cdot 3w^2 + 9\cdot 2w - 6\cdot 1 + 0 && \text{Power Rule} \\
&= 6w^2 + 18w - 6 && \text{Simplify.}
\end{aligned}$$

Related Exercises 19–34

The technique used to differentiate the polynomial in Example 3 may be used for *any* polynomial. Much of the remainder of this chapter is devoted to discovering rules of differentiation for rational, algebraic, and trigonometric functions.

Slopes of Tangent Lines

The derivative rules presented in this section allow us to determine slopes of tangent lines, equations of tangent lines, and rates of change for many functions.

EXAMPLE 4 **Slopes and equations of tangent lines** Let $f(x) = 2x^3 - 15x^2 + 24x$.

a. Find an equation of the line tangent to the graph of f at the point $(2, 4)$.

b. At what points on the graph of f is the tangent line horizontal?

c. For what values of x does the tangent line have a slope of 6?

SOLUTION

a. In general, the line tangent to the graph of f at the point $(x, f(x))$ has slope

$$f'(x) = 6x^2 - 30x + 24.$$

At the point $(2, 4)$, the tangent line has slope $f'(2) = -12$. Therefore, an equation of the tangent line passing through $(2, 4)$ is

$$y - 4 = -12(x - 2) \quad \text{or} \quad y = -12x + 28.$$

b. The line tangent to the graph of f is horizontal at values of x that satisfy

$$f'(x) = 6x^2 - 30x + 24 = 6(x - 4)(x - 1) = 0.$$

The solutions of this equation are $x = 1$ and $x = 4$; therefore, horizontal tangent lines can be found at the points $(1, 11)$ and $(4, -16)$ (Figure 3.21).

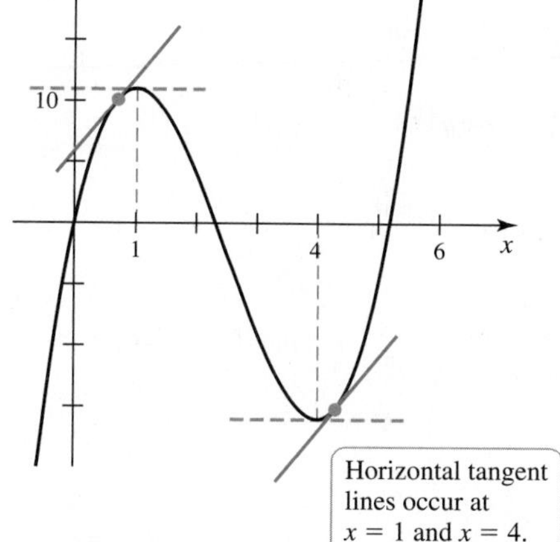

FIGURE 3.21

c. The tangent line has a slope of 6 when

$$f'(x) = 6x^2 - 30x + 24 = 6.$$

Subtracting 6 from both sides of the equation and factoring, we have

$$6(x^2 - 5x + 3) = 0.$$

Using the quadratic formula, the roots are

$$x = \frac{5 - \sqrt{13}}{2} \approx 0.697 \quad \text{and} \quad x = \frac{5 + \sqrt{13}}{2} \approx 4.303.$$

Therefore, the slope of the curve at these points is 6. *Related Exercises 35–41* ◄

QUICK CHECK 4 Determine the point(s) at which $f(x) = x^3 - 12x$ has a horizontal tangent line. ◄

Higher-Order Derivatives

Because the derivative of a function f is a function in its own right, we can take the derivative of f'. The result is the *second derivative of* f, denoted f'' (read f *double prime*). The derivative of the second derivative is the *third derivative of* f, denoted f''' or $f^{(3)}$ (f *triple prime*). For any positive integer n, $f^{(n)}$ represents the nth derivative of f. Other common notations for the nth derivative of $y = f(x)$ include $\frac{d^n f}{dx^n}$ and $y^{(n)}$. In general, derivatives of order $n \geq 2$ are called **higher-order derivatives**.

➤ Parentheses are placed around n to distinguish a derivative from a power. Therefore $f^{(n)}$ is the nth derivative of f and f^n is the function f raised to the nth power.

➤ The notation $\frac{d^2 f}{dx^2}$ comes from $\frac{d}{dx}\left(\frac{df}{dx}\right)$ and is read *d 2 f dx squared.*

DEFINITION Higher-Order Derivatives

Assuming f can be differentiated as often as necessary, the **second derivative** of f is

$$f''(x) = f^{(2)}(x) = \frac{d^2f}{dx^2} = \frac{d}{dx}[f'(x)].$$

For integers $n \geq 1$, the ***n*th derivative** is

$$f^{(n)}(x) = \frac{d^nf}{dx^n} = \frac{d}{dx}[f^{(n-1)}(x)].$$

EXAMPLE 5 Finding higher-order derivatives Find the third derivative of the following functions.

a. $f(x) = 3x^3 - 5x + 12$ **b.** $y = 3t + 2t^{10}$

SOLUTION

➤ In Example 5a, note that $f^{(4)}(x) = 0$, which means that all successive derivatives are also 0. In general, the nth derivative of an nth-degree polynomial is a constant, which implies that derivatives of order $k > n$ are 0.

a.

$$f'(x) = 9x^2 - 5$$

$$f''(x) = \frac{d}{dx}(9x^2 - 5) = 18x$$

$$f'''(x) = 18$$

b. Here we use an alternative notation for higher-order derivatives:

$$\frac{dy}{dt} = \frac{d}{dt}(3t + 2t^{10}) = 3 + 20t^9$$

$$\frac{d^2y}{dt^2} = \frac{d}{dt}(3 + 20t^9) = 180t^8$$

$$\frac{d^3y}{dt^3} = \frac{d}{dt}(180t^8) = 1440t^7$$

Related Exercises 42–46 ◀

QUICK CHECK 5 With $f(x) = x^5$, find $f^{(5)}(x)$, $f^{(6)}(x)$, and $f^{(100)}(x)$. ◀

SECTION 3.2 EXERCISES

Review Questions

Assume the derivatives of f and g exist in Exercises 1–6.

1. If the limit definition of a derivative can be used to find f', then what is the purpose of using other rules to find f'?
2. In this section, it is shown that the rule $\frac{d}{dx}(x^n) = nx^{n-1}$ is valid for what values of n?
3. How do you find the derivative of a constant multiplied by a function?
4. How do you find the derivative of the sum of two functions, $f + g$?
5. Find the derivative of $f(x) = \frac{1}{2}x^6 - 3x^4 + 101x + 7$.
6. How do you find the fifth derivative of a function?

Basic Skills

7–12. Derivatives of power and constant functions *Find the derivative of the following functions.*

7. $y = x^5$ **8.** $f(t) = t^{11}$ **9.** $f(x) = 5$

10. $g(x) = \pi^3$ **11.** $h(t) = t$ **12.** $f(v) = v^{100}$

13–18. Derivatives of constant multiples of functions *Find the derivative of the following functions.*

13. $f(x) = 5x^3$ **14.** $g(w) = \frac{5}{6}w^{12}$ **15.** $p(x) = 8x$

16. $g(t) = 6\sqrt{t}$ **17.** $g(t) = 100t^2$ **18.** $f(s) = \frac{\sqrt{s}}{4}$

19–24. Derivatives of the sum of functions *Find the derivative of the following functions.*

19. $f(x) = 3x^4 + 7x$
20. $g(x) = 6x^5 - x$
21. $f(x) = 10x^4 - 32x + \frac{1}{2}$
22. $f(t) = 6\sqrt{t} - 4t^3 + 9$
23. $g(w) = 2w^3 + 3w$
24. $s(t) = 4\sqrt{t} - \frac{1}{4}t^4 + t + 1$

25–28. Derivatives of products *Find the derivative of the following functions by first expanding the expression. Simplify your answers.*

25. $f(x) = (2x + 1)(3x^2 + 2)$
26. $g(r) = (5r^3 + 3r + 1)(r^2 + 3)$
27. $h(x) = (x^2 + 1)^2$
28. $h(x) = \sqrt{x}(\sqrt{x} - 1)$

29–34. Derivatives of quotients *Find the derivative of the following functions by first simplifying the expression.*

29. $f(w) = \dfrac{w^3 - w}{w}$
30. $y = \dfrac{12s^3 - 8s^2 + 12s}{4s}$
31. $g(x) = \dfrac{x^2 - 1}{x - 1}$
32. $h(x) = \dfrac{x^3 - 6x^2 + 8x}{x^2 - 2x}$
33. $y = \dfrac{x - a}{\sqrt{x} - \sqrt{a}}$; a is a positive constant.
34. $y = \dfrac{x^2 - 2ax + a^2}{x - a}$; a is a constant.

T **35–38. Equations of tangent lines**

a. *Find an equation of the tangent line at $x = a$.*
b. *Use a graphing utility to graph the curve and the tangent line on the same set of axes.*

35. $y = -3x^2 + 2$; $a = 1$
36. $y = x^3 - 4x^2 + 2x - 1$; $a = 2$
37. $y = \sqrt{x}$; $a = 4$
38. $y = \dfrac{1}{2}x^4 + x$; $a = 2$

39. **Finding slope locations** Let $f(x) = x^2 - 6x + 5$.
    a. Find the values of x for which the slope of the curve $y = f(x)$ is 0.
    b. Find the values of x for which the slope of the curve $y = f(x)$ is 2.

40. **Finding slope locations** Let $f(t) = t^3 - 27t + 5$.
    a. Find the values of t for which the slope of the curve $y = f(t)$ is 0.
    b. Find the values of t for which the slope of the curve $y = f(t)$ is 21.

41. **Finding slope locations** Let $f(x) = 2x^3 - 3x^2 - 12x + 4$.
    a. Find all points on the graph of f at which the tangent line is horizontal.
    b. Find all points on the graph of f at which the tangent line has slope 60.

42–46. Higher-order derivatives *Find $f'(x)$, $f''(x)$, and $f^{(3)}(x)$ for the following functions.*

42. $f(x) = 3x^3 + 5x^2 + 6x$
43. $f(x) = 5x^4 + 10x^3 + 3x + 6$
44. $f(x) = 3x^{12} + 4x^3$
45. $f(x) = \dfrac{x^2 - 7x - 8}{x + 1}$
46. $f(x) = \dfrac{1}{8}x^4 - 3x^2 + 1$

Further Explorations

47. **Explain why or why not** Determine whether the following statements are true and give an explanation or counterexample.
    a. The derivative $\dfrac{d}{dx}(10^5)$ equals $5 \cdot 10^4$.
    b. The slope of a line tangent to the curve $y = 4x + 1$ is never 0.
    c. The nth derivative $\dfrac{d^n}{dx^n}(5x^3 + 2x + 5)$ equals 0 for any integer $n \geq 3$.

48. **Tangent lines** Suppose $f(3) = 1$ and $f'(3) = 4$. Let $g(x) = x^2 + f(x)$ and $h(x) = 3f(x)$.
    a. Find an equation of the line tangent to $y = g(x)$ at $x = 3$.
    b. Find an equation of the line tangent to $y = h(x)$ at $x = 3$.

49. **Derivatives from tangent lines** Suppose the line tangent to the graph of f at $x = 2$ is $y = 4x + 1$ and suppose $y = 3x - 2$ is the line tangent to the graph of g at $x = 2$. Find an equation of the line tangent to the following curves at $x = 2$.
    a. $y = f(x) + g(x)$
    b. $y = f(x) - 2g(x)$
    c. $y = 4f(x)$

50–53. Derivatives from a graph *Let $F = f + g$ and $G = 3f - g$, where the graphs of f and g are shown in the figure. Find the following derivatives.*

50. $F'(2)$
51. $G'(2)$
52. $F'(5)$
53. $G'(5)$

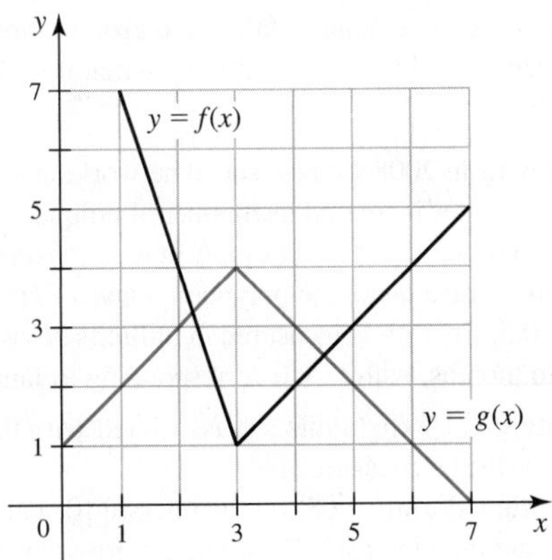

54–56. Derivatives from a table *Use the table to find the following derivatives.*

x	1	2	3	4	5
$f'(x)$	3	5	2	1	4
$g'(x)$	2	4	3	1	5

54. $\left.\dfrac{d}{dx}[f(x) + g(x)]\right|_{x=1}$

55. $\left.\dfrac{d}{dx}[1.5f(x)]\right|_{x=2}$

56. $\left.\dfrac{d}{dx}[2x - 3g(x)]\right|_{x=4}$

57–59. Derivatives from limits *The following limits represent $f'(a)$ for some function f and some real number a.*

a. *Find a function f and a number a.*

b. *Determine the value of the limit by finding $f'(a)$.*

57. $\displaystyle\lim_{h\to 0}\frac{\sqrt{9+h} - \sqrt{9}}{h}$

58. $\displaystyle\lim_{h\to 0}\frac{(1+h)^8 + (1+h)^3 - 2}{h}$

59. $\displaystyle\lim_{x\to 1}\frac{x^{100} - 1}{x - 1}$

Applications

T 60. **Projectile trajectory** The position of a small rocket that is launched vertically upward is given by $s(t) = -5t^2 + 40t + 100$, for $0 \le t \le 10$, where t is measured in seconds and s is measured in meters above the ground.

a. Find the rate of change in the position (instantaneous velocity) of the rocket, for $0 \le t \le 10$.

b. At what time is the instantaneous velocity zero?

c. At what time does the instantaneous velocity have the greatest magnitude, for $0 \le t \le 10$.

d. Graph the position and instantaneous velocity, for $0 \le t \le 10$.

61. **Height estimate** The distance an object falls (under the influence of Earth's gravity, neglecting air resistance) is given by $d(t) = 16t^2$, where d is measured in feet and t is measured in seconds. A rock climber sits on a ledge on a vertical wall and carefully observes the time it takes for a small stone to fall from the ledge to the ground.

a. Compute $d'(t)$. What units are associated with the derivative, and what does it measure?

b. If it takes 6 s for a stone to fall to the ground, how high is the ledge? How fast is the stone moving when it strikes the ground (in mi/hr)?

62. **Twitter growth** In 2008 the new social networking and microblogging service Twitter increased its number of unique visitors from 0.5 million to more than 4.5 million. A fit to the visitor data over several years using a quadratic polynomial gives $V(t) = 0.0173t^2 + 0.1736t + 0.5$, where V is measured in millions of visitors and t is measured in months, with $t = 0$ corresponding to January 1, 2008.

a. Compute $V'(t)$. What units are associated with the derivative and what does it measure?

b. At what time during 2008 (on the interval [0, 12]) was the growth rate the greatest? What was the growth rate at that time?

c. At what time during 2008 was the growth rate the least? What was the growth rate at that time?

63. **Gas mileage** Starting with a full tank of gas, the distance traveled by a particular car is $D(g) = 0.05g^2 + 35g$, where D is measured in miles and g is the amount of gas consumed in gallons.

a. Compute dD/dg. What units are associated with the derivative and what does it measure?

b. Find dD/dg for $g = 0, 5$, and 10 gal (include units). What do your answers say about the gas mileage for this car?

c. What is the range of this car if it has a 12-gal tank?

Additional Exercises

64. **Constant Rule proof** For the constant function $f(x) = c$, use the limit definition of the derivative to show that $f'(x) = 0$.

65. **Alternative proof of the Power Rule** The Binomial Theorem states that for any positive integer n,

$$(a+b)^n = a^n + na^{n-1}b + \frac{n(n-1)}{2\cdot 1}a^{n-2}b^2 + \frac{n(n-1)(n-2)}{3\cdot 2\cdot 1}a^{n-3}b^3 + \cdots + nab^{n-1} + b^n.$$

Use this formula and the definition $f'(x) = \displaystyle\lim_{h\to 0}\frac{f(x+h) - f(x)}{h}$ to show that $\dfrac{d}{dx}(x^n) = nx^{n-1}$ for any positive integer n.

66. **Looking ahead: Power Rule for negative integers** Suppose n is a negative integer and $f(x) = x^n$. Use the following steps to prove that $f'(a) = na^{n-1}$, which means the Power Rule for positive integers extends to all integers. This result is proved in Section 3.3 by a different method.

a. Assume that $m = -n$, so that $m > 0$. Use the definition $f'(a) = \displaystyle\lim_{x\to a}\frac{x^n - a^n}{x - a} = \lim_{x\to a}\frac{x^{-m} - a^{-m}}{x - a}$. Simplify using the factoring rule $x^n - a^n = (x-a)(x^{n-1} + x^{n-2}a + \cdots + xa^{n-2} + a^{n-1})$ until it is possible to take the limit.

b. Use this result to find $\dfrac{d}{dx}(x^{-7})$ and $\dfrac{d}{dx}\left(\dfrac{1}{x^{10}}\right)$.

67. **Extending the Power Rule to $n = \frac{1}{2}, \frac{3}{2}$, and $\frac{5}{2}$** With Theorem 3.3 and Exercise 66, we have shown that the Power Rule, $\dfrac{d}{dx}(x^n) = nx^{n-1}$, applies to any integer n. Later in the chapter, we extend this rule so that it applies to any rational number n.

a. Explain why the Power Rule is consistent with the formula $\dfrac{d}{dx}(\sqrt{x}) = \dfrac{1}{2\sqrt{x}}$.

b. Prove that the Power Rule holds for $n = \frac{3}{2}$. (*Hint:* Use the definition of the derivative: $\dfrac{d}{dx}(x^{3/2}) = \displaystyle\lim_{h\to 0}\frac{(x+h)^{3/2} - x^{3/2}}{h}$.)

c. Prove that the Power Rule holds for $n = \frac{5}{2}$.

d. Propose a formula for $\dfrac{d}{dx}(x^{n/2})$ for any positive integer n.

QUICK CHECK ANSWERS

1. $\dfrac{d}{dx}(5) = 0$ and $\dfrac{d}{dx}(\pi) = 0$ because 5 and π are constants.
2. The slope of the curve $y = x$ is 1 at any point; therefore, $\dfrac{d}{dx}(x) = 1$. 3. $2x + 2$ 4. $x = 2$ and $x = -2$
5. $f^{(5)}(x) = 120, f^{(6)}(x) = 0, f^{(100)}(x) = 0$ ◀

3.3 The Product and Quotient Rules

The derivative of a sum of functions is the sum of the derivatives. So, you might be tempted to assume that the derivative of a product is the product of the derivatives. Consider, however, the functions $f(x) = x^3$ and $g(x) = x^4$. In this case, $\frac{d}{dx}[f(x)g(x)] = \frac{d}{dx}(x^7) = 7x^6$, but $f'(x)g'(x) = 3x^2 \cdot 4x^3 = 12x^5$. Therefore, $\frac{d}{dx}(f \cdot g) \neq f' \cdot g'$. Similarly, the derivative of a quotient is *not* the quotient of the derivatives. The purpose of this section is to develop rules for differentiating products and quotients of functions.

Product Rule

Here is an anecdote that suggests the formula for the Product Rule. Imagine running along a road at a constant speed. Your speed is determined by two factors: the length of your stride and the number of strides you take each second. Therefore,

$$\text{running speed} = \text{stride length} \cdot \text{stride rate}.$$

If your stride length is 3 ft and you take 2 strides/s, then your speed is 6 ft/s.

Now, suppose your stride length increases by 0.5 ft, from 3 to 3.5 ft. Then the change in speed is calculated as follows:

$$\begin{aligned} \textit{change} \text{ in speed} &= \text{change in stride length} \cdot \text{stride rate} \\ &= 0.5 \cdot 2 = 1 \text{ ft/s} \end{aligned}$$

Alternatively, suppose your stride length remains constant but your stride rate increases by 0.25 strides/s, from 2 to 2.25 strides/s. Then

$$\begin{aligned} \textit{change} \text{ in speed} &= \text{stride length} \cdot \text{change in stride rate} \\ &= 3 \cdot 0.25 = 0.75 \text{ ft/s}. \end{aligned}$$

If both your stride rate and stride length change simultaneously, we expect two contributions to the change in your running speed:

$$\begin{aligned} \textit{change} \text{ in speed} &= (\text{change in stride length} \cdot \text{stride rate}) \\ &\quad + (\text{stride length} \cdot \text{change in stride rate}) \\ &= 1 \text{ ft/s} + 0.75 \text{ ft/s} = 1.75 \text{ ft/s} \end{aligned}$$

This argument correctly suggests that the derivative (or rate of change) of a product of two functions has *two components*, as shown by the following rule.

> In words, Theorem 3.6 states that the derivative of the product of two functions equals the derivative of the first function multiplied by the second function plus the first function multiplied by the derivative of the second function.

THEOREM 3.6 Product Rule
If f and g are differentiable at x, then

$$\frac{d}{dx}[f(x)g(x)] = f'(x)g(x) + f(x)g'(x).$$

Proof We apply the definition of the derivative to the function fg:

$$\frac{d}{dx}[f(x)g(x)] = \lim_{h \to 0} \frac{f(x+h)g(x+h) - f(x)g(x)}{h}$$

A useful tactic is to add $-f(x)g(x + h) + f(x)g(x + h)$ (which equals 0) to the numerator, so that

$$\frac{d}{dx}[f(x)g(x)] = \lim_{h \to 0} \frac{f(x + h)g(x + h) - f(x)g(x + h) + f(x)g(x + h) - f(x)g(x)}{h}$$

The fraction is now split and the numerators are factored:

$$\frac{d}{dx}[f(x)g(x)] = \lim_{h \to 0} \frac{f(x + h)g(x + h) - f(x)g(x + h)}{h} + \lim_{h \to 0} \frac{f(x)g(x + h) - f(x)g(x)}{h}$$

$$= \lim_{h \to 0} \left[\underbrace{\frac{f(x + h) - f(x)}{h}}_{\text{approaches } f'(x) \text{ as } h \to 0} \cdot \underbrace{g(x + h)}_{\text{approaches } g(x) \text{ as } h \to 0} \right] + \lim_{h \to 0} \left[\underbrace{f(x)}_{\text{equals } f(x) \text{ as } h \to 0} \cdot \underbrace{\frac{g(x + h) - g(x)}{h}}_{\text{approaches } g'(x) \text{ as } h \to 0} \right]$$

$$= f'(x) \cdot g(x) + f(x) \cdot g'(x)$$

➤ As $h \to 0$, $f(x)$ does not change in value; it is independent of h.

The continuity of g is used to conclude that $\lim_{h \to 0} g(x + h) = g(x)$. ◄

EXAMPLE 1 **Using the Product Rule** Find and simplify the following derivatives.

a. $\frac{d}{dv}[v^2(2\sqrt{v} + 1)]$ **b.** $\frac{d}{dx}[(x^3 - 8)(x^2 + 4)]$

SOLUTION

➤ Recall from Example 4 of Section 3.1 that $\frac{d}{dv}(\sqrt{v}) = \frac{1}{2\sqrt{v}}$.

a. $\frac{d}{dv}[v^2(2\sqrt{v} + 1)] = \left[\frac{d}{dv}(v^2)\right](2\sqrt{v} + 1) + v^2\left[\frac{d}{dv}(2\sqrt{v} + 1)\right]$ Product Rule

$= 2v(2\sqrt{v} + 1) + v^2\left(2 \cdot \frac{1}{2\sqrt{v}}\right)$ Evaluate the derivatives.

$= (4v^{3/2} + 2v) + v^{3/2} = 5v^{3/2} + 2v$ Simplify.

b. $\frac{d}{dx}[(x^3 - 8)(x^2 + 4)] = \underbrace{3x^2}_{\frac{d}{dx}(x^3 - 8)} \cdot (x^2 + 4) + (x^3 - 8) \cdot \underbrace{2x}_{\frac{d}{dx}(x^2 + 4)} = x(5x^3 + 12x - 16)$

Related Exercises 7–16 ◄

QUICK CHECK 1 Find the derivative of $f(x) = x^5$. Then, find the same derivative using the Product Rule with $f(x) = x^2x^3$. ◄

Quotient Rule

Consider the quotient $q(x) = \frac{f(x)}{g(x)}$ and note that $f(x) = g(x)q(x)$. By the Product Rule, we have

$$f'(x) = g'(x)q(x) + g(x)q'(x).$$

Solving for $q'(x)$, we find that

$$q'(x) = \frac{f'(x) - g'(x)q(x)}{g(x)}.$$

Substituting $q(x) = \dfrac{f(x)}{g(x)}$ produces a rule for finding $q'(x)$:

$$q'(x) = \frac{f'(x) - g'(x)\dfrac{f(x)}{g(x)}}{g(x)} \qquad \text{Replace } q(x) \text{ with } \frac{f(x)}{g(x)}.$$

$$= \frac{g(x)\left(f'(x) - g'(x)\dfrac{f(x)}{g(x)}\right)}{g(x)\cdot g(x)} \qquad \text{Multiply numerator and denominator by } g(x).$$

$$= \frac{g(x)f'(x) - f(x)g'(x)}{[g(x)]^2} \qquad \text{Simplify.}$$

This calculation produces the correct result for the derivative of a quotient. However, there is one subtle point: How do we know that the derivative of f/g exists in the first place? A complete proof of the Quotient Rule is outlined in Exercise 66.

➤ In words, Theorem 3.7 states that the derivative of the quotient of two functions equals the denominator multiplied by the derivative of the numerator minus the numerator multiplied by the derivative of the denominator, all divided by the denominator squared.

An easy way to remember the Quotient Rule is

$$\frac{LoD(Hi) - HiD(Lo)}{(Lo)^2}.$$

THEOREM 3.7 The Quotient Rule
If f and g are differentiable at x, then the derivative of f/g at x exists provided $g(x) \neq 0$ and it is given by

$$\frac{d}{dx}\left[\frac{f(x)}{g(x)}\right] = \frac{g(x)f'(x) - f(x)g'(x)}{[g(x)]^2}.$$

EXAMPLE 2 Using the Quotient Rule Find and simplify the following derivatives.

a. $\dfrac{d}{dx}\left[\dfrac{x^2 + 3x + 4}{x^2 - 1}\right]$ **b.** $\dfrac{d}{dx}(2x^{-3})$

SOLUTION

a. $$\frac{d}{dx}\left[\frac{x^2 + 3x + 4}{x^2 - 1}\right] = \frac{\overbrace{(x^2 - 1)(2x + 3)}^{(x^2-1)\cdot\text{the derivative of }(x^2+3x+4)} - \overbrace{(x^2 + 3x + 4)2x}^{(x^2+3x+4)\cdot\text{the derivative of }(x^2-1)}}{\underbrace{(x^2 - 1)^2}_{\text{the denominator }(x^2-1)\text{ squared}}} \qquad \text{Quotient Rule}$$

$$= \frac{2x^3 - 2x + 3x^2 - 3 - 2x^3 - 6x^2 - 8x}{(x^2 - 1)^2} \qquad \text{Expand.}$$

$$= \frac{-3x^2 - 10x - 3}{(x^2 - 1)^2} \qquad \text{Simplify.}$$

➤ The Product and Quotient Rules are used on a regular basis throughout this text. Therefore, it is a good idea to memorize these rules (along with the other derivative rules and formulas presented in this chapter) so that you can evaluate derivatives quickly.

b. We rewrite $2x^{-3}$ as $\dfrac{2}{x^3}$, and use the Quotient Rule:

$$\frac{d}{dx}\left(\frac{2}{x^3}\right) = \frac{x^3 \cdot 0 - 2 \cdot 3x^2}{(x^3)^2} = -\frac{6}{x^4} = -6x^{-4}.$$

Related Exercises 17–26 ◄

QUICK CHECK 2 Find the derivative of $f(x) = x^5$. Then find the same derivative using the Quotient Rule with $f(x) = x^8/x^3$. ◄

EXAMPLE 3 **Finding tangent lines** Find an equation of the line tangent to the graph of $f(x) = \dfrac{x^2 + 1}{x^2 - 4}$ at the point $(3, 2)$. Plot the curve and tangent line.

SOLUTION To find the slope of the tangent line, we compute f' using the Quotient Rule:

$$f'(x) = \frac{(x^2 - 4)\,2x - (x^2 + 1)\,2x}{(x^2 - 4)^2} \qquad \text{Quotient Rule}$$

$$= \frac{2x^3 - 8x - 2x^3 - 2x}{(x^2 - 4)^2} = \frac{-10x}{(x^2 - 4)^2} \qquad \text{Simplify.}$$

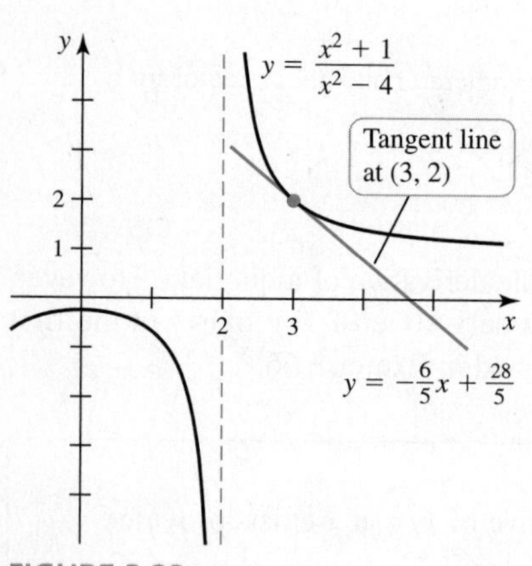

FIGURE 3.22

The slope of the tangent line at $(3, 2)$ is

$$m_{\tan} = f'(3) = \frac{-10(3)}{(3^2 - 4)^2} = -\frac{6}{5}.$$

Therefore, an equation of the tangent line is

$$y - 2 = -\frac{6}{5}(x - 3), \quad \text{or} \quad y = -\frac{6}{5}x + \frac{28}{5}.$$

The graphs of f and the tangent line are shown in Figure 3.22. *Related Exercises 27–30* ◀

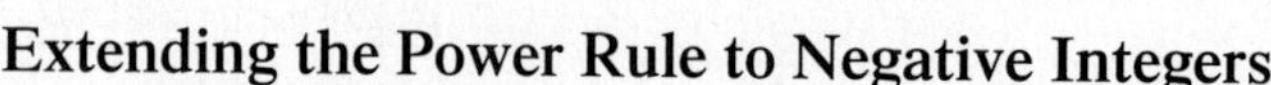

Extending the Power Rule to Negative Integers

The Power Rule in Section 3.2 says that $\dfrac{d}{dx}(x^n) = nx^{n-1}$, for nonnegative integers n. Using the Quotient Rule, we show that the Power Rule also holds if n is a negative integer. Assume n is a negative integer and let $m = -n$, so that $m > 0$. Then

$$\frac{d}{dx}(x^n) = \frac{d}{dx}\left(\frac{1}{x^m}\right) \qquad x^n = \frac{1}{x^{-n}} = \frac{1}{x^m}$$

$$= \frac{x^m \overbrace{\left[\frac{d}{dx}(1)\right]}^{\text{derivative of a constant is 0}} - 1 \overbrace{\left(\frac{d}{dx}x^m\right)}^{\text{equals } mx^{m-1}}}{(x^m)^2} \qquad \text{Quotient Rule}$$

$$= \frac{-mx^{m-1}}{x^{2m}} \qquad \text{Simplify.}$$

$$= -mx^{-m-1} \qquad \frac{x^{m-1}}{x^{2m}} = x^{m-1-2m}$$

$$= nx^{n-1} \qquad \text{Replace } -m \text{ by } n.$$

THEOREM 3.8 **Extended Power Rule**
If n is any integer, then

$$\frac{d}{dx}(x^n) = nx^{n-1}.$$

QUICK CHECK 3 Find the derivative of $f(x) = 1/x^5$ in two different ways: using the Extended Power Rule and using the Quotient Rule. ◀

EXAMPLE 4 Using the Extended Power Rule Find the following derivatives.

a. $\frac{d}{dx}\left(\frac{9}{x^5}\right)$ **b.** $\frac{d}{dt}\left[\frac{3t^{16} - 4}{t^6}\right]$

SOLUTION

a. $\frac{d}{dx}\left(\frac{9}{x^5}\right) = \frac{d}{dx}(9x^{-5}) = 9(-5x^{-6}) = -45x^{-6} = -\frac{45}{x^6}$

b. The derivative of $\frac{3t^{16} - 4}{t^6}$ can be evaluated by the Quotient Rule, but an alternative method is to rewrite the expression using negative powers:

$$\frac{3t^{16} - 4}{t^6} = \frac{3t^{16}}{t^6} - \frac{4}{t^6} = 3t^{10} - 4t^{-6}$$

We now differentiate using the Extended Power Rule:

$$\frac{d}{dt}\left[\frac{3t^{16} - 4}{t^6}\right] = \frac{d}{dt}(3t^{10} - 4t^{-6}) = 30t^9 + 24t^{-7}$$

Related Exercises 31–36 ◀

Rates of Change

The derivative provides information about the instantaneous rate of change of a function. The next example illustrates this concept.

EXAMPLE 5 Population growth rates The population of a culture of cells increases and approaches a constant level (called the *steady state* or *carrying capacity*) and is modeled by the function $p(t) = 400\left(\frac{t^2 + 1}{t^2 + 4}\right)$, where $t \geq 0$ is measured in hours (Figure 3.23).

a. Compute and graph the instantaneous growth rate of the population for $t \geq 0$.

b. At approximately what time is the instantaneous growth rate the greatest?

c. What is the steady-state population?

➤ Methods for determining exactly when the growth rate is a maximum are discussed in Chapter 4.

SOLUTION

a. The instantaneous growth rate is given by the derivative of the population function:

$$p'(t) = \frac{d}{dt}\left[400\left(\frac{t^2 + 1}{t^2 + 4}\right)\right]$$

$$= 400\,\frac{(t^2 + 4)(2t) - (t^2 + 1)(2t)}{(t^2 + 4)^2} \quad \text{Quotient Rule}$$

$$= \frac{2400t}{(t^2 + 4)^2} \quad \text{Simplify.}$$

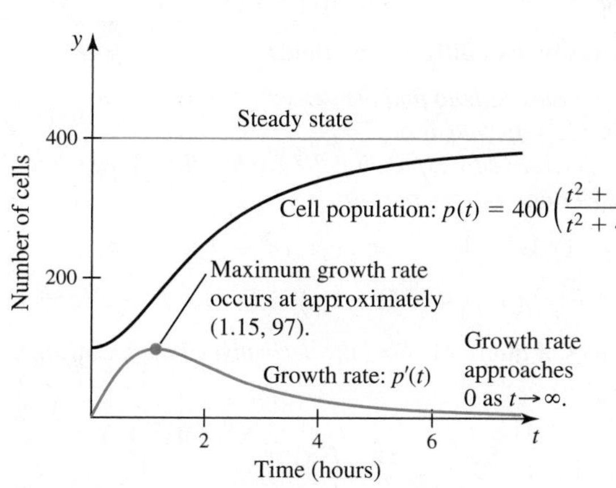

FIGURE 3.23

The growth rate has units of cells per hour; its graph is shown in Figure 3.23.

b. The growth rate p' has a maximum value at the point at which the population curve is steepest. Using a graphing utility, this point corresponds to $t \approx 1.15$ hr and the growth rate has a value of $p'(1.15) \approx 97$ cells/hr.

c. To determine whether the population approaches a fixed value after a long period of time (the steady-state population), we investigate the limit of the population function as $t \to \infty$. In this case, the steady-state population exists and is

$$\lim_{t\to\infty} p(t) = \lim_{t\to\infty}\left[400\underbrace{\left(\frac{t^2+1}{t^2+4}\right)}_{\text{approaches } 1}\right] = 400,$$

which is confirmed by the population curve (Figure 3.23). Notice that as the population approaches its steady state, the growth rate p' approaches zero.

Related Exercises 37–40 ◀

Combining Derivative Rules

Some situations call for the use of multiple differentiation rules. This section concludes with one such example.

EXAMPLE 6 Combining derivative rules Find the derivative of

$$y = \frac{4x(2x^3 - 3x^{-1})}{x^2 + 1}.$$

SOLUTION In this case, we have the quotient of two functions, with a product in the numerator:

$$\frac{dy}{dx} = \frac{(x^2+1)\cdot\frac{d}{dx}[4x(2x^3 - 3x^{-1})] - [4x(2x^3 - 3x^{-1})]\cdot\frac{d}{dx}(x^2+1)}{(x^2+1)^2} \quad \text{Quotient Rule}$$

$$= \frac{(x^2+1)(4(2x^3 - 3x^{-1}) + 4x(6x^2 + 3x^{-2})) - [4x(2x^3 - 3x^{-1})](2x)}{(x^2+1)^2} \quad \text{Product Rule in the numerator}$$

$$= \frac{8x(2x^4 + 4x^2 + 3)}{(x^2+1)^2} \quad \text{Simplify.}$$

Related Exercises 41–44 ◀

SECTION 3.3 EXERCISES

Review Questions

1. How do you find the derivative of the product of two functions that are differentiable at a point?

2. How do you find the derivative of the quotient of two functions that are differentiable at a point?

3. State the Extended Power Rule for differentiating x^n. For what values of n does the rule apply?

4. Give two ways to differentiate $f(x) = 1/x^{10}$.

5. Let n be a positive integer and note that $x^n \cdot x^{-n} = 1$. Differentiate $x^n \cdot x^{-n}$ by the Product Rule and show that the result is $\frac{d}{dx}(1) = 0$.

6. Give two ways to differentiate $f(x) = (x - 3)(x^2 + 4)$.

Basic Skills

7–12. Derivatives of products *Find the derivative of the following functions.*

7. $f(x) = 3x^4(2x^2 - 1)$

8. $g(x) = 6x - 2x(x^{10} - 3x^3)$

9. $h(x) = (5x^7 + 5x)(6x^3 + 3x^2 + 3)$

10. $f(x) = \left(1 + \frac{1}{x^2}\right)(x^2 + 1)$

11. $g(w) = (w^3 + 4)(w^3 - 1)$

12. $s(t) = 4(3t^2 + 2t - 1)\sqrt{t}$

13–16. Derivatives by two different methods

a. *Use the Product Rule to find the derivative of the given function. Simplify your result.*

b. *Find the derivative by expanding the product first. Verify that your answer agrees with part (a).*

13. $f(x) = (x - 1)(3x + 4)$

14. $y = (t^2 + 7t)(3t - 4)$

15. $g(y) = (3y^4 - y^2)(y^2 - 4)$

16. $h(z) = (z^3 + 4z^2 + z)(z - 1)$

17–22. Derivatives of quotients *Find the derivative of the following functions.*

17. $f(x) = \dfrac{x}{x + 1}$

18. $f(x) = \dfrac{x^3 - 4x^2 + x}{x - 2}$

19. $y = (3t - 1)(2t - 2)^{-1}$

20. $h(w) = \dfrac{w^2 - 1}{w^2 + 1}$

21. $g(x) = \dfrac{x^4 + 1}{x^2 - 1}$

22. $y = (2\sqrt{x} - 1)(4x + 1)^{-1}$

23–26. Derivatives by two different methods

a. *Use the Quotient Rule to find the derivative of the given function. Simplify your result.*
b. *Find the derivative by first simplifying the function. Verify that your answer agrees with part (a).*

23. $f(w) = \dfrac{w^3 - w}{w}$

24. $y = \dfrac{12s^3 - 8s^2 + 12s}{4s}$

25. $y = \dfrac{x - a}{\sqrt{x} - \sqrt{a}}$; a is a positive constant.

26. $y = \dfrac{x^2 - 2ax + a^2}{x - a}$; a is a constant.

T **27–30. Equations of tangent lines**

a. *Find an equation of the line tangent to the given curve at a.*
b. *Use a graphing utility to graph the curve and the tangent line on the same set of axes.*

27. $y = \dfrac{x + 5}{x - 1}$; $a = 3$

28. $y = \dfrac{2x^2}{3x - 1}$; $a = 1$

29. $y = x(2x^{-2} + 1)$; $a = -1$

30. $y = \dfrac{x - 2}{x + 1}$; $a = 1$

31–36. Extended Power Rule *Find the derivative of the following functions.*

31. $f(x) = 3x^{-9}$

32. $y = \dfrac{4}{p^3}$

33. $g(t) = 3t^2 + \dfrac{6}{t^7}$

34. $y = \dfrac{w^4 + 5w^2 + w}{w^2}$

35. $g(t) = \dfrac{t^3 + 3t^2 + t}{t^3}$

36. $p(x) = \dfrac{4x^3 + 3x + 1}{2x^5}$

T **37–38. Population growth** *Consider the following population functions.*

a. *Find the instantaneous growth rate of the population, for $t \geq 0$.*
b. *What is the instantaneous growth rate at $t = 5$?*
c. *At what time is the instantaneous growth rate the greatest?*
d. *Evaluate and interpret $\lim_{t\to\infty} p'(t)$.*
e. *Use a graphing utility to graph the population and its growth rate, for $0 \leq t \leq 20$.*

37. $p(t) = \dfrac{200t}{t + 2}$

38. $p(t) = 600\left(\dfrac{t^2 + 3}{t^2 + 9}\right)$

39. Finding slope locations Let $f(x) = \dfrac{x - x^2}{2x^2 + 1}$.

a. Find the values of x for which the slope of the curve $y = f(x)$ is 0.
b. Explain the meaning of your answer to part (a) in terms of tangent lines.

T **40. Finding slope locations** Let $f(t) = \dfrac{3t^2}{t^2 + 1}$.

a. Find the values of t for which the slope of the curve $y = f(t)$ is 0.
b. Does the graph of f have a slope of 3 at any point? Explain.

41–44. Combining rules *Compute the derivative of the following functions.*

41. $g(x) = \dfrac{x(3 - x)}{2x^2}$

42. $h(x) = \dfrac{(x - 1)(2x^2 - 1)}{(x^3 - 1)}$

43. $g(x) = \dfrac{4x}{(x^2 + x)(1 - x)}$

44. $h(x) = \dfrac{(x + 1)}{x^2(2x^3 + 1)}$

Further Explorations

45. Explain why or why not Determine whether the following statements are true and give an explanation or counterexample.

a. Let $f(x) = x^{-n}$, where n is a positive integer. Then $f^{(8)}(1) > 0$.
b. The Quotient Rule must be used to evaluate $\dfrac{d}{dx}\left(\dfrac{x^2 + 3x + 2}{x}\right)$.
c. $\dfrac{d}{dx}\left(\dfrac{1}{x^5}\right) = \dfrac{1}{5x^4}$

46–49. Higher-order derivatives *Find $f'(x)$, $f''(x)$, and $f'''(x)$.*

46. $f(x) = \dfrac{1}{x}$

47. $f(x) = x^2(2 + x^{-3})$

48. $f(x) = \dfrac{x}{x + 2}$

49. $f(x) = \dfrac{x^2 - 7x}{x + 1}$

50–53. Choose your method *Use any method to evaluate the derivative of the following functions.*

50. $f(x) = \dfrac{4 - x^2}{x - 2}$

51. $f(x) = 4x^2 - \dfrac{2x}{5x + 1}$

52. $f(z) = z^2(z + 4) - \dfrac{2z}{z^2 + 1}$

53. $h(r) = \dfrac{2 - r - \sqrt{r}}{r + 1}$

54. Tangent lines Suppose $f(2) = 2$ and $f'(2) = 3$. Let $g(x) = x^2 \cdot f(x)$ and $h(x) = \dfrac{f(x)}{x - 3}$.

a. Find an equation of the line tangent to $y = g(x)$ at $x = 2$.
b. Find an equation of the line tangent to $y = h(x)$ at $x = 2$.

T **55. The Witch of Agnesi** The graph of $y = \dfrac{a^3}{x^2 + a^2}$, where a is a constant is called the *witch of Agnesi* (named after the 18th-century Italian mathematician Maria Agnesi).

a. Let $a = 3$ and find an equation of the line tangent to $y = \dfrac{27}{x^2 + 9}$ at $x = 2$.
b. Plot the function and the tangent line found in part (a).

56–61. Derivatives from a table *Use the following table to find the given derivatives.*

x	1	2	3	4	5
$f(x)$	5	4	3	2	1
$f'(x)$	3	5	2	1	4
$g(x)$	4	2	5	3	1
$g'(x)$	2	4	3	1	5

56. $\dfrac{d}{dx}[f(x)g(x)]\bigg|_{x=1}$

57. $\dfrac{d}{dx}\left[\dfrac{f(x)}{g(x)}\right]\bigg|_{x=2}$

58. $\dfrac{d}{dx}[xf(x)]\bigg|_{x=3}$

59. $\dfrac{d}{dx}\left[\dfrac{f(x)}{x+2}\right]\bigg|_{x=4}$

60. $\dfrac{d}{dx}\left[\dfrac{xf(x)}{g(x)}\right]\bigg|_{x=4}$

61. $\dfrac{d}{dx}\left[\dfrac{f(x)g(x)}{x}\right]\bigg|_{x=4}$

62. Derivatives from tangent lines Suppose the line tangent to the graph of f at $x = 2$ is $y = 4x + 1$ and suppose $y = 3x - 2$ is the line tangent to the graph of g at $x = 2$. Find an equation of the line tangent to the following curves at $x = 2$.

a. $y = f(x)g(x)$ **b.** $y = \dfrac{f(x)}{g(x)}$

Applications

63. Electrostatic force The magnitude of the electrostatic force between two point charges Q and q of the same sign is given by $F(x) = \dfrac{kQq}{x^2}$, where x is the distance between the charges and $k = 9 \times 10^9\ \mathrm{Nm^2/C^2}$ is a physical constant (C stands for coulomb, the unit of charge; N stands for newton, the unit of force).

a. Find the instantaneous rate of change of the force with respect to the distance between the charges.

b. For two identical charges with $Q = q = 1$ C, what is the instantaneous rate of change of the force at a separation of $x = 0.001$ m?

c. Does the instantaneous rate of change of the force increase or decrease with the separation? Explain.

64. Gravitational force The magnitude of the gravitational force between two objects of mass M and m is given by $F(x) = -\dfrac{GMm}{x^2}$, where x is the distance between the centers of mass of the objects and $G = 6.7 \times 10^{-11}\ \mathrm{Nm^2/kg^2}$ is the gravitational constant (N stands for newton, the unit of force; the negative sign indicates an attractive force).

a. Find the instantaneous rate of change of the force with respect to the distance between the objects.

b. For two identical objects of mass $M = m = 0.1$ kg, what is the instantaneous rate of change of the force at a separation of $x = 0.01$ m?

c. Does the instantaneous rate of change of the force increase or decrease with the separation? Explain.

Additional Exercises

65. Means and tangents Suppose f is differentiable on an interval containing a and b, and let $P(a, f(a))$ and $Q(b, f(b))$ be distinct points on the graph of f. Let c be the x-coordinate of the point at which the lines tangent to the curve at P and Q intersect, assuming that the tangent lines are not parallel (see figure).

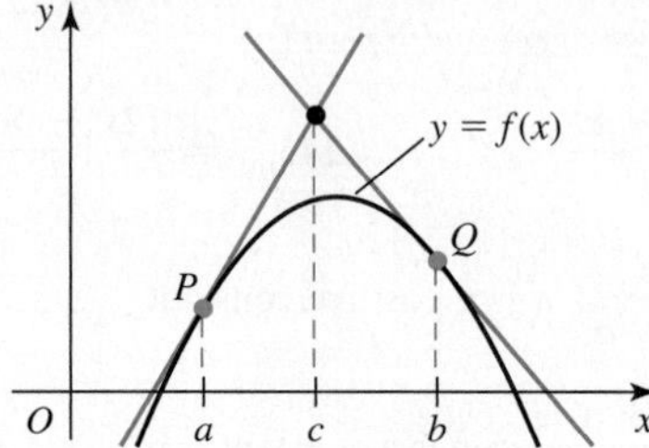

a. If $f(x) = x^2$, show that $c = (a + b)/2$, the arithmetic mean of a and b, for real numbers a and b.

b. If $f(x) = \sqrt{x}$, show that $c = \sqrt{ab}$, the geometric mean of a and b, for $a > 0$ and $b > 0$.

c. If $f(x) = 1/x$, show that $c = 2ab/(a + b)$, the harmonic mean of a and b, for $a > 0$ and $b > 0$.

d. Find an expression for c in terms of a and b for any (differentiable) function f whenever c exists.

66. Proof of the Quotient Rule Let $F = f/g$ be the quotient of two functions that are differentiable at x.

a. Use the definition of F' to show that

$$\frac{d}{dx}\left[\frac{f(x)}{g(x)}\right] = \lim_{h\to 0} \frac{f(x+h)g(x) - f(x)g(x+h)}{h \cdot g(x+h) \cdot g(x)}.$$

b. Now add $-f(x)g(x) + f(x)g(x)$ (which equals 0) to the numerator in the preceding limit to obtain

$$\lim_{h\to 0} \frac{f(x+h)g(x) - f(x)g(x) + f(x)g(x) - f(x)g(x+h)}{h \cdot g(x+h) \cdot g(x)}.$$

Use this limit to obtain the Quotient Rule.

c. Explain why $F' = (f/g)'$ exists, whenever $g(x) \neq 0$.

67. Product Rule for the second derivative Assuming the first and second derivatives of f and g exist at x, find a formula for $\dfrac{d^2}{dx^2}[f(x)g(x)]$.

68. Quotient Rule for the second derivative Assuming the first and second derivatives of f and g exist at x, find a formula for $\dfrac{d^2}{dx^2}\left[\dfrac{f(x)}{g(x)}\right]$.

69. Product Rule for three functions Assume that f, g, and h are differentiable at x.

a. Use the Product Rule (twice) to find a formula for $\dfrac{d}{dx}[f(x)g(x)h(x)]$.

b. Use the formula in (a) to find $\dfrac{d}{dx}[x(x - 1)(x + 3)]$.

70. One of the Leibniz Rules One of several Leibniz Rules in calculus deals with higher-order derivatives of products. Let $(fg)^{(n)}$ denote the nth derivative of the product fg, for $n \geq 1$.

a. Prove that $(fg)^{(2)} = gf'' + 2f'g' + fg''$.

b. Prove that, in general,

$$(fg)^{(n)} = \sum_{k=0}^{n} \binom{n}{k} f^{(k)} g^{(n-k)},$$

where $\binom{n}{k} = \dfrac{n!}{k!(n-k)!}$ are the binomial coefficients.

c. Compare the result of (b) to the expansion of $(a + b)^n$.

QUICK CHECK ANSWERS

1. $f'(x) = 5x^4$ by either method **2.** $f'(x) = 5x^4$ by either method **3.** $f'(x) = -5x^{-6}$ by either method

3.4 Derivatives of Trigonometric Functions

From variations in market trends and ocean temperatures to daily fluctuations in tides and hormone levels, change is often cyclical or periodic. Trigonometric functions are well suited for describing such cyclical behavior. In this section, we investigate the derivatives of trigonometric functions and their many uses.

➤ Results stated in this section assume that angles are measured in *radians*.

Two Special Limits

Our principal goal is to determine derivative formulas for $\sin x$ and $\cos x$. In order to do this, we use two special limits.

Table 3.1

x	$\dfrac{\sin x}{x}$
± 0.1	0.9983341665
± 0.01	0.9999833334
± 0.001	0.9999998333

THEOREM 3.9 Trigonometric Limits

$$\lim_{x \to 0} \frac{\sin x}{x} = 1 \qquad \lim_{x \to 0} \frac{\cos x - 1}{x} = 0$$

Note that these limits cannot be evaluated by direct substitution because in both cases, the numerator and denominator approach zero as $x \to 0$. We first examine numerical and graphical evidence supporting Theorem 3.9, and then we offer an analytic proof.

The values of $\dfrac{\sin x}{x}$, rounded to 10 digits, appear in Table 3.1. As x approaches zero

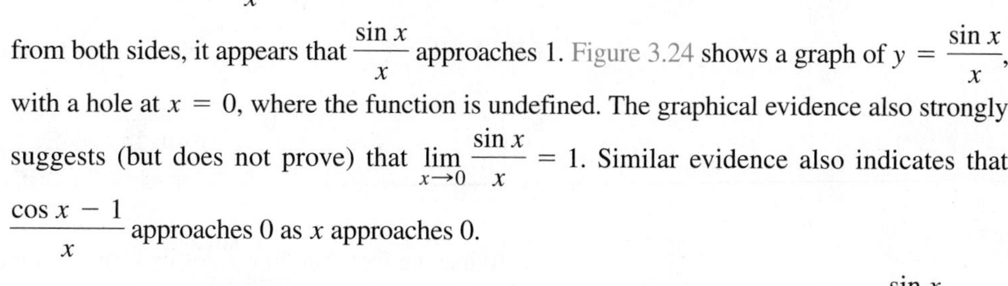

from both sides, it appears that $\dfrac{\sin x}{x}$ approaches 1. Figure 3.24 shows a graph of $y = \dfrac{\sin x}{x}$, with a hole at $x = 0$, where the function is undefined. The graphical evidence also strongly suggests (but does not prove) that $\lim_{x \to 0} \dfrac{\sin x}{x} = 1$. Similar evidence also indicates that $\dfrac{\cos x - 1}{x}$ approaches 0 as x approaches 0.

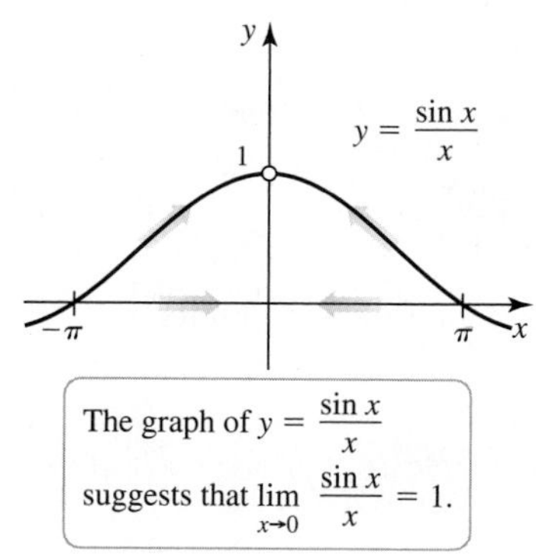

The graph of $y = \dfrac{\sin x}{x}$ suggests that $\lim_{x \to 0} \dfrac{\sin x}{x} = 1$.

FIGURE 3.24

Using a geometric argument and the methods of Chapter 2, we now prove $\lim_{x \to 0} \dfrac{\sin x}{x} = 1$. The proof that $\lim_{x \to 0} \dfrac{\cos x - 1}{x} = 0$ is found in Exercise 61.

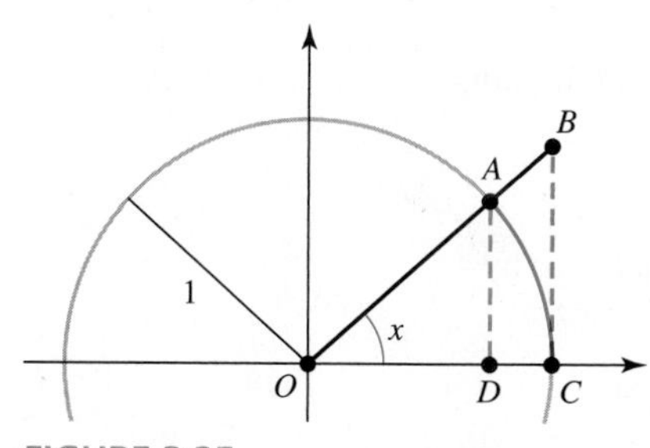

FIGURE 3.25

Proof Consider Figure 3.25, in which $\triangle OAD$, $\triangle OBC$, and the sector OAC of the unit circle (with central angle x) are shown. Observe that $0 < x < \pi/2$ and

$$\text{area of } \triangle OAD < \text{area of sector } OAC < \text{area of } \triangle OBC. \qquad (1)$$

➤ Area of the sector of a circle of radius r formed by a central angle θ:

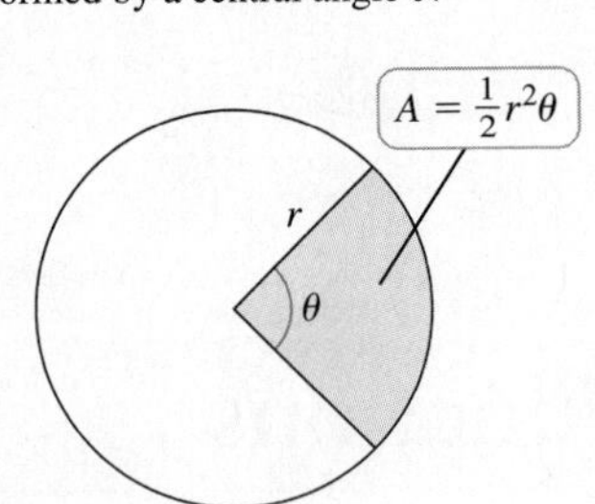

Because the circle in Figure 3.25 is a *unit* circle, $OA = OC = 1$. It follows that $\sin x = \dfrac{AD}{OA} = AD$, $\cos x = \dfrac{OD}{OA} = OD$, and $\tan x = \dfrac{BC}{OC} = BC$. From these observations, we conclude that

- area of $\triangle OAD = \dfrac{1}{2}(OD)(AD) = \dfrac{1}{2}\cos x \sin x$
- area of sector $OAC = \dfrac{1}{2} \cdot 1^2 \cdot x = \dfrac{x}{2}$
- area of $\triangle OBC = \dfrac{1}{2}(OC)(BC) = \dfrac{1}{2}\tan x$

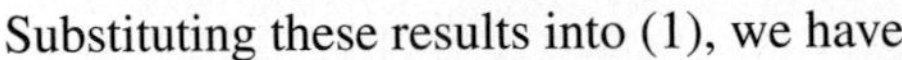

Substituting these results into (1), we have

$$\frac{1}{2}\cos x \sin x < \frac{x}{2} < \frac{1}{2}\tan x.$$

Replacing $\tan x$ with $\dfrac{\sin x}{\cos x}$ and multiplying the inequalities by $\dfrac{2}{\sin x}$ (which is positive) leads to the inequalities

$$\cos x < \frac{x}{\sin x} < \frac{1}{\cos x}.$$

When we take reciprocals and reverse the inequalities, we have

$$\cos x < \frac{\sin x}{x} < \frac{1}{\cos x}, \qquad (2)$$

for $0 < x < \pi/2$.

A similar argument may be used to show that the inequalities in (2) also hold for $-\pi/2 < x < 0$. Taking the limit as $x \to 0$ in (2), we find that

$$\underbrace{\lim_{x\to 0} \cos x}_{1} < \lim_{x\to 0} \frac{\sin x}{x} < \underbrace{\lim_{x\to 0} \frac{1}{\cos x}}_{1}.$$

The Squeeze Theorem (Theorem 2.5) now implies that $\lim\limits_{x\to 0} \dfrac{\sin x}{x} = 1$. ◄

EXAMPLE 1 Calculating trigonometric limits Evaluate the following limits.

a. $\lim\limits_{x\to 0} \dfrac{\sin 4x}{x}$ **b.** $\lim\limits_{x\to 0} \dfrac{\sin 3x}{\sin 5x}$

SOLUTION

a. To use the fact that $\lim\limits_{x\to 0} \dfrac{\sin x}{x} = 1$, the argument of the sine function in the numerator must be the same as the denominator. Multiplying and dividing $\dfrac{\sin 4x}{x}$ by 4, we evaluate the limit as follows:

$$\lim_{x\to 0} \frac{\sin 4x}{x} = \lim_{x\to 0} \frac{4 \sin 4x}{4x} \qquad \text{Multiply and divide by 4.}$$

$$= 4 \lim_{t\to 0} \frac{\sin t}{t} \qquad \text{Factor out 4 and let } t = 4x;\ t \to 0 \text{ as } x \to 0.$$

$$= 4(1) = 4 \qquad \text{Theorem 3.9}$$

b. In order to obtain limits of the form $\lim_{x\to 0} \frac{\sin ax}{ax}$, the first step is to divide the numerator and denominator of $\frac{\sin 3x}{\sin 5x}$ by x:

$$\frac{\sin 3x}{\sin 5x} = \frac{(\sin 3x)/x}{(\sin 5x)/x}$$

As in part (a), we now divide and multiply $\frac{\sin 3x}{x}$ by 3 and divide and multiply $\frac{\sin 5x}{x}$ by 5. In the numerator, we let $t = 3x$, and in the denominator we let $u = 5x$. In each case, $t \to 0$ and $u \to 0$ as $x \to 0$. Therefore,

$$\lim_{x\to 0} \frac{\sin 3x}{\sin 5x} = \lim_{x\to 0} \frac{\dfrac{3 \sin 3x}{3x}}{\dfrac{5 \sin 5x}{5x}} \quad \text{Multiply and divide by 3 and 5.}$$

$$= \frac{3}{5} \frac{\lim_{t\to 0} (\sin t)/t}{\lim_{u\to 0} (\sin u)/u} \quad t = 3x \text{ in numerator and } u = 5x \text{ in denominator}$$

$$= \frac{3}{5} \cdot \frac{1}{1} = \frac{3}{5}. \quad \text{Both limits equal 1.}$$

Related Exercises 7–14 ◀

QUICK CHECK 1 Evaluate $\lim_{x\to 0} \frac{\tan 2x}{x}$. ◀

Derivatives of Sine and Cosine Functions

With the trigonometric limits of Theorem 3.9, the derivative of the sine function can be found. We start with the definition of the derivative

$$f'(x) = \lim_{h\to 0} \frac{f(x+h) - f(x)}{h}$$

with $f(x) = \sin x$ and then appeal to the sine addition identity

$$\sin(x+h) = \sin x \cos h + \cos x \sin h.$$

The derivative is

$$\begin{aligned}
f'(x) &= \lim_{h\to 0} \frac{\sin(x+h) - \sin x}{h} && \text{Definition of derivative} \\
&= \lim_{h\to 0} \frac{\sin x \cos h + \cos x \sin h - \sin x}{h} && \text{Sine addition identity} \\
&= \lim_{h\to 0} \frac{\sin x(\cos h - 1) + \cos x \sin h}{h} && \text{Factor } \sin x. \\
&= \lim_{h\to 0} \frac{\sin x(\cos h - 1)}{h} + \lim_{h\to 0} \frac{\cos x \sin h}{h} && \text{Theorem 2.3} \\
&= \sin x \underbrace{\left[\lim_{h\to 0} \frac{\cos h - 1}{h}\right]}_{0} + \cos x \underbrace{\left[\lim_{h\to 0} \frac{\sin h}{h}\right]}_{1} && \text{Both } \sin x \text{ and } \cos x \text{ are independent of } h. \\
&= (\sin x)(0) + \cos x(1) && \text{Theorem 3.9} \\
&= \cos x. && \text{Simplify.}
\end{aligned}$$

We have proved the important result that $\frac{d}{dx}(\sin x) = \cos x$.

The fact that $\frac{d}{dx}(\cos x) = -\sin x$ is proved in a similar way using a cosine addition identity (Exercise 63).

> **THEOREM 3.10 Derivatives of Sine and Cosine**
>
> $$\frac{d}{dx}(\sin x) = \cos x \qquad \frac{d}{dx}(\cos x) = -\sin x$$

From a geometric point of view, these derivative formulas make sense. Because $f(x) = \sin x$ is a periodic function, we expect its derivative to be periodic. Observe that the horizontal tangent lines on the graph of $f(x) = \sin x$ (Figure 3.26a) occur at the zeros of $f'(x) = \cos x$. Similarly, the horizontal tangent lines on the graph of $f(x) = \cos x$ occur at the zeros of $f'(x) = -\sin x$ (Figure 3.26b).

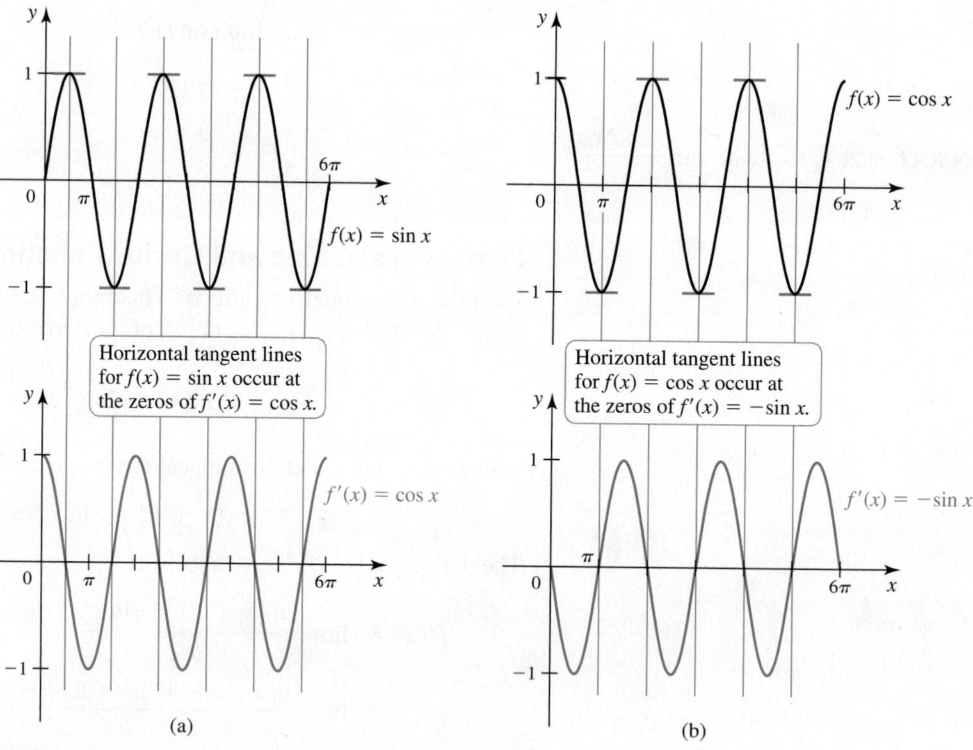

FIGURE 3.26

QUICK CHECK 2 At what points on the interval $[0, 2\pi]$ does the graph of $f(x) = \sin x$ have tangent lines with positive slopes? At what points on the interval $[0, 2\pi]$ is $\cos x > 0$? Explain the connection.

EXAMPLE 2 Derivatives involving trigonometric functions Calculate dy/dx for the following functions.

a. $y = x^2 \cos x$ **b.** $y = \sin x - x\cos x$ **c.** $y = \frac{1 + \sin x}{1 - \sin x}$

SOLUTION

a. $$\frac{dy}{dx} = \frac{d}{dx}(x^2 \cdot \cos x) = \underbrace{2x\cos x}_{\text{derivative of } x^2 \cdot \cos x} + \underbrace{x^2(-\sin x)}_{x^2 \cdot \text{the derivative of } \cos x} \quad \text{Product Rule}$$

$$= x(2\cos x - x\sin x) \quad \text{Simplify.}$$

b. $$\frac{dy}{dx} = \frac{d}{dx}(\sin x) - \frac{d}{dx}(x \cos x) \quad \text{Difference Rule}$$
$$= \cos x - [\underbrace{(1)\cos x}_{\text{derivative of } x \cdot \cos x} + \underbrace{x(-\sin x)}_{x \cdot \text{derivative of } \cos x}] \quad \text{Product Rule}$$
$$= x \sin x \quad \text{Simplify.}$$

c. $$\frac{dy}{dx} = \frac{(1 - \sin x)\overbrace{(\cos x)}^{\text{derivative of } 1+\sin x} - (1 + \sin x)\overbrace{(-\cos x)}^{\text{derivative of } 1-\sin x}}{(1 - \sin x)^2} \quad \text{Quotient Rule}$$
$$= \frac{\cos x - \cos x \sin x + \cos x + \sin x \cos x}{(1 - \sin x)^2} \quad \text{Expand.}$$
$$= \frac{2 \cos x}{(1 - \sin x)^2} \quad \text{Simplify.}$$

Related Exercises 15–22 ◀

Derivatives of Other Trigonometric Functions

The derivatives of $\tan x$, $\cot x$, $\sec x$, and $\csc x$ are obtained using the derivatives of $\sin x$ and $\cos x$ together with the Quotient Rule and trigonometric identities.

EXAMPLE 3 **Derivative of the tangent function** Calculate $\frac{d}{dx}(\tan x)$.

> Recall that $\tan x = \frac{\sin x}{\cos x}$, $\cot x = \frac{\cos x}{\sin x}$, $\sec x = \frac{1}{\cos x}$, and $\csc x = \frac{1}{\sin x}$.

SOLUTION Using the identity $\tan x = \frac{\sin x}{\cos x}$ and the Quotient Rule, we have

$$\frac{d}{dx}(\tan x) = \frac{d}{dx}\left(\frac{\sin x}{\cos x}\right)$$
$$= \frac{\overbrace{\cos x}^{\text{derivative of } \sin x} \cos x - \sin x \overbrace{(-\sin x)}^{\text{derivative of } \cos x}}{\cos^2 x} \quad \text{Quotient Rule}$$
$$= \frac{\cos^2 x + \sin^2 x}{\cos^2 x} \quad \text{Simplify numerator.}$$
$$= \frac{1}{\cos^2 x} = \sec^2 x. \quad \cos^2 x + \sin^2 x = 1$$

Therefore, $\frac{d}{dx}(\tan x) = \sec^2 x$.

Related Exercises 23–25 ◀

> One way to remember Theorem 3.11 is to learn the derivatives of the sine, tangent, and secant functions. Then, replace each function by its corresponding **cofunction** and put a negative sign on the right-hand side of the new derivative formula.
>
> $\frac{d}{dx}(\sin x) = \cos x \quad \leftrightarrow \quad \frac{d}{dx}(\cos x) = -\sin x$
>
> $\frac{d}{dx}(\tan x) = \sec^2 x \quad \leftrightarrow \quad \frac{d}{dx}(\cot x) = -\csc^2 x$
>
> $\frac{d}{dx}(\sec x) = \sec x \tan x \quad \leftrightarrow \quad \frac{d}{dx}(\csc x) = -\csc x \cot x$

The derivatives of $\cot x$, $\sec x$, and $\csc x$ are given in Theorem 3.11 (Exercises 23–25).

THEOREM 3.11 **Derivatives of the Trigonometric Functions**

$$\frac{d}{dx}(\sin x) = \cos x \qquad \frac{d}{dx}(\cos x) = -\sin x$$
$$\frac{d}{dx}(\tan x) = \sec^2 x \qquad \frac{d}{dx}(\cot x) = -\csc^2 x$$
$$\frac{d}{dx}(\sec x) = \sec x \tan x \qquad \frac{d}{dx}(\csc x) = -\csc x \cot x$$

QUICK CHECK 3 The formulas for $\frac{d}{dx}(\cot x)$, $\frac{d}{dx}(\sec x)$, and $\frac{d}{dx}(\csc x)$ can be determined using the Quotient Rule. Why?

EXAMPLE 4 Derivatives involving sec *x* and csc *x* Find the derivative of $y = \sec x \csc x$.

SOLUTION

$$\begin{aligned}
\frac{dy}{dx} &= \frac{d}{dx}(\sec x \cdot \csc x) \\
&= \underbrace{\sec x \tan x}_{\text{derivative of } \sec x} \csc x + \sec x \underbrace{(-\csc x \cot x)}_{\text{derivative of } \csc x} && \text{Product Rule} \\
&= \underbrace{\frac{1}{\cos x}}_{\sec x} \cdot \underbrace{\frac{\sin x}{\cos x}}_{\tan x} \cdot \underbrace{\frac{1}{\sin x}}_{\csc x} - \underbrace{\frac{1}{\cos x}}_{\sec x} \cdot \underbrace{\frac{1}{\sin x}}_{\csc x} \cdot \underbrace{\frac{\cos x}{\sin x}}_{\cot x} && \text{Write functions in terms of } \sin x \text{ and } \cos x. \\
&= \frac{1}{\cos^2 x} - \frac{1}{\sin^2 x} && \text{Cancel and simplify.} \\
&= \sec^2 x - \csc^2 x && \text{Definition of } \sec x \text{ and } \csc x
\end{aligned}$$

Related Exercises 26–32

QUICK CHECK 4 Why is the derivative of $\sec x \csc x$ equal to the derivative of $\frac{1}{\cos x \sin x}$?

Higher-Order Trigonometric Derivatives

Higher-order derivatives of the sine and cosine functions are important in many applications. A few higher-order derivatives of $y = \sin x$ reveal a pattern:

$$\frac{dy}{dx} = \cos x \qquad \frac{d^2y}{dx^2} = \frac{d}{dx}(\cos x) = -\sin x$$

$$\frac{d^3y}{dx^3} = \frac{d}{dx}(-\sin x) = -\cos x \qquad \frac{d^4y}{dx^4} = \frac{d}{dx}(-\cos x) = \sin x$$

We see that the higher-order derivatives of $\sin x$ cycle back periodically to $\pm \sin x$. In general, it can be shown that $\frac{d^{2n}y}{dx^{2n}} = (-1)^n \sin x$, with a similar result for $\cos x$ (Exercise 68). This cyclic behavior in the derivatives of $\sin x$ and $\cos x$ does not occur with the other trigonometric functions.

QUICK CHECK 5 Find $\frac{d^2y}{dx^2}$ and $\frac{d^4y}{dx^4}$ when $y = \cos x$. Find $\frac{d^{40}y}{dx^{40}}$ and $\frac{d^{42}y}{dx^{42}}$ when $y = \sin x$.

EXAMPLE 5 Second-order derivatives Find the second derivative of $y = \csc x$.

SOLUTION By Theorem 3.11, $\frac{dy}{dx} = -\csc x \cot x$.

Applying the Product Rule gives the second derivative:

$$\begin{aligned}
\frac{d^2y}{dx^2} &= \frac{d}{dx}(-\csc x \cot x) \\
&= \left(\frac{d}{dx}(-\csc x)\right)\cot x - \csc x \frac{d}{dx}(\cot x) && \text{Product Rule} \\
&= (\csc x \cot x)\cot x - \csc x(-\csc^2 x) && \text{Calculate derivatives.} \\
&= \csc x(\cot^2 x + \csc^2 x) && \text{Factor.}
\end{aligned}$$

Related Exercises 33–36

SECTION 3.4 EXERCISES

Review Questions

1. Why is it not possible to evaluate $\lim_{x\to 0} \frac{\sin x}{x}$ by direct substitution?
2. How is $\lim_{x\to 0} \frac{\sin x}{x}$ used in this section?
3. Explain why the Quotient Rule is used to determine the derivative of $\tan x$ and $\cot x$.
4. How can you use the derivatives $\frac{d}{dx}(\sin x) = \cos x$, $\frac{d}{dx}(\tan x) = \sec^2 x$, and $\frac{d}{dx}(\sec x) = \sec x \tan x$ to remember the derivatives of $\cos x$, $\cot x$ and $\csc x$?
5. If $f(x) = \sin x$, then what is the value of $f'(\pi)$?
6. Where does $\sin x$ have a horizontal tangent line? Where does $\cos x$ have a value of zero? Explain the connection between these two observations.

Basic Skills

7–14. Trigonometric limits *Use Theorem 3.9 to evaluate the following limits.*

7. $\lim_{x\to 0} \frac{\sin 3x}{x}$
8. $\lim_{x\to 0} \frac{\sin 5x}{3x}$
9. $\lim_{x\to 0} \frac{\tan 5x}{x}$
10. $\lim_{\theta\to 0} \frac{\cos^2\theta - 1}{\theta}$
11. $\lim_{x\to 0} \frac{\tan 7x}{\sin x}$
12. $\lim_{\theta\to 0} \frac{\sec\theta - 1}{\theta}$
13. $\lim_{x\to 2} \frac{\sin(x-2)}{x^2-4}$
14. $\lim_{x\to -3} \frac{\sin(x+3)}{x^2+8x+15}$

15–22. Calculating derivatives *Find dy/dx for the following functions.*

15. $y = \sin x + \cos x$
16. $y = 5x^2 + \cos x$
17. $y = 3x^4 \sin x$
18. $y = \sin x + \frac{4\cos x}{x}$
19. $y = \sin x \cos x$
20. $y = \frac{(x^2-1)\sin x}{\sin x + 1}$
21. $y = \cos^2 x$
22. $y = \frac{x \sin x}{1 + \cos x}$

23–25. Derivatives of other trigonometric functions *Verify the following derivative formulas using the Quotient Rule.*

23. $\frac{d}{dx}(\cot x) = -\csc^2 x$
24. $\frac{d}{dx}(\sec x) = \sec x \tan x$
25. $\frac{d}{dx}(\csc x) = -\csc x \cot x$

26–32. Derivatives involving other trigonometric functions *Find the derivative of the following functions.*

26. $y = \tan x + \cot x$
27. $y = \sec x + \csc x$
28. $y = \frac{\tan w}{1 + \tan w}$
29. $y = \frac{\cot x}{1 + \csc x}$
30. $y = \frac{\tan t}{1 + \sec t}$
31. $y = \frac{1}{\sec z \csc z}$
32. $y = \csc^2\theta - 1$

33–36. Second derivatives *Find y'' for the following functions.*

33. $y = \cot x$
34. $y = \tan x$
35. $y = \sec x \csc x$
36. $y = \cos\theta \sin\theta$

Further Explorations

37. **Explain why or why not** Determine whether the following statements are true and give an explanation or counterexample.
    a. $\frac{d}{dx}(\sin^2 x) = \cos^2 x$
    b. $\frac{d^2}{dx^2}(\sin x) = \sin x$
    c. $\frac{d^4}{dx^4}(\cos x) = \cos x$
    d. The function $\sec x$ is not differentiable at $x = \pi/2$.

38–43. Trigonometric limits *Evaluate the following limits or state that they do not exist.*

38. $\lim_{x\to 0} \frac{\sin ax}{bx}$, where a and b are constants with $b \neq 0$
39. $\lim_{x\to 0} \frac{\sin ax}{\sin bx}$, where a and b are constants with $b \neq 0$
40. $\lim_{x\to\pi/2} \frac{\cos x}{x - (\pi/2)}$
41. $\lim_{x\to 0} \frac{3\sec^5 x}{x^2+4}$
42. $\lim_{x\to\infty} \frac{\cos x}{x}$
43. $\lim_{x\to\pi/4} 3\csc 2x \cot 2x$

44–49. Calculating derivatives *Find dy/dx for the following functions.*

44. $y = \frac{\sin x}{1 + \cos x}$
45. $y = x \cos x \sin x$
46. $y = \frac{1}{2 + \sin x}$
47. $y = \frac{2\cos x}{1 + \sin x}$
48. $y = \frac{x \cos x}{1 + x^3}$
49. $y = \frac{1 - \cos x}{1 + \cos x}$

T **50–53. Equations of tangent lines**
   a. *Find an equation of the line tangent to the following curves at the given value of x.*
   b. *Use a graphing utility to plot the curve and the tangent line.*

50. $y = 4\sin x \cos x;\ x = \pi/3$
51. $y = 1 + 2\sin x;\ x = \pi/6$
52. $y = \csc x;\ x = \pi/4$
53. $y = \frac{\cos x}{1 - \cos x};\ x = \pi/3$

54. Locations of tangent lines

a. For what values of x does $g(x) = x - \sin x$ have a horizontal tangent line?
b. For what values of x does $g(x) = x - \sin x$ have a slope of 1?

55. Locations of horizontal tangent lines For what values of x does $f(x) = x - 2\cos x$ have a horizontal tangent line?

56. Matching Match the graphs of functions a–d with the graphs of derivatives A–D.

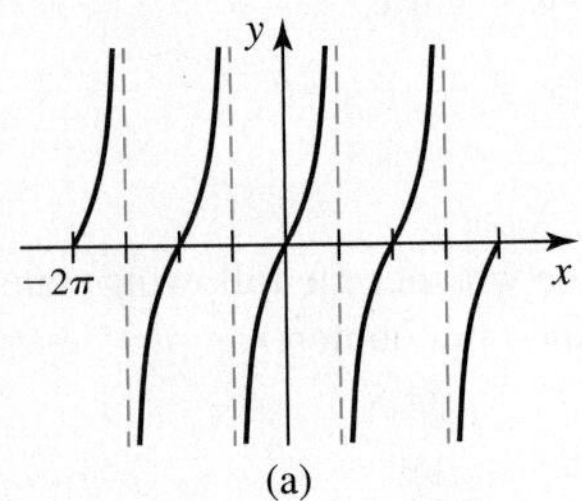

(a)

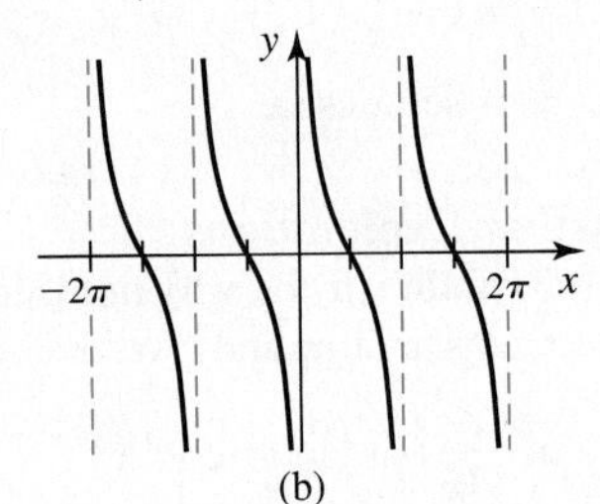

(b)

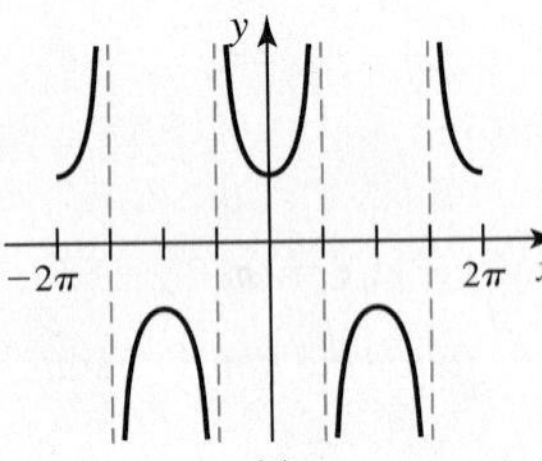

(c)

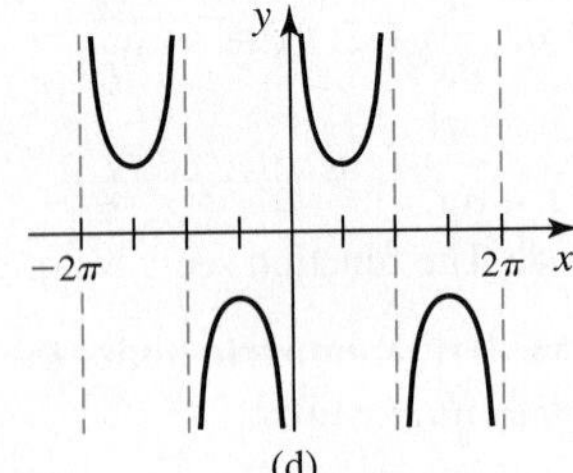

(d)

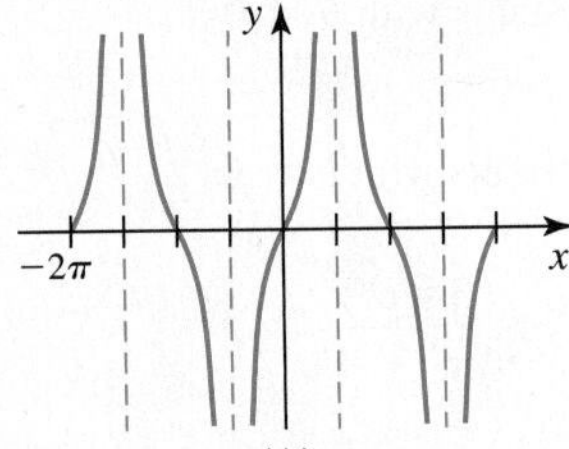

(A)

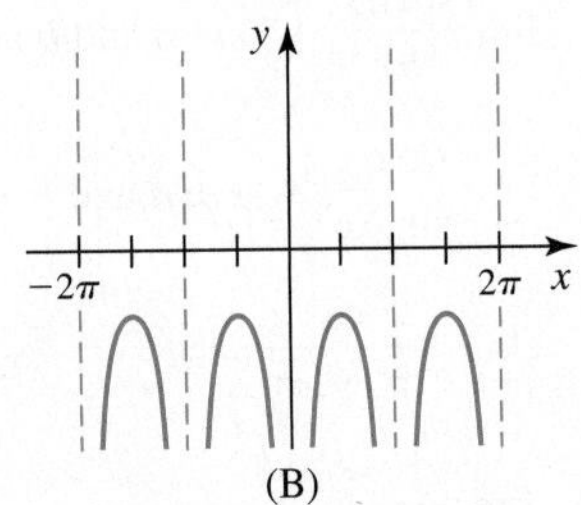

(B)

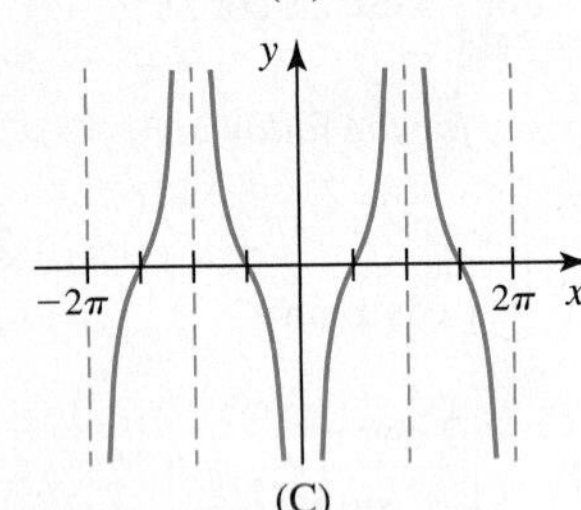

(C)

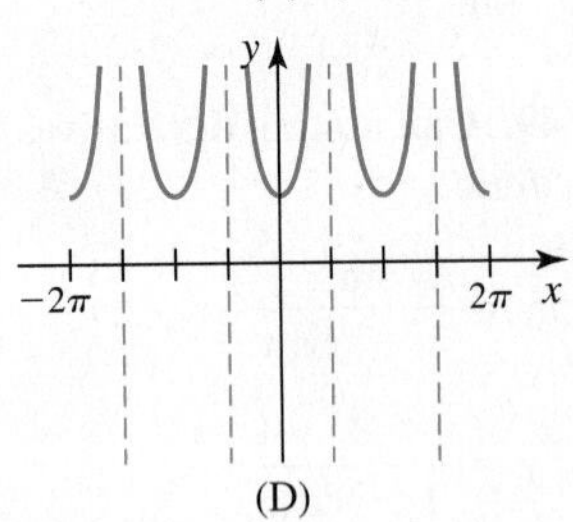

(D)

Applications

57. Velocity of an oscillator An object oscillates along a vertical line, and its displacement in centimeters is given by $y(t) = 30(\sin t - 1)$, where $t \geq 0$ is measured in seconds and y is positive in the upward direction.

a. Graph the position function, for $0 \leq t \leq 10$.
b. Find the velocity of the oscillator, $v(t) = y'(t)$.
c. Graph the velocity function, for $0 \leq t \leq 10$.
d. At what times and positions is the velocity zero?
e. At what times and positions is the velocity a maximum?
f. The acceleration of the oscillator is $a(t) = v'(t)$. Find and graph the acceleration function.

58. Resonance An oscillator (such as a mass on a spring or a component in an electrical circuit) subject to external forces that have the same frequency as the oscillator itself may undergo motion called *resonance* (at least for short periods of time). The position function of an oscillator in resonance has the form $y(t) = At\sin t$, where A is a constant.

a. Graph the position function with $A = \frac{1}{2}$, for $0 \leq t \leq 20$. How does the amplitude of the oscillation (the height of the peaks) change as t increases?
b. Compute and graph the velocity of the object, $v(t) = y'(t)$ (with $A = \frac{1}{2}$), for $0 \leq t \leq 20$.
c. Where do the zeros of the velocity function appear relative to the peaks and valleys of the position function?
d. If the oscillator were a suspension bridge, explain why resonance could be catastrophic.

59. A differential equation A differential equation is an equation involving an unknown function and its derivatives. Consider the differential equation $y''(t) + y(t) = 0$.

a. Show that $y = A\sin t$ satisfies the equation for any constant A.
b. Show that $y = B\cos t$ satisfies the equation for any constant B.
c. Show that $y = A\sin t + B\cos t$ satisfies the equation for any constants A and B.

Additional Exercises

60. Using identities Use the identity $\sin 2x = 2\sin x\cos x$ to find $\frac{d}{dx}(\sin 2x)$. Then use the identity $\cos 2x = \cos^2 x - \sin^2 x$ to express the derivative of $\sin 2x$ in terms of $\cos 2x$.

61. Proof of $\lim_{x\to 0}\frac{\cos x - 1}{x} = 0$ Use the trigonometric identity $\cos^2 x + \sin^2 x = 1$ to prove that $\lim_{x\to 0}\frac{\cos x - 1}{x} = 0$. (*Hint:* Begin by multiplying the numerator and denominator by $\cos x + 1$.)

62. Another method for proving $\lim_{x\to 0}\frac{\cos x - 1}{x} = 0$ Use the half-angle formula $\sin^2 x = \frac{1 - \cos 2x}{2}$ to prove that $\lim_{x\to 0}\frac{\cos x - 1}{x} = 0$.

63. Proof of $\frac{d}{dx}(\cos x) = -\sin x$ Use the limit definition of the derivative and the trigonometric identity

$$\cos(x + h) = \cos x\cos h - \sin x\sin h$$

to prove that $\frac{d}{dx}(\cos x) = -\sin x$.

64. Continuity of a piecewise function Let

$$f(x) = \begin{cases} \dfrac{3\sin x}{x} & \text{if } x \neq 0 \\ a & \text{if } x = 0 \end{cases}$$

For what values of a is f continuous?

65. Continuity of a piecewise function Let

$$g(x) = \begin{cases} \dfrac{1 - \cos x}{2x} & \text{if } x \neq 0 \\ a & \text{if } x = 0 \end{cases}$$

For what values of a is g continuous?

T **66. Computing limits with angles in degrees** Suppose your graphing calculator has two functions, one called $\sin x$, which calculates the sine of x when x is in radians and the other called $s(x)$, which calculates the sine of x when x is in degrees.

a. Explain why $s(x) = \sin\left(\dfrac{\pi}{180}x\right)$.

b. Evaluate $\lim_{x\to 0} \dfrac{s(x)}{x}$. Verify your answer by estimating the limit on your calculator.

67. Derivatives of $\sin^n x$ Calculate the following derivatives using the Product Rule.

a. $\dfrac{d}{dx}(\sin^2 x)$ **b.** $\dfrac{d}{dx}(\sin^3 x)$ **c.** $\dfrac{d}{dx}(\sin^4 x)$

d. Based upon your answers to parts (a)–(c), make a conjecture about $\dfrac{d}{dx}(\sin^n x)$, where n is a positive integer. Then, prove the result by induction.

68. Higher-order derivatives of $\sin x$ and $\cos x$ Prove that

$$\frac{d^{2n}}{dx^{2n}}(\sin x) = (-1)^n \sin x \quad \text{and} \quad \frac{d^{2n}}{dx^{2n}}(\cos x) = (-1)^n \cos x.$$

69–72. Identifying derivatives from limits *The following limits equal the derivative of a function f at a point a.*

a. *Find one possible f and a.* ***b.*** *Evaluate the limit.*

69. $\lim_{h\to 0} \dfrac{\sin\left(\dfrac{\pi}{6} + h\right) - \dfrac{1}{2}}{h}$

70. $\lim_{h\to 0} \dfrac{\cos\left(\dfrac{\pi}{6} + h\right) - \dfrac{\sqrt{3}}{2}}{h}$

71. $\lim_{x\to \pi/4} \dfrac{\cot x - 1}{x - \dfrac{\pi}{4}}$

72. $\lim_{h\to 0} \dfrac{\tan\left(\dfrac{5\pi}{6} + h\right) + \dfrac{1}{\sqrt{3}}}{h}$

QUICK CHECK ANSWERS

1. 2 **2.** $0 < x < \frac{\pi}{2}$ and $\frac{3\pi}{2} < x < 2\pi$. The value of $\cos x$ is the slope of the line tangent to the curve $y = \sin x$. **3.** The Quotient Rule is used because each function is a quotient when written in terms of the sine and cosine functions. **4.** $\dfrac{1}{\cos x \sin x} = \dfrac{1}{\cos x} \cdot \dfrac{1}{\sin x} = \sec x \csc x$ **5.** $\dfrac{d^2 y}{dx^2} = -\cos x$, $\dfrac{d^4 y}{dx^4} = \cos x$, $\dfrac{d^{40}}{dx^{40}}(\sin x) = \sin x$, $\dfrac{d^{42}}{dx^{42}}(\sin x) = -\sin x$ ◀

3.5 Derivatives as Rates of Change

The theme of this section is the *derivative as a rate of change*. Observing the world around us, we see that almost everything is in a state of change: The size of the Internet is increasing; your blood pressure fluctuates; as supply increases, prices decrease; and the universe is expanding. This section explores a few of the many applications of this idea and demonstrates why calculus is called the mathematics of change.

One-Dimensional Motion

Describing the motion of objects such as projectiles and planets was one of the challenges that led to the development of calculus in the 17th century. We begin by considering the motion of an object confined to one dimension; that is, the object moves along a line. This motion could be horizontal (for example, a car moving along a straight highway) or it could be vertical (such as a projectile launched vertically into the air).

➤ When describing the motion of objects, it is customary to use t as the independent variable to represent time. Generally, motion is assumed to begin at $t = 0$.

Position and Velocity Suppose an object moves along a straight line and its location at time t is given by the **position function** $s = f(t)$. All positions are measured relative to a reference point, which is often the origin at $s = 0$. The **displacement** of the object between $t = a$ and $t = a + \Delta t$ is $\Delta s = f(a + \Delta t) - f(a)$, where the elapsed time is Δt units (Figure 3.27).

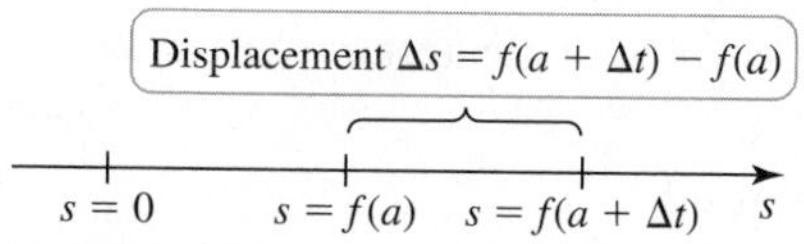

Displacement $\Delta s = f(a + \Delta t) - f(a)$

$s = 0$ $s = f(a)$ $s = f(a + \Delta t)$ s

FIGURE 3.27

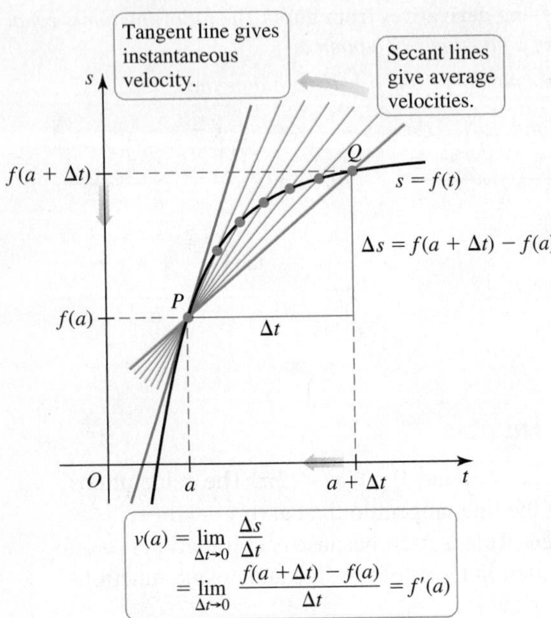

FIGURE 3.28

Recall from Section 2.1 that the *average velocity* of the object over the interval $[a, a + \Delta t]$ is the displacement Δs of the object divided by the elapsed time Δt:

$$\frac{\Delta s}{\Delta t} = \frac{f(a + \Delta t) - f(a)}{\Delta t}.$$

The average velocity is the slope of the secant line passing through the points $P(a, f(a))$ and $Q(a + \Delta t, f(a + \Delta t))$ (Figure 3.28).

As Δt approaches 0, the average velocity is calculated over smaller and smaller time intervals, and the limiting value of these average velocities, when it exists, is the *instantaneous velocity* at a. This is the same argument used to arrive at the derivative. The conclusion is that the instantaneous velocity at time a, denoted $v(a)$, is the derivative of the position function evaluated at a:

$$v(a) = \lim_{\Delta t \to 0} \frac{f(a + \Delta t) - f(a)}{\Delta t} = f'(a).$$

Equivalently, the instantaneous velocity at a is the rate of change in the position function at a; it also equals the slope of the line tangent to the curve $s = f(t)$ at $P(a, f(a))$.

➤ Using the various derivative notations, the velocity is also written $v(t) = s'(t) = ds/dt$. If *average* or *instantaneous* is not specified, *velocity* is understood to mean instantaneous velocity.

DEFINITION Average and Instantaneous Velocity

Let $s = f(t)$ be the position function of an object moving along a line. The **average velocity** of the object over the time interval $[a, a + \Delta t]$ is the slope of the secant line between $(a, f(a))$ and $(a + \Delta t, f(a + \Delta t))$:

$$\frac{f(a + \Delta t) - f(a)}{\Delta t}.$$

The **instantaneous velocity** at a is the slope of the line tangent to the position curve at $(a, f(a))$, which is the derivative of the position function:

$$v(a) = \lim_{\Delta t \to 0} \frac{f(a + \Delta t) - f(a)}{\Delta t} = f'(a).$$

QUICK CHECK 1 Does the speedometer in your car measure average or instantaneous velocity? ◄

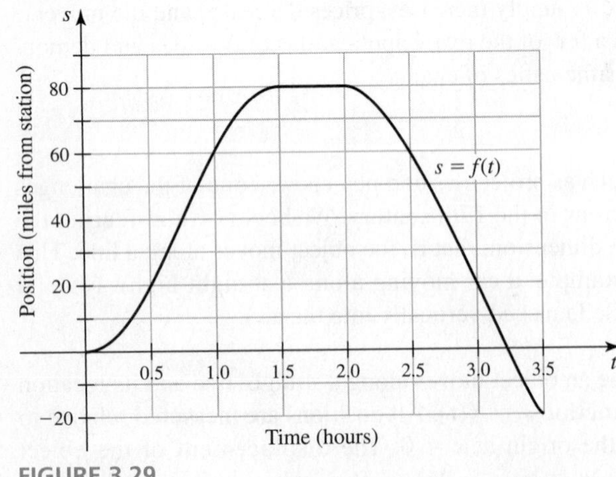

FIGURE 3.29

EXAMPLE 1 Position and velocity of a patrol car Assume a police station is located along a straight east-west freeway. At noon ($t = 0$), a patrol car leaves the station heading east. The position function of the car $s = f(t)$ gives the location of the car in miles east ($s > 0$) or west ($s < 0$) of the station t hours after noon (Figure 3.29).

a. Describe the location of the patrol car during the first 3.5 hr of the trip.

b. Calculate the average velocity of the car between noon and 2:00 P.M. ($0 \le t \le 2$).

c. Calculate the displacement and average velocity of the car between 2:00 P.M. and 3:30 P.M. ($2 \le t \le 3.5$).

d. At what time(s) is the instantaneous velocity greatest *as the car travels east*?

e. At what time(s) is the patrol car at rest?

SOLUTION

a. The graph of the position function indicates the car travels 80 mi east between $t = 0$ (noon) and $t = 1.5$ (1:30 P.M.). The position of the car does not change from $t = 1.5$ to $t = 2$, and therefore the car is at rest from 1:30 P.M. to 2:00 P.M. Starting at $t = 2$, the car's distance from the station decreases, which means the car travels west, eventually ending up 20 mi west of the station at $t = 3.5$ (3:30 P.M.) (Figure 3.30).

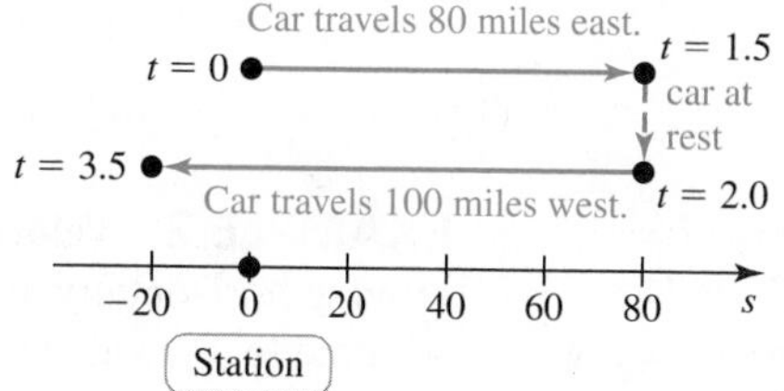

FIGURE 3.30

b. Using Figure 3.29, we find that $f(0) = 0$ mi and $f(2) = 80$ mi. Therefore, the average velocity during the first 2 hours is

$$\frac{\Delta s}{\Delta t} = \frac{f(2) - f(0)}{2 - 0} = \frac{80 \text{ mi}}{2 \text{ hr}} = 40 \text{ mi/hr}.$$

c. The position of the car at 3:30 P.M. is $f(3.5) = -20$ (the negative sign indicates the car is 20 miles *west* of the station), and the position of the car at 2:00 P.M. is $f(2) = 80$. Therefore, the displacement is

$$\Delta s = f(3.5) - f(2) = -20 \text{ mi} - 80 \text{ mi} = -100 \text{ mi}$$

during an elapsed time of $\Delta t = 3.5 - 2 = 1.5$ hr (the *negative* displacement indicates that the car moved 100 miles *west*). The average velocity is

$$\frac{\Delta s}{\Delta t} = \frac{-100 \text{ mi}}{1.5 \text{ hr}} \approx -66.7 \text{ mi/hr}.$$

d. The greatest eastward instantaneous velocity corresponds to points at which the graph has the greatest positive slope. The greatest slope appears to occur between $t = 0.5$ and $t = 1$. During this time interval, the car also has a nearly constant velocity because the curve is approximately linear. We conclude that the eastward velocity is largest from 12:30 to 1:00.

e. The car is at rest when the instantaneous velocity is zero. So, we look for points at which the slope of the curve is zero. These points occur at times between $t = 1.5$ and $t = 2$.

Related Exercises 9–10 ◀

Speed and Acceleration When only the magnitude of the velocity is of interest, we use **speed**, which is the absolute value of the velocity:

$$\text{speed} = |v|$$

For example, a car with an instantaneous velocity of -30 mi/hr has a speed of 30 mi/hr.

A more complete description of an object moving along a line includes its **acceleration**, which is the rate of change of the velocity; that is, acceleration is the derivative of the velocity function with respect to time t. If the acceleration is positive, the object's velocity increases; if it is negative, the object's velocity decreases. Because velocity is the derivative of the position function, acceleration is the second derivative of the position. Therefore,

$$a = \frac{dv}{dt} = \frac{d^2 s}{dt^2}.$$

➤ Newton's first law of motion says that in the absence of external forces, a moving object has no acceleration, which means the magnitude and direction of the velocity are constant.

DEFINITION Velocity, Speed, and Acceleration

Suppose an object moves along a line with position $s = f(t)$.

velocity at time t: $\quad v = \dfrac{ds}{dt} = f'(t)$

speed at time t: $\quad |v| = |f'(t)|$

acceleration at time t: $\quad a = \dfrac{dv}{dt} = \dfrac{d^2s}{dt^2} = f''(t)$

➤ The units of derivatives are consistent with the notation. If s is measured in meters and t is measured in seconds, the units of the velocity $\dfrac{ds}{dt}$ are m/s. The units of the acceleration $\dfrac{d^2s}{dt^2}$ are m/s^2.

EXAMPLE 2 Velocity and acceleration Suppose the position (in feet) of an object moving horizontally at time t (in seconds) is $s = t^2 - 5t$, for $0 \leq t \leq 5$ (Figure 3.31). Assume that positive values of s correspond to positions to the right of $s = 0$.

a. Graph the velocity function on the interval $0 \leq t \leq 5$, and determine when the object is stationary, moving to the left, and moving to the right.

b. Graph the acceleration function on the interval $0 \leq t \leq 5$, and determine the acceleration of the object when its velocity is zero.

c. Describe the motion of the object.

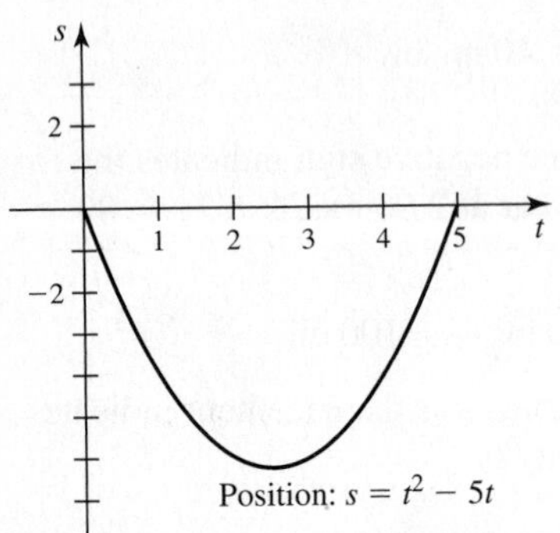

FIGURE 3.31

➤ Figure 3.31 gives the graph of the position function, not the path of the object. The motion is along a horizontal line.

SOLUTION

a. The velocity is $v = s'(t) = 2t - 5$. The object is stationary when $v = 2t - 5 = 0$, or at $t = 2.5$ s. Solving $v = 2t - 5 > 0$, the velocity is positive (motion to the right) for $\frac{5}{2} < t < 5$. Similarly, the velocity is negative (motion to the left) for $0 \leq t < \frac{5}{2}$. The graph of the velocity function (Figure 3.32) confirms these observations.

b. The acceleration is the derivative of the velocity or $a = v'(t) = s''(t) = 2$. This means that the acceleration is 2 ft/s^2, for $0 \leq t \leq 5$ (Figure 3.33).

c. Starting at an initial position of $s(0) = 0$, the object moves in the negative direction (to the left) with decreasing speed until it comes to rest momentarily at $s\left(\frac{5}{2}\right) = -\frac{25}{4}$. The object then moves in the positive direction (to the right) with increasing speed, reaching its initial position at $t = 5$. During this time interval, the acceleration is constant.

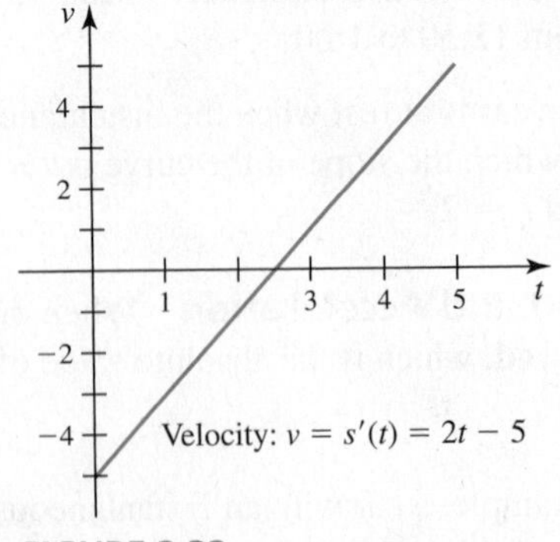

FIGURE 3.32

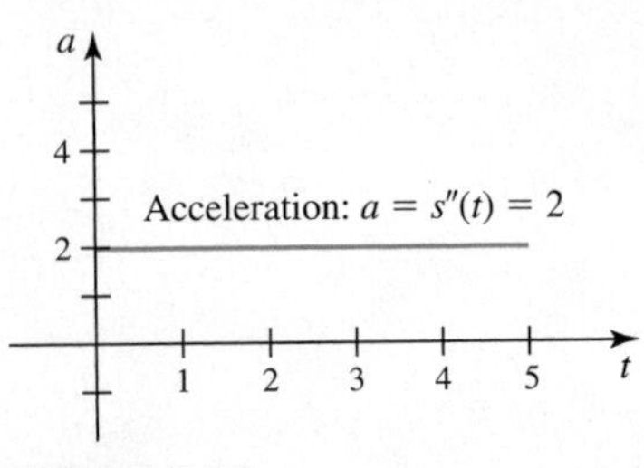

FIGURE 3.33

Related Exercises 11–16 ◄

QUICK CHECK 2 Describe in words the velocity of an object that has a positive constant acceleration. Could an object have a positive acceleration and a decreasing speed? ◄

➤ The acceleration due to Earth's gravitational field is denoted g. In metric units $g \approx 9.8\ \text{m/s}^2$ on the surface of Earth; in the U.S. Customary System (USCS), $g \approx 32\ \text{ft/s}^2$.

➤ The derivation of the position function is given in Section 6.1. Once again we mention that the graph of the position function is not the path of the stone.

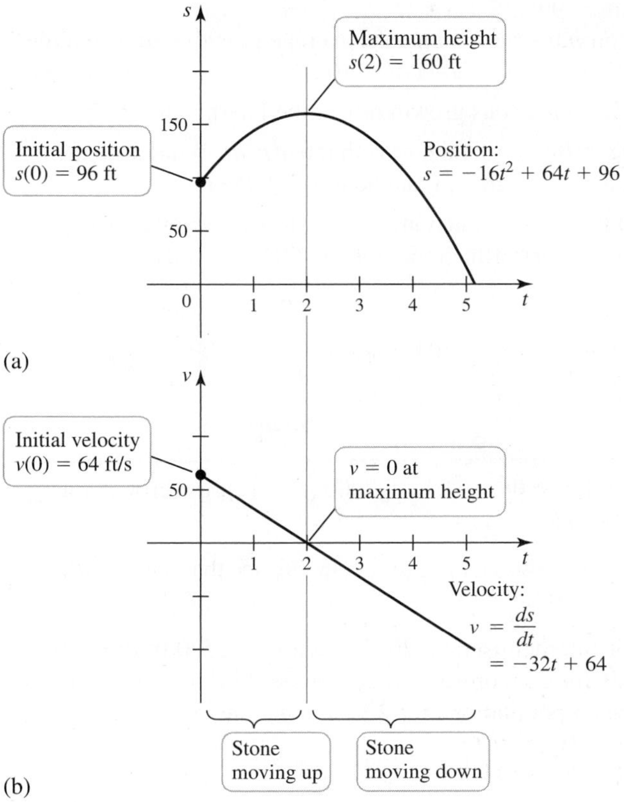

Free Fall We now consider problems in which an object moves vertically in Earth's gravitational field, assuming that no other forces (such as air resistance) are at work.

EXAMPLE 3 **Motion in a gravitational field** Suppose a stone is thrown vertically upward with an initial velocity of 64 ft/s from a bridge 96 ft above a river. By Newton's laws of motion, the position of the stone (measured as the height above the river) after t seconds is

$$s(t) = -16t^2 + 64t + 96,$$

where $s = 0$ is the level of the river (Figure 3.34a).

a. Find the velocity and acceleration functions.

b. What is the highest point above the river reached by the stone?

c. With what velocity will the stone strike the river?

FIGURE 3.34

SOLUTION

a. The velocity of the stone is the derivative of the position function, and its acceleration is the derivative of the velocity function. Therefore,

$$v = \frac{ds}{dt} = -32t + 64 \quad \text{and} \quad a = \frac{dv}{dt} = -32.$$

b. When the stone reaches its high point, its velocity is zero (Figure 3.34b). Solving $v(t) = -32t + 64 = 0$ yields $t = 2$, and thus the stone reaches its maximum height 2 s after it is thrown. Its height at that instant is

$$s(2) = -16(2)^2 + 64(2) + 96 = 160 \text{ ft}.$$

c. To determine the velocity at which the stone strikes the river, we first determine *when* it reaches the river. The stone strikes the river when $s(t) = -16t^2 + 64t + 96 = 0$. Dividing both sides of the equation by -16, we obtain $t^2 - 4t - 6 = 0$. Using the quadratic formula, the solutions are $t \approx 5.16$ or $t \approx -1.16$. Because the stone is thrown at $t = 0$, only positive values of t are of interest; therefore, the relevant root is $t \approx 5.16$. The velocity of the stone (in ft/s) when it strikes the river is approximately

$$v(5.16) = -32(5.16) + 64 = -101.1.$$

Related Exercises 17–18 ◀

QUICK CHECK 3 In Example 3, does the rock have the greater speed at $t = 1$ or $t = 3$? ◀

Growth Models

Much of the change in the world around us can be classified as *growth*: Populations, prices, and computer networks all tend to increase in size. Modeling growth is important because it often leads to an understanding of underlying processes and allows for predictions.

We let $p = f(t)$ be the measure of a quantity of interest (for example, the population of a species or the consumer price index), where $t \geq 0$ represents time. The average growth rate of p between time $t = a$ and a later time $t = a + \Delta t$ is the change Δp divided by elapsed time Δt. Therefore, the **average growth rate** of p on the interval $[a, a + \Delta t]$ is

$$\frac{\Delta p}{\Delta t} = \frac{f(a + \Delta t) - f(a)}{\Delta t}.$$

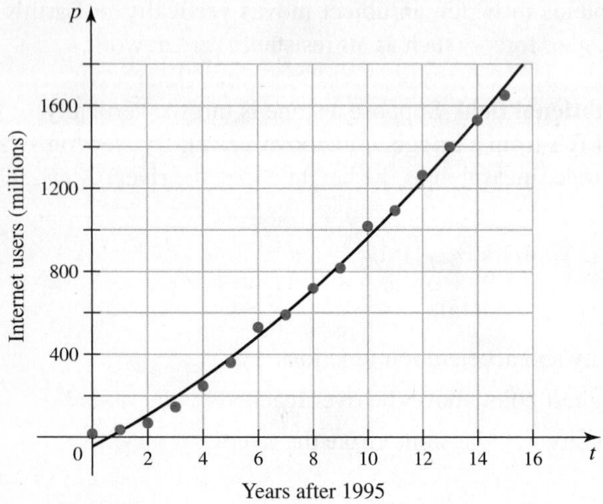

FIGURE 3.35

If we now let $\Delta t \to 0$, then $\frac{\Delta p}{\Delta t}$ approaches the derivative $\frac{dp}{dt}$, which is the **instantaneous growth rate** (or simply **growth rate**) of p with respect to time:

$$\frac{dp}{dt} = \lim_{\Delta t \to 0} \frac{\Delta p}{\Delta t}$$

EXAMPLE 4 **Internet growth** The number of worldwide Internet users between 1995 and 2010 is shown in Figure 3.35. A reasonable fit to the data is given by the function $p(t) = 3.0t^2 + 70.8t - 45.8$, where t measures years after 1995.

a. Use the function p to approximate the average growth rate of Internet users from 2000 ($t = 5$) to 2005 ($t = 10$).

b. What was the instantaneous growth rate of the Internet in 2006?

c. Use a graphing utility to plot the growth rate dp/dt. What does the graph tell you about the growth rate between 1995 and 2010?

d. Assuming that the growth function can be extended beyond 2010, what is the predicted number of Internet users in 2015 ($t = 20$)?

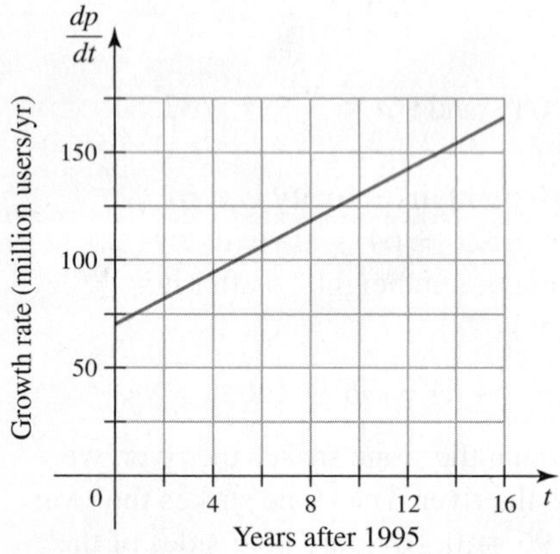

FIGURE 3.36

QUICK CHECK 4 Using the growth function in Example 4, compare the growth rates in 1996 and 2010.

SOLUTION

a. The average growth rate over the interval $[5, 10]$ is

$$\frac{\Delta p}{\Delta t} = \frac{p(10) - p(5)}{10 - 5} \approx \frac{962 - 383}{5} \approx 116 \text{ million users/year.}$$

b. The growth rate at time t is $p'(t) = 6.0t + 70.8$. In 2006 ($t = 11$), the growth rate was $p'(11) \approx 137$ million users/year.

c. The graph of p', for $0 \le t \le 16$, is shown in Figure 3.36. We see that the growth rate is positive and increasing, for $t \ge 0$.

d. A projection of the number of Internet users in 2015 is $p(20) \approx 2570$ million users, or about 2.6 billion users. This figure represents roughly one-third of the world's population, assuming a projected population of 7.2 billion people in 2015.

Related Exercises 19–20

Average and Marginal Cost

Our final example illustrates how derivatives arise in business and economics. As you will see, the mathematics of derivatives is the same in economics as it is in other applications. However, the vocabulary and interpretation used by economists are quite different.

Imagine a company that manufactures large quantities of a product such as mousetraps, DVD players, or snowboards. Associated with the manufacturing process is a **cost function** $C(x)$ that gives the cost of manufacturing x items of the product. A simple cost function might have the form $y = C(x) = 500 + 0.1x$, as shown in Figure 3.37. It includes a **fixed cost** of \$500 (setup costs and overhead) that is independent of the number of items produced. It also includes a **unit cost**, or **variable cost**, of \$0.10 per item produced. For example, the cost of producing 1000 items is $C(1000) = \$600$.

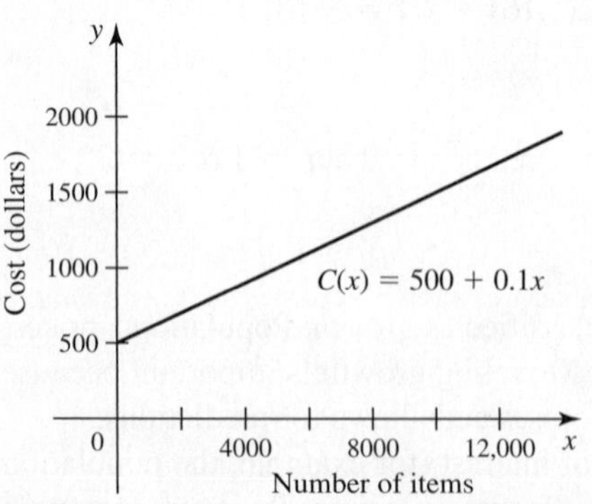

FIGURE 3.37

Although x is a whole number of units, we treat it as a continuous variable, which is reasonable if x is large.

If the company produces x items at a cost of $C(x)$, then the **average cost** is $\frac{C(x)}{x}$ per item. For the cost function $C(x) = 500 + 0.1x$, the average cost is

$$\frac{C(x)}{x} = \frac{500 + 0.1x}{x} = \frac{500}{x} + 0.1.$$

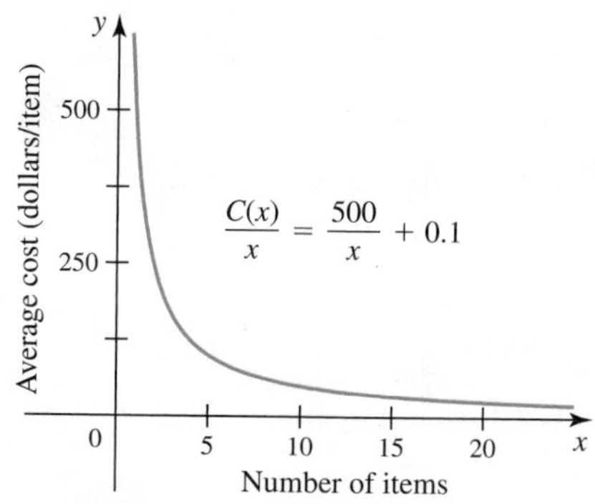

FIGURE 3.38

➤ The average describes the past; the marginal describes the future.
—Old saying

For example, the average cost of manufacturing 1000 items is

$$\frac{C(1000)}{1000} = \frac{\$600}{1000} = \$0.60/\text{unit}.$$

Plotting $C(x)/x$, we see that the average cost decreases as the number of items produced increases (Figure 3.38).

The average cost gives the cost of items already produced. But what about the cost of producing additional items? Having produced x items, the cost of producing another Δx items is $C(x + \Delta x) - C(x)$. Therefore, the average cost per item of producing those Δx additional items is

$$\frac{C(x + \Delta x) - C(x)}{\Delta x} = \frac{\Delta C}{\Delta x}.$$

If we let $\Delta x \rightarrow 0$, we see that

$$\lim_{\Delta x \rightarrow 0} \frac{\Delta C}{\Delta x} = C'(x),$$

which is called the **marginal cost**. In reality, we cannot let $\Delta x \rightarrow 0$ because Δx represents whole numbers of items.

Here is a useful interpretation of the marginal cost. Suppose $\Delta x = 1$. Then, $\Delta C = C(x + 1) - C(x)$ is the cost to produce *one* additional item. In this case we write

$$\frac{\Delta C}{\Delta x} = \frac{C(x + 1) - C(x)}{1}.$$

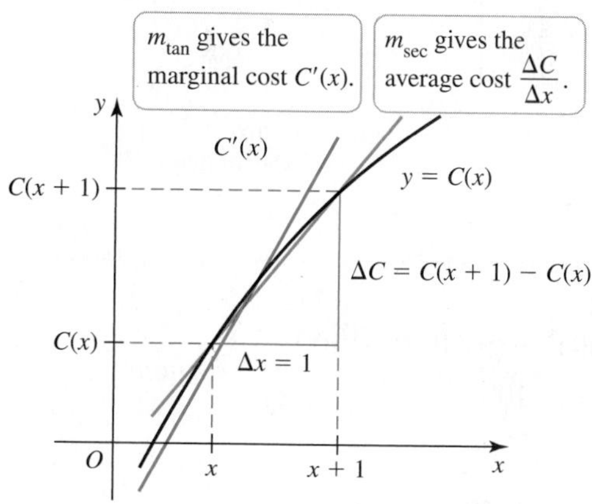

FIGURE 3.39

If the *slope* of the cost curve does not vary significantly near the point x, then (Figure 3.39) we have

$$\frac{\Delta C}{\Delta x} \approx \lim_{\Delta x \rightarrow 0} \frac{\Delta C}{\Delta x} = C'(x).$$

Therefore, the cost of producing one additional item, having already produced x items, is approximated by the marginal cost $C'(x)$. In the preceding example, we have $C'(x) = 0.1$, so if $x = 1000$ items have been produced, then the cost of producing the 1001st item is $C'(1000) = \$0.10$. With this simple linear cost function, the marginal cost tells us what we already know: The cost of producing one additional item is the variable cost of \$0.10. With more realistic cost functions, the marginal cost may be variable.

➤ The approximation $\Delta C/\Delta x \approx C'(x)$ says that the slope of the secant line between $(x, C(x))$ and $(x + 1, C(x + 1))$ is approximately equal to the slope of the tangent line at $(x, C(x))$. This approximation is good if the cost curve is nearly linear over a one-unit interval.

> **DEFINITION Average and Marginal Cost**
>
> The **cost function** $C(x)$ gives the cost to produce the first x items in a manufacturing process. The **average cost** to produce x items is $\overline{C}(x) = C(x)/x$. The **marginal cost** $C'(x)$ is the approximate cost to produce one additional item after producing x items.

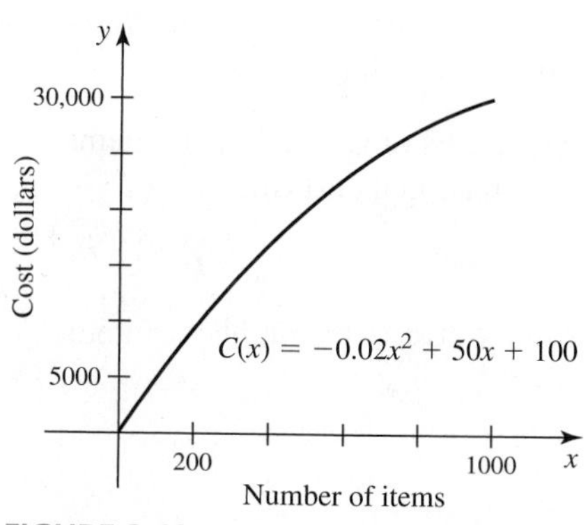

FIGURE 3.40

EXAMPLE 5 Average and marginal costs Suppose the cost of producing x items is given by the function (Figure 3.40)

$$C(x) = -0.02x^2 + 50x + 100, \quad \text{for} \quad 0 \leq x \leq 1000.$$

a. Determine the average and marginal cost functions.

b. Determine the average and marginal cost when $x = 100$ items and interpret these values.

c. Determine the average and marginal cost when $x = 900$ items and interpret these values.

SOLUTION

a. The average cost is

$$\overline{C}(x) = \frac{C(x)}{x} = \frac{-0.02x^2 + 50x + 100}{x} = -0.02x + 50 + \frac{100}{x}$$

and the marginal cost is

$$C'(x) = -0.04x + 50.$$

The average cost decreases as the number of items produced increases (Figure 3.41a). The marginal cost decreases linearly with a slope of -0.04 (Figure 3.41b).

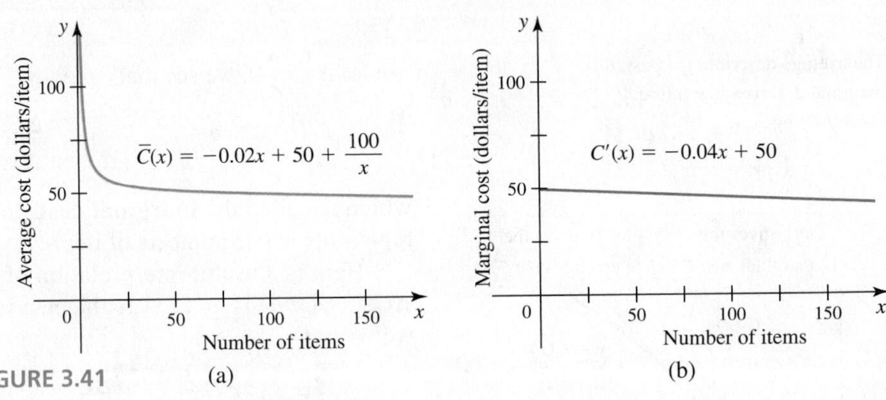

FIGURE 3.41

b. To produce $x = 100$ items, the average cost is

$$\overline{C}(100) = \frac{C(100)}{100} = \frac{-0.02(100)^2 + 50(100) + 100}{100} = \$49/\text{item}$$

and the marginal cost is

$$C'(100) = -0.04(100) + 50 = \$46/\text{item}.$$

These results mean that the average cost of producing 100 items is \$49 per item, but the cost of producing one additional item (the 101st item) is only \$46. Therefore, producing one more item is less expensive than the average cost of producing the first 100 items.

c. To produce $x = 900$ items, the average cost is

$$\overline{C}(900) = \frac{C(900)}{900} = \frac{-0.02(900)^2 + 50(900) + 100}{900} \approx \$32/\text{item}$$

and the marginal cost is

$$C'(900) = -0.04(900) + 50 = \$14/\text{item}.$$

The comparison with part (b) is revealing. The average cost of producing 900 items has dropped to \$32 per item. More striking is that the marginal cost (the cost of producing the 901st item) has dropped to \$14. *Related Exercises 21–24* ◄

QUICK CHECK 5 In Example 5, what happens to the average cost as the number of items produced increases from $x = 1$ to $x = 100$? ◄

SECTION 3.5 EXERCISES

Review Questions

1. Use a graph to explain the difference between the average rate of change and the instantaneous rate of change of a function f.

2. Complete the following statement. If $\frac{dy}{dx}$ is large, then small changes in x will result in relatively _______ changes in the value of y.

3. Complete the following statement: If $\frac{dy}{dx}$ is small, then small changes in x will result in relatively _______ changes in the value of y.

4. What is the difference between the *velocity* and *speed* of an object moving in a straight line?

5. Define the acceleration of an object moving in a straight line.

6. An object moving along a line has a constant negative acceleration. Describe the velocity of the object.

7. Suppose the average cost of producing $x = 200$ gas stoves is \$70 per stove and the marginal cost at $x = 200$ is \$65 per stove. Interpret these costs.

8. Explain in your own words the adage: The average describes the past; the marginal describes the future.

Basic Skills

9. **Highway travel** A state patrol station is located on a straight north-south freeway. A patrol car leaves the station at 9:00 A.M. heading north with position function $s = f(t)$ that gives its location in miles t hours after 9:00 A.M. (see figure). Assume s is positive when the car is north of the patrol station.
   a. Determine the average velocity of the car during the first 45 minutes of the trip.
   b. Find the average velocity of the car over the interval $[0.25, 0.75]$. Is the average velocity a good estimate of the velocity at 9:30 A.M.?
   c. Find the average velocity of the car over the interval $[1.75, 2.25]$. Estimate the velocity of the car at 11:00 A.M. and determine the direction in which the patrol car is moving.
   d. Describe the motion of the patrol car relative to the patrol station between 9:00 A.M. and 12:00 P.M.

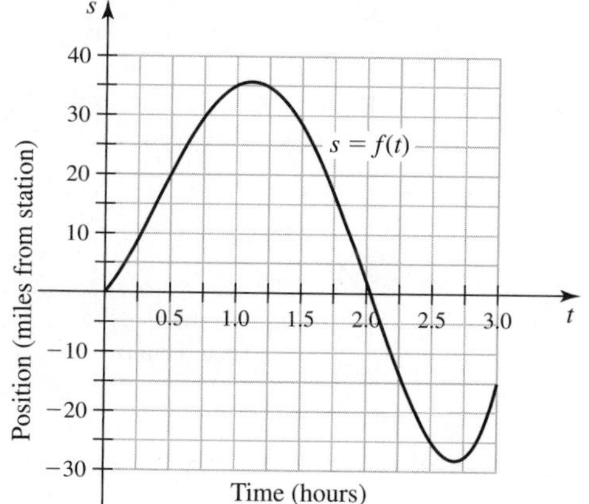

10. **Airline travel** The following figure shows the position function $s = f(t)$ of an airliner on an out-and-back trip from Seattle to Minneapolis, where $s = f(t)$ is the number of ground miles from Seattle t hours after take-off at 6:00 A.M. The plane returns to Seattle 8.5 hours later at 2:30 P.M.
   a. Calculate the average velocity of the airliner during the first 1.5 hours of the trip $(0 \le t \le 1.5)$.
   b. Calculate the average velocity of the airliner between 1:30 P.M. and 2:30 P.M. $(7.5 \le t \le 8.5)$.
   c. At what time(s) is the velocity 0? Give a plausible explanation.
   d. Determine the velocity of the airliner at noon $(t = 6)$ and explain why the velocity is negative.

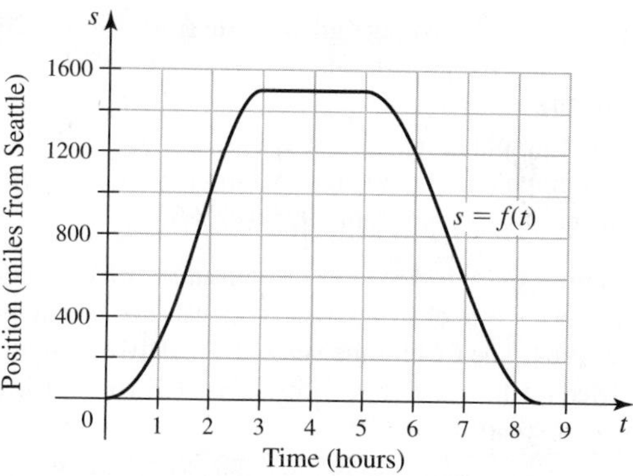

11–16. Position, velocity, and acceleration *Suppose the position of an object moving horizontally after t seconds is given by the following functions $s = f(t)$, where s is measured in feet, with $s > 0$ corresponding to positions right of the origin.*

   a. *Graph the position function.*
   b. *Find and graph the velocity function. When is the object stationary, moving to the right, and moving to the left?*
   c. *Determine the velocity and acceleration of the object at $t = 1$.*
   d. *Determine the acceleration of the object when its velocity is zero.*

11. $f(t) = t^2 - 4t;\ 0 \le t \le 5$

12. $f(t) = -t^2 + 4t - 3;\ 0 \le t \le 5$

13. $f(t) = 2t^2 - 9t + 12;\ 0 \le t \le 3$

14. $f(t) = 18t - 3t^2;\ 0 \le t \le 8$

15. $f(t) = 2t^3 - 21t^2 + 60t;\ 0 \le t \le 6$

16. $f(t) = -6t^3 + 36t^2 - 54t;\ 0 \le t \le 4$

17. **A stone thrown vertically** Suppose a stone is thrown vertically upward from the edge of a cliff with an initial velocity of 64 ft/s from a height of 32 ft above the ground. The height s (in ft) of the stone above the ground t seconds after it is thrown is $s = -16t^2 + 64t + 32$.
   a. Determine the velocity v of the stone after t seconds.
   b. When does the stone reach its highest point?
   c. What is the height of the stone at the highest point?
   d. When does the stone strike the ground?
   e. With what velocity does the stone strike the ground?

18. A stone thrown vertically on Mars Suppose a stone is thrown vertically upward from the edge of a cliff on Mars (where the acceleration due to gravity is only about 12 ft/s^2) with an initial velocity of 64 ft/s from a height of 192 ft above the ground. The height s of the stone above the ground after t seconds is given by $s = -6t^2 + 64t + 192$.

a. Determine the velocity v of the stone after t seconds.
b. When does the stone reach its highest point?
c. What is the height of the stone at the highest point?
d. When does the stone strike the ground?
e. With what velocity does the stone strike the ground?

T **19. Population growth in Georgia** The population of the state of Georgia (in thousands) from 1995 ($t = 0$) to 2005 ($t = 10$) is modeled by the polynomial $p(t) = -0.27t^2 + 101t + 7055$.

a. Determine the average growth rate from 1995 to 2005.
b. What was the growth rate for Georgia in 1997 ($t = 2$) and 2005 ($t = 10$)?
c. Use a graphing utility to graph p', for $0 \le t \le 10$. What does this graph tell you about population growth in Georgia during the period of time from 1995 to 2005?

T **20. Consumer price index** The U.S. consumer price index (CPI) measures the cost of living based on a value of 100 in the years 1982–1984. The CPI for the years 1995–2010 (see figure) is modeled by the function $c(t) = 0.10t^2 + 3.18t + 153.09$, where t represents years after 1995.

a. Was the average growth rate greater between the years 1995–2000 or 2005–2010?
b. Was the growth rate greater in 2000 ($t = 5$) or 2005 ($t = 10$)?
c. Use a graphing utility to graph the growth rate, for $0 \le t \le 15$. What does the graph tell you about growth in the cost of living during this time period?

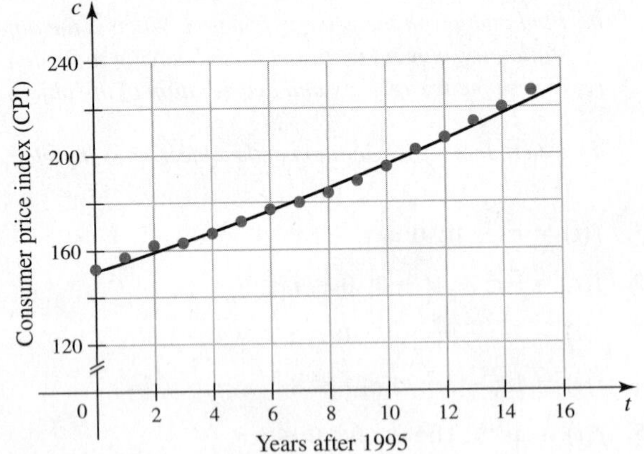

21–24. Average and marginal cost *Consider the following cost functions.*

a. Find the average cost and marginal cost functions.
b. Determine the average and marginal cost when $x = a$.
c. Interpret the values obtained in part (b).

21. $C(x) = 1000 + 0.1x,\ 0 \le x \le 5000,\ a = 2000$

22. $C(x) = 500 + 0.02x,\ 0 \le x \le 2000,\ a = 1000$

23. $C(x) = -0.01x^2 + 40x + 100,\ 0 \le x \le 1500,\ a = 1000$

24. $C(x) = -0.04x^2 + 100x + 800,\ 0 \le x \le 1000,\ a = 500$

Further Explorations

25. Explain why or why not Determine whether the following statements are true and give an explanation or counterexample.

a. If the acceleration of an object remains constant, then its velocity is constant.
b. If the acceleration of an object moving along a line is always 0, then its velocity is constant.
c. It is impossible for the instantaneous velocity at all times $a \le t \le b$ to equal the average velocity over the interval $a \le t \le b$.
d. A moving object can have negative acceleration and increasing speed.

26. A feather dropped on the moon On the moon, a feather will fall to the ground at the same rate as a heavy stone. Suppose a feather is dropped from a height of 40 m above the surface of the moon. Then, its height s (in meters) above the ground after t seconds is $s = 40 - 0.8t^2$. Determine the velocity and acceleration of the feather the moment it strikes the surface of the moon.

27. Velocity of a bullet A bullet is fired vertically into the air at an initial velocity of 1200 ft/s. On Mars, the height s (in feet) of the bullet above the ground after t seconds is $s = 1200t - 6t^2$ and on Earth, $s = 1200t - 16t^2$. How much higher will the bullet travel on Mars than on Earth?

28. Velocity of a car The graph shows the position $s = f(t)$ of a car t hours after 5:00 P.M. relative to its starting point $s = 0$, where s is measured in miles.

a. Describe the velocity of the car. Specifically, when is it speeding up and when is it slowing down?
b. At approximately what time is the car traveling the fastest? The slowest?
c. What is the approximate maximum velocity of the car? The approximate minimum velocity?

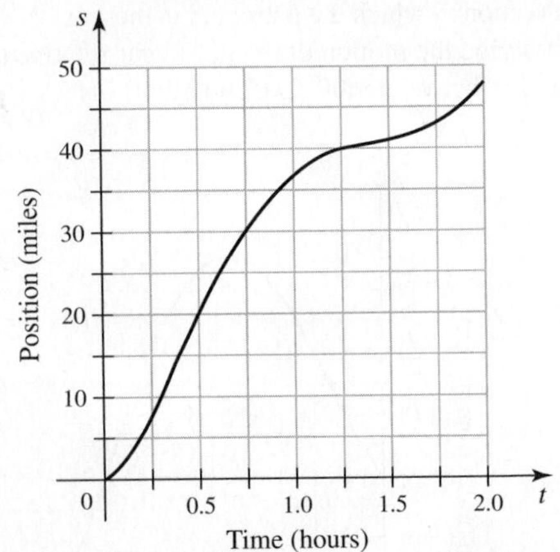

29. Velocity from position The graph of $s = f(t)$ represents the position of an object moving along a line at time $t \geq 0$.

a. Assume the velocity of the object is 0 when $t = 0$. For what other values of t is the velocity of the object zero?
b. When is the object moving in the positive direction and when is it moving in the negative direction?
c. Sketch a graph of the velocity function.

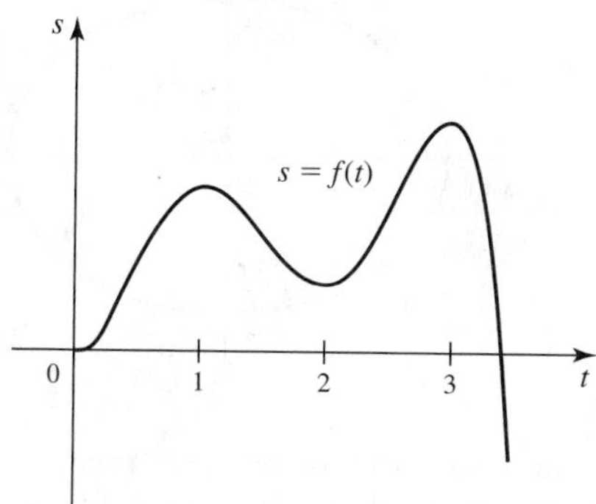

30. Fish length Assume the length L (in cm) of a particular species of fish after t years is modeled by the following graph.

a. What does dL/dt represent and what happens to this derivative as t increases?
b. What does the derivative tell you about how this species of fish grows?
c. Sketch a rough graph of L' and L''.

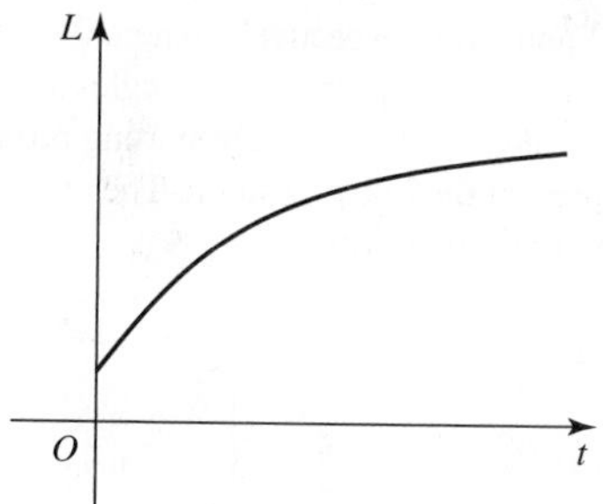

31–34. Average and marginal profit *Let $C(x)$ represent the cost of producing x items and $p(x)$ be the sale price per item if x items are sold. The profit $P(x)$ of selling x items is $P(x) = x\,p(x) - C(x)$ (revenue minus costs). The* ***average profit per item*** *when x items are sold is $P(x)/x$ and the* ***marginal profit*** *is dP/dx. The marginal profit approximates the profit obtained by selling one more item given that x items have already been sold. Consider the following cost functions C and price functions p.*

a. Find the profit function P.
b. Find the average profit function and marginal profit function.
c. Find the average profit and marginal profit if $x = a$ units have been sold.
d. Interpret the meaning of the values obtained in part (c).

31. $C(x) = -0.02x^2 + 50x + 100,\ p(x) = 100,\ a = 500$

32. $C(x) = -0.02x^2 + 50x + 100,\ p(x) = 100 - 0.1x,\ a = 500$

33. $C(x) = -0.04x^2 + 100x + 800,\ p(x) = 200,\ a = 1000$

34. $C(x) = -0.04x^2 + 100x + 800,\ p(x) = 200 - 0.1x,\ a = 1000$

Applications

35. Population growth of the United States Suppose $p(t)$ represents the population of the United States (in millions) t years after the year 1900. The graph of p' is shown in the figure.

a. Approximately when (in what year) was the U.S. population growing most slowly between 1900 to 1990? Estimate the growth rate in that year.
b. Approximately when (in what year) was the U.S. population growing most rapidly between 1900 and 1990? Estimate the growth rate in that year.
c. In what years, if any, was p decreasing?
d. In what years was the population growth rate increasing?

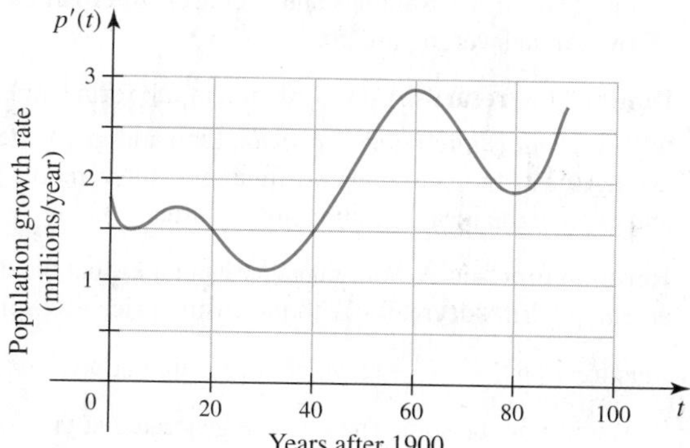

T **36. Average of marginal production** Economists use *production functions* to describe how the output of a system varies with respect to another variable such as labor or capital. For example, the production function $P(L) = 200L + 10L^2 - L^3$ gives the output of a system as a function of the number of laborers L. The *average product* $A(L)$ is the average output per laborer when L laborers are working; that is, $A(L) = P(L)/L$. The *marginal product* $M(L)$ is the approximate change in output when one additional laborer is added to L laborers; that is, $M(L) = \frac{dP}{dL}$.

a. For the given production function, compute and graph P, A, and L.
b. Suppose the peak of the average product curve occurs at $L = L_0$, so that $A'(L_0) = 0$. Show that for a general production function, $M(L_0) = A(L_0)$.

T **37. Velocity of a marble** The position (in meters) of a marble rolling up a long incline is given by $s = \frac{100t}{t + 1}$, where t is measured in seconds and $s = 0$ is the starting point.

a. Graph the position function.
b. Find the velocity function for the marble.
c. Graph the velocity function and give a description of the motion of the marble.
d. At what time is the marble 80 m from its starting point?
e. At what time is the velocity 50 m/s?

T **38. Tree growth** Let b represent the base diameter of a conifer tree and let h represent the height of the tree, where b is measured in centimeters and h is measured in meters. Assume the height is related to the base diameter by the function $h = 5.67 + 0.70b + 0.0067b^2$.

a. Graph the height function.
b. Plot and interpret the meaning of $\frac{dh}{db}$.

39. A different interpretation of marginal cost Suppose a large company makes 25,000 gadgets per year in batches of x items at a time. After analyzing setup costs to produce each batch and taking into account storage costs, it has been determined that the total cost $C(x)$ of producing 25,000 gadgets in batches of x items at a time is given by

$$C(x) = 1{,}250{,}000 + \frac{125{,}000{,}000}{x} + 1.5x.$$

a. Determine the marginal cost and average cost functions. Graph and interpret these functions.
b. Determine the average cost and marginal cost when $x = 5000$.
c. The meaning of average cost and marginal cost here is different than earlier examples and exercises. Interpret the meaning of your answer in part (b).

40. Diminishing returns A cost function of the form $C(x) = \frac{1}{2}x^2$ reflects *diminishing returns to scale*. Find and graph the cost, average cost, and marginal cost functions. Interpret the graphs and explain the idea of diminishing returns.

41. Revenue function A store manager estimates that the demand for an energy drink decreases with increasing price according to the function $d(p) = \frac{100}{p^2 + 1}$, which means that at price p (in dollars), $d(p)$ units can be sold. The revenue generated at price p is $R(p) = p \cdot d(p)$ (price multiplied by number of units).

a. Find and graph the revenue function.
b. Find and graph the marginal revenue $R'(p)$.
c. From the graph of the revenue function and its derivative, estimate the price that should be charged to maximize the revenue.

42. Fuel economy Suppose you own a fuel-efficient hybrid automobile with a monitor on the dashboard that displays the mileage and gas consumption. The number of miles you can drive with g gallons of gas remaining in the tank on a particular stretch of highway is given by $m = 50g - 25.8g^2 + 12.5g^3 - 1.6g^4$, for $0 \le g \le 4$.

a. Graph and interpret the mileage function.
b. Graph and interpret the gas mileage m/g.
c. Graph and interpret dm/dg.

43. Spring oscillations A spring hangs from the ceiling at equilibrium with a mass attached to its end. Suppose you pull downward on the mass and release it 10 in below its equilibrium position. The distance x (in inches) of the mass from its equilibrium position after t seconds is given by the function $x(t) = 10 \sin t - 10 \cos t$, where x is positive when the mass is above the equilibrium position.

a. Graph and interpret this function.
b. Find $\frac{dx}{dt}$ and interpret the meaning of this derivative.
c. At what times is the velocity of the mass zero?
d. The function given here is a model for the motion of an object on a spring. In what ways is this model unrealistic?

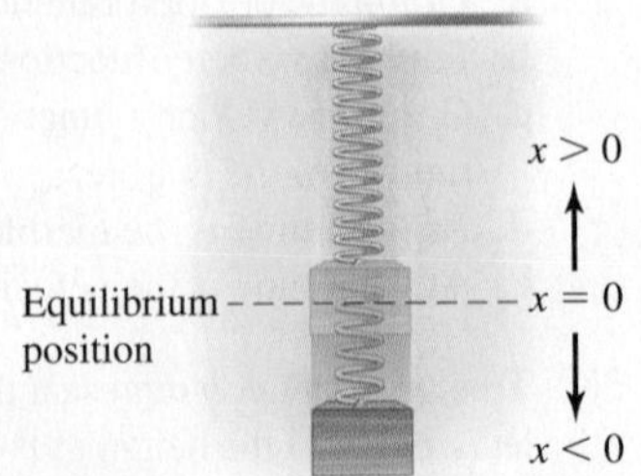

44. Looking ahead: An elliptical orbit As discussed in Chapter 10, the path of an object moving in an elliptical orbit in the xy-plane (see figure) can be described by *parametric equations* of the form

$$x = 400 \cos t \qquad y = 200 \sin t, \qquad \text{for } 0 \le t \le 2\pi.$$

In this case, the length of the orbit in the x-direction is 800 units and the length in the y-direction is 400 units. The object completes one orbit in 2π time units.

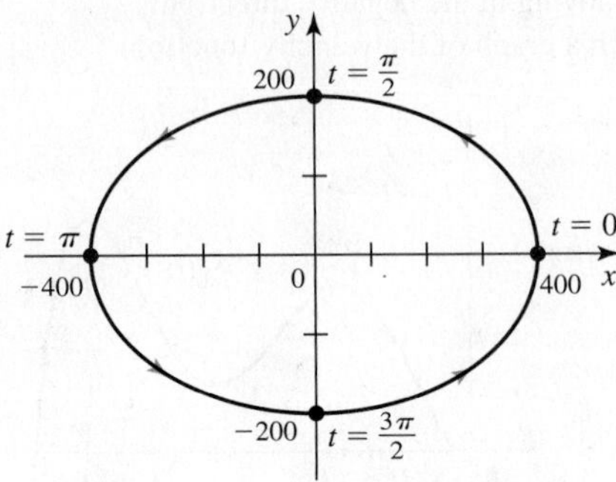

a. Find the components of the object's velocity in the x- and y-directions, which are $x'(t)$ and $y'(t)$.
b. At what times in the interval $0 \le t \le 2\pi$ does the x-component of the velocity reach a maximum?
c. Compute the speed of the object along its path, which is $\sqrt{x'(t)^2 + y'(t)^2}$.
d. Graph the speed as a function of t, for $0 \le t \le 2\pi$. At what approximate times does the object attain its maximum speed?

45. A race Jean and Juan run a one-lap race on a circular track. Their angular positions on the track during the race are given by the functions $\theta(t)$ and $\phi(t)$, respectively, where $0 \le t \le 4$ and t is measured in minutes (see figure). These angles are measured in radians, where $\theta = \phi = 0$ represent the starting position and $\theta = \phi = 2\pi$ represent the finish position. The angular velocities of the runners are $\theta'(t)$ and $\phi'(t)$.

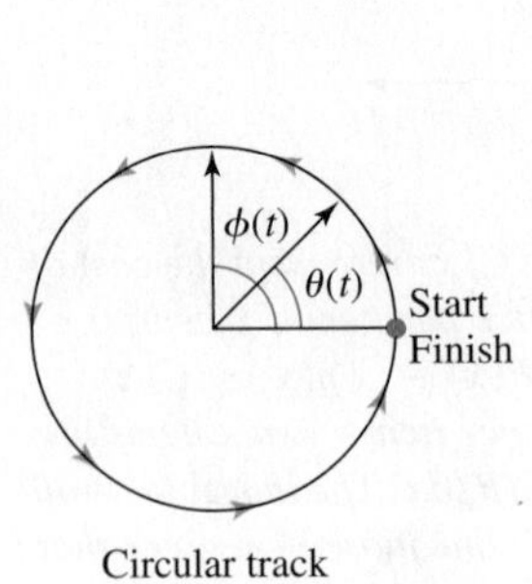

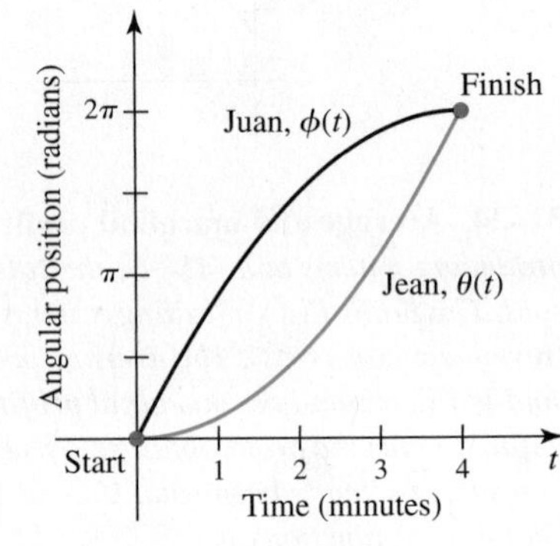

a. Compare in words the angular velocity of the two runners and the progress of the race.
b. Which runner has the greater average angular velocity?
c. Who wins the race?
d. Jean's position is given by $\theta(t) = \pi t^2/8$. What is her angular velocity at $t = 2$ and at what time is her angular velocity the greatest?
e. Juan's position is given by $\phi(t) = \pi t(8 - t)/8$. What is his angular velocity at $t = 2$ and at what time is his angular velocity the greatest?

46. Power and energy Power and energy are often used interchangeably, but they are quite different. **Energy** is what makes matter move or heat up. It is measured in units of **joules** or **Calories**, where 1 Cal = 4184 J. One hour of walking consumes roughly 10^6 J, or 240 Cal. On the other hand, **power** is the rate at which energy is used, which is measured in **watts**, where 1 W = 1 J/s. Other useful units of power are **kilowatts** (1 kW = 10^3 W) and **megawatts** (1 MW = 10^6 W). If energy is used at a rate of 1 kW for one hour, the total amount of energy used is 1 **kilowatt-hour** (1 kWh = 3.6×10^6 J). Suppose the cumulative energy used in a large building over a 24-hr period is given by $E(t) = 100t + 4t^2 - \frac{t^3}{9}$ kWh, where $t = 0$ corresponds to midnight.

a. Graph the energy function.
b. The power is the rate of energy consumption; that is, $P(t) = E'(t)$. Find the power over the interval $0 \le t \le 24$.
c. Graph the power function and interpret the graph. What are the units of power in this case?

47. Flow from a tank A cylindrical tank is full at time $t = 0$ when a valve in the bottom of the tank is opened. By Torricelli's Law, the volume of water in the tank after t hours is $V = 100(200 - t)^2$, measured in m^3.

a. Graph the volume function. What is the volume of water in the tank before the valve is opened?
b. How long does it take for the tank to empty?
c. Find the rate at which water flows from the tank and plot the flow rate function.
d. At what time is the magnitude of the flow rate a minimum? A maximum?

48. Spring runoff The flow of a small stream is monitored for 90 days between May 1 and August 1. The total water that flows past a gauging station is given by

$$V(t) = \begin{cases} \frac{4}{5}t^2 & \text{if } 0 \le t < 45 \\ -\frac{4}{5}(t^2 - 180t + 4050) & \text{if } 45 \le t < 90 \end{cases}$$

where V is measured in ft^3 and t is measured in days, with $t = 0$ corresponding to May 1.

a. Graph the volume function.
b. Find the flow rate function $V'(t)$ and graph it. What are the units of the flow rate?
c. Describe the flow of the stream over the 3-month period. Specifically, when is the flow rate a maximum?

49. Temperature distribution A thin copper rod, 4 m in length, is heated at its midpoint and the ends are held at a constant temperature of 0°. When the temperature reaches equilibrium, the temperature profile is given by $T(x) = 40x(4 - x)$, where $0 \le x \le 4$ is the position along the rod. The **heat flux** at a point on the rod equals $-kT'(x)$, where k is a constant. If the heat flux is positive at a point, heat moves in the positive x-direction at that point, and if the heat flux is negative, heat moves in the negative x-direction.

a. With $k = 1$, what is the heat flux at $x = 1$? At $x = 3$?
b. For what values of x is the heat flux negative? Positive?
c. Explain the statement that heat flows out of the rod at its ends.

QUICK CHECK ANSWERS

1. Instantaneous velocity **2.** If an object has positive acceleration, then its velocity is increasing. If the velocity is negative but increasing, then the acceleration is positive and the speed is decreasing. For example, the velocity may increase from −2 m/s to −1 m/s to 0 m/s. **3.** $v(1) = 32$ ft/s and $v(3) = -32$ ft/s, so the speed is 32 ft/s at both times. **4.** The growth rate in 1996 ($t = 1$) is approximately 77 million users/year. It is less than half of the growth rate in 2010 ($t = 15$), which is approximately 161 million users/year. **5.** As x increases from 1 to 100, the average cost decreases from \$150/item to \$49/item.

3.6 The Chain Rule

The differentiation rules presented so far allow us to find derivatives of many functions. However, these rules are inadequate for finding the derivatives of most *composite functions*. Here is a typical situation. If $f(x) = x^3$ and $g(x) = 5x + 4$, then their composition is $f(g(x)) = (5x + 4)^3$. One way to find the derivative is by expanding $(5x + 4)^3$ and differentiating the resulting polynomial. Unfortunately, this strategy becomes prohibitive for functions such as $(5x + 4)^{100}$. We need a better approach.

QUICK CHECK 1 Explain why it is not practical to calculate $\frac{d}{dx}(5x + 4)^{100}$ by first expanding $(5x + 4)^{100}$.

Chain Rule Formulas

An efficient method for differentiating composite functions, called the *Chain Rule*, is motivated by the following example. Suppose Yancey, Uri, and Xan pick apples. Let y, u, and x represent the number of apples picked in some period of time by Yancey, Uri, and Xan, respectively. Yancey picks apples three times faster than Uri, which means the rate at

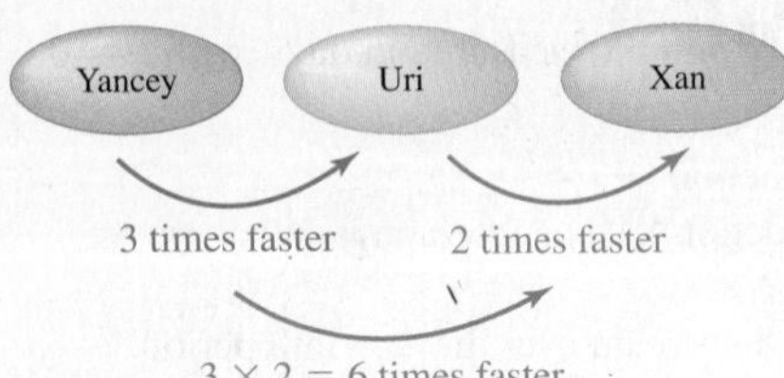

FIGURE 3.42

which Yancey picks apples with respect to Uri is $\frac{dy}{du} = 3$. Uri picks apples twice as fast as Xan, so $\frac{du}{dx} = 2$. Therefore, Yancey picks apples at a rate that is $3 \cdot 2 = 6$ times greater than Xan's rate, which means that $\frac{dy}{dx} = 6$ (Figure 3.42). Observe that

$$\frac{dy}{dx} = \frac{dy}{du} \cdot \frac{du}{dx} = 3 \cdot 2 = 6.$$

The equation $\frac{dy}{dx} = \frac{dy}{du} \cdot \frac{du}{dx}$ is one form of the Chain Rule. It is referred to as Version 1 of the Chain Rule in this text.

Alternatively, the Chain Rule may be expressed in terms of composite functions. Let $y = f(u)$ and $u = g(x)$, which means y is related to x through the composite function $y = f(u) = f(g(x))$. The derivative $\frac{dy}{dx}$ is now expressed as the product

$$\underbrace{\frac{d}{dx}[f(g(x))]}_{\frac{dy}{dx}} = \underbrace{f'(u)}_{\frac{dy}{du}} \cdot \underbrace{g'(x)}_{\frac{du}{dx}}.$$

➤ Expressions such as dy/dx should not be treated as fractions. Nevertheless, you can check symbolically that you have written the Chain Rule correctly by noting that du appears in the "numerator" and "denominator." If it were "canceled," the Chain Rule would have dy/dx on both sides.

Replacing u with $g(x)$ results in

$$\frac{d}{dx}[f(g(x))] = f'(g(x)) \cdot g'(x),$$

which we refer to as Version 2 of the Chain Rule.

➤ The two versions of the Chain Rule differ only in notation. Mathematically, they are identical. Version 2 of the Chain Rule states that the derivative of $y = f(g(x))$ is the derivative of f evaluated at $g(x)$ multiplied by the derivative of g evaluated at x.

THEOREM 3.12 The Chain Rule
Suppose g is differentiable at x and $y = f(u)$ is differentiable at $u = g(x)$. The composite function $y = f(g(x))$ is differentiable at x, and its derivative can be expressed in two equivalent ways:

$$\frac{dy}{dx} = \frac{dy}{du} \cdot \frac{du}{dx} \qquad \text{Version 1}$$

$$\frac{d}{dx}[f(g(x))] = f'(g(x)) \cdot g'(x) \qquad \text{Version 2}$$

A proof of the Chain Rule is given at the end of this section. For now, it's important to learn how to use it. When working with the composite function $f(g(x))$, we refer to g as the *inner function* and f as the *outer function*. The key to using the Chain Rule is identifying the inner and outer functions. The following four steps outline the differentiation process, although you will soon find that the procedure can be streamlined.

➤ There may be different ways to choose an inner function $u = g(x)$ and an outer function $y = f(u)$. Nevertheless, we refer to *the* inner and *the* outer function for the most obvious choices.

Guidelines for Using the Chain Rule
Assume the differentiable function $y = f(g(x))$ is given.

1. Identify the outer function f, the inner function g, and let $u = g(x)$.
2. Replace $g(x)$ by u to express y in terms of u:

$$y = f(\underbrace{g(x)}_{u}) \Rightarrow y = f(u)$$

QUICK CHECK 2 Identify an inner function (call it g) of $y = (5x + 4)^3$. Let $u = g(x)$ and express the outer function f in terms of u.

3. Calculate the product $\frac{dy}{du} \cdot \frac{du}{dx}$.

4. Replace u by $g(x)$ in $\frac{dy}{du}$ to obtain $\frac{dy}{dx}$.

EXAMPLE 1 **Version 1 of the Chain Rule** For each of the following composite functions, find the inner function $u = g(x)$ and the outer function $y = f(u)$. Then, use Version 1 of the Chain Rule to find $\frac{dy}{dx}$.

a. $y = (5x + 4)^3$ **b.** $y = \sin^3 x$ **c.** $y = \sin x^3$

SOLUTION

a. The inner function of $y = (5x + 4)^3$ is $u = 5x + 4$, and the outer function is $y = u^3$. By Version 1 of the Chain Rule, we have

$$\begin{aligned} \frac{dy}{dx} &= \frac{dy}{du} \cdot \frac{du}{dx} && \text{Version 1} \\ &= 3u^2 \cdot (5) && y = u^3 \Rightarrow \frac{dy}{du} = 3u^2,\ u = 5x + 4 \Rightarrow \frac{du}{dx} = 5 \\ &= 3(5x + 4)^2 \cdot (5) && \text{Replace } u \text{ by } 5x + 4. \\ &= 15(5x + 4)^2. \end{aligned}$$

➤ When using trigonometric functions, expressions such as $\sin^n(x)$ always mean $(\sin x)^n$, except when $n = -1$. In Example 1, $\sin^3 x = (\sin x)^3$.

b. Replacing the shorthand form $y = \sin^3 x$ with $y = (\sin x)^3$, we identify the inner function as $u = \sin x$. Letting $y = u^3$, we have

$$\frac{dy}{dx} = \frac{dy}{du} \cdot \frac{du}{dx} = 3u^2 \cdot \cos x = \underbrace{3 \sin^2 x}_{3u^2} \cos x.$$

QUICK CHECK 3 In Example 1a, we showed that $\frac{d}{dx}((5x + 4)^3) = 15(5x + 4)^2$. Verify this result by expanding $(5x + 4)^3$ and differentiating.

c. Although $y = \sin x^3$ appears to be similar to the function $y = \sin^3 x$ in part (b), the inner function in this case is $u = x^3$ and the outer function is $y = \sin u$. Therefore,

$$\frac{dy}{dx} = \frac{dy}{du} \cdot \frac{du}{dx} = (\cos u) \cdot 3x^2 = 3x^2 \cos x^3.$$

Related Exercises 7–16

Version 2 of the Chain Rule, $\frac{d}{dx}[f(g(x))] = f'(g(x)) \cdot g'(x)$, is equivalent to Version 1; it just uses different derivative notation. With Version 2, we identify the outer function $y = f(u)$ and the inner function $u = g(x)$. Then, $\frac{d}{dx}[f(g(x))]$ is the product of $f'(u)$ evaluated at $u = g(x)$ and $g'(x)$.

EXAMPLE 2 **Version 2 of the Chain Rule** Use Version 2 of the Chain Rule to calculate the derivatives of the following functions.

a. $(6x^3 + 3x + 1)^{10}$ **b.** $\sqrt{5x^2 + 1}$ **c.** $\left(\frac{5t^2}{3t^2 + 2}\right)^3$

SOLUTION

a. The inner function of $(6x^3 + 3x + 1)^{10}$ is $g(x) = 6x^3 + 3x + 1$, and the outer function is $f(u) = u^{10}$. The derivative of the outer function is $f'(u) = 10u^9$, which, when evaluated at $g(x)$ is $10(6x^3 + 3x + 1)^9$. The derivative of the inner function is $g'(x) = 18x^2 + 3$. Multiplying the derivatives of the outer and inner functions, we have

$$\frac{d}{dx}[(6x^3 + 3x + 1)^{10}] = \underbrace{10(6x^3 + 3x + 1)^9}_{f'(u) \text{ evaluated at } g(x)} \cdot \underbrace{(18x^2 + 3)}_{g'(x)}$$

$$= 30(6x^2 + 1)(6x^3 + 3x + 1)^9. \quad \text{Factor and simplify.}$$

b. The inner function of $\sqrt{5x^2 + 1}$ is $g(x) = 5x^2 + 1$, and the outer function is $f(u) = \sqrt{u}$. The derivatives of these functions are $f'(u) = \dfrac{1}{2\sqrt{u}}$ and $g'(x) = 10x$.

Therefore,

$$\frac{d}{dx}\sqrt{5x^2 + 1} = \underbrace{\frac{1}{2\sqrt{5x^2 + 1}}}_{f'(u) \text{ evaluated at } g(x)} \cdot \underbrace{10x}_{g'(x)} = \frac{5x}{\sqrt{5x^2 + 1}}.$$

c. The inner function of $\left(\dfrac{5t^2}{3t^2 + 2}\right)^3$ is $g(t) = \dfrac{5t^2}{3t^2 + 2}$. The outer function is $f(u) = u^3$, whose derivative is $f'(u) = 3u^2$. The derivative of the inner function requires the Quotient Rule. Applying the Chain Rule, we have

$$\frac{d}{dt}\left(\frac{5t^2}{3t^2 + 2}\right)^3 = \underbrace{3\left(\frac{5t^2}{3t^2 + 2}\right)^2}_{f'(u) \text{ evaluated at } g(t)} \cdot \underbrace{\frac{(3t^2 + 2)10t - 5t^2(6t)}{(3t^2 + 2)^2}}_{g'(t) \text{ by the Quotient Rule}} = \frac{1500t^5}{(3t^2 + 2)^4}.$$

Related Exercises 17–30 ◀

The Chain Rule is also used to calculate the derivative of a composite function for a specific value of the variable. If $h(x) = f(g(x))$, g is differentiable at a and f is differentiable at $g(a)$, then $h'(a) = f'(g(a))g'(a)$. Therefore, $h'(a)$ is the derivative of f evaluated at $g(a)$ multiplied by the derivative of g evaluated at a.

EXAMPLE 3 Calculating derivatives at a point Let $h(x) = f(g(x))$. Use the values in Table 3.2 to calculate $h'(1)$ and $h'(2)$.

Table 3.2

x	$f'(x)$	$g(x)$	$g'(x)$
1	5	2	3
2	7	1	4

SOLUTION We use $h'(a) = f'(g(a))g'(a)$ with $a = 1$:

$$h'(1) = f'(g(1))g'(1) = f'(2)g'(1) = 7 \cdot 3 = 21$$

With $a = 2$, we have

$$h'(2) = f'(g(2))g'(2) = f'(1)g'(2) = 5 \cdot 4 = 20.$$

Related Exercises 31–32 ◀

Chain Rule for Powers

The Chain Rule leads to a general derivative rule for powers of differentiable functions. In fact, we have already used it in several examples. Consider the function $f(x) = (g(x))^n$, where n is an integer. Letting $f(u) = u^n$ be the outer function and $u = g(x)$ be the inner function, we obtain the Chain Rule for powers of functions.

THEOREM 3.13 Chain Rule for Powers
If g is differentiable for all x in its domain and n is an integer, then

$$\frac{d}{dx}[(g(x))^n] = n(g(x))^{n-1}g'(x).$$

EXAMPLE 4 Chain Rule for powers Find $\frac{d}{dx}(\tan x + 10)^{21}$.

SOLUTION With $g(x) = \tan x + 10$, the Chain Rule gives

$$\begin{aligned}\frac{d}{dx}(\tan x + 10)^{21} &= 21(\tan x + 10)^{20}\frac{d}{dx}(\tan x + 10)\\ &= 21(\tan x + 10)^{20}\sec^2 x.\end{aligned}$$

Related Exercises 33–36

The Composition of Three or More Functions

We can differentiate the composition of three or more functions by applying the Chain Rule repeatedly, as shown in the following example.

EXAMPLE 5 Composition of three functions Calculate the derivative of $\sin(\cos x^2)$.

SOLUTION The inner function of $\sin(\cos x^2)$ is $\cos x^2$. Because $\cos x^2$ is also a composition of two functions, the Chain Rule is used again to calculate $\frac{d}{dx}(\cos x^2)$, where x^2 is the inner function:

$$\begin{aligned}\frac{d}{dx}[\underbrace{\sin}_{\text{outer}}\underbrace{(\cos x^2)}_{\text{inner}}] &= \cos(\cos x^2)\frac{d}{dx}(\cos x^2) && \text{Chain Rule}\\ &= \cos(\cos x^2)\underbrace{(-\sin x^2)\cdot\frac{d}{dx}(x^2)}_{\frac{d}{dx}(\cos x^2)} && \text{Chain Rule}\\ &= \cos(\cos x^2)\cdot(-\sin x^2)\cdot 2x && \text{Differentiate } x^2.\\ &= -2x\cos(\cos x^2)\sin x^2 && \text{Simplify.}\end{aligned}$$

Related Exercises 37–46

QUICK CHECK 4 Let $y = \tan^{10}(x^5)$. Find f, g, and h such that $y = f(u)$, where $u = g(v)$ and $v = h(x)$.

Proof of the Chain Rule

Suppose f and g are differentiable functions and $h(x) = f(g(x))$. By the definition of the derivative of h,

$$h'(a) = \lim_{x\to a}\frac{h(x) - h(a)}{x - a} = \lim_{x\to a}\frac{f(g(x)) - f(g(a))}{x - a}. \quad (1)$$

We assume that $g(a) \neq g(x)$ for values of x near a but not equal to a. This assumption holds for most, but not all, functions encountered in this text. For a proof of the Chain Rule without this assumption, see Exercise 79.

We multiply the right side of equation (1) by $\frac{g(x) - g(a)}{g(x) - g(a)}$, which equals 1, and let $v = g(x)$ and $u = g(a)$. The result is

$$h'(a) = \lim_{x \to a} \frac{f(g(x)) - f(g(a))}{g(x) - g(a)} \cdot \frac{g(x) - g(a)}{x - a}$$

$$= \lim_{x \to a} \frac{f(v) - f(u)}{v - u} \cdot \frac{g(x) - g(a)}{x - a}.$$

By assumption, g is a differentiable function; therefore, it is continuous. This means that $\lim_{x \to a} g(x) = g(a)$, so $v \to u$ as $x \to a$. Consequently,

$$h'(a) = \underbrace{\lim_{v \to u} \frac{f(v) - f(u)}{v - u}}_{f'(u)} \cdot \underbrace{\lim_{x \to a} \frac{g(x) - g(a)}{x - a}}_{g'(a)} = f'(u)g'(a).$$

Because f and g are differentiable, the two limits in this expression exist; therefore, $h'(a)$ exists. Noting that $u = g(a)$, we have $h'(a) = f'(g(a))g'(a)$. Replacing a with the variable x gives the Chain Rule: $h'(x) = f'(g(x))g'(x)$. ◄

SECTION 3.6 EXERCISES

Review Questions

1. Two equivalent forms of the Chain Rule for calculating the derivative of $y = f(g(x))$ are presented in this section. State both forms.

2. Let $h(x) = f(g(x))$, where f and g are differentiable on their domains. If $g(1) = 3$ and $g'(1) = 5$, what else do you need to know to calculate $h'(1)$?

3. Fill in the blanks. The derivative of $f(g(x))$ equals f' evaluated at ________ multiplied by g' evaluated at ________.

4. Identify the inner and outer functions in the composition $\cos^4 x$.

5. Identify the inner and outer functions in the composition $(x^2 + 10)^{-5}$.

6. Express $Q(x) = \cos^4(x^2 + 1)$ as the composition of three functions; that is, identify f, g, and h so that $Q(x) = f(g(h(x)))$.

Basic Skills

7–16. Version 1 of the Chain Rule *Use Version 1 of the Chain Rule to calculate* $\frac{dy}{dx}$.

7. $y = (3x + 7)^{10}$
8. $y = (5x^2 + 11x)^{20}$
9. $y = \sqrt{x^2 + 1}$
10. $y = \sin \sqrt{x}$
11. $y = \tan(5x^2)$
12. $y = \sin\left(\frac{x}{4}\right)$
13. $y = \sqrt{\cos x}$
14. $y = \left(\frac{3x}{4x + 2}\right)^5$
15. $y = \tan x^4$
16. $y = ((x + 2)(3x^3 + 3x))^4$

17–28. Version 2 of the Chain Rule *Use Version 2 of the Chain Rule to calculate the derivatives of the following composite functions.*

17. $y = (3x^2 + 7x)^{10}$
18. $y = \sqrt{x^2 + 9}$
19. $y = 5(7x^3 + 1)^{-3}$
20. $y = \cos(5t + 1)$
21. $y = \tan(3x + 1)$
22. $y = (\tan t)^{-2}$
23. $y = \sin(4x^3 + 3x + 1)$
24. $y = \csc(t^2 + t)$
25. $y = \theta^2 \sec 5\theta$
26. $y = \cos^4 \theta + \sin^4 \theta$
27. $y = (\sec x + \tan x)^5$
28. $y = \sin(4 \cos z)$

29–30. Similar-looking composite functions *Two composite functions are given that look similar, but in fact are quite different. Identify the inner function* $u = g(x)$ *and the outer function* $y = f(u)$; *then evaluate* $\frac{dy}{dx}$ *using the Chain Rule.*

29. **a.** $y = \cos^3 x$ **b.** $y = \cos x^3$

30. **a.** $y = \sin\left(\frac{1}{t}\right)$ **b.** $y = \frac{1}{\sin t}$

31. **Chain Rule using a table** Let $h(x) = f(g(x))$ and $p(x) = g(f(x))$. Use the table to compute the following derivatives.
a. $h'(3)$ **b.** $h'(2)$ **c.** $p'(4)$ **d.** $p'(2)$ **e.** $h'(5)$

x	1	2	3	4	5
$f(x)$	0	3	5	1	0
$f'(x)$	5	2	−5	−8	−10
$g(x)$	4	5	1	3	2
$g'(x)$	2	10	20	15	20

32. **Chain Rule using a table** Let $h(x) = f(g(x))$ and $k(x) = g(g(x))$. Use the table to compute the following derivatives.
a. $h'(1)$ **b.** $h'(2)$ **c.** $h'(3)$ **d.** $k'(3)$ **e.** $k'(1)$ **f.** $k'(5)$

x	1	2	3	4	5
$f'(x)$	−6	−3	8	7	2
$g(x)$	4	1	5	2	3
$g'(x)$	9	7	3	−1	−5

33–36. Chain Rule for powers *Use the Chain Rule to find the derivative of the following functions.*

33. $y = (2x^6 - 3x^3 + 3)^{25}$ **34.** $y = (\cos x + 2 \sin x)^8$

35. $y = (1 + 2 \tan x)^{15}$ **36.** $y = (1 - \sqrt{x})^4$

37–46. Repeated use of the Chain Rule *Calculate the derivative of the following functions.*

37. $\sqrt{1 + \cot^2 x}$ **38.** $\sqrt{(3x - 4)^2 + 3x}$ **39.** $\sin^5 (\cos 3x)$

40. $\cos^4 (7x^3)$ **41.** $\tan (\sqrt{\sec x})$ **42.** $(1 - \sqrt{x + 4})^{-1}$

43. $\sqrt{x + \sqrt{x}}$ **44.** $\sqrt{x + \sqrt{x + \sqrt{x}}}$

45. $f(g(x^2))$, where f and g are differentiable for all real numbers

46. $f(\sqrt{g(x^2)})$, where f and g are differentiable for all real numbers and g is nonnegative

Further Explorations

47. Explain why or why not Determine whether the following statements are true and give an explanation or counterexample.

- **a.** The function $x \sin x$ can be differentiated without using the Chain Rule.
- **b.** The function $(x^2 + 10)^{-2}$ must be differentiated using the Chain Rule.
- **c.** The derivative of a product is *not* the product of the derivatives, but the derivative of a composition is a product of derivatives.
- **d.** $\frac{d}{dx}P(Q(x)) = P'(x)Q'(x)$

48–51. Second derivatives *Find* $\frac{d^2y}{dx^2}$ *for the following functions.*

48. $y = x \cos x^2$ **49.** $y = \sin x^2$

50. $y = \sqrt{3x^3 + 4x + 1}$ **51.** $y = (x^2 + 1)^{-2}$

52. Derivatives by different methods

- **a.** Calculate $\frac{d}{dx}(x^2 + x)^2$ using the Chain Rule. Simplify your answer.
- **b.** Expand $(x^2 + x)^2$ first and then calculate the derivative. Verify that your answer agrees with part (a).

53–54. Square root derivatives *Find the derivative of the following functions.*

53. $y = \sqrt{f(x)}$, where f is differentiable at x and nonnegative

54. $y = \sqrt{f(x)g(x)}$, where f and g are differentiable at x and nonnegative

T **55. Tangent lines** Determine an equation of the line tangent to the graph of $y = \frac{(x^2 - 1)^2}{x^3 - 6x - 1}$ at the point $(3, 8)$. Graph the function and the tangent line.

T **56. Tangent lines** Determine equations of the lines tangent to the graph of $y = x\sqrt{5 - x^2}$ at the points $(1, 2)$ and $(-2, -2)$. Graph the function and the tangent lines.

57. Tangent lines Assume f and g are differentiable on their domains with $h(x) = f(g(x))$. Suppose the equation of the line tangent to the graph of g at the point $(4, 7)$ is $y = 3x - 5$ and the equation of the line tangent to the graph of f at $(7, 9)$ is $y = -2x + 23$.

- **a.** Calculate $h(4)$ and $h'(4)$.
- **b.** Determine an equation of the line tangent to the graph of h at the point on the graph where $x = 4$.

58. Tangent lines Assume f is a differentiable function whose graph passes through the point $(1, 4)$. If $g(x) = f(x^2)$ and the line tangent to the graph of f at $(1, 4)$ is $y = 3x - 1$, determine each of the following.

a. $g(1)$ **b.** $g'(x)$ **c.** $g'(1)$

d. Find an equation of the line tangent to the graph of g when $x = 1$.

59. Tangent line Find the equation of the line tangent to $y = \sec 2x$ at $x = \pi/6$. Graph the function and the tangent line.

60. Composition containing sin *x* Suppose f is differentiable on $[-2, 2]$ with $f'(0) = 3$ and $f'(1) = 5$. Let $g(x) = f(\sin x)$. Evaluate the following expressions.

a. $g'(0)$ **b.** $g'\left(\frac{\pi}{2}\right)$ **c.** $g'(\pi)$

61. Composition containing sin *x* Suppose f is differentiable for all real numbers with $f(0) = -3$, $f(1) = 3$, $f'(0) = 3$, and $f'(1) = 5$. Let $g(x) = \sin (\pi f(x))$. Evaluate the following expressions.

a. $g'(0)$ **b.** $g'(1)$

Applications

62–64. Vibrations of a spring *Suppose an object of mass m is attached to the end of a spring hanging from the ceiling. We say that the mass is at its* equilibrium position $y = 0$ *when the spring hangs at rest. Suppose you push the mass to a position* y_0 *units above its equilibrium position and release it. As the mass oscillates up and down (neglecting any friction in the system), the position y of the mass after t seconds is given by the equation*

$$y = y_0 \cos\left(\sqrt{\frac{k}{m}}\, t\right), \qquad (2)$$

where k is a constant measuring the stiffness of the spring (the larger the value of k, the stiffer the spring) and y is positive in the upward direction.

62. Use equation (2) to answer the following questions.

- **a.** Find $\frac{dy}{dt}$, the velocity of the object. (Assume k and m are constant.)
- **b.** How would the velocity be affected if the experiment were repeated with four times the mass on the end of the spring?
- **c.** How would the velocity be affected if the experiment were repeated with a spring having four times the stiffness (k is increased by a factor of 4)?
- **d.** Assume that y has units of meters, t has units of seconds, m has units of kg, and k has units of kg/s^2. Show that the units of the velocity in part (a) are consistent.

63. Use equation (2) to answer the following questions.

- **a.** Find the second derivative $\frac{d^2y}{dt^2}$.
- **b.** Verify that $\frac{d^2y}{dt^2} = -\frac{k}{m}y$.

64. Use equation (2) to answer the following questions.

a. The *period* T is the time required by the mass to complete one oscillation. Show that $T = 2\pi\sqrt{\frac{m}{k}}$.

b. Assume k is constant and calculate $\frac{dT}{dm}$.

c. Give a physical explanation of why $\frac{dT}{dm}$ is positive.

T 65. Hours of daylight The number of hours of daylight at any point on Earth fluctuates throughout the year. In the northern hemisphere, the shortest day is on the winter solstice and the longest day is on the summer solstice. At 40° north latitude, the length of a day is approximated by

$$D(t) = 12 - 3\cos\left[\frac{2\pi(t + 10)}{365}\right],$$

where D is measured in hours and $0 \leq t \leq 365$ is measured in days, with $t = 0$ corresponding to January 1.

a. Approximately how much daylight is there on March 1 ($t = 59$)?

b. Find the rate at which the daylight function changes.

c. Find the rate at which the daylight function changes on March 1. Convert your answer to units of min/day and explain what this result means.

d. Graph the function $y = D'(t)$ using a graphing utility.

e. At what times of year is the length of day changing most rapidly? Least rapidly?

T 66. A mixing tank A 500-L tank is filled with pure water. At time $t = 0$, a salt solution begins flowing into the tank at a rate of 5 L/min. At the same time, the (fully mixed) solution flows out of the tank at a rate of 5.5 L/min. The mass of salt in grams in the tank at any time $t \geq 0$ is given by

$$M(t) = 250(1000 - t)[1 - 10^{-30}(1000 - t)^{10}]$$

and the volume of solution in the tank is given by $V(t) = 500 - 0.5t$ L.

a. Graph the mass function and verify that $M(0) = 0$.

b. Graph the volume function and verify that the tank is empty when $t = 1000$ min.

c. The concentration of the salt solution in the tank (in g/L) is given by $C(t) = M(t)/V(t)$. Graph the concentration function and comment on its properties. Specifically, what are $C(0)$ and $C(1000)$?

d. Find the rate of change of the mass $M'(t)$, for $0 \leq t \leq 1000$.

e. Find the rate of change of the concentration $C'(t)$, for $0 \leq t \leq 1000$.

f. For what times is the concentration of the solution increasing? Decreasing?

T 67. Power and Energy The total energy in megawatt-hr (MWh) used by a town is given by

$$E(t) = 400t + \frac{2400}{\pi}\sin\left(\frac{\pi t}{12}\right),$$

where $t \geq 0$ is measured in hours, with $t = 0$ corresponding to noon.

a. Find the power, or rate of energy consumption, $P(t) = E'(t)$ in units of megawatts (MW).

b. At what time of day is the rate of energy consumption a maximum? What is the power at that time of day?

c. At what time of day is the rate of energy consumption a minimum? What is the power at that time of day?

d. Sketch a graph of the power function reflecting the times when energy use is a minimum or maximum.

Additional Exercises

68. Deriving Trigonometric Identities

a. Recall that $\cos 2t = \cos^2 t - \sin^2 t$. Use differentiation to find a trigonometric identity for $\sin 2t$.

b. Verify that you obtain the same identity for $\sin 2t$ as in part (a) if you use the identity $\cos 2t = 2\cos^2 t - 1$.

c. Verify that you obtain the same identity for $\sin 2t$ as in part (a) if you use the identity $\cos 2t = 1 - 2\sin^2 t$.

69. Proof of $\cos^2 x + \sin^2 x = 1$ Let $f(x) = \cos^2 x + \sin^2 x$.

a. Use the Chain Rule to show that $f'(x) = 0$.

b. Assume that if $f' = 0$, then f is a constant function. Calculate $f(0)$ and use it with part (a) to explain why $\cos^2 x + \sin^2 x = 1$.

70. General trigonometric derivatives

a. Identify the inner function g and the outer function f for the composition $f(g(x)) = \sin kx$, where k is a real number.

b. Use the Chain Rule to show that $\frac{d}{dx}(\sin kx) = k\cos kx$.

c. Find the derivative of $\cos kx$, $\tan kx$, $\cot kx$, $\sec kx$, and $\csc kx$.

71. Deriving the Quotient Rule using the Product Rule and Chain Rule Suppose you forgot the Quotient Rule for calculating $\frac{d}{dx}\left[\frac{f(x)}{g(x)}\right]$. Use the Chain Rule and Product Rule with the identity $\frac{f(x)}{g(x)} = f(x)(g(x))^{-1}$ to derive the Quotient Rule.

72. The Chain Rule for second derivatives

a. Derive a formula for the second derivative, $\frac{d^2}{dx^2}(f(g(x)))$.

b. Use the formula in part (a) to calculate $\frac{d^2}{dx^2}(\sin(3x^4 + 5x^2 + 2))$.

T 73–76. Calculating limits *The following limits are the derivatives of a composite function h at a point a.*

a. *Find a composite function h and the value of a.*

b. *Use the Chain Rule to find each limit. Verify your answer by using the limit command on a calculator.*

73. $\lim_{x\to 2} \frac{(x^2 - 3)^5 - 1}{x - 2}$

74. $\lim_{x\to 0} \frac{\sqrt{4 + \sin x} - 2}{x}$

75. $\lim_{h\to 0} \frac{\sin(\pi/2 + h)^2 - \sin(\pi^2/4)}{h}$

76. $\lim_{h\to 0} \frac{\frac{1}{3((1 + h)^5 + 7)^{10}} - \frac{1}{3(8)^{10}}}{h}$

77. Limit of a difference quotient Assuming that f is differentiable for all x, simplify $\lim_{x \to 5} \dfrac{f(x^2) - f(25)}{x - 5}$.

78. Derivatives of even and odd functions Recall that f is even if $f(x) = f(-x)$ for all x in the domain of f, and f is odd if $f(x) = -f(-x)$ for all x in the domain of f.

a. If f is a differentiable, even function on its domain, determine whether f' is even, odd, or neither.

b. If f is a differentiable, odd function on its domain, determine whether f' is even, odd, or neither.

79. A general proof of the Chain Rule Let f and g be differentiable functions with $h(x) = f(g(x))$. For a given constant a, let $u = g(a)$ and $v = g(x)$, and define

$$H(v) = \begin{cases} \dfrac{f(v) - f(u)}{v - u} - f'(u) & \text{if } v \neq u \\ 0 & \text{if } v = u \end{cases}$$

a. Show that $\lim_{v \to u} H(v) = 0$.

b. For any value of u show that
$$f(v) - f(u) = (H(v) + f'(u))(v - u).$$

c. Show that

$$h'(a) = \lim_{x \to a} \left[[H(g(x)) + f'(g(a))] \cdot \frac{g(x) - g(a)}{x - a} \right].$$

d. Show that $h'(a) = f'(g(a))g'(a)$.

QUICK CHECK ANSWERS

1. The expansion of $(5x + 4)^{100}$ contains 101 terms. It would take too much time to calculate both the expansion and the derivative. **2.** The inner function is $u = 5x + 4$, and the outer function is $y = u^3$. **4.** $f(u) = u^{10}$; $u = g(v) = \tan v$; $v = h(x) = x^5$ ◄

3.7 Implicit Differentiation

This chapter has been devoted to calculating derivatives of functions of the form $y = f(x)$, where y is defined *explicitly* as a function of x. However, relationships between variables are often expressed *implicitly*. For example, the equation of the unit circle $x^2 + y^2 = 1$, when written $x^2 + y^2 - 1 = 0$, has the *implicit* form $F(x, y) = 0$. This equation does not represent a single function because its graph fails the vertical line test (Figure 3.43a). If, however, the equation $x^2 + y^2 = 1$ is solved for y, then *two* functions, $y = -\sqrt{1 - x^2}$ and $y = \sqrt{1 - x^2}$, emerge (Figure 3.43b). Having identified two explicit functions that form the circle, their derivatives are found using the Chain Rule:

$$\text{If } y = \sqrt{1 - x^2}, \text{ then } \frac{dy}{dx} = -\frac{x}{\sqrt{1 - x^2}}. \qquad (1)$$

$$\text{If } y = -\sqrt{1 - x^2}, \text{ then } \frac{dy}{dx} = \frac{x}{\sqrt{1 - x^2}}. \qquad (2)$$

We use equation (1) to find the slope of the curve at any point on the upper half of the unit circle and equation (2) to find the slope of the curve at any point on the lower half of the circle.

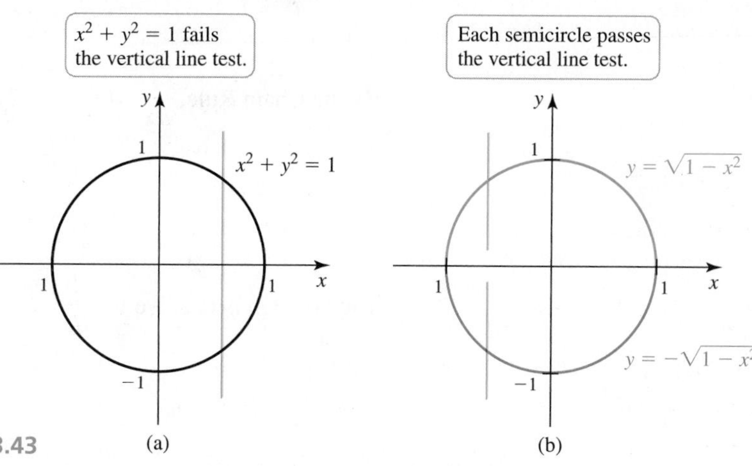

FIGURE 3.43

QUICK CHECK 1 The equation $x - y^2 = 0$ implicitly defines what two functions?

While it is straightforward to solve some implicit equations for y (such as $x^2 + y^2 = 1$ or $x - y^2 = 0$), it is difficult or impossible to solve other equations for y. For example, the graph of $x + y^3 - xy = 1$ (Figure 3.44a) represents three functions: the upper half of a parabola $y = f_1(x)$, the lower half of a parabola $y = f_2(x)$, and the horizontal line $y = f_3(x)$ (Figure 3.44b). Solving for y to obtain these three functions is challenging (Exercise 55), and even after solving for y, derivatives for each of the three functions must be calculated separately. The goal of this section is to find a *single* expression for the derivative *directly* from an equation $F(x, y) = 0$ without first solving for y. This technique, called **implicit differentiation**, is demonstrated through examples.

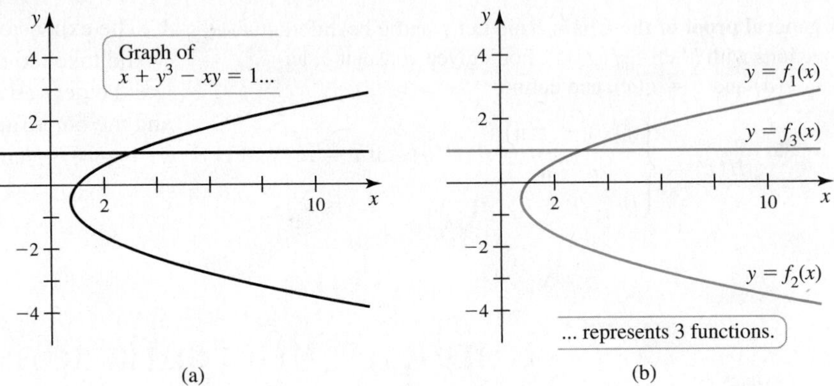

FIGURE 3.44

EXAMPLE 1 Implicit differentiation

a. Calculate $\dfrac{dy}{dx}$ directly from the equation for the unit circle $x^2 + y^2 = 1$.

b. Find the slope of the unit circle at $\left(\dfrac{1}{2}, \dfrac{\sqrt{3}}{2}\right)$ and $\left(\dfrac{1}{2}, -\dfrac{\sqrt{3}}{2}\right)$.

SOLUTION

a. To indicate the choice of x as the independent variable, it is helpful to replace the variable y with $y(x)$:

$$x^2 + (y(x))^2 = 1 \quad \text{Replace } y \text{ by } y(x).$$

We now take the derivative of each term in the equation *with respect to x*:

$$\underbrace{\frac{d}{dx}(x^2)}_{2x} + \underbrace{\frac{d}{dx}[y(x)]^2}_{\text{Use the Chain Rule}} = \underbrace{\frac{d}{dx}(1)}_{0}$$

By the Chain Rule, $\dfrac{d}{dx}[y(x)]^2 = 2y(x)y'(x)$, or more simply, $\dfrac{d}{dx}(y^2) = 2y\dfrac{dy}{dx}$. Using this result, we have

$$2x + 2y\frac{dy}{dx} = 0.$$

The last step is to solve for $\dfrac{dy}{dx}$:

$$2y\frac{dy}{dx} = -2x \quad \text{Subtract } 2x \text{ from both sides.}$$

$$\frac{dy}{dx} = -\frac{x}{y} \quad \text{Divide by } 2y \text{ and simplify.}$$

This result holds provided $y \neq 0$. At the points $(1, 0)$ and $(-1, 0)$, the circle has vertical tangent lines.

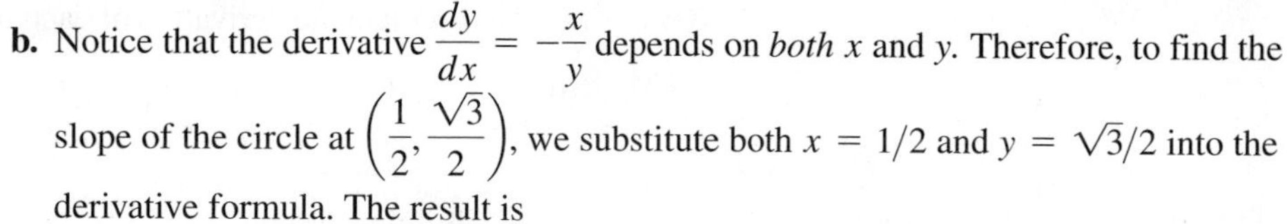

b. Notice that the derivative $\frac{dy}{dx} = -\frac{x}{y}$ depends on *both* x and y. Therefore, to find the slope of the circle at $\left(\frac{1}{2}, \frac{\sqrt{3}}{2}\right)$, we substitute both $x = 1/2$ and $y = \sqrt{3}/2$ into the derivative formula. The result is

$$\left.\frac{dy}{dx}\right|_{\left(\frac{1}{2}, \frac{\sqrt{3}}{2}\right)} = -\frac{1/2}{\sqrt{3}/2} = -\frac{1}{\sqrt{3}}.$$

The slope of the curve at $\left(\frac{1}{2}, -\frac{\sqrt{3}}{2}\right)$ is

$$\left.\frac{dy}{dx}\right|_{\left(\frac{1}{2}, -\frac{\sqrt{3}}{2}\right)} = -\frac{1/2}{-\sqrt{3}/2} = \frac{1}{\sqrt{3}}.$$

The curve and tangent lines are shown in Figure 3.45. *Related Exercises 5–20*

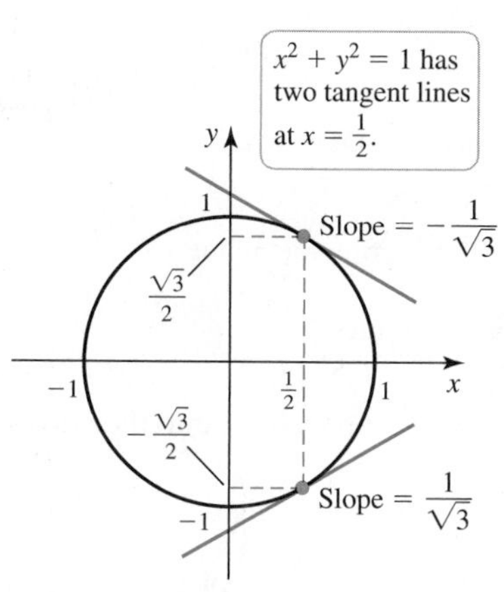

FIGURE 3.45

Example 1 illustrates the technique of implicit differentiation. It is done without solving for y, and it produces $\frac{dy}{dx}$ in terms of *both* x and y. The derivative obtained in Example 1 is consistent with the derivatives calculated explicitly in equations (1) and (2). For the upper half of the circle, substituting $y = \sqrt{1 - x^2}$ into the implicit derivative $\frac{dy}{dx} = -\frac{x}{y}$ gives

$$\frac{dy}{dx} = -\frac{x}{y} = -\frac{x}{\sqrt{1 - x^2}},$$

which agrees with equation (1). For the lower half of the circle, substituting $y = -\sqrt{1 - x^2}$ into $\frac{dy}{dx} = -\frac{x}{y}$ gives

$$\frac{dy}{dx} = -\frac{x}{y} = \frac{x}{\sqrt{1 - x^2}},$$

which is consistent with equation (2). Therefore, implicit differentiation gives a single unified derivative $\frac{dy}{dx} = -\frac{x}{y}$.

QUICK CHECK 2 Use implicit differentiation to find $\frac{dy}{dx}$ for $x - y^2 = 3$.

Slopes of Tangent Lines

Derivatives obtained by implicit differentiation typically depend on x *and* y. Therefore, the slope of a curve at a particular point (x, y) requires both the x- and y-coordinates of the point. These coordinates are also needed to find an equation of the tangent line at that point.

QUICK CHECK 3 If a function is defined explicitly in the form $y = f(x)$, which coordinates are needed to find the slope of a tangent line—the x-coordinate, the y-coordinate, or both?

EXAMPLE 2 **Finding tangent lines with implicit functions** Find an equation of the line tangent to the curve $x^2 + xy - y^3 = 7$ at $(3, 2)$.

➤ Because y is a function of x, we have

$$\frac{d}{dx}(x) = 1 \quad \text{and}$$

$$\frac{d}{dx}(y) = y'.$$

To differentiate y^3 with respect to x, we use the Chain Rule.

SOLUTION We calculate the derivative of each term of the equation $x^2 + xy - y^3 = 7$:

$$\frac{d}{dx}(x^2) + \frac{d}{dx}(xy) - \frac{d}{dx}(y^3) = \frac{d}{dx}(7) \qquad \text{Differentiate each term.}$$

$$2x + \underbrace{y + xy'}_{\text{Product Rule}} - \underbrace{3y^2y'}_{\text{Chain Rule}} = 0 \qquad \text{Calculate the derivatives.}$$

$$3y^2y' - xy' = 2x + y \qquad \text{Group the terms containing } y'.$$

$$y' = \frac{2x + y}{3y^2 - x} \qquad \text{Factor and solve for } y'.$$

To find the slope of the tangent line at $(3, 2)$, we substitute $x = 3$ and $y = 2$ into the derivative formula:

$$\left.\frac{dy}{dx}\right|_{(3,2)} = \left.\frac{2x + y}{3y^2 - x}\right|_{(3,2)} = \frac{8}{9}$$

An equation of the line passing through $(3, 2)$ with slope $\frac{8}{9}$ is

$$y - 2 = \frac{8}{9}(x - 3) \quad \text{or} \quad y = \frac{8}{9}x - \frac{2}{3}.$$

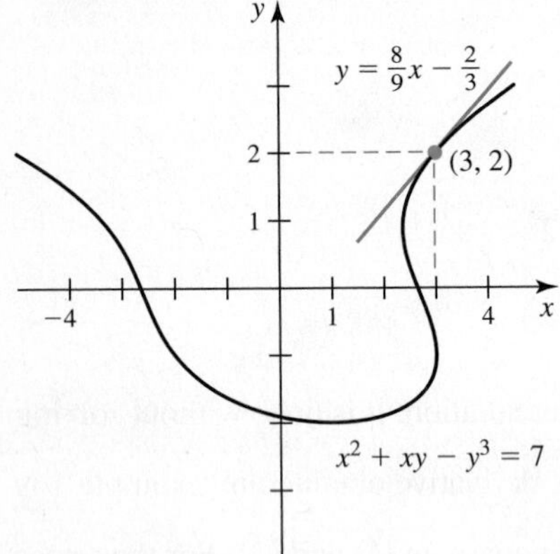

FIGURE 3.46

Figure 3.46 shows the graphs of the curve $x^2 + xy - y^3 = 7$ and the tangent line.

Related Exercises 21–26 ◄

Higher-Order Derivatives of Implicit Functions

In previous sections of this chapter, we found higher-order derivatives $\frac{d^n y}{dx^n}$ by first calculating $\frac{dy}{dx}, \frac{d^2y}{dx^2}, \ldots,$ and $\frac{d^{n-1}y}{dx^{n-1}}$. The same approach is used with implicit differentiation.

EXAMPLE 3 **A second derivative** Find $\frac{d^2y}{dx^2}$ if $x^2 + y^2 = 1$.

SOLUTION The first derivative $\frac{dy}{dx} = -\frac{x}{y}$ was computed in Example 1.

We now calculate the derivative of each side of this equation and solve for the second derivative:

$$\frac{d}{dx}\left(\frac{dy}{dx}\right) = \frac{d}{dx}\left(-\frac{x}{y}\right) \qquad \text{Take derivatives with respect to } x.$$

$$\frac{d^2y}{dx^2} = -\frac{y \cdot 1 - x\frac{dy}{dx}}{y^2} \qquad \text{Quotient Rule}$$

$$= -\frac{y - x\left(-\frac{x}{y}\right)}{y^2} \qquad \text{Substitute for } \frac{dy}{dx}.$$

$$= -\frac{x^2 + y^2}{y^3} \qquad \text{Simplify.}$$

$$= -\frac{1}{y^3} \qquad x^2 + y^2 = 1$$

Related Exercises 27–32 ◄

The Power Rule for Rational Exponents

The Extended Power Rule states that $\frac{d}{dx}(x^n) = nx^{n-1}$ if n is an integer. Using implicit differentiation this rule can be extended to rational values of n such as $\frac{1}{2}$ or $-\frac{5}{3}$. Assume p and q are integers with $q \neq 0$ and let $y = x^{p/q}$, where $x \geq 0$ when q is even. By raising each side of $y = x^{p/q}$ to the power q, we obtain $y^q = x^p$. Assuming that y is a differentiable function of x on its domain, both sides of $y^q = x^p$ are differentiated with respect to x:

$$qy^{q-1}\frac{dy}{dx} = px^{p-1}$$

We divide both sides of this equation by qy^{q-1} and simplify:

$$\frac{dy}{dx} = \frac{p}{q} \cdot \frac{x^{p-1}}{y^{q-1}} = \frac{p}{q} \cdot \frac{x^{p-1}}{(x^{p/q})^{q-1}} \quad \text{Substitute } x^{p/q} \text{ for } y.$$

$$= \frac{p}{q} \cdot \frac{x^{p-1}}{x^{p-p/q}} \quad \text{Multiply exponents in the denominator.}$$

$$= \frac{p}{q} \cdot x^{p/q-1} \quad \text{Simplify by combining exponents.}$$

If we let $n = \frac{p}{q}$, then $\frac{d}{dx}(x^n) = nx^{n-1}$. So, the power rule for rational exponents is the same as the power rule for integer exponents.

> The assumption that $y = x^{p/q}$ is differentiable on its domain is proved in Section 7.3, where the Power Rule is proved for all real powers; that is, we prove that $\frac{d}{dx}(x^n) = nx^{n-1}$ holds for any real number n.

THEOREM 3.14 Power Rule for Rational Exponents
Assume p and q are integers with $q \neq 0$. Then,

$$\frac{d}{dx}(x^{p/q}) = \frac{p}{q}x^{p/q-1},$$

provided that $x \geq 0$ when q is even.

EXAMPLE 4 Rational exponent Calculate $\frac{dy}{dx}$ for the following functions.

a. $y = \sqrt{x}$ **b.** $y = (x^6 + 3x)^{2/3}$

> The derivative of $\sqrt{x}$ (Example 4a) was determined using the limit definition of the derivative in Section 3.1.

SOLUTION

a. $\frac{dy}{dx} = \frac{d}{dx}(x^{1/2}) = \frac{1}{2}x^{-1/2} = \frac{1}{2\sqrt{x}}$

b. We apply the Chain Rule, where the outer function is $u^{2/3}$ and the inner function is $x^6 + 3x$:

$$\frac{dy}{dx} = \frac{d}{dx}((x^6 + 3x)^{2/3}) = \underbrace{\frac{2}{3}(x^6 + 3x)^{-1/3}}_{\text{derivative of outer function}}\underbrace{(6x^5 + 3)}_{\text{derivative of inner function}}$$

$$= \frac{2(2x^5 + 1)}{(x^6 + 3x)^{1/3}}$$

Related Exercises 33–40◄

EXAMPLE 5 Implicit differentiation with rational exponents Find the slope of the curve $2(x + y)^{1/3} = y$ at the point $(4, 4)$.

SOLUTION We begin by differentiating both sides of the given equation:

$$\frac{2}{3}(x + y)^{-2/3}\left(1 + \frac{dy}{dx}\right) = \frac{dy}{dx}$$ Implicit differentiation, Chain Rule, Theorem 3.14

$$\frac{2}{3}(x + y)^{-2/3} = \frac{dy}{dx} - \frac{2}{3}(x + y)^{-2/3}\frac{dy}{dx}$$ Expand and collect like terms.

$$\frac{2}{3}(x + y)^{-2/3} = \frac{dy}{dx}\left(1 - \frac{2}{3}(x + y)^{-2/3}\right)$$ Factor out $\frac{dy}{dx}$.

We now solve for dy/dx:

$$\frac{dy}{dx} = \frac{\frac{2}{3}(x + y)^{-2/3}}{1 - \frac{2}{3}(x + y)^{-2/3}}$$ Divide by $1 - \frac{2}{3}(x + y)^{-2/3}$.

$$\frac{dy}{dx} = \frac{2}{3(x + y)^{2/3} - 2}$$ Multiply by $3(x + y)^{2/3}$ and simplify.

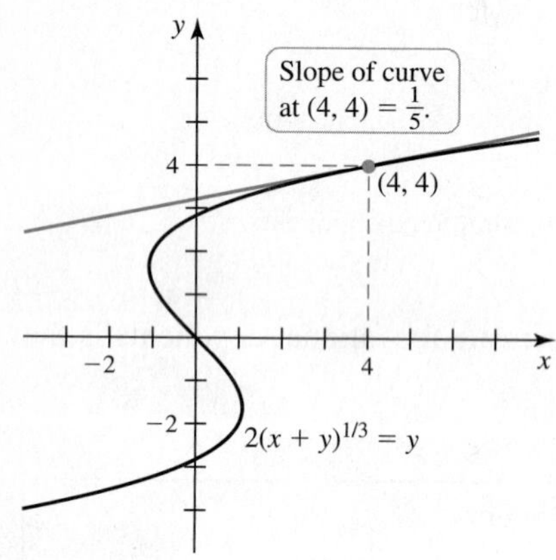

FIGURE 3.47

Note that the point $(4, 4)$ *does* lie on the curve (Figure 3.47). The slope of the curve at $(4, 4)$ is found by substituting $x = 4$ and $y = 4$ into the formula for $\frac{dy}{dx}$:

$$\left.\frac{dy}{dx}\right|_{(4,4)} = \frac{2}{3(8)^{2/3} - 2} = \frac{1}{5}$$

Related Exercises 41–46 ◄

SECTION 3.7 EXERCISES

Review Questions

1. For some equations, such as $x^2 + y^2 = 1$ or $x - y^2 = 0$, it is possible to solve for y and then calculate $\frac{dy}{dx}$. Even in these cases, explain why implicit differentiation is usually a more efficient method for calculating the derivative.

2. Explain the differences between computing the derivatives of functions that are defined implicitly and explicitly.

3. Why are both the x-coordinate and the y-coordinate generally needed to find the slope of the tangent line at a point for an implicitly defined function?

4. In this section, for what values of n did we prove that $\frac{d}{dx}(x^n) = nx^{n-1}$?

Basic Skills

5–10. Implicit differentiation *Carry out the following steps.*

a. *Use implicit differentiation to find* $\frac{dy}{dx}$.

b. *Find the slope of the curve at the given point.*

5. $y^2 = 4x;\ (1, 2)$

6. $y^2 + 3x = 2;\ (-1, \sqrt{5})$

7. $\sin y = 5x^4 - 5;\ (1, \pi)$

8. $5\sqrt{x} - 10\sqrt{y} = \sin x;\ (4\pi, \pi)$

9. $\cos y = x;\ \left(0, \frac{\pi}{2}\right)$

10. $\tan xy = x + y;\ (0, 0)$

11–20. Implicit differentiation *Use implicit differentiation to find* $\frac{dy}{dx}$.

11. $\sin xy = x + y$

12. $\tan(x + y) = 2y$

13. $\cos y^2 + x = y^2$

14. $y = \frac{x + 1}{y - 1}$

15. $x^3 = \frac{x + y}{x - y}$

16. $(xy + 1)^3 = x - y^2 + 8$

17. $6x^3 + 7y^3 = 13xy$

18. $(x^2 + y^2)(x^2 + y^2 + x) = 8xy^2$

19. $\sqrt{x^4 + y^2} = 5x + 2y^3$

20. $\sqrt{3x^7 + y^2} = \sin^2 y + 100xy$

21–26. Tangent lines *Carry out the following steps.*

a. *Verify that the given point lies on the curve.*

b. *Determine an equation of the line tangent to the curve at the given point.*

21. $x^2 + xy + y^2 = 7;\ (2, 1)$

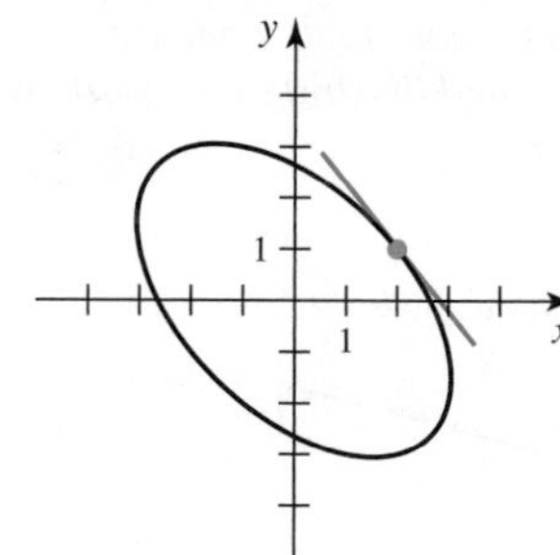

22. $x^4 - x^2y + y^4 = 1;\ (-1, 1)$

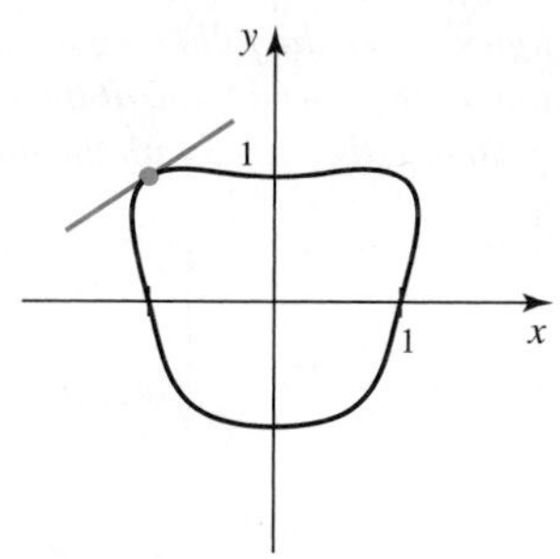

23. $\sin y + 5x = y^2;\ \left(\frac{\pi^2}{5}, \pi\right)$

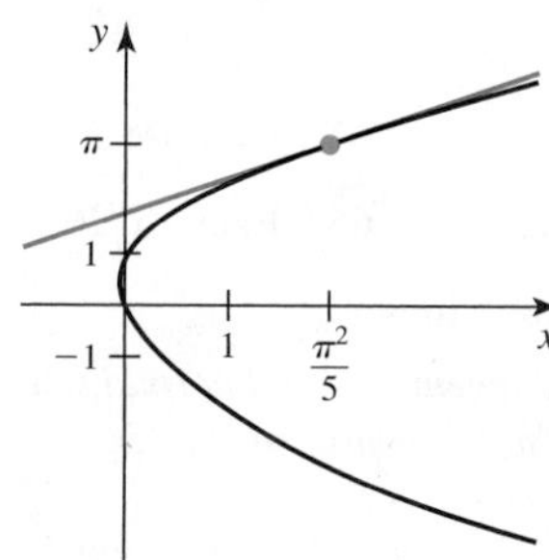

24. $x^3 + y^3 = 2xy;\ (1, 1)$

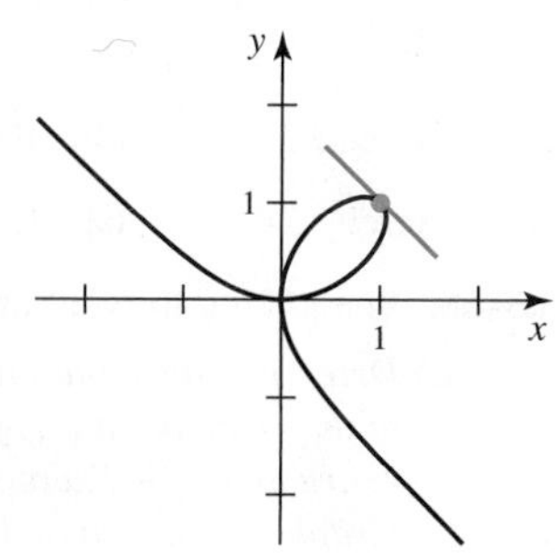

25. $\cos(x - y) + \sin y = \sqrt{2};\ \left(\frac{\pi}{2}, \frac{\pi}{4}\right)$

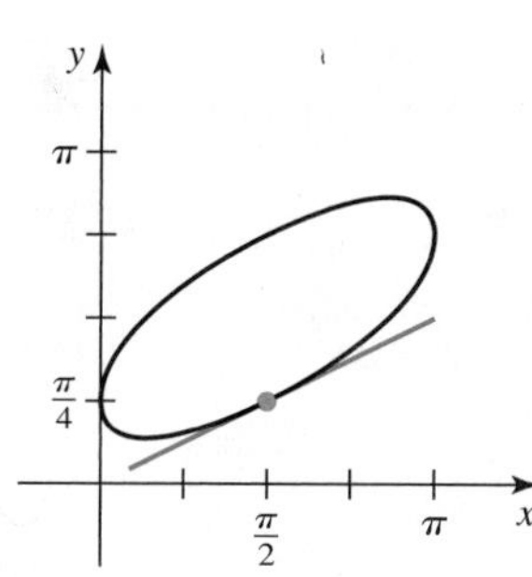

26. $(x^2 + y^2)^2 = \frac{25}{4}xy^2;\ (1, 2)$

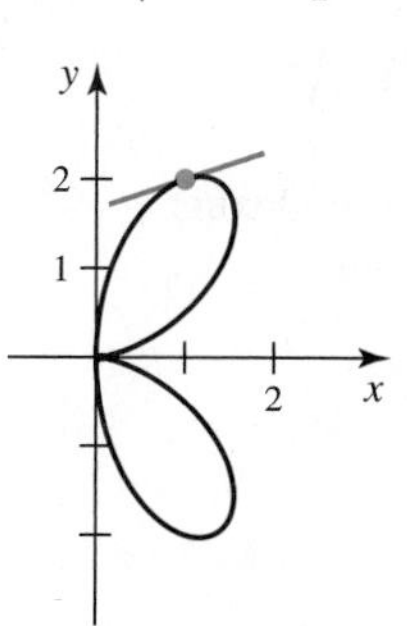

27–32. Second derivatives *Find* $\frac{d^2y}{dx^2}$.

27. $x + y^2 = 1$ **28.** $2x^2 + y^2 = 4$ **29.** $\sqrt{y} + xy = 1$

30. $x^4 + y^4 = 64$ **31.** $\sin y + x = y$ **32.** $\sin x + x^2y = 10$

33–40. Derivatives of functions with rational exponents *Find* $\frac{dy}{dx}$.

33. $y = x^{5/4}$ **34.** $y = \sqrt[3]{x^2 - x + 1}$

35. $y = (5x + 1)^{2/3}$ **36.** $y = \sqrt{x^3}\,(\cos x)$

37. $y = \sqrt[4]{\frac{2x}{4x - 3}}$ **38.** $y = (2x + 3)^2(4x + 6)^{1/4}$

39. $y = x\sqrt[3]{x^2 + 5x + 1}$ **40.** $y = \frac{x}{\sqrt[5]{x} + x}$

41–46. Implicit differentiation with rational exponents *Determine the slope of the following curves at the given point.*

41. $\sqrt[3]{x} + \sqrt[3]{y^4} = 2;\ (1, 1)$ **42.** $x^{2/3} + y^{2/3} = 2;\ (1, 1)$

43. $xy^{1/3} + y = 10;\ (1, 8)$ **44.** $(x + y)^{2/3} = y;\ (4, 4)$

45. $xy + x^{3/2}y^{-1/2} = 2;\ (1, 1)$ **46.** $xy^{5/2} + x^{3/2}y = 12;\ (4, 1)$

Further Explorations

47. Explain why or why not Determine whether the following statements are true and give an explanation or counterexample.

- **a.** For any equation containing the variables x and y, the derivative dy/dx can be found by first using algebra to rewrite the equation in the form $y = f(x)$.
- **b.** For the equation of a circle of radius r, $x^2 + y^2 = r^2$, we have $\frac{dy}{dx} = -\frac{x}{y}$ for $y \neq 0$ and any real number $r > 0$.
- **c.** If $x = 1$, then by implicit differentiation, $1 = 0$.
- **d.** If $xy = 1$, then $y' = 1/x$.

T 48–50. Multiple tangent lines *Complete the following steps.*

- ***a.*** *Find equations of all lines tangent to the curve at the given value of x.*
- ***b.*** *Graph the tangent lines on the given graph.*

48. $x + y^3 - y = 1;\ x = 1$

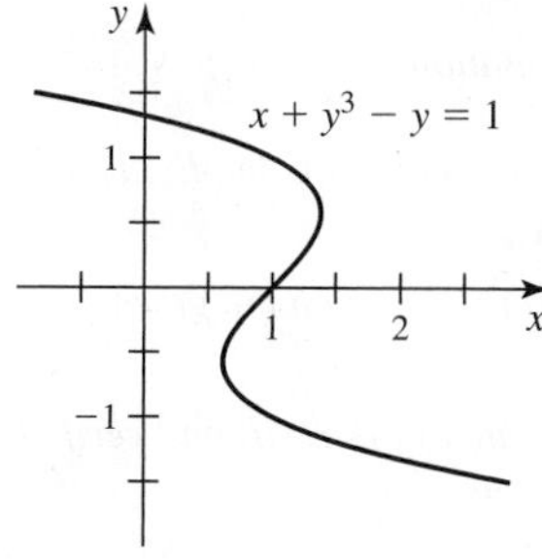

49. $x + y^2 - y = 1;\ x = 1$

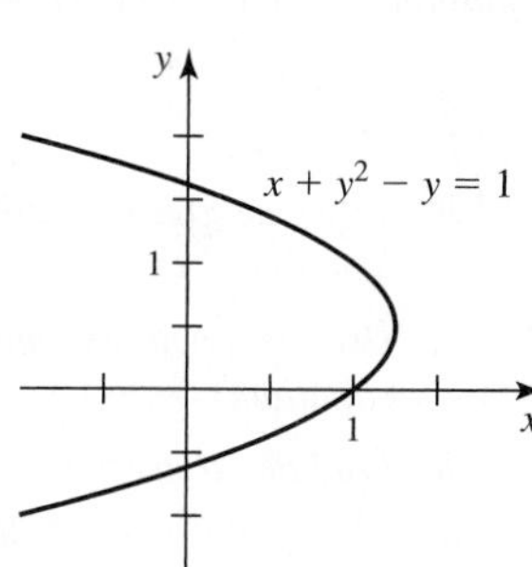

50. $4x^3 = y^2(4 - x);\ x = 2$ (cissoid of Diocles)

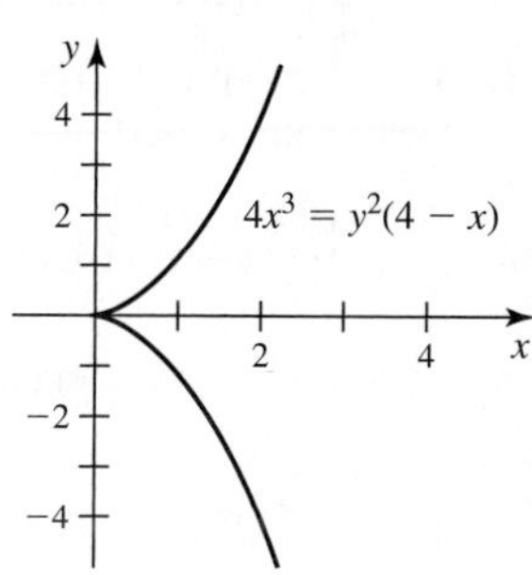

51. Multiple tangent lines Let $y(x^2 + 4) = 8$ (witch of Agnesi).

a. Use implicit differentiation to find $\frac{dy}{dx}$.
b. Find equations of all lines tangent to the curve $y(x^2 + 4) = 8$ when $y = 1$.
c. Solve the equation $y(x^2 + 4) = 8$ for y to find an explicit expression for y and then calculate $\frac{dy}{dx}$.
d. Verify that the results of parts (a) and (c) are consistent.

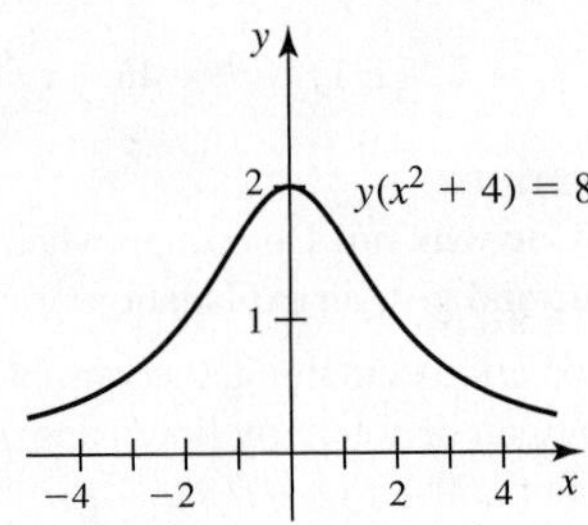

52. Vertical tangent lines

a. Determine the points where the curve $x + y^3 - y = 1$ has a vertical tangent line (see Exercise 48).
b. Does the curve have any horizontal tangent lines? Explain.

53. Vertical tangent lines

a. Determine the points where the curve $x + y^2 - y = 1$ has a vertical tangent line (see Exercise 49).
b. Does the curve have any horizontal tangent lines? Explain.

T **54–58. Identifying functions from an equation** *The following equations implicitly define one or more functions.*

a. Find $\frac{dy}{dx}$ using implicit differentiation.
b. Solve the given equation for y to identify the implicitly defined functions $y = f_1(x), y = f_2(x), \ldots$.
c. Use the functions found in part (b) to graph the given equation.
d. Find the derivative of each function in part (b) and verify that your results are consistent with part (a).

54. $y^3 = ax^2$ (Neile's semicubical parabola)

55. $x + y^3 - xy = 1$ (*Hint:* Rewrite as $y^3 - 1 = xy - x$ and then factor both sides.)

56. $y^2 = \frac{x^2(4 - x)}{4 + x}$ (right strophoid)

57. $x^4 = 2(x^2 - y^2)$ (eight curve)

58. $y^2(x + 2) = x^2(6 - x)$ (trisectrix)

T **59–64. Normal lines** *A* **normal line** *on a curve passes through a point P on the curve perpendicular to the line tangent to the curve at P (see figure). Use the following equations and graphs to determine an equation of the normal line at the given point and illustrate your work by graphing the curve with the normal line.*

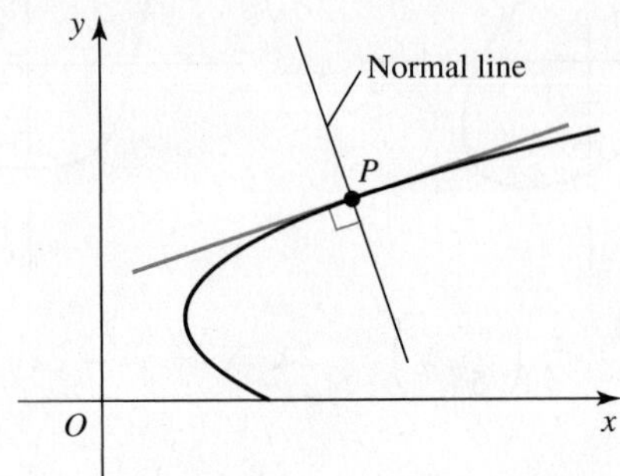

59. Exercise 21 **60.** Exercise 22 **61.** Exercise 23

62. Exercise 24 **63.** Exercise 25 **64.** Exercise 26

T **65–68. Visualizing tangent and normal lines**

a. Determine an equation of the tangent line and normal line at the given point (x_0, y_0) on the following curves. (See instructions for Exercises 59–64.)
b. Graph the tangent and normal lines on the given graph.

65. $3x^3 + 7y^3 = 10y$; $(x_0, y_0) = (1, 1)$

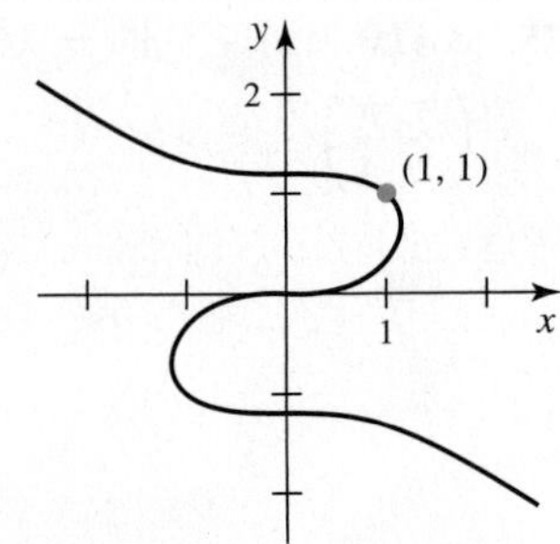

66. $x^4 = 2x^2 + 2y^2$; $(x_0, y_0) = (2, 2)$ (kampyle of Eudoxus)

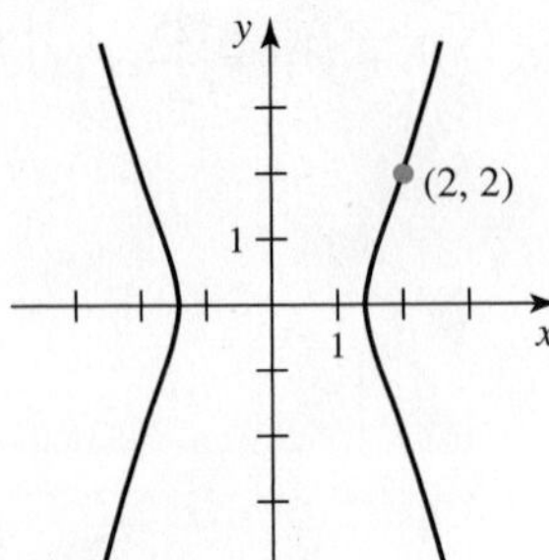

67. $(x^2 + y^2 - 2x)^2 = 2(x^2 + y^2)$; $(x_0, y_0) = (2, 2)$ (limaçon of Pascal)

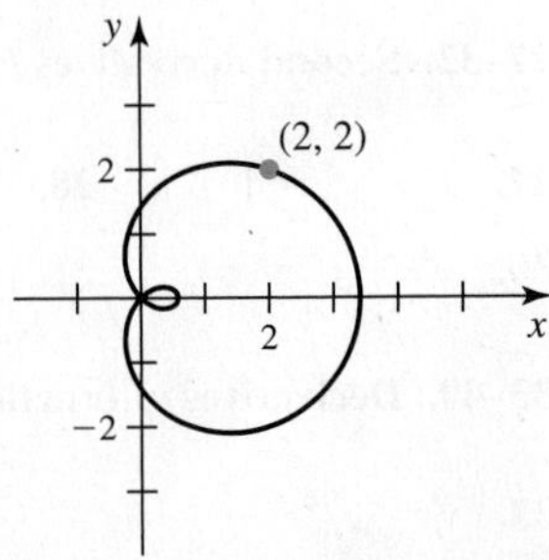

68. $(x^2 + y^2)^2 = \frac{25}{3}(x^2 - y^2)$;
$(x_0, y_0) = (2, -1)$
(lemniscate of Bernoulli)

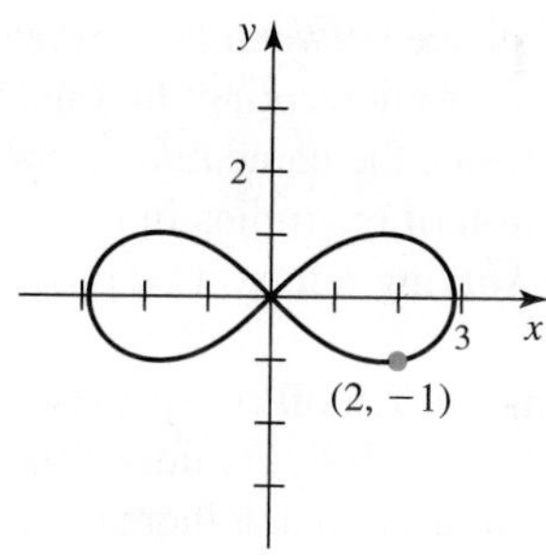

Applications

69. **Cobb-Douglas production function** The output of an economic system Q, subject to two inputs, such as labor L and capital K, is often modeled by the Cobb-Douglas production function $Q = cL^aK^b$. When $a + b = 1$ the case is called *constant returns to scale*. Suppose $Q = 1280$, $a = \frac{1}{3}$, $b = \frac{2}{3}$, and $c = 40$.

   a. Find the rate of change of capital with respect to labor, dK/dL.
   b. Evaluate the derivative in part (a) with $L = 8$ and $K = 64$.

70. **Surface area of a cone** The lateral surface area of a cone of radius r and height h (the surface area excluding the base) is $A = \pi r\sqrt{r^2 + h^2}$.

   a. Find dr/dh for a cone with a lateral surface area of $A = 1500\pi \text{ cm}^2$.
   b. Evaluate this derivative when $r = 30$ cm and $h = 40$ cm.

71. **Volume of a spherical cap** Imagine slicing through a sphere with a plane (sheet of paper). The smaller piece produced is called a spherical cap. Its volume is $V = \pi h^2(3r - h)/3$, where r is the radius of the sphere and h is the thickness of the cap.

   a. Find dr/dh for a spherical cap with a volume of $5\pi/3 \text{ m}^3$.
   b. Evaluate this derivative when $r = 2$ m and $h = 1$ m.

72. **Volume of a torus** The volume of a torus (doughnut or bagel) with an inner radius of a and an outer radius of b is $V = \pi^2(b + a)(b - a)^2/4$.

   a. Find db/da for a torus with a volume of $64\pi^2 \text{ in}^3$.
   b. Evaluate this derivative when $a = 6$ in and $b = 10$ in.

Additional Exercises

73–75. **Orthogonal trajectories** *Two curves are* orthogonal *to each other if their tangent lines are perpendicular at each point of intersection (recall that two lines are perpendicular to each other if their slopes are negative reciprocals). A family of curves forms* **orthogonal trajectories** *with another family of curves if each curve in one family is orthogonal to each curve in the other family. For example, the parabolas $y = cx^2$ form orthogonal trajectories with the family of ellipses $x^2 + 2y^2 = k$, where c and k are constants (see figure).*

Use implicit differentiation if needed to find dy/dx for each equation of the following pairs. Use the derivatives to explain why the families of curves form orthogonal trajectories.

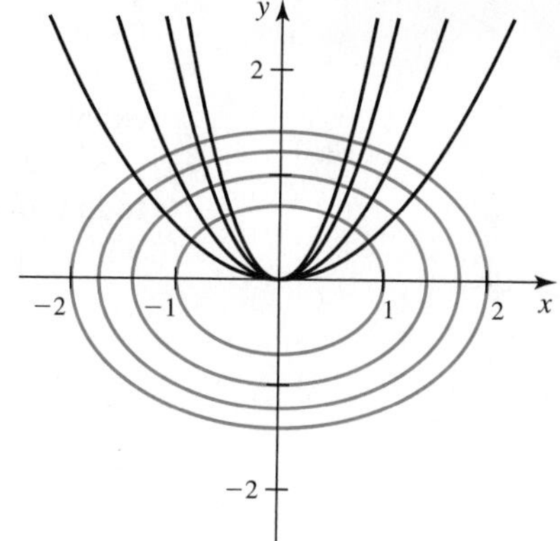

73. $y = mx$; $x^2 + y^2 = a^2$, where m and a are constants

74. $y = cx^2$; $x^2 + 2y^2 = k$, where c and k are constants

75. $xy = a$; $x^2 - y^2 = b$, where a and b are constants

QUICK CHECK ANSWERS

1. $y = \sqrt{x}$ and $y = -\sqrt{x}$ **2.** $\frac{dy}{dx} = \frac{1}{2y}$ **3.** Only the x-coordinate is needed.

3.8 Related Rates

We now return to the theme of derivatives as rates of change in problems in which the variables change with respect to *time*. The essential feature of these problems is that two or more variables, which are related in a known way, are themselves changing in time. Here are two examples illustrating this type of problem.

- An oil rig springs a leak and the oil spreads in a (roughly) circular patch around the rig. If the radius of the oil patch increases at a known rate, how fast is the area of the patch changing (Example 1)?
- Two airliners approach an airport with known speeds, one flying west and one flying north. How fast is the distance between the airliners changing (Example 2)?

In the first problem, the two related variables are the radius and the area of the oil patch. Both are changing in time. The second problem has three related variables: the positions of the two airliners and the distance between them. Again, the three variables change in time. The goal in both problems is to determine the rate of change of one of the variables at a specific moment of time—hence the name *related rates*.

We present a progression of examples in this section. After the first example, a general procedure is given for solving related-rate problems.

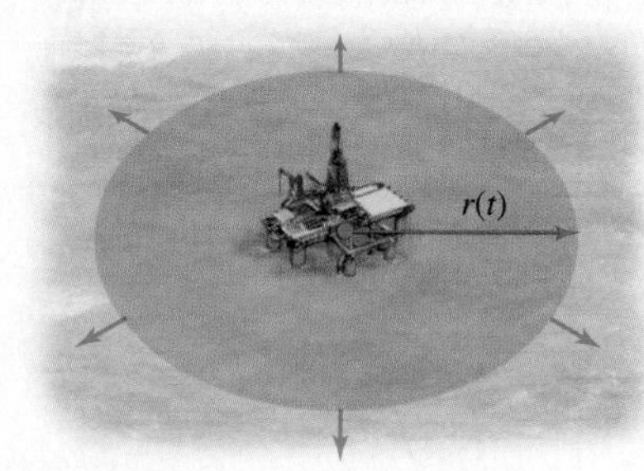

FIGURE 3.48

EXAMPLE 1 **Spreading oil** An oil rig springs a leak in calm seas and the oil spreads in a circular patch around the rig. If the radius of the oil patch increases at a rate of 30 m/hr, how fast is the area of the patch increasing when the patch has a radius of 100 m (Figure 3.48)?

SOLUTION Two variables change simultaneously: the radius of the circle and its area. The key relationship between the radius and area is $A = \pi r^2$. It helps to rewrite the basic relationship showing explicitly which quantities vary in time. In this case, we rewrite A and r as $A(t)$ and $r(t)$ to emphasize that they change with respect to t (time). The general expression relating the radius and area at any time t is $A(t) = \pi r(t)^2$.

The goal is to find the rate of change of the area of the circle, which is $A'(t)$. In order to introduce derivatives into the problem, we differentiate the area relation $A(t) = \pi r(t)^2$ with respect to t:

$$\begin{aligned} A'(t) &= \frac{d}{dt}(\pi r(t)^2) \\ &= \pi \frac{d}{dt}(r(t)^2) \\ &= \pi(2r(t))r'(t) && \text{Chain Rule} \\ &= 2\pi r(t)\,r'(t) && \text{Simplify.} \end{aligned}$$

Substituting the given values $r(t) = 100$ m and $r'(t) = 30$ m/hr, we have (including units)

➤ It is important to remember that substitution of specific values of the variables occurs *after* differentiating.

$$\begin{aligned} A'(t) &= 2\pi r(t)\,r'(t) \\ &= 2\pi(100\text{ m})\left(30\frac{\text{m}}{\text{hr}}\right) \\ &= 6000\,\pi\frac{\text{m}^2}{\text{hr}}. \end{aligned}$$

We see that the area of the oil spill increases at a rate of $6000\pi \approx 18{,}850\text{ m}^2/\text{hr}$. Including units is a simple way to check your work. In this case, we expect an answer with units of area per unit time, so m^2/hr makes sense.

Notice that the rate of change of the area depends on the radius of the spill. As the radius increases, the rate of change of the area also increases—assuming the radius increases at a constant rate. *Related Exercises 5–13* ◀

QUICK CHECK 1 In Example 1, what is the rate of change of the area when the radius is 200 m? 300 m? ◀

Using Example 1 as a template, we offer a set of guidelines for solving related-rate problems. There are always variations that arise for individual problems, but here is a general procedure.

PROCEDURE Steps for Related-Rate Problems

1. Read the problem carefully, making a sketch to organize the given information. Identify the rates that are given and the rate that is to be determined.
2. Write one or more equations that express the basic relationships among the variables.
3. Introduce rates of change by differentiating the appropriate equation(s) with respect to time t.
4. Substitute known values and solve for the desired quantity.
5. Check that units are consistent and the answer is reasonable. (For example, does it have the correct sign?)

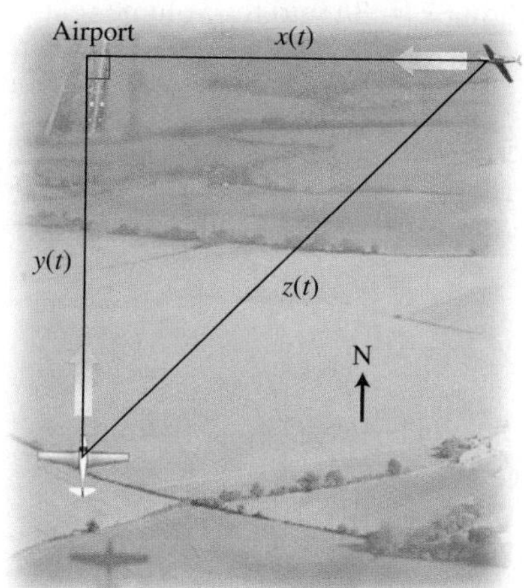

FIGURE 3.49

EXAMPLE 2 Converging airplanes Two small planes approach an airport, one flying due west at 120 mi/hr and the other flying due north at 150 mi/hr. Assuming they fly at the same constant elevation, how fast is the distance between the planes changing when the westbound plane is 180 mi from the airport and the northbound plane is 225 mi from the airport?

SOLUTION A sketch such as Figure 3.49 helps us visualize the problem and organize the information. Let $x(t)$ and $y(t)$ denote the distance from the airport to the westbound and northbound planes, respectively. The paths of the two planes form the legs of a right triangle and the distance between them, denoted $z(t)$, is the hypotenuse. By the Pythagorean theorem, $z^2 = x^2 + y^2$.

Our aim is to find dz/dt, the rate of change of the distance between the planes. We first differentiate both sides of $z^2 = x^2 + y^2$ with respect to t:

$$\frac{d}{dt}(z^2) = \frac{d}{dt}(x^2 + y^2) \Rightarrow 2z\frac{dz}{dt} = 2x\frac{dx}{dt} + 2y\frac{dy}{dt}$$

Notice that the Chain Rule is needed because x, y, and z are functions of t. Solving for dz/dt results in

$$\frac{dz}{dt} = \frac{2x\frac{dx}{dt} + 2y\frac{dy}{dt}}{2z} = \frac{x\frac{dx}{dt} + y\frac{dy}{dt}}{z}.$$

> In Example 1, we replaced A and r by $A(t)$ and $r(t)$, respectively, to remind us of the independent variable. After some practice, this replacement is not necessary.

> One could solve the equation $z^2 = x^2 + y^2$ for z, with the result
> $$z = \sqrt{x^2 + y^2},$$
> and then differentiate. However, it is much easier to differentiate implicitly as shown in the example.

This equation relates the unknown rate dz/dt to the known quantities x, y, z, dx/dt, and dy/dt. For the westbound plane, $dx/dt = -120$ mi/hr (negative because the distance is decreasing), and for the northbound plane, $dy/dt = -150$ mi/hr. At the moment of interest, when $x = 180$ mi and $y = 225$ mi, the distance between the planes is

$$z = \sqrt{x^2 + y^2} = \sqrt{180^2 + 225^2} \approx 288 \text{ mi}.$$

Substituting these values gives

$$\frac{dz}{dt} = \frac{x\frac{dx}{dt} + y\frac{dy}{dt}}{z} \approx \frac{(180\text{ mi})(-120\text{ mi/hr}) + (225\text{ mi})(-150\text{ mi/hr})}{288\text{ mi}}$$
$$\approx -192 \text{ mi/hr}.$$

Notice that $dz/dt < 0$, which means the distance between the planes is *decreasing* at a rate of about 192 mi/hr.

Related Exercises 14–20

QUICK CHECK 2 Assuming the same plane speeds as in Example 2, how fast is the distance between the planes changing if $x = 60$ mi and $y = 75$ mi?

EXAMPLE 3 **Sandpile** Sand falls from an overhead bin, accumulating in a conical pile with a radius that is always three times its height. If the sand falls from the bin at a rate of 120 ft³/min, how fast is the height of the sandpile changing when the pile is 10 ft high?

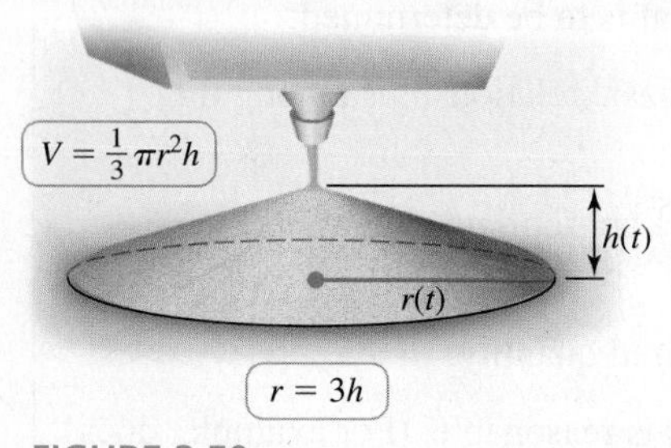

FIGURE 3.50

SOLUTION A sketch of the problem (Figure 3.50) shows the three relevant variables: the volume V, the radius r, and the height h of the sandpile. The aim is to find the rate of change of the height dh/dt at the instant that $h = 10$ ft. The basic relationship among the variables is the formula for the volume of a cone, $V = \frac{1}{3}\pi r^2 h$. We now use the given fact that the radius is always three times the height. Substituting $r = 3h$ into the volume relationship gives V in terms of h:

$$V = \frac{1}{3}\pi r^2 h = \frac{1}{3}\pi(3h)^2 h = 3\pi h^3$$

Rates of change are introduced by differentiating both sides of $V = 3\pi h^3$ with respect to t. Using the Chain Rule, we have

$$\frac{dV}{dt} = 9\pi h^2 \frac{dh}{dt}.$$

Now we find dh/dt at the instant that $h = 10$ ft, given that $dV/dt = 120\text{ ft}^3/\text{min}$. Solving for dh/dt and substituting these values, we have

$$\frac{dh}{dt} = \frac{dV/dt}{9\pi h^2} \qquad \text{Solve for } \frac{dh}{dt}.$$

$$= \frac{120\text{ ft}^3/\text{min}}{9\pi(10\text{ ft})^2} \approx 0.042\,\frac{\text{ft}}{\text{min}}. \qquad \text{Substitute for } \frac{dV}{dt} \text{ and } h.$$

At the instant that the sandpile is 10 ft high, the height is changing at a rate of 0.042 ft/min, or about 30 in/hr. Notice how the units work out consistently. *Related Exercises 21–25* ◄

QUICK CHECK 3 In Example 3, what is the rate of change of the height when $h = 2$ ft? Does the rate of change of the height increase or decrease with increasing height? ◄

EXAMPLE 4 **Observing a launch** An observer stands 200 m from the launch site of a hot-air balloon. The balloon rises vertically at a constant rate of 4 m/s. How fast is the angle of elevation of the balloon increasing 30 s after the launch? (The angle of elevation is the angle between the ground and the observer's line of sight to the balloon.)

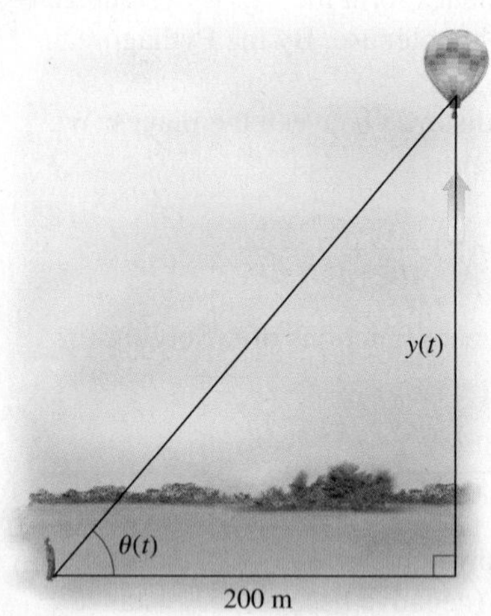

FIGURE 3.51

SOLUTION Figure 3.51 shows the geometry of the launch. As the balloon rises, its distance from the ground y and its angle of elevation θ change simultaneously. An equation expressing the relationship between these variables is $\tan\theta = y/200$. In order to find $d\theta/dt$, we differentiate both sides of this relationship using the Chain Rule:

$$\sec^2\theta \frac{d\theta}{dt} = \frac{1}{200}\frac{dy}{dt}$$

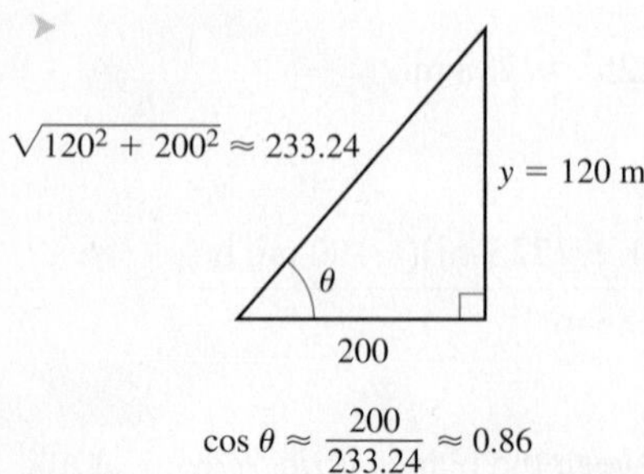

Next we solve for $\dfrac{d\theta}{dt}$:

$$\frac{d\theta}{dt} = \frac{dy/dt}{200\sec^2\theta} = \frac{(dy/dt)\cdot\cos^2\theta}{200}$$

The rate of change of the angle of elevation depends on the angle of elevation and the speed of the balloon. Thirty seconds after the launch, the balloon has risen $y = (4\text{ m/s})(30\text{ s}) = 120$ m.

> The solution to Example 4 is reported in units of rad/s. Where did radians come from? Because a radian has no physical dimensions (it is the ratio of an arc length and a radius), no unit appears. We write rad/s for clarity because $d\theta/dt$ is the rate of change of an angle.

To complete the problem, we need the value of $\cos\theta$. Note that when $y = 120$ m, the distance between the observer and the balloon is

$$d = \sqrt{120^2 + 200^2} \approx 233.24 \text{ m}.$$

Therefore, $\cos\theta \approx 200/233.24 \approx 0.86$ (see margin figure), and the rate of change of the angle of elevation is

$$\frac{d\theta}{dt} = \frac{(dy/dt)\cdot\cos^2\theta}{200} \approx \frac{(4 \text{ m/s})(0.86^2)}{200 \text{ m}} = 0.015 \text{ rad/s}.$$

> Recall that to convert radians to degrees, we use
>
> $$\text{degrees} = \frac{180}{\pi}\cdot\text{radians}.$$

At this instant, the balloon is rising at an angular rate of 0.015 rad/s, or slightly less than 1°/s, as seen by the observer. *Related Exercises 26–31*

QUICK CHECK 4 In Example 4, notice that as the balloon rises (as θ increases), the rate of change of the angle of elevation decreases to zero. When does the maximum value of $\theta'(t)$ occur and what is it?

SECTION 3.8 EXERCISES

Review Questions

1. Give an example in which one dimension of a geometric figure changes and produces a corresponding change in the area or volume of the figure.

2. Explain how implicit differentiation can simplify the work in a related-rates problem.

3. If two opposite sides of a rectangle increase in length, how must the other two opposite sides change if the area of the rectangle is to remain constant?

4. Explain why the term *related rates* describes the problems of this section.

Basic Skills

5. **Expanding square** The sides of a square increase in length at a rate of 2 m/s.
   a. At what rate is the area of the square changing when the sides are 10 m long?
   b. At what rate is the area of the square changing when the sides are 20 m long?
   c. Draw a graph of how the rate of change of the area varies with the side length.

6. **Expanding cube** The edges of a cube increase at a rate of 2 cm/s. How fast is the volume changing when the length of each edge is 50 cm?

7. **Shrinking circle** A circle has an initial radius of 50 ft when the radius begins decreasing at a rate of 2 ft/min. What is the rate of change of the area at the instant the radius is 10 ft?

8. **Shrinking cube** The volume of a cube decreases at a rate of 0.5 ft^3/min. What is the rate of change of the side length when the side lengths are 12 ft?

9. **Balloons** A spherical balloon is inflated and its volume increases at a rate of 15 in^3/min. What is the rate of change of its radius when the radius is 10 in?

10. **Piston compression** A piston is seated at the top of a cylindrical chamber with radius 5 cm when it starts moving into the chamber at a constant speed of 3 cm/s (see figure). What is the rate of change of the volume of the cylinder when the piston is 2 cm from the base of the chamber?

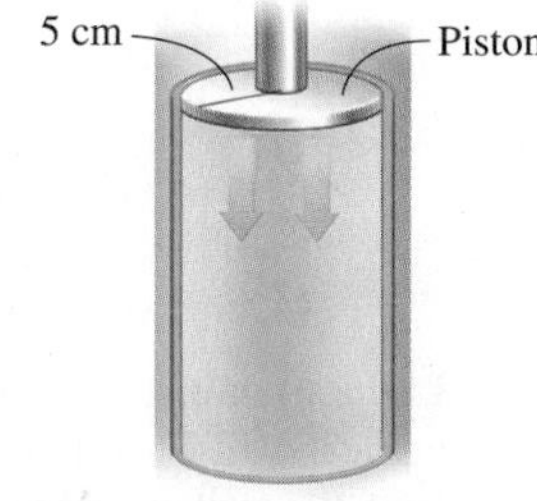

11. **Melting snowball** A spherical snowball melts at a rate proportional to its surface area. Show that the rate of change of the radius is constant. (*Hint:* Surface area $= 4\pi r^2$.)

12. **Expanding rectangle** A rectangle initially has dimensions 2 cm by 4 cm. All sides begin increasing in length at a rate of 1 cm/s. At what rate is the area of the rectangle increasing after 20 s?

13. **Filling a pool** A swimming pool is 50 m long and 20 m wide. Its depth decreases linearly along the length from 3 m to 1 m (see figure). It is initially empty and is filled at a rate of 1 m^3/min. How fast is the water level rising 250 min after the filling begins? How long will it take to fill the pool?

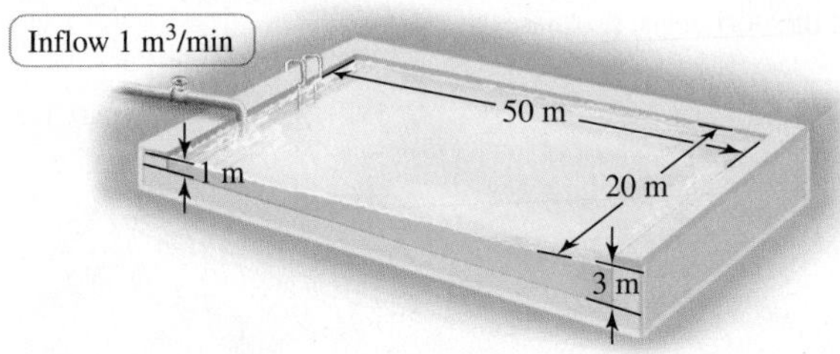

14. **Altitude of a jet** A jet ascends at a 10° angle from the horizontal with an airspeed of 550 mi/hr (its speed along its line of flight is 550 mi/hr). How fast is the altitude of the jet increasing? If the sun is directly overhead, how fast is the shadow of the jet moving on the ground?

15. **Rate of dive of a submarine** A surface ship is moving (horizontally) in a straight line at 10 km/hr. At the same time, an enemy submarine maintains a position directly below the ship while diving at an angle that is 20° below the horizontal. How fast is the submarine's altitude decreasing?

16. **Divergent paths** Two boats leave a port at the same time, one traveling west at 20 mi/hr and the other traveling southwest at 15 mi/hr. At what rate is the distance between them changing 30 min after they leave the port?

17. **Ladder against the wall** A 13-ft ladder is leaning against a vertical wall (see figure) when Jack begins pulling the foot of the ladder away from the wall at a rate of 0.5 ft/s. How fast is the top of the ladder sliding down the wall when the foot of the ladder is 5 ft from the wall?

18. **Ladder against the wall again** A 12-ft ladder is leaning against a vertical wall when Jack begins pulling the foot of the ladder away from the wall at a rate of 0.2 ft/s. What is the configuration of the ladder at the instant that the vertical speed of the top of the ladder equals the horizontal speed of the foot of the ladder?

19. **Moving shadow** A 5-ft-tall woman walks at 8 ft/s toward a street light that is 20 ft above the ground. What is the rate of change of the length of her shadow when she is 15 ft from the street light? At what rate is the tip of her shadow moving?

20. **Baseball runners** Runners stand at first and second base in a baseball game. At the moment a ball is hit, the runner at first base runs to second base at 18 ft/s; simultaneously the runner on second runs to third base at 20 ft/s. How fast is the distance between the runners changing 1 s after the ball is hit (see figure)? (*Hint:* The distance between consecutive bases is 90 ft and the bases lie at the corners of a square.)

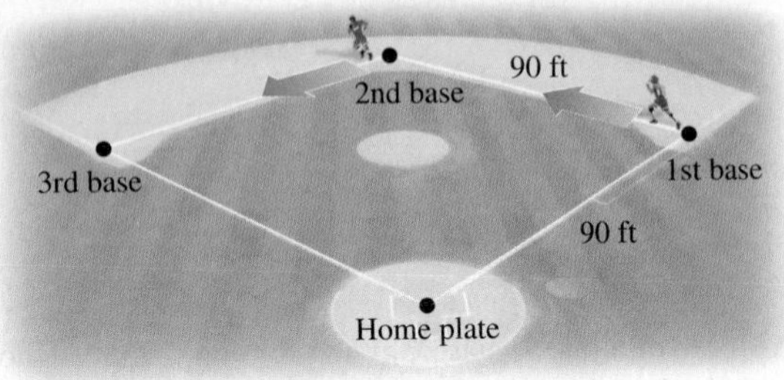

21. **Growing sandpile** Sand falls from an overhead bin and accumulates in a conical pile with a radius that is always three times its height. Suppose the height of the pile increases at a rate of 2 cm/s when the pile is 12 cm high. At what rate is the sand leaving the bin at that instant?

22. **Drinking a soda** At what rate is soda being sucked out of a cylindrical glass that is 6 in tall and has a radius of 2 in? The depth of the soda decreases at a constant rate of 0.25 in/s.

23. **Draining a tank** An inverted conical water tank with a height of 12 ft and a radius of 6 ft is drained through a hole in the vertex at a rate of 2 ft^3/s (see figure). What is the rate of change of the water depth when the water depth is 3 ft? (*Hint:* Use similar triangles.)

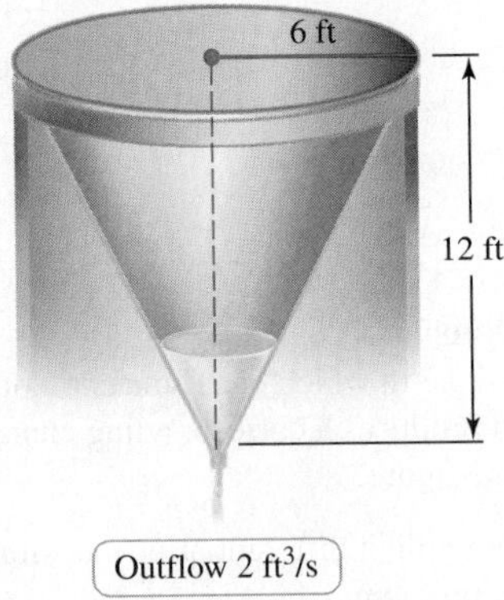

24. **Filling a hemispherical tank** A hemispherical tank with a radius of 10 m is filled from an inflow pipe at a rate of 3 m^3/min (see figure). (*Hint:* The volume of a cap of thickness h sliced from a sphere of radius r is $\pi h^2(3r - h)/3$.)
   a. How fast is the water level rising when the water level is 5 m from the bottom of the tank?
   b. What is the rate of change of the surface area of the water when the water is 5 m deep?

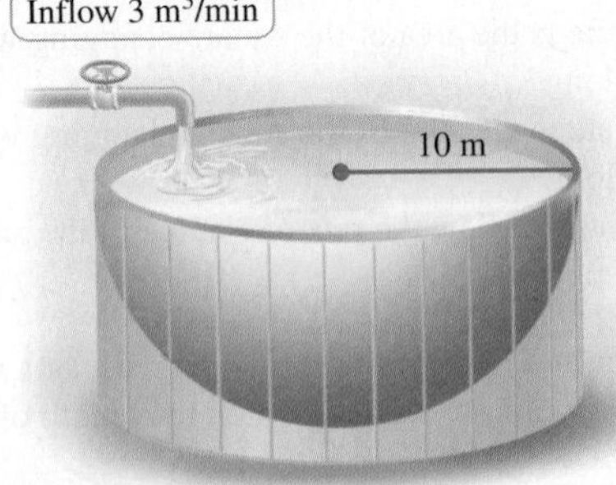

25. **Draining a trough** A trough is shaped like a half cylinder with length 5 m and radius 1 m. The trough is full of water when a valve is opened and water flows out of the bottom of the trough at a rate of 1.5 m^3/hr (see figure). (*Hint:* The area of a sector of a circle of radius r subtended by an angle θ is $r^2\theta/2$.)

a. How fast is the water level changing when the water level is 0.5 m from the bottom of the trough?

b. What is the rate of change of the surface area of the water when the water is 0.5 m deep?

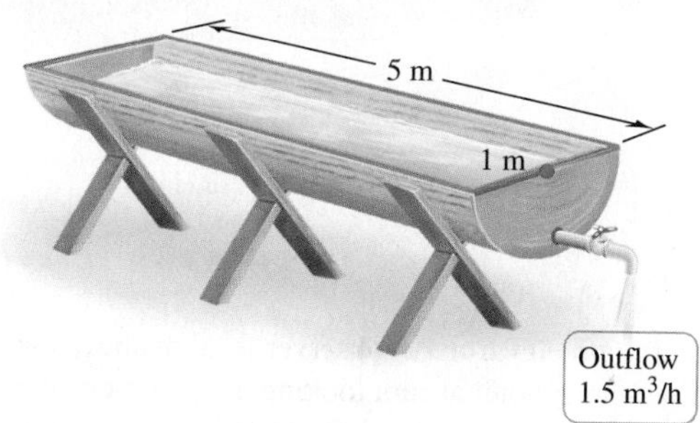

26. Observing a launch An observer stands 300 ft from the launch site of a hot-air balloon. The balloon is launched vertically and maintains a constant upward velocity of 20 ft/s. What is the rate of change of the angle of elevation of the balloon when it is 400 ft from the ground? The angle of elevation is the angle θ between the observer's line of sight to the balloon and the ground.

27. Another balloon story A hot-air balloon is 150 ft above the ground when a motorcycle passes directly beneath it (traveling in a straight line on a horizontal road) going 40 mi/hr (58.67 ft/s). If the balloon is rising vertically at a rate of 10 ft/s, what is the rate of change of the distance between the motorcycle and the balloon 10 s later?

28. Fishing story A fly fisherman hooks a trout and begins turning his circular reel at 1.5 rev/s. If the radius of the reel (and the fishing line on it) is 2 in, then how fast is he reeling in his fishing line?

29. Another fishing story A fisherman hooks a trout and reels in his line at 4 in/s. Assume the tip of the fishing rod is 12 ft above the water directly above the fisherman and the fish is pulled horizontally directly towards the fisherman (see figure). Find the horizontal speed of the fish when it is 20 ft from the fisherman.

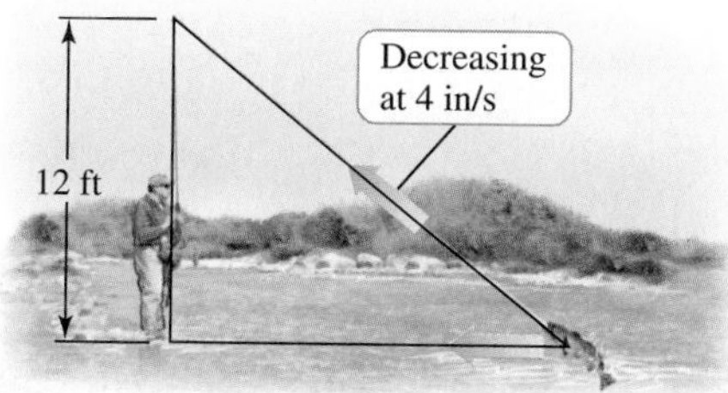

30. Flying a kite Once Kate's kite reaches a height of 50 ft (above her hands), it rises no higher but drifts due east in a wind blowing at 5 ft/s. How fast is the string running through Kate's hands at the moment that she has released 120 ft of string?

31. Rope on a boat A rope passing through a capstan on a dock is attached to a boat offshore. The rope is pulled in at a constant rate of 3 ft/s and the capstan is 5 ft vertically above the water. How fast is the boat traveling when it is 10 ft from the dock?

Further Explorations

32. Parabolic motion An arrow is shot into the air and moves along the parabolic path $y = x(50 - x)$ (see figure). The horizontal component of velocity is always 30 ft/s. What is the vertical component of velocity when (i) $x = 10$ and (ii) $x = 40$?

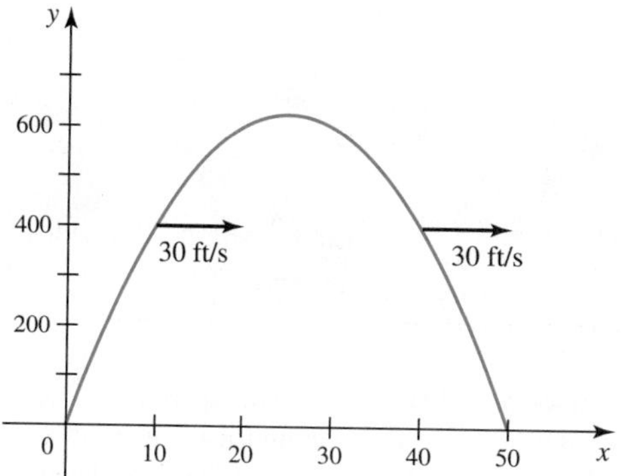

33. Time-lagged flights An airliner passes over an airport at noon traveling 500 mi/hr due west. At 1:00 P.M., another airliner passes over the same airport at the same elevation traveling due north at 550 mi/hr. Assuming both airliners maintain their (equal) elevations, how fast is the distance between them changing at 2:30 P.M.?

34. Disappearing triangle An equilateral triangle initially has sides of length 20 ft when each vertex moves toward the midpoint of the opposite side at a rate of 1.5 ft/min. Assuming the triangle remains equilateral, what is the rate of change of the area of the triangle at the instant the triangle disappears?

35. Clock hands The hands of the clock in the tower of the Houses of Parliament in London are approximately 3 m and 2.5 m in length. How fast is the distance between the tips of the hands changing at 9:00? (*Hint:* Use the Law of Cosines.)

36. Filling two pools Two cylindrical swimming pools are being filled simultaneously at the same rate (in m^3/min; see figure). The smaller pool has a radius of 5 m, and the water level rises at a rate of 0.5 m/min. The larger pool has a radius of 8 m. How fast is the water level rising in the larger pool?

37. Filming a race A camera is set up at the starting line of a drag race 50 ft from a dragster at the starting line (camera 1 in the figure). Two seconds after the start of the race, the dragster has traveled 100 ft and the camera is turning at 0.75 rad/s while filming the dragster.

a. What is the speed of the dragster at this time?
b. A second camera (camera 2 in the figure) filming the dragster is located on the starting line 100 ft away from the dragster at the start of the race. How fast is this camera turning 2 s after the start of the race?

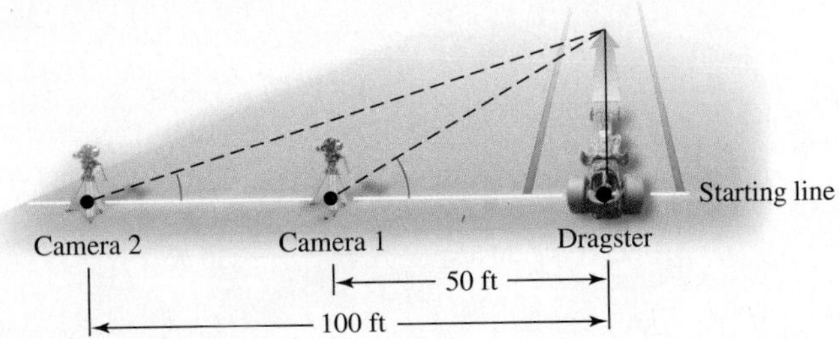

38. **Two tanks** A conical tank with an upper radius of 4 m and a height of 5 m drains into a cylindrical tank with a radius of 4 m and a height of 5 m (see figure). If the water level in the conical tank drops at a rate of 0.5 m/min, at what rate does the water level in the cylindrical tank rise when the water level in the conical tank is 3 m? 1 m?

39. **Oblique tracking** A port and a radar station are 2 mi apart on a straight shore running east and west. A ship leaves the port at noon traveling northeast at a rate of 15 mi/hr. If the ship maintains its speed and course, what is the rate of change of the tracking angle θ between the shore and the line between the radar station and the ship at 12:30 P.M.? (*Hint:* Use the Law of Sines.)

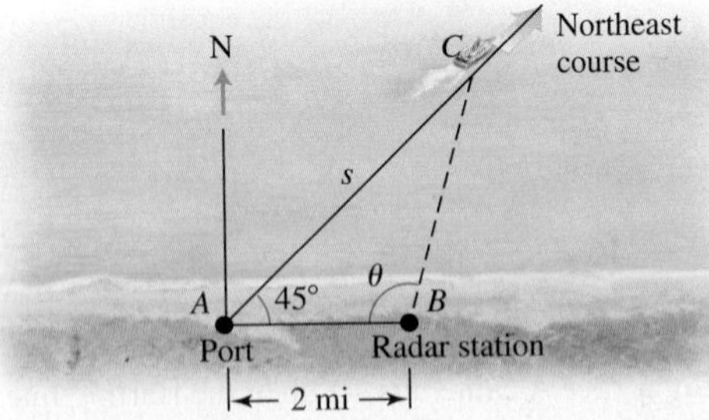

40. **Oblique tracking** A ship leaves port traveling southwest at a rate of 12 mi/hr. At noon, the ship reaches its closest approach to a radar station, which is on the shore 1.5 mi from the port. If the ship maintains its speed and course, what is the rate of change of the tracking angle θ between the radar station and the ship at 1:30 P.M. (see figure)? (*Hint:* Use the Law of Sines.)

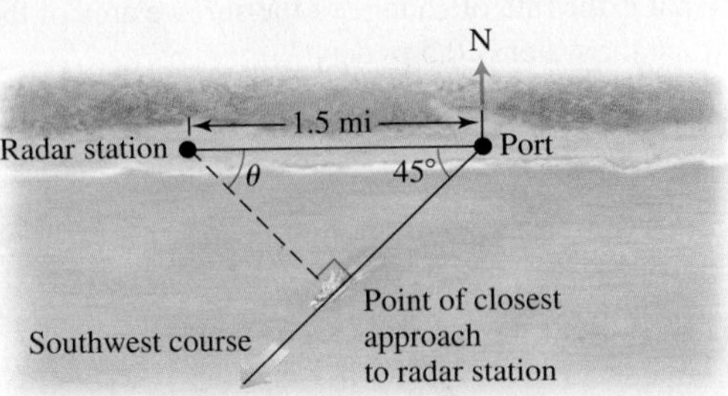

41. **Watching an elevator** An observer is 20 m above the ground floor of a large hotel atrium looking at a glass-enclosed elevator shaft that is 20 m horizontally from the observer (see figure). The angle of elevation of the elevator is the angle that the observer's line of sight makes with the horizontal (it may be positive or negative). Assuming that the elevator rises at a rate of 5 m/s, what is the rate of change of the angle of elevation when the elevator is 10 m above the ground? When the elevator is 40 m above the ground?

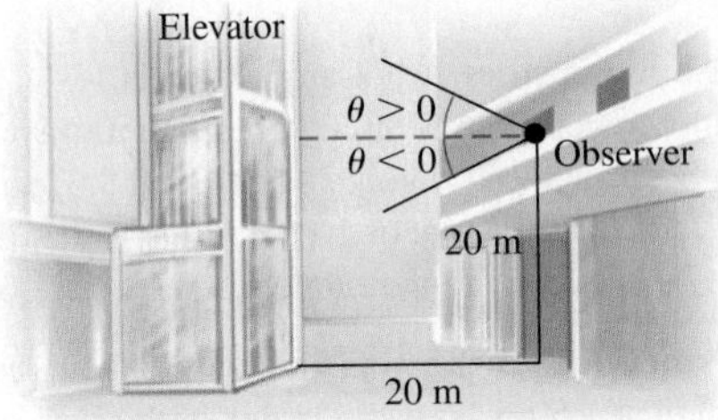

42. **A lighthouse problem** A lighthouse stands 500 m off of a straight shore, the focused beam of its light revolving four times each minute. As shown in the figure, P is the point on shore closest to the lighthouse and Q is a point on the shore 200 m from P. What is the speed of the beam along the shore when it strikes the point Q? Describe how the speed of the beam along the shore varies with the distance between P and Q. Neglect the height of the lighthouse.

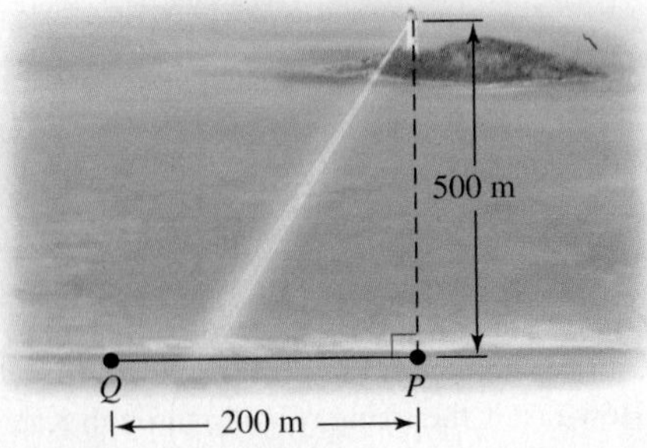

43. **Navigation** A boat leaves a port traveling due east at 12 mi/hr. At the same time, another boat leaves the same port traveling northeast at 15 mi/hr. The angle θ of the line between the boats is measured relative to due north (see figure). What is the rate

of change of this angle 30 min after the boats leave the port? 2 hr after the boats leave the port?

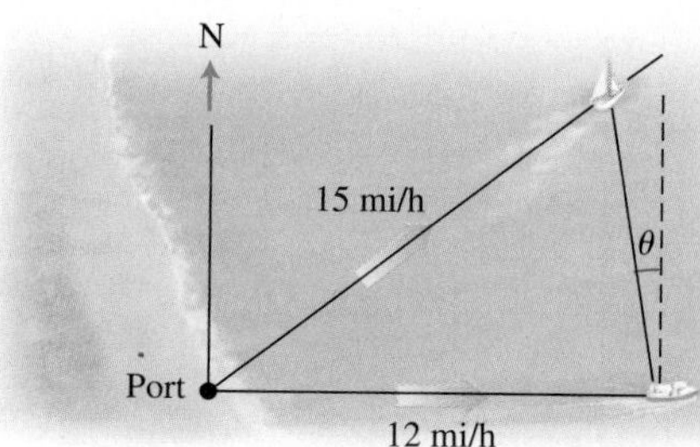

44. Watching a Ferris wheel An observer stands 20 m from the bottom of a 10-m-tall Ferris wheel on a line that is perpendicular to the face of the Ferris wheel. The wheel revolves at a rate of π rad/min and the observer's line of sight with a specific seat on the wheel makes an angle θ with the ground (see figure). Forty seconds after that seat leaves the lowest point on the wheel, what is the rate of change of θ? Assume the observer's eyes are level with the bottom of the wheel.

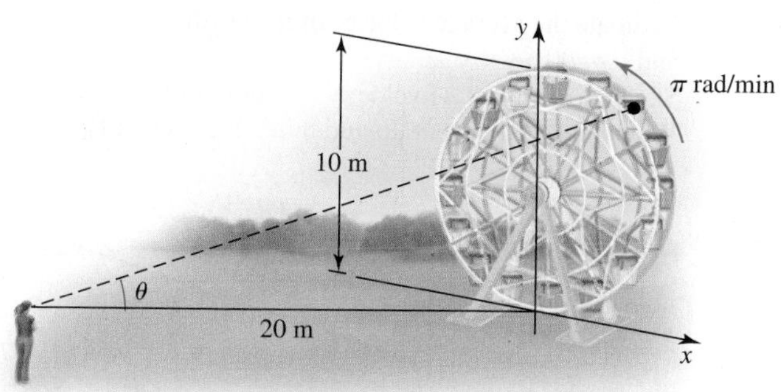

45. Viewing angle The bottom of a large theater screen is 3 ft above your eye level and the top of the screen is 10 ft above your eye level. Assume you walk away from the screen (perpendicular to the screen) at a rate of 3 ft/s while looking at the screen. What is the rate of change of the viewing angle θ when you are 30 ft from the wall on which the screen hangs, assuming the floor is flat (see figure)?

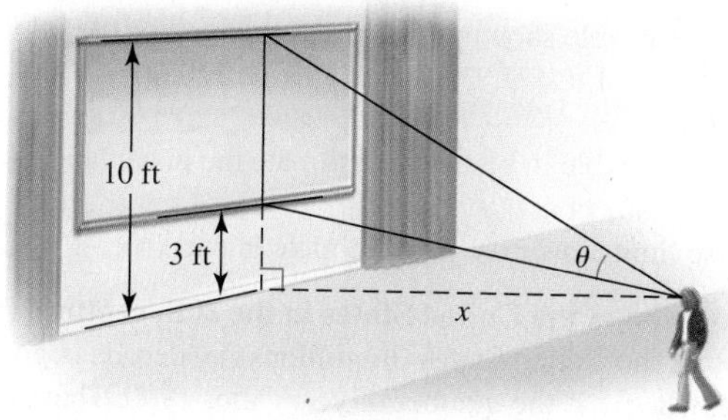

46. Searchlight—wide beam A revolving searchlight, 100 m from the nearest point on the center line of a straight highway, casts a horizontal beam along the highway (see figure). The beam leaves the spotlight at an angle of $\pi/16$ rad and revolves at a rate of $\pi/6$ rad/s. Let w be the width of the beam as it sweeps along the highway and θ be the angle that the center of the beam makes with the perpendicular to the highway. What is the rate of change of w when $\theta = \pi/3$? Neglect the height of the lighthouse.

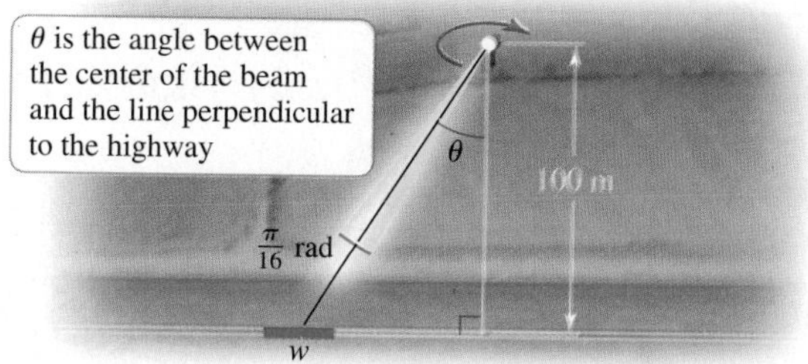

QUICK CHECK ANSWERS

1. $12{,}000\pi\ \text{m}^2/\text{hr}, 18{,}000\pi\ \text{m}^2/\text{hr}$ **2.** -192 mi/hr **3.** 1.1 ft/min; decreases with height **4.** $t = 0, \theta = 0, \theta'(0) = 0.02$ rad/s

CHAPTER 3 REVIEW EXERCISES

1. Explain why or why not Determine whether the following statements are true and give an explanation or counterexample.

a. The function $f(x) = |2x + 1|$ is continuous for all x; therefore, it is differentiable for all x.

b. If $\dfrac{d}{dx}(f(x)) = \dfrac{d}{dx}(g(x))$, then $f = g$.

c. For any function f, $\dfrac{d}{dx}|f(x)| = |f'(x)|$.

d. The value of $f'(a)$ fails to exist only if the curve $y = f(x)$ has a vertical tangent line at $x = a$.

e. An object can have negative acceleration and increasing speed.

T 2–5. Tangent lines

a. *Use either definition of the derivative to determine the slope of the curve $y = f(x)$ at the given point P.*

b. *Find an equation of the line tangent to the curve $y = f(x)$ at P; then, graph the curve and the tangent line.*

2. $f(x) = 4x^2 - 7x + 5;\ P(2, 7)$

3. $f(x) = 5x^3 + x;\ P(1, 6)$

4. $y = f(x) = \dfrac{x + 3}{2x + 1};\ P(0, 3)$

5. $f(x) = \dfrac{1}{2\sqrt{3x + 1}};\ P\left(0, \dfrac{1}{2}\right)$

6. Calculating average and instantaneous velocities Suppose the height s of an object (in meters) above the ground after t seconds is approximated by the function $s = -4.9t^2 + 25t + 1$.

a. Make a table showing the average velocities of the object from time $t = 1$ to $t = 1 + h$ for $h = 0.01, 0.001, 0.0001$, and 0.00001.

b. Use the table in part (a) to estimate the instantaneous velocity of the object at $t = 1$ s.

c. Use limits to verify your estimate in part (b).

7. Population of the United States in the 20th century The population of the United States (in millions) by decade is given in the table, where t is the number of years after 1900. These data are plotted and fitted with a smooth curve $y = p(t)$ in the figure.

a. Compute the average rate of population growth from 1950 to 1960.

b. Explain why the average rate of growth from 1950 to 1960 is a good approximation to the (instantaneous) rate of growth in 1955.

c. Estimate the instantaneous rate of growth in 1985.

Year	1900	1910	1920	1930	1940	1950
t	0	10	20	30	40	50
$p(t)$	76.21	92.23	106.02	123.2	132.16	152.32

Year	1960	1970	1980	1990	2000	2010
t	60	70	80	90	100	110
$p(t)$	179.32	203.30	226.54	248.71	281.42	308.94

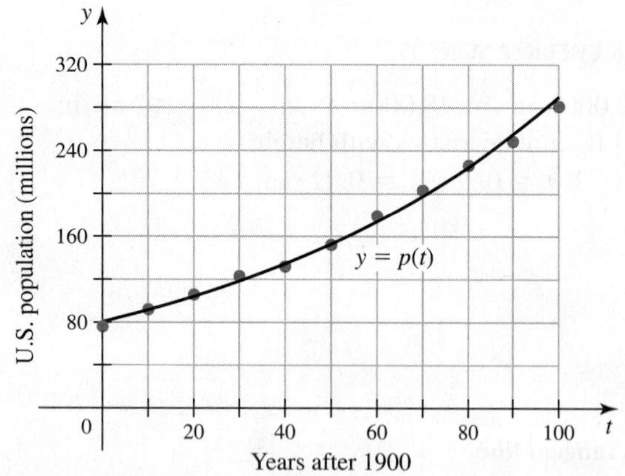

8. Growth rate of bacteria Suppose the following graph represents the number of bacteria in a culture t hours after the start of an experiment.

a. At approximately what time is the instantaneous growth rate the greatest? Estimate the growth rate at this time.

b. At approximately what time in the interval $0 \le t \le 36$ is the instantaneous growth rate the least? Estimate the instantaneous growth rate at this time.

c. What is the average growth rate over the interval $0 \le t \le 36$?

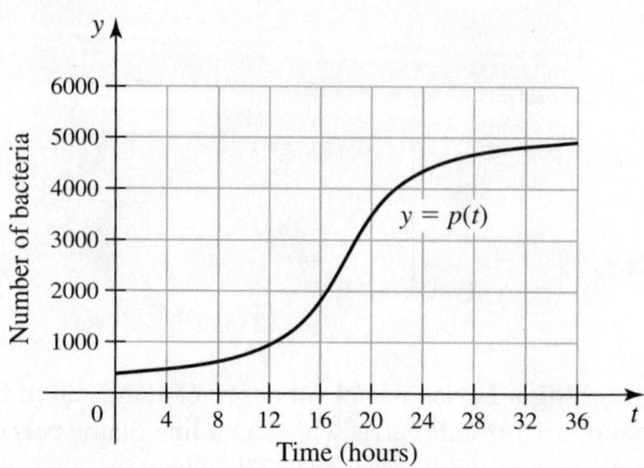

9. Velocity of a skydiver Assume the graph represents the distance (in meters) fallen by a skydiver t seconds after jumping out of a plane.

a. Estimate the velocity of the skydiver at $t = 15$.

b. Estimate the velocity of the skydiver at $t = 70$.

c. Estimate the average velocity of the skydiver between $t = 20$ and $t = 90$.

d. Sketch a graph of the velocity function for $0 \le t \le 120$.

e. What significant event do you think occurred at $t = 30$?

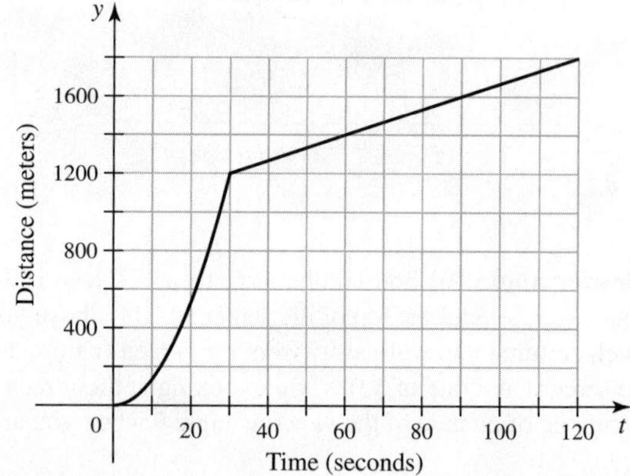

10–11. Using the definition of the derivative *Use the limit definition of the derivative to do the following.*

10. Verify that $f'(x) = 4x - 3$ if $f(x) = 2x^2 - 3x + 1$.

11. Verify that $g'(x) = \dfrac{1}{\sqrt{2x - 3}}$ if $g(x) = \sqrt{2x - 3}$.

12. Sketching a derivative graph Sketch a graph of f' for the function f shown in the figure.

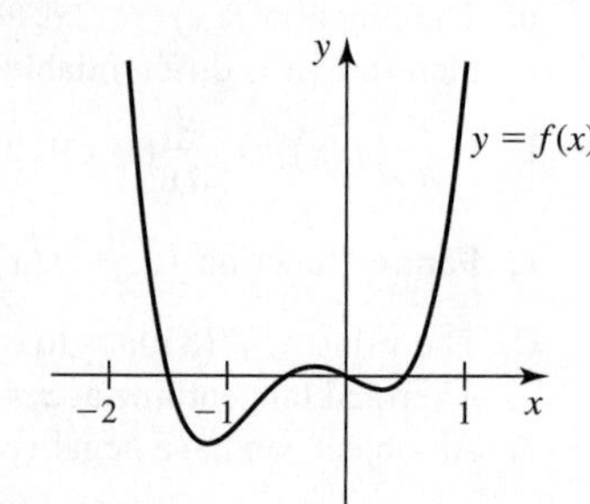

13. Sketching a derivative graph Sketch a graph of g' for the function g shown in the figure.

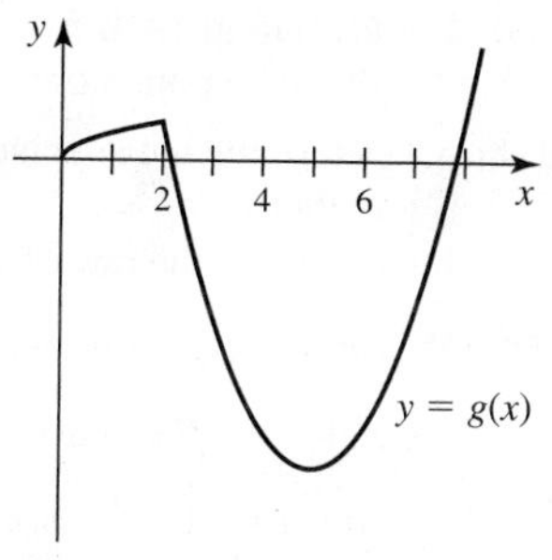

14. Matching functions and derivatives Match functions a–d with derivatives A–D.

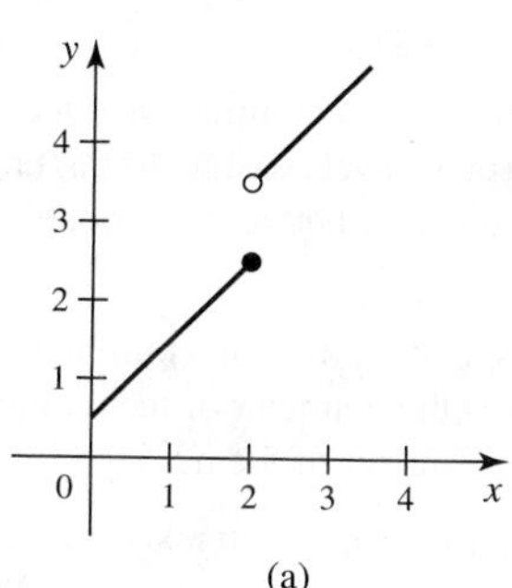
(a)

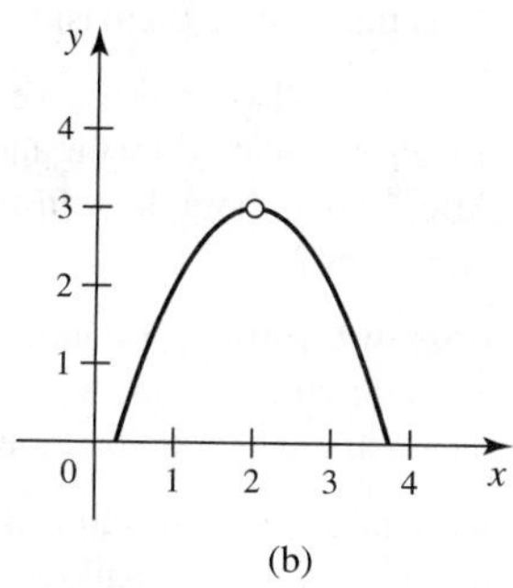
(b)

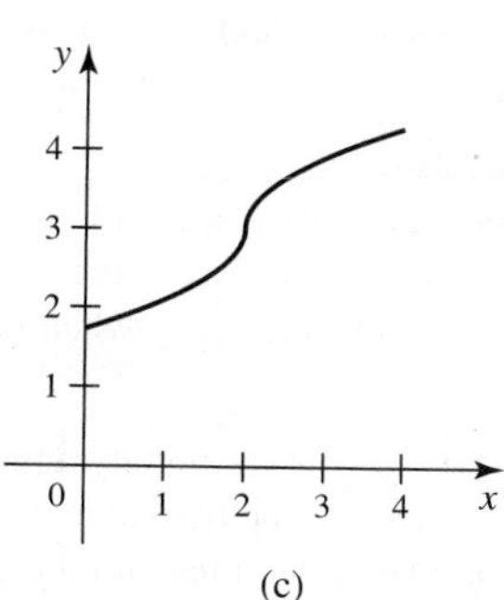
(c)

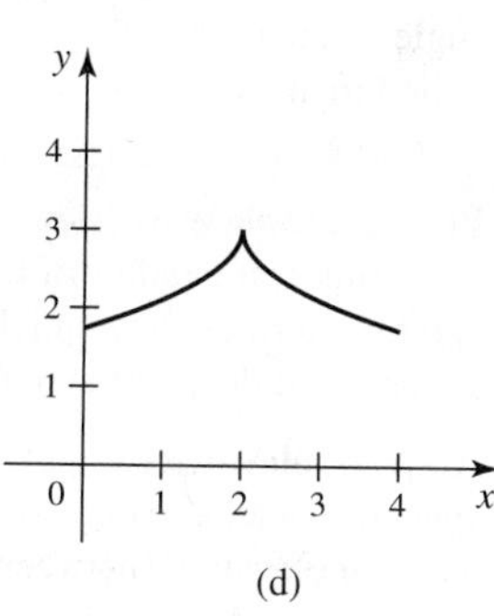
(d)

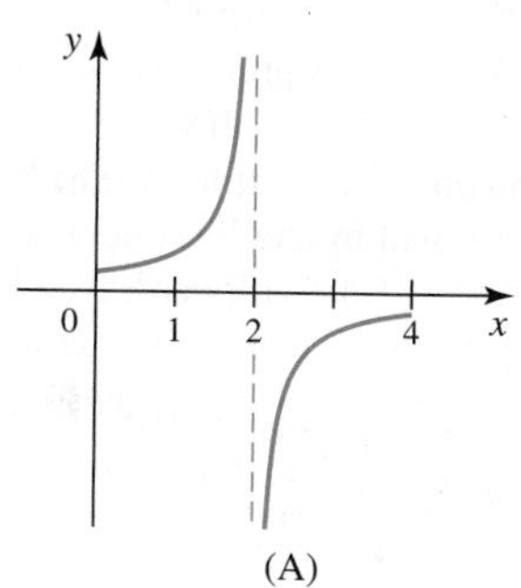
(A)

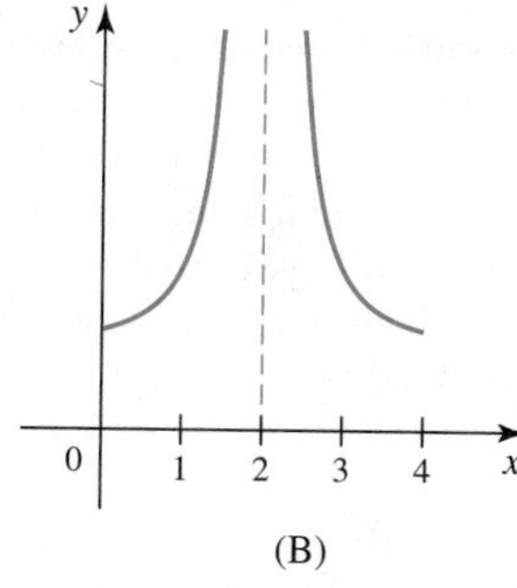
(B)

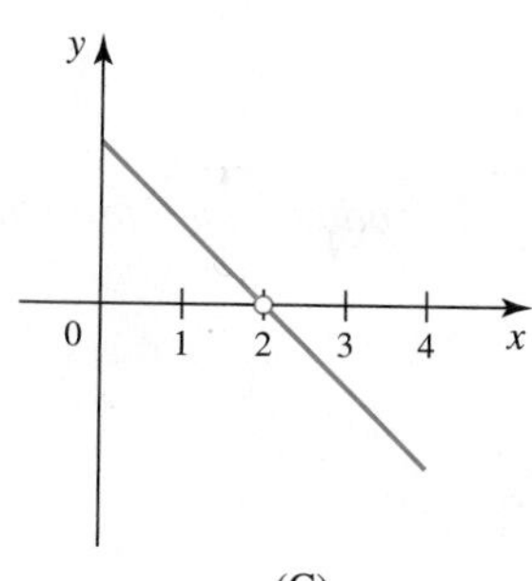
(C)

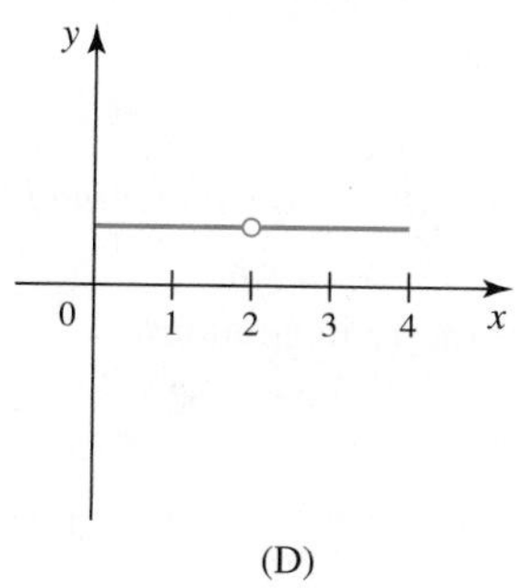
(D)

15–36. Evaluating derivatives *Evaluate and simplify the following derivatives.*

15. $\frac{d}{dx}\left(\frac{2}{3}x^3 + \pi x^2 + 7x + 1\right)$

16. $\frac{d}{dx}\left(2x\sqrt{x^2 - 2x + 2}\right)$

17. $\frac{d}{dt}(5t^2 \sin t)$

18. $\frac{d}{dx}(5x + \sin^3 x + \sin x^3)$

19. $\frac{d}{d\theta}(4\tan(\theta^2 + 3\theta + 2))$

20. $\frac{d}{dx}(\csc^5 3x)$

21. $\frac{d}{du}\left(\frac{4u^2 + u}{8u + 1}\right)$

22. $\frac{d}{dt}\left(\frac{3t^2 - 1}{3t^2 + 1}\right)^{-3}$

23. $\frac{d}{d\theta}(\tan(\sin\theta))$

24. $\frac{d}{dv}\left(\frac{v}{3v^2 + 2v + 1}\right)^{1/3}$

25. $\frac{d}{dx}(2x(\sin x)\sqrt{3x - 1})$

26. $\frac{d}{dx}\left(\frac{\sin^2 x}{\cos^3 4x}\right)$

27–29. Implicit differentiation *Calculate $y'(x)$ for the following relations.*

27. $y = \frac{\cos y}{1 + \sin x}$

28. $\sin x \cos(y - 1) = \frac{1}{2}$

29. $y\sqrt{x^2 + y^2} = 15$

30. Quadratic functions

a. Show that if $(a, f(a))$ is any point on the graph of $f(x) = x^2$, then the slope of the tangent line at that point is $2a$.

b. Show that if $(a, f(a))$ is any point on the graph of $f(x) = bx^2 + cx + d$, then the slope of the tangent line at that point is $2ab + c$.

31–34. Tangent lines *Find an equation of the line tangent to the following curves at the given point.*

31. $y = 3x^3 + \sin x$; $(0, 0)$

32. $y = \frac{4x}{x^2 + 3}$; $(3, 1)$

33. $y + \sqrt{xy} = 6$; $(1, 4)$

34. $x^2y + y^3 = 75$; $(4, 3)$

35. Horizontal tangent line For what value(s) of x is the line tangent to the curve $y = x\sqrt{6 - x}$ horizontal?

36. A parabola property Let $f(x) = x^2$.

a. Show that $\frac{f(x) - f(y)}{x - y} = f'\left(\frac{x + y}{2}\right)$ for all $x \neq y$.

b. Is this property true for $f(x) = ax^2$, where a is a nonzero real number?

c. Give a geometrical interpretation of this property.

d. Is this property true for $f(x) = ax^3$?

37–38. Higher-order derivatives *Find y', y'', and y''' for the following functions.*

37. $y = \sin\sqrt{x}$

38. $y = \sqrt{x + 2}\,(x - 3)$

39–42. Derivative formulas *Evaluate the following derivatives. Express your answers in terms of f, g, f′ and g′.*

39. $\dfrac{d}{dx}(x^2 f(x))$

40. $\dfrac{d}{dx}\sqrt{\dfrac{f(x)}{g(x)}}$

41. $\dfrac{d}{dx}\left(\dfrac{x \cdot f(x)}{g(x)}\right)$

42. $\dfrac{d}{dx}f(\sqrt{g(x)})$

43. Finding derivatives from a table Find the values of the following derivatives using the table.

x	1	3	5	7	9
$f(x)$	3	1	9	7	5
$f'(x)$	7	9	5	1	3
$g(x)$	9	7	5	3	1
$g'(x)$	5	9	3	1	7

a. $\dfrac{d}{dx}[f(x) + 2g(x)]\Big|_{x=3}$ **b.** $\dfrac{d}{dx}\left[\dfrac{x \cdot f(x)}{g(x)}\right]\Bigg|_{x=1}$ **c.** $\dfrac{d}{dx}f[g(x^2)]\Big|_{x=3}$

44–45. Limits *The following limits represent the derivative of a function f at a point a. Find a possible f and a, and then evaluate the limit.*

44. $\displaystyle\lim_{h \to 0} \frac{\sin^2\left(\frac{\pi}{4} + h\right) - \frac{1}{2}}{h}$

45. $\displaystyle\lim_{x \to 5} \frac{\tan\left(\pi\sqrt{3x - 11}\right)}{x - 5}$

T **46. Velocity of a rocket** The height in feet of a rocket above the ground is given by $s(t) = \dfrac{200t^2}{t^2 + 1}$, for $t \geq 0$.

a. Graph the height function and describe the motion of the rocket.
b. Find the velocity of the rocket, $v(t) = s'(t)$.
c. Graph the velocity function and determine the approximate time at which the velocity is a maximum.

47. Marginal and average cost Suppose the cost of producing x lawnmowers is $C(x) = -0.02x^2 + 400x + 5000$.

a. Determine the average and marginal costs for $x = 3000$ lawnmowers.
b. Interpret the meaning of your results in part (a).

48. Marginal and average cost Suppose a company produces fly rods. Assume $C(x) = -0.0001x^3 + 0.05x^2 + 60x + 800$ represents the cost of making x fly rods.

a. Determine the average and marginal costs for $x = 400$ fly rods.
b. Interpret the meaning of your results in part (a).

T **49. Population growth** Suppose $p(t) = -1.7t^3 + 72t^2 + 7200t + 80{,}000$ is the population of a city t years after 1950.

a. Determine the average rate of growth of the city from 1950 to 2000.
b. What was the rate of growth of the city in 1990?

T **50. Position of a piston** The distance between the head of a piston and the end of a cylindrical chamber is given by $x(t) = \dfrac{8t}{t + 1}$ cm, where $t \geq 0$ is measured in seconds. The radius of the cylinder is 4 cm.

a. Find the volume of the chamber, for $t \geq 0$.
b. Find the rate of change of the volume $V'(t)$, for $t \geq 0$.
c. Graph the derivative of the volume function. On what intervals is the volume increasing? Decreasing?

51. Boat rates Two boats leave a dock at the same time. One boat travels south at 30 mi/hr and the other travels east at 40 mi/hr. After half an hour, how fast is the distance between the boats increasing?

52. Rate of inflation of a balloon A spherical balloon is inflated at a rate of 10 cm^3/min. At what rate is the diameter of the balloon increasing when the balloon has a diameter of 5 cm?

53. Rate of descent of a hot-air balloon A rope is attached to the bottom of a hot-air balloon that is floating above a flat field. If the angle of the rope to the ground remains at 65° and the rope is pulled in at 5 ft/s, how quickly is the elevation of the balloon changing?

54. Filling a tank Water flows into a conical tank at a rate of 2 ft^3/min. If the radius of the top of the tank is 4 ft and the height is 6 ft, determine how quickly the water level is rising when the water is 2 ft deep in the tank.

55. Angle of elevation A jet flies horizontally 500 ft directly above a spectator at an air show at 450 mi/hr. Determine how quickly the angle of elevation (between the ground and the line from the spectator to the jet) is changing 2 s later.

56. Viewing angle A man whose eye level is 6 ft above the ground walks toward a billboard at a rate of 2 ft/s. The bottom of the billboard is 10 ft above the ground and it is 15 ft high. The man's viewing angle is the angle formed by the lines between the man's eyes and the top and bottom of the billboard. At what rate is the viewing angle changing when the man is 30 ft from the billboard?

Chapter 3 Guided Projects

Applications of the material in this chapter and related topics can be found in the following Guided Projects. For additional information, see the Preface.

- Numerical differentiation
- Elasticity in economics

4 Applications of the Derivative

Chapter Preview Much of the previous chapter was devoted to the basic mechanics of derivatives: evaluating them and interpreting them as rates of change. We now apply derivatives to a variety of mathematical questions about the properties of functions and their graphs. One outcome of this work is a set of analytical curve-sketching methods that produce accurate graphs of functions. Equally important, derivatives allow us to formulate and solve a wealth of practical problems. For example, a weather probe dropped from an airplane accelerates until it reaches its terminal velocity: When is the acceleration the greatest? An economist has a mathematical model that relates the demand for a product to its price: What price maximizes the revenue? In this chapter, we develop the tools needed to answer such questions. In addition, we begin an ongoing discussion about approximating functions, we present an important result called the Mean Value Theorem, and we work with a powerful method that enables us to evaluate a new kind of limit.

4.1 Maxima and Minima

With a working understanding of derivatives, we now undertake one of the fundamental tasks of calculus: analyzing the behavior and producing accurate graphs of functions. An important question associated with any function concerns its maximum and minimum values: On a given interval (perhaps the entire domain), where does the function assume its largest and smallest values? Questions about maximum and minimum values take on added significance when a function represents a practical quantity, such as the profits of a company, the surface area of a container, or the speed of a space vehicle.

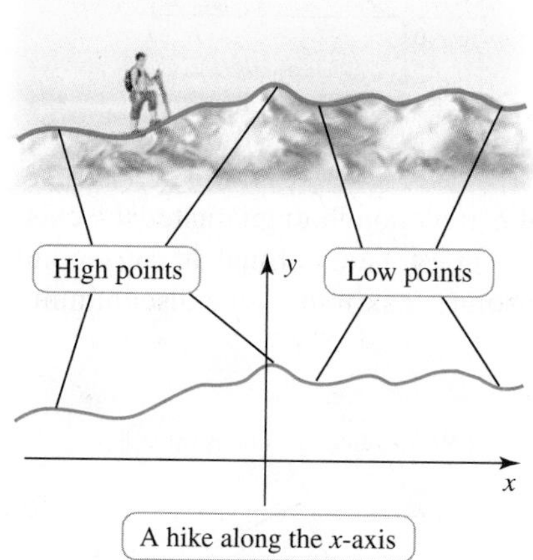

FIGURE 4.1

Absolute Maxima and Minima

Imagine taking a long hike through varying terrain from west to east. Your elevation changes as you walk over hills, through valleys, and across plains, and you reach several high and low points along the journey. Analogously, when we examine a function over an interval on the x-axis, its values increase and decrease, reaching high points and low points (Figure 4.1). You can view our study of functions in this chapter as an exploratory hike along the x-axis.

➤ Absolute maximum and minimum values are also called *global* maximum and minimum values. The plural of maximum is maxima; the plural of minimum is minima. *Extrema* (plural) and *extremum* (singular) refer to either maxima or minima.

> DEFINITION **Absolute Maximum and Minimum**
>
> Let f be defined on an interval I containing c. Then, f has an **absolute maximum** value on I at c if $f(c) \geq f(x)$ for every x in I. Similarly, f has an **absolute minimum** value on I at c if $f(c) \leq f(x)$ for every x in I.

The existence and location of absolute extreme values depend on both the function and the interval of interest. Figure 4.2 shows various cases for the function $f(x) = x^2$. Notice that if the interval of interest is not closed, a function might not attain absolute extreme values (Figure 4.2a, c, and d).

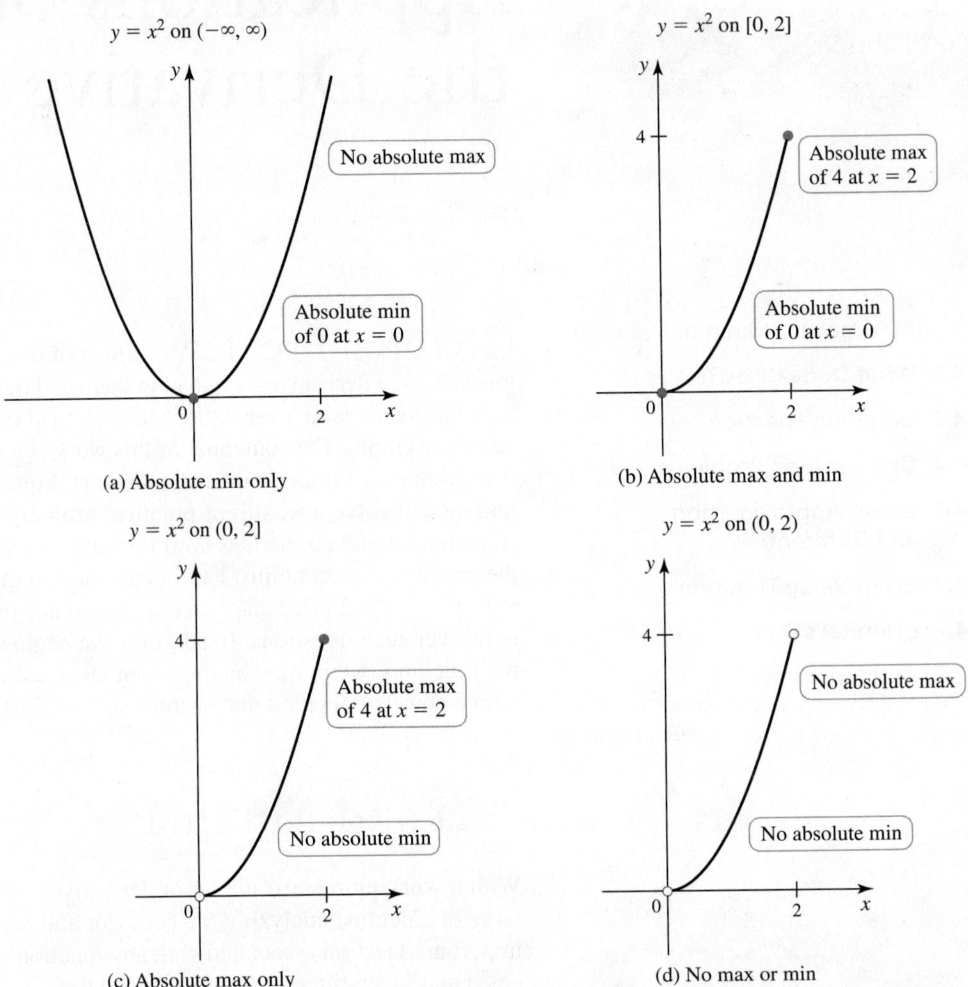

FIGURE 4.2. The function $f(x) = x^2$ has different absolute extrema depending on the interval of interest.

However, defining a function on a closed interval is not enough to guarantee the existence of absolute extreme values. Both functions in Figure 4.3 are defined at every point of a closed interval, but neither function attains an absolute maximum—the discontinuity in each function prevents it from happening.

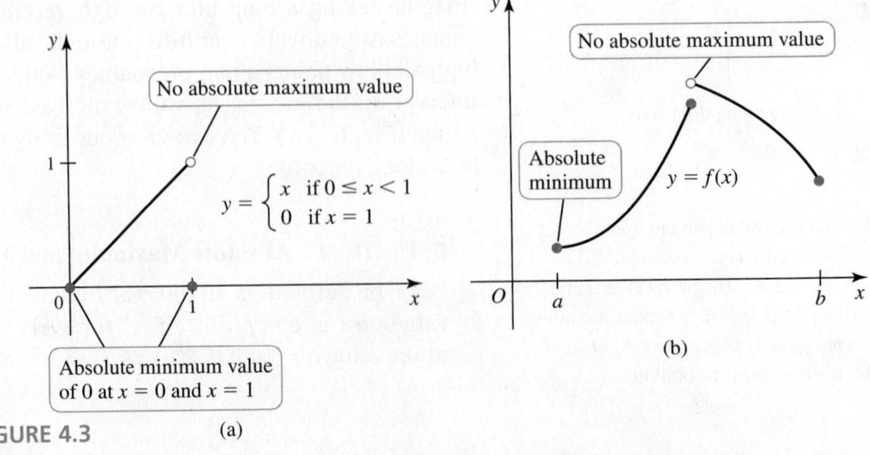

FIGURE 4.3

It turns out that *two* conditions ensure the existence of absolute minimum and maximum values on an interval: The function must be continuous on an interval and the interval must be closed and bounded.

➤ The proof of the Extreme Value Theorem relies on some deep properties of the real numbers found in advanced books.

THEOREM 4.1 Extreme Value Theorem
A function that is continuous on a closed interval $[a, b]$ has an absolute maximum value and an absolute minimum value on that interval.

QUICK CHECK 1 Sketch the graph of a function that is continuous on an interval but does not have an absolute minimum value. Sketch the graph of a function that is defined on a closed interval but does not have an absolute minimum value. ◄

EXAMPLE 1 Locating absolute maximum and minimum values For the functions in Figure 4.4, identify the location of the absolute maximum value and the absolute minimum value on the interval $[a, b]$. Do the functions meet the conditions of the Extreme Value Theorem?

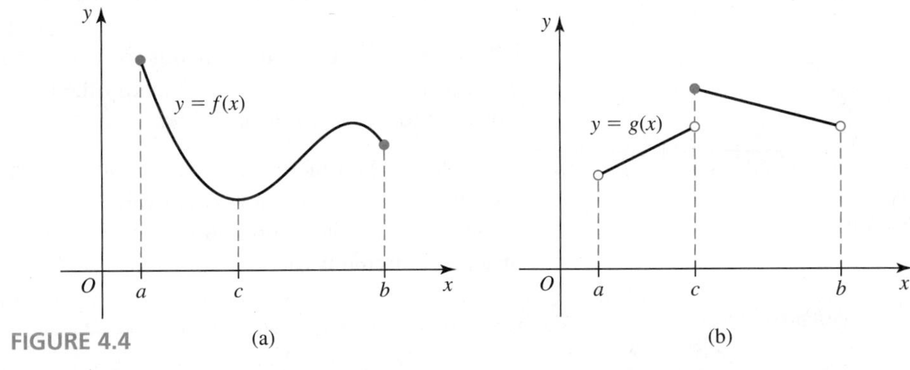

FIGURE 4.4 (a) (b)

SOLUTION

a. The function f is continuous on the closed interval $[a, b]$, so the Extreme Value Theorem guarantees an absolute maximum (which occurs at a) and an absolute minimum (which occurs at c).

b. The function g does not satisfy the conditions of the Extreme Value Theorem because it is not continuous, and it is defined only on the open interval (a, b). It does not have an absolute minimum value. It does, however, have an absolute maximum at c. Therefore, a function may violate the conditions of the Extreme Value Theorem and still have an absolute minimum or maximum (or both). *Related Exercises 11–14* ◄

Local Maxima and Minima

Figure 4.5 shows a function defined on the interval $[a, b]$. It has an absolute minimum at the endpoint a and an absolute maximum at the interior point e. In addition, the function

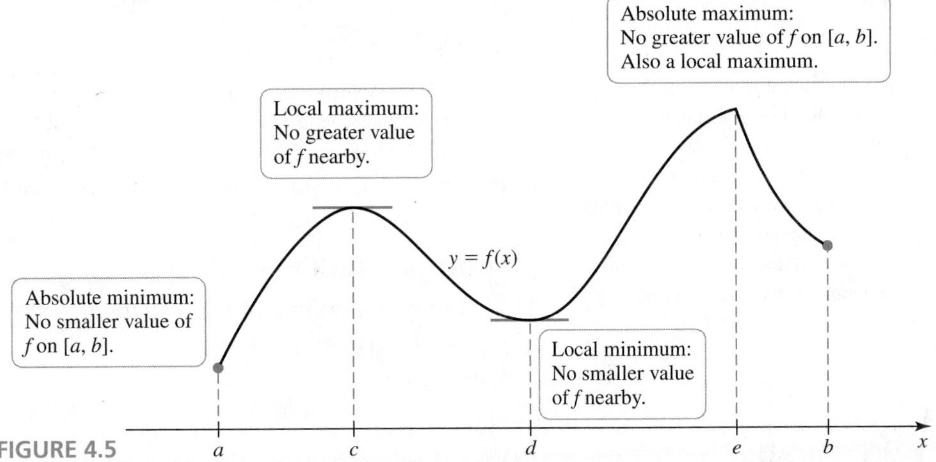

FIGURE 4.5

has special behavior at c, where its value is greatest *among nearby points*, and at d, where its value is least *among nearby points*. A point at which a function takes on the maximum or minimum value among nearby points is important.

➤ Local maximum and minimum values are also called *relative maximum and minimum values. Local extrema* (plural) and *local extremum* (singular) refer to either local maxima or local minima.

DEFINITION Local Maximum and Minimum Values

Suppose I is an interval on which f is defined and c is an interior point of I. If $f(c) \geq f(x)$ for all x in some open interval containing c, then $f(c)$ is a **local maximum** value of f. If $f(c) \leq f(x)$ for all x in some open interval containing c, then $f(c)$ is a **local minimum** value of f.

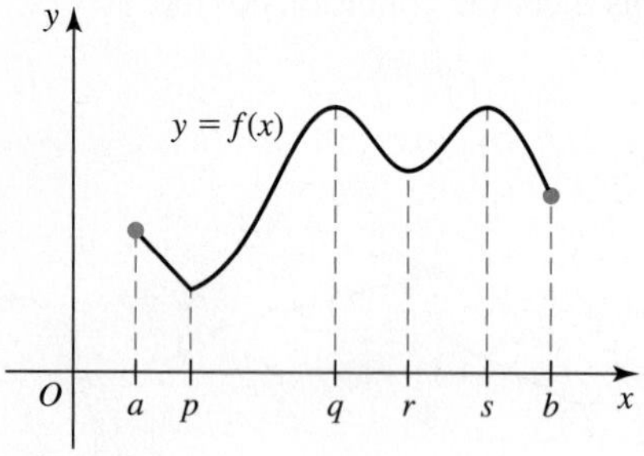

FIGURE 4.6

Note that local maxima and minima occur at interior points of the interval of interest, not at endpoints. For example, in Figure 4.5, the minimum value that occurs at the endpoint a is not a local minimum. However, it is the absolute minimum of the function on $[a, b]$.

EXAMPLE 2 Locating various maxima and minima Figure 4.6 shows the graph of a function defined on $[a, b]$. Identify the location of the various maxima and minima using the terms *absolute* and *local*.

SOLUTION The function f is continuous on a closed interval; by Theorem 4.1, it has absolute maximum and minimum values on $[a, b]$. The function has a local minimum value and its absolute minimum value at p. It has another local minimum value at r. The absolute maximum value of f occurs at both q and s (which are also local maximum values). The function does not have extrema at the endpoints a and b.

Related Exercises 15–22 ◄

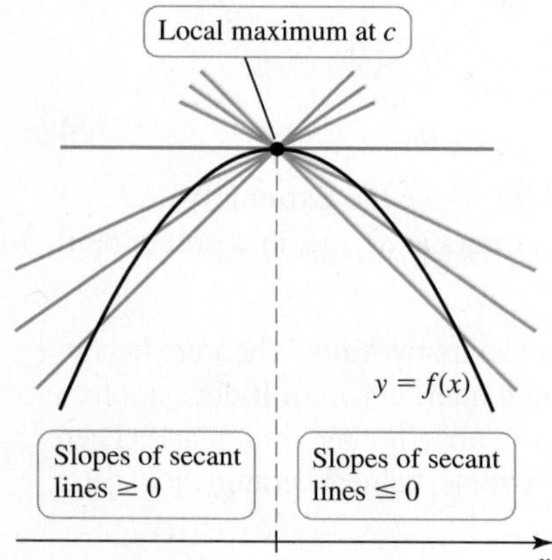

FIGURE 4.7

Critical Points Another look at Figure 4.6 shows that local maxima and minima occur at points in the open interval (a, b) where the derivative is zero ($x = q, r$, and s) and at points where the derivative fails to exist ($x = p$). We now make these observations precise.

Figure 4.7 illustrates a function that is differentiable at c with a local maximum at c. For x near c with $x < c$, the secant lines between the points $(x, f(x))$ and $(c, f(c))$ have nonnegative slopes. For x near c with $x > c$, the secant lines between the points $(x, f(x))$ and $(c, f(c))$ have nonpositive slopes. As $x \rightarrow c$, the slopes of these secant lines approach the slope of the tangent line at $(c, f(c))$. These observations imply that the slope of the tangent line must be both nonnegative and nonpositive, which happens only if $f'(c) = 0$. Similar reasoning leads to the same conclusion for a function with a local minimum at c: $f'(c)$ must be zero. This argument is an outline of the proof (Exercise 71) of the following theorem.

THEOREM 4.2 Local Extreme Point Theorem

If f has a local minimum or maximum value at c and $f'(c)$ exists, then $f'(c) = 0$.

➤ Theorem 4.2, often attributed to Fermat, is one of the clearest examples in mathematics of a necessary, but not sufficient, condition. A local minimum (or maximum) at c necessarily implies a critical point at c, but a critical point at c is not sufficient to imply a local minimum (or maximum) exists there.

Local extrema can also occur at points c where $f'(c)$ does not exist. Figure 4.8 shows two such cases, one in which c is a point of discontinuity and one in which f has a corner point at c. Because local extrema may occur at points c where $f'(c) = 0$ *and* where $f'(c)$ does not exist, we make the following definition.

DEFINITION Critical Point

An interior point c of the domain of f at which $f'(c) = 0$ or $f'(c)$ fails to exist is called a **critical point** of f.

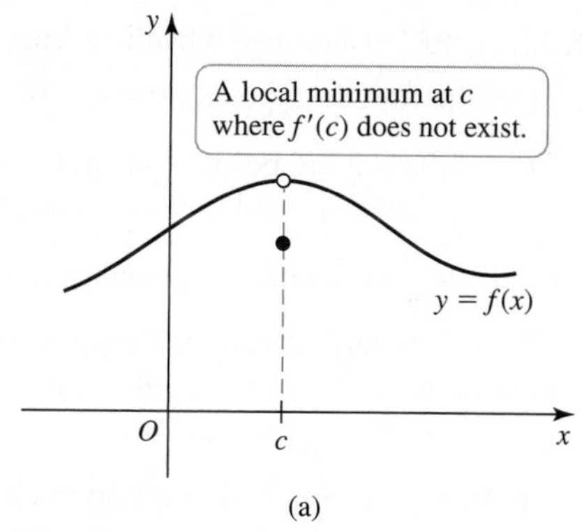

(a)

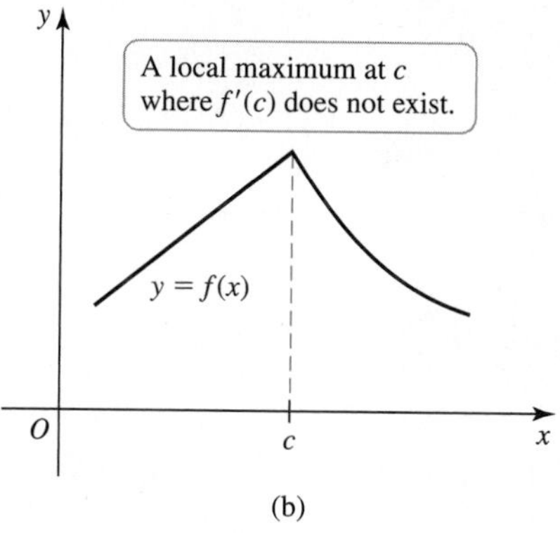

(b)

FIGURE 4.8

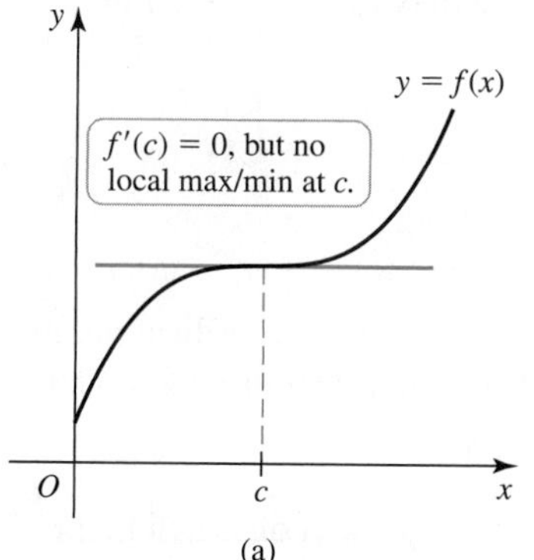

(a)

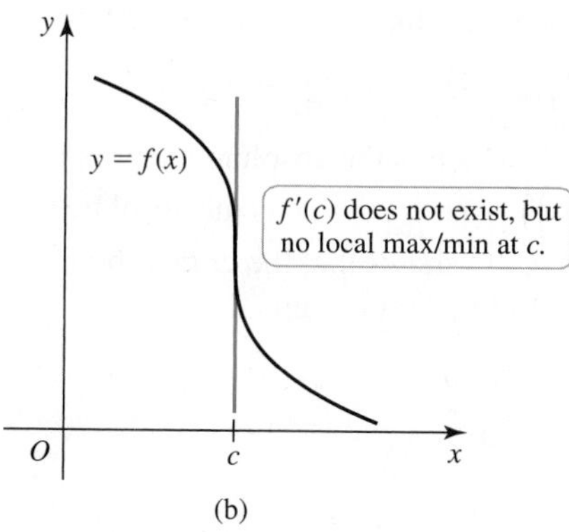

(b)

FIGURE 4.9

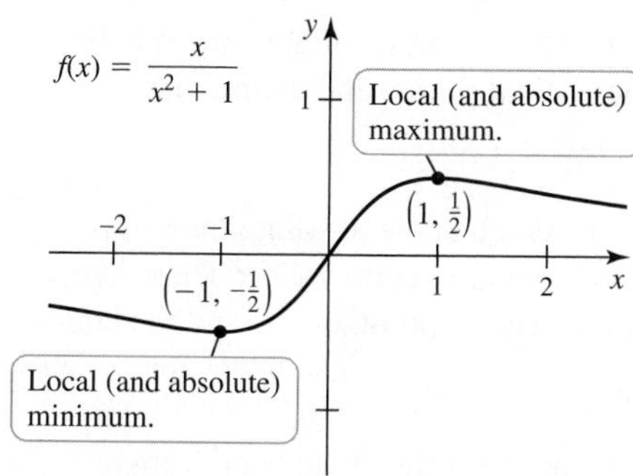

FIGURE 4.10

Note that the converse of Theorem 2 is not necessarily true. It is possible that $f'(c) = 0$ at a point without a local maximum or local minimum value occurring there (Figure 4.9a). It is also possible that $f'(c)$ fails to exist, with no local extreme value occurring at c (Figure 4.9b). Therefore, critical points are *candidates* for local extreme points, but you must determine whether they actually correspond to local maxima or minima. This procedure is discussed in Section 4.2.

EXAMPLE 3 **Locating critical points** Find the critical points of $f(x) = \dfrac{x}{x^2 + 1}$.

SOLUTION Note that f is differentiable on its domain, which is $(-\infty, \infty)$. By the Quotient Rule,

$$f'(x) = \frac{(x^2 + 1) - 2x^2}{(x^2 + 1)^2} = \frac{1 - x^2}{(x^2 + 1)^2}.$$

Setting $f'(x) = 0$ and noting that $x^2 + 1 > 0$ for all x, the critical points satisfy the equation $1 - x^2 = 0$. Therefore, the critical points are $x = 1$ and $x = -1$. The graph of f (Figure 4.10) shows that f has a local (and absolute) maximum at $\left(1, \frac{1}{2}\right)$ and a local (and absolute) minimum at $\left(-1, -\frac{1}{2}\right)$.

Related Exercises 23–30 ◀

QUICK CHECK 2 Consider the function $f(x) = x^3$. Where is the critical point of f? Does f have a local maximum or minimum at the critical point? ◀

Locating Absolute Maxima and Minima

Theorem 4.1 guarantees the existence of absolute extreme values of a continuous function on a closed interval $[a, b]$, but it doesn't say where these values are located. Two observations lead to a procedure for locating absolute extreme values.

- An absolute extreme value in the interior of an interval is also a local extreme value, and we know that local extreme values occur at the critical points of f.
- Absolute extreme values may also occur at the endpoints of the interval of interest.

These two facts suggest the following procedure for locating the absolute extreme values of a continuous function on a closed interval.

PROCEDURE Locating Absolute Maximum and Minimum Values

Assume the function f is continuous on the closed interval $[a, b]$.

1. Locate the critical points c in (a, b), where $f'(c) = 0$ or $f'(c)$ does not exist. These points are candidates for absolute maxima and minima.
2. Evaluate f at the critical points and at the endpoints of $[a, b]$.
3. Choose the largest and smallest values of f from Step 2 for the absolute maximum and minimum values, respectively.

If the interval of interest is an open interval, then absolute extreme values—if they exist—occur at interior points.

EXAMPLE 4 Absolute extreme values Find the absolute maximum and minimum values of the following functions.

a. $f(x) = x^4 - 2x^3$ on the interval $[-2, 2]$

b. $g(x) = x^{2/3}(2 - x)$ on the interval $[-1, 2]$

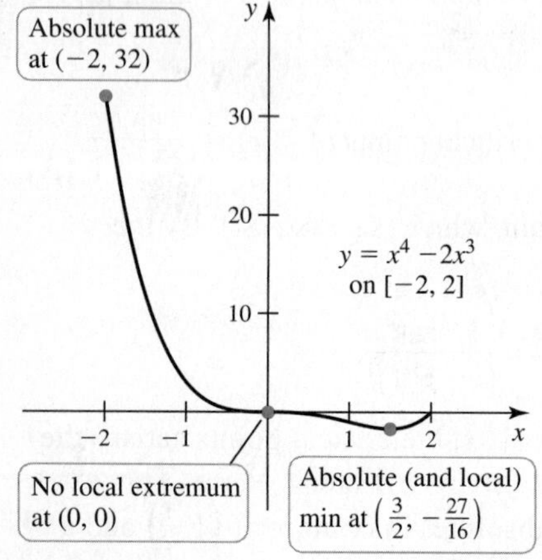

FIGURE 4.11

SOLUTION

a. Because f is a polynomial, its derivative exists everywhere. So, if f has critical points, they are points at which $f'(x) = 0$. Computing f' and setting it equal to zero, we have

$$f'(x) = 4x^3 - 6x^2 = 2x^2(2x - 3) = 0.$$

Solving this equation gives the critical points $x = 0$ and $x = \frac{3}{2}$, both of which lie in the interval $[-2, 2]$; these points and the endpoints are *candidates* for the locations of absolute extrema. Evaluating f at each of these points, we have

$$f(-2) = 32 \qquad f(0) = 0 \qquad f\left(\tfrac{3}{2}\right) = -\tfrac{27}{16} \qquad f(2) = 0.$$

The largest of these function values is $f(-2) = 32$, which is the absolute maximum of f on $[-2, 2]$. The smallest of these values is $f\left(\frac{3}{2}\right) = -\frac{27}{16}$, which is the absolute minimum of f on $[-2, 2]$. The graph of f (Figure 4.11) shows that the critical point $x = 0$ corresponds to neither a local maximum nor a local minimum.

b. Differentiating $g(x) = x^{2/3}(2 - x) = 2x^{2/3} - x^{5/3}$, we have

$$g'(x) = \frac{4}{3}x^{-1/3} - \frac{5}{3}x^{2/3} = \frac{4 - 5x}{3\sqrt[3]{x}}.$$

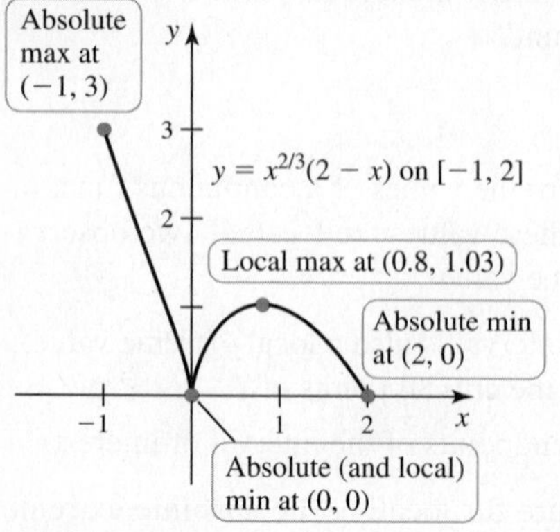

FIGURE 4.12

Because $g'(0)$ is undefined and 0 is in the domain of g, $x = 0$ is a critical point. In addition, $g'(x) = 0$ when $4 - 5x = 0$, so $x = \frac{4}{5}$ is also a critical point. These two critical points and the endpoints are *candidates* for the locations of absolute maxima and minima. The next step is to evaluate g at the critical points and endpoints:

$$g(-1) = 3 \qquad g(0) = 0 \qquad g(4/5) \approx 1.03 \qquad g(2) = 0$$

The largest of these function values is $g(-1) = 3$, which is the absolute maximum value of g on $[-1, 2]$. The least of these values is 0, which occurs twice. Therefore, g has its absolute minimum value on $[-1, 2]$ at the critical point $x = 0$ and the endpoint $x = 2$ (Figure 4.12).

Related Exercises 31–40 ◀

➤ The derivation of the position function for an object moving in a gravitational field is given in Section 6.1.

EXAMPLE 5 Trajectory high point A stone is launched vertically upward from a bridge 80 ft above the ground at a speed of 64 ft/s. Its height above the ground t seconds after the launch is given by

$$f(t) = -16t^2 + 64t + 80, \quad \text{for } 0 \le t \le 5.$$

When does the stone reach its maximum height?

SOLUTION We must evaluate the height function at the critical points and at the endpoints. The critical points satisfy the equation

$$f'(t) = -32t + 64 = -32(t - 2) = 0,$$

so the only critical point is $t = 2$. We now evaluate f at the endpoints and at the critical point:

$$f(0) = 80 \qquad f(2) = 144 \qquad f(5) = 0$$

On the interval $[0, 5]$, the absolute maximum occurs at $t = 2$, at which time the stone reaches a height of 144 ft. Because $f'(t)$ is the velocity of the stone, the maximum height occurs at the instant the velocity is zero.

Related Exercises 41–44 ◄

SECTION 4.1 EXERCISES

Review Questions

1. What does it mean for a function to have an absolute extreme value at a point c of an interval $[a, b]$?
2. What are local maximum and minimum values of a function?
3. What conditions must be met to ensure that a function has an absolute maximum value and an absolute minimum value on an interval?
4. Sketch the graph of a function that is continuous on an open interval (a, b) but has neither an absolute maximum nor an absolute minimum value on (a, b).
5. Sketch the graph of a function that has an absolute maximum, a local minimum, but no absolute minimum on $[0, 3]$.
6. What is a critical point of a function?
7. Sketch the graph of a function f that has a local maximum value at a point c where $f'(c) = 0$.
8. Sketch the graph of a function f that has a local minimum value at a point where $f'(x)$ is undefined.
9. How do you determine the absolute maximum and minimum values of a continuous function on a closed interval?
10. Explain how a function can have an absolute minimum value at an endpoint of an interval.

Basic Skills

11–14. Absolute maximum/minimum values from graphs *Use the following graphs to identify the points (if any) on the interval $[a, b]$ at which the function has an absolute maximum value or an absolute minimum value.*

11.

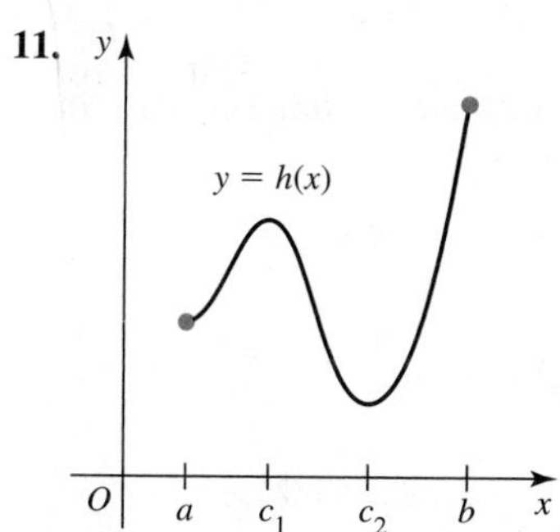

12.

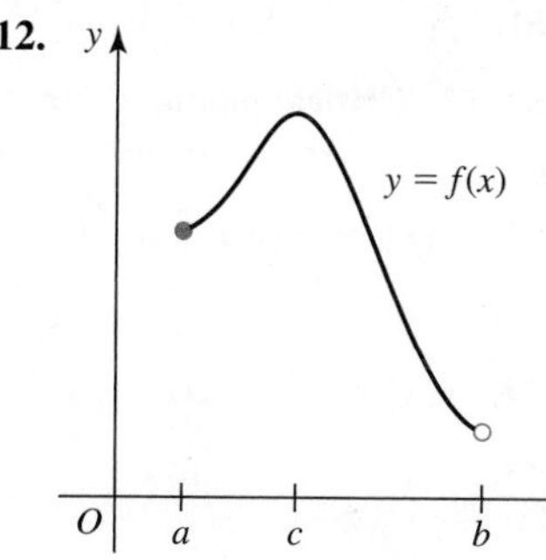

13. 14.

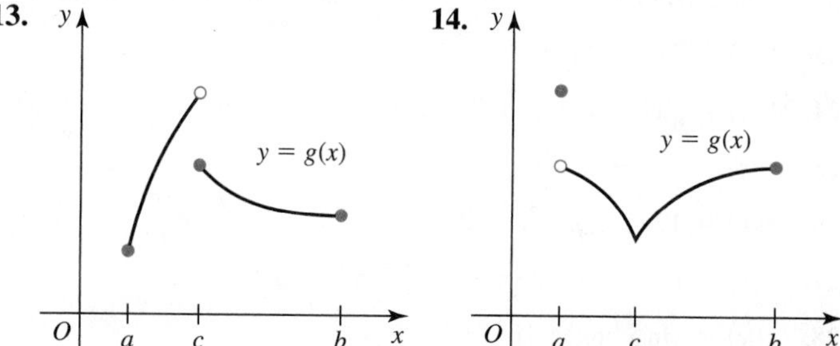

15–18. Local and absolute extreme values *Use the following graphs to identify the points on the interval $[a, b]$ at which local and absolute extreme values occur.*

15.

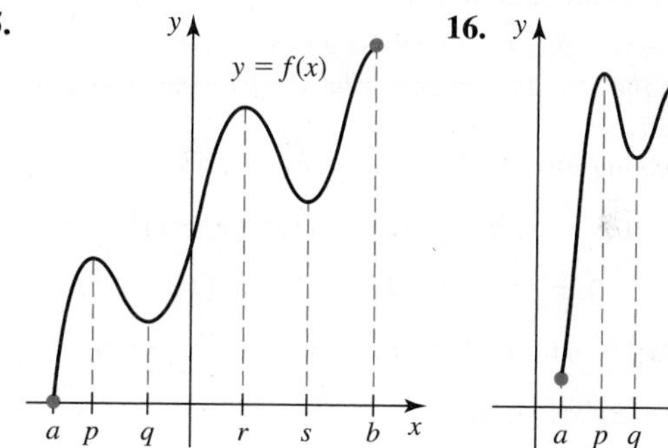

16.

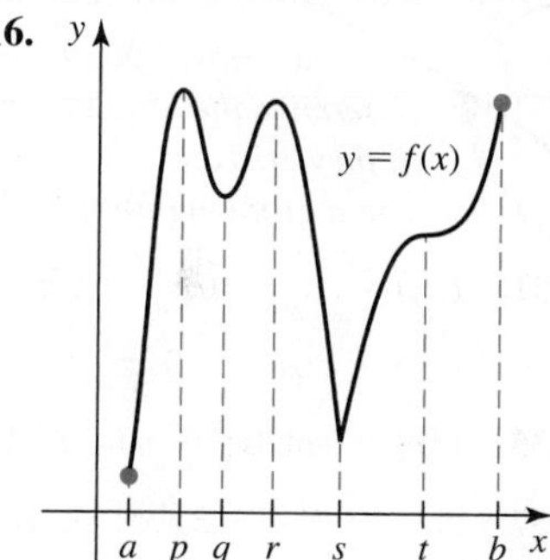

17.

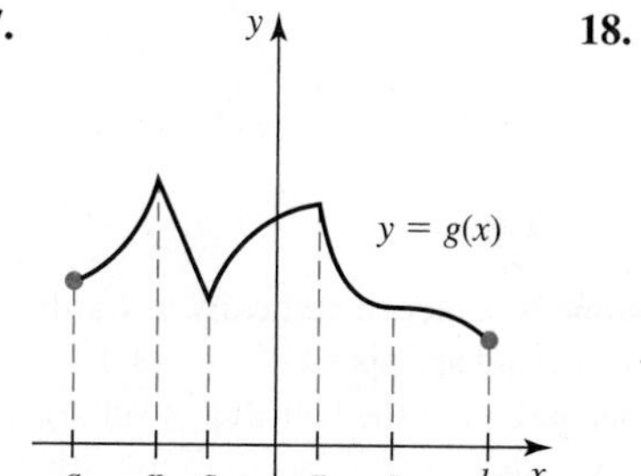

18.

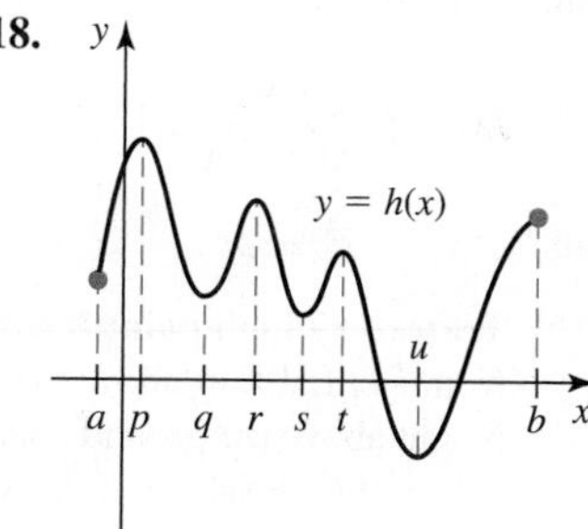

19–22. Designing a function *Sketch the graph of a continuous function f on $[0, 4]$ satisfying the given properties.*

19. $f'(x) = 0$ for $x = 1$ and 2; f has an absolute maximum at $x = 4$; f has an absolute minimum at $x = 0$; and f has a local minimum at $x = 2$.
20. $f'(x) = 0$ for $x = 1, 2$, and 3; f has an absolute minimum at $x = 1$; f has no local extremum at $x = 2$; and f has an absolute maximum at $x = 3$.

21. f' is undefined at $x = 1$ and 3; $f'(2) = 0$; f has a local maximum at $x = 1$; f has a local minimum at $x = 2$; f has an absolute maximum at $x = 3$; and f has an absolute minimum at $x = 4$.

22. $f'(x) = 0$ at $x = 1$ and 3; $f'(2)$ is undefined; f has an absolute maximum at $x = 2$; f has neither a local maximum nor a local minimum at $x = 1$; and f has an absolute minimum at $x = 3$.

T **23–30. Locating critical points**

a. Find the critical points of the following functions on the domain or on the given interval.

b. Use a graphing utility to determine whether each critical point corresponds to a local minimum, local maximum, or neither.

23. $f(x) = 3x^2 - 4x + 2$

24. $f(x) = \frac{1}{8}x^3 - \frac{1}{2}x;\ [-1, 3]$

25. $f(x) = (4x - 3)/(x^2 + 1)$

26. $f(x) = 12x^5 - 20x^3;\ [-2, 2]$

27. $f(x) = \cos 2x + \sqrt{3} \sin 2x;\ [0, \pi]$

28. $f(x) = \sin x \cos x;\ [0, 2\pi]$

29. $f(x) = 1/x - 1/x^2$

30. $f(x) = x^2 \sqrt{1 - x^2}$

T **31–40. Absolute maxima and minima**

a. Find the critical points of f on the given interval.

b. Determine the absolute extreme values of f on the given interval (if they exist).

c. Use a graphing utility to confirm your conclusions.

31. $f(x) = x^2 - 10;\ [-2, 3]$

32. $f(x) = (x + 1)^{4/3};\ [-8, 8]$

33. $f(x) = \cos^2 x;\ [0, \pi]$

34. $f(x) = x/(x^2 + 1)^2;\ [-2, 2]$

35. $f(x) = \sin 3x;\ [-\pi/4, \pi/3]$

36. $f(x) = x^{2/3};\ [-8, 8]$

37. $f(x) = (4x - 3)/x^2;\ [1, 4]$

38. $f(x) = x\sqrt{2 - x^2};\ [-\sqrt{2}, \sqrt{2}]$

39. $f(x) = \dfrac{x}{\sqrt{4 - x^2}};\ (-2, 2)$

40. $f(x) = x^3 - 2x^2 - 5x + 6;\ [4, 8]$

41. Trajectory high point A stone is launched vertically upward from a cliff 192 ft above the ground at a speed of 64 ft/s. Its height above the ground t seconds after the launch is given by $s = -16t^2 + 64t + 192$, for $0 \le t \le 6$. When does the stone reach its maximum height?

42. Maximizing revenue A sales analyst determines that the revenue from sales of fruit smoothies is given by $R(x) = -60x^2 + 300x$, where x is the price in dollars charged per item, with $0 \le x \le 5$.

a. Find the critical points of the revenue function.

b. Determine the absolute maximum value of the revenue function and give the price that maximizes the revenue.

43. Maximizing profit Suppose a tour guide has a bus that holds a maximum of 100 people. Assume his profit (in dollars) for taking n people on a city tour is $P(n) = n(50 - 0.5n) - 100$. (Although P is defined only for positive integers, treat it as a continuous function.)

a. How many people should the guide take on a tour to maximize the profit?

b. Suppose the bus holds a maximum of 45 people. How many people should be taken on a tour to maximize the profit?

44. Maximizing rectangle perimeters All rectangles with an area of 64 m^2 have a perimeter given by $P(x) = 2x + 128/x$, where x is the length of one side of the rectangle. Find the absolute minimum value of the perimeter function. What are the dimensions of the rectangle with minimum perimeter?

Further Explorations

45. Explain why or why not Determine whether the following statements are true and give an explanation or counterexample.

a. The function $f(x) = \sqrt{x}$ has a local maximum on the interval $[0, 1]$.

b. If a function has an absolute maximum, then the function must be continuous on a closed interval.

c. A function f has the property that $f'(2) = 0$. Therefore, f has a local maximum or minimum at $x = 2$.

d. Absolute extreme values on an interval always occur at a critical point or an endpoint of the interval.

e. A function f has the property that $f'(3)$ does not exist. Therefore, $x = 3$ is a critical point of f.

T **46–51. Absolute maxima and minima**

a. Find the critical points of f on the given interval.

b. Determine the absolute extreme values of f on the given interval.

c. Use a graphing utility to confirm your conclusions.

46. $f(x) = (x - 2)^{1/2};\ [2, 6]$

47. $f(x) = x^2(x^2 + 4x - 8);\ [-5, 2]$

48. $f(x) = x^{1/2}(x^2/5 - 4);\ [0, 4]$

49. $f(x) = \sec x;\ [-\pi/4, \pi/4]$

50. $f(x) = x^{1/3}(x + 4);\ [-27, 27]$

51. $f(x) = x/\sqrt{x - 4};\ [6, 12]$

52–55. Critical points of functions with parameters *Find the critical points of f. Assume a and b are constants.*

52. $f(x) = x/\sqrt{x - a}$

53. $f(x) = x\sqrt{x - a}$

54. $f(x) = x^3 - 3ax^2 + 3a^2x - a^3 + b$

55. $f(x) = \frac{1}{5}x^5 - a^4x$

56–61. Critical points and extreme values

a. *Find the critical points of the following functions on the given interval.*
b. *Use a graphing utility to determine whether the critical points correspond to local maxima, local minima, or neither.*
c. *Find the absolute maximum and minimum values on the given interval (if they exist).*

56. $f(x) = 6x^4 - 16x^3 - 45x^2 + 54x + 23$; $[-5, 5]$

57. $f(\theta) = 2\sin\theta + \cos\theta$; $[-2\pi, 2\pi]$

58. $f(x) = x^{2/3}(4 - x^2)$; $[-3, 4]$

59. $g(x) = (x - 3)^{5/3}(x + 2)$; $[-4, 4]$

60. $f(t) = 3t/(t^2 + 1)$; $[-2, 2]$

61. $h(x) = (5 - x)/(x^2 + 2x - 3)$; $[-10, 10]$

62–63. Absolute value functions *Graph the following functions and determine the local and absolute extreme values on the given interval.*

62. $f(x) = |x - 3| + |x + 2|$; $[-4, 4]$

63. $g(x) = |x - 3| - 2|x + 1|$; $[-2, 3]$

Applications

64. **Minimum surface area box** All boxes with a square base and a volume of 50 ft^3 have a surface area given by $S(x) = 2x^2 + 200/x$, where x is the length of the sides of the base. Find the absolute minimum of the surface area function. What are the dimensions of the box with minimum surface area?

65. **Every second counts** You must get from a point P on the straight shore of a lake to a stranded swimmer who is 50 m from a point Q on the shore that is 50 m from you (see figure). Assume you can swim at a speed of 2 m/s and run at a speed of 4 m/s. Use the following steps to determine the point along the shore, x meters from Q, at which you should stop running and start swimming if you want to reach the swimmer in the minimum time.

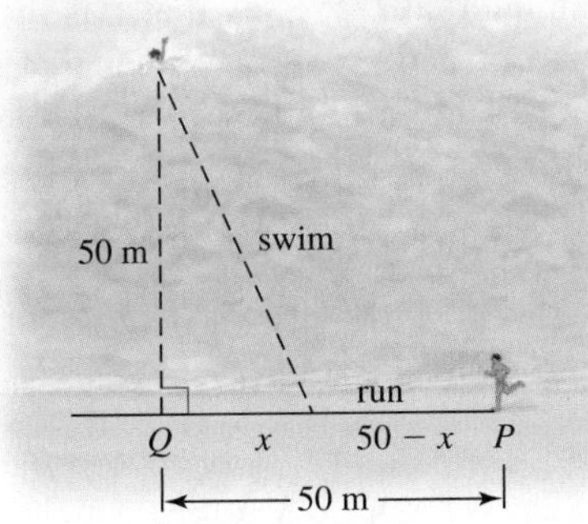

a. Find the function T that gives the travel time as a function of x, where $0 \le x \le 50$.
b. Find the critical point of T on $(0, 50)$.
c. Evaluate T at the critical point and the endpoints ($x = 0$ and $x = 50$) to verify that the critical point corresponds to an absolute minimum. What is the minimum travel time?
d. Graph the function T to check your work.

66. **Dancing on a parabola** Suppose that two people, A and B, walk along the parabola $y = x^2$ in such a way that the line segment L between them is always perpendicular to the line tangent to the parabola at A's position. What are the positions of A and B when L has minimum length?

a. Assume that A's position is (a, a^2), where $a > 0$. Find the slope of the line tangent to the parabola at A and find the slope of the line that is perpendicular to the tangent line at A.
b. Find the equation of the line joining A and B when A is at (a, a^2).
c. Find the position of B on the parabola when A is at (a, a^2).
d. Write the function $F(a)$ that gives the *square* of the distance between A and B as it varies with a. (The square of the distance is minimized at the same point that the distance is minimized; it is easier to work with the square of the distance.)
e. Find the critical point of F on the interval $a > 0$.
f. Evaluate F at the critical point and verify that it corresponds to an absolute minimum. What are the positions of A and B that minimize the length of L? What is the minimum length?
g. Graph the function F to check your work.

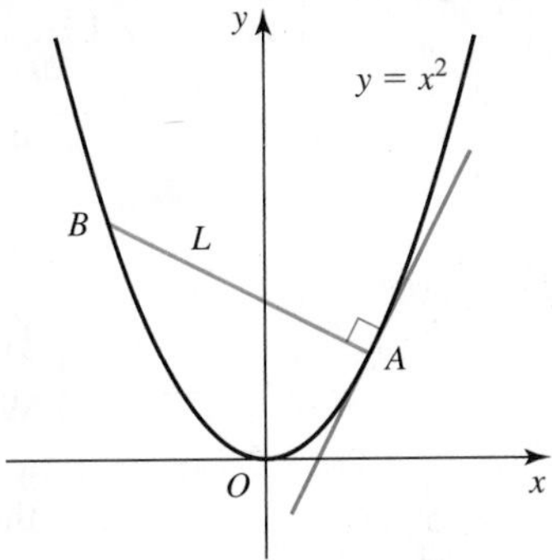

Additional Exercises

67. **Values of related functions** Suppose f is differentiable on $(-\infty, \infty)$ and assume it has a local extreme value at the point $x = 2$ where $f(2) = 0$. Let $g(x) = xf(x) + 1$ and let $h(x) = xf(x) + x + 1$ for all values of x.

a. Evaluate $g(2)$, $h(2)$, $g'(2)$, and $h'(2)$.
b. Does either g or h have a local extreme value at 2? Explain.

68. **Extreme values of parabolas** Consider the function $f(x) = ax^2 + bx + c$, with $a \ne 0$. Explain geometrically why f has exactly one absolute extreme value on $(-\infty, \infty)$. Find the critical points to determine the value of x at which f has an extreme value.

69. **Even and odd functions**

a. Suppose an even function f has a local minimum at c. Does f have a local maximum or minimum at $-c$? Explain. (An even function satisfies $f(x) = f(-x)$.)
b. Suppose an odd function f has a local minimum at c. Does f have a local maximum or minimum at $-c$? Explain. (An odd function satisfies $f(x) = -f(-x)$.)

70. A family of double-humped functions Consider the functions $f(x) = x/(x^2 + 1)^n$, where n is a positive integer.

a. Show that these functions are odd for all positive integers n.

b. Show that the critical points of these functions are $x = \pm\sqrt{\frac{1}{2n - 1}}$ for all positive integers n. (Start with the special cases $n = 1$ and $n = 2$.)

c. Show that as n increases the absolute maximum values of these functions decrease.

d. Use a graphing utility to verify your conclusions.

71. Proof of the Local Extreme Point Theorem Prove Theorem 4.2 for a local maximum: If f has a local maximum at the point c and $f'(c)$ exists, then $f'(c) = 0$. Use the following steps.

a. If f has a local maximum at c, then what is the sign of $f(x) - f(c)$ if x is near c and $x > c$? What is the sign of $f(x) - f(c)$ if x is near c and $x < c$?

b. If $f'(c)$ exists, then it is defined by $\lim_{x \to c} \frac{f(x) - f(c)}{x - c}$. Examine this limit as $x \to c^+$ and conclude that $f'(c) \leq 0$.

c. Examine the limit in part (b) as $x \to c^-$ and conclude that $f'(c) \geq 0$.

d. Combine parts (b) and (c) to conclude that $f'(c) = 0$.

QUICK CHECK ANSWERS

1. The continuous function $f(x) = x$ does not have an absolute minimum on the open interval $(0, 1)$. The function $f(x) = -x$ on $\left[0, \frac{1}{2}\right)$ and $f(x) = 0$ on $\left[\frac{1}{2}, 1\right]$ does not have an absolute minimum on $[0, 1]$; it has a discontinuity at $\frac{1}{2}$. **2.** The critical point is 0. Although $f'(0) = 0$, the function has neither a local minimum nor maximum at $x = 0$.

4.2 What Derivatives Tell Us

In the previous section, we saw that the derivative is a tool for finding critical points, which are related to local maxima and minima. As we show in this section, derivatives (first *and* second derivatives) tell us much more about the behavior of functions.

Increasing and Decreasing Functions

We used the terms *increasing* and *decreasing* informally in earlier sections to describe a function or its graph. For example, the graph in Figure 4.13a rises as x increases, so the corresponding function is increasing. In Figure 4.13b, the graph falls as x increases, so the corresponding function is decreasing. The following definition makes these ideas precise.

> A function is **monotonic** if it is either increasing or decreasing. Some books make a further distinction by defining **nondecreasing** ($f(x_2) \geq f(x_1)$ whenever $x_2 > x_1$) and **nonincreasing** ($f(x_2) \leq f(x_1)$ whenever $x_2 > x_1$).

DEFINITION Increasing and Decreasing Functions

Suppose a function f is defined on an interval I. We say that f is **increasing** on I if $f(x_2) > f(x_1)$ whenever x_1 and x_2 are in I and $x_2 > x_1$. We say that f is **decreasing** on I if $f(x_2) < f(x_1)$ whenever x_1 and x_2 are in I and $x_2 > x_1$.

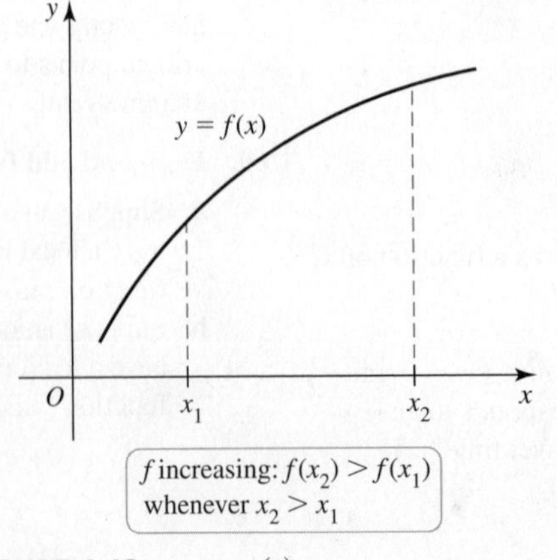

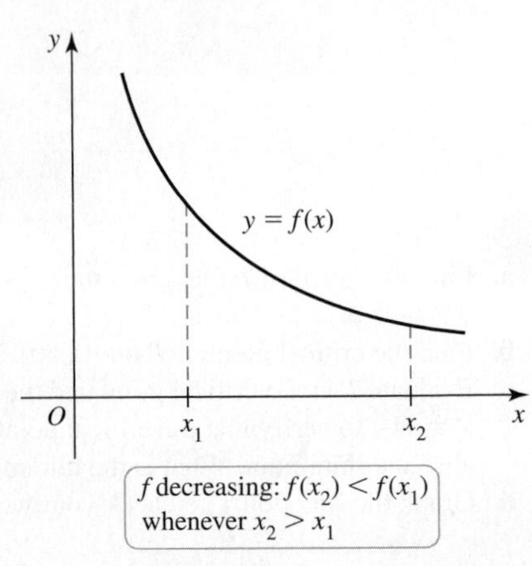

FIGURE 4.13 (a) (b)

Intervals of Increase and Decrease The graph of a function f gives us an idea of the intervals on which f is increasing and decreasing. But how do we determine those intervals precisely? This question is answered by making a connection to the derivative.

Recall that the derivative of a function gives the slopes of tangent lines. If the derivative is positive on an interval, the tangent lines on that interval have positive slopes, and the function is increasing on the interval (Figure 4.14a). Said differently, positive derivatives on an interval imply positive rates of change on the interval, which, in turn, indicate an increase in function values.

Similarly, if the derivative is negative on an interval, the tangent lines on that interval have negative slopes, and the function is decreasing on that interval (Figure 4.14b). These observations are proved in Section 4.6 using a result called the Mean Value Theorem.

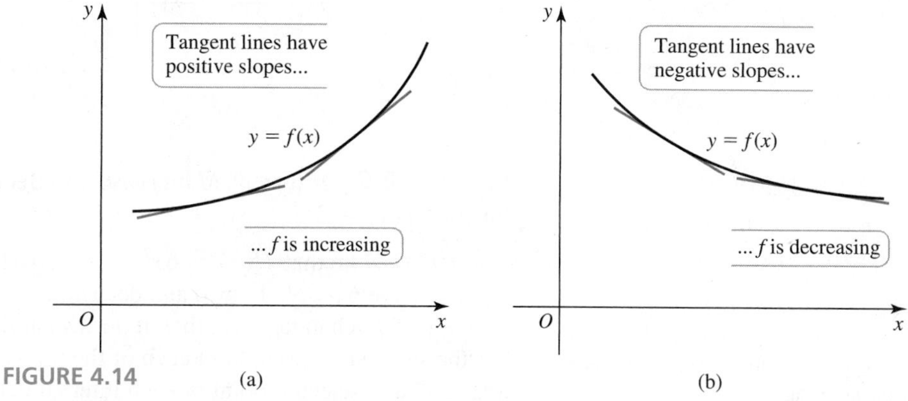

FIGURE 4.14 (a) (b)

> The converse of Theorem 4.3 may not be true. According to the definition, $f(x) = x^3$ is increasing on $(-\infty, \infty)$, but it is not true that $f'(x) > 0$ on $(-\infty, \infty)$ (because $f'(0) = 0$).

THEOREM 4.3 Test for Intervals of Increase and Decrease
Suppose f is continuous on an interval I and differentiable at every interior point of I. If $f'(x) > 0$ at all interior points of I, then f is increasing on I. If $f'(x) < 0$ at all interior points of I, then f is decreasing on I.

QUICK CHECK 1 Explain why a positive derivative on an interval implies that the function is increasing on the interval.

EXAMPLE 1 Sketching a function Sketch a function f that is continuous on its domain $(-\infty, \infty)$ and satisfies the following conditions:

1. $f' > 0$ on $(-\infty, 0)$, $(4, 6)$, and $(6, \infty)$
2. $f' < 0$ on $(0, 4)$
3. $f'(0)$ is undefined
4. $f'(4) = f'(6) = 0$

SOLUTION By condition (1), f is increasing on the intervals $(-\infty, 0)$, $(4, 6)$, and $(6, \infty)$. By condition (2), f is decreasing on $(0, 4)$. Condition (3) implies f has a cusp or corner at $x = 0$, and by condition (4), the graph has a horizontal tangent line at $x = 4$ and $x = 6$. It is useful to summarize these results (Figure 4.15) before sketching a graph. One of many possible graphs satisfying these conditions is shown in Figure 4.16.

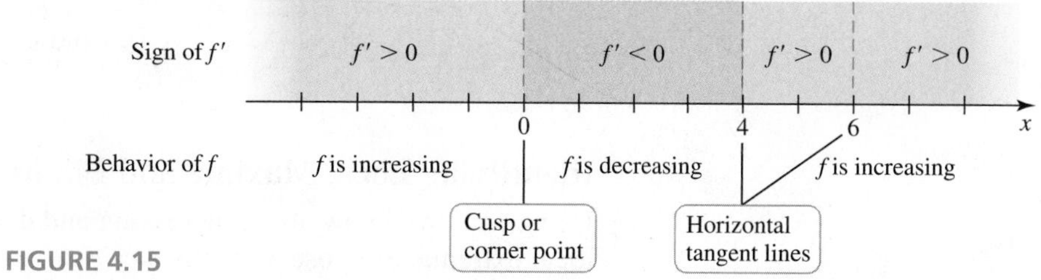

FIGURE 4.15

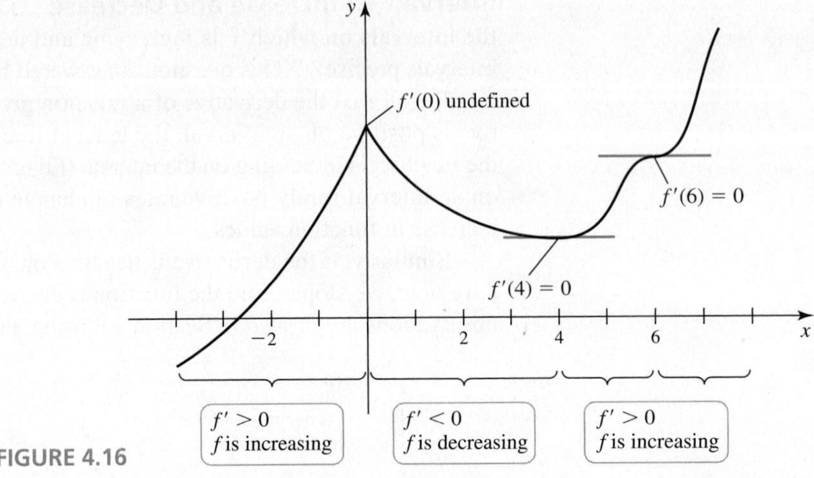

FIGURE 4.16

Related Exercises 11–16 ◀

EXAMPLE 2 **Intervals of increase and decrease** Find the intervals on which the function $f(x) = 2x^3 + 3x^2 + 1$ is increasing and decreasing.

> See Appendix A for solving inequalities using test values.

SOLUTION Note that $f'(x) = 6x^2 + 6x = 6x(x + 1)$. To find the intervals of increase, we first solve $6x(x + 1) = 0$ and determine that the critical points are $x = 0$ and $x = -1$. If f' changes sign, then it does so at these points and nowhere else; that is, f' has the same sign throughout each of the intervals $(-\infty, -1)$, $(-1, 0)$, and $(0, \infty)$. Evaluating f' at a selected point of each interval determines the sign of f' on that interval.

- At $x = -2$, $f'(-2) = 12 > 0$, so $f' > 0$ and f is increasing on $(-\infty, -1)$.
- At $x = -\frac{1}{2}$, $f'\left(-\frac{1}{2}\right) = -\frac{3}{2} < 0$, so $f' < 0$ and f is decreasing on $(-1, 0)$.
- At $x = 1$, $f'(1) = 12 > 0$, so $f' > 0$ and f is increasing on $(0, \infty)$.

The graph of f has a horizontal tangent line at $x = -1$ and $x = 0$. Figure 4.17 shows the graph of f superimposed on the graph of f', confirming our conclusions.

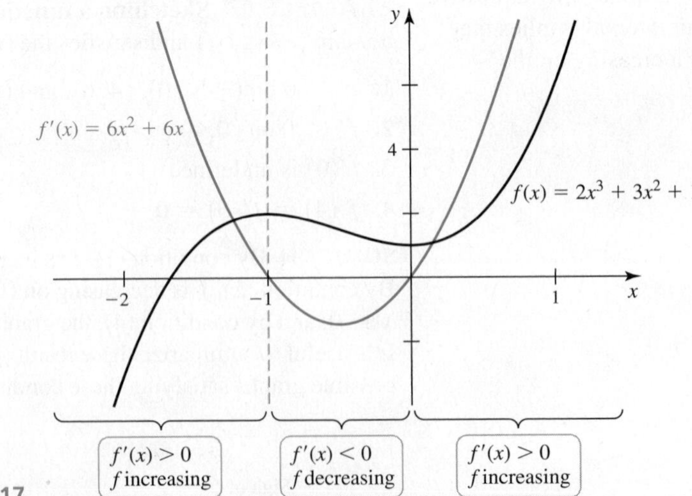

FIGURE 4.17

Related Exercises 17–28 ◀

Identifying Local Maxima and Minima

Using what we know about increasing and decreasing functions, we can now identify local extrema. Suppose $x = c$ is a critical point of f, where $f'(c) = 0$. Suppose also that f' changes sign at c with $f'(x) < 0$ on an interval (a, c) to the left of c and

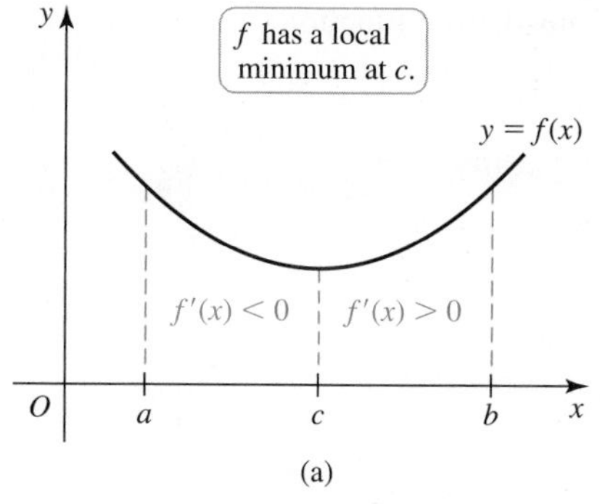

(a)

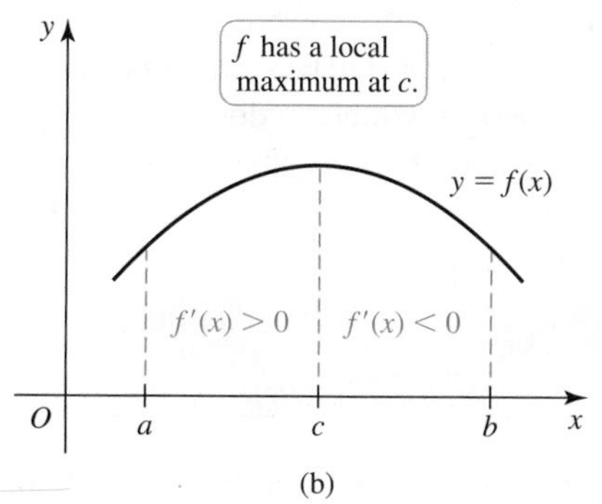

(b)

FIGURE 4.18

$f'(x) > 0$ on an interval (c, b) to the right of c. In this case f' is decreasing to the left of c and increasing to the right of c, which means that f has a local minimum at c, as shown in Figure 4.18a.

Similarly, suppose f' changes sign at c with $f'(x) > 0$ on an interval (a, c) to the left of c and $f'(x) < 0$ on an interval (c, b) to the right of c. Then, f is increasing to the left of c and decreasing to the right of c, so f has a local maximum at c, as shown in Figure 4.18b.

Figure 4.19 shows typical features of a function on an interval $[a, b]$. At local maxima or minima (c_2, c_3, and c_4), f' changes sign. Although c_1 and c_5 are critical points, f' does not change sign at these points, so there is no local maximum or minimum at these points. As emphasized earlier, *critical points do not always correspond to local extreme values.*

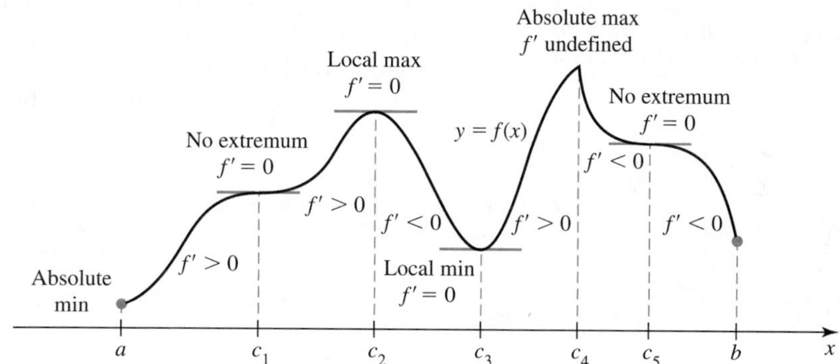

FIGURE 4.19

QUICK CHECK 2 Sketch a function f that is differentiable on $(-\infty, \infty)$ with the following properties: (i) $x = 0$ and $x = 2$ are critical points; (ii) f is increasing on $(-\infty, 2)$; (iii) f is decreasing on $(2, \infty)$. ◀

First Derivative Test The observations used to interpret Figure 4.19 are summarized in a powerful test for identifying local maxima and minima.

> **THEOREM 4.4 First Derivative Test**
> Suppose that f is continuous on an interval I that contains a critical point c and assume f is differentiable on I, except perhaps at c itself.
>
> - If f' changes sign from positive to negative as x increases through c, then f has a **local maximum** at c.
> - If f' changes sign from negative to positive as x increases through c, then f has a **local minimum** at c.
> - If f' does not change sign at c (from positive to negative or vice versa), then f has no local extreme value at c.

Proof Suppose that $f'(x) > 0$ on an interval (a, c), which means that f is increasing on (a, c), which, in turn, implies that $f(x) < f(c)$ for all x in (a, c). Similarly, suppose that $f'(x) < 0$ on an interval (c, b), which means that f is decreasing on (c, b), which, in turn, implies that $f(x) < f(c)$ for all x in (c, b). Therefore, $f(x) \leq f(c)$ for all x in (a, b) and f has a local maximum at c. The proofs of the other two cases are similar. ◀

EXAMPLE 3 **Using the First Derivative Test** Consider the function

$$f(x) = 3x^4 - 4x^3 - 6x^2 + 12x + 1.$$

a. Find the intervals on which f is increasing and decreasing.

b. Identify the local extrema of f.

SOLUTION

a. Differentiating f, we find that

$$\begin{aligned} f'(x) &= 12x^3 - 12x^2 - 12x + 12 \\ &= 12(x^3 - x^2 - x + 1) \\ &= 12(x + 1)(x - 1)^2. \end{aligned}$$

Solving $f'(x) = 0$ gives the critical points $x = -1$ and $x = 1$. The critical points determine the intervals $(-\infty, -1)$, $(-1, 1)$, and $(1, \infty)$ on which f' does not change sign. Choosing a test point in each interval, a sign graph of f' is constructed (Figure 4.20), which summarizes the behavior of f.

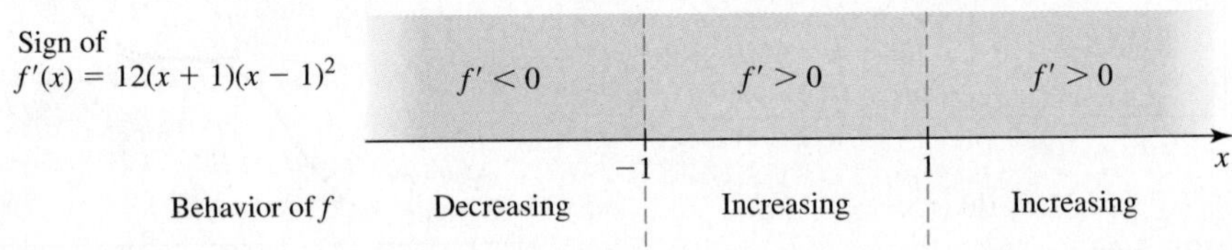

FIGURE 4.20

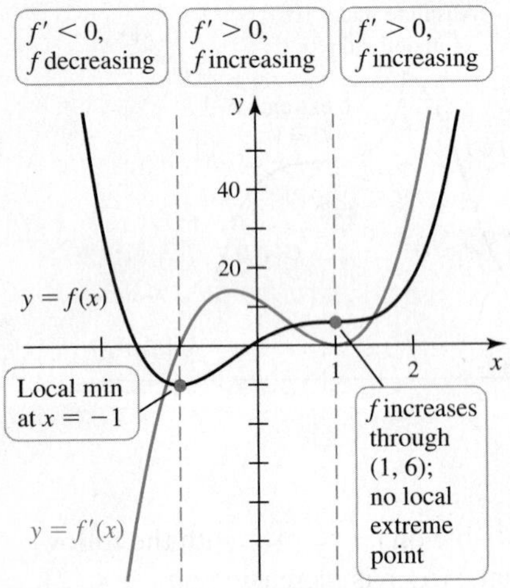

f' < 0, f decreasing
f' > 0, f increasing
f' > 0, f increasing
y = f(x)
Local min at x = −1
f increases through (1, 6); no local extreme point
y = f'(x)

FIGURE 4.21

b. Because f' changes sign from negative to positive as x passes through the critical point $x = -1$, it follows by the First Derivative Test that f has a local minimum value of $f(-1) = -10$ at $x = -1$. As x passes through $x = 1$, f does not change sign, so f does not have a local extreme value at the critical point $x = 1$ (Figure 4.21).

Related Exercises 29–34 ◄

EXAMPLE 4 **Extreme points** Find the local extrema of the function $f(x) = x^{2/3}(2 - x)$.

SOLUTION In Example 4b of Section 4.1, we found that

$$f'(x) = \frac{4}{3}x^{-1/3} - \frac{5}{3}x^{2/3} = \frac{4 - 5x}{3x^{1/3}}$$

and that the critical points of f are $x = 0$ and $x = \frac{4}{5}$. These two critical points are *candidates* for local extrema, and Theorem 4.4 is used to classify each as a local minimum, local maximum, or neither.

Using Figure 4.22, we see that f has a local minimum at $x = 0$ and a local maximum at $x = \frac{4}{5}$. These observations are confirmed by the graphs of f and f' (Figure 4.23).

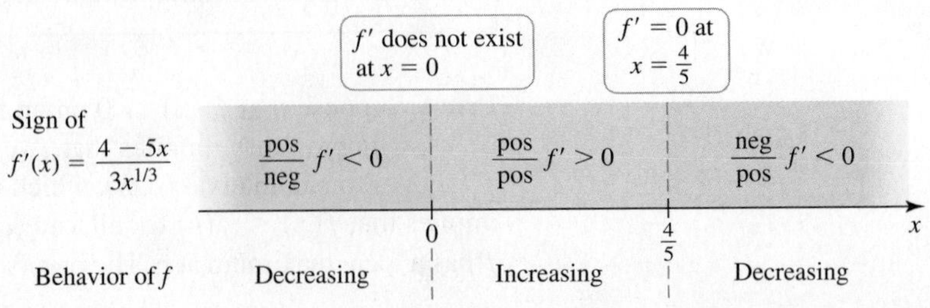

FIGURE 4.22

Related Exercises 29–34 ◄

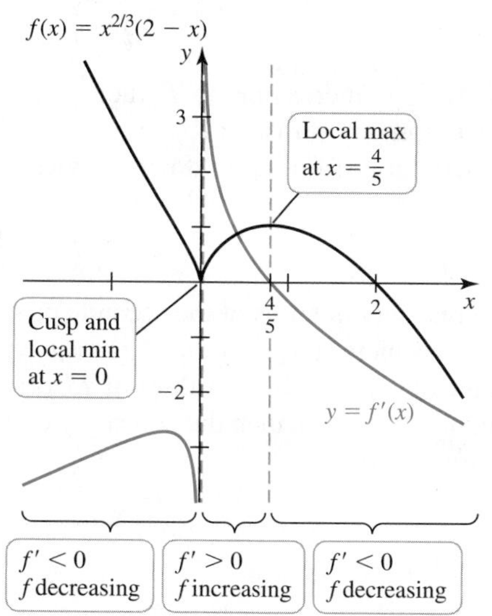

FIGURE 4.23

QUICK CHECK 3 Explain how the First Derivative Test determines whether $f(x) = x^2$ has a local maximum or local minimum at $x = 0$.

Absolute Extreme Values on Any Interval Theorem 4.1 guarantees the existence of absolute extreme values only on closed intervals. What can be said about absolute extrema on intervals that are not closed? The following theorem provides a valuable test.

> **THEOREM 4.5 One Local Extremum Implies Absolute Extremum**
> Suppose f is continuous on an interval I that contains exactly one local extremum at c.
>
> - If a local minimum occurs at c, then $f(c)$ is the absolute minimum of f on I.
> - If a local maximum occurs at c, then $f(c)$ is the absolute maximum of f on I.

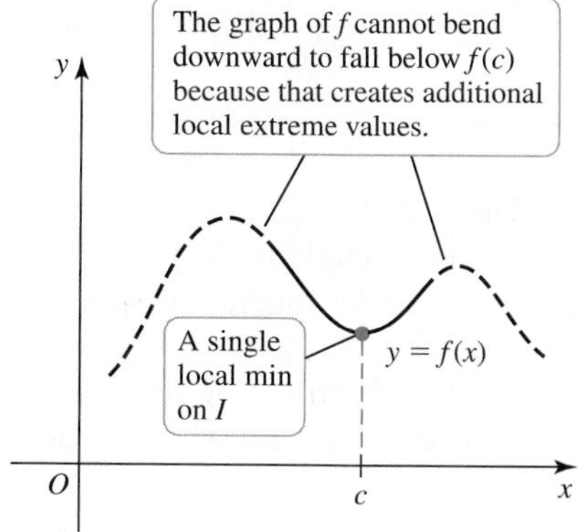

FIGURE 4.24

The proof of Theorem 4.5 is beyond the scope of this text, although Figure 4.24 illustrates why the theorem is plausible. Assume f has exactly one local minimum on I at c. Notice that there is no other point on the graph at which f has a value less than $f(c)$. If such a point did exist, the graph would have to bend downward to drop below $f(c)$. Because f is continuous on I, this cannot happen as it implies additional local extreme values on I. A similar argument applies to a solitary local maximum.

EXAMPLE 5 Finding an absolute extremum Verify that $f(x) = \frac{1}{4}x^4 - x^3 + \frac{3}{2}x^2 - 9x + 2$ has an absolute extreme value on its domain.

SOLUTION As a polynomial, f is differentiable on its domain $(-\infty, \infty)$ with

$$f'(x) = x^3 - 3x^2 + 3x - 9 = (x - 3)(x^2 + 3).$$

Solving $f'(x) = 0$ and noting that $x^2 + 3 > 0$ for all x gives the single critical point $x = 3$. It may be verified that $f'(x) < 0$ for $x < 3$ and $f'(x) > 0$ for $x > 3$. Therefore, by Theorem 4.4, f has a local minimum at $x = 3$. Because it is the only local extremum on $(-\infty, \infty)$, it follows from Theorem 4.5 that the absolute minimum value of f occurs at $x = 3$, where $f(3) = -\frac{73}{4}$ (Figure 4.25).

Related Exercises 35–38

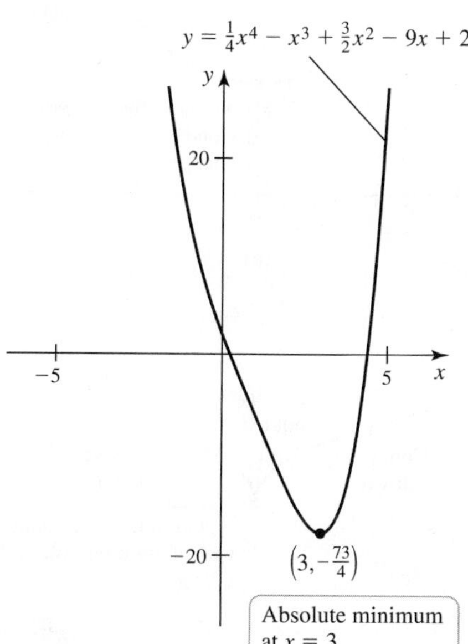

FIGURE 4.25

Concavity and Inflection Points

Just as the first derivative is related to the slope of tangent lines, the second derivative also has geometric meaning. Consider $f(x) = x^3$, shown in Figure 4.26. Its graph bends upward for $x > 0$, reflecting the fact that the tangent lines get steeper as x increases. It follows that the first derivative is increasing for $x > 0$. A function with the property that f' is increasing on an interval is **concave up** on that interval.

Similarly, $f(x) = x^3$ bends downward for $x < 0$ because it has a decreasing first derivative on that interval. A function with the property that f' is decreasing as x increases on an interval is **concave down** on that interval. We now have a useful interpretation of the second derivative: It measures *concavity*.

Here is another useful characterization of concavity. If a function is concave up at a point (any point $x > 0$ in Figure 4.26), then its graph near that point lies *above* the tangent line at that point. Similarly, if a function is concave down at a point (any point $x < 0$ in Figure 4.26), then its graph near that point lies *below* the tangent line at that point (Exercise 76).

Finally, imagine a function that changes concavity (from up to down, or vice versa) at a point c. For example, $f(x) = x^3$ in Figure 4.26 changes from concave down to concave up as x passes through $x = 0$. A point on the graph of f at which f changes concavity is called an **inflection point**.

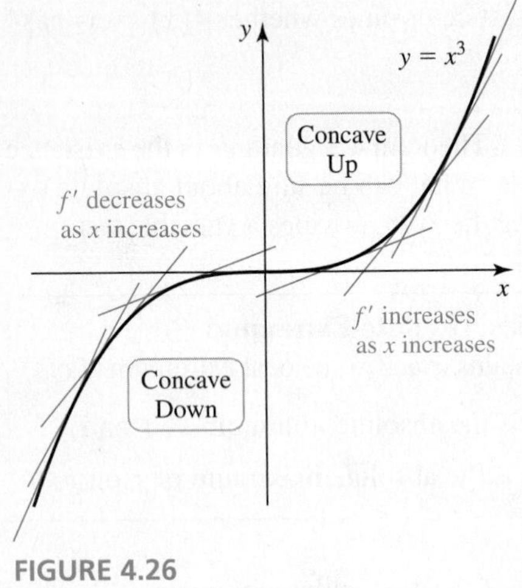

FIGURE 4.26

> **DEFINITION Concavity and Inflection Point**
>
> Let f be differentiable on an open interval I. If f' is increasing on I, then f is **concave up** on I. If f' is decreasing on I, then f is **concave down** on I.
>
> If f is continuous at c and f changes concavity at c (from up to down, or vice versa), then f has an **inflection point** at c.

Applying Theorem 4.3 to f' leads to a test for concavity in terms of the second derivative. Specifically, if $f'' > 0$ on an interval I, then f' is increasing on I and f is concave up on I. Similarly, if $f'' < 0$ on I, then f is concave down on I. If the values of f'' pass through zero at a point c (from positive to negative, or vice versa), then the concavity of f changes at c and f has an inflection point at c (Figure 4.27a).

> **THEOREM 4.6 Test for Concavity**
>
> Suppose that f'' exists on an interval I.
>
> - If $f'' > 0$ on I, then f is concave up on I.
> - If $f'' < 0$ on I, then f is concave down on I.
> - If c is a point of I at which $f''(c) = 0$ and f'' changes sign at c, then f has an inflection point at c.

There are a few important but subtle points here. The fact that $f''(c) = 0$ does not necessarily imply that f has an inflection point at c. A good example is $f(x) = x^4$. Although $f''(0) = 0$, the concavity does not change at $x = 0$ (a similar function is shown in Figure 4.27b).

Typically, if f has an inflection point at c, then $f''(c) = 0$, reflecting the smooth change in concavity. However, an inflection point may also occur at a point where f'' does

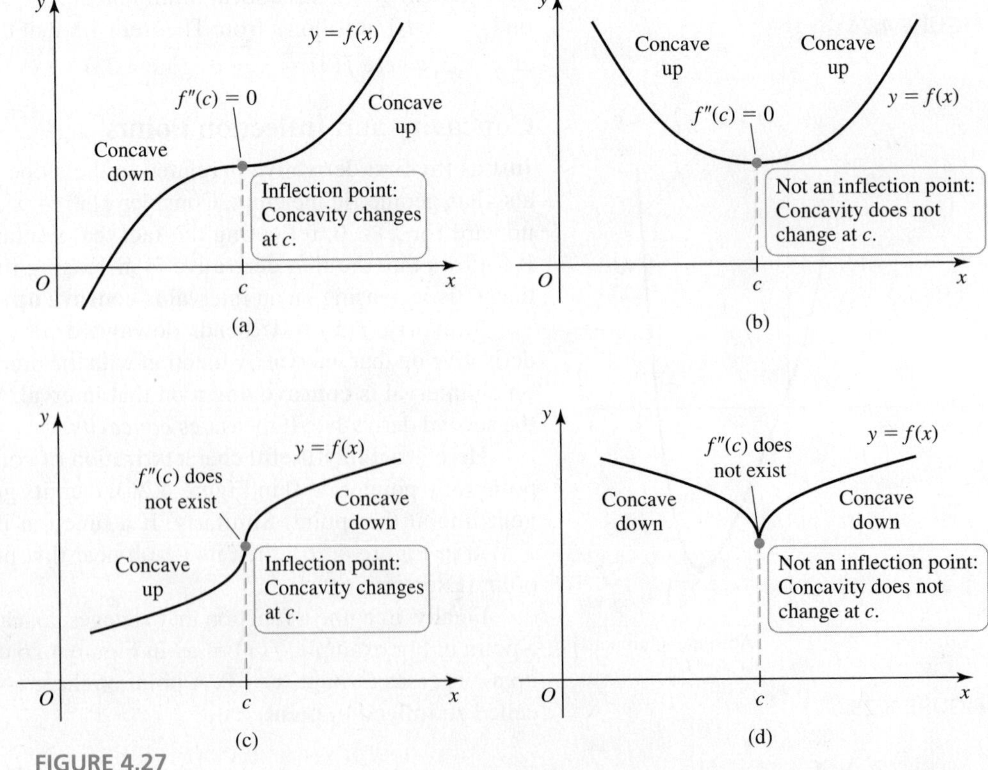

FIGURE 4.27

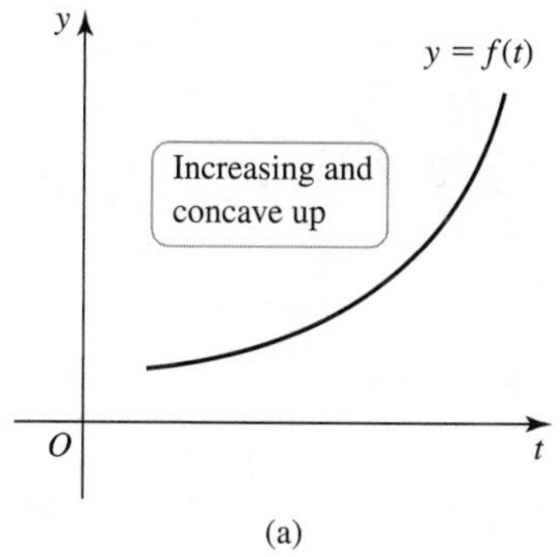

(a)

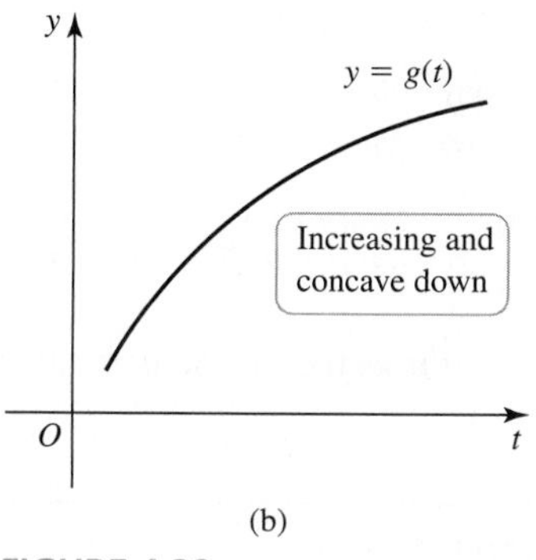

(b)

FIGURE 4.28

not exist. For example, the function $f(x) = x^{1/3}$ has a vertical tangent line and an inflection point at $x = 0$ (a similar function is shown in Figure 4.27c). Finally, the function shown in Figure 4.27d, with behavior similar to that of $f(x) = x^{2/3}$, does not have an inflection point at c and $f''(c)$ does not exist.

QUICK CHECK 4 Verify that the function $f(x) = x^4$ is concave up for $x > 0$ and for $x < 0$. Is $x = 0$ an inflection point? Explain.

EXAMPLE 6 Interpreting concavity Sketch a function satisfying each set of conditions on some interval.

a. $f'(t) > 0$ and $f''(t) > 0$ **b.** $g'(t) > 0$ and $g''(t) < 0$

c. Would you rather have f or g as a function representing the market value of a house that you own?

SOLUTION

a. Figure 4.28a shows the graph of a function that is increasing ($f'(t) > 0$) and concave up ($f''(t) > 0$).

b. Figure 4.28b shows the graph of a function that is increasing ($g'(t) > 0$) and concave down ($g''(t) < 0$).

c. Because f increases at an *increasing* rate and g increases at a *decreasing* rate, f would be a better function for the value of your house. *Related Exercises 39–42*

EXAMPLE 7 Detecting concavity Identify the intervals on which the function $f(x) = 3x^4 - 4x^3 - 6x^2 + 12x + 1$ is concave up or concave down. Then locate the inflection points.

SOLUTION This function was considered in Example 3, where we found that

$$f'(x) = 12(x + 1)(x - 1)^2.$$

It follows that

$$f''(x) = 12(x - 1)(3x + 1).$$

We see that $f''(x) = 0$ at $x = 1$ and $x = -\frac{1}{3}$. These points are *candidates* for inflection points, and it must be determined whether the concavity changes at these points. The sign graph in Figure 4.29 shows that

- $f''(x) > 0$ and f is concave up on $\left(-\infty, -\frac{1}{3}\right)$ and $(1, \infty)$, and
- $f''(x) < 0$ and f is concave down on $\left(-\frac{1}{3}, 1\right)$.

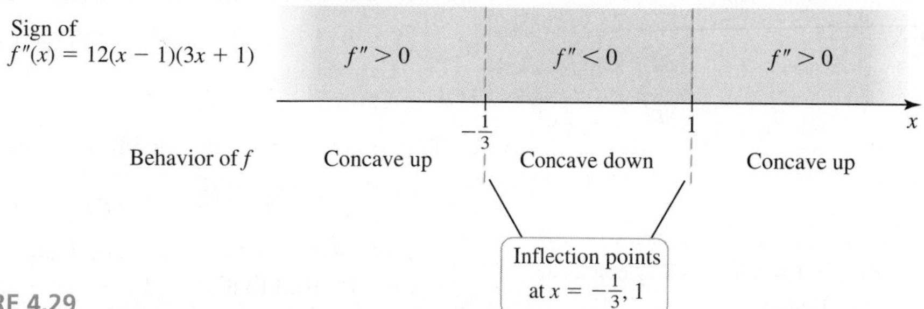

FIGURE 4.29

We see that the sign of f'' changes at $x = -\frac{1}{3}$ and at $x = 1$, so the concavity of f also changes at these points. Therefore, inflection points occur at $x = -\frac{1}{3}$ and $x = 1$. The graphs of f and f'' (Figure 4.30) show that the concavity of f changes at the zeros of f''.

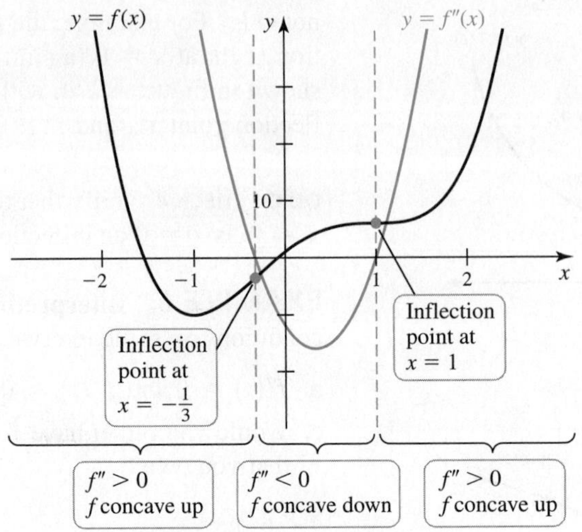

FIGURE 4.30

Related Exercises 43–50 ◀

Second Derivative Test It is now a short step to a test that uses the second derivative to identify local maxima and minima (Figure 4.31).

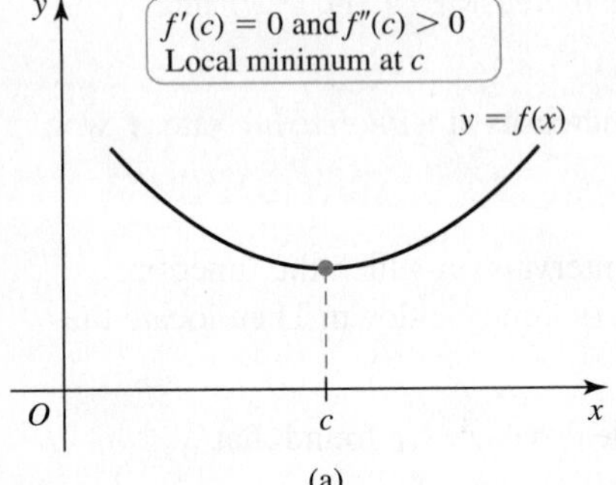

f'(c) = 0 and f''(c) < 0.
Local maximum at c
y = f(x)
y
O
c
x
(b)

FIGURE 4.31

> **THEOREM 4.7 Second Derivative Test for Local Extrema**
> Suppose that f'' is continuous on an open interval containing c with $f'(c) = 0$.
> - If $f''(c) > 0$, then f has a local minimum at c.
> - If $f''(c) < 0$, then f has a local maximum at c.
> - If $f''(c) = 0$, then the test is inconclusive.

Proof Because $f''(c) > 0$ and f'' is continuous on an interval I containing c, it follows that $f'' > 0$ on I and f' is increasing on I. Because $f'(c) = 0$, it follows that f' changes sign at c from negative to positive, which, by the First Derivative Test, implies that f has a local minimum at c. The proofs of the other two cases are similar. ◀

QUICK CHECK 5 Make a sketch of a function with $f'(x) > 0$ and $f''(x) > 0$ on an interval. Make a sketch of a function with $f'(x) < 0$ and $f''(x) < 0$ on an interval. ◀

➤ In the inconclusive case of Theorem 4.7 where $f''(c) = 0$, it is usually best to use the First Derivative Test.

EXAMPLE 8 The Second Derivative Test Use the Second Derivative Test to locate the local extrema of the following functions.

a. $f(x) = 3x^4 - 4x^3 - 6x^2 + 12x + 1$ on $[-2, 2]$ **b.** $f(x) = \sin^2 x$

SOLUTION

a. This function was considered in Examples 3 and 7, where we found that

$$f'(x) = 12(x + 1)(x - 1)^2 \quad \text{and} \quad f''(x) = 12(x - 1)(3x + 1).$$

Therefore, the critical points of f are $x = -1$ and $x = 1$. Evaluating f'' at the critical points, we find that $f''(-1) = 48 > 0$. By the Second Derivative Test, f has a local minimum at $x = -1$. At the other critical point, $f''(1) = 0$, so the test is inconclusive. You can check that the first derivative does not change sign at $x = 1$, which means f does not have a local maximum or minimum at $x = 1$ (Figure 4.32).

b. Using the Chain Rule and a trigonometric identity, we have $f'(x) = 2 \sin x \cos x = \sin 2x$ and $f''(x) = 2 \cos 2x$. The critical points occur when $f'(x) = \sin 2x = 0$, or

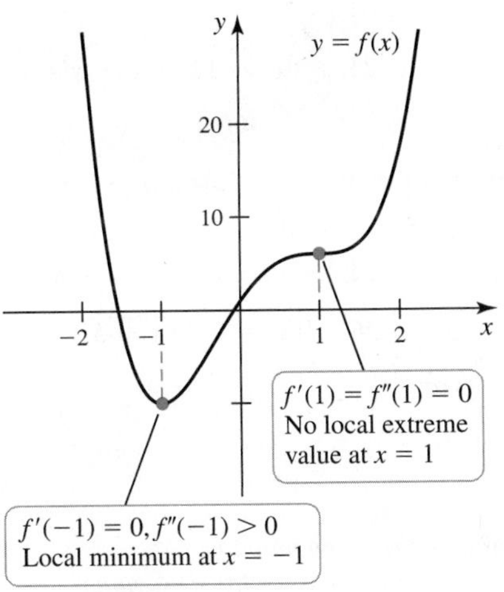

FIGURE 4.32

when $x = 0, \pm\pi/2, \pm\pi, \ldots$. To apply the Second Derivative Test, we evaluate f'' at the critical points:

- $f''(0) = 2 > 0$, so f has a local minimum at $x = 0$.
- $f''(\pm\pi/2) = -2 < 0$, so f has a local maximum at $x = \pm\pi/2$.
- $f''(\pm\pi) = 2 > 0$, so f has a local minimum at $x = \pm\pi$.

This pattern continues, and we see that f has alternating local maxima and minima, evenly spaced every $\pi/2$ units (Figure 4.33).

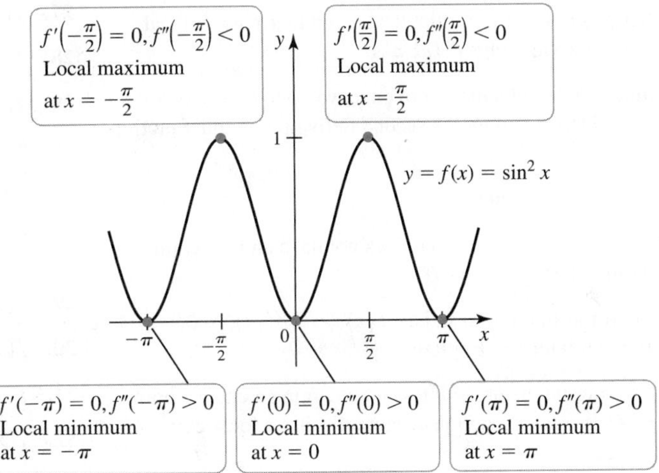

FIGURE 4.33

Related Exercises 51–56

Recap of Derivative Properties

This section has demonstrated that the first and second derivatives of a function provide valuable information about its graph. The relationships among a function's derivatives, and its extreme points and concavity are summarized in Figure 4.34.

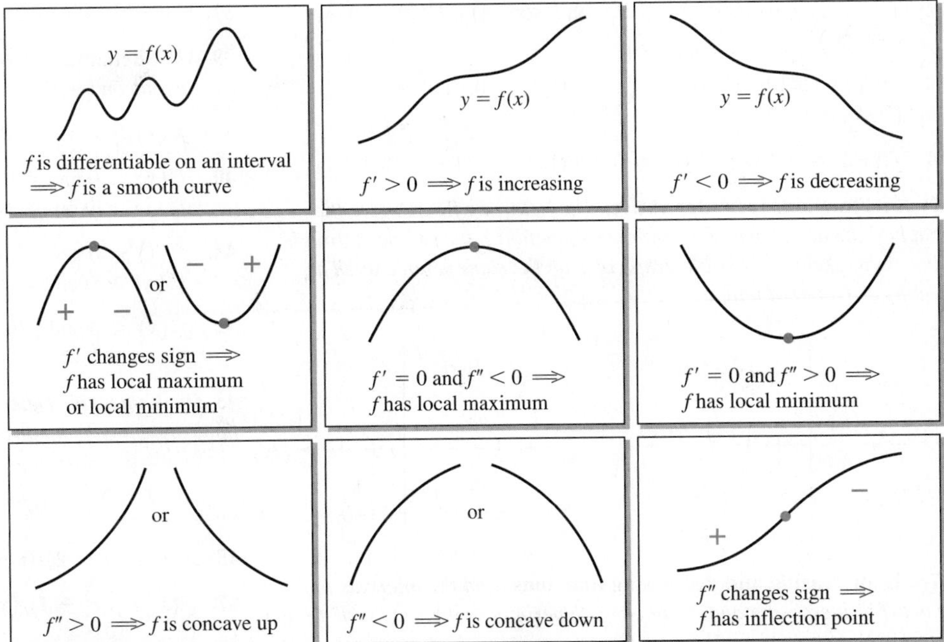

FIGURE 4.34

SECTION 4.2 EXERCISES

Review Questions

1. Explain how the first derivative of a function determines where the function is increasing and decreasing.
2. Explain how to apply the First Derivative Test.
3. Sketch the graph of a function that has neither a local maximum nor a local minimum at a point where $f'(x) = 0$.
4. Explain how to apply the Second Derivative Test.
5. Assume that f is twice differentiable at c and that f has a local maximum at c. Explain why $f''(c) \leq 0$.
6. Sketch a function that changes from concave up to concave down as x increases. Describe how the second derivative of this function changes.
7. What is an inflection point?
8. Sketch the graph of a function that does not have an inflection point at a point where $f''(x) = 0$.
9. Is it possible for a function to satisfy $f(x) > 0, f'(x) > 0$, and $f''(x) > 0$ on an interval? Explain.
10. Suppose f is continuous on an interval containing a critical point c and $f''(c) = 0$. How do you determine if f has a local extreme value at $x = c$?

Basic Skills

11–14. Sketches from properties *Sketch a function that is continuous on $(-\infty, \infty)$ and has the following properties. Use a number line to summarize information about the function.*

11. $f'(x) < 0$ on $(-\infty, 2)$; $f'(x) > 0$ on $(2, 5)$; $f'(x) < 0$ on $(5, \infty)$
12. $f'(-1)$ is undefined; $f'(x) > 0$ on $(-\infty, -1)$; $f'(x) < 0$ on $(-1, \infty)$
13. $f(0) = f(4) = f'(0) = f'(2) = f'(4) = 0$; $f(x) \geq 0$ on $(-\infty, \infty)$
14. $f'(-2) = f'(2) = f'(6) = 0$; $f'(x) \geq 0$ on $(-\infty, \infty)$

15–16. Functions from derivatives *The following figures give the graph of the derivative of a continuous function f that passes through the origin. Sketch a possible graph of f on the same set of axes. The graphs of f are not unique.*

15.

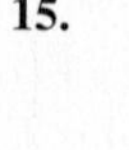

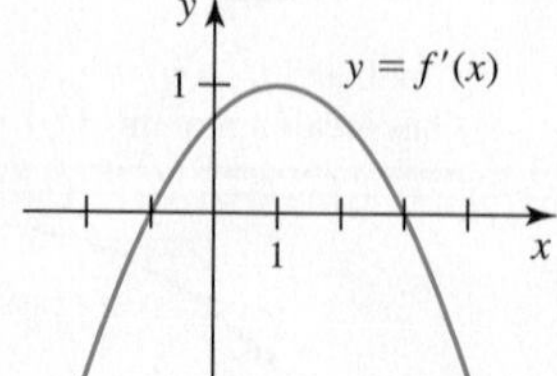

16.

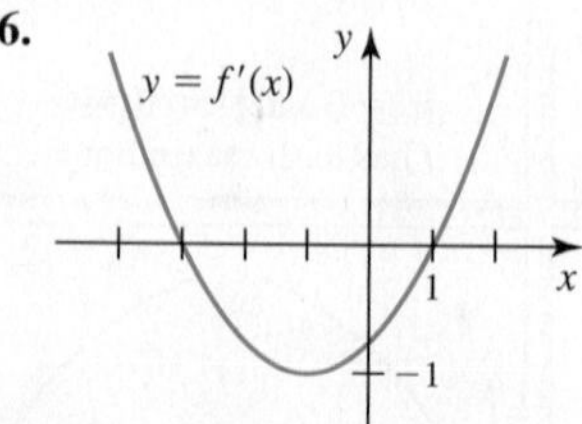

17–22. Increasing and decreasing functions *Find the intervals on which f is increasing and decreasing. Superimpose the graphs of f and f' to verify your work.*

17. $f(x) = 4 - x^2$
18. $f(x) = x^2 - 16$
19. $f(x) = (x - 1)^2$
20. $f(x) = x^3 + 4x$
21. $f(x) = 12 + x - x^2$
22. $f(x) = x^4 - 4x^3 + 4x^2$

23–28. Increasing and decreasing functions *Find the intervals on which f is increasing and decreasing.*

23. $f(x) = 3\cos 3x$ on $[-\pi, \pi]$
24. $f(x) = \cos^2 x$ on $[-\pi, \pi]$
25. $f(x) = x^{4/3}$
26. $f(x) = x^2\sqrt{x + 5}$
27. $f(x) = -12x^5 + 75x^4 - 80x^3$
28. $f(x) = \frac{1}{3}x^3 - 2x^2 + 3x + 10$

29–34. First Derivative Test

a. Locate the critical points of the given function.
b. Use the First Derivative Test to locate the local maximum and minimum values.
c. Identify the absolute minimum and maximum values of the function on the given interval (when they exist).

29. $f(x) = x^2 + 3$; $[-3, 2]$
30. $f(x) = -x^2 - x + 2$; $[-4, 4]$
31. $f(x) = x\sqrt{9 - x^2}$; $[-3, 3]$
32. $f(x) = 2x^3 + 3x^2 - 12x + 1$; $[-2, 4]$
33. $f(x) = x^{2/3}(x - 4)$; $[-5, 5]$
34. $f(x) = \dfrac{x^2}{x^2 - 1}$; $[-4, 4]$

35–38. Absolute extreme values *Verify that the following functions satisfy the conditions of Theorem 4.5 on their domains. Then find the location and value of the absolute extrema guaranteed by the theorem.*

35. $f(x) = -3x^2 + 2x - 5$
36. $f(x) = 4x + 1/\sqrt{x}, x \geq 0$
37. $A(r) = 24/r + 2\pi r^2, r > 0$
38. $f(x) = x\sqrt{3 - x}, x \leq 3$

39–42. Sketching curves *Sketch a graph of the function f that is continuous on $(-\infty, \infty)$ and has the following properties.*

39. $f'(x) > 0, f''(x) > 0$
40. $f'(x) < 0$ and $f''(x) > 0$ on $(-\infty, 0)$; $f'(x) > 0$ and $f''(x) > 0$ on $(0, \infty)$
41. $f'(x) < 0$ and $f''(x) < 0$ on $(-\infty, 0)$; $f'(x) < 0$ and $f''(x) > 0$ on $(0, \infty)$
42. $f'(x) < 0$ and $f''(x) > 0$ on $(-\infty, 0)$; $f'(x) < 0$ and $f''(x) < 0$ on $(0, \infty)$

43–50. Concavity *Determine the intervals on which the following functions are concave up or concave down. Identify any inflection points.*

43. $f(x) = 5x^4 - 20x^3 + 10$
44. $f(x) = \dfrac{1}{1 + x^2}$
45. $g(t) = (t - 2)/(t + 3)$
46. $g(x) = \sqrt[3]{x - 4}$
47. $f(x) = (x^2 - 1)/(x^2 + 1)$
48. $h(t) = 2 + \cos 2t$, for $-\pi \leq t \leq \pi$
49. $g(t) = 3t^5 - 30t^4 + 80t^3 + 100$
50. $f(x) = 2x^4 + 8x^3 + 12x^2 - x - 2$

51–56. Second Derivative Test *Locate the critical points of the following functions. Then use the Second Derivative Test to determine whether they correspond to local minima or local maxima or whether the test is inconclusive.*

51. $f(x) = 4 - x^2$

52. $g(x) = x^3 - 6$

53. $f(x) = 2x^3 - 3x^2 + 12$

54. $p(x) = (x - 4)/(x^2 + 20)$

55. $f(x) = 1/x - 3/x^3$

56. $g(x) = x^4/2 - 12x^2$

Further Explorations

57. Explain why or why not Determine whether the following statements are true and give an explanation or counterexample.

a. If $f'(x) > 0$ and $f''(x) < 0$ on an interval, then f is increasing at a decreasing rate.

b. If $f'(c) > 0$ and $f''(c) = 0$, then f has a local maximum at c.

c. Two functions that differ by a constant increase and decrease on the same intervals.

d. If f and g increase on an interval, then the product fg also increases on that interval.

e. There exists a function f that is continuous on $(-\infty, \infty)$ with exactly three critical points, all of which correspond to local maxima.

58–59. Functions from derivatives *Consider the following graphs of f' and f''. On the same set of axes, sketch the graph of a possible function f. The graphs of f are not unique.*

58.

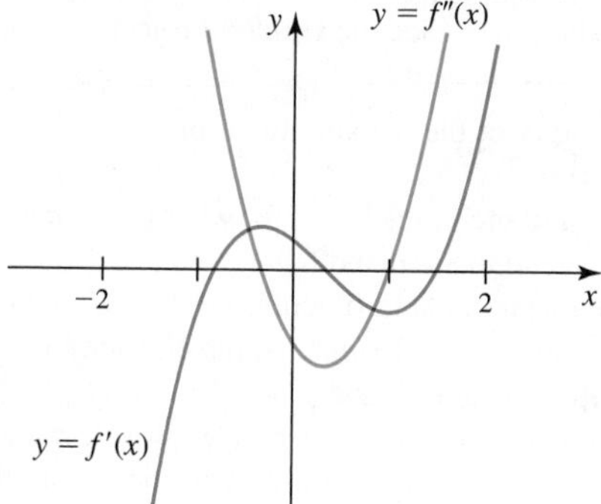

59.

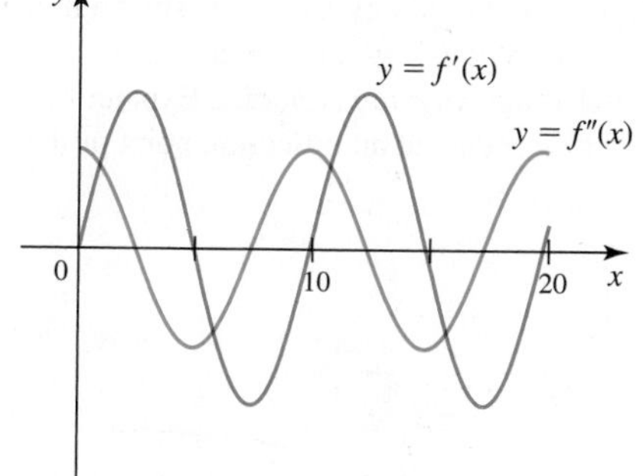

60. Is it possible? Determine whether the following properties can be satisfied by a function that is continuous on $(-\infty, \infty)$. If such a function is possible, provide an example or a sketch of the function. If such a function is not possible, explain why.

a. A function f is concave down and positive everywhere.

b. A function f is increasing and concave down everywhere.

c. A function f has exactly two local extrema and three inflection points.

d. A function f has exactly four zeros and two local extrema.

61. Matching derivatives and functions The following figures show the graphs of three functions (graphs a–c). Match each function with its first derivative (graphs d–f) *and* its second derivative (graphs g–i).

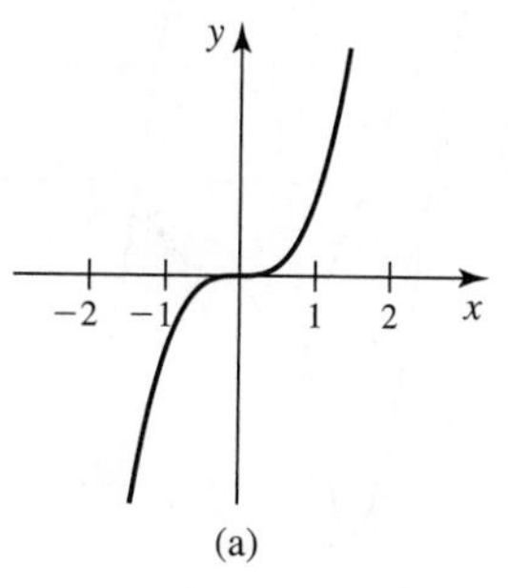
(a)

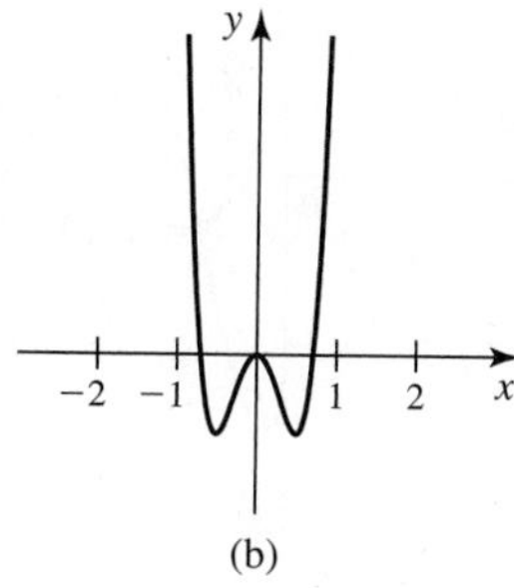
(b)

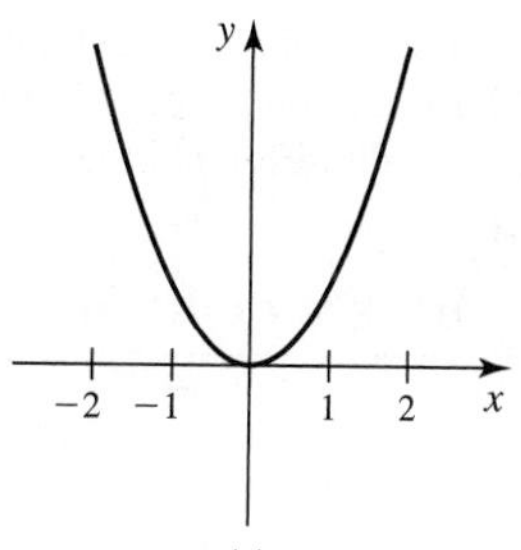
(c)

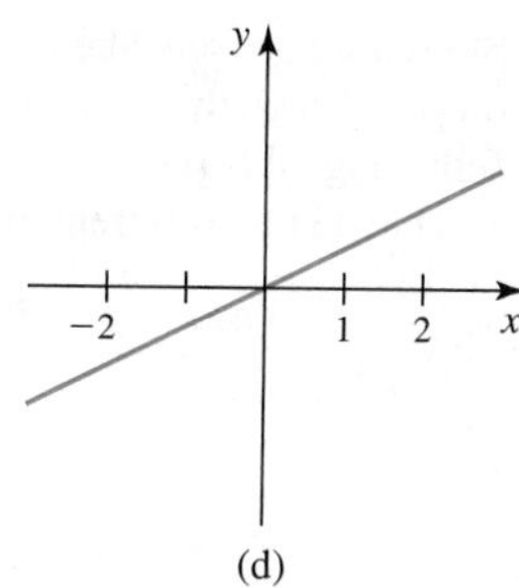
(d)

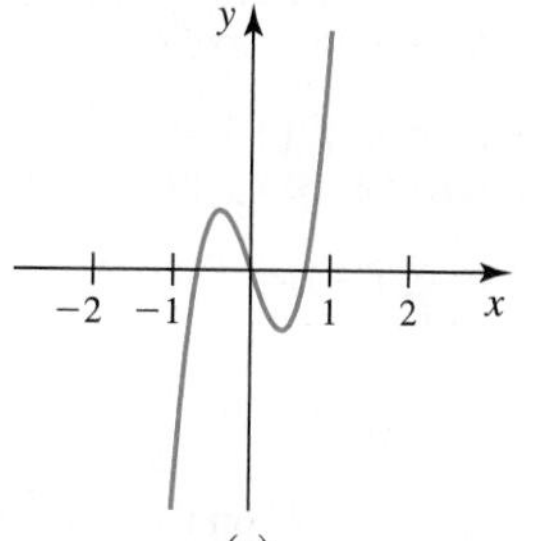
(e)

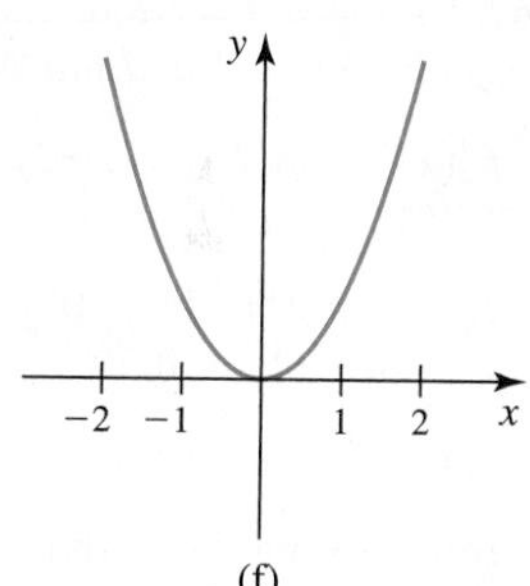
(f)

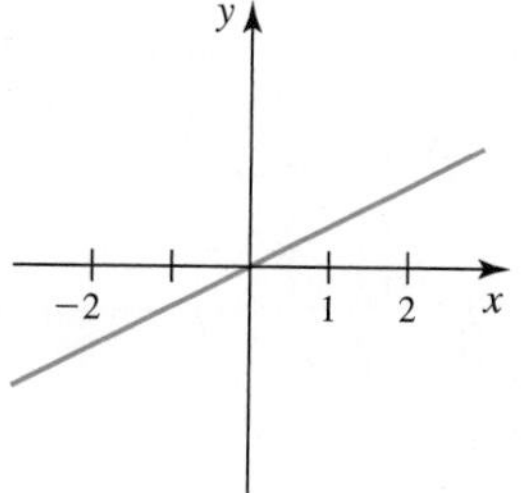
(g)

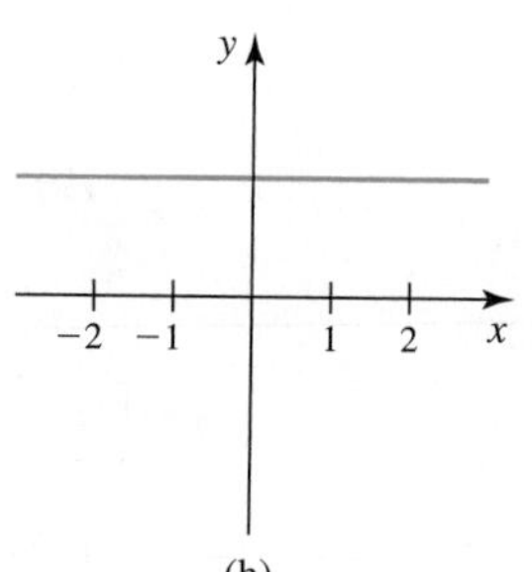
(h)

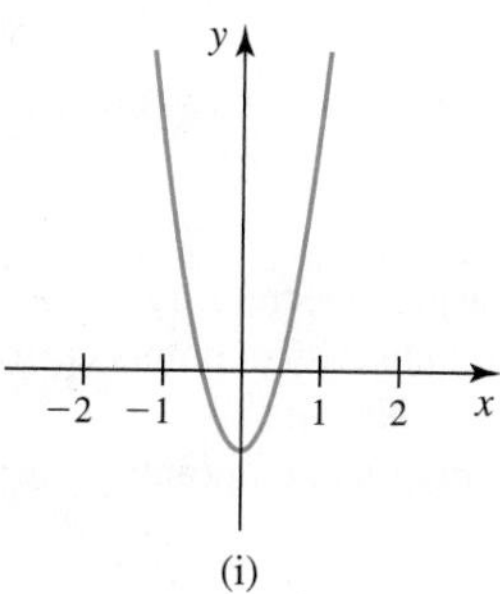
(i)

62. Graphical analysis The accompanying figure shows the graphs of f, f', and f''. Which curve is which?

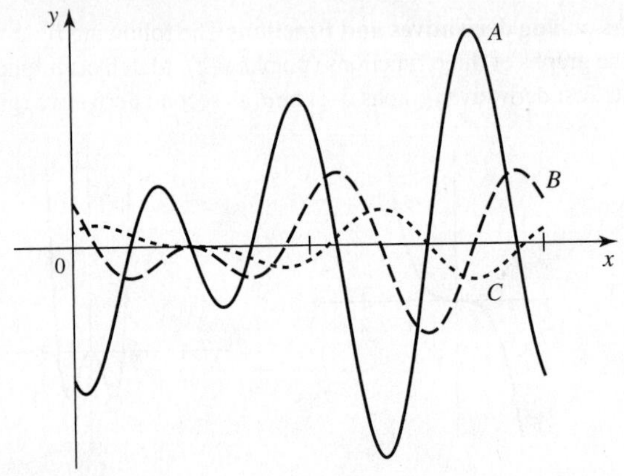

63. Sketching graphs Sketch the graph of a function f continuous on $[a, b]$ such that f, f', and f'' have the signs indicated in the following table on $[a, b]$. There are eight different cases lettered A–H and eight different graphs.

Case	A	B	C	D	E	F	G	H
f	+	+	+	+	−	−	−	−
f'	+	+	−	−	+	+	−	−
f''	+	−	+	−	+	−	+	−

64–67. Designer functions *Sketch the graph of a function that is continuous on* $(-\infty, \infty)$ *and satisfies the following sets of conditions.*

64. $f''(x) > 0$ on $(-\infty, -2)$; $f''(-2) = 0$; $f'(-1) = f'(1) = 0$; $f''(2) = 0$; $f'(3) = 0$; $f''(x) > 0$ on $(4, \infty)$

65. $f(-2) = f''(-1) = 0$; $f'\left(-\frac{3}{2}\right) = 0$; $f(0) = f'(0) = 0$; $f(1) = f'(1) = 0$

66. $f(x) > f'(x) > 0$ for all x; $f''(1) = 0$

67. Interpreting the derivative The graph of f' on the interval $[-3, 2]$ is shown in the figure.

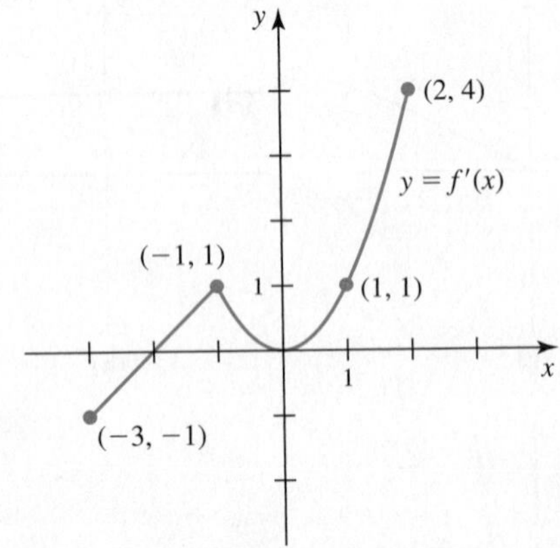

a. On what interval(s) is f increasing? Decreasing?
b. Find the critical points of f. Which critical points correspond to local maxima? Local minima? Neither?
c. At what point(s) does f have an inflection point?
d. On what interval(s) is f concave up? Concave down?
e. Sketch the graph of f''.
f. Sketch one possible graph of f.

68–71. Second Derivative Test *Locate the critical points of the following functions and use the Second Derivative Test to determine whether they correspond to local minima, local maxima, or neither.*

68. $p(t) = 2t^3 + 3t^2 - 36t$

69. $f(x) = \frac{x^4}{4} - \frac{5x^3}{3} - 4x^2 + 48x$

70. $h(x) = (x + a)^4$, *a* constant

71. $f(x) = x^3 + 2x^2 + 4x - 1$

72. Concavity of parabolas Consider the general parabola described by the function $f(x) = ax^2 + bx + c$. For what values of a, b, and c is f concave up? For what values of a, b, and c is f concave down?

Applications

T 73. Demand functions and elasticity Economists use *demand functions* to describe how much of a commodity can be sold at varying prices. For example, the demand function $D(p) = 500 - 10p$ says that at a price of $p = 10$, a quantity of $D(10) = 400$ units of the commodity can be sold. The elasticity $E = \frac{dD}{dp}\frac{p}{D}$ of the demand gives the approximate percent change in the demand for every 1% change in the price. (See the Guided Projects for more on demand functions and elasticity.)

a. Compute the elasticity of the demand function $D(p) = 500 - 10p$.
b. If the price is \$12 and increases by 4.5%, what is the approximate percent change in the demand?
c. Show that for the linear demand function $D(p) = a - bp$, where a and b are positive real numbers, the elasticity is a decreasing function, for $p \geq 0$ and $p \neq a/b$.
d. Show that the demand function $D(p) = a/p^b$, where a and b are positive real numbers, has a constant elasticity for all positive prices.

74. Population models A typical population curve is shown in the figure. The population is small at $t = 0$ and increases toward a steady-state level called the *carrying capacity*. Explain why the maximum growth rate occurs at an inflection point of the population curve.

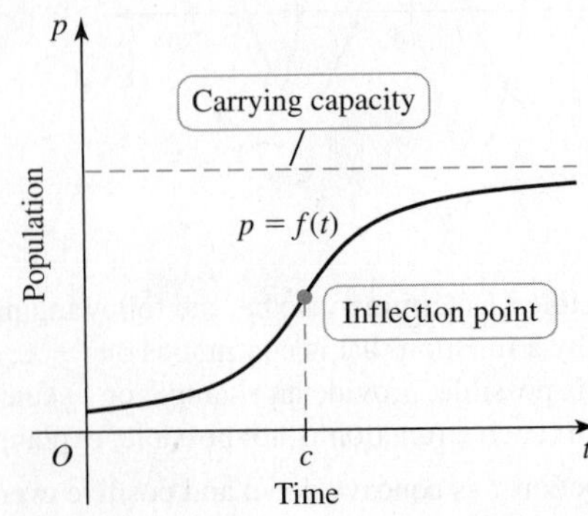

75. Population models The population of a species is given by the function $P(t) = \dfrac{Kt^2}{t^2 + b}$, where $t \geq 0$ is measured in years and K and b are positive real numbers.

a. With $K = 300$ and $b = 30$, what is $\lim_{t\to\infty} P(t)$, the carrying capacity of the population?

b. With $K = 300$ and $b = 30$, when does the maximum growth rate occur?

c. For arbitrary positive values of K and b, when does the maximum growth rate occur (in terms of K and b)?

Additional Exercises

76. Tangent lines and concavity Give an argument to support the claim that if a function is concave up at a point, then the tangent line at that point lies below the curve near that point.

77. Symmetry of cubics Consider the general cubic polynomial $f(x) = x^3 + ax^2 + bx + c$, where a, b, and c are real numbers.

a. Show that f has exactly one inflection point and it occurs at $x^* = -a/3$.

b. Show that f is an odd function with respect to the inflection point $(x^*, f(x^*))$. This means that $f(x^*) - f(x^* + x) = f(x^* - x) - f(x^*)$ for all x.

78. Properties of cubics Consider the general cubic polynomial $f(x) = x^3 + ax^2 + bx + c$, where a, b, and c are real numbers.

a. Prove that f has exactly one local minimum and one local maximum provided that $a^2 > 3b$.

b. Prove that f has no extreme values if $a^2 < 3b$.

c. Prove that for all real values of a, b, and c, the function has exactly one inflection point. Where is the inflection point located?

T 79. A family of single-humped functions Consider the functions $f(x) = \dfrac{1}{x^{2n} + 1}$, where n is a positive integer.

a. Show that these functions are even.

b. Show that the graphs of these functions intersect at the points $\left(\pm 1, \frac{1}{2}\right)$ for all positive values of n.

c. Show that the inflection points of these functions occur at $x = \pm \sqrt[2n]{\dfrac{2n - 1}{2n + 1}}$ for all positive values of n.

d. Use a graphing utility to verify your conclusions.

e. Describe how the inflection points and the shape of the graph change as n increases.

80. Even quartics Consider the quartic (fourth-degree) polynomial $f(x) = x^4 + bx^2 + d$ consisting only of even-powered terms.

a. Show that the graph of f is symmetric about the y-axis.

b. Show that if $b \geq 0$, then f has one critical point and no inflection points.

c. Show that if $b < 0$, then f has three critical points and two inflection points. Find the critical points and inflection points, and show that they alternate along the x-axis. Explain why one critical point is always $x = 0$.

d. Prove that the number of distinct real roots of f depends on the values of the coefficients b and d, as shown in the figure. The curve that divides the plane is the parabola $d = b^2/4$.

e. Find the number of real roots when $b = 0$ or $d = 0$ or $d = b^2/4$.

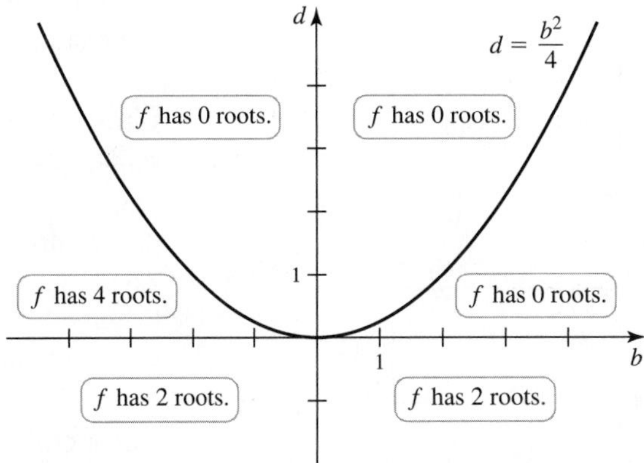

81. General quartic Show that the general quartic (fourth-degree) polynomial $f(x) = x^4 + ax^3 + bx^2 + cx + d$ has either zero or two inflection points, and the latter case occurs provided that $b < 3a^2/8$.

QUICK CHECK ANSWERS

1. Positive derivatives on an interval mean the curve is rising on the interval, which means the function is increasing on the interval. **2.**

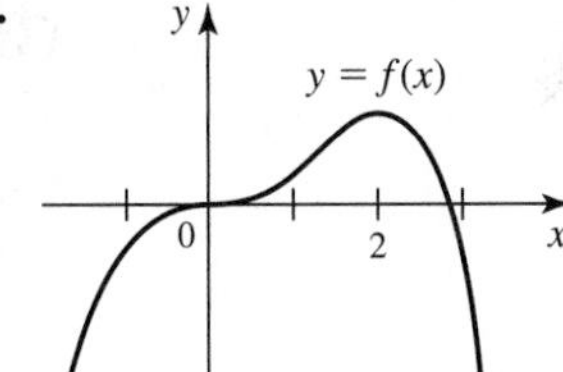

3. $f'(x) < 0$ on $(-\infty, 0)$ and $f'(x) > 0$ on $(0, \infty)$. Therefore, f has a local minimum at $x = 0$ by the First Derivative Test. **4.** $f''(x) = 12x^2$, so $f''(x) > 0$ for $x < 0$ and for $x > 0$. There is no inflection point at $x = 0$ because the second derivative does not change sign. **5.** The first curve should be rising and concave up. The second curve should be falling and concave down.

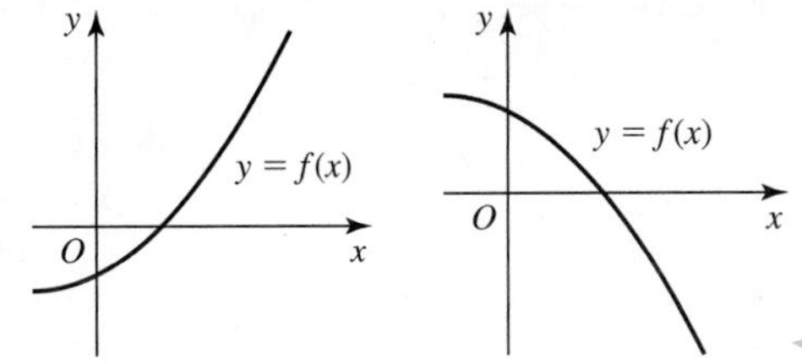

4.3 Graphing Functions

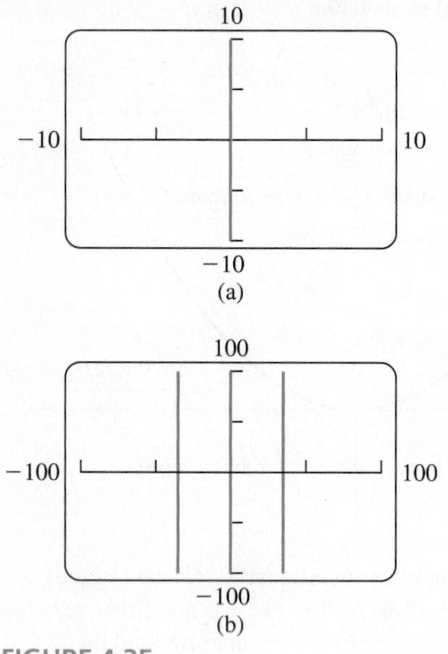

FIGURE 4.35

Over the span of three chapters, we have collected the tools required for a comprehensive approach to graphing functions. These *analytical methods* are indispensable, even with the availability of powerful graphing utilities, as illustrated by the following example.

Calculators and Analysis

Suppose you want to graph the harmless-looking function $f(x) = x^3/3 - 400x$. If you plot f using a typical graphing utility with a default window of $[-10, 10] \times [-10, 10]$, the resulting graph is shown in Figure 4.35a; one vertical line appears on the screen. Zooming out to the window $[-100, 100] \times [-100, 100]$ produces three vertical lines (Figure 4.35b), which is not an accurate graph of the function. Expanding the window even more to $[-1000, 1000] \times [-1000, 1000]$ is no better. So, what do we do?

QUICK CHECK 1 Try to graph $f(x) = x^3/3 - 400x$ by using various windows on a graphing utility. Can you find a window that gives a better graph of f than those in Figure 4.35?

Like most functions, $f(x) = x^3/3 - 400x$ has a reasonable graph, but it cannot be found automatically by letting technology do all the work. Here is the message of this section: Graphing utilities are valuable for exploring functions, producing preliminary graphs, and checking your work. But they should not be relied on exclusively because they cannot explain *why* a graph has its shape. Rather, graphing utilities should be used in an interactive way with the analytical methods presented in this chapter.

Graphing Guidelines

The following set of guidelines need not be followed exactly for every function, and you will find that several steps can often be done at once. Depending on the specific problem, some of the steps are best done analytically, while other steps can be done with a graphing utility. Experiment with both approaches and try to find a good balance. We also present a schematic record-keeping procedure to keep track of discoveries as they are made.

➤ The precise order of these steps may vary from one problem to another.

Graphing Guidelines for $y = f(x)$

1. **Identify the domain or interval of interest.** On what interval should the function be graphed? It may be the domain of the function or some subset of the domain.

2. **Exploit symmetry.** Take advantage of symmetry. For example, is the function even ($f(-x) = f(x)$), odd ($f(-x) = -f(x)$), or neither?

3. **Find the first and second derivatives.** They are needed to determine extreme values, concavity, inflection points, and intervals of increase and decrease. Computing derivatives—particularly second derivatives—may not be practical, so some functions may need to be graphed without complete derivative information.

4. **Find critical points and possible inflection points.** Determine points at which $f'(x) = 0$ or f' is undefined. Determine points at which $f''(x) = 0$ or f'' is undefined.

5. **Find intervals on which the function is increasing/decreasing and concave up/down.** The first derivative determines the intervals of increase and decrease. The second derivative determines the intervals on which the function is concave up or concave down.

6. **Identify extreme values and inflection points.** Use either the First or the Second Derivative Test to classify the critical points. Both x- and y-coordinates of maxima, minima, and inflection points are needed for graphing.

7. **Locate vertical/horizontal asymptotes and determine end behavior.** Vertical asymptotes often occur at zeros of denominators. Horizontal asymptotes require examining limits as $x \to \pm\infty$; these limits determine end behavior.

8. **Find the intercepts.** The y-intercept of the graph is found by setting $x = 0$. The x-intercepts are the real zeros (or roots) of a function: those values of x that satisfy $f(x) = 0$.

9. **Choose an appropriate graphing window and make a graph.** Use the results of the above steps to graph the function. If you use graphing software, check for consistency with your analytical work. Is your graph *complete*—that is, does it show all the essential details of the function?

EXAMPLE 1 **A warm-up** Given the following information about the first and second derivatives of a function f, which is continuous on $(-\infty, \infty)$, summarize the information using a number line, and then sketch a possible graph of f.

$f' < 0, f'' > 0$ on $(-\infty, 0)$ $\quad$ $f' > 0, f'' > 0$ on $(0, 1)$ $\quad$ $f' > 0, f'' < 0$ on $(1, 2)$

$f' < 0, f'' < 0$ on $(2, 3)$ $\quad$ $f' < 0, f'' > 0$ on $(3, 4)$ $\quad$ $f' > 0, f'' > 0$ on $(4, \infty)$

SOLUTION We illustrate the given information on a number line. For example, on the interval $(-\infty, 0)$, f is decreasing and concave up; so we sketch a segment of a curve with these properties on this interval (Figure 4.36). Continuing in this manner, we obtain a useful summary of the properties of f.

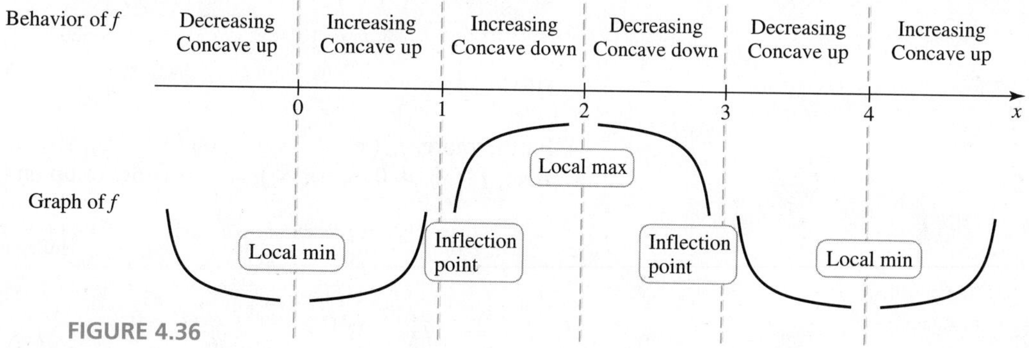

FIGURE 4.36

Assembling the information shown in Figure 4.36, a rough graph of f is produced (Figure 4.37). Notice that derivative information is not sufficient to determine the y-coordinates of points on the curve.

Related Exercises 7–8◀

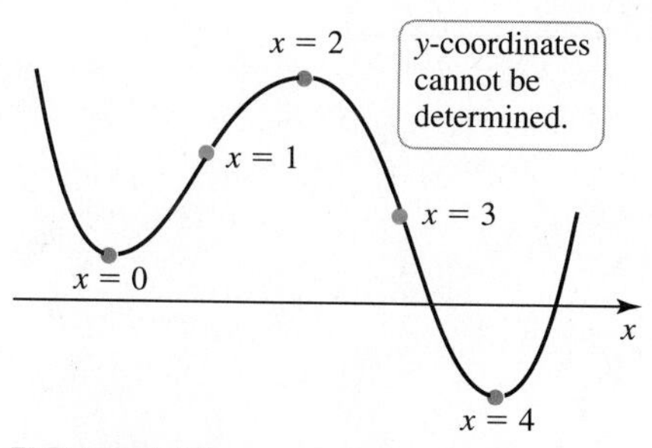

FIGURE 4.37

QUICK CHECK 2 Explain why the function f and $f + C$, where C is a constant, have the same derivative properties.

EXAMPLE 2 A deceptive polynomial Use the graphing guidelines to graph $f(x) = \frac{x^3}{3} - 400x$ on its domain.

SOLUTION

1. **Domain** The domain of any polynomial is $(-\infty, \infty)$.

➤ Notice that the first derivative of an odd polynomial is an even polynomial and the second derivative is an odd polynomial.

2. **Symmetry** Because f consists of odd powers of the variable, it is an odd function. Its graph is symmetric about the origin.

3. **Derivatives** The first two derivatives of f are

$$f'(x) = x^2 - 400 \quad \text{and} \quad f''(x) = 2x.$$

4. **Critical points and possible inflection points** Solving $f'(x) = 0$, we find that the critical points are $x = \pm 20$. Solving $f''(x) = 0$, we see that a possible inflection point occurs at $x = 0$.

➤ See Appendix A for solving inequalities using test values.

5. **Increasing/decreasing and concavity** Note that

$$f'(x) = x^2 - 400 = (x - 20)(x + 20).$$

Solving the inequality $f'(x) < 0$, we find that f is decreasing on the interval $(-20, 20)$. Solving the inequality $f'(x) > 0$ reveals that f is increasing on the intervals $(-\infty, -20)$ and $(20, \infty)$ (Figure 4.38). By the First Derivative Test, we have enough information to conclude that f has a local maximum at $x = -20$ and a local minimum at $x = 20$.

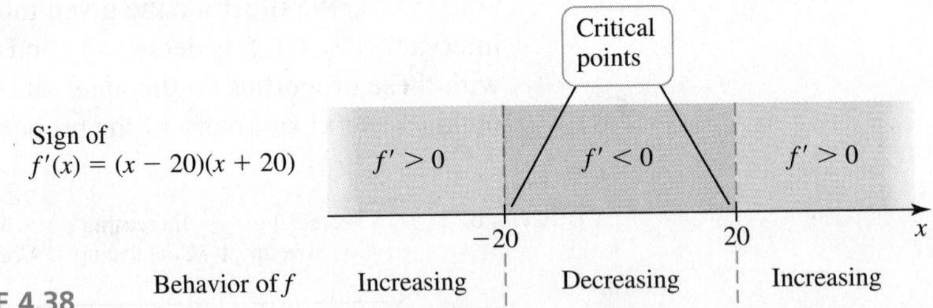

FIGURE 4.38

Furthermore, $f''(x) = 2x < 0$ on $(-\infty, 0)$, so f is concave down on this interval. Also, $f''(x) > 0$ on $(0, \infty)$, so f is concave up on $(0, \infty)$ (Figure 4.39).

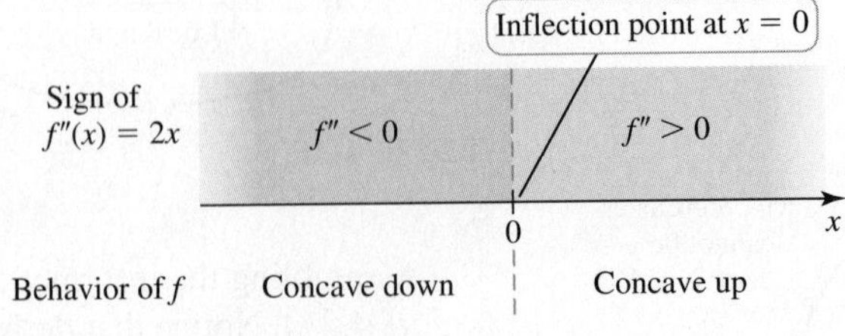

FIGURE 4.39

The evidence obtained so far is summarized in Figure 4.40.

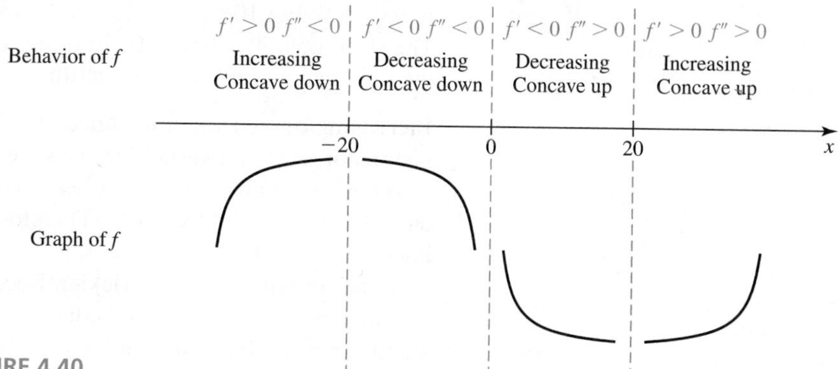

FIGURE 4.40

6. **Extreme values and inflection points** In this case, the Second Derivative Test is easily applied and it confirms what we have already learned. Because $f''(-20) < 0$ and $f''(20) > 0$, f has a local maximum at $x = -20$ and a local minimum at $x = 20$. The corresponding function values are $f(-20) = 16{,}000/3 = 5333\frac{1}{3}$ and $f(20) = -f(-20) = -5333\frac{1}{3}$. Finally, we see that f'' changes sign at $x = 0$, making $(0, 0)$ an inflection point.

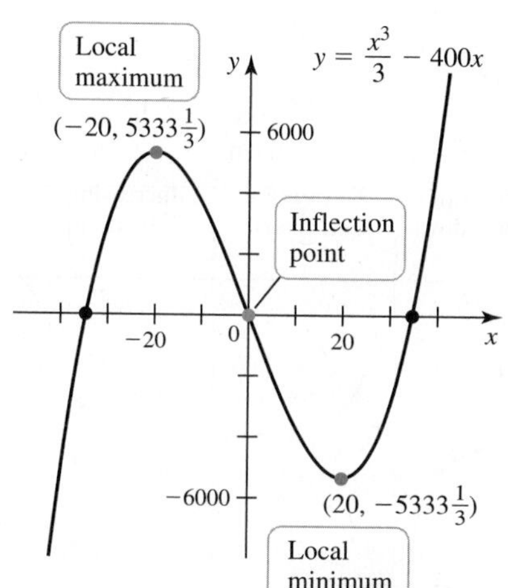

FIGURE 4.41

7. **Asymptotes and end behavior** Polynomials have neither vertical nor horizontal asymptotes. Because the highest-power term in the polynomial is x^3 (an odd power) and the leading coefficient is positive, we have the end behavior

$$\lim_{x\to\infty} f(x) = \infty \quad \text{and} \quad \lim_{x\to-\infty} f(x) = -\infty.$$

8. **Intercepts** The y-intercept is $(0, 0)$. We solve the equation $f(x) = 0$ to find the x-intercepts:

$$\frac{x^3}{3} - 400x = x\left(\frac{x^2}{3} - 400\right) = 0$$

The roots of this equation are $x = 0$ and $x = \pm\sqrt{1200} \approx \pm 34.6$.

9. **Graph the function** Using the information found in Steps 1–8, we choose the graphing window $[-40, 40] \times [-6000, 6000]$ and produce the graph shown in Figure 4.41. Notice that the symmetry detected in Step 2 is evident in this graph.

Related Exercises 9–14

EXAMPLE 3 The surprises of a rational function Use the graphing guidelines to graph $f(x) = \dfrac{10x^3}{x^2 - 1}$ on its domain.

SOLUTION

1. **Domain** The zeros of the denominator are $x = \pm 1$, so the domain is $\{x: x \neq \pm 1\}$.

2. **Symmetry** This function consists of an odd function divided by an even function. The product or quotient of an even function and an odd function is odd. Therefore, the graph is symmetric about the origin.

3. **Derivatives** The Quotient Rule is used to find the first and second derivatives:

$$f'(x) = \frac{10x^2(x^2 - 3)}{(x^2 - 1)^2} \quad \text{and} \quad f''(x) = \frac{20x(x^2 + 3)}{(x^2 - 1)^3}.$$

4. **Critical points and possible inflection points** The solutions of $f'(x) = 0$ occur where the numerator equals 0, provided the denominator is nonzero at those points. Solving $10x^2(x^2 - 3) = 0$ gives the critical points $x = 0$ and $x = \pm\sqrt{3}$. The solutions of $f''(x) = 0$ are found by solving $20x(x^2 + 3) = 0$; we see that the only candidate for an inflection point is $x = 0$.

5. **Increasing/decreasing and concavity** To find the sign of f', first note that the denominator of f' is nonnegative, as is the factor $10x^2$ in the numerator. So, the sign of f' is determined by the factor $x^2 - 3$, which is negative on $(-\sqrt{3}, \sqrt{3})$ and positive on $(-\infty, -\sqrt{3})$ and $(\sqrt{3}, \infty)$. Therefore, f is decreasing on $(-\sqrt{3}, \sqrt{3})$ and increasing on $(-\infty, -\sqrt{3})$ and $(\sqrt{3}, \infty)$.

   The sign of f'' is a bit trickier. Because $x^2 + 3$ is positive, the sign of f'' is determined by the sign of x in the numerator and $(x^2 - 1)^3$ in the denominator. When x and $(x^2 - 1)^3$ have the same sign, $f''(x) > 0$; when x and $(x^2 - 1)^3$ have opposite signs, $f''(x) < 0$ (Table 4.1). The results of this analysis are shown in Figure 4.42.

Table 4.1

	$20x$	$x^2 + 3$	$(x^2 - 1)^3$	Sign of f''
$(-\infty, -1)$	$-$	$+$	$+$	$-$
$(-1, 0)$	$-$	$+$	$-$	$+$
$(0, 1)$	$+$	$+$	$-$	$-$
$(1, \infty)$	$+$	$+$	$+$	$+$

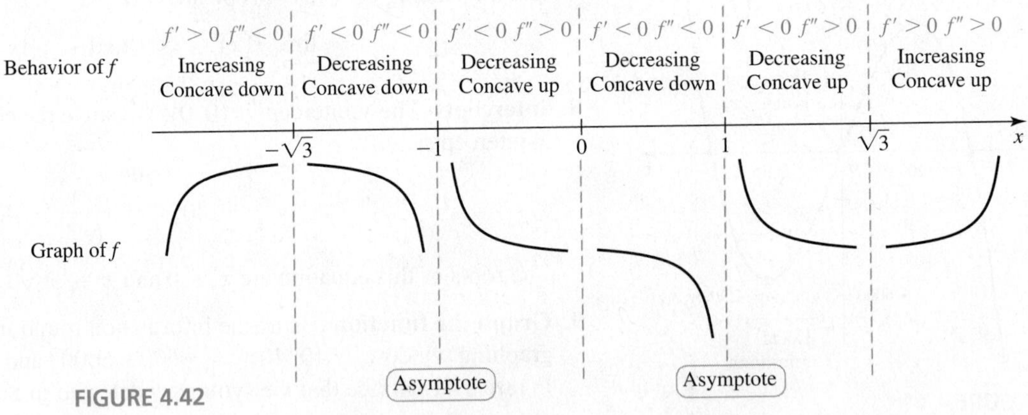

FIGURE 4.42

6. **Extreme values and inflection points** The First Derivative Test is easily applied by looking at Figure 4.42. The function is increasing on $(-\infty, -\sqrt{3})$ and decreasing on $(-\sqrt{3}, \sqrt{3})$; therefore, f has a local maximum at $x = -\sqrt{3}$, where $f(-\sqrt{3}) = -15\sqrt{3}$. Similarly, f has a local minimum at $x = \sqrt{3}$, where $f(\sqrt{3}) = 15\sqrt{3}$. (These results could also be obtained with the Second Derivative Test.) There is no local extreme value at the critical point $x = 0$, only a horizontal tangent line.

   Using the calculations of Step 5, we see that f'' changes sign at $x = \pm 1$ and at $x = 0$. The points $x = \pm 1$ are not in the domain of f, so they cannot correspond to inflection points. However, there is an inflection point at $(0, 0)$.

7. **Asymptotes and end behavior** Recall from Section 2.4 that zeros of the denominator, which in this case are $x = \pm 1$, are candidates for vertical asymptotes. Checking the sign of f on either side of $x = \pm 1$, we find

$$\lim_{x \to -1^-} f(x) = -\infty \qquad \lim_{x \to -1^+} f(x) = +\infty$$

$$\lim_{x \to 1^-} f(x) = -\infty \qquad \lim_{x \to 1^+} f(x) = +\infty$$

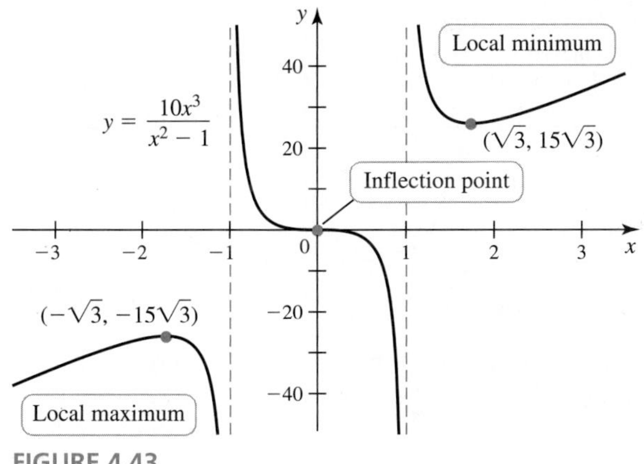

FIGURE 4.43

It follows that f has vertical asymptotes at $x = \pm 1$. The degree of the numerator is greater than the degree of the denominator, so there are no horizontal asymptotes. It can be shown that f has the slant asymptote (see Section 2.5) $y = 10x$.

8. **Intercepts** The zeros of a rational function coincide with the zeros of the numerator, provided that those points are not also zeros of the denominator. In this case the zeros of f satisfy $10x^3 = 0$, or $x = 0$ (which is not a zero of the denominator). Therefore, $(0, 0)$ is both the x- and y-intercept.

9. **Graphing** We now assemble an accurate graph of f, as shown in Figure 4.43. A window of $[-3, 3] \times [-40, 40]$ gives a complete graph of the function. Notice that the symmetry about the origin deduced in Step 2 is apparent in the graph. *Related Exercises 15–20*◀

QUICK CHECK 3 Verify that the function f in Example 3 is symmetric about the origin by showing that $f(-x) = -f(x)$.◀

In the next example, we show how the guidelines may be streamlined to some extent.

EXAMPLE 4 **Roots and cusps** Graph $f(x) = \frac{1}{8}x^{2/3}(9x^2 - 8x - 16)$ on its domain.

SOLUTION The domain of f is $(-\infty, \infty)$. The polynomial factor in f consists of both even and odd powers, so f has no special symmetry. Computing the first derivative is straightforward if you first expand f as a sum of three terms:

$$\begin{aligned} f'(x) &= \frac{d}{dx}\left(\frac{9x^{8/3}}{8} - x^{5/3} - 2x^{2/3}\right) && \text{Expand } f. \\ &= 3x^{5/3} - \frac{5}{3}x^{2/3} - \frac{4}{3}x^{-1/3} && \text{Differentiate.} \\ &= \frac{(x-1)(9x+4)}{3x^{1/3}} && \text{Simplify.} \end{aligned}$$

The critical points are now identified: f' is undefined at $x = 0$ (because $x^{-1/3}$ is undefined there) and $f'(x) = 0$ at $x = 1$ and $x = -\frac{4}{9}$. So we have three critical points to analyze. Table 4.2 tracks the signs of the three factors in f' and shows the sign of f' on the relevant intervals; this information is recorded in Figure 4.44.

Table 4.2

	$\frac{x^{-1/3}}{3}$	$9x + 4$	$x - 1$	Sign of f'
$\left(-\infty, -\frac{4}{9}\right)$	−	−	−	−
$\left(-\frac{4}{9}, 0\right)$	−	+	−	+
$(0, 1)$	+	+	−	−
$(1, \infty)$	+	+	+	+

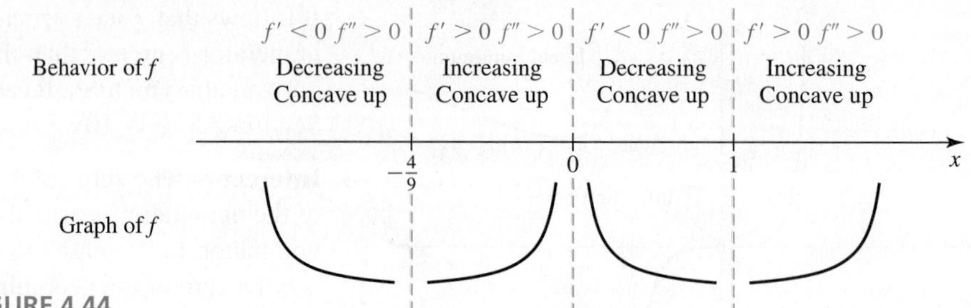

FIGURE 4.44

We use the second line in the calculation of f' to compute the second derivative:

$$\begin{aligned} f''(x) &= \frac{d}{dx}\left(3x^{5/3} - \frac{5}{3}x^{2/3} - \frac{4}{3}x^{-1/3}\right) \\ &= 5x^{2/3} - \frac{10}{9}x^{-1/3} + \frac{4}{9}x^{-4/3} \qquad \text{Differentiate.} \\ &= \frac{45x^2 - 10x + 4}{9x^{4/3}} \qquad \text{Simplify.} \end{aligned}$$

Solving $f''(x) = 0$, we discover that $f''(x) > 0$ for all x, except $x = 0$, where it is undefined. Therefore, f is concave up on $(-\infty, 0)$ and $(0, \infty)$ (Figure 4.44).

By the Second Derivative Test, because $f''(x) > 0$ for $x \neq 0$, the critical points $x = -\frac{4}{9}$ and $x = 1$ correspond to local minima; their y-coordinates are $f\left(-\frac{4}{9}\right) \approx -0.78$ and $f(1) = -\frac{15}{8} = -1.875$.

What about the third critical point $x = 0$? Note that $f(0) = 0$, and f is increasing just to the left of 0 and decreasing just to the right. By the First Derivative Test, f has a local maximum at $x = 0$. Furthermore, $f'(x) \to \infty$ as $x \to 0^-$ and $f'(x) \to -\infty$ as $x \to 0^+$, so the graph of f has a cusp at $x = 0$.

As $x \to \pm\infty$, f is dominated by its highest-power term, which is $9x^{8/3}/8$. This term becomes large and positive as $x \to \pm\infty$; therefore, f has no absolute maximum. Its absolute minimum occurs at $x = 1$ because, comparing the two local minima, $f(1) < f\left(-\frac{4}{9}\right)$.

The roots of f satisfy $\frac{1}{8}x^{2/3}(9x^2 - 8x - 16) = 0$, which gives $x = 0$ and

$$x = \frac{4}{9}(1 \pm \sqrt{10}) \approx -0.96 \quad \text{or} \quad 1.85 \qquad \text{Use the quadratic formula.}$$

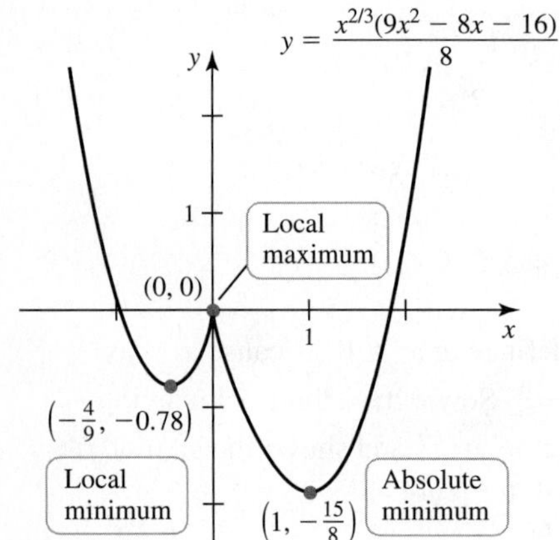

FIGURE 4.45

With the information gathered in this analysis, we obtain the graph shown in Figure 4.45.

Related Exercises 21–32◀

SECTION 4.3 EXERCISES

Review Questions

1. Why is it important to determine the domain of f before graphing f?
2. Explain why it is useful to know about symmetry in a function.
3. Can the graph of a polynomial have vertical or horizontal asymptotes? Explain.
4. Where are the vertical asymptotes of a rational function located?
5. How do you find the absolute maximum and minimum values of a function that is continuous on a closed interval?
6. Describe the possible end behavior of a polynomial.

Basic Skills

7–8. Shape of the curve *Sketch a curve with the following properties.*

7.

$x < 3$	$f' < 0$ and $f'' < 0$
$x > 3$	$f' < 0$ and $f'' > 0$

8.

$x < -1$	$f' < 0$ and $f'' < 0$
$-1 < x < 2$	$f' < 0$ and $f'' > 0$
$2 < x < 8$	$f' > 0$ and $f'' > 0$
$8 < x < 10$	$f' > 0$ and $f'' < 0$
$x > 10$	$f' > 0$ and $f'' > 0$

9–14. Graphing polynomials *Sketch a graph of the following polynomials. Identify local extrema, inflection points, and x- and y-intercepts when they exist.*

9. $f(x) = \frac{1}{3}x^3 - 2x^2 - 5x + 2$

10. $f(x) = \frac{1}{15}x^3 - x + 1$

11. $f(x) = x^4 - 6x^2$

12. $f(x) = 2x^6 - 3x^4$

13. $f(x) = 3x^4 + 4x^3 - 12x^2$

14. $f(x) = x^3 - 33x^2 + 216x - 2$

15–20. Graphing rational functions *Use the guidelines of this section to make a complete graph of f.*

15. $f(x) = \frac{x^2}{x - 2}$

16. $f(x) = \frac{x^2}{x^2 - 4}$

17. $f(x) = \frac{3x - 5}{x^2 - 1}$

18. $f(x) = \frac{2x - 3}{2x - 8}$

19. $f(x) = \frac{x^2 + 12}{2x + 1}$

20. $f(x) = \frac{4x + 4}{x^2 + 3}$

T **21–28. More graphing** *Make a complete graph of the following functions. If an interval is not specified, graph the function on its domain. Use a graphing utility to check your work.*

21. $f(x) = x + 2\cos x$ on $[-2\pi, 2\pi]$

22. $f(x) = x^{1/3}(x - 2)^2$

23. $f(x) = \sin x - x$ on $[0, 2\pi]$

24. $f(x) = x\sqrt{x + 4}$

25. $g(t) = 3/t^2 - 54/t^4$

26. $g(x) = \sqrt{x + 2}/(x + 3)$

27. $f(x) = \sqrt{2 + x^2}/(x - 1)$

28. $f(x) = \cos^4 x$ on $[0, 3\pi/2]$

T **29–32. Graphing with technology** *Make a complete graph of the following functions. A graphing utility is useful in locating local extreme values and inflection points.*

29. $f(x) = \sin x - \cos 2x$ on $[-\pi, \pi]$

30. $f(x) = \frac{\sqrt{4x^2 + 1}}{x^2 + 1}$

31. $f(x) = \frac{x \sin x}{x^2 + 1}$ on $[-2\pi, 2\pi]$

32. $f(x) = \frac{2}{1 + \sin^2 x}$ on $[-\pi, \pi]$

Further Explorations

33. Explain why or why not Determine whether the following statements are true and give an explanation or counterexample.

a. The zeros of f' are $x = -3, 1$, and 4, so the local extrema are located at these points.

b. The zeros of f'' are $x = -2$ and 4, so the inflection points are also located at these points.

c. The zeros of the denominator of f are $x = -3$ and 4, so f has vertical asymptotes at these points.

d. If a rational function has a finite limit as $x \to \infty$, it must have a finite limit as $x \to -\infty$.

34–37. Functions from derivatives *Use the derivative f' to determine the local minima and maxima of f and the intervals of increase and decrease. Sketch a possible graph of f (f is not unique).*

34. $f'(x) = (x - 1)(x + 2)(x + 4)$

35. $f'(x) = 10 \sin 2x$ on $[-2\pi, 2\pi]$

36. $f'(x) = \frac{x - 1}{(x - 2)^2(x - 3)}$

37. $f'(x) = \frac{x + 2}{x^2(x - 6)}$

38–39. Functions from graphs *Use the graphs of f' and f'' to find the critical points and inflection points of f, the intervals on which f is increasing and decreasing, and the intervals of concavity. Then graph f assuming $f(0) = 0$.*

38.

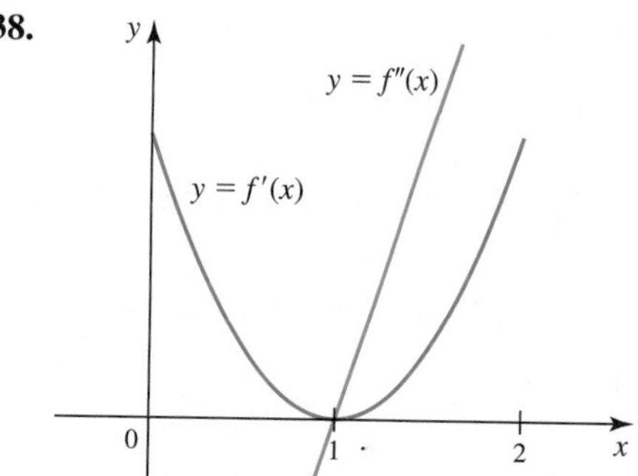

39.

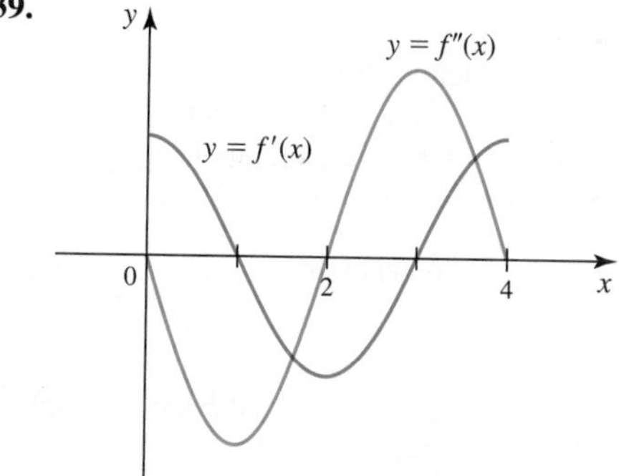

40–42. Nice cubics and quartics *The following third- and fourth-degree polynomials have a property that makes them relatively easy to graph. Make a complete graph and describe the property.*

40. $f(x) = x^4 + 8x^3 - 270x^2 + 1$

41. $f(x) = x^3 - 6x^2 - 135x$

42. $f(x) = x^3 - 147x + 286$

43–46. Designer functions *Sketch a continuous function f on some interval that has the properties described.*

43. The function f has one inflection point but no local extrema.

44. The function f has three real zeros and exactly two local minima.

45. The function f satisfies $f'(-2) = 2, f'(0) = 0, f'(1) = -3, f'(4) = 1$.

46. The function f has the same finite limit as $x \to \pm\infty$ and has exactly one local minimum and one local maximum.

T **47–54. More graphing** *Make a complete graph of the following functions. If an interval is not specified, graph the function on its domain. Use analytical methods and a graphing utility together in a complementary way.*

47. $f(x) = \dfrac{-x\sqrt{x^2 - 4}}{x - 2}$

48. $f(x) = 3\sqrt[4]{x} - \sqrt{x} - 2$

49. $f(x) = 3x^4 - 44x^3 + 60x^2$ (*Hint:* Two different graphing windows may be needed.)

50. $f(x) = \dfrac{1}{1 + \cos(\pi x)}$ on $(1, 3)$

51. $f(x) = 10x^6 - 36x^5 - 75x^4 + 300x^3 + 120x^2 - 720x$

52. $f(x) = \dfrac{\sin(\pi x)}{1 + \sin(\pi x)}$ on $[0, 2]$ (*Hint:* Two different graphing windows may be needed.)

53. $f(x) = \dfrac{x\sqrt{|x^2 - 1|}}{x^4 + 1}$

54. $f(x) = \sin(3\pi \cos x)$ on $[-\pi/2, \pi/2]$

T 55. **Hidden oscillations** Use analytical methods together with a graphing utility to graph the following functions on the interval $[-2\pi, 2\pi]$. Define f at $x = 0$ so that it is continuous there. Be sure to uncover all relevant features of the graph.

a. $f(x) = \dfrac{1 - \cos^3 x}{x^2}$ **b.** $f(x) = \dfrac{1 - \cos^5 x}{x^2}$

56. **Cubic with parameters** Locate all local maxima and minima of $f(x) = x^3 - 3bx^2 + 3a^2x + 23$, where a and b are constants, in the following cases.

a. $|a| < |b|$ **b.** $|a| > |b|$ **c.** $|a| = |b|$

Applications

57. **Height vs. volume** The figure shows six containers, each of which is filled from the top. Assume that water is poured into the containers at a constant rate and each container is filled in 10 s. Assume also that the horizontal cross sections of the containers are always circles. Let $h(t)$ be the depth of water in the container at time t, for $0 \le t \le 10$.

a. For each container, sketch a graph of the function $y = h(t)$, for $0 \le t \le 10$.

b. Explain why h is an increasing function.

c. Describe the concavity of the function. Identify inflection points when they occur.

d. For each container, where does h' (the derivative of h) have an absolute maximum on $[0, 10]$?

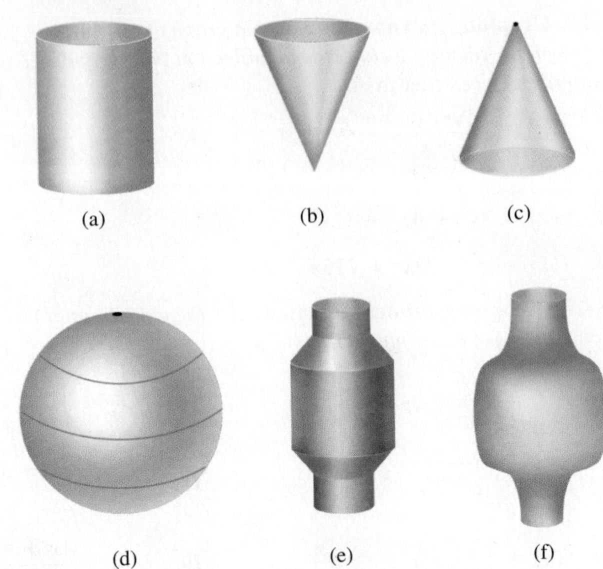

T 58. **A pursuit curve** Imagine a man standing 1 mi east of a crossroads. At noon, a dog starts walking north from the crossroads at 1 mi/hr (see figure). At the same instant, the man starts walking and at all times walks directly toward the dog at a speed of $s > 1$ mi/hr. The path in the xy-plane followed by the man as he pursues the dog is given by the function

$$y = f(x) = \frac{s}{2}\left(\frac{x^{(s+1)/s}}{s + 1} - \frac{x^{(s-1)/s}}{s - 1}\right) + \frac{s}{s^2 - 1}.$$

Select various values of $s > 1$ and graph this pursuit curve. Comment on the changes in the curve as s increases.

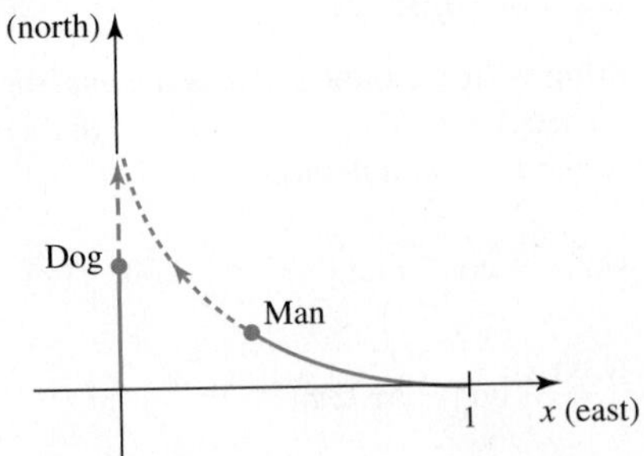

Additional Exercises

59. **Derivative information** Suppose a continuous function f is concave up on $(-\infty, 0)$ and $(0, \infty)$. Assume f has a local maximum at $x = 0$. What, if anything, do you know about $f'(0)$? Explain with an illustration.

T 60. **Power of cos x** Consider the functions $f_n(x) = \cos^{2n} x$, where n is a positive integer.

a. Graph f_n, for $n = 1, 2, 3, 4$, on the interval $[0, \pi]$.

b. Show that f_n has two inflection points on $[0, \pi]$ for any positive integer n.

c. Suppose the inflection points of f_n occur at $x = c_n$. Show that c_n satisfies $\sin c_n = \dfrac{1}{\sqrt{2n}}$.

d. Evaluate $\lim_{n\to\infty} c_n$ and interpret this result on the graphs of part (a).

61–67. Special curves *The following classical curves have been studied by generations of mathematicians. Use analytical methods (including implicit differentiation) and a graphing utility to graph each curve. Include as much detail as possible.*

61. $x^{2/3} + y^{2/3} = 1$ Astroid or hypocycloid with four cusps

62. $y = \dfrac{8}{x^2 + 4}$ Witch of Agnesi

63. $x^3 + y^3 = 3xy$ Folium of Descartes

64. $y^2 = \dfrac{x^3}{2 - x}$ Cissoid of Diocles

65. $y^4 - x^4 - 4y^2 + 5x^2 = 0$ Devil's curve

66. $y^2 = x^3(1 - x)$ Pear curve

67. $x^4 - x^2 + y^2 = 0$ Figure-8 curve

68. Elliptic curves The equation $y^2 = x^3 - ax + 3$, where a is a parameter, defines a well-known family of *elliptic curves.*

a. Verify that if $a = 3$, the graph consists of a single curve.
b. Verify that if $a = 4$, the graph consists of two distinct curves.
c. By experimentation, determine the value of a ($3 < a < 4$) at which the graph separates into two curves.

69. Lamé Curves The equation $|y/a|^n + |x/a|^n = 1$, where n and a are positive real numbers, defines the family of Lamé curves. Make a complete graph of this function with $a = 1$, for $n = \frac{2}{3}, 1, 2, 3$. Describe the progression that you observe as n increases.

70. An exotic curve (Putnam Exam 1942) Find the coordinates of four local maxima of the function $f(x) = \dfrac{x}{1 + x^6 \sin^2 x}$ and graph the function, for $0 \le x \le 10$.

QUICK CHECK ANSWERS

1. Make the window larger in the y-direction.
2. Notice that f and $f + C$ have the same derivatives.
3. $f(-x) = \dfrac{10(-x)^3}{(-x)^2 - 1} = -\dfrac{10x^3}{x^2 - 1} = -f(x)$

4.4 Optimization Problems

The theme of this section is *optimization*, a topic arising in many disciplines that rely on mathematics. A structural engineer may seek the dimensions of a beam that maximizes strength for a specified cost. A packaging designer may seek the dimensions of a container that maximizes the capacity of the container for a given surface area. Airline strategists need to find the best allocation of airliners among several hubs in order to minimize fuel costs and maximize passenger miles. In all these examples, the challenge is to find an *efficient* way to carry out a task, where "efficient" could mean least expensive, most profitable, least time consuming, or, as you will see, many other measures.

To introduce the ideas behind optimization problems, think about pairs of nonnegative real numbers x and y between 0 and 20 with the property that their sum is 20, that is, $x + y = 20$. Of all possible pairs, which has the greatest product?

Table 4.3

x	y	$x + y$	$P = xy$
1	19	20	19
5.5	14.5	20	79.75
9	11	20	99
13	7	20	91
18	2	20	36

Table 4.3 displays a few cases showing how the product of two nonnegative numbers varies while their sum remains constant. The condition that $x + y = 20$ is called a **constraint**: It tells us to consider only (nonnegative) values of x and y satisfying this equation.

The quantity that we wish to maximize (or minimize in other cases) is called the **objective function**; in this case, the objective function is the product $P = xy$. From Table 4.3 it appears that the product is greatest if both x and y are near the middle of the interval $[0, 20]$.

This simple problem has all the essential features of optimization problems. At their heart, all optimization problems take the following form:

What is the maximum (minimum) value of an objective function subject to the given constraint(s)?

For the problem at hand, this question would be stated as "What pair of nonnegative numbers maximizes $P = xy$ subject to the constraint $x + y = 20$?" The first step is to use the constraint to express the objective function $P = xy$ in terms of a single variable. In this case, the constraint is

➤ In this problem it is just as easy to eliminate x as y. In other problems, eliminating one variable may result in less work than eliminating other variables.

$$x + y = 20, \quad \text{or} \quad y = 20 - x.$$

Substituting for y, the objective function becomes

$$P = xy = x(20 - x) = 20x - x^2,$$

which is a function of the single variable x. Notice that the values of x lie in the interval $0 \le x \le 20$ with $P(0) = P(20) = 0$.

To maximize P, we first find the critical points by solving

$$P'(x) = 20 - 2x = 0$$

to obtain the solution $x = 10$. To find the absolute maximum value of P on the interval $[0, 20]$, we check the endpoints and the critical points. Because $P(0) = P(20) = 0$ and $P(10) = 100$, we conclude that P has its absolute maximum value at $x = 10$. By the constraint $x + y = 20$, the numbers with the greatest product are $x = y = 10$, and their product is $P = 100$.

Figure 4.46 summarizes this problem. We see the constraint line $x + y = 20$ in the xy-plane. Above the line is the objective function $P = xy$. As x and y vary along the constraint line, the objective function changes, reaching a maximum value of 100 when $x = y = 10$.

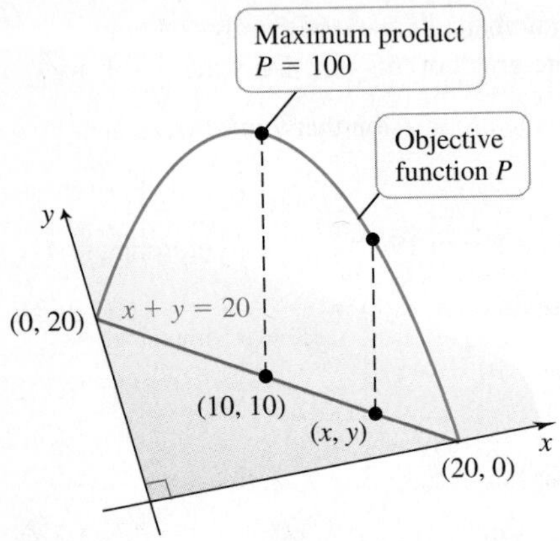

FIGURE 4.46

QUICK CHECK 1 Verify that in the previous example the same result is obtained if the constraint $x + y = 20$ is used to eliminate x rather than y. ◄

Most optimization problems have the same basic structure as the preceding example: There is an objective function, which may involve several variables, and one or more constraints. The methods of calculus (Sections 4.1 and 4.2) are used to find the minimum or maximum values of the objective function.

EXAMPLE 1 **Rancher's dilemma** A rancher has 400 ft of fence for constructing a rectangular corral. One side of the corral will be formed by a barn and requires no fence. Three exterior fences and two interior fences partition the corral into three rectangular regions. What dimensions of the corral maximize the enclosed area? What is the area of that corral?

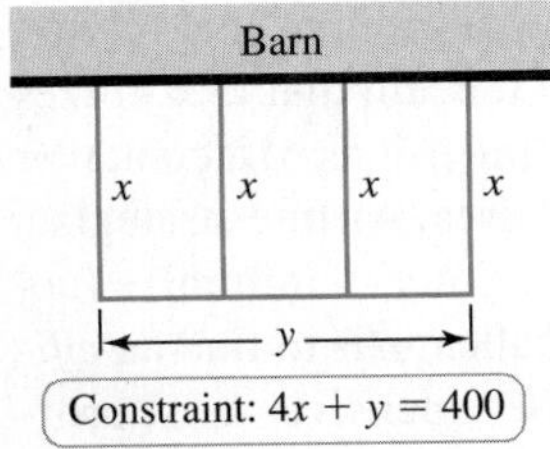

FIGURE 4.47

SOLUTION We first sketch the corral (Figure 4.47), where x is the width and y is the length of the corral. The amount of fence required is $4x + y$, so the constraint is $4x + y = 400$, or $y = 400 - 4x$.

The objective function to be maximized is the area of the corral, $A = xy$. Using $y = 400 - 4x$, we eliminate y and express A as a function of x:

$$A = xy = x(400 - 4x) = 400x - 4x^2$$

➤ Recall from Section 4.1 that the absolute extreme points occur at critical points or endpoints.

Notice that the width of the corral must be at least $x = 0$, and it cannot exceed $x = 100$ (because 400 ft of fence are available). Therefore, we maximize $A(x) = 400x - 4x^2$, for $0 \le x \le 100$. The critical points of the objective function satisfy

$$A'(x) = 400 - 8x = 0,$$

which has the solution $x = 50$. To find the absolute maximum value of A, we check the endpoints of $[0, 100]$ and the critical point $x = 50$. Because $A(0) = A(100) = 0$ and $A(50) = 10{,}000$, the absolute maximum value of A occurs when $x = 50$. Using the constraint, the optimal length of the corral is $y = 400 - 4(50) = 200$ ft. Therefore, the maximum area of 10,000 ft^2 is achieved with dimensions $x = 50$ ft and $y = 200$ ft. The objective function A is shown in Figure 4.48. *Related Exercises 5–10* ◄

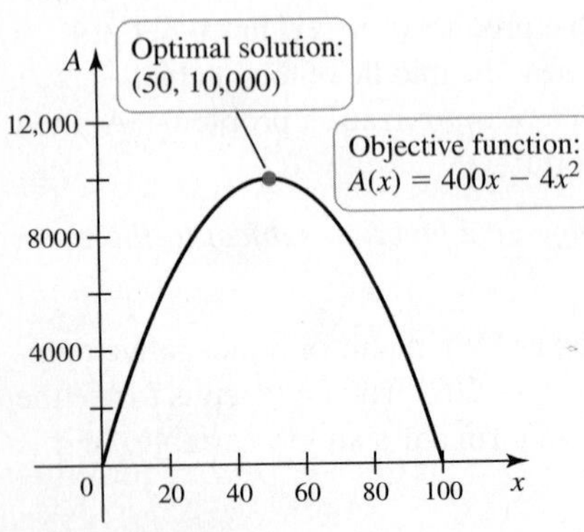

FIGURE 4.48

QUICK CHECK 2 Find the objective function in Example 1 (in terms of x) if there is no interior fence and if there is one interior fence. ◄

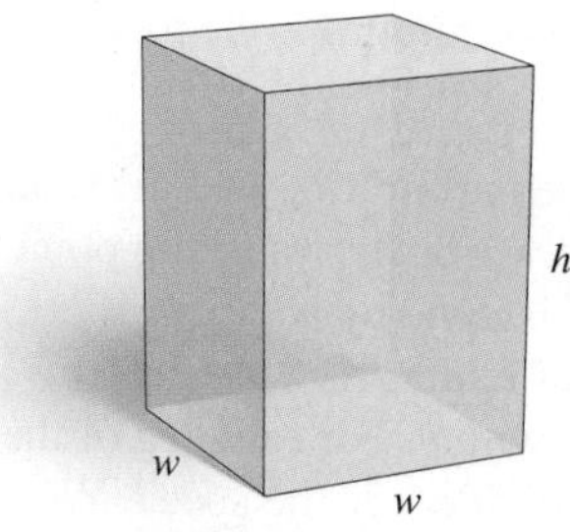

FIGURE 4.49

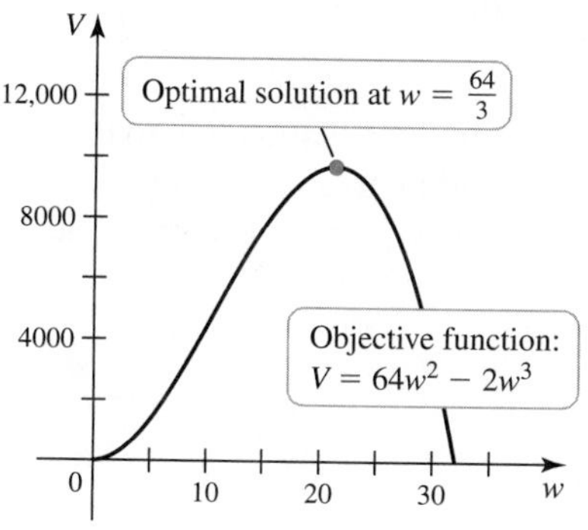

FIGURE 4.50

EXAMPLE 2 **Airline regulations** Suppose an airline policy states that all baggage must be box-shaped with a sum of length, width, and height not exceeding 64 in. What are the dimensions and volume of a square-based box with the greatest volume under these conditions?

SOLUTION We sketch a square-based box whose length and width are w and whose height is h (Figure 4.49). The box with greatest volume satisfies the constraint $2w + h = 64$. The objective function is the volume, $V = w^2h$. Either w or h may be eliminated from the objective function; substituting $h = 64 - 2w$, the volume is

$$V = w^2h = w^2(64 - 2w) = 64w^2 - 2w^3.$$

The objective function has now been expressed in terms of a single variable. Notice that w is nonnegative and cannot exceed 32, so the domain of V is $0 \leq w \leq 32$. The critical points satisfy

$$V'(w) = 128w - 6w^2 = 2w(64 - 3w) = 0,$$

which has roots $w = 0$ and $w = \frac{64}{3} \approx 21.3$. By the First (or Second) Derivative Test, $w = \frac{64}{3}$ corresponds to a local maximum. At the endpoints, $V(0) = V(32) = 0$. Therefore, the volume function has an absolute maximum of $V(64/3) \approx 9709 \text{ in}^3$. The dimensions of the optimal box are $w = \ell = 64/3$ in and $h = 64 - 2w = 64/3$ in, so the optimal box is a cube. A graph of the volume function is shown in Figure 4.50.

Related Exercises 11–13 ◀

QUICK CHECK 3 Find the objective function in Example 2 (in terms of w) if the constraint is that the sum of length and width and height cannot exceed 108 in. ◀

Optimization Guidelines

With two examples providing some insight, we present a procedure for solving optimization problems. These guidelines provide a general framework, but the details may vary depending upon the problem.

Guidelines for Optimization Problems

1. Read the problem carefully, identify the variables, and organize the given information with a picture.
2. Identify the objective function (the function to be optimized). Write it in terms of the variables of the problem.
3. Identify the constraints. Write them in terms of the variables of the problem.
4. Use the constraint to eliminate all but one independent variable of the objective function.
5. With the objective function expressed in terms of a single variable, find the interval of interest for that variable.
6. Use methods of calculus to find the absolute maximum or minimum value of the objective function on the interval of interest. If necessary, check the endpoints.

EXAMPLE 3 **Walking and swimming** Suppose you are standing on the shore of a circular pond with radius 1 mi and you want to get to a point on the shore directly opposite your position (on the other end of a diameter). You plan to swim at 2 mi/hr from your current position to another point P on the shore and then walk at 3 mi/hr along the shore

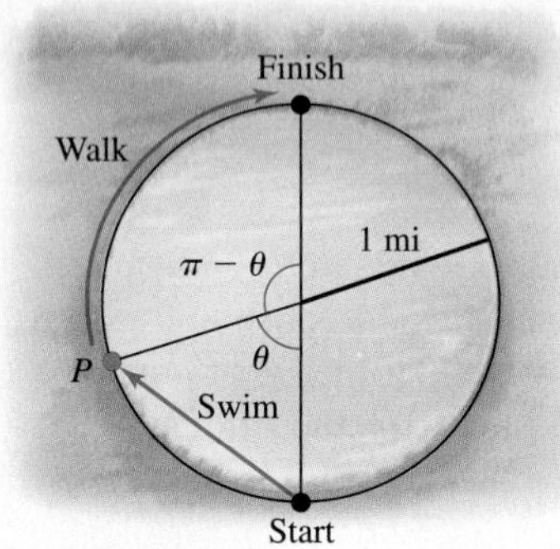

FIGURE 4.51

to the terminal point (Figure 4.51). How should you choose P to minimize the total time for the trip?

SOLUTION As shown in Figure 4.51, the initial point is chosen arbitrarily, and the terminal point is at the other end of a diameter. The easiest way to describe the transition point P is to refer to the central angle θ. If $\theta = 0$, then the entire trip is done by walking; if $\theta = \pi$, the entire trip is done by swimming. So the interval of interest is $0 \le \theta \le \pi$.

The objective function is the total travel time as it varies with θ. For each leg of the trip (swim and walk), the travel time is the distance traveled divided by the speed. We need a few facts from circular geometry. The length of the swimming leg is the length of the chord of the circle corresponding to the angle θ. For a circle of radius r, this chord length is given by $2r \sin(\theta/2)$ (Figure 4.52). So, the time for the swimming leg (with $r = 1$ and speed 2 mi/hr) is

$$\frac{\text{distance}}{\text{rate}} = \frac{2\sin(\theta/2)}{2} = \sin\frac{\theta}{2}.$$

➤ You can check two special cases: If the entire trip is done walking, the travel time is $(\pi \text{ mi})/(3 \text{ mi/hr}) \approx 1.05$ hr. If the entire trip is done swimming, the travel time is $(2 \text{ mi})/(2 \text{ mi/hr}) \approx 1$ hr.

The length of the walking leg is the length of the arc of the circle corresponding to the angle $\pi - \theta$. For a circle of radius r, the arc length corresponding to an angle θ is $r\theta$ (Figure 4.52). Therefore, the time for the walking leg (with an angle $\pi - \theta$, $r = 1$, and speed 3 mi/hr) is

$$\frac{\text{distance}}{\text{rate}} = \frac{\pi - \theta}{3}.$$

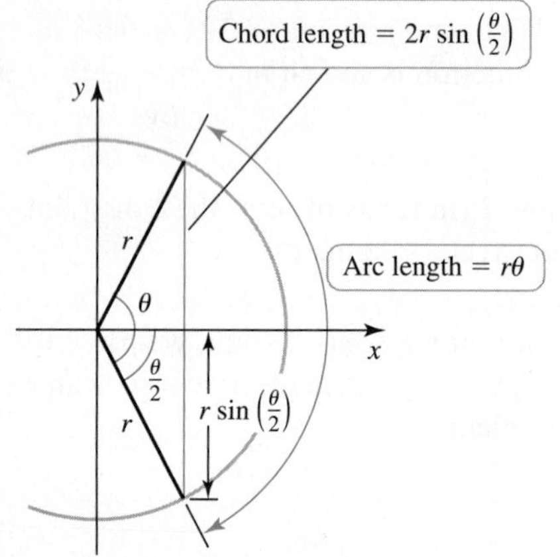

FIGURE 4.52

The total travel time for the trip is the objective function

$$T(\theta) = \sin\frac{\theta}{2} + \frac{\pi - \theta}{3}, \qquad 0 \le \theta \le \pi.$$

We now analyze the objective function. The critical points of T satisfy

$$\frac{dT}{d\theta} = \frac{1}{2}\cos\frac{\theta}{2} - \frac{1}{3} = 0 \quad \text{or} \quad \cos\frac{\theta}{2} = \frac{2}{3}.$$

Using a calculator, the only solution in the interval $[0, \pi]$ is $\theta \approx 1.68 \text{ rad} \approx 96°$, which is the critical point.

Evaluating the objective function at the critical point and at the endpoints, we find that $T(1.68) \approx 1.23$, $T(0) = \pi/3 = 1.05$, and $T(\pi) = 1$. We conclude that the minimum travel time is $T(\pi) = 1$ hr when the entire trip is done swimming. The *maximum* travel time, corresponding to $\theta \approx 96°$, is $T \approx 1.23$ hr.

➤ To show that the chord length of a circle is $2r\sin(\theta/2)$, draw a line from the center of the circle to the midpoint of the chord. This line bisects the angle θ. Using a right triangle, half the length of the chord is $r\sin(\theta/2)$.

The objective function is shown in Figure 4.53. In general, the maximum and minimum travel times depend on the walking and swimming speeds (Exercise 14).

Related Exercises 14–15 ◀

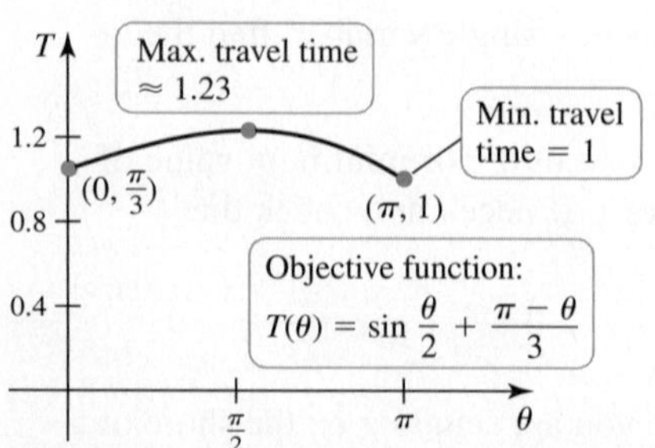

FIGURE 4.53

EXAMPLE 4 Ladder over the fence An 8-foot-tall fence runs parallel to the side of a house 3 feet away (Figure 4.54a). What is the length of the shortest ladder that clears the fence and reaches the house? Assume that the vertical wall of the house and the horizontal ground have infinite extent (see Exercise 17 for more realistic assumptions).

SOLUTION Let's first ask why we expect a minimum ladder length. You could put the foot of the ladder far from the fence, making it clear the fence at a shallow angle; but the ladder would be very long. Or you could put the foot of the ladder close to the fence, making it clear the fence at a steep angle; but again, the ladder would be long. Somewhere between these extremes, there is a ladder position that minimizes the ladder length.

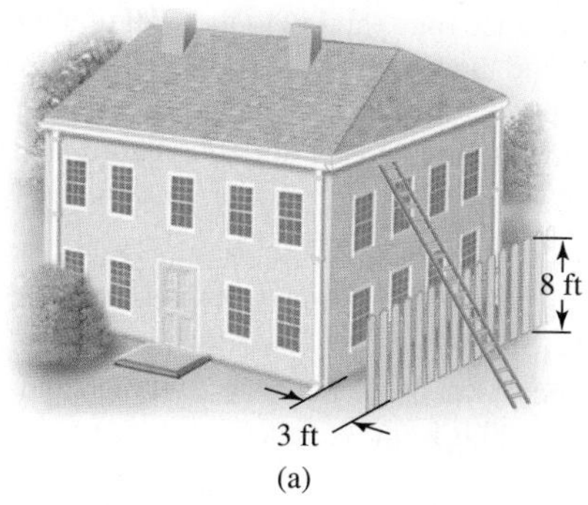

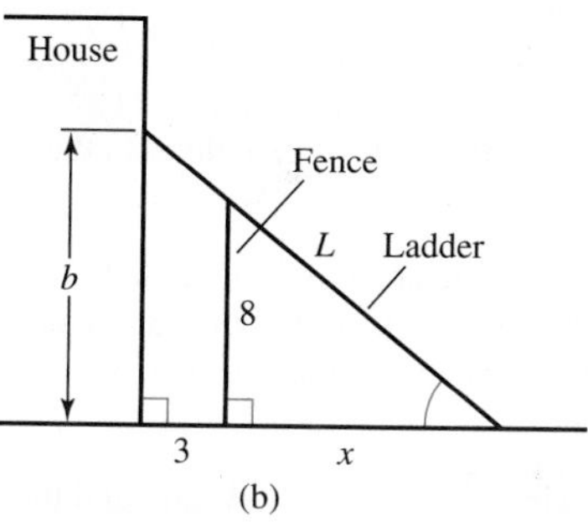

FIGURE 4.54

The objective function in this problem is the ladder length L. The position of the ladder is specified by x, the distance between the foot of the ladder and the fence (Figure 4.54b). The goal is to express L as a function of x, where $x > 0$.

The Pythagorean theorem gives the relationship

$$L^2 = (x + 3)^2 + b^2,$$

where b is the height of the top of the ladder above the ground. Similar triangles give the constraint $8/x = b/(x + 3)$. We now solve the constraint equation for b and substitute to express L^2 in terms of x:

$$L^2 = (x + 3)^2 + \Bigg(\underbrace{\frac{8(x + 3)}{x}}_{b}\Bigg)^2 = (x + 3)^2\left(1 + \frac{64}{x^2}\right)$$

At this juncture, we could find the critical points of L by first solving the preceding equation for L, and then solving $L' = 0$. However, the solution is simplified considerably if we note that L is a nonnegative function. Therefore, L and L^2 have local extrema at the same points, and we choose to minimize L^2. The derivative of L^2 is

$$\frac{d}{dx}\left[(x + 3)^2\left(1 + \frac{64}{x^2}\right)\right] = (x + 3)^2\left(-\frac{128}{x^3}\right) + 2(x + 3)\left(1 + \frac{64}{x^2}\right) \qquad \text{Chain Rule and Product Rule}$$

$$= \frac{2(x + 3)(x^3 - 192)}{x^3}. \qquad \text{Simplify.}$$

Because $x > 0$, we have $x + 3 \neq 0$; so the condition $\frac{d}{dx}(L^2) = 0$ becomes $x^3 - 192 = 0$, or $x = 4\sqrt[3]{3} \approx 5.77$. By the First Derivative Test, this critical point corresponds to a local minimum. By Theorem 4.5, this solitary local minimum is also the absolute minimum on the interval $(0, \infty)$. Therefore, the minimum ladder length occurs when the foot of the ladder is approximately 5.77 ft from the fence. We find that $L^2(5.77) \approx 224.77$ and the minimum ladder length is $\sqrt{224.77} \approx 15$ ft.

Related Exercises 16–17 ◀

SECTION 4.4 EXERCISES

Review Questions

1. Fill in the blanks: The goal of an optimization problem is to find the maximum or minimum value of the ________ function subject to the ________.

2. If the objective function involves more than one independent variable, how are the extra variables eliminated?

3. If the objective function is $Q = x^2y$ and you know that $x + y = 10$, write the objective function first in terms of x and then in terms of y.

4. Suppose you wish to minimize a continuous objective function on a closed interval, but you find that it has only a single local maximum. Where should you look for the solution to the problem?

Basic Skills

5. **Maximum area rectangles** Of all rectangles with a perimeter of 10 m, which one has the maximum area? (Give the dimensions.)

6. **Minimum perimeter rectangles** Of all rectangles with a fixed area A, which one has the minimum perimeter? (Give the dimensions in terms of A.)

7. **Maximum product** What two nonnegative real numbers with a sum of 23 have the largest possible product?

8. **Maximum length** What two nonnegative real numbers a and b whose sum is 23 maximize $a^2 + b^2$? Minimize $a^2 + b^2$?

9. **Minimum sum** What two positive real numbers whose product is 50 have the smallest possible sum?

10. **Pen problems**

    a. A rectangular pen is built with one side against a barn. Two hundred meters of fencing are used for the other three sides of the pen. What dimensions maximize the area of the pen?

    b. A rancher plans to make four identical and adjacent rectangular pens against a barn, each with an area of 100 m^2 (see figure). What are the dimensions of each pen that minimize the amount of fence that must be used?

Barn

100 100 100 100

c. Two rectangular pens are built against a barn. Two hundred meters of fencing are to be used for the three sides and the diagonal dividing fence (see figure). What dimensions maximize the area of the pen?

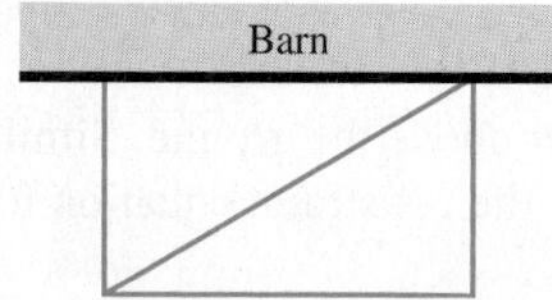

11. **Minimum surface area box** Of all boxes with a square base and a volume of 100 m^3, which one has the minimum surface area? (Give its dimensions.)

12. **Maximum volume box** Suppose an airline policy states that all baggage must be box-shaped with a sum of length, width, and height not exceeding 108 in. What are the dimensions and volume of a square-based box with the greatest volume under these conditions?

13. **Shipping crates** A square-based, box-shaped shipping crate is designed to have a volume of 16 ft^3. The material used to make the base costs twice as much (per ft^2) as the material in the sides, and the material used to make the top costs half as much (per ft^2) as the material in the sides. What are the dimensions of the crate that minimize the cost of materials?

14. **Walking and swimming** A man wishes to get from an initial point on the shore of a circular pond with radius 1 mi to a point on the shore directly opposite (on the other end of the diameter). He plans to swim from the initial point to another point on the shore and then walk along the shore to the terminal point.
    a. If he swims at 2 mi/hr and walks at 4 mi/hr, what are the minimum and maximum times for the trip?
    b. If he swims at 2 mi/hr and walks at 1.5 mi/hr, what are the minimum and maximum times for the trip?
    c. If he swims at 2 mi/hr, what is the minimum walking speed for which it is quickest to walk the entire distance?

15. **Walking and rowing** A boat on the ocean is 4 mi from the nearest point on a straight shoreline; that point is 6 mi from a restaurant on the shore. A woman plans to row the boat straight to a point on the shore and then walk along the shore to the restaurant.

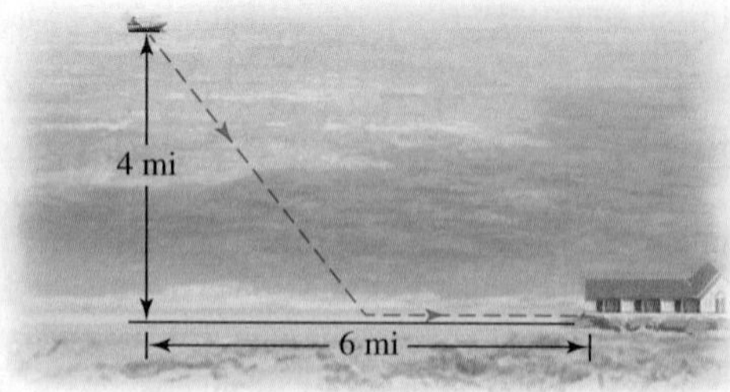

    a. If she walks at 3 mi/hr and rows at 2 mi/hr, at which point on the shore should she land to minimize the total travel time?
    b. If she walks at 3 mi/hr, what is the minimum speed at which she must row so that the quickest way to the restaurant is to row directly (with no walking)?

16. **Shortest ladder** A 10-ft-tall fence runs parallel to the wall of a house at a distance of 4 ft. Find the length of the shortest ladder that extends from the ground, over the fence, to the house. Assume the vertical wall of the house and the horizontal ground have infinite extent.

17. **Shortest ladder—more realistic** An 8-ft-tall fence runs parallel to the wall of a house at a distance of 5 ft. Find the length of the shortest ladder that extends from the ground, over the fence, to the house. Assume that the vertical wall of the house is 20 ft high and the horizontal ground extends 20 ft from the fence.

Further Explorations and Applications

18. **Rectangles beneath a parabola** A rectangle is constructed with its base on the x-axis and two of its vertices on the parabola $y = 16 - x^2$. What are the dimensions of the rectangle with the maximum area? What is the area?

19. **Rectangles beneath a semicircle** A rectangle is constructed with its base on the diameter of a semicircle with radius 5 cm and with two vertices on the semicircle. What are the dimensions of the rectangle with maximum area?

20. **Circle and square** A piece of wire 60 cm in length is cut, and the resulting two pieces are formed to make a circle and a square. Where should the wire be cut to (a) minimize and (b) maximize the combined area of the circle and the square?

21. **Maximum volume cone** A cone is constructed by cutting a sector of angle θ from a circular sheet of metal with radius 20 cm. The cut sheet is then folded up and welded (see figure). What angle θ maximizes the volume of the cone?

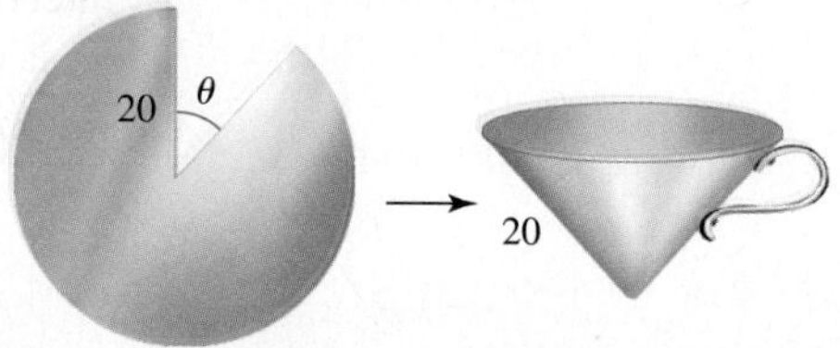

22. **Covering a marble** Imagine a flat-bottomed cylindrical pot with a circular cross section of radius 4 in. A marble with radius $0 < r < 4$ in is placed in the bottom of the pot. What is the radius of the marble that requires the most water to cover it completely?

23. **Optimal garden** A rectangular flower garden with an area of 30 m^2 is surrounded by a grass border 1 m wide on two sides and 2 m wide on the other two sides (see figure). What dimensions of the garden minimize the combined area of the garden and borders?

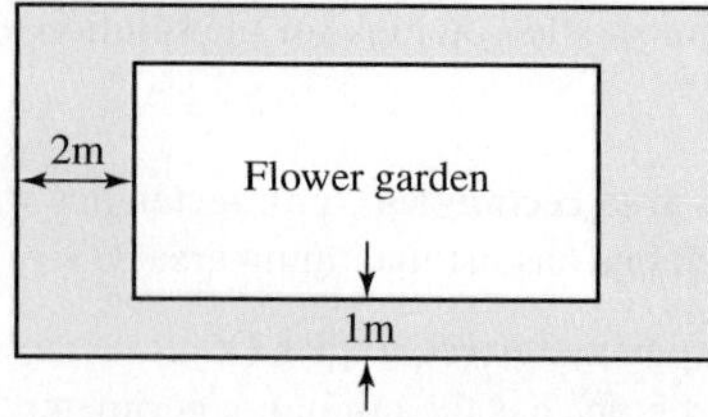

24. Rectangles beneath a line

a. A rectangle is constructed with one side on the positive x-axis, one side on the positive y-axis, and the vertex opposite the origin on the line $y = 10 - 2x$. What dimensions maximize the area of the rectangle? What is the maximum area?

b. Is it possible to construct a rectangle with a greater area than that found in part (a) by placing one side of the rectangle on the line $y = 10 - 2x$ and the two vertices not on that line on the positive x- and y-axes? Find the dimensions of the rectangle of maximum area that can be constructed in this way.

25. Kepler's wine barrel Several mathematical stories originated with the second wedding of the mathematician and astronomer Johannes Kepler. Here is one: While shopping for wine for his wedding, Kepler noticed that the price of a barrel of wine (here assumed to be a cylinder) was determined solely by the length d of a dipstick that was inserted diagonally through a hole in the top of the barrel to the edge of the base of the barrel (see figure). Kepler realized that this measurement does not determine the volume of the barrel and that for a fixed value of d, the volume varies with the radius r and height h of the barrel. For a fixed value of d, what is the ratio r/h that maximizes the volume of the barrel?

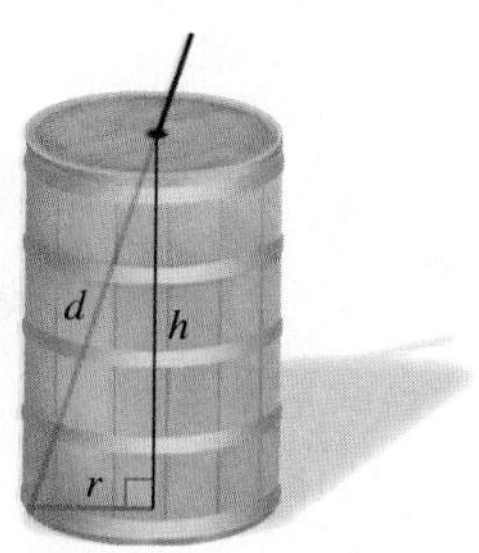

26. Folded boxes

a. Squares with sides of length x are cut out of each corner of a rectangular piece of cardboard measuring 3 ft by 4 ft. The resulting piece of cardboard is then folded into a box without a lid. Find the volume of the largest box that can be formed in this way.

b. Suppose that in part (a) the original piece of cardboard is a square with sides of length ℓ. Find the volume of the largest box that can be formed in this way.

c. Suppose that in part (a) the original piece of cardboard is a rectangle with sides of length ℓ and L. Holding ℓ fixed, find the size of the corner squares x that maximizes the volume of the box as $L \to \infty$. (*Source: Mathematics Teacher*, November 2002)

27. Making silos A grain silo consists of a cylindrical concrete tower surmounted by a metal hemispherical dome. The metal in the dome costs 1.5 times as much as the concrete (per unit of surface area). If the volume of the silo is 750 m^3, what are the dimensions of the silo (radius and height of the cylindrical tower) that minimize the cost of the materials? Assume the silo has no floor and no flat ceiling under the dome.

28. Suspension system A load must be suspended 6 m below a high ceiling using cables attached to two supports that are 2 m apart (see figure). How far below the ceiling (x in the figure) should the cables be joined to minimize the total length of cable used?

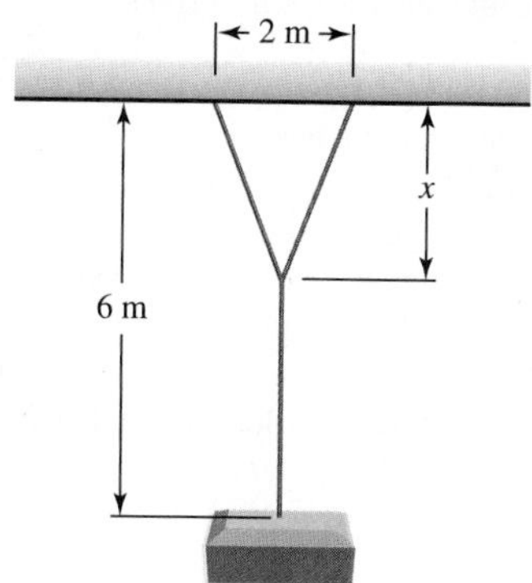

29. Light sources The intensity of a light source at a distance is directly proportional to the strength of the source and inversely proportional to the square of the distance from the source. Two light sources, one twice as strong as the other, are 12 m apart. At what point on the line segment joining the sources is the intensity the weakest?

30. Crease-length problem A rectangular sheet of paper of width a and length b, where $0 < a < b$, is folded by taking one corner of the sheet and placing it at a point P on the opposite long side of the sheet (see figure). The fold is then flattened to form a crease across the sheet. Assuming that the fold is made so that there is no flap extending beyond the original sheet, find the point P that produces the crease of minimum length. What is the length of that crease?

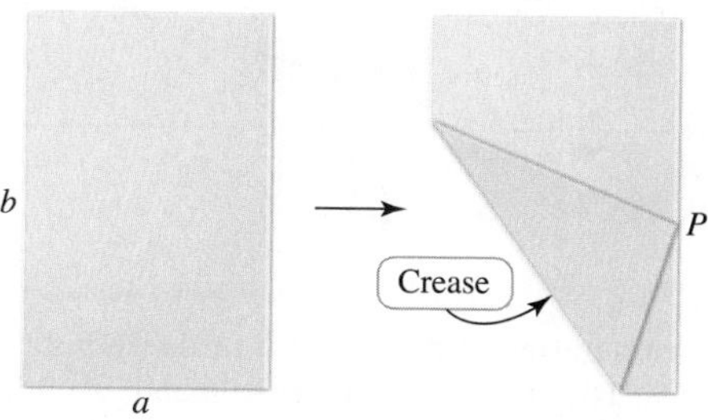

31. Laying cable An island is 3.5 mi from the nearest point on a straight shoreline; that point is 8 mi from a power station (see figure). A utility company plans to lay electrical cable underwater from the island to the shore and then underground along the shore to the power station. Assume that it costs \$2400/mi to lay underwater cable and \$1200/mi to lay underground cable. At what point should the underwater cable meet the shore in order to minimize the cost of the project?

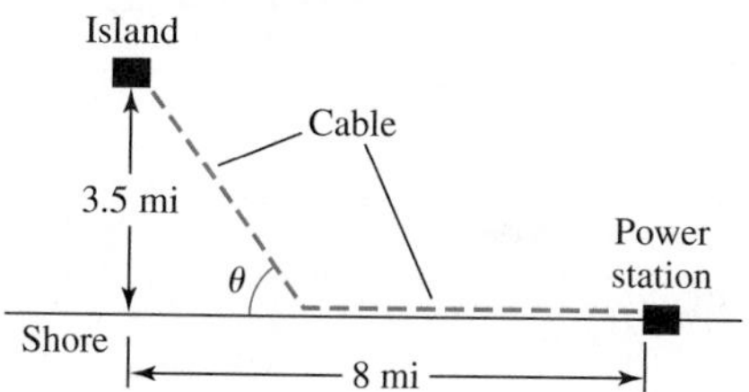

32. Laying cable again Solve the problem in Exercise 31, but this time minimize the cost with respect to the smaller angle θ between the underwater cable and the shore. (You should get the same answer.)

33. Sum of isosceles distances

a. An isosceles triangle has a base of length 4 and two sides of length $2\sqrt{2}$. Let P be a point on the perpendicular bisector of the base. Find the location P that minimizes the sum of the distances between P and the three vertices.

b. Assume in part (a) that the height of the isosceles triangle is $h > 0$ and its base has length 4. Show that the location of P that gives a minimum solution is independent of h for $h \geq \frac{2}{\sqrt{3}}$.

34. Circle in a triangle What are the radius and area of the circle of maximum area that can be inscribed in an isosceles triangle whose two equal sides have length 1?

35. Crankshaft A crank of radius r rotates with a constant angular frequency ω. It is connected to a piston by a connecting rod of length L (see figure). The acceleration of the piston varies with the position of the crank according to the function

$$a(\theta) = \omega^2 r\left(\cos\theta + \frac{r\cos 2\theta}{L}\right).$$

For fixed ω and r, find the values of θ, with $0 \leq \theta \leq 2\pi$, for which the acceleration of the piston is a maximum and minimum.

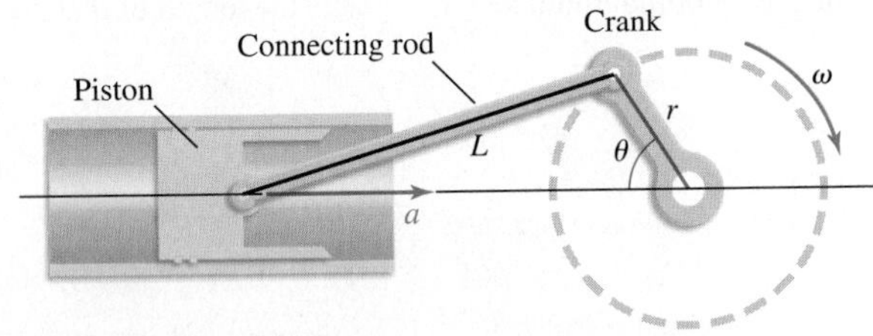

36. Metal rain gutters A rain gutter is made from sheets of metal 9 in wide. The gutters have a 3-in base and two 3-in sides, folded up at an angle θ (see figure). What angle θ maximizes the cross-sectional area of the gutter?

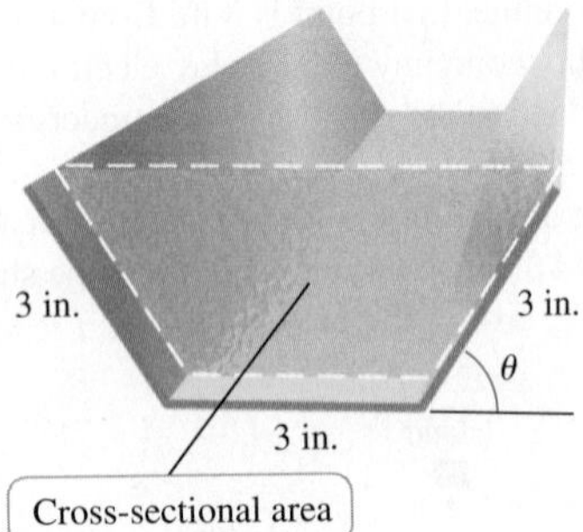

37. Optimal soda can

a. Classical problem Find the radius and height of a cylindrical soda can with a volume of 354 cm^3 that minimize the surface area.

b. Real problem Compare your answer in part (a) to a real soda can, which has a volume of 354 cm^3, a radius of 3.1 cm, and a height of 12.0 cm, to conclude that real soda cans do not seem to have an optimal design. Then use the fact that real soda cans have a double thickness in their top and bottom surfaces to find the radius and height that minimizes the surface area of a real can (the surface areas of the top and bottom are now twice their values in part (a)). Are these dimensions closer to the dimensions of a real soda can?

38. Cylinder and cones (Putnam Exam 1938) Right circular cones of height h and radius r are attached to each end of a right circular cylinder of height h and radius r, forming a double-pointed object. For a given surface area A, what are the dimensions r and h that maximize the volume of the object?

39. Viewing angles An auditorium with a flat floor has a large screen on one wall. The lower edge of the screen is 3 ft above eye level and the upper edge of the screen is 10 ft above eye level (see figure). How far from the screen should you stand to maximize your viewing angle?

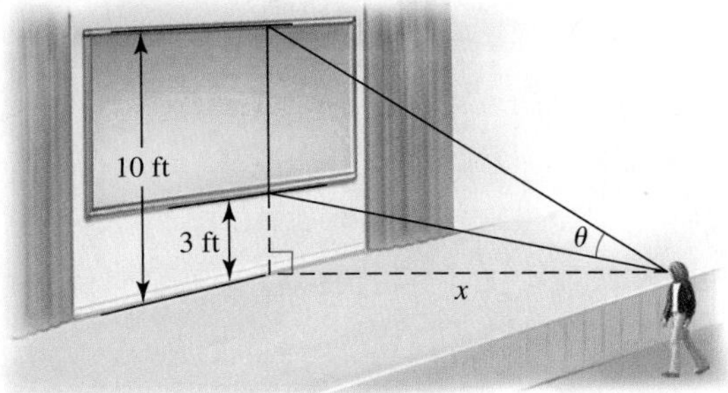

40. Searchlight problem—narrow beam A searchlight is 100 m from the nearest point on a straight highway (see figure). As it rotates, the searchlight casts a horizontal beam that intersects the highway in a point. If the light revolves at a rate of $\pi/6$ rad/s, find the rate at which the beam sweeps along the highway as a function of θ. For what value of θ is this rate minimized?

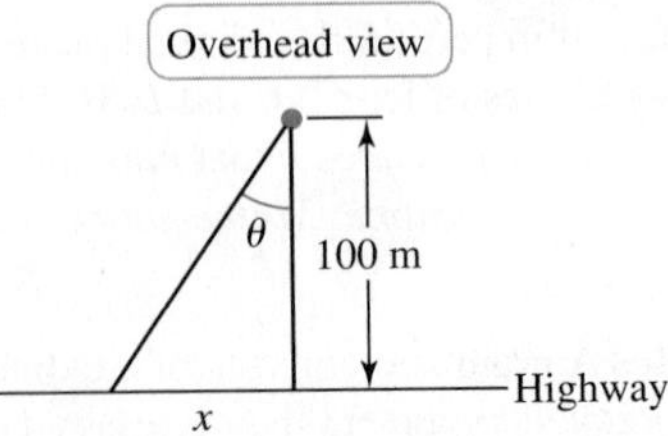

T **41. Watching a Ferris wheel** An observer stands 20 m from the bottom of a Ferris wheel on a line that is perpendicular to the face of the wheel, with her eyes at the level of the bottom of the wheel. The wheel revolves at a rate of π rad/min and the observer's line of sight with a specific seat on the Ferris wheel makes an angle θ with the horizontal (see figure). At what time during a full revolution is θ changing most rapidly?

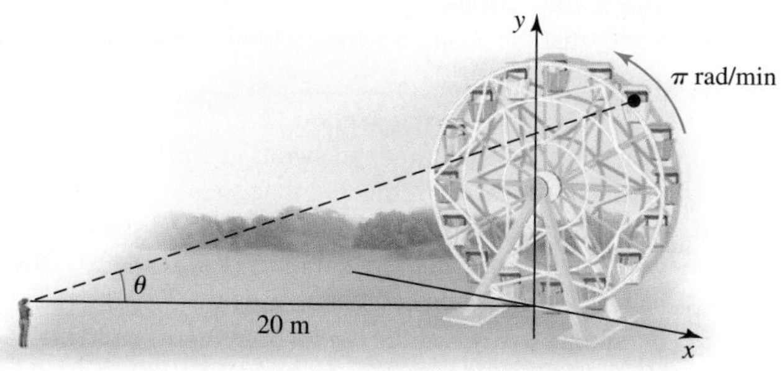

42. Maximum angle Find the value of x that maximizes θ in the figure.

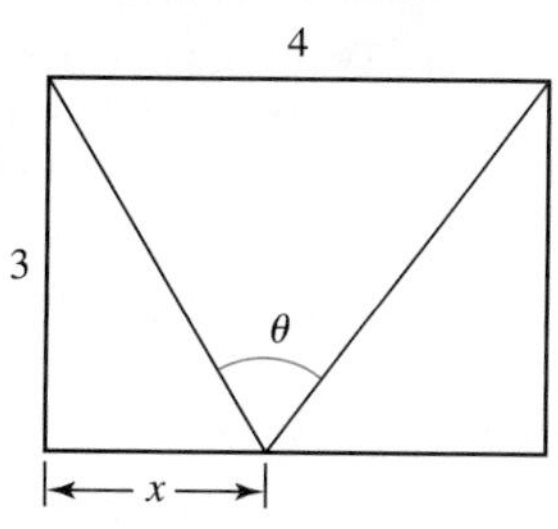

43. Maximum volume cylinder in a sphere Find the dimensions of the right circular cylinder of maximum volume that can be placed inside a sphere of radius R.

44. Rectangles in triangles Find the dimensions and area of the rectangle of maximum area that can be inscribed in the following figures.

a. A right triangle with a given hypotenuse length L
b. An equilateral triangle with a given side length L
c. A right triangle with a given area A
d. An arbitrary triangle with a given area A (The result applies to any triangle, but first consider triangles for which all the angles are less than or equal to 90°.)

45. Cylinder in a cone A right circular cylinder is placed inside a cone of radius R and height H so that the base of the cylinder lies on the base of the cone.

a. Find the dimensions of the cylinder with maximum volume. Specifically, show that the volume of the maximum-volume cylinder is $\frac{4}{9}$ the volume of the cone.
b. Find the dimensions of the cylinder with maximum lateral surface area (area of the curved surface).

46. Maximizing profit Suppose you own a tour bus and you book groups of 20 to 70 people for a day tour. The cost per person is \$30 minus \$0.25 for every ticket sold. If gas and other miscellaneous costs are \$200, how many tickets should you sell to maximize your profit? Treat the number of tickets as a nonnegative real number.

47. Cone in a cone A right circular cone is inscribed inside a larger right circular cone with a volume of 150 cm^3. The axes of the cones coincide and the vertex of the inner cone touches the center of the base of the outer cone. Find the ratio of the heights of the cones that maximizes the volume of the inner cone.

48. Another pen problem A rancher is building a horse pen on the corner of her property using 1000 ft of fencing. Because of the unusual shape of her property, the pen must be built in the shape of a trapezoid (see figure).

a. Determine the lengths of the sides that maximize the area of the pen.
b. Suppose there is already a fence along the side of the property opposite the side of length y. Find the lengths of the sides that maximize the area of the pen, using 1000 ft of fencing.

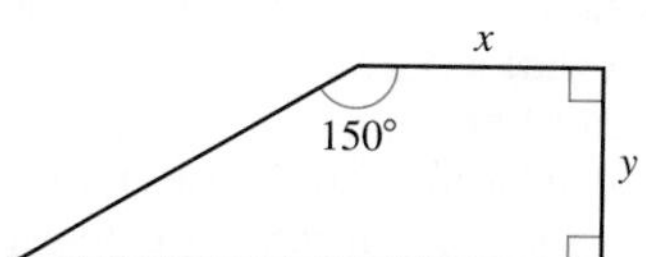

49. Minimum-length roads A house is located at each corner of a square with side lengths of 1 mi. What is the length of the shortest road system with straight roads that connects all of the houses by roads (that is, a road system that allows one to drive from any house to any other house)? (*Hint:* Place two points inside the square at which roads meet.) (*Source:* Halmos, *Problems for Mathematicians Young and Old.*)

50. Light transmission A window consists of a rectangular pane of clear glass surmounted by a semicircular pane of tinted glass. The clear glass transmits twice as much light per unit of surface area as the tinted glass. Of all such windows with a fixed perimeter P, what are the dimensions of the window that transmits the most light?

51. Slowest shortcut Suppose you are standing in a field near a straight section of railroad tracks just as the locomotive of a train passes the point nearest to you, which is $\frac{1}{4}$ mi away. The train, with length $\frac{1}{3}$ mi, is traveling at 20 mi/hr. If you start running in a straight line across the field, how slowly can you run and still catch the train? In which direction should you run?

52. The arbelos An arbelos is the region enclosed by three mutually tangent semicircles; it is the region inside the larger semicircle and outside the two smaller semicircles (see figure).

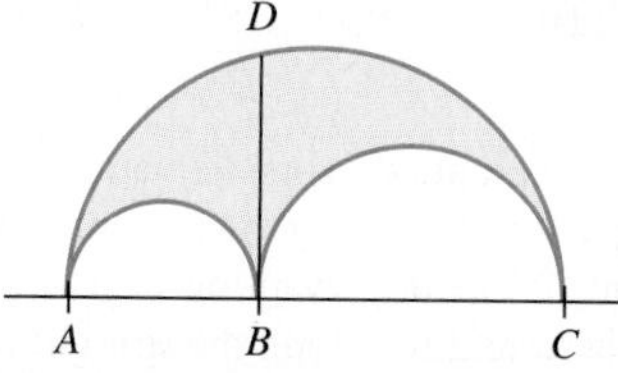

a. Given an arbelos in which the diameter of the largest circle is 1, what positions of point B maximize the area of the arbelos?
b. Show that the area of the arbelos is the area of a circle whose diameter is the distance BD in the figure.

53. Proximity questions

a. What point on the line $y = 3x + 4$ is closest to the origin?
b. What point on the parabola $y = 1 - x^2$ is closest to the point $(1, 1)$?
c. Find the point on the graph of $y = \sqrt{x}$ that is nearest the point $(p, 0)$ if (i) $p > \frac{1}{2}$; and (ii) $0 < p < \frac{1}{2}$. Express the answer in terms of p.

54. Turning a corner with a pole

a. What is the length of the longest pole that can be carried horizontally around a corner at which a 3-ft corridor and a 4-ft corridor meet at right angles?

b. What is the length of the longest pole that can be carried horizontally around a corner at which a corridor that is a ft wide and a corridor that is b ft wide meet at right angles?

c. What is the length of the longest pole that can be carried horizontally around a corner at which a corridor that is $a = 5$ ft wide and a corridor that is $b = 5$ ft wide meet at an angle of $120°$?

d. What is the length of the longest pole that can be carried around a corner at which a corridor that is a ft wide and a corridor that is b ft wide meet at right angles, assuming there is an 8-ft ceiling and that you may tilt the pole at any angle?

55. Travel costs A simple model for travel costs involves the cost of gasoline and the cost of a driver. Specifically, assume that gasoline costs $\$p/\text{gallon}$ and the vehicle gets g miles per gallon. Also, assume that the driver earns $\$w/\text{hour}$.

a. A plausible function to describe how gas mileage (in mi/gal) varies with speed is $g(v) = v(85 - v)/60$. Evaluate $g(0)$, $g(40)$, and $g(60)$ and explain why these values are reasonable.

b. At what speed does the gas mileage function have its maximum?

c. Explain why the cost of a trip of length L miles is $C(v) = Lp/g(v) + Lw/v$.

d. Let $L = 400$ mi, $p = \$4/\text{gal}$, and $w = \$20/\text{hr}$. At what (constant) speed should the vehicle be driven to minimize the cost of the trip?

e. Should the optimal speed be increased or decreased (compared with part (d)) if L is increased from 400 mi to 500 mi? Explain.

f. Should the optimal speed be increased or decreased (compared with part (d)) if p is increased from \$4/gal to \$4.20/gal? Explain.

g. Should the optimal speed be increased or decreased (compared with part (d)) if w is decreased from \$20/hr to \$15/hr? Explain.

56. Do dogs know calculus? A mathematician stands on a beach with his dog at point A. He throws a tennis ball so that it hits the water at point B. The dog, wanting to get to the tennis ball as quickly as possible, runs along the straight beach to point D and then swims from point D to point B to retrieve his ball. Assume C is the closest point on the edge of the beach to the tennis ball (see figure).

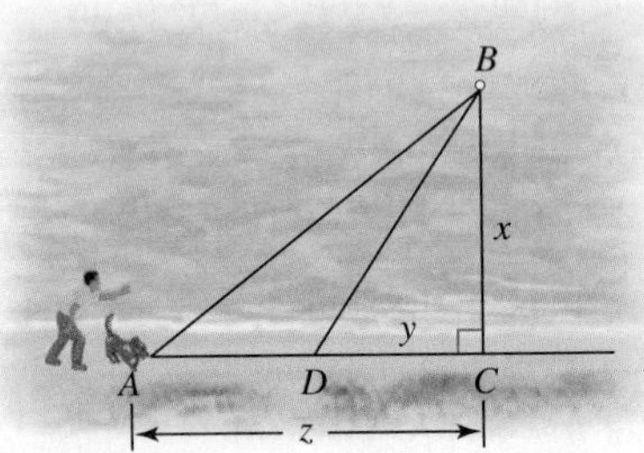

a. Assume the dog runs at r m/s and swims at s m/s, where $r > s$. Also assume the lengths of BC, CD, and AC are x, y, and z, respectively. Find a function $T(y)$ representing the total time it takes for the dog to get to the ball.

b. Verify that the value of y that minimizes the time it takes to retrieve the ball is $y = \dfrac{x}{\sqrt{r/s + 1}\sqrt{r/s - 1}}$.

c. If the dog runs at 8 m/s and swims at 1 m/s, what ratio y/x produces the fastest retrieving time?

d. A dog named Elvis who runs at 6.4 m/s and swims at 0.910 m/s was found to use an average ratio y/x of 0.144 to retrieve his ball. Does Elvis appear to know calculus? (*Source:* Timothy Pennings, *College Mathematics Journal*, May 2003)

57. Fermat's Principle

a. Two poles of heights m and n are separated by a horizontal distance d. A rope is stretched from the top of one pole to the ground and then to the top of the other pole. Show that the configuration that requires the least amount of rope occurs when $\theta_1 = \theta_2$ (see figure).

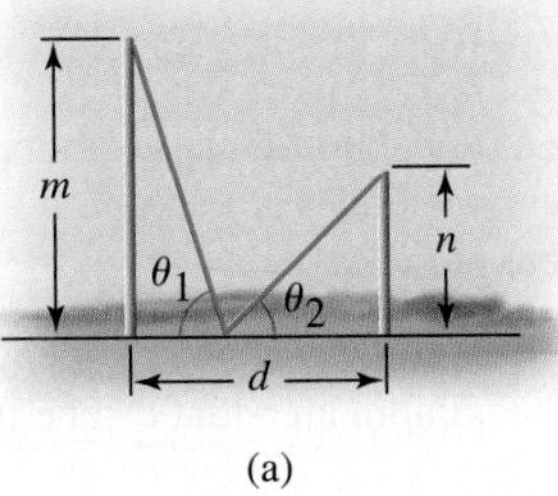

(a)

b. Fermat's Principle states that when light travels between two points in the same medium (at a constant speed), it travels on the path that minimizes the travel time. Show that when light from a source A reflects off of a surface and is received at point B, the angle of incidence equals the angle of reflection, or $\theta_1 = \theta_2$ (see figure).

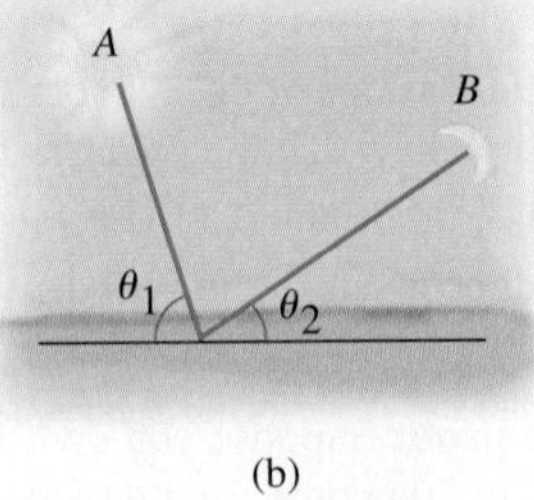

(b)

58. Snell's Law Suppose that a light source at A is in a medium in which light travels at a speed v_1 and the point B is in a medium in which light travels at a speed v_2 (see figure). Using Fermat's Principle, which states that light travels along the path that requires the minimum travel time (Exercise 57), show that the path taken between points A and B satisfies $(\sin \theta_1)/v_1 = (\sin \theta_2)/v_2$.

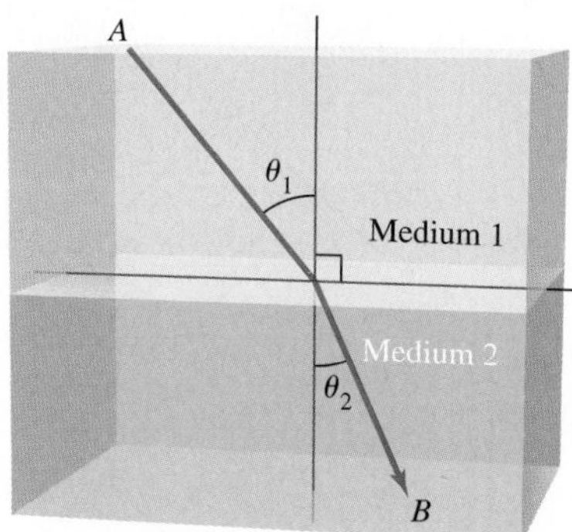

59. **Tree notch (Putnam Exam 1938, rephrased)** A notch is cut in a cylindrical vertical tree trunk. The notch penetrates to the axis of the cylinder and is bounded by two half-planes that intersect on a diameter D of the tree. The angle between the two half planes is θ. Prove that for a given tree and fixed angle θ, the volume of the notch is minimized by taking the bounding planes at equal angles to the horizontal plane that also passes through D.

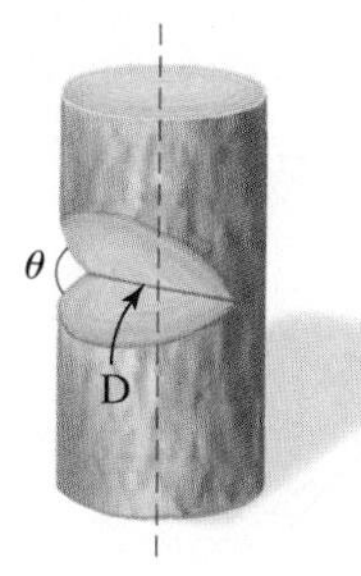

60. **Gliding mammals** Many species of small mammals (such as flying squirrels and marsupial gliders) have the ability to walk and glide. Recent research suggests that these animals choose the most energy-efficient means of travel. According to one empirical model, the energy required for a glider with body mass m to walk a horizontal distance D is $8.46\,Dm^{2/3}$ (where m is measured in grams, D is measured in meters, and energy is measured in microliters of oxygen consumed in respiration). The energy cost of climbing to a height $D \tan \theta$ and gliding at an angle of θ (below the horizontal, with $\theta = 0$ representing horizontal flight and $\theta > 45°$ representing controlled falling) a horizontal distance D is modeled by $1.36\,mD \tan \theta$. Therefore, the function

$$S(m, \theta) = 8.46m^{2/3} - 1.36m \tan \theta$$

gives the energy difference per horizontal meter traveled between walking and gliding: If $S > 0$ for given values of m and θ, then it is more costly to walk than glide.

a. For what glide angles is it more efficient for a 200-gram animal to glide rather than walk?

b. Find the threshold function $\theta = g(m)$ that gives the curve along which walking and gliding are equally efficient. Is it an increasing or decreasing function of body mass?

c. In order to make gliding more efficient than walking, do larger gliders have a larger or smaller selection of glide angles that they can use?

d. Let $\theta = 25°$ (a typical glide angle) and graph S as a function of m, for $0 \le m \le 3000$. For what values of m is gliding more efficient?

e. For $\theta = 25°$, what value of m (call it m^*) maximizes S?

f. Does m^*, as defined in part (e), increase or decrease with increasing θ? That is, as a glider reduces its glide angle, does its optimal size become larger or smaller?

g. Assuming Dumbo is a gliding elephant whose weight is one metric ton (10^6 g), what glide angle would Dumbo use to be more efficient at gliding than walking?

(*Source: Energetic savings and the body size distribution of gliding mammals*, Roman Dial, *Evolutionary Ecology Research*, **5** (2003): 1151–1162.)

QUICK CHECK ANSWERS

2. $A = 400x - 2x^2$, $A = 400x - 3x^2$
3. $V = 108w^2 - 2w^3$

4.5 Linear Approximation and Differentials

Imagine plotting a smooth curve with a graphing utility. Now pick a point P on the curve, draw the line tangent to the curve at P, and zoom in on it several times. As you successively enlarge the curve near P, it looks more and more like the tangent line (Figure 4.55a). This fundamental observation—that smooth curves appear straighter on smaller scales—is the basis of many important mathematical ideas, one of which is *linear approximation.*

Now, consider a curve with a corner or cusp at a point Q (Figure 4.55b). No amount of magnification "straightens out" the curve or removes the corner at Q. The different behavior at P and Q is related to the idea of differentiability: The function in Figure 4.55a is differentiable at P, whereas the function in Figure 4.55b is not differentiable at Q. One of the requirements for the techniques presented in this section is that the function be differentiable at the point in question.

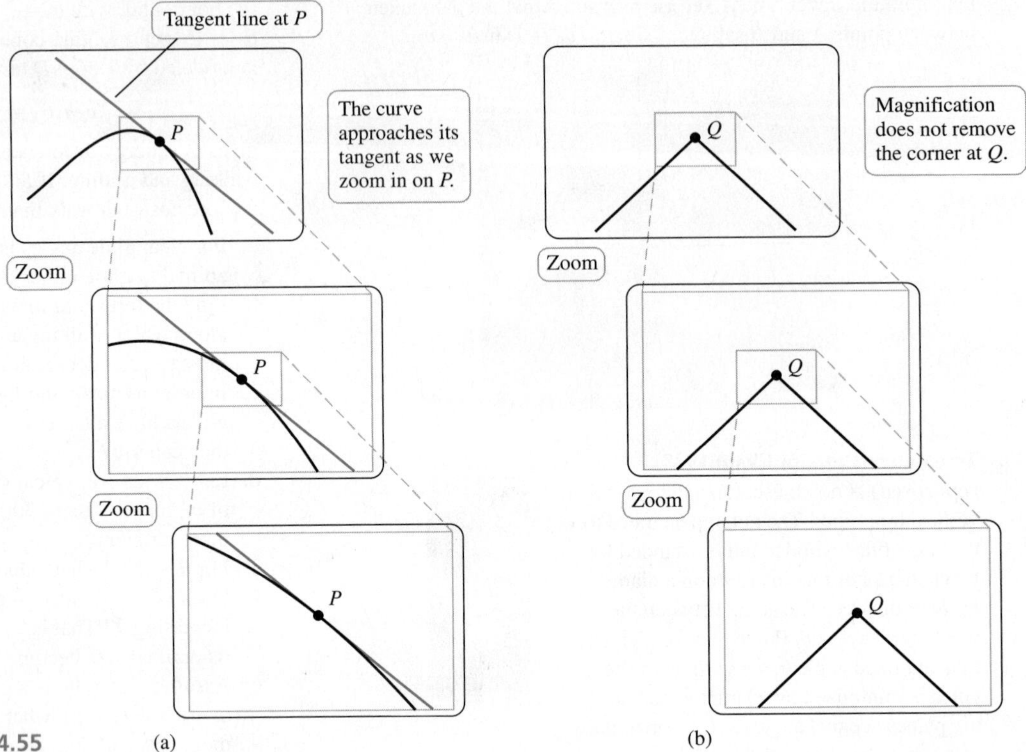

FIGURE 4.55

Linear Approximation

Figure 4.55a suggests that when we zoom in on the graph of a smooth function at a point P, the curve approaches its tangent line at P. This fact is the key to understanding linear approximation. The idea is to use the line tangent to the curve at P to approximate the value of the function at points near P. Here's how it works.

Assume f is differentiable on an interval containing the point a. The slope of the line tangent to the curve at the point $(a, f(a))$ is $f'(a)$. Therefore, the equation of the tangent line is

$$y - f(a) = f'(a)(x - a) \quad \text{or} \quad y = \underbrace{f(a) + f'(a)(x - a)}_{L(x)}.$$

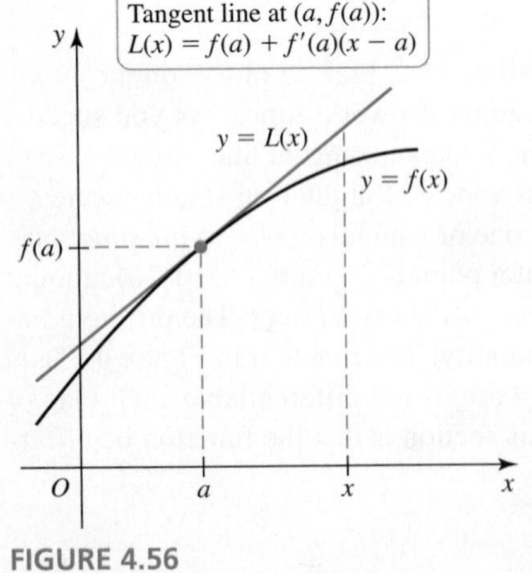

FIGURE 4.56

This tangent line is a new function L that we call the *linear approximation* to f at a (Figure 4.56). If f and f' are easy to evaluate at a, then the value of f at points near a is easily approximated using the linear approximation L. That is,

$$f(x) \approx L(x) = f(a) + f'(a)(x - a).$$

This approximation improves as x approaches a.

DEFINITION Linear Approximation to *f* at *a*

Suppose f is differentiable on an interval I containing the point a. The **linear approximation** to f at a is the linear function

$$L(x) = f(a) + f'(a)(x - a), \qquad \text{for } x \text{ in } I.$$

QUICK CHECK 1 Sketch the graph of a function f that is concave up at a point $(a, f(a))$. Sketch the linear approximation to f at a. Is the graph of the linear approximation above or below the graph of f?

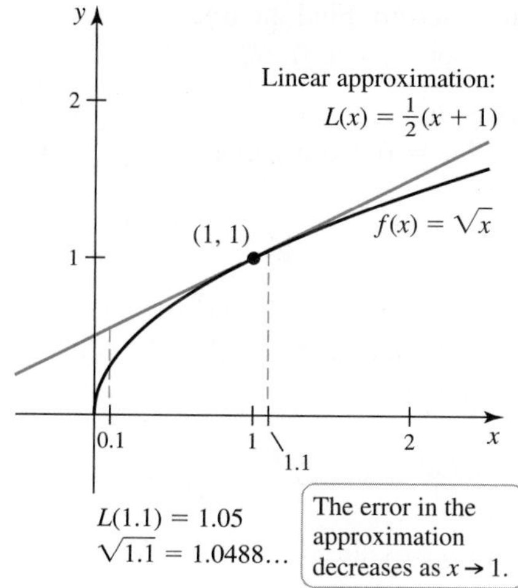

FIGURE 4.57

Table 4.4

x	$L(x)$	Exact $\sqrt{x}$	Percent error
1.2	1.1	1.0954...	0.4%
1.1	1.05	1.0488...	0.1%
1.01	1.005	1.0049...	0.001%
1.001	1.0005	1.0005...	0.00001%

EXAMPLE 1 Linear approximations and errors

a. Find the linear approximation to $f(x) = \sqrt{x}$ at $x = 1$ and use it to approximate $\sqrt{1.1}$.

b. Use linear approximation to estimate the value of $\sqrt{0.1}$.

SOLUTION

a. We construct the linear approximation

$$L(x) = f(a) + f'(a)(x - a),$$

where $f(x) = \sqrt{x}$, $f'(x) = 1/(2\sqrt{x})$, and $a = 1$. Noting that $f(a) = f(1) = 1$ and $f'(a) = f'(1) = \frac{1}{2}$, we have

$$L(x) = 1 + \frac{1}{2}(x - 1) = \frac{1}{2}(x + 1),$$

which is an equation of the line tangent to the curve at the point $(1, 1)$ (Figure 4.57). Because $x = 1.1$ is near $x = 1$, we approximate $\sqrt{1.1}$ by $L(1.1)$:

$$\sqrt{1.1} \approx L(1.1) = \frac{1}{2}(1.1 + 1) = 1.05$$

The exact value is $f(1.1) = \sqrt{1.1} = 1.0488\ldots$; therefore, the linear approximation has an error of about 0.1%. Furthermore, our approximation is an *overestimate* because the tangent line lies above the graph of f. In Table 4.4 we see several approximations to $\sqrt{x}$ for x near 1 and the associated errors. Clearly, the errors decrease as x approaches 1.

b. If the linear approximation $L(x) = \frac{1}{2}(x + 1)$ obtained in part (a) is used to approximate $\sqrt{0.1}$, we have

$$\sqrt{0.1} \approx L(0.1) = \frac{1}{2}(0.1 + 1) = 0.55.$$

A calculator gives $\sqrt{0.1} = 0.3162\ldots$, which shows that the approximation is well off the mark. The error arises because the tangent line through $(1, 1)$ is not close to the curve at $x = 0.1$ (Figure 4.57). For this reason, we seek a different value of a, with the requirement that it is near $x = 0.1$, and both $f(a)$ and $f'(a)$ are easily computed. It is tempting to try $a = 0$, but $f'(0)$ is undefined. One choice that works well is $a = \frac{9}{100} = 0.09$. Using the linear approximation $L(x) = f(a) + f'(a)(x - a)$, we have

$$\begin{aligned}\sqrt{0.1} \approx L(0.1) &= \overbrace{\sqrt{\frac{9}{100}}}^{f(a)} + \overbrace{\frac{1}{2\sqrt{9/100}}}^{f'(a)}\overbrace{\left(\frac{1}{10} - \frac{9}{100}\right)}^{(x-a)} \\ &= \frac{3}{10} + \frac{10}{6}\left(\frac{1}{100}\right) \\ &= \frac{19}{60} \approx 0.3167\end{aligned}$$

➤ We choose $a = \frac{9}{100}$ because it is close to 0.1 and its square root is easy to evaluate.

This approximation agrees with the exact value to three decimal places.

Related Exercises 7–22 ◄

QUICK CHECK 2 Suppose you want to use linear approximation to estimate $\sqrt{0.18}$. What is a good choice for a? ◄

EXAMPLE 2 Linear approximation for the sine function Find the linear approximation to $f(x) = \sin x$ at $x = 0$, and use it to approximate $\sin 2.5°$.

SOLUTION We begin by constructing a linear approximation $L(x) = f(a) + f'(a)(x - a)$, where $f(x) = \sin x$ and $a = 0$. Noting that $f(0) = 0$ and $f'(0) = \cos(0) = 1$, we have

$$L(x) = 0 + 1(x - 0) = x.$$

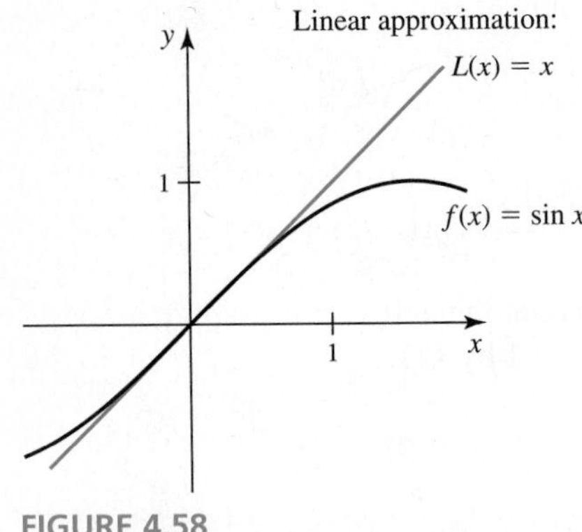

FIGURE 4.58

The linear approximation is the line tangent to the curve at the point (0, 0) (Figure 4.58). Before using $L(x)$ to approximate $\sin 2.5°$, we convert to radian measure (the derivative formulas for trigonometric functions require angles in radians):

$$2.5° = 2.5°\left(\frac{\pi}{180°}\right) = \frac{\pi}{72} \approx 0.04363 \text{ rad}$$

Therefore, $\sin 2.5° \approx L(\pi/72) \approx 0.04363$. A calculator gives $\sin 2.5° \approx 0.04362$, so the approximation is accurate to four decimal places. *Related Exercises 7–22* ◀

In Examples 1 and 2, we used a calculator to check the accuracy of our approximations. This begs the question: Why bother with linear approximation when a calculator does a better job? There are some good answers to that question.

Linear approximation is actually just the first step in the larger process of *polynomial approximation*. While linear approximation does a decent job of estimating function values when x is near a, we can generally do better with higher-degree polynomials. These ideas are explored further in Chapter 10.

Linear approximation also allows us to discover simple approximations to complicated functions. In Example 2, we found the *small-angle approximation to the sine function*; $\sin x \approx x$ for x near 0. Finally, as will be shown in Chapter 10, linear approximation allows us to estimate errors in approximations.

QUICK CHECK 3 Explain why the linear approximation to $f(x) = \cos x$ at $x = 0$ is $L(x) = 1$. ◀

A Variation on Linear Approximation

Linear approximation says that a function f can be approximated as

$$f(x) \approx f(a) + f'(a)(x - a),$$

where a is fixed and x is a nearby point. We first rewrite this expression as

$$\underbrace{f(x) - f(a)}_{\Delta y} \approx f'(a)\underbrace{(x - a)}_{\Delta x}.$$

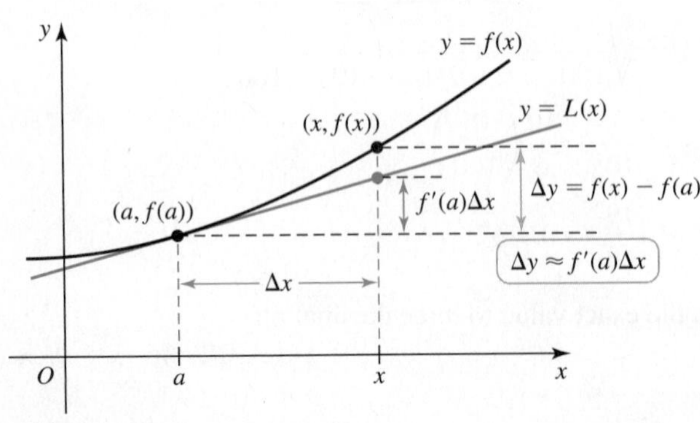

FIGURE 4.59

It is customary to use the notation Δ (capital Greek delta) to denote a change. The factor $x - a$ is the change in the x-coordinate between a and a nearby point x. Similarly, $f(x) - f(a)$ is the corresponding change in the y-coordinate (Figure 4.59). So, we write this approximation as

$$\Delta y \approx f'(a)\,\Delta x.$$

In other words, a change in y (the function value) can be approximated by the corresponding change in x magnified or diminished by a factor of $f'(a)$. This interpretation states the familiar fact that $f'(a)$ is the rate of change of y with respect to x.

Relationship Between Δx and Δy

Suppose f is differentiable on an interval I containing the point a. The change in the value of f between two points a and $a + \Delta x$ is approximately

$$\Delta y \approx f'(a)\,\Delta x,$$

where $a + \Delta x$ is in I.

EXAMPLE 3 Estimating changes with linear approximations

a. Approximate the change in $y = f(x) = x^9 - 2x + 1$ when x changes from 1.00 to 1.05.

b. Approximate the change in the surface area of a spherical hot-air balloon when the radius decreases from 4 m to 3.9 m.

SOLUTION

a. The change in y is $\Delta y \approx f'(a)\,\Delta x$, where $a = 1$, $\Delta x = 0.05$, and $f'(x) = 9x^8 - 2$. Substituting these values, we find that

$$\Delta y \approx f'(a)\,\Delta x = f'(1)\cdot 0.05 = 7\cdot 0.05 = 0.35.$$

If x increases from 1.00 to 1.05, then y increases by approximately 0.35.

b. The surface area of a sphere is $S = 4\pi r^2$, so the change in the surface area when the radius changes by Δr is $\Delta S \approx S'(a)\,\Delta r$. Substituting $S'(r) = 8\pi r$, $a = 4$, and $\Delta r = -0.1$, the approximate change in the surface area is

$$\Delta S \approx S'(a)\,\Delta r = S'(4)\cdot(-0.1) = 32\pi\cdot(-0.1) \approx -10.05.$$

The change in surface area is approximately -10.05 m^2; it is negative, reflecting a decrease.

Related Exercises 23–26

➤ Notice that the units in these calculations are consistent. If r has units of meters (m), S' has units of $\text{m}^2/\text{m} = \text{m}$, so ΔS has units of m^2 as it should.

QUICK CHECK 4 Given that the volume of a sphere is $V = 4\pi r^3/3$, find an expression for the approximate change in the volume when the radius changes from a to $a + \Delta r$.

SUMMARY **Uses of Linear Approximation**

- To approximate f near $x = a$, use

$$f(x) \approx L(x) = f(a) + f'(a)(x - a).$$

- To approximate the change Δy in the dependent variable when x changes from a to $a + \Delta x$, use

$$\Delta y \approx f'(a)\,\Delta x.$$

Differentials

We now introduce an important concept that allows us to distinguish two related quantities:

- The change in the function $y = f(x)$ as x changes from a to $a + \Delta x$ (which we call Δy, as before)
- The change in the linear approximation $y = L(x)$ as x changes from a to $a + \Delta x$ (which we will call the *differential* dy)

Consider a function f that is differentiable on an interval containing a. If the x-coordinate changes from a to $a + \Delta x$, the corresponding change in the function is *exactly*

$$\Delta y = f(a + \Delta x) - f(a).$$

Using the linear approximation $L(x) = f(a) + f'(a)(x - a)$, the change in L as x changes from a to $a + \Delta x$ is

$$\begin{aligned}\Delta L &= L(a + \Delta x) - L(a)\\ &= \underbrace{[f(a) + f'(a)(a + \Delta x - a)]}_{L(a+\Delta x)} - \underbrace{[f(a) + f'(a)(a - a)]}_{L(a)}\\ &= f'(a)\,\Delta x.\end{aligned}$$

In order to distinguish Δy and ΔL, we define two new variables called **differentials**. The differential dx is simply Δx; the differential dy is the change in the linear approximation, which is $\Delta L = f'(a)\,\Delta x$. Using this notation,

$$\Delta L = \underbrace{dy}_{\text{same as }\Delta L} = f'(a)\,\Delta x = f'(a)\,\underbrace{dx}_{\text{same as }\Delta x}.$$

Therefore, at the point a, we have $dy = f'(a)\,dx$. More generally, we replace the fixed point a by a variable point x and write

$$dy = f'(x)\,dx.$$

DEFINITION Differentials

Let f be differentiable on an interval containing x. A small change in x is denoted by the **differential** dx. The corresponding change in f is approximated by the **differential** $dy = f'(x)\,dx$; that is,

$$\Delta y = f(x + dx) - f(x) \approx dy = f'(x)\,dx.$$

Of the two coinventors of calculus, Leibniz relied on the idea of differentials in his development of calculus. Leibniz's notation for differentials is essentially the same as the notation we use today. An Irish philosopher of the day, Bishop Berkeley, called differentials "the ghost of departed quantities."

Figure 4.60 shows that if $\Delta x = dx$ is small, then the change in f, which is Δy, is well approximated by the change in the linear approximation, which is dy. Furthermore, the approximation $\Delta y \approx dy$ improves as dx approaches 0. The notation for differentials is consistent with the notation for the derivative: If we divide both sides of $dy = f'(x)\,dx$ by dx, we have

$$\frac{dy}{dx} = \frac{f'(x)\,dx}{dx} = f'(x).$$

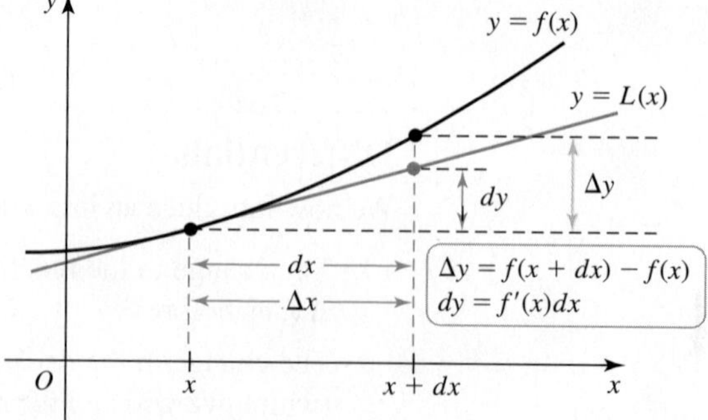

FIGURE 4.60

EXAMPLE 4 Differentials as change Use the notation of differentials to write the approximate change in $f(x) = 3\cos^2 x$ given a small change dx.

Recall that $\sin 2x = 2\sin x\cos x$.

SOLUTION With $f(x) = 3\cos^2 x$, we have $f'(x) = -6\cos x\sin x = -3\sin 2x$. Therefore,

$$dy = f'(x)\,dx = -3\sin 2x\,dx.$$

The interpretation is that a small change dx in the independent variable x produces an approximate change in the dependent variable of $dy = -3 \sin 2x\, dx$ in y. For example, if x increases from $x = \pi/4$ to $x = \pi/4 + 0.1$, then $dx = 0.1$ and

$$dy = -3 \sin(\pi/2)(0.1) = -0.3.$$

The approximate change in the function is -0.3, which means a decrease of approximately 0.3.

Related Exercises 27–34 ◀

SECTION 4.5 EXERCISES

Review Questions

1. Sketch the graph of a smooth function f and label a point $P(a, (f(a))$ on the curve. Draw the line that represents the linear approximation to f at P.
2. Suppose you find the linear approximation to a differentiable function at a local maximum of that function. Describe the graph of the linear approximation.
3. How can linear approximation be used to approximate the value of a function f near a point at which f and f' are easily evaluated?
4. How can linear approximation be used to approximate the change in $y = f(x)$ given a change in x?
5. Given a function f differentiable on its domain, write and explain the relationship between the differentials dx and dy.
6. Does the differential dy represent the change in f or the change in the linear approximation to f? Explain.

Basic Skills

T **7–12. Linear approximation**

a. Write the equation of the line that represents the linear approximation to the following functions at the given point a.
b. Graph the function and the linear approximation near a.
c. Use the linear approximation to estimate the given function value.
d. Compute the percent error in your approximation, $100 \cdot |\text{approx}-\text{exact}|/|\text{exact}|$, *where the exact value is given by a calculator.*

7. $f(x) = 12 - x^2$; $a = 2$; $f(2.1)$
8. $f(x) = \sin x$; $a = \pi/4$; $f(0.75)$
9. $f(x) = 1/(1 + x)$; $a = 0$; $f(-0.1)$
10. $f(x) = x/(x + 1)$; $a = 1$; $f(1.1)$
11. $f(x) = \cos x$; $a = 0$; $f(-0.01)$
12. $f(x) = x^{-3}$; $a = 1$; $f(1.05)$

13–22. Estimations with linear approximation *Use linear approximation to estimate the following quantities. Choose a value of a to produce a small error.*

13. $1/203$
14. $\tan 3°$
15. $\sqrt{146}$
16. $\sqrt[3]{65}$
17. $1/1.05$
18. $\sqrt{5/29}$
19. $\sin(\pi/4 + 0.1)$
20. $1/\sqrt{119}$
21. $1/\sqrt[3]{510}$
22. $\cos 31°$

23–26. Approximating changes

23. Approximate the change in the volume of a sphere when its radius changes from $r = 5$ ft to $r = 5.1$ ft $\left(V(r) = \frac{4}{3}\pi r^3\right)$.
24. Approximate the change in the volume of a right circular cone of fixed height $h = 4$ m when its radius increases from $r = 3$ m to $r = 3.05$ m $(V(r) = \frac{1}{3}\pi r^2 h)$.
25. Approximate the change in the lateral surface area (excluding the area of the base) of a right circular cone of fixed height $h = 6$ m when its radius decreases from $r = 10$ m to $r = 9.9$ m $(S = \pi r\sqrt{r^2 + h^2})$.
26. Approximate the change in the magnitude of the electrostatic force between two charges when the distance between them increases from $r = 20$ m to $r = 21$ m $(F(r) = 0.01/r^2)$.

27–34. Differentials *Consider the following functions and express the relationship between a small change in x and the corresponding change in y in the form* $dy = f'(x)\,dx$.

27. $f(x) = 2x + 1$
28. $\sin^2 x$
29. $f(x) = 1/x^3$
30. $f(x) = \sqrt{x^2 + 1}$
31. $f(x) = 2 - a\cos x$
32. $f(x) = (4 + x)/(4 - x)$
33. $f(x) = 3x^3 - 4x$
34. $f(x) = \tan x$

Further Explorations

35. **Explain why or why not** Determine whether the following statements are true and give an explanation or counterexample.
    a. The linear approximation to $f(x) = x^2$ at the point $(0, 0)$ is $L(x) = 0$.
    b. Linear approximation provides a good approximation to $f(x) = |x|$ at $(0, 0)$.
    c. If $f(x) = mx + b$, then at any point a, the linear approximation to f is $L(x) = f(x)$.

T **36–39. Linear approximation**

a. Write an equation of the line that represents the linear approximation to the following functions at a.
b. Graph the function and the linear approximation near a;
c. use the linear approximation to estimate the given quantity; and
d. compute the percent error in your approximation.

36. $f(x) = \tan x$; $a = 0$; $\tan 1.5°$
37. $f(x) = 1/(x + 1)$; $a = 0$; $1/1.1$

38. $f(x) = \cos x;\quad a = \pi/4;\ \cos(0.8)$

39. $f(x) = \sqrt[3]{64 + x};\quad a = 0;\ \sqrt[3]{62.5}$

Applications

40. Ideal Gas Law The pressure P, temperature T, and volume V of an ideal gas are related by $PV = nRT$, where n is the number of moles of the gas and R is the universal gas constant. For the purposes of this exercise, let $nR = 1$; thus, $P = T/V$.

- **a.** Suppose that the volume is held constant and the temperature increases by $\Delta T = 0.05$. What is the approximate change in the pressure? Does the pressure increase or decrease?
- **b.** Suppose that the temperature is held constant and the volume increases by $\Delta V = 0.1$. What is the approximate change in the pressure? Does the pressure increase or decrease?
- **c.** Suppose that the pressure is held constant and the volume increases by $\Delta V = 0.1$. What is the approximate change in the temperature? Does the temperature increase or decrease?

T **41. Errors in approximations** Suppose $f(x) = \sqrt[3]{x}$ is to be approximated near $x = 8$. Find the linear approximation to f at 8. Then complete the following table, showing the errors in various approximations. Use a calculator to obtain the exact values. The percent error is $100 \cdot |\text{approximation}-\text{exact}|/|\text{exact}|$. Comment on the behavior of the errors as x approaches 8.

x	Linear approx	Exact value	Percent error
8.1			
8.01			
8.001			
8.0001			
7.9999			
7.999			
7.99			
7.9			

T **42. Errors in approximations** Suppose $f(x) = 1/(1 + x)$ is to be approximated near $x = 0$. Find the linear approximation to f at 0. Then complete the following table showing the errors in various approximations. Use a calculator to obtain the exact values. The percent error is $100 \cdot |\text{approximation}-\text{exact}|/|\text{exact}|$. Comment on the behavior of the errors as x approaches 0.

x	Linear approx	Exact value	Percent error
0.1			
0.01			
0.001			
0.0001			
−0.0001			
−0.001			
−0.01			
−0.1			

Additional Exercises

43. Linear approximation and the second derivative Draw the graph of a function f such that $f(1) = f'(1) = f''(1) = 1$. Draw the linear approximation to the function at the point $(1, 1)$. Now draw the graph of another function g such that $g(1) = g'(1) = 1$ and $g''(1) = 10$. (It is not possible to represent the second derivative exactly, but your graphs should reflect the fact that $f''(1)$ is relatively small and $g''(1)$ is relatively large.) Now, suppose that linear approximations are used to approximate $f(1.1)$ and $g(1.1)$.

- **a.** Which function has the more accurate linear approximation near $x = 1$ and why?
- **b.** Explain why the error in the linear approximation to f near a point a is proportional to the magnitude of $f''(a)$.

QUICK CHECK ANSWERS

1. The linear approximation lies below the graph of f for x near a. **2.** $a = 0.16$ **3.** Note that $f(0) = 1$ and $f'(0) = 0$, so $L(x) = 1$ (this is the line tangent to $y = \cos x$ at $(0, 1)$). **4.** $\Delta V \approx 4\pi a^2\,\Delta r$.

4.6 Mean Value Theorem

The *Mean Value Theorem* is a cornerstone in the theoretical framework of calculus. Several critical theorems (some stated in previous sections) rely on the Mean Value Theorem; the theorem also appears in practical applications. We begin with a preliminary result known as Rolle's Theorem.

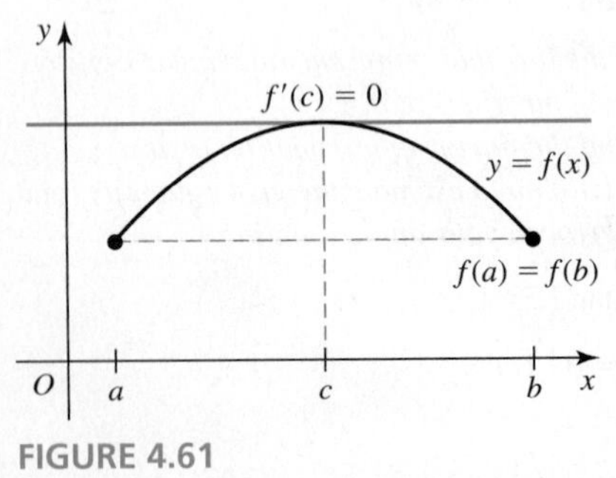

FIGURE 4.61

Rolle's Theorem

Consider a function f that is continuous on a closed interval $[a, b]$ and differentiable on the open interval (a, b). Furthermore, assume f has the special property that $f(a) = f(b)$ (Figure 4.61). The statement of Rolle's Theorem is not surprising: It says that somewhere between a and b, there is at least one point at which f has a horizontal tangent line.

Michel Rolle (1652–1719) is one of the less celebrated mathematicians whose name is nevertheless attached to a theorem. He worked in Paris most of his life as a scribe and published his theorem in 1691.

THEOREM 4.8 Rolle's Theorem
Let f be continuous on a closed interval $[a, b]$ and differentiable on (a, b) with $f(a) = f(b)$. There is at least one point c in (a, b) such that $f'(c) = 0$.

Proof The function f satisfies the conditions of Theorem 4.1 (Extreme Value Theorem) and thus attains its absolute maximum and minimum values on $[a, b]$. Those values are attained either at an endpoint or at an interior point c.

The Extreme Value Theorem, discussed in Section 4.1, states that a function that is continuous on a closed bounded interval attains its absolute maximum and minimum values on that interval.

Case 1: First suppose that f attains both its absolute maximum and minimum values at the endpoints. Because $f(a) = f(b)$, the maximum and minimum values are equal, and it follows that f is a constant function on $[a, b]$. Therefore, $f'(x) = 0$ for all x in (a, b), and the conclusion of the theorem holds.

Case 2: Assume at least one of the absolute extreme values of f does not occur at an endpoint. Then, f must attain an absolute extreme value at an interior point of $[a, b]$; therefore, f must have either a local maximum or a local minimum at a point c in (a, b). Because f is differentiable on (a, b), we know from Theorem 4.2 that at a local extremum the derivative is zero. Therefore, $f'(c) = 0$ for at least one point c of (a, b), and again the conclusion of the theorem holds. ◀

Why does Rolle's Theorem require continuity? A function that is not continuous on $[a, b]$ may have identical values at both endpoints and still not have a horizontal tangent line at any point on the interval (Figure 4.62a). Similarly, a function that is continuous on $[a, b]$ but not differentiable at a point of (a, b) may also fail to have a horizontal tangent line (Figure 4.62b).

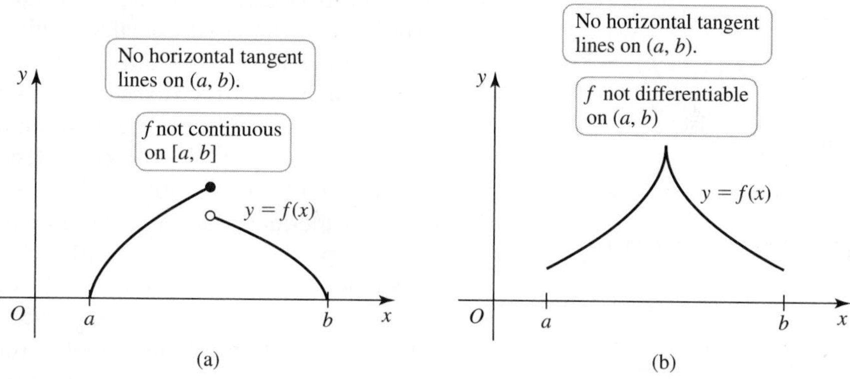

FIGURE 4.62

QUICK CHECK 1 Where on the interval $[0, 4]$ does $f(x) = 4x - x^2$ have a horizontal tangent line? ◀

EXAMPLE 1 Verifying Rolle's Theorem Find an interval on which Rolle's Theorem applies to $f(x) = x^3 - 7x^2 + 10x$. Then find all the points on that interval at which $f'(c) = 0$.

SOLUTION Because f is a polynomial, it is everywhere continuous and differentiable. We need an interval $[a, b]$ with the property that $f(a) = f(b)$. Noting that $f(x) = x(x - 2)(x - 5)$, we choose the interval $[0, 5]$, because $f(0) = f(5) = 0$ (other intervals are possible). The goal is to find points c in the interval $(0, 5)$ at which $f'(c) = 0$, which amounts to the familiar task of finding the critical points of f. The critical points satisfy

$$f'(x) = 3x^2 - 14x + 10 = 0.$$

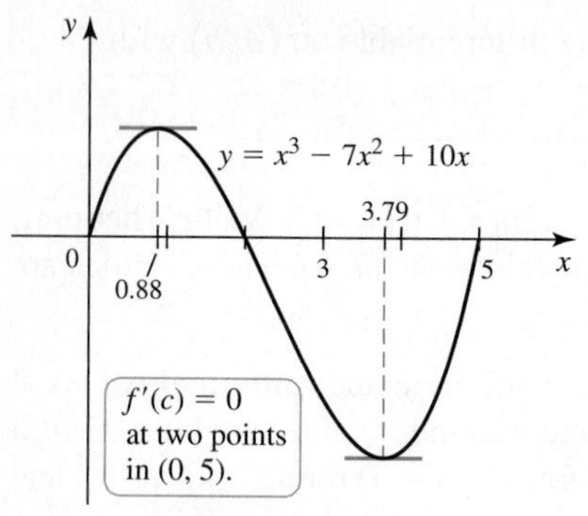

FIGURE 4.63

Using the quadratic formula, the roots are

$$x = \frac{7 \pm \sqrt{19}}{3}, \quad \text{or} \quad x \approx 0.88 \quad \text{and} \quad x \approx 3.79.$$

As shown in Figure 4.63, the graph of f has two points at which the tangent line is horizontal. *Related Exercises 7–12*

Mean Value Theorem

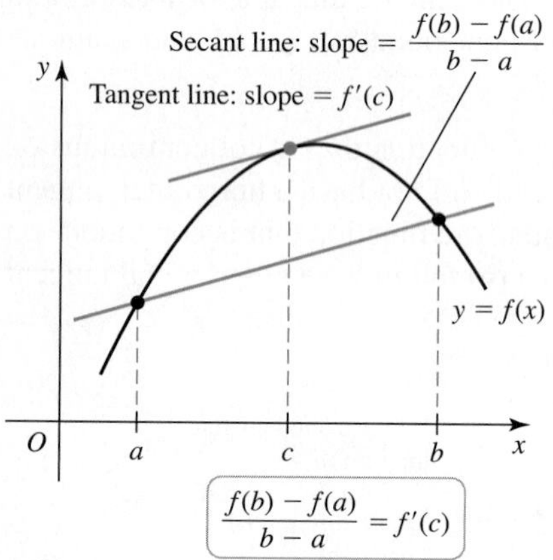

FIGURE 4.64

The Mean Value Theorem is easily understood with the aid of a picture. Figure 4.64 shows a function f differentiable on (a, b) with a secant line passing through $(a, f(a))$ and $(b, f(b))$; its slope is the average rate of change of f over $[a, b]$. The Mean Value Theorem claims that there exists a point c in (a, b) at which the slope of the tangent line at c is equal to the slope of the secant line. In other words, we can find a point on the graph of f where the tangent line is parallel to the secant line.

THEOREM 4.9 Mean Value Theorem
If f is continuous on a closed interval $[a, b]$ and differentiable on (a, b), then there is at least one point c in (a, b) such that

$$\frac{f(b) - f(a)}{b - a} = f'(c).$$

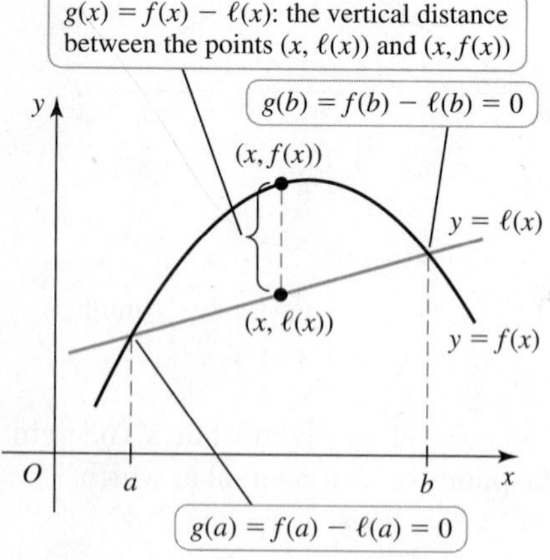

FIGURE 4.65

Proof The strategy of the proof is to use the function f of the Mean Value Theorem to form a new function g that satisfies Rolle's Theorem. Notice that the continuity and differentiability conditions of Rolle's Theorem and the Mean Value Theorem are the same. We devise g so that it satisfies the condition that $g(a) = g(b) = 0$.

As shown in Figure 4.65, the chord between $(a, f(a))$ and $(b, f(b))$ is a segment of the straight line described by a function ℓ. We now define a new function g that measures the vertical distance between the given function f and the line ℓ. This function is simply $g(x) = f(x) - \ell(x)$. Because f and ℓ are continuous on $[a, b]$ and differentiable on (a, b), it follows that g is also continuous on $[a, b]$ and differentiable on (a, b). Furthermore, because the graphs of f and ℓ intersect at $x = a$ and $x = b$, we have $g(a) = f(a) - \ell(a) = 0$ and $g(b) = f(b) - \ell(b) = 0$.

We now have a function g that satisfies the conditions of Rolle's Theorem. By that theorem, we are guaranteed the existence of at least one point c in the interval (a, b) such that $g'(c) = 0$. By the definition of g, this condition implies that $f'(c) - \ell'(c) = 0$, or $f'(c) = \ell'(c)$.

We are almost finished. What is $\ell'(c)$? It is just the slope of the chord, which is

$$\frac{f(b) - f(a)}{b - a}.$$

Therefore, $f'(c) = \ell'(c)$ implies that

$$\frac{f(b) - f(a)}{b - a} = f'(c).$$

QUICK CHECK 2 Sketch the graph of a function that illustrates why the continuity condition of the Mean Value Theorem is needed. Sketch the graph of a function that illustrates why the differentiability condition of the Mean Value Theorem is needed.

➤ The proofs of Rolle's Theorem and the Mean Value Theorem are nonconstructive: The theorems claim that a certain point exists, but their proofs do not say how to find it.

The following situation offers an interpretation of the Mean Value Theorem. Imagine taking 2 hours to drive to a town 100 miles away. While your average speed is $100 \text{ mi}/2 \text{ hr} = 50 \text{ mi/hr}$, your instantaneous speed (measured by the speedometer) almost certainly varies. The Mean Value Theorem says that at some point during the trip, your instantaneous speed equals your average speed, which is 50 mi/hr.

Meteorologists look for "steep" lapse rates in the layer of the atmosphere where the pressure is between 700 and 500 hPa (hectopascals). This range of pressure typically corresponds to altitudes between 3 km and 5.5 km. The data in Example 2 were recorded in Denver at nearly the same time a tornado struck 50 mi to the north.

EXAMPLE 2 **Mean Value Theorem in action** The *lapse rate* is the rate at which the temperature T decreases in the atmosphere with respect to increasing altitude z. It is typically reported in units of °C/km and is defined by $\gamma = -dT/dz$. When the lapse rate rises above 7°C/km in a certain layer of the atmosphere, it indicates favorable conditions for thunderstorm and tornado formation, provided other atmospheric conditions are also present.

Suppose the temperature at $z = 2.9$ km is $T = 7.6$°C and the temperature at $z = 5.6$ km is $T = -14.3$°C. Assume also that the temperature function is continuous and differentiable at all altitudes of interest. What can a meteorologist conclude from these data?

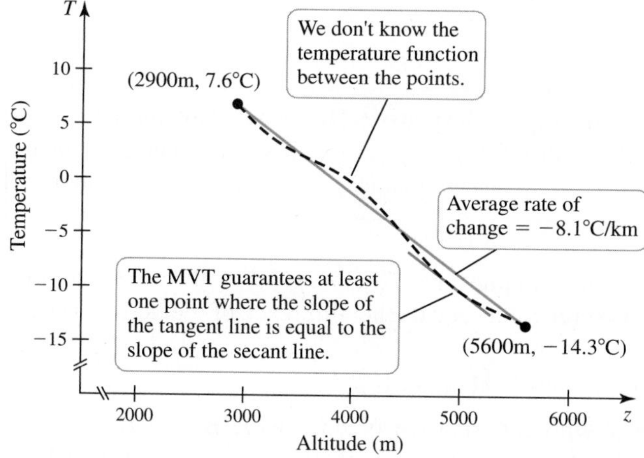

FIGURE 4.66

SOLUTION Figure 4.66 shows the two data points plotted on a graph of altitude and temperature. The slope of the line joining these points is

$$\frac{-14.3\text{°C} - 7.6\text{°C}}{5.6 \text{ km} - 2.9 \text{ km}} = -8.1\text{°C/km},$$

which means, on average, the temperature is decreasing at 8.1°C per km in the layer of air between 2.9 km and 5.6 km. With only two data points, we cannot know the entire temperature profile. The Mean Value Theorem, however, guarantees that there is at least one altitude at which $dT/dz = -8.1$°C/km. At each such altitude, the lapse rate is $\gamma = -dT/dz = 8.1$°C/km. Because this lapse rate is above the 7°C/km threshold associated with unstable weather, the meteorologist might expect an increased likelihood of severe storms.

Related Exercises 13–14

EXAMPLE 3 **Verifying the Mean Value Theorem** Determine whether the function $f(x) = 2x^3 - 3x + 1$ satisfies the conditions of the Mean Value Theorem on the interval $[-2, 2]$. If so, find the point(s) guaranteed to exist by the theorem.

SOLUTION The polynomial f is everywhere continuous and differentiable, so it satisfies the conditions of the Mean Value Theorem. The average rate of change of the function on the interval $[-2, 2]$ is

$$\frac{f(2) - f(-2)}{2 - (-2)} = \frac{11 - (-9)}{4} = 5.$$

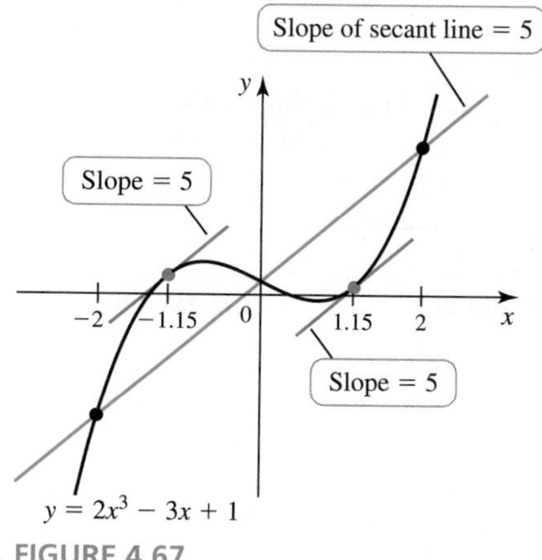

FIGURE 4.67

The goal is to find points in $(-2, 2)$ at which the line tangent to the curve has a slope of 5—that is, to find points at which $f'(x) = 5$. Differentiating f, this condition becomes

$$f'(x) = 6x^2 - 3 = 5 \quad \text{or} \quad x^2 = \frac{4}{3}.$$

Therefore, the points guaranteed to exist by the Mean Value Theorem are $x = \pm 2/\sqrt{3} \approx \pm 1.15$. The tangent lines have slope 5 at the points $(\pm 2/\sqrt{3}, f(\pm 2/\sqrt{3}))$ (Figure 4.67).

Related Exercises 15–22

Consequences of the Mean Value Theorem

We close with several results—some postponed from previous sections—that follow from the Mean Value Theorem.

We already know that the derivative of a constant function is zero; that is, if $f(x) = C$, then $f'(x) = 0$ (Theorem 3.2). Theorem 4.10 states the converse of this result.

THEOREM 4.10 Zero Derivative Implies Constant Function
If f is differentiable and $f'(x) = 0$ at all points of an interval I, then f is a constant function on I.

Proof Suppose $f'(x) = 0$ on $[a, b]$, where a and b are distinct points of I. By the Mean Value Theorem, there exists a point c in (a, b) such that

$$\frac{f(b) - f(a)}{b - a} = \underbrace{f'(c) = 0.}_{f'(x) = 0 \text{ for all } x \text{ in } I}$$

Multiplying both sides of this equation by $b - a \neq 0$, it follows that $f(b) = f(a)$, and this is true for every pair of points a and b in I. If $f(b) = f(a)$ for every pair of points in an interval, then f is a constant function on that interval. ◀

Theorem 4.11 builds on the conclusion of Theorem 4.10.

THEOREM 4.11 Functions with Equal Derivatives Differ by a Constant
If two functions have the property that $f'(x) = g'(x)$ for all x of an interval I, then $f(x) - g(x) = C$ on I, where C is a constant; that is, f and g differ by a constant.

Proof The fact that $f'(x) = g'(x)$ on I implies that $f'(x) - g'(x) = 0$ on I. Recall that the derivative of a difference of two functions equals the difference of the derivatives, so we can write

$$f'(x) - g'(x) = (f - g)'(x) = 0.$$

Now we have a function $f - g$ whose derivative is zero on I. By Theorem 4.10, $f(x) - g(x) = C$ for all x in I, where C is a constant; that is, f and g differ by a constant. ◀

QUICK CHECK 3 Give two linear functions f and g that satisfy $f'(x) = g'(x)$; that is, the lines have equal slopes. Show that f and g differ by a constant. ◀

In Section 4.2, we stated and gave an argument to support the test for intervals of increase and decrease. With the Mean Value Theorem, we can prove this important result.

THEOREM 4.12 Intervals of Increase and Decrease
Suppose f is continuous on an interval I and differentiable at all interior points of I. If $f'(x) > 0$ at all interior points of I, then f is increasing on I. If $f'(x) < 0$ at all interior points of I, then f is decreasing on I.

Proof Let a and b be any two distinct points in the interval I with $b > a$. By the Mean Value Theorem,

$$\frac{f(b) - f(a)}{b - a} = f'(c)$$

for some c between a and b. Equivalently,

$$f(b) - f(a) = f'(c)(b - a).$$

Notice that $b - a > 0$ by assumption. So, if $f'(c) > 0$, then $f(b) - f(a) > 0$. Therefore, for all a and b in I with $b > a$, we have $f(b) > f(a)$, which implies that f is increasing on I. Similarly if $f'(c) < 0$, then $f(b) - f(a) < 0$ or $f(b) < f(a)$. It follows that f is decreasing on I. ◀

SECTION 4.6 EXERCISES

Review Questions

1. Explain Rolle's Theorem with a sketch.

2. Draw the graph of a function for which the conclusion of Rolle's Theorem does not hold.

3. Explain why Rolle's Theorem cannot be applied to the function $f(x) = |x|$ on the interval $[-a, a]$ for any $a > 0$.

4. Explain the Mean Value Theorem with a sketch.

5. Draw the graph of a function for which the conclusion of the Mean Value Theorem does not hold.

6. At what points c does the conclusion of the Mean Value Theorem hold for $f(x) = x^3$ on the interval $[-10, 10]$?

Basic Skills

7–12. Rolle's Theorem *Determine whether Rolle's Theorem applies to the following functions on the given interval. If so, find the point(s) that are guaranteed to exist by Rolle's Theorem.*

7. $f(x) = x(x-1)^2;\ [0, 1]$

8. $f(x) = \sin 2x;\ [0, \pi/2]$

9. $f(x) = \cos 4x;\ [\pi/8, 3\pi/8]$

10. $f(x) = 1 - |x|;\ [-1, 1]$

11. $f(x) = 1 - x^{2/3};\ [-1, 1]$

12. $f(x) = x^3 - 2x^2 - 8x;\ [-2, 4]$

13. **Lapse rates in the atmosphere** Concurrent measurements indicate that at an elevation of 6.1 km, the temperature is $-10.3°$C, and at an elevation of 3.2 km, the temperature is 8.0°C. Based on the Mean Value Theorem, can you conclude that the lapse rate exceeds the threshold value of 7°C/km at some intermediate elevation? Explain.

14. **Drag racer acceleration** The fastest drag racers can reach a speed of 330 mi/hr over a quarter-mile strip in 4.45 s (from a standing start). Complete the following sentence about such a drag racer: At some point during the race, the maximum acceleration of the drag race is at least ________ mi/hr/s.

15–22. Mean Value Theorem

a. *Determine whether the Mean Value Theorem applies to the following functions on the interval $[a, b]$.*

b. *If so, find or approximate the point(s) that are guaranteed to exist by the Mean Value Theorem.*

c. *Make a sketch of the function and the line that passes through $(a, f(a))$ and $(b, f(b))$. Mark the points P (if they exist) at which the slope of the function equals the slope of the secant line. Then sketch the tangent line at P.*

15. $f(x) = 7 - x^2;\ [-1, 2]$

16. $f(x) = 3\sin 2x;\ [0, \pi/4]$

17. $f(x) = \sqrt{x};\ [1, 4]$

18. $f(x) = |x - 1|;\ [-1, 4]$

19. $f(x) = x^{-1/3};\ [1/8, 8]$

20. $f(x) = x + 1/x;\ [1, 3]$

21. $f(x) = 2x^{1/3};\ [-8, 8]$

22. $f(x) = x/(x + 2);\ [-1, 2]$

Further Explorations

23. **Explain why or why not** Determine whether the following statements are true and give an explanation or counterexample.
    a. The continuous function $f(x) = 1 - |x|$ satisfies the conditions of the Mean Value Theorem on the interval $[-1, 1]$.
    b. Two differentiable functions that differ by a constant always have the same derivative.
    c. If $f'(x) = 0$, then $f(x) = 10$.

24–26. Questions about derivatives

24. Without evaluating derivatives, which of the following functions have the same derivative: $f(x) = \sin^2 x$, $g(x) = -\cos^2 x$, $h(x) = 2\sin^2 x$, $p(x) = 1/\csc^2 x$?

25. Without evaluating derivatives, which of the functions $g(x) = 2x^{10}$, $h(x) = x^{10} + 2$, or $p(x) = x^{10} - \cos 2$ have the same derivative as $f(x) = x^{10}$?

26. Find all functions f whose derivative is $f'(x) = x + 1$.

27. **Mean Value Theorem and graphs** By visual inspection, locate all points on the graph at which the slope of the tangent line equals the average rate of change of the function over the interval $[-4, 4]$.

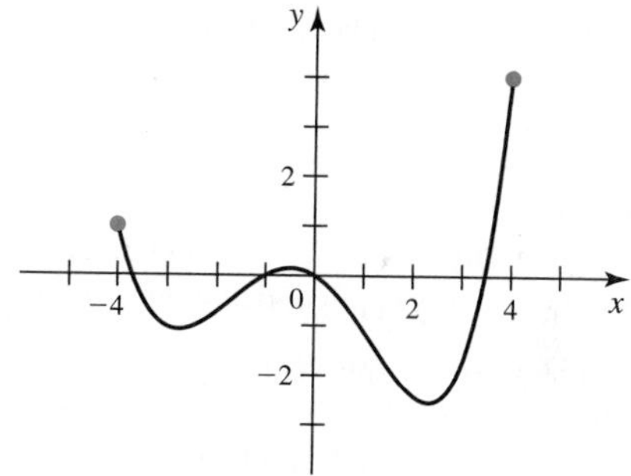

Applications

28. **Avalanche forecasting** Avalanche forecasters measure the *temperature gradient dT/dh*, which is the rate at which the temperature in a snowpack T changes with respect to its depth h. If the temperature gradient is large, it may lead to a weak layer of snow in the snowpack. When these weak layers collapse, avalanches occur. Avalanche forecasters use the following rule of thumb: If dT/dh exceeds 10°C/m anywhere in the snowpack, conditions are favorable for weak layer formation and the risk of avalanche increases. Assume the temperature function is continuous and differentiable.
    a. An avalanche forecaster digs a snow pit and takes two temperature measurements. At the surface ($h = 0$) the temperature is $-12°$C. At a depth of 1.1 m, the temperature is 2°C. Using the Mean Value Theorem, what can he conclude about the temperature gradient? Is the formation of a weak layer likely?
    b. One mile away, a skier finds that the temperature at a depth of 1.4 m is $-1°$C, and at the surface it is $-12°$C. What can be concluded about the temperature gradient? Is the formation of a weak layer in her location likely?

c. Because snow is an excellent insulator, the temperature of snow-covered ground is near 0°C. Furthermore, the surface temperature of snow in a particular area does not vary much from one location to the next. Explain why a weak layer is more likely to form in places where the snowpack is not too deep.

d. The term *isothermal* is used to describe the situation where all layers of the snowpack are at the same temperature (typically near the freezing point). Is a weak layer likely to form in isothermal snow? Explain.

29. **Mean Value Theorem and the police** A state patrol officer saw a car start from rest at a highway on-ramp. She radioed ahead to another officer 30 mi along the highway. When the car reached the location of the second officer 28 min later, it was clocked going 60 mi/hr. The driver of the car was given a ticket for exceeding the 60-mi/hr speed limit. Why can the officer conclude that the driver exceeded the speed limit?

30. **Mean Value Theorem and the police again** Compare carefully to Exercise 29. A state patrol officer saw a car start from rest at a highway on-ramp. She radioed ahead to another officer 30 mi along the highway. When the car reached the location of the second officer 30 min later, it was clocked going 60 mi/hr. Can the patrol officer conclude that the driver exceeded the speed limit?

31. **Running pace** Explain why if a runner completes a 6.2-mi (10-km) race in 32 min, then he must have been running at exactly 11 mi/hr at least twice in the race. Assume the runner's speed at the finish line is zero.

Additional Exercises

32. **Mean Value Theorem for linear functions** Interpret the Mean Value Theorem when it is applied to any linear function.

33. **Mean Value Theorem for quadratic functions** Consider the quadratic function $f(x) = Ax^2 + Bx + C$, where A, B, and C are real numbers with $A \neq 0$. Show that when the Mean Value Theorem is applied to f on the interval $[a, b]$, the number c guaranteed by the theorem is the midpoint of the interval.

34. **Means**

a. Show that the point c guaranteed to exist by the Mean Value Theorem for $f(x) = x^2$ on $[a, b]$ is the arithmetic mean of a and b; that is, $c = (a + b)/2$.

b. Show that the point c guaranteed to exist by the Mean Value Theorem for $f(x) = 1/x$ on $[a, b]$, where $0 < a < b$, is the geometric mean of a and b; that is, $c = \sqrt{ab}$.

35. **Equal derivatives** Verify that the functions $f(x) = \tan^2 x$ and $g(x) = \sec^2 x$ have the same derivative. What can you say about the difference $f - g$? Explain.

36. **Equal derivatives** Verify that the functions $f(x) = \sin^2 x$ and $g(x) = -\cos^2 x$ have the same derivative. What can you say about the difference $f - g$? Explain.

37. **100-m speed** The Jamaican sprinter Usain Bolt set a world record of 9.58 s in the 100-meter dash in the summer of 2009. Did his speed ever exceed 37 km/hr during the race? Explain.

38. **Condition for nondifferentiability** Suppose $f'(x) < 0 < f''(x)$ for $x < a$ and $f'(x) > 0 > f''(x)$ for $x > a$. Prove that f is not differentiable at a. (*Hint:* Assume that f is differentiable at a and apply the Mean Value Theorem to f'.) More generally, show that if f' and f'' change sign at the same point, then f is not differentiable at that point.

39. **Generalized Mean Value Theorem** Suppose f and g are functions that are continuous on $[a, b]$ and differentiable on (a, b), where $g(a) \neq g(b)$. Then, there is a point c in (a, b) at which

$$\frac{f(b) - f(a)}{g(b) - g(a)} = \frac{f'(c)}{g'(c)}.$$

This result is known as the **Generalized (or Cauchy's) Mean Value Theorem**.

a. If $g(x) = x$, then show that the Generalized Mean Value Theorem reduces to the Mean Value Theorem.

b. Suppose $f(x) = x^2 - 1$, $g(x) = 4x + 2$, and $[a, b] = [0, 1]$. Find a value of c satisfying the Generalized Mean Value Theorem.

QUICK CHECK ANSWERS

1. $x = 2$ 2. The functions shown in Figure 4.62 provide examples. 3. The graphs of $f(x) = 3x$ and $g(x) = 3x + 2$ have the same slope. Note that $f(x) - g(x) = -2$, a constant. ◄

4.7 L'Hôpital's Rule

The study of limits in Chapter 2 was thorough but not exhaustive. Some limits, called *indeterminate forms*, cannot generally be evaluated using the techniques presented in Chapter 2. These limits tend to be the more interesting limits that arise in practice. A powerful result called *l'Hôpital's Rule* enables us to evaluate such limits with relative ease.

Here is how indeterminate forms arise. If f is a *continuous* function at a point a, then we know that $\lim_{x \to a} f(x) = f(a)$, allowing the limit to be evaluated by computing $f(a)$. But there are many limits that cannot be evaluated by substitution. In fact, we encountered such a limit in Section 3.4:

$$\lim_{x \to 0} \frac{\sin x}{x} = 1$$

If we attempt to substitute $x = 0$ into $(\sin x)/x$, we get $0/0$, which has no meaning. Yet we proved that $(\sin x)/x$ has limit 1 at $x = 0$ (Theorem 3.9). This limit is an example of an *indeterminate form*.

The meaning of an *indeterminate form* is further illustrated by $\lim_{x \to \infty} \frac{ax}{x}$, where $a \neq 0$. This limit has the indeterminate form ∞/∞ (meaning that the numerator and denominator of ax/x become arbitrarily large in magnitude as $x \to \infty$), but the actual value of the limit is $\lim_{x \to \infty} \frac{ax}{x} = \lim_{x \to \infty} a = a$. In general, a limit with the form ∞/∞ or $0/0$ can have *any* value—which is why these limits must be handled carefully.

➤ The notations $0/0$ and ∞/∞ are merely symbols used to describe various types of indeterminate forms. The notation $0/0$ does not imply division by 0.

L'Hôpital's Rule for the Form 0/0

Consider a function of the form $f(x)/g(x)$ and assume that $\lim_{x \to a} f(x) = \lim_{x \to a} g(x) = 0$. Then, the limit $\lim_{x \to a} \frac{f(x)}{g(x)}$ has the indeterminate form $0/0$. We first state l'Hôpital's Rule and then prove a special case.

➤ Guillaume François l'Hôpital (lo-pee-tal) (1661–1704) is credited with writing the first calculus textbook. Much of the material in the book, including l'Hôpital's Rule, was provided by the Swiss mathematician Johann Bernoulli (1667–1748).

THEOREM 4.13 L'Hôpital's Rule

Suppose f and g are differentiable on an open interval I containing a with $g'(x) \neq 0$ on I when $x \neq a$. If $\lim_{x \to a} f(x) = \lim_{x \to a} g(x) = 0$, then

$$\lim_{x \to a} \frac{f(x)}{g(x)} = \lim_{x \to a} \frac{f'(x)}{g'(x)},$$

provided the limit on the right side exists (or is $\pm\infty$). The rule also applies if $x \to a$ is replaced by $x \to \pm\infty$, $x \to a^+$, or $x \to a^-$.

Proof (special case) The proof of this theorem relies on the Generalized Mean Value Theorem (Exercise 39 of Section 4.6). We prove a special case of the theorem in which we assume that f' and g' are continuous at a, $f(a) = g(a) = 0$, and $g'(a) \neq 0$. We have

➤ The definition of the derivative provides an example of an indeterminate form:

$$f'(x) = \lim_{h \to 0} \frac{f(x + h) - f(x)}{h}$$

has the form $0/0$.

$$\lim_{x \to a} \frac{f'(x)}{g'(x)} = \frac{f'(a)}{g'(a)} \qquad \text{Continuity of } f' \text{ and } g'$$

$$= \frac{\lim_{x \to a} \frac{f(x) - f(a)}{x - a}}{\lim_{x \to a} \frac{g(x) - g(a)}{x - a}} \qquad \text{Definition of } f'(a) \text{ and } g'(a)$$

$$= \lim_{x \to a} \frac{\frac{f(x) - f(a)}{x - a}}{\frac{g(x) - g(a)}{x - a}} \qquad \text{Limit of a quotient, } g'(a) \neq 0$$

$$= \lim_{x \to a} \frac{f(x) - f(a)}{g(x) - g(a)} \qquad \text{Cancel } x - a.$$

$$= \lim_{x \to a} \frac{f(x)}{g(x)}. \qquad f(a) = g(a) = 0$$

◄

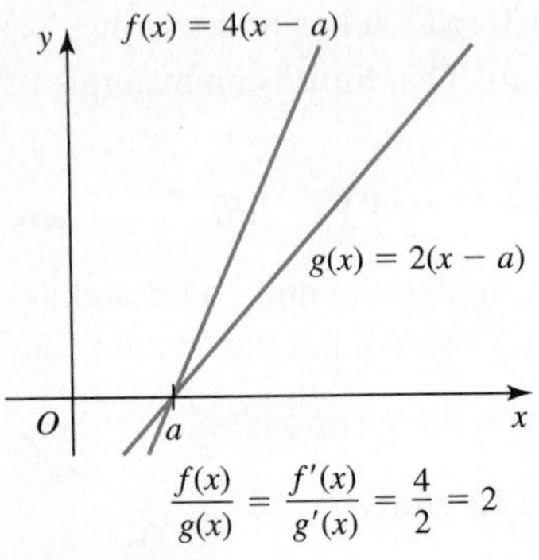

FIGURE 4.68

The geometry of l'Hôpital's Rule offers some insight. First consider two *linear* functions, f and g, whose graphs both pass through the point $(a, 0)$ with slopes 4 and 2, respectively; this means that

$$f(x) = 4(x - a) \quad \text{and} \quad g(x) = 2(x - a).$$

Furthermore $f(a) = g(a) = 0$, $f'(x) = 4$, and $g'(x) = 2$ (Figure 4.68).

Looking at the quotient f/g, we see that

$$\frac{f(x)}{g(x)} = \frac{4(x - a)}{2(x - a)} = \frac{4}{2} = \frac{f'(x)}{g'(x)}. \qquad \text{Exactly}$$

This argument may be generalized, and we find that for any linear functions f and g with $f(a) = g(a) = 0$,

$$\lim_{x \to a} \frac{f(x)}{g(x)} = \lim_{x \to a} \frac{f'(x)}{g'(x)},$$

provided $g'(a) \neq 0$.

If f and g are not linear functions, we replace them by their linear approximations at $(a, 0)$ (Figure 4.69). Zooming in on the point a, the graphs of f and g are close to their respective tangent lines $y = f'(a)(x - a)$ and $y = g'(a)(x - a)$, which have slopes $f'(a)$ and $g'(a) \neq 0$, respectively. Therefore, near $x = a$ we have

$$\frac{f(x)}{g(x)} \approx \frac{f'(a)(x - a)}{g'(a)(x - a)} = \frac{f'(a)}{g'(a)}.$$

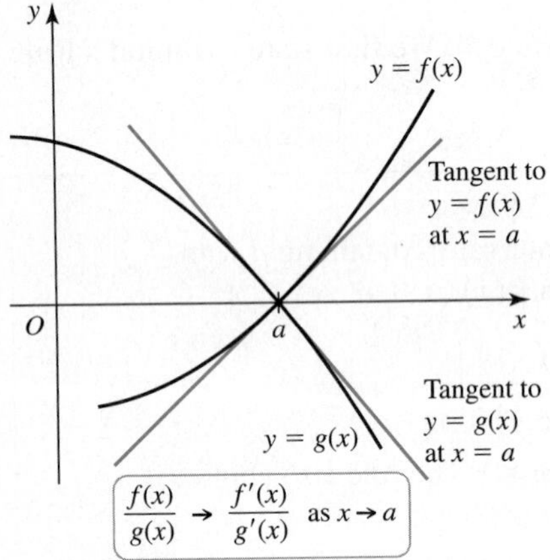

FIGURE 4.69

Therefore, the ratio of the functions is well approximated by the ratio of the derivatives. In the limit as $x \to a$, we again have

$$\lim_{x \to a} \frac{f(x)}{g(x)} = \lim_{x \to a} \frac{f'(x)}{g'(x)}.$$

QUICK CHECK 1 Which of the following functions lead to an indeterminate form as $x \to 0$: $f(x) = x^2/(x + 2)$, $g(x) = (\tan 3x)/x$, or $h(x) = (1 - \cos x)/x^2$?

EXAMPLE 1 Using l'Hôpital's Rule Evaluate the following limits.

a. $\displaystyle\lim_{x \to 1} \frac{x^3 + x^2 - 2x}{x - 1}$ **b.** $\displaystyle\lim_{x \to 0} \frac{\sqrt{9 + 3x} - 3}{x}$

SOLUTION

a. Direct substitution of $x = 1$ into $\dfrac{x^3 + x^2 - 2x}{x - 1}$ produces the indeterminate form $0/0$. Applying l'Hôpital's Rule with $f(x) = x^3 + x^2 - 2x$ and $g(x) = x - 1$ gives

$$\lim_{x \to 1} \frac{x^3 + x^2 - 2x}{x - 1} = \lim_{x \to 1} \frac{f'(x)}{g'(x)} = \lim_{x \to 1} \frac{3x^2 + 2x - 2}{1} = 3.$$

➤ This limit in part (a) can also be evaluated by factoring the numerator and canceling $(x - 1)$:

$$\lim_{x \to 1} \frac{x^3 + x^2 - 2x}{x - 1} = \lim_{x \to 1} \frac{x(x - 1)(x + 2)}{x - 1} = \lim_{x \to 1} x(x + 2) = 3$$

b. Substituting $x = 0$ into this function produces the indeterminate form $0/0$. Let $f(x) = \sqrt{9 + 3x} - 3$ and $g(x) = x$, and note that $f'(x) = \dfrac{3}{2\sqrt{9 + 3x}}$ and $g'(x) = 1$. Applying l'Hôpital's Rule, we have

$$\lim_{x \to 0} \underbrace{\frac{\sqrt{9 + 3x} - 3}{x}}_{f/g} = \lim_{x \to 0} \underbrace{\frac{\frac{3}{2\sqrt{9 + 3x}}}{1}}_{f'/g'} = \frac{1}{2}.$$

Related Exercises 9–14

L'Hôpital's Rule requires evaluating $\lim_{x \to a} f'(x)/g'(x)$. It may happen that this second limit is another indeterminate form to which l'Hôpital's Rule may be applied again.

EXAMPLE 2 L'Hôpital's Rule repeated Evaluate the following limits.

a. $\lim_{x \to 0} \frac{\sec x - 1}{x^2}$ **b.** $\lim_{x \to 2} \frac{x^3 - 3x^2 + 4}{x^4 - 4x^3 + 7x^2 - 12x + 12}$.

SOLUTION

a. This limit has the indeterminate form $0/0$. Applying l'Hôpital's Rule, we have

$$\lim_{x \to 0} \frac{\sec x - 1}{x^2} = \lim_{x \to 0} \frac{\sec x \tan x}{2x},$$

which is another limit of the form $0/0$. Therefore, we apply l'Hôpital's Rule again:

$$\lim_{x \to 0} \frac{\sec x - 1}{x^2} = \lim_{x \to 0} \frac{\sec x \tan x}{2x} \qquad \text{L'Hôpital's Rule}$$

$$= \lim_{x \to 0} \frac{(\sec x \tan x) \tan x + \sec x (\sec^2 x)}{2} \qquad \text{L'Hôpital's Rule again; Product Rule}$$

$$= \lim_{x \to 0} \frac{\overbrace{\sec x \tan^2 x}^{\text{approaches } 0} + \overbrace{\sec^3 x}^{\text{approaches } 1}}{2} = \frac{1}{2} \qquad \text{Evaluate limit.}$$

b. Evaluating the numerator and denominator at $x = 2$, we see that this limit has the form $0/0$. Applying l'Hôpital's Rule twice gives

$$\lim_{x \to 2} \frac{x^3 - 3x^2 + 4}{x^4 - 4x^3 + 7x^2 - 12x + 12} = \underbrace{\lim_{x \to 2} \frac{3x^2 - 6x}{4x^3 - 12x^2 + 14x - 12}}_{\text{limit of the form } 0/0} \qquad \text{L'Hôpital's Rule}$$

$$= \lim_{x \to 2} \frac{6x - 6}{12x^2 - 24x + 14} \qquad \text{L'Hôpital's Rule again}$$

$$= \frac{3}{7}. \qquad \text{Evaluate limit.}$$

It is easy to overlook a crucial step in this computation: After applying l'Hôpital's Rule the first time, you *must* establish that the new limit is an indeterminate form before applying l'Hôpital's Rule a second time. *Related Exercises 15–22* ◀

Indeterminate Form ∞/∞

L'Hôpital's Rule also applies directly to limits of the form $\lim_{x \to a} f(x)/g(x)$, where $\lim_{x \to a} f(x) = \pm\infty$ and $\lim_{x \to a} g(x) = \pm\infty$; this indeterminate form is denoted ∞/∞. The proof of this result is found in advanced books.

THEOREM 4.14 L'Hôpital's Rule (∞/∞)
Suppose that f and g are differentiable on an open interval I containing a, with $g'(x) \neq 0$ on I when $x \neq a$. If $\lim_{x \to a} f(x) = \pm\infty$ and $\lim_{x \to a} g(x) = \pm\infty$, then

$$\lim_{x \to a} \frac{f(x)}{g(x)} = \lim_{x \to a} \frac{f'(x)}{g'(x)},$$

provided the limit on the right side exists (or is $\pm\infty$). The rule also applies for $x \to \pm\infty$, $x \to a^+$, or $x \to a^-$.

QUICK CHECK 2 Which of the following functions lead to an indeterminate form as $x \to \infty$: $f(x) = \sin x/x$, $g(x) = (x - 1)/x^3$, or $h(x) = (3x^2 + 4)/x^2$? ◀

EXAMPLE 3 **L'Hôpital's Rule for ∞/∞** Evaluate the following limits.

a. $\displaystyle\lim_{x\to\infty} \frac{4x^3 - 6x^2 + 1}{2x^3 - 10x + 3}$ **b.** $\displaystyle\lim_{x\to\pi/2^-} \frac{1 + \tan x}{\sec x}$

SOLUTION

▶ As shown in Section 2.5, this limit could also be evaluated by first dividing the numerator and denominator by x^3.

a. This limit has the indeterminate form ∞/∞ because both the numerator and the denominator approach $+\infty$ as $x \to \infty$. Applying l'Hôpital's Rule three times, we have

$$\underbrace{\lim_{x\to\infty} \frac{4x^3 - 6x^2 + 1}{2x^3 - 10x + 3}}_{\infty/\infty} = \underbrace{\lim_{x\to\infty} \frac{12x^2 - 12x}{6x^2 - 10}}_{\infty/\infty} = \underbrace{\lim_{x\to\infty} \frac{24x - 12}{12x}}_{\infty/\infty} = \lim_{x\to\infty} \frac{24}{12} = 2.$$

b. In this limit both the numerator and the denominator approach $+\infty$ as $x \to \pi/2^-$. L'Hôpital's Rule gives us

$$\begin{aligned} \lim_{x\to\pi/2^-} \frac{1 + \tan x}{\sec x} &= \lim_{x\to\pi/2^-} \frac{\sec^2 x}{\sec x \tan x} && \text{L'Hôpital's Rule} \\ &= \lim_{x\to\pi/2^-} \frac{1}{\sin x} && \text{Simplify.} \\ &= 1. && \text{Evaluate limit.} \end{aligned}$$

Related Exercises 23–26 ◀

Related Indeterminate Forms: $0 \cdot \infty$ and $\infty - \infty$

The limit $\lim_{x\to a} f(x)g(x)$, where $\lim_{x\to a} f(x) = 0$ and $\lim_{x\to a} g(x) = \pm\infty$, is an indeterminate form that we denote $0 \cdot \infty$. *L'Hôpital's Rule cannot be directly applied to this limit.* The following examples illustrate how this indeterminate form can be recast in the form $0/0$ or ∞/∞.

EXAMPLE 4 **L'Hôpital's Rule for $0 \cdot \infty$** Evaluate $\displaystyle\lim_{x\to\infty} x^2 \sin\left(\frac{1}{4x^2}\right)$.

SOLUTION This limit has the form $0 \cdot \infty$. A common technique that converts this form to either $0/0$ or ∞/∞ is to *divide by the reciprocal*. We rewrite the limit and apply l'Hôpital's Rule:

$$\begin{aligned} \underbrace{\lim_{x\to\infty} x^2 \sin\left(\frac{1}{4x^2}\right)}_{0\cdot\infty \text{ form}} &= \underbrace{\lim_{x\to\infty} \frac{\sin\left(\frac{1}{4x^2}\right)}{\left(\frac{1}{x^2}\right)}}_{\text{recast in } 0/0 \text{ form}} && x^2 = \frac{1}{1/x^2} \\ &= \lim_{x\to\infty} \frac{\cos\left(\frac{1}{4x^2}\right)\frac{1}{4}(-2x^{-3})}{-2x^{-3}} && \text{L'Hôpital's Rule} \\ &= \frac{1}{4} \lim_{x\to\infty} \cos\left(\frac{1}{4x^2}\right) && \text{Simplify.} \\ &= \frac{1}{4} && \frac{1}{4x^2} \to 0, \cos 0 = 1 \end{aligned}$$

Related Exercises 27–30 ◀

QUICK CHECK 3 What is the form of the limit $\displaystyle\lim_{x\to\pi/2^-} (x - \pi/2)(\tan x)$? Write it in the form $0/0$. ◀

Indeterminate Form $\infty - \infty$ Limits of the form $\lim_{x \to a} (f(x) - g(x))$, where $\lim_{x \to a} f(x) = \infty$ and $\lim_{x \to a} g(x) = \infty$, are indeterminate forms that we denote $\infty - \infty$. L'Hôpital's Rule cannot be applied directly to an $\infty - \infty$ form. It must first be expressed in the form $0/0$ or ∞/∞. With the $\infty - \infty$ form, it is easy to reach erroneous conclusions. For example, if $f(x) = 3x + 5$ and $g(x) = 3x$, then the $\infty - \infty$ form has the limit

$$\lim_{x \to \infty} ((3x + 5) - (3x)) = 5.$$

However, if $f(x) = 3x$ and $g(x) = 2x$, then the $\infty - \infty$ form has the limit

$$\lim_{x \to \infty} (3x - 2x) = \lim_{x \to \infty} x = \infty.$$

These examples show again why indeterminate forms are deceptive. Before proceeding, we introduce another useful technique.

Occasionally, it helps to convert a limit as $x \to \infty$ to a limit as $t \to 0^+$ (or vice versa) by a *change of variables*. To evaluate $\lim_{x \to \infty} f(x)$, we define $t = 1/x$ and note that as $x \to \infty$, $t \to 0^+$. Then,

$$\lim_{x \to \infty} f(x) = \lim_{t \to 0^+} f\left(\frac{1}{t}\right).$$

This idea is illustrated in the next example.

EXAMPLE 5 L'Hôpital's Rule for $\infty - \infty$ Evaluate $\lim_{x \to \infty} (x - \sqrt{x^2 - 3x})$.

SOLUTION As $x \to \infty$, both terms in the difference $x - \sqrt{x^2 - 3x}$ approach ∞ and this limit has the form $\infty - \infty$. We first factor x from the expression and form a quotient:

$$\begin{aligned} \lim_{x \to \infty} (x - \sqrt{x^2 - 3x}) &= \lim_{x \to \infty} (x - \sqrt{x^2(1 - 3/x)}) && \text{Factor } x^2 \text{ under square root.} \\ &= \lim_{x \to \infty} x(1 - \sqrt{1 - 3/x}) && x > 0, \text{ so } \sqrt{x^2} = x \\ &= \lim_{x \to \infty} \frac{1 - \sqrt{1 - 3/x}}{1/x} && \text{Write } 0 \cdot \infty \text{ form as } 0/0 \text{ form; } x = \frac{1}{1/x} \end{aligned}$$

This new limit has the form $0/0$, and l'Hôpital's Rule may be applied.

One way to proceed is to use the change of variables $t = 1/x$:

$$\begin{aligned} \lim_{x \to \infty} \frac{1 - \sqrt{1 - 3/x}}{1/x} &= \lim_{t \to 0^+} \frac{1 - \sqrt{1 - 3t}}{t} && \text{Let } t = 1/x\text{; replace } \lim_{x \to \infty} \text{ by } \lim_{t \to 0^+}. \\ &= \lim_{t \to 0^+} \frac{\dfrac{3}{2\sqrt{1 - 3t}}}{1} && \text{L'Hôpital's Rule} \\ &= \frac{3}{2} && \text{Evaluate limit.} \end{aligned}$$

Related Exercises 31–34 ◀

Pitfalls in Using l'Hôpital's Rule

We close with a short list of common pitfalls of l'Hôpital's Rule.

1. L'Hôpital's Rule says $\lim_{x \to a} \frac{f(x)}{g(x)} = \lim_{x \to a} \frac{f'(x)}{g'(x)}$, not

$$\lim_{x \to a} \frac{f(x)}{g(x)} = \lim_{x \to a} \left[\frac{f(x)}{g(x)}\right]' \quad \text{or} \quad \lim_{x \to a} \frac{f(x)}{g(x)} = \lim_{x \to a} \left[\frac{1}{g(x)}\right]' f'(x).$$

In other words, you should evaluate $f'(x)$ and $g'(x)$, form their quotient, and then take the limit. Don't confuse l'Hôpital's Rule with the Quotient Rule.

2. Be sure that the given limit involves the indeterminate form $0/0$ or ∞/∞ before applying l'Hôpital's Rule. For example, consider the following erroneous use of l'Hôpital's Rule:

$$\lim_{x\to 0} \frac{1 - \sin x}{\cos x} = \lim_{x\to 0} \frac{-\cos x}{\sin x},$$

which does not exist. The limit is not an indeterminate form in the first place. This limit should be evaluated by direct substitution:

$$\lim_{x\to 0} \frac{1 - \sin x}{\cos x} = \frac{1 - \sin 0}{1} = 1$$

3. When using l'Hôpital's Rule repeatedly, be sure to simplify expressions as much as possible at each step and evaluate the limit as soon as the new limit is no longer an indeterminate form.

4. Repeated use of l'Hôpital's Rule occasionally leads to unending cycles, in which case other methods must be used. Limits of the form $\lim_{x\to\infty} \frac{\sqrt{ax + 1}}{\sqrt{bx + 1}}$, where a and b are real numbers, lead to such behavior (see Exercise 49).

5. Be sure that the final limit exists. Consider $\lim_{x\to\infty} \frac{3x + \cos x}{x}$, which has the form ∞/∞. Applying l'Hôpital's Rule, we have

$$\lim_{x\to\infty} \frac{3x + \cos x}{x} = \lim_{x\to\infty} \frac{3 - \sin x}{1}.$$

It is tempting to conclude that because the limit on the right side does not exist, the original limit also does not exist. In fact, the original limit has a value of 3 (divide numerator and denominator by x). In order to reach a conclusion from l'Hôpital's Rule, the final limit in the calculation must exist (or be $\pm\infty$).

SECTION 4.7 EXERCISES

Review Questions

1. Explain with examples what is meant by the indeterminate form $0/0$.
2. Why are special methods, such as l'Hôpital's Rule, needed to evaluate indeterminate forms (as opposed to substitution)?
3. Explain the steps used to apply l'Hôpital's Rule to a limit of the form $0/0$.
4. To which indeterminate forms does l'Hôpital's Rule apply *directly*?
5. Explain how to convert a limit of the form $0 \cdot \infty$ to a limit of the form $0/0$ or ∞/∞.
6. Give an example of a limit of the form ∞/∞ as $x \to 0$.
7. What is the form of the limit $\lim_{x\to 1^-} (x - 1) \tan \frac{\pi x}{2}$?
8. What is the form of the limit $\lim_{x\to 2^+} \frac{1}{x - 2} - \frac{1}{\sqrt{x^2 - 4}}$?

Basic Skills

9–14. 0/0 form *Evaluate the following limits using l'Hôpital's Rule.*

9. $\lim_{x\to 2} \frac{x^2 - 2x}{8 - 6x + x^2}$
10. $\lim_{x\to -1} \frac{x^4 + x^3 + 2x + 2}{x + 1}$
11. $\lim_{x\to 0} \frac{3 \sin 4x}{5x}$
12. $\lim_{x\to 2\pi} \frac{x \sin x + x^2 - 4\pi^2}{x - 2\pi}$
13. $\lim_{u\to \pi/4} \frac{\tan u - \cot u}{u - \pi/4}$
14. $\lim_{z\to 0} \frac{\tan 4z}{\tan 7z}$

15–22. 0/0 form *Evaluate the following limits.*

15. $\lim_{x\to 0} \frac{1 - \cos 3x}{8x^2}$
16. $\lim_{x\to 0} \frac{\sin^2 3x}{x^2}$
17. $\lim_{x\to -1} \frac{x^3 - x^2 - 5x - 3}{x^4 + 2x^3 - x^2 - 4x - 2}$
18. $\lim_{x\to 1} \frac{x^n - 1}{x - 1}$, n is a positive integer
19. $\lim_{v\to 3} \frac{v - 1 - \sqrt{v^2 - 5}}{v - 3}$
20. $\lim_{y\to 2} \frac{y^2 + y - 6}{\sqrt{8 - y^2} - y}$

21. $\lim_{h \to 0} \frac{\sin(x+h) - \sin x}{h}$, x is a real number

22. $\lim_{x \to 2} \frac{\sqrt[3]{3x+2} - 2}{x-2}$

23–26. ∞/∞ form *Evaluate the following limits.*

23. $\lim_{x \to \infty} \frac{3x^4 - x^2}{6x^4 + 12}$

24. $\lim_{x \to \infty} \frac{4x^3 - 2x^2 + 6}{\pi x^3 + 4}$

25. $\lim_{x \to \infty} \frac{8 - 4x^2}{3x^3 + x - 1}$

26. $\lim_{x \to \pi/2} \frac{2 \tan x}{\sec^2 x}$

27–30. $0 \cdot \infty$ form *Evaluate the following limits.*

27. $\lim_{x \to 0} x \csc x$

28. $\lim_{x \to 1^-} (1-x) \tan\left(\frac{\pi x}{2}\right)$

29. $\lim_{x \to (\pi/2)^-} \left(\frac{\pi}{2} - x\right) \sec x$

30. $\lim_{x \to 0^+} (\sin x) \sqrt{\frac{1-x}{x}}$

31–34. $\infty - \infty$ form *Evaluate the following limits.*

31. $\lim_{x \to 0^+} \left(\cot x - \frac{1}{x}\right)$

32. $\lim_{x \to \infty} \left(x - \sqrt{x^2+1}\right)$

33. $\lim_{\theta \to \pi/2^-} (\tan\theta - \sec\theta)$

34. $\lim_{x \to \infty} \left(x - \sqrt{x^2 + 4x}\right)$

Further Explorations

35. **Explain why or why not** Determine whether the following statements are true and give an explanation or counterexample.

a. By l'Hôpital's Rule, $\lim_{x \to 2} \frac{x-2}{x^2-1} = \lim_{x \to 2} \frac{1}{2x} = \frac{1}{4}$.

b. $\lim_{x \to 0} (x \sin x) = \lim_{x \to 0} f(x)g(x) = \lim_{x \to 0} f'(x) \lim_{x \to 0} g'(x) = \left(\lim_{x \to 0} 1\right)\left(\lim_{x \to 0} \cos x\right) = 1$

c. $\lim_{x \to 2} \frac{x^3 - 2x^2 + x - 2}{x^2 - 1} = \lim_{x \to 2} \frac{3x^2 - 4x + 1}{2x}$

d. $\lim_{x \to 2} \frac{x^3 - 2x^2 + x - 2}{x^2 - 4} = \lim_{x \to 2} \frac{3x^2 - 4x + 1}{2x}$

36–37. Two methods *Evaluate the following limits in two different ways: Use the methods of Chapter 2 and use l'Hôpital's Rule.*

36. $\lim_{x \to \infty} \frac{100x^3 - 3}{x^4 - 2}$

37. $\lim_{x \to \infty} \frac{2x^3 - x^2 + 1}{5x^3 + 2x}$

38. **L'Hôpital's example** Evaluate one of the limits l'Hôpital used in his own textbook in about 1700:

$$\lim_{x \to a} \frac{\sqrt{2a^3x - x^4} - a\sqrt[3]{a^2x}}{a - \sqrt[4]{ax^3}}, \text{ where } a \text{ is a real number}$$

39–47. Miscellaneous limits by any means *Use analytical methods to evaluate the following limits.*

39. $\lim_{x \to 6} \frac{\sqrt[5]{5x+2} - 2}{1/x - 1/6}$

40. $\lim_{t \to \pi/2^+} \frac{\tan 3t}{\sec 5t}$

41. $\lim_{x \to \infty} \left(\sqrt{x-2} - \sqrt{x-4}\right)$

42. $\lim_{x \to \pi/2} (\pi - 2x) \tan x$

43. $\lim_{x \to \infty} x^3\left(\frac{1}{x} - \sin\frac{1}{x}\right)$

44. $\lim_{x \to \infty} \left(\sqrt{x^2-1} - \sqrt[3]{x^3-1}\right)$

45. $\lim_{x \to 1^+} \left(\frac{1}{x-1} - \frac{1}{\sqrt{x-1}}\right)$

46. $\lim_{x \to \infty} \frac{3x^2 - \cos x}{2x^2}$

47. $\lim_{\theta \to \infty} \frac{\sin 2\theta - \theta^3}{3\theta^3}$

Applications

48. **An optics limit** The theory of interference of coherent oscillators requires the limit $\lim_{\delta \to 2m\pi} \frac{\sin^2(N\delta/2)}{\sin^2(\delta/2)}$, where N is a positive integer and m is any integer. Show that the value of this limit is N^2.

Additional Exercises

49. **L'Hôpital loops** Consider the limit $\lim_{x \to \infty} \frac{\sqrt{ax+b}}{\sqrt{cx+d}}$, where a, b, c, and d are positive real numbers. Show that l'Hôpital's Rule fails for this limit. Find the limit using another method.

50. **General $\infty - \infty$ result** Let a and b be positive real numbers. Evaluate $\lim_{x \to \infty} \left(ax - \sqrt{a^2x^2 - bx}\right)$ in terms of a and b.

51. **A geometric limit** Let $f(\theta)$ be the area of the triangle ABP (see figure) and let $g(\theta)$ be the area of the region between the chord PB and the arc PB. Evaluate $\lim_{\theta \to 0} g(\theta)/f(\theta)$.

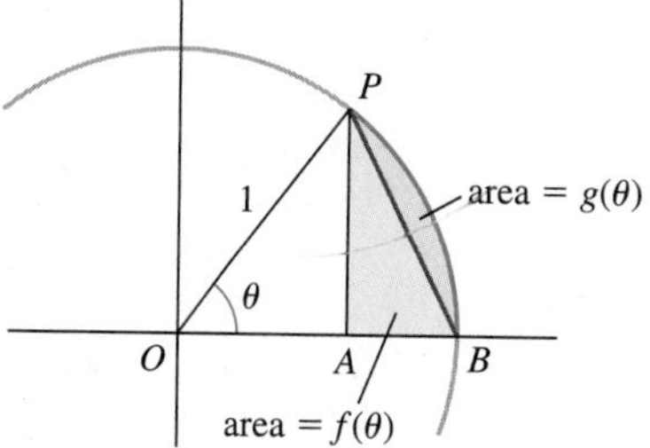

QUICK CHECK ANSWERS

1. g and h 2. g and h 3. $0 \cdot \infty$; $(x - \pi/2)/\cot x$ ◀

4.8 Antiderivatives

The goal of differentiation is to find the derivative f' of a given function f. The reverse process, called *antidifferentiation*, is equally important: Given a function f, we look for an *antiderivative* function F whose derivative is f; that is, a function F such that $F' = f$.

DEFINITION Antiderivative

A function F is an **antiderivative** of f on an interval I provided $F'(x) = f(x)$ for all x in I.

In this section, we revisit derivative formulas developed in previous chapters to discover corresponding antiderivative formulas.

Thinking Backward

Consider the function $f(x) = 1$ and the derivative formula $\frac{d}{dx}(x) = 1$. We see that an antiderivative of f is $F(x) = x$ because $F'(x) = 1 = f(x)$. Using the same logic, we can write

$$\frac{d}{dx}(x^2) = 2x \quad \Rightarrow \quad \text{an antiderivative of } f(x) = 2x \text{ is } F(x) = x^2$$

$$\frac{d}{dx}(\sin x) = \cos x \quad \Rightarrow \quad \text{an antiderivative of } f(x) = \cos x \text{ is } F(x) = \sin x$$

QUICK CHECK 1 Verify by differentiation that x^3 is an antiderivative of $3x^2$ and $-\cos x$ is an antiderivative of $\sin x$. ◄

Each of these proposed antiderivative formulas is easily checked by showing that $F' = f$.

An immediate question arises: Does a function have more than one antiderivative? To answer this question, let's focus on $f(x) = 1$ and the antiderivative $F(x) = x$. Because the derivative of a constant C is zero, we see that $F(x) = x + C$ is also an antiderivative of $f(x) = 1$, which is easy to check:

$$F'(x) = \frac{d}{dx}(x + C) = 1 = f(x)$$

Therefore, $f(x) = 1$ actually has an infinite number of antiderivatives. For the same reason, any function of the form $F(x) = x^2 + C$ is an antiderivative of $f(x) = 2x$, and any function of the form $F(x) = \sin x + C$ is an antiderivative of $f(x) = \cos x$, where C is an arbitrary constant.

We might ask whether there are still *more* antiderivatives of a given function. The following theorem provides the answer.

THEOREM 4.15 The Family of Antiderivatives

Let F be any antiderivative of f. Then *all* the antiderivatives of f have the form $F + C$, where C is an arbitrary constant.

Proof Suppose that F and G are antiderivatives of f on an interval I. Then $F' = f$ and $G' = f$, which implies that $F' = G'$ on I. From Theorem 4.11, which states that functions with equal derivatives differ by a constant, it follows that $G = F + C$. Therefore, all antiderivatives of f have the form $F + C$, where C is an arbitrary constant. ◄

Theorem 4.15 says that while there are infinitely many antiderivatives of a function, they are all of one family, namely, those functions of the form $F + C$. Because the antiderivatives of a particular function differ by a constant, the graphs of the antiderivatives are vertical translations of one another (Figure 4.70).

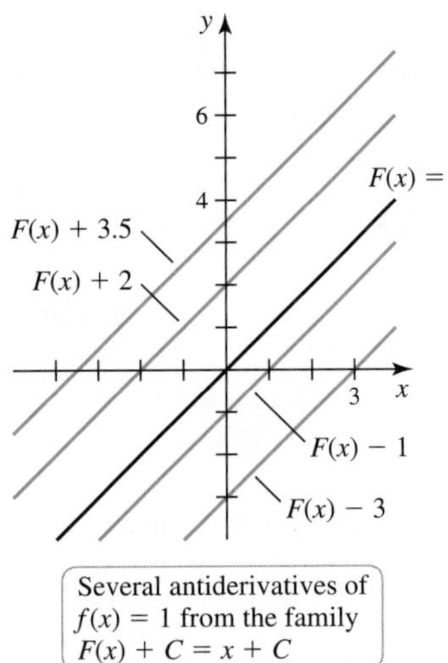

Several antiderivatives of $f(x) = 1$ from the family $F(x) + C = x + C$

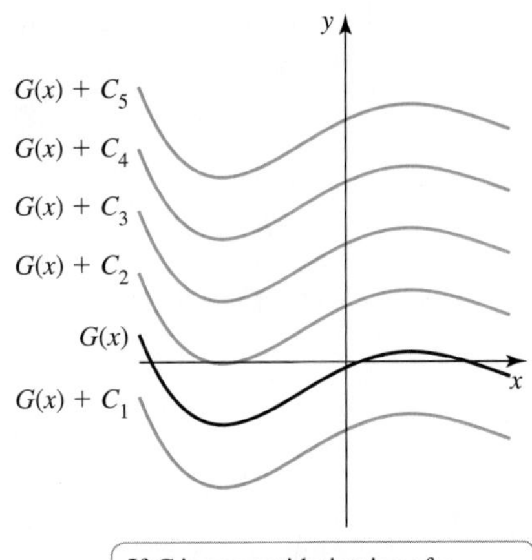

If G is any antiderivative of g, the graphs of $y = G(x) + C$ are vertical translations of one another.

FIGURE 4.70

EXAMPLE 1 **Finding antiderivatives** Use what you know about derivatives to find all antiderivatives of the following functions.

a. $f(x) = 3x^2$ **b.** $f(x) = -\dfrac{9}{x^{10}}$ **c.** $f(x) = \sin x$

SOLUTION

a. Note that $\dfrac{d}{dx}(x^3) = 3x^2$. Reversing this derivative formula says that an antiderivative of $f(x) = 3x^2$ is x^3. By Theorem 4.15, the complete family of antiderivatives is $F(x) = x^3 + C$, where C is an arbitrary constant.

b. Because $\dfrac{d}{dx}(x^{-9}) = -9x^{-10} = -9/x^{10}$, all antiderivatives of f are of the form $F(x) = x^{-9} + C$, where C is an arbitrary constant.

c. Recall that $\dfrac{d}{dx}(\cos x) = -\sin x$. We seek a function whose derivative is $\sin x$, not $-\sin x$. Observing that $\dfrac{d}{dx}(-\cos x) = \sin x$, it follows that the antiderivatives of $\sin x$ are $F(x) = -\cos x + C$, where C is an arbitrary constant. *Related Exercises 9–16*◄

QUICK CHECK 2 Find the family of antiderivatives for each of $f(x) = \dfrac{1}{2\sqrt{x}}$, $g(x) = 4x^3$, and $h(x) = \sec^2 x$.◄

Indefinite Integrals

The notation $\dfrac{d}{dx}(f)$ means *take the derivative of f*. We need analogous notation for antiderivatives. For historical reasons that become apparent in the next chapter, the notation that means *find the antiderivatives of f* is the **indefinite integral** $\int f(x)\,dx$. Every time an indefinite integral sign $\int$ appears, it is followed by a function called the **integrand**, which in turn is followed by dx. For now, dx simply means that x is the independent variable, or the **variable of integration**. The notation $\int f(x)\,dx$ represents *all* of the antiderivatives of f.

Using this new notation, the three results of Example 1 are written as

$$\int 3x^2\,dx = x^3 + C, \quad \int\left(-\frac{9}{x^{10}}\right)dx = x^{-9} + C, \text{ and } \quad \int \sin x\,dx = -\cos x + C,$$

where C is an arbitrary constant called a **constant of integration**. All the derivative formulas presented earlier in the text may be written in terms of indefinite integrals. We begin with the Power Rule.

> Notice that if $p = -1$ in this antiderivative formula, then $F(x)$ is undefined. The antiderivative of $f(x) = x^{-1}$ is discussed in Chapter 7.

THEOREM 4.16 Power Rule for Indefinite Integrals

$$\int x^p\,dx = \frac{x^{p+1}}{p+1} + C,$$

where $p \neq -1$ is a real number and C is an arbitrary constant.

> So far, we have proved that $\frac{d}{dx}(x^p) = px^{p-1}$, for rational numbers p. In Chapter 7, we prove that this result holds for real values of p.

Proof The theorem says that the antiderivatives of $f(x) = x^p$ are of the form $F(x) = \frac{x^{p+1}}{p+1} + C$. Differentiating F, we verify that $F'(x) = f(x)$:

> Any indefinite integral calculation can be checked by differentiation: The derivative of the alleged indefinite integral must equal the integrand.

$$\begin{aligned} F'(x) &= \frac{d}{dx}\left(\frac{x^{p+1}}{p+1} + C\right) \\ &= \frac{d}{dx}\left(\frac{x^{p+1}}{p+1}\right) + \underbrace{\frac{d}{dx}(C)}_{0} \\ &= \frac{(p+1)x^{(p+1)-1}}{p+1} + 0 = x^p \end{aligned}$$

Theorems 3.4 and 3.5 (Section 3.2) state the Constant Multiple and Sum Rules for derivatives. Here are the corresponding antiderivative rules, which are proved by differentiation.

THEOREM 4.17 Constant Multiple and Sum Rules

Constant Multiple Rule: $$\int cf(x)\,dx = c\int f(x)\,dx$$

Sum Rule: $$\int (f(x) + g(x))\,dx = \int f(x)\,dx + \int g(x)\,dx$$

EXAMPLE 2 Indefinite integrals Determine the following indefinite integrals.

a. $\int (3x^5 + 2 - 5x^{-3/2})\,dx$ **b.** $\int \left(\frac{4x^{19} - 5x^{-8}}{x^2}\right) dx$

SOLUTION

> $\int dx$ means $\int 1\,dx$, which is the indefinite integral of the constant function $f(x) = 1$, so $\int dx = x + C$.

> Each indefinite integral produces an arbitrary constant, all of which may be combined in one arbitrary constant called C.

a.
$$\begin{aligned} \int (3x^5 + 2 - 5x^{-3/2})\,dx &= \int 3x^5\,dx + \int 2\,dx - \int 5x^{-3/2}\,dx && \text{Sum Rule} \\ &= 3\int x^5\,dx + 2\int dx - 5\int x^{-3/2}\,dx && \text{Constant Multiple Rule} \\ &= 3\cdot\frac{x^6}{6} + 2\cdot x - 5\cdot\frac{x^{-1/2}}{(-1/2)} + C && \text{Power Rule} \\ &= \frac{x^6}{2} + 2x + 10x^{-1/2} + C && \text{Simplify.} \end{aligned}$$

b. $\displaystyle\int\left(\frac{4x^{19}-5x^{-8}}{x^2}\right)dx = \int(4x^{17}-5x^{-10})\,dx$ Simplify the integrand.

$\displaystyle = 4\int x^{17}\,dx - 5\int x^{-10}\,dx$ Sum and Constant Multiple Rules

$\displaystyle = 4\cdot\frac{x^{18}}{18} - 5\cdot\frac{x^{-9}}{(-9)} + C$ Power Rule

$\displaystyle = \frac{2x^{18}}{9} + \frac{5x^{-9}}{9} + C$ Simplify.

Both of these results should be checked by differentiation. *Related Exercises 17–24* ◄

Indefinite Integrals of Trigonometric Functions

Any derivative formula can be restated in terms of an indefinite integral formula. For example, by the Chain Rule we know that

$$\frac{d}{dx}(\cos 3x) = -3\sin 3x.$$

Therefore, we can immediately write

$$\int -3\sin 3x\,dx = \cos 3x + C.$$

Factoring -3 from the left side and dividing through by -3, we have

$$\int \sin 3x\,dx = -\frac{1}{3}\cos 3x + C.$$

This argument works if we replace 3 by any constant $a \neq 0$. Similar reasoning leads to the results in Table 4.5, where $a \neq 0$ and C is an arbitrary constant.

➤ Table 4.5 is a subset of the table of integrals at the end of the book.

Table 4.5 Indefinite Integrals of Trigonometric Functions

1. $\displaystyle\frac{d}{dx}(\sin ax) = a\cos ax \quad\rightarrow\quad \int \cos ax\,dx = \frac{1}{a}\sin ax + C$
2. $\displaystyle\frac{d}{dx}(\cos ax) = -a\sin ax \quad\rightarrow\quad \int \sin ax\,dx = -\frac{1}{a}\cos ax + C$
3. $\displaystyle\frac{d}{dx}(\tan ax) = a\sec^2 ax \quad\rightarrow\quad \int \sec^2 ax\,dx = \frac{1}{a}\tan ax + C$
4. $\displaystyle\frac{d}{dx}(\cot ax) = -a\csc^2 ax \quad\rightarrow\quad \int \csc^2 ax\,dx = -\frac{1}{a}\cot ax + C$
5. $\displaystyle\frac{d}{dx}(\sec ax) = a\sec ax\tan ax \quad\rightarrow\quad \int \sec ax\tan ax\,dx = \frac{1}{a}\sec ax + C$
6. $\displaystyle\frac{d}{dx}(\csc ax) = -a\csc ax\cot ax \quad\rightarrow\quad \int \csc ax\cot ax\,dx = -\frac{1}{a}\csc ax + C$

QUICK CHECK 3 Use differentiation to verify that $\displaystyle\int \sin 2x\,dx = -\frac{1}{2}\cos 2x + C.$ ◄

EXAMPLE 3 **Indefinite integrals of trigonometric functions** Determine the following indefinite integrals.

a. $\displaystyle\int \sec^2 3x\,dx$ **b.** $\displaystyle\int \cos\left(\frac{x}{2}\right)dx$

SOLUTION These integrals follow directly from Table 4.5 and can be verified by differentiation.

a. Letting $a = 3$ in result (3) of Table 4.5, we have

$$\int \sec^2 3x\, dx = \frac{\tan 3x}{3} + C.$$

b. We let $a = \frac{1}{2}$ in result (1) of Table 4.5, which says that

$$\int \cos\left(\frac{x}{2}\right) dx = \frac{\sin(x/2)}{\frac{1}{2}} + C = 2\sin\left(\frac{x}{2}\right) + C.$$

Related Exercises 25–30◄

Introduction to Differential Equations

Suppose you know that the derivative of a function f satisfies the equation

$$f'(x) = 2x + 10.$$

To solve this *differential equation* for the function f, we note that the solutions are antiderivatives of $2x + 10$, which are $x^2 + 10x + C$, where C is an arbitrary constant. So we have found an infinite number of solutions, all of the form $f(x) = x^2 + 10x + C$.

QUICK CHECK 4 Explain why an antiderivative of f' is f.◄

Now consider a more general differential equation of the form $f'(x) = G(x)$, where G is given and f is unknown. The solution consists of antiderivatives of G, which involve an arbitrary constant. In most practical cases, the differential equation is accompanied by an **initial condition** that allows us to determine the arbitrary constant. Therefore, we consider problems of the form

$$f'(x) = G(x), \quad \text{where } G \text{ is given} \qquad \text{Differential equation}$$
$$f(a) = b, \quad \text{where } a \text{ and } b \text{ are given} \qquad \text{Initial condition}$$

A differential equation coupled with an initial condition is called an **initial value problem**.

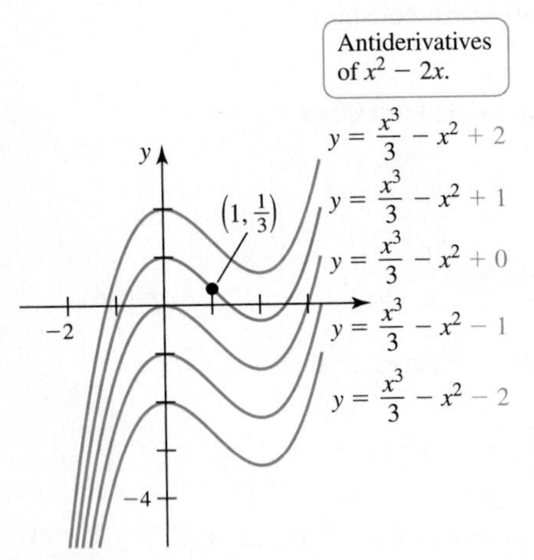

FIGURE 4.71

EXAMPLE 4 An initial value problem Solve the initial value problem $f'(x) = x^2 - 2x$ with $f(1) = \frac{1}{3}$.

SOLUTION The solution is an antiderivative of $x^2 - 2x$. Therefore,

$$f(x) = \frac{x^3}{3} - x^2 + C,$$

where C is an arbitrary constant. We have determined that the solution is a member of a family of functions, all of which differ by a constant. This family of functions, called the **general solution**, is shown in Figure 4.71, where we see curves for various choices of C.

Using the initial condition $f(1) = \frac{1}{3}$, we must find the particular function in the general solution whose graph passes through the point $\left(1, \frac{1}{3}\right)$. Imposing the condition $f(1) = \frac{1}{3}$, we reason as follows:

$$f(x) = \frac{x^3}{3} - x^2 + C \qquad \text{General solution}$$

$$f(1) = \frac{1}{3} - 1 + C \qquad \text{Substitute } x = 1.$$

$$\frac{1}{3} = \frac{1}{3} - 1 + C \qquad f(1) = \tfrac{1}{3}$$

$$C = 1 \qquad \text{Solve for } C.$$

➤ It is advisable to check that the solution satisfies the original problem: We find that $f'(x) = x^2 - 2x$ and $f(1) = \frac{1}{3} - 1 + 1 = \frac{1}{3}$.

Therefore, the solution of the initial value problem is

$$f(x) = \frac{x^3}{3} - x^2 + 1,$$

which is just one of the curves in the family shown in Figure 4.71.

Related Exercises 31–46 ◀

Motion Problems Revisited

QUICK CHECK 5 Position is an antiderivative of velocity. But there are infinitely many antiderivatives that differ by a constant. Explain how two objects can have the same velocity function but two different position functions. ◀

Antiderivatives allow us to revisit the topic of one-dimensional motion introduced in Section 3.5. Suppose the position of an object that moves along a line relative to an origin is $s(t)$, where $t \geq 0$ measures elapsed time. The velocity of the object is $v(t) = s'(t)$, which may now be read in terms of antiderivatives: *The position function is an antiderivative of the velocity.* If we are given the velocity function of an object and its position at a particular time, we can determine its position at all future times by solving an initial value problem.

➤ The convention with motion problems is to assume that motion begins at $t = 0$. This means that initial conditions are specified at $t = 0$.

We also know that the acceleration $a(t)$ of an object moving in one dimension is the rate of change of the velocity, which means $a(t) = v'(t)$. In antiderivative terms, this says that the velocity is an antiderivative of the acceleration. Thus, if we are given the acceleration of an object and its velocity at a particular time, we can determine its velocity at all times. These ideas lie at the heart of modeling the motion of objects.

Initial Value Problems for Velocity and Position

Suppose an object moves along a line with a (known) velocity $v(t)$, for $t \geq 0$. Then its position is found by solving the initial value problem

$$s'(t) = v(t), \; s(0) = s_0, \text{ where } s_0 \text{ is the initial position.}$$

If the acceleration of the object $a(t)$ is given, then its velocity is found by solving the initial value problem

$$v'(t) = a(t), \; v(0) = v_0, \text{ where } v_0 \text{ is the initial velocity.}$$

EXAMPLE 5 **A race** Runner A begins at the point $s(0) = 0$ and runs with velocity $v(t) = 2t$. Runner B begins with a head start at the point $S(0) = 8$ and runs with velocity $V(t) = 2$. Find the positions of the runners for $t \geq 0$ and determine who is ahead at $t = 6$ time units.

SOLUTION Let the position of Runner A be $s(t)$, with an initial position $s(0) = 0$. Then, the position function satisfies the initial value problem

$$s'(t) = v(t) = 2t, \; s(0) = 0.$$

The solution is an antiderivative of $s'(t) = 2t$, which has the form $s(t) = t^2 + C$. Substituting $s(0) = 0$, we find that $C = 0$. Therefore, the position of Runner A is given by $s(t) = t^2$, for $t \geq 0$.

Let the position of Runner B be $S(t)$, with an initial position $S(0) = 8$. This position function satisfies the initial value problem

$$S'(t) = V(t) = 2, \; S(0) = 8.$$

The antiderivatives of $S'(t) = 2$ are $S(t) = 2t + C$. Substituting $S(0) = 8$ implies that $C = 8$. Therefore, the position of Runner B is given by $S(t) = 2t + 8$, for $t \geq 0$.

The graphs of the position functions are shown in Figure 4.72. Runner B begins with a head start but is overtaken when $s(t) = S(t)$, or when $t^2 = 2t + 8$. The solutions of this equation are $t = 4$ and $t = -2$. Only the positive solution is relevant because the race takes place for $t \geq 0$, so Runner A overtakes Runner B at $t = 4$, when $s = S = 16$. When $t = 6$, Runner A has the lead.

Related Exercises 47–54 ◀

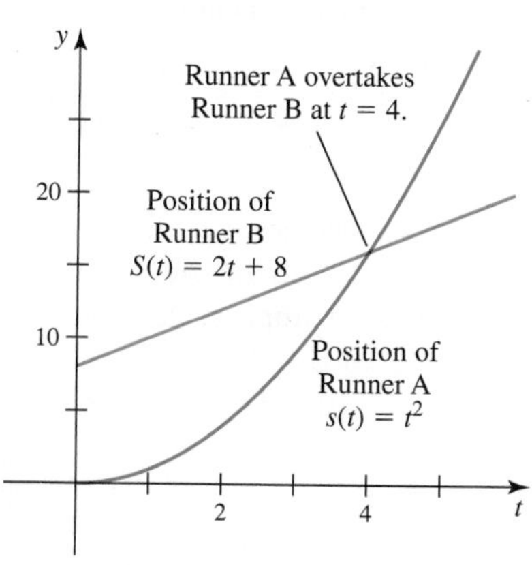

FIGURE 4.72

EXAMPLE 6 **Motion with gravity** Neglecting air resistance, the motion of an object moving vertically near Earth's surface is determined by the acceleration due to gravity, which is approximately 9.8 m/s^2. Suppose a stone is thrown vertically upward at $t = 0$ with a velocity of 40 m/s from the edge of a cliff that is 100 m above a river.

a. Find the velocity $v(t)$ of the object, for $t \geq 0$.

b. Find the position $s(t)$ of the object, for $t \geq 0$.

c. Find the maximum height of the object above the river.

d. With what speed does the object strike the river?

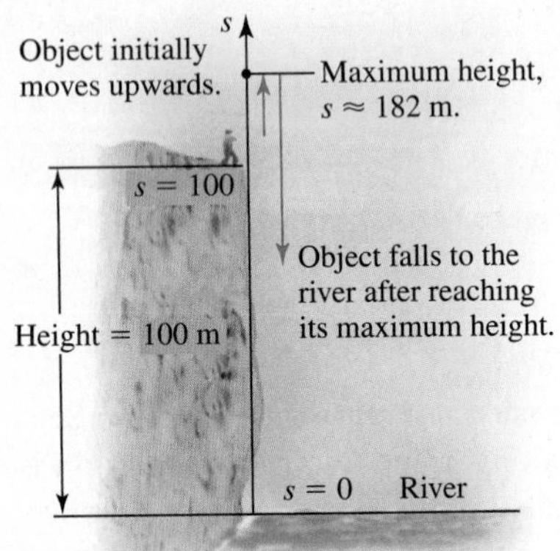

FIGURE 4.73

➤ The acceleration due to gravity at Earth's surface is approximately $g = 9.8\text{ m/s}^2$, or $g = 32\text{ ft/s}^2$. It varies even at sea level from about 9.8640 at the poles to 9.7982 at the equator. The equation $v'(t) = -g$ is an instance of Newton's Second Law of Motion, assuming no other forces (such as air resistance) are present.

SOLUTION We establish a coordinate system in which the positive s-axis points vertically upward with $s = 0$ corresponding to the river (Figure 4.73). Let $s(t)$ be the position of the stone measured relative to the river, for $t \geq 0$. The initial velocity of the stone is $v(0) = 40\text{ m/s}$ and the initial position of the stone is $s(0) = 100\text{ m}$.

a. The acceleration due to gravity points in the *negative* s-direction. Therefore, the initial value problem governing the motion of the object is

$$\text{acceleration} = v'(t) = -9.8, \; v(0) = 40.$$

The antiderivatives of -9.8 are $v(t) = -9.8t + C$. The initial condition $v(0) = 40$ gives $C = 40$. Therefore, the velocity of the stone is

$$v(t) = -9.8t + 40.$$

As shown in Figure 4.74, the velocity decreases from its initial value $v(0) = 40$ until it reaches zero at the high point of the trajectory. This point is reached when

$$v(t) = -9.8t + 40 = 0$$

or when $t \approx 4.1$ s. For $t > 4.1$, the velocity becomes increasingly negative as the stone falls to Earth.

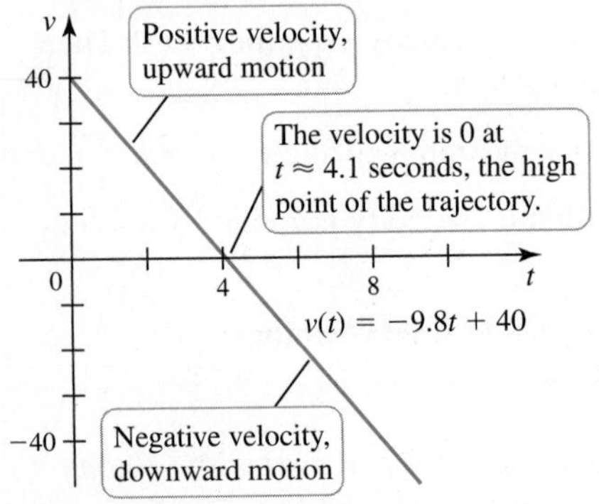

FIGURE 4.74

b. Knowing the velocity of the stone, we can determine its position. The position function satisfies the initial value problem

$$v(t) = s'(t) = -9.8t + 40, \; s(0) = 100.$$

The antiderivatives of $-9.8t + 40$ are

$$s(t) = -4.9t^2 + 40t + C.$$

The initial condition $s(0) = 100$ implies $C = 100$, so the position function of the stone is

$$s(t) = -4.9t^2 + 40t + 100$$

as shown in Figure 4.75. The parabolic graph of the position function is not the actual trajectory of the stone; the stone moves vertically along the s-axis.

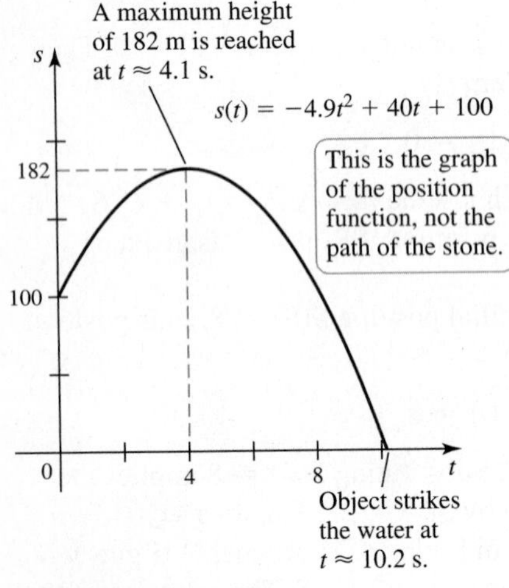

FIGURE 4.75

c. The position function of the stone increases for $0 < t < 4.1$. At $t \approx 4.1$, the stone reaches a high point of $s(4.1) \approx 182$ m.

d. For $t > 4.1$, the position function decreases, and the stone strikes the river when $s(t) = 0$. The roots of this equation are $t \approx 10.2$ and $t \approx -2.0$. Only the first root is relevant because the motion takes place for $t \geq 0$. Therefore, the stone strikes the ground at $t \approx 10.2$ s. Its speed at this instant is $|v(10.2)| \approx |-60| = 60\text{ m/s}$.

Related Exercises 55–58 ◀

SECTION 4.8 EXERCISES

Review Questions

1. Fill in the blank with the words *derivative* or *antiderivative*: If $F'(x) = f(x)$, then f is the ________ of F and F is the ________ of f.

2. Describe the set of antiderivatives of $f(x) = 0$.

3. Describe the set of antiderivatives of $f(x) = 1$.

4. Why do two different antiderivatives of a function differ by a constant?

5. Give the antiderivatives of x^p. For what values of p does your answer apply?

6. Evaluate $\int \cos ax\,dx$ and $\int \sin ax\,dx$.

7. If $F(x) = x^2 - 3x + C$ and $F(-1) = 4$, what is the value of C?

8. For a given function f, explain the steps used to solve the initial value problem $F'(t) = f(t), F(0) = 10$.

Basic Skills

9–16. Finding antiderivatives *Find all the antiderivatives of the following functions. Check your work by taking derivatives.*

9. $f(x) = 5x^4$

10. $g(x) = 11x^{10}$

11. $f(x) = \sin 2x$

12. $g(x) = -4 \cos 4x$

13. $P(x) = 3 \sec^2 x$

14. $Q(s) = \csc^2 s$

15. $f(y) = -2/y^3$

16. $H(z) = -6z^{-7}$

17–24. Indefinite integrals *Determine the following indefinite integrals. Check your work by differentiation.*

17. $\int (3x^5 - 5x^9)\,dx$

18. $\int (3u^{-2} - 4u^2 + 1)\,du$

19. $\int \left(4\sqrt{x} - \frac{4}{\sqrt{x}}\right) dx$

20. $\int \left(\frac{5}{t^2} + 4t^2\right) dt$

21. $\int (5s + 3)^2\,ds$

22. $\int 5m(12m^3 - 10m)\,dm$

23. $\int (3x^{1/3} + 4x^{-1/3} + 6)\,dx$

24. $\int 6\sqrt[3]{x}\,dx$

25–30. Indefinite integrals involving trigonometric functions *Determine the following indefinite integrals. Check your work by differentiation.*

25. $\int (\sin 2y + \cos 3y)\,dy$

26. $\int \left[\sin 4t - \sin\left(\frac{t}{4}\right)\right] dt$

27. $\int (\sec^2 x - 1)\,dx$

28. $\int 2 \sec^2 2v\,dv$

29. $\int (\sec^2 \theta + \sec\theta \tan\theta)\,d\theta$

30. $\int \frac{\sin\theta - 1}{\cos^2\theta}\,d\theta$

31–34. Particular antiderivatives *For the following functions f, find the antiderivative F that satisfies the given condition.*

31. $f(x) = x^5 - 2x^{-2} + 1;\ F(1) = 0$

32. $f(t) = \sec^2 t;\ F(\pi/4) = 1$

33. $f(v) = \sec v \tan v;\ F(0) = 2$

34. $f(x) = (4\sqrt{x} + 6/\sqrt{x})/x^2;\ F(1) = 4$

35–40. Solving initial value problems *Find the solution of the following initial value problems.*

35. $f'(x) = 2x - 3;\ f(0) = 4$

36. $g'(x) = 7x^6 - 4x^3 + 12;\ g(1) = 24$

37. $g'(x) = 7x\left(x^6 - \frac{1}{7}\right);\ g(1) = 2$

38. $h'(t) = 6 \sin 3t;\ h(\pi/6) = 6$

39. $f'(u) = 4(\cos u - \sin 2u);\ f(\pi/6) = 0$

40. $p'(t) = \frac{1}{2\sqrt{t}};\ p(4) = 6$

T **41–46. Graphing general solutions** *Graph several functions that satisfy each of the following differential equations. Then, find and graph the particular function that satisfies the given initial condition.*

41. $f'(x) = 2x - 5;\ f(0) = 4$

42. $f'(x) = 3x^2 - 1;\ f(1) = 2$

43. $f'(x) = 3x + \sin \pi x;\ f(2) = 3$

44. $f'(s) = 4 \sec s \tan s;\ f(\pi/4) = 1$

45. $f'(t) = 1/t^2;\ f(1) = 4$

46. $f'(x) = 2 \cos 2x;\ f(0) = 1$

T **47–52. Velocity to position** *Given the following velocity functions of an object moving along a line, find the position function with the given initial position. Then, graph both the velocity and position functions.*

47. $v(t) = 2t + 4;\ s(0) = 0$

48. $v(t) = 2 \cos t;\ s(0) = 0$

49. $v(t) = 2\sqrt{t};\ s(0) = 1$

50. $v(t) = \sin t + 3 \cos t;\ s(0) = 4$

51. $v(t) = 6t^2 + 4t - 10;\ s(0) = 0$

52. $v(t) = 2 \sin 2t;\ s(0) = 0$

T **53–54. Races** *The velocity function and initial position of Runners A and B are given. Analyze the race that results by graphing the position functions of the runners and finding the time and positions (if any) at which they first pass each other.*

53. A: $v(t) = \sin t,\ s(0) = 0$; B: $V(t) = \cos t,\ S(0) = 0$

54. A: $v(t) = 2t,\ s(0) = 0$; B: $V(t) = 3\sqrt{t},\ S(0) = 0$

55–58. Motion with gravity *Consider the following descriptions of the vertical motion of an object subject only to the acceleration due to gravity.*

a. *Find the velocity of the object for all relevant times.*
b. *Find the position of the object for all relevant times.*
c. *Find the time when the object reaches its highest point. (What is the height?)*
d. *Find the time when the object strikes the ground.*

55. A softball is popped up vertically (from the ground) with a velocity of 30 m/s.

56. A stone is thrown vertically upward with a velocity of 30 m/s from the edge of a cliff 200 m above a river.

57. A payload is released at an elevation of 400 m from a hot-air balloon that is rising at a rate of 10 m/s.

58. A payload is dropped at an elevation of 400 m from a hot-air balloon that is descending at a rate of 10 m/s.

Further Explorations

59. Explain why or why not Determine whether the following statements are true and give an explanation or counterexample.

a. $F(x) = x^3 - 4x + 100$ and $G(x) = x^3 - 4x - 100$ are antiderivatives of the same function.
b. If $F'(x) = f(x)$, then f is an antiderivative of F.
c. If $F'(x) = f(x)$, then $\int f(x)\,dx = F(x) + C$.
d. $f(x) = x^3 + 3$ and $g(x) = x^3 - 4$ are derivatives of the same function.
e. If $F'(x) = G'(x)$, then $F(x) = G(x)$.

60–67. Miscellaneous indefinite integrals *Determine the following indefinite integrals. Check your work by differentiation.*

60. $\int (\sqrt[3]{x^2} + \sqrt{x^3})\,dx$

61. $\int \frac{\sqrt{2x} + \sqrt[3]{8x}}{x}\,dx$

62. $\int (4\cos 4w - 3\sin 3w)\,dw$

63. $\int (\csc^2\theta + 2\theta^2 - 3\theta)\,d\theta$

64. $\int (\csc^2\theta + 1)\,d\theta$

65. $\int \frac{1 + \sqrt{x}}{x^2}\,dx$

66. $\int (\sec^2 4x + 1)\,dx$

67. $\int \sqrt{x}\,(2x^6 - 4\sqrt[3]{x})\,dx$

68–71. Functions from higher derivatives *Find the function F that satisfies the following differential equations and initial conditions.*

68. $F''(x) = 1, F'(0) = 3, F(0) = 4$

69. $F''(x) = \cos x, F'(0) = 3, F(\pi) = 4$

70. $F'''(x) = 4x, F''(0) = 0, F'(0) = 1, F(0) = 3$

71. $F'''(x) = 672x^5 + 24x, F''(0) = 0, F'(0) = 2, F(0) = 1$

Applications

72. Mass on a spring A mass oscillates up and down on the end of a spring. Find its position s relative to the equilibrium position if its acceleration is $a(t) = \sin \pi t$, and its initial velocity and position are $v(0) = 3$ and $s(0) = 0$, respectively.

73. Flow rate A large tank is filled with water when an outflow valve is opened at $t = 0$. Water flows out at a rate in gal/min given by $Q'(t) = 0.1(100 - t^2)$, for $0 \le t \le 10$.

a. Find the amount of water $Q(t)$ that has flowed out of the tank after t minutes, given the initial condition $Q(0) = 0$.
b. Graph the flow function Q, for $0 \le t \le 10$.
c. How much water flows out of the tank in 10 min?

74. General headstart problem Suppose that object A is located at $s = 0$ at time $t = 0$ and starts moving along the s-axis with a velocity given by $v(t) = 2at$, where $a > 0$. Object B is located at $s = c > 0$ at $t = 0$ and starts moving along the s-axis with a constant velocity given by $V(t) = b > 0$. Show that A always overtakes B at time

$$t = \frac{b + \sqrt{b^2 + 4ac}}{2a}.$$

Additional Exercises

75. Using identities Use the identities $\sin^2 x = (1 - \cos 2x)/2$ and $\cos^2 x = (1 + \cos 2x)/2$ to find $\int \sin^2 x\,dx$ and $\int \cos^2 x\,dx$.

76–79. Verifying indefinite integrals *Verify the following indefinite integrals by differentiation. These integrals are derived in later chapters.*

76. $\int \frac{\cos\sqrt{x}}{\sqrt{x}}\,dx = 2\sin\sqrt{x} + C$

77. $\int \frac{x}{\sqrt{x^2 + 1}}\,dx = \sqrt{x^2 + 1} + C$

78. $\int x^2 \cos x^3\,dx = \frac{1}{3}\sin x^3 + C$

79. $\int \frac{x}{(x^2 - 1)^2}\,dx = -\frac{1}{2(x^2 - 1)} + C$

QUICK CHECK ANSWERS

1. $d/dx(x^3) = 3x^2$ and $d/dx(-\cos x) = \sin x$ **2.** $\sqrt{x} + C$, $x^4 + C$, $\tan x + C$ **3.** $d/dx(-\cos(2x)/2 + C) = \sin 2x$ **4.** One function that can be differentiated to get f' is f. Therefore, f is an antiderivative of f'. **5.** The two position functions involve two different initial positions; they differ by a constant.

CHAPTER 4 REVIEW EXERCISES

1. Explain why or why not Determine whether the following statements are true and give an explanation or counterexample.

a. If $f'(c) = 0$, then f has a local minimum or maximum at c.
b. If $f''(c) = 0$, then f has an inflection point at $(c, f(c))$.
c. $F(x) = x^2 + 10$ and $G(x) = x^2 - 100$ are antiderivatives of the same function.
d. Between two local minima of a continuous function on $(-\infty, \infty)$, there must be a local maximum.

2. **Locating extrema** Consider the graph of a function f on the interval $[-3, 3]$.

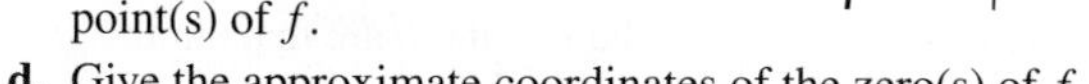

   a. Give the approximate coordinates of the local maxima and minima of f.
   b. Give the approximate coordinates of the absolute maximum and absolute minimum of f (if they exist).
   c. Give the approximate coordinates of the inflection point(s) of f.
   d. Give the approximate coordinates of the zero(s) of f.
   e. On what intervals (approximately) is f concave up?
   f. On what intervals (approximately) is f concave down?

3–4. Designer functions *Sketch the graph of a continuous function that satisfies the following conditions.*

3. f is continuous on the interval $[-4, 4]$, $f'(x) = 0$, for $x = -2, 0$, and 3; f has an absolute minimum at $x = 3$; f has a local minimum at $x = -2$; f has a local maximum at $x = 0$; f has an absolute maximum at $x = -4$.

4. f is continuous on $(-\infty, \infty)$; $f'(x) < 0$ and $f''(x) < 0$ on $(-\infty, 0)$; $f'(x) > 0$ and $f''(x) > 0$ on $(0, \infty)$

5. **Functions from derivatives** Given the graphs of f' and f'', sketch a possible graph of f.

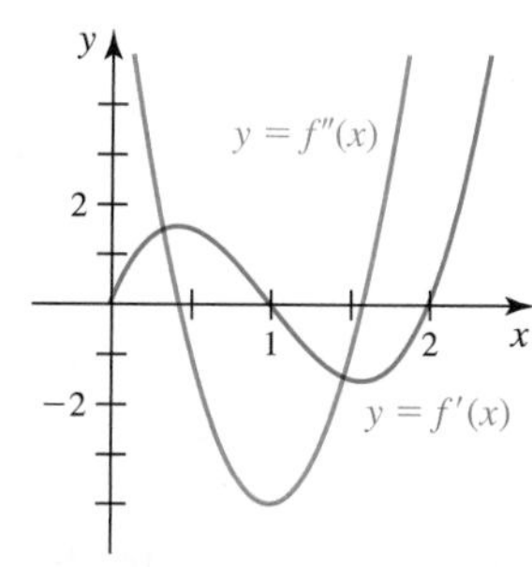

6–10. Critical points *Find the critical points of the following functions on the given intervals. Identify the absolute maximum and absolute minimum values (if possible). Graph the function to confirm your conclusions.*

6. $f(x) = \sin 2x + 3;\ [-\pi, \pi]$

7. $f(x) = 2x^3 - 3x^2 - 36x + 12;\ (-\infty, \infty)$

8. $f(x) = 4x^{1/2} - x^{5/2};\ [0, 4]$

9. $f(x) = (x^2 + 8)/(x + 1);\ [-5, 5]$

10. $g(x) = x^{1/3}(9 - x^2);\ [-4, 4]$

11. **Absolute values** Consider the function $f(x) = |x - 2| + |x + 3|$ on $[-4, 4]$. Graph f, identify the critical points, and give the coordinates of the local and absolute extreme values.

12. **Inflection points** Does $f(x) = 2x^5 - 10x^4 + 20x^3 + x + 1$ have any inflection points? If so, identify them.

13–20. Curve sketching *Use the guidelines of this chapter to make a complete graph of the following functions on their domains or on the given interval. Use a graphing utility to check your work.*

13. $f(x) = x^4/2 - 3x^2 + 4x + 1$

14. $f(x) = \dfrac{3x}{x^2 + 3}$

15. $f(x) = 4\cos(\pi(x - 1))$ on $[0, 2]$

16. $f(x) = \dfrac{x^2 + x}{4 - x^2}$

17. $f(x) = \sqrt[3]{x} - \sqrt{x} + 2$

18. $f(x) = \dfrac{\cos \pi x}{1 + x^2}$ on $[-2, 2]$

19. $f(x) = x^{2/3} + (x + 2)^{1/3}$

20. $f(x) = \dfrac{x^2 + 12}{x - 2}$

21. **Optimization** A right triangle has legs of length h and r and a hypotenuse of length 4 (see figure). It is revolved about the leg of length h to sweep out a right circular cone. What values of h and r maximize the volume of the cone? (Volume of a cone $= \pi r^2 h/3$.)

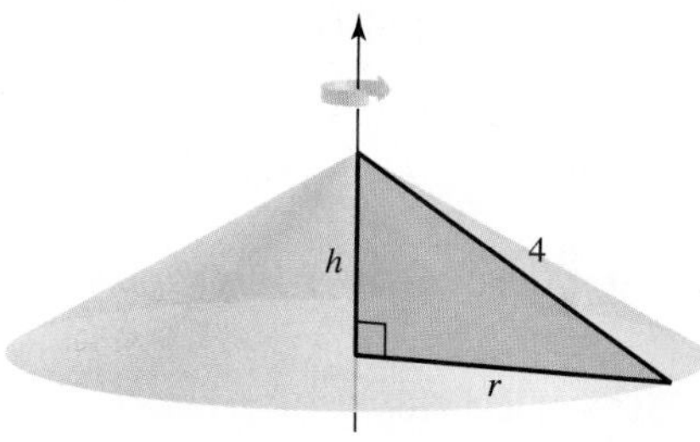

22. **Rectangles beneath a curve** A rectangle is constructed with one side on the positive x-axis, one side on the positive y-axis, and the vertex opposite the origin on the curve $y = \cos x$, for $0 < x < \pi/2$. Approximate the dimensions of the rectangle that maximize the area of the rectangle. What is the area?

23. **Maximum length** What two nonnegative real numbers a and b whose sum is 23 (a) minimize $a^2 + b^2$? (b) Maximize $a^2 + b^2$?

24. **Nearest point** What point of the graph of $f(x) = \frac{5}{2} - x^2$ is closest to the origin? (*Hint:* You can minimize the square of the distance.)

25. **Mean Value Theorem** The population of a culture of cells grows according to the function $P(t) = \dfrac{100t}{t + 1}$, where $t \geq 0$ is measured in weeks.
   a. What is the average rate of change in the population over the interval $[0, 8]$?
   b. At what point of the interval $[0, 8]$ is the instantaneous rate of change equal to the average rate of change?

26–33. Limits *Evaluate the following limits. Use l'Hôpital's Rule when needed.*

26. $\displaystyle\lim_{t \to 2} \frac{t^3 - t^2 - 2t}{t^2 - 4}$

27. $\displaystyle\lim_{t \to 0} \frac{1 - \cos 6t}{2t}$

28. $\displaystyle\lim_{x \to \infty} \frac{5x^2 + 2x - 5}{\sqrt{x^4 - 1}}$

29. $\displaystyle\lim_{\theta \to 0} \frac{3\sin^2 2\theta}{\theta^2}$

30. $\displaystyle\lim_{x \to \infty} \left(\sqrt{x^2 + x + 1} - \sqrt{x^2 - x}\right)$

31. $\displaystyle\lim_{\theta \to 0} 2\theta \cot 3\theta$

32. $\displaystyle\lim_{\theta \to 0} \frac{3\sin 8\theta}{8\sin 3\theta}$

33. $\displaystyle\lim_{x \to 1} \frac{x^4 - x^3 - 3x^2 + 5x - 2}{x^3 + x^2 - 5x + 3}$

34–43. Indefinite integrals *Determine the following indefinite integrals.*

34. $\int (x^8 - 3x^3 + 1)\, dx$

35. $\int \left(\frac{1}{x^2} - \frac{2}{x^{5/2}}\right) dx$

36. $\int \frac{x^4 - 2\sqrt{x} + 2}{x^2}\, dx$

37. $\int (1 + \cos 3\theta)\, d\theta$

38. $\int 2 \sec^2 x\, dx$

39. $\int \sec 2x \tan 2x\, dx$

40. $\int (\sin 2\theta + 2\theta + 1)\, d\theta$

41. $\int (4x^{1/3} - 7x^{2/5} + 10x^{3/7})\, dx$

42. $\int \frac{1 + \tan\theta}{\sec\theta}\, d\theta$

43. $\int \left(\sqrt[4]{x^3} + \sqrt{x^5}\right) dx$

44–47. Functions from derivatives *Find the function with the following properties.*

44. $f'(x) = 3x^2 - 1$ and $f(0) = 10$

45. $f'(t) = \sin t + 2t$ and $f(0) = 5$

46. $g'(t) = t^2 + t^{-2}$ and $g(1) = 1$

47. $h'(x) = \sin^2 x$ and $h(1) = 1$ (*Hint:* $\sin^2 x = (1 - \cos 2x)/2$.)

48. Motion along a line Two objects move along the x-axis with position functions $x_1(t) = 2 \sin t$ and $x_2(t) = \sin(t - \pi/2)$. At what times on the interval $[0, 2\pi]$ are the objects closest to each other and farthest from each other?

49. Vertical motion with gravity A rocket is launched vertically upward with an initial velocity of 120 m/s from a platform that is 125 m above the ground. Assume that the only force at work is gravity. Determine and graph the velocity and position functions of the rocket, for $t \geq 0$. Then describe the motion in words.

50. Critical points of a family of rational functions Consider the functions $f(x) = \frac{x^2 + a}{x - b}$, where a and b are real numbers.

a. What values of a and b guarantee that f has two critical points?

b. What values of a and b guarantee that f has zero critical points?

c. Does f have exactly one critical point for any values of a and b?

51–52. Two methods *Evaluate the following limits in two different ways: Use the methods of Chapter 2 and use l'Hôpital's Rule.*

51. $\lim_{x\to\infty} \frac{2x^5 - x + 1}{5x^6 + x}$

52. $\lim_{x\to\infty} \frac{4x^4 - \sqrt{x}}{2x^4 + x^{-1}}$

53. Cosine limits Let n be a positive integer. Use graphical and/or analytical methods to verify the following limits:

a. $\lim_{x\to 0} \frac{1 - \cos x^n}{x^{2n}} = \frac{1}{2}$

b. $\lim_{x\to 0} \frac{1 - \cos^n x}{x^2} = \frac{n}{2}$

Chapter 4 Guided Projects

Applications of the material in this chapter and related topics can be found in the following Guided Projects. For additional information, see the Preface.

- Newton's method
- Ice cream, geometry, and calculus

5 Integration

Chapter Preview We are now at a critical point in the calculus story. Many would argue that this chapter is the cornerstone of calculus because it explains the relationship between the two processes of calculus: differentiation and integration. We begin by explaining why finding the area of regions bounded by the graphs of functions is such an important problem in calculus. Then you will see how antiderivatives lead to definite integrals, which are used to solve this problem. But there is more to the story. You will also see the remarkable connection between derivatives and integrals, which is expressed in the Fundamental Theorem of Calculus. In this chapter, we develop key properties of definite integrals, investigate a few of their many applications, and present the first of several powerful techniques for evaluating definite integrals.

5.1 Approximating Areas Under Curves

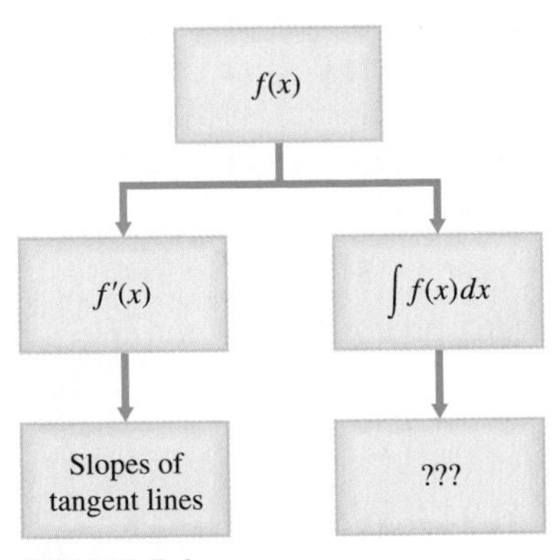

FIGURE 5.1

The derivative of a function is associated with rates of change and slopes of tangent lines. We also know that antiderivatives (or indefinite integrals) reverse the derivative operation. Figure 5.1 summarizes our current understanding and raises the question: What is the geometric meaning of the integral? The following example reveals a clue.

Area under a Velocity Curve

Consider an object moving along a line. You learned in previous chapters that the slope of the line tangent to the graph of the position function at a certain time gives the velocity at that time. We now turn the situation around. If we know the velocity function of a moving object, what can we learn about its position function?

Imagine a car traveling at a constant velocity of 60 mi/hr along a straight highway over a two-hour period. The graph of the velocity function $v = 60$ on the interval $0 \le t \le 2$ is a horizontal line (Figure 5.2). The displacement of the car between $t = 0$ and $t = 2$ hr is found by a familiar formula:

$$\begin{aligned} \text{displacement} &= \text{rate} \cdot \text{time} \\ &= (60 \text{ mi/hr})(2 \text{ hr}) = 120 \text{ mi} \end{aligned}$$

➤ Recall from Section 3.5 that the *displacement* of an object moving along a line is the difference between its final and initial position. If the velocity of an object is positive, its displacement equals the distance traveled.

This product is the area of the rectangle formed by the velocity curve and the t-axis between $t = 0$ and $t = 2$ hr (Figure 5.3). In the case of constant positive velocity, we see that the area between the velocity curve and the t-axis is the displacement of the moving object.

➤ The side lengths of the rectangle in Figure 5.3 have units mi/hr and hr. Therefore, the units of the area are mi/hr · hr = mi, which is a unit of displacement.

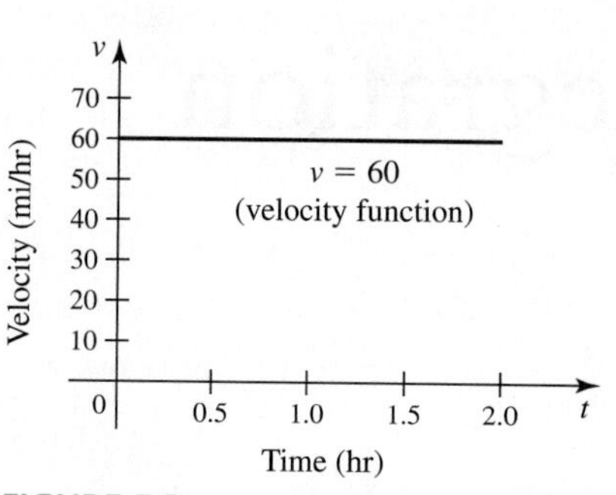

FIGURE 5.2

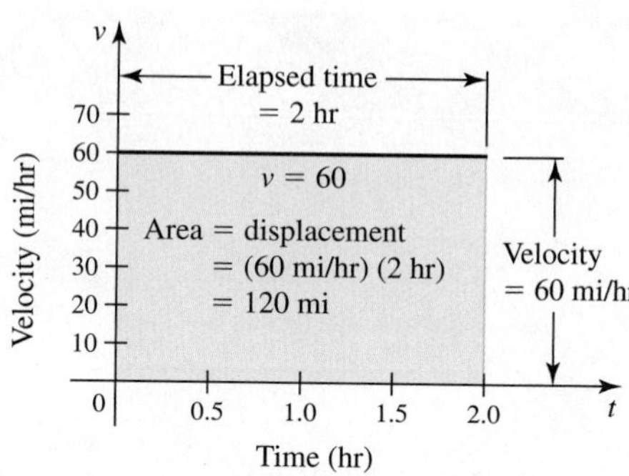

FIGURE 5.3

QUICK CHECK 1 What is the displacement of an object that travels at a constant velocity of 10 mi/hr for a half hour, 20 mi/hr for the next half hour, and 30 mi/hr for the next hour? ◂

Because objects do not necessarily move at a constant velocity, we must extend these ideas to positive velocities that *change* over an interval of time. One strategy is to divide the time interval into many subintervals and approximate the velocity on each subinterval by a constant velocity. Then the displacements on each subinterval are calculated and summed. This strategy produces only an approximation to the displacement; however, this approximation generally improves as the number of subintervals increases.

EXAMPLE 1 **Approximating the displacement** Suppose the velocity in m/s of an object moving along a line is given by the function $v = t^2$, where $0 \le t \le 8$. Approximate the displacement of the object by dividing the time interval $[0, 8]$ into n subintervals of equal length. On each subinterval, approximate the velocity by a constant equal to the value of v evaluated at the midpoint of the subinterval.

a. Begin by dividing $[0, 8]$ into $n = 2$ subintervals: $[0, 4]$ and $[4, 8]$.

b. Divide $[0, 8]$ into $n = 4$ subintervals: $[0, 2]$, $[2, 4]$, $[4, 6]$, and $[6, 8]$.

c. Divide $[0, 8]$ into $n = 8$ subintervals of equal length.

SOLUTION

a. We divide the interval $[0, 8]$ into $n = 2$ subintervals, $[0, 4]$ and $[4, 8]$, each with length 4. The velocity on each subinterval is approximated using the value of v evaluated at the midpoint of that subinterval (Figure 5.4a).

- We approximate the velocity on $[0, 4]$ by $v(2) = 2^2 = 4$ m/s. Traveling at 4 m/s for 4 s results in a displacement of 4 m/s · 4 s = 16 m.
- We approximate the velocity on $[4, 8]$ by $v(6) = 6^2 = 36$ m/s. Traveling at 36 m/s for 4 s results in a displacement of 36 m/s · 4 s = 144 m.

Therefore, an approximation to the displacement over the entire interval $[0, 8]$ is

$$(v(2) \cdot 4\text{ s}) + (v(6) \cdot 4\text{ s}) = (4\text{ m/s} \cdot 4\text{ s}) + (36\text{ m/s} \cdot 4\text{ s}) = 160\text{ m}.$$

b. With $n = 4$ (Figure 5.4b), each subinterval has length 2. The approximate displacement over the entire interval is

$$\underbrace{(1\text{ m/s}\cdot 2\text{ s})}_{v(1)} + \underbrace{(9\text{ m/s}\cdot 2\text{ s})}_{v(3)} + \underbrace{(25\text{ m/s}\cdot 2\text{ s})}_{v(5)} + \underbrace{(49\text{ m/s}\cdot 2\text{ s})}_{v(7)} = 168\text{ m}.$$

c. With $n = 8$ subintervals (Figure 5.4c), the approximation to the displacement is 170 m. In each case, the approximate displacement is the sum of the areas of the rectangles under the velocity curve.

The midpoint of each subinterval is used to approximate the velocity over that subinterval.

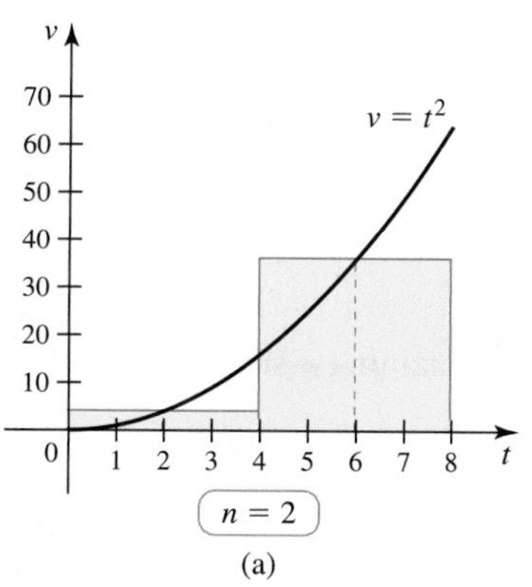

(a)

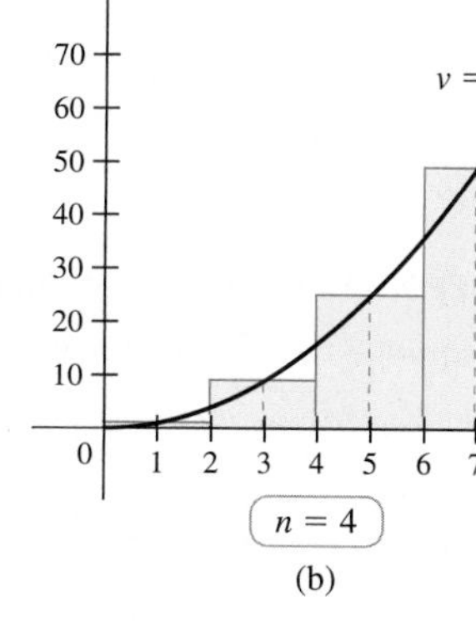

(b)

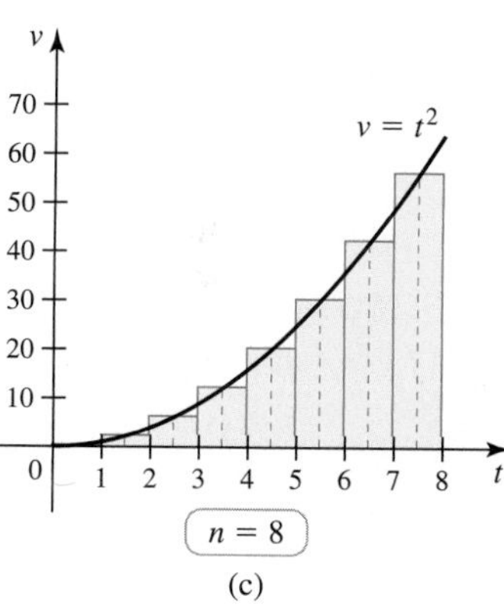

(c)

FIGURE 5.4

Related Exercises 9–14

QUICK CHECK 2 In Example 1, if we used $n = 32$ subintervals of equal length, what would be the length of each subinterval? Find the midpoint of the first and last subinterval.

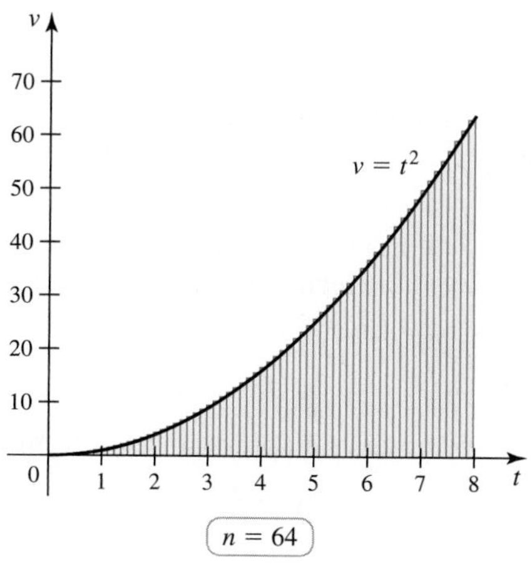

FIGURE 5.5

The progression in Example 1 may be continued. Larger values of n mean more rectangles; in general, more rectangles give a better fit to the region under the curve (Figure 5.5). With the help of a calculator, we can generate the approximations in Table 5.1 using $n = 1$, 2, 4, 8, 16, 32, and 64 subintervals. Observe that as n increases, the approximations appear to approach a limit of approximately 170.7 m. The limit is the exact displacement, which is represented by the area of the region under the velocity curve. This strategy of taking limits of sums is developed fully in Section 5.2.

Table 5.1 Approximations to the area under the velocity curve $v = t^2$ on $[0, 8]$

Number of subintervals	Length of each subinterval	Approximate displacement (area under curve)
1	8 s	128.0 m
2	4 s	160.0 m
4	2 s	168.0 m
8	1 s	170.0 m
16	0.5 s	170.5 m
32	0.25 s	170.625 m
64	0.125 s	170.65625 m

> The language "the area of the region bounded by the graph of a function" is often abbreviated as "the area under the curve."

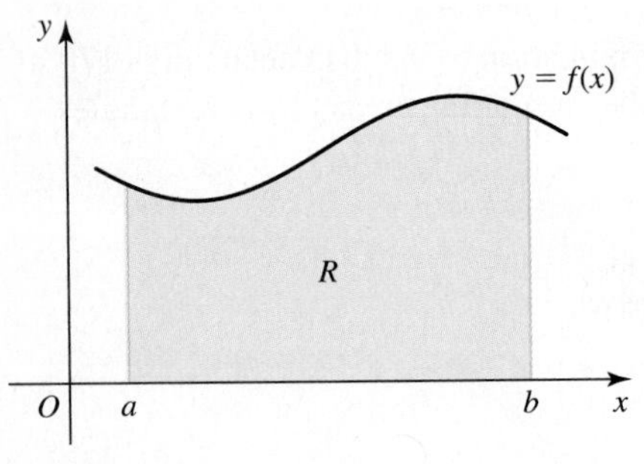

FIGURE 5.6

Approximating Areas by Riemann Sums

We now develop a method for approximating areas under curves. Consider a function f that is continuous and nonnegative on an interval $[a, b]$. The goal is to approximate the area of the region R bounded by the graph of f and the x-axis from $x = a$ to $x = b$ (Figure 5.6). We begin by dividing the interval $[a, b]$ into n subintervals of equal length,

$$[x_0, x_1], [x_1, x_2], \ldots, [x_{n-1}, x_n],$$

where $a = x_0$ and $b = x_n$ (Figure 5.7). The length of each subinterval, denoted Δx, is found by dividing the length of the interval by n:

$$\Delta x = \frac{b - a}{n}$$

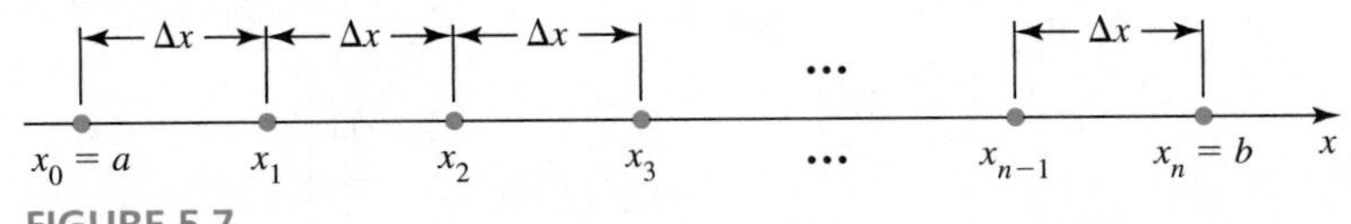

FIGURE 5.7

> **DEFINITION Regular Partition**
>
> Suppose $[a, b]$ is a closed interval containing n subintervals
>
> $$[x_0, x_1], [x_1, x_2], \ldots, [x_{n-1}, x_n]$$
>
> of equal length $\Delta x = \frac{b - a}{n}$ with $a = x_0$ and $b = x_n$. The endpoints $x_0, x_1, x_2, \ldots, x_{n-1}, x_n$ of the subintervals are called **grid points** and they create a **regular partition** of the interval $[a, b]$. In general, the kth grid point is
>
> $$x_k = a + k\,\Delta x, \qquad \text{for } k = 0, 1, 2, \ldots, n.$$

QUICK CHECK 3 If the interval $[1, 9]$ is partitioned into 4 subintervals of equal length, what is Δx? List the grid points x_0, x_1, x_2, x_3, and x_4. ◄

> Although the idea of integration was formulated in the 17th century, it was almost 200 years later that the German mathematician Bernhard Riemann (1826–1866) developed the mathematical theory underlying integration.

In the kth subinterval $[x_{k-1}, x_k]$, we choose any point $\overline{x}_k$ and build a rectangle whose height is $f(\overline{x}_k)$, the value of f at $\overline{x}_k$ (Figure 5.8). The area of the rectangle on the kth subinterval is

$$\text{height} \cdot \text{base} = f(\overline{x}_k)\,\Delta x, \qquad \text{where } k = 1, 2, \ldots, n.$$

Summing the areas of the rectangles in Figure 5.8, we obtain an approximation to the area of R, which is called a **Riemann sum**:

$$f(\overline{x}_1)\,\Delta x + f(\overline{x}_2)\,\Delta x + \cdots + f(\overline{x}_n)\,\Delta x$$

Three notable Riemann sums are the left, right, and midpoint Riemann sums.

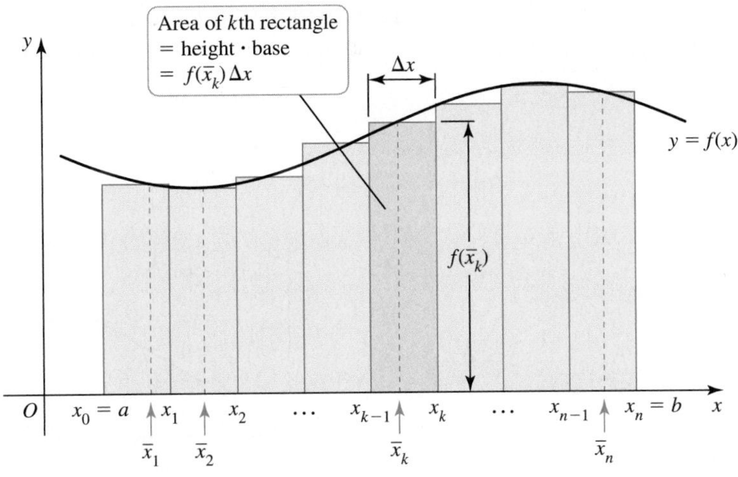

FIGURE 5.8

DEFINITION Riemann Sum

Suppose f is defined on a closed interval $[a, b]$, which is divided into n subintervals of equal length Δx. If $\bar{x}_k$ is any point in the kth subinterval $[x_{k-1}, x_k]$, for $k = 1, 2, \ldots, n$, then

$$f(\bar{x}_1)\Delta x + f(\bar{x}_2)\Delta x + \cdots + f(\bar{x}_n)\Delta x$$

is called a **Riemann sum** for f on $[a, b]$. This sum is

- a **left Riemann sum** if $\bar{x}_k$ is the left endpoint of $[x_{k-1}, x_k]$ (Figure 5.9);
- a **right Riemann sum** if $\bar{x}_k$ is the right endpoint of $[x_{k-1}, x_k]$ (Figure 5.10); and
- a **midpoint Riemann sum** if $\bar{x}_k$ is the midpoint of $[x_{k-1}, x_k]$ (Figure 5.11), for $k = 1, 2, \ldots, n$.

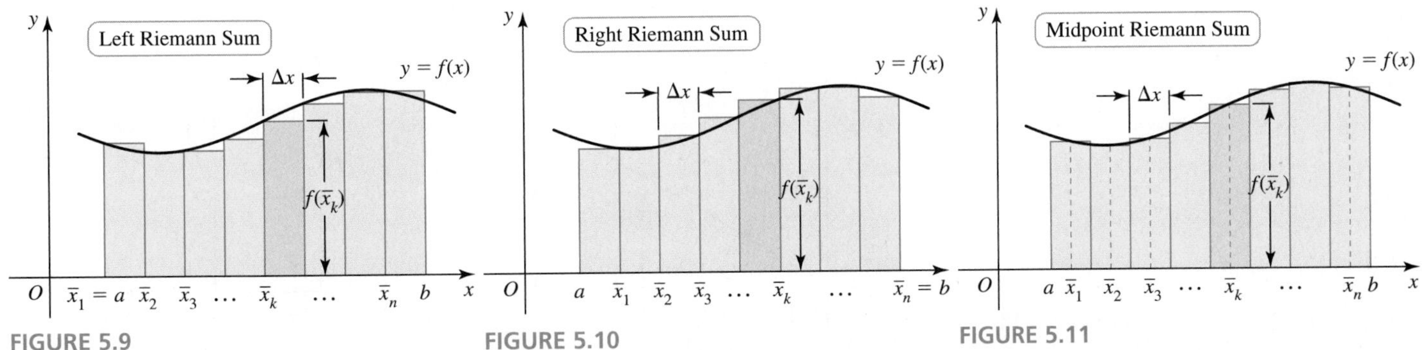

FIGURE 5.9 FIGURE 5.10 FIGURE 5.11

EXAMPLE 2 Area under the sine curve Let R be the region bounded by the graph of $f(x) = \sin x$ and the x-axis between $x = 0$ and $x = \pi/2$.

a. Approximate the area of R using a left Riemann sum with $n = 6$ subintervals. Illustrate the sum with the appropriate rectangles.

b. Approximate the area of R using a right Riemann sum with $n = 6$ subintervals. Illustrate the sum with the appropriate rectangles.

c. How do the area approximations in parts (a) and (b) compare to the actual area under the curve?

SOLUTION Dividing the interval $[a, b] = [0, \pi/2]$ into $n = 6$ subintervals means the length of each subinterval is

$$\Delta x = \frac{b - a}{n} = \frac{\pi/2 - 0}{6} = \frac{\pi}{12}.$$

a. To find the left Riemann sum, we set $\overline{x}_1, \overline{x}_2, \ldots, \overline{x}_6$ equal to the left endpoints of the six subintervals. The heights of the rectangles are $f(\overline{x}_k)$, for $k = 1, \ldots, 6$.

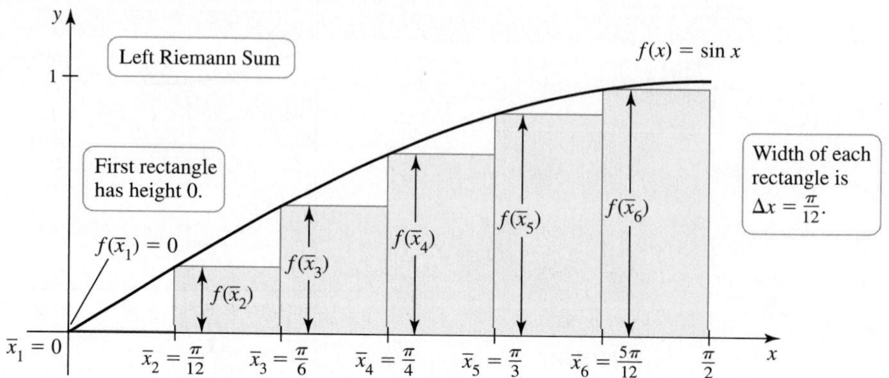

FIGURE 5.12

The resulting left Riemann sum (Figure 5.12) is

$$\begin{aligned} & f(\overline{x}_1)\Delta x + f(\overline{x}_2)\Delta x + \cdots + f(\overline{x}_6)\Delta x \\ &= \left[\sin(0) \cdot \frac{\pi}{12}\right] + \left[\sin\left(\frac{\pi}{12}\right) \cdot \frac{\pi}{12}\right] + \left[\sin\left(\frac{\pi}{6}\right) \cdot \frac{\pi}{12}\right] \\ &\quad + \left[\sin\left(\frac{\pi}{4}\right) \cdot \frac{\pi}{12}\right] + \left[\sin\left(\frac{\pi}{3}\right) \cdot \frac{\pi}{12}\right] + \left[\sin\left(\frac{5\pi}{12}\right) \cdot \frac{\pi}{12}\right] \\ &\approx 0.863. \end{aligned}$$

b. In a right Riemann sum, the right endpoints are used for $\overline{x}_1, \overline{x}_2, \ldots, \overline{x}_6$, and the heights of the rectangles are $f(\overline{x}_k)$, for $k = 1, \ldots, 6$.

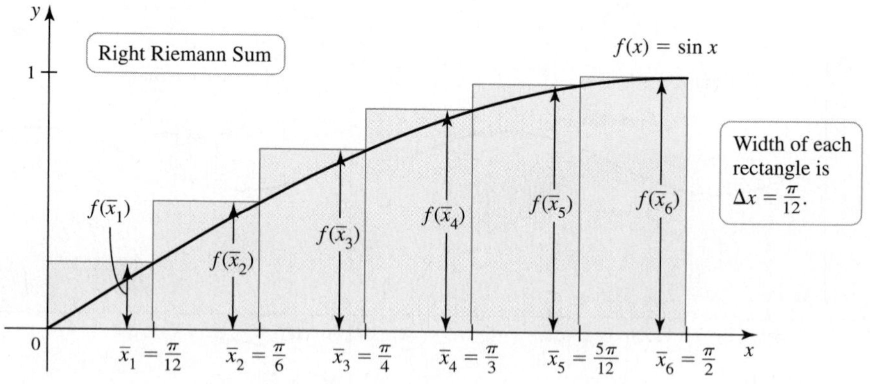

FIGURE 5.13

The resulting right Riemann sum (Figure 5.13) is

$$\begin{aligned} & f(\overline{x}_1)\Delta x + f(\overline{x}_2)\Delta x + \cdots + f(\overline{x}_6)\Delta x \\ &= \left[\sin\left(\frac{\pi}{12}\right) \cdot \frac{\pi}{12}\right] + \left[\sin\left(\frac{\pi}{6}\right) \cdot \frac{\pi}{12}\right] + \left[\sin\left(\frac{\pi}{4}\right) \cdot \frac{\pi}{12}\right] \\ &\quad + \left[\sin\left(\frac{\pi}{3}\right) \cdot \frac{\pi}{12}\right] + \left[\sin\left(\frac{5\pi}{12}\right) \cdot \frac{\pi}{12}\right] + \left[\sin\left(\frac{\pi}{2}\right) \cdot \frac{\pi}{12}\right] \\ &\approx 1.125. \end{aligned}$$

QUICK CHECK 4 If the function in Example 2 is instead $f(x) = \cos x$, does the left Riemann sum or the right Riemann sum overestimate the area under the curve?

c. Looking at the graphs, we see that the left Riemann sum in part (a) underestimates the actual area of R, whereas the right Riemann sum in part (b) overestimates the area of R. Therefore, the area of R is between 0.863 and 1.125. As the number of rectangles increases, these approximations improve.

Related Exercises 15–20

EXAMPLE 3 **A midpoint Riemann sum** Let R be the region bounded by the graph of $f(x) = \sin x$ and the x-axis between $x = 0$ and $x = \pi/2$. Approximate the area of R using a midpoint Riemann sum with $n = 6$ subintervals. Illustrate the sum with the appropriate rectangles.

SOLUTION The grid points and the length of the subintervals $\Delta x = \pi/12$ are the same as in Example 2. To find the midpoint Riemann sum, we set $\overline{x}_1, \overline{x}_2, \ldots, \overline{x}_6$ equal to the midpoints of the subintervals. The midpoint of the first subinterval is the average of x_0 and x_1, which is

$$\overline{x}_1 = \frac{x_1 + x_0}{2} = \frac{\pi/12 + 0}{2} = \frac{\pi}{24}.$$

The remaining midpoints are also computed by averaging the two nearest grid points.

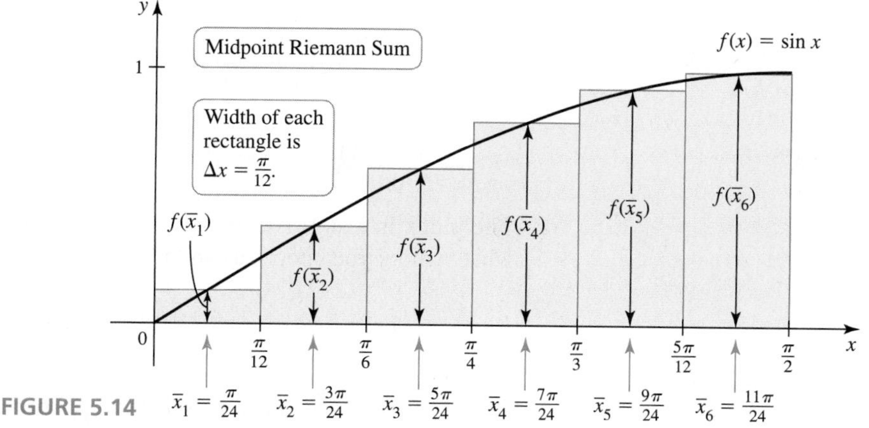

FIGURE 5.14

The resulting midpoint Riemann sum (Figure 5.14) is

$$\begin{aligned} &f(\overline{x}_1)\Delta x + f(\overline{x}_2)\Delta x + \cdots + f(\overline{x}_6)\Delta x \\ &= \left[\sin\left(\frac{\pi}{24}\right)\cdot\frac{\pi}{12}\right] + \left[\sin\left(\frac{3\pi}{24}\right)\cdot\frac{\pi}{12}\right] + \left[\sin\left(\frac{5\pi}{24}\right)\cdot\frac{\pi}{12}\right] \\ &\quad + \left[\sin\left(\frac{7\pi}{24}\right)\cdot\frac{\pi}{12}\right] + \left[\sin\left(\frac{9\pi}{24}\right)\cdot\frac{\pi}{12}\right] + \left[\sin\left(\frac{11\pi}{24}\right)\cdot\frac{\pi}{12}\right] \\ &\approx 1.003. \end{aligned}$$

Comparing the midpoint Riemann sum (Figure 5.14) with the left (Figure 5.12) and right (Figure 5.13) Riemann sums suggests that the midpoint sum is a more accurate estimate of the area under the curve. *Related Exercises 21–26* ◀

Table 5.2

x	$f(x)$
0	1
0.5	3
1.0	4.5
1.5	5.5
2.0	6.0

EXAMPLE 4 **Riemann sums from tables** Estimate the area A under the graph of f on the interval $[0, 2]$ using left and right Riemann sums with $n = 4$, when f is continuous but known only at the points in Table 5.2.

SOLUTION With $n = 4$ subintervals on the interval $[0, 2]$, $\Delta x = 2/4 = 0.5$. Using the left endpoint of each subinterval, the left Riemann sum is

$$A \approx (f(0) + f(0.5) + f(1.0) + f(1.5))\Delta x = (1 + 3 + 4.5 + 5.5)0.5 = 7.0.$$

Using the right endpoint of each subinterval, the right Riemann sum is

$$A \approx (f(0.5) + f(1.0) + f(1.5) + f(2.0))\Delta x = (3 + 4.5 + 5.5 + 6.0)0.5 = 9.5.$$

With only five function values, these estimates of the area are necessarily crude. Better estimates are obtained by using more subintervals and more function values.

Related Exercises 27–30 ◀

Sigma (Summation) Notation

Working with Riemann sums is cumbersome with large numbers of subintervals. Therefore, we pause for a moment to introduce some notation that simplifies our work.

Sigma (or **summation**), **notation** is used to express sums in a compact way. For example, the sum $1 + 2 + 3 + \cdots + 10$ is represented in sigma notation as $\sum_{k=1}^{10} k$. Here is how the notation works. The symbol Σ (*sigma*, the Greek capital S) stands for *sum*. The **index** k takes on all integer values from the lower limit ($k = 1$) to the upper limit ($k = 10$). The expression that immediately follows Σ (the **summand**) is evaluated for each value of k, and the resulting values are summed. Here are some examples:

$$\sum_{k=1}^{99} k = 1 + 2 + 3 + \cdots + 99 = 4950 \qquad \sum_{k=1}^{n} k = 1 + 2 + \cdots + n$$

$$\sum_{k=0}^{3} k^2 = 0^2 + 1^2 + 2^2 + 3^2 = 14 \qquad \sum_{k=1}^{4} (2k + 1) = 3 + 5 + 7 + 9 = 24$$

$$\sum_{k=-1}^{2} (k^2 + k) = ((-1)^2 + (-1)) + (0^2 + 0) + (1^2 + 1) + (2^2 + 2) = 8$$

The index in a sum is a *dummy variable*. It is internal to the sum, so it does not matter what symbol you choose as an index. For example,

$$\sum_{k=1}^{99} k = \sum_{n=1}^{99} n = \sum_{p=1}^{99} p.$$

Two properties of sums are useful in upcoming work. Suppose that $\{a_1, a_2, \ldots, a_n\}$ and $\{b_1, b_2, \ldots, b_n\}$ are two sets of real numbers, and suppose that c is a real number. Then we can factor constants out of a sum:

Constant Multiple Rule $\qquad \sum_{k=1}^{n} ca_k = c\sum_{k=1}^{n} a_k$

We can also split a sum into two sums:

Addition Rule $\qquad \sum_{k=1}^{n} (a_k + b_k) = \sum_{k=1}^{n} a_k + \sum_{k=1}^{n} b_k$

In the coming examples and exercises, the following summation formulas are essential.

> Formulas for the sums of powers of positive integers have been known for centuries. The formulas for powers $p = 0, 1, 2,$ and 3 are relatively simple. The formulas become complicated as p increases.

THEOREM 5.1 Sums of Positive Integers

Let n be a positive integer.

Sum of a constant c $\qquad \sum_{k=1}^{n} c = cn$

Sum of the first n integers $\qquad \sum_{k=1}^{n} k = \dfrac{n(n + 1)}{2}$

Sum of squares of the first n integers $\qquad \sum_{k=1}^{n} k^2 = \dfrac{n(n + 1)(2n + 1)}{6}$

Sum of cubes of the first n integers $\qquad \sum_{k=1}^{n} k^3 = \dfrac{n^2(n + 1)^2}{4}$

Related Exercises 31–34 ◄

Riemann Sums Using Sigma Notation

With sigma notation, a Riemann sum has the convenient compact form

$$f(\overline{x}_1)\,\Delta x + f(\overline{x}_2)\,\Delta x + \cdots + f(\overline{x}_n)\,\Delta x = \sum_{k=1}^{n} f(\overline{x}_k)\,\Delta x.$$

To express left, right, and midpoint Riemann sums in sigma notation, we must identify the points $\overline{x}_k$.

- For left Riemann sums, the left endpoints of the subintervals are $\overline{x}_k = a + (k - 1)\,\Delta x$, for $k = 1, \ldots, n$.
- For right Riemann sums, the right endpoints of the subintervals are $\overline{x}_k = a + k\,\Delta x$, for $k = 1, \ldots, n$.
- For midpoint Riemann sums, the midpoints of the subintervals are $\overline{x}_k = a + \left(k - \frac{1}{2}\right)\Delta x$, for $k = 1, \ldots, n$.

The three Riemann sums are written compactly as follows.

DEFINITION Left, Right, and Midpoint Riemann Sums in Sigma Notation

Suppose f is defined on a closed interval $[a, b]$, which is divided into n subintervals of equal length Δx. If $\overline{x}_k$ is a point in the kth subinterval $[x_{k-1}, x_k]$, for $k = 1, 2, \ldots, n$, then the **Riemann sum** of f on $[a, b]$ is $\sum_{k=1}^{n} f(\overline{x}_k)\,\Delta x$. Three cases arise in practice:

- **left Riemann sum**: $\overline{x}_k = a + (k - 1)\,\Delta x$
- **right Riemann sum**: $\overline{x}_k = a + k\,\Delta x$
- **midpoint Riemann sum**: $\overline{x}_k = a + \left(k - \frac{1}{2}\right)\Delta x$, for $k = 1, 2, \ldots, n$

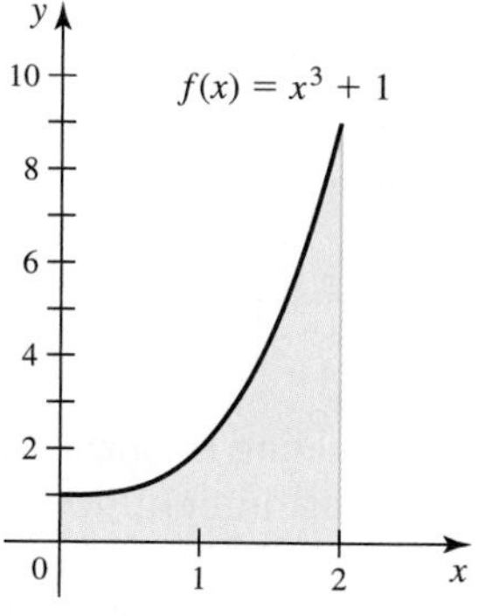

FIGURE 5.15

EXAMPLE 5 Calculating Riemann sums Evaluate the left, right, and midpoint Riemann sums of $f(x) = x^3 + 1$ between $a = 0$ and $b = 2$ using $n = 50$ subintervals. Make a conjecture about the exact area of the region under the curve (Figure 5.15).

SOLUTION With $n = 50$, the length of each subinterval is

$$\Delta x = \frac{b - a}{n} = \frac{2 - 0}{50} = \frac{1}{25} = 0.04.$$

The value of $\overline{x}_k$ for the left Riemann sum is

$$\overline{x}_k = a + (k - 1)\,\Delta x = 0 + 0.04(k - 1) = 0.04k - 0.04,$$

for $k = 1, 2, \ldots, 50$. Therefore, the left Riemann sum, evaluated with a calculator, is

$$\sum_{k=1}^{n} f(\overline{x}_k)\,\Delta x = \sum_{k=1}^{50} f(0.04k - 0.04)0.04 = 5.8416.$$

To evaluate the right Riemann sum, we let $\overline{x}_k = a + k\,\Delta x = 0.04k$ and find that

$$\sum_{k=1}^{n} f(\overline{x}_k)\,\Delta x = \sum_{k=1}^{50} f(0.04k)0.04 = 6.1616.$$

For the midpoint Riemann sum, we let

$$\overline{x}_k = a + \left(k - \frac{1}{2}\right)\Delta x = 0 + 0.04\left(k - \frac{1}{2}\right) = 0.04k - 0.02.$$

The value of the sum is

$$\sum_{k=1}^{n} f(\bar{x}_k)\,\Delta x = \sum_{k=1}^{50} f(0.04k - 0.02)0.04 = 5.9992.$$

Because f is increasing on $[0, 2]$, the left Riemann sum underestimates the area of the shaded region in Figure 5.15, while the right Riemann sum overestimates the area. Therefore, the exact area lies between 5.8416 and 6.1616. The midpoint Riemann sum usually gives the best estimate for increasing or decreasing functions; a reasonable estimate of the area under the curve is 6.

ALTERNATIVE SOLUTION It is worth examining another approach to Example 5 that reappears in Section 5.2. Consider the right Riemann sum given previously:

$$\sum_{k=1}^{n} f(\bar{x}_k)\,\Delta x = \sum_{k=1}^{50} f(0.04k)0.04$$

Rather than evaluating this sum with a calculator, we note that $f(0.04k) = (0.04k)^3 + 1$ and then use the properties of sums:

$$\begin{aligned}\sum_{k=1}^{n} f(\bar{x}_k)\,\Delta x &= \sum_{k=1}^{50} \underbrace{[(0.04k)^3 + 1]}_{f(\bar{x}_k)}\underbrace{0.04}_{\Delta x}\\ &= \sum_{k=1}^{50}(0.04k)^3\,0.04 + \sum_{k=1}^{50} 1\cdot 0.04 \qquad \textstyle\sum(a_k + b_k) = \sum a_k + \sum b_k\\ &= (0.04)^4\sum_{k=1}^{50} k^3 + 0.04\sum_{k=1}^{50} 1 \qquad \textstyle\sum c a_k = c\sum a_k\end{aligned}$$

Using the summation formulas for powers of integers in Theorem 5.1, we find that

$$\sum_{k=1}^{50} 1 = 50 \quad\text{and}\quad \sum_{k=1}^{50} k^3 = \frac{50^2\cdot 51^2}{4}.$$

Substituting the values of these sums into the right Riemann sum, its value is

$$\sum_{k=1}^{50} f(\bar{x}_k)\,\Delta x = \frac{3851}{625} = 6.1616,$$

confirming the result given in the first solution. The idea of evaluating Riemann sums for *arbitrary* values of n is used in Section 5.2, where we evaluate the limit of the Riemann sum as $n \to \infty$.

Related Exercises 35–42 ◀

SECTION 5.1 EXERCISES

Review Questions

1. Suppose an object moves along a line at 15 m/s, for $0 \le t < 2$, and at 25 m/s, for $2 \le t \le 5$, where t is measured in seconds. Sketch the graph of the velocity function and find the displacement of the object, for $0 \le t \le 5$.

2. Given the graph of the positive velocity of an object moving along a line, what is the geometrical representation of its displacement over a time interval $[a, b]$?

3. Suppose you want to approximate the area of the region bounded by the graph of $f(x) = \cos x$ and the x-axis between $x = 0$ and $x = \pi/2$. Explain a possible strategy.

4. Explain how Riemann sum approximations to the area of a region under a curve change as the number of subintervals increases.

5. Suppose the interval $[1, 3]$ is partitioned into $n = 4$ subintervals. What is the subinterval length Δx? List the grid points x_0, x_1, x_2, x_3, x_4. Which points are used for the left, right, and midpoint Riemann sums?

6. Suppose the interval $[2, 6]$ is partitioned into $n = 4$ subintervals with grid points $x_0 = 2$, $x_1 = 3$, $x_2 = 4$, $x_3 = 5$, and $x_4 = 6$. Write but do not evaluate the left, right, and midpoint Riemann sums for $f(x) = x^2$.

7. Does the right Riemann sum underestimate or overestimate the area of the region under the graph of a positive decreasing function? Explain.

8. Does the left Riemann sum underestimate or overestimate the area of the region under the graph of a positive increasing function? Explain.

Basic Skills

9. Approximating displacement The velocity in ft/s of an object moving along a line is given by $v = 3t^2 + 1$ on the interval $0 \le t \le 4$.

a. Divide the interval $[0, 4]$ into $n = 4$ subintervals, $[0, 1]$, $[1, 2]$, $[2, 3]$, and $[3, 4]$. On each subinterval, assume the object moves at a constant velocity equal to the value of v evaluated at the midpoint of the subinterval and use these approximations to estimate the displacement of the object on $[0, 4]$ (see part (a) of the figure).

b. Repeat part (a) for $n = 8$ subintervals (see part (b) of the figure).

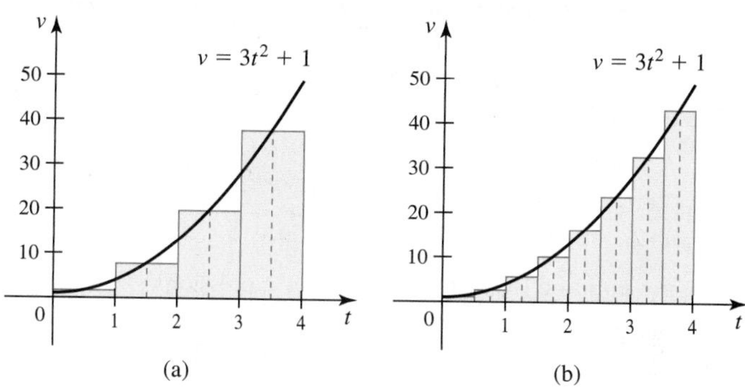

10. Approximating displacement The velocity in ft/s of an object moving along a line is given by $v = \sqrt{10t}$ on the interval $1 \le t \le 7$.

a. Divide the interval $[1, 7]$ into $n = 3$ subintervals, $[1, 3]$, $[3, 5]$, and $[5, 7]$. On each subinterval, assume the object moves at a constant velocity equal to the value of v evaluated at the midpoint of the subinterval and use these approximations to estimate the displacement of the object on $[1, 7]$ (see part (a) of the figure).

b. Repeat part (a) for $n = 6$ subintervals (see part (b) of the figure)).

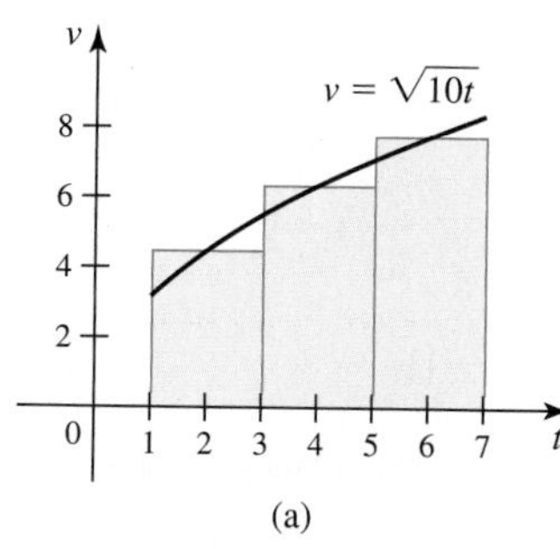

(a)

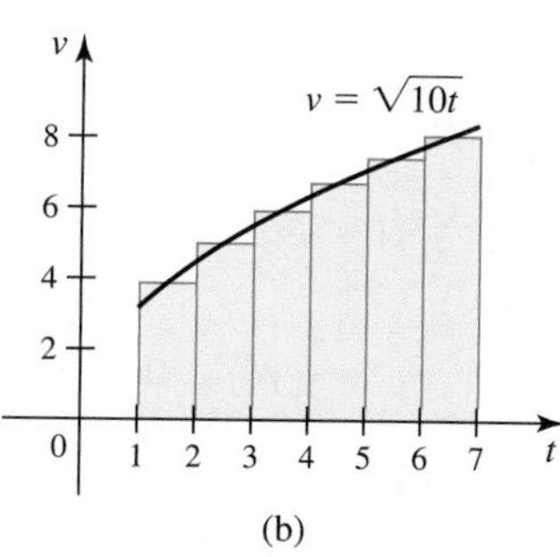

(b)

11–14. Approximating displacement *The velocity of an object is given by the following functions on a specified interval. Approximate the displacement of the object on this interval by subdividing the interval into the indicated number of subintervals. Use the left endpoint of each subinterval to compute the height of the rectangles.*

11. $v = 1/(2t + 1)$ (m/s), for $0 \le t \le 8$; $n = 4$

12. $v = t^2/2 + 4$ (ft/s), for $0 \le t \le 12$; $n = 6$

13. $v = 4\sqrt{t + 1}$ (mi/hr), for $0 \le t \le 15$; $n = 5$

14. $v = (t + 3)/6$ (m/s), for $0 \le t \le 4$; $n = 4$

15–16. Left and right Riemann sums *Use the figures to calculate the left and right Riemann sums for f on the given interval and the given value of n.*

15. $f(x) = x + 1$ on $[1, 6]$; $n = 5$

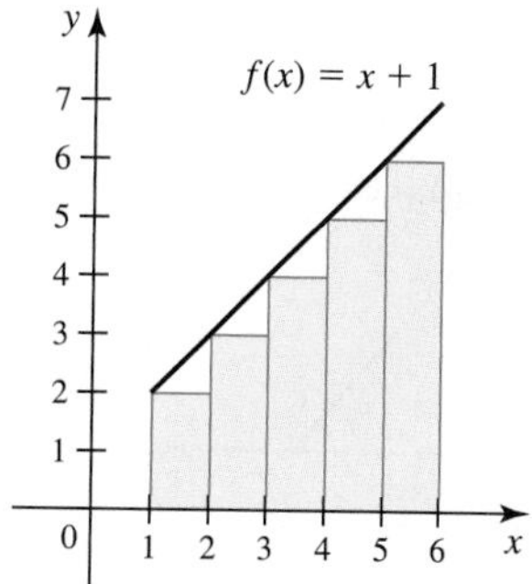

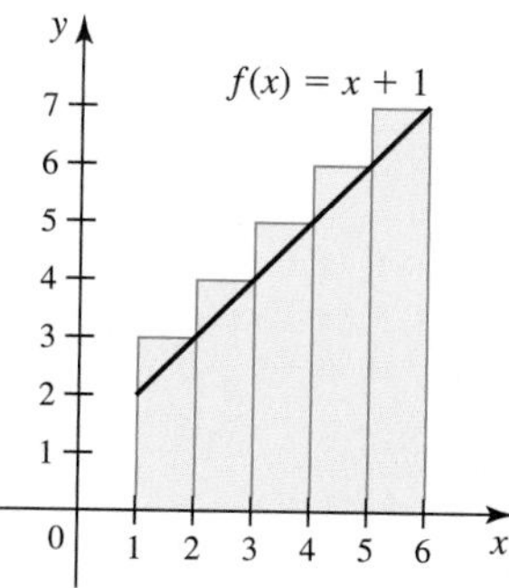

16. $f(x) = \dfrac{1}{x}$ on $[1, 5]$; $n = 4$

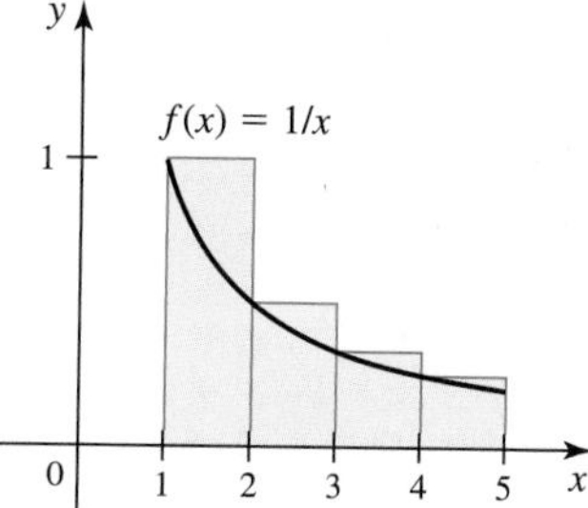

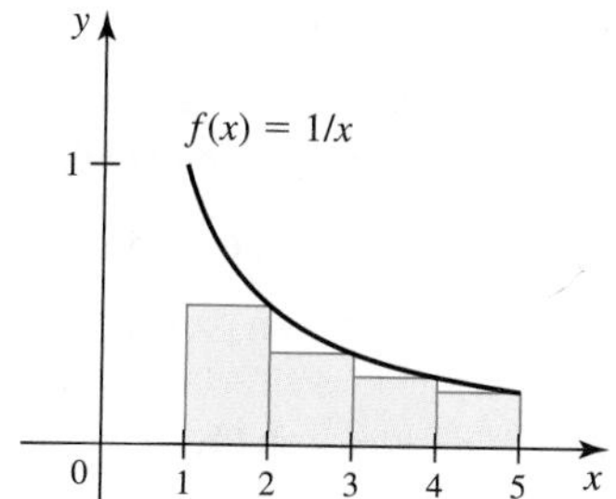

17–20. Left and right Riemann sums *Complete the following steps for the given function, interval, and value of n.*

a. Sketch the graph of the function on the given interval.

b. Calculate Δx and the grid points $x_0, x_1, \ldots, x_n$.

c. Illustrate the left and right Riemann sums. Then determine which Riemann sum underestimates and which sum overestimates the area under the curve.

d. Calculate the left and right Riemann sums.

17. $f(x) = x^2 - 1$ on $[2, 4]$; $n = 4$

18. $f(x) = 2x^2$ on $[1, 6]$; $n = 5$

19. $f(x) = \cos x$ on $[0, \pi/2]$; $n = 4$

20. $f(x) = \cos x$ on $[-\pi/2, \pi/2]$; $n = 6$

21. A midpoint Riemann sum Approximate the area of the region bounded by the graph of $f(x) = 100 - x^2$ and the x-axis on $[0, 10]$ with $n = 5$ subintervals. Use the midpoint of each subinterval to determine the height of each rectangle (see figure).

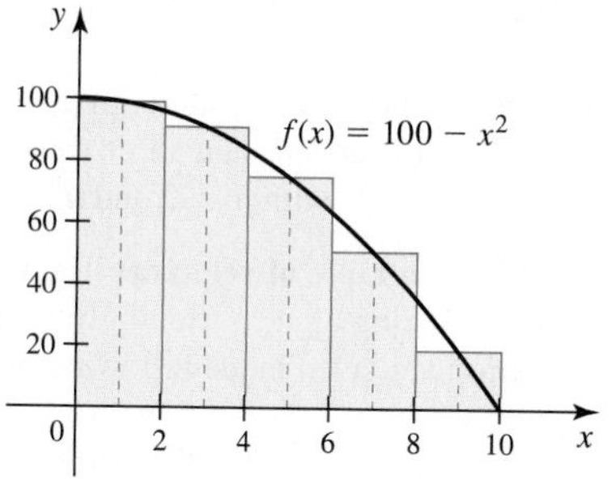

22. A midpoint Riemann sum Approximate the area of the region bounded by the graph of $f(t) = \cos(t/2)$ and the t-axis on $[0, \pi]$ with $n = 4$ subintervals. Use the midpoint of each subinterval to determine the height of each rectangle (see figure).

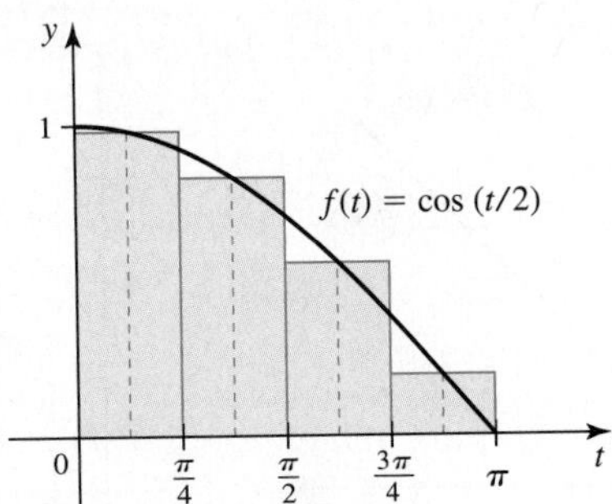

23–26. Midpoint Riemann sums *Complete the following steps for the given function, interval, and value of n.*

a. Sketch the graph of the function on the given interval.
b. Calculate Δx and the grid points $x_0, x_1, \ldots, x_n$.
c. Illustrate the midpoint Riemann sum by sketching the appropriate rectangles.
d. Calculate the midpoint Riemann sum.

23. $f(x) = \sqrt{x}$ on $[1, 3]$; $n = 4$

24. $f(x) = x^2$ on $[0, 4]$; $n = 4$

25. $f(x) = \dfrac{1}{x}$ on $[1, 6]$; $n = 5$

26. $f(x) = 4 - x$ on $[-1, 4]$; $n = 5$

27–28. Riemann sums from tables *Use the tabulated values of f to evaluate the left and right Riemann sums for the given value of n.*

27. $n = 4$; $[0, 2]$

x	0	0.5	1	1.5	2
$f(x)$	5	3	2	1	1

28. $n = 8$; $[1, 5]$

x	1	1.5	2	2.5	3	3.5	4	4.5	5
$f(x)$	0	2	3	2	2	1	0	2	3

29. Displacement from a table of velocities The velocities (in mi/hr) of an automobile moving along a straight highway over a two-hour period are given in the following table.

t (hr)	0	0.25	0.5	0.75	1	1.25	1.5	1.75	2
v (mi/hr)	50	50	60	60	55	65	50	60	70

a. Sketch a smooth curve passing through the data points.
b. Find the midpoint Riemann sum approximation to the displacement on $[0, 2]$ with $n = 2$ and $n = 4$.

30. Displacement from a table of velocities The velocities (in m/s) of an automobile moving along a straight freeway over a four-second period are given in the following table.

t (s)	0	0.5	1	1.5	2	2.5	3	3.5	4
v (m/s)	20	25	30	35	30	30	35	40	40

a. Sketch a smooth curve passing through the data points.
b. Find the midpoint Riemann sum approximation to the displacement on $[0, 4]$ with $n = 2$ and $n = 4$ subintervals.

31. Sigma notation Express the following sums using sigma notation. (Answers are not unique.)

a. $1 + 2 + 3 + 4 + 5$ **b.** $4 + 5 + 6 + 7 + 8 + 9$
c. $1^2 + 2^2 + 3^2 + 4^2$ **d.** $1 + \frac{1}{2} + \frac{1}{3} + \frac{1}{4}$

32. Sigma notation Express the following sums using sigma notation. (Answers are not unique.)

a. $1 + 3 + 5 + 7 + \cdots + 99$
b. $4 + 9 + 14 + \cdots + 44$
c. $3 + 8 + 13 + \cdots + 63$
d. $\dfrac{1}{1 \cdot 2} + \dfrac{1}{2 \cdot 3} + \dfrac{1}{3 \cdot 4} + \cdots + \dfrac{1}{49 \cdot 50}$

33. Sigma notation Evaluate the following expressions.

a. $\sum_{k=1}^{10} k$ **b.** $\sum_{k=1}^{6} (2k + 1)$
c. $\sum_{k=1}^{4} k^2$ **d.** $\sum_{n=1}^{5} (1 + n^2)$
e. $\sum_{m=1}^{3} \dfrac{2m + 2}{3}$ **f.** $\sum_{j=1}^{3} (3j - 4)$
g. $\sum_{p=1}^{5} (2p + p^2)$ **h.** $\sum_{n=0}^{4} \sin \dfrac{n\pi}{2}$

34. Evaluating sums Evaluate the following expressions by two methods.

(i) Use Theorem 5.1. **(ii)** Use a calculator.

a. $\sum_{k=1}^{45} k$ **b.** $\sum_{k=1}^{45} (5k - 1)$ **c.** $\sum_{k=1}^{75} 2k^2$
d. $\sum_{n=1}^{50} (1 + n^2)$ **e.** $\sum_{m=1}^{75} \dfrac{2m + 2}{3}$ **f.** $\sum_{j=1}^{20} (3j - 4)$
g. $\sum_{p=1}^{35} (2p + p^2)$ **h.** $\sum_{n=0}^{40} (n^2 + 3n - 1)$

35–38. Riemann sums for larger values of *n* *Complete the following steps for the given function and interval.*

a. For the given value of n, use sigma notation to write the left, right, and midpoint Riemann sums. Then evaluate each sum using a calculator.
b. Based on the approximations found in part (a), estimate the area of the region bounded by the graph of f and the x-axis on the interval.

35. $f(x) = \sqrt{x}$, for $[0, 4]$; $n = 40$

36. $f(x) = x^2 + 1$, for $[-1, 1]$; $n = 50$

37. $f(x) = x^2 - 1$, for $[2, 7]$; $n = 75$

38. $f(x) = \cos 2x$, for $[0, \pi/4]$; $n = 60$

39–44. Approximating areas with a calculator *Use a calculator and right Riemann sums to approximate the area of the region described. Present your calculations in a table showing the approximations for* $n = 10, 30, 60,$ *and* 80 *subintervals. Comment on whether your approximations appear to approach a limit.*

39. The region bounded by the graph of $f(x) = 4 - x^2$ and the x-axis on the interval $[-2, 2]$

40. The region bounded by the graph of $f(x) = x^2 + 1$ and the x-axis on the interval $[0, 2]$

41. The region bounded by the graph of $f(x) = 2 - 2 \sin x$ and the x-axis on the interval $[-\pi/2, \pi/2]$

42. The region bounded by the graph of $f(x) = \sqrt{x + 1}$ and the x-axis on the interval $[0, 3]$

Further Explorations

43. **Explain why or why not** State whether the following statements are true and give an explanation or counterexample.
    a. Consider the linear function $f(x) = 2x + 5$ and the region bounded by its graph and the x-axis on the interval $[3, 6]$. Suppose the area of this region is approximated using midpoint Riemann sums. Then the approximations give the exact area of the region for any number of subintervals.
    b. A left Riemann sum always overestimates the area of a region bounded by a positive increasing function and the x-axis on an interval $[a, b]$.
    c. For an increasing or decreasing nonconstant function and a given value of n on an interval $[a, b]$, the value of the midpoint Riemann sum always lies between the values of the left and right Riemann sums.

44–45. Riemann sums *Evaluate the Riemann sum for f on the given interval for the given values of n and* $\bar{x}_k$. *Sketch the graph of f and the rectangles used in the Riemann sum.*

44. $f(x) = x^2 + 2$, for $[0, 2]$; $n = 2$; $\bar{x}_1 = 0.25$ and $\bar{x}_2 = 1.75$

45. $f(x) = 1/x$, for $[1, 3]$; $n = 5$; $\bar{x}_1 = 1.1, \bar{x}_2 = 1.5, \bar{x}_3 = 2,$ $\bar{x}_4 = 2.3,$ and $\bar{x}_5 = 3$

46. **Riemann sums for a semicircle** Let $f(x) = \sqrt{1 - x^2}$.
    a. Show that the graph of f is the upper half of a circle of radius 1 centered at the origin.
    b. Estimate the area between the graph of f and the x-axis on the interval $[-1, 1]$ using a midpoint Riemann sum with $n = 25$.
    c. Repeat part (b) using $n = 75$ rectangles.
    d. What happens to the midpoint Riemann sums on $[-1, 1]$ as $n \to \infty$?

47–50. Sigma notation for Riemann sums *Use sigma notation to write the following Riemann sums. Then evaluate each Riemann sum using Theorem 5.1 or a calculator.*

47. The right Riemann sum for $f(x) = x + 1$ on $[0, 4]$ with $n = 50$

48. The left Riemann sum for $f(x) = 3/x$ on $[1, 3]$ with $n = 30$

49. The midpoint Riemann sum for $f(x) = x^3$ on $[3, 11]$ with $n = 32$

50. The midpoint Riemann sum for $f(x) = 1 + \cos(\pi x)$ on $[0, 2]$ with $n = 50$

51–54. Identifying Riemann sums *Fill in the blanks with right, left, or midpoint; an interval; and a value of n. In some cases, more than one answer may work.*

51. $\sum_{k=1}^{4} f(1 + k) \cdot 1$ is a ____ Riemann sum for f on the interval [_, _] with $n =$ ____

52. $\sum_{k=1}^{4} f(2 + k) \cdot 1$ is a ____ Riemann sum for f on the interval [_, _] with $n =$ ____

53. $\sum_{k=1}^{4} f(1.5 + k) \cdot 1$ is a ____ Riemann sum for f on the interval [_, _] with $n =$ ____

54. $\sum_{k=1}^{8} f\left(1.5 + \frac{k}{2}\right) \cdot \frac{1}{2}$ is a ____ Riemann sum for f on the interval [_, _] with $n =$ ____

55. **Approximating areas** Estimate the area of the region bounded by the graph of $f(x) = x^2 + 2$ and the x-axis on $[0, 2]$ in the following ways.
    a. Divide $[0, 2]$ into $n = 4$ subintervals and approximate the area of the region using a left Riemann sum. Illustrate the solution geometrically.
    b. Divide $[0, 2]$ into $n = 4$ subintervals and approximate the area of the region using a midpoint Riemann sum. Illustrate the solution geometrically.
    c. Divide $[0, 2]$ into $n = 4$ subintervals and approximate the area of the region using a right Riemann sum. Illustrate the solution geometrically.

56. **Approximating area from a graph** Approximate the area of the region bounded by the graph (see figure) and the x-axis by dividing the interval $[0, 6]$ into $n = 3$ subintervals. Then use left and right Riemann sums to obtain two different approximations.

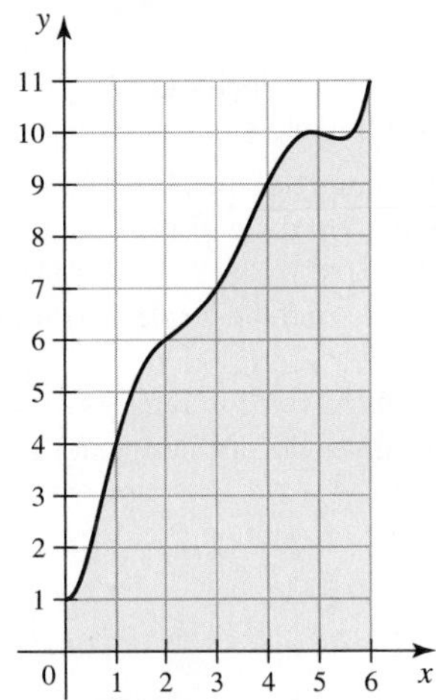

57. Approximating area from a graph Approximate the area of the region bounded by the graph (see figure) and the x-axis by dividing the interval $[1, 7]$ into $n = 6$ subintervals. Then use left and right Riemann sums to obtain two different approximations.

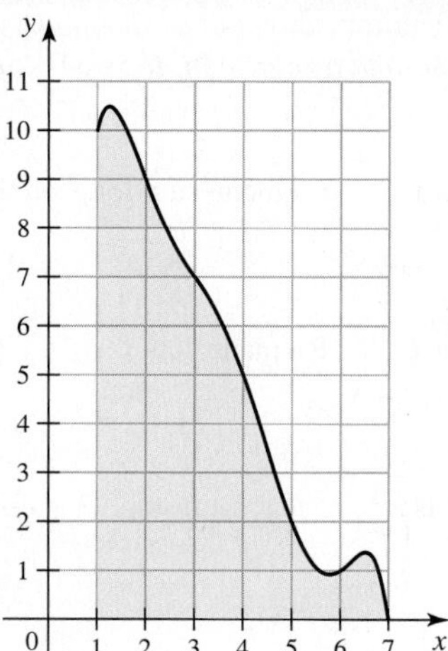

Applications

58. Displacement from a velocity graph Consider the velocity function for an object moving along a line (see figure).

a. Describe the motion of the object over the interval $[0, 6]$.

b. Use geometry to find the displacement of the object between $t = 0$ and $t = 3$.

c. Use geometry to find the displacement of the object between $t = 3$ and $t = 5$.

d. Assuming that the velocity remains 30 m/s for $t \geq 4$, find the function that gives the displacement between $t = 0$ and any time $t \geq 5$.

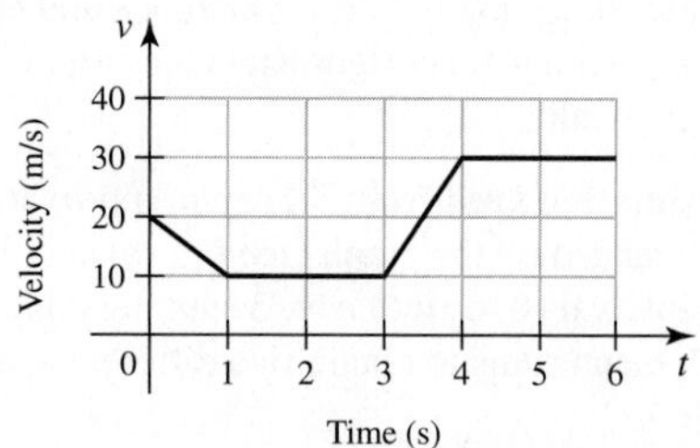

59. Displacement from a velocity graph Consider the velocity function for an object moving along a line (see figure).

a. Describe the motion of the object over the interval $[0, 6]$.

b. Use geometry to find the displacement of the object between $t = 0$ and $t = 2$.

c. Use geometry to find the displacement of the object between $t = 2$ and $t = 5$.

d. Assuming that the velocity remains 10 m/s for $t \geq 5$, find the function that gives the displacement between $t = 0$ and any time $t \geq 5$.

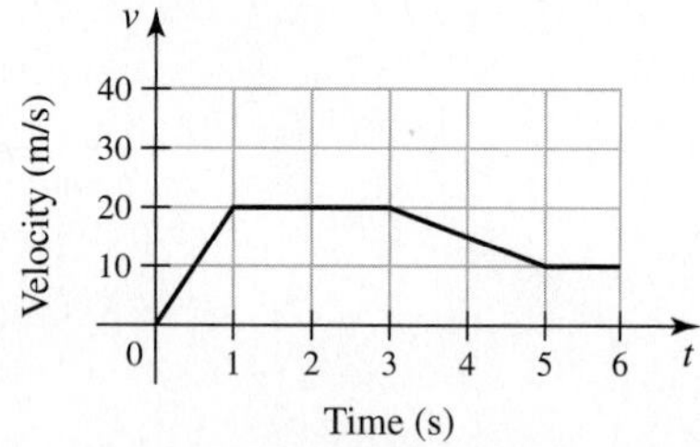

60. Flow rates Suppose a gauge at the outflow of a reservoir measures the flow rate of water in units of ft^3/hr. In Chapter 6 we show that the total amount of water that flows out of the reservoir is the area under the flow rate curve. Consider the flow rate function shown in the figure.

a. Find the amount of water (in units of ft^3) that flows out of the reservoir over the interval $[0, 4]$.

b. Find the amount of water that flows out of the reservoir over the interval $[8, 10]$.

c. Does more water flow out of the reservoir over the interval $[0, 4]$ or $[4, 6]$?

d. Show that the units of your answer are consistent with the units of the variables on the axes.

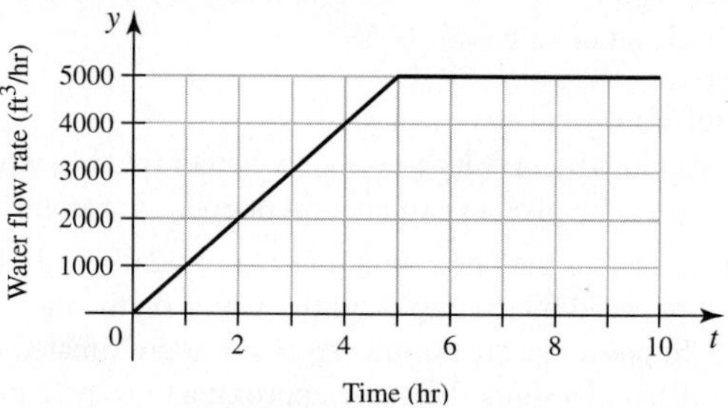

61. Mass from density A thin 10-cm rod is made of an alloy whose density varies along its length according to the function shown in the figure. Assume density is measured in units of g/cm. In Chapter 6, we show that the mass of the rod is the area under the density curve.

a. Find the mass of the left half of the rod ($0 \leq x \leq 5$).

b. Find the mass of the right half of the rod ($5 \leq x \leq 10$).

c. Find the mass of the entire rod ($0 \leq x \leq 10$).

d. Estimate the point along the rod at which it will balance (called the center of mass).

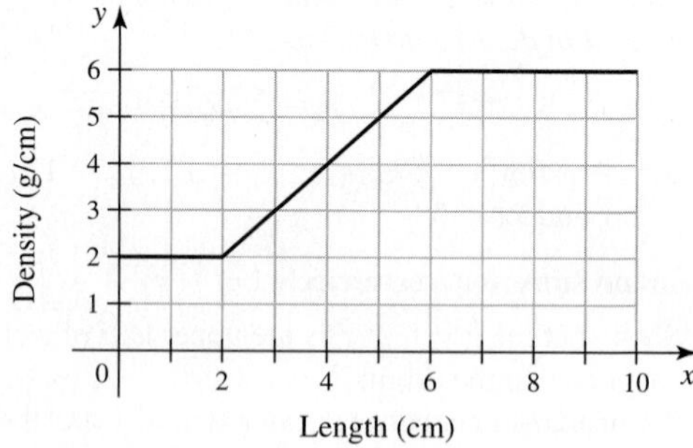

62–63. Displacement from velocity *The following functions describe the velocity of a car (in mi/hr) moving along a straight highway for a 3-hr interval. In each case, find the function that gives the displacement of the car over the interval $[0, t]$, where $0 \leq t \leq 3$.*

62. $v(t) = \begin{cases} 40 & \text{if } 0 \leq t \leq 1.5 \\ 50 & \text{if } 1.5 < t \leq 3 \end{cases}$

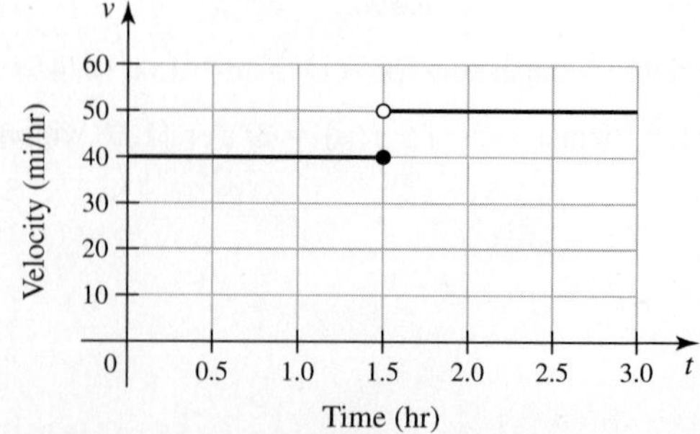

63. $v(t) = \begin{cases} 30 & \text{if } 0 \le t \le 2 \\ 50 & \text{if } 2 < t \le 2.5 \\ 44 & \text{if } 2.5 < t \le 3 \end{cases}$

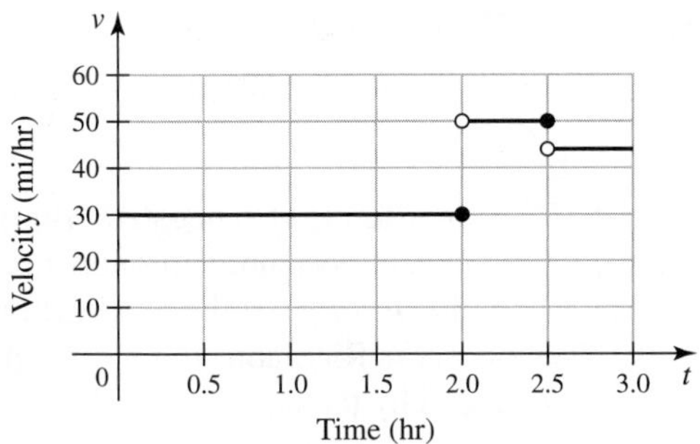

64–67. Functions with absolute value *Use a calculator and the method of your choice to approximate the area of the following regions. Present your calculations in a table, showing approximations using* $n = 16, 32,$ *and* 64 *subintervals. Comment on whether your approximations appear to approach a limit.*

64. The region bounded by the graph of $f(x) = |25 - x^2|$ and the x-axis on the interval $[0, 10]$

65. The region bounded by the graph of $f(x) = |x(x^2 - 1)|$ and the x-axis on the interval $[-1, 1]$

66. The region bounded by the graph of $f(x) = |\cos 2x|$ and the x-axis on the interval $[0, \pi]$

67. The region bounded by the graph of $f(x) = |1 - x^3|$ and the x-axis on the interval $[-1, 2]$

Additional Exercises

68. **Riemann sums for constant functions** Let $f(x) = c$, where $c > 0$, be a constant function on $[a, b]$. Prove that any Riemann sum for any value of n gives the exact area of the region between the graph of f and the x-axis on $[a, b]$.

69. **Riemann sums for linear functions** Assume that the linear function $f(x) = mx + c$ is positive on the interval $[a, b]$. Prove that the midpoint Riemann sum with any value of n gives the exact area of the region between the graph of f and the x-axis on $[a, b]$.

QUICK CHECK ANSWERS

1. 45 mi **2.** 0.25, 0.125, 7.875 **3.** $\Delta x = 2$; $\{1, 3, 5, 7, 9\}$ **4.** The left sum overestimates the area.

5.2 Definite Integrals

We introduced Riemann sums in Section 5.1 as a way to approximate the area of a region bounded by a curve $y = f(x)$ and the x-axis on an interval $[a, b]$. In that discussion, we assumed f to be nonnegative on the interval. Our next task is to discover the geometric meaning of Riemann sums when f is negative on some or all of $[a, b]$. Once this matter is settled, we proceed to the main event of this section, which is to define the *definite integral*. With definite integrals, the approximations given by Riemann sums become exact.

Net Area

How do we interpret Riemann sums when f is negative at some or all points of $[a, b]$? The answer follows directly from the Riemann sum definition.

EXAMPLE 1 Interpreting Riemann Sums Evaluate and interpret the following Riemann sums for $f(x) = 1 - x^2$ on the interval $[a, b]$ with n equally spaced subintervals.

a. A midpoint Riemann sum with $[a, b] = [1, 3]$ and $n = 4$

b. A left Riemann sum with $[a, b] = [0, 3]$ and $n = 6$

SOLUTION

a. The length of each subinterval is $\Delta x = \dfrac{b - a}{n} = \dfrac{3 - 1}{4} = 0.5$. So the grid points are

$$x_0 = 1, \quad x_1 = 1.5, \quad x_2 = 2, \quad x_3 = 2.5, \quad x_4 = 3.$$

To compute the midpoint Riemann sum, we evaluate f at the midpoints of the subintervals, which are

$$\bar{x}_1 = 1.25, \quad \bar{x}_2 = 1.75, \quad \bar{x}_3 = 2.25, \quad \bar{x}_4 = 2.75.$$

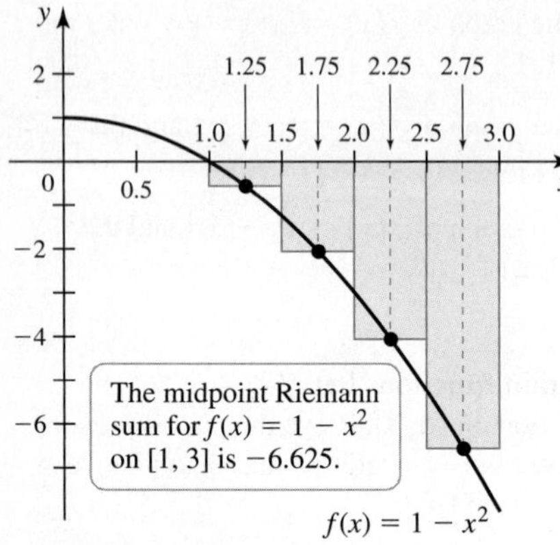

1.25 1.75 2.25 2.75
1.0 1.5 2.0 2.5 3.0
0.5
The midpoint Riemann sum for $f(x) = 1 - x^2$ on [1, 3] is -6.625.
$f(x) = 1 - x^2$

FIGURE 5.16

The resulting midpoint Riemann sum is

$$\begin{aligned}\sum_{k=1}^{n} f(\overline{x}_k)\,\Delta x &= \sum_{k=1}^{4} f(\overline{x}_k)(0.5)\\ &= f(1.25)(0.5) + f(1.75)(0.5) + f(2.25)(0.5) + f(2.75)(0.5)\\ &= (-0.5625 - 2.0625 - 4.0625 - 6.5625)0.5\\ &= -6.625.\end{aligned}$$

All values of $f(\overline{x}_k)$ are negative, so the Riemann sum is also negative. Because area is always a nonnegative quantity, this Riemann sum does not approximate an area. Notice, however, that the values of $f(\overline{x}_k)$ are the *negative* of the heights of the corresponding rectangles (Figure 5.16). Therefore, the Riemann sum is an approximation to the *negative* of the area of the region bounded by the curve.

b. The length of each subinterval is $\Delta x = \dfrac{b - a}{n} = \dfrac{3 - 0}{6} = 0.5$ and the grid points are

$$x_0 = 0, \quad x_1 = 0.5, \quad x_2 = 1, \quad x_3 = 1.5, \quad x_4 = 2, \quad x_5 = 2.5, \quad x_6 = 3.$$

To calculate the left Riemann sum, we set $\overline{x}_1, \overline{x}_2, \ldots, \overline{x}_6$ equal to the left endpoints of the subintervals:

$$\overline{x}_1 = 0, \quad \overline{x}_2 = 0.5, \quad \overline{x}_3 = 1, \quad \overline{x}_4 = 1.5, \quad \overline{x}_5 = 2, \quad \overline{x}_6 = 2.5$$

The resulting left Riemann sum is

$$\begin{aligned}\sum_{k=1}^{n} f(\overline{x}_k)\,\Delta x &= \sum_{k=1}^{6} f(\overline{x}_k)(0.5)\\ &= (\underbrace{f(0) + f(0.5) + f(1)}_{\text{nonnegative contribution}} + \underbrace{f(1.5) + f(2) + f(2.5)}_{\text{negative contribution}})\,0.5\\ &= (1 + 0.75 + 0 - 1.25 - 3 - 5.25)\,0.5\\ &= -3.875.\end{aligned}$$

In this case the values of $f(\overline{x}_k)$ are nonnegative for $k = 1, 2,$ and 3, and negative for $k = 4, 5,$ and 6 (Figure 5.17). Where f is positive, we get positive contributions to the Riemann sum and where f is negative, we get negative contributions to the sum.

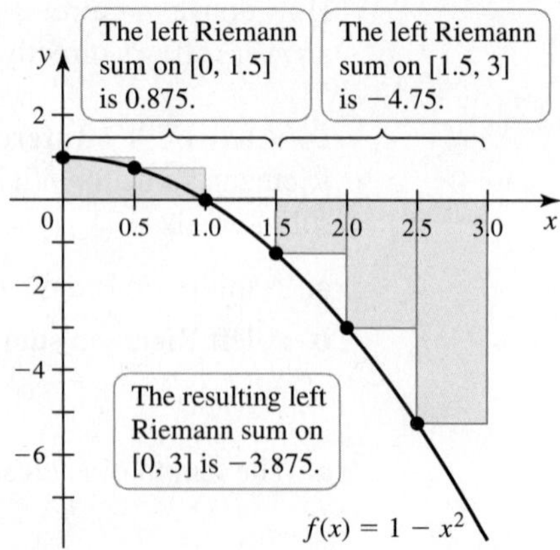

The left Riemann sum on [0, 1.5] is 0.875.
The left Riemann sum on [1.5, 3] is -4.75.
0.5 1.0 1.5 2.0 2.5 3.0
The resulting left Riemann sum on [0, 3] is -3.875.
$f(x) = 1 - x^2$

FIGURE 5.17

Related Exercises 11–18◄

Let's recap what was learned in Example 1. On intervals where $f(x) < 0$, Riemann sums approximate the *negative* of the area of the region bounded by the curve (Figure 5.18).

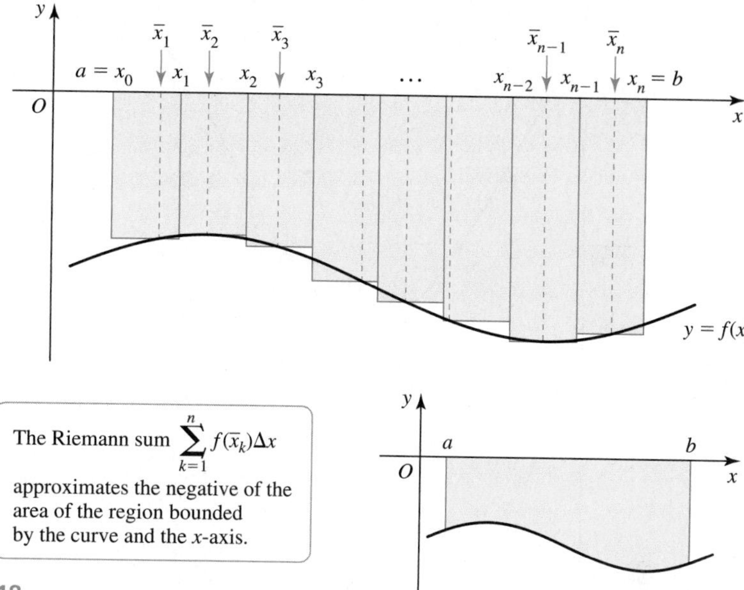

FIGURE 5.18

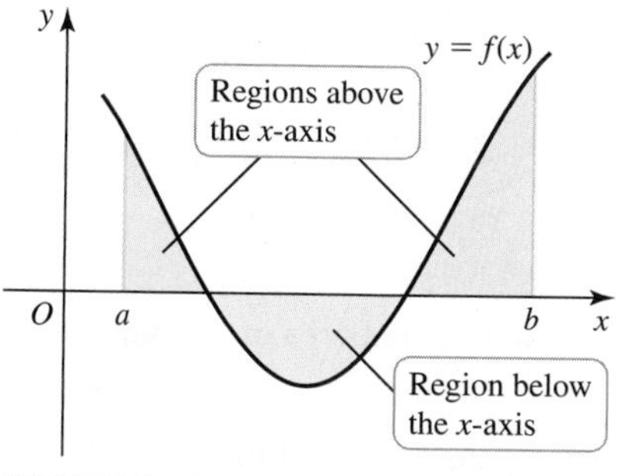

FIGURE 5.19

In the more general case that f is positive on only part of $[a, b]$, we get positive contributions to the sum where f is positive and negative contributions to the sum where f is negative. In this case, Riemann sums approximate the area of the regions that lie above the x-axis *minus* the area of the regions that lie *below* the x-axis (Figure 5.19). This difference between the positive and negative contributions is called the *net area*; it can be positive, negative, or zero.

QUICK CHECK 1 Suppose $f(x) = -5$. What is the net area of the region bounded by the graph of f and the x-axis on the interval $[1, 5]$? Make a sketch of the function and the region.

> Net area suggests the difference between positive and negative contributions much like net change or net profit. Some texts use the term **signed area** for net area.

QUICK CHECK 2 Sketch a function f that is continuous and positive over the interval $[0, 1]$, and continuous and negative over the interval $[1, 2]$, such that the net area of the region bounded by the graph of f and the x-axis on $[0, 2]$ is zero.

DEFINITION Net Area

Consider the region R bounded by the graph of a continuous function f and the x-axis between $x = a$ and $x = b$. The **net area** of R is the area of the parts of R that lie above the x-axis *minus* the area of the parts of R that lie below the x-axis on $[a, b]$.

The Definite Integral

Riemann sums for f on $[a, b]$ give *approximations* to the net area of the region bounded by the graph of f and the x-axis between $x = a$ and $x = b$. How can we make these approximations exact? If f is continuous on $[a, b]$, it is reasonable to expect the Riemann sum approximations to approach the exact value of the net area as the number of subintervals $n \to \infty$ and as the length of the subintervals $\Delta x \to 0$ (Figure 5.20). In terms of limits, we write

$$\text{net area} = \lim_{n\to\infty} \sum_{k=1}^{n} f(\bar{x}_k)\,\Delta x.$$

The Riemann sums we have used so far involve regular partitions in which the subintervals have the same length Δx.

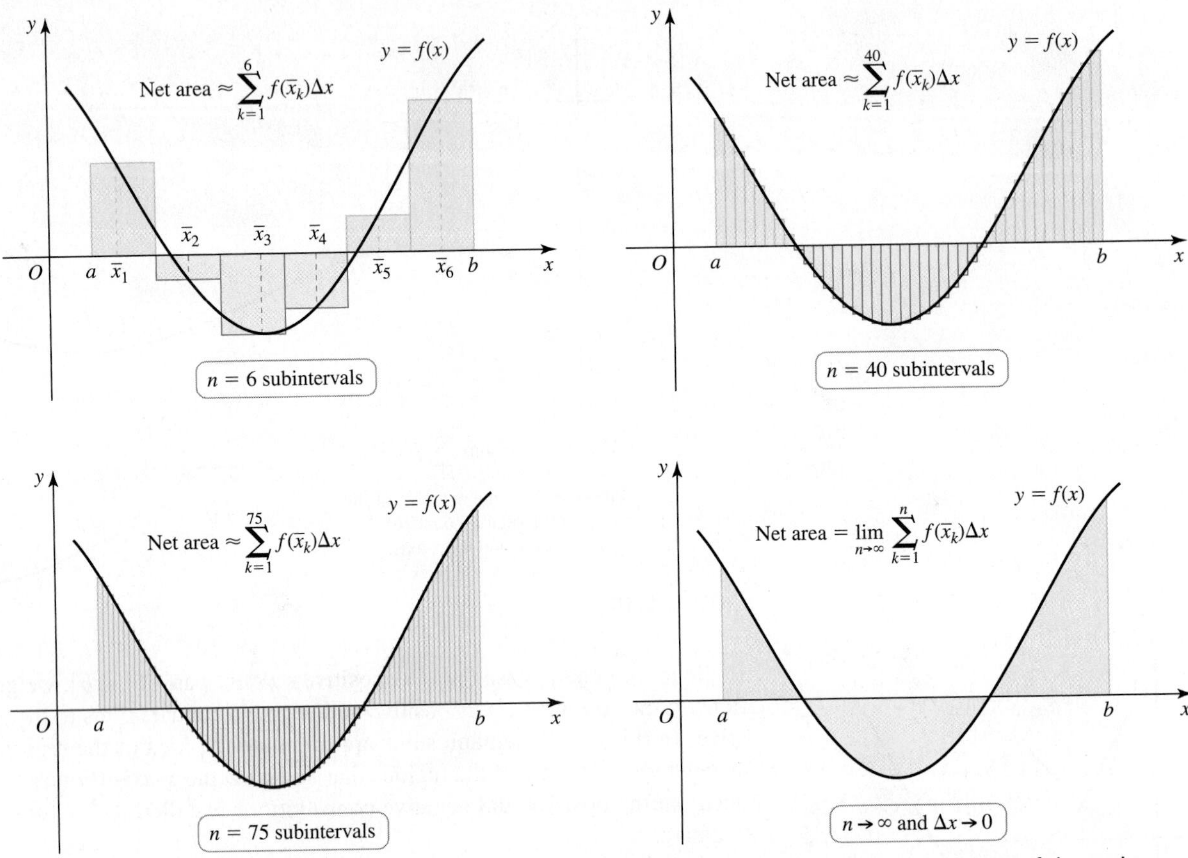

FIGURE 5.20. As the number of subintervals n increases, the Riemann sum approaches the net area of the region between the curve $y = f(x)$ and the x-axis on $[a, b]$.

We now introduce partitions of $[a, b]$ in which the lengths of the subintervals are not necessarily equal. A **general partition** of $[a, b]$ consists of the n subintervals

$$[x_0, x_1], [x_1, x_2], \ldots, [x_{n-1}, x_n],$$

where $x_0 = a$ and $x_n = b$. The length of the kth subinterval is $\Delta x_k = x_k - x_{k-1}$, for $k = 1, \ldots, n$. We let $\bar{x}_k$ be any point in the subinterval $[x_{k-1}, x_k]$. This general partition is used to define the *general Riemann sum*.

DEFINITION General Riemann Sum

Suppose $[x_0, x_1], [x_1, x_2], \ldots, [x_{n-1}, x_n]$ are subintervals of $[a, b]$ with

$$a = x_0 < x_1 < x_2 < \cdots < x_{n-1} < x_n = b.$$

Let Δx_k be the length of the subinterval $[x_{k-1}, x_k]$ and let $\bar{x}_k$ be any point in $[x_{k-1}, x_k]$, for $k = 1, 2, \ldots, n$.

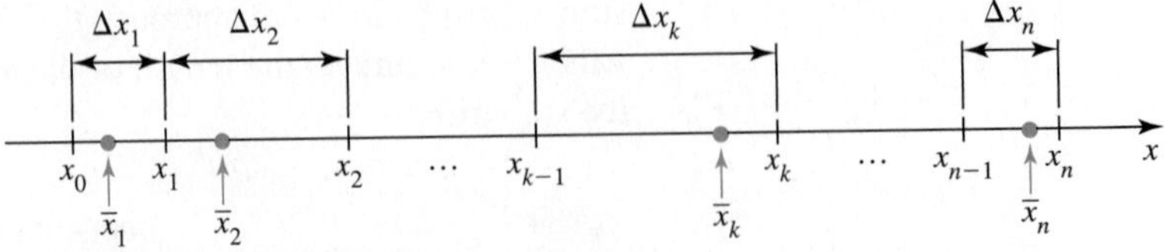

If f is defined on $[a, b]$, the sum

$$\sum_{k=1}^{n} f(\bar{x}_k)\Delta x_k = f(\bar{x}_1)\Delta x_1 + f(\bar{x}_2)\Delta x_2 + \cdots + f(\bar{x}_n)\Delta x_n$$

is called a **general Riemann sum for f on $[a, b]$**.

Now consider the limit of $\sum_{k=1}^{n} f(\overline{x}_k)\,\Delta x_k$ as $n \to \infty$ and as *all* of the $\Delta x_k \to 0$. We let Δ denote the largest value of Δx_k; that is, $\Delta = \max\{\Delta x_1, \Delta x_2, \ldots, \Delta x_n\}$. Observe that if $\Delta \to 0$, then $\Delta x_k \to 0$, for $k = 1, 2, \ldots, n$. In order for the limit $\lim_{\Delta \to 0} \sum_{k=1}^{n} f(\overline{x}_k)\,\Delta x_k$ to exist, it must have the same value over all general partitions of $[a, b]$ and for all choices of $\overline{x}_k$ on a partition.

> Note that letting $\Delta \to 0$ forces all $\Delta x_k \to 0$, which forces $n \to \infty$. Therefore, it suffices to write $\Delta \to 0$ in the limit.

> It is imperative to remember that the indefinite integral $\int f(x)\,dx$ is a family of functions of x, while the definite integral $\int_a^b f(x)\,dx$ is a real number (the net area of a region).

DEFINITION Definite Integral

A function f defined on $[a, b]$ is **integrable** on $[a, b]$ if $\lim_{\Delta \to 0} \sum_{k=1}^{n} f(\overline{x}_k)\,\Delta x_k$ exists and is unique over all partitions of $[a, b]$ and all choices of $\overline{x}_k$ on a partition. This limit is the **definite integral of *f* from *a* to *b***, which we write

$$\int_a^b f(x)\,dx = \lim_{\Delta \to 0} \sum_{k=1}^{n} f(\overline{x}_k)\,\Delta x_k.$$

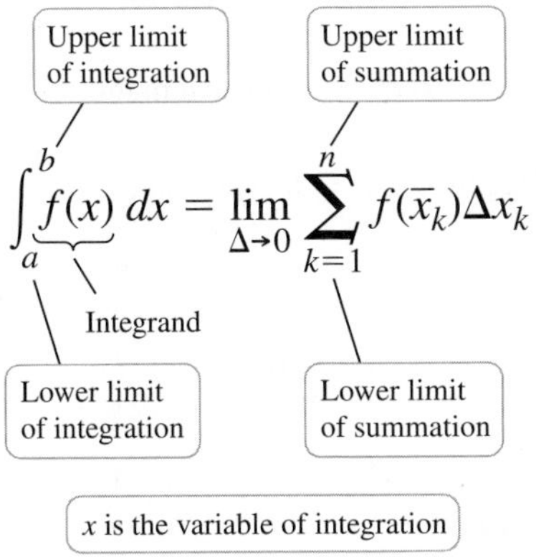

Upper limit of integration; Upper limit of summation

$$\int_a^b f(x)\,dx = \lim_{\Delta \to 0} \sum_{k=1}^{n} f(\overline{x}_k)\Delta x_k$$

Integrand; Lower limit of integration; Lower limit of summation

x is the variable of integration

FIGURE 5.21

Notation The notation for the definite integral requires some explanation. There is a direct match between the notation on either side of the equation in the definition (Figure 5.21). In the limit as $\Delta \to 0$, the finite sum, denoted Σ, becomes a sum with an infinite number of terms, denoted $\int$. The integral sign $\int$ is an elongated S for sum. In this limit, the lengths of the subintervals Δx_k are replaced by dx. The **limits of integration**, a and b, and the limits of summation also match: The lower limit in the sum, $k = 1$, corresponds to the left endpoint of the interval, $x = a$, and the upper limit in the sum, $k = n$, corresponds to the right endpoint of the interval, $x = b$. The function under the integral sign is called the **integrand**. Finally, the factor dx in the integral is an essential part of the notation; it tells us that the **variable of integration** is x.

The variable of integration is a dummy variable that is completely internal to the integral. It does not matter what the variable of integration is called, as long as it does not conflict with other variables that are in use. Therefore, the integrals in Figure 5.22 all have the same meaning.

> For Leibniz, who introduced this notation in 1675, dx represented the width of an infinitesimally thin rectangle and $f(x)\,dx$ represented the area of such a rectangle. He used $\int_a^b f(x)\,dx$ to denote the sum of all these areas from a to b.

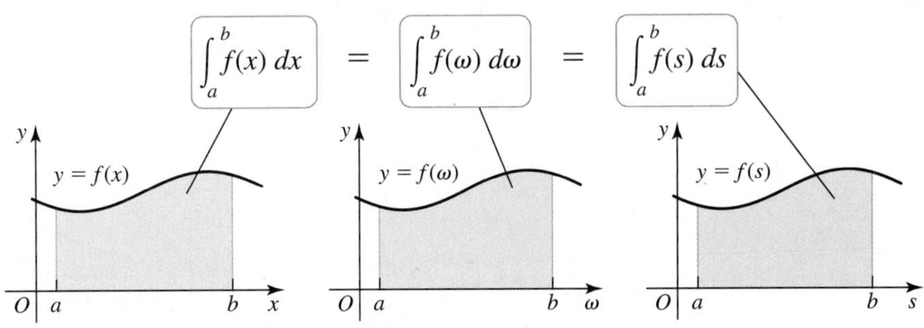

FIGURE 5.22

The strategy of slicing a region into smaller parts, summing the results from the parts, and taking a limit is used repeatedly in calculus and its applications. We call this strategy the **slice-and-sum method**. It often results in a Riemann sum whose limit is a definite integral.

Evaluating Definite Integrals

Most of the functions encountered in this text are integrable on some interval (see Exercise 79 for an exception). In fact, if f is continuous on $[a, b]$ or if f is bounded on $[a, b]$ with a finite number of discontinuities, then f is integrable on $[a, b]$. The proof of this result goes beyond the scope of this text.

> A function f is bounded on an interval I if there is a number M such that $|f(x)| < M$ for all x in I.

> **THEOREM 5.2 Integrable Functions**
> If f is continuous on $[a, b]$ or bounded on $[a, b]$ with a finite number of discontinuities, then f is integrable on $[a, b]$.

Net area $= \int_a^b f(x)\,dx$
= area above x-axis (Regions 1 and 3)
− area below x-axis (Region 2)

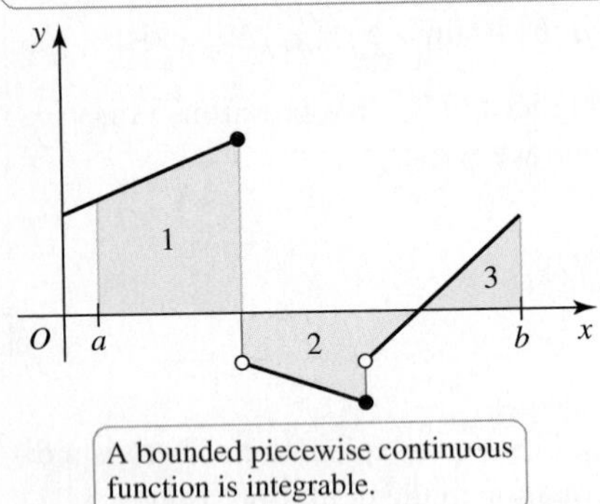

FIGURE 5.23

When f is continuous on $[a, b]$, we have seen that the definite integral $\int_a^b f(x)\,dx$ is the net area of the region bounded by the graph of f and the x-axis on $[a, b]$. Figure 5.23 illustrates how the idea of net area carries over to piecewise continuous functions.

QUICK CHECK 3 Graph $f(x) = x$ and use geometry to evaluate $\int_{-1}^{1} x\,dx$. ◄

EXAMPLE 2 Identifying the limit of a sum Assume that

$$\lim_{\Delta \to 0} \sum_{k=1}^{n} (3\bar{x}_k^2 + 2\bar{x}_k + 1)\,\Delta x_k$$

is the limit of a Riemann sum for a function f on $[1, 3]$. Identify the function f and express the limit as a definite integral. What does the definite integral represent geometrically?

SOLUTION By comparing the sum $\sum_{k=1}^{n} (3\bar{x}_k^2 + 2\bar{x}_k + 1)\,\Delta x_k$ to the general Riemann sum $\sum_{k=1}^{n} f(\bar{x}_k)\,\Delta x_k$, we see that $f(x) = 3x^2 + 2x + 1$. Because f is a polynomial, it is continuous and integrable on $[1, 3]$. It follows that

$$\lim_{\Delta \to 0} \sum_{k=1}^{n} (3\bar{x}_k^2 + 2\bar{x}_k + 1)\,\Delta x_k = \int_1^3 (3x^2 + 2x + 1)\,dx.$$

Because f is positive on $[1, 3]$, the definite integral $\int_1^3 (3x^2 + 2x + 1)\,dx$ is the area of the region bounded by the curve $y = 3x^2 + 2x + 1$ and the x-axis on $[1, 3]$ (Figure 5.24).

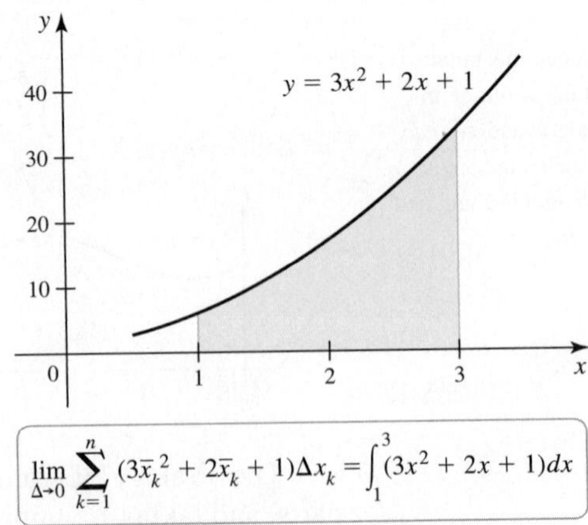

FIGURE 5.24

Related Exercises 19–22 ◄

EXAMPLE 3 Evaluating definite integrals using geometry Use familiar area formulas to evaluate the following definite integrals.

a. $\int_2^4 (2x + 3)\,dx$ **b.** $\int_1^6 (2x - 6)\,dx$ **c.** $\int_3^4 \sqrt{1 - (x - 3)^2}\,dx$

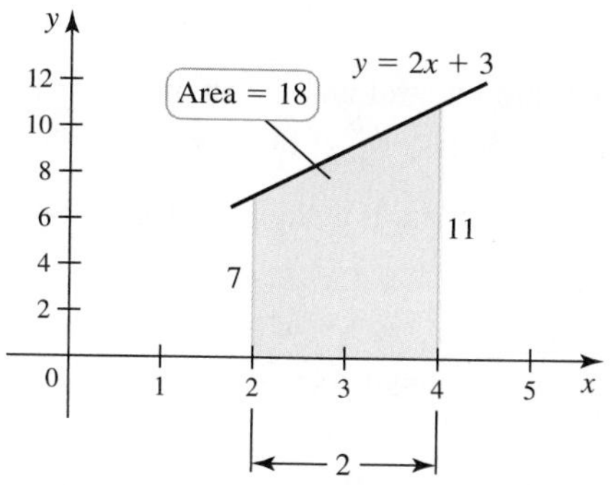

FIGURE 5.25

SOLUTION To evaluate these definite integrals geometrically, a sketch of the corresponding region is essential.

a. The definite integral $\int_2^4 (2x + 3)\,dx$ is the area of the trapezoid bounded by the x-axis and the line $y = 2x + 3$ from $x = 2$ to $x = 4$ (Figure 5.25). The width of its base is 2 and the lengths of its two parallel sides are $f(2) = 7$ and $f(4) = 11$. Using the area formula for a trapezoid we have

$$\int_2^4 (2x + 3)\,dx = \frac{1}{2}\cdot 2(11 + 7) = 18.$$

b. A sketch shows that the regions bounded by the line $y = 2x - 6$ and the x-axis are triangles (Figure 5.26). The area of the triangle on the interval $[1, 3]$ is $\frac{1}{2}\cdot 2\cdot 4 = 4$. Similarly, the area of the triangle on $[3, 6]$ is $\frac{1}{2}\cdot 3\cdot 6 = 9$. The definite integral is the net area of the entire region, which is the area of the triangle above the x-axis minus the area of the triangle below the x-axis:

$$\int_1^6 (2x - 6)\,dx = \text{net area} = 9 - 4 = 5$$

A trapezoid and its area. When $a = 0$ or $b = 0$, we get the area of a triangle. When $a = b$, we get the area of a rectangle.

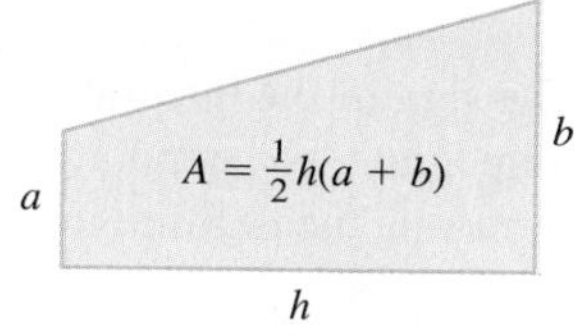

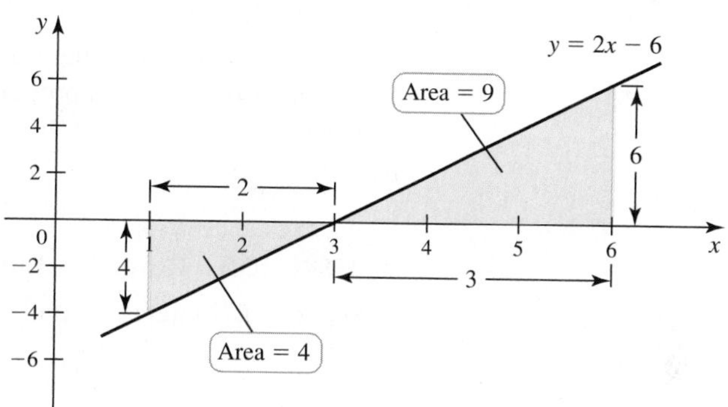

FIGURE 5.26

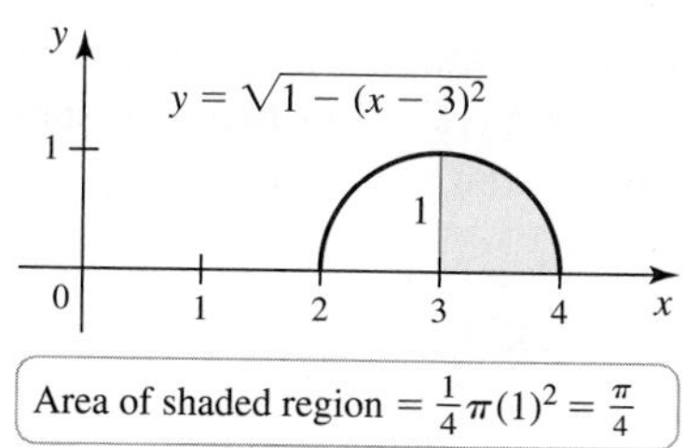

FIGURE 5.27

c. We first let $y = \sqrt{1 - (x - 3)^2}$ and square both sides of the equation. The result is $(x - 3)^2 + y^2 = 1$, whose graph is a circle of radius 1 centered at $(3, 0)$. Because $y \geq 0$, the graph of $y = \sqrt{1 - (x - 3)^2}$ is the upper half of the circle. It follows that the integral $\int_3^4 \sqrt{1 - (x - 3)^2}\,dx$ is the area of a quarter circle of radius 1 (Figure 5.27). Therefore,

$$\int_3^4 \sqrt{1 - (x - 3)^2}\,dx = \frac{1}{4}\pi(1)^2 = \frac{\pi}{4}.$$

Related Exercises 23–30

QUICK CHECK 4 Let $f(x) = 5$ and use geometry to evaluate $\int_1^3 f(x)\,dx$. What is the value of $\int_a^b c\,dx$, where c is a real number?

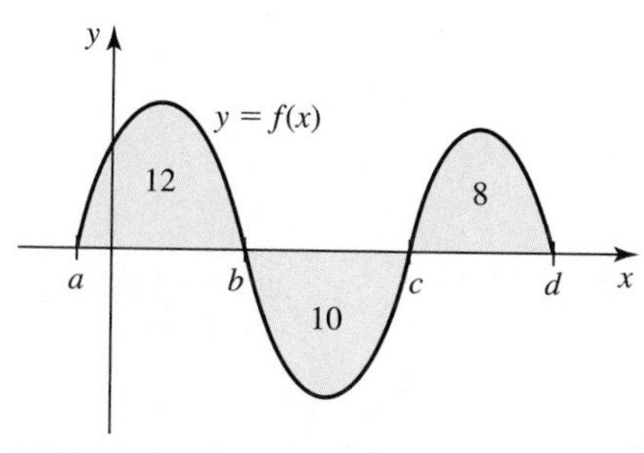

FIGURE 5.28

EXAMPLE 4 Definite integrals from graphs

Figure 5.28 shows the graph of a function f with the areas of the regions bounded by its graph and the x-axis given. Find the values of the following definite integrals.

a. $\displaystyle\int_a^b f(x)\,dx$ **b.** $\displaystyle\int_b^c f(x)\,dx$ **c.** $\displaystyle\int_a^c f(x)\,dx$ **d.** $\displaystyle\int_b^d f(x)\,dx$

SOLUTION

a. Because f is positive on $[a, b]$, the value of the definite integral is the area of the region between the graph and the x-axis on $[a, b]$; that is, $\int_a^b f(x)\,dx = 12$.

b. Because f is negative on $[b, c]$, the value of the definite integral is the negative of the area of the corresponding region; that is, $\int_b^c f(x)\,dx = -10$.

c. The value of the definite integral is the area of the region on $[a, b]$ (where f is positive) minus the area of the region on $[b, c]$ (where f is negative). Therefore, $\int_a^c f(x)\,dx = 12 - 10 = 2$.

d. Reasoning as in part (c), we have $\int_b^d f(x)\,dx = -10 + 8 = -2$.

Related Exercises 31–38◀

Properties of Definite Integrals

Recall that the definite integral $\int_a^b f(x)\,dx$ was defined assuming that $a < b$. There are, however, occasions when it is necessary to allow the limits of integration to be reversed. If f is integrable on $[a, b]$, we define

$$\int_b^a f(x)\,dx = -\int_a^b f(x)\,dx.$$

In other words, reversing the limits of integration changes the sign of the integral.

Another fundamental property of integrals is that if we integrate from a point to itself, then the length of the interval of integration is zero, which means the definite integral is also zero.

QUICK CHECK 5 Evaluate $\int_a^b f(x)\,dx + \int_b^a f(x)\,dx$ if f is integrable on $[a, b]$. ◀

DEFINITION Reversing Limits and Identical Limits

Suppose f is integrable on $[a, b]$.

1. $\int_b^a f(x)\,dx = -\int_a^b f(x)\,dx$ **2.** $\int_a^a f(x)\,dx = 0$

Integral of a Sum Definite integrals possess other properties that often simplify their evaluation. Assume f and g are integrable on $[a, b]$. The first property states that their sum $f + g$ is integrable on $[a, b]$ and the integral of their sum is the sum of their integrals:

$$\int_a^b (f(x) + g(x))\,dx = \int_a^b f(x)\,dx + \int_a^b g(x)\,dx$$

We prove this property, assuming that f and g are continuous on $[a, b]$. In this case, $f + g$ is continuous and integrable on $[a, b]$. We then have

$$\int_a^b (f(x) + g(x))\,dx = \lim_{\Delta \to 0} \sum_{k=1}^{n} [f(\overline{x}_k) + g(\overline{x}_k)]\,\Delta x_k \quad \text{Definition of definite integral}$$

$$= \lim_{\Delta \to 0} \left[\sum_{k=1}^{n} f(\overline{x}_k)\,\Delta x_k + \sum_{k=1}^{n} g(\overline{x}_k)\,\Delta x_k \right] \quad \text{Split into two finite sums.}$$

$$= \lim_{\Delta \to 0} \sum_{k=1}^{n} f(\overline{x}_k)\,\Delta x_k + \lim_{\Delta \to 0} \sum_{k=1}^{n} g(\overline{x}_k)\,\Delta x_k \quad \text{Split into two limits.}$$

$$= \int_a^b f(x)\,dx + \int_a^b g(x)\,dx. \quad \text{Definition of definite integral}$$

Constants in Integrals Another property of definite integrals is that constants can be factored out of definite integrals. If f is integrable on $[a, b]$ and c is a constant, then cf is integrable on $[a, b]$ and

$$\int_a^b cf(x)\,dx = c\int_a^b f(x)\,dx.$$

The justification (Exercise 77) is based on the fact that for finite sums,

$$\sum_{k=1}^{n} cf(\overline{x}_k)\,\Delta x_k = c\sum_{k=1}^{n} f(\overline{x}_k)\,\Delta x_k.$$

Integrals over Subintervals If c lies between a and b, then the integral on $[a, b]$ may be split into two integrals. As shown in Figure 5.29, we have the property

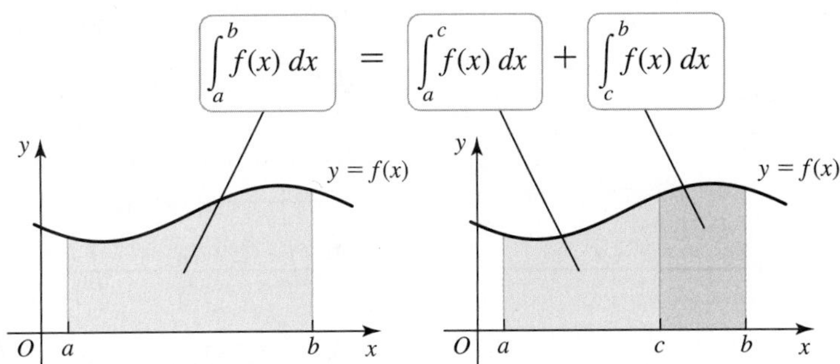

FIGURE 5.29

This same property also holds if c lies outside the interval $[a, b]$. For example, if $a < b < c$ and f is integrable on $[a, c]$, then it follows (Figure 5.30) that

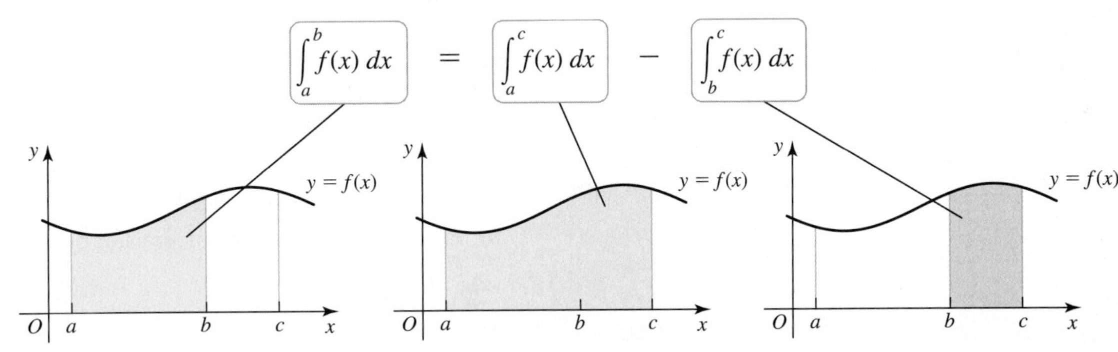

FIGURE 5.30

Because $\int_c^b f(x)\,dx = -\int_b^c f(x)\,dx$, we have the original property $\int_a^b f(x)\,dx = \int_a^c f(x)\,dx + \int_c^b f(x)\,dx$.

Integrals of Absolute Values Finally, how do we interpret $\int_a^b |f(x)|\,dx$, the integral of the absolute value of a function? The graphs f and $|f|$ are shown in Figure 5.31. The integral $\int_a^b |f(x)|\,dx$ gives the area of regions R_1^* and R_2. But R_1 and R_1^* have the same area; therefore, $\int_a^b |f(x)|\,dx$ also gives the area of R_1 and R_2. The conclusion is that $\int_a^b |f(x)|\,dx$ is the area of the entire region (above and below the x-axis) that lies between the graph of f and the x-axis on $[a, b]$.

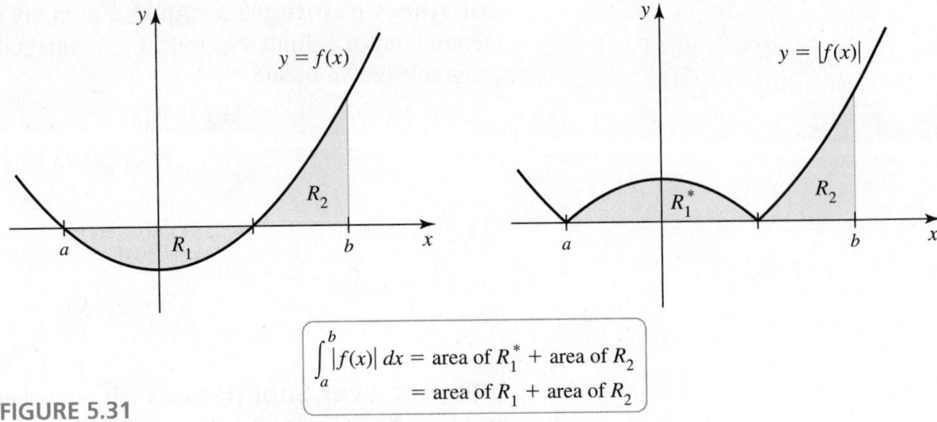

FIGURE 5.31

Table 5.3 Properties of Definite Integrals

Let f and g be integrable functions on an interval that contains a, b, and c.

1. $\displaystyle\int_a^a f(x)\,dx = 0$ Definition

2. $\displaystyle\int_b^a f(x)\,dx = -\int_a^b f(x)\,dx$ Definition

3. $\displaystyle\int_a^b (f(x) + g(x))\,dx = \int_a^b f(x)\,dx + \int_a^b g(x)\,dx$

4. $\displaystyle\int_a^b cf(x)\,dx = c\int_a^b f(x)\,dx$ For any constant c

5. $\displaystyle\int_a^b f(x)\,dx = \int_a^c f(x)\,dx + \int_c^b f(x)\,dx$

6. The function $|f|$ is integrable on $[a, b]$ and $\int_a^b |f(x)|\,dx$ is the sum of the areas of the regions bounded by the graph of f and the x-axis on $[a, b]$.

EXAMPLE 5 **Properties of integrals** Assume that $\int_0^5 f(x)\,dx = 3$ and $\int_0^7 f(x)\,dx = -10$. Evaluate the following integrals, if possible.

a. $\int_0^7 2f(x)\,dx$ **b.** $\int_5^7 f(x)\,dx$ **c.** $\int_5^0 f(x)\,dx$ **d.** $\int_7^0 6f(x)\,dx$ **e.** $\int_0^7 |f(x)|\,dx$

SOLUTION

a. By Property 4 of Table 5.3, $\int_0^7 2f(x)\,dx = 2\int_0^7 f(x)\,dx = 2(-10) = -20$.

b. By Property 5 of Table 5.3, $\int_0^7 f(x)\,dx = \int_0^5 f(x)\,dx + \int_5^7 f(x)\,dx$.
Therefore, $\int_5^7 f(x)\,dx = \int_0^7 f(x)\,dx - \int_0^5 f(x)\,dx = -10 - 3 = -13$.

c. By Property 2 of Table 5.3,

$$\int_5^0 f(x)\,dx = -\int_0^5 f(x)\,dx = -3.$$

d. Reversing limits and using Properties 2 and 4 of Table 5.3, we have

$$\int_7^0 6f(x)\,dx = -\int_0^7 6f(x)\,dx = -6\int_0^7 f(x)\,dx = (-6)(-10) = 60.$$

e. This integral cannot be evaluated without knowing the intervals on which f is positive and negative. In fact, its value is greater than or equal to 10.

Related Exercises 39–44

QUICK CHECK 6 Evaluate $\int_{-1}^{2} x\,dx$ and $\int_{-1}^{2} |x|\,dx$ using geometry.

Evaluating Definite Integrals Using Limits

In Example 3 we used area formulas for trapezoids, triangles, and circles to evaluate definite integrals. Regions bounded by more general functions have curved boundaries for which conventional geometrical methods do not work. At the moment the only way to handle such integrals is to appeal to the definition of the definite integral and the summation formulas given in Theorem 5.1.

We know that if f is integrable on $[a, b]$, then $\int_a^b f(x)\,dx = \lim_{\Delta \to 0} \sum_{k=1}^{n} f(\overline{x}_k)\,\Delta x_k$ for any partition of $[a, b]$ and any points $\overline{x}_k$. To simplify these calculations, we use equally spaced grid points and right Riemann sums. That is, for any value of n we let $\Delta x_k = \Delta x = \dfrac{b - a}{n}$ and $\overline{x}_k = a + k\,\Delta x$, for $k = 1, 2, \ldots, n$. Then, as $n \to \infty$ and $\Delta \to 0$,

$$\int_a^b f(x)\,dx = \lim_{\Delta \to 0} \sum_{k=1}^{n} f(\overline{x}_k)\,\Delta x_k = \lim_{n \to \infty} \sum_{k=1}^{n} f(a + k\,\Delta x)\,\Delta x.$$

EXAMPLE 6 **Evaluating definite integrals** Find the value of $\int_0^2 (x^3 + 1)\,dx$ by evaluating a right Riemann sum and letting $n \to \infty$.

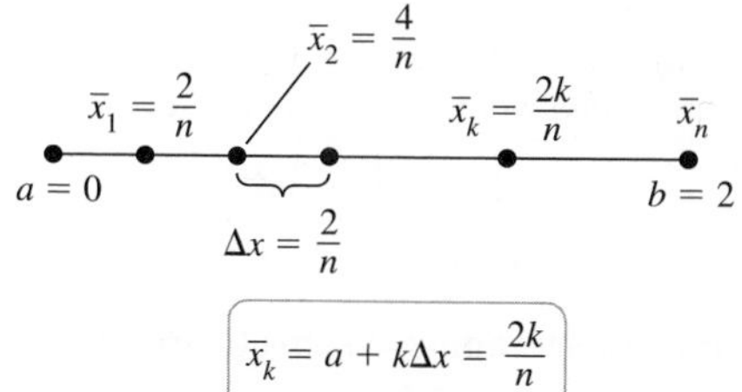

SOLUTION Based on approximations found in Example 5, Section 5.1, we conjectured that the value of this integral is 6. To verify this conjecture, we now evaluate the integral exactly. The interval $[a, b] = [0, 2]$ is divided into n subintervals of length $\Delta x = \dfrac{b - a}{n} = \dfrac{2}{n}$, which produces the grid points

$$\overline{x}_k = a + k\,\Delta x = 0 + k \cdot \frac{2}{n} = \frac{2k}{n}, \qquad \text{for } k = 1, 2, \ldots, n.$$

Letting $f(x) = x^3 + 1$, the right Riemann sum is

$$\begin{aligned}
\sum_{k=1}^{n} f(\overline{x}_k)\,\Delta x &= \sum_{k=1}^{n} \left[\left(\frac{2k}{n}\right)^3 + 1\right]\frac{2}{n} \\
&= \frac{2}{n} \sum_{k=1}^{n} \left(\frac{8k^3}{n^3} + 1\right) && \sum_{k=1}^{n} ca_k = c\sum_{k=1}^{n} a_k \\
&= \frac{2}{n}\left(\frac{8}{n^3}\sum_{k=1}^{n} k^3 + \sum_{k=1}^{n} 1\right) && \sum_{k=1}^{n}(a_k + b_k) = \sum_{k=1}^{n} a_k + \sum_{k=1}^{n} b_k \\
&= \frac{2}{n}\left[\frac{8}{n^3}\left(\frac{n^2(n+1)^2}{4}\right) + n\right] && \sum_{k=1}^{n} k^3 = \frac{n^2(n+1)^2}{4} \text{ and } \sum_{k=1}^{n} 1 = n;\ \text{Theorem 5.1} \\
&= \frac{4(n^2 + 2n + 1)}{n^2} + 2 && \text{Simplify.}
\end{aligned}$$

An analogous calculation could be done using left Riemann sums or midpoint Riemann sums.

Now we evaluate $\int_0^2 (x^3 + 1)\,dx$ by letting $n \to \infty$ in the Riemann sum:

$$\begin{aligned}\int_0^2 (x^3 + 1)\,dx &= \lim_{n\to\infty} \sum_{k=1}^{n} f(\overline{x}_k)\,\Delta x \\ &= \lim_{n\to\infty} \left[\frac{4(n^2 + 2n + 1)}{n^2} + 2\right] \\ &= 4 \lim_{n\to\infty} \underbrace{\left(\frac{n^2 + 2n + 1}{n^2}\right)}_{\text{approaches 1}} + \lim_{n\to\infty} 2 \\ &= 4(1) + 2 = 6\end{aligned}$$

Therefore, $\int_0^2 (x^3 + 1)\,dx = 6$, confirming our conjecture in Example 5, Section 5.1.

Related Exercises 45–50 ◀

The Riemann sum calculations in Example 6 are tedious even if f is a simple function. For polynomials of degree 4 and higher, the calculations are much more challenging, and for rational and transcendental functions, advanced mathematical results are needed. The next section introduces more efficient methods for evaluating definite integrals.

SECTION 5.2 EXERCISES

Review Questions

1. Explain what net area means.

2. How do you interpret geometrically the definite integral of a function that changes sign on the interval of integration?

3. When does the net area of a region equal the area of a region? When does the net area of a region differ from the area of a region?

4. Suppose that $f(x) < 0$ on the interval $[a, b]$. Using Riemann sums, explain why the definite integral $\int_a^b f(x)\,dx$ is negative.

5. Use graphs to evaluate $\int_0^{2\pi} \sin x\,dx$ and $\int_0^{2\pi} \cos x\,dx$.

6. Explain how the notation for Riemann sums, $\sum_{k=1}^{n} f(\overline{x}_k)\,\Delta x$, corresponds to the notation for the definite integral, $\int_a^b f(x)\,dx$.

7. Give a geometrical explanation of why $\int_a^a f(x)\,dx = 0$.

8. Use Table 5.3 to rewrite $\int_1^6 (2x^3 - 4x)\,dx$ as the sum of two integrals.

9. Use geometry to find a formula for $\int_0^a x\,dx$, in terms of a.

10. If f is continuous on $[a, b]$ and $\int_a^b |f(x)|\,dx = 0$, what can you conclude about f?

Basic Skills

11–14. Approximating net area *The following functions are negative on the given interval.*

- **a.** *Sketch the function on the given interval.*
- **b.** *Approximate the net area bounded by the graph of f and the x-axis on the interval using a left, right, and midpoint Riemann sum with n = 4.*

11. $f(x) = -2x - 1;\ [0, 4]$

12. $f(x) = -4 - x^3;\ [3, 7]$

13. $f(x) = \sin 2x;\ [\pi/2, \pi]$

14. $f(x) = x^3 - 1;\ [-2, 0]$

15–18. Approximating net area *The following functions are positive and negative on the given interval.*

- **a.** *Sketch the function on the given interval.*
- **b.** *Approximate the net area bounded by the graph of f and the x-axis on the interval using a left, right, and midpoint Riemann sum with n = 4.*
- **c.** *Use the sketch in part (a) to show which intervals of [a, b] make positive and negative contributions to the net area.*

15. $f(x) = 4 - 2x;\ [0, 4]$

16. $f(x) = 8 - 2x^2;\ [0, 4]$

17. $f(x) = \sin 2x;\ [0, 3\pi/4]$

18. $f(x) = x^3;\ [-1, 2]$

19–22. Identifying definite integrals as limits of sums *Consider the following limits of Riemann sums of a function f on [a, b]. Identify f and express the limit as a definite integral.*

19. $\lim_{\Delta\to 0} \sum_{k=1}^{n} (\overline{x}_k^2 + 1)\,\Delta x_k;\ [0, 2]$

20. $\lim_{\Delta\to 0} \sum_{k=1}^{n} (4 - \overline{x}_k^2)\,\Delta x_k;\ [-2, 2]$

21. $\lim_{\Delta\to 0} \sum_{k=1}^{n} \overline{x}_k \cos \overline{x}_k\,\Delta x_k;\ [1, 2]$

22. $\lim_{\Delta\to 0} \sum_{k=1}^{n} |\overline{x}_k^2 - 1|\,\Delta x_k;\ [-2, 2]$

23–30. Net area and definite integrals *Use geometry (not Riemann sums) to evaluate the following definite integrals. Sketch a graph of the integrand, show the region in question, and interpret your result.*

23. $\int_0^4 (8 - 2x)\,dx$

24. $\int_{-4}^{2} (2x + 4)\,dx$

25. $\int_{-1}^{2} (-|x|)\,dx$

26. $\int_{0}^{2} (1 - |x|)\,dx$

27. $\int_{0}^{4} \sqrt{16 - x^2}\,dx$

28. $\int_{-1}^{3} \sqrt{4 - (x - 1)^2}\,dx$

29. $\int_{0}^{4} f(x)\,dx$ where $f(x) = \begin{cases} 5 & \text{if } x \le 2 \\ 3x - 1 & \text{if } x > 2 \end{cases}$

30. $\int_{1}^{10} g(x)\,dx$ where $g(x) = \begin{cases} 4x & \text{if } 0 \le x \le 2 \\ -8x + 16 & \text{if } 2 < x \le 3 \\ -8 & \text{if } x > 3 \end{cases}$

31–34. Net area from graphs *The figure shows the areas of regions bounded by the graph of f and the x-axis. Evaluate the following integrals.*

31. $\int_{0}^{a} f(x)\,dx$

32. $\int_{0}^{b} f(x)\,dx$

33. $\int_{a}^{c} f(x)\,dx$

34. $\int_{0}^{c} f(x)\,dx$

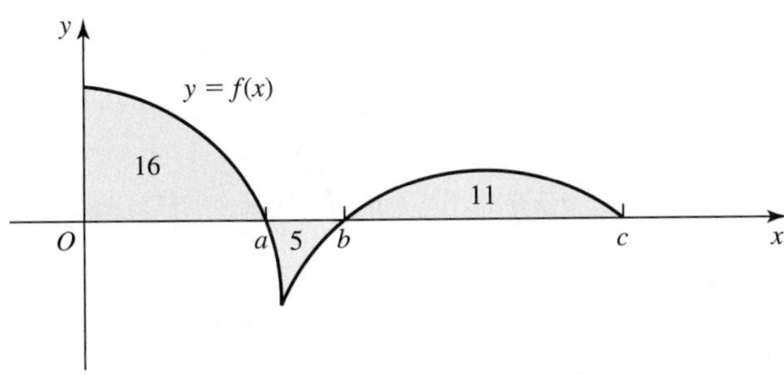

35–38. Net area from graphs *The accompanying figure shows four regions bounded by the graph of $y = x \sin x$: R_1, R_2, R_3, and R_4, whose areas are 1, $\pi - 1$, $\pi + 1$, and $2\pi - 1$, respectively. (We verify these results later in the text.) Use this information to evaluate the following integrals.*

35. $\int_{0}^{\pi} x \sin x\,dx$

36. $\int_{0}^{3\pi/2} x \sin x\,dx$

37. $\int_{0}^{2\pi} x \sin x\,dx$

38. $\int_{\pi/2}^{2\pi} x \sin x\,dx$

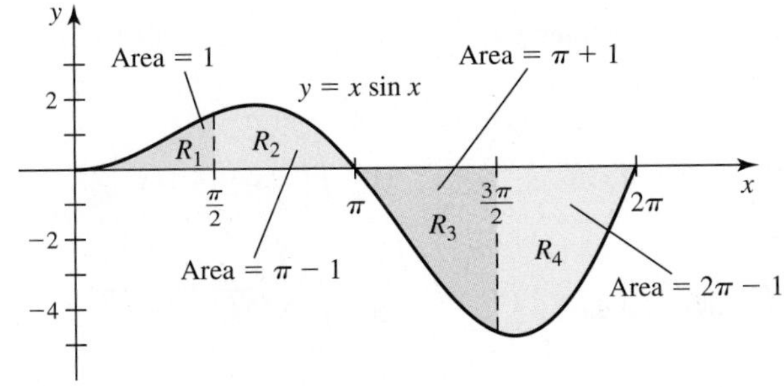

39. **Properties of integrals** Use only the fact that $\int_0^4 3x(4 - x)\,dx = 32$ and the definitions and properties of integrals to evaluate the following integrals, if possible.

a. $\int_{4}^{0} 3x(4 - x)\,dx$

b. $\int_{0}^{4} x(x - 4)\,dx$

c. $\int_{4}^{0} 6x(4 - x)\,dx$

d. $\int_{0}^{8} 3x(4 - x)\,dx$

40. **Properties of integrals** Suppose $\int_1^4 f(x)\,dx = 8$ and $\int_1^6 f(x)\,dx = 5$. Evaluate the following integrals.

a. $\int_{1}^{4} (-3f(x))\,dx$

b. $\int_{1}^{4} 3f(x)\,dx$

c. $\int_{6}^{4} 12\,f(x)\,dx$

d. $\int_{4}^{6} 3\,f(x)\,dx$

41. **Properties of integrals** Suppose $\int_0^3 f(x)\,dx = 2$, $\int_3^6 f(x)\,dx = -5$, and $\int_3^6 g(x)\,dx = 1$. Evaluate the following integrals.

a. $\int_{0}^{3} 5f(x)\,dx$

b. $\int_{3}^{6} [-3g(x)]\,dx$

c. $\int_{3}^{6} (3f(x) - g(x))\,dx$

d. $\int_{6}^{3} [f(x) + 2g(x)]\,dx$

42. **Properties of integrals** Suppose that $f(x) \ge 0$ on $[0, 2]$, $f(x) \le 0$ on $[2, 5]$, $\int_0^2 f(x)\,dx = 6$, and $\int_2^5 f(x)\,dx = -8$. Evaluate the following integrals.

a. $\int_{0}^{5} f(x)\,dx$

b. $\int_{0}^{5} |f(x)|\,dx$

c. $\int_{2}^{5} 4|f(x)|\,dx$

d. $\int_{0}^{5} (f(x) + |f(x)|)\,dx$

43–44. Using properties of integrals *Use the value of the first integral I to evaluate the two given integrals.*

43. $I = \int_{0}^{1} (x^3 - 2x)\,dx = -\dfrac{3}{4}$

a. $\int_{0}^{1} (4x - 2x^3)\,dx$

b. $\int_{1}^{0} (2x - x^3)\,dx$

44. $I = \int_{0}^{\pi/2} (\cos\theta - 2\sin\theta)\,d\theta = -1$

a. $\int_{0}^{\pi/2} (2\sin\theta - \cos\theta)\,d\theta$

b. $\int_{\pi/2}^{0} (4\cos\theta - 8\sin\theta)\,d\theta$

45–50. Limits of sums *Use the definition of the definite integral to evaluate the following definite integrals. Use right Riemann sums and Theorem 5.1.*

45. $\int_0^2 (2x + 1)\,dx$

46. $\int_1^5 (1 - x)\,dx$

47. $\int_3^7 (4x + 6)\,dx$

48. $\int_0^2 (x^2 - 1)\,dx$

49. $\int_1^4 (x^2 - 1)\,dx$

50. $\int_0^2 4x^3\,dx$

Further Explorations

51. **Explain why or why not** Determine whether the following statements are true and give an explanation or counterexample.
   a. If f is a constant function on the interval $[a, b]$, then the right and left Riemann sums give the exact value of $\int_a^b f(x)\,dx$ for any n.
   b. If f is a linear function on the interval $[a, b]$, then a midpoint Riemann sum gives the exact value of $\int_a^b f(x)\,dx$ for any n.
   c. $\int_0^{2\pi/a} \sin ax\,dx = \int_0^{2\pi/a} \cos ax\,dx = 0$ (*Hint:* Graph the functions and use properties of trigonometric functions).
   d. If $\int_a^b f(x)\,dx = \int_b^a f(x)\,dx$, then f is a constant function.
   e. Property 4 of Table 5.3 implies that $\int_a^b xf(x)\,dx = x\int_a^b f(x)\,dx$.

T **52–55. Approximating definite integrals** *Complete the following steps for the given integral and the given value of n.*

a. *Sketch the graph of the integrand on the interval of integration.*
b. *Calculate Δx and the grid points $x_0, x_1, \ldots, x_n$, assuming a regular partition.*
c. *Calculate the left and right Riemann sums for the given value of n.*
d. *Determine which Riemann sum (left or right) underestimates the value of the definite integral and which overestimates the value of the definite integral.*

52. $\int_0^2 (x^2 - 2)\,dx;\ n = 4$

53. $\int_3^6 (1 - 2x)\,dx;\ n = 6$

54. $\int_0^{\pi/2} \cos x\,dx;\ n = 4$

55. $\int_1^7 \frac{1}{x}\,dx;\ n = 6$

T **56–60. Approximating definite integrals with a calculator** *Consider the following definite integrals.*

a. *Write the left and right Riemann sums in sigma notation for $n = 20, 50,$ and 100. Then evaluate the sums using a calculator.*
b. *Based upon your answers to part (a), make a conjecture about the value of the definite integral.*

56. $\int_4^9 3\sqrt{x}\,dx$

57. $\int_0^1 (x^2 + 1)\,dx$

58. $\int_0^1 \tan\left(\frac{\pi x}{4}\right)dx$

59. $\int_1^4 \frac{dx}{2x}$

60. $\int_{-1}^1 \cos\left(\frac{x\pi}{2}\right)dx$

T **61–64. Riemann sums with midpoints and a calculator** *Consider the following definite integrals.*

a. *Write the midpoint Riemann sum in sigma notation for an arbitrary value of n.*
b. *Evaluate each sum using a calculator with $n = 20, 50,$ and 100. Use these values to estimate the value of the integral.*

61. $\int_1^4 2\sqrt{x}\,dx$

62. $\int_{-1}^2 \sin\left(\frac{x\pi}{4}\right)dx$

63. $\int_0^4 (4x - x^2)\,dx$

64. $\int_0^{\pi/4} \tan x\,dx$

65. **More properties of integrals** Consider two functions f and g on $[1, 6]$ such that $\int_1^6 f(x)\,dx = 10$, $\int_1^6 g(x)\,dx = 5$, $\int_4^6 f(x)\,dx = 5$, and $\int_1^4 g(x)\,dx = 2$. Evaluate the following integrals.
   a. $\int_1^4 3f(x)\,dx$
   b. $\int_1^6 (f(x) - g(x))\,dx$
   c. $\int_1^4 (f(x) - g(x))\,dx$
   d. $\int_4^6 (g(x) - f(x))\,dx$
   e. $\int_4^6 8g(x)\,dx$
   f. $\int_4^1 2f(x)\,dx$

66–69. Area versus net area *Graph the following functions. Then use geometry (not Riemann sums) to find the area and the net area of the region described.*

66. The region between the graph of $y = 4x - 8$ and the x-axis, for $-4 \le x \le 8$

67. The region between the graph of $y = -3x$ and the x-axis, for $-2 \le x \le 2$

68. The region between the graph of $y = 3x - 6$ and the x-axis, for $0 \le x \le 6$

69. The region between the graph of $y = 1 - |x|$ and the x-axis, for $-2 \le x \le 2$

70–73. Area by geometry *Use geometry to evaluate the following integrals.*

70. $\int_{-2}^3 |x + 1|\,dx$

71. $\int_1^6 |2x - 4|\,dx$

72. $\int_1^6 (3x - 6)\,dx$

73. $\int_{-6}^4 \sqrt{24 - 2x - x^2}\,dx$

Additional Exercises

74. Integrating piecewise continuous functions Suppose f is continuous on the interval $[a, c]$ and on the interval $(c, b]$, where $a < c < b$, with a finite jump at c. Form a uniform partition on the interval $[a, c]$ with n grid points and another uniform partition on the interval $[c, b]$ with m grid points, where c is a grid point of both partitions. Write a Riemann sum for $\int_a^b f(x)\,dx$ and separate it into two pieces for $[a, c]$ and $[c, b]$. Explain why $\int_a^b f(x)\,dx = \int_a^c f(x)\,dx + \int_c^b f(x)\,dx$.

75–76. Piecewise continuous functions *Use geometry and the result of Exercise 74 to evaluate the following integrals.*

75. $\displaystyle\int_0^{10} f(x)\,dx$ where $f(x) = \begin{cases} 2 & \text{if } 0 \le x \le 5 \\ 3 & \text{if } 5 < x \le 10 \end{cases}$

76. $\displaystyle\int_1^{6} f(x)\,dx$ where $f(x) = \begin{cases} 2x & \text{if } 1 \le x \le 4 \\ 10 - 2x & \text{if } 4 < x \le 6 \end{cases}$

77. Constants in integrals Use the definition of the definite integral to justify the property $\int_a^b cf(x)\,dx = c\int_a^b f(x)\,dx$, where f is continuous and c is a real number.

78. Exact area Consider the linear function $f(x) = 2px + q$ on the interval $[a, b]$, where a, b, p, and q are positive constants.

a. Show that the midpoint Riemann sum with n subintervals equals $\int_a^b f(x)\,dx$ for any value of n.

b. Show that $\int_a^b f(x)\,dx = (b - a)[p(b + a) + q]$.

79. A nonintegrable function Consider the function defined on $[0, 1]$ such that $f(x) = 1$ if x is a rational number and $f(x) = 0$ if x is irrational. This function has an infinite number of discontinuities, and the integral $\int_0^1 f(x)\,dx$ does not exist. Show that the right, left, and midpoint Riemann sums on *regular* partitions with n subintervals equal 1 for all n.

80. Powers of x by Riemann sums Consider the integral $I(p) = \int_0^1 x^p\,dx$ where p is a positive integer.

a. Write the left Riemann sum for the integral with n subintervals.

b. It is a fact (proved by the 17th-century mathematicians Fermat and Pascal) that $\displaystyle\lim_{n\to\infty} \frac{1}{n}\sum_{k=0}^{n-1}\left(\frac{k}{n}\right)^p = \frac{1}{p+1}$. Use this fact to evaluate $I(p)$.

QUICK CHECK ANSWERS

1. -20 **2.** $f(x) = 1 - x$ is one possibility. **3.** 0 **4.** 10; $c(b - a)$ **5.** 0 **6.** $\frac{3}{2}$; $\frac{5}{2}$

5.3 Fundamental Theorem of Calculus

Evaluating definite integrals using limits of Riemann sums, as described in Section 5.2, is usually not possible or practical. Fortunately, there is a powerful and practical method for evaluating definite integrals, which is developed in this section. Along the way, we discover the inverse relationship between differentiation and integration, expressed in the most important result of calculus, the Fundamental Theorem of Calculus.

Area Functions

The concept of an area function is crucial to the discussion about the connection between derivatives and integrals. We start with a continuous function $y = f(t)$ defined for $t \ge a$, where a is a fixed number. The *area function* for f with left endpoint a is denoted $A(x)$; it gives the net area of the region bounded by the graph of f and the t-axis between $t = a$ and $t = x$ (Figure 5.32). The net area of this region is also given by the definite integral

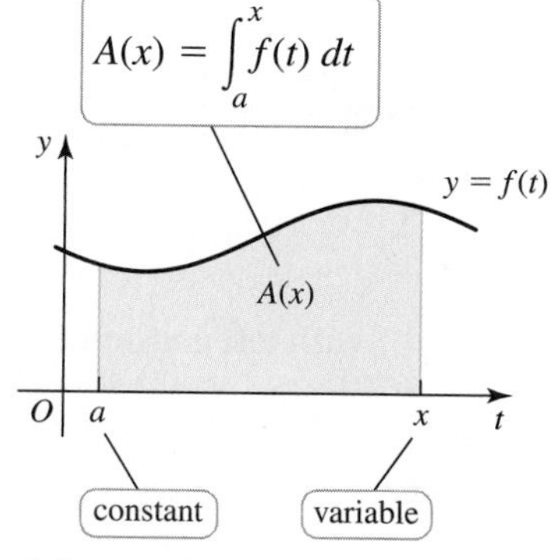

FIGURE 5.32

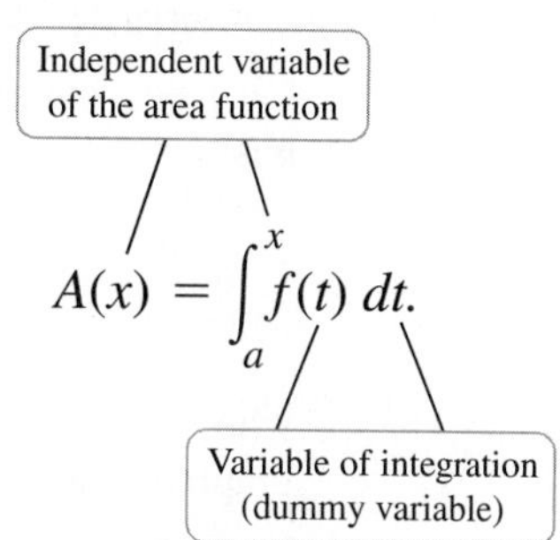

➤ A dummy variable is a placeholder; its role can be played by any symbol that does not conflict with other variables in the problem.

Notice that x is the upper limit of the integral *and* the independent variable of the area function: As x changes, so does the net area under the curve. Because the symbol x is already in use as the independent variable for A, we must choose another symbol for the variable of integration. Any symbol—except x—can be used because it is a *dummy variable*; we have chosen t as the integration variable.

Figure 5.33 gives a general view of how an area function is generated. Suppose that for a fixed number a, f is continuous for $t \geq a$. Now choose a point $b > a$. The net area of the region between the graph of f and the t-axis on the interval $[a, b]$ is $A(b)$. Moving the right endpoint to $(c, 0)$ or $(d, 0)$ produces different regions with net areas $A(c)$ and $A(d)$, respectively. In general, if $x > a$ is a variable point, then $A(x) = \int_a^x f(t)\,dt$ is the net area of the region between the graph of f and the t-axis on the interval $[a, x]$.

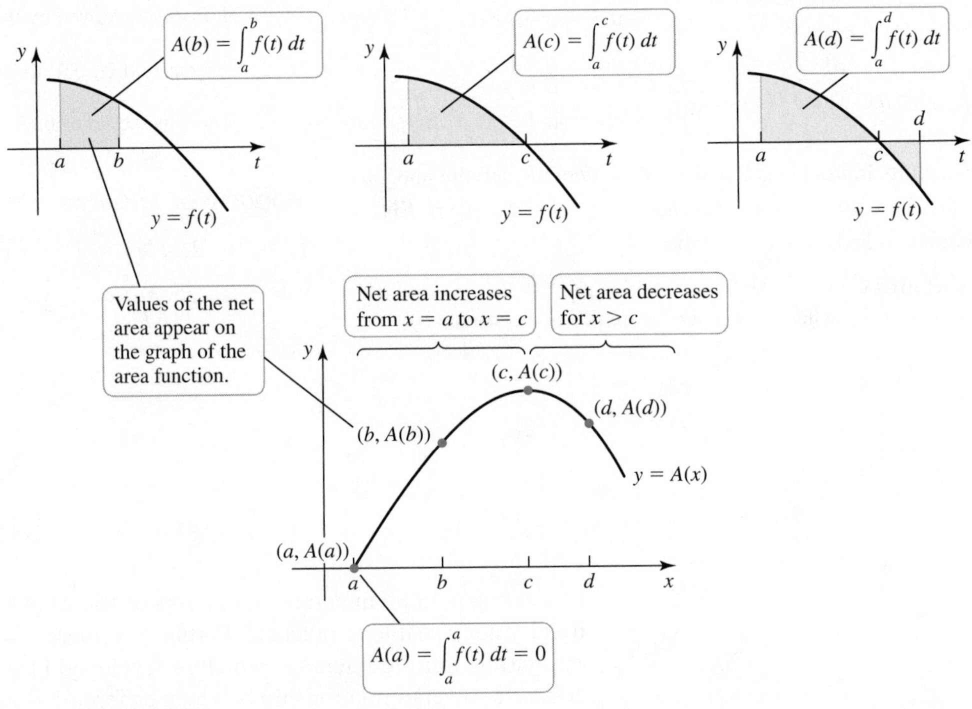

FIGURE 5.33

Figure 5.33 shows how $A(x)$ varies with respect to x. Notice that $A(a) = \int_a^a f(t)\,dt = 0$. Then, for $x > a$ the net area increases until $x = c$, at which point $f(c) = 0$. For $x > c$, the function f is negative, which produces a negative contribution to the area function. As a result, the area function decreases for $x > c$.

DEFINITION Area Function

Let f be a continuous function for $t \geq a$. The **area function for f with left endpoint a** is

$$A(x) = \int_a^x f(t)\,dt,$$

where $x \geq a$. The area function gives the net area of the region bounded by the graph of f and the t-axis on the interval $[a, x]$.

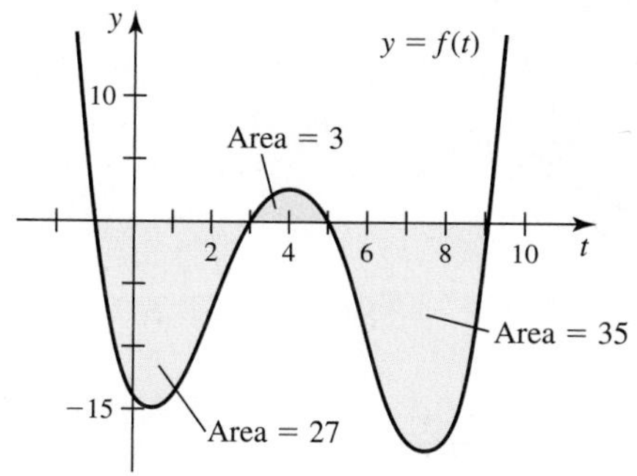

FIGURE 5.34

EXAMPLE 1 **Area of regions** The graph of f is shown in Figure 5.34 with areas of various regions marked. Let $A(x) = \int_{-1}^{x} f(t)\,dt$ and $F(x) = \int_{3}^{x} f(t)\,dt$ be two area functions for f (note the different left endpoints). Evaluate the following area functions.

a. $A(3)$ and $F(3)$ **b.** $A(5)$ and $F(5)$ **c.** $A(9)$ and $F(9)$

SOLUTION

a. The value of $A(3) = \int_{-1}^{3} f(t)\,dt$ is the net area of the region bounded by the graph of f and the t-axis on the interval $[-1, 3]$. Using the graph of f, we see that $A(3) = -27$ (because this region has an area of 27 and lies below the t-axis). On the other hand, $F(3) = \int_{3}^{3} f(t)\,dt = 0$ by Property 1 of Table 5.3.

b. The value of $A(5) = \int_{-1}^{5} f(t)\,dt$ is found by subtracting the area of the region that lies below the t-axis on $[-1, 3]$ from the area of the region that lies above the t-axis on $[3, 5]$. Therefore, $A(5) = 3 - 27 = -24$. Similarly, $F(5)$ is the net area of the region bounded by the graph of f and the t-axis on the interval $[3, 5]$; therefore, $F(5) = 3$.

c. Reasoning as in parts (a) and (b), we see that $A(9) = -27 + 3 - 35 = -59$ and $F(9) = 3 - 35 = -32$.

Related Exercises 11–12 ◀

QUICK CHECK 1 In Example 1, let $B(x)$ be the area function for f with left endpoint 5. Evaluate $B(5)$ and $B(9)$. ◀

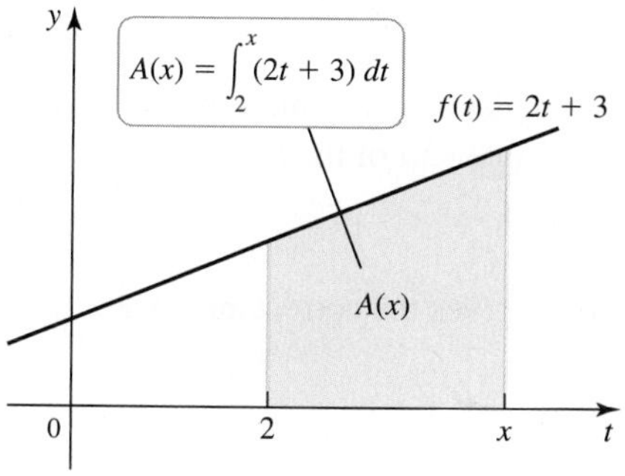

FIGURE 5.35

EXAMPLE 2 **Area of a trapezoid** Consider the trapezoid bounded by the line $f(t) = 2t + 3$ and the t-axis from $t = 2$ to $t = x$ (Figure 5.35). The area function $A(x) = \int_{2}^{x} f(t)\,dt$ gives the area of a trapezoid, for $x \geq 2$.

a. Evaluate $A(2)$.

b. Evaluate $A(5)$.

c. Find and graph the area function $y = A(x)$, for $x \geq 2$.

d. Compare the derivative of A to f.

SOLUTION

a. By Property 1 of Table 5.3, $A(2) = \int_{2}^{2} (2t + 3)\,dt = 0$.

b. Notice that $A(5)$ is the area of a trapezoid (Figure 5.35) bounded by the line $y = 2t + 3$ and the t-axis on the interval $[2, 5]$. Using the area formula for a trapezoid (Figure 5.36), we find that

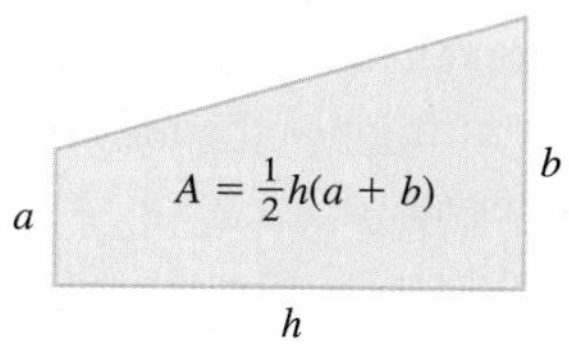

FIGURE 5.36

$$A(5) = \int_{2}^{5} (2t + 3)\,dt = \frac{1}{2} \underbrace{(5 - 2)}_{\text{distance between parallel sides}} \underbrace{(f(2) + f(5))}_{\text{sum of parallel side lengths}} = \frac{1}{2} \cdot 3(7 + 13) = 30.$$

c. Now the right endpoint of the base is a variable $x \geq 2$ (Figure 5.37). The distance between the parallel sides of the trapezoid is $x - 2$. By the area formula for a trapezoid, the area of this trapezoid for any $x \geq 2$ is

$$\begin{aligned} A(x) &= \frac{1}{2} \underbrace{(x - 2)}_{\text{distance between parallel sides}} \underbrace{(f(2) + f(x))}_{\text{sum of parallel side lengths}} \\ &= \frac{1}{2}(x - 2)(7 + 2x + 3) \\ &= (x - 2)(x + 5) \\ &= x^2 + 3x - 10. \end{aligned}$$

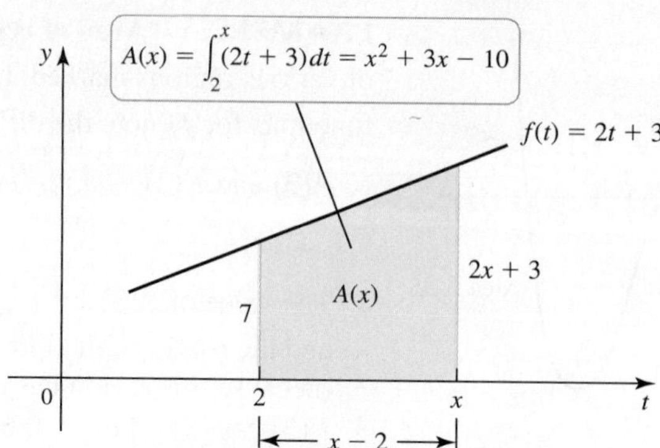

FIGURE 5.37

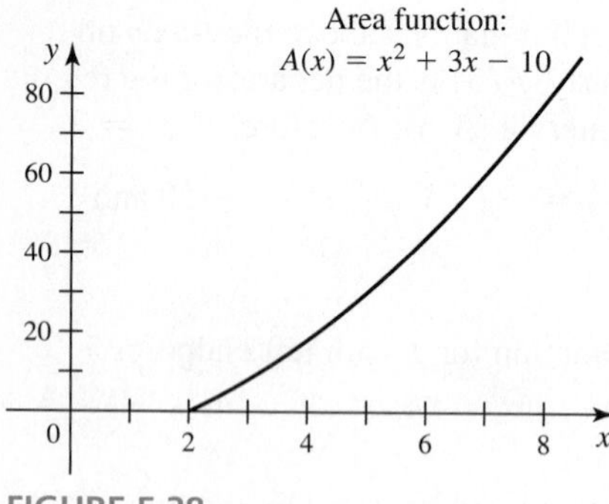

FIGURE 5.38

➤ Recall that if $A'(x) = f(x)$, then f is the derivative of A; equivalently, A is an antiderivative of f.

Expressing the area function in terms of an integral with a variable upper limit we have

$$A(x) = \int_2^x (2t + 3)\,dt = x^2 + 3x - 10.$$

Because the line $f(t) = 2t + 3$ is above the t-axis for $t \geq 2$, the area function $A(x) = x^2 + 3x - 10$ is an increasing function of x with $A(2) = 0$ (Figure 5.38).

d. Differentiating the area function, we find that

$$A'(x) = \frac{d}{dx}(x^2 + 3x - 10) = 2x + 3 = f(x).$$

Therefore, $A'(x) = f(x)$, or equivalently, the area function A is an antiderivative of f. We soon show this relationship is not an accident; it is one part of the Fundamental Theorem of Calculus.

Related Exercises 13–22 ◄

QUICK CHECK 2 Verify that the area function in Example 2 gives the correct area when $x = 6$ and $x = 10$. ◄

Fundamental Theorem of Calculus

Example 2 suggests that the area function A for a linear function f is an antiderivative of f; that is, $A'(x) = f(x)$. Our goal is to show that this conjecture is true for more general functions. Let's start with an intuitive argument.

Assume that f is a continuous function defined on an interval $[a, b]$. As before, $A(x) = \int_a^x f(t)\,dt$ is the area function for f with a left endpoint a: It gives the net area of the region bounded by the graph of f and the t-axis on the interval $[a, x]$, for $x \geq a$. Figure 5.39 is the key to the argument.

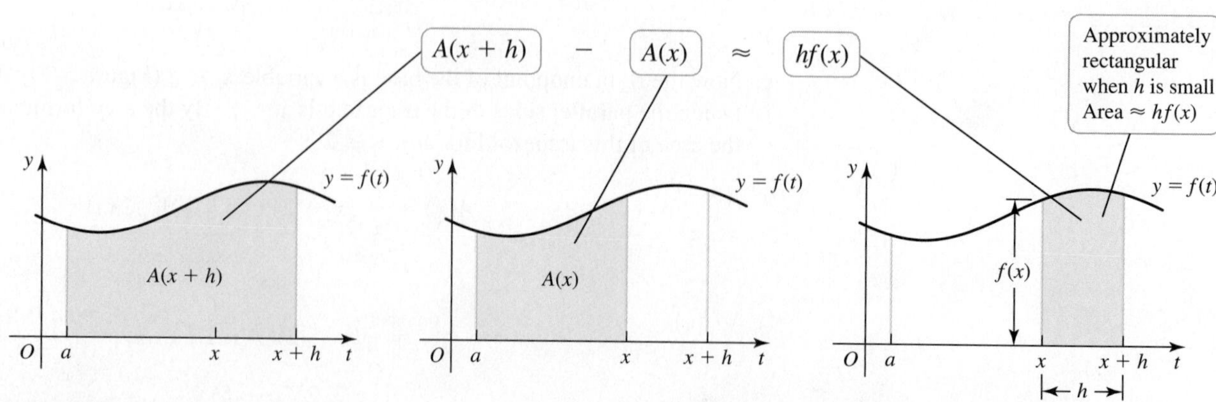

FIGURE 5.39

Note that with $h > 0$, $A(x + h)$ is the area of the region whose base is the interval $[a, x + h]$, while $A(x)$ is the area of the region whose base is the interval $[a, x]$. So the difference $A(x + h) - A(x)$ is the area of the region whose base is the interval $[x, x + h]$. If h is small, this region is nearly rectangular with a base of length h and a height $f(x)$. Therefore, the area of this region is approximately

$$A(x + h) - A(x) \approx h\,f(x).$$

Dividing by h, we have

$$\frac{A(x + h) - A(x)}{h} \approx f(x).$$

➤ Recall that

$$f'(x) = \lim_{h \to 0} \frac{f(x + h) - f(x)}{h}.$$

If the function f is replaced by A, then

$$A'(x) = \lim_{h \to 0} \frac{A(x + h) - A(x)}{h}.$$

An analogous argument can be made with $h < 0$. Now observe that as h tends to zero, this approximation improves. In the limit as $h \to 0$, we have

$$\underbrace{\lim_{h \to 0} \frac{A(x + h) - A(x)}{h}}_{A'(x)} = \underbrace{\lim_{h \to 0} f(x)}_{f(x)}.$$

We see that indeed $A'(x) = f(x)$. Because $A(x) = \int_a^x f(t)\,dt$, the result can also be written

$$A'(x) = \frac{d}{dx}\underbrace{\int_a^x f(t)\,dt}_{A(x)} = f(x),$$

which says that the derivative of the integral of f is f. A formal proof that $A'(x) = f(x)$ is given at the end of the section; but for the moment, we have a plausible argument. This conclusion is the first part of the Fundamental Theorem of Calculus.

THEOREM 5.3 (PART 1) Fundamental Theorem of Calculus
If f is continuous on $[a, b]$, then the area function

$$A(x) = \int_a^x f(t)\,dt, \qquad \text{for } a \le x \le b,$$

is continuous on $[a, b]$ and differentiable on (a, b). The area function satisfies $A'(x) = f(x)$; or, equivalently,

$$A'(x) = \frac{d}{dx}\int_a^x f(t)\,dt = f(x),$$

which means that the area function of f is an antiderivative of f.

Given that A is an antiderivative of f, it is one short step to a powerful method for evaluating definite integrals. Remember (Section 4.8) that any two antiderivatives of f differ by a constant. Assuming that F is any other antiderivative of f, we have

$$F(x) = A(x) + C, \qquad \text{for all } x.$$

Noting that $A(a) = 0$, it follows that

$$F(b) - F(a) = (A(b) + C) - (\underbrace{A(a)}_{0} + C) = A(b).$$

Writing $A(b)$ in terms of a definite integral leads to the remarkable result

$$A(b) = \int_a^b f(x)\,dx = F(b) - F(a).$$

We have shown that to evaluate a definite integral of f, we

- find any antiderivative of f, call it F
- compute $F(b) - F(a)$, the difference in the values of F between the upper and lower limits of integration.

This process is the essence of the second part of the Fundamental Theorem of Calculus.

> **THEOREM 5.3 (PART 2) Fundamental Theorem of Calculus**
> If f is continuous on $[a, b]$ and F is any antiderivative of f, then
>
> $$\int_a^b f(x)\,dx = F(b) - F(a).$$

It is customary and convenient to denote the difference $F(b) - F(a)$ by $F(x)|_a^b$. Using this shorthand, the Fundamental Theorem is summarized in Figure 5.40.

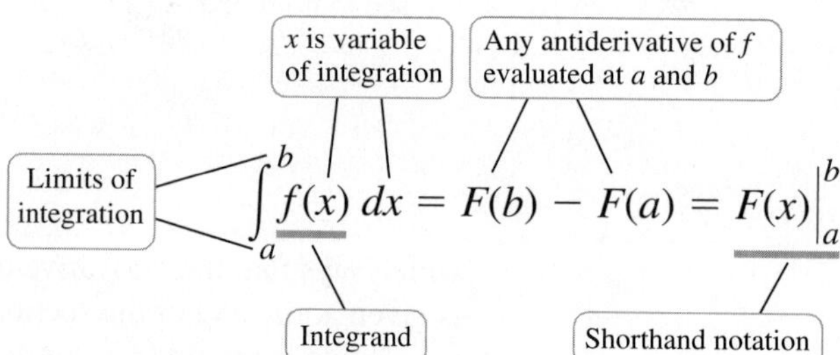

FIGURE 5.40

QUICK CHECK 3 Evaluate $\left(\dfrac{x}{x+1}\right)\Big|_1^2$. ◄

The Inverse Relationship between Differentiation and Integration It is worth pausing to observe that the two parts of the Fundamental Theorem express the inverse relationship between differentiation and integration. Part 1 of the Fundamental Theorem says

$$\frac{d}{dx}\int_a^x f(t)\,dt = f(x)$$

or the derivative of the integral of f is f itself.

Noting that f is an antiderivative of f', Part 2 of the Fundamental Theorem says

$$\int_a^b f'(x)\,dx = f(b) - f(a),$$

or the definite integral of the derivative of f is given in terms of f evaluated at two points. In other words, the integral "undoes" the derivative.

QUICK CHECK 4 Explain why f is an antiderivative of f'. ◄

EXAMPLE 3 Evaluating definite integrals Evaluate the following definite integrals using the Fundamental Theorem of Calculus, Part 2. Interpret each result geometrically.

a. $\displaystyle\int_0^{10} (60x - 6x^2)\,dx$ **b.** $\displaystyle\int_0^{2\pi} 3\sin x\,dx$ **c.** $\displaystyle\int_{1/16}^{1/4} \frac{\sqrt{t} - 2t}{t}\,dt$

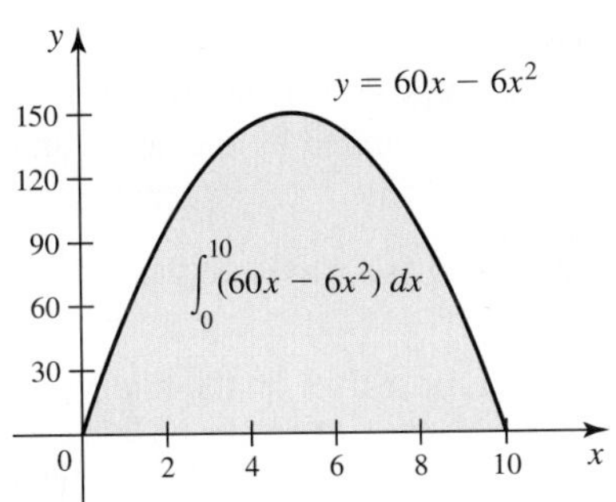

FIGURE 5.41

> The arbitrary constant C may always be omitted when evaluating definite integrals. It is added in when evaluating at the upper limit and then subtracted out when evaluating at the lower limit.

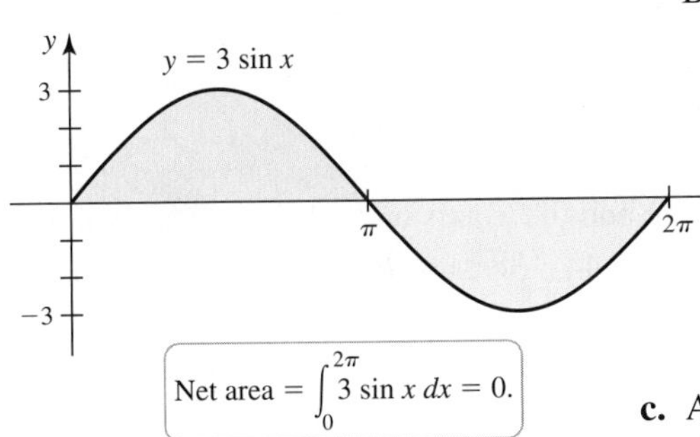

FIGURE 5.42

> We know that

$$\frac{d}{dt}(t^{1/2}) = \frac{1}{2}t^{-1/2}.$$

Therefore,

$$\int \frac{1}{2}t^{-1/2}\,dt = t^{1/2} + C$$

and

$$\int \frac{dt}{\sqrt{t}} = \int t^{-1/2}\,dt = 2t^{1/2} + C.$$

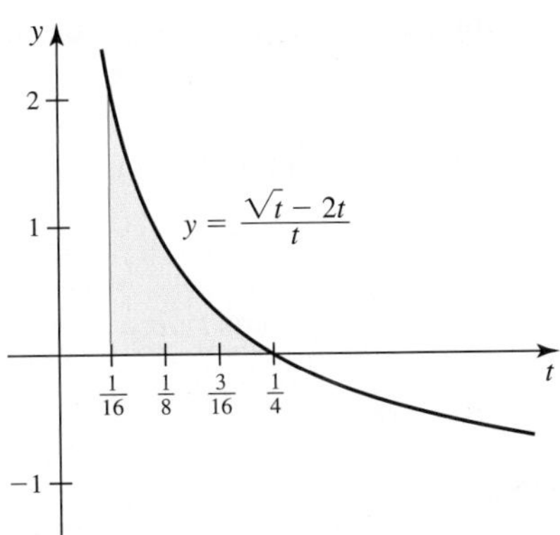

FIGURE 5.43

SOLUTION

a. Using the antiderivative rules of Section 4.8, an antiderivative of $60x - 6x^2$ is $30x^2 - 2x^3$. By the Fundamental Theorem, the value of the definite integral is

$$\begin{aligned}
\int_0^{10} (60x - 6x^2)\,dx &= (30x^2 - 2x^3)\Big|_0^{10} && \text{Fundamental Theorem}\\
&= (30 \cdot 10^2 - 2 \cdot 10^3) - (30 \cdot 0^2 - 2 \cdot 0^3) && \text{Evaluate at } x = 10 \text{ and } x = 0.\\
&= (3000 - 2000) - 0\\
&= 1000. && \text{Simplify.}
\end{aligned}$$

Because f is positive on $[0, 10]$, the definite integral $\int_0^{10}(60x - 6x^2)\,dx$ is the area of the region between the graph of f and the x-axis on the interval $[0, 10]$ (Figure 5.41).

b. As shown in Figure 5.42, the region bounded by the graph of $f(x) = 3 \sin x$ and the x-axis on $[0, 2\pi]$ consists of two parts, one above the x-axis and one below the x-axis. By the symmetry of f, these two regions have the same area, so the definite integral over $[0, 2\pi]$ is zero. Let's confirm this fact. An antiderivative of $f(x) = 3 \sin x$ is $-3 \cos x$. Therefore, the value of the definite integral is

$$\begin{aligned}
\int_0^{2\pi} 3 \sin x\,dx &= -3 \cos x\Big|_0^{2\pi} && \text{Fundamental Theorem}\\
&= (-3 \cos(2\pi)) - (-3 \cos(0)) && \text{Substitute.}\\
&= -3 - (-3) = 0. && \text{Simplify.}
\end{aligned}$$

c. Although the variable of integration is t, rather than x, we proceed as before after simplifying the integrand:

$$\frac{\sqrt{t} - 2t}{t} = \frac{1}{\sqrt{t}} - 2$$

Finding antiderivatives with respect to t and applying the Fundamental Theorem, we have

$$\begin{aligned}
\int_{1/16}^{1/4} \frac{\sqrt{t} - 2t}{t}\,dt &= \int_{1/16}^{1/4} \left(t^{-1/2} - 2\right) dt && \text{Simplify the integrand.}\\
&= 2t^{1/2} - 2t\Big|_{1/16}^{1/4} && \text{Fundamental Theorem}\\
&= \left[2\left(\frac{1}{4}\right)^{1/2} - \frac{1}{2}\right] - \left[2\left(\frac{1}{16}\right)^{1/2} - \frac{1}{8}\right] && \text{Evaluate.}\\
&= 1 - \frac{1}{2} - \frac{1}{2} + \frac{1}{8} && \text{Simplify.}\\
&= \frac{1}{8}.
\end{aligned}$$

The definite integral is positive because the graph of f lies above the t-axis (Figure 5.43).

Related Exercises 23–38 ◀

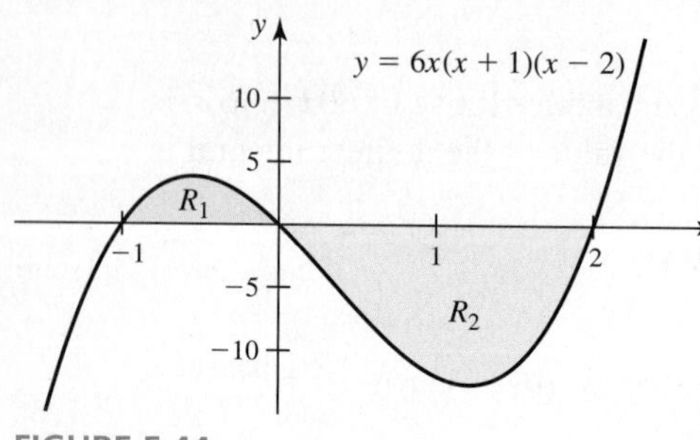

FIGURE 5.44

EXAMPLE 4 Net areas and definite integrals The graph of $f(x) = 6x(x + 1)(x - 2)$ is shown in Figure 5.44. The region R_1 is bounded by the curve and the x-axis on the interval $[-1, 0]$, and R_2 is bounded by the curve and the x-axis on the interval $[0, 2]$.

a. Find the *net area* of the region bounded by the curve and the x-axis on the interval $[-1, 2]$.

b. Find the *area* of the region bounded by the curve and the x-axis on the interval $[-1, 2]$.

SOLUTION

a. The net area of the region is given by a definite integral. The integrand f is first expanded in order to find an antiderivative:

$$\int_{-1}^{2} f(x)\,dx = \int_{-1}^{2} (6x^3 - 6x^2 - 12x)\,dx \quad \text{Expanding } f$$

$$= \left(\frac{3}{2}x^4 - 2x^3 - 6x^2\right)\Big|_{-1}^{2} \quad \text{Fundamental Theorem}$$

$$= -\frac{27}{2} \quad \text{Simplify.}$$

The net area of the region between the curve and the x-axis on $[-1, 2]$ is $-\frac{27}{2}$, which is the area of R_1 *minus* the area of R_2 (Figure 5.44). Because R_2 has a larger area than R_1, the net area is negative.

b. The region R_1 lies above the x-axis, so its area is

$$\int_{-1}^{0} (6x^3 - 6x^2 - 12x)\,dx = \left(\frac{3}{2}x^4 - 2x^3 - 6x^2\right)\Big|_{-1}^{0} = \frac{5}{2}.$$

The region R_2 lies below the x-axis, so its net area is negative:

$$\int_{0}^{2} (6x^3 - 6x^2 - 12x)\,dx = \left(\frac{3}{2}x^4 - 2x^3 - 6x^2\right)\Big|_{0}^{2} = -16$$

Therefore, the *area* of R_2 is $-(-16) = 16$. The combined area of R_1 and R_2 is $\frac{5}{2} + 16 = \frac{37}{2}$. We could also find the area of this region directly by evaluating $\int_{-1}^{2} |f(x)|\,dx$.

Related Exercises 39–48 ◀

Examples 3 and 4 make use of Part 2 of the Fundamental Theorem, which is the most potent tool for evaluating definite integrals. The remaining examples illustrate the use of the equally important Part 1 of the Fundamental Theorem.

EXAMPLE 5 Derivatives of integrals Use Part 1 of the Fundamental Theorem to simplify the following expressions.

a. $\dfrac{d}{dx}\displaystyle\int_{1}^{x} \sin^2 t\,dt$ **b.** $\dfrac{d}{dx}\displaystyle\int_{x}^{5} \sqrt{t^2 + 1}\,dt$ **c.** $\dfrac{d}{dx}\displaystyle\int_{0}^{x^2} \cos t^2\,dt$

SOLUTION

a. Using Part 1 of the Fundamental Theorem, we see that

$$\frac{d}{dx}\int_{1}^{x} \sin^2 t\,dt = \sin^2 x.$$

b. To apply Part 1 of the Fundamental Theorem, the variable must appear in the upper limit. Therefore, we use the fact that $\int_a^b f(t)\,dt = -\int_b^a f(t)\,dt$ and then apply the Fundamental Theorem:

$$\frac{d}{dx}\int_x^5 \sqrt{t^2+1}\,dt = -\frac{d}{dx}\int_5^x \sqrt{t^2+1}\,dt = -\sqrt{x^2+1}$$

c. The upper limit of the integral is not x, but a function of x. Therefore, the function to be differentiated is a composite function, which requires the Chain Rule. We let $u = x^2$ to produce

$$y = g(u) = \int_0^u \cos t^2\,dt.$$

By the Chain Rule,

$$\frac{d}{dx}\int_0^{x^2} \cos t^2\,dt = \frac{dy}{du}\frac{du}{dx} \quad \text{Chain Rule}$$

$$= \left[\frac{d}{du}\int_0^u \cos t^2\,dt\right](2x) \quad \text{Substitute for } y\text{; note that } u'(x) = 2x.$$

$$= (\cos u^2)(2x) \quad \text{Fundamental Theorem}$$

$$= 2x\cos x^4. \quad \text{Substitute } u = x^2.$$

Related Exercises 49–54 ◀

➤ Example 5c illustrates one case of Leibniz's Rule:

$$\frac{d}{dx}\int_a^{g(x)} f(t)\,dt = f(g(x))g'(x)$$

EXAMPLE 6 **Working with area functions** Consider the function f shown in Figure 5.45 and its area function $A(x) = \int_0^x f(t)\,dt$, for $0 \le x \le 17$. Assume that the four regions R_1, R_2, R_3, and R_4 have the same area. Based on the graph of f, do the following.

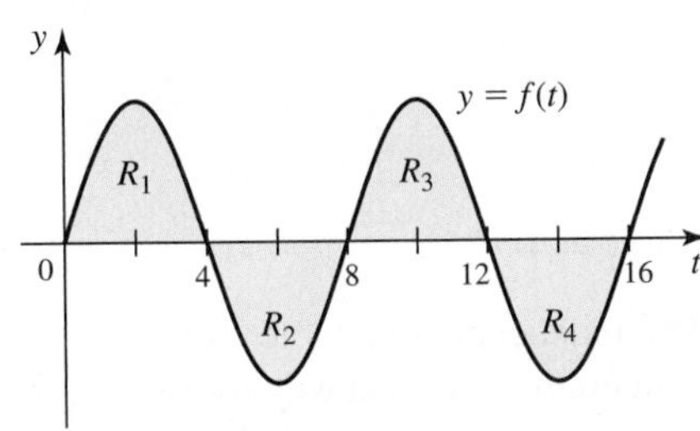

FIGURE 5.45

a. Find the zeros of A on $[0, 17]$.

b. Find the points on $[0, 17]$ at which A has local maxima or local minima.

c. Sketch a graph of A, for $0 \le x \le 17$.

SOLUTION

a. The area function $A(x) = \int_0^x f(t)\,dt$ gives the net area bounded by the graph of f and the t-axis on the interval $[0, x]$ (Figure 5.46a). Therefore, $A(0) = \int_0^0 f(t)\,dt = 0$. Because R_1 and R_2 have the same area but lie on opposite sides of the t-axis, it follows that $A(8) = \int_0^8 f(t)\,dt = 0$. Similarly, $A(16) = \int_0^{16} f(t)\,dt = 0$. Therefore, the zeros of A are 0, 8, and 16.

b. Observe that the function f is positive for $0 < t < 4$, which implies that $A(x)$ increases as x increases from 0 to 4 (Figure 5.46b). Then, as x increases from 4 to 8, $A(x)$ decreases because f is negative for $4 < t < 8$ (Figure 5.46c). Similarly, $A(x)$ increases as x increases from $x = 8$ to $x = 12$ (Figure 5.46d) and decreases from $x = 12$ to $x = 16$. By the First Derivative Test, A has local maxima at $x = 4$ and $x = 12$ and local minima at $x = 8$ and $x = 16$ (Figure 5.46e).

➤ Recall that local extrema occur only at interior points of the domain.

c. Combining the observations in parts (a) and (b) leads to a qualitative sketch of A (Figure 5.46e). Note that $A(x) \ge 0$ for all $x \ge 0$. It is not possible to determine function values (y-coordinates) on the graph of A.

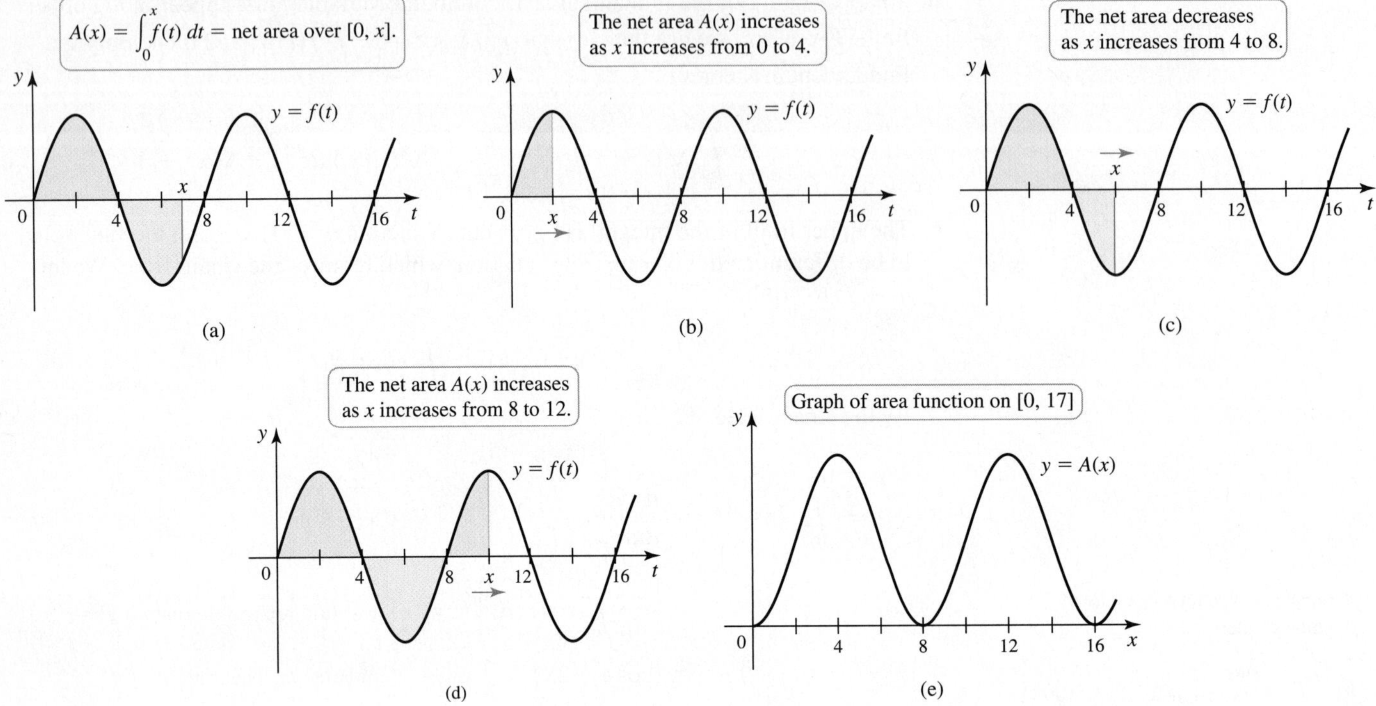

FIGURE 5.46

Related Exercises 55–66 ◀

EXAMPLE 7 **The sine integral function** Let

$$g(t) = \begin{cases} \dfrac{\sin t}{t} & \text{if } t > 0 \\ 1 & \text{if } t = 0 \end{cases}$$

Graph the *sine integral function* $S(x) = \int_0^x g(t)\,dt$, for $x \geq 0$.

SOLUTION Notice that S is an area function for g. The independent variable of S is x, while t has been chosen as the (dummy) variable of integration. A good way to start is by graphing the integrand g (Figure 5.47a). The function oscillates with a decreasing amplitude with $g(0) = 1$. Beginning with $S(0) = 0$, the area function S increases until $x = \pi$ because g is positive on $(0, \pi)$. However, on $(\pi, 2\pi)$, g is negative and the net area decreases. Then, on $(2\pi, 3\pi)$, g is positive again, so S again increases. Therefore, the graph of S has alternating local maxima and minima. Because the amplitude of g decreases, each maximum is less than the previous maximum and each minimum is greater than the previous minimum (Figure 5.47b). Determining the exact value of S at these maxima and minima is difficult.

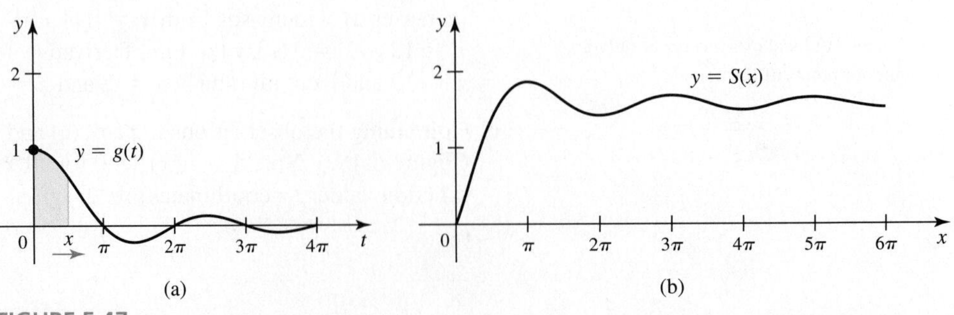

FIGURE 5.47

Appealing to the second part of the Fundamental Theorem, we find that

$$S'(x) = \frac{d}{dx}\int_0^x \frac{\sin t}{t}\,dt = \frac{\sin x}{x}, \qquad \text{for } x > 0.$$

As anticipated, the derivative of S changes sign at integer multiples of π. Specifically, S' is positive and S increases on the intervals $(0, \pi), (2\pi, 3\pi), \ldots, (2n\pi, (2n + 1)\pi), \ldots,$ while S' is negative and S decreases on the remaining intervals. It is clear that S has local maxima at $x = \pi, 3\pi, 5\pi, \ldots,$ and it has local minima at $x = 2\pi, 4\pi, 6\pi, \ldots.$

> Note that
> $$\lim_{x\to\infty} S'(x) = \lim_{x\to\infty} g(x) = 0$$

One more observation is helpful. It can be shown that, while S oscillates for increasing x, its graph gradually flattens out and approaches a horizontal asymptote. (Finding the exact value of this horizontal asymptote is challenging; see Exercise 93.) Assembling all these observations, the graph of the sine integral function emerges (Figure 5.47b).

Related Exercises 67–70 ◀

Proof of the Fundamental Theorem Let f be continuous on $[a, b]$ and let A be the area function for f with left endpoint a. The first step is to prove that $A'(x) = f(x)$, which is Part 1 of the Fundamental Theorem. The proof of Part 2 then follows.

Step 1. We use the definition of the derivative,

$$A'(x) = \lim_{h\to 0} \frac{A(x + h) - A(x)}{h}.$$

First assume that $h > 0$. Using Figure 5.48 and Property 5 of Table 5.3, we have

$$A(x + h) - A(x) = \int_a^{x+h} f(t)\,dt - \int_a^x f(t)\,dt = \int_x^{x+h} f(t)\,dt.$$

That is, $A(x + h) - A(x)$ is the net area of the region bounded by the curve on the interval $[x, x + h]$.

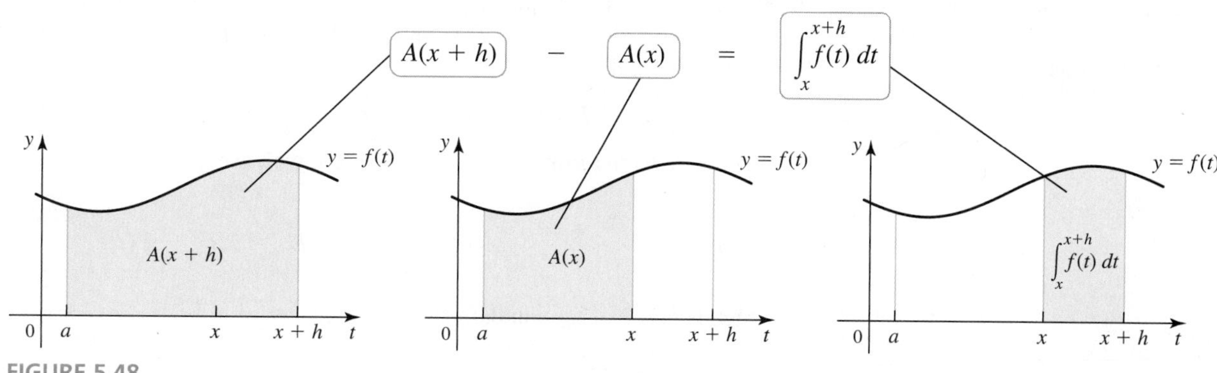

FIGURE 5.48

Let m and M be the minimum and maximum values of f on $[x, x + h]$, respectively, which exist by the continuity of f (Figure 5.49). In the case that $0 \le m \le M$, $A(x + h) - A(x)$ is greater than or equal to the area of a rectangle with height m and width h and it is less than or equal to the area of a rectangle with height M and width h; that is,

> The quantities m and M exist for any $h > 0$; however, they also depend on h. Figure 5.48 illustrates the case $0 \le m \le M$. The argument that follows holds for the general case.

$$mh \le A(x + h) - A(x) \le Mh.$$

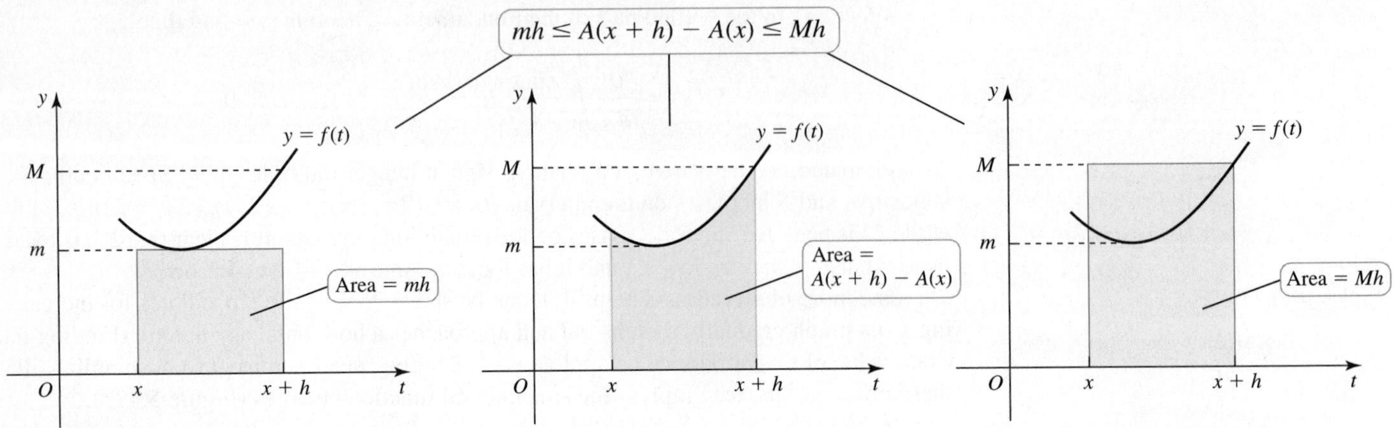

FIGURE 5.49

Dividing these inequalities by h, we have

$$m \leq \frac{A(x + h) - A(x)}{h} \leq M.$$

The case $h < 0$ is handled similarly and leads to the same conclusion.

We now take the limit as $h \to 0$ across these inequalities. As $h \to 0$, m and M squeeze together toward the value of f at x, because f is continuous at x. At the same time, as $h \to 0$, the quotient that is sandwiched between m and M approaches $A'(x)$:

$$\underbrace{\lim_{h\to 0} m}_{f(x)} = \underbrace{\lim_{h\to 0} \frac{A(x + h) - A(x)}{h}}_{A'(x)} = \underbrace{\lim_{h\to 0} M}_{f(x)}$$

By the Squeeze Theorem (Theorem 2.5), we conclude that $A'(x) = f(x)$.

➤ Once again we use an important fact: Two antiderivatives of the same function differ by a constant.

Step 2. Having established that the area function A is an antiderivative of f, we know that $F(x) = A(x) + C$, where F is any antiderivative of f and C is a constant. Noting that $A(a) = 0$, it follows that

$$F(b) - F(a) = (A(b) + C) - (A(a) + C) = A(b).$$

Writing $A(b)$ in terms of a definite integral, we have

$$A(b) = \int_a^b f(x)\,dx = F(b) - F(a),$$

which is part 2 of the Fundamental Theorem. ◀

SECTION 5.3 EXERCISES

Review Questions

1. Suppose A is an area function of f. What is the relationship between f and A?

2. Suppose F is an antiderivative of f and A is an area function of f. What is the relationship between F and A?

3. Explain in words and write mathematically how the Fundamental Theorem of Calculus is used to evaluate definite integrals.

4. Let $f(x) = c$, where c is a positive constant. Explain why an area function of f is an increasing function.

5. The linear function $f(x) = 3 - x$ is decreasing on the interval $[0, 3]$. Is its area function on the interval $[0, 3]$ increasing or decreasing? Draw a picture and explain.

6. Evaluate $\int_0^2 3x^2\,dx$ and $\int_{-2}^2 3x^2\,dx$.

7. Explain in words and express mathematically the inverse relationship between differentiation and integration as given by the Fundamental Theorem of Calculus.

8. Why can the constant of integration be omitted from the antiderivative when evaluating a definite integral?

9. Evaluate $\frac{d}{dx}\int_a^x f(t)\,dt$ and $\frac{d}{dx}\int_a^b f(t)\,dt$, where a and b are constants.

10. Explain why $\int_a^b f'(x)\,dx = f(b) - f(a)$.

Basic Skills

11. **Area functions** The graph of f is shown in the figure. Let $A(x) = \int_{-2}^x f(t)\,dt$ and $F(x) = \int_4^x f(t)\,dt$ be two area functions for f. Evaluate the following area functions.

a. $A(-2)$ **b.** $F(8)$ **c.** $A(4)$ **d.** $F(4)$ **e.** $A(8)$

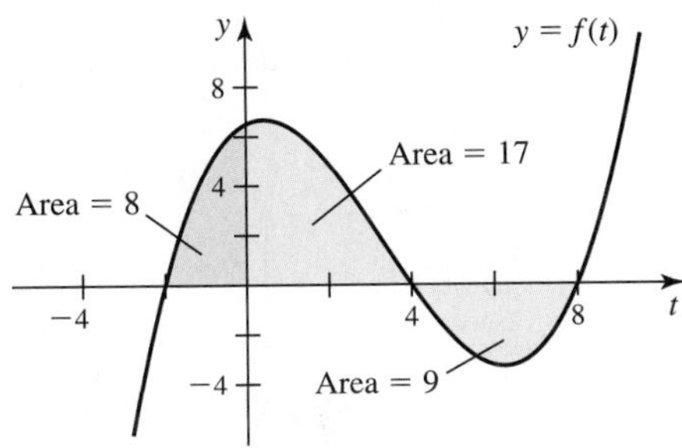

12. **Area functions** The graph of f is shown in the figure. Let $A(x) = \int_0^x f(t)\,dt$ and $F(x) = \int_2^x f(t)\,dt$ be two area functions for f. Evaluate the following area functions.

a. $A(2)$ **b.** $F(5)$ **c.** $A(0)$ **d.** $F(8)$ **e.** $A(8)$
f. $A(5)$ **g.** $F(2)$

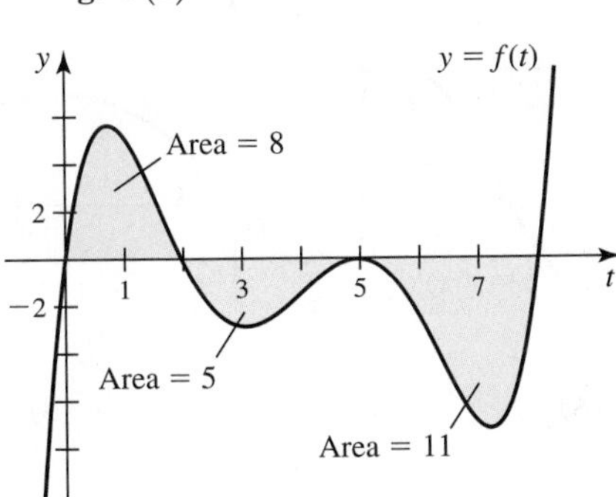

13–16. Area functions for constant functions *Consider the following functions f and real numbers a (see figure).*

a. *Find and graph the area function $A(x) = \int_a^x f(t)\,dt$ for f.*
b. *Verify that $A'(x) = f(x)$.*

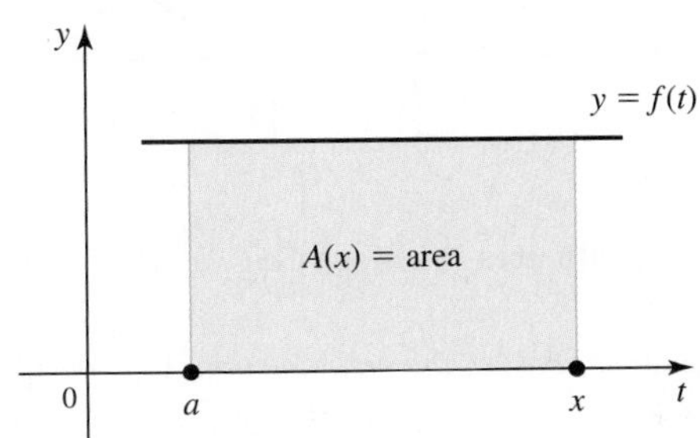

13. $f(t) = 5,\ a = 0$

14. $f(t) = 10,\ a = 4$

15. $f(t) = 5,\ a = -5$

16. $f(t) = 2,\ a = -3$

17. **Area functions for the same linear function** Let $f(t) = t$ and consider the two area functions $A(x) = \int_0^x f(t)\,dt$ and $F(x) = \int_2^x f(t)\,dt$.
   a. Evaluate $A(2)$ and $A(4)$. Then use geometry to find an expression for $A(x)$, for all $x \geq 0$.
   b. Evaluate $F(4)$ and $F(6)$. Then use geometry to find an expression for $F(x)$, for all $x \geq 2$.
   c. Show that $A(x) - F(x)$ is a constant.

18. **Area functions for the same linear function** Let $f(t) = 2t - 2$ and consider the two area functions $A(x) = \int_1^x f(t)\,dt$ and $F(x) = \int_4^x f(t)\,dt$.
   a. Evaluate $A(2)$ and $A(3)$. Then use geometry to find an expression for $A(x)$, for all $x \geq 1$.
   b. Evaluate $F(5)$ and $F(6)$. Then use geometry to find an expression for $F(x)$, for all $x \geq 4$.
   c. Show that $A(x) - F(x)$ is a constant.

19–22. Area functions for linear functions *Consider the following functions f and real numbers a (see figure).*

a. *Find and graph the area function $A(x) = \int_a^x f(t)\,dt$.*
b. *Verify that $A'(x) = f(x)$.*

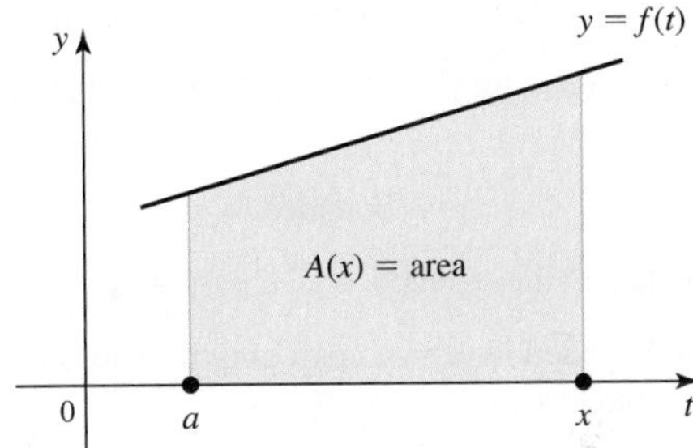

19. $f(t) = t + 5,\ a = -5$

20. $f(t) = 2t + 5,\ a = 0$

21. $f(t) = 3t + 1,\ a = 2$

22. $f(t) = 4t + 2,\ a = 0$

23–24. Definite integrals *Evaluate the following integrals using the Fundamental Theorem of Calculus. Discuss whether your result is consistent with the figure.*

23. $\displaystyle\int_0^1 (x^2 - 2x + 3)\,dx$

24. $\displaystyle\int_{-\pi/4}^{7\pi/4} (\sin x + \cos x)\,dx$

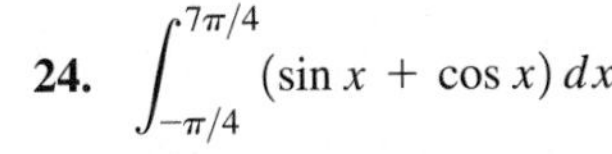

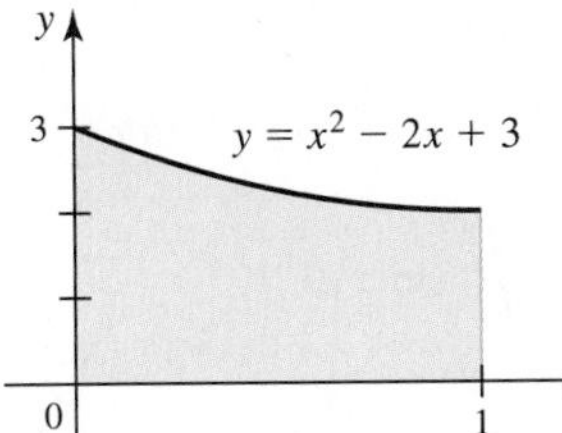

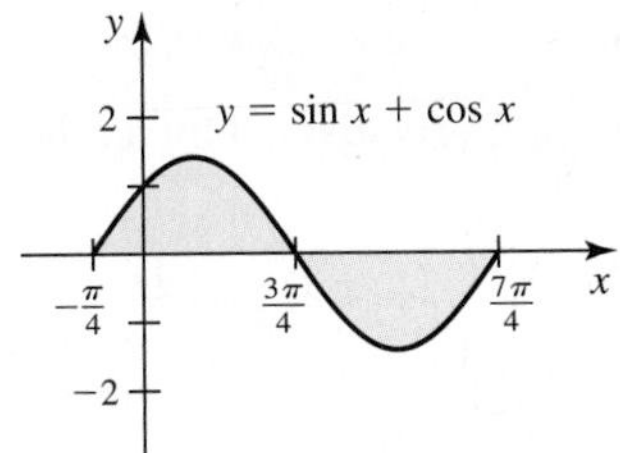

25–30. Definite integrals *Evaluate the following integrals using the Fundamental Theorem of Calculus. Sketch a graph of the integrand and shade the region whose net area you have found.*

25. $\displaystyle\int_1^4 (1 - x)(x - 4)\,dx$

26. $\displaystyle\int_0^{\pi} (1 - \sin x)\,dx$

27. $\int_{-2}^{3} (x^2 - x - 6)\, dx$ **28.** $\int_{0}^{1} (x - \sqrt{x})\, dx$

29. $\int_{0}^{5} (x^2 - 9)\, dx$ **30.** $\int_{1/2}^{2} \left(1 - \frac{1}{x^2}\right) dx$

31–38. Definite integrals *Evaluate the following integrals using the Fundamental Theorem of Calculus.*

31. $\int_{-2}^{2} (x^2 - 4)\, dx$ **32.** $\int_{1/2}^{1} (x^{-3} - 8)\, dx$

33. $\int_{0}^{4} x(x - 2)(x - 4)\, dx$ **34.** $\int_{0}^{\pi/4} \sec^2 \theta\, d\theta$

35. $\int_{-2}^{-1} x^{-3}\, dx$ **36.** $\int_{-\pi/2}^{\pi/2} (\cos x - 1)\, dx$

37. $\int_{1}^{4} \frac{5t^6 - \sqrt{t}}{t^2}\, dt$ **38.** $\int_{4}^{9} \frac{x - \sqrt{x}}{x^3}\, dx$

39–42. Areas *Find (i) the net area and (ii) the area of the following regions. Graph the function and indicate the region in question.*

39. The region bounded by $y = x^{1/2}$ and the x-axis between $x = 1$ and $x = 4$

40. The region above the x-axis bounded by $y = 4 - x^2$

41. The region below the x-axis bounded by $y = x^4 - 16$

42. The region bounded by $y = 6 \cos x$ and the x-axis between $x = -\pi/2$ and $x = \pi$

T **43–48. Areas of regions** *Find the area of the region R bounded by the graph of f and the x-axis on the given interval. Graph f and the region R.*

43. $f(x) = x^2 - 25;\ [2, 4]$ **44.** $f(x) = x^3 - 1;\ [-1, 2]$

45. $f(x) = \frac{1}{x^3};\ [-2, -1]$

46. $f(x) = x(x + 1)(x - 2);\ [-1, 2]$

47. $f(x) = \sin x;\ [-\pi/4, 3\pi/4]$

48. $f(x) = \cos x;\ [\pi/2, \pi]$

49–54. Derivatives of integrals *Simplify the following expressions.*

49. $\frac{d}{dx} \int_{3}^{x} (t^2 + t + 1)\, dt$ **50.** $\frac{d}{dx} \int_{0}^{x} \sin^2 t\, dt$

51. $\frac{d}{dx} \int_{2}^{x^3} \frac{dp}{p^2}$ **52.** $\frac{d}{dx} \int_{x^2}^{10} \frac{dz}{z^2 + 1}$

53. $\frac{d}{dx} \int_{x}^{1} \sqrt{t^4 + 1}\, dt$ **54.** $\frac{d}{dx} \int_{x}^{0} \frac{dp}{p^2 + 1}$

55. Matching functions with area functions Match the functions f whose graphs are given in (a)–(d) with the area functions $A(x) = \int_0^x f(t)\, dt$, whose graphs are given in (A)–(D).

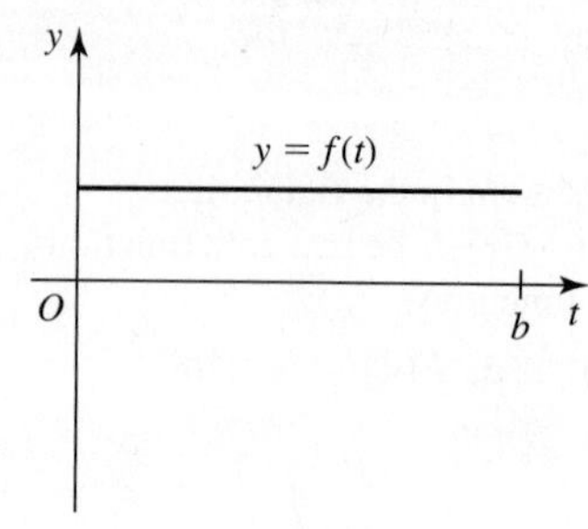

(a)

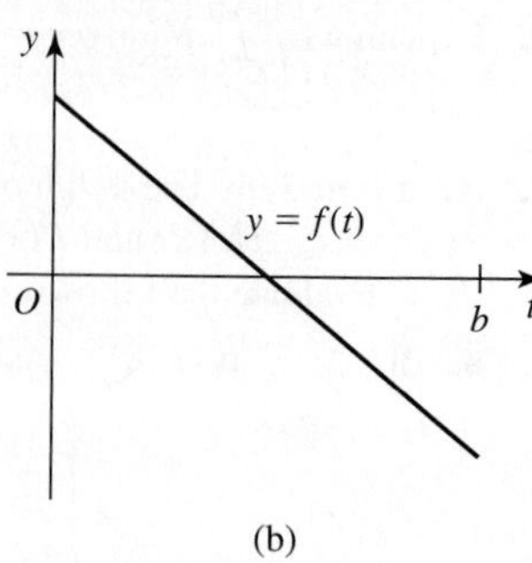

(b)

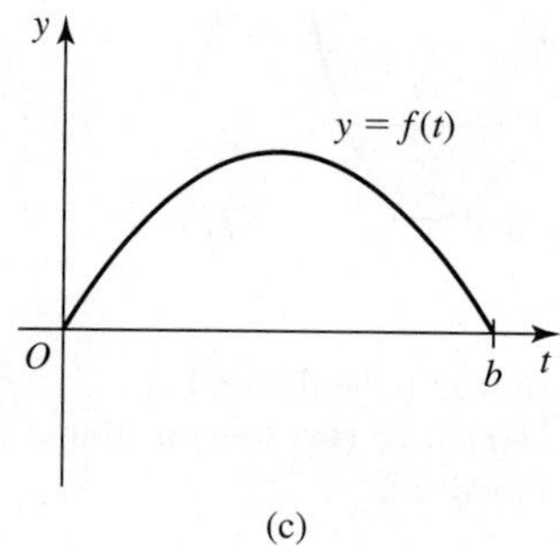

(c)

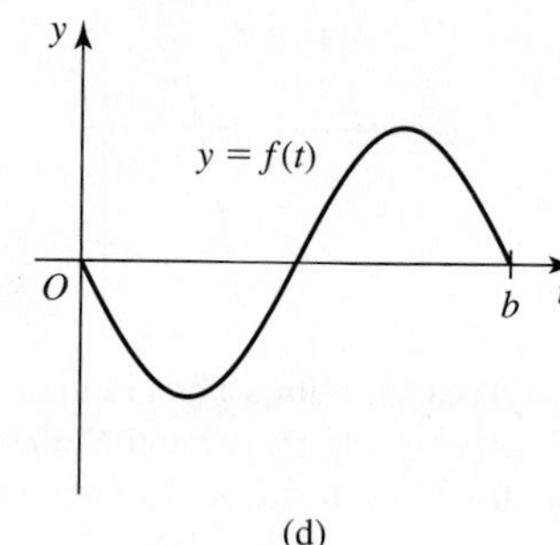

(d)

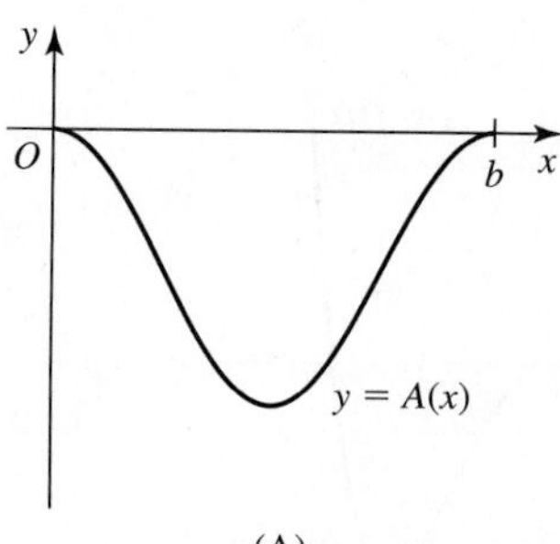

(A)

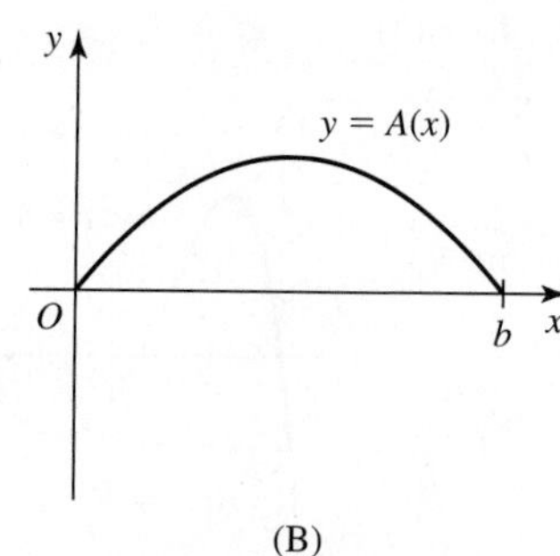

(B)

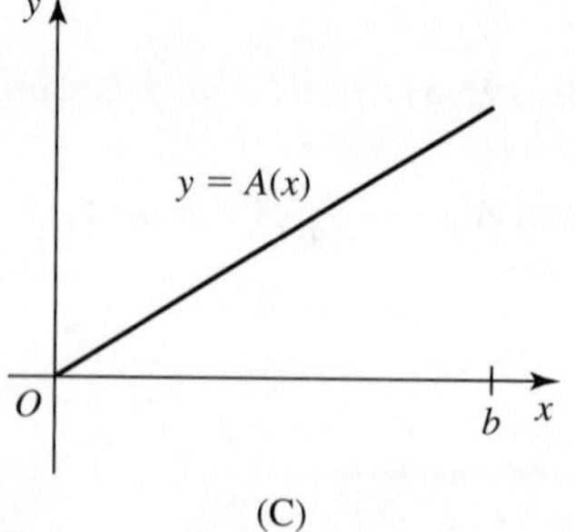

(C)

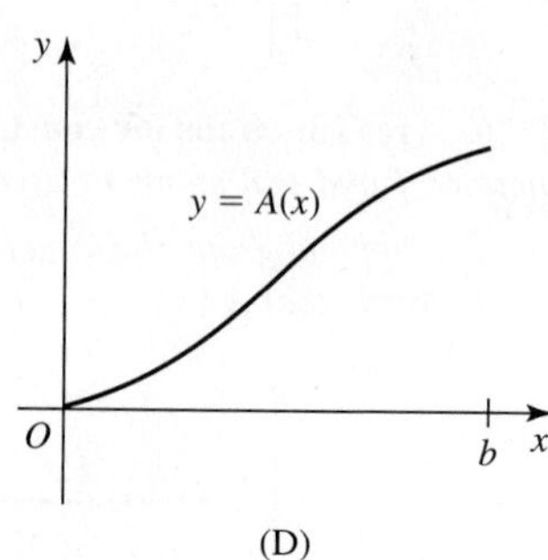

(D)

56–59. Working with area functions *Consider the following graphs of functions f.*

a. *Estimate the zeros of the area function $A(x) = \int_0^x f(t)\, dt$, for $0 \le x \le 10$.*

b. *Estimate the points (if any) at which A has a local maximum or minimum.*

c. *Sketch a rough graph of A, for $0 \le x \le 10$, without a scale on the y-axis.*

56.

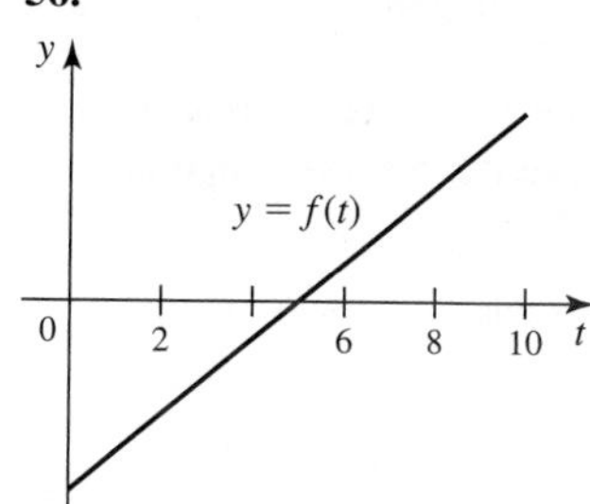

57.

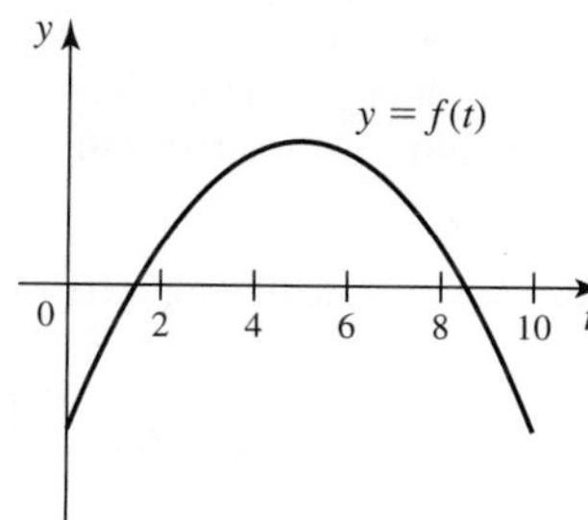

58.

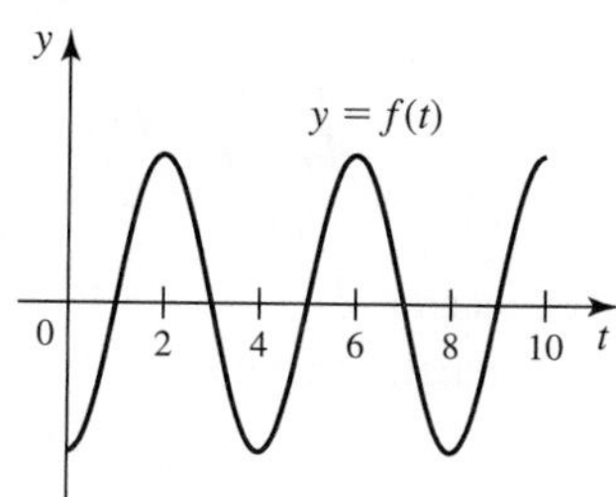

59.

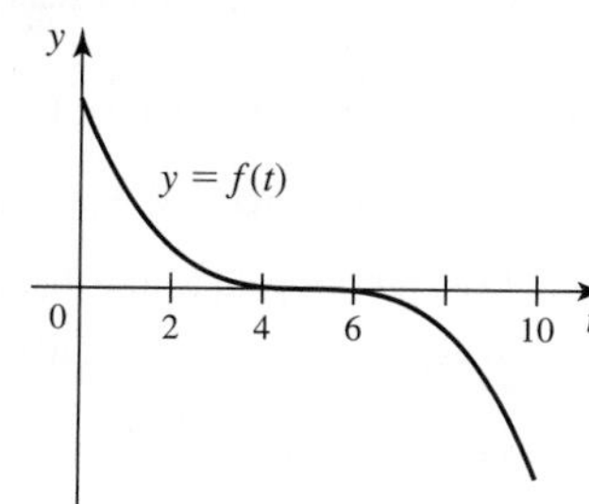

60. **Area functions from graphs** The graph of f is given in the figure. Let $A(x) = \int_0^x f(t)\,dt$ and evaluate $A(1)$, $A(2)$, $A(4)$, and $A(6)$.

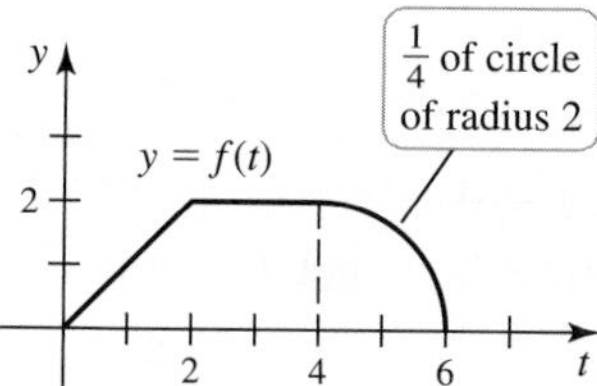

61. **Area functions from graphs** The graph of f is given in the figure. Let $A(x) = \int_0^x f(t)\,dt$ and evaluate $A(2)$, $A(5)$, $A(8)$, and $A(12)$.

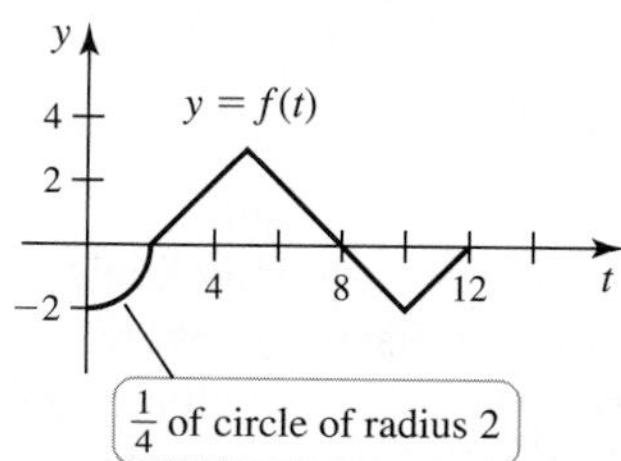

62–66. Working with area functions *Consider the function f and the points a, b, and c.*

a. *Find the area function $A(x) = \int_a^x f(t)\,dt$ using the Fundamental Theorem.*

b. *Graph f and A.*

c. *Evaluate A(b) and A(c) and interpret the results using the graphs of part (b).*

62. $f(x) = \sin x;\ a = 0, b = \pi/2, c = \pi$

63. $f(x) = \cos x;\ a = 0, b = \pi/2, c = \pi$

64. $f(x) = x^3 + 1;\ a = 0, b = 2, c = 3$

65. $f(x) = x^{1/2};\ a = 1, b = 4, c = 9$

66. $f(x) = 1/x^2;\ a = 1, b = 2, c = 4$

T **67–70. Functions defined by integrals** *Consider the function g, which is given in terms of a definite integral with a variable upper limit.*

a. *Graph the integrand.*

b. *Calculate $g'(x)$.*

c. *Graph g, showing all of your work and reasoning.*

67. $g(x) = \int_0^x \sin^2 t\,dt$

68. $g(x) = \int_0^x (t^2 + 1)\,dt$

69. $g(x) = \int_0^x \sin(\pi t^2)\,dt$ (a Fresnel integral)

70. $g(x) = \int_0^x \cos(\pi\sqrt{t})\,dt$

Further Explorations

71. **Explain why or why not** Determine whether the following statements are true and give an explanation or counterexample.

a. Suppose that f is a positive decreasing function, for $x > 0$. Then the area function $A(x) = \int_0^x f(t)\,dt$ is an increasing function of x.

b. Suppose that f is a negative increasing function, for $x > 0$. Then the area function $A(x) = \int_0^x f(t)\,dt$ is a decreasing function of x.

c. The functions $p(x) = \sin 3x$ and $q(x) = 4 \sin 3x$ are antiderivatives of the same function.

d. If $A(x) = 3x^2 - x + 2$ is an area function for f, then $B(x) = 3x^2 - x$ is also an area function for f.

72–78. Definite integrals *Evaluate the following definite integrals using the Fundamental Theorem of Calculus.*

72. $\frac{1}{2}\int_1^4 \frac{x^2 - 1}{x^2}\,dx$

73. $\int_1^4 \frac{x - 2}{\sqrt{x}}\,dx$

74. $\int_1^2 \left(\frac{2}{s^2} - \frac{4}{s^3}\right) ds$

75. $\int_0^{\pi/3} \sec x \tan x\,dx$

76. $\int_{\pi/4}^{\pi/2} \csc^2\theta\,d\theta$

77. $\int_1^8 \sqrt[3]{y}\,dy$

78. $\int_1^2 \frac{x^2 + 6x + 8}{x^4 + 2x^3}\,dx$

T **79–82. Areas of regions** *Find the area of the region R bounded by the graph of f and the x-axis on the given interval. Graph f and show the region R.*

79. $f(x) = 2 - |x|;\ [-2, 4]$

80. $f(x) = 16 - x^4;\ [-2, 2]$

81. $f(x) = x^4 - 4;\ [1, 4]$

82. $f(x) = x^2(x - 2);\ [-1, 3]$

83–86. Derivatives and integrals *Simplify the given expressions. Assume that derivatives are continuous on the interval of integration.*

83. $\int_3^8 f'(t)\,dt$

84. $\frac{d}{dx}\int_0^{x^2} \frac{1}{t^2 + 4}\,dt$

85. $\frac{d}{dx}\int_0^{\cos x} (t^4 + 6)\,dt$

86. $\frac{d}{dx}\int_x^1 \cos^3 t\,dt$

Additional Exercises

87. Zero net area Consider the function $f(x) = x^2 - 4x$.

a. Graph f on the interval $x \geq 0$.

b. For what value of $b > 0$ is $\int_0^b f(x)\,dx = 0$?

c. In general, for the function $f(x) = x^2 - ax$, where $a > 0$, for what value of $b > 0$ (as a function of a) is $\int_0^b f(x)\,dx = 0$?

88. Cubic zero net area Consider the graph of the cubic $y = x(x - a)(x - b)$ where $0 < a < b$. Verify that the graph bounds a region above the x-axis for $0 < x < a$ and bounds a region below the x-axis for $a < x < b$. What is the relationship between a and b if the areas of these two regions are equal?

89. Maximum net area What value of $b > -1$ maximizes the integral

$$\int_{-1}^{b} x^2 (3 - x)\,dx?$$

T **90. Maximum net area** Graph the function $f(x) = 8 + 2x - x^2$ and determine the values of a and b that maximize the value of the integral

$$\int_a^b (8 + 2x - x^2)\,dx.$$

91. An integral equation Use the Fundamental Theorem of Calculus, Part 1, to find the function f that satisfies the equation

$$\int_0^x f(t)\,dt = 2\cos x + 3x + 2.$$

92. Max/min of area functions Suppose f is continuous on $[0, \infty)$ and $A(x)$ is the net area of the region bounded by the graph of f and the t-axis on $[0, x]$. Show that the maxima and minima of A occur at the zeros of f. Verify this fact with the function $f(x) = x^2 - 10x$.

T **93. Asymptote of sine integral** Use a calculator to approximate

$$\lim_{x\to\infty} S(x) = \lim_{x\to\infty} \int_0^x \frac{\sin t}{t}\,dt,$$

where S is the sine integral function (see Example 7). Show your work and describe your reasoning.

94. Sine integral Show that the sine integral $S(x) = \int_0^x \frac{\sin t}{t}\,dt$ satisfies the (differential) equation $xS'(x) + 2S''(x) + xS'''(x) = 0$.

95. Fresnel integral Show that the Fresnel integral $S(x) = \int_0^x \sin(t^2)\,dt$ satisfies the (differential) equation

$$(S'(x))^2 + \left(\frac{S''(x)}{2x}\right)^2 = 1.$$

96. Variable integration limits Evaluate $\frac{d}{dx}\int_{-x}^{x} (t^2 + t)\,dt$. (*Hint:* Separate the integral into two pieces.)

QUICK CHECK ANSWERS

1. $0, -35$ **2.** $A(6) = 44$; $A(10) = 120$ **3.** $\frac{2}{3} - \frac{1}{2} = \frac{1}{6}$ **4.** If f is differentiated, we get f'. Thus f is an antiderivative of f'. ◄

5.4 Working with Integrals

With the Fundamental Theorem of Calculus in hand, we may begin an investigation of integration and its applications. In this section we discuss the role of symmetry in integrals, use the slice-and-sum strategy to define the average value of a function, and then explore a theoretical result called the Mean Value Theorem for integrals.

Integrating Even and Odd Functions

Symmetry appears throughout mathematics in many different forms, and its use often leads to insights and efficiencies. Here we use the symmetry of a function to simplify integral calculations.

Section 1.1 introduced the symmetry of even and odd functions. An **even function** satisfies the property that $f(-x) = f(x)$, which means that its graph is symmetric about the y-axis (Figure 5.50a). Examples of even functions are $f(x) = \cos x$ and $f(x) = x^n$, where n is an even integer. An **odd function** satisfies the property that $f(-x) = -f(x)$, which means that its graph is symmetric about the origin (Figure 5.50b). Examples of odd functions are $f(x) = \sin x$ and $f(x) = x^n$, where n is an odd integer.

Special things happen when we integrate even and odd functions on intervals centered at the origin. First, suppose f is an even function and consider $\int_{-a}^{a} f(x)\,dx$. From

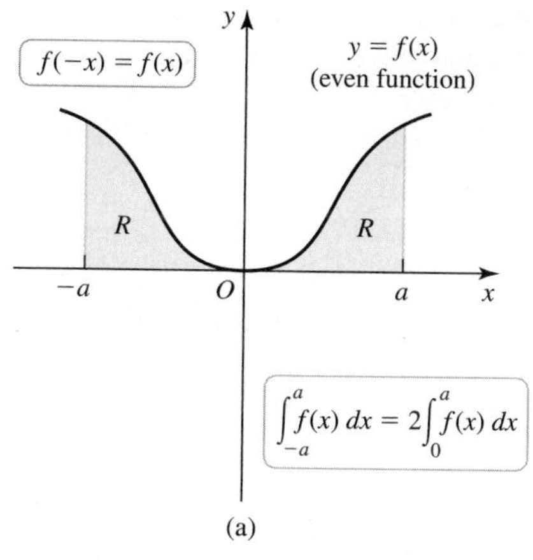

(a)

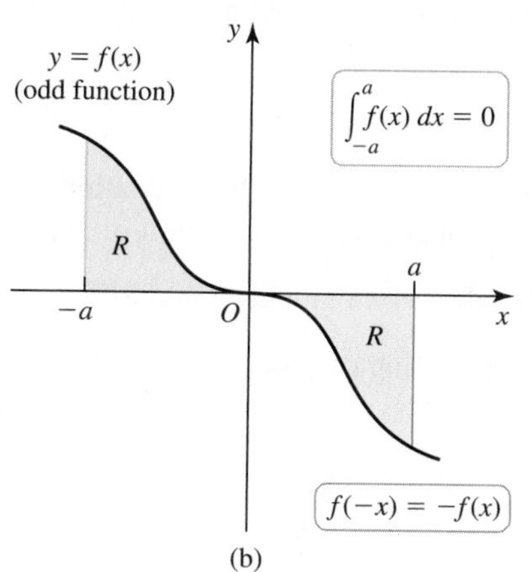

(b)

FIGURE 5.50

Figure 5.50a, we see that the integral of f on $[-a, 0]$ equals the integral of f on $[0, a]$. Therefore, the integral on $[-a, a]$ is twice the integral on $[0, a]$, or

$$\int_{-a}^{a} f(x)\,dx = 2\int_{0}^{a} f(x)\,dx.$$

On the other hand, suppose f is an odd function and consider $\int_{-a}^{a} f(x)\,dx$. As shown in Figure 5.50b, the integral on the interval $[-a, 0]$ is the negative of the integral on $[0, a]$. Therefore, the integral on $[-a, a]$ is zero, or

$$\int_{-a}^{a} f(x)\,dx = 0.$$

We summarize these results in the following theorem.

THEOREM 5.4 Integrals of Even and Odd Functions
Let a be a positive real number and let f be an integrable function on the interval $[-a, a]$.

- If f is even, $\int_{-a}^{a} f(x)\,dx = 2\int_{0}^{a} f(x)\,dx$.
- If f is odd, $\int_{-a}^{a} f(x)\,dx = 0$.

QUICK CHECK 1 If f and g are both even functions, is the product fg even or odd? Use the facts that $f(-x) = f(x)$ and $g(-x) = g(x)$.

EXAMPLE 1 Integrating symmetric functions Evaluate the following integrals using symmetry arguments.

a. $\displaystyle\int_{-2}^{2} (x^4 - 3x^3)\,dx$ **b.** $\displaystyle\int_{-\pi/2}^{\pi/2} (\cos x - 4\sin^3 x)\,dx$

SOLUTION

a. Using Properties 3 and 4 of Table 5.3, we split the integral into two integrals and use symmetry:

$$\begin{aligned}
\int_{-2}^{2} (x^4 - 3x^3)\,dx &= \int_{-2}^{2} x^4\,dx - 3\int_{-2}^{2} x^3\,dx \\
&= 2\int_{0}^{2} x^4\,dx - 0 && x^4 \text{ is even, } x^3 \text{ is odd.} \\
&= 2\left(\frac{x^5}{5}\right)\bigg|_0^2 && \text{Fundamental Theorem} \\
&= 2\left(\frac{32}{5}\right) = \frac{64}{5} && \text{Simplify.}
\end{aligned}$$

Notice how the odd-powered term of the integrand is eliminated by symmetry. Integration of the even-powered term is simplified because the lower limit is zero.

➤ There are several ways to see that $\sin^3 x$ is an odd function. Its graph is symmetric about the origin. Or by analogy, take an odd power of x and raise it to an odd power. For example, $(x^5)^3 = x^{15}$, which is odd. See Exercises 45–48 and 57 for direct proofs of symmetry in composite functions.

b. The $\cos x$ term is an even function, so it can be integrated on the interval $[0, \pi/2]$. What about $\sin^3 x$? It is an odd function raised to an odd power, which results in an odd function; its integral on $[-\pi/2, \pi/2]$ is zero. Therefore,

$$\begin{aligned}\int_{-\pi/2}^{\pi/2} (\cos x - 4\sin^3 x)\,dx &= 2\int_0^{\pi/2} \cos x\,dx - 0 && \text{Symmetry}\\ &= 2\sin x\Big|_0^{\pi/2} && \text{Fundamental Theorem}\\ &= 2(1-0) = 2. && \text{Simplify.}\end{aligned}$$

Related Exercises 7–18 ◄

Average Value of a Function

If five people weigh 155, 143, 180, 105, and 123 lb, their average (mean) weight is

$$\frac{155 + 143 + 180 + 105 + 123}{5} = 141.2 \text{ lb}.$$

This idea generalizes quite naturally to functions. Consider a function f that is continuous on $[a, b]$. Let the grid points $x_0 = a, x_1, x_2, \ldots, x_n = b$ form a regular partition of $[a, b]$ with $\Delta x = \dfrac{b-a}{n}$. We now select a point $\overline{x}_k$ in each subinterval and compute $f(\overline{x}_k)$ for $k = 1, \ldots, n$. The values of $f(\overline{x}_k)$ may be viewed as a sampling of f on $[a, b]$. The average of these function values is

$$\frac{f(\overline{x}_1) + f(\overline{x}_2) + \cdots + f(\overline{x}_n)}{n}.$$

Noting that $n = \dfrac{b-a}{\Delta x}$, we write the average of the n sample values as the Riemann sum

$$\frac{f(\overline{x}_1) + f(\overline{x}_2) + \cdots + f(\overline{x}_n)}{(b-a)/\Delta x} = \frac{1}{b-a}\sum_{k=1}^{n} f(\overline{x}_k)\,\Delta x.$$

Now suppose we increase n, taking more and more samples of f, while Δx decreases to zero. The limit of this sum is a definite integral that gives the average value $\overline{f}$ on $[a, b]$:

$$\begin{aligned}\overline{f} &= \frac{1}{b-a}\lim_{n\to\infty}\sum_{k=1}^{n} f(\overline{x}_k)\,\Delta x\\ &= \frac{1}{b-a}\int_a^b f(x)\,dx\end{aligned}$$

This definition of the average value of a function is analogous to the definition of the average of a finite set of numbers.

DEFINITION Average Value of a Function

The average value of an integrable function f on the interval $[a, b]$ is

$$\overline{f} = \frac{1}{b-a}\int_a^b f(x)\,dx.$$

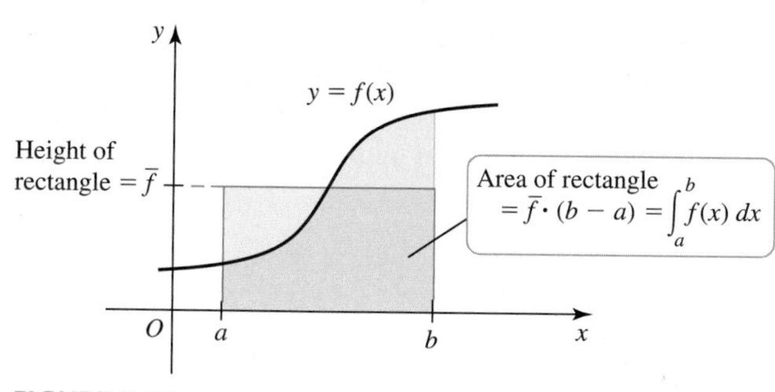

FIGURE 5.51

The average value of a function f on an interval $[a, b]$ has a clear geometrical interpretation. Multiplying both sides of the definition of average value by $(b - a)$, we have

$$\underbrace{(b-a)\bar{f}}_{\text{net area of rectangle}} = \underbrace{\int_a^b f(x)\,dx.}_{\text{net area of region bounded by curve}}$$

We see that the average value is the height of the rectangle with base $[a, b]$ that has the same net area as the region bounded by the graph of f on the interval $[a, b]$ (Figure 5.51). (We need to use net area in case f is negative on part of $[a, b]$, which could make $\bar{f}$ negative.)

QUICK CHECK 2 What is the average value of a constant function on an interval? What is the average value of an odd function on an interval $[-a, a]$?

EXAMPLE 2 **Average elevation** A hiking trail has an elevation given by

$$f(x) = 60x^3 - 650x^2 + 1200x + 4500,$$

where f is measured in feet above sea level and x represents horizontal distance along the trail in miles, with $0 \le x \le 5$. What is the average elevation of the trail?

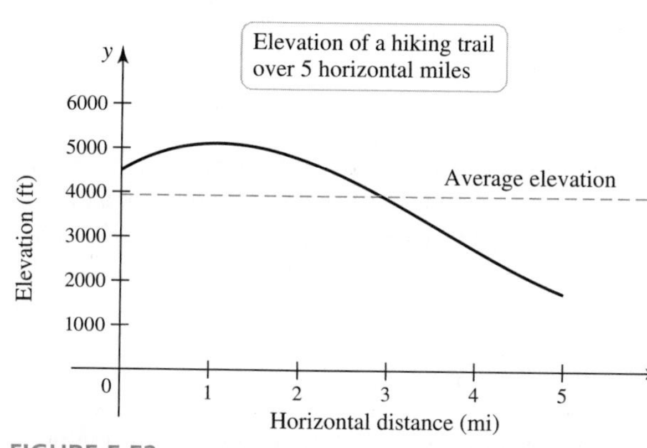

FIGURE 5.52

SOLUTION The trail ranges between elevations of about 2000 and 5000 ft (Figure 5.52). If we let the endpoints of the trail correspond to the horizontal distances $a = 0$ and $b = 5$ mi, the average elevation of the trail is

$$\begin{aligned}\bar{f} &= \frac{1}{5}\int_0^5 (60x^3 - 650x^2 + 1200x + 4500)\,dx \\ &= \frac{1}{5}\left(60\frac{x^4}{4} - 650\frac{x^3}{3} + 1200\frac{x^2}{2} + 4500x\right)\Big|_0^5 && \text{Fundamental Theorem} \\ &= 3958\tfrac{1}{3}\text{ ft.} && \text{Simplify.}\end{aligned}$$

The average elevation of the trail is slightly less than 3960 ft.

Related Exercises 19–26

EXAMPLE 3 **Average distance** Suppose you walk at constant speed along a semicircle with a radius of 1 km. What is your average distance from the *base* of the semicircle over your entire trip?

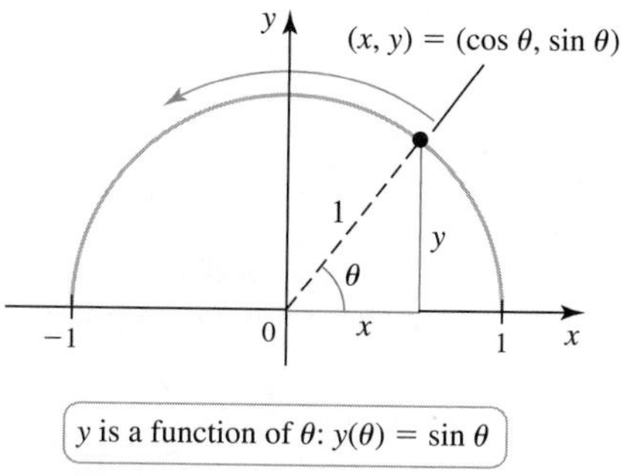

(x, y) = (cos θ, sin θ)

y is a function of θ: y(θ) = sin θ

FIGURE 5.53

SOLUTION As you walk along the semicircle, your x- and y-coordinates change continuously (Figure 5.53). The goal is to find the average value of the y-coordinate. The easiest way to describe the walk is in terms of the angle θ, which varies from 0 to π. For each value of θ corresponding to a point along the path, the y-coordinate is $y = \sin\theta$. Therefore, the average value of the y-coordinate as you walk along the path is

$$\begin{aligned}\bar{y} &= \frac{1}{\pi - 0}\int_0^\pi y(\theta)\,d\theta = \frac{1}{\pi}\int_0^\pi \sin\theta\,d\theta && \text{Substitute for } y. \\ &= \frac{1}{\pi}(-\cos\theta)\Big|_0^\pi && \text{Fundamental Theorem} \\ &= -\frac{1}{\pi}[(-1)-1] = \frac{2}{\pi}. && \text{Simplify.}\end{aligned}$$

Your average distance from the base of the semicircle is $2/\pi \approx 0.64$ km.

Related Exercises 27–28

In Example 3, the average distance to the x-axis is computed relative to a person walking on the semicircle. One could also compute the average height of the semicircle above the x-axis, which is $\pi/4$.

Mean Value Theorem for Integrals

The average value of a function brings us close to an important theoretical result. The **Mean Value Theorem for Integrals** says that if f is continuous on $[a, b]$ then there is at least one point c in the interval $[a, b]$ such that $f(c)$ equals the average value of f on $[a, b]$. In other words, the horizontal line $y = \overline{f} = f(c)$ intersects the graph of f for some point c in $[a, b]$ (Figure 5.54). If f were not continuous, such a point might not exist.

➤ Compare this statement to that of the Mean Value Theorem for derivatives: There is at least one point c in (a, b) such that $f'(c)$ equals the average slope of f.

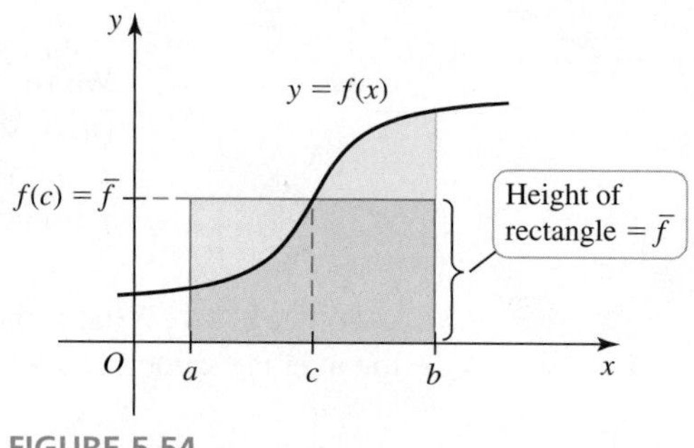

FIGURE 5.54

> **THEOREM 5.5 Mean Value Theorem for Integrals**
> Let f be continuous on the interval $[a, b]$. There exists a point c in $[a, b]$ such that
> $$f(c) = \overline{f} = \frac{1}{b-a}\int_a^b f(x)\,dx.$$

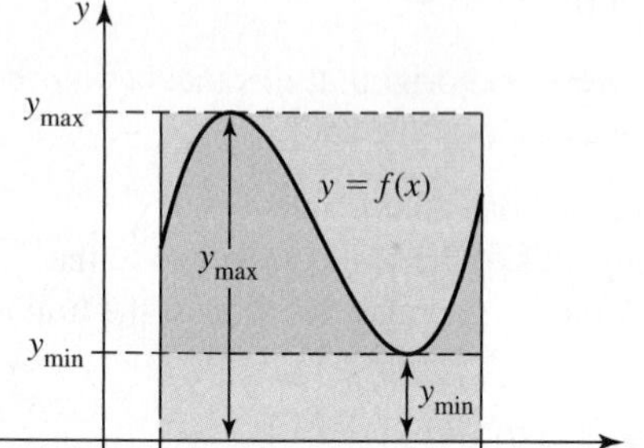

Area of smallest rectangle (red) $= (b - a)\,y_{min}$
Area under curve (red + green) $= \int_a^b f(x)\,dx$
Area of largest rectangle (red + green + blue) $= (b - a)\,y_{max}$

FIGURE 5.55

Proof The proof offers a nice application of the Extreme Value Theorem (Theorem 4.1) and the Intermediate Value Theorem (Theorem 2.13). Because f is continuous on a closed interval $[a, b]$, it attains its minimum value y_{min} and its maximum value y_{max} on $[a, b]$. Also note that

$$(b-a)y_{min} \le \int_a^b f(x)\,dx \le (b-a)y_{max} \qquad \text{(Figure 5.55).}$$

These inequalities hold because if every function value in the Riemann sum for the integral is replaced by y_{min}, we obtain a lower bound on the integral. If every function value in the Riemann sum for the integral is replaced by y_{max}, we obtain an upper bound on the integral. Dividing through these inequalities by $(b - a)$, we have

$$y_{min} \le \underbrace{\frac{1}{b-a}\int_a^b f(x)\,dx}_{\overline{f}} \le y_{max}.$$

Because f is continuous on $[a, b]$, f assumes all values between y_{min} and y_{max} by the Intermediate Value Theorem. In particular, $y_{min} \le \overline{f} \le y_{max}$, so there must be a point c in $[a, b]$ for which $f(c) = \overline{f} = \frac{1}{b-a}\int_a^b f(x)\,dx$. ◄

➤ A more general form of the Mean Value Theorem for Integrals states that if f and g are continuous on $[a, b]$ with $g(x) \ge 0$ on $[a, b]$, then there exists a number c in $[a, b]$ such that
$$\int_a^b f(x)g(x)dx = f(c)\int_a^b g(x)dx.$$

QUICK CHECK 3 Explain why $f(x) = 0$ for at least one point of $[a, b]$ if f is continuous and $\int_a^b f(x)\,dx = 0$. ◄

EXAMPLE 4 Average value equals function value Find the point(s) on the interval $[0, 1]$ at which $f(x) = 2x(1 - x)$ equals its average value on $[0, 1]$.

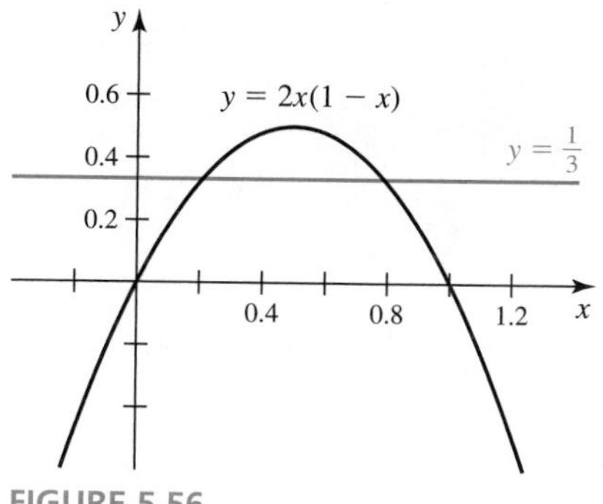

FIGURE 5.56

SOLUTION The average value of f on $[0, 1]$ is

$$\bar{f} = \frac{1}{1-0}\int_0^1 2x(1-x)\,dx = \left(x^2 - \frac{2}{3}x^3\right)\Big|_0^1 = \frac{1}{3}.$$

We must find the points on $[0, 1]$ at which $f(x) = \frac{1}{3}$ (Figure 5.56). Using the quadratic formula, the two solutions of $f(x) = 2x(1 - x) = \frac{1}{3}$ are

$$\frac{1 - \sqrt{1/3}}{2} \approx 0.211 \quad \text{and} \quad \frac{1 + \sqrt{1/3}}{2} \approx 0.789.$$

These two points are located symmetrically on either side of $x = \frac{1}{2}$. The two solutions, 0.211 and 0.789, are the same for $f(x) = ax(1 - x)$ for any value of a (Exercise 49).

Related Exercises 29–34 ◀

SECTION 5.4 EXERCISES

Review Questions

1. If f is an odd function, why is $\int_{-a}^{a} f(x)\,dx = 0$?
2. If f is an even function, why is $\int_{-a}^{a} f(x)\,dx = 2\int_0^a f(x)\,dx$?
3. Is x^{12} an even or odd function? Is $\sin x^2$ an even or odd function?
4. Explain how to find the average value of a function on an interval $[a, b]$ and why this definition is analogous to the definition of the average of a finite set of numbers.
5. Explain the statement that a continuous function on an interval $[a, b]$ equals its average value at some point on $[a, b]$.
6. Sketch the function $y = x$ on the interval $[0, 2]$ and let R be the region bounded by $y = x$ and the x-axis on $[0, 2]$. Now sketch a rectangle in the first quadrant whose base is $[0, 2]$ and whose area equals the area of R.

Basic Skills

7–14. Symmetry in integrals *Use symmetry to evaluate the following integrals.*

7. $\int_{-2}^{2} (3x^8 - 2)\,dx$
8. $\int_{-\pi/4}^{\pi/4} \cos x\,dx$
9. $\int_{-2}^{2} (x^9 - 3x^5 + 2x^2 - 10)\,dx$
10. $\int_{-\pi/2}^{\pi/2} 5\sin x\,dx$
11. $\int_{-10}^{10} \frac{x}{\sqrt{200 - x^2}}\,dx$
12. $\int_{-\pi/2}^{\pi/2} (\cos 2x + \cos x \sin x - 3\sin x^5)\,dx$
13. $\int_{-\pi/4}^{\pi/4} \sin^5 x\,dx$
14. $\int_{-1}^{1} (1 - |x|)\,dx$

15–18. Symmetry and definite integrals *Use symmetry to evaluate the following integrals. Draw a figure to interpret your result.*

15. $\int_{-\pi}^{\pi} \sin x\,dx$
16. $\int_0^{2\pi} \cos x\,dx$
17. $\int_0^{\pi} \cos x\,dx$
18. $\int_0^{2\pi} \sin x\,dx$

19–22. Average values *Find the average value of the following functions on the given interval. Draw a graph of the function and indicate the average value.*

19. $f(x) = \cos x;\ [-\pi/2, \pi/2]$
20. $f(x) = x(1 - x);\ [0, 1]$
21. $f(x) = x^n;\ [0, 1]$ for any positive integer n
22. $f(x) = x^{1/n};\ [0, 1]$ for any positive integer n
23. **Average distance on a parabola** What is the average distance between the parabola $y = 10x(20 - x)$ and the x-axis on the interval $[0, 20]$?
24. **Average elevation** The elevation of a path is given by $f(x) = x^3 - 5x^2 + 10$, where x measures horizontal distances. Draw a graph of the elevation function and find its average value, for $0 \le x \le 4$.
25. **Average height of an arch** The height of an arch above the ground is given by the function $y = 10\sin x$, for $0 \le x \le \pi$. What is the average height of the arch above the ground?
26. **Average height of a wave** The surface of a water wave is described by $y = 5(1 + \cos x)$, for $-\pi \le x \le \pi$, where $y = 0$ corresponds to a trough of the wave (see Figure). Find the average height of the wave above the trough on $[-\pi, \pi]$.

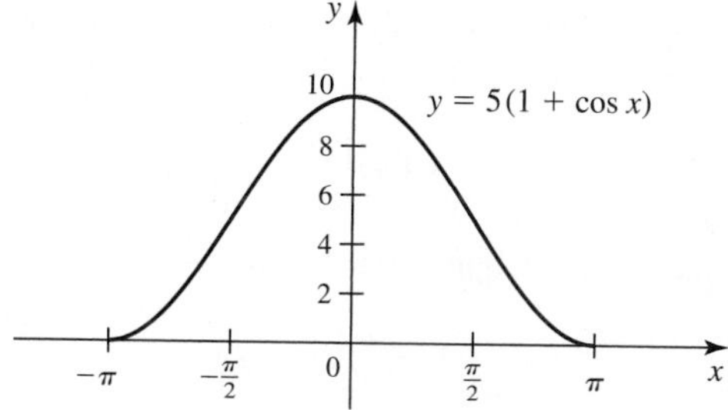

27. **Average distance on a semicircle** Suppose you walk the length of a semicircle with radius 2 km at a constant speed. What is your average distance from the *base* of the semicircle?

28. Average distance on a semicircle Suppose you walk the length of a semicircle with radius 2 km at a constant speed. What is your average distance from the *center* of the semicircle?

29–34. Mean Value Theorem for Integrals *Find or approximate the point(s) at which the given function equals its average value on the given interval.*

T **29.** $f(x) = 8 - 2x;\ [0, 4]$

30. $f(x) = \cos x;\ \left[-\frac{\pi}{2}, \frac{\pi}{2}\right]$

31. $f(x) = 1 - x^2/a^2;\ [0, a]$, where a is a positive real number

32. $f(x) = \frac{\pi}{4}\sin x;\ [0, \pi]$

33. $f(x) = 1 - |x|;\ [-1, 1]$

34. $f(x) = 1/x^2;\ [1, 4]$

Further Explorations

35. Explain why or why not Determine whether the following statements are true and give an explanation or counterexample.

a. If f is symmetric about the line $x = 2$, then $\int_0^4 f(x)\,dx = 2\int_0^2 f(x)\,dx$.

b. If f has the property $f(a + x) = -f(a - x)$ for all x, where a is a constant, then $\int_{a-2}^{a+2} f(x)\,dx = 0$.

c. The average value of a linear function on an interval $[a, b]$ is the function value at the midpoint of the interval.

d. Consider the function $f(x) = x(a - x)$ on the interval $[0, a]$ for $a > 0$. Its average value on $[0, a]$ is $\frac{1}{2}$ of its maximum value.

36–39. Symmetry in integrals *Use symmetry to evaluate the following integrals.*

36. $\displaystyle\int_{-\pi/4}^{\pi/4} \tan x\,dx$

37. $\displaystyle\int_{-\pi/4}^{\pi/4} \sec^2 x\,dx$

38. $\displaystyle\int_{-2}^{2} (1 - |x|^3)\,dx$

39. $\displaystyle\int_{-2}^{2} \frac{x^3 - 4x}{x^2 + 1}\,dx$

Applications

40. Root mean square The root mean square (or RMS) is used to measure the average value of oscillating functions (for example, sine and cosine functions that describe the current, voltage, or power in an alternating circuit). The RMS of a function f on the interval $[0, T]$ is

$$\bar{f}_{RMS} = \sqrt{\frac{1}{T}\int_0^T f(t)^2\,dt}.$$

Compute the RMS of $f(t) = A\sin\omega t$, where A and ω are positive constants and T is any integer multiple of the period of f, which is $2\pi/\omega$.

41. Gateway Arch The Gateway Arch in St. Louis is 630 ft high and has a 630-ft base. Its shape can be modeled by the parabola

$$y = 630\left[1 - \left(\frac{x}{315}\right)^2\right].$$

Find the average height of the arch above the ground.

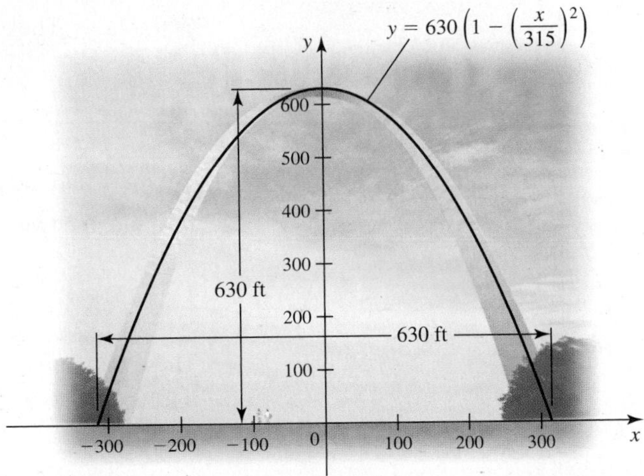

42. Looking ahead—surface area of a parabolic mirror Consider the segment of the parabola $f(x) = 2\sqrt{x}$ on the interval $[0, 1]$. When this segment is revolved about the x-axis, it sweeps out a surface S that might be used as a parabolic mirror (in a telescope or a transmitter). It can be shown that the area of S is $A = 2\pi\int_0^1 f(x)\sqrt{1 + f'(x)^2}\,dx$.

a. Compute and simplify the integrand of this integral and show that $A = 4\pi\int_0^1 \sqrt{1 + x}\,dx$.

b. Use the fact that $\frac{d}{dx}((x + a)^{3/2}) = \frac{3}{2}(x + a)^{1/2}$, where a is a constant, to find the area of S.

43. Planetary orbits The planets orbit the Sun in elliptical orbits with the Sun at one focus (see Section 11.4 for more on ellipses). The equation of an ellipse whose dimensions are $2a$ in the x-direction and $2b$ in the y-direction is $\frac{x^2}{a^2} + \frac{y^2}{b^2} = 1$.

a. Let d^2 denote the square of the distance from a planet to the center of the ellipse at $(0, 0)$. Integrate over the interval $[-a, a]$ to show that the average value of d^2 is $(a^2 + 2b^2)/3$.

b. Show that in the case of a circle ($a = b = R$), the average value in part (a) is R^2.

c. Assuming $0 < b < a$, the coordinates of the Sun are $\left(\sqrt{a^2 - b^2}, 0\right)$. Let D^2 denote the square of the distance from the planet to the Sun. Integrate over the interval $[-a, a]$ to show that the average value of D^2 is $(4a^2 - b^2)/3$.

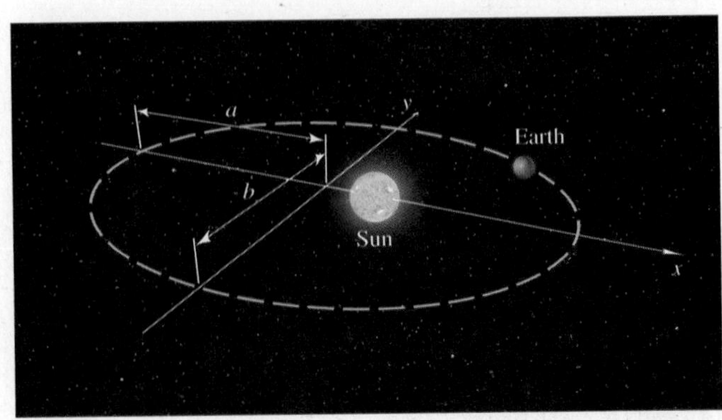

Additional Exercises

44. Comparing a sine and a quadratic function Consider the functions $f(x) = \sin x$ and $g(x) = \frac{4}{\pi^2}x(\pi - x)$.

a. Carefully graph f and g on the same set of axes. Verify that both functions have a single local maximum on the interval $[0, \pi]$ and they have the same maximum value on $[0, \pi]$.
b. On the interval $[0, \pi]$, which is true: $f(x) \geq g(x)$, $g(x) \geq f(x)$, or neither?
c. Compute and compare the average values of f and g on $[0, \pi]$.

45–48. Symmetry of composite functions *Prove that the integrand is either even or odd. Then give the value of the integral or show how it can be simplified. Assume that f and g are even functions and p and q are odd functions.*

45. $\int_{-a}^{a} f(g(x))\,dx$

46. $\int_{-a}^{a} f(p(x))\,dx$

47. $\int_{-a}^{a} p(g(x))\,dx$

48. $\int_{-a}^{a} p(q(x))\,dx$

49. Average value with a parameter Consider the function $f(x) = ax(1 - x)$ on the interval $[0, 1]$, where a is a positive real number.

a. Find the average value of f as a function of a.
b. Find the points at which the value of f equals its average value and prove that they are independent of a.

50. Square of the average For what functions f is it true that the square of the average value of f equals the average value of the square of f over all intervals $[a, b]$?

51. Problems of antiquity Several calculus problems were solved by Greek mathematicians long before the discovery of calculus. The following problems were solved by Archimedes using methods that predated calculus by 2000 years.

a. Show that the area of a segment of a parabola is 4/3 that of its inscribed triangle of greatest area. In other words, the area bounded by the parabola $y = a^2 - x^2$ and the x-axis is 4/3 the area of the triangle with vertices $(\pm a, 0)$ and $(0, a^2)$. Assume that $a > 0$, but is unspecified.
b. Show that the area bounded by the parabola $y = a^2 - x^2$ and the x-axis is 2/3 the area of the rectangle with vertices $(\pm a, 0)$ and $(\pm a, a^2)$. Assume that $a > 0$, but is unspecified.

52. Unit area sine curve Find the value of c such that the region bounded by $y = c \sin x$ and the x-axis on the interval $[0, \pi]$ has area 1.

53. Unit area cubic Find the value of $c > 0$ such that the region bounded by the cubic $y = x(x - c)^2$ and the x-axis on the interval $[0, c]$ has area 1.

54. Unit area

a. Consider the curve $y = 1/\sqrt{x}$, for $x \geq 1$. For what value of $b > 0$ does the region bounded by this curve and the x-axis on the interval $[1, b]$ have an area of 1?
b. Consider the curve $y = 1/x^p$, where $x \geq 1$ and $p < 2$ is a rational number. For what value of b (as a function of p) does the region bounded by this curve and the x-axis on the interval $[1, b]$ have unit area?
c. Is $b(p)$ in part (b) an increasing or decreasing function of p? Explain.

55. A sine integral by Riemann sums Consider the integral $I = \int_0^{\pi/2} \sin x\,dx$.

a. Write the left Riemann sum for I with n subintervals.
b. Show that $\lim_{\theta \to 0} \theta\left(\frac{\cos\theta + \sin\theta - 1}{2(1 - \cos\theta)}\right) = 1$.
c. It is a fact that $\sum_{k=0}^{n-1} \sin\left(\frac{\pi k}{2n}\right) = \frac{\cos\left(\frac{\pi}{2n}\right) + \sin\left(\frac{\pi}{2n}\right) - 1}{2\left[1 - \cos\left(\frac{\pi}{2n}\right)\right]}$.

Use this fact and part (b) to evaluate I by taking the limit of the Riemann sum as $n \to \infty$.

56. Alternate definitions of means Consider the function

$$f(t) = \frac{\int_a^b x^{t+1}\,dx}{\int_a^b x^t\,dx}.$$

Show that the following means can be defined in terms of f.

a. Arithmetic mean: $f(0) = \frac{a + b}{2}$
b. Geometric mean: $f\left(-\frac{3}{2}\right) = \sqrt{ab}$
c. Harmonic mean: $f(-3) = \frac{2ab}{a + b}$

(*Source: Mathematics Magazine* 78, No. 5 (December 2005))

57. Fill in the following table with either **even** or **odd** and prove each result. Assume n is an integer and f^n means the nth power of f.

	f is even	*f* is odd
n is even	f^n is ______	f^n is ______
n is odd	f^n is ______	f^n is ______

58. Average value of the derivative Suppose that f' is a continuous function for all real numbers. Show that the average value of the derivative on an interval $[a, b]$ is $\overline{f'} = \frac{f(b) - f(a)}{b - a}$. Interpret this result in terms of secant lines.

59. Symmetry about a point A function f is symmetric about a point (c, d) if whenever $(c - x, d - y)$ is on the graph, then so is $(c + x, d + y)$. Functions that are symmetric about a point (c, d) are easily integrated on an interval with midpoint c.

a. Show that if f is continuous and symmetric about (c, d) and $a > 0$, then $\int_{c-a}^{c+a} f(x)\,dx = 2af(c) = 2ad$.

b. Graph the function $f(x) = \sin^2 x$ on the interval $[0, \pi/2]$ and show that the function is symmetric about the point $(\pi/4, 1/2)$.

c. Using only the graph of f (and no integration), show that $\int_0^{\pi/2} \sin^2 x\,dx = \frac{\pi}{4}$.

(See the Guided Projects for more on symmetry in integrals.)

60. Bounds on an integral Suppose f is continuous on $[a, b]$ with $f''(x) > 0$ on the interval. It can be shown that

$$(b - a)f\left(\frac{a + b}{2}\right) \le \int_a^b f(x)\,dx \le (b - a)\frac{f(a) + f(b)}{2}.$$

a. Assuming f is nonnegative on $[a, b]$, draw a figure to illustrate the geometric meaning of these inequalities. Discuss your conclusions.

b. Divide these inequalities by $(b - a)$ and interpret the resulting inequalities in terms of the average value of f on $[a, b]$.

QUICK CHECK ANSWERS

1. $f(-x)g(-x) = f(x)g(x)$; therefore, fg is even. **2.** The average value is the constant; the average value is 0. **3.** The average value is zero on the interval; by the Mean Value Theorem for Integrals, $f(x) = 0$ at some point on the interval. ◀

5.5 Substitution Rule

Given just about any differentiable function, with enough know-how and persistence, you can compute its derivative. But the same cannot be said of antiderivatives. Many functions, even relatively simple ones, do not have antiderivatives that can be expressed in terms of familiar functions. Examples are $\sin x^2$, $(\sin x)/x$, and x^x. At the moment, the number of functions for which we can find antiderivatives is extremely limited. The immediate goal of this section is to enlarge the family of functions for which we can find antiderivatives. This campaign resumes in Chapter 8, where additional integration methods are developed.

Indefinite Integrals

One way to find new antiderivative rules is to start with familiar derivative rules and work backward. When applied to the Chain Rule, this strategy leads to the Substitution Rule. A few examples illustrate the technique.

EXAMPLE 1 Antiderivatives by trial and error Find $\int \cos 2x\,dx$.

SOLUTION The closest familiar indefinite integral related to this problem is

➤ We assume C is an arbitrary constant without stating so each time it appears.

$$\int \cos x\,dx = \sin x + C,$$

which is true because

$$\frac{d}{dx}(\sin x + C) = \cos x.$$

Therefore, we might *incorrectly* conclude that the indefinite integral of $\cos 2x$ is $\sin 2x + C$. However, by the Chain Rule,

$$\frac{d}{dx}(\sin 2x + C) = 2\cos 2x \neq \cos 2x.$$

Note that $\sin 2x$ fails to be an antiderivative of $\cos 2x$ by a multiplicative factor of 2. A small adjustment corrects this problem. Let's try $\frac{1}{2}\sin 2x$:

$$\frac{d}{dx}\left(\frac{1}{2}\sin 2x\right) = \frac{1}{2}\cdot 2\cos 2x = \cos 2x.$$

It works! So we have

$$\int \cos 2x\, dx = \frac{1}{2}\sin 2x + C.$$

Related Exercises 9–12 ◀

The trial-and-error approach of Example 1 does not work for complicated integrals. To develop a systematic method, consider a composite function $F(g(x))$, where F is an antiderivative of f; that is, $F' = f$. Using the Chain Rule to differentiate the composite function $F(g(x))$, we find that

$$\frac{d}{dx}[F(g(x))] = \underbrace{F'(g(x))}_{f(g(x))}g'(x) = f(g(x))g'(x).$$

This equation says that $F(g(x))$ is an antiderivative of $f(g(x))g'(x)$, which is written

$$\int f(g(x))g'(x)\, dx = F(g(x)) + C, \qquad (1)$$

where F is any antiderivative of f.

Why is this approach called the *Substitution Rule* (or *Change of Variables Rule*)? In the composite function $f(g(x))$ in equation (1), we identify the "inner function" as $u = g(x)$, which implies that $du = g'(x)\, dx$. Making this identification, the integral in equation (1) is written

➤ You can call the new variable anything you want because it is just another variable of integration. Typically, u is a standard choice for the new variable.

$$\int \underbrace{f(g(x))}_{f(u)}\underbrace{g'(x)dx}_{du} = \int f(u)\, du = F(u) + C.$$

We see that the integral $\int f(g(x))g'(x)\, dx$ with respect to x is replaced by a new integral $\int f(u)du$ with respect to the new variable u. In other words, we have substituted the new variable u for the old variable x. Of course, if the new integral with respect to u is no easier to find than the original integral, then the change of variables has not helped. The Substitution Rule requires some practice until certain patterns become familiar.

THEOREM 5.6 Substitution Rule for Indefinite Integrals

Let $u = g(x)$, where g' is continuous on an interval, and let f be continuous on the corresponding range of g. On that interval,

$$\int f(g(x))g'(x)\, dx = \int f(u)\, du.$$

PROCEDURE Substitution Rule (Change of Variables)

1. Given an indefinite integral involving a composite function $f(g(x))$, identify an inner function $u = g(x)$ such that a constant multiple of $u'(x)$ (equivalently, $g'(x)$) appears in the integrand.
2. Substitute $u = g(x)$ and $du = u'(x)\,dx$ in the integral.
3. Evaluate the new indefinite integral with respect to u.
4. Write the result in terms of x using $u = g(x)$.

Disclaimer: Not all integrals yield to the Substitution Rule.

EXAMPLE 2 Perfect substitution Use the Substitution Rule to evaluate $\int 2(2x + 1)^3\,dx$. Check your work by differentiating.

SOLUTION We identify $u = 2x + 1$ as the inner function of the composite function $(2x + 1)^3$. Therefore, we choose the new variable $u = 2x + 1$, which implies that $du = 2\,dx$. Notice that $du = 2\,dx$ appears as a factor in the integrand. The change of variables looks like this:

$$\int \underbrace{(2x+1)^3}_{u^3} \cdot \underbrace{2\,dx}_{du} = \int u^3\,du \qquad \text{Substitute } u = 2x+1,\ du = 2\,dx.$$

$$= \frac{u^4}{4} + C \qquad \text{Antiderivative}$$

$$= \frac{(2x+1)^4}{4} + C \qquad \text{Replace } u \text{ by } 2x+1.$$

Notice that the final step uses $u = 2x + 1$ to return to the original variable.

Related Exercises 13–16 ◀

➤ It is a good idea to check the result. By the Chain Rule, we have

$$\frac{d}{dx}\left[\frac{(2x+1)^4}{4} + C\right] = 2(2x+1)^3.$$

QUICK CHECK 1 Find a new variable u so that $\int 4x^3(x^4 + 5)^{10}\,dx = \int u^{10}\,du$. ◀

EXAMPLE 3 Introducing a constant Find the following indefinite integrals.

a. $\int x^4(x^5 + 6)^9\,dx$ **b.** $\int \cos^3 x \sin x\,dx$

SOLUTION

a. The inner function of the composite function $(x^5 + 6)^9$ is $x^5 + 6$ and a multiple of its derivative $5x^4$ also appears in the integrand. Therefore, we use the substitution $u = x^5 + 6$, which implies that $du = 5x^4\,dx$ or $x^4\,dx = 1/5\,du$. By the Substitution Rule,

$$\int \underbrace{(x^5+6)^9}_{u^9}\,\underbrace{x^4\,dx}_{\frac{1}{5}du} = \int u^9\,\frac{1}{5}\,du \qquad \text{Substitute } u = x^5+6,\ du = 5x^4\,dx \Rightarrow x^4\,dx = \frac{1}{5}\,du$$

$$= \frac{1}{5}\int u^9\,du \qquad \int c\,f(x)\,dx = c\int f(x)\,dx$$

$$= \frac{1}{5}\cdot\frac{u^{10}}{10} + C \qquad \text{Antiderivative}$$

$$= \frac{1}{50}(x^5+6)^{10} + C. \qquad \text{Replace } u \text{ by } x^5+6.$$

b. The integrand can be written as $(\cos x)^3 \sin x$. The inner function in the composition is $\cos x$, which suggests the substitution $u = \cos x$. Note that $du = -\sin x\,dx$ or $\sin x\,dx = -du$. The change of variables appears as

$$\int \underbrace{\cos^3 x}_{u^3} \underbrace{\sin x\,dx}_{-du} = -\int u^3\,du \qquad \text{Substitute } u = \cos x,\ du = -\sin x\,dx.$$

$$= -\frac{u^4}{4} + C \qquad \text{Antiderivative}$$

$$= -\frac{\cos^4 x}{4} + C. \qquad \text{Replace } u \text{ by } \cos x.$$

Related Exercises 17–28

QUICK CHECK 2 In Example 3a, explain why the same substitution would not work as well for the integral $\int x^3(x^5 + 6)^9\,dx$.

Sometimes the choice for a u-substitution is not so obvious *or* more than one u-substitution works. The following example illustrates both of these points.

EXAMPLE 4 Variations on the substitution method Find $\displaystyle\int \frac{x}{\sqrt{x+1}}\,dx$.

SOLUTION

Substitution 1 The composite function $\sqrt{x+1}$ suggests the new variable $u = x + 1$. You might doubt whether this choice will work because $du = dx$ and the x in the numerator of the integrand is unaccounted for. But let's proceed. Letting $u = x + 1$, we have $x = u - 1$, $du = dx$, and

$$\int \frac{x}{\sqrt{x+1}}\,dx = \int \frac{u-1}{\sqrt{u}}\,du \qquad \text{Substitute } u = x + 1,\ du = dx.$$

$$= \int \left(\sqrt{u} - \frac{1}{\sqrt{u}}\right) du \qquad \text{Rewrite integrand.}$$

$$= \int (u^{1/2} - u^{-1/2})\,du. \qquad \text{Fractional powers}$$

We integrate each term individually and then return to the original variable x:

$$\int (u^{1/2} - u^{-1/2})\,du = \frac{2}{3}u^{3/2} - 2u^{1/2} + C \qquad \text{Antiderivatives}$$

$$= \frac{2}{3}(x+1)^{3/2} - 2(x+1)^{1/2} + C \qquad \text{Replace } u \text{ by } x + 1.$$

$$= \frac{2}{3}(x+1)^{1/2}(x-2) + C \qquad \text{Factor out } (x+1)^{1/2} \text{ and simplify.}$$

Substitution 2 Another possible substitution is $u = \sqrt{x+1}$. Now $u^2 = x + 1$, $x = u^2 - 1$, and $dx = 2u\,du$. Making these substitutions leads to

$$\int \frac{x}{\sqrt{x+1}}\,dx = \int \frac{u^2-1}{u}\,2u\,du \qquad \text{Substitute } u = \sqrt{x+1},\ x = u^2 - 1.$$

$$= 2\int (u^2 - 1)\,du \qquad \text{Simplify the integrand.}$$

$$= 2\left(\frac{u^3}{3} - u\right) + C \qquad \text{Antiderivatives}$$

➤ In Substitution 2, you could also use the fact that

$$u'(x) = \frac{1}{2\sqrt{x+1}},$$

which implies

$$du = \frac{1}{2\sqrt{x+1}}\,dx.$$

$$= \frac{2}{3}(x+1)^{3/2} - 2(x+1)^{1/2} + C \quad \text{Replace } u \text{ by } \sqrt{x+1}.$$

$$= \frac{2}{3}(x+1)^{1/2}(x-2) + C. \quad \text{Factor out } (x+1)^{1/2} \text{ and simplify.}$$

The same indefinite integral is found using either substitution. *Related Exercises 29–34* ◀

Definite Integrals

The Substitution Rule is also used for definite integrals; in fact, there are two ways to proceed.

- You may use the Substitution Rule to find an antiderivative F, as described above, and then use the Fundamental Theorem to evaluate $F(b) - F(a)$.
- Alternatively, once you have changed variables from x to u, you may also change the limits of integration and complete the integration with respect to u. Specifically, if $u = g(x)$, the lower limit $x = a$ is replaced by $u = g(a)$ and the upper limit $x = b$ is replaced by $u = g(b)$.

The second option tends to be more efficient, and we use it whenever possible. A few examples illustrate this idea.

THEOREM 5.7 Substitution Rule for Definite Integrals
Let $u = g(x)$, where g' is continuous on $[a, b]$, and let f be continuous on the range of g. Then

$$\int_a^b f(g(x))g'(x)\,dx = \int_{g(a)}^{g(b)} f(u)\,du.$$

EXAMPLE 5 Definite integrals Evaluate the following integrals.

a. $\displaystyle\int_0^2 \frac{dx}{(x+3)^3}$ **b.** $\displaystyle\int_{-1}^2 \frac{x^2}{(x^3+2)^3}\,dx$ **c.** $\displaystyle\int_0^{\pi/2} \sin^4 x \cos x\,dx$

SOLUTION

> When the integrand has the form $f(ax+b)$, the substitution $u = ax + b$ is often effective.

a. Let the new variable be $u = x + 3$; then $du = dx$. Because we have changed the variable of integration from x to u, the limits of integration must also be expressed in terms of u. In this case,

$$x = 0 \text{ implies } u = 0 + 3 = 3 \quad \text{Lower limit}$$
$$x = 2 \text{ implies } u = 2 + 3 = 5 \quad \text{Upper limit}$$

The entire integration is carried out as follows:

$$\int_0^2 \frac{dx}{(x+3)^3} = \int_3^5 u^{-3}\,du \quad \text{Substitute } u = x + 3,\ du = dx.$$

$$= \left.\frac{u^{-2}}{-2}\right|_3^5 \quad \text{Fundamental Theorem}$$

$$= -\frac{1}{2}(5^{-2} - 3^{-2}) = \frac{8}{225} \quad \text{Simplify.}$$

b. Notice that a multiple of the derivative of $x^3 + 2$ appears in the numerator; therefore, we let $u = x^3 + 2$. Then $du = 3x^2\,dx$, or $x^2\,dx = \frac{1}{3}\,du$. We also change the limits of integration:

$$x = -1 \text{ implies } u = -1 + 2 = 1 \quad \text{Lower limit}$$
$$x = 2 \text{ implies } u = 2^3 + 2 = 10 \quad \text{Upper limit}$$

Changing variables, we have

$$\int_{-1}^{2} \frac{x^2}{(x^3+2)^3}\,dx = \frac{1}{3}\int_1^{10} u^{-3}\,du \quad \text{Substitute } u = x^3 + 2,\ du = 3x^2\,dx.$$
$$= \frac{1}{3}\left(\frac{u^{-2}}{-2}\right)\Bigg|_1^{10} \quad \text{Fundamental Theorem}$$
$$= \frac{1}{3}\left[-\frac{1}{200} - \left(-\frac{1}{2}\right)\right] \quad \text{Simplify.}$$
$$= \frac{33}{200}.$$

c. Let $u = \sin x$, which implies that $du = \cos x\,dx$. The lower limit of integration becomes $u = 0$ and the upper limit becomes $u = 1$. Changing variables, we have

$$\int_0^{\pi/2} \sin^4 x \cos x\,dx = \int_0^1 u^4\,du \quad u = \sin x,\ du = \cos x\,dx$$
$$= \left(\frac{u^5}{5}\right)\Bigg|_0^1 = \frac{1}{5}. \quad \text{Fundamental Theorem}$$

Related Exercises 35–44 ◀

The Substitution Rule enables us to find two standard integrals that appear frequently in practice, $\int \sin^2\theta\,d\theta$ and $\int \cos^2\theta\,d\theta$. These integrals are handled using the identities

$$\sin^2\theta = \frac{1-\cos 2\theta}{2} \quad \text{and} \quad \cos^2\theta = \frac{1+\cos 2\theta}{2}.$$

EXAMPLE 6 **Integral of $\cos^2\theta$** Evaluate $\int_0^{\pi/2} \cos^2\theta\,d\theta$.

SOLUTION Working with the indefinite integral first, we use the identity for $\cos^2\theta$:

$$\int \cos^2\theta\,d\theta = \int \frac{1+\cos 2\theta}{2}\,d\theta = \frac{1}{2}\int d\theta + \frac{1}{2}\int \cos 2\theta\,d\theta.$$

The change of variables $u = 2\theta$ is now used for the second integral, and we have

$$\int \cos^2\theta\,d\theta = \frac{1}{2}\int d\theta + \frac{1}{2}\int \cos 2\theta\,d\theta$$
$$= \frac{1}{2}\int d\theta + \frac{1}{2}\cdot\frac{1}{2}\int \cos u\,du \quad u = 2\theta,\ du = 2\,d\theta$$
$$= \frac{\theta}{2} + \frac{1}{4}\sin 2\theta + C. \quad \text{Evaluate integrals; } u = 2\theta.$$

➤ See Exercise 82 for a generalization of Example 6. Trigonometric integrals involving powers of $\sin x$ and $\cos x$ are explored in greater detail in Section 8.2.

Using the Fundamental Theorem of Calculus, the value of the definite integral is

$$\int_0^{\pi/2} \cos^2\theta\,d\theta = \left(\frac{\theta}{2} + \frac{1}{4}\sin 2\theta\right)\Bigg|_0^{\pi/2}$$
$$= \left(\frac{\pi}{4} + \frac{1}{4}\sin\pi\right) - \left(0 + \frac{1}{4}\sin 0\right) = \frac{\pi}{4}.$$

Related Exercises 45–50 ◀

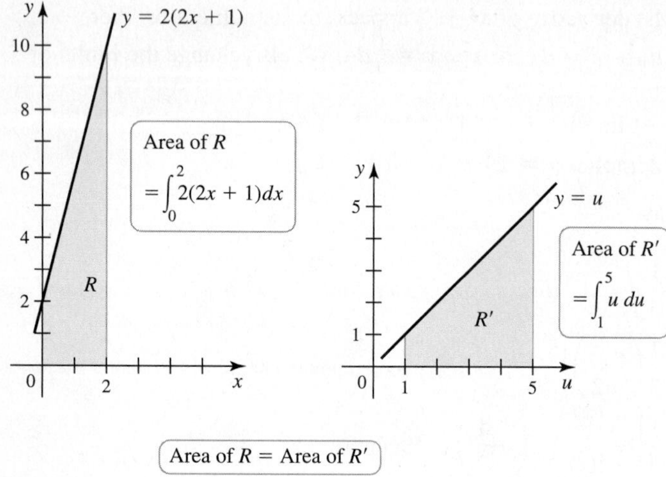

FIGURE 5.57

Geometry of Substitution

The Substitution Rule may be interpreted graphically. To keep matters simple, consider the integral $\int_0^2 2(2x+1)\,dx$. The graph of the integrand $y = 2(2x+1)$ on the interval $[0,2]$ is shown in Figure 5.57, along with the region R whose area is given by the integral. The change of variables $u = 2x + 1, du = 2\,dx$, $u(0) = 1$, and $u(2) = 5$ leads to the new integral

$$\int_0^2 2(2x+1)\,dx = \int_1^5 u\,du.$$

Figure 5.57 also shows the graph of the new integrand $y = u$ on the interval $[1,5]$ and the region R' whose area is given by the new integral. You can check that the areas of R and R' are equal. An analogous interpretation may be given to more complicated integrands and substitutions.

QUICK CHECK 3 Changes of variables occur frequently in mathematics. For example, suppose you want to solve the equation $x^4 - 13x^2 + 36 = 0$. If you use the substitution $u = x^2$, what is the new equation that must be solved for u? What are the roots of the original equation?◀

SECTION 5.5 EXERCISES

Review Questions

1. On which derivative rule is the Substitution Rule based?
2. Explain why the Substitution Rule is referred to as a change of variables.
3. The composite function $f(g(x))$ consists of an inner function g and an outer function f. When doing a change of variables, which function is often a likely choice for a new variable u?
4. Find a suitable substitution for evaluating $\int \tan x \sec^2 x\,dx$, and explain your choice.
5. When using a change of variables $u = g(x)$ to evaluate the definite integral $\int_a^b f(g(x))g'(x)\,dx$, how are the limits of integration transformed?
6. If the change of variables $u = x^2 - 4$ is used to evaluate the definite integral $\int_2^4 f(x)\,dx$, what are the new limits of integration?
7. Find $\int \cos^2 x\,dx$.
8. What identity is needed to find $\int \sin^2 x\,dx$?

Basic Skills

9–12. Trial and error *Find an antiderivative of the following functions by trial and error. Check your answer by differentiation.*

9. $f(x) = (x+1)^{12}$
10. $f(x) = \sin 10x$
11. $f(x) = \sqrt{2x+1}$
12. $f(x) = \cos(2x+5)$

13–16. Substitution given *Use the given substitution to find the following indefinite integrals. Check your answer by differentiation.*

13. $\int 2x(x^2+1)^4\,dx,\ u = x^2 + 1$
14. $\int 8x\cos(4x^2+3)\,dx,\ u = 4x^2 + 3$
15. $\int \sin^3 x \cos x\,dx,\ u = \sin x$
16. $\int (6x+1)\sqrt{3x^2+x}\,dx,\ u = 3x^2 + x$

17–28. Indefinite integrals *Use a change of variables to find the following indefinite integrals. Check your work by differentiation.*

17. $\int 2x(x^2-1)^{99}\,dx$
18. $\int x\cos x^2\,dx$
19. $\int \frac{2x^2}{\sqrt{1-4x^3}}\,dx$
20. $\int \frac{(\sqrt{x}+1)^4}{2\sqrt{x}}\,dx$
21. $\int (x^2+x)^{10}(2x+1)\,dx$
22. $\int \frac{1}{(10x-3)^2}\,dx$
23. $\int x^3(x^4+16)^6\,dx$
24. $\int \sin^{10}\theta\cos\theta\,d\theta$
25. $\int \frac{x}{\sqrt{4-9x^2}}\,dx$
26. $\int x^9\sin x^{10}\,dx$
27. $\int (x^6-3x^2)^4(x^5-x)\,dx$
28. $\int \frac{x}{(x-2)^3}\,dx$ (*Hint:* Let $u = x - 2$.)

29–34. Variations on the substitution method *Find the following integrals.*

29. $\int \frac{x}{\sqrt{x-4}}\,dx$
30. $\int \frac{y^2}{(y+1)^4}\,dy$

31. $\int \frac{x}{\sqrt[3]{x+4}}\,dx$

32. $\int \frac{2x}{\sqrt{3x+2}}\,dx$

33. $\int x\sqrt[3]{2x+1}\,dx$

34. $\int (x+1)\sqrt{3x+2}\,dx$

35–44. Definite integrals *Use a change of variables to evaluate the following definite integrals.*

35. $\int_0^1 2x(4-x^2)\,dx$

36. $\int_0^2 \frac{2x}{(x^2+1)^2}\,dx$

37. $\int_0^{\pi/2} \sin^2\theta\cos\theta\,d\theta$

38. $\int_0^{\pi/4} \frac{\sin x}{\cos^2 x}\,dx$

39. $\int_{-\pi/12}^{\pi/8} \sec^2 2y\,dy$

40. $\int_0^4 \frac{p}{\sqrt{9+p^2}}\,dp$

41. $\int_{\pi/4}^{\pi/2} \frac{\cos x}{\sin^2 x}\,dx$

42. $\int_0^{\pi/4} \frac{\sin x}{\cos^3 x}\,dx$

43. $\int_2^6 \frac{x}{\sqrt{2x-3}}\,dx$

44. $\int_0^3 \frac{v^2+1}{\sqrt{v^3+3v+4}}\,dv$

45–50. Integrals with $\sin^2 x$ and $\cos^2 x$ *Evaluate the following integrals.*

45. $\int_{-\pi}^{\pi} \cos^2 x\,dx$

46. $\int \sin^2 x\,dx$

47. $\int \sin^2\left(\theta+\frac{\pi}{6}\right)d\theta$

48. $\int_0^{\pi/4} \cos^2 8\theta\,d\theta$

49. $\int_{-\pi/4}^{\pi/4} \sin^2 2\theta\,d\theta$

50. $\int x\cos^2(x^2)\,dx$

Further Explorations

51. **Explain why or why not** Determine whether the following statements are true and give an explanation or counterexample. Assume that f, f', and f'' are continuous functions for all real numbers.

   a. $\int f(x)f'(x)\,dx = \frac{1}{2}(f(x))^2 + C$

   b. $\int (f(x))^n f'(x)\,dx = \frac{1}{n+1}(f(x))^{n+1} + C,\ n \neq -1$

   c. $\int \sin 2x\,dx = 2\int \sin x\,dx$

   d. $\int (x^2+1)^9 dx = \frac{(x^2+1)^{10}}{10} + C$

   e. $\int_a^b f'(x)f''(x)\,dx = f'(b) - f'(a)$

52–62. Additional integrals *Use a change of variables to evaluate the following integrals.*

52. $\int \sec 4w\tan 4w\,dw$

53. $\int \sec^2 10x\,dx$

54. $\int (\sin^5 x + 3\sin^3 x - \sin x)\cos x\,dx$

55. $\int \frac{\csc^2 x}{\cot^3 x}\,dx$

56. $\int (x^{3/2}+8)^5\sqrt{x}\,dx$

57. $\int \sin x\sec^8 x\,dx$

58. $\int_0^1 x\sqrt{1-x^2}\,dx$

59. $\int_2^3 \frac{x}{\sqrt[3]{x^2-1}}\,dx$

60. $\int_1^3 \frac{(1+4/x)^2}{x^2}\,dx$

61. $\int_0^2 x^3\sqrt{16-x^4}\,dx$

62. $\int_{\sqrt{2}}^{\sqrt{3}} (x-1)(x^2-2x)^{11}\,dx$

63–66. Areas of regions *Find the area of the following regions.*

63. The region bounded by the graph of $f(x) = x\sin x^2$ and the x-axis between $x = 0$ and $x = \sqrt{\pi}$

64. The region bounded by the graph of $f(\theta) = \cos\theta\sin\theta$ and the θ-axis between $\theta = 0$ and $\theta = \pi/2$

65. The region bounded by the graph of $f(x) = (x-4)^4$ and the x-axis between $x = 2$ and $x = 6$

66. The region bounded by the graph of $f(x) = \frac{x}{\sqrt{x^2-9}}$ and the x-axis between $x = 4$ and $x = 5$

67. **Morphing parabolas** The family of parabolas $y = (1/a) - x^2/a^3$, where $a > 0$, has the property that for $x \geq 0$, the x-intercept is $(a, 0)$ and the y-intercept is $(0, 1/a)$. Let $A(a)$ be the area of the region in the first quadrant bounded by the parabola and the x-axis. Find $A(a)$ and determine whether it is an increasing, decreasing, or constant function of a.

Applications

68. **Periodic motion** An object moves in one dimension with a velocity in m/s given by $v(t) = 8\cos(\pi t/6)$.

   a. Graph the velocity function.

   b. As will be discussed in Chapter 6, the position of the object is given by $s(t) = \int_0^t v(y)\,dy$, for $t \geq 0$. Find the position function, for $t \geq 0$.

   c. What is the period of the motion—that is, starting at any point, how long does it take the object to return to that position?

69. **Population models** The population of a culture of bacteria has a growth rate given by $p'(t) = \frac{200}{(t+1)^r}$ bacteria per hour, for $t \geq 0$, where $r > 1$ is a real number. In Chapter 6 it will be shown that the increase in the population over the time interval $[0, t]$ is given by $\int_0^t p'(s)\,ds$. (Note that the growth rate decreases in time, reflecting competition for space and food.)

   a. Using the population model with $r = 2$, what is the increase in the population over the time interval $0 \leq t \leq 4$?

   b. Using the population model with $r = 3$, what is the increase in the population over the time interval $0 \leq t \leq 6$?

   c. Let ΔP be the increase in the population over a fixed time interval $[0, T]$. For fixed T, does ΔP increase or decrease with the parameter r? Explain.

d. A lab technician measures an increase in the population of 350 bacteria over the 10-hr period $[0, 10]$. Estimate the value of r that best fits this data point.

e. Looking ahead: Work with the population model using $r = 3$ (part (b)) and find the increase in population over the time interval $[0, T]$ for any $T > 0$. If the culture is allowed to grow indefinitely ($T \to \infty$), does the bacteria population increase without bound? Or does it approach a finite limit?

70. Consider the right triangle with vertices $(0, 0)$, $(0, b)$, and $(a, 0)$, where $a > 0$ and $b > 0$. Show that the average vertical distance from points on the x-axis to the hypotenuse is $b/2$ for all $a > 0$.

T **71. Average value of sine functions** Use a graphing utility to verify that the functions $f(x) = \sin kx$ have a period of $2\pi/k$, where $k = 1, 2, 3, \ldots$. Equivalently, the first "hump" of $f(x) = \sin kx$ occurs on the interval $[0, \pi/k]$. Verify that the average value of the first hump of $f(x) = \sin kx$ is independent of k. What is the average value? (See Section 5.4 for average value.)

Additional Exercises

72. Equal areas The area of the shaded region under the curve $y = 2\sin 2x$ in (a) equals the area of the shaded region under the curve $y = \sin x$ in (b). Explain why this is true without computing areas.

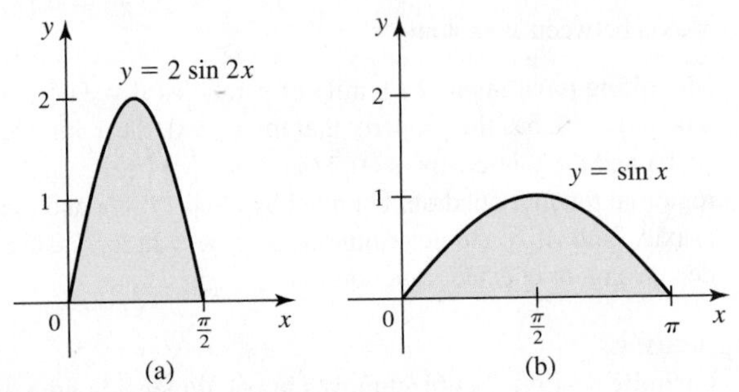

73. Equal areas The area of the shaded region under the curve $y = \dfrac{(\sqrt{x} - 1)^2}{2\sqrt{x}}$ on the interval $[4, 9]$ in (a) equals the area of the shaded region under the curve $y = x^2$ on the interval $[1, 2]$ in (b). Without computing areas, explain why.

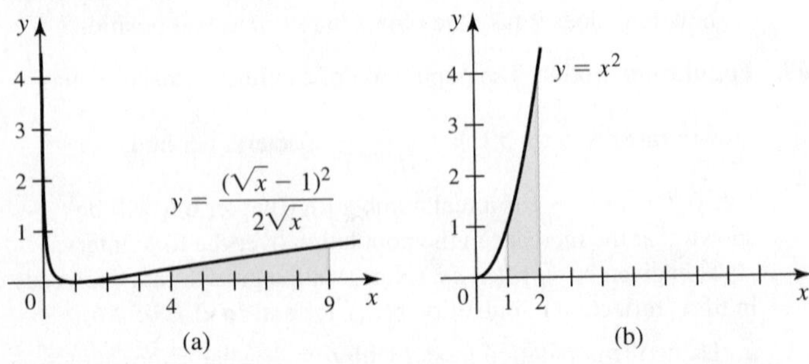

74–78. General results *Evaluate the following integrals in which the function f is unspecified. Note $f^{(p)}$ is the pth derivative of f and f^p is the pth power of f. Assume f and its derivatives are continuous for all real numbers.*

74. $\displaystyle\int (5f^3(x) + 7f^2(x) + f(x))f'(x)\,dx$

75. $\displaystyle\int_1^2 (5f(x)^3 + 7f(x)^2 + f(x))f'(x)\,dx$, where $f(1) = 4$, $f(2) = 5$

76. $\displaystyle\int_0^1 f'(x)f''(x)\,dx$, where $f'(0) = 3$ and $f'(1) = 2$

77. $\displaystyle\int (f^{(p)}(x))^n f^{(p+1)}(x)\,dx$, where p is a positive integer, $n \neq -1$

78. $\displaystyle\int 2(f(x)^2 + 2f(x))f(x)f'(x)\,dx$

79–81. More than one way *Occasionally, two different substitutions do the job. Use both of the given substitutions to evaluate the following integrals.*

79. $\displaystyle\int_0^1 x\sqrt{x + a}\,dx;\ a > 0 \qquad (u = \sqrt{x + a} \text{ and } u = x + a)$

80. $\displaystyle\int_0^1 x\sqrt[p]{x + a}\,dx;\ a > 0 \qquad (u = \sqrt[p]{x + a} \text{ and } u = x + a)$

81. $\displaystyle\int \sec^3\theta \tan\theta\,d\theta \qquad (u = \cos\theta \text{ and } u = \sec\theta)$

82. $\sin^2 ax$ and $\cos^2 ax$ integrals Use the Substitution Rule to prove that

$$\int \sin^2 ax\,dx = \frac{x}{2} - \frac{\sin(2ax)}{4a} + C \quad \text{and}$$

$$\int \cos^2 ax\,dx = \frac{x}{2} + \frac{\sin(2ax)}{4a} + C$$

83. Integral of $\sin^2 x \cos^2 x$ Consider the integral

$$I = \int \sin^2 x \cos^2 x\,dx.$$

a. Find I using the identity $\sin 2x = 2\sin x \cos x$.

b. Find I using the identity $\cos^2 x = 1 - \sin^2 x$.

c. Confirm that the results in parts (a) and (b) are consistent and compare the work involved in each method.

84. Substitution: shift Perhaps the simplest change of variables is the shift or translation given by $u = x + c$, where c is a real number.

a. Prove that shifting a function does not change the net area under the curve, in the sense that

$$\int_a^b f(x + c)\,dx = \int_{a+c}^{b+c} f(u)\,du.$$

b. Draw a picture to illustrate this change of variables in the case that $f(x) = \sin x$, $a = 0$, $b = \pi$, $c = \pi/2$.

85. Substitution: scaling Another change of variables that can be interpreted geometrically is the scaling $u = cx$, where c is a real number. Prove and interpret the fact that

$$\int_a^b f(cx)\,dx = \frac{1}{c}\int_{ac}^{bc} f(u)\,du.$$

Draw a picture to illustrate this change of variables in the case that $f(x) = \sin x$, $a = 0$, $b = \pi$, $c = \frac{1}{2}$.

86–89. Multiple substitutions *Use two or more substitutions to find the following integrals.*

86. $\int x \sin^4 x^2 \cos x^2 \, dx$

(*Hint:* Begin with $u = x^2$, then use $v = \sin u$.)

87. $\int \frac{dx}{\sqrt{1 + \sqrt{1 + x}}}$ $\left(\textit{Hint: } \text{Begin with } u = \sqrt{1 + x}.\right)$

88. $\int \tan^{10} 4x \sec^2 4x \, dx$ (*Hint:* Begin with $u = 4x$.)

89. $\int_0^{\pi/2} \frac{\cos\theta \sin\theta}{\sqrt{\cos^2\theta + 16}} \, d\theta$ (*Hint:* Begin with $u = \cos\theta$.)

QUICK CHECK ANSWERS

1. $u = x^4 + 5$ **2.** With $u = x^5 + 6$, we have $du = 5x^4$, and x^4 does not appear in the integrand. **3.** New equation: $u^2 - 13u + 36 = 0$; roots: $x = \pm 2, \pm 3$ ◂

CHAPTER 5 REVIEW EXERCISES

1. **Explain why or why not** Determine whether the following statements are true and give an explanation or counterexample. Assume f and f' are continuous functions for all real numbers.
   a. If $A(x) = \int_a^x f(t)\,dt$ and $f(t) = 2t - 3$, then A is a quadratic function.
   b. Given an area function $A(x) = \int_a^x f(t)\,dt$ and an antiderivative F of f, it follows that $A'(x) = F(x)$.
   c. $\int_a^b f'(x)\,dx = f(b) - f(a)$
   d. If $\int_a^b |f(x)|\,dx = 0$, then $f(x) = 0$ on $[a, b]$.
   e. If the average value of f on $[a, b]$ is zero, then $f(x) = 0$ on $[a, b]$.
   f. $\int_a^b (2f(x) - 3g(x))\,dx = 2\int_a^b f(x)\,dx + 3\int_b^a g(x)\,dx$
   g. $\int f'(g(x))g'(x)\,dx = f(g(x)) + C$

2. **Velocity to displacement** An object travels on the x-axis with a velocity given by $v(t) = 2t + 5$, for $0 \le t \le 4$.
   a. How far does the object travel, for $0 \le t \le 4$?
   b. What is the average value of v on the interval $[0, 4]$?
   c. True or false: The object would travel as far as in part (a) if it traveled at its average velocity (a constant), for $0 \le t \le 4$.

3. **Area by geometry** Use geometry to evaluate $\int_0^7 f(x)\,dx$, where the graph of f is given in the figure.

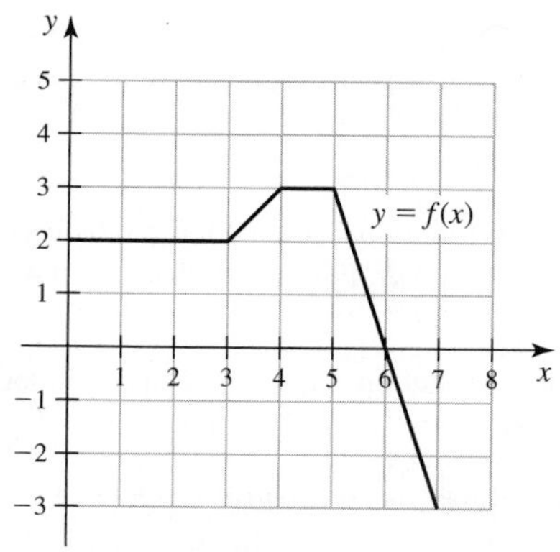

4. **Displacement by geometry** Use geometry to find the displacement of an object moving along a line, for $0 \le t \le 8$, where the graph of its velocity $v = g(t)$ is given in the figure.

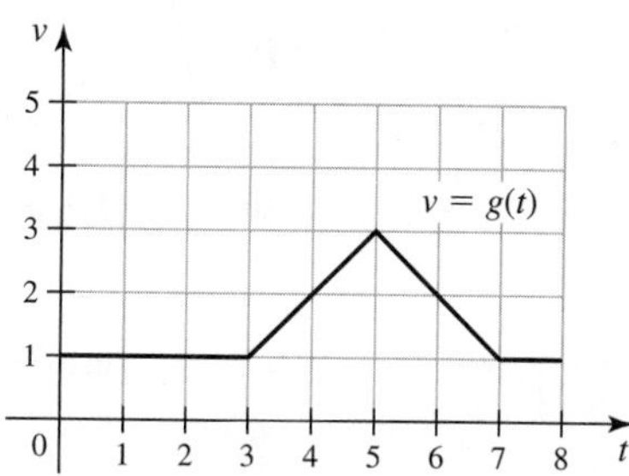

5. **Area by geometry** Use geometry to evaluate $\int_0^4 \sqrt{8x - x^2}\,dx$ (*Hint:* Complete the square of $8x - x^2$ first).

6. **Bagel output** The manager of a bagel bakery collects the following production rate data (in bagels per minute) at six different times during the morning. Estimate the total number of bagels produced between 6:00 and 7:30 a.m.

Time of day (a.m.)	Production rate (bagels/min)
6:00	45
6:15	60
6:30	75
6:45	60
7:00	50
7:15	40

7. **Integration by Riemann sums** Consider the integral $\int_1^4 (3x - 2)\,dx$.
   a. Evaluate the right Riemann sum for the integral with $n = 3$.
   b. Use summation notation to write the right Riemann sum for an arbitrary positive integer n.
   c. Evaluate the definite integral by taking the limit as $n \to \infty$ of the Riemann sum in part (b).

8. **Evaluating Riemann sums** Consider the function $f(x) = 3x + 4$ on the interval $[3, 7]$. Show that the midpoint Riemann sum with $n = 4$ gives the exact area of the region bounded by the graph.

9. **Sum to integral** Evaluate the following limit by identifying the integral that it represents:

$$\lim_{n\to\infty} \sum_{k=1}^{n} \left[\left(\frac{4k}{n} \right)^8 + 1 \right] \left(\frac{4}{n} \right).$$

10. **Area function by geometry** Use geometry to find the area $A(x)$ that is bounded by the graph of $f(t) = 2t - 4$ and the t-axis between the point $(2, 0)$ and the variable point $(x, 0)$, where $x \geq 2$. Verify that $A'(x) = f(x)$.

11–26. Evaluating integrals *Evaluate the following integrals.*

11. $\int_{-2}^{2} (3x^4 - 2x + 1)\,dx$

12. $\int \cos 3x\,dx$

13. $\int_0^2 (x + 1)^3\,dx$

14. $\int_0^1 (4x^{21} - 2x^{16} + 1)\,dx$

15. $\int (9x^8 - 7x^6)\,dx$

16. $\int_{1/2}^{1} \sin\left(\frac{\pi x}{2} - \frac{\pi}{4}\right) dx$

17. $\int_0^1 \sqrt{x}(\sqrt{x} + 1)\,dx$

18. $\int \frac{x^2}{(x^3 + 27)^2}\,dx$

19. $\int_0^1 \frac{6x}{(4 - x^2)^{3/2}}\,dx$

20. $\int y^2(3y^3 + 1)^4\,dy$

21. $\int_0^3 \frac{x}{\sqrt{25 - x^2}}\,dx$

22. $\int x \sin x^2 \cos^8 x^2\,dx$

23. $\int \sin^2 5\theta\,d\theta$

24. $\int_0^{\pi} (1 - \cos^2 3\theta)\,d\theta$

25. $\int \frac{x^2 + 2x - 2}{(x^3 + 3x^2 - 6x)^2}\,dx$

26. $\int_1^4 \frac{1 + x^{3/2}}{x^{1/2}}\,dx$

27. **Symmetry properties** Suppose that $\int_0^4 f(x)\,dx = 10$ and $\int_0^4 g(x)\,dx = 20$. Furthermore, suppose that f is an even function and g is an odd function. Evaluate the following integrals.

a. $\int_{-4}^{4} f(x)\,dx$ b. $\int_{-4}^{4} 3g(x)\,dx$ c. $\int_{-4}^{4} (4f(x) - 3g(x))\,dx$

28. **Properties of integrals** The figure shows the areas of regions bounded by the graph of f and the x-axis. Evaluate the following integrals.

a. $\int_a^c f(x)\,dx$ b. $\int_b^d f(x)\,dx$ c. $2\int_c^b f(x)\,dx$

d. $4\int_a^d f(x)\,dx$ e. $3\int_a^b f(x)\,dx$ f. $2\int_b^d f(x)\,dx$

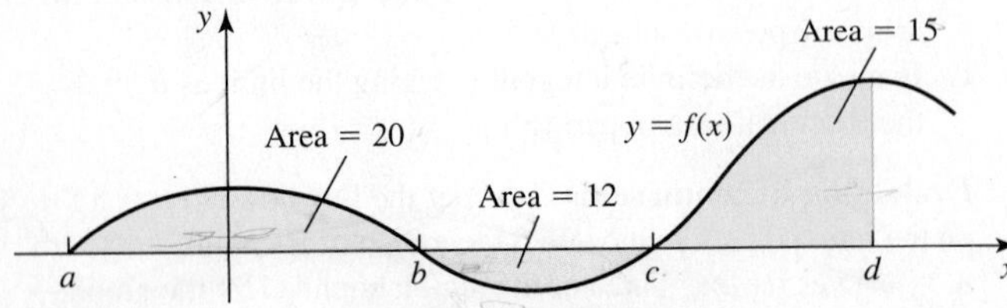

29–34. Properties of integrals *Suppose that* $\int_1^4 f(x)\,dx = 6$, $\int_1^4 g(x)\,dx = 4$, *and* $\int_3^4 f(x)\,dx = 2$. *Evaluate the following integrals or state that there is not enough information.*

29. $\int_1^4 3f(x)\,dx$

30. $-\int_4^1 2f(x)\,dx$

31. $\int_1^4 (3f(x) - 2g(x))\,dx$

32. $\int_1^4 f(x)g(x)\,dx$

33. $\int_1^3 \frac{f(x)}{g(x)}\,dx$

34. $\int_3^1 (f(x) - g(x))\,dx$

35. **Displacement from velocity** A particle moves along a line with a velocity given by $v(t) = 5\sin(\pi t)$ starting with an initial position $s(0) = 0$. Find the displacement of the particle between $t = 0$ and $t = 2$, which is given by $s(t) = \int_0^2 v(t)\,dt$. Find the distance traveled by the particle during this interval, which is $\int_0^2 |v(t)|\,dt$.

36. **Average height** A baseball is launched into the outfield on a parabolic trajectory given by $y = 0.01x(200 - x)$. Find the average height of the baseball over the horizontal extent of its flight.

37. **Average values** Find the average value of the functions shown in (a) and (b). Integration is not needed.

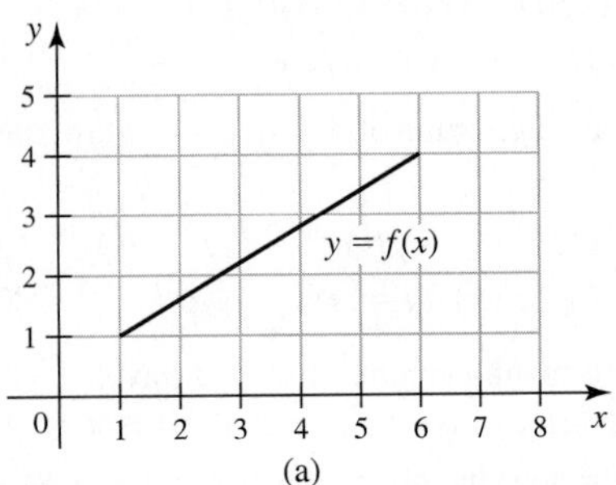

(a)

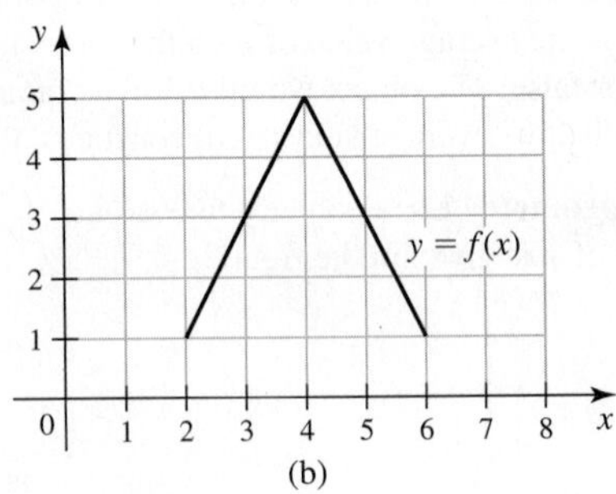

(b)

38. **An unknown function** The function f satisfies the equation $3x^4 - 2 = \int_a^x f(t)\,dt$. Find f and check your answer by substitution.

39. **An unknown function** Assume f' is a continuous function, $\int_1^2 f'(2x)\,dx = 10$, and $f(2) = 4$. Evaluate $f(4)$.

40. **Function defined by an integral** Let $H(x) = \int_0^x \sqrt{4 - t^2}\,dt$.

a. Evaluate $H(0)$.

b. Evaluate $H'(1)$.

c. Evaluate $H'(2)$.

d. Use geometry to evaluate $H(2)$.

e. Find the value of s such that $H(x) = sH(-x)$.

41. Function defined by an integral Make a graph of the function $f(x) = \int_1^x \frac{dt}{t}$, for $x \geq 1$. Be sure to include all of the evidence you used to arrive at the graph.

42. Identifying functions Match graphs A, B, and C in the figure with the functions $f(x)$, $f'(x)$, and $\int_0^x f(t)\,dt$.

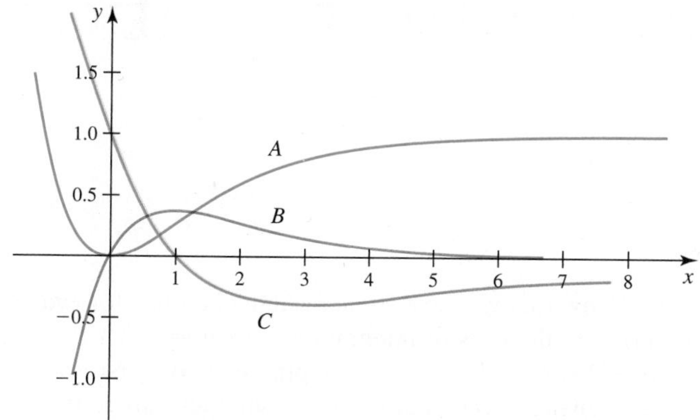

43. Geometry of integrals Without evaluating the integrals, explain why the following statement is true for positive integers n:

$$\int_0^1 x^n\,dx + \int_0^1 \sqrt[n]{x}\,dx = 1.$$

44. Change of variables Use the change of variables $u^3 = x^2 - 1$ to evaluate the integral $\int_1^3 x\sqrt[3]{x^2 - 1}\,dx$.

45. Multiple substitutions Evaluate

$$\int \sec^8(\tan x^2)\sin(\tan x^2)\,x\sec^2 x^2\,dx.$$

46. Area with a parameter Let $a > 0$ be a real number and consider the family of functions $f(x) = \sin ax$ on the interval $[0, \pi/a]$.

a. Graph f for $a = 1, 2, 3$.

b. Let $g(a)$ be the area of the region bounded by the graph of f and the x-axis on the interval $[0, \pi/a]$. Graph g for $0 < a < \infty$. Is g an increasing function, a decreasing function, or neither?

47. Equivalent equations Explain why a function that satisfies the equation $u(x) + 2\int_0^x u(t)\,dt = 10$ also satisfies the equation $u'(x) + 2u(x) = 0$.

T **48. Area function properties** Consider the function $f(x) = x^2 - 5x + 4$ and the area function $A(x) = \int_0^x f(t)\,dt$.

a. Graph f on the interval $[0, 6]$.

b. Compute and graph A on the interval $[0, 6]$.

c. Show that the local extrema of A occur at the zeros of f.

d. Give a geometrical and analytical explanation for the observation in part (c).

e. Find the approximate zeros of A, other than 0, and call them x_1 and x_2.

f. Find b such that the area bounded by the graph of f and the x-axis on the interval $[0, x_1]$ equals the area bounded by the graph of f and the x-axis on the interval $[x_1, b]$.

g. If f is an integrable function and $A(x) = \int_a^x f(t)\,dt$, is it always true that the local extrema of A occur at the zeros of f? Explain.

49. Function defined by an integral Let $f(x) = \int_0^x (t - 1)^{15}(t - 2)^9\,dt$.

a. Find the intervals on which f is increasing and the intervals on which f is decreasing.

b. Find the intervals on which f is concave up and the intervals on which f is concave down.

c. For what values of x does f have local minima? Local maxima?

d. Where are the inflection points of f?

Chapter 5 Guided Projects

Applications of the material in this chapter and related topics can be found in the following Guided Projects. For additional information, see the Preface.

- Limits of sums
- Symmetry in integrals
- Distribution of wealth

6

Applications of Integration

Chapter Preview Now that we have some basic techniques for evaluating integrals, we turn our attention to the uses of integration, which are virtually endless. Some uses of integration are theoretical and some are practical. We first illustrate the general rule that if the rate of change of a quantity is known, then integration can be used to determine the net change or future value of that quantity over a certain time interval. Next, we explore some rich geometric applications of integration: computing the area of regions bounded by several curves, the volume of three-dimensional solids, and the length of curves. A variety of physical applications of integration include finding the work done in the presence of a variable force and computing the total force exerted by water behind a dam. All these applications are unified by their use of the *slice-and-sum* strategy.

6.1 Velocity and Net Change

In previous chapters we established the relationship between the position and velocity of an object moving along a line. With integration, we can now say much more about this relationship. Once we relate velocity and position through integration, we can make analogous observations about a variety of other practical problems, which include fluid flow, population growth, manufacturing costs, and consumption of natural resources. The ideas in this section come directly from the Fundamental Theorem of Calculus, and they are among the most powerful applications of calculus.

Velocity, Position, and Displacement

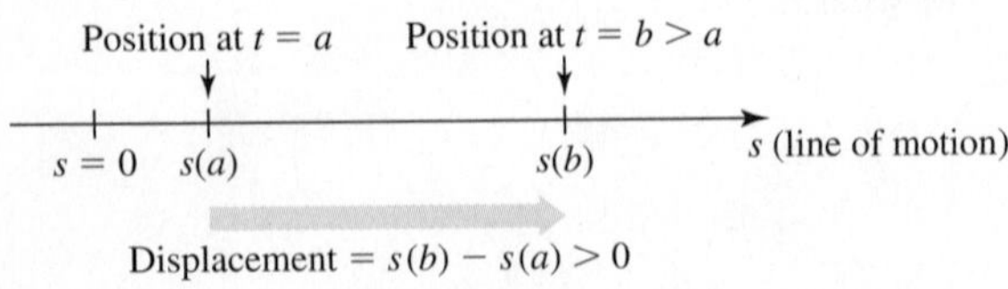

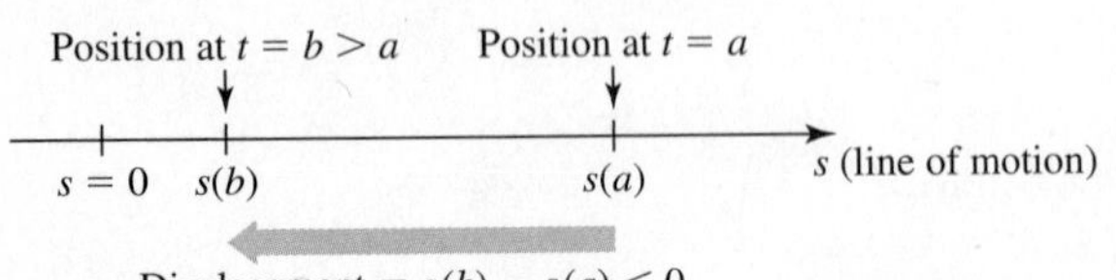

FIGURE 6.1

Suppose you are driving along a straight highway and your position relative to a reference point or origin is $s(t)$, for times $t \geq 0$ (Figure 6.1). Your *displacement* over a time interval $[a, b]$ is the change in position $s(b) - s(a)$. If $s(b) > s(a)$, then your displacement is positive; when $s(b) < s(a)$, your displacement is negative.

Now assume that $v(t)$ is the velocity of the object at a particular time t. Recall from Chapter 3 that $v(t) = s'(t)$, which means that s is an antiderivative of v. From the Fundamental Theorem of Calculus, it follows that

$$\int_a^b v(t)\,dt = \int_a^b s'(t)\,dt = s(b) - s(a) = \text{displacement}.$$

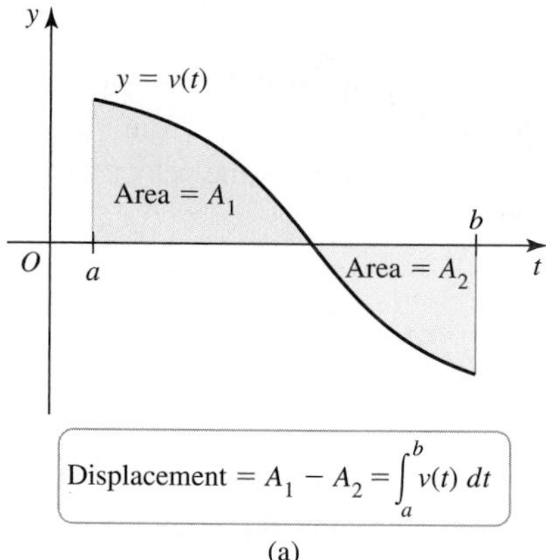

(a)

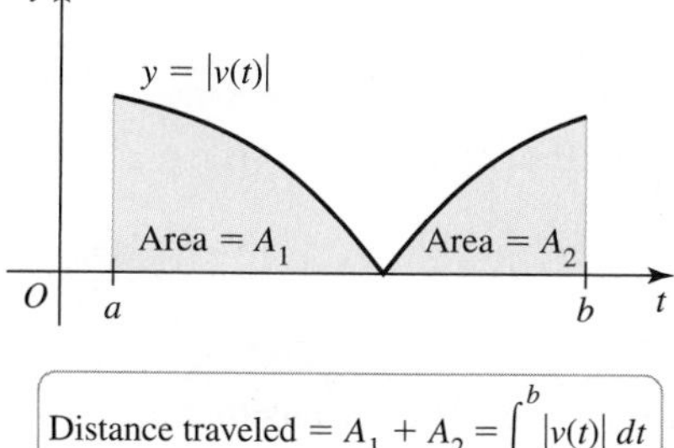

(b)

FIGURE 6.2

We see that the definite integral $\int_a^b v(t)\,dt$ is the displacement (change in position) between times $t = a$ and $t = b$. Equivalently, the displacement over the time interval $[a, b]$ is the net area under the velocity curve over $[a, b]$ (Figure 6.2a).

Not to be confused with the displacement is the *distance traveled* over a time interval, which is the total distance traveled by the object, independent of the direction of motion. If the velocity is positive, the object moves in the positive direction and the displacement equals the distance traveled. However, if the velocity changes sign, then the displacement and the distance traveled are not generally equal.

QUICK CHECK 1 A police officer leaves his station on a north-south freeway at 9 a.m., traveling north (the positive direction) for 40 mi between 9 a.m. and 10 a.m. From 10 a.m. to 11 a.m., he travels south to a point 20 mi south of the station. What is the distance traveled and the displacement between 9:00 a.m. and 11:00 a.m.?

To compute the distance traveled, we need the magnitude, not the sign of the velocity. The magnitude of the velocity $|v(t)|$ is called the *speed*. The distance traveled over a small time interval dt is $|v(t)|\,dt$ (speed multiplied by elapsed time). Summing these distances, the distance traveled over the time interval $[a, b]$ is the integral of the speed; that is,

$$\text{distance traveled} = \int_a^b |v(t)|\,dt.$$

As shown in Figure 6.2b, integrating the speed produces the area (not net area) bounded by the velocity curve and the t-axis, which corresponds to the distance traveled. The distance traveled is always nonnegative.

DEFINITIONS Position, Velocity, Displacement, and Distance

1. The **position** of an object at time t, denoted $s(t)$, is the location of the object relative to the origin.
2. The **velocity** of an object at time t is $v(t) = s'(t)$.
3. The **displacement** of the object between $t = a$ and $t = b > a$ is

$$s(b) - s(a) = \int_a^b v(t)\,dt.$$

4. The **distance traveled** by the object between $t = a$ and $t = b > a$ is

$$\int_a^b |v(t)|\,dt,$$

where $|v(t)|$ is the **speed** of the object at time t.

QUICK CHECK 2 Describe a possible motion of an object along a line for $0 \le t \le 5$ for which the displacement and the distance traveled are different.

EXAMPLE 1 Displacement from velocity A cyclist pedals along a straight road with velocity (in mi/hr) $v(t) = 2t^2 - 8t + 6$, for $0 \le t \le 3$.

a. Graph the velocity function over the interval $[0, 3]$. Determine when the cyclist moves in the positive direction and when she moves in the negative direction.

b. Find the displacement of the cyclist (in miles) on the time intervals $[0, 1]$, $[1, 3]$, and $[0, 3]$. Interpret these results.

c. Find the distance traveled over the interval $[0, 3]$.

SOLUTION

a. By solving $v(t) = 2t^2 - 8t + 6 = 2(t-1)(t-3) = 0$, we find that the velocity is zero at $t = 1$ and $t = 3$. The velocity is positive on the interval $0 \le t < 1$ (Figure 6.3a), which means the cyclist moves in the positive direction. For $1 < t < 3$, the velocity is negative and the cyclist moves in the negative direction.

b. The displacement (in miles) over the interval $[0, 1]$ is

$$s(1) - s(0) = \int_0^1 v(t)\,dt$$

$$= \int_0^1 (2t^2 - 8t + 6)\,dt \qquad \text{Substitute for } v.$$

$$= \left(\frac{2}{3}t^3 - 4t^2 + 6t\right)\bigg|_0^1 = \frac{8}{3}. \qquad \text{Evaluate integral.}$$

A similar calculation shows that the displacement over the interval $[1, 3]$ is

$$s(3) - s(1) = \int_1^3 v(t)\,dt = -\frac{8}{3}.$$

Over the interval $[0, 3]$, the displacement is $\frac{8}{3} + \left(-\frac{8}{3}\right) = 0$. This means that the cyclist returns to the starting point after three hours.

c. From part (b), we can deduce the total distance traveled by the cyclist. On the interval $[0, 1]$ the distance traveled is $\frac{8}{3}$ mi; on the interval $[1, 3]$, the distance traveled is also $\frac{8}{3}$ mi. Therefore, the distance traveled on $[0, 3]$ is $\frac{16}{3}$ mi. Alternatively (Figure 6.3b), we can integrate the speed and get the same result:

$$\int_0^3 |v(t)|\,dt = \int_0^1 (2t^2 - 8t + 6)\,dt + \int_1^3 (-(2t^2 - 8t + 6))\,dt \qquad \text{Definition of } |v(t)|$$

$$= \left(\frac{2}{3}t^3 - 4t^2 + 6t\right)\bigg|_0^1 + \left(-\frac{2}{3}t^3 + 4t^2 - 6t\right)\bigg|_1^3 \qquad \text{Evaluate integrals.}$$

$$= \frac{16}{3} \qquad \text{Simplify.}$$

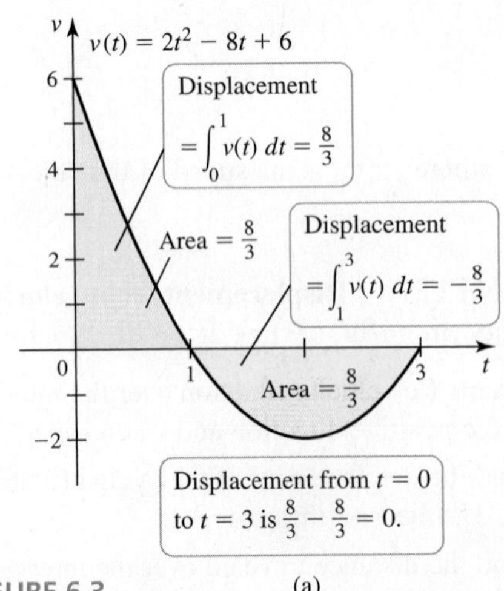

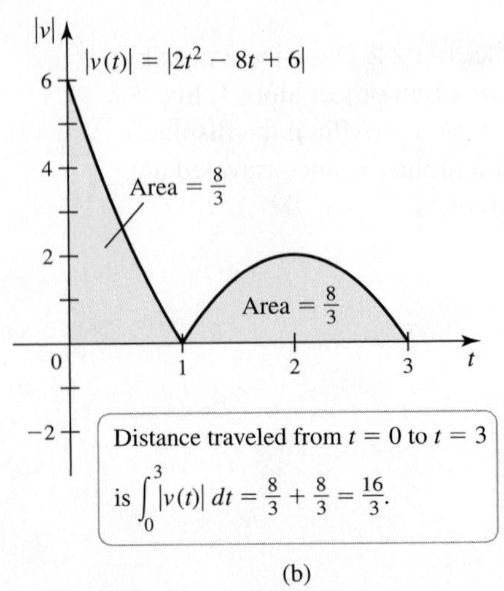

FIGURE 6.3 (a) (b)

Related Exercises 7–10

Future Value of the Position Function

To find the displacement of an object, we do not need to know its initial position. For example, whether an object moves from $s = -20$ to $s = -10$ or from $s = 50$ to $s = 60$, its displacement is 10 units. What happens if we are interested in the actual *position* of the object at some future time?

Suppose we know the velocity of an object and its initial position $s(0)$. The goal is to find the position $s(t)$ at some future time $t \geq 0$. The Fundamental Theorem of Calculus gives us the answer directly. Because the position s is an antiderivative of the velocity v, we have

> Note that t is the independent variable of the position function. Therefore, another (dummy) variable, in this case x, is used as the variable of integration.

$$\int_0^t v(x)\,dx = \int_0^t s'(x)\,dx = s(x)\Big|_0^t = s(t) - s(0).$$

Rearranging this expression, we have the following result.

> Theorem 6.1 is a consequence (actually a restatement) of the Fundamental Theorem of Calculus.

THEOREM 6.1 Position from Velocity
Given the velocity v of an object moving along a line and its initial position $s(0)$, the position function of the object for future times $t \geq 0$ is

$$\underbrace{s(t)}_{\text{position at time } t} = \underbrace{s(0)}_{\text{initial position}} + \underbrace{\int_0^t v(x)\,dx}_{\text{displacement over } [0,\,t]}.$$

Theorem 6.1 says that to find the position $s(t)$, we add the displacement over the interval $[0, t]$ to the initial position $s(0)$.

QUICK CHECK 3 Is the position $s(t)$ a number or a function? For fixed times $t = a$ and $t = b$, is the displacement $s(b) - s(a)$ a number or a function?

There are two *equivalent* ways to determine the position function:

- Using antiderivatives (Section 4.8)
- Using Theorem 6.1

The latter method is usually more efficient, but either method produces the same result. The following example illustrates both approaches.

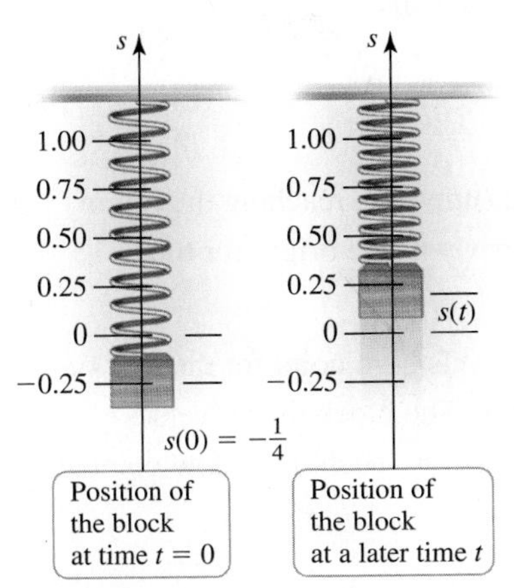

FIGURE 6.4

EXAMPLE 2 Position from velocity A block hangs at rest from a massless spring at the origin ($s = 0$). At $t = 0$, the block is pulled downward $\frac{1}{4}$ m to its initial position $s(0) = -\frac{1}{4}$ and released (Figure 6.4). Its velocity (in m/s) is given by $v(t) = \frac{1}{4}\sin t$, for $t \geq 0$. Assume that the upward direction is positive.

a. Find the position of the block, for $t \geq 0$.

b. Graph the position function, for $0 \leq t \leq 3\pi$.

c. When does the block move through the origin for the first time?

d. When does the block reach its high point for the first time and what is its position at that time? When does the block return to its lowest point?

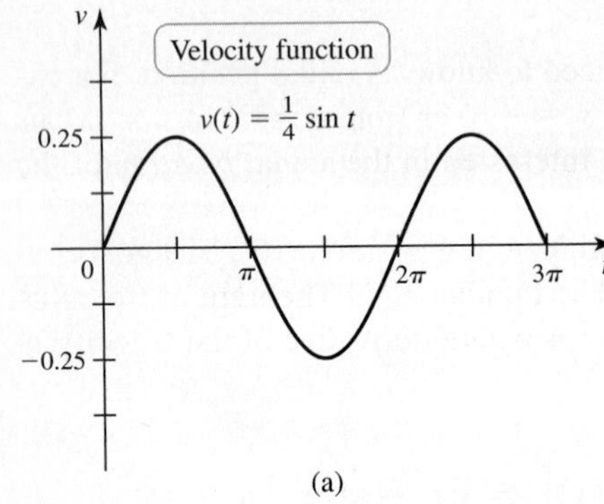

(a)

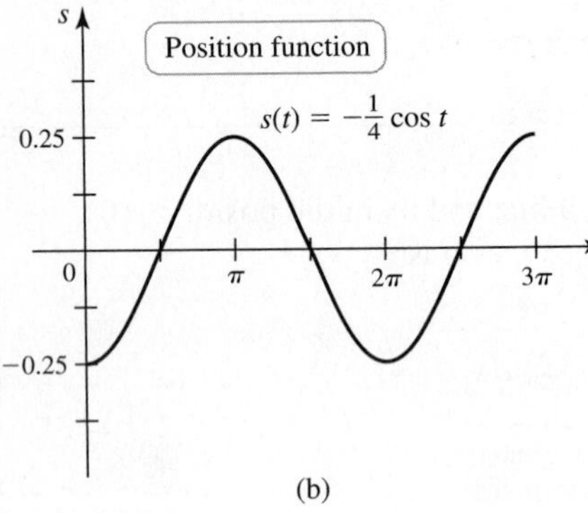

(b)

FIGURE 6.5

SOLUTION

a. The velocity function (Figure 6.5a) is positive for $0 < t < \pi$, which means the block moves in the positive (upward) direction. At $t = \pi$, the block comes to rest momentarily; for $\pi < t < 2\pi$, the block moves in the negative (downward) direction. We let $s(t)$ be the position at time $t \geq 0$ with the initial position $s(0) = -\frac{1}{4}$ m.

Method 1: Using antiderivatives Because the position is an antiderivative of the velocity, we have

$$s(t) = \int v(t)\,dt = \int \frac{1}{4}\sin t\,dt = -\frac{1}{4}\cos t + C.$$

To determine the arbitrary constant C, we substitute the initial condition $s(0) = -\frac{1}{4}$ into the expression for $s(t)$:

$$-\frac{1}{4} = -\frac{1}{4}\cos 0 + C$$

Solving for C, we find that $C = 0$. Therefore, the position for any time $t \geq 0$ is

$$s(t) = -\frac{1}{4}\cos t.$$

Method 2: Using Theorem 6.1 Alternatively, we may use the relationship

$$s(t) = s(0) + \int_0^t v(x)\,dx.$$

Substituting $v(x) = \frac{1}{4}\sin x$ and $s(0) = -\frac{1}{4}$, the position function is

$$\begin{aligned}
s(t) &= \underbrace{-\frac{1}{4}}_{s(0)} + \int_0^t \underbrace{\frac{1}{4}\sin x}_{v(x)}\,dx \\
&= -\frac{1}{4} - \left(\frac{1}{4}\cos x\right)\Big|_0^t && \text{Evaluate integral.} \\
&= -\frac{1}{4} - \frac{1}{4}(\cos t - 1) && \text{Simplify.} \\
&= -\frac{1}{4}\cos t. && \text{Simplify.}
\end{aligned}$$

b. The graph of the position function is shown in Figure 6.5b. We see that $s(0) = -\frac{1}{4}$, as prescribed.

➤ It is worth repeating that to find the displacement, we need to know only the velocity. To find the position, we must know both the velocity and the initial position $s(0)$.

c. The block initially moves in the positive s direction (upward), reaching the origin ($s = 0$) when $s(t) = -\frac{1}{4}\cos t = 0$. So the block arrives at the origin for the first time when $t = \pi/2$.

d. The block moves in the positive direction and reaches its high point for the first time when $t = \pi$; the position at that moment is $s(\pi) = \frac{1}{4}$. The block then reverses direction and moves in the negative (downward) direction, reaching its low point at $t = 2\pi$. This motion repeats every 2π seconds. *Related Exercises 11–18* ◄

QUICK CHECK 4 Without doing further calculations, what are the displacement and distance traveled by the block in Example 2 over the interval $[0, 2\pi]$? ◄

➤ The terminal velocity of an object depends on its density, shape, size, and the medium through which it falls. Estimates for human beings in free fall vary from 120 mi/hr (54 m/s) to 180 mi/hr (80 m/s).

EXAMPLE 3 **Skydiving** Suppose a skydiver leaps from a hovering helicopter and falls in a straight line. He falls at a terminal velocity of 80 m/s for 19 seconds, at which time he opens his parachute. The velocity decreases linearly to 6 m/s over a two-second period and then remains constant until he reaches the ground at $t = 40$ s. The motion is described by the velocity function

$$v(t) = \begin{cases} 80 & \text{if } 0 \leq t < 19 \\ 783 - 37t & \text{if } 19 \leq t < 21 \\ 6 & \text{if } 21 \leq t \leq 40 \end{cases}$$

Determine the altitude from which the skydiver jumped.

SOLUTION We let the position of the skydiver increase *downward* with the origin ($s = 0$) corresponding to the position of the helicopter. The velocity (Figure 6.6) is positive, so the distance traveled by the skydiver equals the displacement, which is

$$\begin{aligned} \int_0^{40} |v(t)|\, dt &= \int_0^{19} 80\, dt + \int_{19}^{21} (783 - 37t)\, dt + \int_{21}^{40} 6\, dt \\ &= 80t\Big|_0^{19} + \left(783t - \frac{37t^2}{2}\right)\Big|_{19}^{21} + 6t\Big|_{21}^{40} \qquad \text{Fundamental Theorem} \\ &= 1720. \qquad \text{Evaluate and simplify.} \end{aligned}$$

The skydiver jumped from 1720 m above the ground. Notice that the displacement of the skydiver is the area under the velocity curve.

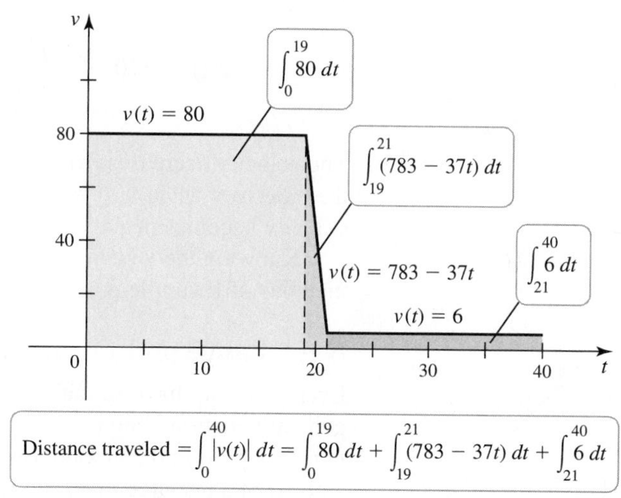

FIGURE 6.6

Related Exercises 19–20 ◄

QUICK CHECK 5 Suppose (unrealistically) in Example 3 that the velocity of the skydiver is 80 m/s, for $0 < t < 20$ and then it changes instantaneously to 6 m/s, for $20 < t < 40$. Sketch the velocity function and, without integrating, find the distance the skydiver falls in 40 s. ◄

Acceleration

Because the acceleration of an object moving along a line is given by $a(t) = v'(t)$, the relationship between velocity and acceleration is the same as the relationship between position and velocity. Given the acceleration of an object, the change in velocity over an interval $[a, b]$ is

$$\text{change in velocity} = v(b) - v(a) = \int_a^b v'(t)\,dt = \int_a^b a(t)\,dt.$$

Furthermore, if we know the acceleration and initial velocity $v(0)$, then the velocity at future times can also be found.

> Theorem 6.2 is a consequence of the Fundamental Theorem of Calculus.

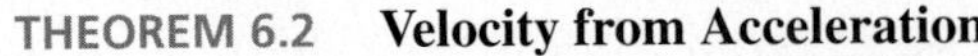

THEOREM 6.2 Velocity from Acceleration
Given the acceleration $a(t)$ of an object moving along a line and its initial velocity $v(0)$, the velocity of the object for future times $t \geq 0$ is

$$v(t) = v(0) + \int_0^t a(x)\,dx.$$

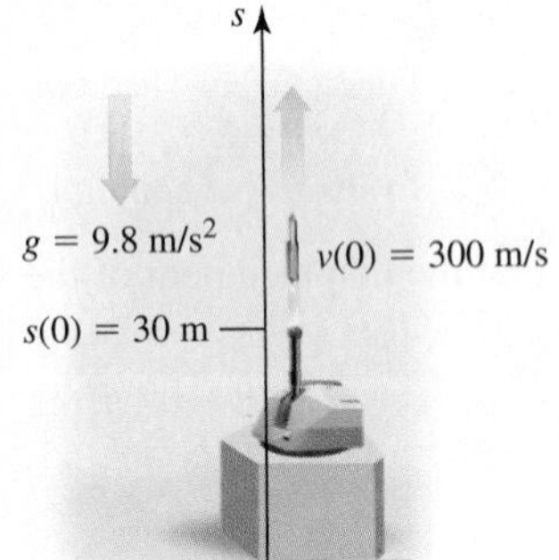

FIGURE 6.7

EXAMPLE 4 Motion in a gravitational field An artillery shell is fired directly upward with an initial velocity of 300 m/s from a point 30 m above the ground (Figure 6.7). Assume that only the force of gravity acts on the shell and it produces an acceleration of 9.8 m/s^2. Find the velocity of the shell, for $t \geq 0$.

SOLUTION We let the positive direction be upward with the origin $(s = 0)$ corresponding to the ground. The initial velocity of the shell is $v(0) = 300$ m/s. The acceleration due to gravity is downward; therefore, $a(t) = -9.8\text{ m/s}^2$. The velocity for $t \geq 0$ is

$$v(t) = \underbrace{v(0)}_{300\text{ m/s}} + \int_0^t \underbrace{a(x)}_{-9.8\text{ m/s}^2}\,dx = 300 + \int_0^t (-9.8)\,dx = 300 - 9.8t.$$

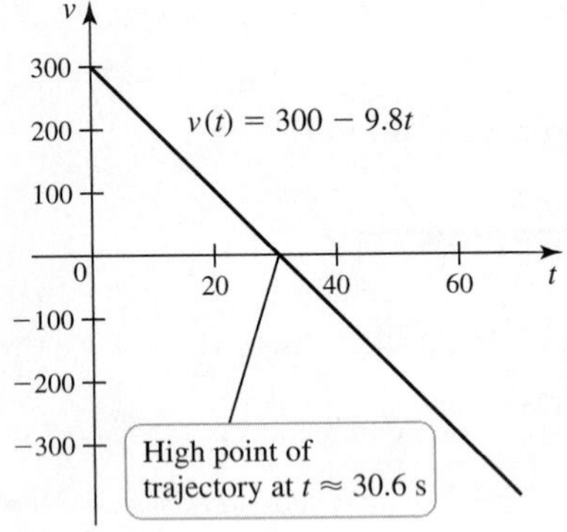

FIGURE 6.8

The velocity decreases from its initial value of 300 m/s, reaching zero at the high point of the trajectory when $v(t) = 300 - 9.8t = 0$, or at $t \approx 30.6$ s (Figure 6.8). At this point the velocity becomes negative, and the shell begins its descent to Earth.

Knowing the velocity function, you could now find the position function using the methods of Example 3. *Related Exercises 21–27* ◄

Net Change and Future Value

Everything we have said about velocity, position, and displacement carries over to more general situations. Suppose you are interested in some quantity Q that changes over *time*; Q may represent the amount of water in a reservoir, the population of a cell culture, or the amount of a resource that is consumed or produced. If you are given the rate Q' at which Q changes, then integration allows you to calculate either the net change in the quantity Q or the future value of Q.

We argue just as we did for velocity and position: Because Q is an antiderivative of Q', the Fundamental Theorem of Calculus tells us that

$$\int_a^b Q'(t)\,dt = Q(b) - Q(a) = \text{net change in } Q \text{ over } [a, b].$$

Geometrically, the net change in Q over the time interval $[a, b]$ is the net area under the graph of Q' over $[a, b]$.

Alternatively, suppose we are given both the rate of change Q' and the initial value $Q(0)$. Integrating over the interval $[0, t]$, where $t \geq 0$, we have

> Note that the units in the integral are consistent. For example, if Q' has units of gal/second, and t and x have units of seconds, then $Q'(x)\,dx$ has units of (gal/second)(second) = gal, which are the units of Q.

$$\int_0^t Q'(x)\,dx = Q(t) - Q(0).$$

Rearranging this equation, we write the value of Q at any future time $t \geq 0$ as

$$\underbrace{Q(t)}_{\text{future value}} = \underbrace{Q(0)}_{\text{initial value}} + \underbrace{\int_0^t Q'(x)\,dx}_{\text{net change over } [0,t]}.$$

> At the risk of being repetitious, Theorem 6.3 is also a consequence of the Fundamental Theorem of Calculus. We assume that Q' is an integrable function.

THEOREM 6.3 Net Change and Future Value

Suppose a quantity Q changes over time at a known rate Q'. Then the **net change** in Q between $t = a$ and $t = b$ is

$$\underbrace{Q(b) - Q(a)}_{\text{net change in } Q} = \int_a^b Q'(t)\,dt.$$

Given the initial value $Q(0)$, the **future value** of Q at times $t \geq 0$ is

$$Q(t) = Q(0) + \int_0^t Q'(x)\,dx.$$

The correspondences between velocity-displacement problems and more general problems are shown in Table 6.1.

Table 6.1

Velocity-Displacement Problems	General Problems
Position $s(t)$	Quantity $Q(t)$ (such as volume or population size)
Velocity: $s'(t) = v(t)$	Rate of change: $Q'(t)$
Displacement: $s(b) - s(a) = \int_a^b v(t)\,dt$	Net change: $Q(b) - Q(a) = \int_a^b Q'(t)\,dt$
Future position: $s(t) = s(0) + \int_0^t v(x)\,dx$	Future value of Q: $Q(t) = Q(0) + \int_0^t Q'(x)\,dx$

EXAMPLE 5 Emptying a tank Imagine an open cylindrical tank with radius R and height H filled to the top with water. At time $t = 0$, a circular drain of radius r in the bottom of the tank is opened and water flows out of the tank (Figure 6.9). Using a result known as **Torricelli's Law** (proposed in 1643) it can be shown that under ideal conditions the rate of change of the volume of water in the tank at time $t \geq 0$ is

$$V'(t) = \frac{\pi r^4 g}{R^2}t - \pi r^2\sqrt{2gH},$$

where $g = 980\ \text{cm/s}^2$ is the acceleration due to gravity. In the specific case that $r = 5$ cm, $R = 50$ cm, and $H = 100$ cm, we have $V'(t) = 769.690t - 34{,}771.059$, where t is measured in seconds and $V(0) = 785{,}398.163\ \text{cm}^3$. Find the function that gives the volume of water remaining in the tank until the tank is empty.

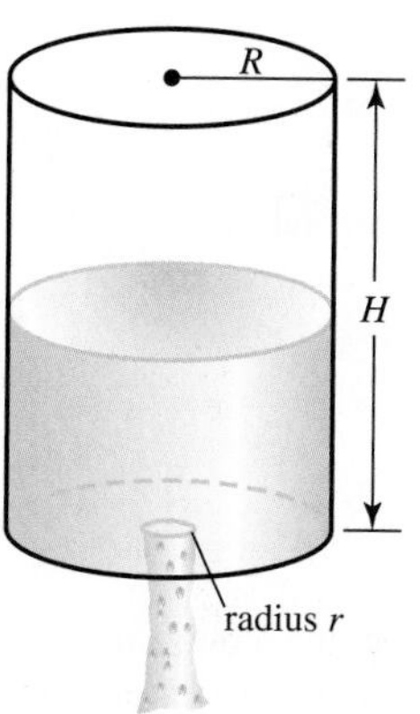

FIGURE 6.9

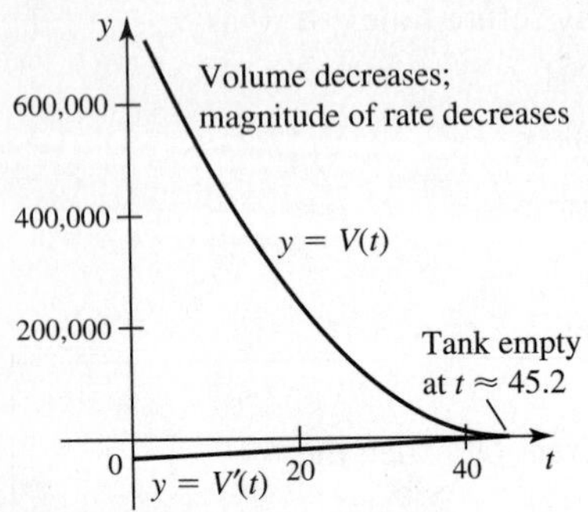

FIGURE 6.10

SOLUTION

As shown in Figure 6.10, the rate of change of the volume is negative, reflecting the decreasing volume of water in the tank. Knowing the initial volume $V(0)$ and the rate of change $V'(t)$, Theorem 6.3 gives the volume of water in the tank:

$$V(t) = V(0) + \int_0^t V'(x)\,dx \qquad \text{Theorem 6.3}$$

$$= \underbrace{785{,}398.163}_{V(0)} + \int_0^t \underbrace{(769.690x - 34{,}771.059)}_{V'(x)}\,dx \qquad \text{Substitute.}$$

$$= 785{,}398.163 + \left(\frac{769.690x^2}{2} - 34{,}771.059x\right)\Bigg|_0^t \qquad \text{Fundamental Theorem}$$

$$= 785{,}398.163 - 34{,}771.059t + 384.845t^2 \qquad \text{Simplify.}$$

The graph of the volume function (Figure 6.10) shows that the volume decreases until the volume reaches zero at $t \approx 45.2$ seconds—the same time at which the rate of change equals zero.

Related Exercises 28–34 ◀

EXAMPLE 6 **Production costs** A book publisher estimates that the marginal cost of a particular title (in dollars/book) is given by

$$C'(x) = 12 - 0.0002x,$$

where $0 \leq x \leq 50{,}000$ is the number of books printed. What is the cost of producing the 12,001st through the 15,000th book?

> Although x is a positive integer (the number of books produced), we treat it as a continuous variable in this example.

SOLUTION Recall from Section 3.5 that the cost function $C(x)$ is the cost required to produce x units of a product. The marginal cost $C'(x)$ is the approximate cost of producing one additional unit after x units have already been produced. The cost of producing books $x = 12{,}001$ through $x = 15{,}000$ is the cost of producing 15,000 books minus the cost of producing the first 12,000 books. Therefore, the cost in dollars of producing books 12,001 through 15,000 is

$$C(15{,}000) - C(12{,}000) = \int_{12{,}000}^{15{,}000} C'(x)\,dx$$

$$= \int_{12{,}000}^{15{,}000} (12 - 0.0002x)\,dx \qquad \text{Substitute for } C'(x).$$

$$= (12x - 0.0001x^2)\Big|_{12{,}000}^{15{,}000} \qquad \text{Fundamental Theorem}$$

$$= 27{,}900. \qquad \text{Simplify.}$$

Related Exercises 35–38 ◀

QUICK CHECK 6 Would the cost of increasing the production from 9000 books to 12,000 books be more or less than the cost of increasing the production from 12,000 books to 15,000 books? Explain. ◀

SECTION 6.1 EXERCISES

Review Questions

1. Explain the meaning of position, displacement, and distance traveled as they apply to an object moving along a line.

2. Suppose the velocity of an object moving along a line is positive. Are position, displacement, and distance traveled equal? Explain.

3. Given the velocity function v of an object moving along a line, explain how definite integrals can be used to find the displacement of the object.

4. Explain how to use definite integrals to find the net change in a quantity, given the rate of change of that quantity.

5. Given the rate of change of a quantity Q and its initial value $Q(0)$, explain how to find the value of Q at a future time $t \geq 0$.

6. What is the result of integrating a population growth rate between two times $t = a$ and $t = b$, where $b > a$?

Basic Skills

T **7–10. Displacement from velocity** *Assume t is time measured in seconds and velocities have units of m/s.*

a. Graph the velocity function over the given interval. Then determine when the motion is in the positive direction and when it is in the negative direction.
b. Find the displacement over the given interval.
c. Find the distance traveled over the given interval.

7. $v(t) = 6 - 2t;\ 0 \leq t \leq 6$

8. $v(t) = 10 \sin 2t;\ 0 \leq t \leq 2\pi$

9. $v(t) = t^3 - 5t^2 + 6t;\ 0 \leq t \leq 5$

10. $v(t) = 50/(t + 1)^2,\ 0 \leq t \leq 4$

T **11–14. Position from velocity** *Consider an object moving along a line with the following velocities and initial positions.*

a. Graph the velocity function on the given interval and determine when the object is moving in the positive direction and when it is moving in the negative direction.
b. Determine the position function for $t \geq 0$ using both the antiderivative method and the Fundamental Theorem of Calculus (Theorem 6.1). Check for agreement between the two methods.
c. Graph the position function on the given interval.

11. $v(t) = 6 - 2t$ on $[0, 5]$; $s(0) = 0$

12. $v(t) = 3 \sin \pi t$ on $[0, 4]$; $s(0) = 1$

13. $v(t) = 9 - t^2$ on $[0, 4]$; $s(0) = -2$

14. $v(t) = 20/\sqrt{t + 1}$ on $[0, 8]$; $s(0) = -4$

T 15. **Oscillating motion** A mass hanging from a spring is set in motion and its ensuing velocity is given by $v(t) = 2\pi \cos \pi t$, for $t \geq 0$. Assume that the positive direction is upward and $s(0) = 0$.
   a. Determine the position function, for $t \geq 0$.
   b. Graph the position function on the interval $[0, 4]$.
   c. At what times does the mass reach its lowest point the first three times?
   d. At what times does the mass reach its highest point the first three times?

16. **Cycling distance** A cyclist rides down a long straight road at a velocity (in m/min) given by $v(t) = 400 - 20t$, for $0 \leq t \leq 10$ min.
   a. How far does the cyclist travel in the first 5 min?
   b. How far does the cyclist travel in the first 10 min?
   c. How far has the cyclist traveled when her velocity is 250 m/min?

17. **Flying into a headwind** The velocity (in mi/hr) of an airplane flying into a headwind is given by $v(t) = 30(16 - t^2)$, for $0 \leq t \leq 3$. Assume that $s(0) = 0$.
   a. Determine and graph the position function, for $0 \leq t \leq 3$.
   b. How far does the airplane travel in the first 2 hr?
   c. How far has the airplane traveled at the instant its velocity reaches 400 mi/hr?

18. **Day hike** The velocity (in mi/hr) of a hiker walking along a straight trail is given by $v(t) = 3 \sin^2 (\pi t/2)$, for $0 \leq t \leq 4$. Assume that $s(0) = 0$.
   a. Determine and graph the position function, for $0 \leq t \leq 4$.
   b. What is the distance traveled by the hiker in the first 15 minutes of the hike? (*Hint*: $\sin^2 t = \frac{1}{2}(1 - \cos 2t)$.)
   c. What is the hiker's position at $t = 3$?

19. **Piecewise velocity** The velocity of a (fast) automobile on a straight highway is given by the function

$$v(t) = \begin{cases} 3t & \text{if } 0 \leq t < 20 \\ 60 & \text{if } 20 \leq t < 45 \\ 240 - 4t & \text{if } t \geq 45 \end{cases}$$

where t is measured in seconds and v has units of m/s.
   a. Graph the velocity function, for $0 \leq t \leq 70$. When is the velocity a maximum? When is the velocity zero?
   b. What is the distance traveled by the automobile in the first 30 s?
   c. What is the distance traveled by the automobile in the first 60 s?
   d. What is the position of the automobile when $t = 75$?

20. **Probe speed** A data collection probe is dropped from a stationary balloon and it falls with a velocity (in m/s) given by $v(t) = 9.8t$, neglecting air resistance. After 10 s, a chute deploys and the probe immediately slows to a constant speed of 10 m/s, which it maintains until it enters the ocean.
   a. Graph the velocity function.
   b. How far does the probe fall in the first 30 s after it is released?
   c. If the probe was released from an altitude of 3 km, when does it enter the ocean?

21–24. Position and velocity from acceleration *Find the position and velocity of an object moving along a straight line with the given acceleration, initial velocity, and initial position.*

21. $a(t) = -9.8,\ v(0) = 20,\ s(0) = 0$

22. $a(t) = 20 - 4t,\ v(0) = 60,\ s(0) = 40$

23. $a(t) = -0.01t,\ v(0) = 10,\ s(0) = 0$

24. $a(t) = 20/(t + 2)^{3/2},\ v(0) = 20,\ s(0) = 10$

25. **Acceleration** A drag racer accelerates at $a(t) = 88\ \text{ft/s}^2$. Assume that $v(0) = 0$ and $s(0) = 0$.
   a. Determine and graph the position function, for $t \geq 0$.
   b. How far does the racer travel in the first 4 seconds?
   c. At this rate, how long will it take the racer to travel $\frac{1}{4}$ mi?
   d. How long does it take the racer to travel 300 ft?
   e. How far has the racer traveled when it reaches a speed of 178 ft/s?

26. **Deceleration** A car slows down with an acceleration of $a(t) = -15\ \text{ft/s}^2$. Assume that $v(0) = 60$ ft/s and $s(0) = 0$.
   a. Determine and graph the position function, for $t \geq 0$.
   b. How far does the car travel in the time it takes to come to rest?

27. **Approaching a station** At $t = 0$, a train approaching a station begins decelerating from a speed of 80 mi/hr according to the acceleration function $a(t) = -1280(1 + 8t)^{-3}$, where $t \geq 0$. How far does the train travel between $t = 0$ and $t = 0.2$? Between $t = 0.2$ and $t = 0.4$? The units of acceleration are mi/hr^2.

28. Peak oil extraction The owners of an oil reserve begin extracting oil at time $t = 0$. Based on estimates of the reserves, suppose the projected extraction rate is given by $Q'(t) = 3t^2(40 - t)^2$, where $0 \le t \le 40$, Q is measured in millions of barrels, and t is measured in years.

a. When does the peak extraction rate occur?
b. How much oil is extracted in the first 10, 20, and 30 years?
c. What is the total amount of oil extracted in 40 years?
d. Is one-fourth of the total oil extracted in the first one-fourth of the extraction period? Explain.

29. Oil production An oil refinery produces oil at a variable rate given by

$$Q'(t) = \begin{cases} 800 & \text{if } 0 \le t < 30 \\ 2600 - 60t & \text{if } 30 \le t < 40 \\ 200 & \text{if } t \ge 40 \end{cases}$$

where t is measured in days and Q is measured in barrels.

a. How many barrels are produced in the first 35 days?
b. How many barrels are produced in the first 50 days?
c. Without using calculus, determine the number of barrels produced over the interval $[60, 80]$.

30–33. Population growth

30. Starting with an initial value of $P(0) = 55$, the population of a prairie dog community grows at a rate of $P'(t) = 20 - t/5$ (in units of prairie dogs/month), for $0 \le t \le 200$.

a. What is the population 6 months later?
b. Find the population $P(t)$, for $0 \le t \le 200$.

31. When records were first kept ($t = 0$), the population of a rural town was 250 people. During the following years, the population grew at a rate of $P'(t) = 30(1 + \sqrt{t})$, where t is measured in years.

a. What is the population after 20 years?
b. Find the population $P(t)$ at any time $t \ge 0$.

32. The population of a community of foxes is observed to fluctuate on a 10-year cycle due to variations in the availability of prey. When population measurements began ($t = 0$), the population was 35 foxes. The growth rate in units of foxes/yr was observed to be

$$P'(t) = 5 + 10\sin\left(\frac{\pi t}{5}\right).$$

a. What is the population 15 years later? 35 years later?
b. Find the population $P(t)$ at any time $t \ge 0$.

33. A culture of bacteria in a petri dish has an initial population of 1500 cells and grows at a rate (in cells/day) of $N'(t) = 200(t + 2)^{-1/2}$.

a. What is the population after 14 days? after 34 days?
b. Find the population $N(t)$ at any time $t \ge 0$.

34. Endangered species The population of an endangered species changes at a rate given by $P'(t) = 30 - 20t$ (individuals/year). Assume the initial population of the species is 300 individuals.

a. What is the population after 5 years?
b. When will the species become extinct?
c. How does the extinction time change if the initial population is 100 individuals? 400 individuals?

35–38. Marginal cost *Consider the following marginal cost functions.*

a. *Find the additional cost incurred in dollars when production is increased from 100 units to 150 units.*
b. *Find the additional cost incurred in dollars when production is increased from 500 units to 550 units.*

35. $C'(x) = 2000 - 0.5x$

36. $C'(x) = 200 - 0.05x$

37. $C'(x) = 300 + 10x - 0.01x^2$

38. $C'(x) = 3000 - x - 0.001x^2$

Further Explorations

39. Explain why or why not Determine whether the following statements are true and give an explanation or counterexample.

a. The distance traveled by an object moving along a line is the same as the displacement of the object.
b. When the velocity is positive on an interval, the displacement and the distance traveled on that interval are equal.
c. Consider a tank that is filled and drained at a flow rate of $V'(t) = 1 - t^2/100$ (gal/min), for $t \ge 0$. It follows that the volume of water in the tank increases for 10 min and then decreases until the tank is empty.
d. A particular marginal cost function has the property that it is positive and decreasing. The cost of increasing production from A units to $2A$ units is greater than the cost of increasing production from $2A$ units to $3A$ units.

40–41. Velocity graphs *The figures show velocity functions for motion along a straight line. Assume the motion begins with an initial position of $s(0) = 0$. Determine the following:*

a. *The displacement between $t = 0$ and $t = 5$*
b. *The distance traveled between $t = 0$ and $t = 5$*
c. *The position at $t = 5$*
d. *A piecewise function for $s(t)$*

40.

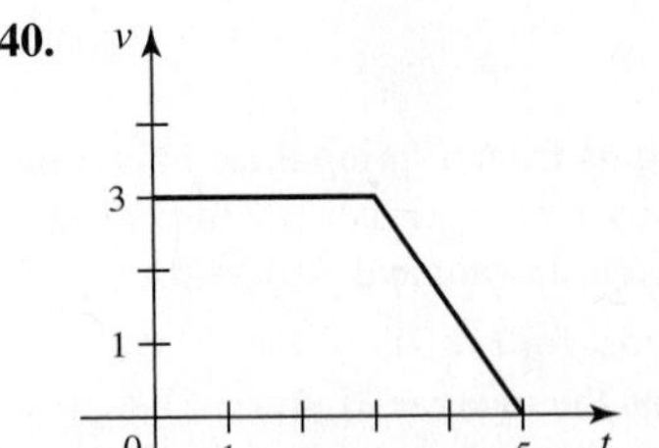

41.

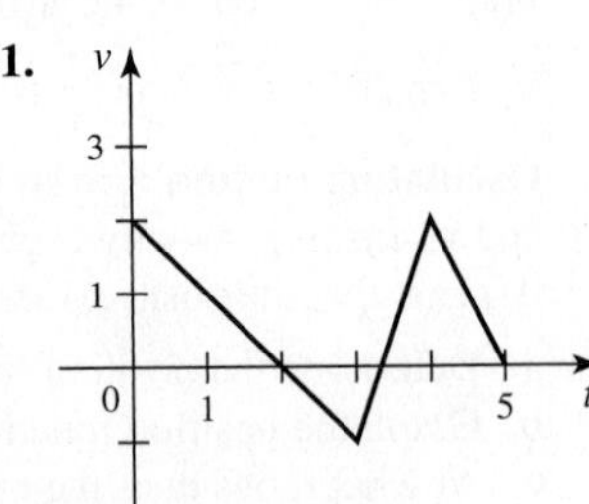

42–45. Equivalent constant velocity *Consider the following velocity functions. In each case, complete the sentence: The same distance could have been traveled over the given time period at a* constant *velocity of* ________.

42. $v(t) = 2t + 6, \quad \text{for } 0 \le t \le 8$

43. $v(t) = 1 - t^2/16, \quad \text{for } 0 \le t \le 4$

44. $v(t) = 2\sin t, \quad \text{for } 0 \le t \le \pi$

45. $v(t) = t(25 - t^2)^{1/2}, \quad \text{for } 0 \le t \le 5$

46. Where do they meet? Kelly started at noon ($t = 0$) riding a bike from Niwot to Berthoud, a distance of 20 km, with velocity $v(t) = 15/(t + 1)^2$ (decreasing because of fatigue). Sandy started at noon ($t = 0$) riding a bike in the opposite direction from

Berthoud to Niwot with velocity $u(t) = 20/(t + 1)^2$ (also decreasing because of fatigue). Assume distance is measured in kilometers and time is measured in hours.

a. Make a graph of Kelly's distance from Niwot as a function of time.
b. Make a graph of Sandy's distance from Berthoud as a function of time.
c. How far has each person traveled when they meet? When do they meet?
d. If the riders' speeds are $v(t) = A/(t + 1)^2$ and $u(t) = B/(t + 1)^2$ and the distance between the towns is D, what conditions on A, B, and D must be met to ensure that the riders will pass each other?
e. Looking ahead: With the velocity functions given in part (d), make a conjecture about the maximum distance each person can ride (given unlimited time).

47. Bike race Theo and Sasha start at the same place on a straight road riding bikes with the following velocities (measured in mi/hr):

Theo: $v_T(t) = 10$, for $t \geq 0$
Sasha: $v_S(t) = 15t$, for $0 \leq t \leq 1$ and
$v_S(t) = 15$, for $t > 1$

a. Graph the velocity functions for both riders.
b. If the riders ride for 1 hr, who rides farther? Interpret your answer geometrically using the graphs of part (a).
c. If the riders ride for 2 hr, who rides farther? Interpret your answer geometrically using the graphs of part (a).
d. Which rider arrives first at the 10-, 15-, and 20-mi markers of the race? Interpret your answer geometrically using the graphs of part (a).
e. Suppose Sasha gives Theo a head start of 0.2 mi and the riders ride for 20 mi. Who wins the race?
f. Suppose Sasha gives Theo a head start of 0.2 hr and the riders ride for 20 mi. Who wins the race?

48. Two runners At noon $(t = 0)$, Alicia starts running along a long straight road at 4 mi/hr. Her velocity decreases according to the function $v(t) = 4/(t + 1)^2$, for $t \geq 0$. At noon, Boris also starts running along the same road with a 2-mi head start on Alicia; his velocity is given by $u(t) = 2/(t + 1)^2$, for $t \geq 0$.

a. Find the position functions for Alicia and Boris, where $s = 0$ corresponds to Alice's starting point.
b. When, if ever, does Alicia overtake Boris?

49. Running in a wind A strong west wind blows across a circular running track. Abe and Bess start at the south end of the track and at the same time, Abe starts running clockwise and Bess starts running counterclockwise. Abe runs with a speed (in units of mi/hr) given by $u(\varphi) = 3 - 2\cos\varphi$ and Bess runs with a speed given by $v(\theta) = 3 + 2\cos\theta$, where φ and θ are the central angles of the runners.

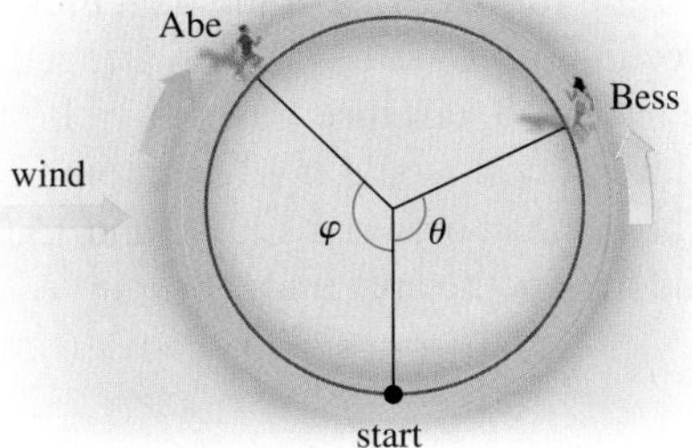

a. Graph the speed functions u and v, and explain why they describe the runners' speeds (in light of the wind).
b. Which runner has the greater average speed for one lap?
c. Challenge: If the track has a radius of $\frac{1}{10}$ mi, how long does it take each runner to complete one lap and who wins the race?

Applications

50. Filling a tank A 200-L cistern is empty when water begins flowing into it (at $t = 0$) at a rate in L/min given by $Q'(t) = 3\sqrt{t}$.

a. How much water flows into the cistern in 1 hr?
b. Find and graph the function that gives the amount of water in the tank at any time $t \geq 0$.
c. When will the tank be full?

T **51. Filling a reservoir** A reservoir with a capacity of 2500 m^3 is filled with a single inflow pipe. The reservoir is empty when the inflow pipe is opened at $t = 0$. Letting $Q(t)$ be the amount of water in the reservoir at time t, the flow rate of water into the reservoir (in m^3/hr) oscillates on a 24-hr cycle (see figure) and is given by

$$Q'(t) = 20\left[1 + \cos\left(\frac{\pi t}{12}\right)\right].$$

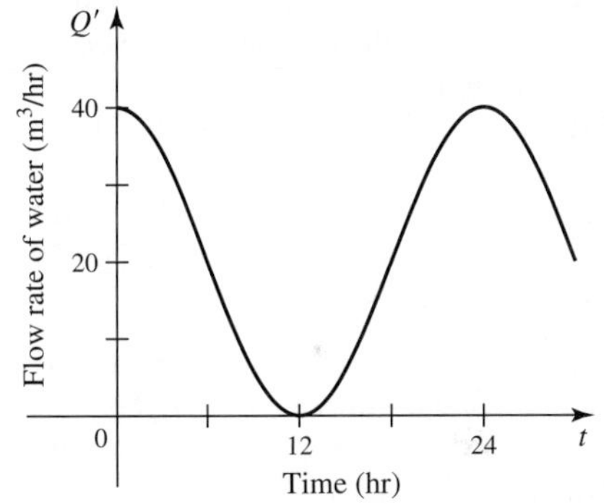

a. How much water flows into the reservoir in the first 2 hr?
b. Find and graph the function that gives the amount of water in the reservoir over the interval $[0, t]$, where $t \geq 0$.
c. When is the reservoir full?

52. Blood flow A typical human heart pumps 20 mL of blood with each stroke (stroke volume). Assuming a heart rate of 60 beats/min, a reasonable model for the outflow rate of the heart is $V'(t) = 20(1 + \sin(2\pi t))$, where $V(t)$ is the amount of blood (in ml) pumped over the interval $[0, t]$, $V(0) = 0$, and t is measured in seconds.

a. Graph the outflow rate function.
b. Verify that the amount of blood pumped over a one-second interval is 20 mL.
c. Find the function that gives the total blood pumped between $t = 0$ and a future time $t > 0$.
d. What is the cardiac output over a period of 1 min? (Use calculus, then check your answer with algebra.)

53. Air flow in the lungs A reasonable model (with different parameters for different people) for the flow of air in and out of the lungs is

$$V'(t) = -\frac{\pi V_0}{10}\sin\left(\frac{\pi t}{5}\right),$$

where $V(t)$ is the volume of air in the lungs at time $t \geq 0$, measured in liters, t is measured in seconds, and V_0 is the capacity of the lungs. The time $t = 0$ corresponds to a time at which the lungs are full and exhalation begins.

a. Graph the flow rate function with $V_0 = 10$ L.
b. Find and graph the function V, assuming that $V(0) = V_0 = 10$ L.
c. What is the breathing rate in breaths/min?

54. Oscillating growth rates Some species have growth rates that oscillate with an (approximately) constant period P. Consider the growth rate function

$$N'(t) = A \sin\left(\frac{2\pi t}{P}\right) + r,$$

where A and r are constants with units of individuals/yr. A species becomes extinct if its population ever reaches 0 after $t = 0$.

a. Suppose $P = 10$, $A = 20$, and $r = 0$. If the initial population is $N(0) = 10$, does the population ever become extinct? Explain.
b. Suppose $P = 10$, $A = 20$, and $r = 0$. If the initial population is $N(0) = 100$, does the population ever become extinct? Explain.
c. Suppose $P = 10$, $A = 50$, and $r = 5$. If the initial population is $N(0) = 10$, does the population ever become extinct? Explain.
d. Suppose $P = 10$, $A = 50$, and $r = -5$. Find the initial population $N(0)$ needed to ensure that the population never becomes extinct.

55. Power and energy Power and energy are often used interchangeably, but they are quite different. **Energy** is what makes matter move or heat up and is measured in units of **joules** (J) or **Calories** (Cal), where 1 Cal = 4184 J. One hour of walking consumes roughly 10^6 J, or 250 Cal. On the other hand, **power** is the rate at which energy is used and is measured in **watts** (W; 1 W = 1 J/s). Other useful units of power are **kilowatts** (1 kW = 10^3 W) and **megawatts** (1 MW = 10^6 W). If energy is used at a rate of 1 kW for 1 hr, the total amount of energy used is 1 **kilowatt-hour** (kWh), which is 3.6×10^6 J.

Suppose the power function of a large city over a 24-hr period is given by

$$P(t) = E'(t) = 300 - 200 \sin\left(\frac{\pi t}{12}\right),$$

where P is measured in MW and $t = 0$ corresponds to 6:00 p.m. (see figure).

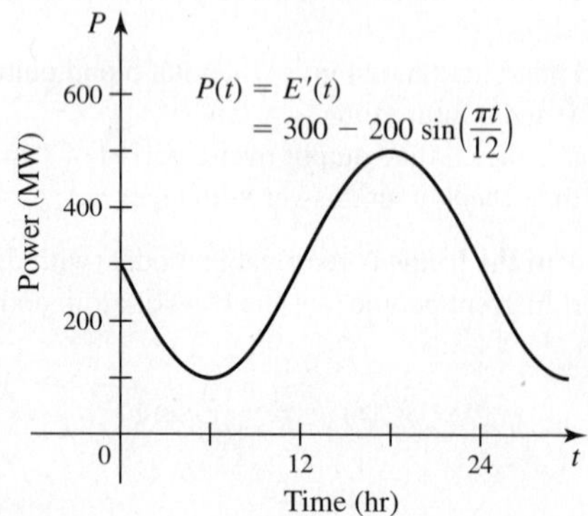

a. How much energy is consumed by this city in a typical 24-hr period? Express the answer in MWh and in J.
b. Burning 1 kg of coal produces about 450 kWh of energy. How many kg of coal are required to meet the energy needs of the city for 1 day? For 1 yr?
c. Fission of 1 gram of uranium-235 (U-235) produces about 16,000 kWh of energy. How many grams of uranium are needed to meet the energy needs of the city for 1 day? For 1 yr?
d. A typical wind turbine can generate electricity at a rate of about 200 kW. Approximately how many wind turbines are needed to meet the average energy needs of the city?

56. Variable gravity At Earth's surface the acceleration due to gravity is approximately $g = 9.8 \text{ m/s}^2$ (with local variations). However, the acceleration decreases with distance from the surface according to Newton's law of gravitation. At a distance of y meters from Earth's surface, the acceleration is given by

$$a(y) = -\frac{g}{(1 + y/R)^2},$$

where $R = 6.4 \times 10^6$ m is the radius of Earth.

a. Suppose a projectile is launched upward with an initial velocity of v_0 m/s. Let $v(t)$ be its velocity and $y(t)$ its height (in meters) above the surface t seconds after the launch. Neglecting forces such as air resistance, explain why $\frac{dv}{dt} = a(y)$ and $\frac{dy}{dt} = v(t)$.
b. Use the Chain Rule to show that $\frac{dv}{dt} = \frac{1}{2}\frac{d}{dy}(v^2)$.
c. Show that the equation of motion for the projectile is $\frac{1}{2}\frac{d}{dy}(v^2) = a(y)$, where $a(y)$ is given previously.
d. Integrate both sides of the equation in part (c) with respect to y using the fact that when $y = 0$, $v = v_0$. Show that

$$\frac{1}{2}(v^2 - v_0^2) = gR\left(\frac{1}{1 + y/R} - 1\right).$$

e. When the projectile reaches its maximum height, $v = 0$. Use this fact to determine that the maximum height is

$$y_{\max} = \frac{Rv_0^2}{2gR - v_0^2}.$$

f. Graph $y_{\max}$ as a function of v_0. What is the maximum height when $v_0 = 500$ m/s, 1500 m/s, and 5 km/s?
g. Show that the value of v_0 needed to put the projectile into orbit (called the escape velocity) is $\sqrt{2gR}$.

QUICK CHECK ANSWERS

1. Displacement = −20 mi (20 mi south); distance traveled = 100 mi. **2.** Suppose the object moves in the positive direction for $0 \leq t \leq 3$ and then moves in the negative direction for $3 < t \leq 5$. **3.** A function; a number **4.** Displacement = 0; distance traveled = 1 **5.** 1720 m **6.** The production cost would increase more between 9000 and 12,000 books than between 12,000 and 15,000 books. Graph C' and look at the area under the curve. ◄

6.2 Regions Between Curves

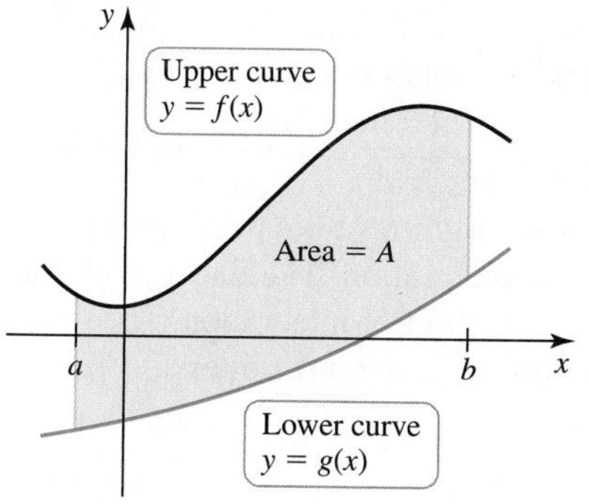

FIGURE 6.11

In this section, the method for finding the area of a region bounded by a single curve is generalized to regions bounded by two or more curves. Consider two functions f and g that are continuous on an interval $[a, b]$ on which $f(x) \geq g(x)$ (Figure 6.11). The goal is to find the area A of the region bounded by the two curves and the vertical lines $x = a$ and $x = b$.

Once again we rely on the *slice-and-sum* strategy (Section 5.2) for finding areas by Riemann sums. The interval $[a, b]$ is partitioned into n subintervals using uniformly spaced grid points separated by a distance $\Delta x = (b - a)/n$ (Figure 6.12). On each subinterval, we build a rectangle extending from the lower curve to the upper curve. On the kth subinterval, a point $\overline{x}_k$ is chosen, and the height of the corresponding rectangle is taken to be $f(\overline{x}_k) - g(\overline{x}_k)$. Therefore, the area of the kth rectangle is $(f(\overline{x}_k) - g(\overline{x}_k))\,\Delta x$ (Figure 6.13). Summing the areas of the n rectangles gives an approximation to the area of the region between the curves:

$$A \approx \sum_{k=1}^{n} (f(\overline{x}_k) - g(\overline{x}_k))\,\Delta x$$

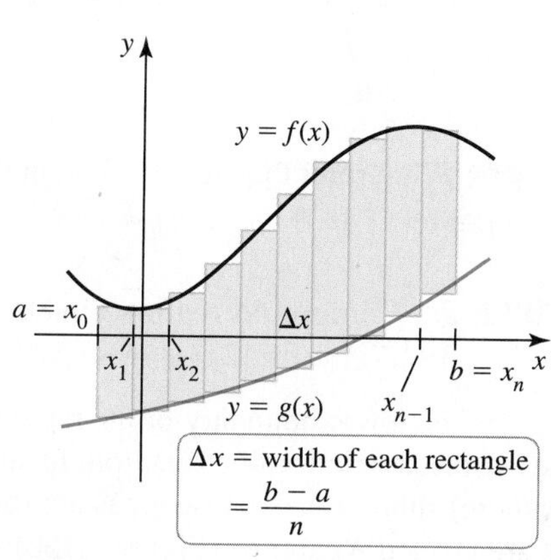

FIGURE 6.12

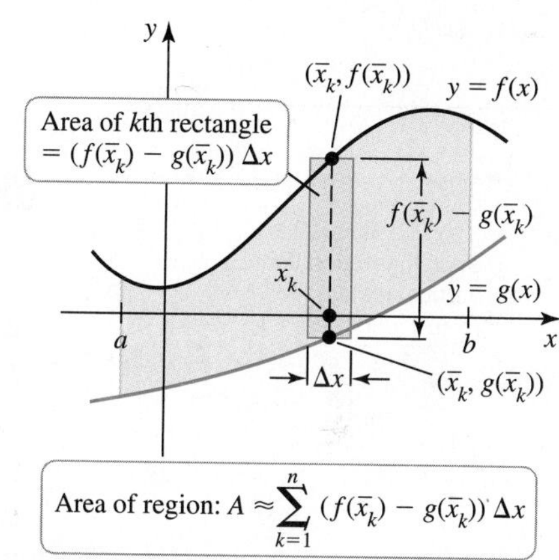

FIGURE 6.13

As the number of grid points increases, Δx approaches zero and these sums approach the area between the curves; that is,

$$A = \lim_{n\to\infty} \sum_{k=1}^{n} (f(\overline{x}_k) - g(\overline{x}_k))\,\Delta x.$$

The limit of these Riemann sums is a definite integral of the function $f - g$.

> It is helpful to interpret the area formula: $f(x) - g(x)$ is the length of a rectangle and dx is its width. We sum (integrate) the areas of the rectangles $(f(x) - g(x))\,dx$ to obtain the area of the region.

DEFINITION Area of a Region Between Two Curves

Suppose that f and g are continuous functions with $f(x) \geq g(x)$ on the interval $[a, b]$. The area of the region bounded by the graphs of f and g on $[a, b]$ is

$$A = \int_a^b (f(x) - g(x))\,dx.$$

QUICK CHECK 1 In the area formula for a region between two curves, verify that if the lower curve is $g(x) = 0$, the formula becomes the usual formula for the area of the region bounded by $y = f(x)$ and the x-axis.

EXAMPLE 1 **Area between curves** Find the area of the region bounded by the graphs of $f(x) = \dfrac{4}{\sqrt{x+1}}$, $g(x) = x - 1$, and the y-axis (Figure 6.14).

➤ A graphing calculator can be used to approximate the roots of $4/\sqrt{x+1} = x - 1$ and then we can confirm that $x = 3$ is the only real root.

SOLUTION A key step in the solution of many area problems is finding the intersection points of the boundary curves, which often determine the limits of integration. The intersection point of these two curves satisfies the equation $\dfrac{4}{\sqrt{x+1}} = x - 1$, whose only real solution is $x = 3$. Because the intersection point is the rightmost boundary point of the region, its x-coordinate becomes the upper limit of integration. The line $x = 0$ (the y-axis) bounds the region on the left, which gives the lower limit of integration. The graph of f is the upper curve and the graph of g is the lower curve on the interval $[0, 3]$, so the area of the region is

$$\begin{aligned} A &= \int_0^3 \left[\frac{4}{\sqrt{x+1}} - (x-1)\right] dx && \text{Substitute for } f \text{ and } g. \\ &= \left(8\sqrt{x+1} - \frac{x^2}{2} + x\right)\Big|_0^3 && \text{Fundamental Theorem} \\ &= \left(8\sqrt{4} - \frac{9}{2} + 3\right) - 8 = \frac{13}{2}. && \text{Evaluate and simplify.} \end{aligned}$$

Related Exercises 5–14 ◄

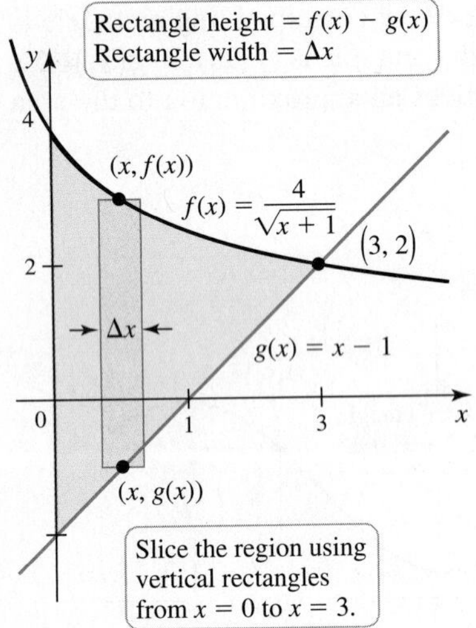

FIGURE 6.14

QUICK CHECK 2 Interpret the area formula in the form $A = \int_a^b f(x)\,dx - \int_a^b g(x)\,dx$, where $f(x) \geq g(x) \geq 0$ on $[a, b]$. ◄

EXAMPLE 2 **Compound region** Find the area of the region between the graphs of $f(x) = x + 3$ and $g(x) = |2x|$ (Figure 6.15a).

SOLUTION The lower boundary of the region in question is bounded by two different branches of the absolute value function. In situations like this, the region is divided into two (or more) subregions, whose areas are found independently and then summed; these regions are labeled R_1 and R_2 (Figure 6.15b). By the definition of absolute value,

$$g(x) = |2x| = \begin{cases} 2x & \text{if } x \geq 0 \\ -2x & \text{if } x < 0 \end{cases}$$

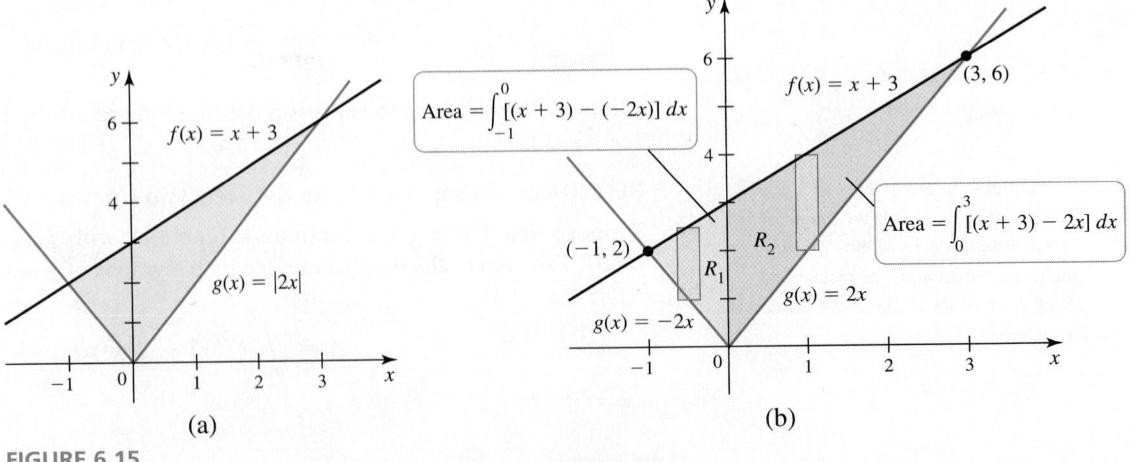

FIGURE 6.15

The left intersection point of f and g satisfies $-2x = x + 3$, or $x = -1$. The right intersection point satisfies $2x = x + 3$, or $x = 3$. We see that the region R_1 is bounded by the lines $y = x + 3$ and $y = -2x$ on the interval $[-1, 0]$. Similarly, region R_2 is bounded by the lines $y = x + 3$ and $y = 2x$ on $[0, 3]$ (Figure 6.15b). Therefore,

$$\begin{aligned} A &= \underbrace{\int_{-1}^{0} [(x + 3) - (-2x)]\,dx}_{\text{area of region } R_1} + \underbrace{\int_{0}^{3} [(x + 3) - 2x]\,dx}_{\text{area of region } R_2} \\ &= \int_{-1}^{0} (3x + 3)\,dx + \int_{0}^{3} (-x + 3)\,dx. \qquad \text{Simplify.} \\ &= \left(\frac{3}{2}x^2 + 3x\right)\bigg|_{-1}^{0} + \left(-\frac{x^2}{2} + 3x\right)\bigg|_{0}^{3} \qquad \text{Fundamental Theorem} \\ &= 0 - \left(\frac{3}{2} - 3\right) + \left(-\frac{9}{2} + 9\right) - 0 = 6. \qquad \text{Simplify.} \end{aligned}$$

Related Exercises 15–22 ◀

Integrating with Respect to y

There are occasions when it is convenient to reverse the roles of x and y. Consider the regions shown in Figure 6.16 that are bounded by the graphs of $x = f(y)$ and $x = g(y)$, where $f(y) \geq g(y)$, for $c \leq y \leq d$ (the graph of f lies to the right of the graph of g). The lower and upper boundaries of the regions are $y = c$ and $y = d$, respectively.

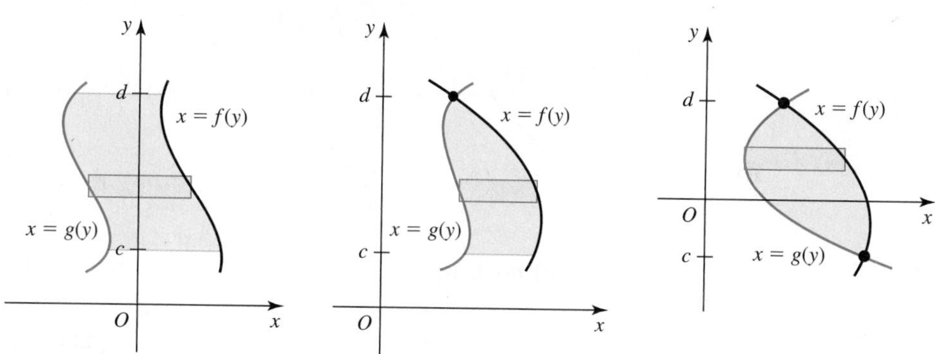

FIGURE 6.16

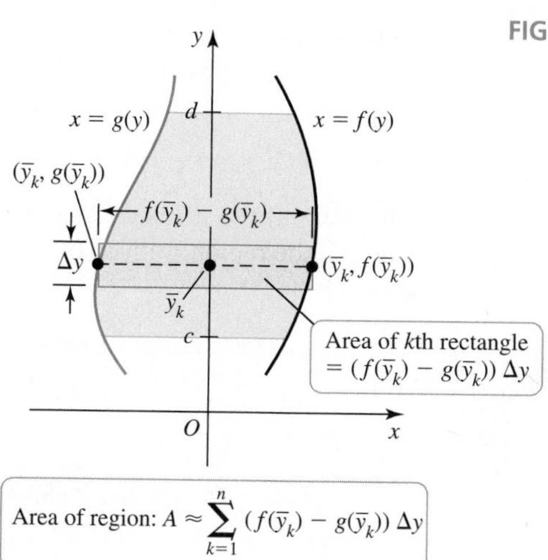

FIGURE 6.17

In cases such as these, we treat y as the independent variable and divide the interval $[c, d]$ into n subintervals of width $\Delta y = (d - c)/n$ (Figure 6.17). On the kth subinterval, a point $\bar{y}_k$ is selected and we construct a rectangle that extends from the left curve to the right curve. The kth rectangle has length $f(\bar{y}_k) - g(\bar{y}_k)$, and so the area of the kth rectangle is $(f(\bar{y}_k) - g(\bar{y}_k))\,\Delta y$. The area of the region is approximated by the sum of the areas of the rectangles. In the limit as $n \to \infty$ and $\Delta y \to 0$, the area of the region is given as the definite integral

$$A = \lim_{n \to \infty} \sum_{k=1}^{n} (f(\bar{y}_k) - g(\bar{y}_k))\,\Delta y = \int_{c}^{d} (f(y) - g(y))\,dy.$$

> This area formula is identical to the one given on page 327; it is now expressed with respect to the y-axis. In this case, $f(y) - g(y)$ is the length of a rectangle and dy is its width. We sum (integrate) the areas of the rectangles $(f(y) - g(y))\,dy$ to obtain the area of the region.

DEFINITION Area of a Region Between Two Curves with Respect to y

Suppose that f and g are continuous functions with $f(y) \geq g(y)$ on the interval $[c, d]$. The area of the region bounded by the graphs $x = f(y)$ and $x = g(y)$ on $[c, d]$ is

$$A = \int_c^d (f(y) - g(y))\,dy.$$

EXAMPLE 3 Integrating with respect to y Find the area of the region R bounded by the graphs of $y = x^3$, $y = x + 6$, and the x-axis.

SOLUTION The area of this region could be found by integrating with respect to x. But this approach requires splitting the region into two pieces (Figure 6.18). Alternatively, we can view y as the independent variable, express the bounding curves as functions of y, and make horizontal slices parallel to the x-axis (Figure 6.19).

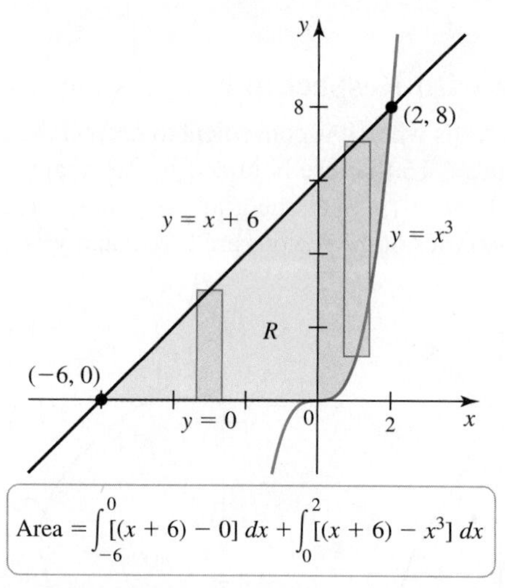

FIGURE 6.18

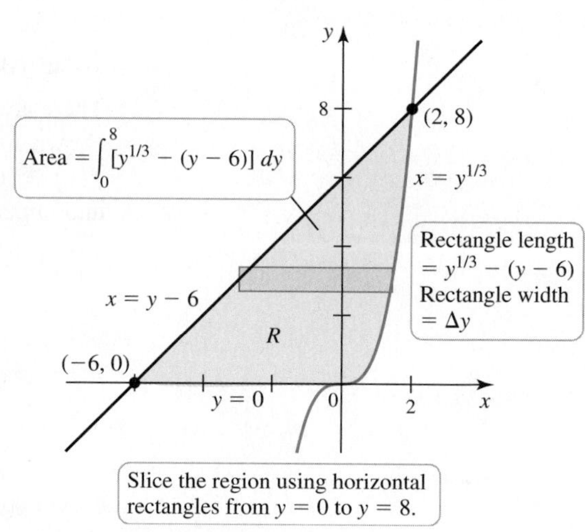

FIGURE 6.19

Solving for x in terms of y, the right curve $y = x^3$ becomes $x = f(y) = y^{1/3}$. The left curve $y = x + 6$ becomes $x = g(y) = y - 6$. The intersection point of the curves satisfies the equation $y^{1/3} = y - 6$, or $y = (y - 6)^3$. Expanding this equation gives the cubic equation

> You may use synthetic division or a root finder to factor this cubic polynomial. Then the quadratic formula shows that the equation
> $$y^2 - 10y + 27 = 0$$
> has no real roots.

$$y^3 - 18y^2 + 107y - 216 = (y - 8)(y^2 - 10y + 27) = 0,$$

whose only real root is $y = 8$. As shown in Figure 6.19, the areas of the slices through the region are summed from $y = 0$ to $y = 8$. Therefore, the area of the region is given by

$$\int_0^8 (y^{1/3} - (y - 6))\,dy = \left(\frac{3}{4}y^{4/3} - \frac{y^2}{2} + 6y\right)\Bigg|_0^8 \qquad \text{Fundamental Theorem}$$

$$= \left(\frac{3}{4}\cdot 16 - 32 + 48\right) - 0 = 28. \qquad \text{Simplify.}$$

Related Exercises 23–32 ◀

QUICK CHECK 3 The region R is bounded by the curve $y = \sqrt{x}$, the line $y = x - 2$, and the x-axis. Express the area of R in terms of (a) integral(s) with respect to x and (b) integral(s) with respect to y. ◀

EXAMPLE 4 **Calculus and geometry** Find the area of the region R in the first quadrant bounded by the curves $y = x^{2/3}$ and $y = x - 4$ (Figure 6.20).

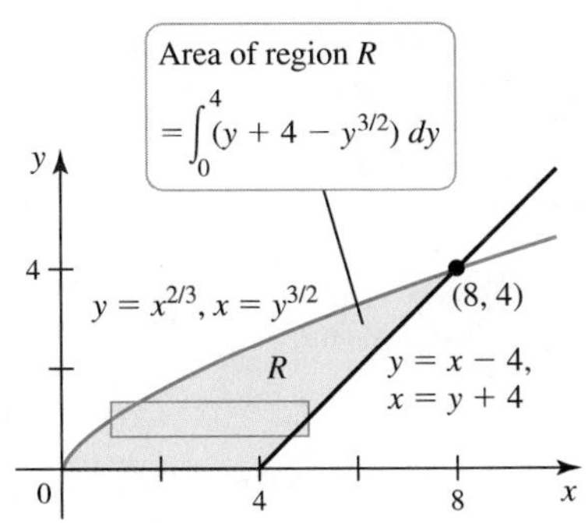

FIGURE 6.20

SOLUTION Slicing the region vertically and integrating with respect to x requires two integrals. Slicing the region horizontally requires a single integral with respect to y. The second approach appears to involve less work.

Slicing horizontally, the right bounding curve is $x = y + 4$ and the left bounding curve is $x = y^{3/2}$. The two curves intersect at $(8, 4)$, so the limits of integration are $y = 0$ and $y = 4$. The area of R is

$$\int_0^4 (\underbrace{y + 4}_{\text{right curve}} - \underbrace{y^{3/2}}_{\text{left curve}})\,dy = \left(\frac{y^2}{2} + 4y - \frac{2}{5}y^{5/2}\right)\bigg|_0^4 = \frac{56}{5}.$$

Can this area be found using a different approach? Sometimes it helps to use geometry. Notice that the region R can be formed by taking the entire region under the curve $y = x^{2/3}$ on the interval $[0, 8]$ and then removing a triangle whose base is the interval $[4, 8]$ (Figure 6.21). The area of the region R_1 under the curve $y = x^{2/3}$ is

$$\int_0^8 x^{2/3}\,dx = \frac{3}{5}x^{5/3}\bigg|_0^8 = \frac{96}{5}.$$

The triangle R_2 has a base of length 4 and a height of 4, so its area is $\frac{1}{2} \cdot 4 \cdot 4 = 8$. Therefore, the area of R is $\frac{96}{5} - 8 = \frac{56}{5}$, which agrees with the first calculation.

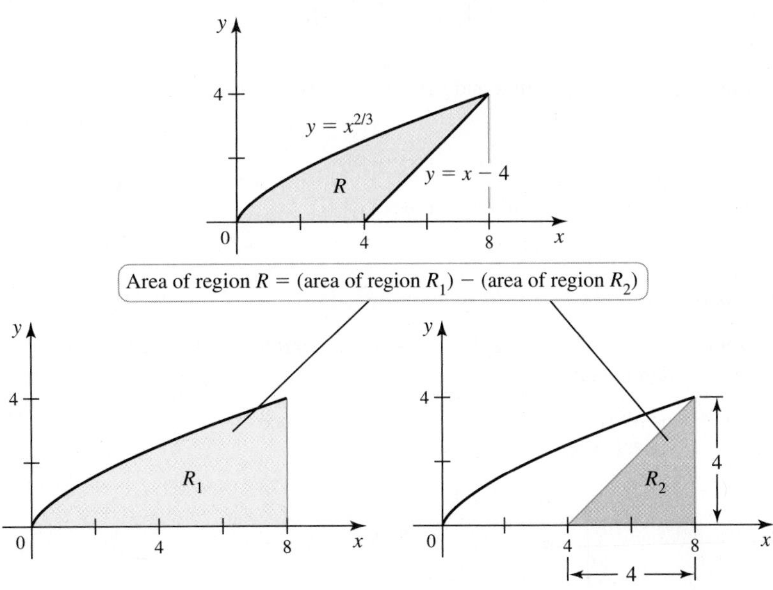

FIGURE 6.21

QUICK CHECK 4 An alternative way to determine the area of the region in Example 3 (Figure 6.18) is to compute $18 + \int_0^2 (x + 6 - x^3)\,dx$. Why?

Related Exercises 33–38

SECTION 6.2 EXERCISES

Review Questions

1. Draw the graphs of two functions f and g that are continuous and intersect exactly twice on an interval $[a, b]$. Explain how to use integration to find the area of the region bounded by the two curves.

2. Draw the graphs of two functions f and g that are continuous and intersect exactly three times on an interval $[a, b]$. Explain how to use integration to find the area of the region bounded by the two curves.

3. Make a sketch to show a case in which the area bounded by two curves is most easily found by integrating with respect to x.

4. Make a sketch to show a case in which the area bounded by two curves is most easily found by integrating with respect to y.

Basic Skills

5–8. Finding area *Determine the area of the shaded region in the following figures.*

5.

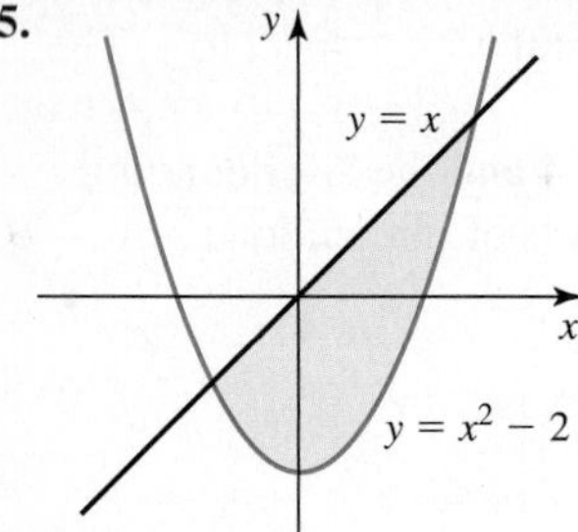

6.

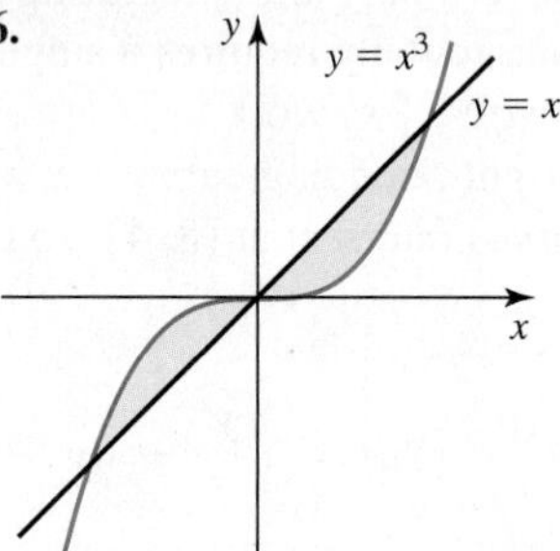

7.

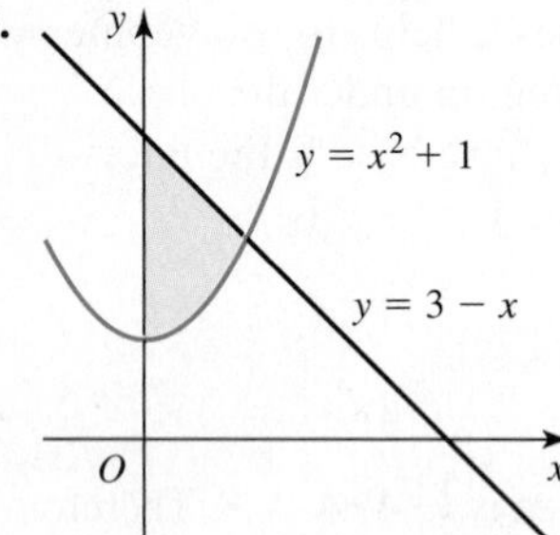

8.

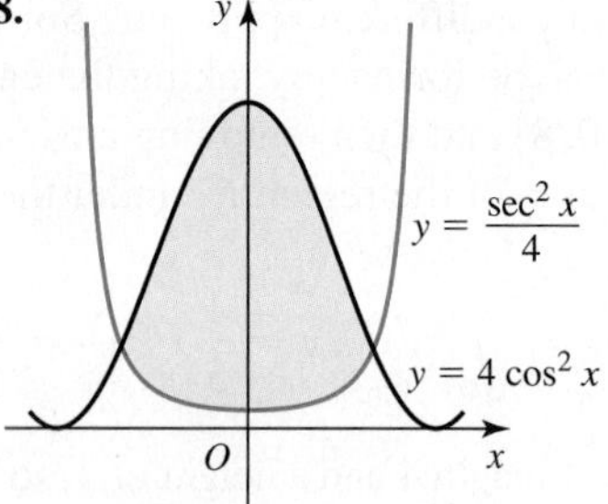

9–14. Regions between curves *Sketch the region and find its area.*

9. The region bounded by $y = 2(x + 1)$, $y = 3(x + 1)$, and $x = 4$

10. The region bounded by $y = \cos x$ and $y = \sin x$ between $x = \pi/4$ and $x = 5\pi/4$

11. The region bounded by $y = 2x^2$ and $y = x^2 + 4$

12. The region bounded by $y = x$ and $y = x^2 - 2$

13. The region bounded by $y = x^4 - 9$ and $y = 7$

14. The region bounded by $y = 64\sqrt{x}$ and $y = 8x^2$

15–22. Compound regions *Sketch the following regions (if a figure is not given) and then find the area.*

15. The region bounded by $y = \sin x$, $y = \cos x$, and the x-axis between $x = 0$ and $x = \pi/2$

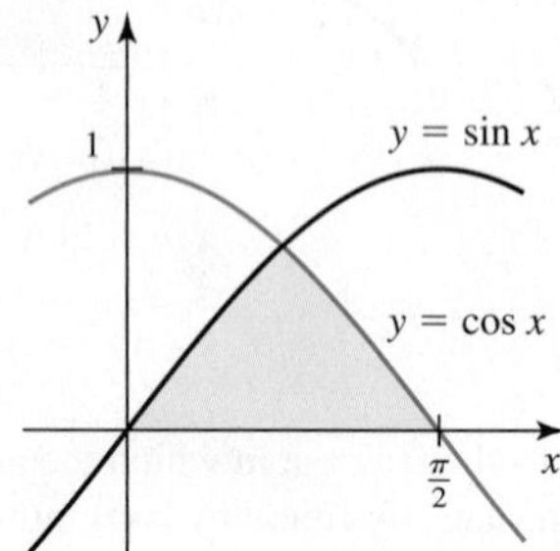

16. The regions between $y = \sin x$ and $y = \sin 2x$, for $0 \le x \le \pi$

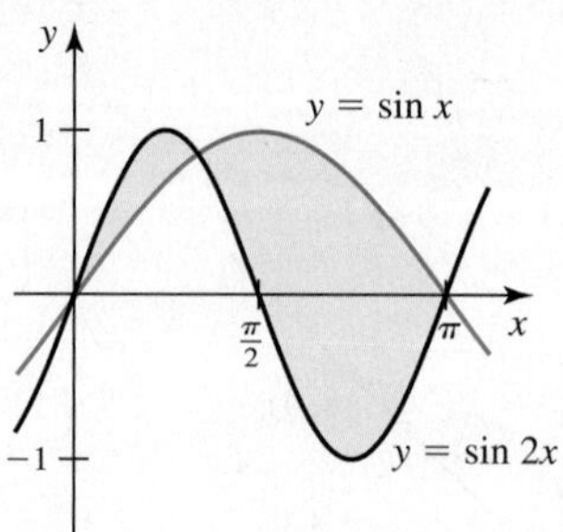

17. The region bounded by $y = x$, $y = 1/x^2$, $y = 0$, and $x = 2$

18. The region in the first quadrant bounded by $y = (x - 1)^3$ and $y = x - 1$

19. The region bounded by $y = 1 - |x|$ and the x-axis

20. The regions bounded by $y = x^3$ and $y = 9x$

21. The region bounded by $y = |x - 3|$ and $y = x/2$

22. The regions bounded by $y = x^2(3 - x)$ and $y = 12 - 4x$

23–26. Integrating with respect to y *Sketch the following regions (if a figure is not given) and find the area.*

23. The region bounded by $y = 8 - 2x$, $y = x + 8$, and $y = 0$

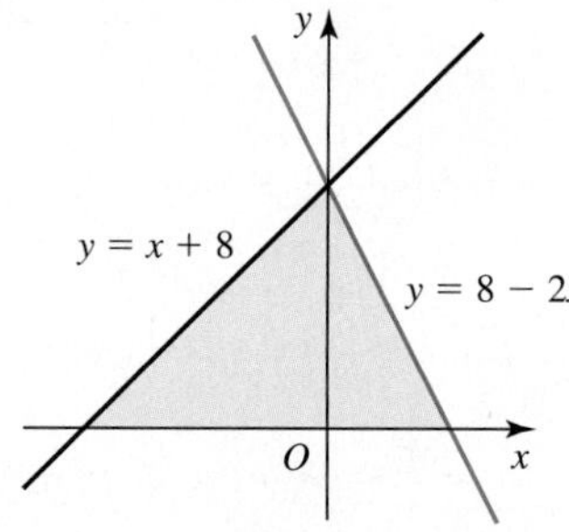

24. The region bounded by $y = \sqrt{x - 1}$, $y = 2$, $y = 0$, and $x = 0$

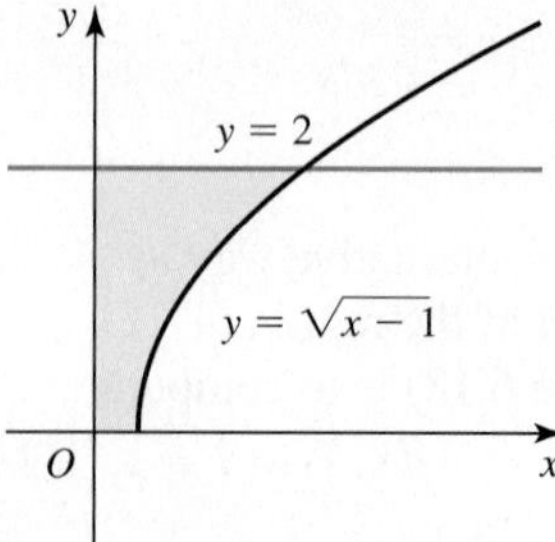

25. The region bounded by $y = 4 - x^2$ and $y - x - 2 = 0$

26. The region bounded by $y = x$ and $x = (y - 2)^2$

27–30. Two approaches *Express the area of the following shaded regions in terms of (a) one or more integrals with respect to x, and (b) one or more integrals with respect to y. You do not need to evaluate the integrals.*

27. $y = x$, $y = x^2 - 2$

28. $y = x^2 - 4x$, $y = 2x - 8$

29. $x = 2y$, $x = y^2 - 3$

30. $y = x^3$, $y = \sqrt{x}$

31–32. Two approaches *Find the area of the following regions by (a) integrating with respect to x, and then (b) integrating with respect to y. Be sure your results agree. In each case, sketch the bounding curves and the region in question.*

31. The region bounded by $y = \sqrt{x}$, $y = 2x - 15$, and $y = 0$

32. The region in the first quadrant bounded by $y = x^{1/3}$, $18y - x - 27 = 0$, and $y = 0$

33–38. Any method *Use any method (including geometry) to find the area of the following regions. In each case, sketch the bounding curves and the region in question.*

33. The region in the first quadrant bounded by $y = x^{2/3}$ and $y = 4$

34. The region in the first quadrant bounded by $y = 2$ and $y = 2 \sin x$ on the interval $[0, \pi/2]$

35. The region bounded by $y = x/4$ and $x = y^3$

36. The region below the line $y = 2$ and above the curve $y = \sec^2 x$ on the interval $[0, \pi/4]$

37. The region between the line $y = x$ and the curve $y = 2x\sqrt{1 - x^2}$ in the first quadrant

38. The region bounded by $x = y^2 - 4$ and $y = x/3$

Further Explorations

39. **Explain why or why not** Determine whether the following statements are true and give an explanation or counterexample.
   a. The area of the region bounded by $y = x$ and $x = y^2$ can be found only by integrating with respect to x.
   b. The area of the region between $y = \sin x$ and $y = \cos x$ on the interval $[0, \pi/2]$ is $\int_0^{\pi/2} (\cos x - \sin x)\, dx$.
   c. $\int_0^1 (x - x^2)\, dx = \int_0^1 (\sqrt{y} - y)\, dy$ (without evaluating integrals).

40–43. Regions between curves *Sketch the region and find its area.*

40. The region bounded by $y = \sin x$ and $y = x(x - \pi)$, for $0 \le x \le \pi$

41. The region bounded by $y = (x - 1)^2$ and $y = 7x - 19$

42. The region bounded by $y = 17$ and $y = x^{2/3} + 1$

43. The region bounded by $y = x^2 - 2x + 1$ and $y = 5x - 9$

44–50. *Either* method *Use the most efficient strategy for computing the area of the following regions.*

44. The region bounded by $x = y(y - 1)$ and $x = -y(y - 1)$

45. The region bounded by $x = y(y - 1)$ and $y = x/3$

46. The region bounded by $y = x^3$, $y = -x^3$, and $3y - 7x - 10 = 0$

47. The region bounded by $y = \sqrt{x}$, $y = 2x - 15$, and $y = 0$

48. The region bounded by $y = x^2 - 4$, $4y - 5x - 5 = 0$, and $y = 0$

49. The regions bounded by $y = 1 - \cos x$ and $y = \sin x$ on $[0, \pi/2]$ and on $[\pi/2, 2\pi]$ (two area calculations).

50. The region in the first quadrant bounded by $y = x^{-2}$, $y = 8x$, and $y = x/8$

51. **Comparing areas** Let $f(x) = x^p$ and $g(x) = x^{1/q}$, where $p > 1$ and $q > 1$ are positive integers. Let R_1 be the region in the first quadrant between $y = f(x)$ and $y = x$ and let R_2 be the region in the first quadrant between $y = g(x)$ and $y = x$.
   a. Find the area of R_1 and R_2 when $p = q$, and determine which region has the greater area.
   b. Find the area of R_1 and R_2 when $p > q$, and determine which region has the greater area.
   c. Find the area of R_1 and R_2 when $p < q$, and determine which region has the greater area.

52–55. Complicated regions *Find the area of the regions shown in the following figures.*

52. $y = 4\sqrt{2x}$, $y = 2x^2$, $y = -4x + 6$

53.

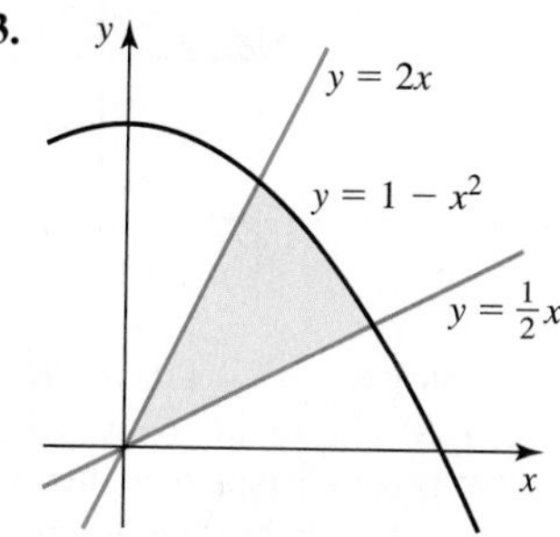

54.

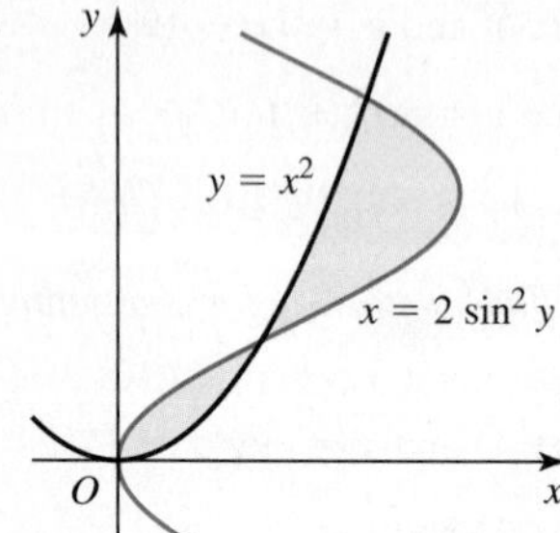

55.

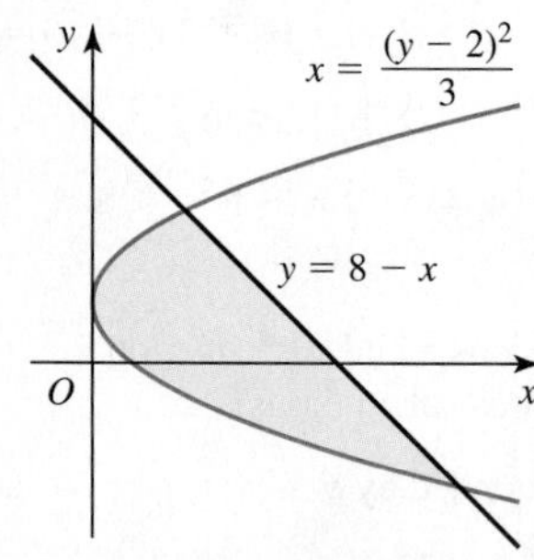

56–59. Roots and powers *Find the area of the following regions, expressing your results in terms of the positive integer $n \geq 2$.*

56. The region bounded by $f(x) = x$ and $g(x) = x^n$, for $x \geq 0$

57. The region bounded by $f(x) = x$ and $g(x) = x^{1/n}$, for $x \geq 0$

58. The region bounded by $f(x) = x^{1/n}$ and $g(x) = x^n$, for $x \geq 0$

59. Let A_n be the area of the region bounded by $f(x) = x^{1/n}$ and $g(x) = x^n$ on the interval $[0, 1]$, where n is a positive integer. Evaluate $\lim_{n \to \infty} A_n$ and interpret the result.

Applications

60. Geometric probability Suppose a dartboard occupies the square $\{(x, y): 0 \leq |x| \leq 1, 0 \leq |y| \leq 1\}$. A dart is thrown randomly at the board many times (meaning it is equally likely to land at any point in the square). On average, in what fraction of the throws does the dart land closer to the edge of the board than the center? Equivalently, what is the probability that the dart lands closer to the edge of the board than the center? Proceed as follows.

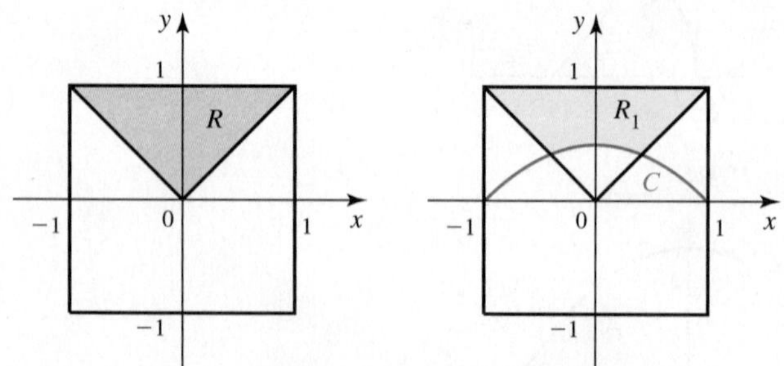

a. Argue that by symmetry it is necessary to consider only one quarter of the board, say the region R: $\{(x, y): |x| \leq y \leq 1\}$.

b. Find the curve C in this region that is equidistant from the center of the board and the top edge of the board (see figure).

c. The probability that the dart lands closer to the edge of the board than the center is the ratio of the area of the region R_1 above C to the area of the entire region R. Compute this probability.

61. Lorenz curves and the Gini index A **Lorenz curve** is given by $y = L(x)$, where $0 \leq x \leq 1$ represents the lowest fraction of the population of a society in terms of wealth and $0 \leq y \leq 1$ represents the fraction of the total wealth that is owned by that fraction of the society. For example, the Lorenz curve in the figure shows that $L(0.5) = 0.2$, which means that the lowest 0.5 (50%) of the society owns 0.2 (20%) of the wealth. (See Guided Projects for more on Lorenz curves.)

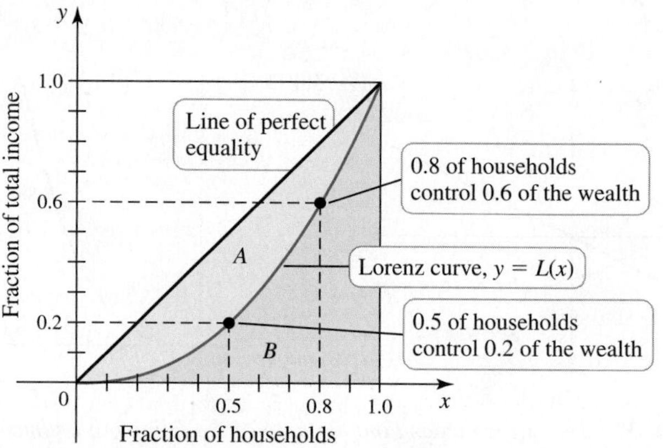

a. A Lorenz curve $y = L(x)$ is accompanied by the line $y = x$, called the **line of perfect equality**. Explain why this line is given this name.

b. Explain why a Lorenz curve satisfies the conditions $L(0) = 0$, $L(1) = 1$, and $L'(x) \geq 0$ on $[0, 1]$.

c. Graph the Lorenz curves $L(x) = x^p$ corresponding to $p = 1.1, 1.5, 2, 3, 4$. Which value of p corresponds to the *most* equitable distribution of wealth (closest to the line of perfect equality)? Which value of p corresponds to the *least* equitable distribution of wealth? Explain.

d. The information in the Lorenz curve is often summarized in a single measure called the **Gini index**, which is defined as follows. Let A be the area of the region between $y = x$ and $y = L(x)$ (see figure) and let B be the area of the region between $y = L(x)$ and the x-axis. Then the Gini index is $G = \frac{A}{A + B}$. Show that $G = 2A = 1 - 2\int_0^1 L(x)\,dx$.

e. Compute the Gini index for the cases $L(x) = x^p$ and $p = 1.1, 1.5, 2, 3, 4$.

f. What is the smallest interval $[a, b]$ on which values of the Gini index lie for $L(x) = x^p$ with $p \geq 1$? Which endpoints of $[a, b]$ correspond to the least and most equitable distribution of wealth?

g. Consider the Lorenz curve described by $L(x) = 5x^2/6 + x/6$. Show that it satisfies the conditions $L(0) = 0$, $L(1) = 1$ and $L'(x) \geq 0$ on $[0, 1]$. Find the Gini index for this function.

Additional Exercises

62. Equal area properties for parabolas Consider the parabola $y = x^2$. Let P, Q, and R be points on the parabola with R between P and Q on the curve. Let ℓ_P, ℓ_Q, and ℓ_R be the lines tangent to the parabola at P, Q, and R, respectively (see figure). Let P' be the intersection point of ℓ_Q, and ℓ_R; let Q' be the intersection point of ℓ_P and ℓ_R; and let R' be the intersection point of ℓ_P and ℓ_Q. Prove that Area $\Delta PQR = 2 \cdot$ Area $\Delta P'Q'R'$ in the following cases.

(In fact, the property holds for any three points on any parabola.) (*Mathematics Magazine* 81, No. 2 (April 2008): 83–95.)

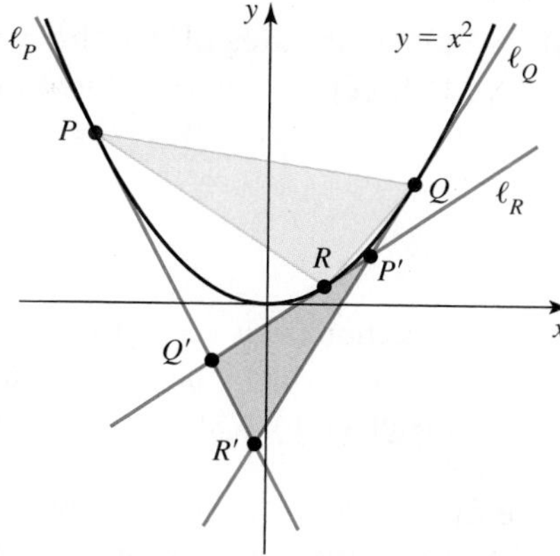

a. $P(-a, a^2)$, $Q(a, a^2)$, and $R(0, 0)$, where a is a positive real number

b. $P(-a, a^2)$, $Q(b, b^2)$, and $R(0, 0)$, where a and b are positive real numbers

c. $P(-a, a^2)$, $Q(b, b^2)$, and R is any point between P and Q on the curve

T **63. Minimum area** Graph the curves $y = (x + 1)(x - 2)$ and $y = ax + 1$ for various values of a. For what value of a is the area of the region between the two curves a minimum?

T **64. An area function** Graph the curves $y = a^2x^3$ and $y = \sqrt{x}$ for various values of $a > 0$. Note how the area $A(a)$ between the curves varies with a. Find and graph the area function $A(a)$. For what value of a is $A(a) = 16$?

65. Area of a curve defined implicitly Determine the area of the shaded region bounded by the curve $x^2 = y^4(1 - y^3)$ (see figure).

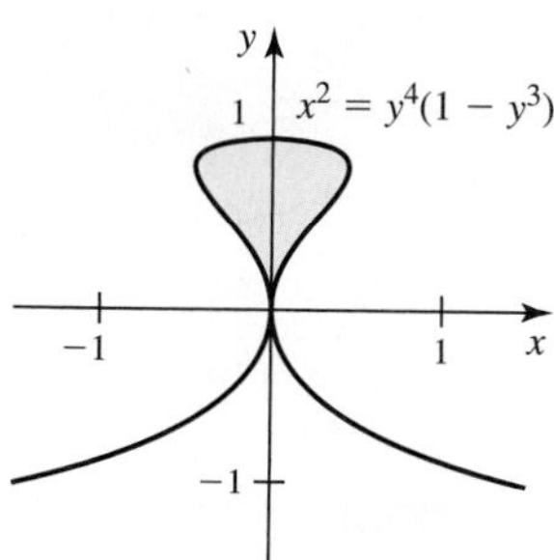

66. Rewrite first Find the area of the region bounded by the curve $x = \dfrac{y}{\sqrt{1 - y^2}}$ and the line $x = 1$ in the first quadrant. (*Hint:* Express y in terms of x.)

T **67. Area function for a cubic** Consider the cubic polynomial $f(x) = x(x - a)(x - b)$, where $0 \le a \le b$.

a. For a fixed value of b, find the function $F(a) = \int_0^b f(x)\,dx$. For what value of a (which depends on b) is $F(a) = 0$?

b. For a fixed value of b, find the function $A(a)$ that gives the area of the region bounded by the graph of f and the x-axis between $x = 0$ and $x = b$. Graph this function and show that it has a minimum at $a = b/2$. What is the maximum value of $A(a)$, and where does it occur (in terms of b)?

68. Differences of even functions Assume f and g are even, integrable functions on $[-a, a]$, where $a > 1$. Suppose $f(x) > g(x) > 0$ on $[-a, a]$ and that the area bounded by the graphs of f and g on $[-a, a]$ is 10. What is the value of $\int_0^{\sqrt{a}} x[f(x^2) - g(x^2)]\,dx$?

T **69. Roots and powers** Consider the functions $f(x) = x^n$ and $g(x) = x^{1/n}$, where $n \ge 2$ is a positive integer.

a. Graph f and g for $n = 2, 3$, and 4, for $x \ge 0$.

b. Give a geometric interpretation of the area function $A_n(x) = \int_0^x (f(s) - g(s))\,ds$, for $n = 2, 3, 4, \ldots$ and $x > 0$.

c. Find the positive root of $A_n(x) = 0$ in terms of n. Does the root increase or decrease with n?

T **70. Shifting sines** Consider the functions $f(x) = a \sin 2x$ and $g(x) = (\sin x)/a$, where $a > 0$ is a real number.

a. Graph the two functions on the interval $[0, \pi/2]$, for $a = \frac{1}{2}$, 1, and 2.

b. Show that the curves have an intersection point x^* (other than $x = 0$) on $[0, \pi/2]$ that satisfies $\cos x^* = 1/(2a^2)$, provided $a \ge 1/\sqrt{2}$.

c. Find the area of the region between the two curves on $[0, x^*]$ when $a = 1$.

d. Show that as $a \to 1/\sqrt{2}$, the area of the region between the two curves on $[0, x^*]$ approaches zero.

QUICK CHECK ANSWERS

1. If $g(x) = 0$ and $f(x) \ge 0$, then the area between the curves is $\int_a^b (f(x) - 0)\,dx = \int_a^b f(x)\,dx$, which is the area between $y = f(x)$ and the x-axis. **2.** $\int_a^b f(x)\,dx$ is the area of the region between the graph of f and the x-axis. $\int_a^b g(x)\,dx$ is the area of the region between the graph of g and the x-axis. The difference of the two integrals is the area of the region between the graphs of f and g. **3. a.** $\int_0^2 \sqrt{x}\,dx + \int_2^4 (\sqrt{x} - x + 2)\,dx$ **b.** $\int_0^2 (y + 2 - y^2)\,dy$. **4.** The area of the triangle to the left of the y-axis is 18. The area of the region to the right of the y-axis is given by the integral.

6.3 Volume by Slicing

We have seen that integration is used to compute the area of two-dimensional regions bounded by curves. Integrals are also used to find the volume of three-dimensional regions (or solids). Once again, the slice-and-sum method is the key to solving these problems.

General Slicing Method

Consider a solid object that extends in the x-direction from $x = a$ to $x = b$. Imagine cutting through the solid, perpendicular to the x-axis at a particular point x, and suppose the area of the cross section created by the cut is given by a known integrable function A (Figure 6.22).

To find the volume of this solid, we first divide $[a, b]$ into n subintervals of length $\Delta x = (b - a)/n$. The endpoints of the subintervals are the grid points $x_0 = a, x_1, x_2, \ldots, x_n = b$. We now make cuts through the solid perpendicular to the x-axis at each grid point, which produces n slices of thickness Δx. (Imagine cutting a loaf of bread to create n slices of equal width.) On each subinterval, an arbitrary point $\overline{x}_k$ is identified. The kth slice through the solid has a thickness Δx, and we take $A(\overline{x}_k)$ as a representative cross-sectional area of the slice. Therefore, the volume of the kth slice is approximately $A(\overline{x}_k)\,\Delta x$ (Figure 6.23). Summing the volumes of the slices, the approximate volume of the solid is

$$V \approx \sum_{k=1}^{n} A(\overline{x}_k)\,\Delta x.$$

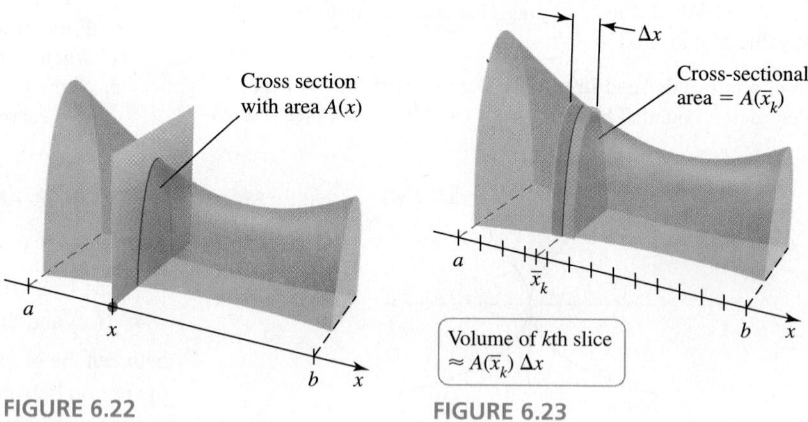

FIGURE 6.22

FIGURE 6.23

As the number of slices increases ($n \to \infty$) and the thickness of each slice approaches zero ($\Delta x \to 0$), the exact volume V is obtained in terms of a definite integral (Figure 6.24):

$$V = \lim_{n \to \infty} \sum_{k=1}^{n} A(\overline{x}_k)\,\Delta x = \int_a^b A(x)\,dx.$$

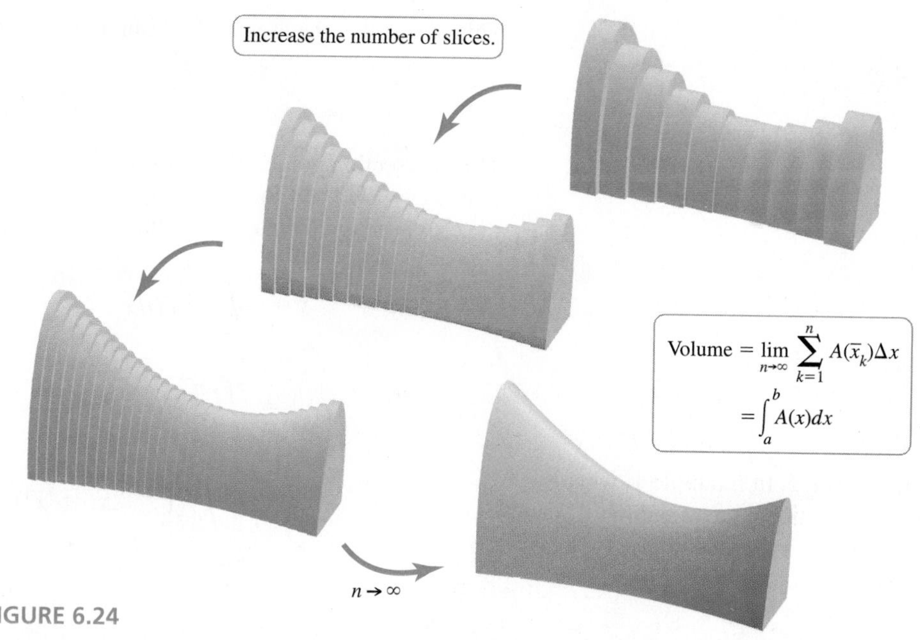

FIGURE 6.24

➤ The factors in this volume integral have meaning: $A(x)$ is the cross-sectional area of a slice and dx is its thickness. Summing (integrating) the volumes of the slices $A(x)\,dx$ gives the volume of the solid.

General Slicing Method

Suppose a solid object extends from $x = a$ to $x = b$ and the cross section of the solid perpendicular to the x-axis has an area given by a function A that is integrable on $[a, b]$. The volume of the solid is

$$V = \int_a^b A(x)\,dx.$$

QUICK CHECK 1 Explain why the volume, as given by the general slicing method, is equal to the average value of $A(x)$ on $[a, b]$ multiplied by $b - a$. ◀

EXAMPLE 1 Volume of a "parabolic hemisphere" A solid has a base that is bounded by the curves $y = x^2$ and $y = 2 - x^2$ in the xy-plane. Cross sections through the solid perpendicular to the x-axis are semicircular disks. Find the volume of the solid.

SOLUTION Because a typical cross section perpendicular to the x-axis is a semicircular disk (Figure 6.25), the area of a cross section is $\frac{1}{2}\pi r^2$, where r is the radius of the cross section. The key observation is that this radius is one-half of the distance between the upper bounding curve $y = 2 - x^2$ and the lower bounding curve $y = x^2$. So the radius at the point x is

$$r = \frac{1}{2}((2 - x^2) - x^2) = 1 - x^2.$$

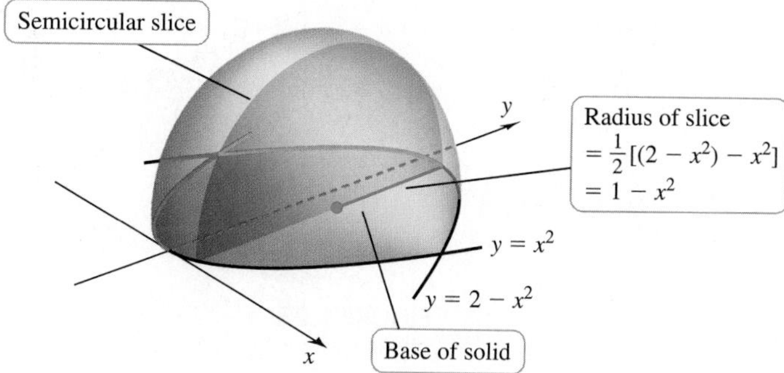

FIGURE 6.25

This means that the area of the semicircular cross section at the point x is

$$A(x) = \frac{1}{2}\pi r^2 = \frac{\pi}{2}(1 - x^2)^2.$$

The intersection points of the two bounding curves satisfy $2 - x^2 = x^2$, which has solutions $x = \pm 1$. Therefore, the cross sections lie between $x = -1$ and $x = 1$. Integrating the cross-sectional areas, the volume of the solid is

$$\begin{aligned} V &= \int_{-1}^{1} A(x)\,dx && \text{General slicing method} \\ &= \int_{-1}^{1} \frac{\pi}{2}(1 - x^2)^2\,dx && \text{Substitute for } A(x). \\ &= \frac{\pi}{2}\int_{-1}^{1} (1 - 2x^2 + x^4)\,dx && \text{Expand integand.} \\ &= \frac{8\pi}{15}. && \text{Evaluate.} \end{aligned}$$

Related Exercises 7–14 ◄

QUICK CHECK 2 In Example 1, what is the cross-sectional area function $A(x)$ if cross sections perpendicular to the base are squares rather than semicircles? ◄

The Disk Method

We now consider a specific type of solid known as a *solid of revolution*. Suppose f is a continuous function with $f(x) \geq 0$ on an interval $[a, b]$. Let R be the region bounded by the graph of f, the x-axis, and the lines $x = a$ and $x = b$ (Figure 6.26). Now revolve R around the x-axis. As R revolves once around the x-axis, it sweeps out a three-dimensional **solid of revolution** (Figure 6.27). The goal is to find the volume of this solid, and it may be done using the general slicing method.

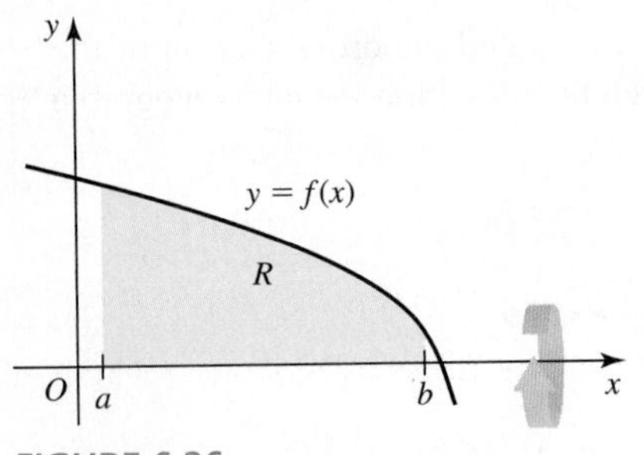

FIGURE 6.26

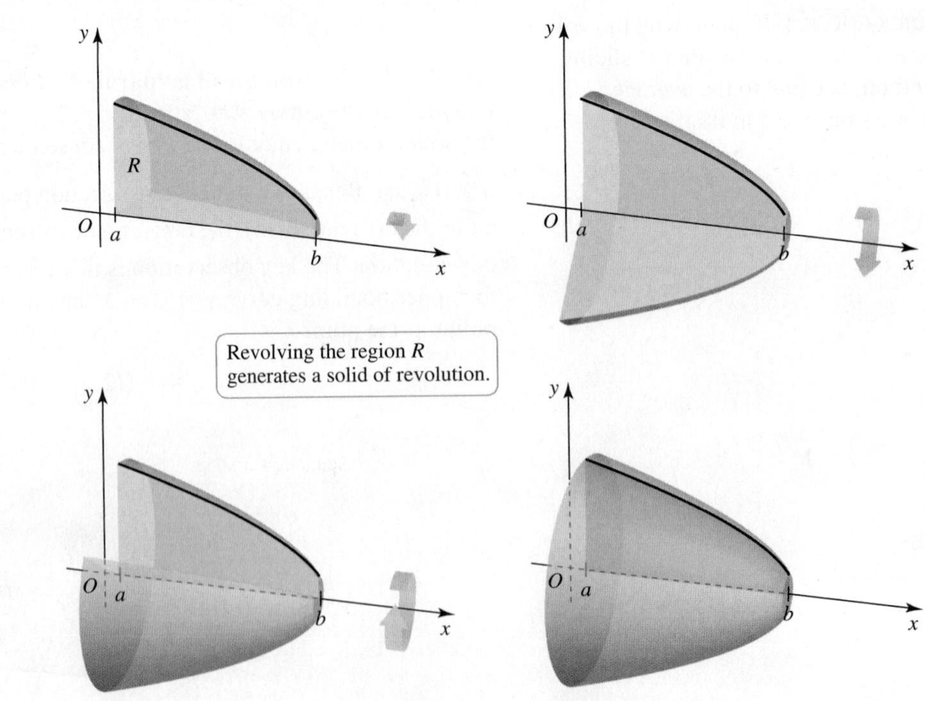

FIGURE 6.27

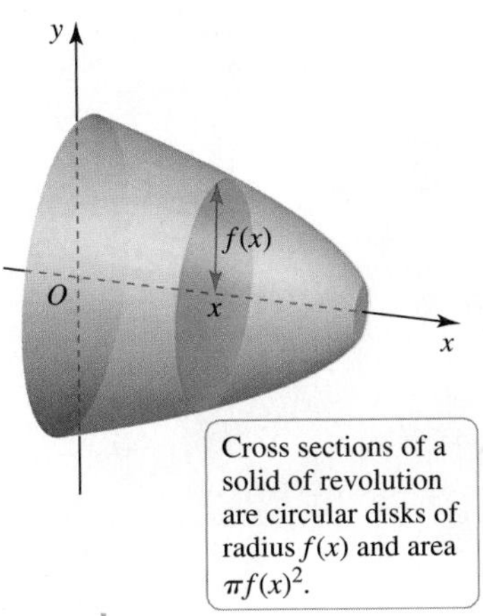

FIGURE 6.28

QUICK CHECK 3 What solid results when the region R is revolved about the x-axis if (a) R is a square with vertices $(0, 0)$, $(0, 2)$, $(2, 0)$, and $(2, 2)$ and (b) R is a triangle with vertices $(0, 0)$, $(0, 2)$, and $(2, 0)$?

With a solid of revolution, the cross-sectional area function has a special form because all cross sections perpendicular to the x-axis are *circular disks* with radius $f(x)$ (Figure 6.28). Therefore, the cross section at the point x, where $a \le x \le b$, has area

$$A(x) = \pi(\text{radius})^2 = \pi f(x)^2.$$

By the general slicing method, the volume of the solid is

$$V = \int_a^b A(x)\,dx = \int_a^b \pi f(x)^2\,dx.$$

Because each slice through the solid is a circular disk, the resulting method is called the **disk method**.

Disk Method About the x-Axis

Let f be continuous with $f(x) \ge 0$ on the interval $[a, b]$. If the region R bounded by the graph of f, the x-axis, and the lines $x = a$ and $x = b$ is revolved about the x-axis, the volume of the resulting solid of revolution is

$$V = \int_a^b \pi f(x)^2\,dx.$$

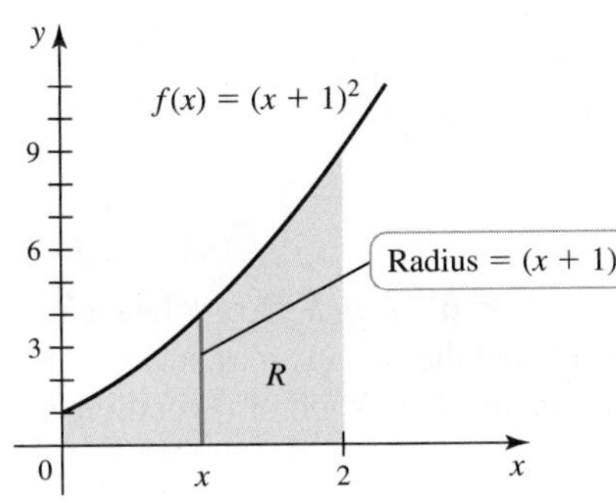

EXAMPLE 2 **Disk method at work** Let R be the region bounded by the curve $f(x) = (x + 1)^2$, the x-axis, and the lines $x = 0$ and $x = 2$. Find the volume of the solid of revolution obtained by revolving R about the x-axis.

SOLUTION When the region R is revolved about the x-axis, it generates a solid of revolution (Figure 6.29). A cross section perpendicular to the x-axis at the point $0 \le x \le 2$ is a circular disk of radius $f(x)$. Therefore, a typical cross section has area

$$A(x) = \pi f(x)^2 = \pi((x + 1)^2)^2 = \pi(x + 1)^4.$$

Integrating these cross-sectional areas between $x = 0$ and $x = 2$ gives the volume of the solid:

$$V = \int_0^2 A(x)\,dx = \int_0^2 \pi(x + 1)^4\,dx \quad \text{Substitute for } A(x).$$

$$= \pi \frac{u^5}{5}\bigg|_1^3 = \frac{242\,\pi}{5} \quad \text{Let } u = x + 1 \text{ and evaluate.}$$

Related Exercises 15–22

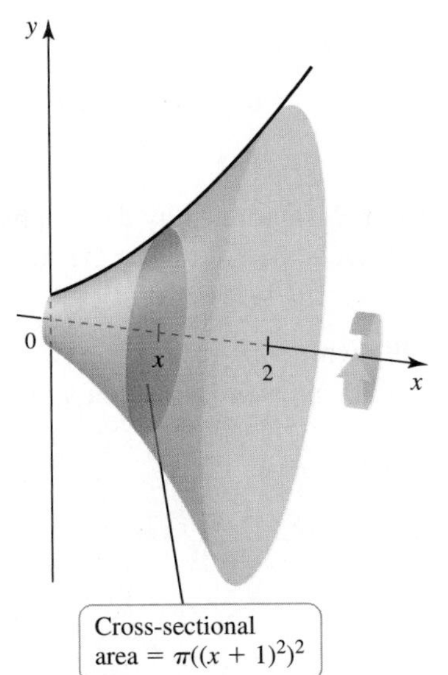

FIGURE 6.29

Washer Method A slight variation on the disk method enables us to compute the volume of more exotic solids of revolution. Suppose that R is the region bounded by the graphs of f and g between $x = a$ and $x = b$, where $f(x) \ge g(x) \ge 0$ (Figure 6.30). If R is revolved about the x-axis to generate a solid of revolution, the resulting solid generally has a hole through it.

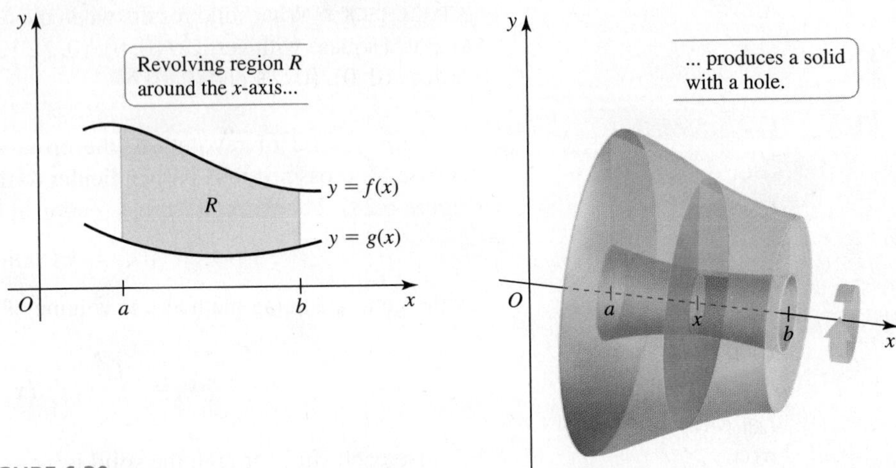

FIGURE 6.30

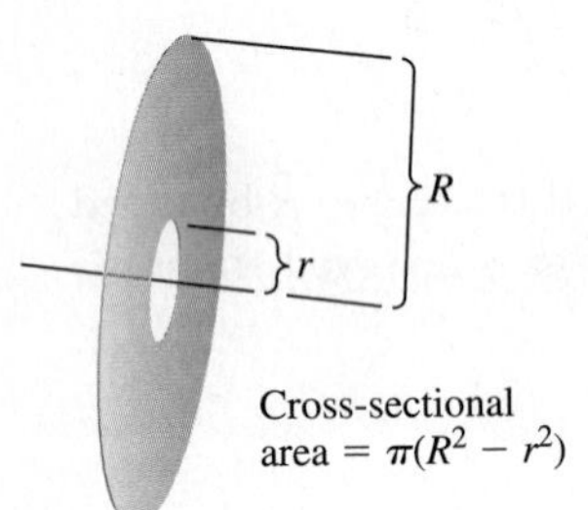
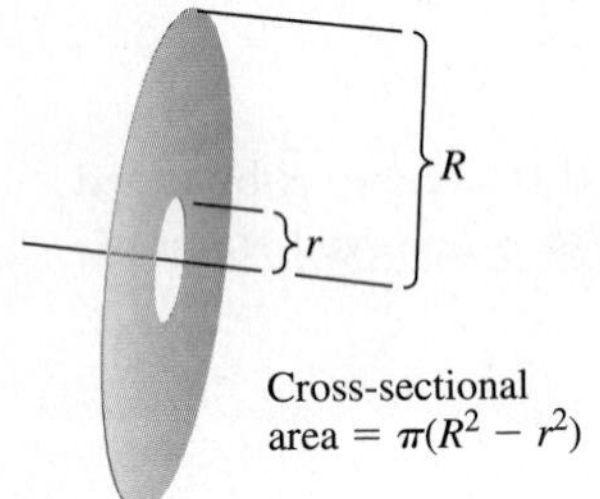

Once again we apply the general slicing method. In this case, a cross section through the solid perpendicular to the x-axis is a circular *washer* with an outer radius of $R = f(x)$ and a hole with a radius of $r = g(x)$, where $a \le x \le b$. The area of the cross section is the area of the entire disk minus the area of the hole, or

$$A(x) = \pi(R^2 - r^2) = \pi(f(x)^2 - g(x)^2)$$

(Figure 6.31). The general slicing method gives the area of the solid.

> **Washer Method About the x-Axis**
>
> Let f and g be continuous functions with $f(x) \ge g(x) \ge 0$ on $[a, b]$. Let R be the region bounded by the curves $y = f(x)$ and $y = g(x)$, and the lines $x = a$ and $x = b$. When R is revolved about the x-axis, the volume of the resulting solid of revolution is
>
> $$V = \int_a^b \pi(f(x)^2 - g(x)^2)\,dx.$$

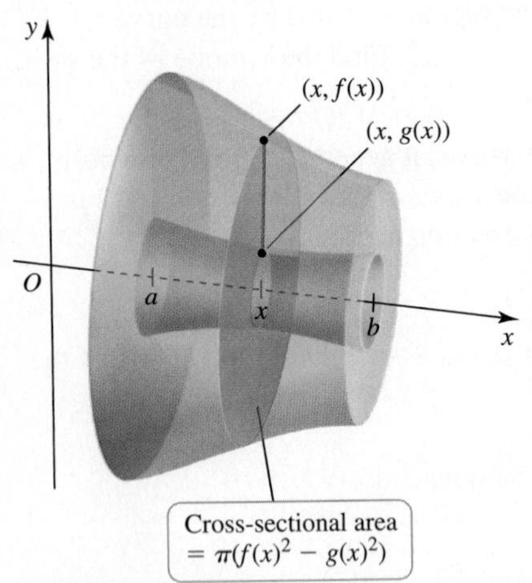

FIGURE 6.31

➤ The washer method is really two applications of the disk method. We compute the volume of the entire solid without the hole (by the disk method) and then subtract the volume of the hole (also computed by the disk method).

QUICK CHECK 4 Show that when $g(x) = 0$ in the washer method, the result is the disk method. ◄

EXAMPLE 3 Volume by the washer method The region R is bounded by the graphs of $f(x) = \sqrt{x}$ and $g(x) = x^2$ between $x = 0$ and $x = 1$. What is the volume of the solid that results when R is revolved about the x-axis?

SOLUTION The region R is bounded by the graphs of f and g with $f(x) \ge g(x)$ on $[0, 1]$, so the washer method is applicable (Figure 6.32). The area of a typical cross section at the point x is

$$A(x) = \pi(f(x)^2 - g(x)^2) = \pi((\sqrt{x})^2 - (x^2)^2) = \pi(x - x^4).$$

Therefore, the volume of the solid is

$$V = \int_0^1 \pi(x - x^4)\,dx \qquad \text{Washer method}$$

$$= \pi\left(\frac{x^2}{2} - \frac{x^5}{5}\right)\Big|_0^1 = \frac{3\pi}{10}. \qquad \text{Fundamental Theorem of Calculus}$$

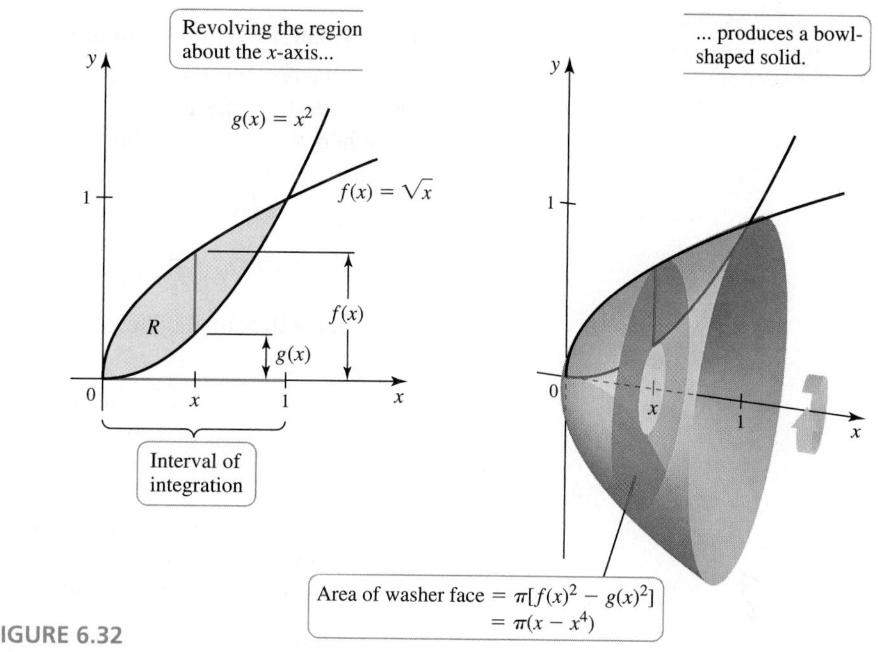

FIGURE 6.32

Related Exercises 23–30

> See Exercises 54–58 for problems in which regions are revolved about lines other than coordinate axes.

QUICK CHECK 5 Suppose the region in Example 3 is revolved about the line $y = -1$ instead of the x-axis. (a) What is the inner radius of a typical washer? (b) What is the outer radius of a typical washer?

Revolving About the y-Axis

Everything you learned about revolving regions about the x-axis applies to revolving regions about the y-axis. Consider a region R bounded by the curve $x = p(y)$ on the right, the curve $x = q(y)$ on the left, and the horizontal lines $y = c$ and $y = d$ (Figure 6.33).

To find the volume of the solid generated when R is revolved about the y-axis, we use the general slicing method—now with respect to the y-axis. The area of a typical cross section is $A(y) = \pi(p(y)^2 - q(y)^2)$, where $c \leq y \leq d$. As before, integrating these cross-sectional areas of the solid gives the volume.

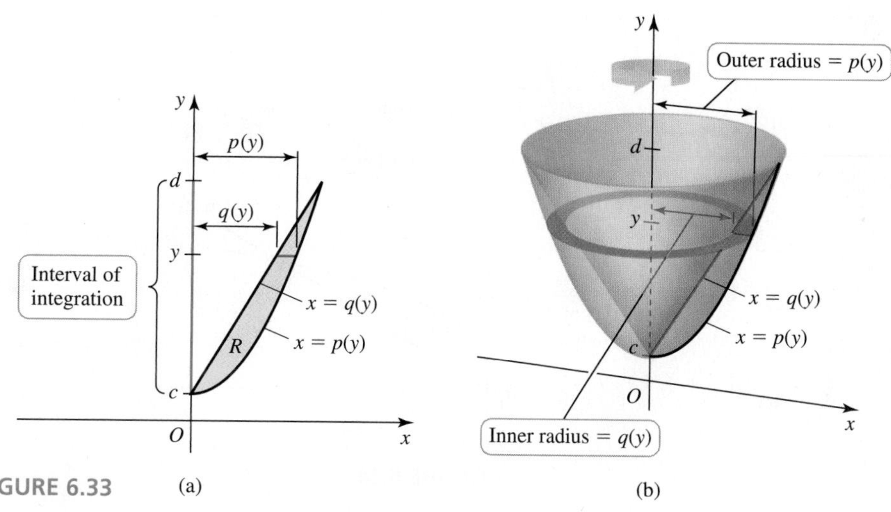

FIGURE 6.33

➤ The disk/washer method about the y-axis is the disk/washer method about the x-axis with x replaced by y.

Disk and Washer Methods About the y-Axis

Let p and q be continuous functions with $p(y) \geq q(y) \geq 0$ on $[c, d]$. Let R be the region bounded by the curves $x = p(y)$ and $x = q(y)$, and the lines $y = c$ and $y = d$. When R is revolved about the y-axis, the volume of the resulting solid of revolution is given by

$$V = \int_c^d \pi(p(y)^2 - q(y)^2)\, dy$$

If $q(y) = 0$, the disk method results:

$$V = \int_c^d \pi p(y)^2\, dy$$

EXAMPLE 4 Which solid has greater volume? Let R be the region in the first quadrant bounded by the graphs of $x = y^3$ and $x = 4y$. Which is greater, the volume of the solid generated when R is revolved about the x-axis or the y-axis?

SOLUTION Solving $y^3 = 4y$—or, equivalently, $y(y^2 - 4) = 0$—we find that the bounding curves of R intersect at the points $(0, 0)$ and $(8, 2)$. When the region R is revolved about the y-axis, it generates a funnel with a curved inner surface (Figure 6.34). Washer-shaped cross sections perpendicular to the y-axis extend from $y = 0$ to $y = 2$. The outer radius of the cross section at the point y is determined by the line $x = p(y) = 4y$. The inner radius of the cross section at the point y is determined by the curve $x = q(y) = y^3$. Applying the washer method, the volume of this solid is

$$\begin{aligned} V &= \int_0^2 \pi(p(y)^2 - q(y)^2)\, dy && \text{Washer method} \\ &= \int_0^2 \pi(16y^2 - y^6)\, dy && \text{Substitute for } p \text{ and } q. \\ &= \pi\left(\frac{16}{3}y^3 - \frac{y^7}{7}\right)\Bigg|_0^2 && \text{Fundamental Theorem} \\ &= \frac{512\pi}{21} \approx 76.60. && \text{Evaluate.} \end{aligned}$$

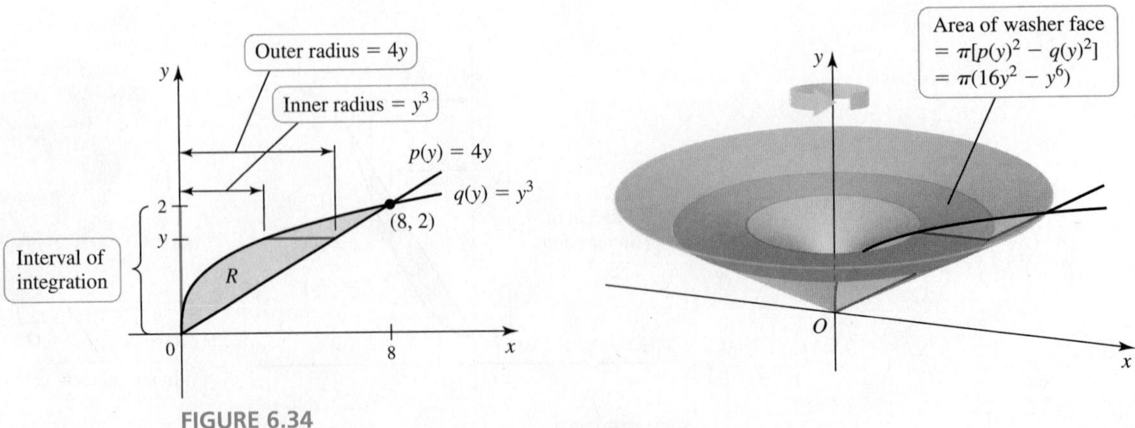

FIGURE 6.34

When the region R is revolved about the x-axis, it generates a funnel with a flat inner surface (Figure 6.35). Vertical slices through the solid between $x = 0$ and $x = 8$ produce washers. The outer radius of the washer at the point x is determined by the curve $x = y^3$, or $y = f(x) = x^{1/3}$. The inner radius is determined by $x = 4y$, or $y = g(x) = x/4$. The volume of the resulting solid is

$$V = \int_0^8 \pi(f(x)^2 - g(x)^2)\,dx \quad \text{Washer method}$$

$$= \int_0^8 \pi\left(x^{2/3} - \frac{x^2}{16}\right)dx \quad \text{Substitute for } f \text{ and } g.$$

$$= \pi\left(\frac{3}{5}x^{5/3} - \frac{x^3}{48}\right)\Big|_0^8 \quad \text{Fundamental Theorem}$$

$$= \frac{128\pi}{15} \approx 26.81. \quad \text{Evaluate.}$$

We see that revolving the region about the y-axis produces a solid of greater volume.

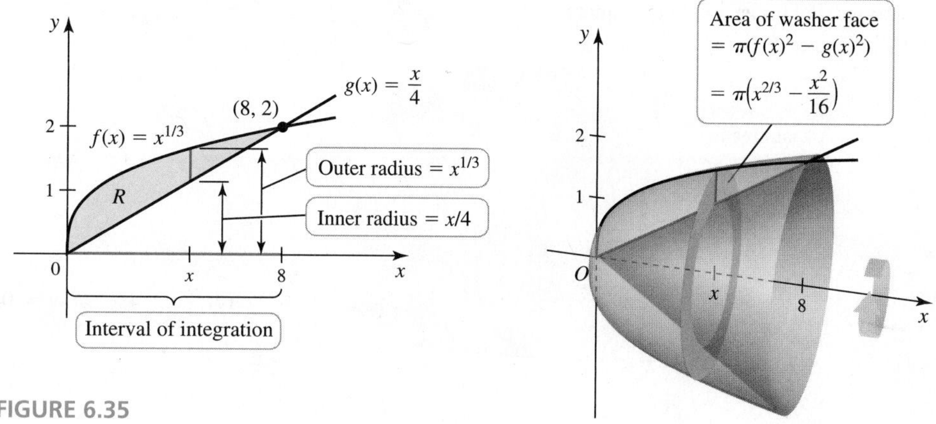

FIGURE 6.35

Related Exercises 31–40

QUICK CHECK 6 The region in the first quadrant bounded by $y = x$ and $y = x^3$ is revolved about the y-axis. Give the integral for the volume of the solid that is generated.

SECTION 6.3 EXERCISES

Review Questions

1. Suppose a cut is made through a solid object perpendicular to the x-axis at a particular point x. Explain the meaning of $A(x)$.

2. Describe how a solid of revolution is generated.

3. The region bounded by the curves $y = 2x$ and $y = x^2$ is revolved about the x-axis. Give an integral for the volume of the solid that is generated.

4. The region bounded by the curves $y = 2x$ and $y = x^2$ is revolved about the y-axis. Give an integral for the volume of the solid that is generated.

5. Why is the disk method a special case of the general slicing method?

6. A solid has a circular base and cross sections perpendicular to the base are squares. What method should be used to find the volume of the solid?

Basic Skills

7–14. General slicing method *Use the general slicing method to find the volume of the following solids.*

7. A triangular wedge whose perpendicular sides have lengths 3, 4, and 5 (Use calculus.)

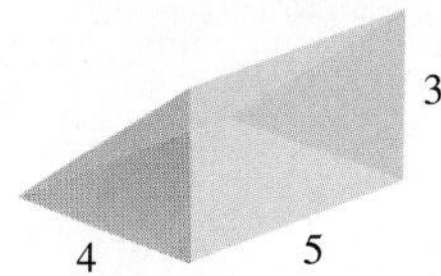

8. The solid with a circular base of radius 5 whose cross sections perpendicular to the base and parallel to the x-axis are equilateral triangles

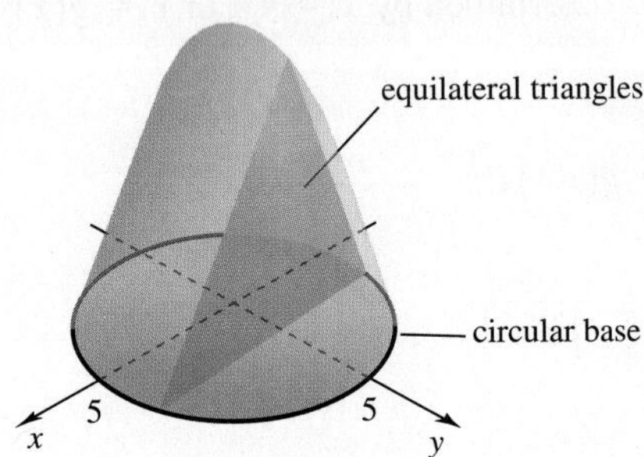

9. The solid with a semicircular base of radius 5 whose cross sections perpendicular to the base and parallel to the diameter are squares

10. The solid whose base is the region bounded by $y = x^2$ and the line $y = 1$ and whose cross sections perpendicular to the base and parallel to the x-axis are squares

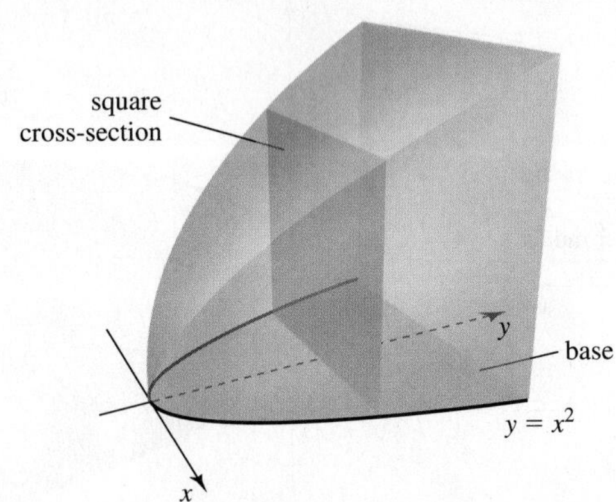

11. The solid whose base is the triangle with vertices $(0, 0)$, $(2, 0)$, and $(0, 2)$ and whose cross sections perpendicular to the base and parallel to the y-axis are semicircles

12. The pyramid with a square base 4 m on a side and a height of 2 m (Use calculus.)

13. The tetrahedron (pyramid with four triangular faces), all of whose edges have length 4

14. A circular cylinder of radius r and height h whose axis is at an angle of $\pi/4$ to the base

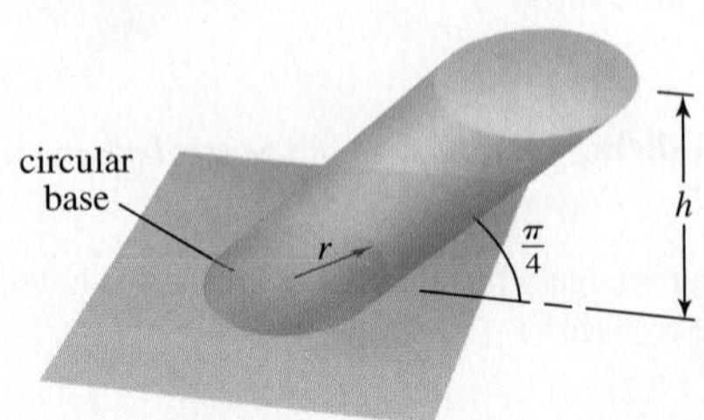

15–22. Disk method *Let R be the region bounded by the following curves. Use the disk method to find the volume of the solid generated when R is revolved about the x-axis.*

15. $y = 2x, y = 0, x = 3$ (Verify that your answer agrees with the volume formula for a cone.)

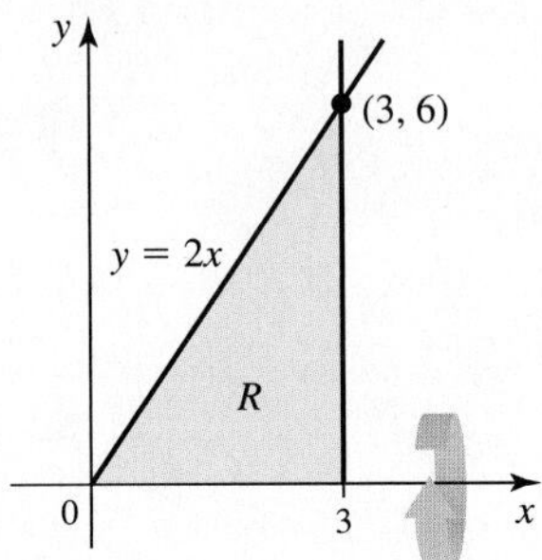

16. $y = 2 - 2x, y = 0, x = 0$ (Verify that your answer agrees with the volume formula for a cone.)

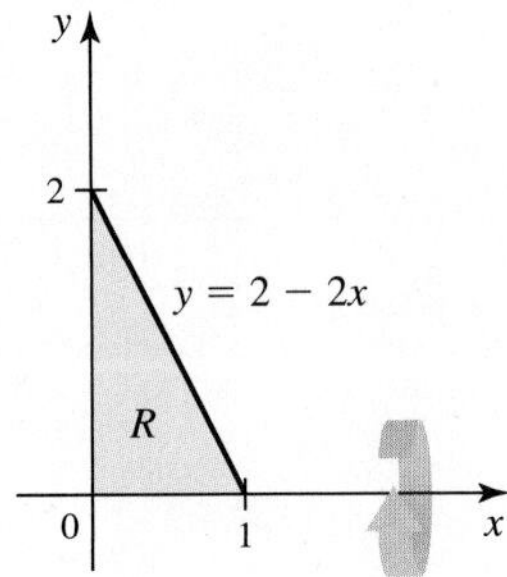

17. $y = 4 - x^2, y = 0, x = 0$

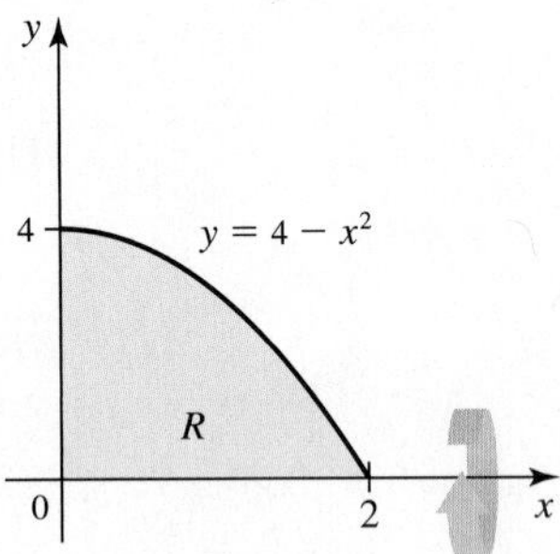

18. $y = \cos x, y = 0, x = 0$ (Recall that $\cos^2 x = \frac{1}{2}(1 + \cos 2x)$.)

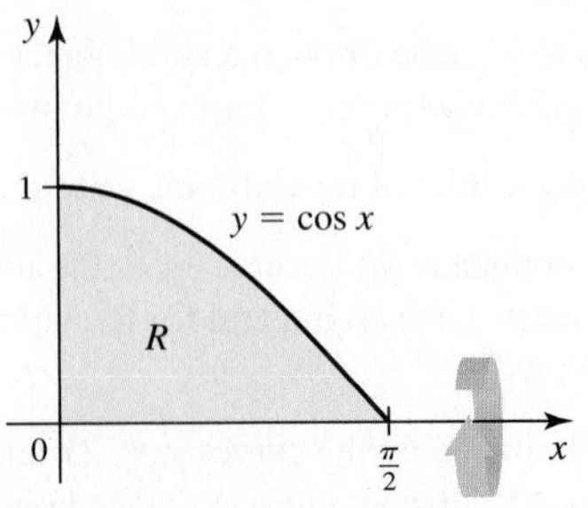

19. $y = \sin x, y = 0$, for $0 \le x \le \pi$ (Recall that $\sin^2 x = \frac{1}{2}(1 - \cos 2x)$.)

20. $y = \sqrt{25 - x^2}, y = 0$ (Verify that your answer agrees with the volume formula for a sphere.)

21. $y = \dfrac{1}{\sqrt[4]{1 - x}}, y = 0, x = 0$ and $x = \frac{1}{2}$

22. $y = \sec x, y = 0, x = 0$ and $x = \pi/4$

23–30. Washer method *Let R be the region bounded by the following curves. Use the washer method to find the volume of the solid generated when R is revolved about the x-axis.*

23. $y = x, y = 2\sqrt{x}$

24. $y = 2x, y = 16x^{1/4}$

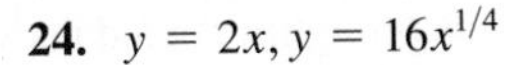

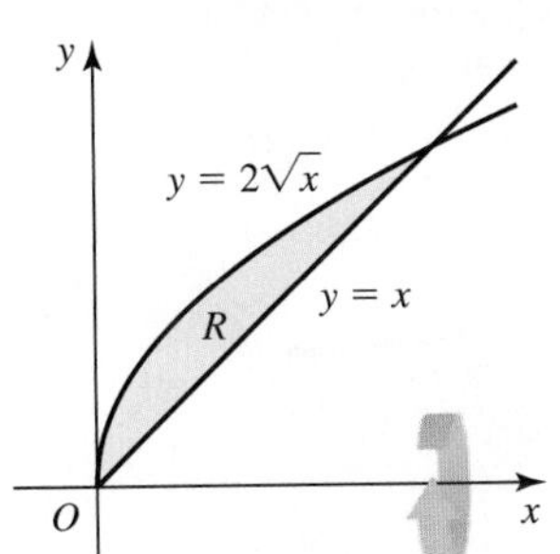

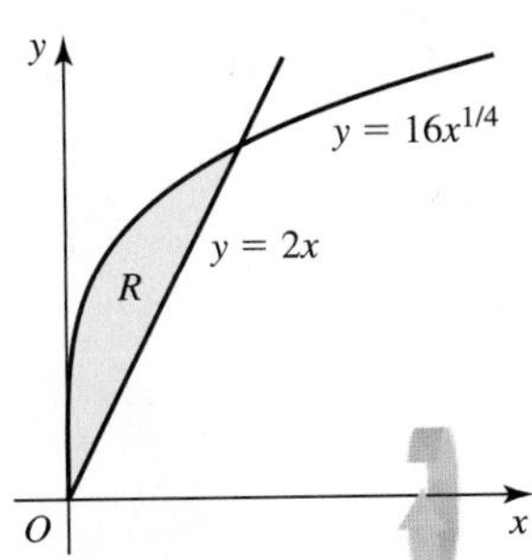

25. $y = \sin x, y = 1 - \sin x, x = \pi/6, x = 5\pi/6$

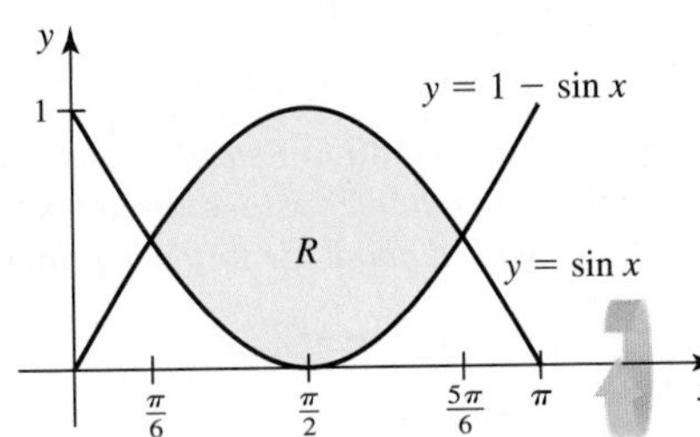

26. $y = x, y = x + 2, x = 0, x = 4$

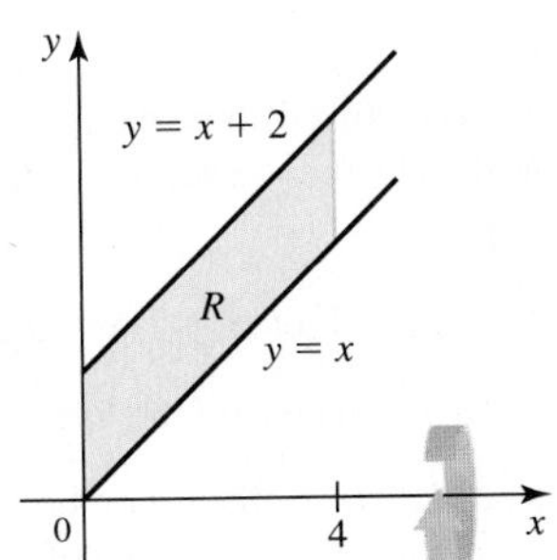

27. $y = 4x, y = 4x^2 - x^3$

28. $y = \sqrt{\sin x}, y = 1, x = 0$

29. $y = \sin x, y = \sqrt{\sin x}$, for $0 \le x \le \pi/2$

30. $y = |x|, y = 12 - x^2$

31–36. Disks/washers about the y-axis *Let R be the region bounded by the following lines and curves. Use the disk or washer method to find the volume of the solid generated when R is revolved about the y-axis.*

31. $y = x, y = 2x, y = 6$

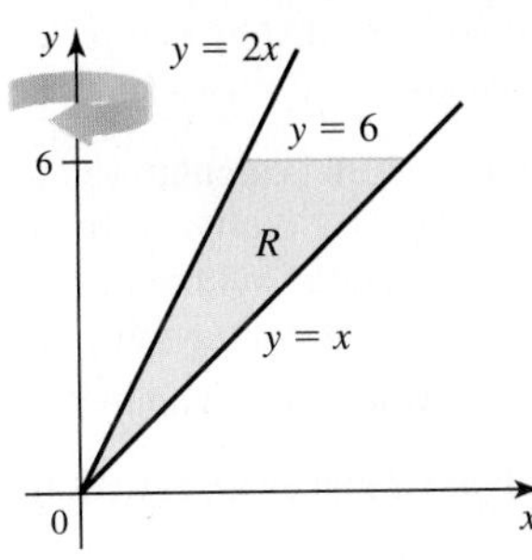

32. $y = 0, y = \sqrt{x - 1}, y = 2, x = 0$

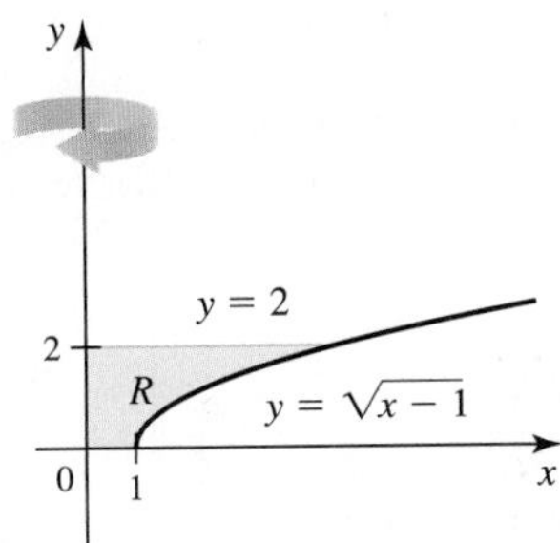

33. $y = x^3, y = 0, x = 2$

34. $y = \sqrt{x}, y = 0, x = 4$

35. $x = \sqrt{16 - y^2}, x = 0$

36. $y = 2 + \sqrt{x}, y = 2 - \sqrt{x}, x = 4$

37–40. Which is greater? *For the following regions R, determine which is greater—the volume of the solid generated when R is revolved about the x-axis or about the y-axis.*

37. R is bounded by $y = 2x$, the x-axis, and $x = 5$.

38. R is bounded by $y = 4 - 2x$, the x-axis, and the y-axis.

39. R is bounded by $y = 1 - x^3$, the x-axis, and the y-axis.

40. R is bounded by $y = x^2$ and $y = \sqrt{8x}$.

Further Explorations

41. **Explain why or why not** Determine whether the following statements are true and give an explanation or counterexample.
    a. A pyramid is a solid of revolution.
    b. The volume of a hemisphere can be computed using the disk method.
    c. Let R_1 be the region bounded by $y = \cos x$ and the x-axis on $[-\pi/2, \pi/2]$. Let R_2 be the region bounded by $y = \sin x$ and the x-axis on $[0, \pi]$. The volumes of the solids generated when R_1 and R_2 are revolved about the x-axis are equal.

42–46. Solids of revolution *Find the volume of the solid of revolution. Sketch the region in question.*

42. The region bounded by $y = 4/\sqrt{x + 1}, y = 1$, and $x = 0$ revolved about the y-axis

43. The region bounded by $y = x^{-3/2}, y = 1, x = 1$, and $x = 6$ revolved about the x-axis

44. The region bounded by $y = \sec x, y = 2$, and $x = 0$ revolved about the x-axis

45. The region bounded by $y = x^{1/3}, y = 4 - x^{1/3}$ and $x = 0$ revolved about the y-axis

46. The region bounded by $y = x^{-1}$, $y = 0$, $x = 1$, and $x = p > 0$ revolved about the x-axis (Is the volume bounded as $p \to \infty$?)

47. Fermat's volume calculation (1636) Let R be the region bounded by $y = \sqrt{x + a}$ (with $a > 0$), the y-axis, and the x-axis. Let S be the solid generated by rotating R about the y-axis. Let T be the inscribed cone that has the same circular base as S and height $\sqrt{a}$. Show that volume (S)/volume$(T) = \frac{8}{5}$.

48. Solid from a piecewise function Let

$$f(x) = \begin{cases} x & \text{if } 0 \le x \le 2 \\ 2x - 2 & \text{if } 2 < x \le 5 \\ -2x + 18 & \text{if } 5 < x \le 6 \end{cases}$$

Find the volume of the solid formed when the region bounded by the graph of f, the x-axis, and the line $x = 6$ is revolved about the x-axis.

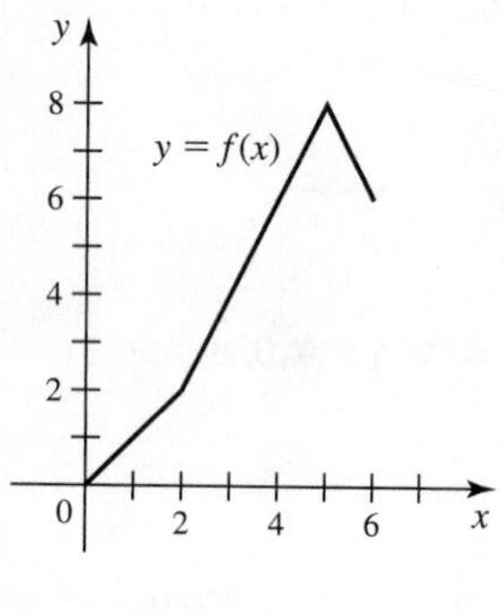

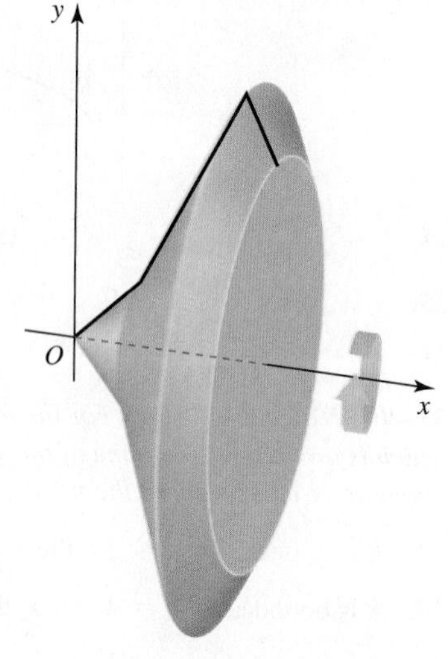

49. Solids from integrals Sketch a solid of revolution whose volume by the disk method is given by the following integrals. Indicate the function that generates the solid. Solutions are not unique.

a. $\int_0^{\pi} \pi \sin^2 x \, dx$ **b.** $\int_0^{2} \pi(x^2 + 2x + 1) \, dx$

Applications

50. Volume of a wooden object A solid wooden object turned on a lathe has a length of 50 cm and diameters (measured in cm) shown in the figure. (A lathe is a tool that spins and cuts a block of wood so that it has circular cross sections.) Use left Riemann sums to estimate the volume of the object.

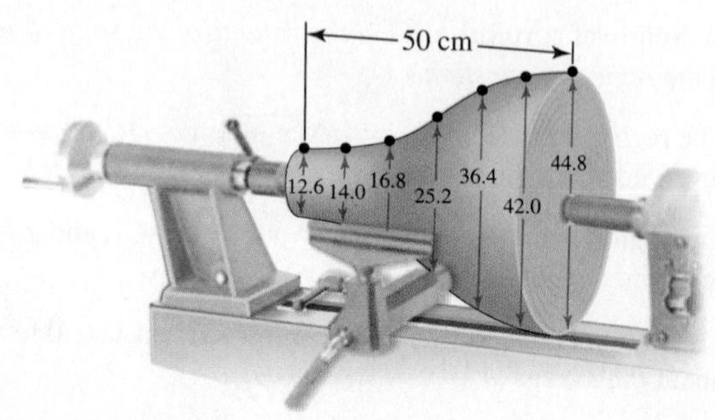

51. Cylinder, cone, hemisphere A right circular cylinder with height R and radius R has a volume of $V_C = \pi R^3$ (height = radius).

a. Find the volume of the cone that is inscribed in the cylinder with the same base as the cylinder and height R. Express the volume in terms of V_C.

b. Find the volume of the hemisphere that is inscribed in the cylinder with the same base as the cylinder. Express the volume in terms of V_C.

52. Water in a bowl A hemispherical bowl of radius 8 inches is filled to a depth of h in, where $0 \le h \le 8$. Find the volume of water in the bowl as a function of h. (Check the special cases $h = 0$ and $h = 8$.)

53. A torus (doughnut) Find the volume of the torus formed when the circle of radius 2 centered at $(3, 0)$ is revolved about the y-axis. Use geometry to evaluate the integral.

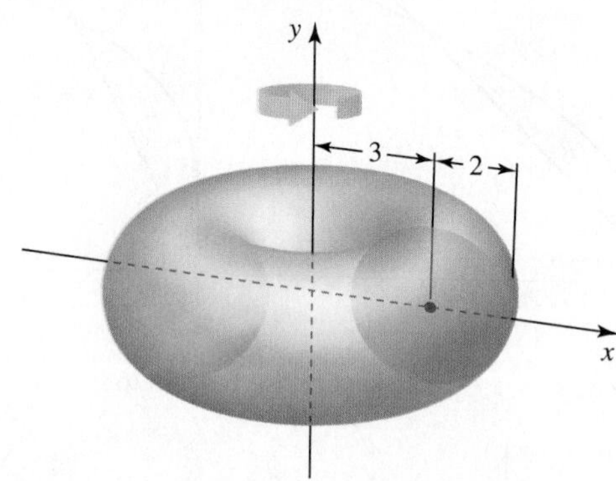

54–58. Different axes of revolution *Find the volume of the solid that is generated when the region in the first quadrant bounded by* $y = x^2$, $y = 4$, *and* $x = 0$ *is revolved about the following lines.*

54. y-axis **55.** $y = -2$ **56.** $x = -1$

57. $y = 6$ **58.** $x = 2$

59. Different axes of revolution Suppose R is the region bounded by $y = f(x)$ and $y = g(x)$ on the interval $[a, b]$, where $f(x) \ge g(x) \ge 0$.

a. Show that if R is revolved about the horizontal line $y = y_0$ that lies below R, then by the washer method, the volume of the resulting solid is

$$V = \int_a^b \pi[(f(x) - y_0)^2 - (g(x) - y_0)^2] \, dx.$$

b. How is this formula changed if the line $y = y_0$ lies above R?

60. Which is greater? Let R be the region bounded by $y = x^2$ and $y = \sqrt{x}$. Which is greater, the volume of the solid generated when R is revolved about the x-axis or about the line $y = 1$?

Additional Exercises

61. Cavalieri's principle *Cavalieri's principle* states that if two solids with equal altitudes have the same cross-sectional areas at every height, then they have equal volumes (see figure).

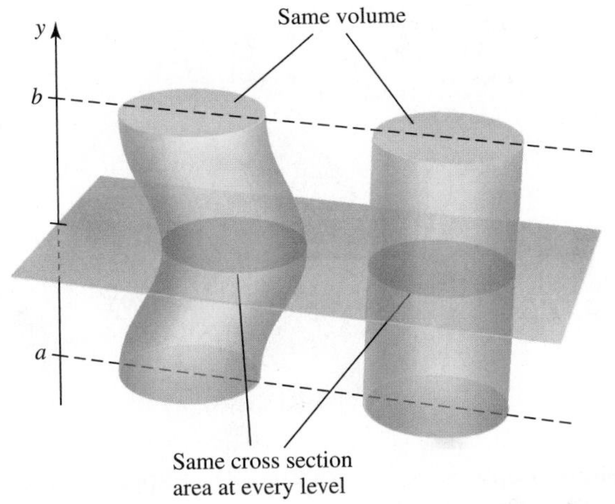

a. Use the theory of this section to justify Cavalieri's principle.
b. Find the radius of a circular cylinder of height 10 m that has the same volume as a 2-m by 2-m by 10-m box.

62. Limiting volume Consider the region R in the first quadrant bounded by $y = x^{1/n}$ and $y = x^n$, where n is a positive number.

a. Find the volume $V(n)$ of the solid generated when R is revolved about the x-axis. Express your answer in terms of n.
b. Evaluate $\lim_{n\to\infty} V(n)$. Interpret this limit geometrically.

QUICK CHECK ANSWERS

1. The average value of A on $[a, b]$ is $\overline{A} = \dfrac{1}{b-a}\displaystyle\int_a^b A(x)\,dx.$ Therefore, $V = (b - a)\overline{A}$. **2.** $A(x) = (2 - 2x^2)^2$ **3.** (a) A cylinder with height 2 and radius 2; (b) a cone with height 2 and base radius 2 **4.** When $g(x) = 0$, the washer method $V = \int_a^b \pi(f(x)^2 - g(x)^2)\,dx$ reduces to the disk method $V = \int_a^b \pi(f(x)^2)\,dx$. **5.** (a) Inner radius $= \sqrt{x} + 1$; (b) outer radius $= x^2 + 1$ **6.** $\int_0^1 \pi(y^{2/3} - y^2)\,dy$

6.4 Volume by Shells

You can solve a lot of challenging volume problems using the disk/washer method. There are, however, some volume problems that are difficult to solve with this method. For this reason, we extend our discussion of volume problems to the *shell method*, which—like the disk/washer method—is used to compute the volume of solids of revolution.

Cylindrical Shells

Let R be a region bounded by the graph of f, the x-axis, and the lines $x = a$ and $x = b$, where $f(x) \geq 0$ on $[a, b]$. When R is revolved about the y-axis, a solid is generated (Figure 6.36) whose volume is computed with the slice-and-sum strategy.

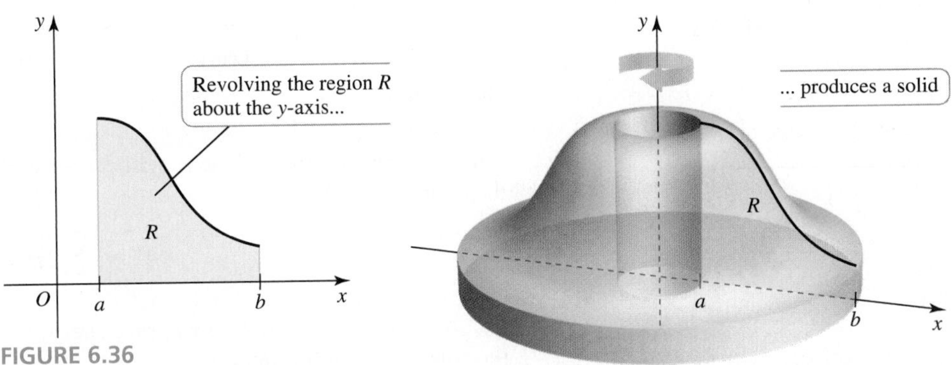

FIGURE 6.36

We divide $[a, b]$ into n subintervals of length $\Delta x = (b - a)/n$, and identify an arbitrary point $\overline{x}_k$ on the kth subinterval, for $k = 1, \ldots, n$. Now observe the rectangle built on the kth subinterval with a height of $f(\overline{x}_k)$ and a width Δx (Figure 6.37). As it revolves about the y-axis, this rectangle sweeps out a thin *cylindrical shell*.

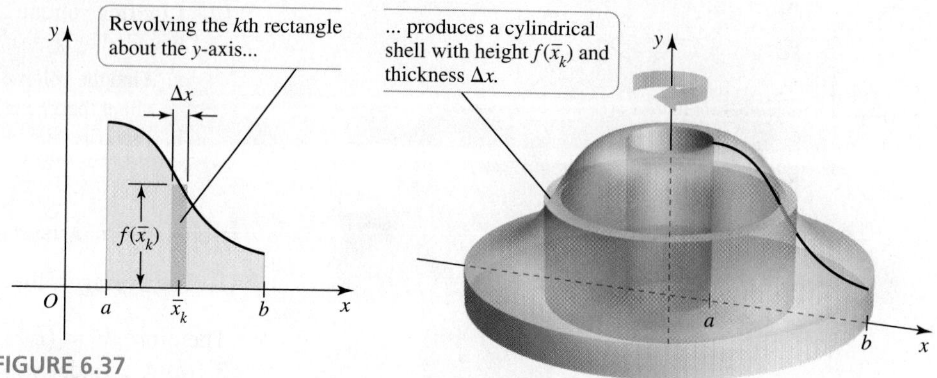

FIGURE 6.37

When the kth cylindrical shell is unwrapped (Figure 6.38), it approximates a thin rectangular slab. The approximate length of the slab is the circumference of a circle with radius $\bar{x}_k$, which is $2\pi\bar{x}_k$. The height of the slab is the height of the original rectangle $f(\bar{x}_k)$ and its thickness is Δx; therefore, the volume of the kth shell is approximately

$$\underbrace{2\pi\bar{x}_k}_{\text{length}} \cdot \underbrace{f(\bar{x}_k)}_{\text{height}} \cdot \underbrace{\Delta x}_{\text{thickness}} = 2\pi\bar{x}_k f(\bar{x}_k)\,\Delta x.$$

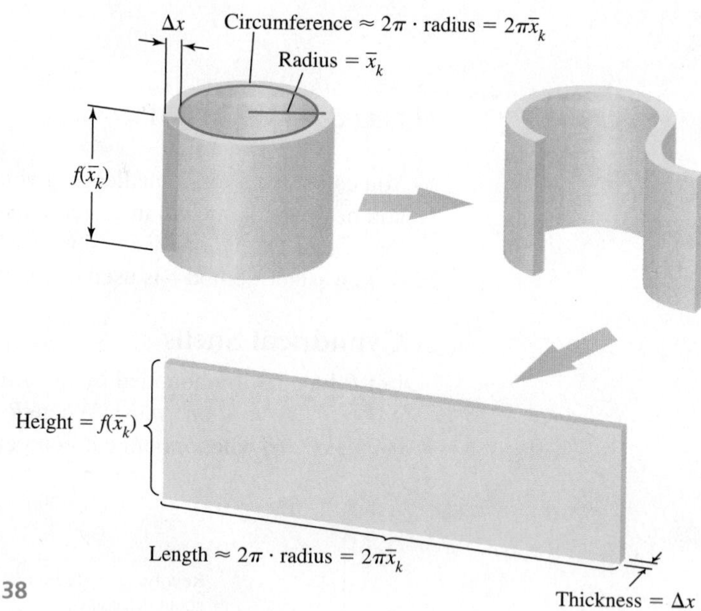

FIGURE 6.38

Summing the volumes of the n cylindrical shells gives an approximation to the volume of the entire solid:

$$V \approx \sum_{k=1}^{n} 2\pi\bar{x}_k f(\bar{x}_k)\,\Delta x$$

As n increases and as Δx approaches 0 (Figure 6.39), we obtain the exact volume of the solid as a definite integral:

$$V = \lim_{n\to\infty} \sum_{k=1}^{n} \underbrace{2\pi\,\bar{x}_k}_{\substack{\text{shell}\\\text{circumference}}}\, \overbrace{f(\bar{x}_k)}^{\substack{\text{shell}\\\text{height}}}\, \underbrace{\Delta x}_{\substack{\text{shell}\\\text{thickness}}} = \int_a^b 2\pi x f(x)\,dx$$

➤ Rather than memorizing, think of the meaning of the factors in this formula: $f(x)$ is the height of a single cylindrical shell, $2\pi x$ is the circumference of the shell, and dx corresponds to the thickness of a shell. Therefore, $2\pi x f(x)\,dx$ represents the volume of a single shell, and we sum the volumes from $x = a$ to $x = b$. Notice that the integrand for the shell method is the function $A(x)$ that gives the surface area of the shell of radius x for $a \le x \le b$.

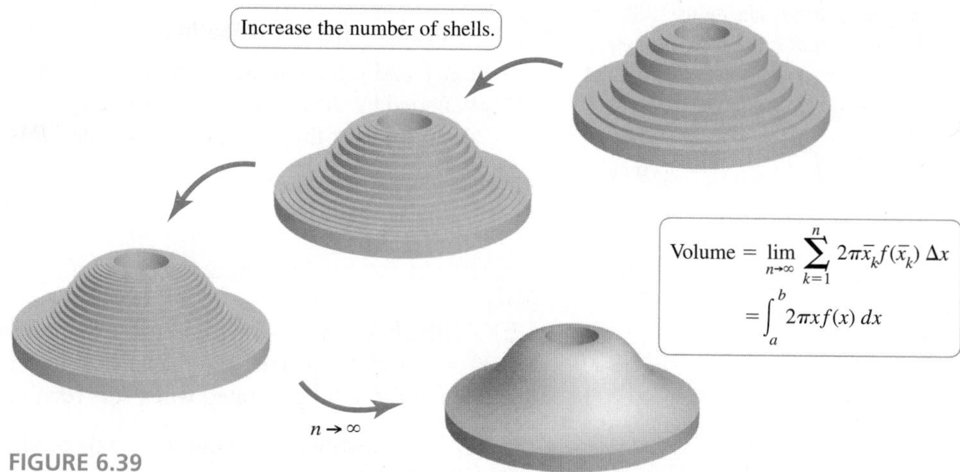

FIGURE 6.39

Before doing examples, we generalize this method as we did for the disk method. Suppose that the region R is bounded by two curves, $y = f(x)$ and $y = g(x)$, where $f(x) \ge g(x)$ on $[a, b]$ (Figure 6.40). What is the volume of the solid generated when R is revolved about the y-axis?

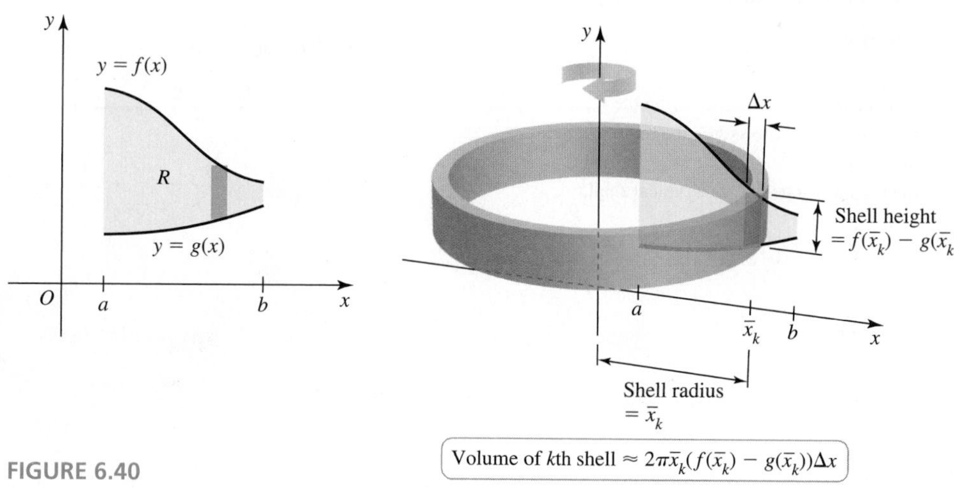

FIGURE 6.40

The situation is similar to the case we just considered. A typical rectangle in R sweeps out a cylindrical shell, but now the height of the kth shell is $f(\bar{x}_k) - g(\bar{x}_k)$, for $k = 1, \ldots, n$. As before, we take the radius of the kth shell to be $\bar{x}_k$, which means the volume of the kth shell is approximated by $2\pi\bar{x}_k(f(\bar{x}_k) - g(\bar{x}_k))\,\Delta x$ (Figure 6.40). Summing the volumes of all the shells gives an approximation to the volume of the entire solid:

$$V \approx \sum_{k=1}^{n} \underbrace{2\pi\bar{x}_k}_{\text{circumference of shell}} \underbrace{(f(\bar{x}_k) - g(\bar{x}_k))}_{\text{height of shell}}\,\Delta x$$

Taking the limit as $n \to \infty$ (which implies that $\Delta x \to 0$), the volume is the definite integral

$$V = \lim_{n\to\infty} \sum_{k=1}^{n} 2\pi\,\bar{x}_k(f(\bar{x}_k) - g(\bar{x}_k))\,\Delta x = \int_a^b 2\pi x\,(f(x) - g(x))\,dx.$$

➤ An analogous formula for the shell method when R is revolved about the x-axis is obtained by reversing the roles of x and y:

$$V = \int_c^d 2\pi y(f(y) - g(y))\,dy$$

Volume by the Shell Method

Let f and g be continuous functions with $f(x) \ge g(x)$ on $[a, b]$. If R is the region bounded by the curves $y = f(x)$ and $y = g(x)$ between the lines $x = a$ and $x = b$, the volume of the solid generated when R is revolved about the y-axis is

$$V = \int_a^b 2\pi x(f(x) - g(x))\,dx.$$

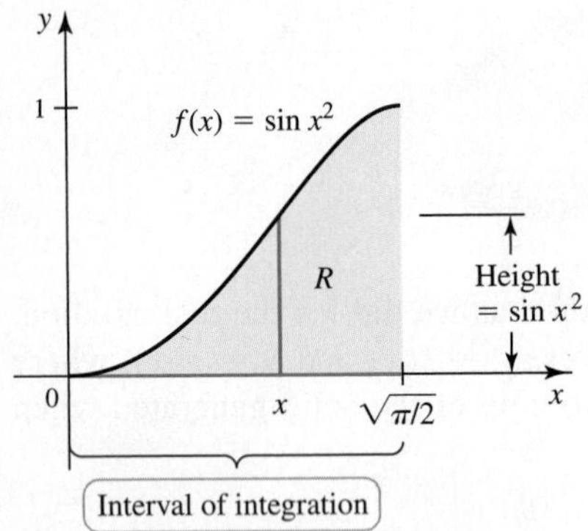

FIGURE 6.41

➤ When computing volumes using the shell method, it is best to sketch the region R in the xy-plane and draw a slice through the region that generates a typical shell.

EXAMPLE 1 **A sine bowl** Let R be the region bounded by the graph of $f(x) = \sin x^2$, the x-axis, and the vertical line $x = \sqrt{\pi/2}$ (Figure 6.41). Find the volume of the solid generated when R is revolved about the y-axis.

SOLUTION Revolving R about the y-axis produces a bowl-shaped region (Figure 6.42). The radius of a typical cylindrical shell is x and its height is $f(x) = \sin x^2$. Therefore, the volume by the shell method is

$$V = \int_a^b 2\pi x f(x)\,dx = \int_0^{\sqrt{\pi/2}} 2\pi x \sin x^2\,dx.$$

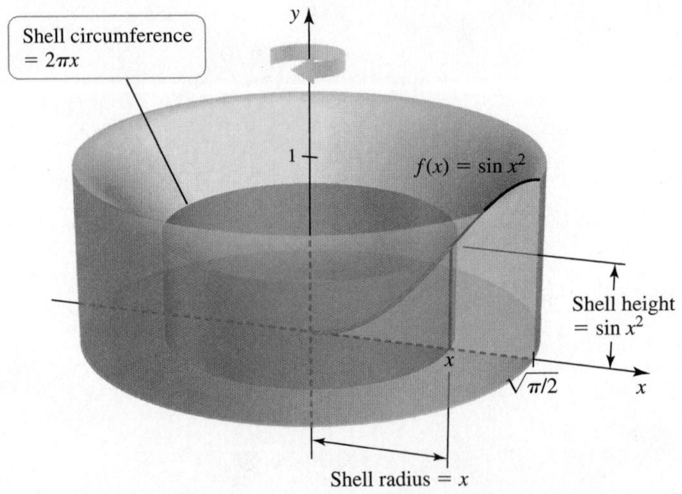

FIGURE 6.42

Now we make the change of variables $u = x^2$, which means that $du = 2x\,dx$. The lower limit $x = 0$ becomes $u = 0$ and the upper limit $x = \sqrt{\pi/2}$ becomes $u = \pi/2$. The volume of the solid is

$$\begin{aligned} V = \int_0^{\sqrt{\pi/2}} 2\pi x \sin x^2\,dx &= \pi \int_0^{\pi/2} \sin u\,du && u = x^2, du = 2x\,dx \\ &= \pi\,(-\cos u)\Big|_0^{\pi/2} && \text{Fundamental Theorem} \\ &= \pi[0 - (-1)] = \pi. && \text{Simplify.} \end{aligned}$$

Related Exercises 5–10 ◀

QUICK CHECK 1 The triangle bounded by the x-axis, the line $y = 2x$, and the line $x = 1$ is revolved about the y-axis. Give an integral that equals the volume of the resulting solid using the shell method. ◀

> We could use the disk/washer method to compute the volume, but notice that this approach requires splitting the region into two subregions. A better approach is to use the shell method and integrate along the y-axis.

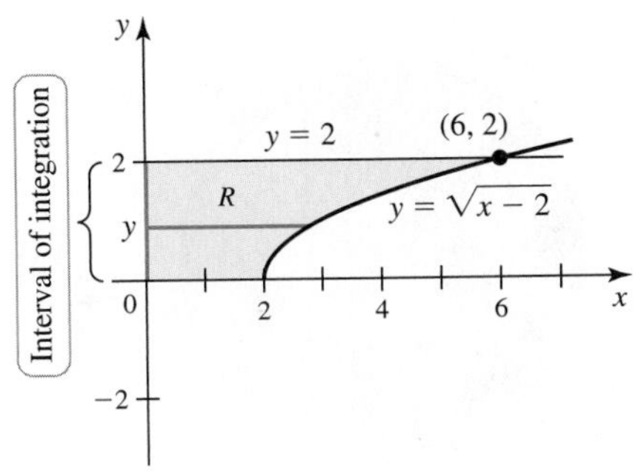

FIGURE 6.43

EXAMPLE 2 **Shells about the x-axis** Let R be the region in the first quadrant bounded by the graph of $y = \sqrt{x - 2}$ and the line $y = 2$.

a. Find the volume of the solid generated when R is revolved about the x-axis.

b. Find the volume of the solid generated when R is revolved about the line $y = -2$.

SOLUTION

a. The revolution is about the x-axis, so the integration in the shell method is with respect to y. A typical shell runs parallel to the x-axis and has radius y, where $0 \le y \le 2$; the shells extend from the y-axis to the curve $y = \sqrt{x - 2}$ (Figure 6.43). Solving $y = \sqrt{x - 2}$ for x, we have $x = y^2 + 2$, which is the height of the shell at the point y (Figure 6.44a). Integrating with respect to y, the volume of the solid is

$$V = \int_0^2 \underbrace{2\pi y}_{\text{shell circumference}} \underbrace{(y^2 + 2)}_{\text{shell height}}\, dy = 2\pi \int_0^2 (y^3 + 2y)\, dy = 16\pi.$$

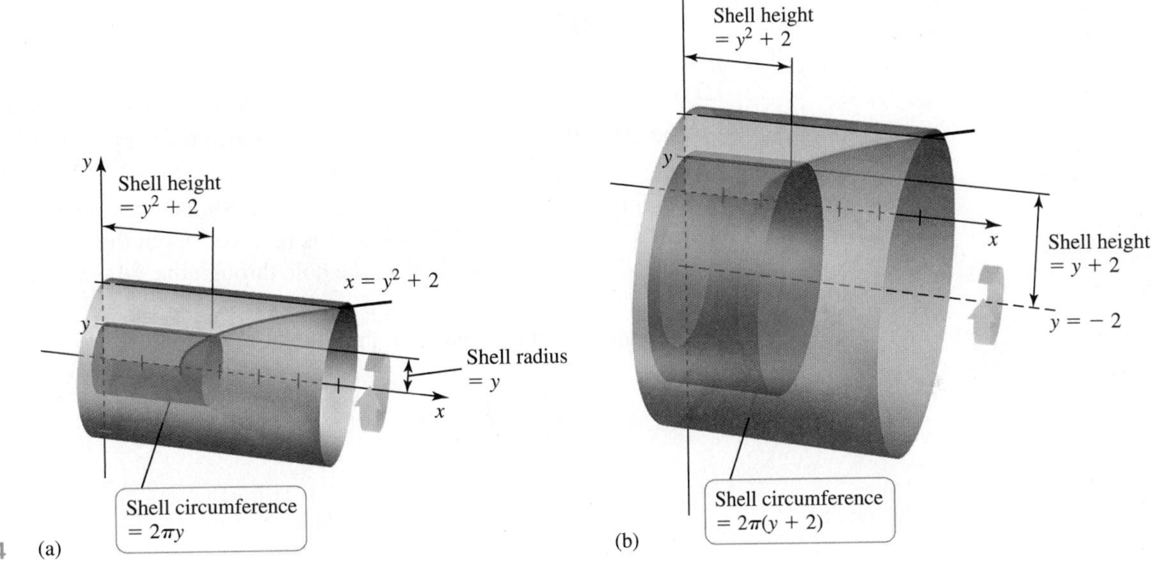

FIGURE 6.44 (a) (b)

b. Revolving R about the line $y = -2$ produces a solid with a cylindrical hole through it (Figure 6.44b). To find the volume of this solid, we carry out the calculation in part (a) with a single change: The radius of a typical shell at a point y is now $y + 2$ (the distance to the x-axis plus 2 units from the x-axis to the axis of revolution). With this change, the volume of this solid is

$$V = \int_0^2 \underbrace{2\pi(y + 2)}_{\text{shell circumference}} \underbrace{(y^2 + 2)}_{\text{shell height}}\, dy = 2\pi \int_0^2 (y^3 + 2y^2 + 2y + 4)\, dy = \frac{128\pi}{3}.$$

Related Exercises 11–20 ◄

QUICK CHECK 2 Write the volume integral in Example 2 in the case that R is revolved about the line $y = -5$. ◄

EXAMPLE 3 **Volume of a drilled sphere** A cylindrical hole with radius r is drilled symmetrically through the center of a sphere with radius R, where $r \le R$. What is the volume of the remaining material?

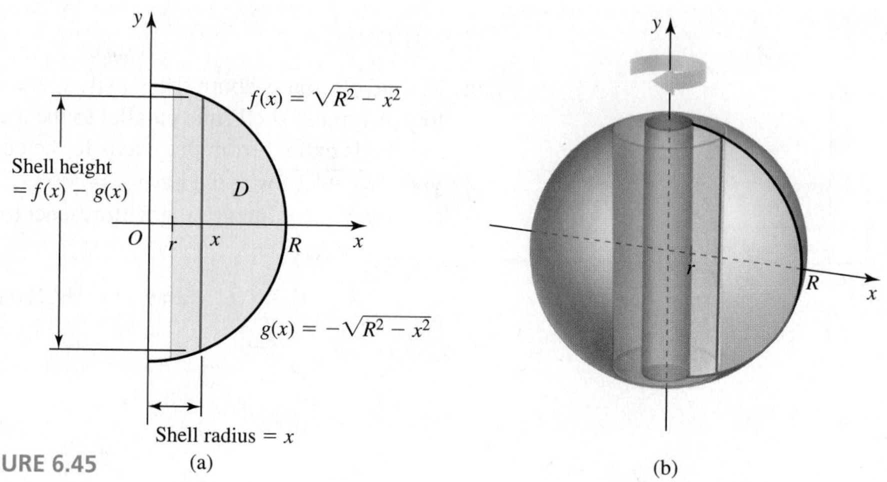

FIGURE 6.45

SOLUTION The y-axis is chosen to coincide with the axis of the cylindrical hole. We let D be the region in the xy-plane bounded above by $f(x) = \sqrt{R^2 - x^2}$, the upper half of a circle of radius R, and bounded below by $g(x) = -\sqrt{R^2 - x^2}$, the lower half of a circle of radius R, for $r \le x \le R$ (Figure 6.45a). Slices are taken perpendicular to the x-axis from $x = r$ to $x = R$. When a slice is revolved about the y-axis, it sweeps out a cylindrical shell that is concentric with the hole through the sphere (Figure 6.45b). The radius of a typical shell is x and its height is $f(x) - g(x) = 2\sqrt{R^2 - x^2}$. Therefore, the volume of the material that remains in the sphere is

$$
\begin{aligned}
V &= \int_r^R 2\pi x\left(2\sqrt{R^2 - x^2}\right) dx \\
&= -2\pi \int_{R^2-r^2}^{0} \sqrt{u}\, du && u = R^2 - x^2,\ du = -2x\,dx \\
&= 2\pi\left(\frac{2}{3}u^{3/2}\right)\Bigg|_0^{R^2-r^2} && \text{Fundamental Theorem of Calculus} \\
&= \frac{4\pi}{3}(R^2 - r^2)^{3/2}. && \text{Simplify.}
\end{aligned}
$$

It is important to check the result by examining special cases. In the case that $r = R$ (the radius of the hole equals the radius of the sphere), our calculation gives a volume of 0, which is correct. In the case that $r = 0$ (no hole in the sphere), our calculation gives the correct volume of a sphere, $\frac{4}{3}\pi R^3$.

Related Exercises 21–26 ◀

Restoring Order

After working with slices, disks, washers, and shells, you may feel somewhat overwhelmed. How do you choose a method and which method is best?

First, notice that the disk method is just a special case of the washer method. So, for solids of revolution, the choice is between the washer method and the shell method. In *principle*, either method can be used. In *practice*, one method usually produces an integral that is easier to evaluate than the other method. The following table summarizes these methods.

SUMMARY Disk/washer and Shell Methods

Integration with respect to x

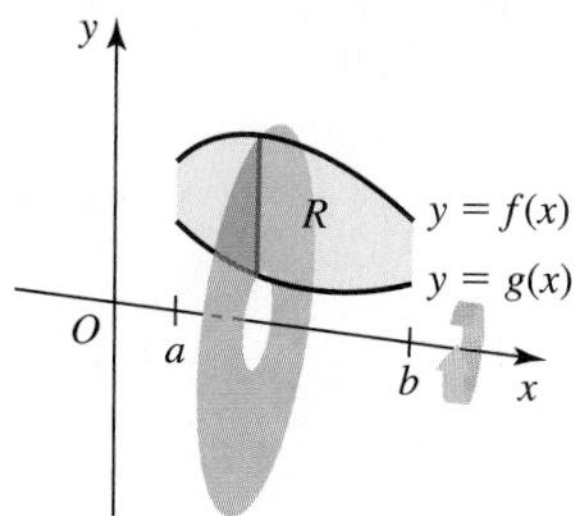

Disk/washer method about the x-axis
Disks/washers are *perpendicular* to the x-axis.

$$\int_a^b \pi(f(x)^2 - g(x)^2)\,dx$$

Shell method about the y-axis
Shells are *parallel* to the y-axis.

$$\int_a^b 2\pi x(f(x) - g(x))\,dx$$

Integration with respect to y

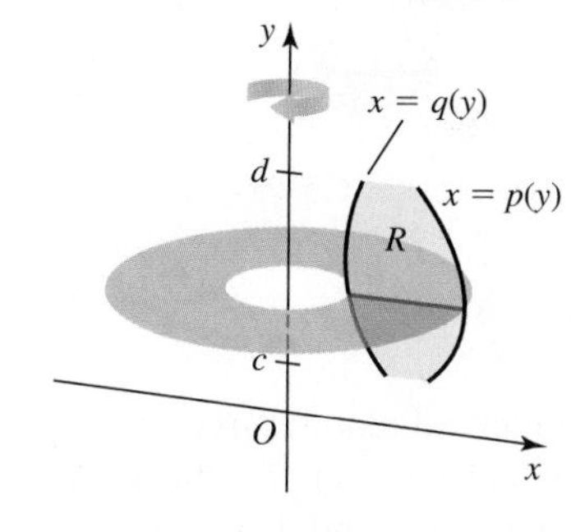

Disk/washer method about the y-axis
Disks/washers are *perpendicular* to the y-axis.

$$\int_c^d \pi(p(y)^2 - q(y)^2)\,dy$$

Shell method about the x-axis
Shells are *parallel* to the x-axis.

$$\int_c^d 2\pi y(p(y) - q(y))\,dy$$

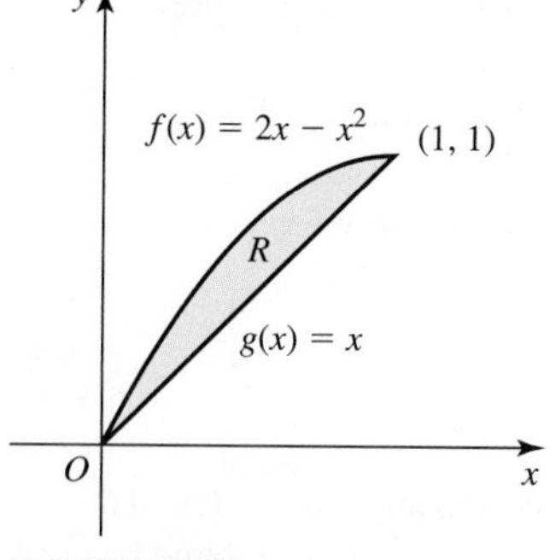

FIGURE 6.46

EXAMPLE 4 Volume by which method? The region R is bounded by the graphs of $f(x) = 2x - x^2$ and $g(x) = x$ on the interval $[0, 1]$ (Figure 6.46). Use the washer method and the shell method to find the volume of the solid formed when R is revolved about the x-axis.

SOLUTION Solving $f(x) = g(x)$, we find that the curves intersect at the points $(0, 0)$ and $(1, 1)$. Using the washer method, the upper bounding curve is the graph of f, the lower bounding curve is the graph of g, and a typical washer is perpendicular to the x-axis (Figure 6.47). Therefore, the volume is

$$V = \int_0^1 \pi((2x - x^2)^2 - x^2)\,dx \quad \text{Washer method}$$

$$= \pi \int_0^1 (x^4 - 4x^3 + 3x^2)\,dx \quad \text{Expand integrand.}$$

$$= \pi\left(\frac{x^5}{5} - x^4 + x^3\right)\Big|_0^1 = \frac{\pi}{5}. \quad \text{Evaluate integral.}$$

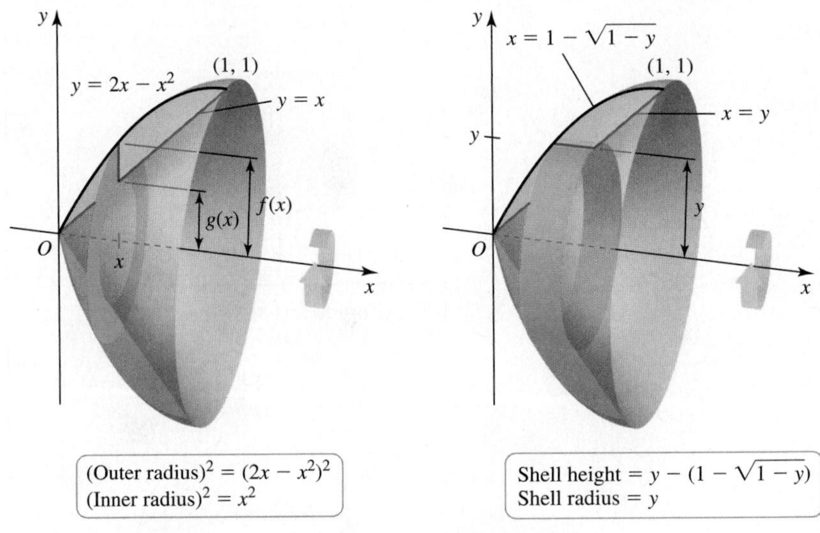

FIGURE 6.47 FIGURE 6.48

➤ To solve $y = 2x - x^2$ for x, write the equation as $x^2 - 2x + y = 0$ and complete the square or use the quadratic formula.

The shell method requires expressing the bounding curves in the form $x = p(y)$ for the right curve and $x = q(y)$ for the left curve. The right curve is $x = y$. Solving $y = 2x - x^2$ for x, we find that $x = 1 - \sqrt{1 - y}$ describes the left curve. A typical shell is parallel to the x-axis (Figure 6.48). Therefore, the volume is

$$V = \int_0^1 2\pi y[\underbrace{y}_{p(y)} - \underbrace{(1 - \sqrt{1 - y})}_{q(y)}]\,dy.$$

Although this integral can be evaluated $\left(\text{and equals } \frac{\pi}{5}\right)$, it is decidedly more difficult than the integral required by the washer method. In this case, the washer method is preferable. Of course, the shell method may be preferable for other problems.

Related Exercises 27–32 ◄

QUICK CHECK 3 Suppose the region in Example 4 is revolved about the y-axis. Which method (washer or shell) leads to an easier integral? ◄

SECTION 6.4 EXERCISES

Review Questions

1. Assume f and g are continuous with $f(x) \geq g(x) \geq 0$ on $[a, b]$. The region bounded by the graphs of f and g and the lines $x = a$ and $x = b$ is revolved about the y-axis. Write the integral given by the shell method that equals the volume of the resulting solid.

2. Fill in the blanks: A region R is revolved about the y-axis. The volume of the resulting solid could (in principle) be found by using the disk/washer method and integrating with respect to ________ or using the shell method and integrating with respect to ________.

3. Fill in the blanks: A region R is revolved about the x-axis. The volume of the resulting solid could (in principle) be found by using the disk/washer method and integrating with respect to ________ or using the shell method and integrating with respect to ________.

4. Are shell method integrals easier to evaluate than washer method integrals? Explain.

Basic Skills

5–10. Shell method *Let R be the region bounded by the following curves. Use the shell method to find the volume of the solid generated when R is revolved about the y-axis.*

5. $y = \frac{x}{2} + 1, y = 0, x = 0$, and $x = 2$

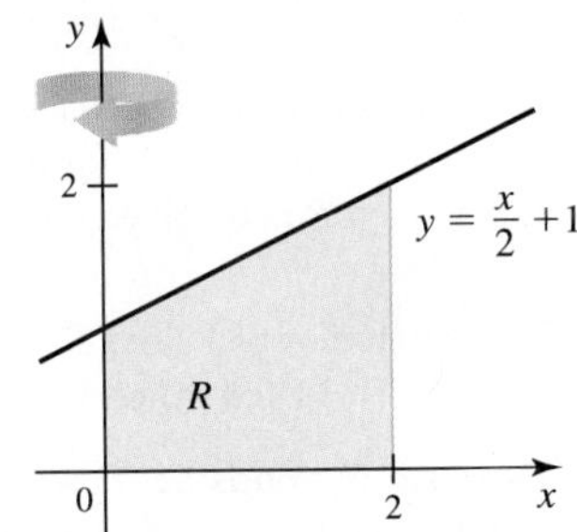

6. $y = 6 - x, y = 0, x = 2$, and $x = 4$

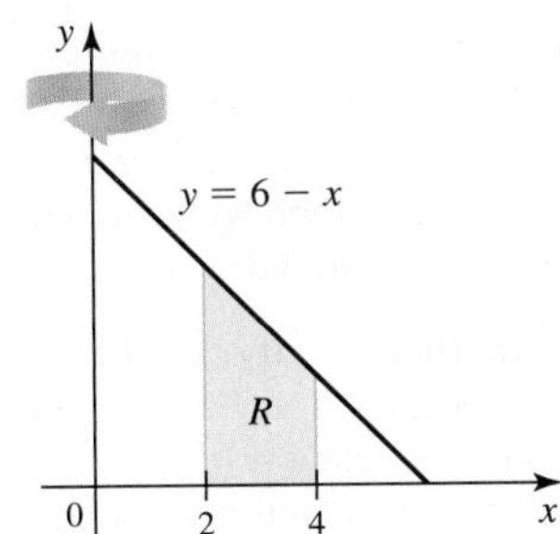

7. $y = 3x, y = 3$, and $x = 0$ (Use calculus.)

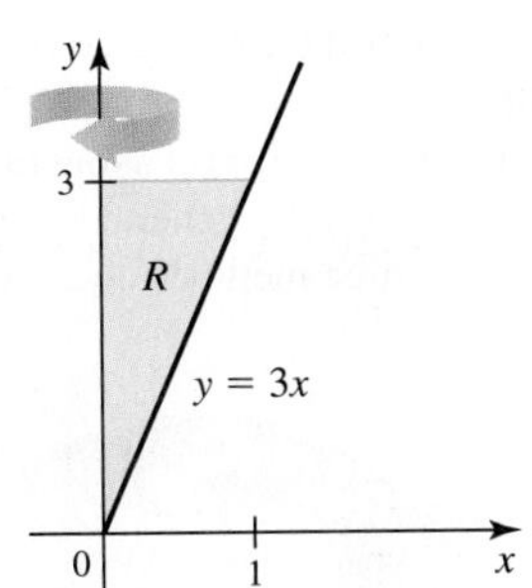

8. $y = \sqrt{x}, y = 0$, and $x = 4$

9. $y = \cos x^2, y = 0$, for $0 \le x \le \sqrt{\pi/2}$

10. $y = \sqrt{4 - 2x^2}, y = 0$, and $x = 0$, in the first quadrant

11–16. Shell method *Let R be the region bounded by the following curves. Use the shell method to find the volume of the solid generated when R is revolved about the x-axis.*

11. $y = \sqrt{x}, y = 0$, and $x = 4$

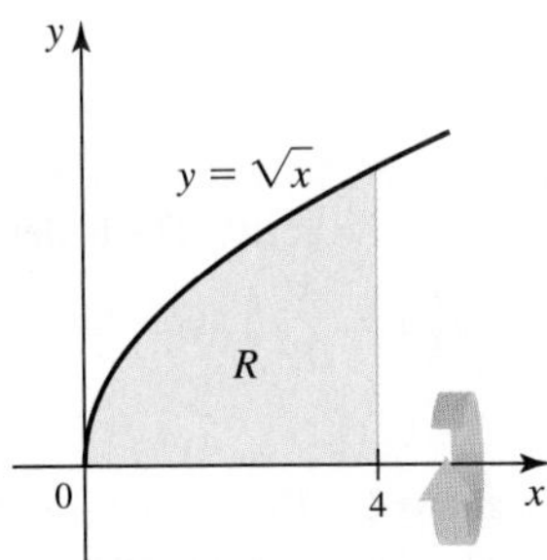

12. $y = 8, y = 2x + 2, x = 0$, and $x = 2$

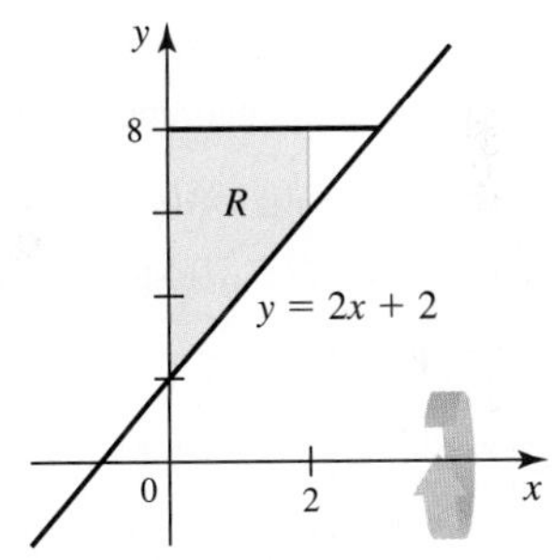

13. $y = 4 - x, y = 2$, and $x = 0$

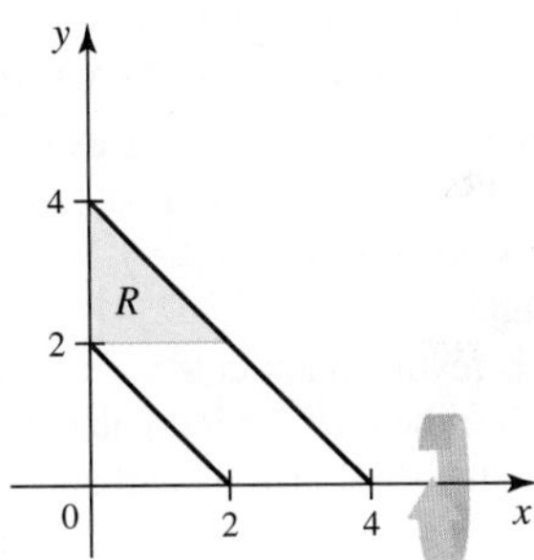

14. $y = x^3, y = 8$, and $x = 0$

15. $y = 2x^{-3/2}, y = 2, y = 16$, and $x = 0$

16. $y = \sqrt{50 - 2x^2}$, in the first quadrant

17–20. Shell method about other lines *Let R be the region bounded by $y = x^2, x = 1$, and $y = 0$. Use the shell method to find the volume of the solid generated when R is revolved about the following lines.*

17. $x = -2$ 18. $x = 2$ 19. $y = -2$ 20. $y = 2$

21–26. Shell method *Use the shell method to find the volume of the following solids.*

21. A right circular cone of radius 3 and height 8

22. The solid formed when a hole of radius 2 is drilled symmetrically along the axis of a right circular cylinder of height 6 and radius 4

23. The solid formed when a hole of radius 3 is drilled symmetrically along the axis of a right circular cone of radius 6 and height 9

24. The solid formed when a hole of radius 3 is drilled symmetrically through the center of a sphere of radius 6

25. The *ellipsoid* formed when the ellipse $x^2 + 2y^2 = 4$ is revolved about the y-axis

26. The solid formed when a hole of radius $r \le R$ is drilled symmetrically along the axis of a bullet. The bullet is formed by revolving the parabola $y = 6\left(1 - \frac{x^2}{R^2}\right)$ about the y-axis, where $0 \le x \le R$.

27–32. Washers vs. shells *Let R be the region bounded by the following curves. Let S be the solid generated when R is revolved about the given axis. If possible, find the volume of S by both the disk/washer and shell methods. Check that your results agree and state which method is easiest to apply.*

27. $y = x, y = x^{1/3}$; in the first quadrant; revolved about the x-axis

28. $y = x^2/8, y = 2 - x, x = 0$; revolved about the y-axis

29. $y = 1/(x + 1), y = 1 - x/3$; revolved about the x-axis

30. $y = (x - 2)^3 - 2, x = 0, y = 25$; revolved about the y-axis

31. $y = 16 - x^2, y = 8 - 2x, x = 0$; revolved about the x-axis

32. $y = 6/(x + 3), y = 2 - x$; revolved about the x-axis

Further Explorations

33. **Explain why or why not** Determine whether the following statements are true and give an explanation or counterexample.
   a. When using the shell method, the axis of the cylindrical shells is parallel to the axis of revolution.
   b. If a region is revolved about the y-axis, then the shell method must be used.
   c. If a region is revolved about the x-axis, then in principle it is possible to use the disk/washer method and integrate with respect to x or the shell method and integrate with respect to y.

34–36. Solids of revolution *Find the volume of the following solids of revolution. Sketch the region in question.*

T 34. The region bounded by $y = (1 - x)^{-1/2}, y = 1, y = 2$, and $x = 0$ revolved about the y-axis

35. The region bounded by $y = 1/x^3, y = 0, x = 2$, and $x = 4$ revolved about the y-axis

T 36. The region bounded by $y = (x^2 + 1)^{-1/3}, y = 0, x = 0$, and $x = \sqrt{7}$ revolved about the y-axis

37–44. Choose your method *Find the volume of the following solids using the method of your choice.*

37. The solid formed when the region bounded by $y = x^2$ and $y = 2 - x^2$ is revolved about the x-axis

38. The solid formed when the region bounded by $y = \sec x$ and $y = 2$ on the interval $[0, \pi/3]$ is revolved about the x-axis

39. The solid formed when the region bounded by $y = x, y = 2x + 2, x = 2$, and $x = 6$ is revolved about the y-axis

40. The solid formed when the region bounded by $y = x^3$, the x-axis, and $x = 2$ is revolved about the x-axis

41. The solid whose base is the region bounded by $y = x^2$ and the line $y = 1$ and whose cross sections perpendicular to the base and parallel to the x-axis are semicircles

42. The solid formed when the region bounded by $y = 2, y = 2x + 2$, and $x = 6$ is revolved about the y-axis

43. The solid whose base in the xy-plane is the square with vertices $(1, 0), (0, 1), (-1, 0)$, and $(0, -1)$ and whose cross sections perpendicular to the base and perpendicular to the x-axis are semicircles

44. The solid formed when the region bounded by $y = \sqrt{x}$, the x-axis, and $x = 4$ is revolved about the x-axis

T 45. **Equal volumes** Consider the region R bounded by the curves $y = ax^2 + 1, y = 0, x = 0$, and $x = 1$, for $a \ge -1$. Let S_1 and S_2 be solids generated when R is revolved about the x- and y-axes, respectively.
   a. Find V_1 and V_2, the volumes of S_1 and S_2, as functions of a.
   b. Are there values of $a \ge -1$ for which $V_1(a) = V_2(a)$?

46. **A hemisphere by several methods** Let R be the region in the first quadrant bounded by the circle $x^2 + y^2 = r^2$ and the coordinate axes. Find the volume of a hemisphere of radius r in the following ways.
   a. Revolve R about the x-axis and use the disk method.
   b. Revolve R about the x-axis and use the shell method.
   c. Assume the base of the hemisphere is in the xy-plane and use the general slicing method with slices perpendicular to the xy-plane and parallel to the x-axis.

47. **A cone by two methods** Verify that the volume of a right circular cone with a base radius of r and a height of h is $\pi r^2 h/3$. Use the region bounded by the line $y = rx/h$, the x-axis, and the line $x = h$, where the region is rotated around the x-axis. Then (a) use the disk method and integrate with respect to x, and (b) use the shell method and integrate with respect to y.

48. **A spherical cap** Consider the cap of thickness h that has been sliced from a sphere of radius r (see figure). Verify that the volume of the cap is $\pi h^2 (3r - h)/3$ using (a) the washer method, (b) the shell method, and (c) the general slicing method. Check for consistency among the three methods and check the special cases $h = r$ and $h = 0$.

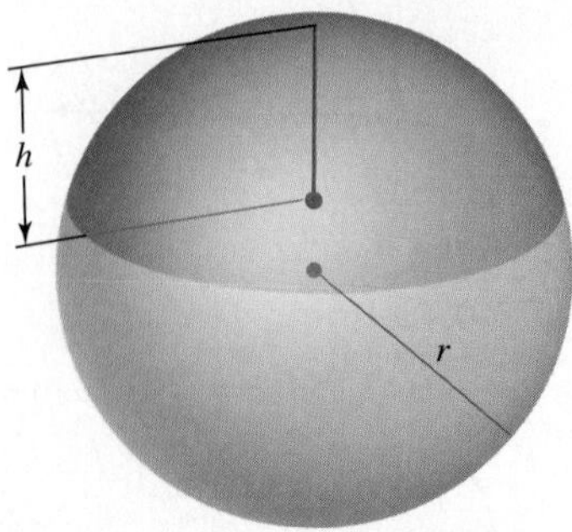

Applications

49. Water in a bowl A hemispherical bowl of radius 8 inches is filled to a depth of h inches, where $0 \le h \le 8$ ($h = 0$ corresponds to an empty bowl). Use the shell method to find the volume of water in the bowl as a function of h. (Check the special cases $h = 0$ and $h = 8$.)

50. Wedge from a tree Imagine a cylindrical tree of radius a. A wedge is cut from the tree by making two cuts: one in a horizontal plane P perpendicular to the axis of the cylinder, and one that makes an angle θ with P, intersecting P along a diameter of the cylinder (see figure). What is the volume of the wedge?

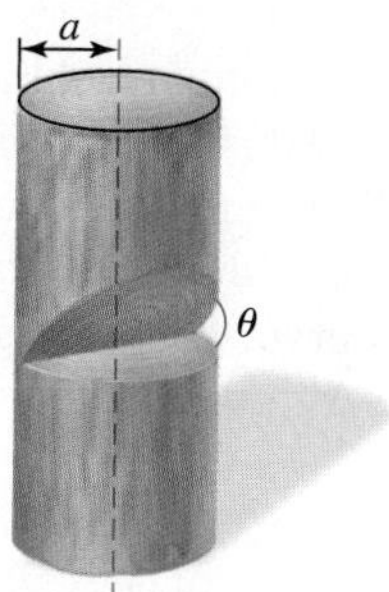

51. A torus (doughnut) Find the volume of the torus formed when a circle of radius 2 centered at $(3, 0)$ is revolved about the y-axis. Use the shell method. You may need a computer algebra system or table of integrals to evaluate the integral.

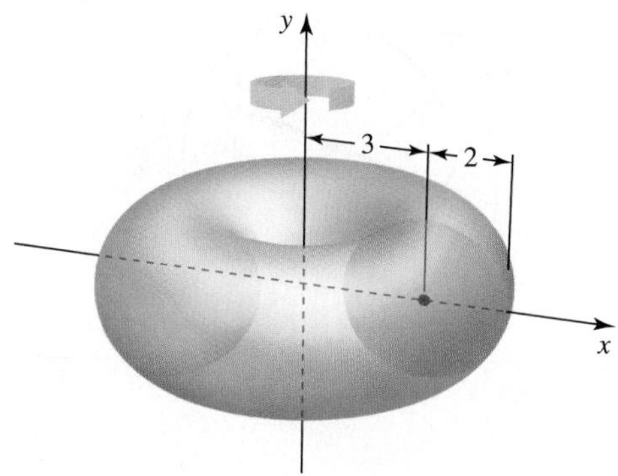

52. Different axes of revolution Suppose R is the region bounded by $y = f(x)$ and $y = g(x)$ on the interval $[a, b]$, where $f(x) \ge g(x)$.

a. Show that if R is revolved about the vertical line $x = x_0$, where $x_0 < a$, then by the shell method, the volume of the resulting solid is $V = \int_a^b 2\pi(x - x_0)(f(x) - g(x))\,dx$.

b. How is this formula changed if $x_0 > b$?

Additional Exercises

53. Ellipsoids An ellipse centered at the origin is described by the equation $x^2/a^2 + y^2/b^2 = 1$. If an ellipse R is revolved about either axis, the resulting solid is an *ellipsoid*.

a. Find the volume of the ellipsoid generated when R is revolved about the x-axis (in terms of a and b).

b. Find the volume of the ellipsoid generated when R is revolved about the y-axis (in terms of a and b).

c. Should the results of parts (a) and (b) agree? Explain.

54. Change of variables Suppose $f(x) > 0$ for all x and $\int_0^4 f(x)\,dx = 10$. Let R be the region in the first quadrant bounded by the coordinate axes, $y = f(x^2)$, and $x = 2$. Find the volume of the solid generated by revolving R around the y-axis.

55. Equal integrals Without evaluating integrals, explain why the following equalities are true. (*Hint:* Draw pictures.)

a. $\pi \int_0^4 (8 - 2x)^2\,dx = 2\pi \int_0^8 y\left(4 - \frac{y}{2}\right)dy$

b. $\int_0^2 (25 - (x^2 + 1)^2)\,dx = 2\int_1^5 y\sqrt{y - 1}\,dy$

56. Volumes without calculus Solve the following problems with *and* without calculus. A good picture helps!

a. A cube with side length r is inscribed in a sphere, which is inscribed in a right circular cone, which is inscribed in a right circular cylinder. The side length (slant height) of the cone is equal to its diameter. What is the volume of the cylinder?

b. A cube is inscribed in a right circular cone with a radius of 1 and a height of 3. What is the volume of the cube?

c. A cylindrical hole 10 in long is drilled symmetrically through the center of a sphere. How much material is left in the sphere? (There *is* enough information given.)

QUICK CHECK ANSWERS

1. $\int_0^1 2\pi x(2x)\,dx$ **2.** $V = \int_0^2 2\pi(y + 5)(y^2 + 2)\,dy$
3. The shell method is easier.

6.5 Length of Curves

A space shuttle orbits Earth in an elliptical path. How far does it travel in one orbit? A baseball slugger launches a home run into the upper deck and the sportscaster claims it landed 480 feet from home plate. But how far did the ball actually travel along its flight path? These questions deal with the length of trajectories or, more generally, with *arc length*. As you will see, their answers can be found by integration.

There are two common ways to formulate problems about arc length: The curve may be given explicitly in the form $y = f(x)$ or it may be defined *parametrically*. In this section we deal with the first case. Parametric curves are introduced in Section 11.1 and the associated arc length problem is discussed in Section 12.8.

Arc Length for $y = f(x)$

Suppose a curve is given by $y = f(x)$, where f is a function with a continuous first derivative on the interval $[a, b]$. The goal is to determine how far you would travel if you walked along the curve from $(a, f(a))$ to $(b, f(b))$. This distance is the arc length, which we denote L.

> More generally, we may choose any point in the kth subinterval and Δx may vary from one subinterval to the next. Using right endpoints, as we do here, simplifies the discussion and leads to the same result.

As shown in Figure 6.49, we divide $[a, b]$ into n subintervals of length $\Delta x = (b - a)/n$, where x_k is the right endpoint of the kth subinterval, for $k = 1, \ldots, n$. Joining the corresponding points on the curve by line segments, we obtain a polygonal line with n line segments. If n is large and Δx is small, the length of the polygonal line is a good approximation to the length of the actual curve. The strategy is to find the length of the polygonal line and then let n increase, while Δx goes to zero, to get the exact length of the curve.

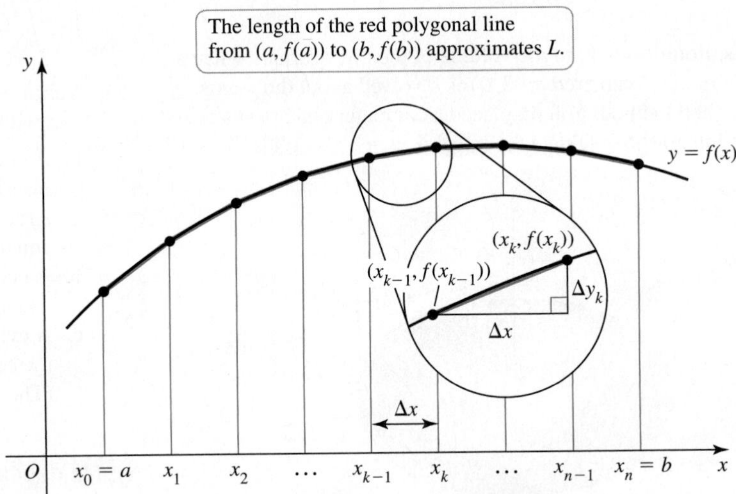

FIGURE 6.49

> Notice that Δx is the same for each subinterval, but Δy_k depends on the subinterval.

The kth segment of the polygonal line is the hypotenuse of a right triangle with sides of length Δx and $|\Delta y_k| = |f(x_k) - f(x_{k-1})|$. The length of each line segment is

$$\sqrt{(\Delta x)^2 + (\Delta y_k)^2}, \quad \text{for} \quad k = 1, 2, \ldots, n.$$

Summing these lengths, we obtain the length of the polygonal line, which approximates the length L of the curve:

$$L \approx \sum_{k=1}^{n} \sqrt{(\Delta x)^2 + (\Delta y_k)^2}$$

In previous applications of the integral, we would, at this point, take the limit as $n \to \infty$ and $\Delta x \to 0$ to obtain a definite integral. However, because of the presence of the Δy_k term, we must complete one additional step before taking a limit. Notice that the slope of the line segment on the kth subinterval is $\Delta y_k/\Delta x$ (rise over run). By the

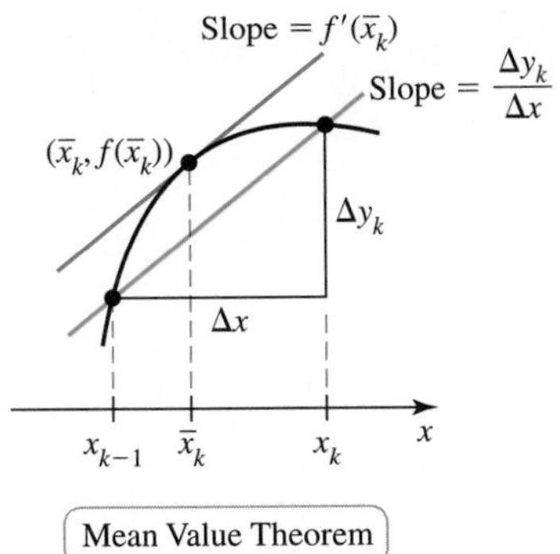

Mean Value Theorem (see the margin figure and Section 4.6), this slope equals $f'(\bar{x}_k)$, for some point $\bar{x}_k$ on the kth subinterval. Therefore,

$$\begin{aligned} L &\approx \sum_{k=1}^{n} \sqrt{(\Delta x)^2 + (\Delta y_k)^2} \\ &= \sum_{k=1}^{n} \sqrt{(\Delta x)^2 \left[1 + \left(\frac{\Delta y_k}{\Delta x}\right)^2\right]} && \text{Factor out } (\Delta x)^2. \\ &= \sum_{k=1}^{n} \sqrt{1 + \left(\frac{\Delta y_k}{\Delta x}\right)^2}\, \Delta x && \text{Bring } \Delta x \text{ out of the square root.} \\ &= \sum_{k=1}^{n} \sqrt{1 + f'(\bar{x}_k)^2}\, \Delta x. && \text{Mean Value Theorem} \end{aligned}$$

Now we have a Riemann sum. As n increases and as Δx approaches zero, the sum approaches a definite integral, which is also the length of the curve. We have

$$L = \lim_{n\to\infty} \sum_{k=1}^{n} \sqrt{1 + f'(\bar{x}_k)^2}\, \Delta x = \int_a^b \sqrt{1 + f'(x)^2}\, dx.$$

Note that $1 + f'(x)^2$ is positive, so the square root in the integrand is defined whenever f' exists. To ensure that $\sqrt{1 + f'(x)^2}$ is integrable on $[a, b]$, we require that f' be continuous on $[a, b]$.

DEFINITION Arc Length for $y = f(x)$

Let f have a continuous first derivative on the interval $[a, b]$. The length of the curve from $(a, f(a))$ to $(b, f(b))$ is

$$L = \int_a^b \sqrt{1 + f'(x)^2}\, dx.$$

QUICK CHECK 1 What does the arc length formula give for the length of the line $y = x$ between $x = 0$ and $x = a$, where $a \geq 0$?

EXAMPLE 1 Arc length Find the length of the curve $f(x) = x^{3/2}$ on the interval $[0, 4]$ (Figure 6.50).

FIGURE 6.50

SOLUTION Notice that $f'(x) = \frac{3}{2}x^{1/2}$, which is continuous on $[0, 4]$. Using the arc length formula, we have

$$\begin{aligned} L = \int_a^b \sqrt{1 + f'(x)^2}\, dx &= \int_0^4 \sqrt{1 + \left(\frac{3}{2}x^{1/2}\right)^2}\, dx && \text{Substitute for } f'(x). \\ &= \int_0^4 \sqrt{1 + \frac{9}{4}x}\, dx && \text{Simplify.} \\ &= \frac{4}{9}\int_1^{10} \sqrt{u}\, du && u = 1 + \frac{9x}{4},\ du = \frac{9}{4}dx \\ &= \frac{4}{9}\left(\frac{2}{3}u^{3/2}\right)\Big|_1^{10} && \text{Fundamental Theorem} \\ &= \frac{8}{27}(10^{3/2} - 1). && \text{Simplify.} \end{aligned}$$

The length of the curve is $\frac{8}{27}(10^{3/2} - 1) \approx 9.1$ units. *Related Exercises 3–10*

EXAMPLE 2 **Arc length calculation** Find the length of the curve $f(x) = x^3 + \frac{1}{12x}$ on the interval $\left[\frac{1}{2}, 2\right]$ (Figure 6.51).

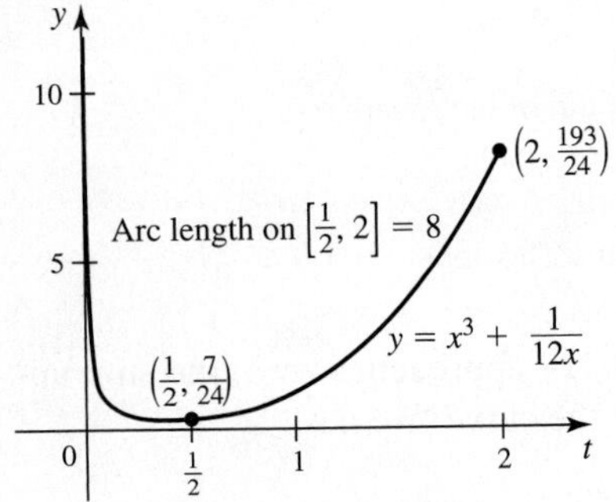

FIGURE 6.51

SOLUTION We first calculate $f'(x) = 3x^2 - \frac{1}{12x^2}$ and $f'(x)^2 = 9x^4 - \frac{1}{2} + \frac{1}{144x^4}$. The length of the curve on $\left[\frac{1}{2}, 2\right]$ is

$$\begin{aligned}
L &= \int_{1/2}^{2} \sqrt{1 + f'(x)^2}\, dx = \int_{1/2}^{2} \sqrt{1 + \left(9x^4 - \frac{1}{2} + \frac{1}{144x^4}\right)}\, dx && \text{Substitute.} \\
&= \int_{1/2}^{2} \sqrt{\left(3x^2 + \frac{1}{12x^2}\right)^2}\, dx && \text{Factor.} \\
&= \int_{1/2}^{2} \left(3x^2 + \frac{1}{12x^2}\right) dx && \text{Simplify.} \\
&= \left(x^3 - \frac{1}{12x}\right)\Bigg|_{1/2}^{2} = 8. && \text{Evaluate the integral.}
\end{aligned}$$

Related Exercises 3–10 ◄

EXAMPLE 3 **Looking ahead** Consider the segment of the parabola $f(x) = x^2$ on the interval $[0, 2]$.

a. Write the integral for the length of the curve.

b. Use a calculator to evaluate the integral.

SOLUTION

a. Noting that $f'(x) = 2x$, the arc length integral is

$$\int_0^2 \sqrt{1 + f'(x)^2}\, dx = \int_0^2 \sqrt{1 + 4x^2}\, dx.$$

b. Even simple functions can lead to arc length integrals that are difficult, if not impossible, to evaluate analytically. Using integration techniques presented so far, this integral cannot be evaluated (the required method is given in Section 8.3). Without an analytical method, we may use numerical integration to *approximate* the value of a definite integral (Section 8.6). Many calculators have built-in functions for this purpose. For this integral, the approximate arc length is

$$\int_0^2 \sqrt{1 + 4x^2}\, dx \approx 4.647.$$

Related Exercises 11–20 ◄

➤ When relying on technology, it is a good idea to check whether an answer is plausible. In Example 3, we found the arc length of $y = x^2$ on $[0, 2]$ is approximately 4.647. The straight-line distance between $(0, 0)$ and $(2, 4)$ is $\sqrt{20} \approx 4.472$, so our answer is reasonable.

Arc Length for $x = g(y)$

When evaluating arc length integrals, it is sometimes advantageous to describe a curve as a function of y—that is, $x = g(y)$. The arc length formula in this case is derived exactly as in the case of $y = f(x)$, switching the roles of x and y. The result is the following arc length formula.

QUICK CHECK 2 What does the arc length formula give for the length of the line $x = y$ between $y = c$ and $y = d$, where $d \geq c$? Is the result consistent with the result given by the Pythagorean theorem?

DEFINITION Arc Length for $x = g(y)$

Let $x = g(y)$ have a continuous first derivative on the interval $[c, d]$. The length of the curve from $(g(c), c)$ to $(g(d), d)$ is

$$L = \int_c^d \sqrt{1 + g'(y)^2}\, dy.$$

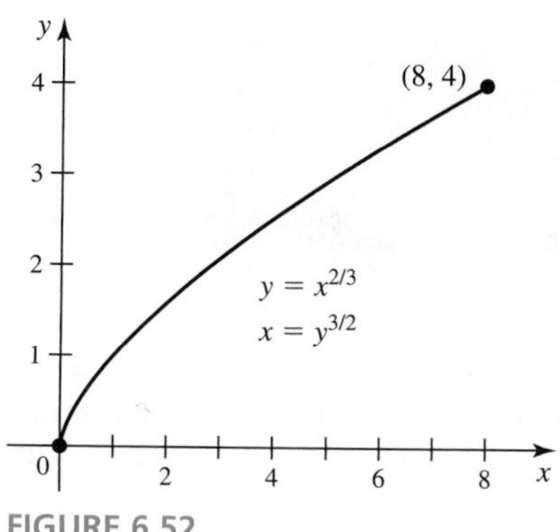

FIGURE 6.52

EXAMPLE 4 Arc length Find the length of the curve $y = f(x) = x^{2/3}$ between $x = 0$ and $x = 8$ (Figure 6.52).

SOLUTION The derivative of $f(x) = x^{2/3}$ is $f'(x) = \frac{2}{3}x^{-1/3}$, which is undefined at $x = 0$. Therefore, the arc length formula with respect to x cannot be used, yet the curve certainly appears to have a well-defined length.

The key is to describe the curve with y as the independent variable. Solving $y = x^{2/3}$ for x, we have $x = g(y) = \pm y^{3/2}$. Notice that when $x = 8$, $y = 8^{2/3} = 4$, which says that we should use the positive branch of $\pm y^{3/2}$. Therefore, finding the length of the curve $y = f(x) = x^{2/3}$ from $x = 0$ to $x = 8$ is equivalent to finding the length of the curve $x = g(y) = y^{3/2}$ from $y = 0$ to $y = 4$. This is precisely the problem solved in Example 1. The arc length is $\frac{8}{27}(10^{3/2} - 1) \approx 9.1$ units. *Related Exercises 21–24*

QUICK CHECK 3 Write the integral for the length of the curve $x = \sin y$ on the interval $0 \leq y \leq \pi$.

SECTION 6.5 EXERCISES

Review Questions

1. Explain the steps required to find the length of a curve $y = f(x)$ between $x = a$ and $x = b$.
2. Explain the steps required to find the length of a curve $x = g(y)$ between $y = c$ and $y = d$.

Basic Skills

3–10. Arc length calculations *Find the arc length of the following curves on the given interval by integrating with respect to x.*

3. $y = 2x + 1$; $[1, 5]$ (Use calculus.)
4. $y = \dfrac{x^3}{3} + \dfrac{1}{4x}$; $[1, 5]$
5. $y = \dfrac{1}{3}x^{3/2}$; $[0, 60]$
6. $y = \dfrac{3}{10}x^{1/3} - \dfrac{3}{2}x^{5/3}$; $[1, 3]$
7. $y = \dfrac{(x^2 + 2)^{3/2}}{3}$; $[0, 1]$
8. $y = \dfrac{x^{3/2}}{3} - x^{1/2}$; $[4, 16]$
9. $y = \dfrac{x^4}{4} + \dfrac{1}{8x^2}$; $[1, 2]$
10. $y = \frac{2}{3}x^{3/2} - \frac{1}{2}x^{1/2}$; $[1, 9]$

T **11–20. Arc length by calculator**

a. *Write and simplify the integral that gives the arc length of the following curves on the given interval.*
b. *If necessary, use a calculator to evaluate or approximate the integral.*

11. $y = x^2$; $[-1, 1]$
12. $y = \sin x$; $[0, \pi]$
13. $y = \tan x$; $[0, \pi/4]$
14. $y = \dfrac{x^3}{3}$; $[-1, 1]$
15. $y = \sqrt{x - 2}$; $[3, 4]$
16. $y = \dfrac{8}{x^2}$; $[1, 4]$
17. $y = \cos 2x$; $[0, \pi]$
18. $y = 4x - x^2$; $[0, 4]$
19. $y = \dfrac{1}{x}$; $[1, 10]$
20. $y = \dfrac{1}{x^2 + 1}$; $[-5, 5]$

T **21–24. Arc length calculations with respect to y** *Find the arc length of the following curves by integrating with respect to y.*

21. $x = 2y - 4$, for $-3 \leq y \leq 4$
22. $x = \dfrac{y^5}{5} + \dfrac{1}{12y^3}$, for $2 \leq y \leq 4$

23. $x = \frac{y^4}{4} + \frac{1}{8y^2}$, for $1 \le y \le 2$

24. $x = \frac{9}{4}y^{2/3} - \frac{1}{8}y^{4/3}$, for $1 \le y \le 2$

Further Explorations

25. **Explain why or why not** Determine whether the following statements are true and give an explanation or counterexample.

 a. $\int_a^b \sqrt{1 + f'(x)^2}\, dx = \int_a^b (1 + f'(x))\, dx$

 b. Assuming f' is continuous on the interval $[a, b]$, the length of the curve $y = f(x)$ on $[a, b]$ is the area under the curve $y = \sqrt{1 + f'(x)^2}$ on $[a, b]$.

 c. Arc length may be negative if $f(x) < 0$ on part of the interval in question.

26. **Arc length for a line** Consider the segment of the line $y = mx + c$ on the interval $[a, b]$. Use the arc length formula to show that the length of the line segment is $(b - a)\sqrt{1 + m^2}$. Verify this result by computing the length of the line segment using the distance formula.

27. **Functions from arc length** What differentiable functions have an arc length on the interval $[a, b]$ given by the following integrals? Note that the answers are not unique. Give a family of functions that satisfy the conditions.

 a. $\int_a^b \sqrt{1 + 16x^4}\, dx$ b. $\int_a^b \sqrt{1 + 36\cos^2(2x)}\, dx$

28. **Function from arc length** Find the equation of a curve that passes through the point $(1, 5)$ and has an arc length on the interval $[2, 6]$ given by $\int_2^6 \sqrt{1 + 16x^{-6}}\, dx$.

T 29. **Cosine vs. parabola** Which curve has the greater length on the interval $[-1, 1]$, $y = 1 - x^2$ or $y = \cos(\pi x/2)$?

30. **Function defined as an integral** Write the integral that gives the length of the curve $y = f(x) = \int_0^x \sin t\, dt$ on the interval $[0, \pi]$.

Applications

T 31. **Golden Gate cables** The profile of the cables on a suspension bridge may be modeled by a parabola. The central span of the Golden Gate Bridge (see figure) is 1280 m long and 152 m high. The parabola $y = 0.00037x^2$ gives a good fit to the shape of the cables, where $|x| \le 640$, and x and y are measured in meters. Approximate the length of the cables that stretch between the tops of the two towers.

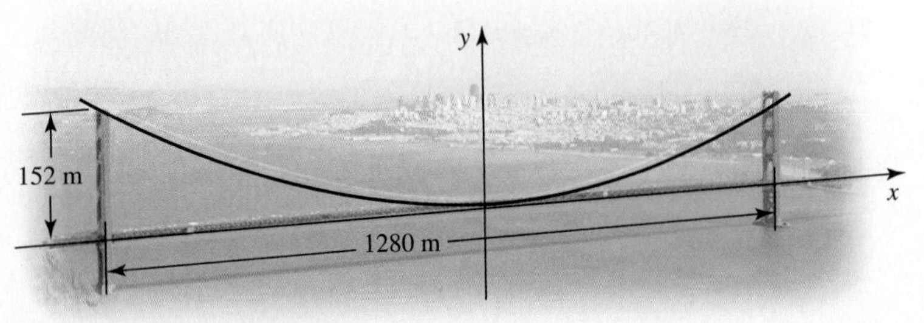

T 32. **Gateway Arch** The shape of the Gateway Arch in St. Louis (with a height and a base length of 630 ft) is modeled by the function $y = 630\left[1 - \left(\frac{x}{315}\right)^2\right]$, where $|x| \le 315$, and x and y are measured in feet (see figure). Estimate the length of the Gateway Arch.

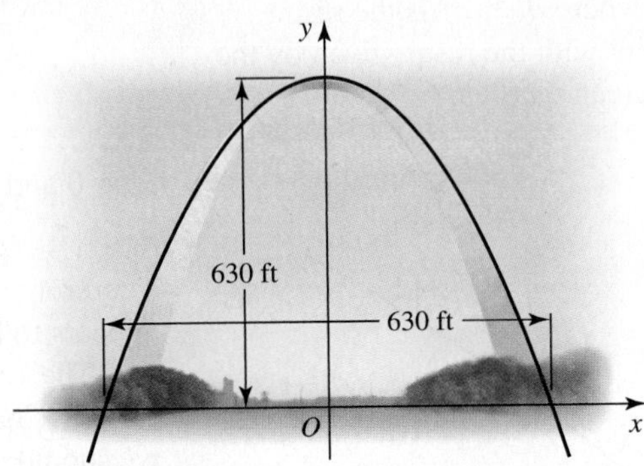

Additional Exercises

33. **Lengths of related curves** Suppose the graph of f on the interval $[a, b]$ has length L, where f' is continuous on $[a, b]$. Evaluate the following integrals in terms of L.

 a. $\int_{a/2}^{b/2} \sqrt{1 + f'(2x)^2}\, dx$ b. $\int_{a/c}^{b/c} \sqrt{1 + f'(cx)^2}\, dx$ if $c \ne 0$

34. **Lengths of symmetric curves** Suppose a curve is described by $y = f(x)$ on the interval $[-b, b]$, where f' is continuous on $[-b, b]$. Show that if f is symmetric about the origin (f is odd) *or* f is symmetric about the y-axis (f is even), then the length of the curve $y = f(x)$ from $x = -b$ to $x = b$ is twice the length of the curve from $x = 0$ to $x = b$. Use a geometric argument and then prove it analytically using calculus.

35. **A family of algebraic functions**

 a. Show that the arc length integral for the function $f(x) = ax^n + \frac{1}{4an(n - 2)x^{n-2}}$, where a and n are positive real numbers with $n \ne 2$, may be integrated using methods you already know.

 b. Verify that the arc length of the curve $y = f(x)$ on the interval $[1, 2]$ is

$$a(2^n - 1) + \frac{1 - 2^{2-n}}{4an(n - 2)}.$$

T 36. **Bernoulli's "parabolas"** Johann Bernoulli (1667–1748) evaluated the arc length of curves of the form $y = x^{(2n+1)/2n}$, where n is a positive integer, on the interval $[0, a]$.

 a. Write the arc length integral.

 b. Make the change of variables $u^2 = 1 + \left(\frac{2n + 1}{2n}\right)^2 x^{1/n}$ to obtain a new integral with respect to u.

 c. Use the Binomial Theorem to expand this integrand and evaluate the integral.

d. The case $n = 1$ $(y = x^{3/2})$ was considered in Example 1. With $a = 1$, evaluate the arc length in the cases $n = 2$ and $n = 3$. Does the arc length increase or decrease with n?

e. Graph the arc length of the parabolas for $a = 1$ as a function of n.

QUICK CHECK ANSWERS

1. $\sqrt{2}a$ (The length of the line segment joining the points)
2. $\sqrt{2}(d - c)$ (The length of the line segment joining the points)
3. $L = \int_0^\pi \sqrt{1 + \cos^2 y}\, dy$

6.6 Physical Applications

We conclude this chapter on applications of integration with several problems from physics and engineering. The physical themes in these problems are mass, work, pressure, and force. The common mathematical theme is the use of the slice-and-sum strategy, which always leads to a definite integral.

Density and Mass

Density is the concentration of mass in an object and is usually measured in units of mass per volume (for example, g/cm^3). An object with *uniform* density satisfies the basic relationship

$$\text{mass} = \text{density} \cdot \text{volume}.$$

When the density of an object *varies*, this formula no longer holds, and we must appeal to calculus.

In this section we introduce mass calculations for thin objects that can be viewed as line segments (such as wires or thin bars). The bar shown in Figure 6.53 has a density ρ that varies along its length. For one-dimensional objects we use *linear density* with units of mass per length (for example, g/cm). What is the mass of such an object?

> In Chapter 14, we return to mass calculations for two- and three-dimensional objects (plates and solids).

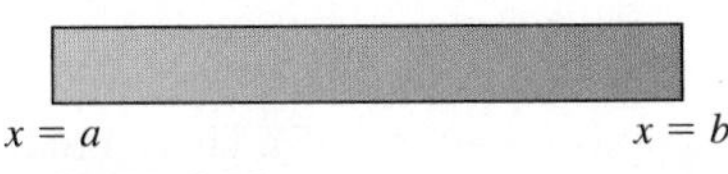

FIGURE 6.53

QUICK CHECK 1 In Figure 6.53, suppose $a = 0$, $b = 3$, and the density of the rod in g/cm is $\rho(x) = (4 - x)$. (a) Where is the rod lightest and heaviest? (b) What is the density at the middle of the bar?

We begin by dividing the bar, represented by the interval $a \le x \le b$, into n subintervals of equal length $\Delta x = (b - a)/n$ (Figure 6.54). Let $\bar{x}_k$ be any point in the kth subinterval, for $k = 1, \ldots, n$. The mass of the kth segment of the bar, denoted m_k, is approximately the density at $\bar{x}_k$ multiplied by the length of the interval, or $m_k \approx \rho(\bar{x}_k)\,\Delta x$. So the approximate mass of the entire bar is

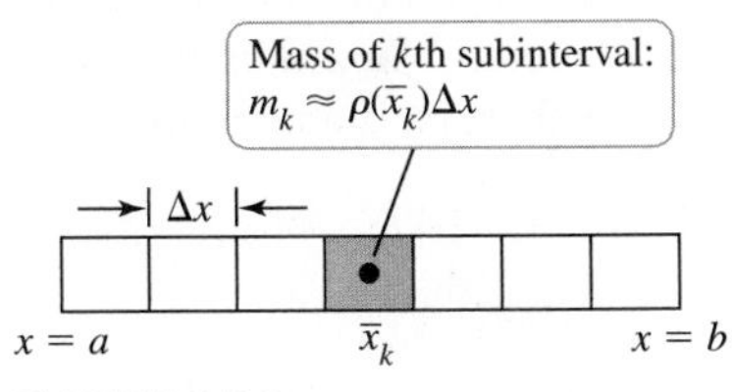

FIGURE 6.54

$$\sum_{k=1}^{n} m_k \approx \sum_{k=1}^{n} \underbrace{\rho(\bar{x}_k)\,\Delta x}_{m_k}.$$

The exact mass is obtained by taking the limit as $n \to \infty$ and as $\Delta x \to 0$, which produces a definite integral.

> Note that the units of the integral work out as they should: ρ has units of mass per length and dx has units of length; so $\rho(x)\,dx$ has units of mass.

> Another interpretation of the mass integral is that mass equals the average value of the density multiplied by the length of the bar $b - a$.

DEFINITION Mass of a One-Dimensional Object

Suppose a thin bar or wire is represented by a line segment on the interval $a \le x \le b$ with a density function ρ (with units of mass per length). The **mass** of the object is

$$m = \int_a^b \rho(x)\,dx.$$

EXAMPLE 1 **Mass from variable density** A thin 2-m bar, represented by the interval $0 \leq x \leq 2$, is made of an alloy whose density in units of kg/m is given by $\rho(x) = (1 + x^2)$. What is the mass of the bar?

SOLUTION The mass of the bar in kilograms is

$$m = \int_a^b \rho(x)\,dx = \int_0^2 (1 + x^2)\,dx = \left(x + \frac{x^3}{3}\right)\Big|_0^2 = \frac{14}{3}.$$

Related Exercises 9–16 ◀

QUICK CHECK 2 A thin bar occupies the interval $0 \leq x \leq 2$ and it has a density in kg/m of $\rho(x) = 1 + x^2$. Using the minimum value of the density, what is a lower bound for the mass of the object? Using the maximum value of the density, what is an upper bound for the mass of the object? ◀

Work

Work can be described as the change in energy when a force causes a displacement of an object. When you carry a refrigerator up a flight of stairs or push a stalled car, you apply a force that results in the displacement of an object, and work is done. If a *constant* force F displaces an object a distance d in the direction of the force, the work done is the force multiplied by the distance:

$$\text{work} = \text{force} \cdot \text{distance}$$

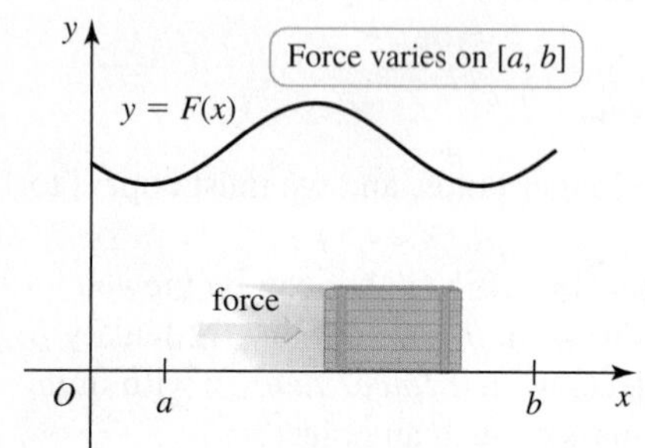

FIGURE 6.55

It is easiest to use metric units for force and work. A newton (N) is the force required to give a 1-kg mass an acceleration of 1 m/s^2. A joule (J) is 1 newton-meter (N m), the work done by a 1-N force over a distance of 1 m.

Calculus enters the picture with *variable* forces. Suppose an object is moved along the x-axis by a variable force F that is directed along the x-axis (Figure 6.55). How much work is done in moving the object between $x = a$ and $x = b$? Once again, we use the slice-and-sum strategy.

The interval $[a, b]$ is divided into n subintervals of equal length $\Delta x = (b - a)/n$. We let $\overline{x}_k$ be any point in the kth subinterval, for $k = 1, \ldots, n$. On that subinterval the force is approximately constant with a value of $F(\overline{x}_k)$. Therefore, the work done in moving the object across the kth subinterval is approximately $F(\overline{x}_k)\Delta x$ (force · distance). Summing the work done over each of the n subintervals, the total work over the interval $[a, b]$ is approximately

$$W \approx \sum_{k=1}^{n} F(\overline{x}_k)\Delta x.$$

QUICK CHECK 3 Explain why the sum of the work over n subintervals is only an approximation to the total work. ◀

This approximation becomes exact when we take the limit as $n \to \infty$ and $\Delta x \to 0$. The total work done is the integral of the force over the interval $[a, b]$ (or, equivalently, the net area under the force curve in Figure 6.55).

> **DEFINITION** **Work**
>
> The work done by a variable force F in moving an object along a line from $x = a$ to $x = b$ in the direction of the force is
>
> $$W = \int_a^b F(x)\,dx.$$

An application of force and work that is easy to visualize is the stretching and compression of a spring. Suppose an object is attached to a spring on a frictionless horizontal surface; the object slides back and forth under the influence of the spring. We say that the spring is at *equilibrium* when it is neither compressed nor stretched. It is convenient to let x be the position of the object, where $x = 0$ is the equilibrium position (Figure 6.56).

➤ Hooke's law was proposed by the English scientist Robert Hooke (1635–1703), who also coined the biological term *cell*.

Larger values of the spring constant k correspond to stiffer springs. Hooke's law works well for springs made of many common materials. However, some springs obey more complicated (nonlinear) spring laws (see Exercise 41).

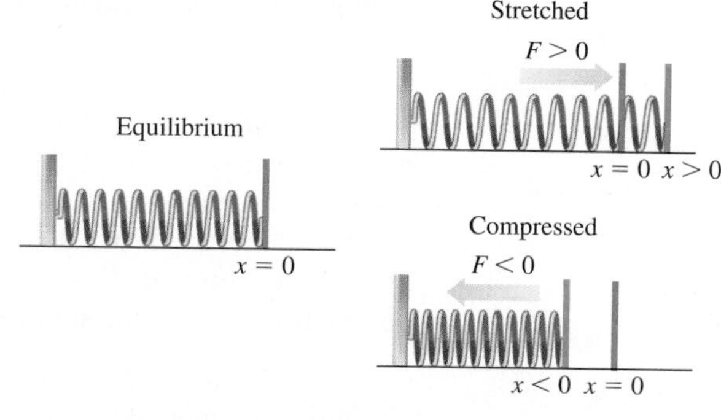

FIGURE 6.56

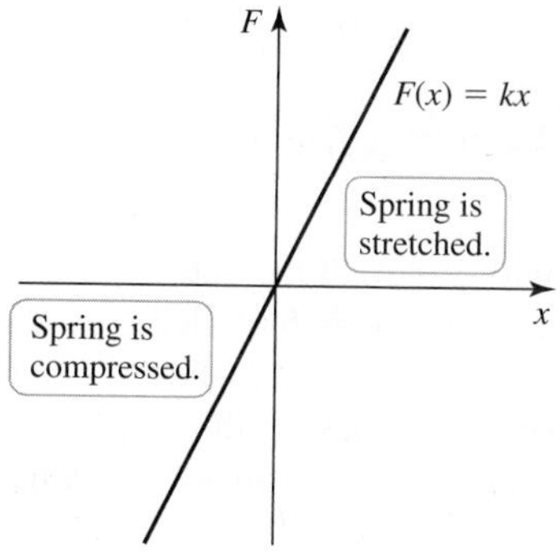

F(x) = kx

Spring is stretched.

Spring is compressed.

FIGURE 6.57

According to **Hooke's law**, the force required to keep the spring in a compressed or stretched position x units from the equilibrium position is $F(x) = kx$, where the spring constant k measures the stiffness of the spring. Note that to stretch the spring to a position $x > 0$, a force $F > 0$ (in the positive direction) is required. To compress the spring to a position $x < 0$, a force $F < 0$ (in the negative direction) is required (Figure 6.57). In other words, the force required to displace the spring is always in the direction of the displacement.

EXAMPLE 2 **Compressing a spring** Suppose a force of 10 N is required to stretch a spring 0.1 m from its equilibrium position and hold it in that position.

a. Assuming that the spring obeys Hooke's law, find the spring constant k.

b. How much work is needed to *compress* the spring 0.5 m from its equilibrium position?

c. How much work is needed to *stretch* the spring 0.25 m from its equilibrium position?

d. How much additional work is required to stretch the spring 0.25 m if it has already been stretched 0.1 m from its equilibrium position?

SOLUTION

a. The fact that a force of 10 N is required to keep the spring stretched at $x = 0.1$ m means (by Hooke's law) that $F(0.1) = k(0.1\text{ m}) = 10$ N. Solving for the spring constant, we find that $k = 100\text{ N/m}$. Therefore, Hooke's law for this spring is $F(x) = 100x$.

b. The work in joules required to compress the spring from $x = 0$ to $x = -0.5$ is

$$W = \int_a^b F(x)\,dx = \int_0^{-0.5} 100x\,dx = 50x^2\Big|_0^{-0.5} = 12.5.$$

➤ Notice again that the units in the integral are consistent. If F has units of N and x has units of m, then W has units of $F\,dx$, or N m, which are the units of work (1 N m = 1 J).

c. The work in joules required to stretch the spring from $x = 0$ to $x = 0.25$ is

$$W = \int_a^b F(x)\,dx = \int_0^{0.25} 100x\,dx = 50x^2\Big|_0^{0.25} = 3.125.$$

d. The work in joules required to stretch the spring from $x = 0.1$ to $x = 0.35$ is

$$W = \int_a^b F(x)\,dx = \int_{0.1}^{0.35} 100x\,dx = 50x^2\Big|_{0.1}^{0.35} = 5.625.$$

Comparing parts (c) and (d), we see that more work is required to stretch the spring 0.25 m starting at $x = 0.1$ than starting at $x = 0$.

Related Exercises 17–22 ◀

QUICK CHECK 4 In Example 2, explain why more work is needed in part (d) than in part (c), even though the displacement is the same. ◀

Lifting Problems Another common work problem arises when the motion is vertical and the force is the gravitational force. The gravitational force exerted on an object with a mass of m is $F = mg$, where $g \approx 9.8\ \text{m/s}^2$ is the acceleration due to gravity near Earth's surface. The work in joules required to lift an object of mass m a vertical distance of y meters is

$$\text{work} = \text{force} \cdot \text{distance} = mgy.$$

This type of problem becomes interesting when the object being lifted is a body of water, a rope, or chain. In these situations, different parts of the object are lifted different distances—so integration is necessary. Here is a typical situation and the strategy used.

Suppose a fluid such as water is pumped out of a tank to a height h above the bottom of the tank. How much work is required, assuming the tank is full of water? Three key observations lead to the solution:

- Water from different levels of the tank is lifted different vertical distances, requiring different amounts of work.
- Water from the same horizontal plane is lifted the same distance, requiring the same amount of work.
- A volume V of water has mass ρV, where $\rho = 1\ \text{g/cm}^3 = 1000\ \text{kg/m}^3$ is the density of water.

➤ The choice of a coordinate system is somewhat arbitrary and may depend on the geometry of the problem. You can let the y-axis point upward or downward, and there are usually several logical choices for the location of $y = 0$. You should experiment with different coordinate systems.

To solve this problem, we let the y-axis point upward with $y = 0$ at the bottom of the tank. The body of water that must be lifted extends from $y = 0$ to $y = b$ (which *may* be the top of the tank). The level to which the water must be raised is $y = h$, where $h \geq b$ (Figure 6.58). We now slice the water into n horizontal layers, each having thickness Δy. The kth layer occupying the interval $[y_{k-1}, y_k]$, for $k = 1, \ldots, n$, is approximately $\bar{y}_k$ units above the bottom of the tank, where $\bar{y}_k$ is any point in $[y_{k-1}, y_k]$.

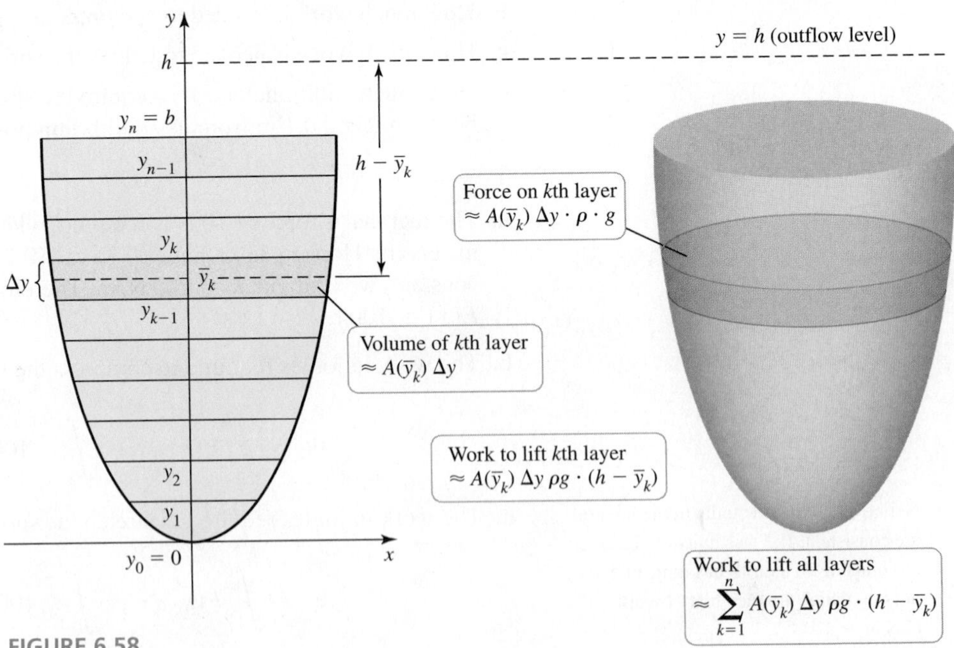

FIGURE 6.58

The cross-sectional area of the kth layer at $\bar{y}_k$, denoted $A(\bar{y}_k)$, is determined by the shape of the tank; the solution depends on being able to find A for all values of y. Because the volume of the kth layer is approximately $A(\bar{y}_k)\,\Delta y$, the force on the kth layer (its weight) is

$$F_k = mg \approx \overbrace{\underbrace{A(\bar{y}_k)\,\Delta y}_{\text{volume}} \cdot \underbrace{\rho}_{\text{density}}}^{\text{mass}} \cdot g.$$

To reach the level $y = h$, the kth layer is lifted an approximate distance of $(h - \bar{y}_k)$ (Figure 6.58). So the work in lifting the kth layer to a height h is approximately

$$W_k = \underbrace{A(\bar{y}_k)\,\Delta y \rho g}_{\text{force}} \cdot \underbrace{(h - \bar{y}_k)}_{\text{distance}}.$$

Summing the work required to lift all the layers to a height h, the total work is

$$W \approx \sum_{k=1}^{n} W_k = \sum_{k=1}^{n} A(\bar{y}_k)\rho g(h - \bar{y}_k)\,\Delta y.$$

This approximation becomes more accurate as the width of the layers Δy tends to zero and the number of layers tends to infinity. In this limit, we obtain a definite integral from $y = 0$ to $y = b$. The total work required to empty the tank is

$$W = \lim_{n\to\infty} \sum_{k=1}^{n} A(\bar{y}_k)\rho g(h - \bar{y}_k)\,\Delta y = \int_0^b \rho g A(y)(h - y)\,dy.$$

This derivation assumes that the *bottom* of the tank is at $y = 0$, in which case the distance that the slice at level y must be lifted is $D(y) = h - y$. If you choose a different location for the origin, the function D will be different. Here is a general procedure for any choice of origin.

Solving Lifting Problems

1. Draw a y-axis in the vertical direction and choose a convenient origin. Assume the interval $[a, b]$ corresponds to the vertical extent of the fluid.
2. For $a \le y \le b$, find the cross-sectional area $A(y)$ of the horizontal slices and the distance $D(y)$ the slices must be lifted.
3. The work required to lift the water is

$$W = \int_a^b \rho g A(y) D(y)\,dy.$$

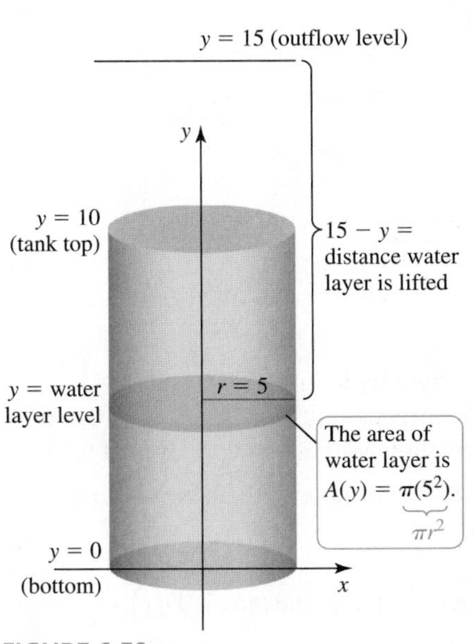

FIGURE 6.59

EXAMPLE 3 **Pumping water** How much work is needed to pump all the water out of a cylindrical tank with a height of 10 m and a radius of 5 m? The water is pumped to an outflow pipe 15 m above the bottom of the tank.

SOLUTION Figure 6.59 shows the cylindrical tank filled to capacity and the outflow 15 m above the bottom of the tank. We let $y = 0$ represent the bottom of the tank and $y = 10$ represent the top of the tank. In this case, all horizontal slices are circular disks of radius $r = 5$ m. Therefore, for $0 \le y \le 10$, the cross-sectional area is

$$A(y) = \pi r^2 = \pi 5^2 = 25\pi.$$

Note that the water is pumped to a level $h = 15$ m above the bottom of the tank, so the lifting distance is $D(y) = 15 - y$. The resulting work integral is

$$W = \int_0^{10} \rho g \underbrace{A(y)}_{25\pi} \underbrace{D(y)}_{15-y}\,dy = 25\pi\rho g \int_0^{10} (15 - y)\,dy.$$

Recall that $g \approx 9.8\ \text{m/s}^2$. You should verify that the units are consistent in this calculation: The units of ρ, g, $A(y)$, $D(y)$, and dy are kg/m^3, m/s^2, m^2, m, and m, respectively. The resulting units of W are $\text{kg} \cdot \text{m}^2/\text{s}^2$, or J. A more convenient unit for large amounts of work and energy is the kilowatt-hr, which is 3.6 million joules.

Substituting $\rho = 1000\ \text{kg/m}^3$ and $g = 9.8\ \text{m/s}^2$, the total work is

$$W = 25\pi\rho g \int_0^{10} (15 - y)\, dy$$

$$= 25\pi \underbrace{(1000)}_{\rho} \underbrace{(9.8)}_{g} \left(15y - \frac{1}{2}y^2 \right) \Big|_0^{10}$$

$$\approx 7.7 \times 10^7.$$

The work required to pump the water out of the tank is approximately 77 million J.

Related Exercises 23–29

QUICK CHECK 5 In the previous example, how would the integral change if the outflow pipe were at the top of the tank?

EXAMPLE 4 **Pumping gasoline** A cylindrical tank with a length of 10 m and a radius of 5 m is on its side and half-full of gasoline (Figure 6.60). How much work is required to empty the tank through an outlet pipe at the top of the tank? The density of gasoline is $\rho \approx 737\ \text{kg/m}^3$.

The equation of the right side of the circle is $x = \sqrt{25 - y^2}$.

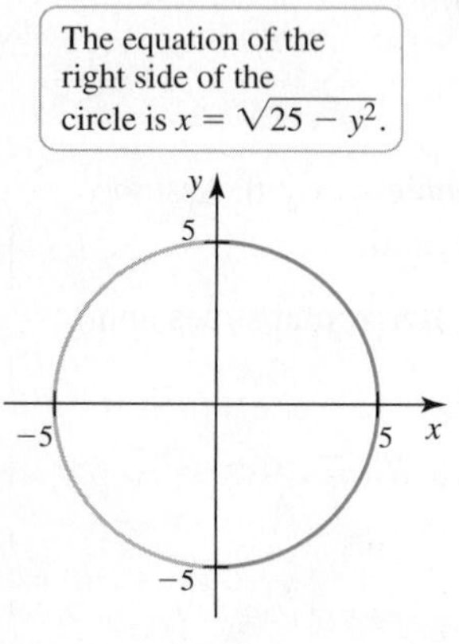

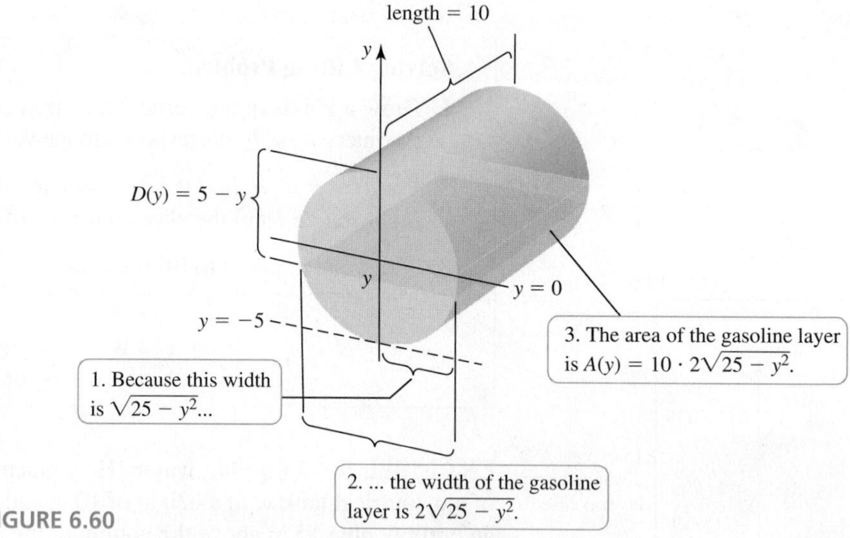

FIGURE 6.60

Again, there are several choices for the location of the origin. The location in this example makes $A(y)$ easy to compute.

SOLUTION In this problem we choose a different origin by letting $y = 0$ and $y = -5$ correspond to the center and the bottom of the tank, respectively. For $-5 \le y \le 0$, a horizontal layer of gasoline located at a depth y is a rectangle with a length of 10 and width of $2\sqrt{25 - y^2}$ (Figure 6.60). Therefore, the cross-sectional area of the layer at depth y is

$$A(y) = 20\sqrt{25 - y^2}.$$

The distance the layer at level y must be lifted to reach the top of the tank is $D(y) = 5 - y$, where $5 \le D(y) \le 10$. The resulting work integral is

$$W = \underbrace{737}_{\rho}\underbrace{(9.8)}_{g} \int_{-5}^{0} \underbrace{20\sqrt{25 - y^2}}_{A(y)}\, \underbrace{(5 - y)}_{D(y)}\, dy = 144{,}452 \int_{-5}^{0} \sqrt{25 - y^2}\,(5 - y)\, dy.$$

This integral is evaluated by splitting it into two pieces and recognizing that one piece is the area of a quarter circle of radius 5:

$$\int_{-5}^{0} \sqrt{25 - y^2}\,(5 - y)\,dy = 5\underbrace{\int_{-5}^{0} \sqrt{25 - y^2}\,dy}_{\text{area of quarter circle}} - \underbrace{\int_{-5}^{0} y\sqrt{25 - y^2}\,dy}_{\text{let } u = 25 - y^2;\ du = -2y\,dy}$$

$$= 5 \cdot \frac{25\pi}{4} + \frac{1}{2}\int_{0}^{25} \sqrt{u}\,du$$

$$= \frac{125\pi}{4} + \frac{1}{3}u^{3/2}\Big|_{0}^{25} = \frac{375\pi + 500}{12}.$$

Multiplying this result by 144,452, we find that the work required is approximately 20.2 million joules.

Related Exercises 23–29

Force and Pressure

Another application of integration deals with the force exerted on a surface by a body of water. Again, we need a few physical principles.

Pressure is a force per unit area, measured in units such as newtons per square meter (N/m^2). For example, the pressure of the atmosphere on the surface of Earth is about $14\ \text{lb}/\text{in}^2$ (approximately 100 kilopascals, or $10^5\ \text{N}/\text{m}^2$). As another example, if you stood on the bottom of a swimming pool, you would feel pressure due to the weight (force) of the column of water above your head. If your head is flat and has surface area $A\ \text{m}^2$ and it is h meters below the surface, then the column of water above your head has volume $Ah\ \text{m}^3$. That column of water exerts a force:

$$F = \text{mass} \cdot \text{acceleration} = \underbrace{\text{volume} \cdot \text{density}}_{\text{mass}} \cdot\, g = Ah\rho g,$$

where ρ is the density of water and g is the acceleration due to gravity. Therefore, the pressure on your head is the force divided by the surface area of your head:

$$\text{pressure} = \frac{\text{force}}{A} = \frac{Ah\rho g}{A} = \rho g h.$$

➤ We have chosen $y = 0$ to be the base of the dam. Depending on the geometry of the problem, it may be more convenient (less computation) to let $y = 0$ be at the top of the dam. Experiment with different choices.

This pressure is called **hydrostatic pressure** (meaning the pressure of *water at rest*), and it has the following important property: *It has the same magnitude in all directions*. Specifically, the hydrostatic pressure on a vertical wall of the swimming pool at a depth h is also $\rho g h$. This is the only fact needed to find the total force on vertical walls such as dams. We assume that the water completely covers the face of the dam.

The first step in finding the force on the face of the dam is to introduce a coordinate system. We choose a y-axis pointing upward with $y = 0$ corresponding to the base of the dam and $y = a$ corresponding to the top of the dam (Figure 6.61). Because the pressure varies with depth (y-direction), the dam is sliced horizontally into n strips of equal thickness Δy. The kth strip corresponds to the interval $[y_{k-1}, y_k]$, and we let $\bar{y}_k$ be any point in that interval. The depth of that strip is approximately $h = a - \bar{y}_k$, so the hydrostatic pressure on that strip is approximately $\rho g(a - \bar{y}_k)$.

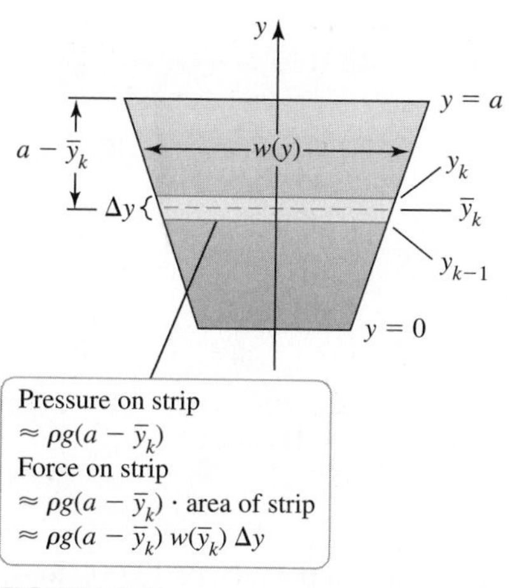

FIGURE 6.61

The crux of any dam problem is finding the width of the strips as a function of y, which we denote $w(y)$. Each dam has its own width function; however, once the width function is known, the solution follows directly. The approximate area of the kth strip is its width multiplied by its thickness, or $w(\bar{y}_k)\,\Delta y$. The force on the kth strip (which is the area of the strip multiplied by the pressure) is approximately

$$F_k = \underbrace{w(\bar{y}_k)\,\Delta y}_{\text{area of strip}}\ \underbrace{\rho g(a - \bar{y}_k)}_{\text{pressure}}.$$

Summing the forces over the n strips, the total force is approximately

$$F \approx \sum_{k=1}^{n} F_k = \sum_{k=1}^{n} \rho g(a - \bar{y}_k)w(\bar{y}_k)\,\Delta y.$$

To find the exact force, we let the thickness of the strips tend to zero and the number of strips tend to infinity, which produces a definite integral. The limits of integration correspond to the base ($y = 0$) and top ($y = a$) of the dam. Therefore, the total force on the dam is

$$F = \lim_{n \to \infty} \sum_{k=1}^{n} \rho g(a - \bar{y}_k)w(\bar{y}_k)\,\Delta y = \int_0^a \rho g(a - y)w(y)\,dy.$$

Solving Force/Pressure Problems

1. Draw a y-axis on the face of the dam in the vertical direction and choose a convenient origin (often taken to be the base of the dam).
2. Find the function $w(y)$ that gives the width of the dam for $0 \le y \le a$.
3. If the base of the dam is at $y = 0$ and the top of the dam is at $y = a$, then the total force on the dam is

$$F = \int_0^a \rho g \underbrace{(a - y)}_{\text{depth}} \underbrace{w(y)}_{\text{width}}\,dy.$$

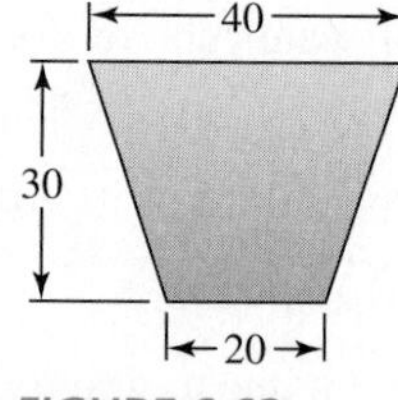

FIGURE 6.62

EXAMPLE 5 **Pressure on a dam** A large vertical dam in the shape of a symmetric trapezoid has a height of 30 m, a width of 20 m at its base, and a width of 40 m at the top (Figure 6.62). What is the total force on the face of the dam when the reservoir is full?

SOLUTION We place the origin at the center of the base of the dam (Figure 6.63). The right slanted edge of the dam is a segment of the line that passes through the points $(10, 0)$ and $(20, 30)$. An equation of that line is

$$y - 0 = \frac{30}{10}(x - 10) \quad \text{or} \quad y = 3x - 30 \quad \text{or} \quad x = \frac{1}{3}(y + 30).$$

➤ You should check the width function: $w(0) = 20$ (the width of the dam at its base) and $w(30) = 40$ (the width of the dam at its top).

Notice that at a depth of y, where $0 \le y \le 30$, the width of the dam is

$$w(y) = 2x = \frac{2}{3}(y + 30).$$

Using $\rho = 1000\text{ kg/m}^3$ and $g = 9.8\text{ m/s}^2$, the total force on the dam in newtons is

$$\begin{aligned} F &= \int_0^a \rho g(a - y)w(y)\,dy && \text{Force integral} \\ &= \rho g \int_0^{30} \underbrace{(30 - y)}_{a - y} \underbrace{\frac{2}{3}(y + 30)}_{w(y)}\,dy && \text{Substitute.} \\ &= \frac{2}{3}\rho g \int_0^{30} (900 - y^2)\,dy && \text{Simplify.} \\ &= \frac{2}{3}\rho g\left(900y - \frac{y^3}{3}\right)\Bigg|_0^{30} && \text{Fundamental Theorem} \\ &\approx 1.18 \times 10^8. \end{aligned}$$

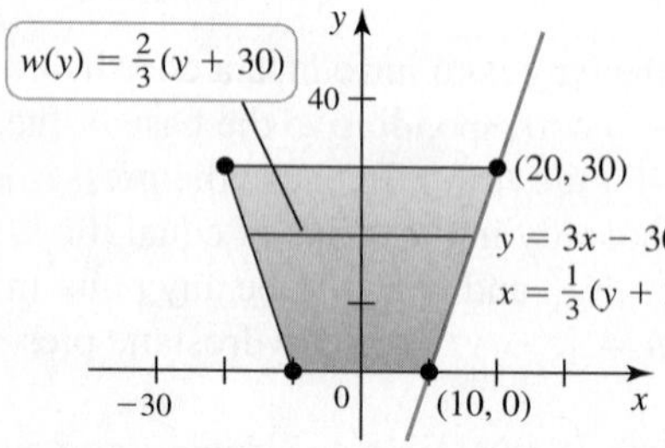

FIGURE 6.63

The force of 1.18×10^8 N on the dam amounts to about 26 million pounds, or 13,000 tons.

Related Exercises 30–38 ◄

SECTION 6.6 EXERCISES

Review Questions

1. If a 1-m cylindrical bar has a constant density of 1 g/cm for its left half and a constant density 2 g/cm for its right half, what is its mass?

2. Explain how to find the mass of a one-dimensional object with a variable density ρ.

3. Explain how to find the work done in moving an object along a line in the direction of a constant force.

4. Why must integration be used to find the work done by a variable force?

5. Why must integration be used to find the work required to pump water out of a tank?

6. Why must integration be used to find the total force on the face of a dam?

7. What is the pressure on a horizontal surface with an area of 2 m^2 that is 4 m underwater?

8. Explain why you integrate in the vertical direction (parallel to the acceleration due to gravity) rather than the horizontal direction to find the force on the face of a dam.

Basic Skills

9–16. Mass of one-dimensional objects *Find the mass of the following thin bars with the given density function.*

9. $\rho(x) = 1 + \sin x$, for $0 \le x \le \pi$

10. $\rho(x) = 1 + x^3$, for $0 \le x \le 1$

11. $\rho(x) = 2 - x/2$, for $0 \le x \le 2$

12. $\rho(x) = 1 + 3 \sin x$, for $0 \le x \le \pi$

13. $\rho(x) = x\sqrt{2 - x^2}$, for $0 \le x \le 1$

14. $\rho(x) = \begin{cases} 1 & \text{if } 0 \le x \le 2 \\ 2 & \text{if } 2 < x \le 3 \end{cases}$

15. $\rho(x) = \begin{cases} 1 & \text{if } 0 \le x \le 2 \\ 1 + x & \text{if } 2 < x \le 4 \end{cases}$

16. $\rho(x) = \begin{cases} x^2 & \text{if } 0 \le x \le 1 \\ x(2 - x) & \text{if } 1 < x \le 2 \end{cases}$

17. **Work from force** How much work is required to move an object from $x = 0$ to $x = 5$ (measured in meters) in the presence of a constant force of 5 N acting along the x-axis?

18. **Work from force** How much work is required to move an object from $x = 1$ to $x = 3$ (measured in meters) in the presence of a force (in N) given by $F(x) = 2/x^2$ acting along the x-axis?

19. **Working a spring** A spring on a horizontal surface can be stretched and held 0.5 m from its equilibrium position with a force of 50 N.
    a. How much work is done in stretching the spring 1.5 m from its equilibrium position?
    b. How much work is done in compressing the spring 0.5 m from its equilibrium position?

20. **Shock absorber** A heavy-duty shock absorber is compressed 2 cm from its equilibrium position by a mass of 500 kg. How much work is required to compress the shock absorber 4 cm from its equilibrium position? (A mass of 500 kg exerts a force (in N) of $500g$, where $g \approx 9.8\,\text{m/s}^2$.)

21. **Additional stretch** It takes 100 J of work to stretch a spring 0.5 m from its equilibrium position. How much work is needed to stretch it an additional 0.75 m?

22. **Work function** A spring has a restoring force given by $F(x) = 25x$. Let $W(x)$ be the work required to stretch the spring from its equilibrium position ($x = 0$) to a variable distance x. Graph the work function. Compare the work required to stretch the spring x units from equilibrium to the work required to compress the spring x units from equilibrium.

23. **Emptying a swimming pool** A swimming pool has the shape of a box with a base that measures 25 m by 15 m and a depth of 2.5 m. How much work is required to pump the water out of the pool when it is full?

24. **Emptying a cylindrical tank** A cylindrical water tank has height 8 m and radius 2 m (see figure).
    a. If the tank is full of water, how much work is required to pump the water to the level of the top of the tank and out of the tank?
    b. Is it true that it takes half as much work to pump the water out of the tank when it is half full as when it is full? Explain.

25. **Emptying a conical tank** A water tank is shaped like an inverted cone with height 6 m and base radius 1.5 m (see figure).
    a. If the tank is full, how much work is required to pump the water to the level of the top of the tank and out of the tank?
    b. Is it true that it takes half as much work to pump the water out of the tank when it is filled to half its depth as when it is full? Explain.

26. **Emptying a real swimming pool** A swimming pool is 20 m long and 10 m wide, with a bottom that slopes uniformly from a depth of 1 m at one end to a depth of 2 m at the other end (see figure). Assuming the pool is full, how much work is required to pump the water to a level 0.2 m above the top of the pool?

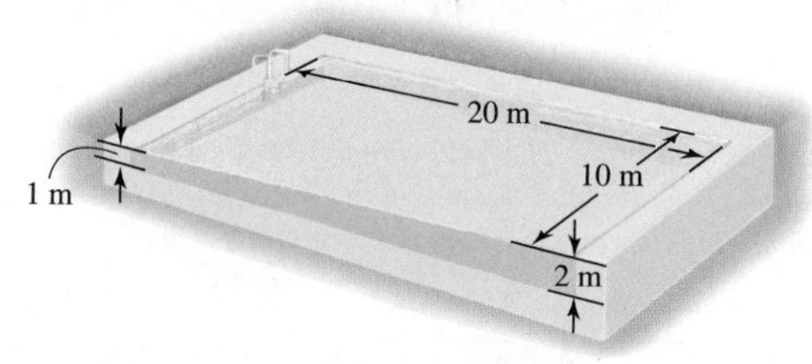

27. **Filling a spherical tank** A spherical water tank with an inner radius of 8 m has its lowest point 2 m above the ground. It is filled by a pipe that feeds the tank at its lowest point (see figure).
   a. Neglecting the volume of the inflow pipe, how much work is required to fill the tank if it is initially empty?
   b. Now assume that the inflow pipe feeds the tank at the top of the tank. Neglecting the volume of the inflow pipe, how much work is required to fill the tank if it is initially empty?

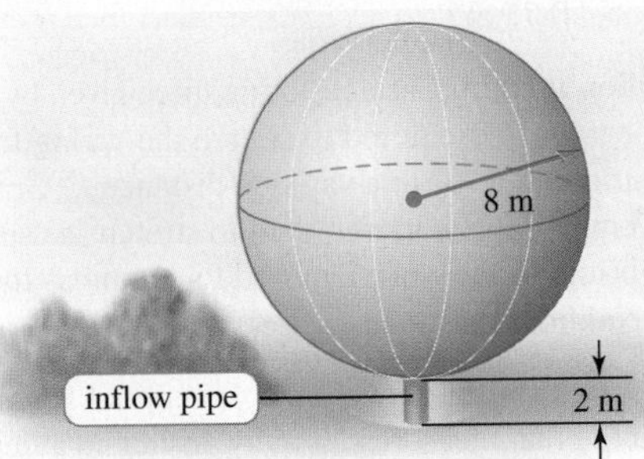

28. **Emptying a water trough** A water trough has a semicircular cross section with a radius of 0.25 m and a length of 3 m (see figure).
   a. How much work is required to pump water out of the trough (to the level of the top of the trough) when it is full?
   b. If the length is doubled, is the required work doubled? Explain.
   c. If the radius is doubled, is the required work doubled? Explain.

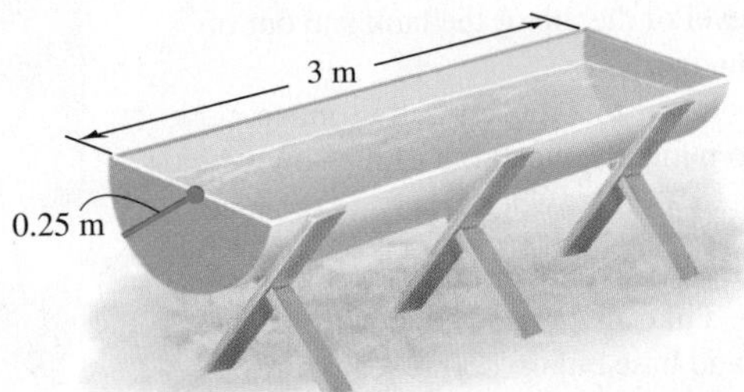

29. **Emptying a water trough** A cattle trough has a trapezoidal cross section with a height of 1 m and horizontal sides of width $\frac{1}{2}$ m and 1 m. Assume the length of the trough is 10 m (see figure).
   a. How much work is required to pump water out of the trough (to the level of the top of the trough) when it is full?
   b. If the length is doubled, is the required work doubled? Explain.

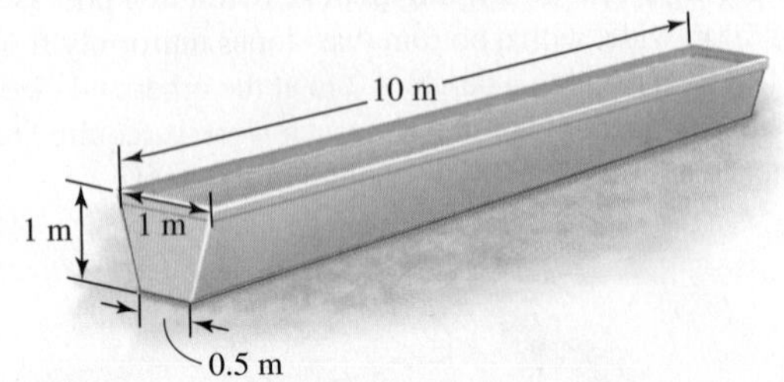

30–33. Force on dams *The following figures show the shape and dimensions of small dams. Assuming the water level is at the top of the dam, find the total force on the face of the dam.*

30.
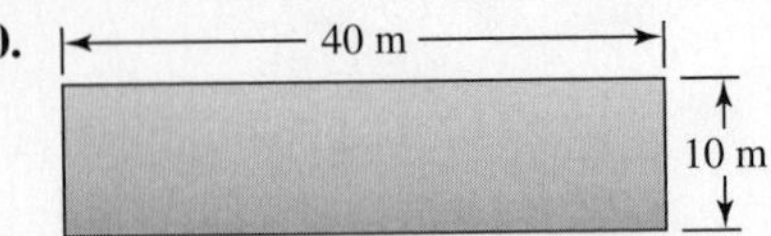

31.
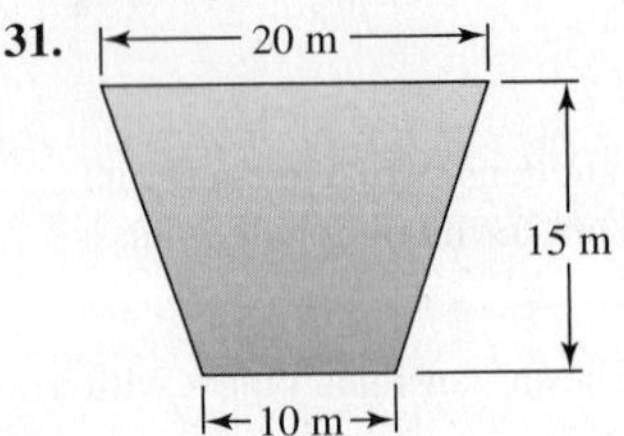

32.
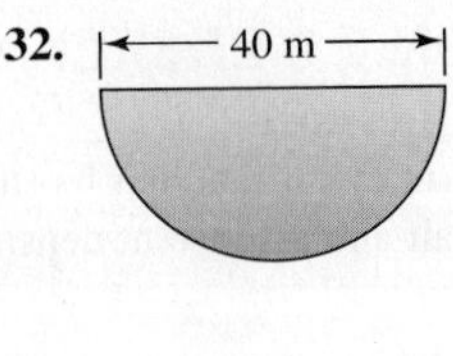

33.
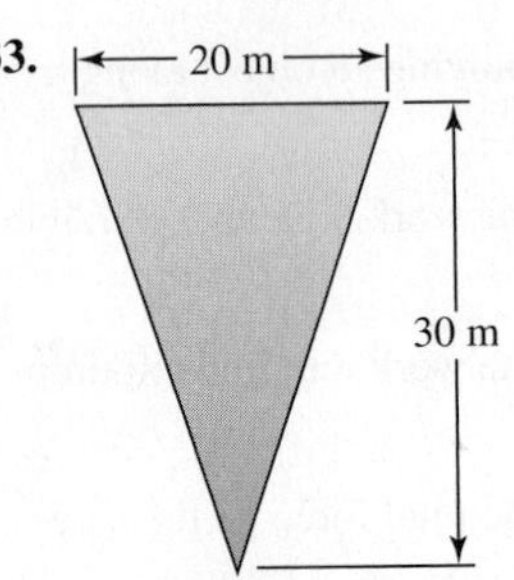

34. **Parabolic dam** The lower edge of a dam is defined by the parabola $y = x^2/16$ (see figure). Use a coordinate system with $y = 0$ at the bottom of the dam to determine the total force on the dam. Lengths are measured in meters.

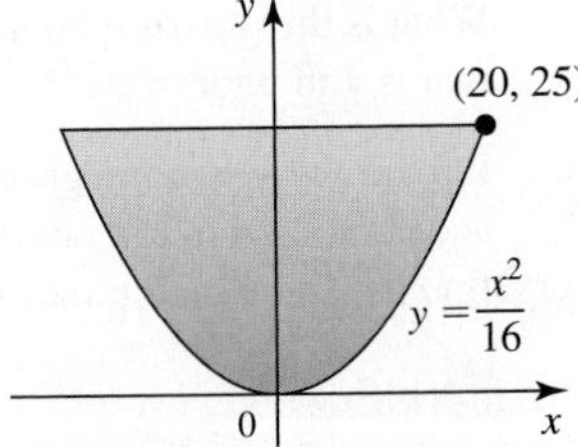

35. **Force on a building** A large building shaped like a box is 50 m high with a face that is 80 m wide. A strong wind blows directly at the face of the building, exerting a pressure of 150 N/m^2 at the ground and increasing with height according to $P(y) = 150 + 2y$, where y is the height above the ground. Calculate the total force on the building, which is a measure of the resistance that must be included in the design of the building.

36–38. Force on a window *A diving pool that is 4 m deep and full of water has a viewing window on one of its vertical walls. Find the force on the following windows.*

36. The window is a square, 0.5 m on a side, with the lower edge of the window on the bottom of the pool.

37. The window is a square, 0.5 m on a side, with the lower edge of the window 1 m from the bottom of the pool.

38. The window is a circle, with a radius of 0.5 m, tangent to the bottom of the pool.

Further Explorations

39. **Explain why or why not** Determine whether the following statements are true and give an explanation or counterexample.
   a. The mass of a thin wire is the length of the wire times its average density over its length.
   b. The work required to stretch a linear spring (that obeys Hooke's law) 100 cm from equilibrium is the same as the work required to compress it 100 cm from equilibrium.
   c. The work required to lift a 10-kg object vertically 10 m is the same as the work required to lift a 20-kg object vertically 5 m.
   d. The total force on a 10-ft^2 region on the (horizontal) floor of a pool is the same as the total force on a 10-ft^2 region on a (vertical) wall of the pool.

40. **Mass of two bars** Two bars of length L have densities of $\rho_1(x) = 4(x+1)^{-2}$ and $\rho_2(x) = 6(x+1)^{-3}$, for $0 \le x \le L$.
   a. For what values of L is bar 1 heavier than bar 2?
   b. As the lengths of the bars increase, do their masses increase without bound? Explain.

41. **A nonlinear spring** Hooke's law is applicable to idealized (linear) springs that are not stretched or compressed too far. Consider a nonlinear spring whose restoring force is given by $F(x) = 16x - 0.1x^3$, for $|x| \le 7$.
   a. Graph the restoring force and interpret it.
   b. How much work is done in stretching the spring from its equilibrium position ($x = 0$) to $x = 1.5$?
   c. How much work is done in compressing the spring from its equilibrium position ($x = 0$) to $x = -2$?

42. **A vertical spring** A 10-kg mass is attached to a spring that hangs vertically and is stretched 2 m from the equilibrium position of the spring. Assume a linear spring with $F(x) = kx$.
   a. How much work is required to compress the spring and lift the mass 0.5 m?
   b. How much work is required to stretch the spring and lower the mass 0.5 m?

43. **Drinking juice** A glass has circular cross sections that taper (linearly) from a radius of 5 cm at the top of the glass to a radius of 4 cm at the bottom. The glass is 15 cm high and full of orange juice. How much work is required to drink all the juice through a straw if your mouth is 5 cm above the top of the glass? Assume the density of orange juice equals the density of water.

44. **Upper and lower half** A cylinder with height 8 m and radius 3 m is filled with water and must be emptied through an outlet pipe 2 m above the top of the cylinder.
   a. Compute the work required to empty the water in the top half of the tank.
   b. Compute the work required to empty the (equal amount of) water in the lower half of the tank.
   c. Interpret the results of parts (a) and (b).

Applications

45. **Work in a gravitational field** For large distances from the surface of Earth, the gravitational force is given by $F(x) = GMm/(x+R)^2$, where $G = 6.7 \times 10^{-11}\,\text{N m}^2/\text{kg}^2$ is the gravitational constant, $M = 6 \times 10^{24}$ kg is the mass of Earth, m is the mass of the object in the gravitational field, $R = 6.378 \times 10^6$ m is the radius of Earth, and $x \ge 0$ is the distance above the surface of Earth (in meters).
   a. How much work is required to launch a rocket with a mass of 500 kg in a vertical flight path to a height of 2500 km (from Earth's surface)?
   b. Find the work required to launch the rocket to a height of x kilometers, for $x > 0$.
   c. How much work is required to reach outer space ($x \to \infty$)?
   d. Equate the work in part (c) to the initial kinetic energy of the rocket, $\frac{1}{2}mv^2$, to compute the escape velocity of the rocket.

46. **Work by two different integrals** A rigid body with a mass of 2 kg moves along a line due to a force that produces a position function $x(t) = 4t^2$, where x is measured in meters and t is measured in seconds. Find the work done during the first 5 s in two ways.
   a. Note that $x''(t) = 8$; then use Newton's second law, ($F = ma = mx''(t)$) to evaluate the work integral $W = \int_{x_0}^{x_f} F(x)\,dx$, where x_0 and x_f are the initial and final positions, respectively.
   b. Change variables in the work integral and integrate with respect to t. Be sure your answer agrees with part (a).

47. **Winding a chain** A 30-m-long chain hangs vertically from a cylinder attached to a winch. Assume there is no friction in the system and that the chain has a density of 5 kg/m.
   a. How much work is required to wind the entire chain onto the cylinder using the winch?
   b. How much work is required to wind the chain onto the cylinder if a 50-kg block is attached to the end of the chain?

48. **Coiling a rope** A 60-m-long, 9.4-mm-diameter rope hangs free from a ledge. The density of the rope is 55 g/m. How much work is needed to pull the entire rope to the ledge?

49. **Lifting a pendulum** A body of mass m is suspended by a rod of length L that pivots without friction (see figure). The mass is slowly lifted along a circular arc to a height h.
   a. Assuming that the only force acting on the mass is the gravitational force, show that the component of this force acting along the arc of motion is $F = mg \sin\theta$.
   b. Noting that an element of length along the path of the pendulum is $ds = L\,d\theta$, evaluate an integral in θ to show that the work done in lifting the mass to a height h is mgh.

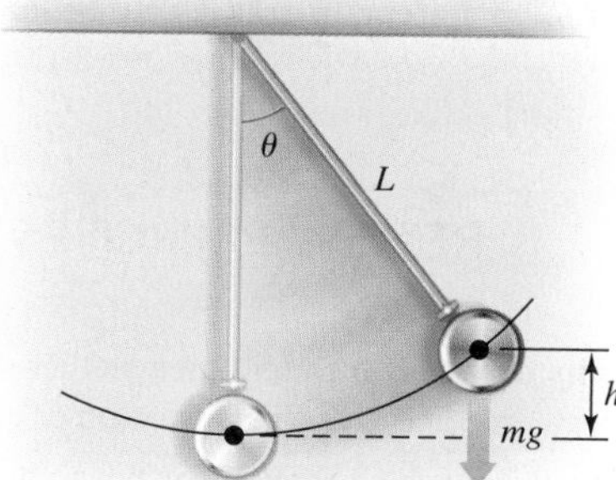

50. **Orientation and force** A plate shaped like an equilateral triangle 1 m on a side is placed on a vertical wall 1 m below the surface of a pool filled with water. On which plate in the figure is the force greater? Try to anticipate the answer and then compute the force on each plate.

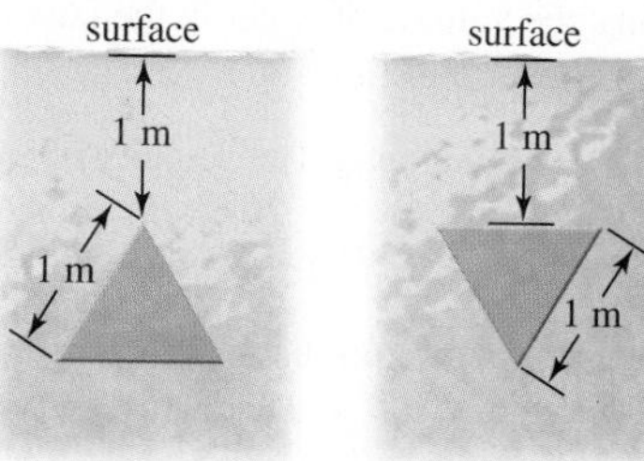

51. **Orientation and force** A square plate 1 m on a side is placed on a vertical wall 1 m below the surface of a pool filled with water. On which plate in the figure is the force greater? Try to anticipate the answer and then compute the force on each plate.

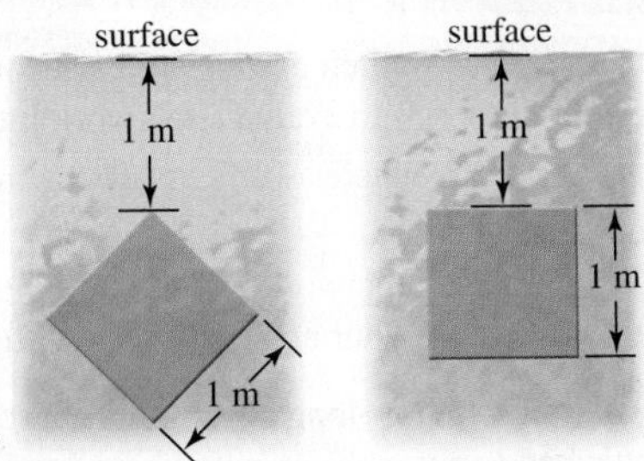

52. **A calorie-free milkshake?** Suppose a cylindrical glass with a diameter of $\frac{1}{12}$ m and a height of $\frac{1}{10}$ m is filled to the brim with a 400-Cal milkshake. If you have a straw that is 1.1 m long (so the top of the straw is 1 m above the top of the glass), do you burn off all the calories in the milkshake in drinking it? Assume that the density of the milkshake is 1 g/cm^3 (1 Cal = 4184 J).

53. **Critical depth** A large tank has a plastic window on one wall that is designed to withstand a force of 90,000 N. The square window is 2 m on a side, and its lower edge is 1 m from the bottom of the tank.
   - **a.** If the tank is filled to a depth of 4 m, will the window withstand the resulting force?
   - **b.** What is the maximum depth to which the tank can be filled without the window failing?

54. **Buoyancy** Archimedes' principle says that the buoyant force exerted on an object that is (partially or totally) submerged in water is equal to the weight of the water displaced by the object (see figure). Let $\rho_w = 1\text{ g/cm}^3 = 1000\text{ kg/m}^3$ be the density of water and let ρ be the density of an object in water. Let $f = \rho/\rho_w$. If $0 < f \leq 1$, then the object floats with a fraction f of its volume submerged; if $f > 1$, then the object sinks.

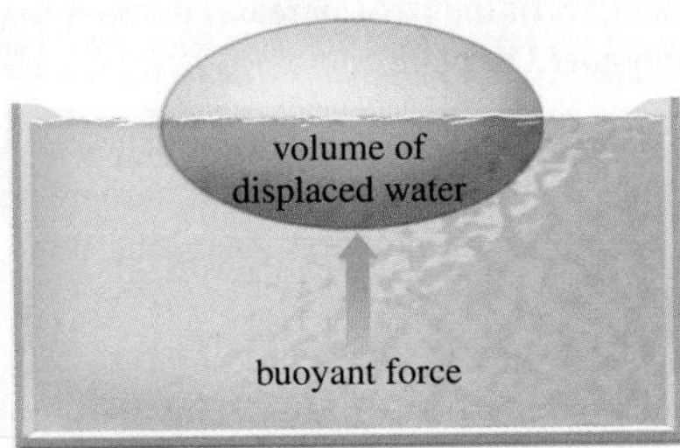

Consider a cubical box with sides 2 m long floating in water with one-half of its volume submerged ($\rho = \rho_w/2$). Find the force required to fully submerge the box (so its top surface is at the water level).

(See Guided Projects for further explorations of buoyancy problems.)

QUICK CHECK ANSWERS

1. (a) The bar is heaviest at the left end and lightest at the right end. (b) $\rho = 2.5\text{ g/cm}$. **2.** Minimum mass $= 2$ kg; maximum mass $= 10$ kg **3.** We assume that the force is constant over each subinterval, when, in fact, it varies over each subinterval. **4.** The restoring force of the spring increases as the spring is stretched ($F(x) = 100x$). Greater restoring forces are encountered on the interval $[0.1, 0.35]$ than on the interval $[0, 0.25]$. **5.** The factor $(15 - y)$ in the integral is replaced by $(10 - y)$.

CHAPTER 6 REVIEW EXERCISES

1. **Explain why or why not** Determine whether the following statements are true and give an explanation or counterexample.
   - **a.** A region R is revolved about the y-axis to generate a solid S. To find the volume of S, you could use either the disk/washer method and integrate with respect to y or the shell method and integrate with respect to x.
   - **b.** Given only the velocity of an object moving on a line, it is possible to find its displacement, but not its position.
   - **c.** If water flows into a tank at a constant rate (for example 6 gal/min), the volume of water in the tank increases according to a linear function of time.

2. **Displacement from velocity** The velocity of an object moving along a line is given by $v(t) = 20\cos \pi t$ (in ft/s). What is the displacement of the object after 1.5 s?

3. **Position, displacement, and distance** A projectile is launched vertically from the ground at $t = 0$ and its velocity in flight (in m/s) is given by $v(t) = 20 - 10t$. Find the position, displacement, and distance traveled after t seconds, for $0 \leq t \leq 4$, assuming $s(0) = 0$.

4. **Deceleration** At $t = 0$, a car begins decelerating from a velocity of 80 ft/s at a constant rate of 5 ft/s^2. Find its position function assuming $s(0) = 0$.

5. **An oscillator** The acceleration of an object moving along a line is given by $a(t) = 2\sin\left(\frac{\pi t}{4}\right)$. The initial velocity and position are $v(0) = -\frac{8}{\pi}$ and $s(0) = 0$.
   - **a.** Find the velocity and position, for $t \geq 0$.
   - **b.** What are the minimum and maximum values of s?
   - **c.** Find the average velocity and average position over the interval $[0, 8]$.

6. **A race** Starting at the same point on a straight road, Anna and Benny begin running with velocities (in mi/hr) given by $v_A(t) = 2t + 1$ and $v_B(t) = 4 - t$, respectively.
   a. Graph the velocity functions, for $0 \le t \le 4$.
   b. If the runners run for 1 hr, who runs farther? Interpret your conclusion geometrically using the graph in part (a).
   c. If the runners run for 6 mi, who wins the race? Interpret your conclusion geometrically using the graph in part (a).

7. **Fuel consumption** A small plane in flight consumes fuel at a rate (in gal/min) given by

$$R'(t) = \begin{cases} 4t^{1/3} & \text{if } 0 \le t \le 8 \text{ (take-off)} \\ 2 & \text{if } t > 8 \text{ (cruising)} \end{cases}$$

   a. Find a function R that gives the total fuel consumed, for $0 \le t \le 8$.
   b. Find a function R that gives the total fuel consumed, for $t \ge 0$.
   c. If the fuel tank capacity is 150 gal, when does the fuel run out?

T 8. **Decreasing velocity** A projectile is fired upward and its velocity (in m/s) is given by $v(t) = \dfrac{200}{\sqrt{t+1}}$, for $t \ge 0$.
   a. Graph the velocity function, for $t \ge 0$.
   b. Find and graph the position function for the projectile, for $t \ge 0$, assuming $s(0) = 0$.
   c. Given unlimited time, can the projectile travel 2500 m? If so, at what time does the distance traveled equal 2500 m?

T **9–13. Areas of regions** *Use any method to find the area of the region described.*

9. The region in the first quadrant bounded by $y = x^p$ and $y = \sqrt[p]{x}$, where $p = 100$ and $p = 1000$.

10. The regions R_1 and R_2 (separately) shown in the figure, which are formed by the graphs of $y = 16 - x^2$ and $y = 5x - 8$

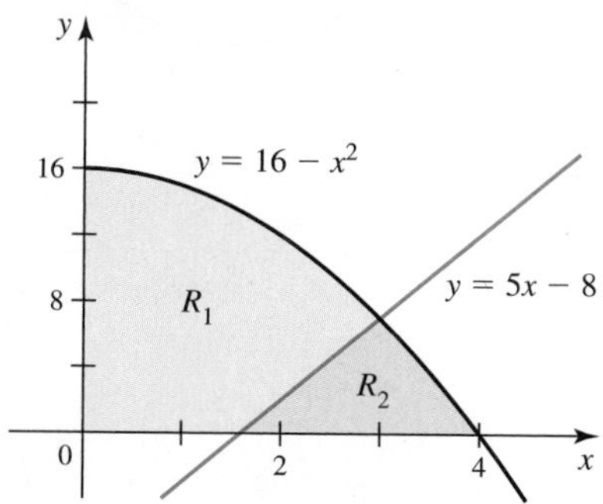

11. The region bounded by $y = x^2$, $y = 2x^2 - 4x$, and $y = 0$

12. The region in the first quadrant bounded by the curve $\sqrt{x} + \sqrt{y} = 1$

13. The region in the first quadrant bounded by $y = x/6$ and $y = 1 - |x/2 - 1|$

14. **An area function** Let $R(x)$ be the area of the shaded region between the graphs of $y = f(t)$ and $y = g(t)$ in the figure.
   a. Sketch a plausible graph of R, for $a \le x \le c$.
   b. Give expressions for $R(x)$ and $R'(x)$, for $a \le x \le c$.

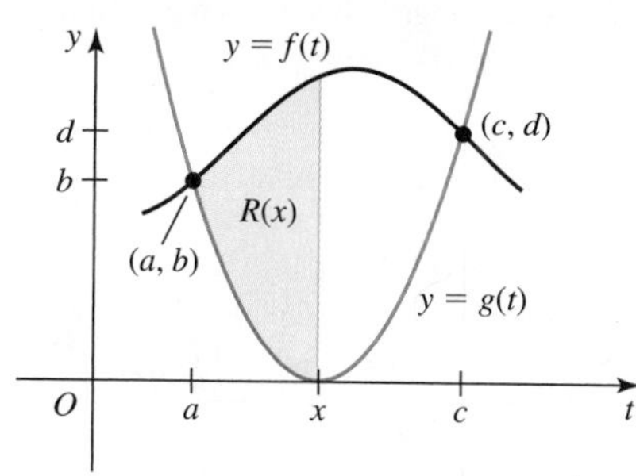

T 15. **An area function** Consider the functions $y = \dfrac{x^2}{a}$ and $y = \sqrt{\dfrac{x}{a}}$, where $a > 0$. Find $A(a)$, the area of the region between the curves.

16. **Three methods** The quarter circle of radius R in the first quadrant ($x^2 + y^2 = R^2$, for $x \ge 0$ and $y \ge 0$) is revolved about the x-axis to produce a hemisphere. Verify that the volume of the hemisphere is $\frac{2}{3}\pi R^3$ in the following ways:
   a. Apply the disk method and integrate with respect to x.
   b. Apply the shell method and integrate with respect to y.
   c. Apply the general slicing method and integrate with respect to y.

17–21. Volumes of solids *Choose the general slicing method, the disk/washer method, or the shell method to find the volume of the following solids.*

17. A pyramid has a square base in the xy-plane with vertices at $(1, 1)$, $(1, -1)$, $(-1, 1)$, and $(-1, -1)$. All cross sections of the pyramid parallel to the xy-plane are squares and the height of the pyramid is 12 units. What is the volume of the pyramid?

18. The region bounded by the curves $y = -x^2 + 2x + 2$ and $y = 2x^2 - 4x + 2$ is revolved about the x-axis. What is the volume of the solid that is generated?

19. The region bounded by the curves $y = 1 + \sqrt{x}$ and $y = 1 - \sqrt{x}$, and the line $x = 1$ is revolved about the y-axis. Find the volume of the resulting solid by (a) integrating with respect to x and (b) integrating with respect to y. Be sure your answers agree.

20. The region bounded by the curves $y = x + 1$, $y = 12/x$, and $y = 1$ is revolved about the x-axis. What is the volume of the solid that is generated?

21. Find the volume of a right circular cone with radius r and height h by treating it as a solid of revolution.

22. **Area and volume** The region R is bounded by the curves $x = y^2 + 2$, $y = x - 4$, and $y = 0$ (see figure).
   a. Write a single integral that gives the area of R.
   b. Write a single integral that gives the volume of the solid generated when R is revolved about the x-axis.
   c. Write a single integral that gives the volume of the solid generated when R is revolved about the y-axis.

d. Suppose S is a solid whose base is R and whose cross sections perpendicular to R and parallel to the x-axis are semicircles. Write a single integral that gives the volume of S.

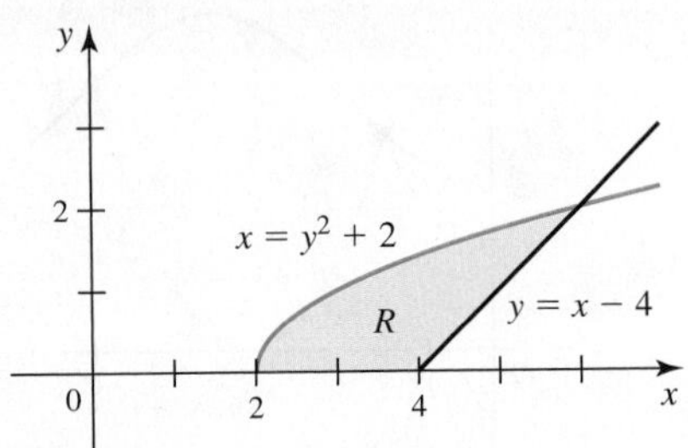

23. Comparing volumes Let R be the region bounded by $y = 1/x^p$ and the x-axis on the interval $[1, a]$, where $p > 0$ and $a > 1$ (see figure). Let V_x and V_y be the volumes of the solids generated when R is revolved about the x- and y-axes, respectively.

a. With $a = 2$ and $p = 1$, which is greater, V_x or V_y?

b. With $a = 4$ and $p = 3$, which is greater, V_x or V_y?

c. Find a general expression for V_x in terms of a and p, where $p \neq \frac{1}{2}$.

d. Find a general expression for V_y in terms of a and p, where $p \neq 2$.

e. Can you find any values of a and p for which $V_x > V_y$?

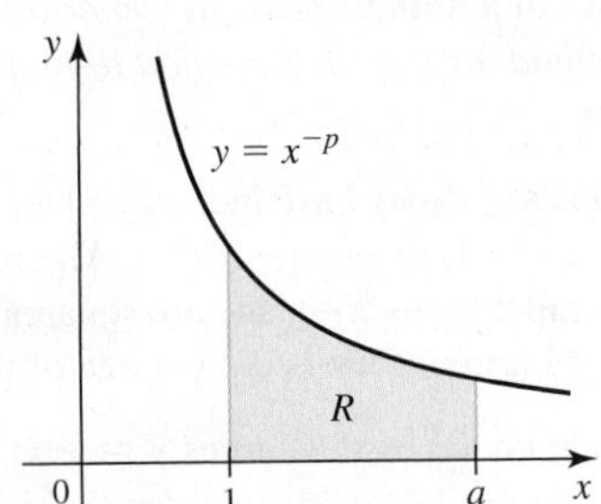

24–26. Arc length *Find the length of the following curves.*

24. $y = x^3/6 + 1/(2x)$ on the interval $[1, 2]$.

25. $y = x^{1/2} - x^{3/2}/3$ on the interval $[1, 3]$.

T **26.** $y = x^3/3 + x^2 + x + 1/(4x + 4)$ on the interval $[0, 4]$.

27–28. Variable density in one dimension *Find the mass of the following thin bars.*

27. A bar on the interval $0 \leq x \leq 9$ with a density (in g/cm) given by $\rho(x) = 3 + 2\sqrt{x}$

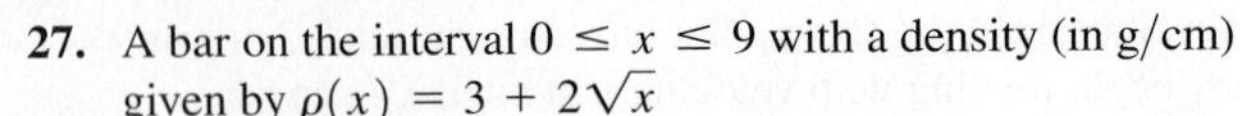

28. A bar on the interval $0 \leq x \leq 6$ with a density

$$\rho(x) = \begin{cases} 1 & \text{if } 0 \leq x < 2 \\ 2 & \text{if } 2 \leq x < 4 \\ 4 & \text{if } 4 \leq x \leq 6 \end{cases}$$

29. Spring work It takes 50 J of work to stretch a spring 0.2 m from its equilibrium position. How much work is needed to stretch it an additional 0.5 m?

30. Pumping water A cylindrical water tank has a height of 6 m and a radius of 4 m. How much work is required to empty the full tank by pumping the water to an outflow pipe at the top of the tank?

31. Force on a dam Find the total force on the face of a semicircular dam with a radius of 20 m when its reservoir is full of water. The diameter of the semicircle is the top of the dam.

32. Equal area property for parabolas Let $f(x) = ax^2 + bx + c$ be an arbitrary quadratic function and choose two points $x = p$ and $x = q$. Let L_1 be the line tangent to the graph of f at the point $(p, f(p))$, and let L_2 be the line tangent to the graph at the point $(q, f(q))$. Let $x = s$ be the vertical line through the intersection point of L_1 and L_2. Finally, let R_1 be the region bounded by $y = f(x)$, L_1, and the vertical line $x = s$, and let R_2 be the region bounded by $y = f(x)$, L_2, and the vertical line $x = s$. Prove that the area of R_1 equals the area of R_2.

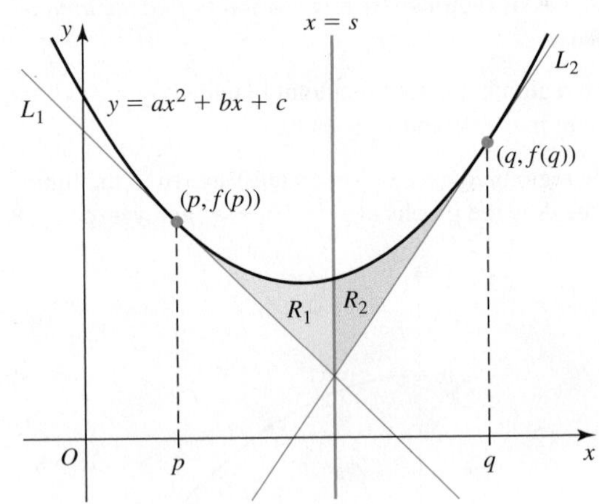

Chapter 6 Guided Projects

Applications of the material in this chapter and related topics can be found in the following Guided Projects. For additional information, see the Preface.

- Geometric probability
- Designing a water clock
- Dipstick problems
- Mathematics of the CD player
- Buoyancy and Archimedes' principle

7

Logarithmic and Exponential Functions

Chapter Preview Until now, we have studied the calculus of polynomial, algebraic, and trigonometric functions, and explored some of their applications. However, many areas of mathematics rely on other functions, known to you from algebra as exponential and logarithmic functions. It turns out that an exponential function of the form b^x, where $b > 0$, is the *inverse function* of the logarithmic function $\log_b x$ (and vice versa). In light of this fact, the chapter opens with a general discussion of inverse functions—pairs of functions that "undo" each other. We then give a definition of the logarithmic function base e, which is called the *natural logarithm*; this function satisfies all the familiar algebraic properties of all logarithmic functions, and it has important derivative properties. Using the properties of inverse functions, we take the important step of introducing the inverse of the natural logarithm, which is the exponential function base e. At this point, a short excursion allows us to develop logarithmic and exponential functions with general (positive) bases. Inverse functions are next put to work to define the inverse trigonometric functions and produce their derivative and integral properties. Finally, with exponential and logarithmic functions in the picture, we can resume the discussion of l'Hôpital's Rule that began in Chapter 4. New indeterminate forms are explored, leading to a ranking of functions by their growth rates. Throughout the chapter, we emphasize the many practical applications of exponential and logarithmic functions.

7.1 Inverse Functions

From your study of algebra, you know that when a function has an *inverse function*, the two functions are related in special ways. Roughly speaking, the action of one function undoes the action of the other. In this section, we begin with a review of inverse functions: when they exist, how to find them, and how to graph them. We then investigate the relationship between the derivative of a function and the derivative of its inverse function. With this background, we devote the rest of the chapter to developing new functions that arise as the inverses of familiar functions.

Existence of Inverse Functions

Consider the linear function $f(x) = 2x$, which takes any value of x and doubles it. The function that reverses this process by taking any value of $f(x) = 2x$ and mapping it back to x is called the *inverse function* of f, denoted f^{-1}. In this case, the inverse function is $f^{-1}(x) = x/2$. The effect of applying these two functions in succession looks like this:

$$x \xrightarrow{f} 2x \xrightarrow{f^{-1}} x$$

We now generalize this idea.

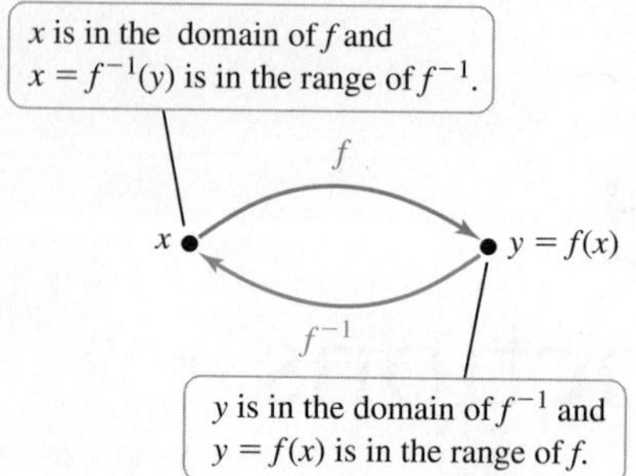

FIGURE 7.1

> The notation f^{-1} for the inverse can be confusing. The inverse is not the reciprocal; that is, $f^{-1}(x)$ is not $1/f(x) = (f(x))^{-1}$. We adopt the common convention of using simply *inverse* to mean *inverse function*.

DEFINITION Inverse Function

Given a function f, its inverse (if it exists) is a function f^{-1} such that whenever $y = f(x)$, then $f^{-1}(y) = x$ (Figure 7.1).

QUICK CHECK 1 What is the inverse of $f(x) = \frac{1}{3}x$? What is the inverse of $f(x) = x - 7$?

Because the inverse undoes the original function, if we start with a value of x, apply f to it, and then apply f^{-1} to the result, we recover the original value of x; that is,

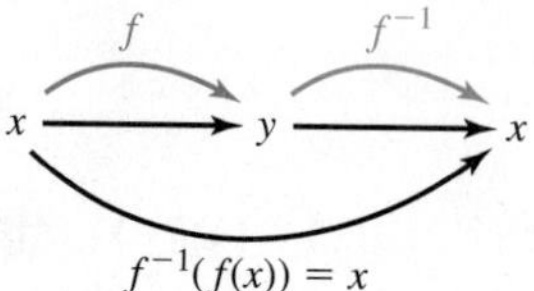

Similarly, if we apply f^{-1} to a value of y and then apply f to the result, we recover the original value of y; that is,

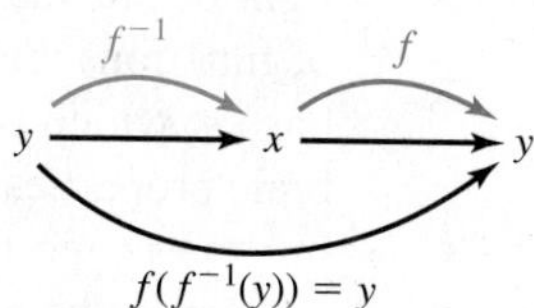

One-to-One Functions We have defined the inverse of a function but said nothing about when it exists. To ensure that f has an inverse on a domain, f must be *one-to-one* on that domain. This property means that every output of the function f must correspond to exactly one input. The one-to-one property is checked graphically by using the *horizontal line test*.

> The vertical line test determines whether f is a function. The horizontal line test determines whether f is one-to-one.

DEFINITION One-to-One Functions and the Horizontal Line Test

A function f is **one-to-one** on a domain D if each value of $f(x)$ corresponds to exactly one value of x in D. More precisely, f is one-to-one on D if $f(x_1) \neq f(x_2)$ whenever $x_1 \neq x_2$, for x_1 and x_2 in D. The **horizontal line test** says that every horizontal line intersects the graph of a one-to-one function at most once (Figure 7.2).

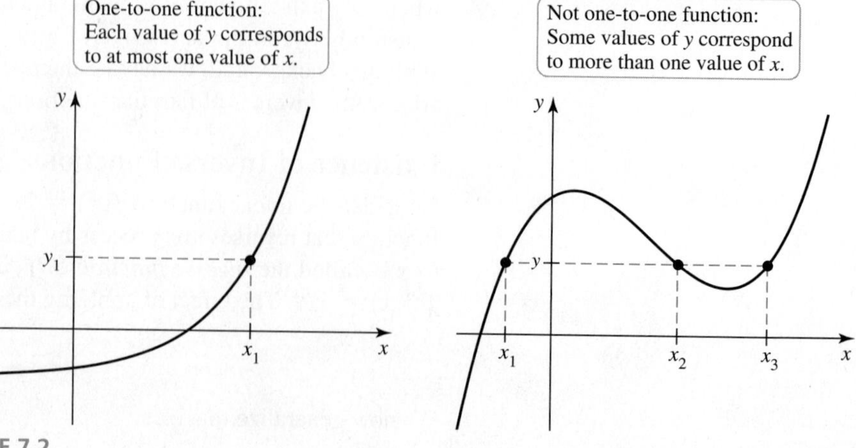

FIGURE 7.2

For example, in Figure 7.3, some horizontal lines intersect the graph of $f(x) = x^2$ twice. Therefore, f does not have an inverse function on the interval $(-\infty, \infty)$. However, if f is restricted to the interval $(-\infty, 0]$ or $[0, \infty)$, then it does pass the horizontal line test and it is one-to-one on these intervals.

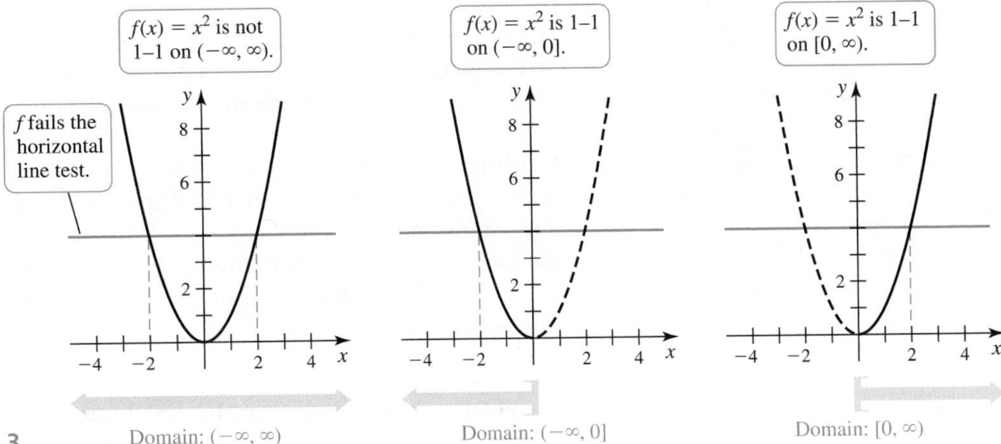

FIGURE 7.3

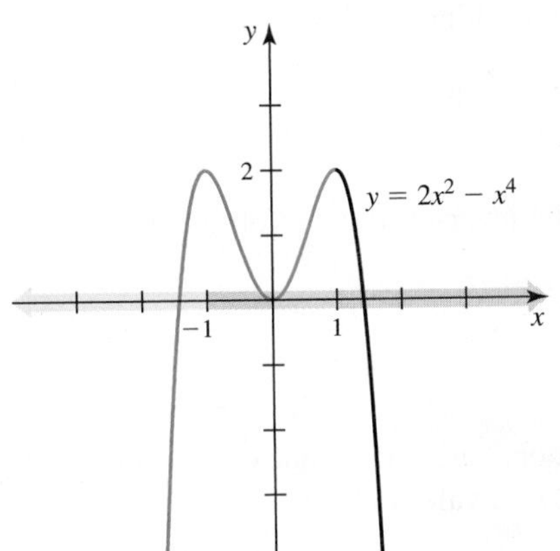

FIGURE 7.4

EXAMPLE 1 One-to-one functions Determine the (largest possible) intervals on which the function $f(x) = 2x^2 - x^4$ (Figure 7.4) is one-to-one.

SOLUTION The graph of f shows that it is not one-to-one on the entire real line because it fails the horizontal line test. However, on the intervals $(-\infty, -1]$, $[-1, 0]$, $[0, 1]$, and $[1, \infty)$, f is one-to-one. The function is also one-to-one on any subinterval of these four intervals.

Related Exercises 9–10 ◀

Conditions for the Existence of Inverse Functions

Figure 7.5a illustrates the actions of a one-to-one function f and its inverse f^{-1}. We see that f maps a value of x to a unique value of y. In turn, f^{-1} maps that value of y back to the original value of x. When f is *not* one-to-one, this procedure cannot be carried out (Figure 7.5b).

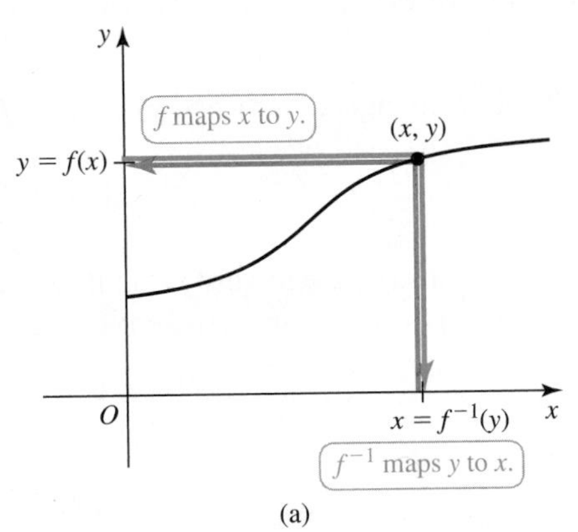

FIGURE 7.5

➤ The statement that a one-to-one function has an inverse may be plausible based on its graph. However, the proof of this theorem is fairly technical and is omitted.

THEOREM 7.1 Existence of Inverse Functions

Let f be a one-to-one function on a domain D with a range R. Then f has a unique inverse f^{-1} with domain R and range D such that

$$f^{-1}(f(x)) = x \quad \text{and} \quad f(f^{-1}(y)) = y,$$

where x is in D and y is in R.

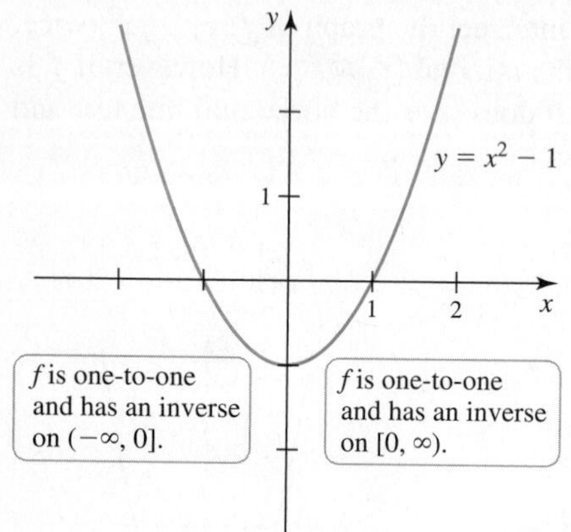

$y = x^2 - 1$
f is one-to-one and has an inverse on $(-\infty, 0]$.
f is one-to-one and has an inverse on $[0, \infty)$.

FIGURE 7.6

QUICK CHECK 2 The function that gives degrees Fahrenheit in terms of degrees Celsius is $F = 9C/5 + 32$. Explain why this function has an inverse.

EXAMPLE 2 **Does an inverse exist?** Determine intervals on which $f(x) = x^2 - 1$ has an inverse function.

SOLUTION On the interval $(-\infty, \infty)$ the function does not pass the horizontal line test and is not one-to-one (Figure 7.6). However, if f is restricted to the interval $(-\infty, 0]$ or $[0, \infty)$, then it is one-to-one and an inverse exists. *Related Exercises 11–14*

Finding Inverse Functions The crux of finding an inverse for a function f is solving the equation $y = f(x)$ for x in terms of y. If it is possible to do so, then we have found a relationship of the form $x = f^{-1}(y)$. Interchanging x and y in $x = f^{-1}(y)$ so that x is the independent variable (which is the customary role for x), the inverse has the form $y = f^{-1}(x)$. Notice that if f is not one-to-one, this process leads to more than one inverse function.

PROCEDURE **Finding an Inverse Function**

Suppose f is one-to-one on an interval I. To find f^{-1}:

1. Solve $y = f(x)$ for x. If necessary, restrict the resulting function so that x lies in I.
2. Interchange x and y and write $y = f^{-1}(x)$.

➤ Once you find a formula for f^{-1} you can check your work by verifying that $f^{-1}(f(x)) = x$ and $f(f^{-1}(x)) = x$.

EXAMPLE 3 **Finding inverse functions** Find the inverse(s) of the following functions. Restrict the domain of f if necessary.

a. $f(x) = 2x + 6$ **b.** $f(x) = x^2 - 1$

SOLUTION

➤ A constant function (whose graph is a horizontal line) fails the horizontal line test and does not have an inverse.

a. Linear functions (except for constant linear functions) are one-to-one on the entire real line. Therefore, an inverse function for f exists for all values of x.

Step 1: Solve $y = f(x)$ for x: We see that $y = 2x + 6$ implies that $2x = y - 6$, or $x = (y - 6)/2$.

Step 2: Interchange x and y and write $y = f^{-1}(x)$:

$$y = f^{-1}(x) = \frac{x - 6}{2}$$

It is instructive to verify that the inverse relations $f(f^{-1}(x)) = x$ and $f^{-1}(f(x)) = x$ are satisfied:

$$f(f^{-1}(x)) = f\left(\frac{x-6}{2}\right) = \underbrace{2\left(\frac{x-6}{2}\right) + 6}_{f(x) = 2x + 6} = x - 6 + 6 = x$$

$$f^{-1}(f(x)) = f^{-1}(2x + 6) = \underbrace{\frac{(2x + 6) - 6}{2}}_{f^{-1}(x) = (x - 6)/2} = x$$

b. As shown in Example 2, the function $f(x) = x^2 - 1$ is not one-to-one on the entire real line; however, it is one-to-one on $(-\infty, 0]$ and on $[0, \infty)$. If we restrict our attention to either of these intervals, then an inverse function can be found.

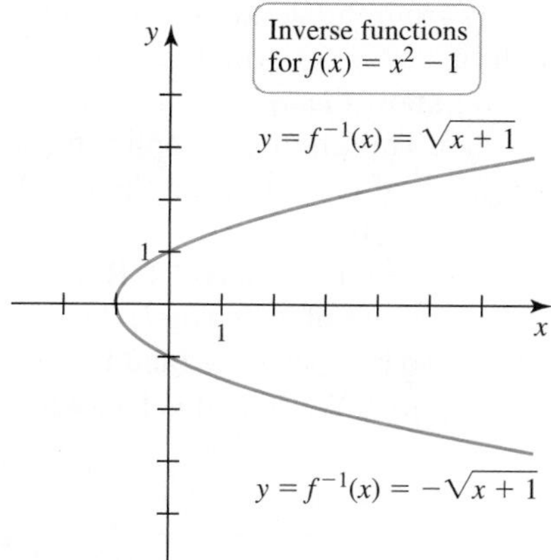

FIGURE 7.7

Step 1: Solve $y = f(x)$ for x:

$$y = x^2 - 1$$
$$x^2 = y + 1$$
$$x = \begin{cases} \sqrt{y+1} \\ -\sqrt{y+1} \end{cases}$$

Each branch of the square root corresponds to an inverse function.

Step 2: Interchange x and y and write $y = f^{-1}(x)$:

$$y = f^{-1}(x) = \sqrt{x+1} \quad \text{or} \quad y = f^{-1}(x) = -\sqrt{x+1}$$

The interpretation of this result is important. Taking the positive branch of the square root, the inverse function $y = f^{-1}(x) = \sqrt{x+1}$ gives positive values of y; it corresponds to the branch of $f(x) = x^2 - 1$ on the interval $[0, \infty)$ (Figure 7.7). The negative branch of the square root, $y = f^{-1}(x) = -\sqrt{x+1}$, is another inverse function that gives negative values of y; it corresponds to the branch of $f(x) = x^2 - 1$ on the interval $(-\infty, 0]$.

Related Exercises 15–22

QUICK CHECK 3 On what interval(s) does the function $f(x) = x^3$ have an inverse?

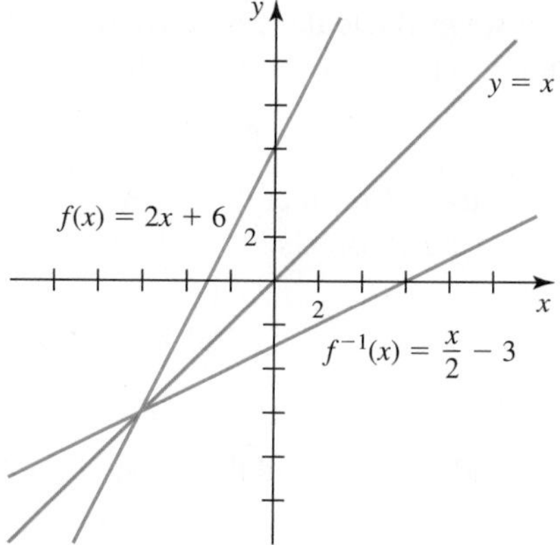

FIGURE 7.8

Graphing Inverse Functions

The graphs of a function and its inverse have a special relationship, which is illustrated in the following example.

EXAMPLE 4 Graphing inverse functions Plot f and f^{-1} on the same coordinate axes.

a. $f(x) = 2x + 6$ **b.** $f(x) = \sqrt{x - 1}$

SOLUTION

a. The inverse of $f(x) = 2x + 6$, found in Example 3, is

$$y = f^{-1}(x) = \frac{x-6}{2} = \frac{x}{2} - 3.$$

The graphs of f and f^{-1} are shown in Figure 7.8. Notice that both f and f^{-1} are increasing linear functions and they intersect at $(-6, -6)$.

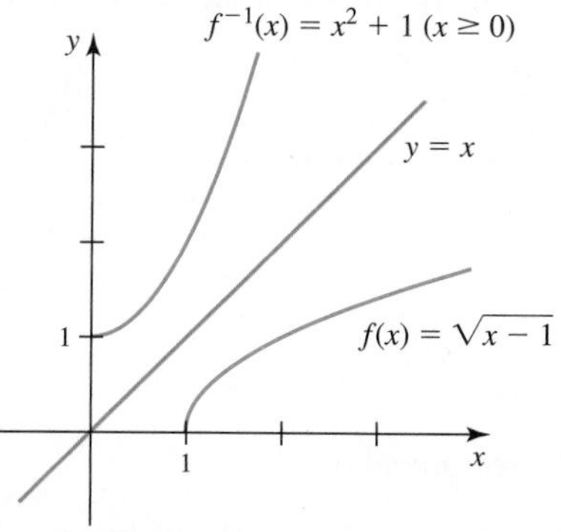

FIGURE 7.9

b. The domain of $f(x) = \sqrt{x - 1}$ is the set $\{x: x \geq 1\}$. On this domain f is one-to-one and has an inverse. It can be found in two steps:

Step 1: Solve $y = \sqrt{x-1}$ for x:

$$y^2 = x - 1 \quad \text{or} \quad x = y^2 + 1$$

Step 2: Interchange x and y and write $y = f^{-1}(x)$:

$$y = f^{-1}(x) = x^2 + 1$$

The graphs of f and f^{-1} are shown in Figure 7.9. *Related Exercises 23–30*

Looking closely at the graphs in Figure 7.8 and Figure 7.9, you see a symmetry that always occurs when a function and its inverse are plotted on the same set of axes. In each figure, one curve is the reflection of the other curve across the line $y = x$. These curves are *symmetric about the line* $y = x$, which means that the point (a, b) is on one curve whenever the point (b, a) is on the other curve (Figure 7.10).

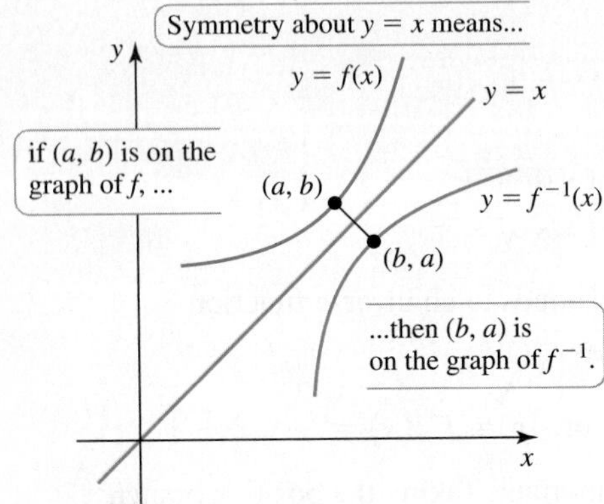

FIGURE 7.10

The explanation for the symmetry comes directly from the definition of the inverse. Suppose that the point (a, b) is on the graph of $y = f(x)$, which means that $b = f(a)$. By the definition of the inverse function, we know that $a = f^{-1}(b)$, which means that the point (b, a) is on the graph of $y = f^{-1}(x)$. This argument applies to all relevant points (a, b), so whenever (a, b) is on the graph of f, (b, a) is on the graph of f^{-1}. As a consequence, the graphs are symmetric about the line $y = x$.

Now suppose a function f is continuous and one-to-one on an interval I. Reflecting the graph of f through the line $y = x$ generates the graph of f^{-1}. The reflection process introduces no discontinuities in the graph of f^{-1}, so it is plausible (and indeed, true) that f^{-1} is continuous on the interval corresponding to I. We state this fact without a formal proof.

THEOREM 7.2 Continuity of Inverse Functions
If a continuous function f has an inverse on an interval I, then its inverse f^{-1} is also continuous (on the interval consisting of the points $f(x)$, where x is in I).

Derivatives of Inverse Functions

Here is an important question that bears on upcoming work: Given a function f that is one-to-one on an interval and its derivative f', how do we evaluate the derivative of f^{-1}? The key to finding the derivative of the inverse function lies in the symmetry of the graphs of f and f^{-1}.

EXAMPLE 5 Linear functions, inverses, and derivatives Consider the general linear function $y = f(x) = mx + b$, where $m \neq 0$ and b are constants.

a. Write the inverse of f in the form $y = f^{-1}(x)$.

b. Find the derivative of the inverse $\dfrac{d}{dx}[f^{-1}(x)]$.

c. Consider the specific case $f(x) = 2x - 6$. Graph f and f^{-1}, and find the slope of each line.

SOLUTION

a. Solving $y = mx + b$ for x, we find that $mx = y - b$, or

$$x = \frac{y}{m} - \frac{b}{m}.$$

Writing this function in the form $y = f^{-1}(x)$ (by reversing the roles of x and y), we have

$$y = f^{-1}(x) = \frac{x}{m} - \frac{b}{m},$$

which describes a line with slope $1/m$.

b. The derivative of f^{-1} is

$$(f^{-1})'(x) = \frac{1}{m} = \frac{1}{f'(x)}.$$

Notice that $f'(x) = m$, so the derivative of f^{-1} is the reciprocal of f'.

c. In the case that $f(x) = 2x - 6$, we have $f^{-1}(x) = x/2 + 3$. The graphs of these two lines are symmetric about the line $y = x$ (Figure 7.11). Furthermore, the slope of the line $y = f(x)$ is 2 and the slope of $y = f^{-1}(x)$ is $\frac{1}{2}$; that is, the slopes (and, therefore, the derivatives) are reciprocals of each other. *Related Exercise 31* ◀

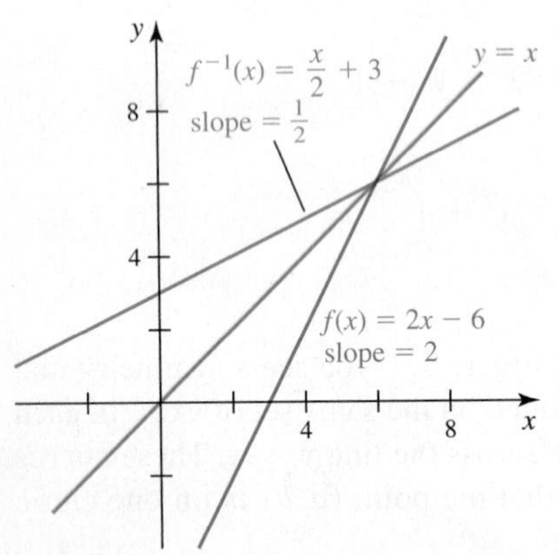

FIGURE 7.11

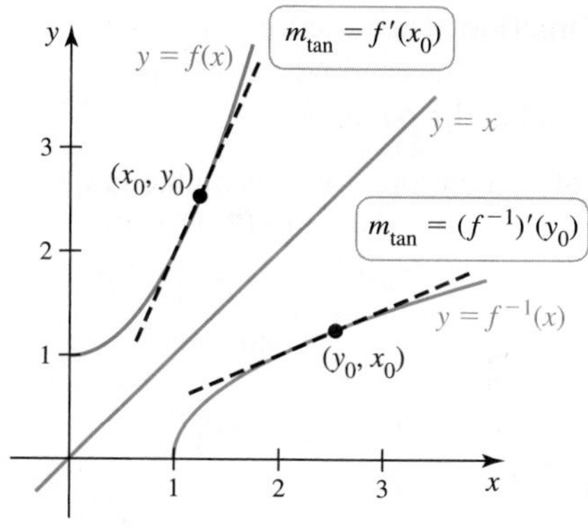

FIGURE 7.12

➤ The result of Theorem 7.3 is also written in the form

$$(f^{-1})'(f(x_0)) = \frac{1}{f'(x_0)}$$

or

$$(f^{-1})'(y_0) = \frac{1}{f'(f^{-1}(y_0))}$$

The reciprocal property obeyed by f' and $(f^{-1})'$ in Example 5 holds for all functions. Figure 7.12 shows the graphs of a typical one-to-one function and its inverse. It also shows a pair of symmetric points—(x_0, y_0) on the graph of f and (y_0, x_0) on the graph of f^{-1}—along with the tangent lines at these points. Notice that as the lines tangent to the graph of f get steeper (as x increases), the corresponding lines tangent to the graph of f^{-1} get less steep. The next theorem makes this relationship precise.

THEOREM 7.3 Derivative of the Inverse Function
Let f be differentiable and have an inverse on an interval I. If x_0 is a point of I at which $f'(x_0) \neq 0$, then f^{-1} is differentiable at $y_0 = f(x_0)$ and

$$(f^{-1})'(y_0) = \frac{1}{f'(x_0)}, \quad \text{where} \quad y_0 = f(x_0).$$

To understand this theorem, suppose that (x_0, y_0) is a point on the graph of f, which means that (y_0, x_0) is the corresponding point on the graph of f^{-1}. Then the slope of the line tangent to the graph of f^{-1} at the point (y_0, x_0) is the reciprocal of the slope of the line tangent to the graph of f at the point (x_0, y_0). Importantly, the theorem says that we can evaluate the derivative of the inverse function without finding the inverse function itself.

Proof Before doing a short calculation, we note two facts:

- At a point x_0 where f is differentiable, $y_0 = f(x_0)$ and $x_0 = f^{-1}(y_0)$.
- Because f is differentiable at x_0, f is continuous at x_0 (Theorem 3.1), which implies that f^{-1} is also continuous at y_0 (Theorem 7.2). Therefore, as $y \to y_0$, $x \to x_0$.

Using the definition of the derivative, we have

$$(f^{-1})'(y_0) = \lim_{y \to y_0} \frac{f^{-1}(y) - f^{-1}(y_0)}{y - y_0} \quad \text{Definition of derivative of } f^{-1}$$

$$= \lim_{x \to x_0} \frac{x - x_0}{f(x) - f(x_0)} \quad y = f(x) \text{ and } x = f^{-1}(y);\ x \to x_0 \text{ as } y \to y_0$$

$$= \lim_{x \to x_0} \frac{1}{\dfrac{f(x) - f(x_0)}{x - x_0}} \quad \frac{a}{b} = \frac{1}{b/a}$$

$$= \frac{1}{f'(x_0)}. \quad \text{Definition of derivative of } f$$

We have shown that $(f^{-1})'(y_0)$ exists (f^{-1} is differentiable at y_0) and it equals the reciprocal of $f'(x_0)$. ◀

QUICK CHECK 4 Sketch the graphs of $f(x) = x^3$ and $f^{-1}(x) = x^{1/3}$. Then verify that Theorem 7.3 holds at the point $(1, 1)$. ◀

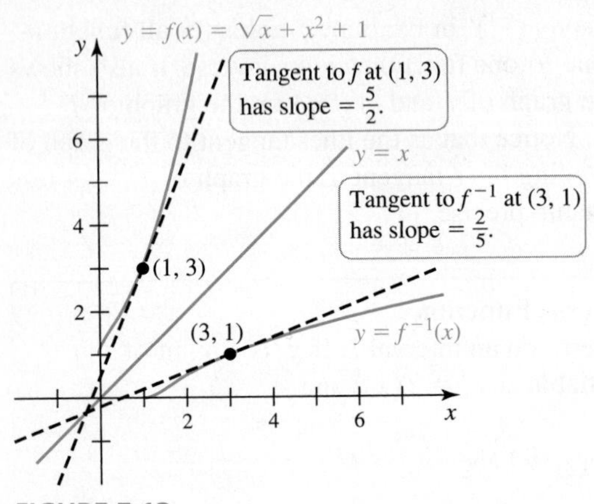

FIGURE 7.13

EXAMPLE 6 Derivative of an inverse function The function $f(x) = \sqrt{x} + x^2 + 1$ is one-to-one for $x \geq 0$ and has an inverse on that interval. Find the slope of the curve $y = f^{-1}(x)$ at the point $(3, 1)$.

SOLUTION The point $(1, 3)$ is on the graph of f; therefore, $(3, 1)$ is on the graph of f^{-1}. In this case, the slope of the curve $y = f^{-1}(x)$ at the point $(3, 1)$ is the reciprocal of the slope of the curve $y = f(x)$ at $(1, 3)$ (Figure 7.13). Note that $f'(x) = \dfrac{1}{2\sqrt{x}} + 2x$, which means that $f'(1) = \dfrac{1}{2} + 2 = \dfrac{5}{2}$. Therefore,

$$(f^{-1})'(3) = \frac{1}{f'(1)} = \frac{1}{5/2} = \frac{2}{5}.$$

Observe that it is not necessary to find a formula for f^{-1} in order to evaluate its derivative at a point.

Related Exercises 32–42 ◄

SECTION 7.1 EXERCISES

Review Questions

1. Give an example of a function that is one-to-one on the entire real number line.
2. Explain why a function that is not one-to-one on an interval I cannot have an inverse function on I.
3. Explain with pictures why (a, b) is on the graph of f whenever (b, a) is on the graph of f^{-1}.
4. Sketch a function that is one-to-one and positive for $x \geq 0$. Make a rough sketch of its inverse.
5. Express the inverse of $f(x) = 3x - 4$ in the form $y = f^{-1}(x)$.
6. Express the inverse of $f(x) = x^2$, for $x \leq 0$, in the form $y = f^{-1}(x)$.
7. If f is a one-to-one function with $f(2) = 8$ and $f'(2) = 4$, what is the value of $(f^{-1})'(8)$?
8. Explain how to find $(f^{-1})'(y_0)$ given that $y_0 = f(x_0)$.

Basic Skills

9–10. One-to-one functions *Answer the questions in the following exercises using the graph of f.*

9. Find three intervals on which f is one-to-one, making each interval as large as possible.

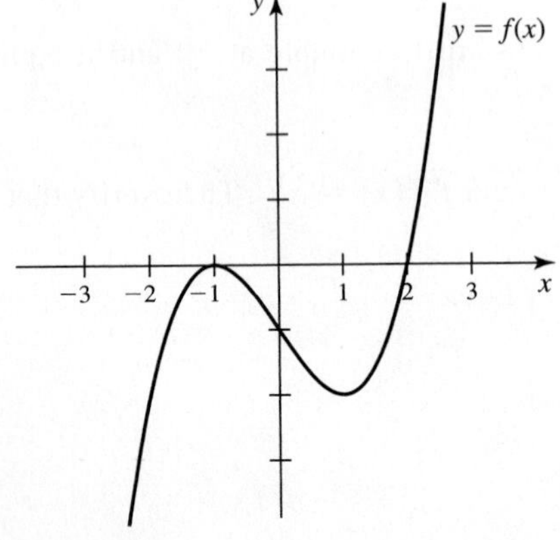

10. Find four intervals on which f is one-to-one, making each interval as large as possible.

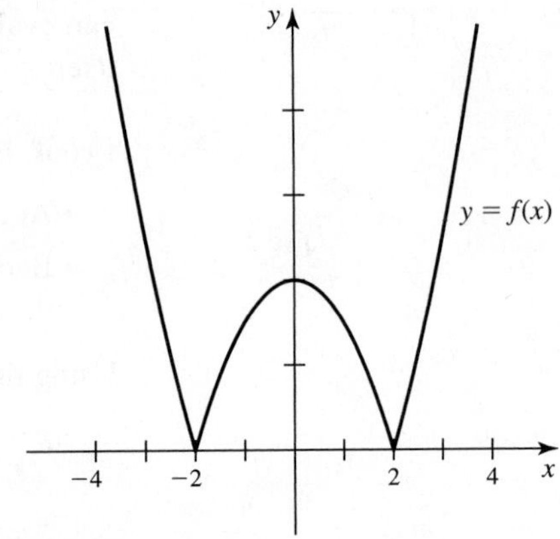

11–14. Where do inverses exist? *Use analytical and/or graphical methods to determine the intervals on which the following functions have an inverse (make each interval as large as possible).*

11. $f(x) = 3x + 4$
12. $f(x) = |2x + 1|$
13. $f(x) = 1/(x - 5)$
14. $f(x) = -(6 - x)^2$

15–20. Finding inverse functions

a. *Find the inverse of each function (on the given interval, if specified) and write it in the form $y = f^{-1}(x)$.*
b. *Verify the relationships $f(f^{-1}(x)) = x$ and $f^{-1}(f(x)) = x$.*

15. $f(x) = 6 - 4x$
16. $f(x) = 3x^3$
17. $f(x) = 3x + 5$
18. $f(x) = x^2 + 4$, for $x \geq 0$
19. $f(x) = \sqrt{x + 2}$, for $x \geq -2$
20. $f(x) = 2/(x^2 + 1)$, for $x \geq 0$

21. **Splitting up curves** The unit circle $x^2 + y^2 = 1$ consists of four one-to-one functions $f_1(x)$, $f_2(x)$, $f_3(x)$, and $f_4(x)$ (see figure).

 a. Find the domain and a formula for each function.
 b. Find the inverse of each function and write it as $y = f^{-1}(x)$.

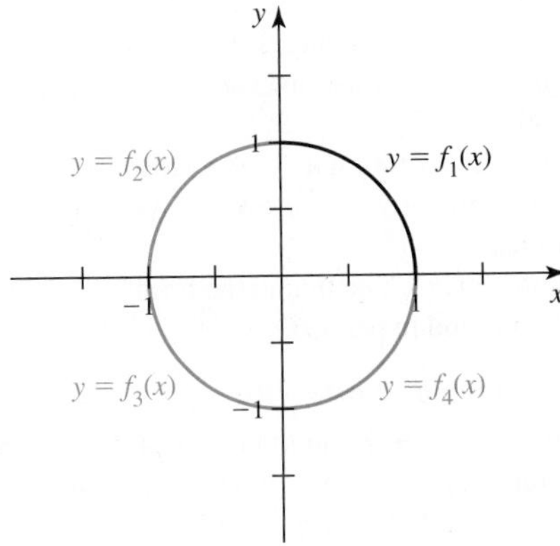

22. **Splitting up curves** The equation $y^4 = 4x^2$ is associated with four one-to-one functions $f_1(x)$, $f_2(x)$, $f_3(x)$, and $f_4(x)$ (see figure).

 a. Find the domain and a formula for each function.
 b. Find the inverse of each function and write it as $y = f^{-1}(x)$.

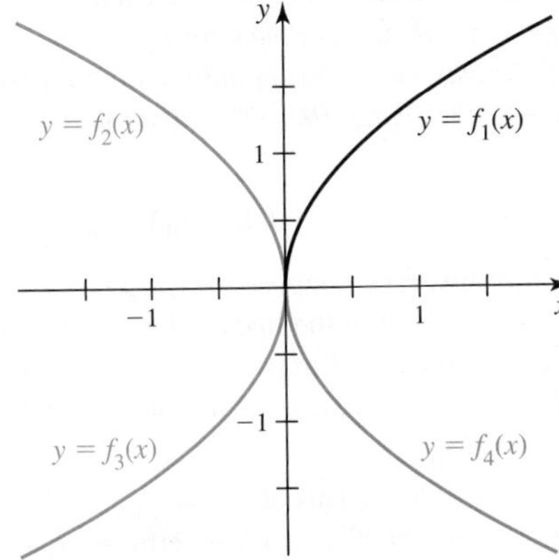

T **23–28. Graphing inverse functions** *Find the inverse function (on the given interval, if specified) and graph both f and f^{-1} on the same set of axes. Check your work by looking for the required symmetry in the graphs.*

23. $f(x) = 8 - 4x$

24. $f(x) = 4x - 12$

25. $f(x) = \sqrt{x}$, for $x \geq 0$

26. $f(x) = \sqrt{3 - x}$, for $x \leq 3$

27. $f(x) = x^4 + 4$, for $x > 0$

28. $f(x) = 6/(x^2 - 9)$, for $x > 3$

29–30. Graphs of inverses *Sketch the graph of the inverse function.*

29.

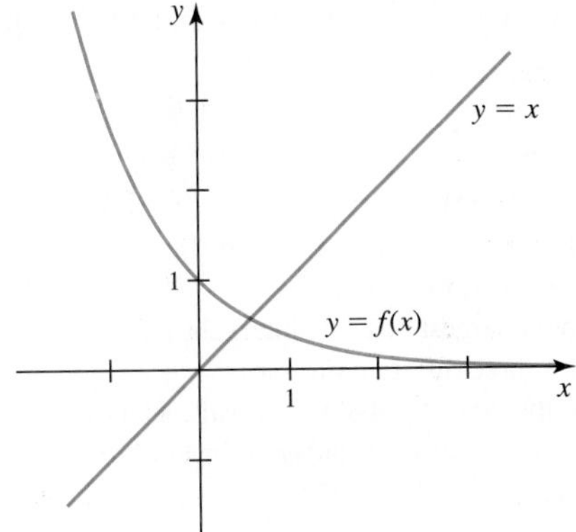

30.

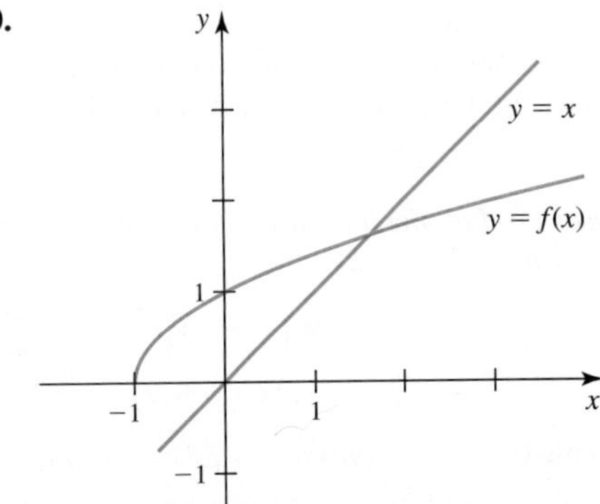

31–34. Derivatives of inverse functions at a point *Find the derivative of the inverse of the following functions at the specified point on the graph of the inverse function. You do not need to find f^{-1}.*

31. $f(x) = 3x + 4$; $(16, 4)$

32. $f(x) = x^2 + 1$, for $x \geq 0$; $(5, 2)$

33. $f(x) = \tan x$; $(1, \pi/4)$

34. $f(x) = x^2 - 2x - 3$, for $x \leq 1$; $(12, -3)$

35–38. Slopes of tangent lines *Given the function f, find the slope of the line tangent to the graph of f^{-1} at the specified point on the graph of f^{-1}.*

35. $f(x) = \sqrt{x}$; $(2, 4)$

36. $f(x) = x^3$; $(8, 2)$

37. $f(x) = (x + 2)^2$; $(36, 4)$

38. $f(x) = -x^2 + 8$; $(7, 1)$

39–42. Derivatives and inverse functions

39. Find $(f^{-1})'(3)$ if $f(x) = x^3 + x + 1$.

40. Find the slope of the curve $y = f^{-1}(x)$ at $(4, 7)$ if the slope of the curve $y = f(x)$ at $(7, 4)$ is $\frac{2}{3}$.

41. If the slope of the curve $y = f^{-1}(x)$ at $(4, 7)$ is $\frac{4}{5}$, find $f'(7)$.

42. If the slope of the curve $y = f(x)$ at $(4, 7)$ is $\frac{1}{5}$, find $(f^{-1})'(7)$.

Further Explorations

43. Explain why or why not Determine whether the following statements are true and give an explanation or counterexample.

a. If $f(x) = x^2 + 1$, then $f^{-1}(x) = 1/(x^2 + 1)$.
b. If $f(x) = 1/x$, then $f^{-1}(x) = 1/x$.
c. When restricted to the largest possible intervals, the function $f(x) = x^3 + x$ has three different inverses.
d. When restricted to the largest possible intervals, a tenth-degree polynomial could have at most ten different inverses.
e. If $f(x) = 1/x$, then $(f^{-1}(x))' = -1/x^2$.

T **44. Piecewise linear function** Consider the function $f(x) = |x| - 2|x - 1|$.

a. Find the largest possible intervals on which f is one-to-one.
b. Find explicit formulas for the inverse of f on the intervals in part (a).

45–48. Finding all inverses *Find all the inverses associated with the following functions and state their domains.*

45. $f(x) = (x + 1)^3$ **46.** $f(x) = (x - 4)^2$

47. $f(x) = 2/(x^2 + 2)$ **48.** $f(x) = 2x/(x + 2)$

49–56. Derivatives of inverse functions *Consider the following functions (on the given interval, if specified). Find the inverse function, express it as a function of x, and find the derivative of the inverse function.*

49. $f(x) = 3x - 4$

50. $f(x) = |x + 2|$, for $x \leq -2$

51. $f(x) = x^2 - 4$, for $x > 0$

52. $f(x) = \dfrac{x}{x + 5}$

53. $f(x) = \sqrt{x + 2}$

54. $f(x) = x^{2/3}$, for $x > 0$

55. $f(x) = x^{-1/2}$, for $x > 0$

56. $f(x) = x^3 + 3$

Applications

57–60. Geometry functions *Each function describes the volume V or surface area S of three-dimensional solids in terms of their radius. Find the inverse of each function that gives the radius in terms of V or S. Assume that r, V, and S are nonnegative. Express your answer in the form* $r = f^{-1}(S)$ *or* $r = f^{-1}(V)$.

57. Sphere: $V = \frac{4}{3}\pi r^3$

58. Sphere: $S = 4\pi r^2$

59. Cylinder with height 10: $V = 10\pi r^2$

60. Cone with height 12: $V = 4\pi r^2$

Additional Exercises

T **61. Inverses of a quartic** Consider the quartic polynomial $y = f(x) = x^4 - x^2$.

a. Graph f and find the largest intervals on which it is one-to-one. The goal is to find the inverse function on each of these intervals.
b. Make the substitution $u = x^2$ to solve the equation $y = f(x)$ for x in terms of y. Be sure you have included all possible solutions.
c. Write the inverse function in the form $y = f^{-1}(x)$ for each of the intervals found in part (a).

62. Inverse of composite functions

a. Let $g(x) = 2x + 3$ and $h(x) = x^3$. Consider the composite function $f(x) = g(h(x))$. Find f^{-1} directly and then express the inverse of f in terms of g^{-1} and h^{-1}.
b. Let $g(x) = x^2 + 1$ and $h(x) = \sqrt{x}$, for $x \geq 0$. Consider the composite function $f(x) = g(h(x))$. Find f^{-1} directly and then express the inverse of f in terms of g^{-1} and h^{-1}.
c. Explain why if h and g are one-to-one, the inverse of $f(x) = g(h(x))$ exists.

63–64. Inverses of (some) cubics *Finding the inverse of a cubic polynomial is equivalent to solving a cubic equation. A special case that is simpler than the general case is the cubic* $f(x) = x^3 + ax$. *Find the inverse of the following cubics using the substitution (known as Vieta's substitution)* $x = z - a/(3z)$. *Be sure to determine where the function is one-to-one.*

63. $f(x) = x^3 + 2x$ **64.** $f(x) = x^3 - 2x$

65. Tangents and inverses Suppose $y = L(x) = ax + b$ (with $a \neq 0$) is the equation of the line tangent to the graph of a one-to-one function f at (x_0, y_0). Also, suppose that $y = M(x) = cx + d$ is the equation of the line tangent to the graph of f^{-1} at (y_0, x_0).

a. Express a and b in terms of x_0 and y_0.
b. Express c in terms of a, and d in terms of a, x_0, and y_0.
c. Prove that $L^{-1}(x) = M(x)$.

QUICK CHECK ANSWERS

1. $f^{-1}(x) = 3x$; $f^{-1}(x) = x + 7$. **2.** For every Fahrenheit temperature, there is exactly one Celsius temperature, and vice versa. The given relation is also a linear function. It is one-to-one, so it has an inverse function. **3.** The function $f(x) = x^3$ is one-to-one on $(-\infty, \infty)$, so it has an inverse for all values of x. **4.** $f'(1) = 3$, $(f^{-1})'(1) = \frac{1}{3}$.

7.2 The Natural Logarithmic and Exponential Functions

Logarithms were invented around 1600 for calculating purposes by the Scotsman John Napier and the Englishman Henry Briggs. Unfortunately, the word *logarithm*, derived from the Greek for reasoning (*logos*) with numbers (*arithmos*), doesn't help with the meaning of the word. **When you see *logarithm*, you should think *exponent*.**

Your understanding of logarithms and exponentials as algebraic operations is important, and it will be put to use in the coming pages. For example, you may recall the following relationship that will be used frequently: If b denotes a *base* with $b > 0$ and $b \neq 1$, then

$$y = b^x \quad \text{if and only if} \quad x = \log_b y.$$

However, to do calculus with logarithms and exponentials, we must view them not just as operations, but as functions. Once we define logarithmic and exponential *functions*, many important questions quickly follow.

- What are the domains of b^x and $\log_b x$?
- How do we assign a meaning to expressions such as 2^π or $\log_3 \pi$?
- Are these functions continuous on their domains?
- What are their derivatives?
- What new integrals can be evaluated using these functions?

It all begins with the definition of the *natural logarithm function* in terms of a definite integral. We show that this definition indeed produces a function that satisfies the algebraic properties of a logarithm. Of critical importance, the base of the natural logarithm function is identified as the number e. The theory of inverse functions (Section 7.1) is next applied to develop the *natural exponential function* (also with base e). Results involving derivatives and integrals of the natural logarithm and exponential functions emerge quite naturally at this point. In Section 7.3, we derive analogous properties of logarithmic and exponential functions with an arbitrary positive base b. This is all important work, so let's begin.

The Natural Logarithm

Our aim is to develop the properties of the natural logarithm using definite integrals.

DEFINITION The Natural Logarithm

The **natural logarithm** of a number $x > 0$, denoted $\ln x$, is defined as

$$\ln x = \int_1^x \frac{1}{t}\,dt.$$

All the essential properties of the natural logarithmic function follow directly from this new integral definition.

Properties of the Natural Logarithm

Domain, range, and sign Because the natural logarithm is defined as a definite integral, its value is the net area bounded by the curve $y = 1/t$ and the t-axis between $t = 1$ and $t = x$. The integrand is undefined at $t = 0$, so the domain of $\ln x$ is $(0, \infty)$. On the interval $(1, \infty)$, $\ln x$ is positive because the net area of the region under the curve is positive (Figure 7.14a). On $(0, 1)$, we have $\int_1^x \frac{1}{t}\,dt = -\int_x^1 \frac{1}{t}\,dt$, which implies $\ln x$ is negative (Figure 7.14b). As expected, when $x = 1$, we have $\ln 1 = \int_1^1 \frac{1}{t}\,dt = 0$. The net area interpretation of $\ln x$ also implies that the range of $\ln x$ is $(-\infty, \infty)$. (See Exercise 78 for an outline of a proof.)

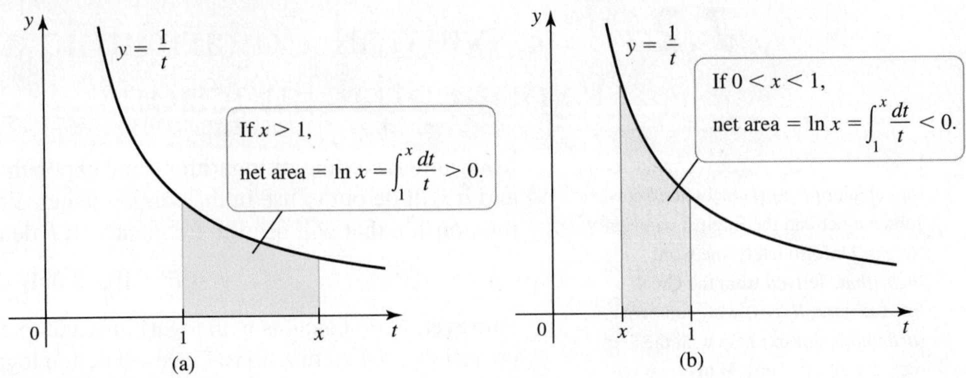

FIGURE 7.14

Derivative The derivative of the natural logarithm follows immediately from its definition and the Fundamental Theorem of Calculus:

➤ Recall that by the Fundamental Theorem of Calculus

$$\frac{d}{dx}\int_a^x f(t)\,dt = f(x).$$

$$\frac{d}{dx}(\ln x) = \frac{d}{dx}\int_1^x \frac{dt}{t} = \frac{1}{x}, \qquad \text{for } x > 0$$

We have two important consequences:

- Because the derivative of $\ln x$ is defined for $x > 0$, $\ln x$ is differentiable for $x > 0$, which means it is continuous on its domain (Theorem 3.1).
- Because $1/x > 0$ for $x > 0$, $\ln x$ is strictly increasing and one-to-one on its domain; therefore, it has a well-defined inverse.

The Chain Rule allows us to extend the derivative property to all nonzero real numbers (Exercise 76). By differentiating $\ln(-x)$ for $x < 0$, we find that

$$\frac{d}{dx}(\ln |x|) = \frac{1}{x}.$$

More generally, by the Chain Rule,

$$\frac{d}{dx}(\ln |u(x)|) = \frac{d}{du}(\ln |u(x)|)u'(x) = \frac{u'(x)}{u(x)}.$$

QUICK CHECK 1 What is the domain of $\ln |x|$? ◄

$\frac{d}{dx}(\ln x) > 0 \Longrightarrow \ln x$ is increasing for $x > 0$

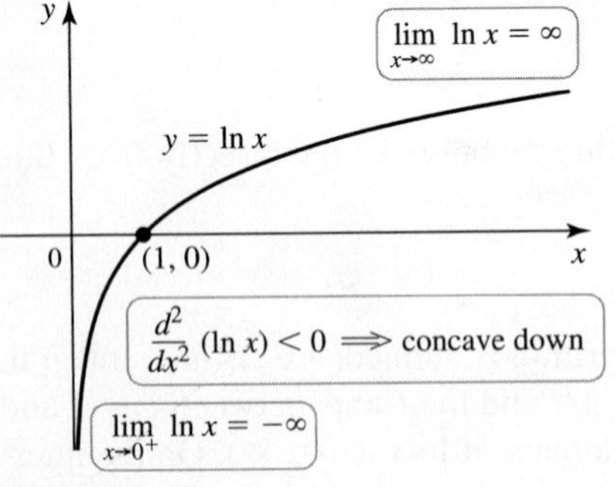

FIGURE 7.15

Graph of $\ln x$ As noted before, $\ln x$ is continuous and strictly increasing for $x > 0$. The second derivative, $\frac{d^2}{dx^2}(\ln x) = -\frac{1}{x^2}$, is negative for all x, which implies the graph of $\ln x$ is concave down for $x > 0$. As demonstrated in Exercise 78,

$$\lim_{x\to\infty} \ln x = \infty, \quad \text{and} \quad \lim_{x\to 0^+} \ln x = -\infty.$$

This information, coupled with the fact that $\ln 1 = 0$, gives the graph of $y = \ln x$ (Figure 7.15). The graphs of $y = \ln x$, $y = \ln |x|$, and their derivatives are shown in Figure 7.16.

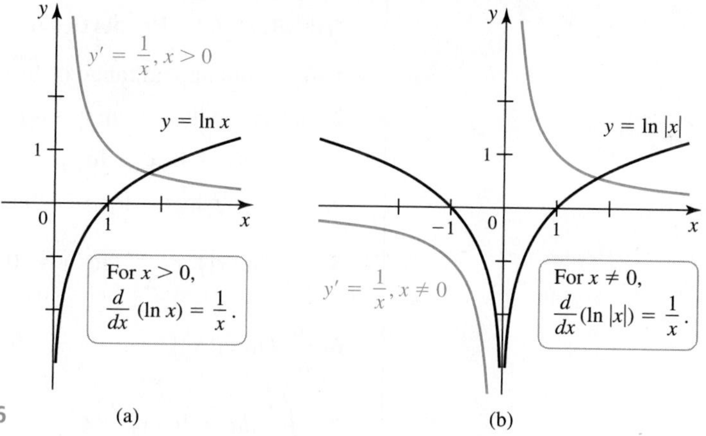

FIGURE 7.16

Logarithm of a product The familiar logarithm property

$$\ln xy = \ln x + \ln y, \qquad \text{for } x > 0, \quad y > 0$$

may be proved using the integral definition:

$$\begin{aligned}
\ln xy &= \int_1^{xy} \frac{dt}{t} && \text{Definition of } \ln xy \\
&= \int_1^{x} \frac{dt}{t} + \int_x^{xy} \frac{dt}{t} && \text{Additive property of integrals} \\
&= \int_1^{x} \frac{dt}{t} + \int_1^{y} \frac{du}{u} && \text{Substitute } u = t/x \text{ in second integral; } \frac{dt}{t} = \frac{du}{u} \\
&= \ln x + \ln y && \text{Definition of ln}
\end{aligned}$$

Logarithm of a quotient Assuming $x > 0$ and $y > 0$, the product property and a bit of algebra give

$$\ln x = \ln\left(y \cdot \frac{x}{y}\right) = \ln y + \ln\left(\frac{x}{y}\right).$$

Solving for $\ln(x/y)$, we have

$$\ln\left(\frac{x}{y}\right) = \ln x - \ln y,$$

which is the quotient property for logarithms. (Also see Exercise 48.)

Logarithm of a power By the product rule for logarithms, if $x > 0$ and p is a positive integer, then

$$\ln x^p = \ln(\underbrace{x \cdot x \cdots x}_{p \text{ factors}}) = \underbrace{\ln x + \cdots + \ln x}_{p \text{ factors}} = p \ln x.$$

Later in this section, we prove that $\ln x^p = p \ln x$, for $x > 0$ and for all real numbers p.

Integrals Because $\frac{d}{dx}(\ln|x|) = \frac{1}{x}$, we have

$$\int \frac{1}{x}\,dx = \ln|x| + C.$$

We have shown that the following properties of $\ln x$ are consequences of the integral definition.

THEOREM 7.4 Properties of the Natural Logarithm

1. The domain and range of $\ln x$ are $(0, \infty)$ and $(-\infty, \infty)$, respectively.
2. $\ln(xy) = \ln x + \ln y$, for $x > 0, y > 0$
3. $\ln(x/y) = \ln x - \ln y$, for $x > 0, y > 0$
4. $\ln x^p = p \ln x$, for $x > 0$ and p a real number
5. $\dfrac{d}{dx}(\ln|x|) = \dfrac{1}{x}$, for $x \neq 0$
6. $\dfrac{d}{dx}(\ln|u(x)|) = \dfrac{u'(x)}{u(x)}$, for $u(x) \neq 0$
7. $\displaystyle\int \frac{1}{x}\,dx = \ln|x| + C$

EXAMPLE 1 Derivatives involving $\ln x$ Find $\dfrac{dy}{dx}$ for the following functions.

a. $y = \ln(4x)$ **b.** $y = x \ln x$ **c.** $y = \ln|\sec x|$ **d.** $y = \dfrac{\ln x^2}{x^2}$

SOLUTION

a. Using the Chain Rule,

$$\frac{dy}{dx} = \frac{d}{dx}(\ln(4x)) = \frac{1}{4x} \cdot 4 = \frac{1}{x}.$$

➤ Because $\ln x$ and $\ln 4x$ differ by a constant ($\ln 4x = \ln x + \ln 4$), the derivatives of $\ln x$ and $\ln 4x$ are equal.

An alternative method uses a property of logarithms before differentiating:

$$\frac{d}{dx}(\ln 4x) = \frac{d}{dx}(\ln 4 + \ln x) \quad \ln(xy) = \ln x + \ln y$$

$$= 0 + \frac{1}{x} = \frac{1}{x} \quad \ln 4 \text{ is a constant.}$$

b. By the Product Rule,

$$\frac{dy}{dx} = \frac{d}{dx}(x \ln x) = 1 \cdot \ln x + x \cdot \frac{1}{x} = \ln x + 1.$$

c. Using property 6 of Theorem 7.4,

$$\frac{dy}{dx} = \frac{1}{\sec x}\left[\frac{d}{dx}(\sec x)\right] = \frac{1}{\sec x}(\sec x \tan x) = \tan x.$$

d. The Quotient Rule and Chain Rule give

$$\frac{dy}{dx} = \frac{x^2\left(\frac{1}{x^2} \cdot 2x\right) - (\ln x^2)\,2x}{(x^2)^2} = \frac{2x - 4x \ln x}{x^4} = \frac{2 - 4 \ln x}{x^3}.$$

➤ The fact that $\ln x^2 = 2 \ln x$ was used to simplify the result in Example 1d. It could also have been used prior to differentiation.

Related Exercises 7–14 ◄

QUICK CHECK 2 Find $\dfrac{d}{dx}(\ln x^p)$, where $x > 0$ and p is a real number, in two ways: (1) using the Chain Rule and (2) by first using a property of logarithms. ◄

EXAMPLE 2 Integrals with ln *x* Evaluate $\displaystyle\int_0^4 \frac{x}{x^2+9}\,dx$.

SOLUTION

$$\begin{aligned}\int_0^4 \frac{x}{x^2+9}\,dx &= \frac{1}{2}\int_9^{25}\frac{du}{u} && \text{Let } u = x^2+9;\ du = 2x\,dx.\ x=0 \Rightarrow u=9,\ x=4\Rightarrow u=25\\ &= \frac{1}{2}\ln|u|\Big|_9^{25} && \text{Fundamental Theorem}\\ &= \frac{1}{2}(\ln 25 - \ln 9) && \text{Evaluate.}\\ &= \ln\frac{5}{3} && \text{Properties of logarithms}\end{aligned}$$

Related Exercises 15–22 ◀

The Question of Base

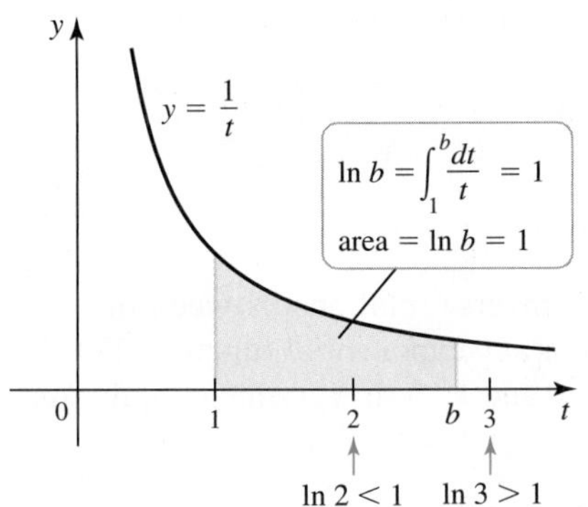

FIGURE 7.17

The natural logarithm *is* a logarithm, but what is its base? We now determine the base b such that $\ln x = \log_b x$. Two steps are needed: We show that b exists; then we identify the value of b.

An algebraic property of any logarithm is that $\log_b b = 1$, for $b > 0$. Therefore, the number b that we seek has the property $\ln b = 1$, or

$$\ln b = \int_1^b \frac{dt}{t} = 1.$$

We see that b is the number that makes the area of the region under the curve $y = 1/t$ on the interval $[1, b]$ exactly 1 (Figure 7.17).

Computations with Riemann sums show that $\ln 2 = \int_1^2 \frac{dt}{t} < 1$ and that $\ln 3 = \int_1^3 \frac{dt}{t} > 1$ (Exercise 79). Because $\ln x$ is a continuous function, the Intermediate Value Theorem says that there is a number b with $2 < b < 3$ such that $\ln b = 1$. That completes the first step: We know that b exists and lies between 2 and 3.

➤ Because $\frac{d}{dx}(\ln x) = \frac{1}{x}$, $\frac{d}{dx}(\ln x)\Big|_{x=1} = \frac{1}{1} = 1.$

To estimate b, we use the fact that the derivative of $\ln x$ at $x = 1$ is 1. By the definition of the derivative, it follows that

$$\begin{aligned}1 = \frac{d}{dx}(\ln x)\Big|_{x=1} &= \lim_{h\to 0}\frac{\ln(1+h) - \ln 1}{h} && \text{Derivative of } \ln x \text{ at } x = 1\\ &= \lim_{h\to 0}\frac{\ln(1+h)}{h} && \ln 1 = 0\\ &= \lim_{h\to 0}\ln(1+h)^{1/h} && p\ln x = \ln x^p\end{aligned}$$

➤ We rely on Theorem 2.10 of Section 2.6 here. If f is continuous at $g(a)$ and g is continuous at a, then $\lim_{x\to a} f(g(x)) = f(\lim_{x\to a} g(x))$.

The natural logarithm is continuous for $x > 0$, so it is permissible to interchange the order of $\lim_{h\to 0}$ and the evaluation of $\ln(1+h)^{1/h}$. The result is that

$$\ln\Big(\underbrace{\lim_{h\to 0}(1+h)^{1/h}}_{b}\Big) = 1.$$

Observe that the limit within the bracket is b because $\ln b = 1$ and only one number satisfies this equation. Therefore, we have isolated b as a limit:

$$b = \lim_{h\to 0}(1+h)^{1/h}$$

Table 7.1

h	$(1+h)^{1/h}$	h	$(1+h)^{1/h}$
10^{-1}	2.593742	-10^{-1}	2.867972
10^{-2}	2.704814	-10^{-2}	2.731999
10^{-3}	2.716924	-10^{-3}	2.719642
10^{-4}	2.718146	-10^{-4}	2.718418
10^{-5}	2.718268	-10^{-5}	2.718295
10^{-6}	2.718280	-10^{-6}	2.718283
10^{-7}	2.718282	-10^{-7}	2.718282

It is evident from the values in Table 7.1 that $(1+h)^{1/h} \to 2.718282\ldots$ as $h \to 0$. The value of this limit is the mathematical constant e, and it has been computed to millions of digits. A better approximation is

$$e \approx 2.718281828459045.$$

With this argument, we have identified the base of the natural logarithm: it is $b = e$.

> The constant e was identified and named by the Swiss mathematician Leonhard Euler (1707–1783) (pronounced "oiler") and is also called Euler's constant.

DEFINITION The Natural Logarithm and the Number e

The **natural logarithm** is the logarithm with a base of $e = \lim_{h\to 0} (1+h)^{1/h} \approx 2.71828$. It follows that $\ln e = 1$.

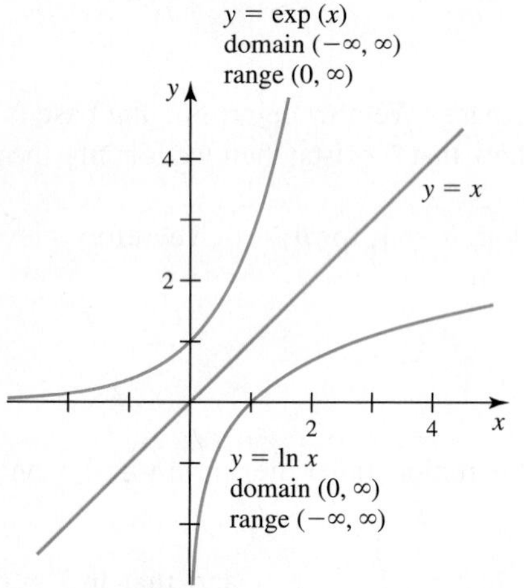

FIGURE 7.18

The Exponential Function

We have established that $f(x) = \ln x$ is a continuous, increasing function on the interval $(0, \infty)$. Therefore, it is one-to-one on this interval and its inverse function exists. We denote the inverse function $f^{-1}(x) = \exp(x)$. Its graph is obtained by reflecting the graph of $f(x) = \ln x$ about the line $y = x$ (Figure 7.18). The domain of $\exp(x)$ is $(-\infty, \infty)$ because the range of $\ln x$ is $(-\infty, \infty)$, and the range of $\exp(x)$ is $(0, \infty)$ because the domain of $\ln x$ is $(0, \infty)$.

The usual relationships between a function and its inverse also hold:

- $y = \exp(x)$ if and only if $x = \ln y$
- $\exp(\ln x) = x$, for $x > 0$, and $\ln(\exp(x)) = x$, for all x

We now appeal to the properties of $\ln x$ and use the inverse relations between $\ln x$ and $\exp(x)$ to show that $\exp(x)$ satisfies the properties of any exponential function. For example, if $x_1 = \ln y_1$ (which implies that $y_1 = \exp(x_1)$) and $x_2 = \ln y_2$ (which implies that $y_2 = \exp(x_2)$), then

$$\begin{aligned}
\exp(x_1 + x_2) &= \exp(\underbrace{\ln y_1 + \ln y_2}_{\ln y_1 y_2}) && \text{Substitute } x_1 = \ln y_1, x_2 = \ln y_2. \\
&= \exp(\ln y_1 y_2) && \text{Properties of logarithms} \\
&= y_1 y_2 && \text{Inverse property of } \exp x \text{ and } \ln x \\
&= \exp(x_1)\exp(x_2). && y_1 = \exp(x_1), y_2 = \exp(x_2)
\end{aligned}$$

> Note that we already know two important values of $\exp(x)$. Because $\ln e = 1$, we have $\exp(1) = e$. Because $\ln 1 = 0$, $\exp(0) = 1$.

Therefore, $\exp(x)$ satisfies the property of exponential functions $b^{x_1+x_2} = b^{x_1}b^{x_2}$. Similar arguments show that $\exp(x)$ satisfies other characteristic properties of all exponential functions (Exercise 77).

We conclude that $\exp(x)$ is an exponential function and it is the inverse function of $\ln x$. We also know that $\ln x$ is the logarithmic function base e. Therefore, the base for $\exp(x)$ is also the number e, and we have $\exp(x) = e^x$, for all real numbers x.

DEFINITION The Exponential Function

The **(natural) exponential function** is the exponential function with the base $e \approx 2.71828$. It is the inverse function of the natural logarithm $\ln x$.

The inverse properties of $\ln x$ and e^x imply that $\ln(e^x) = x$, for all real numbers x, and that $e^{\ln x} = x$, for all real numbers $x > 0$. We may now prove the property that $\ln x^p = p \ln x$, for $x > 0$ and all real numbers p. We begin by using $e^{\ln x} = x$ and writing

$$x^p = (\underbrace{e^{\ln x}}_{x})^p = e^{p \ln x}.$$

> Because $\ln x$ is a one-to-one function for $x > 0$, if $x = y$, then $\ln x = \ln y$. Therefore, we can take the ln of both sides of an equation and produce a valid equation.

Taking the natural logarithm of both sides and using $\ln(e^x) = x$, we have

$$\ln(x^p) = \ln(e^{p\ln x}) = p\ln x.$$

The essential properties of the exponential function are summarized in the following theorem.

THEOREM 7.5 Properties of e^x
The exponential function e^x satisfies the following properties, all of which follow from the integral definition of $\ln x$. Let x and y be real numbers.

1. $e^{x+y} = e^x e^y$
2. $e^{x-y} = e^x/e^y$
3. $(e^x)^y = e^{xy}$
4. $\ln(e^x) = x$, for all x
5. $e^{\ln x} = x$, for $x > 0$

QUICK CHECK 3 Simplify $e^{\ln 2x}$, $\ln(e^{2x})$, $e^{2\ln x}$, $\ln(2e^x)$.

Derivatives and Integrals The derivative of the exponential function follows directly from Theorem 7.3 (derivatives of inverse functions) or by using the Chain Rule. Taking the latter course, we observe that $\ln(e^x) = x$ and then differentiate both sides with respect to x:

$$\frac{d}{dx}(\ln e^x) = \underbrace{\frac{d}{dx}(x)}_{1}$$

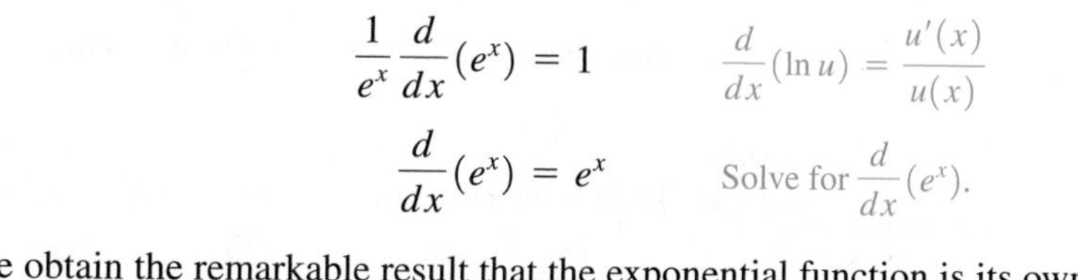

$$\frac{1}{e^x}\frac{d}{dx}(e^x) = 1 \qquad \frac{d}{dx}(\ln u) = \frac{u'(x)}{u(x)}$$

$$\frac{d}{dx}(e^x) = e^x \qquad \text{Solve for } \frac{d}{dx}(e^x).$$

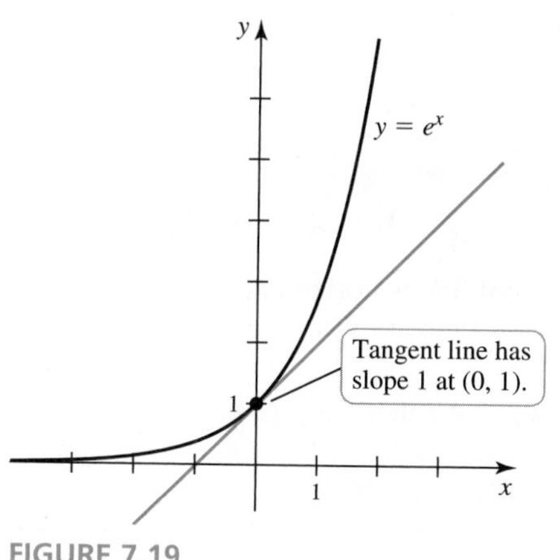

FIGURE 7.19

We obtain the remarkable result that the exponential function is its own derivative, which implies that the line tangent to the graph of $y = e^x$ at $(0, 1)$ has slope 1 (Figure 7.19). It immediately follows that e^x is its own antiderivative up to a constant; that is,

$$\int e^x\,dx = e^x + C.$$

Extending these results using the Chain Rule, we have the following theorem.

THEOREM 7.6 Derivative and Integral of the Exponential Function
For real numbers x,

$$\frac{d}{dx}(e^{u(x)}) = e^{u(x)}u'(x) \quad \text{and} \quad \int e^x\,dx = e^x + C.$$

QUICK CHECK 4 What is the slope of the curve $y = e^x$ at $x = \ln 2$? What is the area of the region bounded by the graph of $y = e^x$ and the x-axis between $x = 0$ and $x = \ln 2$?

EXAMPLE 3 **Derivatives involving exponential functions** Evaluate the following derivatives.

a. $\dfrac{d}{dx}(3e^{2x} - 4e^{x} + e^{-3x})$ **b.** $\dfrac{d}{dt}\left(\dfrac{e^{t}}{e^{2t} - 1}\right)$ **c.** $\dfrac{d}{dx}(e^{\cos \pi x})\Big|_{x=1/2}$

SOLUTION

a.
$$\begin{aligned} \frac{d}{dx}(3e^{2x} - 4e^{x} + e^{-3x}) &= 3\frac{d}{dx}(e^{2x}) - 4\frac{d}{dx}(e^{x}) + \frac{d}{dx}(e^{-3x}) && \text{Sum and Constant Multiple Rules} \\ &= 3\cdot 2\cdot e^{2x} - 4e^{x} + (-3)e^{-3x} && \text{Chain Rule} \\ &= 6e^{2x} - 4e^{x} - 3e^{-3x} && \text{Simplify.} \end{aligned}$$

b.
$$\frac{d}{dt}\left(\frac{e^{t}}{e^{2t} - 1}\right) = \frac{(e^{2t} - 1)e^{t} - e^{t}\cdot 2e^{2t}}{(e^{2t} - 1)^2} = -\frac{e^{3t} + e^{t}}{(e^{2t} - 1)^2} \qquad \text{Quotient Rule}$$

c. First note that by the Chain Rule, we have

$$\frac{d}{dx}(e^{\cos \pi x}) = -\pi \sin \pi x \cdot e^{\cos \pi x}.$$

Therefore,

$$\frac{d}{dx}(e^{\cos \pi x})\Big|_{x=1/2} = (-\underbrace{\pi \sin \pi x}_{1} \cdot \underbrace{e^{\cos \pi x}}_{e^0 = 1})\Big|_{x=1/2} = -\pi.$$

Related Exercises 23–28 ◄

EXAMPLE 4 **Finding tangent lines**

a. Write an equation of the line tangent to the graph of $f(x) = 2x - \dfrac{e^{x}}{2}$ at the point $\left(0, -\frac{1}{2}\right)$.

b. Find the point(s) on the graph of f where the tangent line is horizontal.

SOLUTION

a. To find the slope of the tangent line at $\left(0, -\frac{1}{2}\right)$, we first calculate $f'(x)$:

$$\begin{aligned} f'(x) &= \frac{d}{dx}\left(2x - \frac{e^{x}}{2}\right) \\ &= \frac{d}{dx}(2x) - \frac{d}{dx}\left(\frac{1}{2}e^{x}\right) && \text{Difference Rule} \\ &= 2 - \frac{1}{2}e^{x} && \text{Evaluate derivatives.} \end{aligned}$$

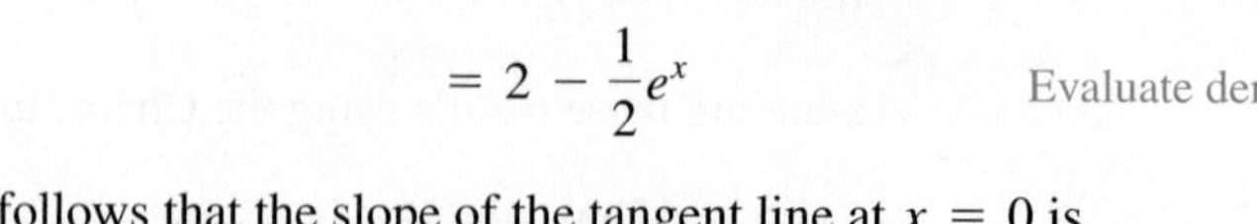

It follows that the slope of the tangent line at $x = 0$ is

$$f'(0) = 2 - \frac{1}{2}e^{0} = \frac{3}{2}.$$

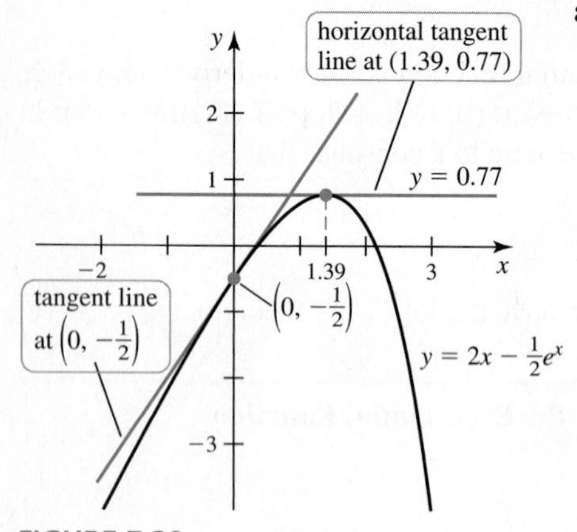

FIGURE 7.20

Figure 7.20 shows the tangent line passing through $\left(0, -\frac{1}{2}\right)$; it has the equation

$$y - \left(-\frac{1}{2}\right) = \frac{3}{2}(x - 0) \quad \text{or} \quad y = \frac{3}{2}x - \frac{1}{2}.$$

b. Because the slope of a horizontal tangent line is 0, our goal is to solve $f'(x) = 2 - \frac{1}{2}e^{x} = 0$. Multiplying both sides of this equation by 2 and rearranging gives the equation $e^{x} = 4$. Taking the natural logarithm of both sides, we find that $x = \ln 4$. Thus, $f'(x) = 0$ at $x = \ln 4 \approx 1.39$, and f has a horizontal tangent at $(\ln 4, f(\ln 4)) \approx (1.39, 0.77)$ (Figure 7.20).

Related Exercises 29–30 ◄

EXAMPLE 5 **Integrals with e^x** Evaluate $\displaystyle\int \frac{e^x}{1 + e^x}\,dx$.

SOLUTION The change of variables $u = 1 + e^x$ implies $du = e^x\,dx$:

$$\int \underbrace{\frac{1}{1 + e^x}}_{u} \underbrace{e^x\,dx}_{du} = \int \frac{1}{u}\,du \qquad u = 1 + e^x,\ du = e^x\,dx$$

$$= \ln |u| + C \qquad \text{Antiderivative of } u^{-1}$$

$$= \ln (1 + e^x) + C \qquad \text{Replace } u \text{ by } 1 + e^x.$$

Note that the absolute value may be removed from $\ln |u|$ because $1 + e^x > 0$ for all x.

Related Exercises 31–38 ◀

EXAMPLE 6 **Arc length of an exponential curve** Find the length of the curve $f(x) = 2e^x + \frac{1}{8}e^{-x}$ on the interval $[0, \ln 2]$.

SOLUTION We first calculate $f'(x) = 2e^x - \frac{1}{8}e^{-x}$ and $f'(x)^2 = 4e^{2x} - \frac{1}{2} + \frac{1}{64}e^{-2x}$. The length of the curve on the interval $[0, \ln 2]$ is

$$L = \int_0^{\ln 2} \sqrt{1 + f'(x)^2}\,dx = \int_0^{\ln 2} \sqrt{1 + \left(4e^{2x} - \tfrac{1}{2} + \tfrac{1}{64}e^{-2x}\right)}\,dx$$

$$= \int_0^{\ln 2} \sqrt{4e^{2x} + \tfrac{1}{2} + \tfrac{1}{64}e^{-2x}}\,dx \qquad \text{Simplify.}$$

$$= \int_0^{\ln 2} \sqrt{\left(2e^x + \tfrac{1}{8}e^{-x}\right)^2}\,dx \qquad \text{Factor.}$$

$$= \int_0^{\ln 2} \left(2e^x + \tfrac{1}{8}e^{-x}\right)dx \qquad \text{Simplify.}$$

$$= \left(2e^x - \tfrac{1}{8}e^{-x}\right)\Big|_0^{\ln 2} = \frac{33}{16}. \qquad \text{Evaluate the integral.}$$

Related Exercises 31–38 ◀

Logarithmic Differentiation

Products, quotients, and powers of functions are usually differentiated using the derivative rules of the same name (perhaps combined with the Chain Rule). There are times, however, when the direct computation of a derivative is tedious. Consider the function

$$f(x) = \frac{(x^3 - 1)^4\sqrt{3x - 1}}{x^2 + 4}.$$

We would need the Quotient, Product, and Chain Rules just to compute $f'(x)$, and simplifying the result would require additional work. The properties of logarithms developed in this section are useful for differentiating such functions.

➤ The properties of logarithms needed for logarithmic differentiation are:

1. $\ln (xy) = \ln x + \ln y$
2. $\ln (x/y) = \ln x - \ln y$
3. $\ln x^p = p \ln x$

All three properties are used in Example 7.

EXAMPLE 7 **Logarithmic differentiation** Let $f(x) = \dfrac{(x^3 - 1)^4\sqrt{3x - 1}}{x^2 + 4}$ and compute $f'(x)$.

SOLUTION We begin by taking the natural logarithm of both sides and simplifying the result:

> In the event that $f(x) \le 0$ for some values of x, $\ln(f(x))$ is not defined. In that case, we generally find the derivative of $|y| = |f(x)|$.

$$\begin{aligned}\ln(f(x)) &= \ln\left[\frac{(x^3-1)^4\sqrt{3x-1}}{x^2+4}\right]\\ &= \ln(x^3-1)^4 + \ln\sqrt{3x-1} - \ln(x^2+4) && \log(xy) = \log x + \log y\\ &= 4\ln(x^3-1) + \tfrac{1}{2}\ln(3x-1) - \ln(x^2+4) && \log x^p = p\log x\end{aligned}$$

We now differentiate both sides using the Chain Rule; specifically the derivative of the left side is $\frac{d}{dx}(\ln f(x)) = \frac{f'(x)}{f(x)}$. Therefore,

$$\frac{f'(x)}{f(x)} = 4\cdot\frac{1}{x^3-1}\cdot 3x^2 + \frac{1}{2}\cdot\frac{1}{3x-1}\cdot 3 - \frac{1}{x^2+4}\cdot 2x.$$

Solving for $f'(x)$, we have

$$f'(x) = f(x)\left[\frac{12x^2}{x^3-1} + \frac{3}{2(3x-1)} - \frac{2x}{x^2+4}\right].$$

Finally, we replace $f(x)$ with the original function:

$$f'(x) = \frac{(x^3-1)^4\sqrt{3x-1}}{x^2+4}\left[\frac{12x^2}{x^3-1} + \frac{3}{2(3x-1)} - \frac{2x}{x^2+4}\right]$$

Related Exercises 39–46 ◀

Logarithmic differentiation also provides a method for finding derivatives of functions of the form $g(x)^{h(x)}$. The derivative of $f(x) = x^x$ is computed as follows, assuming $x > 0$:

$$\begin{aligned}f(x) &= x^x\\ \ln(f(x)) &= \ln(x^x) = x\ln x && \text{Take logarithms of both sides; use properties.}\\ \frac{1}{f(x)}f'(x) &= \left(1\cdot\ln x + x\cdot\frac{1}{x}\right) && \text{Differentiate both sides.}\\ f'(x) &= f(x)(\ln x + 1) && \text{Solve for } f'(x) \text{ and simplify.}\\ f'(x) &= x^x(\ln x + 1) && \text{Replace } f(x) \text{ with } x^x.\end{aligned}$$

SECTION 7.2 EXERCISES

Review Questions

1. What are the domain and range of $\ln x$?
2. Give a geometric interpretation of the function $\ln x = \int_1^x \frac{dt}{t}$.
3. Differentiate both sides of $x = e^y$ with respect to x to show that $\frac{d}{dx}(\ln x) = \frac{1}{x}$, for $x > 0$.
4. Sketch the graph of $f(x) = \ln|x|$ and explain how the graph shows that $f'(x) = 1/x$.
5. Show that $\frac{d}{dx}(\ln kx) = \frac{d}{dx}(\ln x)$, where $x > 0$ and $k > 0$ is a real number.
6. Explain the general procedure of logarithmic differentiation.

Basic Skills

7–14. Derivatives involving ln *x* *Find the following derivatives. Give the intervals on which the results are valid.*

7. $\frac{d}{dx}(\ln x^2)$
8. $\frac{d}{dx}(\ln 2x^8)$
9. $\frac{d}{dx}\left[\ln\left(\frac{x+1}{x-1}\right)\right]$
10. $\frac{d}{dx}(e^x \ln x)$
11. $\frac{d}{dx}((x^2+1)\ln x)$
12. $\frac{d}{dx}(\ln|x^2-1|)$
13. $\frac{d}{dx}(\ln(\ln x))$
14. $\frac{d}{dx}(\ln(\cos^2 x))$

15–22. Integrals with ln *x* *Evaluate the following integrals. Include absolute values only when needed.*

15. $\int \frac{3}{x-10}\,dx$
16. $\int \frac{dx}{4x-3}$

17. $\int \left(\frac{2}{x-4} - \frac{3}{2x+1}\right) dx$

18. $\int \frac{x^2}{2x^3+1}\, dx$

19. $\int_0^3 \frac{2x-1}{x+1}\, dx$

20. $\int \tan x\, dx$

21. $\int_3^4 \frac{dx}{2x \ln x \ln^3 (\ln x)}$

22. $\int_0^{\pi/2} \frac{\sin x}{1+\cos x}\, dx$

23–28. Derivatives with the exponential function *Find the derivative of the following functions.*

23. $f(x) = 9e^{-x} - 5e^{2x} - 6e^x$

24. $g(x) = xe^{-x} - e^{2x}$

25. $f(x) = \frac{e^{2x}}{e^{-x}+2}$

26. $h(x) = \cot e^x$

27. $f(x) = e^{\sin 2x}$ evaluated at $x = \pi/4$

28. $h(x) = \ln (e^{2x}+1)$ evaluated at $x = \ln 2$

29–30. Equations of tangent lines *Find an equation of the line tangent to the following curves at the point $(a, f(a))$.*

29. $y = \frac{e^x}{4} - x, \quad a = 0$

30. $y = 2e^x - 1, \quad a = \ln 3$

31–38. Integrals with e^x *Evaluate the following integrals.*

31. $\int (e^{2x}+1)\, dx$

32. $\int 3e^{-4t}\, dt$

33. $\int_0^{\ln 3} e^x(e^{3x} + e^{2x} + e^x)\, dx$

34. $\int (2e^{-10z} + 3e^{5z})\, dz$

35. $\int \frac{e^x + e^{-x}}{e^x - e^{-x}}\, dx$

36. $\int \frac{e^{\sin x}}{\sec x}\, dx$

37. $\int \frac{e^{\sqrt{x}}}{\sqrt{x}}\, dx$

38. $\int_{-2}^{2} \frac{e^{x/2}}{e^{x/2}+1}\, dx$

39–46. Logarithmic differentiation *Use logarithmic differentiation to evaluate $f'(x)$.*

39. $f(x) = \frac{(x+1)^{10}}{(2x-4)^8}$

40. $f(x) = x^2 \cos x$

41. $f(x) = x^{\ln x}$

42. $f(x) = \frac{\tan^{10} x}{(5x+3)^6}$

43. $f(x) = \frac{(x+1)^{3/2}(x-4)^{5/2}}{(5x+3)^{2/3}}$

44. $f(x) = \frac{x^8 \cos^3 x}{\sqrt{x-1}}$

45. $f(x) = (\sin x)^{\tan x}$

46. $f(x) = \left(1 + \frac{1}{x}\right)^{2x}$

Further Explorations

47. **Explain why or why not** Determine whether the following statements are true and give an explanation or counterexample. Assume $x > 0$ and $y > 0$.

   a. $\ln (xy) = \ln x + \ln y$

   b. $\ln 0 = 1$

   c. $\ln (x + y) = \ln x + \ln y$

   d. If $f(x) = e^{kx}$, then $f^{(n)}(x) = k^n e^{kx}$.

   e. The area under the curve $y = 1/x$ and the x-axis on the interval $[1, e]$ is 1.

48. **Logarithm properties** Use the integral definition of the natural logarithm to prove directly that $\ln (x/y) = \ln x - \ln y$.

T **49–52. Calculator limits** *Use a calculator to make a table similar to Table 7.1 to approximate the following limits. If possible, confirm your result with l'Hôpital's Rule.*

49. $\lim_{h\to 0} (1 + 2h)^{1/h}$

50. $\lim_{h\to 0} (1 + 3h)^{2/h}$

51. $\lim_{x\to 0} \frac{2^x - 1}{x}$

52. $\lim_{x\to 0} \frac{\ln (1+x)}{x}$

53. **Looking ahead: Integrals of tan *x* and cot *x***

   a. Use a change of variables to show that

$$\int \tan x\, dx = -\ln |\cos x| + C = \ln |\sec x| + C.$$

   b. Show that

$$\int \cot x\, dx = \ln |\sin x| + C.$$

T 54. **Behavior at the origin** Using calculus and accurate sketches, explain how the graphs of $f(x) = x^p \ln x$ differ as $x \to 0^+$ for $p = \frac{1}{2}, 1, 2$.

55. **Average value** What is the average value of $f(x) = 1/x$ on the interval $[1, p]$ for $p > 1$? What is the average value of f as $p \to \infty$?

56–62. Miscellaneous derivatives *Compute the following derivatives using a method of your choice.*

56. $\frac{d}{dx}(x^{2x})$

57. $\frac{d}{dx}(e^{-10x^2})$

58. $\frac{d}{dx}(x^{\tan x})$

59. $\frac{d}{dx}(\ln \sqrt{10x})$

60. $\frac{d}{dx}(x^e + e^x)$

61. $\frac{d}{dx}\left[\frac{(x^2+1)(x-3)}{(x+2)^3}\right]$

62. $\frac{d}{dx}(\ln (\sec^4 x \tan^2 x))$

63–68. Miscellaneous integrals *Evaluate the following integrals.*

63. $\int x^2 e^{x^3}\, dx$

64. $\int_0^{\pi} \cos x \cdot e^{\sin x}\, dx$

65. $\int_1^{2e} \frac{e^{\ln x}}{x}\, dx$

66. $\int \frac{\sin (\ln x)}{4x}\, dx$

67. $\int_1^{e^2} \frac{(\ln x)^5}{x}\, dx$

68. $\int \frac{\ln^2 x + 2\ln x - 1}{x}\, dx$

Applications

69. **Probability as an integral** Two points P and Q are chosen randomly, one on each of two adjacent sides of a unit square (see figure). What is the probability that the area of the triangle formed by the sides of the square and the line segment PQ is less

than one-fourth the area of the square? Begin by showing that x and y must satisfy $xy < \frac{1}{2}$ in order for the area condition to be met.

Then argue that the required probability is $\frac{1}{2} + \int_{1/2}^{1} \frac{dx}{2x}$ and evaluate the integral.

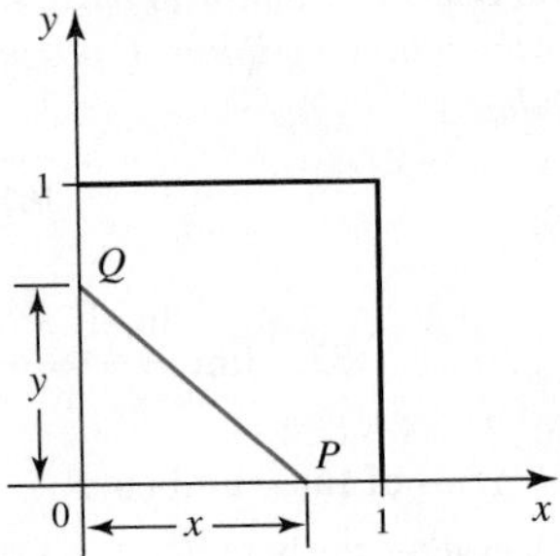

Applications

70–75. Logistic growth *Scientists often use the* logistic growth *function* $P(t) = \frac{P_0 K}{P_0 + (K - P_0)e^{-r_0 t}}$ *to model population growth, where P_0 is the initial population at time $t = 0$, K is the* **carrying capacity**, *and r_0 is the* base growth rate. *The carrying capacity is a theoretical upper bound on the total population that the surrounding environment can support. The figure shows the* sigmoid *(S-shaped) curve associated with a typical logistic model.*

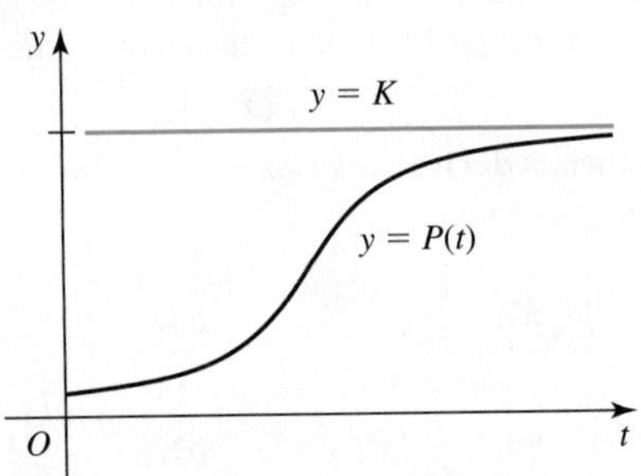

T **70. Population crash** The logistic model can be used for situations in which the initial population P_0 is above the carrying capacity K. For example, consider a deer population of 1500 on an island where a large fire has reduced the carrying capacity to 1000 deer.

a. Assuming a base growth rate of $r_0 = 0.1$ and an initial population of $P(0) = 1500$, write a logistic growth function for the deer population and graph it. Based on the graph, what happens to the deer population in the long run?

b. How fast (in deer per year) is the population declining immediately after the fire at $t = 0$?

c. How long does it take for the deer population to decline to 1200 deer?

T **71. Gone fishing** When a reservoir is created by a new dam, 50 fish are introduced into the reservoir, which has an estimated carrying capacity of 8000 fish. A logistic model of the fish population is $P(t) = \frac{400{,}000}{50 + 7950e^{-0.5t}}$, where t is measured in years.

a. Graph P using a graphing utility. Experiment with different windows until you produce an S-shaped curve characteristic of the logistic model. What window works well for this function?

b. How long does it take for the population to reach 5000 fish? How long does it take for the population to reach 90% of the carrying capacity?

c. How fast (in fish per year) is the population growing at $t = 0$? At $t = 5$?

d. Graph P' and use the graph to estimate the year in which the population is growing fastest.

T **72. World population (part 1)** The population of the world reached 6 billion in 1999 ($t = 0$). Assume the carrying capacity is 15 billion and the base growth rate is $r_0 = 0.025$ per year.

a. Write a logistic growth function for the world's population (in billions), and graph your equation on the interval $0 \le t \le 200$ using a graphing utility.

b. What will the population be in the year 2020? When will it reach 12 billion?

73. World population (part 2) The *relative growth rate r* of a function f measures the rate of change of the function compared to its value at a particular point. It is computed as $r(t) = f'(t)/f(t)$.

a. Confirm that the relative growth rate in 1999 ($t = 0$) for the logistic model in Exercise 72 is $r(0) = P'(0)/P(0) = 0.015$. This means the world's population was growing at 1.5% per year in 1999.

b. Compute the relative growth rate of the world's population in 2010 and 2020. What appears to be happening to the relative growth rate as time increases?

c. Evaluate $\lim_{t\to\infty} r(t) = \lim_{t\to\infty} \frac{P'(t)}{P(t)}$, where $P(t)$ is the logistic growth function from Exercise 72. What does your answer say about populations that follow a logistic growth pattern?

74. Snow plow problem With snow on the ground and falling at a constant rate, a snow plow began plowing down a long straight road at noon. The plow traveled twice as far in the first hour as it did in the second hour. At what time did the snow start falling? Assume the plowing rate is inversely proportional to the depth of the snow.

75. Depletion of natural resources Suppose that $r(t) = r_0 e^{-kt}$ is the rate at which a nation extracts oil, where $r_0 = 10^7$ barrels/yr is the current rate of extraction. Suppose also that the estimate of the total oil reserve is 2×10^9 barrels.

a. Find the minimum decay constant k for which the total oil reserves will last forever.

b. Suppose $r_0 = 2 \times 10^7$ barrels/yr and the decay constant k is the minimum value found in part (a). How long will the total oil reserves last?

Additional Exercises

76. Derivative of ln $|x|$ Differentiate $\ln x$ for $x > 0$ and differentiate $\ln(-x)$ for $x < 0$ to conclude that $\frac{d}{dx}(\ln|x|) = \frac{1}{x}$.

77. Properties of e^x Use the inverse relations between $\ln x$ and e^x and the properties of $\ln x$ to prove the following properties.

a. $e^{x-y} = \frac{e^x}{e^y}$ **b.** $(e^x)^y = e^{xy}$

78. ln x is unbounded Use the following argument to show that $\lim_{x\to\infty} \ln x = \infty$ and $\lim_{x\to 0^+} \ln x = -\infty$.

a. Make a sketch of the function $f(x) = 1/x$ on the interval $[1, 2]$. Explain why the area of the region bounded by $y = f(x)$ and the x-axis on $[1, 2]$ is ln 2.

b. Construct a rectangle over the interval $[1, 2]$ with height $\frac{1}{2}$. Explain why $\ln 2 > \frac{1}{2}$.

c. Show that $\ln 2^n > n/2$ and $\ln 2^{-n} < -n/2$.

d. Conclude that $\lim_{x\to\infty} \ln x = \infty$ and $\lim_{x\to 0^+} \ln x = -\infty$.

79. Bounds on e Use a left Riemann sum with $n = 2$ subintervals of equal length to approximate $\ln 2 = \int_1^2 \frac{dt}{t}$ and show that $\ln 2 < 1$. Use a right Riemann sum with $n = 7$ subintervals of equal length to approximate $\ln 3 = \int_1^3 \frac{dt}{t}$ and show that $\ln 3 > 1$.

80. Alternate proof of product property Assume that $y > 0$ is fixed and that $x > 0$. Show that $\frac{d}{dx}(\ln xy) = \frac{d}{dx}(\ln x)$. Recall that if two functions have the same derivative, they differ by a constant. Set $x = 1$ to evaluate the constant and prove that $\ln xy = \ln x + \ln y$.

81. Harmonic sum In Chapter 9, we will encounter the harmonic sum $1 + \frac{1}{2} + \frac{1}{3} + \cdots + \frac{1}{n}$. Use a right Riemann sum to approximate $\int_1^n \frac{dx}{x}$ (with unit spacing between the grid points) to show that $1 + \frac{1}{2} + \frac{1}{3} + \cdots + \frac{1}{n} > \ln(n + 1)$. Use this fact to conclude that $\lim_{n\to\infty}\left(1 + \frac{1}{2} + \frac{1}{3} + \cdots + \frac{1}{n}\right)$ does not exist.

T **82. Tangency question** It is easily verified that the graphs of $y = x^2$ and $y = e^x$ have no points of intersection (for $x > 0$), while the graphs of $y = x^3$ and $y = e^x$ have two points of intersection. It follows that for some real number $2 < p < 3$, the graphs of $y = x^p$ and $y = e^x$ have exactly one point of intersection (for $x > 0$). Using analytical and/or graphical methods, determine p and the coordinates of the single point of intersection.

QUICK CHECK ANSWERS

1. $\{x: x \neq 0\}$ **2.** p/x **3.** $2x, 2x, x^2, \ln 2 + x$
4. Slope $= 2$; area $= 1$.

7.3 Logarithmic and Exponential Functions with Other Bases

Situations occasionally arise in which it is more convenient to work with bases other than e. In this section, we establish the properties of the exponential function b^x and the logarithmic function $\log_b x$, where the base b is a positive number with $b \neq 1$. Before doing so, it might be helpful to outline the entire program of this and the previous section, in the order in which it is carried out:

1. We first defined the natural logarithm function $\ln x = \int_1^x \frac{dt}{t}$, for $x > 0$ (Section 7.2).
2. Applying the properties of inverse functions to $\ln x$, we then introduced the natural exponential function e^x (Section 7.2).
3. In this section, we use the properties of e^x to define the exponential function b^x with base b.
4. We then apply the properties of inverse functions to b^x to define the logarithmic function $\log_b x$ with base b.

The result of this process is a family of logarithmic functions with base b, each corresponding to an exponential function, which is its inverse.

Exponential Functions

First, it is important to note that the function b^x is defined for all bases b, with $b > 0$ and $b \neq 1$, and for all real numbers x. The reason is that

$$b^x = (e^{\ln b})^x = e^{x \ln b},$$

where we now know that e^x is defined for all real numbers x. We can now state the following properties of the exponential function b^x.

QUICK CHECK 1 Is it possible to raise a positive number b to a power and obtain a negative number? Is it possible to obtain zero?

Properties of $f(x) = b^x$

1. Because $f(x) = b^x$ is defined for all real numbers x, the domain of f is $\{x: -\infty < x < \infty\}$. Because $b^x = e^{x \ln b}$ and the range of e^x is $(0, \infty)$, the range of b^x is $\{y: 0 < y < \infty\}$.
2. For all $b > 0$, $b^0 = e^{0 \ln b} = 1$. Therefore, $f(0) = 1$.
3. If $b > 1$, then $\ln b > 0$ and $b^x = e^{x \ln b}$ is an increasing function (Figure 7.21). For example, if $b = 2$, then $2^x > 2^y$ whenever $x > y$.
4. If $0 < b < 1$, then $\ln b < 0$ and $b^x = e^{x \ln b}$ is a decreasing function (Figure 7.22). For example, if $b = \frac{1}{2}$,

$$f(x) = \left(\frac{1}{2}\right)^x = \frac{1}{2^x} = 2^{-x}$$

and because 2^x increases with x, 2^{-x} decreases with x.

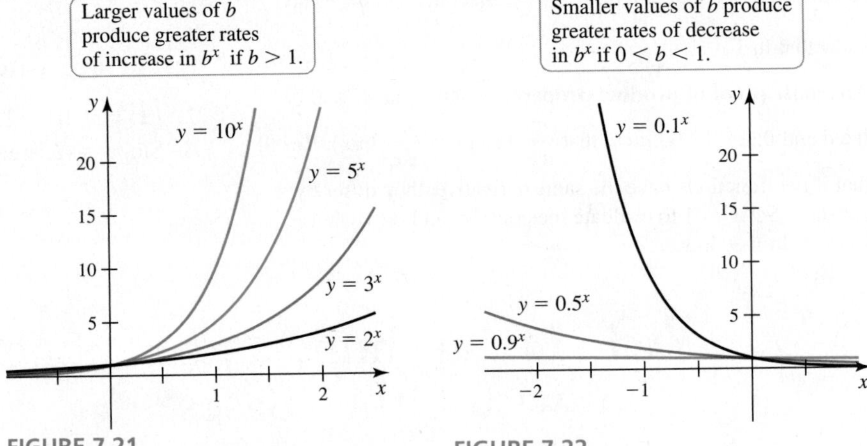

Larger values of b produce greater rates of increase in b^x if $b > 1$.
$y = 10^x$
$y = 5^x$
$y = 3^x$
$y = 2^x$
Smaller values of b produce greater rates of decrease in b^x if $0 < b < 1$.
$y = 0.1^x$
$y = 0.5^x$
$y = 0.9^x$

FIGURE 7.21

FIGURE 7.22

QUICK CHECK 2 Explain why $f(x) = (1/3)^x$ is a decreasing function.

Logarithmic Functions

Everything we learned about inverse functions is now applied to the exponential function $f(x) = b^x$. For any $b > 0$, with $b \neq 1$, this function is one-to-one on the interval $(-\infty, \infty)$. Therefore, it has an inverse.

> **DEFINITION Logarithmic Function Base b**
>
> For any base $b > 0$, with $b \neq 1$, the **logarithmic function base b**, denoted $\log_b x$, is the inverse of the exponential function b^x.

The inverse relationship between logarithmic and exponential functions may be stated concisely in several ways. First, we have

$$y = \log_b x \quad \text{provided} \quad b^y = x.$$

Combining these two conditions results in two important relations.

> **Inverse Relations for Exponential and Logarithmic Functions**
>
> For any base $b > 0$, with $b \neq 1$, the following inverse relations hold:
>
> **I1.** $b^{\log_b x} = x$, for $x > 0$.
>
> **I2.** $\log_b b^x = x$, for all x.

Graphs of b^x and $\log_b x$ are symmetric about $y = x$.

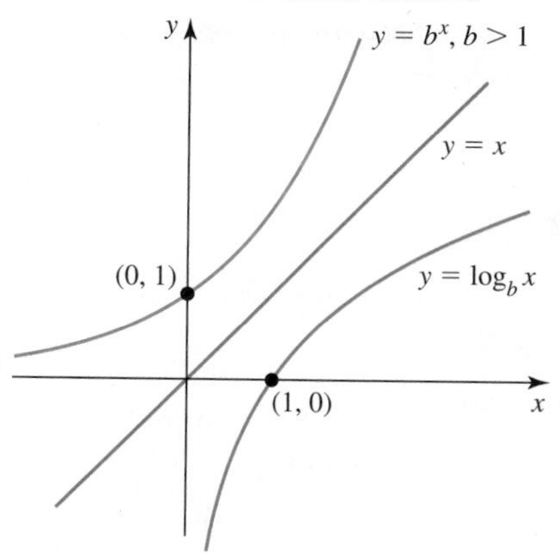

FIGURE 7.23

The graph of the logarithmic function is generated using the symmetry of the graphs of a function and its inverse. Figure 7.23 shows how the graph of $y = b^x$, for $b > 1$, is reflected across the line $y = x$ to obtain the graph of $y = \log_b x$.

The graphs of $y = \log_b x$ are shown (Figure 7.24) for several bases $b > 1$. Logarithms with rational bases $(0 < b < 1)$, although well defined, are generally not used. In fact, rational bases can always be converted to bases with $b > 1$.

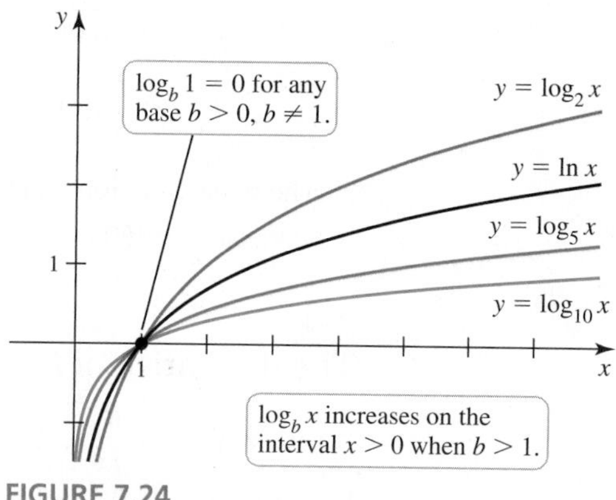

FIGURE 7.24

Logarithmic functions with base $b > 0$ satisfy properties that parallel the properties of the exponential functions given earlier.

Properties of $\log_b x$

1. Because the range of b^x is $\{y: 0 < y < \infty\}$, the domain of $\log_b x$ is $\{x: 0 < x < \infty\}$.
2. The domain of b^x is all real numbers, which implies that the range of $\log_b x$ is all real numbers.
3. Because $b^0 = 1$, it follows that $\log_b 1 = 0$.
4. If $b > 1$, then $\log_b x$ is an increasing function of x. For example, if $b = e$, then $\ln x > \ln y$ whenever $x > y$.

QUICK CHECK 3 What is the domain of $f(x) = \log_b (x^2)$? What is the range of $f(x) = \log_b (x^2)$?

EXAMPLE 1 **Using inverse relations** One thousand grams of a particular radioactive substance decays according to the function $m(t) = 1000e^{-t/850}$, where $t \geq 0$ measures time in years and m is measured in grams.

a. When does the mass of the substance reach the safe level of 1 g?

b. Write the mass function to the base $\frac{1}{2}$.

SOLUTION

a. Setting $m(t) = 1$, we solve $1000e^{-t/850} = 1$ by dividing both sides by 1000 and taking the natural logarithm of both sides:

$$\ln (e^{-t/850}) = \ln \left(\frac{1}{1000}\right)$$

This equation is simplified by calculating $\ln (1/1000) \approx -6.908$ and observing that $\ln (e^{-t/850}) = -\frac{t}{850}$ (inverse property I2). Therefore,

$$-\frac{t}{850} \approx -6.908.$$

Solving for t, we find that $t \approx (-850)(-6.908) \approx 5872$ years.

b. We seek a function $p(t)$ such that $m(t) = 1000\, e^{-t/850} = 1000\left(\frac{1}{2}\right)^{p(t)}$. Canceling 1000 and taking the natural logarithm of both sides, we proceed as follows:

$$\ln\left(e^{-t/850}\right) = \ln\left(\frac{1}{2}\right)^{p(t)}$$

$$-\frac{t}{850} = p(t)\ln\left(\frac{1}{2}\right) = -p(t)\ln 2 \qquad \text{Properties of logarithms}$$

$$p(t) = \frac{t}{850 \ln 2} \qquad \text{Solve for } p(t).$$

The mass function can be written $m(t) = 1000\left(\frac{1}{2}\right)^{t/(850 \ln 2)}$, which says that when t increases by $850 \ln 2 \approx 589$ years, the mass decreases by a factor of $\frac{1}{2}$.

Related Exercises 9–20 ◀

The derivative of b^x

A rule similar to $\frac{d}{dx}(e^x) = e^x$ exists for computing the derivative of b^x, where $b > 0$. Because $b^x = e^{x \ln b}$, the derivative of b^x is

$$\frac{d}{dx}(b^x) = \frac{d}{dx}\left(e^{x\ln b}\right) = \underbrace{e^{x \ln b}}_{b^x} \cdot \ln b. \qquad \text{Chain Rule}$$

Noting that $e^{x \ln b} = b^x$ results in the following theorem. The second part of the theorem follows by the Chain Rule, assuming u is differentiable at x.

> Check that when $b = e$, Theorem 7.7 becomes
> $$\frac{d}{dx}(e^x) = e^x.$$

THEOREM 7.7 Derivative of b^x
If $b > 0$ and $b \neq 1$, then

$$\frac{d}{dx}(b^x) = b^x \ln b, \quad \text{for all } x \qquad \frac{d}{dx}\left(b^{u(x)}\right) = b^{u(x)}(\ln b)\, u'(x)$$

Notice that when $b > 1$, $\ln b > 0$ and the graph of $y = b^x$ has tangent lines with positive slopes for all x. When $0 < b < 1$, $\ln b < 0$ and the graph of $y = b^x$ has tangent lines with negative slopes for all x. In either case, the tangent line at $(0, 1)$ has slope $\ln b$ (Figure 7.25).

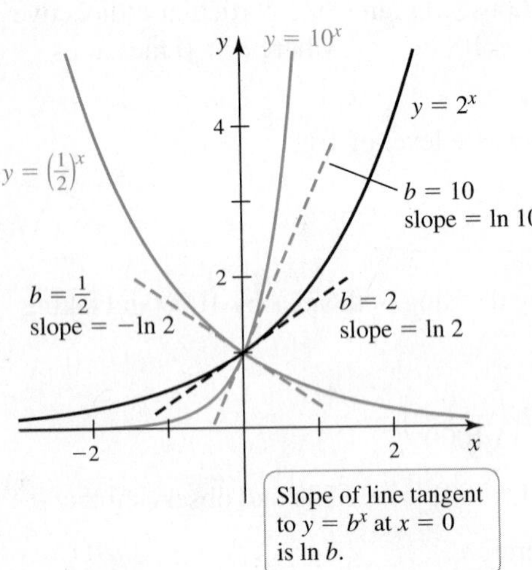

FIGURE 7.25

EXAMPLE 2 Derivatives with b^x Find the derivative of the following functions.

a. $f(x) = 3^x$ **b.** $g(t) = 108 \cdot 2^{t/12}$

SOLUTION

a. Using Theorem 7.7, $f'(x) = 3^x \cdot \ln 3$.

b.

$$g'(t) = 108\frac{d}{dt}\left(2^{t/12}\right) \qquad \text{Constant Multiple Rule}$$

$$= 108 \cdot 2^{t/12} \cdot \ln 2 \cdot \underbrace{\frac{d}{dt}\left(\frac{t}{12}\right)}_{1/12} \qquad \text{Chain Rule}$$

$$= 9 \ln 2 \cdot 2^{t/12} \qquad \text{Simplify.}$$

Related Exercises 21–26 ◀

Table 7.2

Mother's Age	Incidence of Down Syndrome	Decimal Equivalent
30	1 in 900	0.00111
35	1 in 400	0.00250
36	1 in 300	0.00333
37	1 in 230	0.00435
38	1 in 180	0.00556
39	1 in 135	0.00741
40	1 in 105	0.00952
42	1 in 60	0.01667
44	1 in 35	0.02875
46	1 in 20	0.05000
48	1 in 16	0.06250
49	1 in 12	0.08333

Source: E.G. Hook and A. Lindsjo, *Down Syndrome in Live Births by Single Year Maternal Age.*

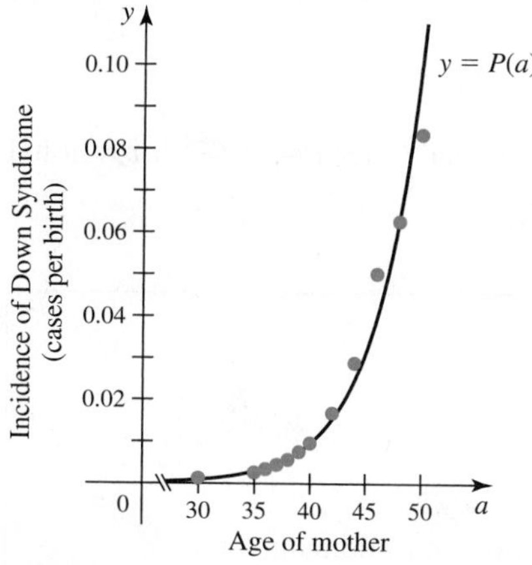

FIGURE 7.26

➤ The model in Example 3 was created using a method called *exponential regression*. The parameters A and B are chosen so that the function $P(a) = A\,B^a$ fits the data as closely as possible.

QUICK CHECK 4 Suppose $A = 500(1.045)^t$. Compute $\dfrac{dA}{dt}$.

EXAMPLE 3 **An exponential model** Table 7.2 and Figure 7.26 show how the incidence of Down syndrome in newborn infants increases with the age of the mother. The data can be modeled with the exponential function $P(a) = \dfrac{1}{1{,}613{,}000}1.2733^a$, where a is the age of the mother (in years) and $P(a)$ is the incidence (number of Down syndrome children per total births).

a. According to the model, at what age is the incidence of Down syndrome equal to 0.01 (that is, 1 in 100)?

b. Compute $P'(a)$.

c. Find $P'(35)$ and $P'(46)$, and interpret each.

SOLUTION

a. We let $P(a) = 0.01$ and solve for a:

$$0.01 = \frac{1}{1{,}613{,}000}1.2733^a$$

$$\ln 16{,}130 = \ln(1.2733^a)$$ Multiply both sides by 1,613,000, and take logarithms of both sides.

$$\ln 16{,}130 = a \ln 1.2733$$ Property of logarithms

$$a = \frac{\ln 16{,}130}{\ln 1.2733} \approx 40 \text{ years old}$$ Solve for a.

b.
$$P'(a) = \frac{1}{1{,}613{,}000}\frac{d}{da}(1.2733^a) = \frac{1}{1{,}613{,}000}1.2733^a \cdot \ln 1.2733 \approx \frac{1}{6{,}676{,}000}1.2733^a$$

c. The derivative measures the rate of change of the incidence with respect to age. For a 35-year-old woman,

$$P'(35) = \frac{1}{6{,}676{,}000}1.2733^{35} \approx 0.0007,$$

which means the incidence increases at a rate of about 0.0007/year. By age 46, the rate of change is

$$P'(46) = \frac{1}{6{,}676{,}000}1.2733^{46} \approx 0.01,$$

which is a significant increase over the rate of change of the incidence at age 35.

Related Exercises 27–29 ◀

Integral of b^x

The fact that $\dfrac{d}{dx}(b^x) = b^x \ln b$ leads immediately to the following indefinite integral result.

THEOREM 7.8 **Indefinite integral of b^x**

For $b > 0$ and $b \neq 1$, $\displaystyle\int b^x\,dx = \frac{1}{\ln b}b^x + C.$

EXAMPLE 4 **Integrals involving exponentials with other bases** Evaluate the following integrals.

a. $\int x\, 3^{x^2}\, dx$ **b.** $\int_1^4 \frac{6^{-\sqrt{x}}}{\sqrt{x}}\, dx$

SOLUTION

a.
$$\int x\, 3^{x^2}\, dx = \frac{1}{2}\int 3^u\, du \qquad u = x^2,\ du = 2x\, dx$$
$$= \frac{1}{2}\frac{1}{\ln 3} 3^u + C \qquad \text{Integrate.}$$
$$= \frac{1}{2\ln 3} 3^{x^2} + C \qquad \text{Substitute } u = x^2.$$

b.
$$\int_1^4 \frac{6^{-\sqrt{x}}}{\sqrt{x}}\, dx = -2\int_{-1}^{-2} 6^u\, du \qquad u = -\sqrt{x},\ du = -\frac{1}{2\sqrt{x}}\, dx$$
$$= -\frac{2}{\ln 6} 6^u \Big|_{-1}^{-2} \qquad \text{Fundamental Theorem}$$
$$= \frac{5}{18\ln 6} \qquad \text{Simplify.}$$

Related Exercises 30–34 ◀

The General Power Rule

As it stands now, the Power Rule for derivatives says that $\frac{d}{dx}(x^p) = px^{p-1}$ for rational powers p. The rule is now extended to all real powers.

THEOREM 7.9 **General Power Rule**
For real numbers p and for $x > 0$,
$$\frac{d}{dx}(x^p) = px^{p-1}.$$
Furthermore, if u is a positive differentiable function on its domain, then
$$\frac{d}{dx}(u(x)^p) = p(u(x))^{p-1} \cdot u'(x).$$

Proof For $x > 0$ and real numbers p, the derivative of x^p is computed as follows:
$$\frac{d}{dx}(x^p) = \frac{d}{dx}(e^{p\ln x}) \qquad x^p = e^{p\ln x}$$
$$= \underbrace{e^{p\ln x}}_{x^p} \cdot \frac{p}{x} \qquad \text{Chain Rule}$$
$$= x^p \cdot \frac{p}{x} \qquad e^{p\ln x} = x^p$$
$$= px^{p-1} \qquad \text{Simplify.}$$

We see that $\frac{d}{dx}(x^p) = px^{p-1}$ for all real powers p. The second part of the General Power Rule follows from the Chain Rule. ◀

EXAMPLE 5 **Computing derivatives** Find the derivative of the following functions.

a. $y = x^{\pi}$ **b.** $y = \pi^x$ **c.** $y = (x^2 + 4)^e$

> Recall that power functions have the variable in the base, while exponential functions have the variable in the exponent.

SOLUTION

a. With $y = x^{\pi}$, we have a power function with an irrational exponent; by the General Power Rule,

$$\frac{dy}{dx} = \pi x^{\pi - 1}, \quad \text{for } x > 0.$$

b. Here we have an exponential function with base $b = \pi$. By Theorem 7.7,

$$\frac{dy}{dx} = \pi^x \cdot \ln \pi.$$

c. The Chain Rule and General Power Rule are required:

$$\frac{dy}{dx} = e(x^2 + 4)^{e-1} \cdot 2x = 2ex\,(x^2 + 4)^{e-1}$$

Because $x^2 + 4 > 0$ for all x, the result is valid for all x. *Related Exercises 35–40* ◀

Functions of the form $f(x) = (g(x))^{h(x)}$, where both g and h are nonconstant functions, are neither exponential functions nor power functions (they are sometimes called *tower functions*). In order to compute their derivatives, we use the identity $b^x = e^{x \ln b}$ to rewrite f with base e:

$$f(x) = (g(x))^{h(x)} = e^{h(x) \ln g(x)}.$$

This function carries the restriction $g(x) > 0$. The derivative of f is then computed using the methods developed in this section.

> Recall that the derivative of $f(x) = x^x$ was determined using logarithmic differentiation in Section 7.2. Either method is acceptable; in fact, they are equivalent.

EXAMPLE 6 **Finding a horizontal tangent line** Determine whether the graph of $f(x) = x^x$, for $x > 0$, has any horizontal tangent lines.

SOLUTION A horizontal tangent occurs when $f'(x) = 0$. In order to find the derivative, we first write $f(x) = x^x = e^{x \ln x}$. Then,

$$\begin{aligned}
\frac{d}{dx}(x^x) &= \frac{d}{dx}(e^{x \ln x}) \\
&= e^{x \ln x} \cdot \frac{d}{dx}(x \ln x) && \text{Chain Rule} \\
&= e^{x \ln x}\left(1 \cdot \ln x + x \cdot \frac{1}{x}\right) && \text{Product Rule} \\
&= x^x (\ln x + 1) && \text{Simplify; } e^{x \ln x} = x^x.
\end{aligned}$$

The equation $f'(x) = 0$ implies that $x^x = 0$ or $\ln x + 1 = 0$. The first equation has no solution because $x^x = e^{x \ln x} > 0$ for all $x > 0$. We solve the second equation, $\ln x + 1 = 0$, as follows:

$$\begin{aligned}
\ln x &= -1 \\
e^{\ln x} &= e^{-1} && \text{Exponentiate both sides.} \\
x &= \frac{1}{e} && e^{\ln x} = x
\end{aligned}$$

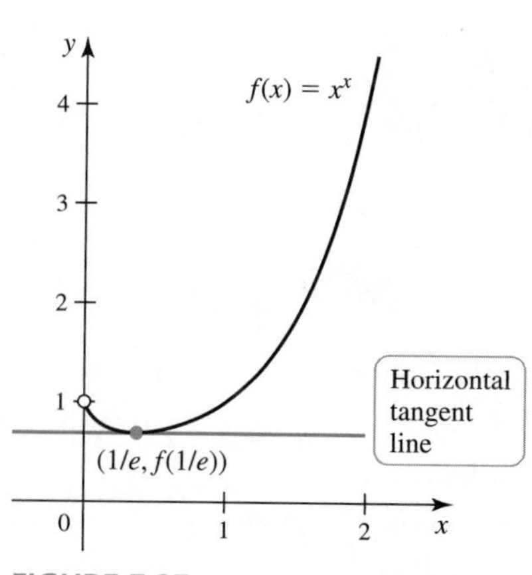

FIGURE 7.27

Therefore, the graph of $f(x) = x^x$ (Figure 7.27) has a single horizontal tangent at $(e^{-1}, f(e^{-1})) \approx (0.368, 0.692)$. *Related Exercises 41–50* ◀

Derivatives of General Logarithmic Functions

The general exponential function $f(x) = b^x$ is one-to-one when $b > 0$. The inverse function is $f^{-1}(x) = \log_b x$, the logarithmic function with base b. To find the derivative of the logarithmic function, we begin with the inverse relationship

$$y = \log_b x \iff x = b^y.$$

Differentiating both sides of $x = b^y$ with respect to x, we obtain

$$1 = b^y \cdot \ln b \cdot \frac{dy}{dx} \quad \text{Chain Rule}$$

$$\frac{dy}{dx} = \frac{1}{b^y \ln b} \quad \text{Solve for } \frac{dy}{dx}.$$

$$\frac{dy}{dx} = \frac{1}{x \ln b}. \quad b^y = x$$

➤ An alternative proof of Theorem 7.10 uses the change-of-base formula $\log_b x = \frac{\ln x}{\ln b}$. Differentiating both sides of this equation gives the same result.

THEOREM 7.10 Derivative of $\log_b x$
If $b > 0$ with $b \neq 1$, then

$$\frac{d}{dx}(\log_b x) = \frac{1}{x \ln b}, \quad \text{for } x > 0 \qquad \frac{d}{dx}(\log_b |x|) = \frac{1}{x \ln b}, \quad \text{for } x \neq 0$$

QUICK CHECK 5 Compute dy/dx for $y = \log_3 x$. ◄

EXAMPLE 7 Derivatives with general logarithms Compute the derivative of each function.

a. $f(x) = \log_5 (2x + 1)$ **b.** $T(n) = n \log_2 n$

SOLUTION

a. We use Theorem 7.10 with the Chain Rule assuming $2x + 1 > 0$:

$$f'(x) = \frac{1}{(2x + 1) \ln 5} \cdot 2 = \frac{2}{\ln 5} \cdot \frac{1}{2x + 1}$$

b. $$T'(n) = \log_2 n + n \cdot \frac{1}{n \ln 2} = \log_2 n + \frac{1}{\ln 2} \quad \text{Product Rule}$$

We can change bases and write the result in base e:

$$T'(n) = \frac{\ln n}{\ln 2} + \frac{1}{\ln 2} = \frac{\ln n + 1}{\ln 2}$$

Related Exercises 51–56 ◄

➤ The function in Example 7b is used in computer science as an estimate on the computing time needed to carry out a *sorting algorithm* on a list of n items.

QUICK CHECK 6 Show that the derivative computed in Example 7b can be expressed in base 2 as $T'(n) = \log_2 (en)$. ◄

SECTION 7.3 EXERCISES

Review Questions

1. State the derivative rule for the exponential function $f(x) = b^x$. How does it differ from the derivative rule for e^x?

2. State the derivative rule for the logarithmic function $f(x) = \log_b x$. How does it differ from the derivative rule for $\ln x$?

3. Explain why $b^x = e^{x \ln b}$.

4. Express the function $f(x) = g(x)^{h(x)}$ in terms of the natural logarithm and natural exponential functions (base e).

5. Evaluate $\int 4^x\,dx$.

6. What is the inverse function of b^x, and what are its domain and range?

7. Express 3^x, x^π, $x^{\sin x}$ using the base e.

8. Evaluate $\frac{d}{dx}(3^x)$.

Basic Skills

9–20. Solving equations *Solve the following equations without using a calculator.*

9. $\log_{10} x = 3$

10. $\log_5 x = -1$

11. $\log_8 x = \frac{1}{3}$

12. $\log_b 125 = 3$

13. $10^{x^2-4} = 1$

14. $3^{x^2-5x-5} = \frac{1}{3}$

15. $2^{|x|} = 16$

16. $9^x + 3^{x+1} - 18 = 0$

17. $7^x = 21$

18. $2^x = 55$

19. $3^{3x-4} = 15$

20. $5^{3x} = 29$

21–26. Derivatives of b^x *Find the derivatives of the following functions.*

21. $y = 5 \cdot 4^x$

22. $y = 4^{-x} \sin x$

23. $y = x^3 \cdot 3^x$

24. $P = \dfrac{40}{1 + 2^{-t}}$

25. $A = 250(1.045)^{4t}$

26. $y = \ln(10^x)$

27. Exponential model The following table shows the *time of useful consciousness* at various altitudes in the situation where a pressurized airplane suddenly loses pressure. The change in pressure drastically reduces available oxygen, and hypoxia sets in. The upper value of each time interval is roughly modeled by $T = 10 \cdot 2^{-0.274a}$, where T measures time in minutes and a is the altitude over 22,000 in thousands of feet ($a = 0$ corresponds to 22,000 ft).

Altitude (in ft)	Time of useful consciousness
22,000	5 to 10 min
25,000	3 to 5 min
28,000	2.5 to 3 min
30,000	1 to 2 min
35,000	30 to 60 s
40,000	15 to 20 s
45,000	9 to 15 s

a. A Learjet flying at 38,000 ft ($a = 16$) suddenly loses pressure when the seal on a window fails. According to this model, how long do the pilot and passengers have to deploy oxygen masks before they become incapacitated?

b. What is the average rate of change of T with respect to a over the interval from 24,000 to 30,000 ft (include units)?

c. Find the instantaneous rate of change dT/da, compute it at 30,000 ft, and interpret its meaning.

28. Magnitude of an earthquake The energy (in joules) released by an earthquake of magnitude M is given by the equation $E = 25{,}000 \cdot 10^{1.5M}$. (This equation can be solved for M to define the magnitude of a given earthquake; it is a refinement of the original Richter scale created by Charles Richter in 1935.)

a. Compute the energy released by earthquakes of magnitude 1, 2, 3, 4, and 5. Plot the points on a graph and join them with a smooth curve.

b. Compute dE/dM and evaluate it for $M = 3$. What does this derivative mean? (M has no units, so the units of the derivative are J per change in magnitude.)

29. Diagnostic scanning Iodine-123 is a radioactive isotope used in medicine to test the function of the thyroid gland. If a 350-microcurie (μCi) dose of iodine-123 is administered to a patient, the quantity Q left in the body after t hours is approximately $Q = 350\left(\frac{1}{2}\right)^{t/13.1}$.

a. How long does it take for the level of iodine-123 to drop to 10 μCi?

b. Find the rate of change of the quantity of iodine-123 at 12 hours, 1 day, and 2 days. What do your answers say about the rate at which iodine decreases as time increases?

30–34. Integrals with general bases *Evaluate the following integrals.*

30. $\displaystyle\int 2^{3x}\,dx$

31. $\displaystyle\int_{-1}^{1} 10^x\,dx$

32. $\displaystyle\int_0^{\pi/2} 4^{\sin x} \cos x\,dx$

33. $\displaystyle\int_1^2 (1 + \ln x)x^x\,dx$

34. $\displaystyle\int_{1/3}^{1/2} \frac{10^{1/x}}{x^2}\,dx$

35–40. General Power Rule *Use the General Power Rule where appropriate to find the derivative of the following functions.*

35. $g(y) = e^y \cdot y^e$

36. $f(x) = 2x^{\sqrt{2}}$

37. $s(t) = \cos(2^t)$

38. $y = \ln(x^3 + 1)^\pi$

39. $f(x) = (2x - 3)x^{3/2}$

40. $y = \tan(x^{0.74})$

41–46. Derivatives *Evaluate the derivatives of the following functions.*

41. $f(x) = (2x)^{4x}$

42. $f(x) = x^\pi$

43. $h(x) = 2^{(x^2)}$

44. $h(t) = (\sin t)^{\sqrt{t}}$

45. $H(x) = (x + 1)^{2x}$

46. $p(x) = x^{-\ln x}$

47–50. Tangent lines and general exponential functions

47. Find an equation of the line tangent to $y = x^{\sin x}$ at the point $x = 1$.

48. Determine whether the graph of $y = x^{\sqrt{x}}$ has any horizontal tangent lines.

49. The graph of $y = (x^2)^x$ has two horizontal tangent lines. Find equations for both of them.

50. The graph of $y = x^{\ln x}$ has one horizontal tangent line. Find an equation for it.

51–56. Derivatives of logarithmic functions *Calculate the derivative of the following functions.*

51. $y = 4\log_3(x^2 - 1)$

52. $y = \log_{10} x$

53. $y = (\cos x)\ln(\cos^2 x)$

54. $y = \log_8 |\tan x|$

55. $y = \dfrac{1}{\log_4 x}$

56. $y = \log_2 \log_2 x$

Further Explorations

57. Explain why or why not Determine whether the following statements are true and give an explanation or counterexample.

a. The derivative of $\log_2 9$ is $1/(9 \ln 2)$.

b. $\ln(x + 1) + \ln(x - 1) = \ln(x^2 - 1)$

c. The exponential function 2^{x+1} can be written in base e as $e^{2\ln(x+1)}$.

d. $\frac{d}{dx}(\sqrt{2}^x) = x\sqrt{2}^{x-1}$

e. $\frac{d}{dx}\left(x^{\sqrt{2}}\right) = \sqrt{2}x^{\sqrt{2}-1}$

58. Graphs of exponential functions The following figure shows the graphs of $y = 2^x$, $y = 3^x$, $y = 2^{-x}$, and $y = 3^{-x}$. Match each curve with the correct function.

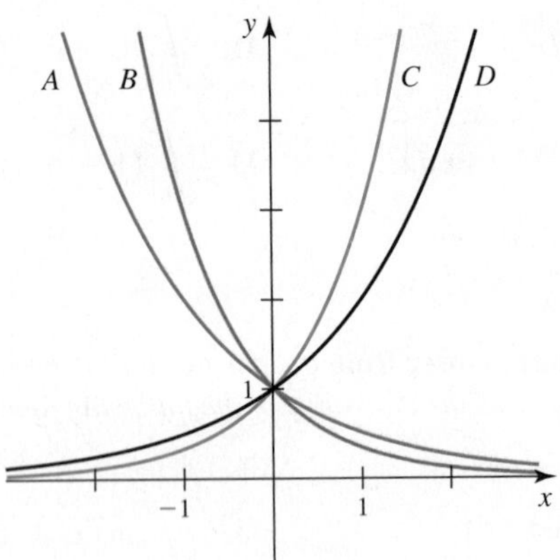

59. Graphs of logarithmic functions The following figure shows the graphs of $y = \log_2 x$, $y = \log_4 x$, and $y = \log_{10} x$. Match each curve with the correct function.

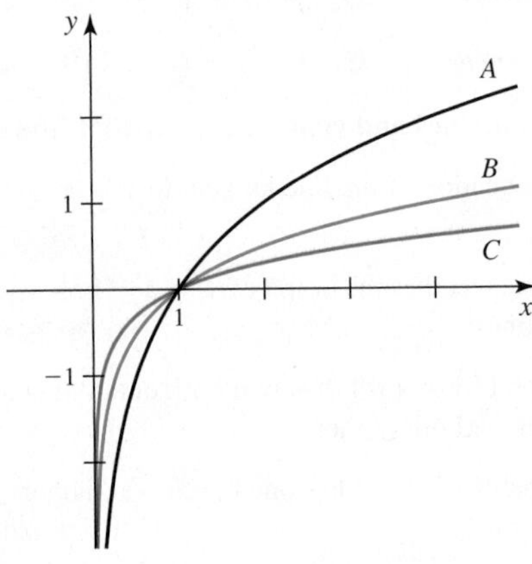

60. Graphs of modified exponential functions Without using a graphing utility, sketch the graph of $y = 2^x$. Then, on the same set of axes, sketch the graphs of $y = 2^{-x}$, $y = 2^{x-1}$, $y = 2^x + 1$, and $y = 2^{2x}$.

61. Graphs of modified logarithmic functions Without using a graphing utility, sketch the graph of $y = \log_2 x$. Then, on the same set of axes, sketch the graphs of $y = \log_2 (x - 1)$, $y = \log_2 x^2$, $y = (\log_2 x)^2$, and $y = \log_2 x + 1$.

T **62. Large intersection point** Use any means to approximate the point(s) of intersection of the graphs of $f(x) = e^x$ and $g(x) = x^{123}$. Consider using logarithms.

63–66. Higher-order derivatives *Find the following higher-order derivatives.*

63. $\frac{d^2}{dx^2}(\log x)$

64. $\frac{d^3}{dx^3}\left(x^{4.2}\right)\Big|_{x=1}$

65. $\frac{d^3}{dx^3}(x^2 \ln x)$

66. $\frac{d^n}{dx^n}(2^x)$

67–68. Derivatives by different methods *Calculate the derivative of the following functions (i) using the fact that $b^x = e^{x\ln b}$ and (ii) by using logarithmic differentiation. Verify that both answers are the same.*

67. $y = 3^x$

68. $y = (x^2 + 1)^x$

69–72. Derivatives of logarithmic functions *Use the properties of logarithms to simplify the following functions before computing $f'(x)$.*

69. $f(x) = \log_{10} \sqrt{10x}$

70. $f(x) = \log_2 \frac{8}{\sqrt{x+1}}$

71. $f(x) = \ln \frac{(2x-1)(x+2)^3}{(1-4x)^2}$

72. $f(x) = \ln (\sec^4 x \tan^2 x)$

T **73. Tangent lines** Find the equation of the line tangent to $y = 2^{\sin x}$ at $x = \pi/2$. Graph the function and the tangent line.

74. Horizontal tangents The graph of $y = \cos x \cdot \ln \cos^2 x$ has seven horizontal tangent lines on the interval $[0, 2\pi]$. Find the x-coordinates of all points at which these tangent lines occur.

75–82. General logarithmic and exponential derivatives *Compute the following derivatives. Use logarithmic differentiation where appropriate.*

75. $\frac{d}{dx}(x^{10x})$

76. $\frac{d}{dx}(2x)^{2x}$

77. $\frac{d}{dx}(x^{\cos x})$

78. $\frac{d}{dx}(x^\pi + \pi^x)$

79. $\frac{d}{dx}\left(1 + \frac{1}{x}\right)^x$

80. $\frac{d}{dx}(1 + x^2)^{\sin x}$

81. $\frac{d}{dx}\left[x^{(x^{10})}\right]$

82. $\frac{d}{dx}(\ln x)^{x^2}$

83–87. Miscellaneous integrals *Evaluate the following integrals.*

83. $\int 3^{-2x}\, dx$

84. $\int_0^5 5^{5x}\, dx$

85. $\int x^2 10^{x^3}\, dx$

86. $\int_0^\pi \cos x \cdot 2^{\sin x}\, dx$

87. $\int_1^{2e} \frac{3^{\ln x}}{x}\, dx$

Additional Exercises

T **88. Triple intersection** Graph the functions $f(x) = x^3$, $g(x) = 3^x$, and $h(x) = x^x$ and find their common intersection point (exactly).

89–92. Calculating limits exactly *Use the definition of the derivative to evaluate the following limits.*

89. $\lim_{x\to e} \frac{\ln x - 1}{x - e}$

90. $\lim_{h\to 0} \frac{\ln (e^8 + h) - 8}{h}$

91. $\lim_{h\to 0} \frac{(3+h)^{3+h} - 27}{h}$

92. $\lim_{x\to 2} \frac{5^x - 25}{x - 2}$

93. Derivative of $u(x)^{v(x)}$ Use logarithmic differentiation to prove that

$$\frac{d}{dx}[u(x)^{v(x)}] = u(x)^{v(x)}\left[\frac{v(x)}{u(x)}\frac{du}{dx} + \ln u(x)\frac{dv}{dx}\right].$$

T **94. Tangency question** It is easily verified that the graphs of $y = 1.1^x$ and $y = x$ have two points of intersection, while the graphs of $y = 2^x$ and $y = x$ have no points of intersection. It follows that for some real number $1 < p < 2$, the graphs of $y = p^x$ and $y = x$ have exactly one point of intersection. Using analytical and/or graphical methods, determine p and the coordinates of the single point of intersection.

95. Nice property Prove that $(\log_b c)(\log_c b) = 1$, for $b > 0$ and $c > 0$.

QUICK CHECK ANSWERS

1. b^x is always positive (and never zero) for all x and for positive bases b. **2.** Because $(1/3)^x = 1/3^x$ and 3^x increases as x increases, it follows that $(1/3)^x$ decreases as x increases. **3.** $\{x: x \neq 0\}, \mathbf{R}$
4. $\frac{dA}{dt} = 500(1.045)^t \cdot \ln 1.045 \approx 22(1.045)^t$ **5.** $\frac{dy}{dx} = \frac{1}{x \ln 3}$
6. $T'(n) = \log_2 n + \frac{1}{\ln 2} = \log_2 n + \frac{1}{\frac{\log_2 2}{\log_2 e}}$
$= \log_2 n + \log_2 e = \log_2(en)$

7.4 Exponential Models

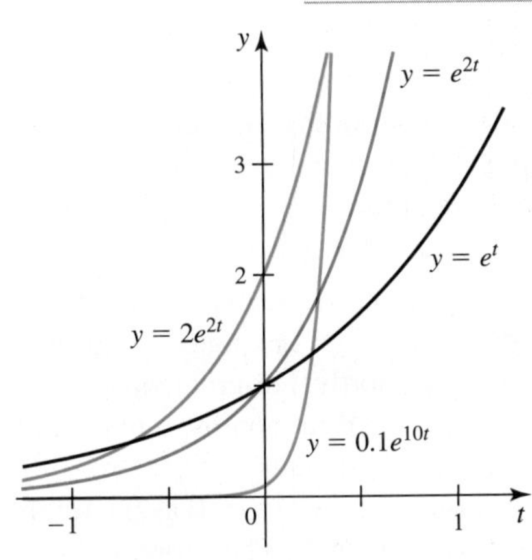

FIGURE 7.28

The uses of exponential functions are wide-ranging. In this section, you will see them applied to problems in finance, medicine, ecology, biology, economics, pharmacokinetics, anthropology, and physics.

Exponential Growth

Exponential growth models use functions of the form $y(t) = Ce^{kt}$, where t represents time, C is a constant, and the **rate constant** k is positive (Figure 7.28).

If we start with the exponential growth function $y(t) = Ce^{kt}$ and take its derivative, we find that

$$\frac{dy}{dt} = \frac{d}{dt}(Ce^{kt}) = C \cdot ke^{kt} = k(\underbrace{Ce^{kt}}_{y}),$$

that is, $\frac{dy}{dt} = ky$. Here is the first insight about exponential functions: *Their rate of change is proportional to their value*. If y represents a population, then $\frac{dy}{dt}$ is the **growth rate** with units such as people/month. Therefore, the more people present, the faster the population grows.

➤ The derivative $\frac{dy}{dt}$ is the *absolute* growth rate but is usually more simply called the *growth rate*.

Another way to talk about growth rates is to use the **relative growth rate**, which is the growth rate divided by the current value of that quantity—that is, $\frac{1}{y}\frac{dy}{dt}$. For example, if y is a population, the relative growth rate is the fraction or percentage by which the population grows each unit of time. Examples of relative growth rates are *5% per year* or *a factor of 1.2 per month*. When the equation $\frac{dy}{dt} = ky$ is written in the form $\frac{1}{y}\frac{dy}{dt} = k$, it has another interpretation. It says that *a quantity that grows exponentially has a constant relative growth rate*. Constant relative or percentage change is the hallmark of exponential growth.

➤ A consumer price index that increases at a constant rate of 4% per year increases exponentially. A currency that is devalued at a constant rate of 3% per month decreases exponentially. By contrast, linear growth is characterized by constant absolute growth rates, such as 500 people per year or $400 per month.

EXAMPLE 1 **Linear vs. exponential growth** Suppose the population of the town of Pine is given by $P(t) = 1500 + 125t$, while the population of the town of Spruce is given by $S(t) = 1500e^{0.1t}$, where $t \geq 0$ is measured in years. Find the growth rates and the relative growth rates of the two towns.

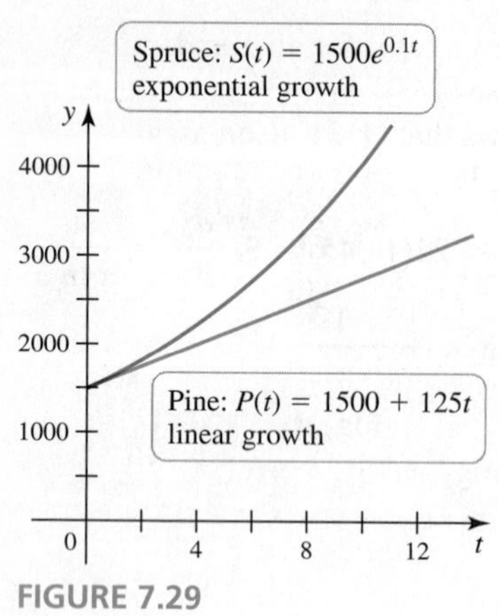

FIGURE 7.29

SOLUTION Note that Pine grows according to a linear function, while Spruce grows exponentially (Figure 7.29). The growth rate of Pine is $\frac{dP}{dt} = 125$ people/year, which is constant for all times. The growth rate of Spruce is

$$\frac{dS}{dt} = 0.1(\underbrace{1500e^{0.1t}}_{S(t)}) = 0.1S(t),$$

showing that the growth rate is proportional to the population. The relative growth rate of Pine is $\frac{1}{P}\frac{dP}{dt} = \frac{125}{1500 + 125t}$, which decreases in time. The relative growth rate of Spruce is

$$\frac{1}{S}\frac{dS}{dt} = \frac{0.1 \cdot 1500e^{0.1t}}{1500e^{0.1t}} = 0.1,$$

which is constant for all times. In summary, the linear population function has a *constant absolute growth rate*, while the exponential population function has a *constant relative growth rate*.

Related Exercises 9–10 ◀

QUICK CHECK 1 Population A increases at a constant rate of 4%/yr. Population B increases at a constant rate of 500 people/yr. Which population exhibits exponential growth? What kind of growth is exhibited by the other population? ◀

The rate constant k in $y(t) = Ce^{kt}$ determines the growth rate of the exponential function. We adopt the convention that $k > 0$; then $y(t) = Ce^{kt}$ describes exponential growth and $y(t) = Ce^{-kt}$ describes exponential decay, to be discussed shortly. For problems that involve time, the units of k are time^{-1}; for example, if t is measured in months, the units of k are month^{-1}. In this way, the exponent kt is dimensionless (without units).

➤ The unit time^{-1} is read *per unit time*. For example, month^{-1} is read *per month*.

Unless there is good reason to do otherwise, it is customary to take $t = 0$ as the reference point for time. Notice that with $y(t) = Ce^{kt}$, we have $y(0) = C$. Therefore, C has a simple meaning: It is the **initial value** of the quantity of interest, which we denote y_0. In the examples that follow, two pieces of information are typically given: the initial value and clues for determining the rate constant k. The initial value and the rate constant determine an exponential growth function completely.

Exponential Growth Functions

Exponential growth is described by functions of the form $y(t) = y_0e^{kt}$. The initial value of y at $t = 0$ is $y(0) = y_0$ and the **rate constant** $k > 0$ determines the rate of growth. Exponential growth is characterized by a constant relative growth rate.

Because exponential growth is characterized by a constant relative growth rate, the time required for a quantity to double (a 100% increase) is constant. Therefore, one way to describe an exponentially growing quantity is to give its *doubling time*. To compute the time it takes for the function $y(t) = y_0e^{kt}$ to double in value, say from y_0 to $2y_0$, we find the value of t that satisfies

$$y(t) = 2y_0 \quad \text{or} \quad y_0e^{kt} = 2y_0.$$

➤ Note that the initial value y_0 appears on both sides of this equation. It may be canceled, meaning that the doubling time is independent of the initial value: *The doubling time is constant for all t.*

Canceling y_0 from the equation $y_0e^{kt} = 2y_0$ leaves the equation $e^{kt} = 2$. Taking logarithms of both sides, we have $\ln e^{kt} = \ln 2$, or $kt = \ln 2$, which has the solution $t = \frac{\ln 2}{k}$.

We denote this doubling time T_2 so that $T_2 = \frac{\ln 2}{k}$. If y increases exponentially, the time it takes to double from 100 to 200 is the same as the time it takes to double from 1000 to 2000.

QUICK CHECK 2 Verify that the time needed for $y(t) = y_0e^{kt}$ to double from y_0 to $2y_0$ is the same as the time needed to double from $2y_0$ to $4y_0$.

> **DEFINITION Doubling Time**
>
> The quantity described by the function $y(t) = y_0e^{kt}$, for $k > 0$, has a constant **doubling time** of $T_2 = \frac{\ln 2}{k}$, with the same units as t.

EXAMPLE 2 World population Human population growth rates vary geographically and fluctuate over time. The overall growth rate for world population peaked at an annual rate of 2.1% per year in the 1960s. Assume a world population of 6.0 billion in 1999 ($t = 0$) and 6.9 billion in 2009 ($t = 10$).

World population

1804	1 billion
1927	2 billion
1960	3 billion
1974	4 billion
1987	5 billion
1999	6 billion
2011	7 billion (proj.)

a. Find an exponential growth function for the world population that fits the two data points.

b. Find the doubling time for the world population using the model in part (a).

c. Find the (absolute) growth rate $y'(t)$ and graph it for $0 \le t \le 50$.

d. How fast was the population growing in 2010 ($t = 11$)?

SOLUTION

It is a common mistake to assume that if the annual growth rate is 1.4% per year, then $k = 1.4\% = 0.014\text{ yr}^{-1}$. The rate constant k must be calculated, as it is in Example 2 to give $k = 0.013976$. For larger growth rates, the difference between k and the growth rate is greater.

a. Let $y(t)$ be world population measured in billions of people t years after 1999. We use the growth function $y(t) = y_0e^{kt}$, where y_0 and k must be determined. The initial value is $y_0 = 6$ (billion). To determine the rate constant k, we use the fact that $y(10) = 6.9$. Substituting $t = 10$ into the growth function with $y_0 = 6$ implies

$$y(10) = 6e^{10k} = 6.9.$$

Solving for k yields the rate constant $k = \frac{\ln(6.9/6)}{10} \approx 0.013976 \approx 0.014\text{ yr}^{-1}$.

Therefore, the growth function is

$$y(t) = 6e^{0.014t}.$$

b. The doubling time of the population is

$$T_2 = \frac{\ln 2}{k} \approx \frac{\ln 2}{0.014} \approx 50 \text{ years}.$$

c. Working with the growth function $y(t) = 6e^{0.014t}$, we find that

$$y'(t) = 6(0.014)e^{0.014t} = 0.084e^{0.014t},$$

which has units of billions of people/yr. As shown in Figure 7.30 the growth rate itself increases exponentially.

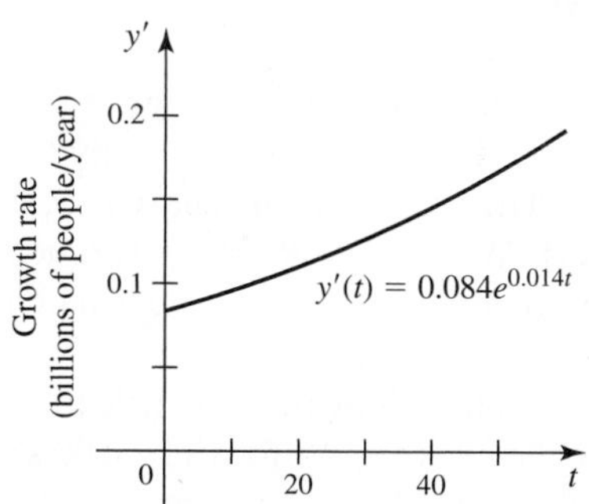

FIGURE 7.30

d. In 2010 ($t = 11$), the growth rate was

$$y'(11) = 0.084e^{(0.014)(11)} \approx 0.098 \text{ billion people/yr}$$

or roughly 98 million people/yr.

Converted to a daily rate (dividing by 365), the world population in 2010 increased at a rate of roughly 268,000 people per day.

Related Exercises 11–16

QUICK CHECK 3 Assume $y(t) = 100e^{0.05t}$. By what percentage does y increase when t increases by 1 unit?

A Financial Model Exponential functions are used in many financial applications, several of which are explored in the exercises. For now, consider a simple savings account in which an initial deposit earns interest that is reinvested in the account. Interest payments are made on a regular basis (for example, annually, monthly, daily) or interest may be compounded continuously. In all cases, the balance in the account increases exponentially at a rate that can be determined from the advertised **annual percentage yield** (or **APY**) of the account. Assuming that no additional deposits are made, the balance in the account is given by the exponential growth function $y(t) = y_0e^{kt}$, where y_0 is the initial deposit, t is measured in years, and k is determined by the annual percentage yield.

EXAMPLE 3 Continuous compounding The APY of a savings account is the percentage increase in the balance over the course of a year. Suppose you deposit \$500 in a savings account that has an APY of 6.18% per year. Assume that the interest rate remains constant and that no additional deposits or withdrawals are made. How long will it take for the balance to reach \$2500?

> The rate constant k, in this case $0.06 = 6\%$, is the factor by which the balance increases if interest is compounded once at the end of the year. It is often advertised by banks as the *annual percentage rate* (or APR). If the balance increases by 6.18% in one year, it increases by a factor of 1.0618 in one year.

SOLUTION Because the balance grows by a fixed percentage every year, it grows exponentially. Letting $y(t)$ be the balance t years after the initial deposit of $y_0 = \$500$, we have $y(t) = y_0e^{kt}$, where the rate constant k must be determined. Note that if the initial balance is y_0, one year later the balance is 6.18% more, or

$$y(1) = 1.0618\, y_0 = y_0e^k.$$

Solving for k, we find that the rate constant is

$$k = \ln 1.0618 \approx 0.060\ \text{yr}^{-1}.$$

Therefore, the balance at any time $t \geq 0$ is $y(t) = 500e^{0.060t}$. To determine the time required for the balance to reach \$2500, we solve the equation

$$y(t) = 500e^{0.060t} = 2500.$$

Dividing by 500 and taking the natural logarithm of both sides yields

$$0.060t = \ln 5.$$

The balance reaches \$2500 in $t = (\ln 5)/0.060 \approx 26.8$ yr. *Related Exercises 11–16* ◀

Resource Consumption Among the many resources that people use, energy is certainly one of the most important. The basic unit of energy is the **joule** (J), roughly the energy needed to lift a 0.1-kg object (say an orange) 1 m. The *rate* at which energy is consumed is called **power**. The basic unit of power is the **watt** (W), where 1 W = 1 J/s. If you turn on a 100-W lightbulb for 1 min, the bulb consumes energy at a rate of 100 J/s and it uses a total of $100\ \text{J/s} \cdot 60\ \text{s} = 6000$ J of energy.

A more useful measure of energy for large quantities is the **kilowatt-hour** (kWh). A kilowatt is 1000 W or 1000 J/s. If you consume energy at the rate of 1 kW for 1 hr (3600 s), you use a total of $1000\ \text{J/s} \cdot 3600\ \text{s} = 3.6 \times 10^6$ J, which is 1 kWh. A person running for 1 hr consumes roughly 1 kWh of energy. A typical house uses on the order of 1000 kWh of energy in a month.

Assume that the total energy used (by a person, machine, or city) is given by the function $E(t)$. Because the power $P(t)$ is the rate at which energy is used, we have $P(t) = E'(t)$. Using the ideas of Section 6.1, the total amount of energy used between the times $t = a$ and $t = b$ is

$$\text{total energy used} = \int_a^b E'(t)\,dt = \int_a^b P(t)\,dt.$$

We see that energy is the area under the power curve. With this background, we can investigate a situation in which the rate of energy consumption increases exponentially.

EXAMPLE 4 **Energy consumption** At the beginning of 2006, the rate of energy consumption for the city of Denver was 7000 megawatts (MW), where 1 MW $= 10^6$ W. That rate was expected to increase at an annual growth rate of 2% per year.

a. Find the function that gives the power or rate of energy consumption for all times after the beginning of 2006.

b. Find the total amount of energy used during the year 2010.

c. Find the function that gives the total (cumulative) amount of energy used by the city between 2006 and any time $t \geq 0$.

SOLUTION

➤ In one year, the power function increases by 2% or by a factor of 1.02.

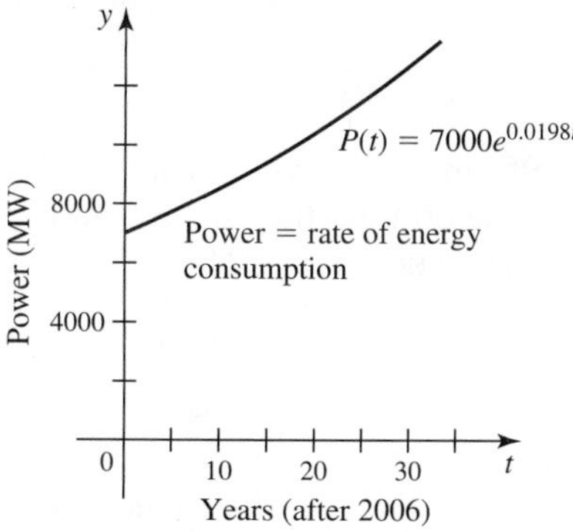

FIGURE 7.31

a. Let $t \geq 0$ be the number of years after the beginning of 2006, and let $P(t)$ be the power function that gives the rate of energy consumption at time t. Because P increases at a constant rate of 2% per year, it increases exponentially. Therefore, $P(t) = P_0 e^{kt}$, where $P_0 = 7000$ MW. We determine k as before by setting $t = 1$; after one year the power is

$$P(1) = P_0 e^k = 1.02 P_0.$$

Canceling P_0 and solving for k, we find that $k = \ln(1.02) \approx 0.0198$. Therefore, the power function (Figure 7.31) is

$$P(t) = 7000e^{0.0198t}, \quad \text{for } t \geq 0.$$

b. The entire year 2010 corresponds to the interval $4 \leq t \leq 5$. Substituting $P(t) = 7000e^{0.0198t}$, the total energy used in 2010 was

$$\begin{aligned} \int_4^5 P(t)\,dt &= \int_4^5 7000e^{0.0198t}\,dt && \text{Substitute for } P(t). \\ &= \frac{7000}{0.0198} e^{0.0198t} \Big|_4^5 && \text{Fundamental Theorem} \\ &\approx 7652. && \text{Evaluate.} \end{aligned}$$

Because the units of P are MW and t is measured in years, the units of energy are MW-yr. To convert to MWh, we multiply by 8760 hr/yr to get the total energy of about 6.7×10^7 MWh (or 6.7×10^{10} kWh).

c. The total energy used between $t = 0$ and at any future time t is given by the future value formula (Section 6.1):

$$E(t) = E(0) + \int_0^t E'(s)\,ds = E(0) + \int_0^t P(s)\,ds.$$

Assuming $t = 0$ corresponds to the beginning of 2006, we take $E(0) = 0$. Substituting again for the power function P, the total energy in MW-yr at time t is

$$\begin{aligned} E(t) &= E(0) + \int_0^t P(s)\,ds \\ &= 0 + \int_0^t 7000e^{0.0198s}\,ds && \text{Substitute for } P(s) \text{ and } E(0). \\ &= \frac{7000}{0.0198} e^{0.0198s} \Big|_0^t && \text{Fundamental Theorem} \\ &\approx 353{,}535(e^{0.0198t} - 1). && \text{Evaluate.} \end{aligned}$$

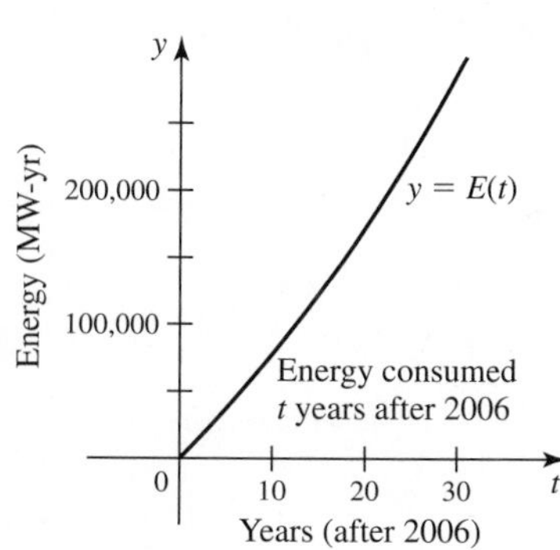

FIGURE 7.32

As shown in Figure 7.32, when the rate of energy consumption increases exponentially, the total amount of energy consumed also increases exponentially.

Related Exercises 11–16 ◂

Exponential Decay

Everything you have learned about exponential growth carries over directly to exponential decay. A function that decreases exponentially has the form $y(t) = y_0 e^{-kt}$, where $y_0 = y(0)$ is the initial value and $k > 0$ is the rate constant.

Exponential decay is characterized by a constant relative decay rate and by a constant **half-life**. For example, radioactive plutonium has a half-life of 24,000 years. An initial sample of 1 mg decays to 0.5 mg after 24,000 years and to 0.25 mg after 48,000 years. To compute the half-life, we determine the time required for the quantity $y(t) = y_0 e^{-kt}$ to reach one half of its current value; that is, we solve $y_0 e^{-kt} = y_0/2$ for t. Canceling y_0 and taking logarithms of both sides, we find that

$$e^{-kt} = \frac{1}{2} \Rightarrow -kt = \ln\left(\frac{1}{2}\right) = -\ln 2 \Rightarrow t = \frac{\ln 2}{k}.$$

QUICK CHECK 4 If a quantity decreases by a factor of 8 every 30 years, what is its half-life?◄

The half-life is given by the same formula as the doubling time.

Exponential Decay Functions

Exponential decay is described by functions of the form $y(t) = y_0 e^{-kt}$. The initial value of y is $y(0) = y_0$, and the rate constant $k > 0$ determines the rate of decay. Exponential decay is characterized by a constant relative decay rate. The constant half-life is $T_{1/2} = \frac{\ln 2}{k}$, with the same units as t.

Radiometric Dating A powerful method for estimating the age of ancient objects (for example, rocks, bones, meteorites, and cave paintings) relies on the radioactive decay of certain elements. A common version of radiometric dating uses the carbon isotope C-14, which is present in all living matter. When a living organism dies, it ceases to replace C-14, and the C-14 that is present decays with a half-life of about $T_{1/2} = 5730$ yr. Comparing the C-14 in a living organism to the amount in a dead sample provides an estimate of its age.

EXAMPLE 5 **Radiometric dating** Researchers determine that a fossilized bone has 30% of the C-14 of a live bone. Estimate the age of the bone. Assume a half-life for C-14 of 5730 yr.

SOLUTION The exponential decay function $y(t) = y_0 e^{-kt}$ may be invoked as it applies to all decay processes with a constant half-life. By the half-life formula, $T_{1/2} = (\ln 2)/k$. Substituting $T_{1/2} = 5730$ yr, the rate constant is

$$k = \frac{\ln 2}{T_{1/2}} = \frac{\ln 2}{5730 \text{ yr}} \approx 0.000121 \text{ yr}^{-1}.$$

Assume that the amount of C-14 in a living bone is y_0. Over t years, the amount of C-14 in the fossilized bone decays to 30% of its initial value, or $0.3y_0$. Using the decay function, we have

$$0.3y_0 = y_0 e^{-0.000121t}.$$

Solving for t, the age of the bone in years is

$$t = \frac{\ln 0.3}{-0.000121} \approx 9950.$$

Related Exercises 17–24◄

Pharmacokinetics Pharmacokinetics describes the processes by which drugs are assimilated by the body. The elimination of most drugs from the body may be modeled by an exponential decay function with a known half-life (alcohol is a notable exception). The simplest models assume that an entire drug dose is immediately absorbed into the blood. This assumption is a bit of an idealization; more refined mathematical models can account for the absorption process.

Half-lives of common drugs

Penicillin	1 hr
Amoxicillin	1 hr
Nicotine	2 hr
Morphine	3 hr
Tetracycline	9 hr
Digitalis	33 hr
Phenobarbitol	2–6 days

EXAMPLE 6 **Pharmacokinetics** An exponential decay function $y(t) = y_0 e^{-kt}$ models the amount of a drug in the blood t hr after an initial dose of $y_0 = 100$ mg is administered. Assume the half-life of a particular drug is 16 hours.

a. Find the exponential decay function that governs the amount of drug in the blood.

b. How much time is required for the drug to reach 1% of the initial dose (1 mg)?

c. If a second 100-mg dose is given 12 hr after the first dose, how much time is required for the drug level to reach 1 mg?

SOLUTION

a. Knowing that the half-life is 16 hr, the rate constant is

$$k = \frac{\ln 2}{T_{1/2}} = \frac{\ln 2}{16 \text{ hr}} \approx 0.0433 \text{ hr}^{-1}.$$

Therefore, the decay function is $y(t) = 100e^{-0.0433t}$.

b. The time required for the drug to reach 1 mg is the solution of

$$100e^{-0.0433t} = 1.$$

Solving for t, we have

$$t = \frac{\ln 0.01}{-0.0433 \text{ hr}^{-1}} \approx 106 \text{ hr}.$$

It takes more than 4 days for the drug to be reduced to 1% of the initial dose.

c. Using the exponential decay function of part (a), the amount of drug in the blood after 12 hr is

$$y(12) = 100e^{-0.0433 \cdot 12} \approx 59.5 \text{ mg}.$$

The second 100-mg dose given after 12 hr increases the amount of drug (assuming instantaneous absorption) to 159.5 mg. This amount becomes the new initial value for another exponential decay process (Figure 7.33). Measuring t from the time of the second dose, the amount of drug in the blood is

$$y(t) = 159.5e^{-0.0433t}.$$

The amount of drug reaches 1 mg when

$$y(t) = 159.5e^{-0.0433t} = 1,$$

which implies that

$$t = \frac{-\ln 159.5}{-0.0433 \text{ hr}^{-1}} = 117.1 \text{ hr}.$$

Approximately 117 hr after the second dose (or 129 hr after the first dose), the drug reaches 1% of the initial dose.

Related Exercises 17–24

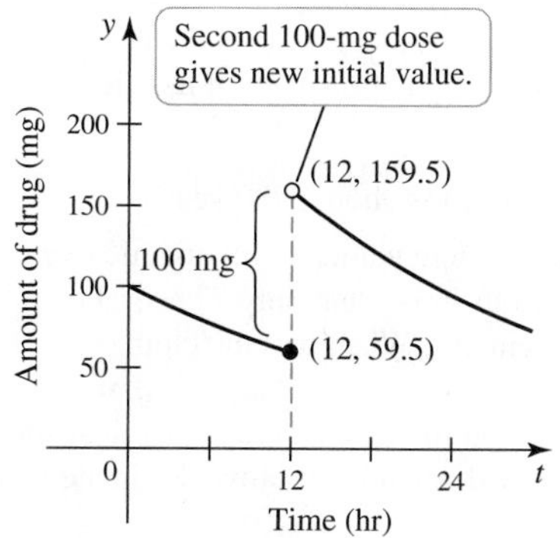

FIGURE 7.33

SECTION 7.4 EXERCISES

Review Questions

1. In terms of relative growth rate, what is the defining property of exponential growth?
2. Give two pieces of information that may be used to formulate an exponential growth or decay function.
3. Explain the meaning of doubling time.
4. Explain the meaning of half-life.
5. How are the rate constant and the doubling time related?
6. How are the rate constant and the half-life related?
7. Give two examples of processes that are modeled by exponential growth.
8. Give two examples of processes that are modeled by exponential decay.

Basic Skills

9–10. Absolute and relative growth rates *Two functions f and g are given. Show that the growth rate of the linear function is constant and the relative growth rate of the exponential function is constant.*

9. $f(t) = 100 + 10.5t,\ g(t) = 100e^{t/10}$
10. $f(t) = 2200 + 400t,\ g(t) = 400 \cdot 2^{t/20}$

11–14. Designing exponential growth functions *Devise the exponential growth function that fits the given data, then answer the accompanying questions. Be sure to identify the reference point ($t = 0$) and units of time.*

11. **Population** The population of a town with a 2010 population of 90,000 grows at a rate of 2.4%/yr. In what year will the population double its initial value (to 180,000)?
12. **Population** The population of Clark County, Nevada, was 1.9 million in 2008. Assuming an annual growth rate of 4.5%/yr, what will the county population be in 2020?
13. **Rising costs** Between 2005 and 2010, the average rate of inflation was about 3%/yr (as measured by the Consumer Price Index). If a cart of groceries cost $100 in 2005, what will it cost in 2015 assuming the rate of inflation remains constant?
14. **Cell growth** The number of cells in a tumor doubles every 6 weeks starting with 8 cells. After how many weeks does the tumor have 1500 cells?
15. **Projection sensitivity** According to the 2000 census, the U.S. population was 281 million with an estimated growth rate of 0.7%/yr.
    a. Based on these figures, find the doubling time and project the population in 2100.
    b. Suppose the actual growth rates are just 0.2 percentage points lower and higher than 0.7%/yr (0.5% and 0.9%). What are the resulting doubling times and projected 2100 population?
    c. Comment on the sensitivity of these projections to the growth rate.
16. **Oil consumption** Starting in 2010 ($t = 0$), the rate at which oil is consumed by a small country increases at a rate of 1.5%/yr, starting with an initial rate of 1.2 million barrels/yr.
    a. How much oil is consumed over the course of the year 2010 (between $t = 0$ and $t = 1$)?
    b. Find the function that gives the amount of oil consumed between $t = 0$ and any future time t.
    c. How many years after 2010 will the amount of oil consumed since 2010 reach 10 million barrels?

17–20. Designing exponential decay functions *Devise an exponential decay function that fits the following data; then answer the accompanying questions. Be sure to identify the reference point ($t = 0$) and units of time.*

17. **Crime rate** The homicide rate decreases at a rate of 3%/yr in a city that had 800 homicides/yr in 2010. At this rate, when will the homicide rate reach 600 homicides/yr?
18. **Drug metabolism** A drug is eliminated from the body at a rate of 15%/hr. After how many hours does the amount of drug reach 10% of the initial dose?
19. **Atmospheric pressure** The pressure of Earth's atmosphere at sea level is approximately 1000 millibars and decreases exponentially with elevation. At an elevation of 30,000 ft (approximately the altitude of Mt. Everest), the pressure is one-third of the sea-level pressure. At what elevation is the pressure half of the sea-level pressure? At what elevation is it 1% of the sea-level pressure?
20. **China's population** China's one-child policy was implemented with a goal of reducing China's population to 700 million by 2050 (from 1.2 billion in 2000). Suppose China's population declines at a rate of 0.5%/yr. Will this rate of decline be sufficient to meet the goal?
21. **Valium metabolism** The drug valium is eliminated from the bloodstream with a half-life of 36 hr. Suppose that a patient receives an initial dose of 20 mg of valium at midnight.
    a. How much valium is in the patient's blood at noon the next day?
    b. When will the valium concentration reach 10% of its initial level?
22. **Carbon dating** The half-life of C-14 is about 5730 years.
    a. Archaeologists find a piece of cloth painted with organic dyes. Analysis of the dye in the cloth shows that only 77% of the C-14 originally in the dye remains. When was the cloth painted?
    b. A well-preserved piece of wood found at an archaeological site has 6.2% of the C-14 that it had when it was alive. Estimate when the wood was cut.
23. **Uranium dating** Uranium-238 (U-238) has a half-life of 4.5 billion years. Geologists find a rock containing a mixture of U-238 and lead, and determine that 85% of the original U-238 remains; the other 15% has decayed into lead. How old is the rock?
24. **Radioiodine treatment** Roughly 12,000 Americans are diagnosed with thyroid cancer every year, which accounts for 1% of all cancer

cases. It occurs in women three times as frequently as in men. Fortunately, thyroid cancer can be treated successfully in many cases with radioactive iodine (I-131). This unstable form of iodine has a half-life of 8 days and is given in small doses measured in millicuries.

a. Suppose a patient is given an initial dose of 100 millicuries. Find the function that gives the amount of I-131 in the body after $t \geq 0$ days.
b. How long does it take for the amount of I-131 to reach 10% of the initial dose?
c. Finding the initial dose to give a particular patient is a critical calculation. How does the time to reach 10% of the initial dose change if the initial dose is increased by 5%?

Further Explorations

25. **Explain why or why not** Determine whether the following statements are true and give an explanation or counterexample.
   a. A quantity that increases at 6%/yr obeys the growth function $y(t) = y_0e^{0.06t}$.
   b. If a quantity increases by 10%/yr, it increases by 30% over 3 years.
   c. A quantity decreases by one-third every month. Therefore, it decreases exponentially.
   d. If the rate constant of an exponential growth function is increased, its doubling time is decreased.
   e. If a quantity increases exponentially, the time required to increase by a factor of 10 remains constant for all time.

26. **Tripling time** A quantity increases according to the exponential function $y(t) = y_0e^{kt}$. What is the tripling time for the quantity? What is the time required for the quantity to increase p-fold?

27. **Constant doubling time** Prove that the doubling time for an exponentially increasing quantity is constant for all time.

28. **Overtaking** City A has a current population of 500,000 people and grows at a rate of 3%/yr. City B has a current population of 300,000 and grows at a rate of 5%/yr.
   a. When will the cities have the same population?
   b. Suppose City C has a current population of $y_0 < 500{,}000$ and a growth rate of $p > 3\%$/yr. What is the relationship between y_0 and p such that the Cities A and C have the same population in 10 years?

T 29. **A slowing race** Starting at the same time and place, Abe and Bob race, running at velocities $u(t) = 4/(t + 1)$ mi/hr and $v(t) = 4e^{-t/2}$ mi/hr, respectively, for $t \geq 0$.
   a. Who is ahead after $t = 5$ hr? After $t = 10$ hr?
   b. Find and graph the position functions of both runners. Which runner can run only a finite distance in an unlimited amount of time?

Applications

30. **Law of 70** Bankers use the law of 70, which says that if an account increases at a fixed rate of $p\%$/yr, its doubling time is approximately $70/p$. Explain why and when this statement is true.

31. **Compounded inflation** The U.S. government reports the rate of inflation (as measured by the Consumer Price Index) both monthly and annually. Suppose that, for a particular month, the *monthly* rate of inflation is reported as 0.8%. Assuming that this rate remains constant, what is the corresponding *annual* rate of inflation? Is the annual rate 12 times the monthly rate? Explain.

32. **Acceleration, velocity, position** Suppose the acceleration of an object moving along a line is given by $a(t) = -kv(t)$, where k is a positive constant and v is the object's velocity. Assume that the initial velocity and position are given by $v(0) = 10$ and $s(0) = 0$, respectively.
   a. Use $a(t) = v'(t)$ to find the velocity of the object as a function of time.
   b. Use $v(t) = s'(t)$ to find the position of the object as a function of time.
   c. Use the fact that $dv/dt = (dv/ds)(ds/dt)$ (by the Chain Rule) to find the velocity as a function of position.

T 33. **Free fall** (adapted from Putnam Exam, 1939) An object moves freely in a straight line except for air resistance, which is proportional to its speed; this means its acceleration is $a(t) = -kv(t)$. The speed of the object decreases from 1000 ft/s to 900 ft/s over a distance of 1200 ft. Approximate the time required for this deceleration to occur. (Exercise 32 may be useful.)

T 34. **A running model** A model for the startup of a runner in a short race results in the velocity function $v(t) = a(1 - e^{-t/c})$, where a and c are positive constants and v has units of m/s. [Source: "A Theory of Competitive Running," Joe Keller, *Physics Today*, 26 (Sept 1973).]
   a. Graph the velocity function for $a = 12$ and $c = 2$. What is the runner's maximum velocity?
   b. Using the velocity in part (a) and assuming $s(0) = 0$, find the position function $s(t)$ for $t \geq 0$.
   c. Graph the position function and estimate the time required to run 100 m.

35. **Tumor growth** Suppose the cells of a tumor are idealized as spheres each with a radius of 5 μm (micrometer). The number of cells has a doubling time of 35 days. Approximately how long will it take a single cell to grow into a multi-celled spherical tumor with a volume of 0.5 cm^3 (1 cm = 10,000 μm)? Assume that the tumor spheres are tightly packed.

36. **Carbon emissions from China and the United States** The burning of fossil fuels releases greenhouse gases into the atmosphere. In 1995, the United States emitted about 1.4 billion tons of carbon into the atmosphere, nearly one-fourth of the world total. China was the second largest contributor, emitting about 850 million tons of carbon. However, emissions from China were rising at a rate of about 4%/yr, while U.S. emissions were rising at about 1.3%/yr. Using these growth rates, project greenhouse gas emissions from the United States and China in 2020. Graph the projected emissions for both countries. Comment on your observations.

37. **A revenue model** The owner of a clothing store understands that the demand for shirts decreases with the price. In fact, she has developed a model that predicts that at a price of \$$x$ per shirt, she can sell $D(x) = 40e^{-x/50}$ shirts in a day. It follows that the revenue (total money taken in) in a day is $R(x) = xD(x)$ (\$$x$/shirt $\cdot$ $D(x)$ shirts). What price should the owner charge to maximize revenue?

Additional Exercises

38. Geometric means A quantity grows exponentially according to $y(t) = y_0e^{kt}$. What is the relationship between m, n, and p such that $y(p) = \sqrt{y(m)y(n)}$?

39. Equivalent growth functions The same exponential growth function can be written in the forms $y(t) = y_0e^{kt}$, $y(t) = y_0(1 + r)^t$, and $y(t) = y_0 2^{t/T_2}$. Derive the relationships among k, r, and T_2.

40. General relative growth rates Define the relative growth rate of the function f over the time interval T to be the relative change in f over an interval of length T:

$$R_T = \frac{f(t + T) - f(t)}{f(t)}.$$

Show that for the exponential function $y(t) = y_0e^{kt}$, the relative growth rate R_T is constant for any T; that is, choose any T and show that R_T is constant for all t.

QUICK CHECK ANSWERS

1. Population A grows exponentially; population B grows linearly. **3.** The function $100e^{0.05t}$ increases by a factor of 1.0513, or by 5.13%, in 1 unit of time. **4.** 10 yr.

7.5 Inverse Trigonometric Functions

We used the idea of an inverse function to relate the natural logarithm function to the natural exponential function. We now carry out a similar procedure with trigonometric functions. Our goal is to develop the inverses of the sine and cosine in detail. The inverses of the other four trigonometric functions then follow in an analogous way. When we investigate the calculus of inverse trigonometric functions, we discover several new and important derivatives and integrals.

Inverse Sine and Cosine

So far, we have asked the question, Given an angle x, what is $\sin x$ or $\cos x$? Now we ask the opposite questions: Given a number y, what is the angle x such that $\sin x = y$? Or, what is the angle x such that $\cos x = y$? These are inverse questions.

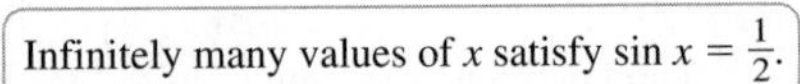
Infinitely many values of x satisfy $\sin x = \frac{1}{2}$.

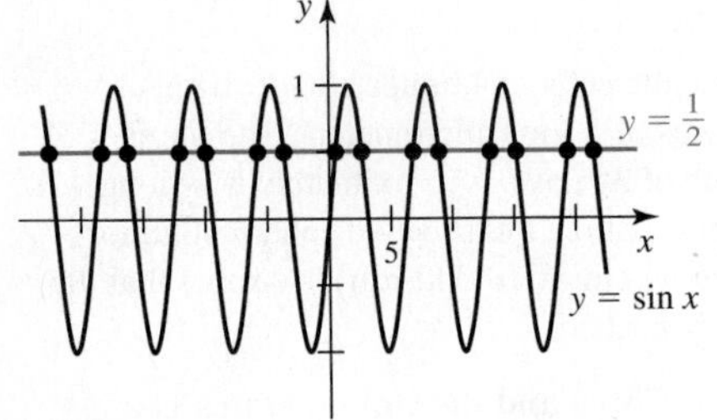

FIGURE 7.34

There are a few things to notice right away. First, these questions do not make sense if $|y| > 1$, because $-1 \le \sin x \le 1$ and $-1 \le \cos x \le 1$. Next, let's select an acceptable value of y, say $y = \frac{1}{2}$, and find the angle x that satisfies $\sin x = y = \frac{1}{2}$. It is apparent that infinitely many angles satisfy $\sin x = \frac{1}{2}$; all angles of the form $\pi/6 \pm 2n\pi$ and $5\pi/6 \pm 2n\pi$, where n is an integer, answer the inverse question (Figure 7.34). A similar situation occurs with the cosine function.

These inverse questions do not have unique answers because $\sin x$ and $\cos x$ are not one-to-one on their domains. To define their inverses, these functions must be restricted to intervals on which they are one-to-one. For the sine function, the standard choice is $[-\pi/2, \pi/2]$; for cosine, it is $[0, \pi]$ (Figure 7.35). Now when we ask for the angle x on the interval $[-\pi/2, \pi/2]$ such that $\sin x = \frac{1}{2}$, there is one answer: $x = \pi/6$. When we ask for the angle x on the interval $[0, \pi]$ such that $\cos x = -\frac{1}{2}$, there is one answer: $x = 2\pi/3$.

➤ The notation for the inverse trigonometric functions invites confusion: $\sin^{-1} x$ and $\cos^{-1} x$ do not mean the reciprocals of $\sin x$ and $\cos x$. The expression $\sin^{-1} x$ should be read "*angle whose sine is x*," and $\cos^{-1} x$ should be read "*angle whose cosine is x*." The values of $\sin^{-1}$ and $\cos^{-1}$ are angles.

We define the **inverse sine**, or **arcsine**, denoted $y = \sin^{-1} x$ or $y = \arcsin x$, such that y is the angle whose sine is x, with the provision that y lies in the interval $[-\pi/2, \pi/2]$. Similarly, we define the **inverse cosine**, or **arccosine**, denoted $y = \cos^{-1} x$ or $y = \arccos x$, such that y is the angle whose cosine is x, with the provision that y lies in the interval $[0, \pi]$.

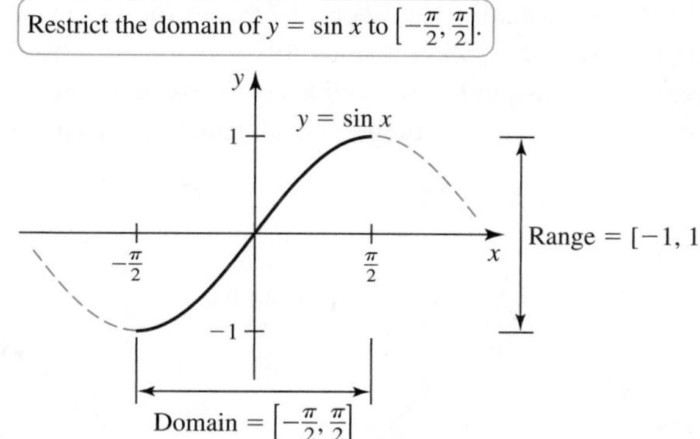

(a)

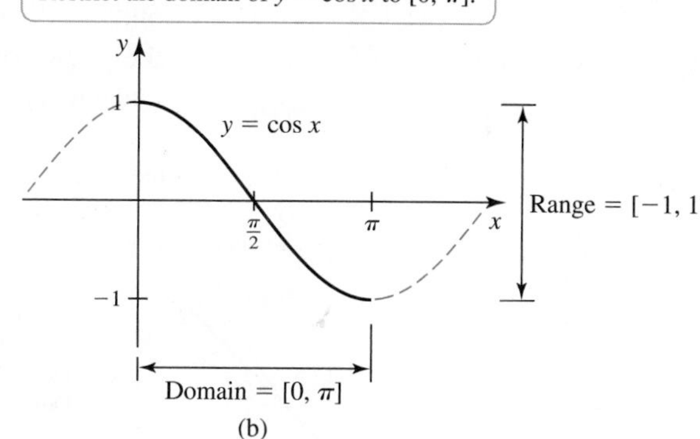

(b)

FIGURE 7.35

DEFINITION Inverse Sine and Cosine

$y = \sin^{-1} x$ is the value of y such that $x = \sin y$, where $-\pi/2 \le y \le \pi/2$.
$y = \cos^{-1} x$ is the value of y such that $x = \cos y$, where $0 \le y \le \pi$.
The domain of both $\sin^{-1} x$ and $\cos^{-1} x$ is $\{x: -1 \le x \le 1\}$.

Any invertible function and its inverse satisfy the properties

$$f(f^{-1}(y)) = y \quad \text{and} \quad f^{-1}(f(x)) = x.$$

These properties apply to the inverse sine and cosine, as long as we observe the restrictions on the domains. Here is what we can say:

- $\sin(\sin^{-1} x) = x$ and $\cos(\cos^{-1} x) = x$, for $-1 \le x \le 1$.
- $\sin^{-1}(\sin y) = y$, for $-\pi/2 \le y \le \pi/2$.
- $\cos^{-1}(\cos y) = y$, for $0 \le y \le \pi$.

QUICK CHECK 1 Explain why $\sin^{-1}(\sin 0) = 0$, but $\sin^{-1}(\sin 2\pi) \ne 2\pi$. ◂

EXAMPLE 1 Working with inverse sine and cosine Evaluate the following expressions.

a. $\sin^{-1}(\sqrt{3}/2)$ **b.** $\cos^{-1}(-\sqrt{3}/2)$ **c.** $\cos^{-1}(\cos 3\pi)$ **d.** $\sin\left(\sin^{-1}\left(\frac{1}{2}\right)\right)$

SOLUTION

a. $\sin^{-1}(\sqrt{3}/2) = \pi/3$ because $\sin(\pi/3) = \sqrt{3}/2$ and $\pi/3$ is in the interval $[-\pi/2, \pi/2]$.

b. $\cos^{-1}(-\sqrt{3}/2) = 5\pi/6$ because $\cos(5\pi/6) = -\sqrt{3}/2$ and $5\pi/6$ is in the interval $[0, \pi]$.

c. It's tempting to conclude that $\cos^{-1}(\cos 3\pi) = 3\pi$, but the result of an inverse cosine operation must lie in the interval $[0, \pi]$. Because $\cos(3\pi) = -1$ and $\cos^{-1}(-1) = \pi$, we have

$$\cos^{-1}\underbrace{(\cos 3\pi)}_{-1} = \cos^{-1}(-1) = \pi.$$

d. $$\sin\underbrace{\left(\sin^{-1}\left(\frac{1}{2}\right)\right)}_{\pi/6} = \sin\frac{\pi}{6} = \frac{1}{2}.$$

Related Exercises 11–16 ◂

Graphs and Properties Recall from Section 7.1 that the graph of the inverse f^{-1} is obtained by reflecting the graph of f about the identity line $y = x$. This operation produces the graphs of the inverse sine (Figure 7.36) and inverse cosine (Figure 7.37). The graphs make it easy to compare the domain and range of each function and its inverse.

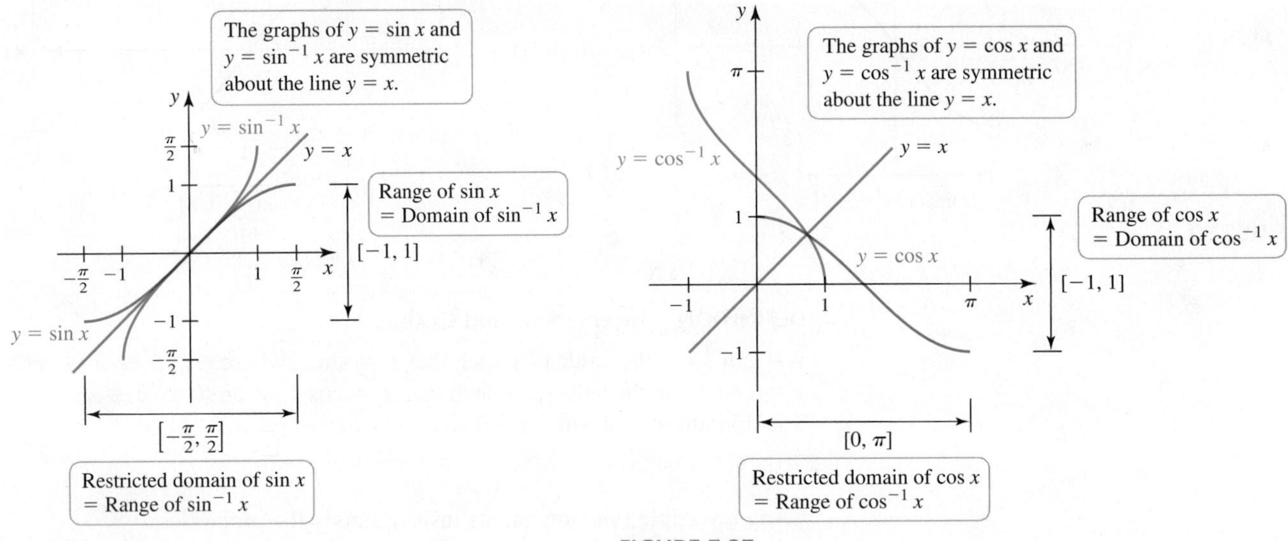

The graphs of y = sin x and y = sin⁻¹ x are symmetric about the line y = x.
y = sin⁻¹ x
y = x
Range of sin x = Domain of sin⁻¹ x
[−1, 1]
y = sin x
[−π/2, π/2]
Restricted domain of sin x = Range of sin⁻¹ x
The graphs of y = cos x and y = cos⁻¹ x are symmetric about the line y = x.
y = cos⁻¹ x
y = x
y = cos x
Range of cos x = Domain of cos⁻¹ x
[−1, 1]
[0, π]
Restricted domain of cos x = Range of cos⁻¹ x

FIGURE 7.36

FIGURE 7.37

EXAMPLE 2 Right-triangle relationships

a. Suppose $\theta = \sin^{-1}(2/5)$. Find $\cos\theta$ and $\tan\theta$.

b. Find an alternative form for $\cot(\cos^{-1}(x/4))$ in terms of x.

SOLUTION

$\sin\theta = \frac{2}{5}$, $\cos\theta = \frac{\sqrt{21}}{5}$, $\tan\theta = \frac{2}{\sqrt{21}}$

$\sqrt{5^2 - 2^2} = \sqrt{21}$

FIGURE 7.38

a. Relationships between the trigonometric functions and their inverses can often be simplified using a right-triangle sketch. The right triangle in Figure 7.38 satisfies the relationship $\sin\theta = \frac{2}{5}$, or, equivalently, $\theta = \sin^{-1}\left(\frac{2}{5}\right)$. We label the angle θ and the lengths of two sides; we then see the length of the third side is $\sqrt{21}$ (by the Pythagorean theorem). Now it is easy to read directly from the triangle:

$$\cos\theta = \frac{\sqrt{21}}{5} \quad \text{and} \quad \tan\theta = \frac{2}{\sqrt{21}}.$$

$\sqrt{16 - x^2}$

$\cos\theta = \frac{x}{4}$

FIGURE 7.39

b. We draw a right triangle with an angle θ satisfying $\cos\theta = x/4$, or, equivalently, $\theta = \cos^{-1}(x/4)$ (Figure 7.39). The length of the third side of the triangle is $\sqrt{16 - x^2}$. It now follows that

$$\cot\Bigg(\underbrace{\cos^{-1}\left(\frac{x}{4}\right)}_{\theta}\Bigg) = \frac{x}{\sqrt{16 - x^2}}.$$

Related Exercises 17–22 ◀

EXAMPLE 3 A useful identity Use right triangles to explain why $\cos^{-1}x + \sin^{-1}x = \pi/2$.

$\sin\varphi = x \Rightarrow \varphi = \sin^{-1}x$

$\cos\theta = x \Rightarrow \theta = \cos^{-1}x$

(x, y)

FIGURE 7.40

SOLUTION We draw a right triangle in a unit circle and label the acute angles θ and φ (Figure 7.40). These angles satisfy $\cos\theta = x$, or $\theta = \cos^{-1}x$, and $\sin\varphi = x$, or $\varphi = \sin^{-1}x$. Because θ and φ are complementary angles, we have

$$\frac{\pi}{2} = \theta + \varphi = \cos^{-1}x + \sin^{-1}x.$$

This result holds for $0 \le x \le 1$. An analogous argument extends the property to $-1 \le x \le 1$.

Related Exercises 23–24 ◀

Other Inverse Trigonometric Functions

The procedures that led to the inverse sine and inverse cosine functions can be used to obtain the other four inverse trigonometric functions. Each of these functions carries a restriction that must be imposed to ensure that an inverse exists.

- The tangent function is one-to-one on $(-\pi/2, \pi/2)$, which becomes the range of $y = \tan^{-1} x$.
- The cotangent function is one-to-one on $(0, \pi)$, which becomes the range of $y = \cot^{-1} x$.
- The secant function is one-to-one on $[0, \pi]$, excluding $x = \pi/2$; this set becomes the range of $y = \sec^{-1} x$.
- The cosecant function is one-to-one on $[-\pi/2, \pi/2]$, excluding $x = 0$; this set becomes the range of $y = \csc^{-1} x$.

The inverse tangent, cotangent, secant, and cosecant are defined as follows.

> Tables and books differ on the definition of the inverse secant and cosecant. In some books, $\sec^{-1} x$ is defined to lie in the interval $[-\pi, -\pi/2)$ when $x < 0$.

DEFINITION Other Inverse Trigonometric Functions

$y = \tan^{-1} x$ is the value of y such that $x = \tan y$, where $-\pi/2 < y < \pi/2$.
$y = \cot^{-1} x$ is the value of y such that $x = \cot y$, where $0 < y < \pi$.

The domain of both $\tan^{-1} x$ and $\cot^{-1} x$ is $\{x: -\infty < x < \infty\}$.

$y = \sec^{-1} x$ is the value of y such that $x = \sec y$, where $0 \le y \le \pi$, with $y \ne \pi/2$.
$y = \csc^{-1} x$ is the value of y such that $x = \csc y$, where $-\pi/2 \le y \le \pi/2$, with $y \ne 0$.

The domain of both $\sec^{-1} x$ and $\csc^{-1} x$ is $\{x: |x| \ge 1\}$.

The graphs of these inverse functions are obtained by reflecting the graphs of the original trigonometric functions about the line $y = x$ (Figures 7.41–7.44). The inverse secant and cosecant are somewhat irregular. The domain of the secant function

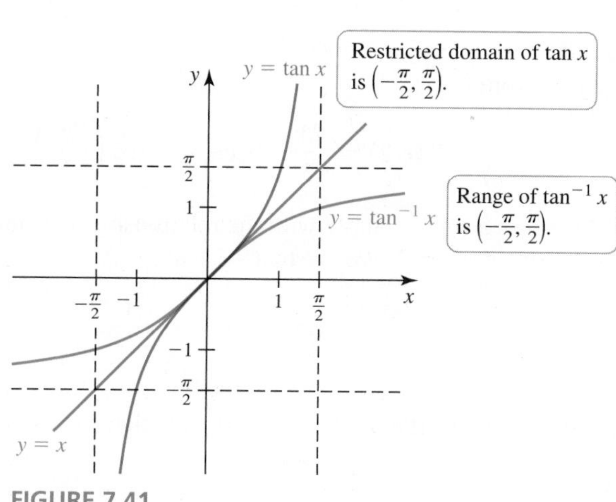

FIGURE 7.41

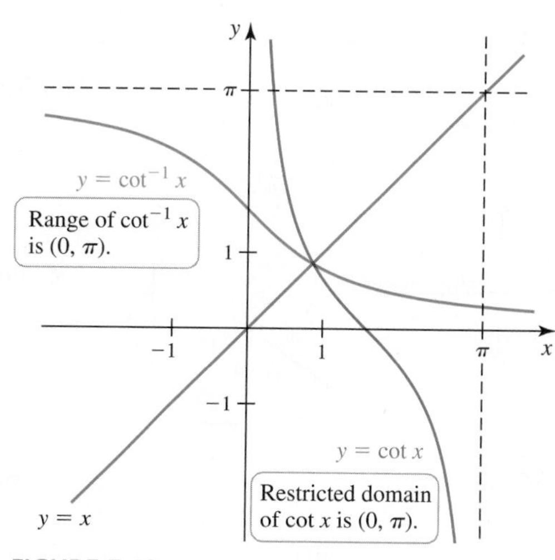

FIGURE 7.42

(Figure 7.43) is restricted to the set $[0, \pi]$, excluding $x = \pi/2$, where the secant has a vertical asymptote. This asymptote splits the range of the secant into two disjoint intervals $(-\infty, -1]$ and $[1, \infty)$, which, in turn, splits the domain of the inverse secant into the same two intervals. A similar situation occurs with the cosecant.

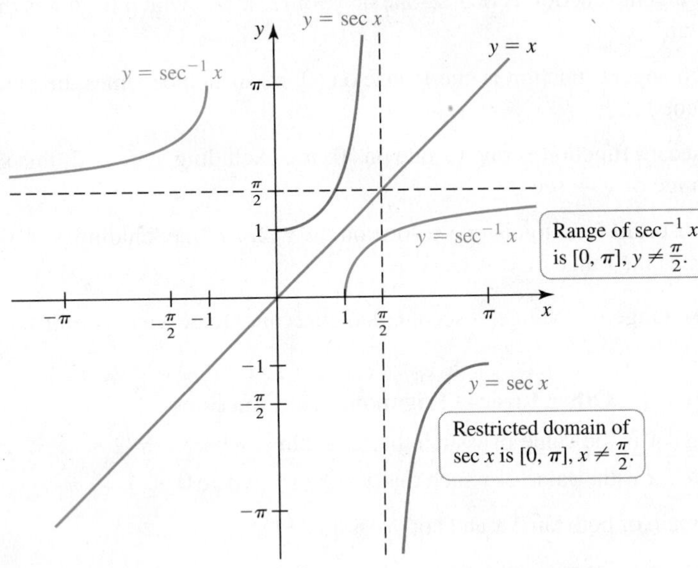

FIGURE 7.43

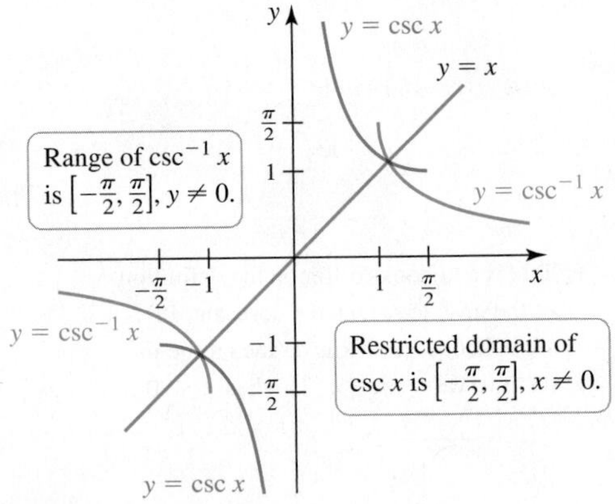

FIGURE 7.44

EXAMPLE 4 Working with inverse trigonometric functions Evaluate or simplify the following expressions.

a. $\tan^{-1}(-1/\sqrt{3})$ **b.** $\sec^{-1}(-2)$ **c.** $\sin(\tan^{-1} x)$

SOLUTION

a. The result of an inverse tangent operation must lie in the interval $(-\pi/2, \pi/2)$. Therefore,

$$\tan^{-1}\left(-\frac{1}{\sqrt{3}}\right) = -\frac{\pi}{6} \quad \text{because} \quad \tan\left(-\frac{\pi}{6}\right) = -\frac{1}{\sqrt{3}}.$$

b. The result of an inverse secant operation when $x \leq -1$ must lie in the interval $(\pi/2, \pi]$. Therefore,

$$\sec^{-1}(-2) = \frac{2\pi}{3} \quad \text{because} \quad \sec\left(\frac{2\pi}{3}\right) = -2.$$

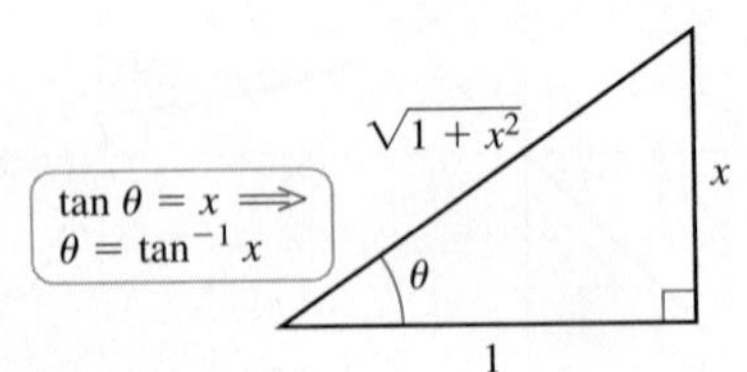

FIGURE 7.45

c. Figure 7.45 shows a right triangle with the relationship $x = \tan\theta$ or $\theta = \tan^{-1} x$, in the case that $0 \leq \theta < \pi/2$. We see that

$$\sin(\underbrace{\tan^{-1} x}_{\theta}) = \frac{x}{\sqrt{1 + x^2}}.$$

The same result follows if $-\pi/2 < \theta < 0$, in which case $x < 0$ and $\sin\theta < 0$.

Related Exercises 25–40 ◀

QUICK CHECK 2 Evaluate $\sec^{-1} 1$ and $\tan^{-1} 1$. ◀

Inverse Sine and Its Derivative

Recall that $y = \sin^{-1} x$ is the value of y such that $x = \sin y$, where $-\pi/2 \leq y \leq \pi/2$. The domain of $\sin^{-1} x$ is $\{x: -1 \leq x \leq 1\}$ (Figure 7.46). The derivative of $y = \sin^{-1} x$

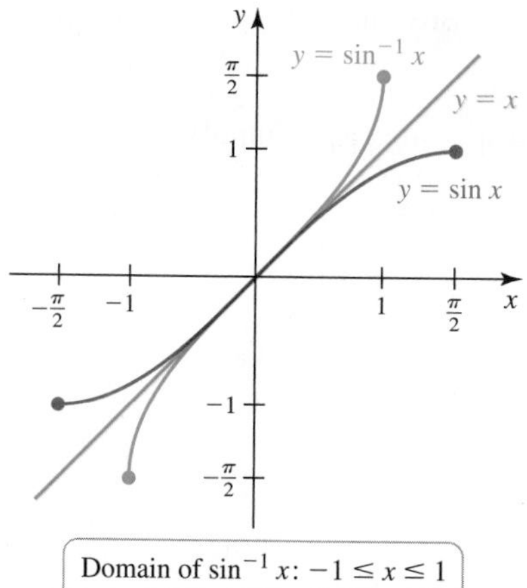

FIGURE 7.46

follows by differentiating both sides of $x = \sin y$ with respect to x, simplifying, and solving for dy/dx:

$$x = \sin y \qquad y = \sin^{-1} x \Leftrightarrow x = \sin y$$

$$\frac{d}{dx}(x) = \frac{d}{dx}(\sin y) \qquad \text{Differentiate with respect to } x.$$

$$1 = (\cos y)\frac{dy}{dx} \qquad \text{Chain Rule on the right side}$$

$$\frac{dy}{dx} = \frac{1}{\cos y} \qquad \text{Solve for } \frac{dy}{dx}.$$

The identity $\sin^2 y + \cos^2 y = 1$ is used to express this derivative in terms of x. Solving for $\cos y$ yields

$$\cos y = \pm\sqrt{1 - \underbrace{\sin^2 y}_{x^2}} \qquad x = \sin y \Rightarrow x^2 = \sin^2 y$$

$$= \pm\sqrt{1 - x^2}.$$

Because y is restricted to the interval $-\pi/2 \le y \le \pi/2$, we have $\cos y \ge 0$. Therefore, we choose the positive branch of the square root, and it follows that

$$\frac{dy}{dx} = \frac{d}{dx}(\sin^{-1} x) = \frac{1}{\sqrt{1 - x^2}}.$$

This result is consistent with the graph of $f(x) = \sin^{-1} x$ (Figure 7.47).

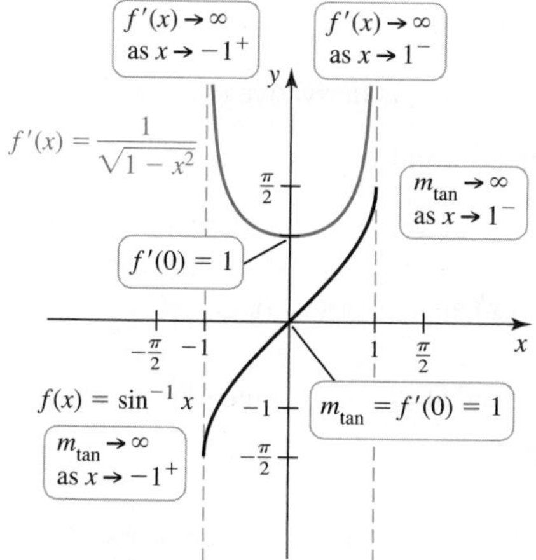

FIGURE 7.47

THEOREM 7.11 Derivative of Inverse Sine

$$\frac{d}{dx}(\sin^{-1} x) = \frac{1}{\sqrt{1 - x^2}}, \qquad \text{for } -1 < x < 1$$

EXAMPLE 5 Derivatives involving the inverse sine Compute the following derivatives.

a. $\frac{d}{dx}(\sin^{-1}(x^2 - 1))$ **b.** $\frac{d}{dx}(\cos(\sin^{-1} x))$

QUICK CHECK 3 Is $f(x) = \sin^{-1} x$ an even or odd function? Is $f'(x)$ an even or odd function?

SOLUTION We apply the Chain Rule for both derivatives.

a. $$\frac{d}{dx}(\sin^{-1}\underbrace{(x^2 - 1)}_{u}) = \underbrace{\frac{1}{\sqrt{1 - (x^2 - 1)^2}}}_{\text{derivative of } \sin^{-1} u \text{ evaluated at } u = x^2 - 1} \cdot \underbrace{2x}_{u'(x)} = \frac{2x}{\sqrt{2x^2 - x^4}}$$

b. $$\frac{d}{dx}(\cos\underbrace{(\sin^{-1} x)}_{u}) = \underbrace{-\sin(\sin^{-1} x)}_{\text{the derivative of the outer function } \cos u \text{ evaluated at } u = \sin^{-1} x} \cdot \underbrace{\frac{1}{\sqrt{1 - x^2}}}_{\text{the derivative of the inner function } \sin^{-1} x} = -\frac{x}{\sqrt{1 - x^2}}$$

> The result in Example 5b could have been obtained by noting that $\cos(\sin^{-1} x) = \sqrt{1 - x^2}$ and differentiating this expression (Exercise 94).

This result is valid for $-1 < x < 1$, where $\sin(\sin^{-1} x) = x$. *Related Exercises 41–46*

Derivatives of Inverse Tangent and Inverse Secant

The derivatives of the inverse tangent and inverse secant are derived using a method similar to that used for the inverse sine. Once these three derivative results are known, the derivatives of the inverse cosine, cotangent, and cosecant follow immediately.

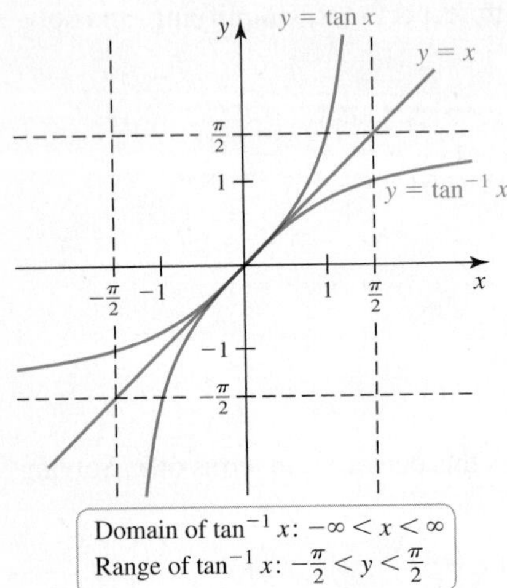

FIGURE 7.48

Inverse Tangent Recall that $y = \tan^{-1} x$ is the value of y such that $x = \tan y$, where $-\pi/2 < y < \pi/2$. The domain of $y = \tan^{-1} x$ is $\{x: -\infty < x < \infty\}$ (Figure 7.48). To find $\dfrac{dy}{dx}$, we differentiate both sides of $x = \tan y$ with respect to x and simplify:

$$x = \tan y \qquad y = \tan^{-1} x \Leftrightarrow x = \tan y$$

$$\frac{d}{dx}(x) = \frac{d}{dx}(\tan y) \qquad \text{Differentiate with respect to } x.$$

$$1 = \sec^2 y \cdot \frac{dy}{dx} \qquad \text{Chain Rule}$$

$$\frac{dy}{dx} = \frac{1}{\sec^2 y} \qquad \text{Solve for } \frac{dy}{dx}.$$

To express this derivative in terms of x, we combine the trigonometric identity $\sec^2 y = 1 + \tan^2 y$ with $x = \tan y$ to obtain $\sec^2 y = 1 + x^2$. Substituting this result into the expression for dy/dx, it follows that

$$\frac{dy}{dx} = \frac{d}{dx}(\tan^{-1} x) = \frac{1}{1 + x^2}.$$

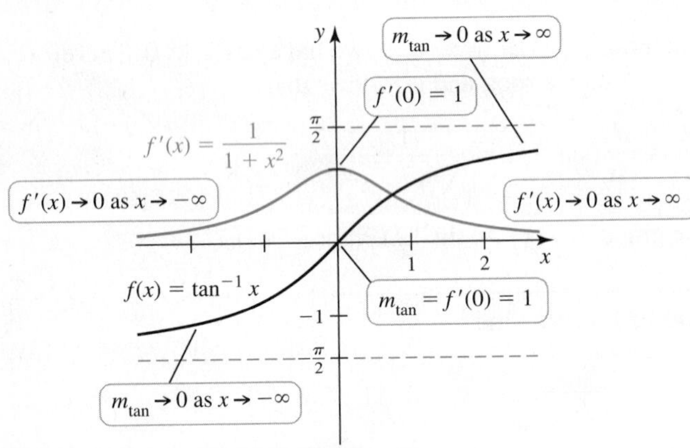

FIGURE 7.49

The graphs of the inverse tangent and its derivative (Figure 7.49) are informative. Letting $f(x) = \tan^{-1} x$ and $f'(x) = \dfrac{1}{1 + x^2}$, we see that $f'(0) = 1$, which is the maximum value of the derivative; that is, $\tan^{-1} x$ has its maximum slope at $x = 0$. As $x \to \infty$, $f'(x)$ approaches zero; likewise, as $x \to -\infty$, $f'(x)$ approaches zero.

QUICK CHECK 4 How do the slopes of the lines tangent to the graph of $y = \tan^{-1} x$ behave as $x \to \infty$?

Inverse Secant Recall that $y = \sec^{-1} x$ is the value of y such that $x = \sec y$, where $0 \le y \le \pi$, with $y \ne \pi/2$. The domain of $y = \sec^{-1} x$ is $\{x: |x| \ge 1\}$ (Figure 7.50).

The derivative of the inverse secant presents a new twist. Let $y = \sec^{-1} x$, or $x = \sec y$, and then differentiate both sides of $x = \sec y$ with respect to x:

$$1 = \sec y \tan y \frac{dy}{dx}.$$

Solving for $\dfrac{dy}{dx}$ produces

$$\frac{dy}{dx} = \frac{d}{dx}(\sec^{-1} x) = \frac{1}{\sec y \tan y}.$$

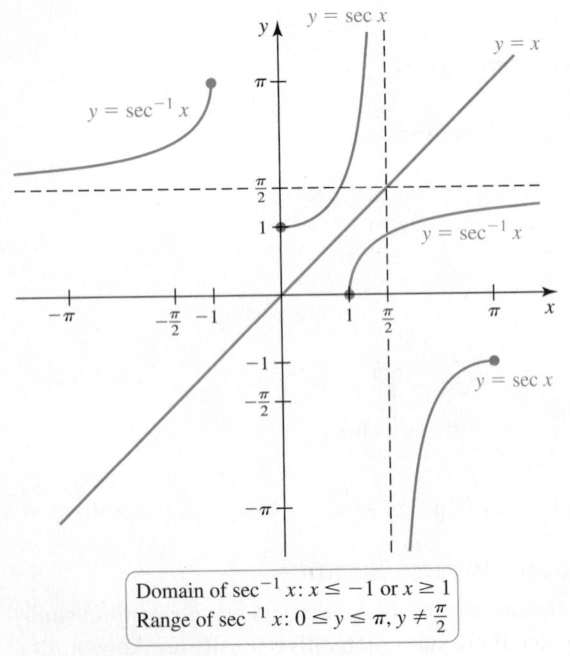

FIGURE 7.50

The final step is to express $\sec y \tan y$ in terms of x by using the identity $\sec^2 y = 1 + \tan^2 y$. Solving this equation for $\tan y$, we have

$$\tan y = \pm\sqrt{\underbrace{\sec^2 y}_{x^2} - 1} = \pm\sqrt{x^2 - 1}.$$

Two cases must be examined to resolve the sign on the square root:

- By the definition of $y = \sec^{-1} x$, if $x \ge 1$, then $0 \le y < \pi/2$ and $\tan y > 0$. In this case we choose the positive branch and take $\tan y = \sqrt{x^2 - 1}$.

- However, if $x \le -1$, then $\pi/2 < y \le \pi$ and $\tan y < 0$. Now we choose the negative branch.

This argument accounts for the $\tan y$ factor in the derivative. For the $\sec y$ factor, we have $\sec y = x$. Therefore, the derivative of the inverse secant is

$$\frac{d}{dx}(\sec^{-1} x) = \begin{cases} \dfrac{1}{x\sqrt{x^2 - 1}} & \text{if } x > 1 \\ -\dfrac{1}{x\sqrt{x^2 - 1}} & \text{if } x < -1 \end{cases}$$

which is an awkward result. The absolute value helps here: Recall that $|x| = x$ if $x > 0$ and $|x| = -x$ if $x < 0$. It follows that

$$\frac{d}{dx}(\sec^{-1} x) = \frac{1}{|x|\sqrt{x^2 - 1}}, \qquad \text{for } |x| > 1.$$

We see that the slope of the inverse secant function is always positive, which is consistent with this derivative result (Figure 7.50).

Derivatives of Other Inverse Trigonometric Functions The hard work is complete. The derivative of the inverse cosine results from the identity

$$\cos^{-1} x + \sin^{-1} x = \frac{\pi}{2}.$$

➤ This identity was proved in Example 3 of this section.

Differentiating both sides of this equation with respect to x, we find that

$$\frac{d}{dx}(\cos^{-1} x) + \underbrace{\frac{d}{dx}(\sin^{-1} x)}_{1/\sqrt{1 - x^2}} = \underbrace{\frac{d}{dx}\left(\frac{\pi}{2}\right)}_{0}.$$

Solving for $\frac{d}{dx}(\cos^{-1} x)$, the required derivative is

$$\frac{d}{dx}(\cos^{-1} x) = -\frac{1}{\sqrt{1 - x^2}}.$$

In a similar manner, the analogous identities

$$\cot^{-1} x + \tan^{-1} x = \frac{\pi}{2} \quad \text{and} \quad \csc^{-1} x + \sec^{-1} x = \frac{\pi}{2}$$

are used to show that the derivatives of $\cot^{-1} x$ and $\csc^{-1} x$ are the negative of the derivatives of $\tan^{-1} x$ and $\sec^{-1} x$, respectively (Exercise 93).

THEOREM 7.12 Derivatives of Inverse Trigonometric Functions

$$\frac{d}{dx}(\sin^{-1} x) = \frac{1}{\sqrt{1 - x^2}}, \quad \frac{d}{dx}(\cos^{-1} x) = -\frac{1}{\sqrt{1 - x^2}}, \quad \text{for } -1 < x < 1$$

$$\frac{d}{dx}(\tan^{-1} x) = \frac{1}{1 + x^2}, \quad \frac{d}{dx}(\cot^{-1} x) = -\frac{1}{1 + x^2}, \quad \text{for } -\infty < x < \infty$$

$$\frac{d}{dx}(\sec^{-1} x) = \frac{1}{|x|\sqrt{x^2 - 1}}, \quad \frac{d}{dx}(\csc^{-1} x) = -\frac{1}{|x|\sqrt{x^2 - 1}}, \quad \text{for } |x| > 1$$

QUICK CHECK 5 Summarize how the derivatives of inverse trigonometric functions are related to the derivatives of the corresponding inverse cofunctions (for example, inverse tangent and inverse cotangent). ◄

EXAMPLE 6 Derivatives of inverse trigonometric functions

a. Evaluate $f'(2\sqrt{3})$, where $f(x) = x \tan^{-1}(x/2)$.

b. Find an equation of the line tangent to the graph of $g(x) = \sec^{-1}(2x)$ at the point $(1, \pi/3)$.

SOLUTION

a. $$f'(x) = 1 \cdot \tan^{-1}\left(\frac{x}{2}\right) + x \underbrace{\frac{1}{1 + (x/2)^2} \cdot \frac{1}{2}}_{\frac{d}{dx}(\tan^{-1}(x/2))} \quad \text{Product Rule and Chain Rule}$$

$$= \tan^{-1}\left(\frac{x}{2}\right) + \frac{2x}{4 + x^2} \quad \text{Simplify.}$$

We evaluate f' at $x = 2\sqrt{3}$ and note that $\tan^{-1}(\sqrt{3}) = \pi/3$:

$$f'(2\sqrt{3}) = \tan^{-1}(\sqrt{3}) + \frac{2(2\sqrt{3})}{4 + (2\sqrt{3})^2} = \frac{\pi}{3} + \frac{\sqrt{3}}{4}.$$

b. The slope of the tangent line at $(1, \pi/3)$ is $g'(1)$. Using the Chain Rule, we have

$$g'(x) = \frac{d}{dx}(\sec^{-1}(2x)) = \frac{2}{|2x|\sqrt{4x^2 - 1}} = \frac{1}{|x|\sqrt{4x^2 - 1}}.$$

It follows that $g'(1) = 1/\sqrt{3}$. An equation of the tangent line is

$$\left(y - \frac{\pi}{3}\right) = \frac{1}{\sqrt{3}}(x - 1) \quad \text{or} \quad y = \frac{1}{\sqrt{3}}x + \frac{\pi}{3} - \frac{1}{\sqrt{3}}.$$

Related Exercises 47–62 ◀

EXAMPLE 7 Shadows in a ballpark As the sun descends behind the 150-ft wall of a baseball stadium, the shadow of the wall moves across the field (Figure 7.51). Let ℓ be the line segment between the edge of the shadow and the sun, and let θ be the angle of elevation of the sun—the angle between ℓ and the horizontal. The length of the shadow s is the distance between the edge of the shadow and the base of the wall.

FIGURE 7.51

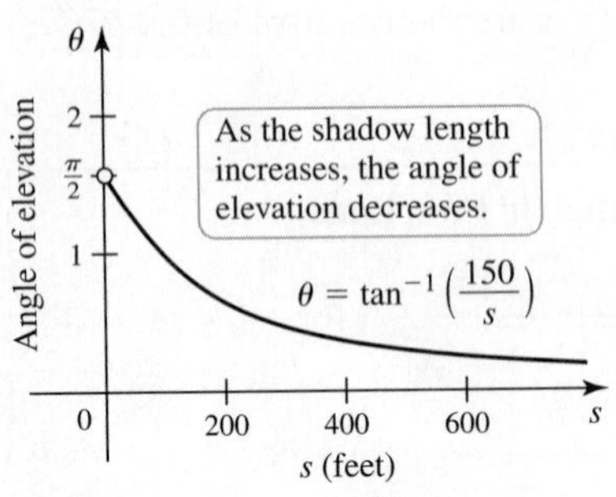

FIGURE 7.52

a. Express θ as a function of the shadow length s.

b. Compute $d\theta/ds$ when $s = 200$ ft and explain what this rate of change measures.

SOLUTION

a. The tangent of θ is

$$\tan\theta = \frac{150}{s},$$

where $s > 0$. Taking the inverse tangent of both sides of this equation, we find that

$$\theta = \tan^{-1}\left(\frac{150}{s}\right).$$

As shown in Figure 7.52, as the shadow length approaches zero, the sun's angle of elevation θ approaches $\pi/2$, ($\theta = \pi/2$ means the sun is overhead). As the shadow length increases, θ decreases and approaches zero.

b. Using the Chain Rule, we have

$$\begin{aligned}\frac{d\theta}{ds} &= \frac{1}{1 + (150/s)^2}\frac{d}{ds}\left(\frac{150}{s}\right) && \text{Chain Rule; } \frac{d}{du}(\tan^{-1} u) = \frac{1}{1+u^2}\\ &= \frac{1}{1 + (150/s)^2}\left(-\frac{150}{s^2}\right) && \text{Evaluate the derivative.}\\ &= -\frac{150}{s^2 + 22{,}500}. && \text{Simplify.}\end{aligned}$$

Notice that $d\theta/ds$ is negative for all values of s, which means longer shadows are associated with smaller angles of elevation (Figure 7.52). At $s = 200$ ft, we have

$$\left.\frac{d\theta}{ds}\right|_{s=200} = -\frac{150}{200^2 + 150^2} = -0.0024\,\frac{\text{rad}}{\text{ft}}.$$

When the length of the shadow is $s = 200$ ft, the angle of elevation is changing at a rate of -0.0024 rad/ft, or $-0.138°$/ft. *Related Exercises 63–64* ◂

QUICK CHECK 6 Example 7 makes the claim that $d\theta/ds = -0.0024$ rad/ft is equivalent to $-0.138°$/ft. Verify this claim. ◂

Integrals Involving Inverse Trigonometric Functions

It is now a straightforward matter to write the results of Theorem 7.12 in terms of indefinite integrals. Notice that only three (rather than six) new integrals arise in this way. However, they are important integrals that are used frequently in upcoming chapters.

We generalize the integrals using the follwing observation applied to the inverse sine derivative. Because

$$\frac{d}{dx}(\sin^{-1} x) = \frac{1}{\sqrt{1 - x^2}}, \quad \text{for } |x| < 1,$$

the Chain Rule gives

$$\frac{d}{dx}\left[\sin^{-1}\left(\frac{x}{a}\right)\right] = \frac{1}{\sqrt{1 - (x/a)^2}}\cdot\frac{1}{a} = \frac{1}{\sqrt{a^2 - x^2}}, \quad \text{for } |x| < a,$$

where $a > 0$ is a constant. Writing this result as an indefinite integral, we have

$$\int \frac{dx}{\sqrt{a^2 - x^2}} = \sin^{-1}\left(\frac{x}{a}\right) + C.$$

QUICK CHECK 7 Why do the derivatives of the six inverse trigonometric functions lead to only three independent indefinite integrals? ◂

A similar calculation with the inverse tangent and inverse secant derivatives gives the following indefinite integrals.

THEOREM 7.13 Integrals Involving Inverse Trigonometric Functions

1. $\displaystyle\int \frac{dx}{\sqrt{a^2 - x^2}} = \sin^{-1}\left(\frac{x}{a}\right) + C, \quad a > 0$

2. $\displaystyle\int \frac{dx}{a^2 + x^2} = \frac{1}{a}\tan^{-1}\left(\frac{x}{a}\right) + C, \quad a \neq 0$

3. $\displaystyle\int \frac{dx}{x\sqrt{x^2 - a^2}} = \frac{1}{a}\sec^{-1}\left|\frac{x}{a}\right| + C, \quad a > 0$

EXAMPLE 8 **Evaluating integrals** Determine the following integrals.

a. $\displaystyle\int \frac{4}{\sqrt{9 - x^2}}\,dx$ **b.** $\displaystyle\int \frac{dx}{16x^2 + 1}$ **c.** $\displaystyle\int_{5/\sqrt{3}}^{5} \frac{dx}{x\sqrt{4x^2 - 25}}$

SOLUTION

a. Setting $a = 3$ in the first result at Theorem 7.13, we have

$$\int \frac{4}{\sqrt{9 - x^2}}\,dx = 4\int \frac{dx}{\sqrt{3^2 - x^2}} = 4\sin^{-1}\left(\frac{x}{3}\right) + C.$$

b. An algebra step is needed to put this integral in a form that matches Theorem 7.13. We first write

$$\int \frac{dx}{16x^2 + 1} = \frac{1}{16}\int \frac{dx}{x^2 + \left(\frac{1}{16}\right)} = \frac{1}{16}\int \frac{dx}{x^2 + \left(\frac{1}{4}\right)^2}.$$

Setting $a = \frac{1}{4}$ in part 2 of Theorem 7.13 gives

$$\int \frac{dx}{16x^2 + 1} = \frac{1}{16}\int \frac{dx}{x^2 + \left(\frac{1}{4}\right)^2} = \left(\frac{1}{16}\right) 4\tan^{-1} 4x + C = \frac{1}{4}\tan^{-1} 4x + C.$$

c. A change of variables puts the integral in the form of the third integral in Theorem 7.13. Letting $u = 2x$, we have

$$\int_{5/\sqrt{3}}^{5} \frac{dx}{x\sqrt{4x^2 - 25}} = \int_{10/\sqrt{3}}^{10} \frac{\frac{1}{2}\,du}{\frac{1}{2}u\sqrt{u^2 - 25}} \qquad u = 2x,\ du = 2\,dx$$

$$= \int_{10/\sqrt{3}}^{10} \frac{du}{u\sqrt{u^2 - 25}} \qquad \text{Simplify.}$$

$$= \frac{1}{5}\sec^{-1}\left(\frac{u}{5}\right)\bigg|_{10/\sqrt{3}}^{10} \qquad \text{Theorem 7.13, } a = 5$$

$$= \frac{1}{5}\left[\sec^{-1} 2 - \sec^{-1}\left(\frac{2}{\sqrt{3}}\right)\right] \qquad \text{Evaluate.}$$

$$= \frac{1}{5}\left(\frac{\pi}{3} - \frac{\pi}{6}\right) = \frac{\pi}{30}. \qquad \text{Simplify.}$$

Related Exercises 65–72 ◀

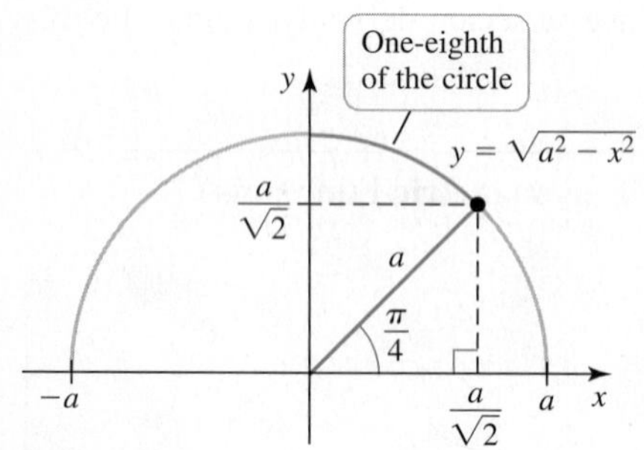

FIGURE 7.53

EXAMPLE 9 **Circumference of a circle** Confirm that the circumference of a circle of radius a is $2\pi a$.

SOLUTION The upper half of a circle of radius a centered at $(0, 0)$ is given by the function $f(x) = \sqrt{a^2 - x^2}$, for $|x| \le a$ (Figure 7.53). So we might consider using the arc length formula on the interval $[-a, a]$ to find the length of a semicircle. However, the circle has vertical tangent lines at $x = \pm a$ and $f'(\pm a)$ is undefined, which prevents us from using the arc length formula. An alternative approach is to use symmetry and avoid the points $x = \pm a$. For example, let's compute the length of one-eighth of the circle on the interval $[0, a/\sqrt{2}]$ (Figure 7.53).

We first determine that $f'(x) = -\dfrac{x}{\sqrt{a^2 - x^2}}$, which is continuous on $[0, a/\sqrt{2}]$. The length of one-eighth of the circle is

$$\begin{aligned}
\int_0^{a/\sqrt{2}} \sqrt{1 + f'(x)^2}\, dx &= \int_0^{a/\sqrt{2}} \sqrt{1 + \left(-\frac{x}{\sqrt{a^2 - x^2}}\right)^2}\, dx \\
&= a \int_0^{a/\sqrt{2}} \frac{dx}{\sqrt{a^2 - x^2}} && \text{Simplify;} \\
&= a \sin^{-1}\left(\frac{x}{a}\right)\Big|_0^{a/\sqrt{2}} && \text{Integrate.} \\
&= a\left[\sin^{-1}\left(\frac{1}{\sqrt{2}}\right) - 0\right] && \text{Evaluate.} \\
&= \frac{\pi a}{4}. && \text{Simplify. } a > 0.
\end{aligned}$$

➤ The arc length integral for the semicircle on $[-a, a]$ is an example of an *improper integral*, a topic considered in Section 8.7.

It follows that the circumference of the full circle is $8(\pi a/4) = 2\pi a$ units.

Related Exercises 65–72 ◀

SECTION 7.5 EXERCISES

Review Questions

1. Explain why the domain of the sine function must be restricted in order to define its inverse function.
2. Why do values of $\cos^{-1} x$ lie in the interval $[0, \pi]$?
3. Is it true that $\tan(\tan^{-1} x) = x$? Is it true that $\tan^{-1}(\tan x) = x$?
4. Sketch the graphs of $y = \cos x$ and $y = \cos^{-1} x$ on the same set of axes.
5. The function $\tan x$ is undefined at $x = \pm\pi/2$. How does this fact appear in the graph of $y = \tan^{-1} x$?
6. What are the domain and range of $\sec^{-1} x$?
7. State the derivative formulas for $\sin^{-1} x$, $\tan^{-1} x$, and $\sec^{-1} x$.
8. What is the slope of the line tangent to the graph of $y = \sin^{-1} x$ at $x = 0$?
9. What is the slope of the line tangent to the graph of $y = \tan^{-1} x$ at $x = -2$?
10. How are the derivatives of $\sin^{-1} x$ and $\cos^{-1} x$ related?

Basic Skills

11–16. Inverse sines and cosines *Without using a calculator, evaluate, if possible, the following expressions.*

11. $\sin^{-1}(\sqrt{3}/2)$ **12.** $\cos^{-1} 2$ **13.** $\cos^{-1}(-1/2)$

14. $\sin^{-1}(-1)$ **15.** $\cos(\cos^{-1}(-1))$ **16.** $\cos^{-1}(\cos 7\pi/6)$

17–22. Right-triangle relationships *Draw a right triangle to simplify the given expressions.*

17. $\cos(\sin^{-1} x)$ **18.** $\cos(\sin^{-1}(x/3))$

19. $\sin(\cos^{-1}(x/2))$ **20.** $\sin^{-1}(\cos\theta)$

21. $\sin(2\cos^{-1} x)$ (*Hint:* Use $\sin 2\theta = 2\sin\theta\cos\theta$.)

22. $\cos(2\sin^{-1} x)$ (*Hint:* Use $\cos 2\theta = \cos^2\theta - \sin^2\theta$.)

23–24. Identities *Use right triangles to explain why the following identities are true.*

23. $\cos^{-1} x + \cos^{-1}(-x) = \pi$ **24.** $\sin^{-1} y + \sin^{-1}(-y) = 0$

25–32. Evaluating inverse trigonometric functions *Without using a calculator, evaluate or simplify the following expressions.*

25. $\tan^{-1}\sqrt{3}$ **26.** $\cot^{-1}(-1/\sqrt{3})$ **27.** $\sec^{-1} 2$

28. $\csc^{-1}(-1)$ **29.** $\tan^{-1}(\tan\pi/4)$ **30.** $\tan^{-1}(\tan 3\pi/4)$

31. $\csc^{-1}(\sec 2)$ **32.** $\tan(\tan^{-1} 1)$

33–38. Right-triangle relationships *Draw a right triangle to simplify the given expressions.*

33. $\cos(\tan^{-1} x)$ **34.** $\tan(\cos^{-1} x)$

35. $\cos(\sec^{-1} x)$ **36.** $\cot(\tan^{-1} 2x)$

37. $\sin\left[\sec^{-1}\left(\dfrac{\sqrt{x^2 + 16}}{4}\right)\right]$ **38.** $\cos\left(\tan^{-1}\left(\dfrac{x}{\sqrt{9 - x^2}}\right)\right)$

39–40. Right-triangle pictures *Express θ in terms of x using the inverse sine, inverse tangent, and inverse secant functions.*

39.

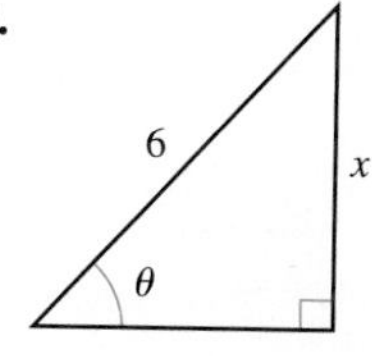

40.

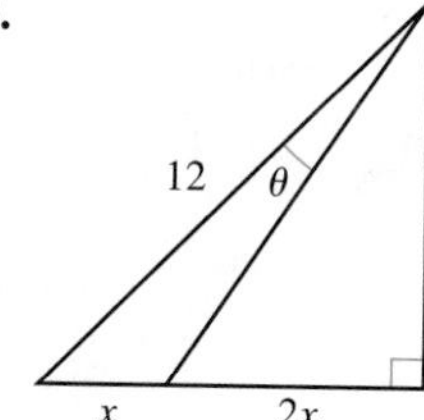

41–46. Derivatives of inverse sine *Evaluate the derivatives of the following functions.*

41. $f(x) = \sin^{-1}(2x)$

42. $f(x) = x\sin^{-1} x$

43. $f(w) = \cos(\sin^{-1}(2w))$

44. $f(x) = \sin^{-1}(\ln x)$

45. $f(x) = \sin^{-1}(e^{-2x})$

46. $f(x) = \sin^{-1}(e^{\sin x})$

47–62. Derivatives *Evaluate the derivatives of the following functions.*

47. $f(y) = \tan^{-1}(2y^2 - 4)$

48. $g(z) = \tan^{-1}(1/z)$

49. $f(z) = \cot^{-1}\sqrt{z}$

50. $f(x) = \sec^{-1}\sqrt{x}$

51. $f(x) = \cos^{-1}(1/x)$

52. $f(t) = (\cos^{-1} t)^2$

53. $f(u) = \csc^{-1}(2u + 1)$

54. $f(t) = \ln(\tan^{-1} t)$

55. $f(y) = \cot^{-1}(1/(y^2 + 1))$

56. $f(w) = \sin(\sec^{-1}(2w))$

57. $f(x) = \sec^{-1}(\ln x)$

58. $f(x) = \tan^{-1}(e^{4x})$

59. $f(x) = \csc^{-1}(\tan e^x)$

60. $f(x) = \sin(\tan^{-1}(\ln x))$

61. $f(s) = \cot^{-1}(e^s)$

62. $f(x) = 1/(\tan^{-1}(x^2 + 4))$

63. Angular size A boat sails directly toward a 150-m skyscraper that stands on the edge of a harbor. The angular size θ of the building is the angle formed by lines from the top and bottom of the building to the observer (see figure).

a. What is the rate of change of the angular size, $d\theta/dx$, when the boat is 500 m from the building?

b. Graph $d\theta/dx$ as a function of x and determine the point at which the angular size changes most rapidly.

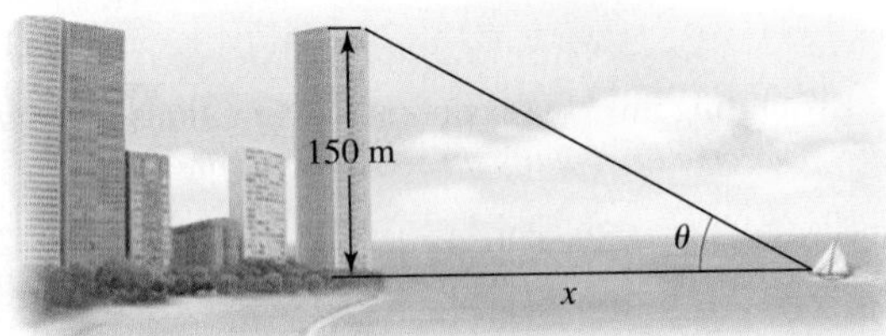

64. Angle of elevation A small plane flies horizontally on a line 400 m directly above an observer with a speed of 70 m/s. Let θ be the angle of elevation of the plane (see figure).

a. What is the rate of change of the angle of elevation, $d\theta/dx$, when the plane is 500 m past the observer?

b. Graph $d\theta/dx$ as a function of x and determine the point at which θ changes most rapidly.

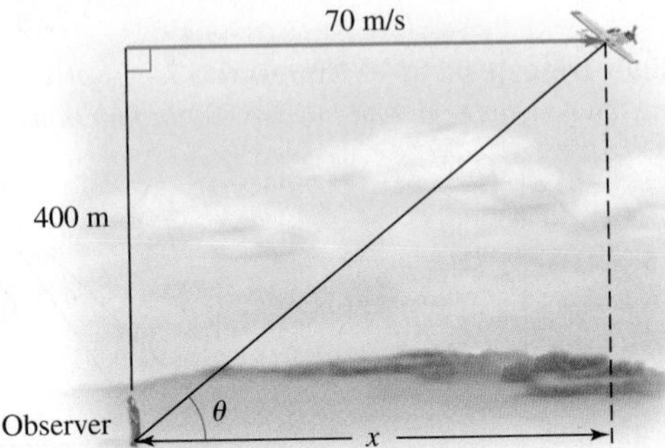

65–72. Integrals involving inverse trigonometric functions *Evaluate the following integrals.*

65. $\displaystyle\int \frac{6}{\sqrt{25 - x^2}}\,dx$

66. $\displaystyle\int \frac{3}{4 + v^2}\,dv$

67. $\displaystyle\int \frac{dx}{x\sqrt{x^2 - 100}}$

68. $\displaystyle\int \frac{2}{16z^2 + 25}\,dz$

69. $\displaystyle\int_0^3 \frac{dx}{\sqrt{36 - x^2}}$

70. $\displaystyle\int_2^{2\sqrt{3}} \frac{5}{x^2 + 4}\,dx$

71. $\displaystyle\int_0^{3/2} \frac{dx}{\sqrt{36 - 4x^2}}$

72. $\displaystyle\int_0^{5/4} \frac{3}{64x^2 + 100}\,dx$

Further Explorations

73. Explain why or why not Determine whether the following statements are true and give an explanation or counterexample.

a. $\dfrac{\sin^{-1} x}{\cos^{-1} x} = \tan^{-1} x$

b. $\cos^{-1}(\cos(15\pi/16)) = 15\pi/16$

c. $\sin^{-1} x = 1/\sin x$

d. $\dfrac{d}{dx}(\sin^{-1} x + \cos^{-1} x) = 0$

e. $\dfrac{d}{dx}(\tan^{-1} x) = \sec^2 x$

f. The lines tangent to the graph of $y = \sin^{-1} x$ on the interval $[-1, 1]$ have a minimum slope of 1.

g. The lines tangent to the graph of $y = \sin x$ on the interval $[-\pi/2, \pi/2]$ have a maximum slope of 1.

74–77. One function gives all six *Given the following information about one trigonometric function, evaluate the other five functions.*

74. $\sin\theta = -\frac{4}{5}$ and $\pi < \theta < 3\pi/2$ (Find $\cos\theta$, $\tan\theta$, $\cot\theta$, $\sec\theta$, and $\csc\theta$.)

75. $\cos\theta = \frac{5}{13}$ and $0 < \theta < \pi/2$

76. $\sec\theta = \frac{5}{3}$ and $3\pi/2 < \theta < 2\pi$

77. $\csc\theta = \frac{13}{12}$ and $0 < \theta < \pi/2$

78–81. Graphing f and f'

a. Graph f with a graphing utility.
b. Compute and graph f'.
c. Verify that the zeros of f' correspond to points at which f has a horizontal tangent line.

78. $f(x) = (x - 1)\sin^{-1} x$ on $[-1, 1]$

79. $f(x) = (x^2 - 1)\sin^{-1} x$ on $[-1, 1]$

80. $f(x) = (\sec^{-1} x)/x$ on $[1, \infty)$

81. $f(x) = e^{-x}\tan^{-1} x$ on $[0, \infty)$

82. Graphing with inverse trigonometric functions

a. Graph the function $f(x) = \dfrac{\tan^{-1} x}{x^2 + 1}$.

b. Compute and graph f' and determine (perhaps approximately) the points at which $f'(x) = 0$.

c. Verify that the zeros of f' correspond to points at which f has a horizontal tangent line.

83–86. Miscellaneous integrals *Evaluate the following integrals. A preliminary step such as completing the square or a change of variables is required.*

83. $\int \frac{dy}{y^2 - 4y + 5}$

84. $\int \frac{dx}{(x+3)\sqrt{x^2+6x}}$

85. $\int \frac{e^x}{e^{2x}+4}\,dx$

86. $\int \frac{dx}{x^3 + x^{-1}}$

Applications

87. Towing a boat A boat is towed toward a dock by a cable attached to a winch that stands 10 ft above the water level (see figure). Let θ be the angle of elevation of the winch and let ℓ be the length of the cable as the boat is towed toward the dock.

a. Show that the rate of change of θ with respect to ℓ is $\frac{d\theta}{d\ell} = \frac{-10}{\ell\sqrt{\ell^2 - 100}}$.

b. Compute $\frac{d\theta}{d\ell}$ when $\ell = 50, 20$, and 11 ft.

c. Find $\lim_{\ell \to 10^+} \frac{d\theta}{d\ell}$, and explain what is happening as the last foot of cable is reeled in (note that the boat is at the dock when $\ell = 10$).

d. It is evident from the figure that θ increases as the boat is towed to the dock. Why, then, is $d\theta/d\ell$ negative?

88. Tracking a dive A biologist standing at the bottom of an 80-ft vertical cliff watches a peregrine falcon dive from the top of the cliff at a 45° angle from the horizontal (see figure).

a. Express the angle of elevation θ from the biologist to the falcon as a function of the height h of the bird above the ground. (*Hint:* The vertical distance between the top of the cliff and the falcon is $80 - h$.)

b. What is the rate of change of θ with respect to the bird's height when it is 60 ft above the ground?

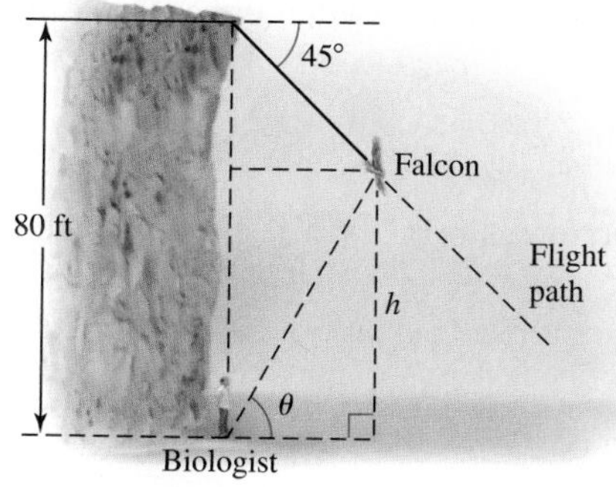

89. Angle to a particle A particle travels clockwise on a circular path of diameter R, monitored by a sensor on the circle at point P; the other endpoint of the diameter on which the sensor lies is Q (see figure). Let θ be the angle between the diameter PQ and the line from the sensor to the particle. Let c be the length of the chord from the particle's position to Q.

a. Calculate $d\theta/dc$.

b. Evaluate $\left.\frac{d\theta}{dc}\right|_{c=0}$.

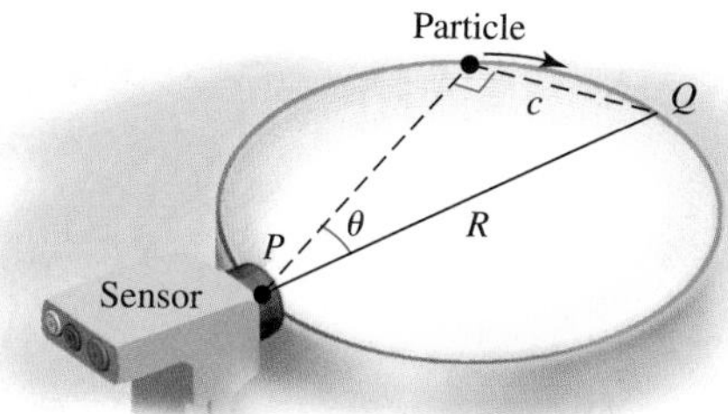

90. Angle to a particle, part II The figure in Exercise 89 shows the particle traveling away from the sensor, which may have influenced your solution (we expect you used the inverse sine function). Suppose instead that the particle approaches the sensor (see figure). How would this change the solution? Explain the differences in the two answers.

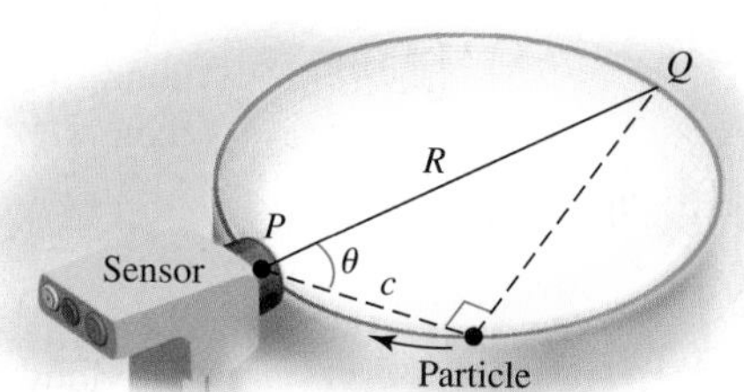

Additional Exercises

91. Derivative of the inverse sine Find the derivative of the inverse sine using Theorem 7.3.

92. Derivative of the inverse cosine Find the derivative of the inverse cosine in the following two ways.

a. Using Theorem 7.3

b. Using the identity $\sin^{-1} x + \cos^{-1} x = \pi/2$

93. Derivative of $\cot^{-1} x$ and $\csc^{-1} x$ Use a trigonometric identity to show that the derivatives of the inverse cotangent and inverse cosecant differ from the derivatives of the inverse tangent and inverse secant, respectively, by a multiplicative factor of -1.

94–97. Identity proofs *Prove the following identities and give the values of x for which they are true.*

94. $\cos(\sin^{-1} x) = \sqrt{1 - x^2}$

95. $\cos(2\sin^{-1} x) = 1 - 2x^2$

96. $\tan(2\tan^{-1} x) = \dfrac{2x}{1 - x^2}$

97. $\sin(2\sin^{-1} x) = 2x\sqrt{1 - x^2}$

QUICK CHECK ANSWERS

1. $\sin^{-1}(\sin 0) = \sin^{-1} 0 = 0$ and $\sin^{-1}(\sin(2\pi)) = \sin^{-1} 0 = 0$ **2.** $0, \pi/4$ **3.** $f(x) = \sin^{-1} x$ is odd, while $f'(x) = 1/\sqrt{1 - x^2}$ is even. **4.** The slopes of the tangent lines approach 0. **5.** One is the negative of the other. **6.** Recall that $1° = \pi/180$ rad. So, 0.0024 rad/ft is equivalent to 0.138°/ft. **7.** Because $\sin^{-1} x$ and $\cos^{-1} x$ differ by a constant, they are both antiderivatives of $(1 - x^2)^{-1/2}$. A similar argument applies to $\tan^{-1} x$ and $\cot^{-1} x$, and $\sec^{-1} x$ and $\csc^{-1} x$.

7.6 L'Hôpital's Rule and Growth Rates of Functions

We first encountered l'Hôpital's Rule in Section 4.7, where it was applied directly to the indeterminate forms $0/0$ and ∞/∞. We may now combine properties of the exponential function with l'Hôpital's Rule to evaluate limits with the indeterminate forms that we denote 1^∞, 0^0, and ∞^0. This technique greatly expands our limit-taking capabilities and it offers some surprising results. A valuable outcome of this section is a ranking of functions according to their growth rates as $x \to \infty$. (For example, which function grows faster as $x \to \infty$, 1.001^x or x^{100}?) This ranking should become part of your mathematical intuition and is used often in upcoming chapters.

First, recall l'Hôpital's Rule (Theorems 4.13 and 4.14). It says that under suitable conditions on f and g, if $\lim_{x\to a} f(x) = \lim_{x\to a} g(x) = 0$ or $\lim_{x\to a} |f(x)| = \lim_{x\to a} |g(x)| = \infty$, then

$$\lim_{x\to a} \frac{f(x)}{g(x)} = \lim_{x\to a} \frac{f'(x)}{g'(x)},$$

provided the limit on the right side exists (or is $\pm\infty$). The rule also applies if $x \to a$ is replaced by $x \to \pm\infty$, $x \to a^+$, or $x \to a^-$.

Indeterminate Forms 1^∞, 0^0, and ∞^0

The indeterminate forms 1^∞, 0^0, and ∞^0 all arise in limits of the form $\lim_{x\to a} f(x)^{g(x)}$. However, l'Hôpital's Rule cannot be applied directly to these indeterminate forms. They must first be expressed in the form $0/0$ or ∞/∞. Here is how we proceed.

The inverse relationship between $\ln x$ and e^x says that $f^g = e^{g \ln f}$, so we first write

$$\lim_{x\to a} f(x)^{g(x)} = \lim_{x\to a} e^{g(x)\ln f(x)}.$$

By the continuity of the exponential function, we switch the order of the limit and the exponential function; therefore,

$$\lim_{x\to a} f(x)^{g(x)} = \lim_{x\to a} e^{g(x)\ln f(x)} = e^{\lim_{x\to a} g(x)\ln f(x)},$$

provided $\lim_{x\to a} g(x)\ln f(x)$ exists. Therefore, $\lim_{x\to a} f(x)^{g(x)}$ is evaluated using the following two steps.

➤ Notice the following:

- For 1^∞, L has the form $\infty \cdot \ln 1 = \infty \cdot 0$.
- For 0^0, L has the form $0 \cdot \ln 0 = 0 \cdot \infty$.
- For ∞^0, L has the form $0 \cdot \ln \infty = 0 \cdot \infty$.

PROCEDURE Indeterminate forms 1^∞, 0^0, and ∞^0

Assume $\lim_{x \to a} f(x)^{g(x)}$ has the indeterminate form 1^∞, 0^0, or ∞^0.

1. Evaluate $L = \lim_{x \to a} g(x) \ln f(x)$. This limit can be put in the form $0/0$ or ∞/∞, both of which are handled by l'Hôpital's Rule.
2. Then $\lim_{x \to a} f(x)^{g(x)} = e^L$.

QUICK CHECK 1 Explain why a limit of the form 0^∞ is not an indeterminate form. ◄

EXAMPLE 1 Indeterminate forms

Evaluate the following limits.

a. $\lim_{x \to 0^+} x^x$ **b.** $\lim_{x \to \infty} \left(1 + \frac{1}{x}\right)^x$ **c.** $\lim_{x \to 0^+} (\csc x)^x$

SOLUTION

a. This limit has the form 0^0. Using the given two-step procedure, we note that $x^x = e^{x \ln x}$ and first evaluate

$$L = \lim_{x \to 0^+} x \ln x.$$

This limit has the form $0 \cdot \infty$, which may be put in the form ∞/∞ so that l'Hôpital's Rule can be applied:

$$\begin{aligned} L = \lim_{x \to 0^+} x \ln x &= \lim_{x \to 0^+} \frac{\ln x}{1/x} && x = \frac{1}{1/x} \\ &= \lim_{x \to 0^+} \frac{1/x}{-1/x^2} && \text{L'Hôpital's Rule for } \infty/\infty \text{ form} \\ &= \lim_{x \to 0^+} (-x) = 0 && \text{Simplify and evaluate the limit.} \end{aligned}$$

The second step is to exponentiate:

$$\lim_{x \to 0^+} x^x = e^L = e^0 = 1$$

We conclude that $\lim_{x \to 0^+} x^x = 1$ (Figure 7.54).

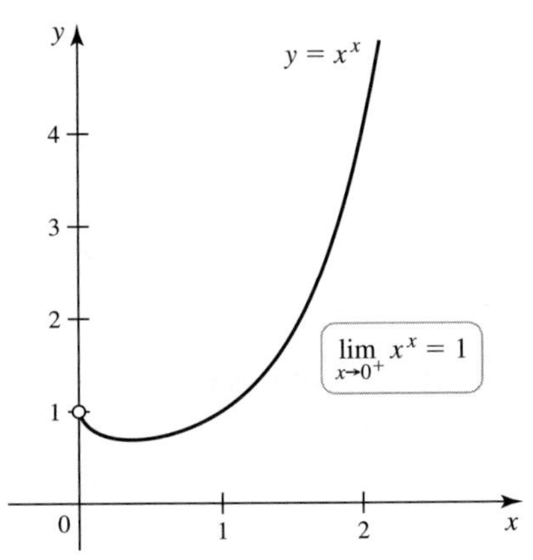

FIGURE 7.54

b. This limit has the form 1^∞. Noting that $(1 + 1/x)^x = e^{x \ln (1 + 1/x)}$, the first step is to evaluate

$$L = \lim_{x \to \infty} x \ln \left(1 + \frac{1}{x}\right),$$

which has the form $0 \cdot \infty$. Proceeding as in part (a), we have

$$\begin{aligned} L = \lim_{x \to \infty} x \ln \left(1 + \frac{1}{x}\right) &= \lim_{x \to \infty} \frac{\ln (1 + 1/x)}{1/x} && x = \frac{1}{1/x} \\ &= \lim_{x \to \infty} \frac{\frac{1}{1 + 1/x} \cdot \left(-\frac{1}{x^2}\right)}{\left(-\frac{1}{x^2}\right)} && \text{L'Hôpital's Rule for } 0/0 \text{ form} \\ &= \lim_{x \to \infty} \frac{1}{1 + 1/x} = 1 && \text{Simplify and evaluate.} \end{aligned}$$

➤ The limit in Example 1b is often given as a definition of e. It is a special case of the more general limit

$$\lim_{x \to \infty} \left(1 + \frac{a}{x}\right)^x = e^a.$$

See Exercise 49.

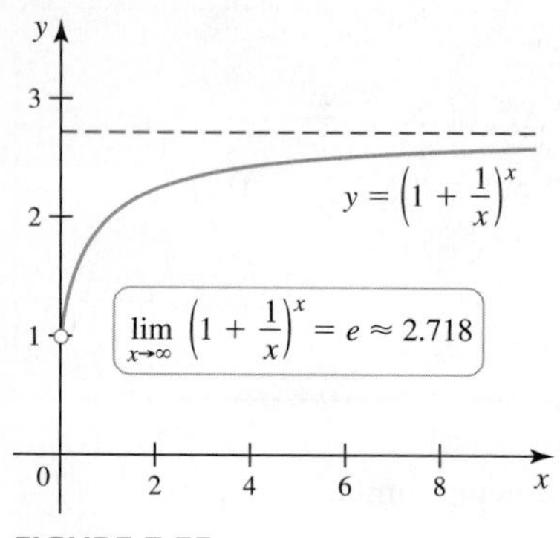

FIGURE 7.55

The second step is to exponentiate:

$$\lim_{x\to\infty}\left(1 + \frac{1}{x}\right)^x = e^L = e^1 = e$$

The function $y = (1 + 1/x)^x$ (Figure 7.55) has a horizontal asymptote $y = e \approx 2.71828$.

c. Note that $\lim_{x\to 0^+} \csc x = \infty$, so the limit has the form ∞^0. Using the two-step procedure with $(\csc x)^x = e^{x \ln \csc x}$, the first step is to evaluate

$$L = \lim_{x\to 0^+} x \ln \csc x = \lim_{x\to 0^+} \frac{\ln \csc x}{x^{-1}},$$

which has the form ∞/∞. Applying l'Hôpital's Rule, we find that

$$L = \lim_{x\to 0^+} \frac{\ln \csc x}{x^{-1}} = \lim_{x\to 0^+} \frac{\frac{1}{\csc x}(-\csc x \cot x)}{-x^{-2}} = \lim_{x\to 0^+} \frac{\cot x}{x^{-2}}.$$

The resulting limit is another indeterminate form. However, some simplification reveals that

$$L = \lim_{x\to 0^+} \frac{\cot x}{x^{-2}} = \lim_{x\to 0^+} \frac{x^2 \cos x}{\sin x} = \underbrace{\lim_{x\to 0^+} \frac{x}{\sin x}}_{1} \cdot \underbrace{\lim_{x\to 0^+} x}_{0} \cdot \underbrace{\lim_{x\to 0^+} \cos x}_{1} = 0.$$

Therefore, $L = 0$ and $\lim_{x\to 0^+} (\csc x)^x = e^L = e^0 = 1$.

Related Exercises 7–16 ◄

Growth Rates of Functions

An important use of l'Hôpital's Rule is to compare the growth rates of functions. Here are two questions—one practical and one theoretical—that demonstrate the importance of comparative growth rates of functions.

➤ Models of epidemics produce more complicated functions than the one given here, but they have the same general features.

- A particular theory for modeling the spread of an epidemic predicts that the number of infected people t days after the start of the epidemic is given by the function

$$N(t) = 2.5t^2 e^{-0.01t} = 2.5\frac{t^2}{e^{0.01t}}.$$

Question: In the long run (as $t \to \infty$), does the epidemic spread or does it die out?

➤ The Prime Number Theorem was proved simultaneously (two different proofs) in 1896 by Jacques Hadamard and Charles de la Vallée Poussin, relying on fundamental ideas contributed by Riemann.

- A prime number is an integer $p \geq 2$ that has only two divisors, 1 and itself. The first few prime numbers are 2, 3, 5, 7, and 11. A celebrated theorem states that the number of prime numbers less than x is approximately

$$P(x) = \frac{x}{\ln x}, \qquad \text{for large values of } x.$$

Question: According to this function, is the number of prime numbers infinite?

These two questions involve a comparison of two functions. In the first question, if t^2 grows faster than $e^{0.01t}$ as $t \to \infty$, then $\lim_{t\to\infty} N(t) = \infty$ and the epidemic grows. If $e^{0.01t}$ grows faster than t^2 as $t \to \infty$, then $\lim_{t\to\infty} N(t) = 0$ and the epidemic eventually dies out. We will explain what is meant by *grows faster than* in a moment.

In the second example, the comparison is between x and $\ln x$. If x grows faster than $\ln x$ as $x \to \infty$, then $\lim_{x\to\infty} P(x) = \infty$ and the number of prime numbers is infinite.

Our goal is to obtain a ranking of the following families of functions based on their growth rates:

- mx, where $m > 0$ (represents linear functions)
- x^p, where $p > 0$ (represents polynomials and algebraic functions)
- x^x (sometimes called a *superexponential* or *tower function*)
- $\ln x$ (represents logarithmic functions)
- $\ln^q x$, where $q > 0$ (represents powers of logarithmic functions)
- $x^p \ln x$, where $p > 0$ (a combination of powers and logarithms)
- e^x (represents exponential functions)

➤ Another function with a large growth rate is the factorial function, defined for integers as $f(n) = n! = n(n-1)\cdots 2\cdot 1$.

QUICK CHECK 2 Before proceeding, use your intuition and rank the classes of functions given above in order of their growth rates. ◀

We need to be precise about growth rates and what it means for f to grow faster than g as $x \to \infty$. We work with the following definitions.

DEFINITION Growth Rates of Functions (as $x \to \infty$)

Suppose f and g are functions with $\lim_{x\to\infty} f(x) = \lim_{x\to\infty} g(x) = \infty$. Then ***f* grows faster than *g*** as $x \to \infty$ if

$$\lim_{x\to\infty} \frac{g(x)}{f(x)} = 0 \quad \text{or, equivalently, if} \quad \lim_{x\to\infty} \frac{f(x)}{g(x)} = \infty.$$

The functions f and g have **comparable growth rates** if

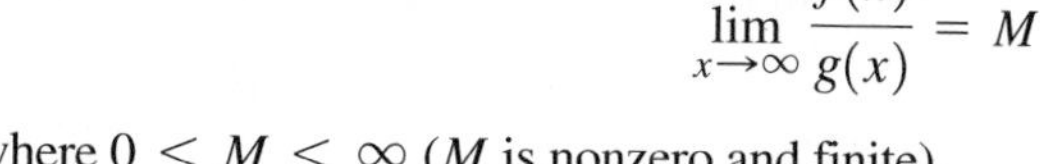

$$\lim_{x\to\infty} \frac{f(x)}{g(x)} = M,$$

where $0 < M < \infty$ (M is nonzero and finite).

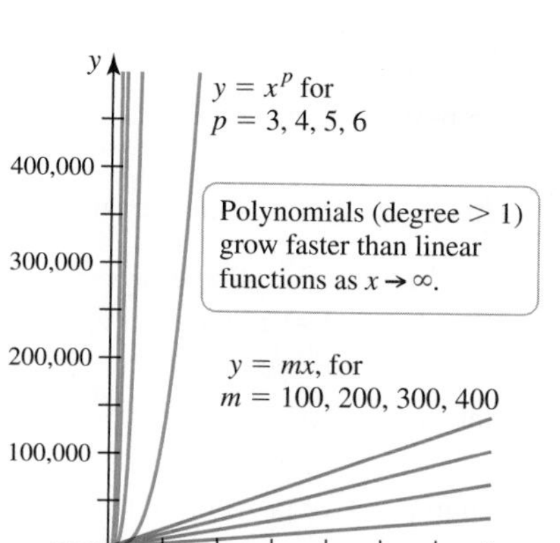

FIGURE 7.56

The idea of growth rates is illustrated nicely with graphs. Figure 7.56 shows a family of linear functions of the form $y = mx$, where $m > 0$, and a family of polynomials of the form $y = x^p$, where $p > 1$. We see that the polynomials grow faster (their curves rise at a greater rate) than the linear functions as $x \to \infty$.

Figure 7.57 shows that exponential functions of the form $y = b^x$, where $b > 1$, grow faster than polynomials of the form $y = x^p$, where $p > 0$, as $x \to \infty$.

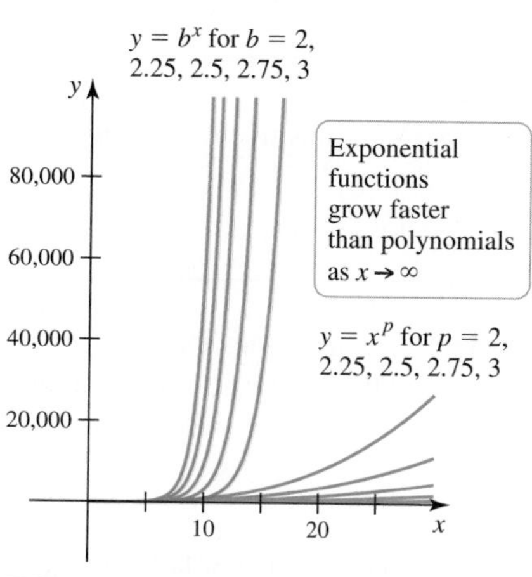

FIGURE 7.57

QUICK CHECK 3 Compare the growth rates of $f(x) = x^2$ and $g(x) = x^3$ as $x \to \infty$. Compare the growth rates of $f(x) = x^2$ and $g(x) = 10x^2$ as $x \to \infty$. ◀

We now begin a systematic comparison of growth rates. Note that a growth rate limit involves an indeterminate form ∞/∞, so l'Hôpital's Rule is always in the picture.

EXAMPLE 2 Powers of *x* vs. powers of ln *x* Compare the growth rates as $x \to \infty$ of the following pairs of functions.

a. $f(x) = \ln x$ and $g(x) = x^p$, where $p > 0$

b. $f(x) = \ln^q x$ and $g(x) = x^p$, where $p > 0$ and $q > 0$

SOLUTION

a. The limit of the ratio of the two functions is

$$\begin{aligned} \lim_{x\to\infty} \frac{\ln x}{x^p} &= \lim_{x\to\infty} \frac{1/x}{px^{p-1}} && \text{L'Hôpital's Rule} \\ &= \lim_{x\to\infty} \frac{1}{px^p} && \text{Simplify.} \\ &= 0. && \text{Evaluate the limit.} \end{aligned}$$

We see that any positive power of x grows faster than $\ln x$.

b. We compare $\ln^q x$ and x^p by observing that

$$\lim_{x\to\infty} \frac{\ln^q x}{x^p} = \lim_{x\to\infty} \left(\frac{\ln x}{x^{p/q}}\right)^q = \Big(\underbrace{\lim_{x\to\infty} \frac{\ln x}{x^{p/q}}}_{0}\Big)^q.$$

By part (a), $\lim_{x\to\infty} \dfrac{\ln x}{x^{p/q}} = 0$ (because $p/q > 0$). Therefore, $\lim_{x\to\infty} \dfrac{\ln^q x}{x^p} = 0$ (because $q > 0$). We conclude that positive powers of x grow faster than positive powers of $\ln x$.

Related Exercises 17–28 ◀

EXAMPLE 3 **Powers of x vs. exponentials** Compare the rates of growth of $f(x) = x^p$ and $g(x) = e^x$ as $x \to \infty$, where p is a positive real number.

SOLUTION The goal is to evaluate $\lim_{x\to\infty} \dfrac{x^p}{e^x}$ for $p > 0$. This comparison is most easily done using Example 2 and a change of variables. We let $x = \ln t$ and note that as $x \to \infty$, we also have $t \to \infty$. With this substitution, $x^p = \ln^p t$ and $e^x = e^{\ln t} = t$. Therefore,

$$\lim_{x\to\infty} \frac{x^p}{e^x} = \lim_{t\to\infty} \frac{\ln^p t}{t} = 0. \quad \text{Example 2}$$

We see that increasing exponential functions grow faster than positive powers of x.

Related Exercises 17–28 ◀

These examples, together with the comparison of exponential functions b^x and the superexponential x^x (see Exercise 50), establish a ranking of growth rates.

> **THEOREM 7.13** **Ranking Growth Rates as $x \to \infty$**
> Let $f \ll g$ mean that g grows faster than f as $x \to \infty$. With positive real numbers p, q, r, and s and $b > 1$,
>
> $$\ln^q x \ll x^p \ll x^p \ln^r x \ll x^{p+s} \ll b^x \ll x^x.$$

You should try to build these relative growth rates into your intuition. They are useful in future chapters (Chapter 9 on sequences, in particular), and they can be used to evaluate limits at infinity quickly.

SECTION 7.6 EXERCISES

Review Questions

1. Explain why the form 1^∞ is indeterminate and cannot be evaluated by substitution.
2. Give the two-step method for attacking a limit of the form $\lim_{x\to a} f(x)^{g(x)}$.
3. In terms of limits, what does it mean for f to grow faster than g as $x \to \infty$?
4. In terms of limits, what does it mean for the rates of growth of f and g to be comparable as $x \to \infty$?

5. Rank the functions x^3, $\ln x$, x^x, and 2^x in order of increasing growth rates as $x \to \infty$.

6. Rank the functions x^{100}, $\ln x^{10}$, x^x, and 10^x in order of increasing growth rates as $x \to \infty$.

Basic Skills

7–16. $1^\infty, 0^0, \infty^0$ forms *Evaluate the following limits or explain why they do not exist. Check your results by graphing.*

7. $\lim_{x\to 0^+} x^{2x}$ 8. $\lim_{x\to 0} (1 + 4x)^{3/x}$ 9. $\lim_{\theta\to \pi/2^-} (\tan\theta)^{\cos\theta}$

10. $\lim_{\theta\to 0^+} (\sin\theta)^{\tan\theta}$ 11. $\lim_{x\to 0^+} (1 + x)^{\cot x}$ 12. $\lim_{x\to\infty} \left(1 + \frac{1}{x}\right)^{\ln x}$

13. $\lim_{x\to 0^+} (\tan x)^x$ 14. $\lim_{z\to\infty} \left(1 + \frac{10}{z^2}\right)^{z^2}$

15. $\lim_{x\to 0} (x + \cos x)^{1/x}$ 16. $\lim_{x\to 0^+} \left(\frac{1}{3}\cdot 3^x + \frac{2}{3}\cdot 2^x\right)^{1/x}$

17–28. Comparing growth rates *Use limit methods to determine which of the two given functions grows faster, or state that they have comparable growth rates.*

17. x^{10}; $e^{0.01x}$ 18. $x^2 \ln x$; $\ln^2 x$ 19. $\ln x^{20}$; $\ln x$

20. $\ln x$; $\ln(\ln x)$ 21. 100^x; x^x 22. $x^2\ln x$; x^3

23. x^{20}; 1.00001^x 24. $x^{10}\ln^{10} x$; x^{11} 25. x^x; $(x/2)^x$

26. $\ln\sqrt{x}$; $\ln^2 x$ 27. e^{x^2}; e^{10x} 28. e^{x^2}; $x^{x/10}$

Further Explorations

29. **Explain why or why not** Determine whether the following statements are true and give an explanation or counterexample.

a. $\lim_{x\to 0^+} x^{1/x}$ is an indeterminate form.

b. The number 1 raised to any fixed power is 1. Therefore, because $(1 + x) \to 1$ as $x \to 0$, $(1 + x)^{1/x} \to 1$ as $x \to 0$.

c. The functions $\ln x^{100}$ and $\ln x$ have comparable growth rates as $x \to \infty$.

d. The function e^x grows faster than 2^x as $x \to \infty$.

30–36. Miscellaneous limits by any means *Use analytical methods to evaluate the following limits.*

30. $\lim_{x\to 0^+} x^{\ln x}$ 31. $\lim_{x\to 0} \left(\frac{\sin x}{x}\right)^{1/x^2}$ 32. $\lim_{x\to 0^+} (\cot x)^x$

33. $\lim_{x\to\infty} x^{1/x}$ 34. $\lim_{x\to\infty} \left(\frac{1}{2x}\right)^{3/x}$ 35. $\lim_{x\to 1^+} (\sqrt{x} - 1)^{\sin \pi x}$

36. $\lim_{x\to 2^+} (\ln(x^2 - 3))^{x^3-2x-4}$

T 37. **It may take time** The ranking of growth rates given in the text applies for $x \to \infty$. However, these rates may not be evident for small values of x. For example, an exponential grows faster than any power of x. However, for $1 < x < 19{,}800$, x^2 is greater than $e^{x/1000}$. For the following pairs of functions, estimate the point at which the faster growing function overtakes the slower growing function (for the last time), as $x \to \infty$.

a. $\ln^3 x$ and $x^{0.3}$ b. $2^{x/100}$ and x^3
c. $x^{x/100}$ and e^x d. $\ln^{10} x$ and $e^{x/10}$

T **38–41. Limits with parameters** *Evaluate the following limits in terms of the parameters a and b, which are positive real numbers. In each case, graph the function for specific values of the parameters to check your results.*

38. $\lim_{x\to 0} (1 + ax)^{b/x}$ 39. $\lim_{x\to 0^+} (a^x - b^x)^x$, $a > b > 0$

40. $\lim_{x\to 0^+} (a^x - b^x)^{1/x}$, $a > b > 0$ 41. $\lim_{x\to 0} \frac{a^x - b^x}{x}$

42. **Avoiding l'Hôpital's Rule** Let $L = \lim_{x\to 0} \frac{x - \sin x}{x^3}$.

a. Compute L using l'Hôpital's Rule.

b. Now compute L using the following interesting detour. First use the sine triplication formula $\sin 3x = 3\sin x - 4\sin^3 x$ to replace $\sin x$ by $3\sin(x/3) - 4\sin^3(x/3)$ in the expression for L.

c. Let $t = x/3$ and note that as $x \to 0$, $t \to 0$. Use $\lim_{t\to 0} \frac{\sin t}{t} = 1$ to show that $L = \frac{L}{9} + \frac{4}{27}$.

d. Solve for L and check for agreement with part (a).

Source: "Teaching Mathematics and its Applications," Fabio Cavallini, no. 3 (1988): 161.

Applications

43. **Compound interest** Suppose you make a deposit of $\$P$ into a savings account that earns interest at a rate of $100r\%$ per year.

a. Show that if interest is compounded once per year, then the balance after t years is $B(t) = P(1 + r)^t$.

b. If interest is compounded m times per year, then the balance after t years is $B(t) = P(1 + r/m)^{mt}$. For example, $m = 12$ corresponds to monthly compounding, and the interest rate for each month is $r/12$. In the limit $m \to \infty$, the compounding is said to be *continuous*. Show that with continuous compounding, the balance after t years is $B(t) = Pe^{rt}$.

T 44. **Algorithm complexity** The complexity of a computer algorithm is the number of operations or steps the algorithm needs to complete its task assuming there are n pieces of input (for example, the number of steps needed to put n numbers in ascending order). Four algorithms for doing the same task have complexities of A: $n^{3/2}$, B: $n\log_2 n$, C: $n(\log_2 n)^2$, and D: $\sqrt{n}\log_2 n$. Rank the algorithms in order of increasing efficiency for large values of n. Graph the complexities as they vary with n and comment on your observations.

Additional Exercises

45. **Exponential functions and powers** Show that any exponential, b^x, for $b > 1$, grows faster than x^p, for $p > 0$.

46. **Exponentials with different bases** Show that $f(x) = a^x$ grows faster than $g(x) = b^x$ as $x \to \infty$ if $1 < b < a$.

47. **Logs with different bases** Show that $f(x) = \log_a x$ and $g(x) = \log_b x$, where $a > 1$ and $b > 1$, grow at a comparable rate as $x \to \infty$.

48. Factorial growth rate The factorial function is usually defined for positive integers as $n! = n(n-1)(n-2)\cdots 3\cdot 2\cdot 1$. For example, $5! = 5\cdot 4\cdot 3\cdot 2\cdot 1 = 120$. A valuable result that gives good approximations to $n!$ for large values of n is Stirling's formula, $n! \approx \sqrt{2\pi n}\, n^n e^{-n}$ (see Guided Projects for more on Stirling's formula). Use this formula and a calculator to determine where the factorial function appears in the ranking of growth rates.

49. Exponential limit Prove that $\lim_{x\to\infty}\left(1+\frac{a}{x}\right)^x = e^a$ for $a \neq 0$.

50. Exponentials vs. super exponentials Show that x^x grows faster than b^x as $x\to\infty$ for $b > 1$.

51. Exponential growth rates

a. For what values of $b > 0$ does b^x grow faster than e^x as $x\to\infty$?
b. Compare the growth rates of e^x and e^{ax} as $x\to\infty$ for $a > 0$.

52. A fascinating function Consider the function $f(x) = (ab^x + (1-a)c^x)^{1/x}$, where a, b, and c are positive real numbers with $0 < a < 1$.

a. Graph f for several sets of (a, b, c). Verify that in all cases that f is an increasing function for all x with a single inflection point.
b. Use analytical methods to determine $\lim_{x\to 0} f(x)$ in terms of a, b, and c.
c. Show that $\lim_{t\to\infty} f(t) = \max\{b, c\}$ and $\lim_{t\to-\infty} f(t) = \min\{b, c\}$, for any $0 < a < 1$.
d. Use analytical methods to determine $\lim_{x\to\infty} f(x)$ and $\lim_{x\to-\infty} f(x)$.
e. Estimate the location of the inflection point (in terms of a, b, and c).

QUICK CHECK ANSWERS

1. The form 0^∞ (for example, $\lim_{x\to 0^+} x^{1/x}$) is not indeterminate, because as the base goes to zero, raising it to larger and larger powers drives the entire function to zero. **3.** x^3 grows faster than x^2 as $x\to\infty$, whereas x^2 and $10x^2$ have comparable growth rates as $x\to\infty$.

CHAPTER 7 REVIEW EXERCISES

1. Explain why or why not Determine whether the following statements are true and give an explanation or counterexample.

a. If $f(x) = 2/x$, then $f^{-1}(x) = 2/x$.
b. $\ln xy = (\ln x)(\ln y)$.
c. The function $y = Ae^{0.1t}$ increases by 10% when t increases by one unit.
d. $\frac{d}{dx}(b^x) = b^x$ for exactly one positive value of b.
e. $\lim_{x\to 0^+} x^{1/x}$ is an indeterminate form.
f. The domain of $\tan^{-1} x$ is $\{x: |x| < \pi/2\}$.
g. $\pi^{3x} = e^{\pi \ln 3x}$

2–4. Properties of logarithms and exponentials *Use properties of logarithms and exponentials, not a calculator, for the following exercises.*

2. Solve the equation $48 = 6e^{4k}$ for k.

3. Solve the equation $\log x^2 + 3\log x = \log 32$ for x. Does the answer depend on the base of the log?

4. Graphs of logarithmic and exponential functions The figure shows the graphs of $y = 2^x$, $y = 3^{-x}$, and $y = -\ln x$. Match each curve with the correct function.

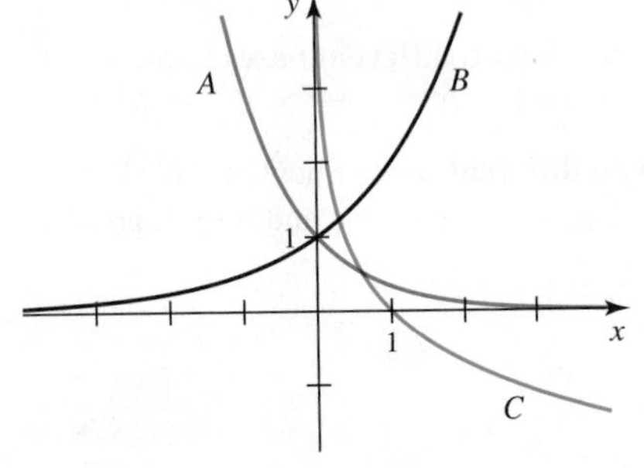

5–6. Existence of inverses *Use analytical methods and/or graphing to determine the intervals on which the following functions have an inverse.*

5. $f(x) = x^3 - 3x^2$ **6.** $g(t) = 2\sin(t/3)$

7–8. Finding inverses *Find the inverse on the specified interval and express it in the form $y = f^{-1}(x)$. Then graph f and f^{-1}.*

7. $f(x) = x^2 - 4x + 5$, for $x > 2$

8. $f(x) = 1/x^2$, for $x > 0$

9–11. Derivative of the inverse at a point *Consider the following functions. In each case, without finding the inverse, evaluate the derivative of the inverse at the given point.*

9. $f(x) = \cos x$ at $f(\pi/4)$

10. $f(x) = 1/(x+1)$ at $f(0)$

11. $f(x) = x^4 - 2x^2 - x$ at $f(0)$

12–13. Derivative of the inverse *Find the derivative of the inverse of the following functions. Express the result with x as the independent variable.*

12. $f(x) = 12x - 16$ **13.** $f(x) = x^{-1/3}$

14. A function and its inverse function The function $f(x) = \frac{x}{x+1}$ is one-to-one for $x > -1$ and has an inverse on that interval.

a. Graph f for $x > -1$.
b. Find the inverse f^{-1} corresponding to the function graphed in part (a). Graph f^{-1} on the same set of axes as in part (a).
c. Evaluate the derivative of f^{-1} at the point $\left(\frac{1}{2}, 1\right)$.
d. Sketch the tangent lines on the graphs of f and f^{-1} at $\left(1, \frac{1}{2}\right)$ and $\left(\frac{1}{2}, 1\right)$, respectively.

15–22. Derivatives of inverse functions *Consider the following functions (on the given interval, if specified). Find the inverse function, express it as a function of x, and find the derivative of the inverse function.*

15. $f(x) = 3x - 4$

16. $f(x) = |x + 2|,\ x \le -2$

17. $f(x) = x^2 - 4,\ x > 0$

18. $f(x) = \dfrac{x}{x + 5}$

19. $f(x) = \sqrt{x + 2},\ x \ge -2$

20. $f(x) = x^{2/3},\ x > 0$

21. $f(x) = x^{-1/2},\ x > 0$

22. $f(x) = x^3 + 3$

23. **Derivative of the inverse in two ways** Let $f(x) = \sin x$, $f^{-1}(x) = \sin^{-1} x$, and $(x_0, y_0) = (\pi/4, 1/\sqrt{2})$.
   a. Evaluate $(f^{-1})'(1/\sqrt{2})$ using Theorem 7.3 $((f^{-1})'(y_0) = 1/f'(x_0))$.
   b. Evaluate $(f^{-1})'(1/\sqrt{2})$ directly by differentiating f^{-1}. Check for agreement with part (a).

24–34. Evaluating derivatives *Evaluate and simplify the following derivatives.*

24. $\dfrac{d}{dx}(xe^{-10x})$

25. $\dfrac{d}{dx}(x \ln^2 x)$

26. $\dfrac{d}{dw}(e^{-w} \ln w)$

27. $\dfrac{d}{dx}(2^{x^2-x})$

28. $\dfrac{d}{dx}(\log_3 (x + 8))$

29. $\dfrac{d}{dx}\left[\sin^{-1}\left(\dfrac{1}{x}\right)\right]$

30. $\dfrac{d}{dx}(x^{\sin x})$

31. $f'(1)$ when $f(x) = x^{1/x}$

32. $f'(1)$ when $f(x) = \tan^{-1}(4x^2)$

33. $\dfrac{d}{dx}(x \sec^{-1} x)\Big|_{x=\frac{2}{\sqrt{3}}}$

34. $\dfrac{d}{dx}\left[\tan^{-1}(e^{-x})\right]\Big|_{x=0}$

35–40. Inverse sines and cosines *Without using a calculator, evaluate or simplify the following expressions.*

35. $\cos^{-1}(\sqrt{3}/2)$

36. $\cos^{-1}\left(-\frac{1}{2}\right)$

37. $\sin^{-1}(-1)$

38. $\cos(\cos^{-1}(-1))$

39. $\sin(\sin^{-1} x)$

40. $\cos^{-1}(\sin 3\pi)$

41. **Right triangles** Given that $\theta = \sin^{-1}\left(\frac{12}{13}\right)$, evaluate $\cos\theta$, $\tan\theta$, $\cot\theta$, $\sec\theta$, and $\csc\theta$.

42–49. Right-triangle relationships *Draw a right triangle to simplify the given expression. Assume $x > 0$ and $0 \le \theta \le \pi/2$.*

42. $\cos(\tan^{-1} x)$

43. $\sin(\cos^{-1}(x/2))$

44. $\tan(\sec^{-1}(x/2))$

45. $\cot^{-1}(\tan\theta)$

46. $\csc^{-1}(\sec\theta)$

47. $\sin^{-1} x + \sin^{-1}(-x)$

48. $\sin(2\sin^{-1} x)$ (*Hint:* Use $\sin 2\theta = 2\sin\theta\cos\theta$.)

49. $\cos(2\sin^{-1} x)$ (*Hint:* Use $\cos 2\theta = \cos^2\theta - \sin^2\theta$.)

50–59. Integrals *Evaluate the following integrals.*

50. $\displaystyle\int \frac{e^x}{4e^x + 6}\,dx$

51. $\displaystyle\int_{e^2}^{e^8} \frac{dx}{x \ln x}$

52. $\displaystyle\int_1^4 \frac{10^{\sqrt{x}}}{\sqrt{x}}\,dx$

53. $\displaystyle\int \frac{x + 4}{x^2 + 8x + 25}\,dx$

54. $\displaystyle\int \frac{dx}{\sqrt{49 - 4x^2}}$

55. $\displaystyle\int \frac{3}{2x^2 + 1}\,dx$

56. $\displaystyle\int \frac{dt}{2t\sqrt{t^2 - 4}}$

57. $\displaystyle\int_{-1}^{2\sqrt{3}-1} \frac{dx}{x^2 + 2x + 5}$

58. $\displaystyle\int \frac{(\ln \ln x)^4}{x \ln x}\,dx$

59. $\displaystyle\int_{-2/3}^{2/\sqrt{3}} \frac{dx}{\sqrt{16 - 9x^2}}$

60–63. Arc length *Compute the arc length of the following curves.*

60. $y = \dfrac{1}{2}(e^x + e^{-x})$ on $[-\ln 2, \ln 2]$

61. $y = 3\ln x - \dfrac{x^2}{24}$ on $[1, 6]$

62. $y = \ln(x - \sqrt{x^2 - 1})$ on $[1, \sqrt{2}]$

63. $x = 2e^{\sqrt{2}y} + \dfrac{1}{16}e^{-\sqrt{2}y}$, for $0 \le y \le \dfrac{\ln 2}{\sqrt{2}}$

64–66. Volume problems *Compute the volume of the following solids of revolution.*

64. The region bounded by the curve $y = e^{-x^2}$ and the x-axis on the interval $[0, \sqrt{\ln 3}]$ is revolved about the y-axis.

65. The region bounded by the curve $y = \dfrac{2}{1 + x^2}$ and the x-axis on the interval $[0, 4]$ is revolved about the y-axis.

66. The region bounded by the curve $y = (4 - x^2)^{-1/4}$ and the x-axis on the interval $[0, 1]$ is revolved about the x-axis.

T 67. **An exponential bike ride** Tom and Sue took a bike ride, both starting at the same time and position. Tom started riding at 20 mi/hr, and his velocity decreased according to the function $v(t) = 20e^{-2t}$, for $t \ge 0$. Sue started riding at 15 mi/hr, and her velocity decreased according to the function $u(t) = 15e^{-t}$, for $t \ge 0$.
   a. Find and graph the position functions of Tom and Sue.
   b. Find the times at which the riders had the same position at the same time.
   c. Who ultimately took the lead and remained in the lead?

68. **Radioactive decay** The mass of radioactive material in a sample has decreased by 30% since the decay began. Assuming a half-life of 1500 years, how long ago did the decay begin?

69. **Population growth** Growing from an initial population of 150,000 at a constant annual growth rate of 4%/yr, how long will it take a city to reach a population of 1 million?

70. **Savings account** A savings account advertises an annual percentage yield (APY) of 5.4%, which means that the balance in the account increases at an annual growth rate of 5.4%/yr.
   a. Find the balance in the account for $t \ge 0$ with an initial deposit of \$1500, assuming the APY remains fixed and no additional deposits or withdrawals are made.
   b. What is the doubling time of the balance?
   c. After how many years does the balance reach \$5000?

71–72. Curve sketching *Use the graphing techniques of Section 4.3 to graph the following functions on their domains. Identify local extreme points, inflection points, concavity, and end behavior. Use a graphing utility only to check your work.*

71. $f(x) = e^x(x^2 - x)$ **72.** $f(x) = \ln x - \ln^2 x$

T 73. Find the length of the curve $y = \ln x$ between $x = 1$ and $x = b > 1$ given that

$$\int \frac{\sqrt{x^2 + a^2}}{x}\,dx = \sqrt{x^2 + a^2} - a \ln\left(\frac{a + \sqrt{x^2 + a^2}}{x}\right) + C.$$

Use any means to approximate the value of b for which the curve has length 2.

T 74–79. 1^∞, 0^0, ∞^0 forms *Evaluate the following limits. Check your results by graphing.*

74. $\lim_{x\to\infty} \frac{\ln x^{100}}{\sqrt{x}}$ **75.** $\lim_{x\to\pi/2^-} (\sin x)^{\tan x}$ **76.** $\lim_{x\to\infty} \frac{\ln^3 x}{\sqrt{x}}$

77. $\lim_{x\to\infty} \ln\left(\frac{x+1}{x-1}\right)$ **78.** $\lim_{x\to\infty} x^{1/x}$ **79.** $\lim_{x\to\infty}\left(1 - \frac{3}{x}\right)^x$

80–87. Comparing growth rates *Determine which of the two functions grows faster, or state that they have comparable growth rates.*

80. $10x$ and $\ln x$ **81.** $x^{1/2}$ and $x^{1/3}$ **82.** $\ln x$ and $\log_{10} x$

83. $\sqrt{x}$ and $\ln^{10} x$ **84.** $10x$ and $\ln x^2$ **85.** e^x and 3^x

86. $\sqrt{x^6 + 10}$ and x^3 **87.** 2^x and $4^{x/2}$

88. Logs of logs Compare the growth rates of $\ln x$, $\ln(\ln x)$, and $\ln(\ln(\ln x))$.

T 89. Two limits with exponentials Evaluate $\lim_{x\to 0^+} \frac{x}{\sqrt{1 - e^{-x^2}}}$ and $\lim_{x\to 0^+} \frac{x^2}{1 - e^{-x^2}}$ and confirm your result by graphing.

90. Geometric mean Prove that $\lim_{r\to 0}\left(\frac{a^r + b^r + c^r}{3}\right)^{1/r} = \sqrt[3]{abc}$, where a, b, and c are positive real numbers.

91. Towers of exponents The functions $f(x) = (x^x)^x$ and $g(x) = x^{(x^x)}$ are different functions. For example, $f(3) = 19{,}683$ and $g(3) \approx 7.6 \times 10^{12}$. Determine whether $\lim_{x\to 0^+} f(x)$ and $\lim_{x\to 0^+} g(x)$ are indeterminate forms and evaluate the limits.

T 92. A family of super-exponential functions Let $f(x) = (a + x)^x$, where $a > 0$.

a. What is the domain of f (in terms of a)?
b. Describe the end behavior of f (near the boundary of its domain or as $|x| \to \infty$).
c. Compute f'. Then graph f and f' for $a = 0.5, 1, 2, 3$.
d. Show that f has a single local minimum at the point z that satisfies $(z + a)\ln(z + a) + z = 0$.
e. Describe how z (found in part (d)) varies as a increases. Describe how $f(z)$ varies as a increases.

93. Limits for e Consider the function $g(x) = (1 + 1/x)^{x+a}$. Show that if $0 \le a < \frac{1}{2}$, then $g(x) \to e$ from *below* as $x \to \infty$; if $\frac{1}{2} \le a < 1$, then $g(x) \to e$ from *above* as $x \to \infty$.

94. Arc length of family of exponential functions

a. Show that the arc length integral for the function $f(x) = Ae^{ax} + \frac{1}{4Aa^2}e^{-ax}$, where $a > 0$ and $A > 0$, may be integrated using methods you already know.
b. Verify that the arc length of the curve $y = f(x)$ on the interval $[0, \ln 2]$ is
$$A(2^a - 1) - \frac{1}{4a^2 A}(2^{-a} - 1).$$

T 95. Log-normal probability distribution A commonly used distribution in probability and statistics is the log-normal distribution. (If the logarithm of a random variable has a normal distribution, then the variable itself has a log-normal distribution.) The distribution function is

$$f(x) = \frac{1}{x\sigma\sqrt{2\pi}} e^{-\ln^2 x/(2\sigma^2)}, \quad \text{for } x \ge 0,$$

where $\ln x$ has zero mean and standard deviation $\sigma > 0$.

a. Graph f for $\sigma = \frac{1}{2}, 1, 2$. Based on your graphs, does $\lim_{x\to 0} f(x)$ appear to exist?
b. Evaluate $\lim_{x\to 0} f(x)$. (*Hint:* Let $x = e^y$.)
c. Show that f has a single local maximum at $x^* = e^{-\sigma^2}$.
d. Evaluate $f(x^*)$ and express the result as a function of σ.
e. For what value of $\sigma > 0$ in part (d) does $f(x^*)$ have a minimum?

T 96. A rush hour function The function $f(t) = \sin(e^{a\cos t}) + 1$ is a periodic function with the property that the number of local extrema on the interval $[0, 2\pi]$ is determined by the parameter $a > 0$. For some values of a, the function could be used to model traffic flow (two rush hours per day) or ocean tides (two low tides and two high tides per day).

a. Graph f on the interval $[0, 2\pi]$ for $a = 0.3, 1.3$, and 1.7. Confirm that in these cases, f has one, three, and five local extrema on $(0, 2\pi)$, respectively.
b. Prove that the period of f is 2π, for all $a > 0$.
c. Prove that f has an extreme point at $0, \pi, 2\pi$, for all $a > 0$.
d. Prove that if $0 < a < \ln(\pi/2)$, then f has one local minimum on $(0, 2\pi)$.
e. Prove that if $\ln(\pi/2) < a < \ln(3\pi/2)$, then f has one local minimum and two local maxima on $(0, 2\pi)$.
f. Prove that if $a > \ln(3\pi/2)$, then f has at least five local extreme points on $(0, 2\pi)$.

T 97. Blood testing Suppose that a blood test for a disease must be given to a population of N people, where N is large. At most N individual blood tests must be done. The following strategy reduces the number of tests. Suppose 100 people are selected from the population and their blood samples are pooled. One test determines whether any of the 100 people test positive. If the test is positive, those 100 people are tested individually, making 101 tests necessary. However, if the pooled sample tests negative, then 100 people have been tested with one test. This procedure is then repeated. Probability theory shows that if the group size is x (for example, $x = 100$, as described here), then the average number of blood tests required to test N people is $N(1 - q^x + 1/x)$, where q is the probability that any one person tests negative. What group size x minimizes the average number of tests in the case that $N = 10{,}000$ and $q = 0.95$? Assume that x is a nonnegative real number.

Chapter 7 Guided Projects

Applications of the material in this chapter and related topics can be found in the following Guided Projects. For additional information, see the Preface.

- Means and tangent lines
- Optimizing fuel use
- Oscillators
- Acid, noise, and earthquakes
- Hyperbolic functions
- Inverse sine from geometry
- Enzyme kinetics
- Pharmacokinetics–drug metabolism
- Landing an airliner
- Atmospheric CO_2

8

Integration Techniques

Chapter Preview The Substitution Rule introduced in Chapter 5 is a powerful method for evaluating a wide range of integrals. However, there are many commonly occurring integrals that *cannot* be handled by the Substitution Rule. Therefore, this chapter has a critical purpose: to develop additional integration techniques that enable us to evaluate a far greater number of integrals. The new *analytical methods* (pencil-and-paper methods) we introduce here are integration by parts, trigonometric substitution, and partial fractions. And yet, even with these new methods, it is important to recognize that there are still many integrals that do not yield to them. For this reason, we also introduce alternative strategies for evaluating indefinite integrals and computer-based methods for approximating definite integrals. The discussion then turns to integrals that have either infinite integrands or infinite intervals of integration. These *improper integrals* offer surprising results and have many practical applications. The chapter closes with an introductory survey of differential equations, a vast topic that has a central place in both the theory and applications of mathematics.

8.1 Integration by Parts

The Substitution Rule (Section 5.5) arises when we reverse the Chain Rule for derivatives. In this section, we employ a similar strategy and reverse the Product Rule for derivatives. The result is an integration technique called *integration by parts*. To illustrate the importance of integration by parts, consider the indefinite integrals

$$\int e^x\,dx = e^x + C \quad \text{and} \quad \int xe^x\,dx = ?$$

The first integral is an elementary integral that we have already encountered. The second integral is only slightly different—and yet, the appearance of the product xe^x in the integrand makes this integral (at the moment) impossible to evaluate. Integration by parts is ideally suited for evaluating integrals of *products* of functions. Such integrals arise frequently.

Integration by Parts for Indefinite Integrals

Given two differentiable functions u and v, the Product Rule states that

$$\frac{d}{dx}[u(x)v(x)] = u'(x)v(x) + u(x)v'(x).$$

By integrating both sides, we can write this rule in terms of an indefinite integral:

$$u(x)v(x) = \int [u'(x)v(x) + u(x)v'(x)]\,dx$$

Rearranging this expression in the form

$$\int \underbrace{u(x)v'(x)\,dx}_{dv} = u(x)v(x) - \int \underbrace{v(x)u'(x)\,dx}_{du}$$

leads to the basic relationship for **integration by parts**. It is expressed more compactly by letting $du = u'(x)\,dx$ and $dv = v'(x)\,dx$. Suppressing the independent variable x, we have

$$\int u\,dv = uv - \int v\,du.$$

The integral $\int u\,dv$ is viewed as the given integral, and we use integration by parts to express it in terms of a new integral $\int v\,du$. The technique is successful if the new integral can be evaluated.

Integration by Parts

Suppose that u and v are differentiable functions. Then,

$$\int u\,dv = uv - \int v\,du.$$

EXAMPLE 1 **Integration by parts** Evaluate $\int xe^x\,dx$.

SOLUTION The presence of *products* in the integrand often suggests integration by parts. We split the product into two factors, one of which must be identified as u and the other as dv (the latter always includes the differential dx). Powers of x are *often* good choices for u. The choice for dv should be easy to integrate because it produces the function v on the right side of the integration by parts formula ($v = \int dv$). In this case, the choices $u = x$ and $dv = e^x\,dx$ are advisable. It follows that $du = dx$. The relationship $dv = e^x\,dx$ means that v is an antiderivative of e^x, which implies $v = e^x$. A table is helpful for organizing these calculations.

➤ The integration by parts calculation may be done without including the constant of integration—as long as it is included in the final result.

Functions in original integral	$u = x$	$dv = e^x\,dx$
Functions in new integral	$du = dx$	$v = e^x$

The integration by parts rule is now applied:

$$\int \underbrace{x}_{u}\,\underbrace{e^x\,dx}_{dv} = \underbrace{x}_{u}\,\underbrace{e^x}_{v} - \int \underbrace{e^x}_{v}\,\underbrace{dx}_{du}$$

The original integral $\int xe^x\,dx$ has been replaced by the integral of e^x, which is easier to evaluate: $\int e^x\,dx = e^x + C$. The entire procedure looks like this:

$$\int xe^x\,dx = xe^x - \int e^x\,dx \quad \text{Integration by parts}$$

$$= xe^x - e^x + C \quad \text{Evaluate the new integral.}$$

Related Exercises 7–22 ◀

➤ To make the table, first write the functions in the original integral:

$u =$ ______, $dv =$ ______.

Then find the functions in the new integral by differentiating u and integrating dv:

$du =$ ______, $v =$ ______.

EXAMPLE 2 **Integration by parts** Evaluate $\int x \sin x\,dx$.

SOLUTION Remembering that powers of x are often a good choice for u, we form the following table.

$u = x$	$dv = \sin x\,dx$
$du = dx$	$v = -\cos x$

Applying integration by parts, we have

$$\int \underbrace{x}_{u} \underbrace{\sin x\, dx}_{dv} = \underbrace{x}_{u} \underbrace{(-\cos x)}_{v} - \int \underbrace{(-\cos x)}_{v} \underbrace{dx}_{du} \quad \text{Integration by parts}$$

$$= -x \cos x + \sin x + C \quad \text{Evaluate } \int \cos x\, dx = \sin x.$$

Related Exercises 7–22 ◀

QUICK CHECK 1 What is the best choice for u and dv in evaluating $\int x \cos x\, dx$? ◀

In general, integration by parts works when we can easily integrate the choice for dv and when the new integral is easier to evaluate than the original. Integration by parts is often used for integrals of the form $\int x^n f(x)\, dx$, where n is a positive integer. Such integrals generally require the repeated use of integration by parts, as shown in the following example.

EXAMPLE 3 Repeated use of integration by parts

a. Evaluate $\int x^2 e^x\, dx$.

b. How would you evaluate $\int x^n e^x\, dx$, where n is a positive integer?

SOLUTION

$u = x^2$	$dv = e^x\, dx$
$du = 2x\, dx$	$v = e^x$

a. The factor x^2 is a good choice for u, leaving $dv = e^x\, dx$. We then have

$$\int \underbrace{x^2}_{u} \underbrace{e^x\, dx}_{dv} = \underbrace{x^2}_{u} \underbrace{e^x}_{v} - \int \underbrace{e^x}_{v} \underbrace{2x\, dx}_{du}.$$

Notice that the new integral on the right side is simpler than the original integral because the power of x has been reduced by one. In fact, the new integral was evaluated in Example 1. Therefore, after using integration by parts twice, we have

$$\int x^2 e^x\, dx = x^2 e^x - 2\int x e^x\, dx \quad \text{Integration by parts}$$

$$= x^2 e^x - 2(xe^x - e^x) + C \quad \text{Result of Example 1}$$

$$= e^x (x^2 - 2x + 2) + C. \quad \text{Simplify.}$$

$u = x^n$	$dv = e^x\, dx$
$du = nx^{n-1}\, dx$	$v = e^x$

b. We now let $u = x^n$ and $dv = e^x\, dx$. The integration takes the form

$$\int x^n e^x\, dx = x^n e^x - n\int x^{n-1} e^x\, dx.$$

➤ An integral identity in which the power of the variable is reduced is called a **reduction formula**. Other examples of reduction formulas are explored in Exercises 42–49.

We see that integration by parts reduces the power of the variable in the integrand. The integral in part (a) with $n = 2$ requires two uses of integration by parts. You can probably anticipate that evaluating the integral $\int x^n e^x\, dx$ requires n applications of integration by parts to reach the integral $\int e^x\, dx$, which is easily evaluated.

Related Exercises 7–22 ◀

EXAMPLE 4 Repeated use of integration by parts Evaluate $\int e^{2x} \sin x\, dx$.

➤ In Example 4, we could also use $u = \sin x$ and $dv = e^{2x}\, dx$. In general, some trial and error may be required when using integration by parts. Effective choices come with practice.

SOLUTION The integrand consists of a product, which suggests integration by parts. In this case there is no obvious choice for u and dv, so let's try the following choices:

$u = e^{2x}$	$dv = \sin x\, dx$
$du = 2e^{2x}\, dx$	$v = -\cos x$

The integral then becomes

$$\int e^{2x} \sin x \, dx = -e^{2x} \cos x + 2 \int e^{2x} \cos x \, dx. \tag{1}$$

The original integral has been expressed in terms of a new integral, $\int e^{2x} \cos x \, dx$, which appears no easier to evaluate than the original integral. It is tempting to start over with a new choice of u and dv, but a little persistence pays off. Suppose we evaluate $\int e^{2x} \cos x \, dx$ using integration by parts with the following choices:

$u = e^{2x}$	$dv = \cos x \, dx$
$du = 2e^{2x} \, dx$	$v = \sin x$

Integrating by parts, we have

$$\int e^{2x} \cos x \, dx = e^{2x} \sin x - 2 \int e^{2x} \sin x \, dx. \tag{2}$$

Now observe that equation (2) contains the original integral, $\int e^{2x} \sin x \, dx$. Substituting the result of equation (2) into equation (1), we find that

$$\begin{aligned}\int e^{2x} \sin x \, dx &= -e^{2x} \cos x + 2 \int e^{2x} \cos x \, dx \\ &= -e^{2x} \cos x + 2\left(e^{2x} \sin x - 2 \int e^{2x} \sin x \, dx\right) && \text{Substitute for } \textstyle\int e^{2x} \cos x \, dx. \\ &= -e^{2x} \cos x + 2e^{2x} \sin x - 4 \int e^{2x} \sin x \, dx. && \text{Simplify.}\end{aligned}$$

Now it is a matter of solving for $\int e^{2x} \sin x \, dx$ and including the constant of integration. We find that

$$\int e^{2x} \sin x \, dx = \frac{1}{5} e^{2x} (2 \sin x - \cos x) + C.$$

Related Exercises 23–28 ◀

Integration by Parts for Definite Integrals

Integration by parts with definite integrals presents two options. You can use the method outlined in Examples 1–4 to find an antiderivative and then evaluate it at the upper and lower limits of integration. Alternatively, the limits of integration can be incorporated directly into the integration by parts process. With the second approach, integration by parts for definite integrals has the following form.

➤ Integration by parts for definite integrals still has the form

$$\int u \, dv = uv - \int v \, du.$$

However, both definite integrals must be written with respect to x.

Integration by Parts for Definite Integrals

Let u and v be differentiable. Then,

$$\int_a^b u(x)v'(x) \, dx = u(x)v(x)\Big|_a^b - \int_a^b v(x)u'(x) \, dx.$$

EXAMPLE 5 **A definite integral** Evaluate $\int_1^2 \ln x \, dx$.

SOLUTION This example is instructive because the integrand does not appear to be a product. The key is to view the integrand as the product $(\ln x)(1 \, dx)$. Then, the following choices are plausible:

$u = \ln x$	$dv = dx$
$du = \frac{1}{x} \, dx$	$v = x$

Using integration by parts, we have

$$\int_1^2 \underbrace{\ln x}_{u}\,\underbrace{dx}_{dv} = \left((\underbrace{\ln x}_{u})\,\underbrace{x}_{v}\right)\Big|_1^2 - \int_1^2 \underbrace{x}_{v}\,\underbrace{\frac{1}{x}\,dx}_{du} \quad \text{Integration by parts}$$

$$= x\ln x\Big|_1^2 - \int_1^2 dx \quad \text{Simplify.}$$

$$= (2\ln 2 - 0) - (2 - 1) \quad \text{Evaluate.}$$

$$= 2\ln 2 - 1 \approx 0.386. \quad \text{Simplify.}$$

Related Exercises 29–36 ◀

In Example 5 we evaluated a definite integral of $\ln x$. The corresponding indefinite integral can be added to our list of integration formulas.

Integral of ln *x*

$$\int \ln x\,dx = x\ln x - x + C$$

QUICK CHECK 2 Verify by differentiation that $\int \ln x\,dx = x\ln x - x + C$. ◀

EXAMPLE 6 **Solids of revolution** Let R be the region bounded by $y = \ln x$, the x-axis, and the line $x = a$, where $a > 1$ (Figure 8.1). Find the volume of the solid that is generated when the region R is revolved about the x-axis.

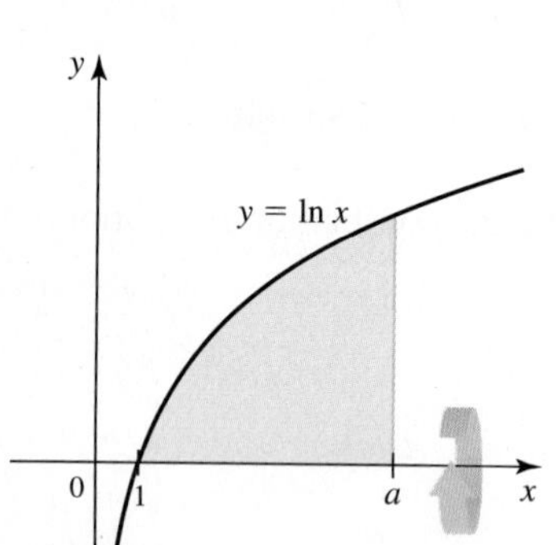

FIGURE 8.1

SOLUTION Revolving R about the x-axis generates a solid whose volume is computed with the disk method (Section 6.3). Its volume is

$$V = \pi\int_1^a (\ln x)^2\,dx.$$

We integrate by parts with the following assignments:

$u = (\ln x)^2$	$dv = dx$
$du = \frac{2\ln x}{x}\,dx$	$v = x$

➤ Recall that if $f(x) \geq 0$ on $[a, b]$ and the region bounded by the graph of f and the x-axis on $[a, b]$ is revolved about the x-axis, then the volume of the solid generated is

$$V = \pi\int_a^b f(x)^2\,dx.$$

The integration is carried out as follows, using the indefinite integral of $\ln x$ given above:

$$V = \pi\int_1^a (\ln x)^2\,dx \quad \text{Disk method}$$

$$= \pi\left[\underbrace{(\ln x)^2}_{u}\,\underbrace{x}_{v}\Big|_1^a - \int_1^a \underbrace{x}_{v}\,\underbrace{\frac{2\ln x}{x}\,dx}_{du}\right] \quad \text{Integration by parts}$$

$$= \pi\left[x(\ln x)^2\Big|_1^a - 2\int_1^a \ln x\,dx\right] \quad \text{Simplify.}$$

$$= \pi\left(x(\ln x)^2\Big|_1^a - 2(x\ln x - x)\Big|_1^a\right) \quad \int \ln x\,dx = x\ln x - x + C$$

$$= \pi(a(\ln a)^2 - 2a\ln a + 2a - 2) \quad \text{Evaluate and simplify.}$$

Related Exercises 37–40 ◀

QUICK CHECK 3 How many times do you need to integrate by parts to reduce $\int_1^a (\ln x)^6\,dx$ to an integral of $\ln x$? ◀

SECTION 8.1 EXERCISES

Review Questions

1. On which derivative rule is integration by parts based?

2. How would you choose the term dv when evaluating $\int x^n e^{ax}\,dx$ using integration by parts?

3. How would you choose the term u when evaluting $\int x^n \cos ax\,dx$ using integration by parts?

4. Explain how integration by parts is used to evaluate a definite integral.

5. For what type of integrand is integration by parts useful?

6. How would you choose u and dv to simplify $\int x^4 e^{-2x}\,dx$?

Basic Skills

7–22. Integration by parts *Evaluate the following integrals.*

7. $\int x\cos x\,dx$ 8. $\int x\sin 2x\,dx$ 9. $\int te^t\,dt$

10. $\int 2xe^{3x}\,dx$ 11. $\int x^2\sin 2x\,dx$ 12. $\int se^{-2s}\,ds$

13. $\int x^2e^{4x}\,dx$ 14. $\int \theta\sec^2\theta\,d\theta$ 15. $\int x^2\ln x\,dx$

16. $\int x\ln x\,dx$ 17. $\int \frac{\ln x}{x^{10}}\,dx$ 18. $\int \sin^{-1}x\,dx$

19. $\int \tan^{-1}x\,dx$ 20. $\int x\sec^{-1}x\,dx,\ x \ge 1$

21. $\int x\sin x\cos x\,dx$ 22. $\int x\tan^{-1}(x^2)\,dx$

23–28. Repeated integration by parts *Evaluate the following integrals.*

23. $\int e^x\cos x\,dx$ 24. $\int e^{3x}\cos 2x\,dx$

25. $\int e^{-x}\sin 4x\,dx$ 26. $\int x^2\ln^2 x\,dx$

27. $\int t^3e^{-t}\,dt$ 28. $\int e^{-2\theta}\sin 6\theta\,d\theta$

29–36. Definite integrals *Evaluate the following definite integrals.*

29. $\int_0^{\pi} x\sin x\,dx$ 30. $\int_1^{e} \ln 2x\,dx$

31. $\int_0^{\pi/2} x\cos 2x\,dx$ 32. $\int_0^{\ln 2} xe^x\,dx$

33. $\int_1^{e^2} x^2\ln x\,dx$ 34. $\int_0^{1/\sqrt{2}} y\tan^{-1}y^2\,dy$

35. $\int_{1/2}^{\sqrt{3}/2} \sin^{-1}y\,dy$ 36. $\int_{2/\sqrt{3}}^{2} z\sec^{-1}z\,dz$

37–40. Volumes of solids *Find the volume of the solid that is generated when the region is revolved as described.*

37. The region bounded by $f(x) = e^{-x}$, $x = \ln 2$, and the coordinate axes is revolved about the y-axis.

38. The region bounded by $f(x) = \sin x$ and the x-axis on $[0, \pi]$ is revolved about the y-axis.

39. The region bounded by $f(x) = x\ln x$ and the x-axis on $[1, e^2]$ is revolved about the x-axis.

40. The region bounded by $f(x) = e^{-x}$ and the x-axis on $[0, \ln 2]$ is revolved about the line $x = \ln 2$.

Further Explorations

41. **Explain why or why not** Determine whether the following statements are true and give an explanation or counterexample.

    a. $\int uv'\,dx = \left(\int u\,dx\right)\left(\int v'\,dx\right)$

    b. $\int uv'\,dx = uv - \int vu'\,dx$

42–45. Reduction formulas *Use integration by parts to derive the following* reduction formulas.

42. $\int x^n e^{ax}\,dx = \frac{x^ne^{ax}}{a} - \frac{n}{a}\int x^{n-1}e^{ax}\,dx$ for $a \ne 0$

43. $\int x^n\cos ax\,dx = \frac{x^n\sin ax}{a} - \frac{n}{a}\int x^{n-1}\sin ax\,dx$ for $a \ne 0$

44. $\int x^n\sin ax\,dx = -\frac{x^n\cos ax}{a} + \frac{n}{a}\int x^{n-1}\cos ax\,dx$ for $a \ne 0$

45. $\int \ln^n x\,dx = x\ln^n x - n\int \ln^{n-1}x\,dx$

46–49. Applying reduction formulas *Use the reduction formulas in Exercises 42–45 to evaluate the following integrals.*

46. $\int x^2e^{3x}\,dx$ 47. $\int x^2\cos 5x\,dx$

48. $\int x^3\sin x\,dx$ 49. $\int \ln^4 x\,dx$

50–51. Integrals involving $\int \ln x\,dx$ *Use a substitution to reduce the following integrals to $\int \ln u\,du$. Then, evaluate the resulting integral.*

50. $\int \cos x\ln(\sin x)\,dx$ 51. $\int \sec^2 x\ln(\tan x + 2)\,dx$

52. **Two methods**

    a. Evaluate $\int x\ln x^2\,dx$ using the substitution $u = x^2$ and evaluating $\int \ln u\,du$.

    b. Evaluate $\int x\ln x^2\,dx$ using integration by parts.

    c. Verify that your answers to parts (a) and (b) are consistent.

53. **Logarithm base b** Prove that $\int \log_b x\,dx = \frac{1}{\ln b}(x\ln x - x) + C$.

54. Two integration methods Evaluate $\int \sin x \cos x\, dx$ using integration by parts. Then evaluate the integral using a substitution. Reconcile your answers.

55. Combining two integration methods Evaluate $\int \cos(\sqrt{x})\, dx$ using a substitution followed by integration by parts.

56. Combining two integration methods Evaluate $\int_0^{\pi^2/4} \sin(\sqrt{x})\, dx$ using a substitution followed by integration by parts.

57. Function defined as an integral Find the arc length of the function $f(x) = \int_e^x \sqrt{\ln^2 t - 1}\, dt$ on $[e, e^3]$.

58. A family of exponentials The curves $y = xe^{-ax}$ are shown in the figure for $a = 1, 2$, and 3.

a. Find the area of the region bounded by $y = xe^{-x}$ and the x-axis on the interval $[0, 4]$.

b. Find the area of the region bounded by $y = xe^{-ax}$ and the x-axis on the interval $[0, 4]$, where $a > 0$.

c. Find the area of the region bounded by $y = xe^{-ax}$ and the x-axis on the interval $[0, b]$. Because this area depends on a and b, we call it $A(a, b)$, where $a > 0$ and $b > 0$.

d. Use part (c) to show that $A(1, \ln b) = 4A(2, (\ln b)/2)$.

e. Does this pattern continue? Is it true that $A(1, \ln b) = a^2 A(a, (\ln b)/a)$?

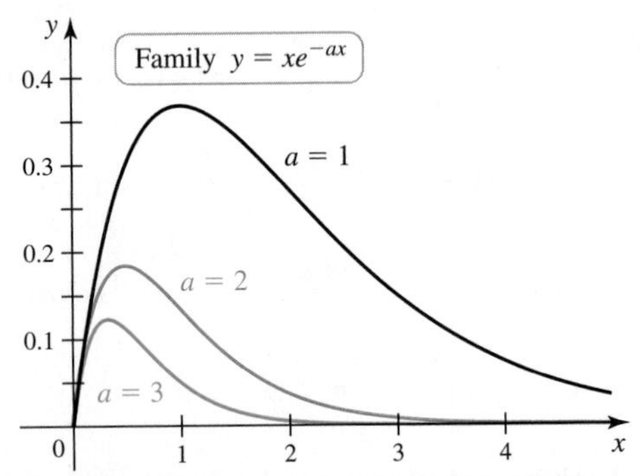

59. Solid of revolution Find the volume of the solid generated when the region bounded by $y = \cos x$ and the x-axis on the interval $[0, \pi/2]$ is revolved about the y-axis.

60. Between the sine and inverse sine Find the area of the region bounded by the curves $y = \sin x$ and $y = \sin^{-1} x$ on the interval $[0, 1]$.

61. Comparing volumes Let R be the region bounded by $y = \sin x$ and the x-axis on the interval $[0, \pi]$. Which is greater, the volume of the solid generated when R is revolved about the x-axis or the volume of the solid generated when R is revolved about the y-axis?

62. Log integrals Use integration by parts to show that for $m \neq -1$,

$$\int x^m \ln x\, dx = \frac{x^{m+1}}{m+1}\left(\ln x - \frac{1}{m+1}\right) + C$$

and for $m = -1$,

$$\int \frac{\ln x}{x}\, dx = \frac{1}{2}\ln^2 x + C.$$

63. A useful integral

a. Use integration by parts to show that if f' is continuous

$$\int xf'(x)\, dx = xf(x) - \int f(x)\, dx.$$

b. Use part (a) to evaluate $\int xe^{3x}\, dx$.

64. Integrating inverse functions

a. Let $y = f^{-1}(x)$, which means $x = f(y)$ and $dx = f'(y)\, dy$. Show that

$$\int f^{-1}(x)\, dx = \int yf'(y)\, dy.$$

b. Use the result of Exercise 63 to show that

$$\int f^{-1}(x)\, dx = yf(y) - \int f(y)\, dy.$$

c. Use the result of part (b) to evaluate $\int \ln x\, dx$ (express the result in terms of x).

d. Use the result of part (b) to evaluate $\int \sin^{-1} x\, dx$.

e. Use the result of part (b) to evaluate $\int \tan^{-1} x\, dx$.

65. Integral of $\sec^3 x$ Use integration by parts to show that

$$\int \sec^3 x\, dx = \frac{1}{2}\sec x \tan x + \frac{1}{2}\int \sec x\, dx.$$

66. Two useful exponential integrals Use integration by parts to derive the following formulas for real numbers a and b.

$$\int e^{ax} \sin bx\, dx = \frac{e^{ax}(a \sin bx - b \cos bx)}{a^2 + b^2} + C$$

$$\int e^{ax} \cos bx\, dx = \frac{e^{ax}(a \cos bx + b \sin bx)}{a^2 + b^2} + C$$

Applications

T **67. Oscillator displacements** Suppose an oscillator (such as a pendulum or a mass on a spring) that is slowed by friction has the position function $s(t) = e^{-t} \sin t$.

a. Graph the position function. At what times does the oscillator pass through the position $s = 0$?

b. Find the average value of the position on the interval $[0, \pi]$.

c. Generalize part (b) and find the average value of the position on the interval $[n\pi, (n + 1)\pi]$ for $n = 0, 1, 2, \ldots$.

d. Let a_n be the absolute value of the average position on the intervals $[n\pi, (n + 1)\pi]$ for $n = 0, 1, 2, \ldots$. Describe the pattern in the numbers $a_0, a_1, a_2, \ldots$.

Additional Exercises

68. Find the error Suppose you evaluate $\int \frac{dx}{x}$ using integration by parts. With $u = 1/x$ and $dv = dx$, you find that $du = -1/x^2\, dx$, $v = x$, and

$$\int \frac{dx}{x} = \left(\frac{1}{x}\right)x - \int x\left(-\frac{1}{x^2}\right) dx = 1 + \int \frac{dx}{x}.$$

You conclude that $0 = 1$. Explain the problem with the calculation.

69. Proof without words Explain how the diagram in the figure illustrates integration by parts for definite integrals.

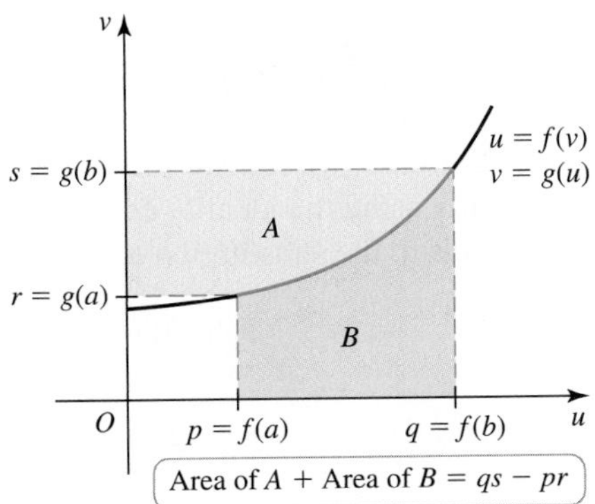

70. An identity Show that if f and g have continuous second derivatives and $f(0) = f(1) = g(0) = g(1) = 0$, then

$$\int_0^1 f''(x)g(x)\,dx = \int_0^1 f(x)g''(x)\,dx.$$

71. Possible and impossible integrals Let $I_n = \int x^n e^{-x^2}\,dx$, where n is a nonnegative integer.

a. $I_0 = \int e^{-x^2}\,dx$ cannot be expressed in terms of elementary functions. Evaluate I_1.

b. Use integration by parts to evaluate I_3.

c. Use integration by parts and the result of part (b) to evaluate I_5.

d. Show that, in general, if n is odd, then $I_n = -\frac{1}{2}e^{-x^2}p_{n-1}(x)$, where p_{n-1} is an even polynomial of degree $n - 1$.

e. Argue that if n is even, then I_n cannot be expressed in terms of elementary functions.

72. Looking ahead (to Chapter 10) Suppose that a function f has derivatives of all orders near $x = 0$. By the Fundamental Theorem of Calculus,

$$f(x) - f(0) = \int_0^x f'(t)\,dt.$$

a. Evaluate the integral using integration by parts to show that

$$f(x) = f(0) + xf'(0) + \int_0^x f''(t)(x - t)\,dt.$$

b. Show (by observing a pattern or using induction) that by integrating by parts n times,

$$f(x) = f(0) + xf'(0) + \frac{1}{2!}x^2 f''(0) + \cdots + \frac{1}{n!}x^n f^{(n)}(0)$$
$$+ \frac{1}{n!}\int_0^x f^{(n+1)}(t)(x - t)^n\,dt + \cdots$$

This expression, called the *Taylor series* for f at $x = 0$, is revisited in Chapter 10.

QUICK CHECK ANSWERS

1. Let $u = x$ and $dv = \cos x\,dx$.
2. $\frac{d}{dx}(x \ln x - x + C) = \ln x$
3. Integration by parts must be applied five times.

8.2 Trigonometric Integrals

At the moment, our inventory of integrals involving trigonometric functions is rather limited. For example, we can integrate $\sin ax$ and $\cos ax$, where a is a constant, but missing from the list are integrals of $\tan ax$, $\cot ax$, $\sec ax$, and $\csc ax$. It turns out that integrals of powers of trigonometric functions, such as $\int \cos^5 x\,dx$ and $\int \cos^2 x \sin^4 x\,dx$, are also important. The goal of this section is to develop techniques for integrating integrals involving trigonometric functions. These techniques are indispensable when we use *trigonometric substitutions* in the next section.

Integrating Powers of sin *x* and cos *x*

Two strategies are employed when evaluating integrals of the form $\int \sin^m x\,dx$ or $\int \cos^n x\,dx$, where m and n are positive integers. Both use trigonometric identities to recast the integrand, as shown in the first example.

EXAMPLE 1 **Powers of sine or cosine** Evaluate the following integrals.

a. $\int \cos^5 x\, dx$ **b.** $\int \sin^4 x\, dx$

SOLUTION

➤ Pythagorean identities:

$$\cos^2 x + \sin^2 x = 1$$
$$1 + \tan^2 x = \sec^2 x$$
$$\cot^2 x + 1 = \csc^2 x$$

a. Integrals involving odd powers of $\cos x$ (or $\sin x$) are most easily evaluated by splitting off a single factor of $\cos x$ (or $\sin x$). In this case, we rewrite $\cos^5 x$ as $\cos^4 x \cdot \cos x$. Now, $\cos^4 x$ can be written in terms of $\sin x$ using the identity $\cos^2 x = 1 - \sin^2 x$. The result is an integrand that readily yields to the substitution $u = \sin x$:

$$\begin{aligned}
\int \cos^5 x\, dx &= \int \cos^4 x \cdot \cos x\, dx && \text{Split off } \cos x.\\
&= \int (1 - \sin^2 x)^2 \cdot \cos x\, dx && \text{Pythagorean identity}\\
&= \int (1 - u^2)^2\, du && \text{Let } u = \sin x;\ du = \cos x\, dx.\\
&= \int (1 - 2u^2 + u^4)\, du && \text{Expand.}\\
&= u - \frac{2}{3}u^3 + \frac{1}{5}u^5 + C && \text{Integrate.}\\
&= \sin x - \frac{2}{3}\sin^3 x + \frac{1}{5}\sin^5 x + C && \text{Replace } u \text{ with } \sin x.
\end{aligned}$$

➤ Use the phrase "sine is minus" to remember that a minus sign is associated with the half-angle formula for $\sin^2 x$, while a positive sign is used for $\cos^2 x$.

b. With even powers of $\sin x$ or $\cos x$, we use the half-angle formulas

$$\sin^2 x = \frac{1 - \cos 2x}{2} \quad \text{and} \quad \cos^2 x = \frac{1 + \cos 2x}{2}$$

to reduce the powers in the integrand:

$$\begin{aligned}
\int \sin^4 x\, dx &= \int \Bigg(\underbrace{\frac{1 - \cos 2x}{2}}_{\sin^2 x}\Bigg)^2 dx && \text{Half-angle formula}\\
&= \frac{1}{4}\int (1 - 2\cos 2x + \cos^2 2x)\, dx && \text{Expand the integrand.}
\end{aligned}$$

Using the half-angle formula again for $\cos^2 2x$, the evaluation may be completed:

$$\begin{aligned}
\int \sin^4 x\, dx &= \frac{1}{4}\int \Bigg(1 - 2\cos 2x + \underbrace{\frac{1 + \cos 4x}{2}}_{\cos^2 2x}\Bigg) dx && \text{Half-angle formula}\\
&= \frac{1}{4}\int \left(\frac{3}{2} - 2\cos 2x + \frac{1}{2}\cos 4x\right) dx && \text{Simplify.}\\
&= \frac{3x}{8} - \frac{1}{4}\sin 2x + \frac{1}{32}\sin 4x + C && \text{Evaluate the integrals.}
\end{aligned}$$

Related Exercises 9–12 ◀

QUICK CHECK 1 Evaluate $\int \sin^3 x\, dx$ by splitting off a factor of $\sin x$, rewriting $\sin^2 x$ in terms of $\cos x$, and using an appropriate u-substitution. ◀

Integrating Products of sin x and cos x

We now consider integrals of the form $\int \sin^m x \cos^n x\, dx$. If m is an odd, positive integer, we split off a factor of $\sin x$ and write the remaining even power of $\sin x$ in terms of cosine functions. This step prepares the integrand for the substitution $u = \cos x$, and the resulting integral is readily solved. A similar strategy is used when n is an odd, positive integer.

If both m and n are even, positive integers, the half-angle formulas are used to transform the integrand into a polynomial in $\cos 2x$, each of whose terms can be integrated, as shown in Example 2.

EXAMPLE 2 **Products of sine and cosine** Evaluate the following integrals.

a. $\int \sin^4 x \cos^2 x\, dx$ **b.** $\int \sin^3 x \cos^{-2} x\, dx$

SOLUTION

a. When both powers are even, the half-angle formulas are used:

$$\int \sin^4 x \cos^2 x\, dx = \int \underbrace{\left(\frac{1-\cos 2x}{2}\right)^2}_{\sin^2 x}\underbrace{\left(\frac{1+\cos 2x}{2}\right)}_{\cos^2 x} dx \qquad \text{Half-angle formulas}$$

$$= \frac{1}{8}\int (1 - \cos 2x - \cos^2 2x + \cos^3 2x)\, dx \qquad \text{Expand.}$$

The third term in the integrand is rewritten with a half-angle formula. For the last term, a factor of $\cos 2x$ is split off, and the resulting even power of $\cos 2x$ is written in terms of $\sin 2x$ to prepare for a u-substitution:

$$\int \sin^4 x \cos^2 x\, dx =$$

$$\frac{1}{8}\int \left[1 - \cos 2x - \overbrace{\left(\frac{1+\cos 4x}{2}\right)}^{\cos^2 2x}\right] dx + \frac{1}{8}\int \overbrace{(1 - \sin^2 2x)}^{\cos^2 2x} \cdot \cos 2x\, dx$$

Finally, the integrals are evaluated, using the substitution $u = \sin 2x$ for the second integral. After simplification, we find that

$$\int \sin^4 x \cos^2 x\, dx = \frac{1}{16}x - \frac{1}{64}\sin 4x - \frac{1}{48}\sin^3 2x + C.$$

b. When at least one power is odd, the following approach works:

$$\int \sin^3 x \cos^{-2} x\, dx = \int \sin^2 x \cos^{-2} x \cdot \sin x\, dx \qquad \text{Split off } \sin x.$$

$$= \int (1 - \cos^2 x)\cos^{-2} x \cdot \sin x\, dx \qquad \text{Pythagorean identity}$$

$$= -\int (1 - u^2) u^{-2}\, du \qquad u = \cos x;\ du = -\sin x\, dx$$

$$= \int (1 - u^{-2})\, du = u + \frac{1}{u} + C \qquad \text{Evaluate the integral.}$$

$$= \cos x + \sec x + C \qquad \text{Replace } u \text{ with } \cos x.$$

Related Exercises 13–18

QUICK CHECK 2 What strategy would you use to evaluate $\int \sin^3 x \cos^3 x\, dx$?

Table 8.1 summarizes the techniques used to evaluate integrals of the form $\int \sin^m x \cos^n x\,dx$.

Table 8.1

$\int \sin^m x \cos^n x\,dx$	Strategy
m odd, n real	Split off $\sin x$, rewrite the resulting even power of $\sin x$ in terms of $\cos x$, and then use $u = \cos x$.
n odd, m real	Split off $\cos x$, rewrite the resulting even power of $\cos x$ in terms of $\sin x$, and then use $u = \sin x$.
m and n both even, nonnegative integers	Use half-angle identities to transform the integrand into a polynomial in $\cos 2x$, and apply the preceding strategies once again to powers greater than 1 ($\cos^2 2x, \cos^3 2x$, etc.).

Reduction Formulas

Evaluating an integral such as $\int \sin^8 x\,dx$ using the method of Example 1b would be tedious, at best. For this reason, *reduction formulas* have been developed to ease the work-load. A reduction formula equates an integral involving a power of a function with another integral in which the power is reduced; several reduction formulas were encountered in Exercises 42–45 of Section 8.1. Here are some frequently used reduction formulas for trigonometric integrals.

Reduction Formulas

Assume n is a positive integer.

1. $$\int \sin^n x\,dx = -\frac{\sin^{n-1} x \cos x}{n} + \frac{n-1}{n}\int \sin^{n-2} x\,dx$$

2. $$\int \cos^n x\,dx = \frac{\cos^{n-1} x \sin x}{n} + \frac{n-1}{n}\int \cos^{n-2} x\,dx$$

3. $$\int \tan^n x\,dx = \frac{\tan^{n-1} x}{n-1} - \int \tan^{n-2} x\,dx, \quad n \neq 1$$

4. $$\int \sec^n x\,dx = \frac{\sec^{n-2} x \tan x}{n-1} + \frac{n-2}{n-1}\int \sec^{n-2} x\,dx, \quad n \neq 1$$

Formulas 1, 3, and 4 are derived in Exercises 52–54. The derivation of formula 2 is similar to that of formula 1.

EXAMPLE 3 **Powers of tan x** Evaluate $\int \tan^4 x\,dx$.

SOLUTION Reduction formula 3 gives

$$\begin{aligned}\int \tan^4 x\,dx &= \frac{1}{3}\tan^3 x - \underbrace{\int \tan^2 x\,dx}_{\text{use (3) again}}\\ &= \frac{1}{3}\tan^3 x - (\tan x - \int \underbrace{\tan^0 x}_{=1}\,dx)\\ &= \frac{1}{3}\tan^3 x - \tan x + x + C\end{aligned}$$

An alternative solution uses the identity $\tan^2 x = \sec^2 x - 1$:

$$\int \tan^4 x\,dx = \int \tan^2 x\,(\sec^2 x - 1)\,dx$$
$$= \int \tan^2 x \sec^2 x\,dx - \int \tan^2 x\,dx$$

The substitution $u = \tan x$, $du = \sec^2 x\,dx$ is used in the first integral, while the identity $\tan^2 x = \sec^2 x - 1$ is used again in the second integral:

$$\int \tan^4 x\,dx = \int \underbrace{\tan^2 x}_{u^2}\,\underbrace{\sec^2 x\,dx}_{du} - \int \tan^2 x\,dx$$

$$= \int u^2\,du - \int (\sec^2 x - 1)\,dx \quad \text{Substitution and identity}$$

$$= \frac{u^3}{3} - \tan x + x + C \quad \text{Evaluate integrals.}$$

$$= \frac{1}{3}\tan^3 x - \tan x + x + C \quad u = \tan x$$

Related Exercises 19–24

Note that for odd powers of $\tan x$ and $\sec x$, the use of reduction formula 3 or 4 will eventually lead to $\int \tan x\,dx$ or $\int \sec x\,dx$. Theorem 8.1 gives these integrals, along with the integrals of $\cot x$ and $\csc x$.

THEOREM 8.1 Integrals of $\tan x$, $\cot x$, $\sec x$, and $\csc x$

$$\int \tan x\,dx = -\ln|\cos x| + C = \ln|\sec x| + C \qquad \int \cot x\,dx = \ln|\sin x| + C$$

$$\int \sec x\,dx = \ln|\sec x + \tan x| + C \qquad \int \csc x\,dx = -\ln|\csc x + \cot x| + C$$

Proof In the first integral, $\tan x$ is expressed as the ratio of $\sin x$ and $\cos x$ to prepare for a standard substitution:

$$\int \tan x\,dx = \int \frac{\sin x}{\cos x}\,dx$$

$$= -\int \frac{1}{u}\,du \quad u = \cos x;\ du = -\sin x\,dx$$

$$= -\ln|u| + C = -\ln|\cos x| + C$$

Using properties of logarithms, the integral can also be written

$$\int \tan x\,dx = -\ln|\cos x| + C = \ln|(\cos x)^{-1}| + C = \ln|\sec x| + C.$$

Derivations of the remaining integrals are left to Exercises 34–36.

Integrating Products of $\tan x$ and $\sec x$

Integrals of the form $\int \tan^m x \sec^n x\,dx$ are evaluated using methods analogous to those used for $\int \sin^m x \cos^n x\,dx$. For example, if n is even, we split off a factor of $\sec^2 x$ and write the remaining even power of $\sec x$ in terms of $\tan x$. This step prepares the integral for the substitution $u = \tan x$. If m is odd, we split off a factor of $\sec x \tan x$ (the derivative of $\sec x$), which prepares the integral for the substitution $u = \sec x$. If m is even and n is odd, the integrand is expressed as a polynomial in $\sec x$, each of whose terms is handled by a reduction formula. Example 4 illustrates these techniques.

EXAMPLE 4 **Products of $\tan x$ and $\sec x$** Evaluate the integrals.

a. $\int \tan^3 x \sec^4 x\, dx$ **b.** $\int \tan^2 x \sec x\, dx$

SOLUTION

a. With an even power of $\sec x$, we split off a factor of $\sec^2 x$, and prepare the integral for the substitution $u = \tan x$:

$$\begin{aligned}\int \tan^3 x \sec^4 x\, dx &= \int \tan^3 x \sec^2 x \cdot \sec^2 x\, dx \\ &= \int \tan^3 x\,(\tan^2 x + 1) \cdot \sec^2 x\, dx && \sec^2 x = \tan^2 x + 1 \\ &= \int u^3 (u^2 + 1)\, du && u = \tan x;\ du = \sec^2 x\, dx \\ &= \frac{1}{6}\tan^6 x + \frac{1}{4}\tan^4 x + C && \text{Evaluate; } u = \tan x.\end{aligned}$$

Because the integrand also has an odd power of $\tan x$, an alternative solution is to split off a factor of $\sec x \tan x$, and prepare the integral for the substitution $u = \sec x$.

➤ In Example 4a, the two methods produce results that look different, but are equivalent. This is common when evaluating trigonometric integrals. For instance, try $\int \sin^4 x\, dx$ using reduction formula 1, and compare your answer to

$$\frac{3x}{8} - \frac{1}{4}\sin 2x + \frac{1}{32}\sin 4x + C,$$

the solution found in Example 1b.

$$\begin{aligned}\int \tan^3 x \sec^4 x\, dx &= \int \underbrace{\tan^2 x}_{\sec^2 x - 1} \sec^3 x \cdot \sec x \tan x\, dx \\ &= \int (\sec^2 x - 1) \sec^3 x \cdot \sec x \tan x\, dx \\ &= \int (u^2 - 1) u^3\, du && u = \sec x;\ du = \sec x \tan x\, dx \\ &= \frac{1}{6}\sec^6 x - \frac{1}{4}\sec^4 x + C && \text{Evaluate; } u = \sec x.\end{aligned}$$

The apparent difference in the two solutions given here is reconciled by using the identity $1 + \tan^2 x = \sec^2 x$ to transform the second result into the first, the only difference being an additive constant, which is part of C.

b. In this case, we write the even power of $\tan x$ in terms of $\sec x$:

$$\begin{aligned}\int \tan^2 x \sec x\, dx &= \int (\sec^2 x - 1) \sec x\, dx && \tan^2 x = \sec^2 x - 1 \\ &= \int \sec^3 x\, dx - \int \sec x\, dx \\ &= \overbrace{\frac{1}{2}\sec x \tan x + \frac{1}{2}\int \sec x\, dx}^{\text{reduction formula 4}} - \int \sec x\, dx \\ &= \frac{1}{2}\sec x \tan x - \frac{1}{2}\ln|\sec x + \tan x| + C && \text{Add secant integrals; use Theorem 8.1.}\end{aligned}$$

Related Exercises 25–32 ◀

Table 8.2 summarizes the methods used to integrate $\int \tan^m x \sec^n x\, dx$. Analogous techniques are used for $\int \cot^m x \csc^n x\, dx$.

Table 8.2

$\int \tan^m x \sec^n x\, dx$	Strategy
n even	Split off $\sec^2 x$, rewrite the remaining even power of $\sec x$ in terms of $\tan x$, and use $u = \tan x$.
m odd	Split off $\sec x \tan x$, rewrite the remaining even power of $\tan x$ in terms of $\sec x$, and use $u = \sec x$.
m even and n odd	Rewrite the even power of $\tan x$ in terms of $\sec x$ to produce a polynomial in $\sec x$; apply reduction formula 4 to each term.

SECTION 8.2 EXERCISES

Review Questions

1. State the half-angle identities used to integrate $\sin^2 x$ and $\cos^2 x$.
2. State the three Pythagorean identities.
3. Describe the method used to integrate $\sin^3 x$.
4. Describe the method used to integrate $\sin^m x \cos^n x$ for m even and n odd.
5. What is a reduction formula?
6. How would you evaluate $\int \cos^2 x \sin^3 x\, dx$?
7. How would you evaluate $\int \tan^{10} x \sec^2 x\, dx$?
8. How would you evaluate $\int \sec^{12} x \tan x\, dx$?

Basic Skills

9–12. Integrals of $\sin x$ or $\cos x$ *Evaluate the following integrals.*

9. $\int \sin^2 x\, dx$
10. $\int \cos^4 2x\, dx$
11. $\int \sin^5 x\, dx$
12. $\int \cos^3 20x\, dx$

13–18. Integrals of $\sin x$ and $\cos x$ *Evaluate the following integrals.*

13. $\int \sin^2 x \cos^2 x\, dx$
14. $\int \sin^3 x \cos^5 x\, dx$
15. $\int \sin^5 x \cos^{-2} x\, dx$
16. $\int \sin^{-3/2} x \cos^3 x\, dx$
17. $\int \sin^2 x \cos^4 x\, dx$
18. $\int \sin^3 x \cos^{3/2} x\, dx$

19–24. Integrals of $\tan x$ or $\cot x$ *Evaluate the following integrals.*

19. $\int \tan^2 x\, dx$
20. $\int 6 \sec^4 x\, dx$
21. $\int \tan^3 4x\, dx$
22. $\int \sec^5 \theta\, d\theta$
23. $\int 20 \tan^6 x\, dx$
24. $\int \cot^5 3x\, dx$

25–32. Integrals of $\tan x$ and $\sec x$ *Evaluate the following integrals.*

25. $\int \sec^2 x \tan^{1/2} x\, dx$
26. $\int \sec^{-2} x \tan^3 x\, dx$
27. $\int \frac{\csc^4 x}{\cot^2 x}\, dx$
28. $\int \csc^{10} x \cot^3 x\, dx$
29. $\int_0^{\pi/4} \sec^4 \theta\, d\theta$
30. $\int \tan^5 \theta \sec^4 \theta\, d\theta$
31. $\int_{\pi/6}^{\pi/3} \cot^3 \theta\, d\theta$
32. $\int_0^{\pi/4} \tan^3 \theta \sec^2 \theta\, d\theta$

Further Explorations

33. **Explain why or why not** Determine whether the following statements are true and give an explanation or counterexample.
    a. If m is a positive integer, then $\int_0^{\pi} \cos^{2m+1} x\, dx = 0$.
    b. If m is a positive integer, then $\int_0^{\pi} \sin^m x\, dx = 0$.

34–37. Integrals of $\cot x$, $\sec x$, and $\csc x$

34. Use a change of variables to prove that $\int \cot x\, dx = \ln |\sin x| + C$.
35. Prove that $\int \sec x\, dx = \ln |\sec x + \tan x| + C$. (*Hint:* Multiply numerator and denominator of the integrand by $\sec x + \tan x$; then make a change of variables with $u = \sec x + \tan x$.)
36. Prove that $\int \csc x\, dx = -\ln |\csc x + \cot x| + C$. (*Hint:* Use a method analogous to that used in Exercise 35.)
37. Use the results of Theorem 8.1 to find the indefinite integral of $\tan ax$ and $\sec ax$, where a is a nonzero real number.
38. **Comparing areas** The region R_1 is bounded by the graph of $y = \tan x$ and the x-axis on the interval $[0, \pi/3]$. The region R_2 is bounded by the graph of $y = \sec x$ and the x-axis on the interval $[0, \pi/6]$. Which region has the greater area?
39. **Region between curves** Find the area of the region bounded by the graphs of $y = \tan x$ and $y = \sec x$ on the interval $[0, \pi/4]$.

40–45. Additional integrals *Evaluate the following integrals.*

40. $\displaystyle\int_0^{\sqrt{\pi/2}} x \sin^3(x^2)\, dx$

41. $\displaystyle\int \frac{\sec^4(\ln\theta)}{\theta}\, d\theta$

42. $\displaystyle\int_{\pi/6}^{\pi/2} \frac{dy}{\sin y}$

43. $\displaystyle\int_{-\pi/3}^{\pi/3} \sqrt{\sec^2\theta - 1}\, d\theta$

44. $\displaystyle\int_{-\pi/4}^{\pi/4} \tan^3 x \sec^2 x\, dx$

45. $\displaystyle\int_0^{\pi} (1 - \cos 2x)^{3/2}\, dx$

46–49. Square roots *Evaluate the following integrals.*

46. $\displaystyle\int_{-\pi/4}^{\pi/4} \sqrt{1 + \cos 4x}\, dx$

47. $\displaystyle\int_0^{\pi/2} \sqrt{1 - \cos 2x}\, dx$

48. $\displaystyle\int_0^{\pi/8} \sqrt{1 - \cos 8x}\, dx$

49. $\displaystyle\int_0^{\pi/4} (1 + \cos 4x)^{3/2}\, dx$

50. Sine football Find the volume of the solid generated when the region bounded by the graph of $y = \sin x$ and the x-axis on the interval $[0, \pi]$ is revolved about the x-axis.

51. Arc length Find the length of the curve $y = \ln(\cos x)$ for $0 \le x \le \pi/4$.

52. A sine reduction formula Use integration by parts to obtain the following reduction formula for positive integers n:

$$\int \sin^n x\, dx = -\sin^{n-1} x \cos x + (n - 1)\int \sin^{n-2} x \cos^2 x\, dx.$$

Then use an identity to obtain the reduction formula

$$\int \sin^n x\, dx = -\frac{\sin^{n-1} x \cos x}{n} + \frac{n-1}{n}\int \sin^{n-2} x\, dx.$$

Use this reduction formula to evaluate $\int \sin^6 x\, dx$.

53. A tangent reduction formula Prove that for positive integers $n \ne 1$,

$$\int \tan^n x\, dx = \frac{\tan^{n-1} x}{n-1} - \int \tan^{n-2} x\, dx.$$

Use the formula to evaluate $\int_0^{\pi/4} \tan^3 x\, dx$.

54. A secant reduction formula Prove that for positive integers $n \ne 1$,

$$\int \sec^n x\, dx = \frac{\sec^{n-2} x \tan x}{n-1} + \frac{n-2}{n-1}\int \sec^{n-2} x\, dx.$$

(*Hint:* Integrate by parts with $u = \sec^{n-2} x$ and $dv = \sec^2 x\, dx$.)

Applications

55–59. Integrals of the form $\int \sin mx \cos nx\, dx$ *Use the following three identities to evaluate the given integrals.*

$$\sin mx \sin nx = \frac{1}{2}[\cos((m - n)x) - \cos((m + n)x)]$$

$$\sin mx \cos nx = \frac{1}{2}[\sin((m - n)x) + \sin((m + n)x)]$$

$$\cos mx \cos nx = \frac{1}{2}[\cos((m - n)x) + \cos((m + n)x)]$$

55. $\int \sin 3x \cos 7x\, dx$

56. $\int \sin 5x \sin 7x\, dx$

57. $\int \sin 3x \sin 2x\, dx$

58. $\int \cos x \cos 2x\, dx$

59. Prove the following **orthogonality relations** (which are used to generate *Fourier series*). Assume m and n are integers with $m \ne n$.

a. $\displaystyle\int_0^{\pi} \sin mx \sin nx\, dx = 0$

b. $\displaystyle\int_0^{\pi} \cos mx \cos nx\, dx = 0$

c. $\displaystyle\int_0^{\pi} \sin mx \cos nx\, dx = 0$

60. Mercator map projection The Mercator map projection was proposed by the Flemish geographer Gerardus Mercator (1512–1594). The stretching of the Mercator map as a function of the latitude θ is given by the function

$$G(\theta) = \int_0^{\theta} \sec x\, dx.$$

Graph G for $0 \le \theta < \pi/2$. (See the Guided Projects for a derivation of this integral.)

Additional Exercises

61. Exploring powers of sine and cosine

a. Graph the functions $f_1(x) = \sin^2 x$ and $f_2(x) = \sin^2 2x$ on the interval $[0, \pi]$. Find the area under these curves on $[0, \pi]$.

b. Graph a few more of the functions $f_n(x) = \sin^2 nx$ on the interval $[0, \pi]$, where n is a positive integer. Find the area under these curves on $[0, \pi]$. Comment on your observations.

c. Prove that $\int_0^{\pi} \sin^2(nx)\, dx$ has the same value for all positive integers n.

d. Does the conclusion of part (c) hold if sine is replaced by cosine?

e. Repeat parts (a), (b), and (c) with $\sin^2 x$ replaced by $\sin^4 x$. Comment on your observations.

f. Challenge problem: Show that for $m = 1, 2, 3, \ldots,$

$$\int_0^{\pi} \sin^{2m} x\, dx = \int_0^{\pi} \cos^{2m} x\, dx = \pi \cdot \frac{1 \cdot 3 \cdot 5 \cdots (2m - 1)}{2 \cdot 4 \cdot 6 \cdots 2m}.$$

QUICK CHECK ANSWERS

1. $\frac{1}{3}\cos^3 x - \cos x + C$ **2.** Write $\int \sin^3 x \cos^3 x\, dx = \int \sin^2 x \cos^3 x \sin x\, dx = \int (1 - \cos^2 x)\cos^3 x \sin x\, dx$. Then, use the substitution $u = \cos x$. Or, begin by writing $\int \sin^3 x \cos^3 x\, dx = \int \sin^3 x \cos^2 x \cos x\, dx$.

8.3 Trigonometric Substitutions

In Section 6.5, we wrote the arc length integral for the segment of the parabola $y = x^2$ on the interval $[0, 2]$ as

$$\int_0^2 \sqrt{1 + 4x^2}\, dx = \int_0^2 2\sqrt{\tfrac{1}{4} + x^2}\, dx.$$

At the time, we did not have the analytical methods needed to evaluate this integral. The goal of this section is to develop the tools needed to evaluate such integrals.

Integrals similar to the arc length integral for the parabola arise in many different situations. For example, electrostatic, magnetic, and gravitational forces obey an inverse square law (their strength is proportional to $1/r^2$, where r is a distance). Computing these force fields in two dimensions leads to integrals such as $\displaystyle\int \frac{dx}{\sqrt{x^2 + a^2}}$ or $\displaystyle\int \frac{dx}{(x^2 + a^2)^{3/2}}$. It turns out that integrals containing the terms $a^2 \pm x^2$ or $x^2 - a^2$, where a is a constant, can be simplified using somewhat unexpected substitutions involving trigonometric functions. The new integrals produced by these substitutions are often trigonometric integrals of the variety studied in the preceding section.

Integrals Involving $a^2 - x^2$

Suppose you are faced with an integral whose integrand contains the term $a^2 - x^2$, where a is a positive constant. Observe what happens when x is replaced with $a \sin\theta$:

$$\begin{aligned} a^2 - x^2 &= a^2 - (a\sin\theta)^2 && \text{Replace } x \text{ with } a\sin\theta. \\ &= a^2 - a^2\sin^2\theta && \text{Simplify.} \\ &= a^2(1 - \sin^2\theta) && \text{Factor.} \\ &= a^2\cos^2\theta && 1 - \sin^2\theta = \cos^2\theta \end{aligned}$$

➤ The following thinking might lead you to the substitution $x = a\sin\theta$. The term $\sqrt{a^2 - x^2}$ looks like the length of one side of a right triangle whose hypotenuse has length a and whose other side has length x. Labeling one acute angle θ, we see that $x = a\sin\theta$.

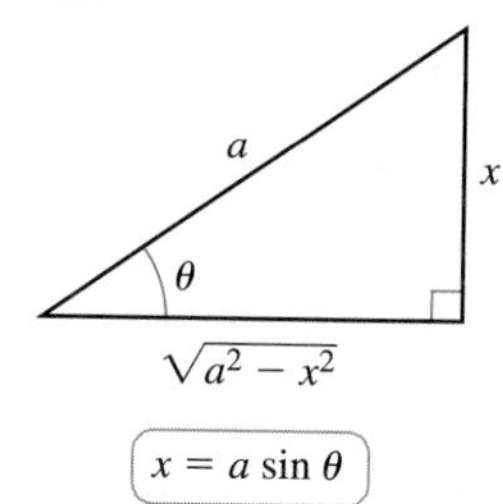

$x = a\sin\theta$

This calculation shows that the substitution $x = a\sin\theta$ turns the difference $a^2 - x^2$ into the product $a^2\cos^2\theta$. The resulting integral—now with respect to θ—is often easier to evaluate than the original integral. The details of this procedure are spelled out in the following examples.

QUICK CHECK 1 Use a substitution of the form $x = a\sin\theta$ to transform $9 - x^2$ into a product. ◄

EXAMPLE 1 Area of a circle Verify that the area of a circle of radius a is πa^2.

SOLUTION The function $f(x) = \sqrt{a^2 - x^2}$ describes the upper half of a circle centered at the origin with radius a (Figure 8.2). The region under this curve on the interval $[0, a]$ is a quarter-circle. Therefore, the area of the full circle is $4\int_0^a \sqrt{a^2 - x^2}\, dx$.

Because the integrand contains the expression $a^2 - x^2$, we use the trigonometric substitution $x = a\sin\theta$. As with all substitutions, the differential associated with the substitution must be computed:

$$x = a\sin\theta \quad \text{implies that} \quad dx = a\cos\theta\, d\theta$$

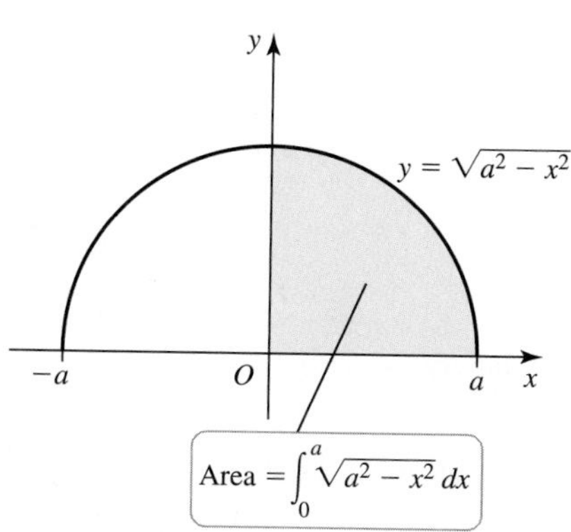

FIGURE 8.2

The substitution $x = a\sin\theta$ can also be written $\theta = \sin^{-1}(x/a)$, where $-\pi/2 \le \theta \le \pi/2$ (Figure 8.3). Notice that the new variable θ plays the role of an angle. The substitution works nicely, because when x is replaced by $a\sin\theta$ in the integrand, we have

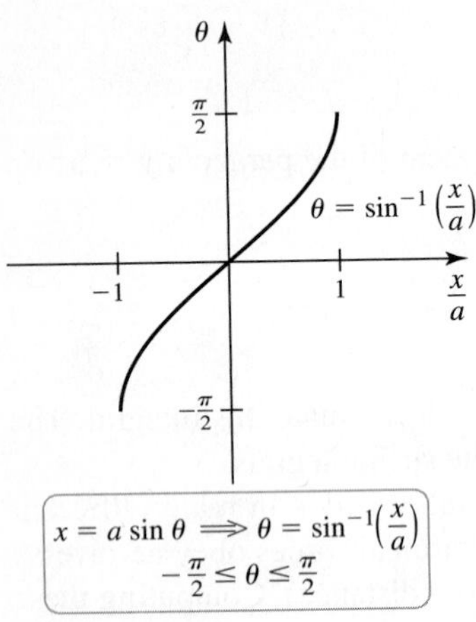

FIGURE 8.3

➤ The key identities for integrating $\sin^2 \theta$ and $\cos^2 \theta$ are

$$\sin^2 \theta = \frac{1 - \cos 2\theta}{2}$$

$$\cos^2 \theta = \frac{1 + \cos 2\theta}{2}$$

$$\begin{aligned}
\sqrt{a^2 - x^2} &= \sqrt{a^2 - (a \sin \theta)^2} && \text{Replace } x \text{ with } a \sin \theta. \\
&= \sqrt{a^2(1 - \sin^2 \theta)} && \text{Factor.} \\
&= \sqrt{a^2 \cos^2 \theta} && 1 - \sin^2 \theta = \cos^2 \theta \\
&= |a \cos \theta| && \sqrt{x^2} = |x| \\
&= a \cos \theta && a > 0, \cos \theta > 0 \text{ for } -\frac{\pi}{2} \le \theta \le \frac{\pi}{2}
\end{aligned}$$

We also change the limits of integration: When $x = 0$, $\theta = \sin^{-1} 0 = 0$; when $x = a$, $\theta = \sin^{-1}(a/a) = \sin^{-1} 1 = \pi/2$. Making these substitutions, the integral is evaluated as follows:

$$\begin{aligned}
4\int_0^a \sqrt{a^2 - x^2}\, dx &= 4\int_0^{\pi/2} \underbrace{a \cos \theta}_{\substack{\text{integrand} \\ \text{simplified}}} \cdot \underbrace{a \cos \theta\, d\theta}_{dx} && x = a \sin \theta, dx = a \cos \theta\, d\theta \\
&= 4a^2 \int_0^{\pi/2} \cos^2 \theta\, d\theta && \text{Simplify.} \\
&= 4a^2 \left(\frac{\theta}{2} + \frac{\sin 2\theta}{4}\right)\Bigg|_0^{\pi/2} && \cos^2 \theta = \frac{1 + \cos 2\theta}{2} \\
&= 4a^2 \left[\left(\frac{\pi}{4} + 0\right) - (0 + 0)\right] = \pi a^2 && \text{Simplify.}
\end{aligned}$$

A similar calculation (Exercise 56) gives the area of an ellipse. *Related Exercises 7–10* ◀

EXAMPLE 2 **Sine substitution** Evaluate $\displaystyle\int \frac{dx}{(16 - x^2)^{3/2}}$.

SOLUTION The factor $16 - x^2$ has the form $a^2 - x^2$ with $a = 4$, so we use the substitution $x = 4 \sin \theta$. It follows that $dx = 4 \cos \theta\, d\theta$. We now simplify $(16 - x^2)^{3/2}$:

$$\begin{aligned}
(16 - x^2)^{3/2} &= \left(16 - (4 \sin \theta)^2\right)^{3/2} && \text{Substitute } x = 4 \sin \theta. \\
&= \left(16(1 - \sin^2 \theta)\right)^{3/2} && \text{Factor.} \\
&= (16 \cos^2 \theta)^{3/2} && 1 - \sin^2 \theta = \cos^2 \theta \\
&= 64 \cos^3 \theta && \text{Simplify.}
\end{aligned}$$

Replacing the factors $(16 - x^2)^{3/2}$ and dx of the original integral with appropriate expressions in θ, we have

$$\begin{aligned}
\int \frac{\overbrace{dx}^{4 \cos \theta\, d\theta}}{\underbrace{(16 - x^2)^{3/2}}_{64 \cos^3 \theta}} &= \int \frac{4 \cos \theta}{64 \cos^3 \theta}\, d\theta \\
&= \frac{1}{16} \int \frac{d\theta}{\cos^2 \theta} \\
&= \frac{1}{16} \int \sec^2 \theta\, d\theta && \text{Simplify.} \\
&= \frac{1}{16} \tan \theta + C && \text{Evaluate the integral.}
\end{aligned}$$

The final step is to express this result in terms of x. In many integrals, this step is most easily done with a reference triangle showing the relationship between x and θ. Figure 8.4

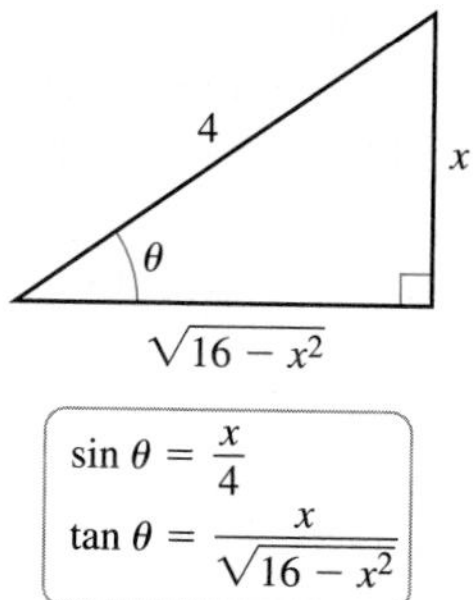

FIGURE 8.4

shows a right triangle with an angle θ and with the sides labeled such that $x = 4\sin\theta$ (or $\sin\theta = x/4$). Using this triangle, we see that $\tan\theta = \dfrac{x}{\sqrt{16 - x^2}}$, which implies that

$$\int \frac{dx}{(16 - x^2)^{3/2}} = \frac{1}{16}\tan\theta + C = \frac{x}{16\sqrt{16 - x^2}} + C.$$

Related Exercises 11–14 ◀

Integrals Involving $a^2 + x^2$ or $x^2 - a^2$

The other standard trigonometric substitutions, involving tangent and secant, use a procedure similar to that used for the sine substitution. Figure 8.5 and Table 8.3 summarize the three basic trigonometric substitutions for real numbers $a > 0$.

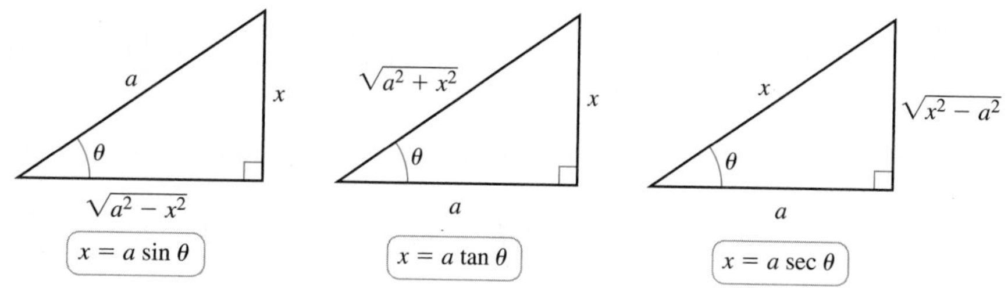

FIGURE 8.5

Table 8.3

The Integral Contains...	Corresponding Substitution	Useful Identity
$a^2 - x^2$	$x = a\sin\theta, -\frac{\pi}{2} \le \theta \le \frac{\pi}{2}$	$a^2 - a^2\sin^2\theta = a^2\cos^2\theta$
$a^2 + x^2$	$x = a\tan\theta, -\frac{\pi}{2} < \theta < \frac{\pi}{2}$	$a^2 + a^2\tan^2\theta = a^2\sec^2\theta$
$x^2 - a^2$	$x = a\sec\theta, \begin{cases} 0 \le \theta < \frac{\pi}{2} & \text{for } x \ge a \\ \frac{\pi}{2} < \theta \le \pi & \text{for } x \le -a \end{cases}$	$a^2\sec^2\theta - a^2 = a^2\tan^2\theta$

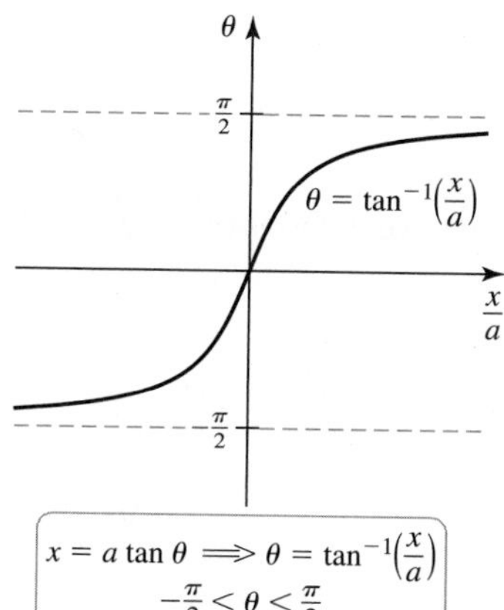

FIGURE 8.6

In order for the tangent substitution $x = a\tan\theta$ to be well defined, the angle θ must be restricted to the interval $-\pi/2 < \theta < \pi/2$, which is consistent with the definition of $\tan^{-1}(x/a)$ (Figure 8.6). On this interval, $\sec\theta > 0$ and with $a > 0$, it is valid to write

$$\sqrt{a^2 + x^2} = \sqrt{a^2 + (a\tan\theta)^2} = \sqrt{a^2\underbrace{(1 + \tan^2\theta)}_{\sec^2\theta}} = a\sec\theta.$$

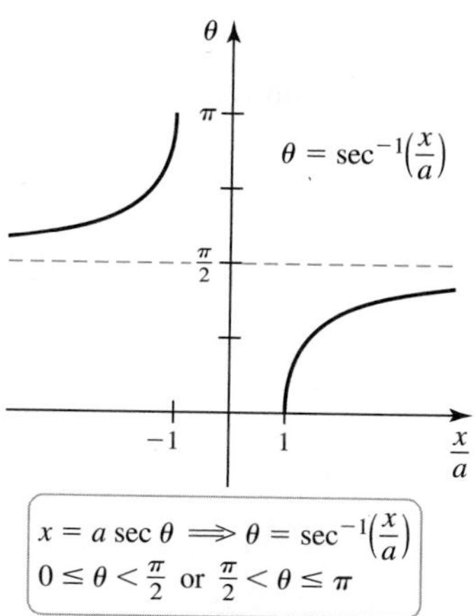

FIGURE 8.7

With the secant substitution, there is a technicality. As discussed in Section 7.5, $\theta = \sec^{-1}(x/a)$ is defined for $x \ge a$, in which case $0 \le \theta < \pi/2$, *and* for $x \le -a$, in which case $\pi/2 < \theta \le \pi$ (Figure 8.7). These restrictions on θ must be treated carefully when simplifying integrands with a factor of $\sqrt{x^2 - a^2}$. Because $\tan\theta$ is positive in the first quadrant but negative in the second, we have

$$\sqrt{x^2 - a^2} = \sqrt{a^2\underbrace{(\sec^2\theta - 1)}_{\tan^2\theta}} = |a\tan\theta| = \begin{cases} a\tan\theta & \text{if } 0 \le \theta < \frac{\pi}{2} \\ -a\tan\theta & \text{if } \frac{\pi}{2} < \theta \le \pi \end{cases}$$

QUICK CHECK 2 What change of variables would you try on the integrals

(a) $\int \frac{x^2}{\sqrt{x^2 + 9}}\,dx$ and

(b) $\int \frac{3}{x\sqrt{16 - x^2}}\,dx$? ◄

When evaluating a definite integral, you should check the limits of integration to see which of these two cases applies. For indefinite integrals, a piecewise formula is often needed, unless a restriction on the variable is given in the problem (see Exercises 75–78).

EXAMPLE 3 **Arc length of a parabola** Evaluate $\int_0^2 \sqrt{1 + 4x^2}\,dx$, the arc length of the segment of the parabola $y = x^2$ on $[0, 2]$.

SOLUTION Removing a factor of 4 from the square root, we have

$$\int_0^2 \sqrt{1 + 4x^2}\,dx = 2\int_0^2 \sqrt{\tfrac{1}{4} + x^2}\,dx = 2\int_0^2 \sqrt{\left(\tfrac{1}{2}\right)^2 + x^2}\,dx.$$

The integrand contains the expression $a^2 + x^2$, with $a = \frac{1}{2}$, which suggests the substitution $x = \frac{1}{2}\tan\theta$. It follows that $dx = \frac{1}{2}\sec^2\theta\,d\theta$, and

$$\sqrt{\left(\tfrac{1}{2}\right)^2 + x^2} = \sqrt{\left(\tfrac{1}{2}\right)^2 + \left(\tfrac{1}{2}\tan\theta\right)^2} = \frac{1}{2}\underbrace{\sqrt{1 + \tan^2\theta}}_{\sec^2\theta} = \frac{1}{2}\sec\theta.$$

➤ Because we are evaluating a definite integral, we could change the limits of integration to $\theta = 0$ and $\theta = \tan^{-1} 4$. However, $\tan^{-1} 4$ is not a standard angle, so it is easier to express the antiderivative in terms of x and use the original limits of integration.

Setting aside the limits of integration for the moment, we compute the antiderivative

$$2\int \sqrt{\left(\tfrac{1}{2}\right)^2 + x^2}\,dx = 2\int \tfrac{1}{2}\sec\theta\,\underbrace{\tfrac{1}{2}\sec^2\theta\,d\theta}_{dx} \qquad x = \frac{1}{2}\tan\theta,\ dx = \frac{1}{2}\sec^2\theta\,d\theta$$

$$= \frac{1}{2}\int \sec^3\theta\,d\theta \qquad \text{Simplify.}$$

$$= \frac{1}{4}(\sec\theta\tan\theta + \ln|\sec\theta + \tan\theta|) \qquad \text{Reduction formula 4, Section 8.2}$$

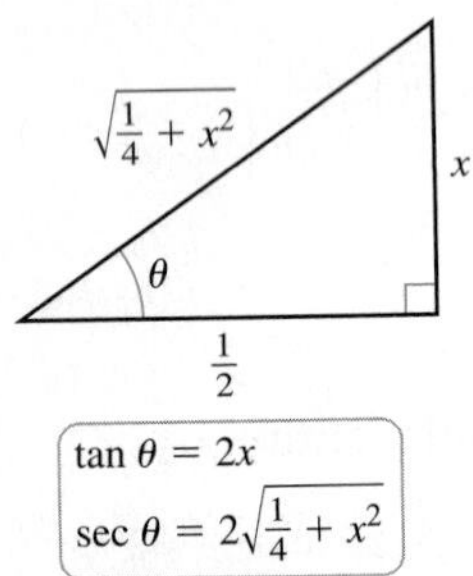

$\tan\theta = 2x$

$\sec\theta = 2\sqrt{\frac{1}{4} + x^2}$

FIGURE 8.8

Using a reference triangle (Figure 8.8), we express the antiderivative in terms of the original variable x and evaluate the definite integral:

$$2\int_0^2 \sqrt{\left(\tfrac{1}{2}\right)^2 + x^2}\,dx = \frac{1}{4}\left(\underbrace{2\sqrt{\tfrac{1}{4} + x^2}}_{\sec\theta}\,\underbrace{2x}_{\tan\theta} + \ln\left|\underbrace{2\sqrt{\tfrac{1}{4} + x^2}}_{\sec\theta} + \underbrace{2x}_{\tan\theta}\right|\right)\Bigg|_0^2 \qquad \tan\theta = 2x,\ \sec\theta = 2\sqrt{\tfrac{1}{4} + x^2}$$

$$= \frac{1}{4}\left(4\sqrt{17} + \ln(\sqrt{17} + 4)\right) \approx 4.65$$

Related Exercises 15–46 ◄

QUICK CHECK 3 The integral $\int \frac{dx}{a^2 + x^2} = \frac{1}{a}\tan^{-1}\frac{x}{a} + C$ was given in Section 7.5. Verify this result with the appropriate trigonometric substitution. ◄

EXAMPLE 4 **Another tangent substitution** Evaluate $\int \frac{dx}{(1 + x^2)^2}$.

SOLUTION The factor $1 + x^2$ suggests the substitution $x = \tan\theta$. It follows that $dx = \sec^2\theta\,d\theta$ and

$$(1 + x^2)^2 = (1 + \tan^2\theta)^2 = \sec^4\theta.$$

Substituting these factors leads to

$$\int \frac{dx}{(1 + x^2)^2} = \int \frac{\sec^2\theta}{\sec^4\theta}\,d\theta \qquad x = \tan\theta,\ dx = \sec^2\theta\,d\theta$$

$$= \int \cos^2\theta\,d\theta \qquad \text{Simplify.}$$

$$= \left(\frac{\theta}{2} + \frac{\sin 2\theta}{4}\right) + C \qquad \text{Integrate } \cos^2\theta = \frac{1 + \cos 2\theta}{2}.$$

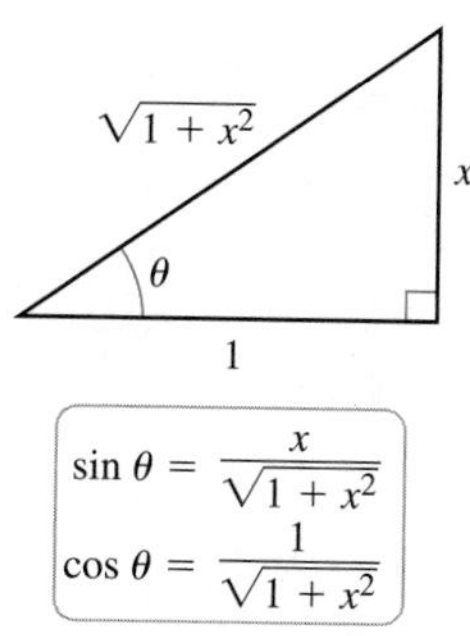

$\sin\theta = \dfrac{x}{\sqrt{1+x^2}}$

$\cos\theta = \dfrac{1}{\sqrt{1+x^2}}$

FIGURE 8.9

The final step is to return to the original variable x. The first term $\theta/2$ is replaced by $\frac{1}{2}\tan^{-1} x$. The second term involving $\sin 2\theta$ requires the identity $\sin 2\theta = 2\sin\theta\cos\theta$. The reference triangle (Figure 8.9) tells us that

$$\frac{1}{4}\sin 2\theta = \frac{1}{2}\sin\theta\cos\theta = \frac{1}{2}\cdot\frac{x}{\sqrt{1+x^2}}\cdot\frac{1}{\sqrt{1+x^2}} = \frac{1}{2}\cdot\frac{x}{1+x^2}.$$

The integration can now be completed:

$$\int\frac{dx}{(1+x^2)^2} = \left(\frac{\theta}{2}+\frac{\sin 2\theta}{4}\right)+C$$

$$= \frac{1}{2}\tan^{-1}x + \frac{x}{2(1+x^2)} + C$$

Related Exercises 15–46 ◂

EXAMPLE 5 A secant substitution Evaluate $\displaystyle\int_1^4 \frac{\sqrt{x^2+4x-5}}{x+2}\,dx.$

➤ Recall that to complete the square with x^2+bx+c, you add and subtract $(b/2)^2$ to the expression, and then factor to form a perfect square. You could also make the single substitution $x+2=3\sec\theta$ in Example 5.

SOLUTION This example illustrates a useful preliminary step before making a trigonometric substitution. The integrand does not contain any of the patterns in Table 8.3 that suggest a trigonometric substitution. Completing the square does, however, lead to one of those patterns. Noting that $x^2+4x-5=(x+2)^2-9$, we change variables with $u=x+2$ and write the integral as

$$\int_1^4\frac{\sqrt{x^2+4x-5}}{x+2}\,dx = \int_1^4\frac{\sqrt{(x+2)^2-9}}{x+2}\,dx \quad \text{Complete the square.}$$

$$= \int_3^6\frac{\sqrt{u^2-9}}{u}\,du \quad u=x+2,\ du=dx \text{ Change limits of integration.}$$

➤ The substitution $u=3\sec\theta$ can be rewritten as $\theta=\sec^{-1}(u/3)$. Because $u\ge 3$ in the integral $\displaystyle\int_3^6\frac{\sqrt{u^2-9}}{u}\,du$, we have $0\le\theta<\dfrac{\pi}{2}$.

This new integral calls for the secant substitution $u=3\sec\theta$ (where $0\le\theta<\pi/2$), which implies that $du=3\sec\theta\tan\theta\,d\theta$ and $\sqrt{u^2-9}=3\tan\theta$. We also change the limits of integration: When $u=3,\theta=0$, and when $u=6,\theta=\pi/3$. The complete integration can now be done:

$$\int_1^4\frac{\sqrt{x^2+4x-5}}{x+2}\,dx = \int_3^6\frac{\sqrt{u^2-9}}{u}\,du \quad u=x+2,\ du=dx$$

$$= \int_0^{\pi/3}\frac{3\tan\theta}{3\sec\theta}\,3\sec\theta\tan\theta\,d\theta \quad u=3\sec\theta,\ du=3\sec\theta\tan\theta\,d\theta$$

$$= 3\int_0^{\pi/3}\tan^2\theta\,d\theta \quad \text{Simplify.}$$

$$= 3\int_0^{\pi/3}(\sec^2\theta-1)\,d\theta \quad \tan^2\theta=\sec^2\theta-1$$

$$= 3(\tan\theta-\theta)\Big|_0^{\pi/3} \quad \text{Evaluate integrals.}$$

$$= 3\sqrt{3}-\pi \quad \text{Simplify.}$$

Related Exercises 15–46 ◂

SECTION 8.3 EXERCISES

Review Questions

1. What change of variables is suggested by an integral containing $\sqrt{x^2 - 9}$?
2. What change of variables is suggested by an integral containing $\sqrt{x^2 + 36}$?
3. What change of variables is suggested by an integral containing $\sqrt{100 - x^2}$?
4. If $x = 4 \tan \theta$, express $\sin \theta$ in terms of x.
5. If $x = 2 \sin \theta$, express $\cot \theta$ in terms of x.
6. If $x = 8 \sec \theta$, express $\tan \theta$ in terms of x.

Basic Skills

7–10. *Evaluate the following integrals.*

7. $\displaystyle\int_0^{5/2} \frac{dx}{\sqrt{25 - x^2}}$

8. $\displaystyle\int_0^{3/2} \frac{dx}{(9 - x^2)^{3/2}}$

9. $\displaystyle\int_5^{10} \sqrt{100 - x^2}\, dx$

10. $\displaystyle\int_0^{\sqrt{2}} \frac{x^2}{\sqrt{4 - x^2}}\, dx$

11–14. *Evaluate the following integrals.*

11. $\displaystyle\int \frac{dx}{(16 - x^2)^{1/2}}$

12. $\displaystyle\int \sqrt{36 - x^2}\, dx$

13. $\displaystyle\int \frac{\sqrt{9 - x^2}}{x}\, dx$

14. $\displaystyle\int (36 - 9x^2)^{-3/2}\, dx$

15–40. *Evaluate the following integrals.*

15. $\displaystyle\int \sqrt{64 - x^2}\, dx$

16. $\displaystyle\int \frac{dx}{\sqrt{x^2 - 49}},\ x > 7$

17. $\displaystyle\int \frac{dx}{\sqrt{36 - x^2}}$

18. $\displaystyle\int \frac{dx}{\sqrt{16 + 4x^2}}$

19. $\displaystyle\int \frac{dx}{\sqrt{x^2 - 81}},\ x > 9$

20. $\displaystyle\int \frac{dx}{\sqrt{1 - 2x^2}}$

21. $\displaystyle\int \frac{dx}{(1 + 4x^2)^{3/2}}$

22. $\displaystyle\int \frac{dx}{(x^2 - 36)^{3/2}},\ x > 6$

23. $\displaystyle\int \frac{x^2}{\sqrt{16 - x^2}}\, dx$

24. $\displaystyle\int \frac{dx}{(81 + x^2)^2}$

25. $\displaystyle\int \frac{\sqrt{x^2 - 9}}{x}\, dx,\ x > 3$

26. $\displaystyle\int \sqrt{9 - 4x^2}\, dx$

27. $\displaystyle\int \frac{x^2}{\sqrt{4 + x^2}}\, dx$

28. $\displaystyle\int \frac{\sqrt{4x^2 - 1}}{x^2}\, dx,\ x > \frac{1}{2}$

29. $\displaystyle\int \frac{dx}{\sqrt{3 - 2x - x^2}}$

30. $\displaystyle\int \frac{x^4}{1 + x^2}\, dx$

31. $\displaystyle\int \frac{\sqrt{9x^2 - 25}}{x^3}\, dx,\ x > \frac{5}{3}$

32. $\displaystyle\int \frac{\sqrt{9 - x^2}}{x^2}\, dx$

33. $\displaystyle\int \frac{x^2}{(25 + x^2)^2}\, dx$

34. $\displaystyle\int \frac{dx}{x^2\sqrt{9x^2 - 1}},\ x > \frac{1}{3}$

35. $\displaystyle\int \frac{x^2}{(100 - x^2)^{3/2}}\, dx$

36. $\displaystyle\int \frac{dx}{x^3\sqrt{x^2 - 100}},\ x > 10$

37. $\displaystyle\int \frac{x^3}{(81 - x^2)^2}\, dx$

38. $\displaystyle\int \frac{dx}{x^3\sqrt{x^2 - 1}},\ x > 1$

39. $\displaystyle\int \frac{dx}{x(x^2 - 1)^{3/2}},\ x > 1$

40. $\displaystyle\int \frac{x^3}{(x^2 - 16)^{3/2}}\, dx,\ x < -4$

41–46. Evaluating definite integrals *Evaluate the following definite integrals.*

41. $\displaystyle\int_0^1 \frac{dx}{\sqrt{x^2 + 16}}$

42. $\displaystyle\int_{8\sqrt{2}}^{16} \frac{dx}{\sqrt{x^2 - 64}}$

43. $\displaystyle\int_0^{1/3} \frac{dx}{(9x^2 + 1)^{3/2}}$

44. $\displaystyle\int_{10/\sqrt{3}}^{10} \frac{dx}{\sqrt{x^2 - 25}}$

45. $\displaystyle\int_{4/\sqrt{3}}^{4} \frac{dx}{x^2(x^2 - 4)}$

46. $\displaystyle\int_6^{6\sqrt{3}} \frac{x^2}{(x^2 + 36)^2}\, dx$

Further Explorations

47. **Explain why or why not** Determine whether the following statements are true and give an explanation or counterexample.
    a. If $x = 4 \tan \theta$, then $\csc \theta = 4/x$.
    b. The integral $\int_1^2 \sqrt{1 - x^2}\, dx$ does not have a finite real value.
    c. The integral $\int_1^2 \sqrt{x^2 - 1}\, dx$ does not have a finite real value.
    d. The integral $\displaystyle\int \frac{dx}{x^2 + 4x + 9}$ cannot be evaluated using a trigonometric substitution.

48–55. Completing the square *Evaluate the following integrals.*

48. $\displaystyle\int \frac{dx}{x^2 - 2x + 10}$

49. $\displaystyle\int \frac{dx}{x^2 + 6x + 18}$

50. $\displaystyle\int \frac{dx}{2x^2 - 12x + 36}$

51. $\displaystyle\int \frac{x^2 - 2x + 1}{\sqrt{x^2 - 2x + 10}}\, dx$

52. $\displaystyle\int \frac{x^2 + 2x + 4}{\sqrt{x^2 - 4x}}\, dx,\ x > 4$

53. $\displaystyle\int \frac{x^2 - 8x + 16}{(9 + 8x - x^2)^{3/2}}\, dx$

54. $\displaystyle\int_1^4 \frac{dx}{x^2 - 2x + 10}$

55. $\displaystyle\int_{1/2}^{(\sqrt{2}+3)/(2\sqrt{2})} \frac{dx}{8x^2 - 8x + 11}$

56. Area of an ellipse The upper half of the ellipse centered at the origin with axes of length $2a$ and $2b$ is described by $y = \frac{b}{a}\sqrt{a^2 - x^2}$ (see figure). Find the area of the ellipse in terms of a and b.

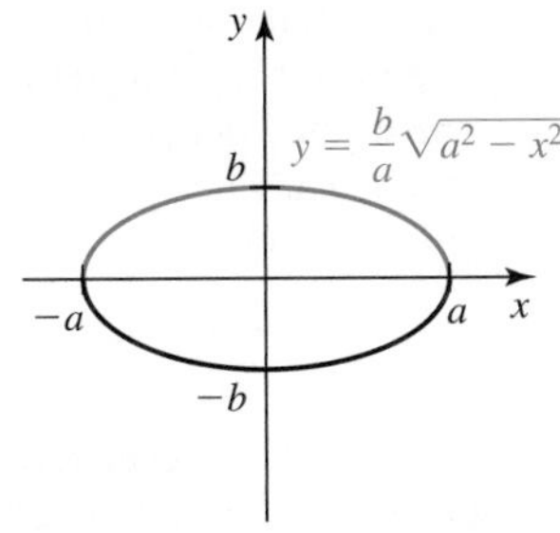

57. Area of a segment of a circle Use two approaches to show that the area of a cap (or segment) of a circle of radius r subtended by an angle θ (see figure) is given by

$$A_{\text{seg}} = \frac{1}{2} r^2 (\theta - \sin\theta).$$

a. Find the area using geometry (no calculus).
b. Find the area using calculus.

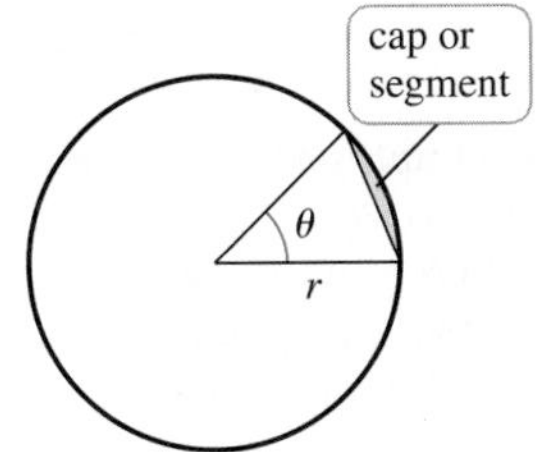

58. Area of a lune A lune is a crescent-shaped region bounded by the arcs of two circles. Let C_1 be a circle of radius 4 centered at the origin. Let C_2 be a circle of radius 3 centered at the point $(2, 0)$. Find the area of the lune (shaded in the figure) that lies inside C_1 and outside C_2.

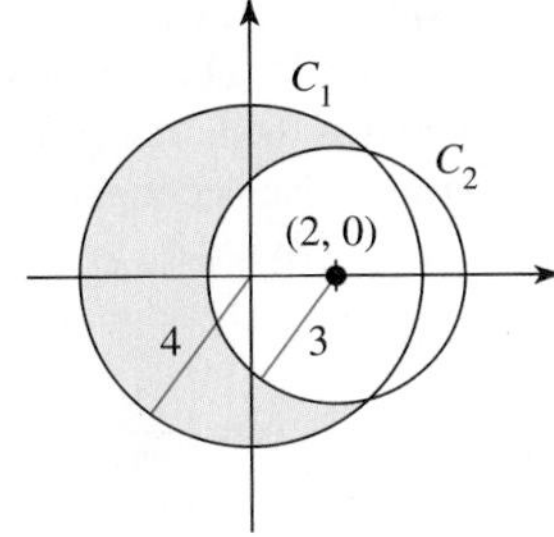

59. Area and volume Consider the function $f(x) = (9 + x^2)^{-1/2}$ and the region R on the interval $[0, 4]$ (see figure).

a. Find the area of R.
b. Find the volume of the solid generated when R is revolved about the x-axis.
c. Find the volume of the solid generated when R is revolved about the y-axis.

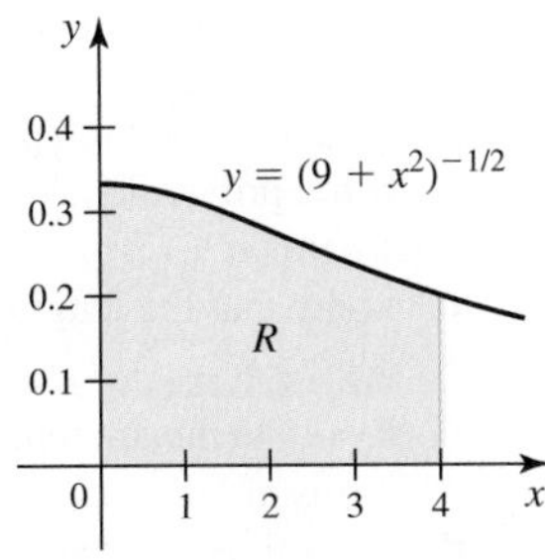

T **60. Area of a region** Graph the function $f(x) = (16 + x^2)^{-3/2}$ and find the area of the region bounded by the curve and the x-axis on the interval $[0, 3]$.

61. Arc length of a parabola Find the length of the curve $y = ax^2$ from $x = 0$ to $x = 10$, where $a > 0$ is a real number.

62. Comparing areas On the interval $[0, 2]$, the graphs of $f(x) = x^2/3$ and $g(x) = x^2(9 - x^2)^{-1/2}$ have similar shapes.

a. Find the area of the region bounded by the graph of f and the x-axis on the interval $[0, 2]$.
b. Find the area of the region bounded by the graph of g and the x-axis on the interval $[0, 2]$.
c. Which region has the greater area?

T **63–65. Using the integral of $\sec^3 u$** *By reduction formula 4 in Section 8.2,*

$$\int \sec^3 u\, du = \frac{1}{2}\left(\sec u \tan u + \ln|\sec u + \tan u|\right) + C.$$

Graph the following functions and find the area under the curve on the given interval.

63. $f(x) = (9 - x^2)^{-2}$, $\left[0, \frac{3}{2}\right]$

64. $f(x) = (4 + x^2)^{1/2}$, $[0, 2]$

65. $f(x) = (x^2 - 25)^{1/2}$, $[5, 10]$

66–67. Asymmetric integrands *Evaluate the following integrals. Consider completing the square.*

66. $\displaystyle\int \frac{dx}{\sqrt{(x - 1)(3 - x)}}$

67. $\displaystyle\int_{2+\sqrt{2}}^{4} \frac{dx}{\sqrt{(x - 1)(x - 3)}}$

68. Clever substitution Evaluate $\displaystyle\int \frac{dx}{1 + \sin x + \cos x}$ using the substitution $x = 2\tan^{-1}\theta$. The identities $\sin x = 2\sin\frac{x}{2}\cos\frac{x}{2}$ and $\cos x = \cos^2\frac{x}{2} - \sin^2\frac{x}{2}$ are helpful.

Applications

69. A torus (doughnut) Find the volume of the solid torus formed when the circle of radius 4 centered at $(0, 6)$ is revolved about the x-axis.

70. Bagel wars Bob and Bruce bake bagels (shaped like tori). They both make standard bagels that have an inner radius of 0.5 in and an outer radius of 2.5 in. Bob plans to increase the volume of his bagels by decreasing the inner radius by 20% (leaving the outer radius unchanged). Bruce plans to increase the volume of his bagels by increasing the outer radius by 20% (leaving the inner radius unchanged). Whose new bagels will have the greater volume? Does this result depend on the size of the original bagels? Explain.

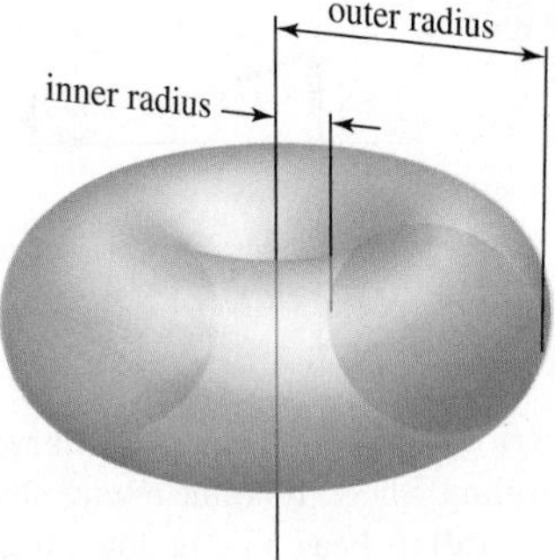

71. Electric field due to a line of charge A total charge of Q is distributed uniformly on a line segment of length $2L$ along the y-axis (see figure). The x-component of the electric field at a point $(a, 0)$ on the x-axis is given by

$$E_x(a) = \frac{kQa}{2L}\int_{-L}^{L} \frac{dy}{(a^2 + y^2)^{3/2}},$$

where k is a physical constant and $a > 0$.

a. Confirm that $E_x(a) = \dfrac{kQ}{a\sqrt{a^2 + L^2}}$.

b. Letting $\rho = Q/2L$ be the charge density on the line segment, show that if $L \to \infty$, then $E_x(a) = 2k\rho/a$.

(See the Guided Projects for a derivation of this and other similar integrals.)

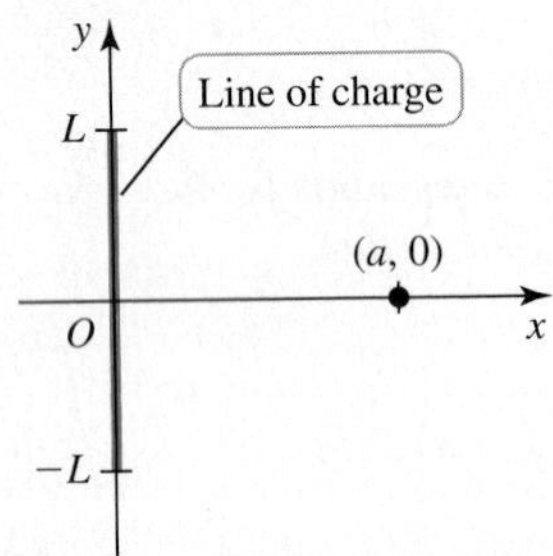

72. Magnetic field due to current in a straight wire A long straight wire of length $2L$ on the y-axis carries a current I. According to the Biot-Savart Law, the magnitude of the magnetic field due to the current at a point $(a, 0)$ is given by

$$B(a) = \frac{\mu_0 I}{4\pi}\int_{-L}^{L} \frac{\sin\theta}{r^2}\,dy,$$

where μ_0 is a physical constant, $a > 0$, and θ, r, and y are related as shown in the figure.

a. Show that the magnitude of the magnetic field at $(a, 0)$ is $B(a) = \dfrac{\mu_0 IL}{2\pi a\sqrt{a^2 + L^2}}$.

b. What is the magnitude of the magnetic field at $(a, 0)$ due to an infinitely long wire $(L \to \infty)$?

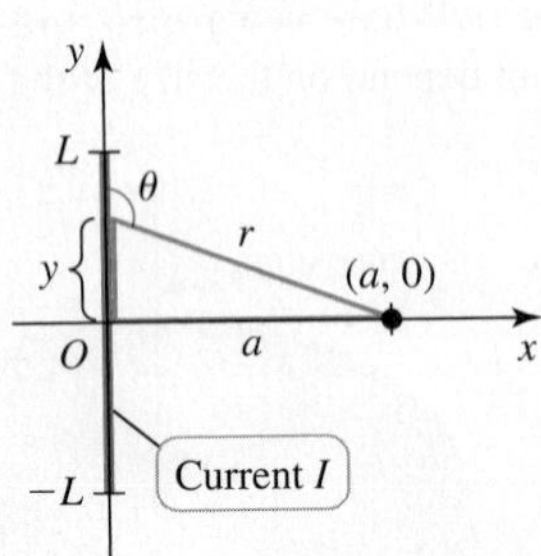

73. Fastest descent time The cycloid is the curve traced by a point on the rim of a rolling wheel. Imagine a wire shaped like an inverted cycloid (see figure). A bead sliding down this wire without friction has some remarkable properties. Among all wire shapes, the cycloid is the shape that produces the fastest descent time (see the Guided Project *The Amazing Cycloid* for more about this *brachistochrone property*). It can be shown that the descent time between any two points $0 \le a \le b \le \pi$ on the curve is

$$\text{descent time} = \int_a^b \sqrt{\frac{1 - \cos t}{g(\cos a - \cos t)}}\,dt,$$

where g is the acceleration due to gravity, $t = 0$ corresponds to the top of the wire, and $t = \pi$ corresponds to the lowest point on the wire.

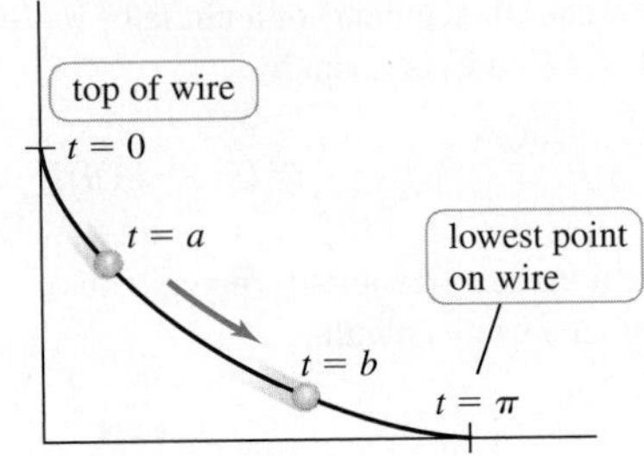

a. Find the descent time on the interval $[a, b]$ by making the substitution $u = \cos t$.

b. Show that when $b = \pi$, the descent time is the same for all values of a; that is, the descent time to the bottom of the wire is the same for all starting points.

T 74. Maximum path length of a projectile (Adapted from Putnam Exam 1940) A projectile is launched from the ground with an initial speed V at an angle θ from the horizontal. Assume that the x-axis is the horizontal ground and y is the height above the ground. Neglecting air resistance and letting g be the acceleration due to gravity, it can be shown that the trajectory of the projectile is given by

$$y = -\frac{1}{2}kx^2 + y_{\max}, \quad \text{where} \quad k = \frac{g}{(V\cos\theta)^2}$$

$$\text{and} \quad y_{\max} = \frac{(V\sin\theta)^2}{2g}.$$

a. Note that the high point of the trajectory occurs at $(0, y_{\max})$. If the projectile is on the ground at $(-a, 0)$ and $(a, 0)$, what is a?

b. Show that the length of the trajectory (arc length) is $2\int_0^a \sqrt{1 + k^2x^2}\,dx$.

c. Evaluate the arc length integral and express your result in terms of V, g, and θ.

d. For a fixed value of V and g, show that the launch angle θ that maximizes the length of the trajectory satisfies $(\sin\theta)\ln(\sec\theta + \tan\theta) = 1$.

e. Use a graphing utility to approximate the optimal launch angle.

Additional Exercises

T 75–78. Care with the secant substitution *Recall that the substitution $x = a\sec\theta$ implies that $x \ge a$ (in which case $0 \le \theta < \pi/2$ and $\tan\theta \ge 0$) or $x \le -a$ (in which case $\pi/2 < \theta \le \pi$ and $\tan\theta \le 0$).*

75. Show that

$$\int \frac{dx}{x\sqrt{x^2-1}} = \begin{cases} \sec^{-1} x + C = \tan^{-1}\sqrt{x^2-1} + C & \text{if } x > 1 \\ -\sec^{-1} x + C = -\tan^{-1}\sqrt{x^2-1} + C & \text{if } x < -1 \end{cases}$$

76. Evaluate for $\int \frac{\sqrt{x^2-1}}{x^3}\,dx$ for $x > 1$ and for $x < -1$.

77. Graph the function $f(x) = \frac{\sqrt{x^2-9}}{x}$ and consider the region bounded by the curve and the x-axis on $[-6, -3]$. Then, evaluate $\int_{-6}^{-3} \frac{\sqrt{x^2-9}}{x}\,dx$. Be sure the result is consistent with the graph.

78. Graph the function $f(x) = \frac{1}{x\sqrt{x^2-36}}$ on its domain. Then, find the area of the region R_1 bounded by the curve and the x-axis on $[-12, -12/\sqrt{3}]$ and the region R_2 bounded by the curve and the x-axis on $[12/\sqrt{3}, 12]$. Be sure your results are consistent with the graph.

79. Visual Proof Let $F(x) = \int_0^x \sqrt{a^2 - t^2}\,dt$. The figure shows that $F(x)$ = area of sector OAB + area of triangle OBC.

a. Use the figure to prove that

$$F(x) = \frac{a^2 \sin^{-1}(x/a)}{2} + \frac{x\sqrt{a^2-x^2}}{2}.$$

b. Conclude that

$$\int \sqrt{a^2 - x^2}\,dx = \frac{a^2 \sin^{-1}(x/a)}{2} + \frac{x\sqrt{a^2-x^2}}{2} + C.$$

[*Source: The College Mathematics Journal* 34, no. 3 (May 2003)]

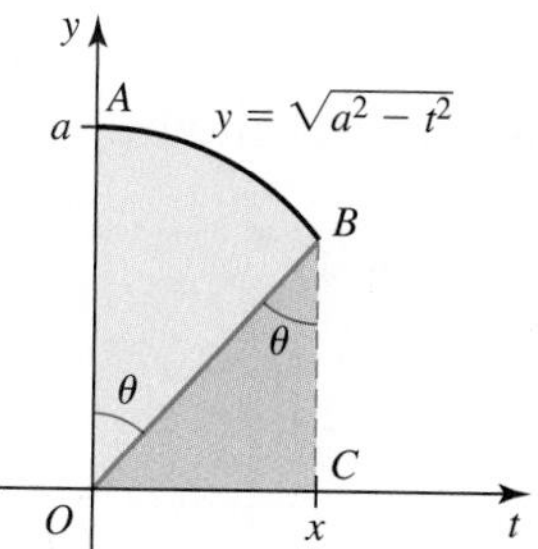

QUICK CHECK ANSWERS

1. Use $x = 3\sin\theta$ to obtain $9\cos^2\theta$. **2.** (a) Use $x = 3\tan\theta$. (b) Use $x = 4\sin\theta$. **3.** Let $x = a\tan\theta$, so that $dx = a\sec^2\theta\,d\theta$. The new integral is $\int \frac{a\sec^2\theta\,d\theta}{a^2(1+\tan^2\theta)} = \frac{1}{a}\int d\theta = \frac{1}{a}\theta + C = \frac{1}{a}\tan^{-1}\frac{x}{a} + C.$

8.4 Partial Fractions

Later in this chapter, we will see that finding the velocity of a skydiver requires evaluating an integral of the form $\int \frac{dv}{a - bv^2}$, where a and b are constants. Similarly, finding the population of a species that is limited in size involves an integral of the form $\int \frac{dP}{aP(1-bP)}$, where a and b are constants. These integrals have the common feature that their integrands are rational functions. Similar integrals result from modeling mechanical and electrical networks. The goal of this section is to introduce the *method of partial fractions* for integrating rational functions. When combined with standard and trigonometric substitutions, this method allows us (in principle) to integrate any rational function.

➤ Recall that a rational function has the form p/q, where p and q are polynomials.

Method of Partial Fractions

Given a function such as

$$f(x) = \frac{1}{x-2} + \frac{2}{x+4},$$

it is a straightforward task to find a common denominator and write the equivalent expression

$$f(x) = \frac{(x+4) + 2(x-2)}{(x-2)(x+4)} = \frac{3x}{(x-2)(x+4)} = \frac{3x}{x^2+2x-8}.$$

The purpose of partial fractions is to reverse this process. Given a rational function that is difficult to integrate, the method of partial fractions produces an equivalent function that is much easier to integrate.

rational function — *method of partial fractions* → *partial fraction decomposition*

$$\frac{3x}{(x-2)(x+4)} = \frac{3x}{x^2+2x-8} \longrightarrow \frac{1}{x-2} + \frac{2}{x+4}$$

Difficult to integrate: $\int \frac{3x}{x^2+2x-8}\,dx$

Easy to integrate: $\int \left(\frac{1}{x-2} + \frac{2}{x+4}\right) dx$

QUICK CHECK 1 Find an antiderivative of $f(x) = \frac{1}{x-2} + \frac{2}{x+4}$.

The Key Idea Working with the same function, $f(x) = \frac{3x}{(x-2)(x+4)}$, our objective is to write it in the form

$$\frac{A}{x-2} + \frac{B}{x+4}$$

where A and B are constants to be determined. This expression is called the **partial fraction decomposition** of the original function; in this case, it has two terms, one for each factor in the denominator of the original function.

> Notice that the numerator of the original rational function does not affect the form of the partial fraction decomposition. The constants A and B are called *undetermined coefficients*.

The constants A and B are determined using the condition that the original function f and its partial fraction decomposition must be equal for all values of x; that is,

$$\frac{3x}{(x-2)(x+4)} = \frac{A}{x-2} + \frac{B}{x+4}. \quad (1)$$

Multiplying both sides of equation (1) by $(x-2)(x+4)$ gives

$$3x = A(x+4) + B(x-2).$$

> This step requires that $x \neq 2$ and $x \neq -4$; both values are outside the domain of f.

Collecting like powers of x results in

$$3x = (A+B)x + (4A - 2B). \quad (2)$$

If equation (2) is to hold for all values of x, then

- the coefficients of x^1 on both sides of the equation must match;
- the coefficients of x^0 (that is, the constants) on both sides of the equation must match.

$$3x + 0 = (A+B)x + (4A - 2B)$$

This observation leads to two equations for A and B.

Match coefficients of x^1: $\quad 3 = A + B$

Match coefficients of x^0: $\quad 0 = 4A - 2B$

The first equation says that $A = 3 - B$. Substituting $A = 3 - B$ into the second equation gives the equation $0 = 4(3 - B) - 2B$. Solving for B, we find that $6B = 12$, or $B = 2$. The value of A now follows; we have $A = 3 - B = 1$.

Substituting these values of A and B into equation (1), the partial fraction decomposition is

$$\frac{3x}{(x-2)(x+4)} = \frac{1}{x-2} + \frac{2}{x+4}.$$

Simple Linear Factors

The previous example illustrates the case of **simple linear factors**; this means the denominator of the original function consists only of linear factors of the form $(x - r)$, which appear to the first power and no higher power. Here is the general procedure for this case.

> Like a fraction, a rational function is said to be in **reduced form** if the numerator and denominator have no common factors and it is said to be **proper** if the degree of the numerator is less than the degree of the denominator.

PROCEDURE Partial Fractions with Simple Linear Factors

Suppose $f(x) = p(x)/q(x)$, where p and q are polynomials with no common factors and with the degree of p less than the degree of q. Assume that q is the product of simple linear factors. The partial fraction decomposition is obtained as follows.

Step 1. Factor the denominator q in the form $(x - r_1)(x - r_2)\cdots(x - r_n)$, where $r_1, \ldots, r_n$ are real numbers.

Step 2. Partial fraction decomposition Form the partial fraction decomposition by writing

$$\frac{p(x)}{q(x)} = \frac{A_1}{(x - r_1)} + \frac{A_2}{(x - r_2)} + \cdots + \frac{A_n}{(x - r_n)}.$$

Step 3. Clear denominators Multiply both sides of the equation in Step 2 by $q(x) = (x - r_1)(x - r_2)\cdots(x - r_n)$, which produces conditions for $A_1, \ldots, A_n$.

Step 4. Solve for coefficients Match like powers of x in Step 3 to solve for the undetermined coefficients $A_1, \ldots, A_n$.

QUICK CHECK 2 If the denominator of a rational function is $(x - 1)(x + 5)(x - 10)$, what is the general form of its partial fraction decomposition?

EXAMPLE 1 Integrating with partial fractions

a. Find the partial fraction decomposition for $f(x) = \dfrac{3x^2 + 7x - 2}{x^3 - x^2 - 2x}$.

b. Evaluate $\int f(x)\,dx$.

SOLUTION

a. The partial fraction decomposition is done in four steps.

Step 1: Factoring the denominator, we find that

$$x^3 - x^2 - 2x = x(x + 1)(x - 2)$$

in which only simple linear factors appear.

Step 2: The partial fraction decomposition has one term for each factor in the denominator:

$$\frac{3x^2 + 7x - 2}{x(x + 1)(x - 2)} = \frac{A}{x} + \frac{B}{x + 1} + \frac{C}{x - 2} \qquad (3)$$

The goal is to find the undetermined coefficients A, B, and C.

> You can call the undetermined coefficients $A_1, A_2, A_3, \ldots$ or $A, B, C, \ldots$. The latter may be preferable because it avoids subscripts.

Step 3: We multiply both sides of equation (3) by $x(x + 1)(x - 2)$:

$$\begin{aligned} 3x^2 + 7x - 2 &= A(x + 1)(x - 2) + Bx(x - 2) + Cx(x + 1) \\ &= (A + B + C)x^2 + (-A - 2B + C)x - 2A \end{aligned}$$

Step 4: We now match coefficients of x^2, x^1, and x^0 on both sides of the equation in Step 3.

Match coefficients of x^2: $\quad A + B + C = 3$

Match coefficients of x^1: $\quad -A - 2B + C = 7$

Match coefficients of x^0: $\quad -2A = -2$

The third equation implies that $A = 1$, which is substituted into the first two equations to give

$$B + C = 2 \quad \text{and} \quad -2B + C = 8$$

Solving for B and C, we conclude that $A = 1, B = -2$, and $C = 4$. Substituting the values of A, B, and C into equation (3), the partial fraction decomposition is

$$f(x) = \frac{1}{x} - \frac{2}{x+1} + \frac{4}{x-2}.$$

b. Integration is now straightforward:

$$\int \frac{3x^2 + 7x - 2}{x^3 - x^2 - 2x}\,dx = \int \left(\frac{1}{x} - \frac{2}{x+1} + \frac{4}{x-2}\right) dx \quad \text{Partial fractions}$$

$$= \ln|x| - 2\ln|x+1| + 4\ln|x-2| + K \quad \text{Integrate; arbitrary constant } K.$$

$$= \ln\frac{|x|(x-2)^4}{(x+1)^2} + K \quad \text{Properties of logarithms}$$

Related Exercises 5–18 ◀

A Shortcut Solving for more than three unknown coefficients in a partial fraction decomposition may be difficult. In the case of simple linear factors, a shortcut saves work. In Example 1, Step 3 led to the equation

$$3x^2 + 7x - 2 = A(x+1)(x-2) + Bx(x-2) + Cx(x+1).$$

Because this equation holds for *all* values of x, it must hold for any particular value of x. By choosing values of x judiciously, it is easy to solve for A, B, and C. For example, setting $x = 0$ in this equation results in $-2 = -2A$, or $A = 1$. Setting $x = -1$ results in $-6 = 3B$, or $B = -2$, and setting $x = 2$ results in $24 = 6C$, or $C = 4$. In each case, we choose a value of x that eliminates all but one term on the right side of the equation.

➤ In cases other than simple linear factors, the shortcut can be used to determine some, but not all, of the coefficients, which reduces the work required to find the remaining coefficients.

Repeated Linear Factors

The preceding discussion relies on the assumption that the denominator of the rational function can be factored into simple linear factors of the form $(x - r)$. But what about denominators such as $x^2(x-3)$, or $(x+2)^2(x-4)^3$, in which linear factors are raised to integer powers greater than 1? In these cases we have **repeated linear factors**, and a modification to the previous procedure must be made.

➤ *Simple* means the factor is raised to the first power; *repeated* means the factor is raised to a power higher than the first power.

Here is the modification: Suppose the factor $(x - r)^m$ appears in the denominator, where $m > 1$ is an integer. Then there must be a partial fraction for each power of $(x - r)$ up to and including the mth power. For example, if $x^2(x-3)^4$ appears in the denominator, then the partial fraction decomposition includes the terms

$$\frac{A}{x} + \frac{B}{x^2} + \frac{C}{(x-3)} + \frac{D}{(x-3)^2} + \frac{E}{(x-3)^3} + \frac{F}{(x-3)^4}.$$

➤ Think of x^2 as the repeated linear factor $(x - 0)^2$.

The rest of the partial fraction procedure remains the same, although the amount of work increases as the number of coefficients increases.

PROCEDURE Partial Fractions for Repeated Linear Factors

Suppose the repeated linear factor $(x - r)^m$ appears in the denominator of a proper rational function in reduced form. The partial fraction decomposition has a partial fraction for each power of $(x - r)$ up to and including the mth power; that is, the partial fraction decomposition contains the sum

$$\frac{A_1}{(x-r)} + \frac{A_2}{(x-r)^2} + \frac{A_3}{(x-r)^3} + \cdots + \frac{A_m}{(x-r)^m},$$

where $A_1, \ldots, A_m$ are constants to be determined.

EXAMPLE 2 Integrating with repeated linear factors Evaluate $\int f(x)\,dx$, where $f(x) = \dfrac{5x^2 - 3x + 2}{x^3 - 2x^2}$.

QUICK CHECK 3 State the form of the partial fraction decomposition of the rational function $p(x)/q(x)$ if $q(x) = x^2(x - 3)^2(x - 1)$. ◄

SOLUTION The denominator factors as $x^3 - 2x^2 = x^2(x - 2)$, so it has one simple linear factor $(x - 2)$ and one repeated linear factor x^2. The partial fraction decomposition has the form

$$\frac{5x^2 - 3x + 2}{x^2(x - 2)} = \frac{A}{x} + \frac{B}{x^2} + \frac{C}{(x - 2)}.$$

Multiplying both sides of the partial fraction decomposition by $x^2(x - 2)$, we find

$$\begin{aligned} 5x^2 - 3x + 2 &= Ax(x - 2) + B(x - 2) + Cx^2 \\ &= (A + C)x^2 + (-2A + B)x - 2B \end{aligned}$$

The coefficients A, B, and C are determined by matching the coefficients of x^2, x^1, and x^0:

➤ The shortcut can be used to obtain two of the three coefficients easily. Choosing $x = 0$ allows B to be determined. Choosing $x = 2$ determines C. To find A, any other value of x may be substituted.

Match coefficients of x^2: $\quad A + C = 5$

Match coefficients of x^1: $\quad -2A + B = -3$

Match coefficients of x^0: $\quad -2B = 2$

Solving these three equations in three unknowns results in the solution $A = 1, B = -1$, and $C = 4$. When A, B, and C are substituted, the partial fraction decomposition is

$$f(x) = \frac{1}{x} - \frac{1}{x^2} + \frac{4}{x - 2}.$$

Integration is now straightforward:

$$\begin{aligned} \int \frac{5x^2 - 3x + 2}{x^3 - 2x^2}\,dx &= \int \left(\frac{1}{x} - \frac{1}{x^2} + \frac{4}{x - 2}\right) dx && \text{Partial fractions} \\ &= \ln|x| + \frac{1}{x} + 4\ln|x - 2| + K && \text{Integrate; arbitrary constant } K. \\ &= \frac{1}{x} + \ln\left(|x|(x - 2)^4\right) + K. && \text{Properties of logarithms} \end{aligned}$$

Related Exercises 19–25 ◄

Irreducible Quadratic Factors

➤ The quadratic $ax^2 + bx + c$ has no real roots and cannot be factored over the real numbers if $b^2 - 4ac < 0$.

It is a fact that a polynomial with real-valued coefficients can be written as the product of linear factors of the form $x - r$ and *irreducible quadratic factors* of the form $ax^2 + bx + c$, where r, a, b, and c are real numbers. By irreducible, we mean that $ax^2 + bx + c$ cannot be factored further over the real numbers. For example, the polynomial

$$x^9 + 4x^8 + 6x^7 + 34x^6 + 64x^5 - 84x^4 - 287x^3 - 500x^2 - 354x - 180$$

factors as

$$\underbrace{(x - 2)}_{\text{linear factor}}\underbrace{(x + 3)^2}_{\text{repeated linear factor}}\underbrace{(x^2 - 2x + 10)}_{\text{irreducible quadratic factor}}\underbrace{(x^2 + x + 1)^2}_{\text{repeated irreducible quadratic factor}}.$$

In this factored form, we see linear factors (simple and repeated) and irreducible quadratic factors (simple and repeated).

With irreducible quadratic factors, two cases must be considered: simple and repeated factors. Simple quadratic factors are examined in the following examples, and repeated quadratic factors (which generally involve long computations) are explored in the exercises.

PROCEDURE Partial Fractions with Simple Irreducible Quadratic Factors

Suppose a simple irreducible factor $ax^2 + bx + c$ appears in the denominator of a proper rational function in reduced form. The partial fraction decomposition contains a term of the form

$$\frac{Ax + B}{ax^2 + bx + c}$$

where A and B are unknown coefficients to be determined.

EXAMPLE 3 Setting up partial fractions Give the appropriate form of the partial fraction decomposition for the following functions.

a. $\dfrac{x^2 + 1}{x^4 - 4x^3 - 32x^2}$ **b.** $\dfrac{10}{(x - 2)^2(x^2 + 2x + 2)}$

SOLUTION

a. The denominator factors as $x^2(x^2 - 4x - 32) = x^2(x - 8)(x + 4)$. Therefore, x is a repeated linear factor, and $(x - 8)$ and $(x + 4)$ are simple linear factors. The required form of the decomposition is

$$\frac{A}{x} + \frac{B}{x^2} + \frac{C}{x - 8} + \frac{D}{x + 4}.$$

We see that the factor $x^2 - 4x - 32$ is quadratic, but it can be further factored, so it is not irreducible.

b. The denominator is already fully factored. The quadratic factor $x^2 + 2x + 2$ cannot be factored further using real numbers; therefore, it is irreducible. The form of the decomposition is

$$\frac{A}{x - 2} + \frac{B}{(x - 2)^2} + \frac{Cx + D}{x^2 + 2x + 2}.$$

Related Exercises 26–29 ◀

EXAMPLE 4 Integrating with partial fractions Evaluate

$$\int \frac{7x^2 - 13x + 13}{(x - 2)(x^2 - 2x + 3)}\, dx.$$

SOLUTION The appropriate form of the partial fraction decomposition is

$$\frac{7x^2 - 13x + 13}{(x - 2)(x^2 - 2x + 3)} = \frac{A}{x - 2} + \frac{Bx + C}{x^2 - 2x + 3}.$$

Note that the irreducible quadratic factor requires $Bx + C$ in the numerator of the second fraction. Multiplying both sides of this equation by $(x - 2)(x^2 - 2x + 3)$ leads to

$$\begin{aligned} 7x^2 - 13x + 13 &= A(x^2 - 2x + 3) + (Bx + C)(x - 2) \\ &= (A + B)x^2 + (-2A - 2B + C)x + (3A - 2C) \end{aligned}$$

Matching coefficients of equal powers of x results in the equations

$$A + B = 7 \qquad -2A - 2B + C = -13 \qquad 3A - 2C = 13.$$

Solving this system of equations gives $A = 5$, $B = 2$, and $C = 1$; therefore, the original integral can be written as

$$\int \frac{7x^2 - 13x + 13}{(x - 2)(x^2 - 2x + 3)}\, dx = \int \frac{5}{x - 2}\, dx + \int \frac{2x + 1}{x^2 - 2x + 3}\, dx.$$

Let's work on the second (more difficult) integral. The substitution $u = x^2 - 2x + 3$ would work if $du = (2x - 2)\, dx$ appeared in the numerator. For this reason, we write the numerator as $2x + 1 = (2x - 2) + 3$ and split the integral:

$$\int \frac{2x + 1}{x^2 - 2x + 3}\, dx = \int \frac{2x - 2}{x^2 - 2x + 3}\, dx + \int \frac{3}{x^2 - 2x + 3}\, dx$$

Assembling all the pieces, we have

$$\begin{aligned} &\int \frac{7x^2 - 13x + 13}{(x - 2)(x^2 - 2x + 3)}\, dx \\ &= \int \frac{5}{x - 2}\, dx + \underbrace{\int \frac{2x - 2}{x^2 - 2x + 3}\, dx}_{\text{let } u = x^2 - 2x + 3} + \underbrace{\int \frac{3}{x^2 - 2x + 3}\, dx}_{(x - 1)^2 + 2} \\ &= 5 \ln |x - 2| + \ln |x^2 - 2x + 3| + \frac{3}{\sqrt{2}} \tan^{-1}\left(\frac{x - 1}{\sqrt{2}}\right) + C \qquad \text{Integrate.} \\ &= \ln |(x - 2)^5(x^2 - 2x + 3)| + \frac{3}{\sqrt{2}} \tan^{-1}\left(\frac{x - 1}{\sqrt{2}}\right) + C \qquad \text{Property of logarithms} \end{aligned}$$

To evaluate the last integral $\int \frac{3\, dx}{x^2 - 2x + 3}$, we completed the square in the denominator and used the substitution $u = x - 1$ to produce $\int \frac{3\, du}{u^2 + 2}$, which is a standard form.

Related Exercises 30–36 ◄

Final Note The preceding discussion of partial fraction decomposition assumes that $f(x) = p(x)/q(x)$ is a proper rational function. If this is not the case and we are faced with an improper rational function f, we divide the denominator into the numerator and express f in two parts. One part will be a polynomial, and the other will be a proper rational function. For example, given the function

$$f(x) = \frac{2x^3 + 11x^2 + 28x + 33}{x^2 - x + 6}$$

we perform long division:

$$\begin{array}{r} 2x + 13 \\ x^2 - x + 6 \overline{)\, 2x^3 + 11x^2 + 28x + 33} \\ \underline{2x^3 - 2x^2 + 12x} \qquad \\ 13x^2 + 16x + 33 \\ \underline{13x^2 - 13x + 78} \\ 29x - 45 \end{array}$$

It follows that

$$f(x) = \underbrace{2x + 13}_{\substack{\text{polynomial} \\ \text{easy to} \\ \text{integrate}}} + \underbrace{\frac{29x - 45}{x^2 - x + 6}}_{\substack{\text{apply partial fraction} \\ \text{decomposition}}}.$$

The first piece is easily integrated, and the second piece now qualifies for the methods described in this section.

SUMMARY Partial Fraction Decompositions

Let $f(x) = p(x)/q(x)$ be a proper rational function in reduced form. Assume the denominator q has been factored completely over the real numbers and m is a positive integer.

1. **Simple linear factor** A factor $x - r$ in the denominator requires the partial fraction $\frac{A}{x - r}$.

2. **Repeated linear factor** A factor $(x - r)^m$ with $m > 1$ in the denominator requires the partial fractions
$$\frac{A_1}{(x - r)} + \frac{A_2}{(x - r)^2} + \frac{A_3}{(x - r)^3} + \cdots + \frac{A_m}{(x - r)^m}.$$

3. **Simple irreducible quadratic factor** An irreducible factor $ax^2 + bx + c$ in the denominator requires the partial fraction
$$\frac{Ax + B}{ax^2 + bx + c}.$$

4. **Repeated irreducible quadratic factor** (See Exercises 67–70.) An irreducible factor $(ax^2 + bx + c)^m$ with $m > 1$ in the denominator requires the partial fractions
$$\frac{A_1x + B_1}{ax^2 + bx + c} + \frac{A_2x + B_2}{(ax^2 + bx + c)^2} + \cdots + \frac{A_mx + B_m}{(ax^2 + bx + c)^m}.$$

SECTION 8.4 EXERCISES

Review Questions

1. What kinds of functions can be integrated using partial fraction decomposition?
2. Give an example of each of the following.
   a. A simple linear factor
   b. A repeated linear factor
   c. A simple irreducible quadratic factor
   d. A repeated irreducible quadratic factor
3. What term(s) should appear in the partial fraction decomposition of a proper rational function with each of the following?
   a. A factor of $x - 3$ in the denominator
   b. A factor of $(x - 4)^3$ in the denominator
   c. A factor of $x^2 + 2x + 6$ in the denominator
4. What is the first step in integrating $\frac{x^2 + 2x - 3}{x + 1}$?

Basic Skills

5–8. Setting up partial fraction decomposition *Give the appropriate form of the partial fraction decomposition for the following functions.*

5. $\frac{2}{x^2 - 2x - 8}$
6. $\frac{x - 9}{x^2 - 3x - 18}$
7. $\frac{x^2}{x^3 - 16x}$
8. $\frac{x^2 - 3x}{x^3 - 3x^2 - 4x}$

9–18. Simple linear factors *Evaluate the following integrals.*

9. $\int \frac{dx}{(x - 1)(x + 2)}$
10. $\int \frac{8}{(x - 2)(x + 6)}\,dx$
11. $\int \frac{3}{x^2 - 1}\,dx$
12. $\int \frac{dt}{t^2 - 9}$
13. $\int \frac{2}{x^2 - x - 6}\,dx$
14. $\int \frac{3}{x^3 - x^2 - 12x}\,dx$
15. $\int \frac{dx}{x^2 - 2x - 24}$
16. $\int \frac{y + 1}{y^3 + 3y^2 - 18y}\,dy$
17. $\int \frac{1}{x^4 - 10x^2 + 9}\,dx$
18. $\int \frac{2}{x^2 - 4x - 32}\,dx$

19–25. Repeated linear factors *Evaluate the following integrals.*

19. $\int \frac{3}{x^3 - 9x^2}\,dx$
20. $\int \frac{x}{(x - 6)(x + 2)^2}\,dx$
21. $\int \frac{x}{(x + 3)^2}\,dx$
22. $\int \frac{dx}{x^3 - 2x^2 - 4x + 8}$

23. $\int \frac{2}{x^3 + x^2}\,dx$

24. $\int \frac{2}{t^3(t + 1)}\,dt$

25. $\int \frac{x - 5}{x^2(x + 1)}\,dx$

26–29. Setting up partial fraction decompositions *Give the appropriate form of the partial fraction decomposition for the following functions.*

26. $\frac{2}{x(x^2 - 6x + 9)}$

27. $\frac{20x}{(x - 1)^2(x^2 + 1)}$

28. $\frac{x^2}{x^3(x^2 + 1)}$

29. $\frac{2x^2 + 3}{(x^2 - 8x + 16)(x^2 + 3x + 4)}$

30–36. Simple irreducible quadratic factors *Evaluate the following integrals.*

30. $\int \frac{x^2 + 2}{x(x^2 + 5x + 8)}\,dx$

31. $\int \frac{2}{(x - 4)(x^2 + 2x + 6)}\,dx$

32. $\int \frac{z + 1}{z(z^2 + 4)}\,dz$

33. $\int \frac{x^2}{(x - 1)(x^2 + 4x + 5)}\,dx$

34. $\int \frac{2x + 1}{x^2 + 4}\,dx$

35. $\int \frac{x^2}{x^3 - x^2 + 4x - 4}\,dx$

36. $\int \frac{1}{(y^2 + 1)(y^2 + 2)}\,dy$

Further Explorations

37. Explain why or why not Determine whether the following statements are true and give an explanation or counterexample.

a. To evaluate $\int \frac{4x^6}{x^4 + 3x^2}\,dx$, the first step is to find the partial fraction decomposition of the integrand.

b. The easiest way to evaluate $\int \frac{6x + 1}{3x^2 + x}\,dx$ is with a partial fraction decomposition of the integrand.

c. The rational function $f(x) = \frac{1}{x^2 - 13x + 42}$ has an irreducible quadratic denominator.

d. The rational function $f(x) = \frac{1}{x^2 - 13x + 43}$ has an irreducible quadratic denominator.

T **38–41. Areas of regions** *Find the area of the following regions. In each case, graph the relevant functions and show the region in question.*

38. The region bounded by the curve $y = x/(1 + x)$, the x-axis, and the line $x = 4$.

39. The region bounded by the curve $y = 10/(x^2 - 2x - 24)$, the x-axis, and the lines $x = -2$ and $x = 2$.

40. The region bounded by the curves $y = 1/x$, $y = x/(3x + 4)$, and the line $x = 10$.

41. The region bounded entirely by the curve $y = \frac{x^2 - 4x - 4}{x^2 - 4x - 5}$ and the x-axis.

42–47. Volumes of solids *Find the volume of the following solids.*

42. The region bounded by $y = 1/(x + 1)$, $y = 0$, $x = 0$, and $x = 2$ is revolved about the y-axis.

43. The region bounded by $y = x/(x + 1)$, the x-axis, and $x = 4$ is revolved about the x-axis.

44. The region bounded by $y = (1 - x^2)^{-1/2}$ and $y = 4$ is revolved about the x-axis.

45. The region bounded by $y = \frac{1}{\sqrt{x(3 - x)}}$, $y = 0$, $x = 1$, and $x = 2$ is revolved about the x-axis.

46. The region bounded by $y = \frac{1}{\sqrt{4 - x^2}}$, $y = 0$, $x = -1$, and $x = 1$ is revolved about the x-axis.

47. The region bounded by $y = 1/(x + 2)$, $y = 0$, $x = 0$, and $x = 3$ is revolved about the line $x = -1$.

48. **What's wrong?** Explain why the coefficients A and B cannot be found if we set

$$\frac{x^2}{(x - 4)(x + 5)} = \frac{A}{x - 4} + \frac{B}{x + 5}.$$

49–59. Preliminary steps *The following integrals require a preliminary step such as long division or a change of variables before using partial fractions. Evaluate these integrals.*

49. $\int \frac{dx}{1 + e^x}$

50. $\int \frac{x^4 + 1}{x^3 + 9x}\,dx$

51. $\int \frac{3x^2 + 4x - 6}{x^2 - 3x + 2}\,dx$

52. $\int \frac{2x^3 + x^2 - 6x + 7}{x^2 + x - 6}\,dx$

53. $\int \frac{dt}{2 + e^{-t}}$

54. $\int \frac{dx}{e^x + e^{2x}}$

55. $\int \frac{\sec\theta}{1 + \sin\theta}\,d\theta$

56. $\int \sqrt{e^x + 1}\,dx$

57. $\int \frac{e^x}{(e^x - 1)(e^x + 2)}\,dx$

58. $\int \frac{\cos x}{(\sin^3 x - 4\sin x)}\,dx$

59. $\int \frac{dx}{(e^x + e^{-x})^2}$

60–65. Fractional powers *Use the indicated substitution to convert the given integral to an integral of a rational function. Evaluate the resulting integral.*

60. $\int \frac{dx}{x - \sqrt[3]{x}}$; $x = u^3$

61. $\int \frac{dx}{\sqrt[4]{x + 2} + 1}$; $x + 2 = u^4$

62. $\int \frac{dx}{x\sqrt{1 + 2x}}$; $1 + 2x = u^2$

63. $\int \frac{dx}{\sqrt{x} + \sqrt[3]{x}}$; $x = u^6$

64. $\int \frac{dx}{x - \sqrt[4]{x}}$; $x = u^4$

65. $\int \frac{dx}{\sqrt{1 + \sqrt{x}}}$; $x = (u^2 - 1)^2$

T 66. **Arc length of the natural logarithm** Consider the curve $y = \ln x$.
   a. Find the length of the curve from $x = 1$ to $x = a$ and call it $L(a)$. (*Hint:* The change of variables $u = \sqrt{x^2 + 1}$ allows evaluation by partial fractions.)
   b. Graph $L(a)$.
   c. As a increases, $L(a)$ increases as what power of a?

67–70. Repeated quadratic factors *Refer to the summary box on p. 472 and evaluate the following integrals.*

67. $\int \frac{2}{x(x^2 + 1)^2}\,dx$

68. $\int \frac{dx}{(x + 1)(x^2 + 2x + 2)^2}$

69. $\int \frac{x}{(x - 1)(x^2 + 2x + 2)^2}\,dx$

70. $\int \frac{x^3 + 1}{x(x^2 + x + 1)^2}\,dx$

71. **Two methods** Evaluate $\int \frac{dx}{x^2 - 1}$ for $x > 1$ in two ways: using partial fractions and a trigonometric substitution. Reconcile your two answers.

72–78. Rational functions of trigonometric functions *An integrand with trigonometric functions in the numerator and denominator can often be converted to a rational integrand using the substitution $u = \tan(x/2)$ or $x = 2\tan^{-1} u$. The following relations are used in making this change of variables.*

$$A:\ dx = \frac{2}{1 + u^2}\,du \qquad B:\ \sin x = \frac{2u}{1 + u^2} \qquad C:\ \cos x = \frac{1 - u^2}{1 + u^2}$$

72. Verify relation A by differentiating $x = 2\tan^{-1} u$. Verify relations B and C using a right-triangle diagram and the double-angle formulas

$$\sin x = 2\sin\left(\frac{x}{2}\right)\cos\left(\frac{x}{2}\right) \text{ and } \cos x = 2\cos^2\left(\frac{x}{2}\right) - 1.$$

73. Evaluate $\int \frac{dx}{1 + \sin x}$.

74. Evaluate $\int \frac{dx}{2 + \cos x}$.

75. Evaluate $\int \frac{dx}{1 - \cos x}$.

76. Evaluate $\int \frac{dx}{1 + \sin x + \cos x}$.

77. Evaluate $\int \frac{d\theta}{\cos\theta - \sin\theta}$.

78. Evaluate $\int \sec t\,dt$.

Applications

79. **Three start-ups** Three cars, A, B, and C, start from rest and accelerate along a line according to the following velocity functions:

$$v_A(t) = \frac{88t}{t + 1} \qquad v_B(t) = \frac{88t^2}{(t + 1)^2} \qquad v_C(t) = \frac{88t^2}{t^2 + 1}$$

   a. After $t = 1$ s, which car has traveled farthest?
   b. After $t = 5$ s, which car has traveled farthest?
   c. Find the position functions for the three cars assuming that all cars start at the origin.
   d. Which car ultimately gains the lead and remains in front?

T 80. **Skydiving** A skydiver has a downward velocity given by

$$v(t) = V\left(\frac{1 - e^{-2gt/V}}{1 + e^{-2gt/V}}\right),$$

where $t = 0$ is the instant the skydiver starts falling, $g \approx 9.8\ \text{m/s}^2$ is the acceleration due to gravity, and V is the terminal velocity of the skydiver.
   a. Evaluate $v(0)$ and $\lim_{t\to\infty} v(t)$ and interpret these results.
   b. Graph the velocity function.
   c. Verify by integration that the position function is given by

$$s(t) = Vt + \frac{V^2}{g}\ln\left(\frac{1 + e^{-2gt/V}}{2}\right)$$

   where $s'(t) = v(t)$ and $s(0) = 0$.
   d. Graph the position function.

(See the Guided Projects for more details on free fall and terminal velocity.)

Additional Exercises

81. $\pi < \frac{22}{7}$ One of the earliest approximations to π is $\frac{22}{7}$. Verify that $0 < \int_0^1 \frac{x^4(1 - x)^4}{1 + x^2}\,dx = \frac{22}{7} - \pi$. Why can you conclude that $\pi < \frac{22}{7}$?

82. **Challenge** Show that with the change of variables $u = \sqrt{\tan x}$, the integral $\int \sqrt{\tan x}\,dx$ can be converted to an integral amenable to partial fractions. Evaluate $\int_0^{\pi/4} \sqrt{\tan x}\,dx$.

QUICK CHECK ANSWERS

1. $\ln|x - 2| + 2\ln|x + 4| = \ln|(x - 2)(x + 4)^2|$
2. $A/(x - 1) + B/(x + 5) + C/(x - 10)$
3. $A/x + B/x^2 + C/(x - 3) + D/(x - 3)^2 + E/(x - 1)$ ◀

8.5 Other Integration Strategies

The integration methods studied so far—various substitutions, integration by parts, and partial fractions—are examples of *analytical methods*; they are done with pencil and paper and they give exact results. While many important integrals can be evaluated with analytical methods, many more integrals lie beyond their reach. For example, the following integrals cannot be evaluated in terms of familiar functions:

$$\int e^{x^2}\,dx \qquad \int \sin(x^2)\,dx \qquad \int \frac{\sin x}{x}\,dx \qquad \int \frac{e^{-x}}{x}\,dx \qquad \int \ln(\ln x)\,dx$$

The next two sections survey alternative strategies for evaluating integrals when standard analytical methods do not work. These strategies fall into three categories.

1. **Tables of integrals** The endpapers of this text contain a table of many standard integrals. Because these integrals were evaluated analytically, using tables is considered an analytical method. Tables of integrals also contain reduction formulas like those discussed in Sections 8.1 and 8.2.
2. **Computer algebra systems** Computer algebra systems have elaborate sets of rules to evaluate difficult integrals. Many definite and indefinite integrals can be evaluated exactly with such systems.
3. **Numerical methods** The value of a definite integral can be approximated accurately using numerical methods introduced in the next section. *Numerical* means that these methods compute numbers rather than manipulate symbols. Computers and calculators often have built-in functions to carry out these calculations.

Figure 8.10 is a chart of the various integration strategies and how they are related.

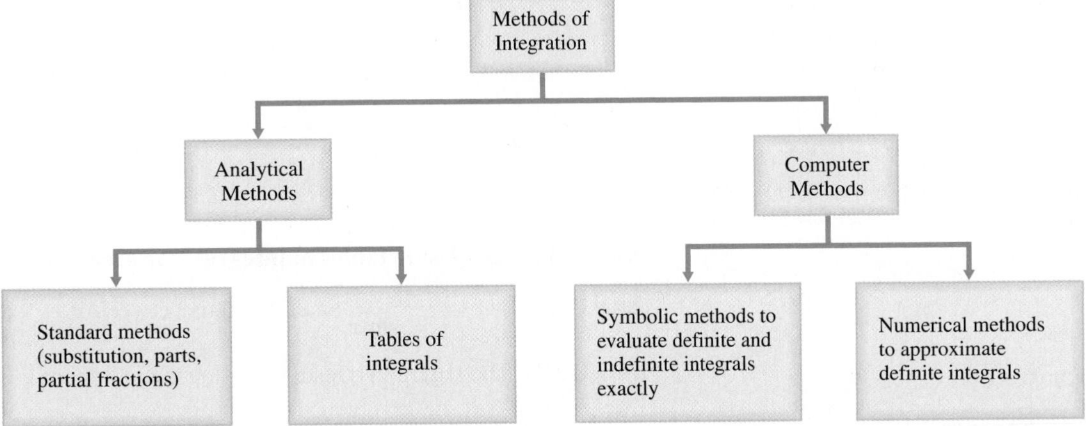

FIGURE 8.10

➤ A short table of integrals can be found at the end of the book. Longer tables of integrals are found online and in venerable collections such as the *CRC Mathematical Tables* and *Handbook of Mathematical Functions*, by Abramowitz and Stegun.

Using Tables of Integrals

Given a specific integral, you *may* be able to find the identical integral in a table of integrals. More likely, some preliminary work is needed to convert the given integral into one that appears in a table. Most tables give only indefinite integrals, although some tables include special definite integrals. The following examples illustrate various ways in which tables of integrals are used.

EXAMPLE 1 **Using tables of integrals** Evaluate the integral $\displaystyle\int \frac{dx}{x\sqrt{2x-9}}$.

➤ Letting $u^2 = 2x - 9$, we have $u\,du = dx$ and $x = \frac{1}{2}(u^2 + 9)$. Therefore,

$$\int \frac{dx}{x\sqrt{2x-9}} = 2\int \frac{du}{u^2+9}.$$

SOLUTION It is worth noting that this integral may be evaluated with the change of variables $u^2 = 2x - 9$. Alternatively, a table of integrals includes the integral

$$\int \frac{dx}{x\sqrt{ax-b}} = \frac{2}{\sqrt{b}} \tan^{-1}\sqrt{\frac{ax-b}{b}} + C, \quad \text{where} \quad b > 0,$$

which matches the given integral. Letting $a = 2$ and $b = 9$, we find that

$$\int \frac{dx}{x\sqrt{2x-9}} = \frac{2}{\sqrt{9}} \tan^{-1}\sqrt{\frac{2x-9}{9}} + C = \frac{2}{3}\tan^{-1}\frac{\sqrt{2x-9}}{3} + C.$$

Related Exercises 5–20 ◄

EXAMPLE 2 **Preliminary work** Evaluate $\int \sqrt{x^2 + 6x}\,dx$.

SOLUTION Most tables of integrals do not include this integral. The nearest integral you are likely to find is $\int \sqrt{x^2 \pm a^2}\,dx$. The given integral can be put into this form by completing the square and using a substitution:

$$x^2 + 6x = x^2 + 6x + 9 - 9 = (x+3)^2 - 9$$

With the change of variables $u = x + 3$, the evaluation appears as follows:

$$\begin{aligned}
\int \sqrt{x^2+6x}\,dx &= \int \sqrt{(x+3)^2 - 9}\,dx && \text{Complete the square.}\\
&= \int \sqrt{u^2-9}\,du && u = x+3,\ du = dx\\
&= \frac{u}{2}\sqrt{u^2-9} - \frac{9}{2}\ln|u + \sqrt{u^2-9}| + C && \text{Table of integrals}\\
&= \frac{x+3}{2}\sqrt{(x+3)^2-9} - \frac{9}{2}\ln|x+3+\sqrt{(x+3)^2-9}| + C\\
&= \frac{x+3}{2}\sqrt{x^2+6x} - \frac{9}{2}\ln|x+3+\sqrt{x^2+6x}| + C.
\end{aligned}$$

Related Exercises 21–32 ◄

EXAMPLE 3 **Using tables of integrals for area** Find the area of the region bounded by the curve $y = \dfrac{1}{1+\sin x}$ and the x-axis between $x = 0$ and $x = \pi$.

SOLUTION The region in question (Figure 8.11) lies entirely above the x-axis, so its area is $\displaystyle\int_0^{\pi} \frac{dx}{1+\sin x}$. A matching integral in a table of integrals is

$$\int \frac{dx}{1+\sin ax} = -\frac{1}{a}\tan\left(\frac{\pi}{4} - \frac{ax}{2}\right) + C.$$

Evaluating the definite integral with $a = 1$, we have

$$\int_0^{\pi} \frac{dx}{1+\sin x} = -\tan\left(\frac{\pi}{4} - \frac{x}{2}\right)\bigg|_0^{\pi} = -\tan\left(-\frac{\pi}{4}\right) - \left(-\tan\frac{\pi}{4}\right) = 2.$$

Related Exercises 33–40 ◄

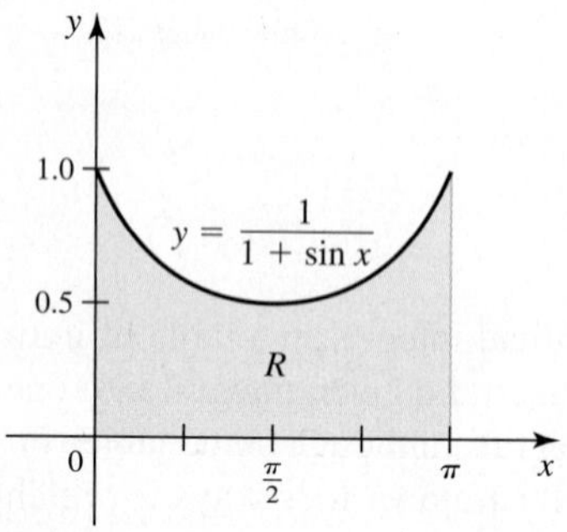

FIGURE 8.11

QUICK CHECK 1 Use the result of Example 3 to evaluate $\displaystyle\int_0^{\pi/2} \frac{dx}{1+\sin x}$. ◄

Using a Computer Algebra System

Computer algebra systems evaluate many integrals exactly using symbolic methods, and they approximate many definite integrals using numerical methods. Different software packages may produce different results for the same indefinite integral; but, ultimately, they must agree. The discussion that follows does not rely on one particular computer algebra system. Rather, it illustrates results from different systems and shows some of the idiosyncrasies of using a computer algebra system.

QUICK CHECK 2 Using one computer algebra system, it was found that $\int \sin x \cos x\, dx = \frac{1}{2}\sin^2 x + C$; using another computer algebra system, it was found that $\int \sin x \cos x\, dx = -\frac{1}{2}\cos^2 x + C$. Reconcile the two answers. ◀

➤ Most computer algebra systems do not include the constant of integration after evaluating an indefinite integral. But, it should always be included when reporting the result.

EXAMPLE 4 Apparent discrepancies Evaluate $\int \frac{dx}{\sqrt{e^x + 1}}$ using tables and a computer algebra system.

SOLUTION Using one particular computer algebra system, we find that

$$\int \frac{dx}{\sqrt{e^x + 1}} = -2\tanh^{-1}\left(\sqrt{e^x + 1}\right) + C,$$

➤ The *hyperbolic tangent* is defined as

$$\tanh x = \frac{e^x - e^{-x}}{e^x + e^{-x}}.$$

Its inverse is the *inverse hyperbolic tangent*, written $\tanh^{-1} x$.

where $\tanh^{-1}$ is the *inverse hyperbolic tangent* function. However, we can obtain a result in terms of more familiar functions by first using the substitution $u = e^x$, which implies that $du = e^x\, dx$ or $dx = du/e^x = du/u$. The integral becomes

$$\int \frac{dx}{\sqrt{e^x + 1}} = \int \frac{du}{u\sqrt{u + 1}}.$$

Using a computer algebra system again, we obtain

➤ Some computer algebra systems use $\log x$ for $\ln x$.

$$\begin{aligned} \int \frac{dx}{\sqrt{e^x + 1}} = \int \frac{du}{u\sqrt{u + 1}} &= \ln\left(\sqrt{1 + u} - 1\right) - \ln\left(\sqrt{1 + u} + 1\right) \\ &= \ln\left(\sqrt{1 + e^x} - 1\right) - \ln\left(\sqrt{1 + e^x} + 1\right). \end{aligned}$$

A table of integrals leads to a third equivalent form of the integral:

$$\begin{aligned} \int \frac{dx}{\sqrt{e^x + 1}} = \int \frac{du}{u\sqrt{u + 1}} &= \ln\left(\frac{\sqrt{u + 1} - 1}{\sqrt{u + 1} + 1}\right) + C \\ &= \ln\left(\frac{\sqrt{e^x + 1} - 1}{\sqrt{e^x + 1} + 1}\right) + C \end{aligned}$$

➤ Some computer algebra systems use $\log x$ for $\ln x$.

Often, the difference between two results is a few steps of algebra or a trigonometric identity. In this case, the final two results are reconciled using logarithm properties. This example illustrates that computer algebra systems generally do not include constants of integration and may omit absolute values when logarithms appear. It is important for the user to determine whether integration constants and absolute values are needed.

Related Exercises 41–56 ◀

QUICK CHECK 3 Using partial fractions, we know that $\int \frac{dx}{x(x + 1)} = \ln\left|\frac{x}{x + 1}\right| + C$. Using a computer algebra system, we find that $\int \frac{dx}{x(x + 1)} = \ln x - \ln(x + 1)$. What is wrong with the result from the computer algebra system? ◀

EXAMPLE 5 **Symbolic vs. numerical integration** Use a computer algebra system to evaluate $\int_0^1 \sin(x^2)\,dx$.

SOLUTION Sometimes a computer algebra system gives the exact value of an integral in terms of an unfamiliar function, or it may not be able to evaluate the integral exactly. For example, one particular computer algebra system returns the result

$$\int_0^1 \sin(x^2)\,dx = \sqrt{\frac{\pi}{2}}\,S\left(\sqrt{\frac{2}{\pi}}\right)$$

where S is a function called the *Fresnel integral function* $\left(S(x) = \int_0^x \sin\left(\frac{\pi t^2}{2}\right)dt\right)$. However, if the computer algebra system is instructed to compute an approximate solution, the result is

$$\int_0^1 \sin(x^2)\,dx \approx 0.3102683017,$$

which is an excellent approximation.

Related Exercises 41–56 ◀

SECTION 8.5 EXERCISES

Review Questions

1. Give some examples of analytical methods for evaluating integrals.

2. Does a computer algebra system give an exact result for an indefinite integral? Explain.

3. Why might an integral found in a table differ from the same integral evaluated by a computer algebra system?

4. Is a reduction formula an analytical method or a numerical method? Explain.

Basic Skills

5–20. Table lookup integrals *Use a table of integrals to evaluate the following indefinite integrals.*

5. $\int \frac{dx}{\sqrt{x^2 + 16}}$

6. $\int \frac{dx}{\sqrt{x^2 - 25}}$

7. $\int \frac{3u}{2u + 7}\,du$

8. $\int \frac{dy}{y(2y + 9)}$

9. $\int \frac{dx}{1 - \cos 4x}$

10. $\int \frac{dx}{x\sqrt{81 - x^2}}$

11. $\int \frac{dx}{\sqrt{4x + 1}}$

12. $\int \sqrt{4x + 12}\,dx$

13. $\int \frac{dx}{\sqrt{9x^2 - 100}}$

14. $\int \frac{dx}{225 - 16x^2}$

15. $\int \frac{dx}{(16 + 9x^2)^{3/2}}$

16. $\int \sqrt{4x^2 - 9}\,dx$

17. $\int \frac{dx}{x\sqrt{144 - x^2}}$

18. $\int \frac{dx}{x(x^3 + 8)}$

19. $\int \frac{dx}{x(x^{10} + 1)}$

20. $\int \frac{dx}{x(x^8 - 256)}$

21–32. Preliminary work *Use a table of integrals to evaluate the following indefinite integrals. These integrals require preliminary work, such as completing the square or changing variables, before they can be found in a table.*

21. $\int \frac{dx}{x^2 + 2x + 10}$

22. $\int \sqrt{x^2 - 4x + 8}\,dx$

23. $\int \frac{dx}{\sqrt{x^2 - 6x}}$

24. $\int \frac{dx}{\sqrt{x^2 + 10x}}$

25. $\int \frac{e^x}{\sqrt{e^{2x} + 4}}\,dx$

26. $\int \frac{\sqrt{\ln^2 x + 4}}{x}\,dx$

27. $\int \frac{\cos x}{\sin^2 x + 2\sin x}\,dx$

28. $\int \frac{\cos^{-1}\sqrt{x}}{\sqrt{x}}\,dx$

29. $\int \frac{\tan^{-1} x^3}{x^4}\,dx$

30. $\int \frac{e^t}{\sqrt{3 + 4e^t}}\,dt$

31. $\int \frac{\ln x \sin^{-1}(\ln x)}{x}\,dx$

32. $\int \frac{dt}{\sqrt{1 + 4e^t}}$

33–40. Geometry problems *Use a table of integrals to solve the following problems.*

33. Find the length of the curve $y = x^2/4$ on the interval $[0, 8]$.

34. Find the length of the curve $y = x^{3/2} + 8$ on the interval $[0, 2]$.

35. Find the length of the curve $y = e^x$ on the interval $[0, \ln 2]$.

36. The region bounded by the graph of $y = 1/(x + 10)$ and the x-axis on the interval $[0, 3]$ is revolved about the x-axis. What is the volume of the solid that is formed?

37. The region bounded by the graph of $y = \frac{1}{\sqrt{x+4}}$ and the x-axis on the interval $[0, 12]$ is revolved about the y-axis. What is the volume of the solid that is formed?

38. Find the area of the region bounded by the graph of $y = \frac{1}{\sqrt{x^2 - 2x + 2}}$ and the x-axis between $x = 0$ and $x = 3$.

39. The region bounded by the graphs of $y = \pi/2$, $y = \sin^{-1} x$, and the y-axis is revolved about the y-axis. What is the volume of the solid that is formed?

40. The graphs of $f(x) = \frac{2}{x^2 + 1}$ and $g(x) = \frac{7}{4\sqrt{x^2 + 1}}$ are shown in the accompanying figure. Which is greater, the average value of f or that of g on the interval $[-1, 1]$?

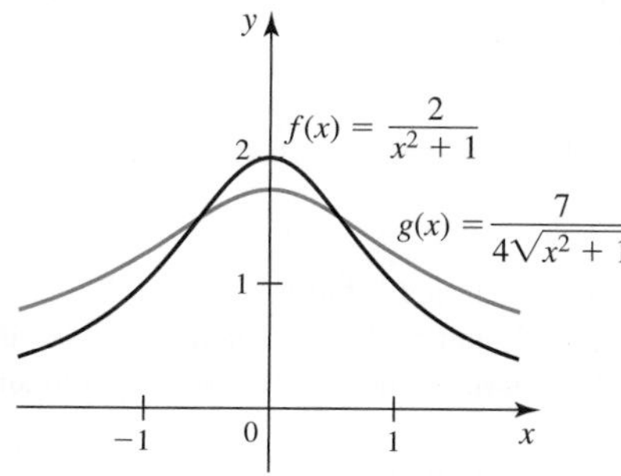

41–48. Indefinite integrals *Use a computer algebra system to evaluate the following indefinite integrals. Assume that a is a positive real number.*

41. $\int \frac{x}{\sqrt{2x + 3}}\,dx$ **42.** $\int \sqrt{4x^2 + 36}\,dx$ **43.** $\int \tan^2 3x\,dx$

44. $\int (a^2 - x^2)^{-2}\,dx$ **45.** $\int \frac{(x^2 - a^2)^{3/2}}{x}\,dx$ **46.** $\int \frac{dx}{x(a^2 - x^2)^2}$

47. $\int (a^2 - x^2)^{3/2}\,dx$ **48.** $\int (x^2 + a^2)^{-5/2}\,dx$

49–56. Definite integrals *Use a computer algebra system to evaluate the following definite integrals. In each case, find an exact value of the integral (obtained by a symbolic method) and find an approximate value (obtained by a numerical method). Compare the results.*

49. $\int_{2/3}^{4/5} x^8\,dx$ **50.** $\int_0^{\pi/2} \cos^6 x\,dx$

51. $\int_0^4 (9 + x^2)^{3/2}\,dx$ **52.** $\int_{1/2}^{1} \frac{\sin^{-1} x}{x}\,dx$

53. $\int_0^{\pi/2} \frac{dx}{1 + \tan^2 x}$ **54.** $\int_0^{2\pi} \frac{dx}{(4 + 2\sin x)^2}$

55. $\int_0^1 \ln x \ln(1 + x)\,dx$ **56.** $\int_0^{\pi/4} \ln(1 + \tan x)\,dx$

Further Explorations

57. Explain why or why not Determine whether the following statements are true and give an explanation or counterexample.

a. It is possible that a computer algebra system says $\int \frac{dx}{x(x-1)} = \ln(x - 1) - \ln x$ and a table of integrals says $\int \frac{dx}{x(x-1)} = \ln\left|\frac{x-1}{x}\right| + C$.

b. A computer algebra system working in symbolic mode could give the result $\int_0^1 x^8\,dx = \frac{1}{9}$, and a computer algebra system working in approximate (numerical) mode could give the result $\int_0^1 x^8\,dx = 0.11111111$.

58. Apparent discrepancy Three different computer algebra systems give the following results:

$$\int \frac{dx}{x\sqrt{x^4 - 1}} = \frac{1}{2}\cos^{-1}\sqrt{x^{-4}} = \frac{1}{2}\cos^{-1} x^{-2} = \frac{1}{2}\tan^{-1}\sqrt{x^4 - 1}.$$

Explain how they can all be correct.

59. Reconciling results Using one computer algebra system, it was found that $\int \frac{dx}{1 + \sin x} = \frac{\sin x - 1}{\cos x}$ and using another computer algebra system, it was found that $\int \frac{dx}{1 + \sin x} = \frac{2\sin(x/2)}{\cos(x/2) + \sin(x/2)}$. Reconcile the two answers.

60. Apparent discrepancy Resolve the apparent discrepancy between

$$\int \frac{dx}{x(x-1)(x+2)} = \frac{1}{6}\ln\frac{(x-1)^2|x+2|}{|x|^3} + C \quad \text{and}$$

$$\int \frac{dx}{x(x-1)(x+2)} = \frac{\ln|x-1|}{3} + \frac{\ln|x+2|}{6} - \frac{\ln|x|}{2} + C$$

61–64. Reduction formulas *Use the reduction formulas in a table of integrals to evaluate the following integrals.*

61. $\int x^3 e^{2x}\,dx$ **62.** $\int x^2 e^{-3x}\,dx$

63. $\int \tan^4 3y\,dy$ **64.** $\int \sec^4 4x\,dx$

65–70. Double table lookup *The following integrals may require more than one table lookup. Evaluate the integrals using a table of integrals, then check your answer with a computer algebra system. When the parameter a appears, assume $a > 0$.*

65. $\int x \sin^{-1} 2x\,dx$ **66.** $\int 4x \cos^{-1} 10x\,dx$ **67.** $\int \frac{\tan^{-1} x}{x^2}\,dx$

68. $\int \frac{\sin^{-1} ax}{x^2}\,dx$ **69.** $\int \frac{dx}{\sqrt{2ax - x^2}}$ **70.** $\int \sqrt{2ax - x^2}\,dx$

Applications

71. Period of a pendulum Consider a pendulum with a length of L meters swinging only under the influence of gravity. Suppose the pendulum starts swinging with an initial displacement of

θ_0 radians (see figure). The period (time to complete one full cycle) is given by

$$T = \frac{4}{\omega}\int_0^{\pi/2} \frac{d\varphi}{\sqrt{1 - k^2 \sin^2 \varphi}}$$

where $\omega^2 = g/L$, $g \approx 9.8\,\text{m/s}^2$ is the acceleration due to gravity, and $k^2 = \sin^2(\theta_0/2)$. Assume $L = 9.8$ m, which means $\omega = 1\,\text{s}^{-1}$.

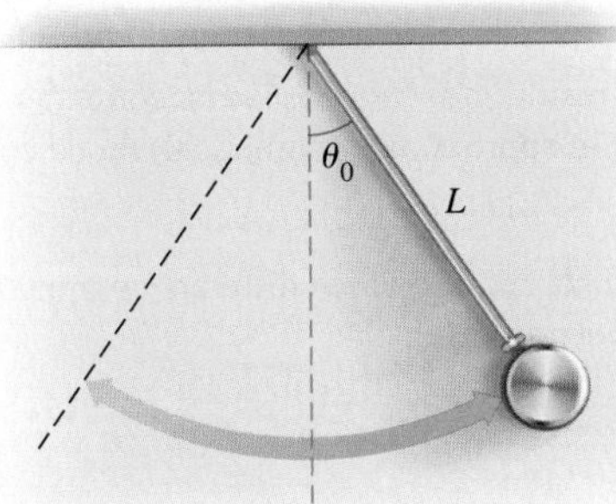

a. Use a computer algebra system to find the period of the pendulum for $\theta_0 = 0.1, 0.2, \ldots, 0.9, 1.0$ rad.
b. For small values of θ_0, the period should be approximately 2π s. For what values of θ_0 are your computed values within 10% of 2π (relative error less than 0.1)?

Additional Exercises

T **72. Arc length of a parabola** Let $L(c)$ be the length of the parabola $f(x) = x^2$ from $x = 0$ to $x = c$, where $c \geq 0$ is a constant.

a. Find an expression for L and graph the function.
b. Is L concave up or concave down on $[0, \infty)$?
c. Show that as c becomes large and positive, the arc length function increases as c^2; that is, $L(c) \approx kc^2$, where k is a constant.

73–76. Deriving formulas *Evaluate the following integrals. Assume a and b are real numbers and n is an integer.*

73. $\displaystyle\int \frac{x}{ax + b}\,dx$; Use $u = ax + b$.

74. $\displaystyle\int \frac{x}{\sqrt{ax + b}}\,dx$; Use $u^2 = ax + b$.

75. $\int x(ax + b)^n\,dx$; Use $u = ax + b$.

76. $\int x^n \sin^{-1} x\,dx$; Use integration by parts.

T **77. Powers of sine and cosine** It can be shown that

$$\int_0^{\pi/2} \sin^n x\,dx = \int_0^{\pi/2} \cos^n x\,dx = \begin{cases} \dfrac{1\cdot 3\cdot 5\cdots(n-1)}{2\cdot 4\cdot 6\cdots n}\cdot\dfrac{\pi}{2} & \text{if } n \geq 2 \text{ is an even integer} \\[2ex] \dfrac{2\cdot 4\cdot 6\cdots(n-1)}{3\cdot 5\cdot 7\cdots n} & \text{if } n \geq 3 \text{ is an odd integer} \end{cases}$$

a. Use a computer algebra system to confirm this result for $n = 2, 3, 4$, and 5.
b. Evaluate the integrals with $n = 10$ and confirm the result.
c. Using graphing and/or symbolic computation, determine whether the values of the integrals increase or decrease as n increases.

T **78. A remarkable integral** It is a fact that $\displaystyle\int_0^{\pi/2} \frac{dx}{1 + \tan^m x} = \frac{\pi}{4}$ for *all* real numbers m.

a. Graph the integrand for $m = -2, -3/2, -1, -1/2, 0, 1/2, 1, 3/2$, and 2, and explain geometrically how the area under the curve on the interval $[0, \pi/2]$ remains constant as m varies.
b. Use a computer algebra system to confirm that the integral is constant for all m.

QUICK CHECK ANSWERS

1. 1 **2.** Because $\sin^2 x = 1 - \cos^2 x$, the two results differ by a constant, which can be absorbed in the arbitrary constant C. **3.** The second result agrees with the first for $x > 0$ after using $\ln a - \ln b = \ln(a/b)$. The second result should have absolute values and an arbitrary constant.

8.6 Numerical Integration

Situations arise in which the analytical methods we have developed so far cannot be used to evaluate a definite integral. For example, an integrand may not have an obvious antiderivative (such as $\cos(x^2)$ and $1/\ln x$), or perhaps the integrand is represented by individual data points, which makes finding an antiderivative impossible.

When analytical methods fail, we often turn to *numerical methods*, which are typically done on a calculator or computer. These methods do not produce exact values of definite integrals, but they provide approximations that are generally quite accurate. Many calculators, software packages, and computer algebra systems have built-in numerical integration methods. In this section, we explore some of these methods.

Absolute and Relative Error

Because numerical methods do not typically produce exact results, we should be concerned about the accuracy of approximations, which leads to the ideas of *absolute* and *relative error.*

> **DEFINITIONS Absolute and Relative Error**
>
> Suppose c is a computed numerical solution to a problem having an exact solution x. There are two common measures of the error in c as an approximation to x:
>
> $$\textbf{absolute error} = |c - x|$$
>
> and
>
> $$\textbf{relative error} = \frac{|c - x|}{|x|} \quad (\text{if } x \neq 0)$$

➤ Because the exact solution is usually not known, the goal in practice is to estimate the maximum size of the error.

EXAMPLE 1 Absolute and relative error The ancient Greeks used $\frac{22}{7}$ to approximate the value of π. Determine the absolute and relative error in this approximation to π.

SOLUTION Letting $c = \frac{22}{7}$ be the approximate value of $x = \pi$, we find that

$$\text{absolute error} = \left|\frac{22}{7} - \pi\right| \approx 0.00126$$

and

$$\text{relative error} = \frac{|22/7 - \pi|}{|\pi|} \approx 0.000402 \approx 0.04\%$$

Related Exercises 7–10 ◀

Midpoint Rule

Many numerical integration methods are based on the ideas that underlie Riemann sums; these methods approximate the net area of regions bounded by curves. A typical problem is shown in Figure 8.12, where we see a function f defined on an interval $[a, b]$. The goal is to approximate the value of $\int_a^b f(x)\,dx$. As with Riemann sums, we first partition the

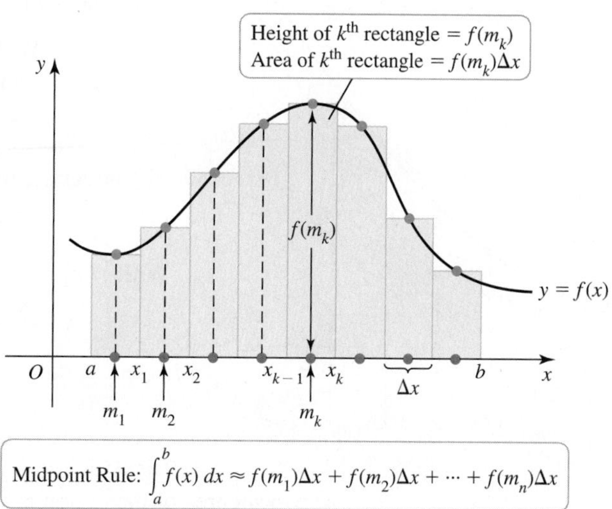

FIGURE 8.12

interval $[a, b]$ into n subintervals of equal length $\Delta x = (b - a)/n$. This partition establishes $n + 1$ grid points

$$x_0 = a, \quad x_1 = a + \Delta x, \quad x_2 = a + 2\Delta x, \ldots, \quad x_k = a + k\Delta x, \ldots, \quad x_n = b.$$

The kth subinterval is $[x_{k-1}, x_k]$, for $k = 1, 2, \ldots, n$.

> The Midpoint Rule is a Riemann sum that uses midpoints of subintervals for $\bar{x}_k$.

The Midpoint Rule approximates the region under the curve using rectangles. The bases of the rectangles have width Δx. The height of the kth rectangle is $f(m_k)$, where $m_k = (x_{k-1} + x_k)/2$ is the midpoint of the kth subinterval (Figure 8.12). Therefore, the net area of the kth rectangle is $f(m_k)\,\Delta x$.

Let $M(n)$ be the Midpoint Rule approximation to the integral using n rectangles. Summing the net areas of the rectangles, we have

$$\begin{aligned}\int_a^b f(x)\,dx &\approx M(n)\\ &= f(m_1)\Delta x + f(m_2)\Delta x + \cdots + f(m_n)\Delta x\\ &= \sum_{k=1}^{n} f\left(\frac{x_{k-1} + x_k}{2}\right)\Delta x\end{aligned}$$

> Recall that if $f(m_k) < 0$ for some k, then the net area of that rectangle is negative, which makes a negative contribution to the approximation (Section 5.2).

Just as with Riemann sums, the Midpoint Rule approximations to $\int_a^b f(x)\,dx$ generally improve as n increases.

DEFINITION Midpoint Rule

Suppose f is defined and integrable on $[a, b]$. The Midpoint Rule approximation to $\int_a^b f(x)\,dx$ using n equally spaced subintervals on $[a, b]$ is

$$\begin{aligned}M(n) &= f(m_1)\Delta x + f(m_2)\Delta x + \cdots + f(m_n)\Delta x\\ &= \sum_{k=1}^{n} f\left(\frac{x_{k-1} + x_k}{2}\right)\Delta x,\end{aligned}$$

where $\Delta x = (b - a)/n$, $x_k = a + k\Delta x$, and m_k is the midpoint of $[x_{k-1}, x_k]$, for $k = 1, \ldots, n$.

QUICK CHECK 1 To apply the Midpoint Rule on the interval $[3, 11]$ with $n = 4$, at what points must the integrand be evaluated?

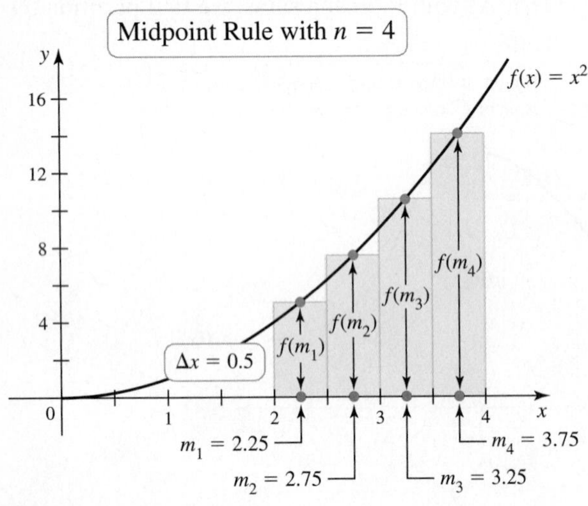

FIGURE 8.13

EXAMPLE 2 Applying the Midpoint Rule Approximate $\int_2^4 x^2\,dx$ using the Midpoint Rule with $n = 4$ and $n = 8$ subintervals.

SOLUTION With $a = 2$, $b = 4$, and $n = 4$ subintervals, the length of each subinterval is $\Delta x = (b - a)/n = 2/4 = 0.5$. The grid points are

$$x_0 = 2, \quad x_1 = 2.5, \quad x_2 = 3, \quad x_3 = 3.5, \quad \text{and} \quad x_4 = 4.$$

The integrand must be evaluated at the midpoints (Figure 8.13):

$$m_1 = 2.25, \quad m_2 = 2.75, \quad m_3 = 3.25, \quad m_4 = 3.75$$

With $f(x) = x^2$ and $n = 4$, the Midpoint Rule approximation is

$$\begin{aligned}M(4) &= f(m_1)\Delta x + f(m_2)\Delta x + f(m_3)\Delta x + f(m_4)\Delta x\\ &= (m_1^2 + m_2^2 + m_3^2 + m_4^2)\Delta x\\ &= (2.25^2 + 2.75^2 + 3.25^2 + 3.75^2)\cdot 0.5\\ &= 18.625.\end{aligned}$$

The exact area of the region is $\frac{56}{3}$, so the Midpoint Rule has an absolute error of

$$|18.625 - 56/3| \approx 0.0417$$

and a relative error of

$$\left|\frac{18.625 - 56/3}{56/3}\right| \approx 0.00223 = 0.223\%.$$

Using $n = 8$ subintervals, the midpoint approximation is

$$M(8) = \sum_{k=1}^{8} f(m_k)\Delta x = 18.65625,$$

which has an absolute error of about 0.0104 and a relative error of about 0.0558%. We see that increasing n and using more rectangles decreases the error in the approximations.

Related Exercises 11–14

The Trapezoid Rule

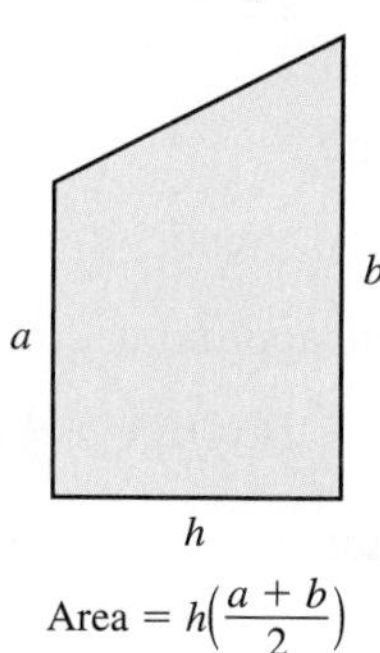

Another method for estimating $\int_a^b f(x)\,dx$ is the Trapezoid Rule, which uses the same partition of the interval $[a, b]$ described for the Midpoint Rule. Instead of approximating the region under the curve by rectangles, the Trapezoid Rule uses (what else?) trapezoids. The bases of the trapezoids have length Δx. The sides of the kth trapezoid have lengths $f(x_{k-1})$ and $f(x_k)$, for $k = 1, 2, \ldots, n$ (Figure 8.14). Therefore, the net area of the kth trapezoid is $\left(\frac{f(x_{k-1}) + f(x_k)}{2}\right)\Delta x$.

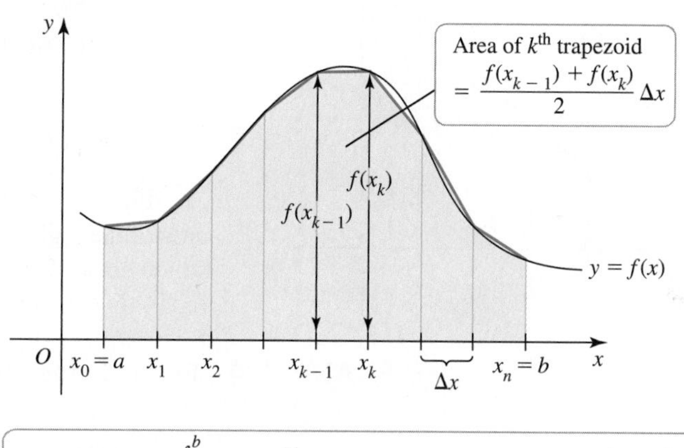

FIGURE 8.14

Letting $T(n)$ be the Trapezoid Rule approximation to the integral using n subintervals, we have

$$\int_a^b f(x)\,dx \approx T(n)$$

$$= \underbrace{\left(\frac{f(x_0) + f(x_1)}{2}\right)\Delta x}_{\text{first trapezoid}} + \underbrace{\left(\frac{f(x_1) + f(x_2)}{2}\right)\Delta x}_{\text{second trapezoid}} + \cdots + \underbrace{\left(\frac{f(x_{n-1}) + f(x_n)}{2}\right)\Delta x}_{n\text{th trapezoid}}$$

$$= \left(\frac{f(x_0)}{2} + \underbrace{\frac{f(x_1)}{2} + \frac{f(x_1)}{2}}_{f(x_1)} + \cdots + \underbrace{\frac{f(x_{n-1})}{2} + \frac{f(x_{n-1})}{2}}_{f(x_{n-1})} + \frac{f(x_n)}{2}\right)\Delta x$$

$$= \left(\frac{f(x_0)}{2} + \underbrace{f(x_1) + \cdots + f(x_{n-1})}_{\sum_{k=1}^{n-1} f(x_k)} + \frac{f(x_n)}{2}\right)\Delta x$$

As with the Midpoint Rule, the Trapezoid Rule approximations generally improve as n increases.

DEFINITION Trapezoid Rule

Suppose f is defined and integrable on $[a, b]$. The Trapezoid Rule approximation to $\int_a^b f(x)\,dx$ using n equally spaced subintervals on $[a, b]$ is

$$T(n) = \left(\frac{1}{2}f(x_0) + \sum_{k=1}^{n-1} f(x_k) + \frac{1}{2}f(x_n)\right)\Delta x,$$

where $\Delta x = (b - a)/n$ and $x_k = a + k\Delta x$, for $k = 0, 1, \ldots, n$.

QUICK CHECK 2 Does the Trapezoid Rule underestimate or overestimate the value of $\int_0^4 x^2\,dx$? ◄

EXAMPLE 3 Applying the Trapezoid Rule Approximate $\int_2^4 x^2\,dx$ using the Trapezoid Rule with $n = 4$ subintervals.

SOLUTION As in Example 2, the grid points are

$$x_0 = 2, \quad x_1 = 2.5, \quad x_2 = 3, \quad x_3 = 3.5, \quad \text{and} \quad x_4 = 4.$$

With $f(x) = x^2$ and $n = 4$, the Trapezoid Rule approximation is

$$\begin{aligned} T(4) &= \tfrac{1}{2}f(x_0)\Delta x + f(x_1)\Delta x + f(x_2)\Delta x + f(x_3)\Delta x + \tfrac{1}{2}f(x_4)\Delta x \\ &= \left(\tfrac{1}{2}x_0^2 + x_1^2 + x_2^2 + x_3^2 + \tfrac{1}{2}x_4^2\right)\Delta x \\ &= \left(\tfrac{1}{2}\cdot 2^2 + 2.5^2 + 3^2 + 3.5^2 + \tfrac{1}{2}\cdot 4^2\right)\cdot 0.5 \\ &= 18.75. \end{aligned}$$

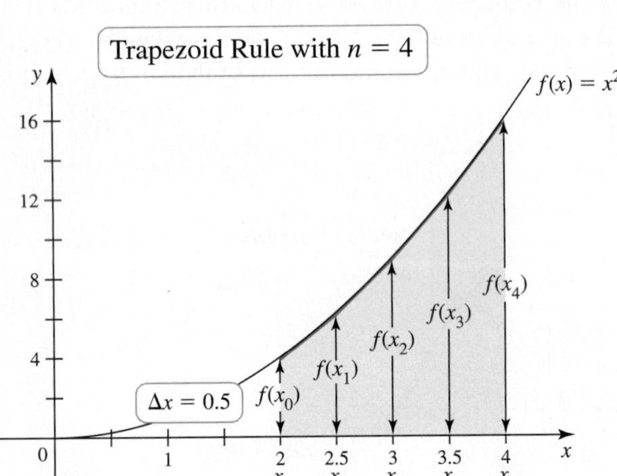

FIGURE 8.15

Figure 8.15 shows the approximation with $n = 4$ trapezoids. The exact area of the region is $56/3$, so the Trapezoid Rule approximation has an absolute error of about 0.0833 and a relative error of approximately 0.00446, or 0.446%. Increasing n decreases this error. *Related Exercises 15–18* ◄

EXAMPLE 4 Errors in the Midpoint and Trapezoid Rules Given that

$$\int_0^1 xe^{-x}\,dx = 1 - 2e^{-1},$$

find the absolute errors in the Midpoint Rule and Trapezoid Rule approximations to the integral with $n = 4, 8, 16, 32, 64$, and 128 subintervals.

SOLUTION Because the exact value of the integral is known (which often does *not* happen in practice), we can compute the error in various approximations. For example, if $n = 16$, then

$$\Delta x = \frac{1}{16} \quad \text{and} \quad x_k = \frac{k}{16}, \quad \text{for } k = 0, 1, \ldots, n.$$

Using sigma notation and a computer algebra system, we have

$$M(16) = \sum_{k=1}^{\overbrace{16}^{n}} f\left(\frac{\overbrace{(k-1)/16}^{x_{k-1}} + \overbrace{k/16}^{x_k}}{2}\right)\overbrace{\frac{1}{16}}^{\Delta x} = \sum_{k=1}^{16} f\left(\frac{2k-1}{32}\right)\frac{1}{16} \approx 0.26440383609318$$

and

$$T(16) = \left(\frac{1}{2}\underbrace{f(0)}_{x_0 = a} + \sum_{k=1}^{\overbrace{15}^{n-1}} \underbrace{f(k/16)}_{x_k} + \frac{1}{2}\underbrace{f(1)}_{x_{16} = b}\right)\frac{1}{16} \approx 0.26391564480235.$$

The absolute error in the Midpoint Rule approximation with $n = 16$ is $|M(16) - (1 - 2e^{-1})| \approx 0.000163$. The absolute error in the Trapezoid Rule approximation with $n = 16$ is $|T(16) - (1 - 2e^{-1})| \approx 0.000325$.

The Midpoint Rule and Trapezoid Rule approximations to the integral, together with the associated absolute errors, are shown in Table 8.4 for various values of n. Notice that as n increases, the errors in both methods decrease, as expected. With $n = 128$ subintervals, the approximations $M(128)$ and $T(128)$ agree to four decimal places. Based on these approximations, a good approximation to the integral is 0.2642. The way in which the errors decrease is also worth noting. If you look carefully at both error columns in Table 8.4, you will see that each time n is doubled (or Δx is halved), the error decreases by a factor of approximately 4.

Table 8.4

n	$M(n)$	$T(n)$	Error $M(n)$	Error $T(n)$
4	0.26683456310319	0.25904504019141	0.00259	0.00520
8	0.26489148795740	0.26293980164730	0.000650	0.00130
16	0.26440383609318	0.26391564480235	0.000163	0.000325
32	0.26428180513718	0.26415974044777	0.0000407	0.0000814
64	0.26425129001915	0.26422077279247	0.0000102	0.0000203
128	0.26424366077837	0.26423603140581	0.00000254	0.00000509

Related Exercises 19–26

QUICK CHECK 3 Compute the approximate factor by which the error decreases in Table 8.4 between $T(16)$ and $T(32)$; between $T(32)$ and $T(64)$.

Table 8.5

Year	World Oil Production (billions barrels/yr)
1992	22.3
1993	21.9
1994	21.5
1995	21.9
1996	22.3
1997	23.0
1998	23.7
1999	24.5
2000	23.7
2001	25.2
2002	24.8
2003	24.5
2004	25.2
2005	25.9
2006	26.3
2007	27.0
2008	27.5

EXAMPLE 5 World oil production Table 8.5 and Figure 8.16 show data for the rate of world oil production (in billions of barrels/yr) over a 16-year period. If the rate of oil production is given by the function R, then the total amount of oil produced in billions of barrels over the time period $a \le t \le b$ is $Q = \int_a^b R(t)\,dt$ (Section 6.1). Use the Midpoint and Trapezoid Rules to approximate the total oil produced between 1992 and 2008.

SOLUTION For convenience, let $t = 0$ represent 1992 and $t = 16$ represent 2008. We let $R(t)$ be the rate of oil production in the year corresponding to t (for example, $R(6) = 23.7$ is the rate in 1998). The goal is to approximate $Q = \int_0^{16} R(t)\,dt$. If we use $n = 4$ subintervals, then $\Delta t = 4$ yr. The resulting Midpoint and Trapezoid Rule approximations (in billions of barrels) are

$$\begin{aligned} Q \approx M(4) &= [R(2) + R(6) + R(10) + R(14)]\Delta t \\ &= (21.5 + 23.7 + 24.8 + 26.3)4 \\ &= 385.2 \end{aligned}$$

and

$$\begin{aligned} Q \approx T(4) &= \left[\frac{1}{2}R(0) + R(4) + R(8) + R(12) + \frac{1}{2}R(16)\right]\Delta t \\ &= \left(\frac{1}{2}\cdot 22.3 + 22.3 + 23.7 + 25.2 + \frac{1}{2}\cdot 27.5\right)4 \\ &= 384.4. \end{aligned}$$

The two methods give reasonable agreement. Using $n = 8$ subintervals, with $\Delta t = 2$ yr, similar calculations give the approximations

$$Q \approx M(8) = 387.8 \quad \text{and} \quad Q \approx T(8) = 384.8.$$

The given data do not allow us to compute the next Midpoint Rule approximation $M(16)$. However, we can compute the next Trapezoid Rule approximation $T(16)$ and here is a good way to do it. If $T(n)$ and $M(n)$ are known, then the next Trapezoid Rule approximation is (Exercise 58)

$$T(2n) = \frac{T(n) + M(n)}{2}.$$

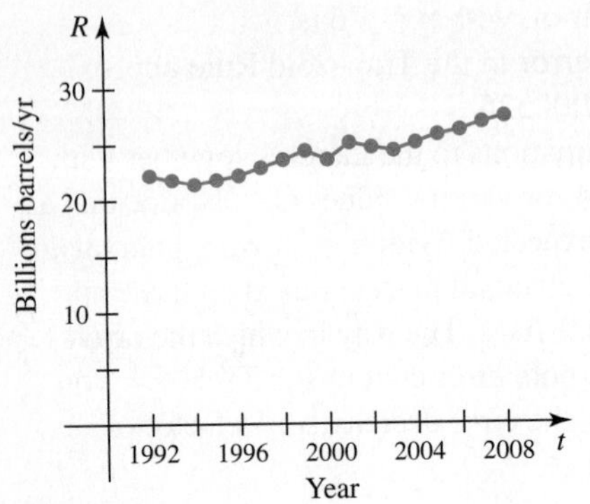

FIGURE 8.16

Source: U.S. Energy Information Administration

Using this trick, we find that

$$T(16) = \frac{T(8) + M(8)}{2} = \frac{384.8 + 387.8}{2} = 386.3.$$

Based on these calculations, the best approximation to the total oil produced between 1992 and 2008 is 386.3 billion barrels. *Related Exercises 27–30*

Simpson's Rule

The Midpoint Rule and the Trapezoid Rule can be improved by approximating the graph of f with curves, rather than line segments. Let's return to the partition used by the Midpoint and Trapezoid Rules, but now suppose we work with three neighboring points on the curve $y = f(x)$, say $(x_0, f(x_0))$, $(x_1, f(x_1))$, and $(x_2, f(x_2))$. These three points determine a *parabola*, and it is easy to find the net area bounded by the parabola on the interval $[x_0, x_2]$. When this idea is applied to every group of three consecutive points along the interval of integration, the result is **Simpson's Rule**. With n subintervals, Simpson's Rule is denoted $S(n)$ and is given by

$$\int_a^b f(x)\,dx \approx S(n)$$

$$= (f(x_0) + 4f(x_1) + 2f(x_2) + 4f(x_3) + \cdots + 2f(x_{n-2}) + 4f(x_{n-1}) + f(x_n))\frac{\Delta x}{3}$$

Notice that apart from the first and last terms, the coefficients alternate between 4 and 2; **n must be an even integer** for this rule to work.

You can use the formula for Simpson's Rule given above; but here is an easier way. If you already have the Trapezoid Rule approximations $T(n)$ and $T(2n)$, the next Simpson's Rule approximation follows immediately with a simple calculation (Exercise 60):

$$S(2n) = \frac{4T(2n) - T(n)}{3}.$$

DEFINITION Simpson's Rule

Suppose f is defined and integrable on $[a, b]$. The Simpson's Rule approximation to $\int_a^b f(x)\,dx$ using n equally spaced subintervals on $[a, b]$ is

$$S(n) = [f(x_0) + 4f(x_1) + 2f(x_2) + 4f(x_3) + \cdots + 4f(x_{n-1}) + f(x_n)]\frac{\Delta x}{3},$$

where n is an even integer, $\Delta x = (b - a)/n$, and $x_k = a + k\Delta x$, for $k = 0, 1, \ldots, n$. Alternatively, if the Trapezoid Rule approximations $T(2n)$ and $T(n)$ are known, then

$$S(2n) = \frac{4T(2n) - T(n)}{3}.$$

EXAMPLE 6 Errors in the Trapezoid Rule and Simpson's Rule Given that $\int_0^1 xe^{-x}\,dx = 1 - 2e^{-1}$, find the absolute errors in the Trapezoid Rule and Simpson's Rule approximations to the integral with $n = 8, 16, 32, 64$, and 128 subintervals.

SOLUTION Because the shortcut formula for Simpson's Rule is based on values generated by the Trapezoid Rule, it is best to calculate the Trapezoid Rule approximations first. The second column of Table 8.6 shows the Trapezoid Rule approximations computed in

Example 4. Having a column of Trapezoid Rule approximations, the corresponding Simpson's Rule approximations are easily found. For example, if $n = 8$, we have

$$S(8) = \frac{4T(8) - T(4)}{3} \approx 0.26423805546593.$$

The table also shows the absolute errors in the approximations. The Simpson's Rule errors decrease much more quickly than the Trapezoid Rule errors. By careful inspection, you will see that the Simpson's Rule errors decrease with a clear pattern: Each time n is doubled (or Δx is halved), the errors decrease by a factor of approximately 16, which makes Simpson's Rule a more efficient and accurate method.

Table 8.6

n	$T(n)$	$S(n)$	Error $T(n)$	Error $S(n)$
4	0.25904504019141		0.00520	
8	0.26293980164730	0.26423805546593	0.00130	0.00000306
16	0.26391564480235	0.26424092585404	0.000325	0.000000192
32	0.26415974044777	0.26424110566291	0.0000814	0.0000000120
64	0.26422077279247	0.26424111690738	0.0000203	0.000000000750
128	0.26423603140581	0.26424111761026	0.00000509	0.0000000000469

QUICK CHECK 4 Compute the approximate factor by which the error decreases in Table 8.6 between $S(16)$ and $S(32)$ and between $S(32)$ and $S(64)$.

Related Exercises 31–38

Errors in Numerical Integration

A detailed analysis of the errors in the three methods we have discussed goes beyond the scope of the book. We state without proof the standard error theorems for the methods and note that Examples 3, 4, and 6 are consistent with these results.

THEOREM 8.2 Errors in Numerical Integration

Assume that f'' is continuous on the interval $[a, b]$ and that k is a real number such that $|f''(x)| < k$ for all x in $[a, b]$. The absolute errors in approximating the integral $\int_a^b f(x)\,dx$ by the Midpoint Rule and Trapezoid Rule with n subintervals satisfy the inequalities

$$E_M \le \frac{k(b-a)}{24}(\Delta x)^2 \quad \text{and} \quad E_T \le \frac{k(b-a)}{12}(\Delta x)^2$$

respectively, where $\Delta x = (b-a)/n$.

Assume that $f^{(4)}$ is continuous on the interval $[a, b]$ and that K is a real number such that $|f^{(4)}(x)| < K$ on $[a, b]$. The error in approximating the integral $\int_a^b f(x)\,dx$ by Simpson's Rule with n subintervals satisfies the inequality

$$E_S \le \frac{K(b-a)}{180}(\Delta x)^4.$$

The absolute errors associated with the Midpoint Rule and Trapezoid Rule are proportional to $(\Delta x)^2$. So, if Δx is reduced by a factor of 2, the errors decrease roughly by a factor of 4, as seen in Example 4. Simpson's Rule is a more accurate method; its error is proportional to $(\Delta x)^4$, which means that if Δx is reduced by a factor of 2, the errors decrease roughly by a factor of 16, as seen in Example 6. Computing both the Trapezoid Rule and Simpson's Rule together, as shown in Example 6, is a powerful method that produces accurate approximations with relatively little work.

SECTION 8.6 EXERCISES

Review Questions

1. If the interval $[4, 18]$ is partitioned into $n = 28$ subintervals of equal width, what is Δx?

2. Explain geometrically how the Midpoint Rule is used to approximate a definite integral.

3. Explain geometrically how the Trapezoid Rule is used to approximate a definite integral.

4. If the Midpoint Rule is used on the interval $[-1, 11]$ with $n = 3$ subintervals, at what x-coordinates is the integrand evaluated?

5. If the Trapezoid Rule is used on the interval $[-1, 9]$ with $n = 5$ subintervals, at what x-coordinates is the integrand evaluated?

6. State how to compute the Simpson's Rule approximation $S(2n)$ if the Trapezoid Rule approximations $T(2n)$ and $T(n)$ are known.

Basic Skills

7–10. Absolute and relative error *Compute the absolute and relative errors in using c to approximate x.*

7. $x = \pi$; $c = 3.14$

8. $x = \sqrt{2}$; $c = 1.414$

9. $x = e$; $c = 2.72$

10. $x = e$; $c = 2.718$

11–14. Midpoint Rule approximations *Find the indicated Midpoint Rule approximations to the following integrals.*

11. $\int_2^{10} 2x^2\,dx$ using $n = 1, 2,$ and 4 subintervals

12. $\int_1^{9} x^3\,dx$ using $n = 1, 2,$ and 4 subintervals

13. $\int_0^{1} \sin \pi x\,dx$ using $n = 6$ subintervals

14. $\int_0^{1} e^{-x}\,dx$ using $n = 8$ subintervals

15–18. Trapezoid Rule approximations *Find the indicated Trapezoid Rule approximations to the following integrals.*

15. $\int_2^{10} 2x^2\,dx$ using $n = 2, 4,$ and 8 subintervals

16. $\int_1^{9} x^3\,dx$ using $n = 2, 4,$ and 8 subintervals

17. $\int_0^{1} \sin \pi x\,dx$ using $n = 6$ subintervals

18. $\int_0^{1} e^{-x}\,dx$ using $n = 8$ subintervals

19. **Midpoint Rule, Trapezoid Rule and relative error** Find the Midpoint and Trapezoid Rule approximations to $\int_0^1 \sin \pi x\,dx$ using $n = 25$ subintervals. Compute the relative error of each approximation.

20. **Midpoint Rule, Trapezoid Rule and relative error** Find the Midpoint and Trapezoid Rule approximations to $\int_0^1 e^{-x}\,dx$ using $n = 50$ subintervals. Compute the relative error of each approximation.

21–26. Comparing the Midpoint and Trapezoid Rules *Apply the Midpoint and Trapezoid Rules to the following integrals. Make a table similar to Table 8.4 showing the approximations and errors for* $n = 4, 8, 16,$ *and* 32. *The exact values of the integrals are given for computing the error.*

21. $\int_1^{5} (3x^2 - 2x)\,dx = 100$

22. $\int_{-2}^{6} \left(\frac{x^3}{16} - x\right) dx = 4$

23. $\int_0^{\pi/4} 3 \sin 2x\,dx = \frac{3}{2}$

24. $\int_1^{e} \ln x\,dx = 1$

25. $\int_0^{\pi} \sin x \cos 3x\,dx = 0$

26. $\int_0^{8} e^{-2x}\,dx = \frac{1 - e^{-16}}{2} \approx 0.4999999$

27–30. Temperature data *Hourly temperature data for Boulder, CO, San Francisco, CA, Nantucket, MA, and Duluth, MN, over a 12-hr period on the same day of January are shown in the figure. Assume that these data are taken from a continuous temperature function* $T(t)$. *The average temperature over the 12-hr period is* $\overline{T} = \frac{1}{12}\int_0^{12} T(t)\,dt$.

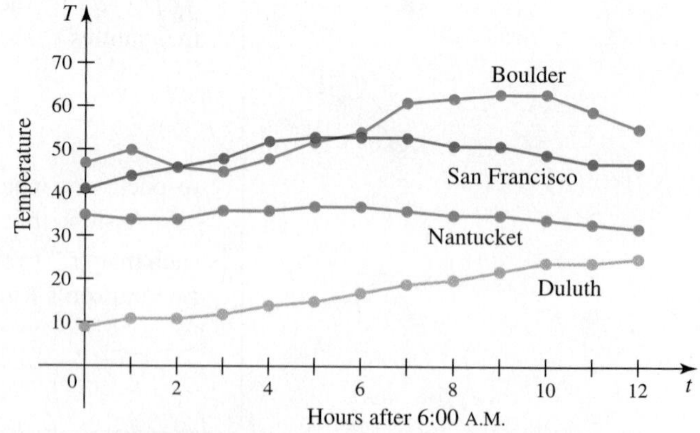

t	0	1	2	3	4	5	6	7	8	9	10	11	12
B	47	50	46	45	48	52	54	61	62	63	63	59	55
SF	41	44	46	48	52	53	53	53	51	51	49	47	47
N	35	34	34	36	36	37	37	36	35	35	34	33	32
D	9	11	11	12	14	15	17	19	20	22	24	24	25

27. Find an accurate approximation to the average temperature over the 12-hr period for Boulder. State your method.

28. Find an accurate approximation to the average temperature over the 12-hour period for San Francisco. State your method.

29. Find an accurate approximation to the average temperature over the 12-hr period for Nantucket. State your method.

30. Find an accurate approximation to the average temperature over the 12-hr period for Duluth. State your method.

T **31–34. Trapezoid Rule and Simpson's Rule** *Consider the following integrals and the given values of n.*

a. *Find the Trapezoid Rule approximations to the integral using n and 2n subintervals.*

b. *Find the Simpson's Rule approximation to the integral using 2n subintervals. It is easiest to obtain Simpson's Rule approximations from the Trapezoid Rule approximations, as in Example 6.*

c. *Compute the absolute errors in the Trapezoid Rule and Simpson's Rule with 2n subintervals.*

31. $\int_0^1 e^{2x}\,dx;\ n = 25$

32. $\int_0^2 x^4\,dx;\ n = 30$

33. $\int_1^e \frac{1}{x}\,dx;\ n = 50$

34. $\int_0^{\pi/4} \frac{1}{1 + x^2}\,dx;\ n = 64$

T **35–38. Simpson's Rule** *Apply Simpson's Rule to the following integrals. It is easiest to obtain the Simpson's Rule approximations from the Trapezoid Rule approximations, as in Example 6. Make a table similar to Table 8.6 showing the approximations and errors for $n = 4, 8, 16,$ and 32. The exact values of the integrals are given for computing the error.*

35. $\int_0^4 (3x^5 - 8x^3)\,dx = 1536$

36. $\int_1^e \ln x\,dx = 1$

37. $\int_0^{\pi} e^{-t}\sin t\,dt = \frac{1}{2}(e^{-\pi} + 1)$

38. $\int_0^6 3e^{-3x}\,dx = 1 - e^{-18} \approx 1.000000$

Further Explorations

39. **Explain why or why not** Determine whether the following statements are true and give an explanation or counterexample.

a. The Trapezoid Rule is exact when used to approximate the definite integral of a linear function.

b. If the number of subintervals used in the Midpoint Rule is increased by a factor of 3, the error is expected to decrease by a factor of 8.

c. If the number of subintervals used in the Trapezoid Rule is increased by a factor of 4, the error is expected to decrease by a factor of 16.

T **40–43. Comparing the Midpoint and Trapezoid Rules** *Compare the errors in the Midpoint and Trapezoid Rules with $n = 4, 8, 16,$ and 32 subintervals when they are applied to the following integrals (with their exact values given).*

40. $\int_0^{\pi/2} \sin^6 x\,dx = \frac{5\pi}{32}$

41. $\int_0^{\pi/2} \cos^9 x\,dx = \frac{128}{315}$

42. $\int_0^1 \left(8x^7 - 7x^8\right)dx = \frac{2}{9}$

43. $\int_0^{\pi} \ln(5 + 3\cos x)\,dx = \pi \ln \frac{9}{2}$

T **44–47. Using Simpson's Rule** *Approximate the following integrals using Simpson's Rule. Experiment with values of n to ensure that the error is less than 10^{-3}.*

44. $\int_0^{2\pi} \frac{dx}{(5 + 3\sin x)^2} = \frac{5\pi}{32}$

45. $\int_0^{\pi} \frac{\cos x}{\frac{5}{4} - \cos x}\,dx = \frac{2\pi}{3}$

46. $\int_0^{\pi} \ln(2 + \cos x)\,dx = \pi \ln\left(\frac{2 + \sqrt{3}}{2}\right)$

47. $\int_0^{\pi} \sin 6x \cos 3x\,dx = \frac{4}{9}$

Applications

T 48. **Period of a pendulum** A standard pendulum of length L swinging under only the influence of gravity (no resistance) has a period of

$$T = \frac{4}{\omega}\int_0^{\pi/2} \frac{d\varphi}{\sqrt{1 - k^2\sin^2\varphi}}$$

where $\omega^2 = g/L$, $k^2 = \sin^2(\theta_0/2)$, $g \approx 9.8\ \text{m/s}^2$ is the acceleration due to gravity, and θ_0 is the initial angle from which the pendulum is released (in radians). Use numerical integration to approximate the period of a pendulum with $L = 1$ m that is released from an angle of $\theta_0 = \pi/4$ rad.

T 49. **Arc length of an ellipse** The length of an ellipse with axes of length $2a$ and $2b$ is

$$\int_0^{2\pi} \sqrt{a^2\cos^2 t + b^2\sin^2 t}\,dt.$$

Use numerical integration and experiment with different values of n to approximate the length of an ellipse with $a = 4$ and $b = 8$.

T 50. **Sine Integral** The theory of diffraction produces the sine integral function $\text{Si}(x) = \int_0^x \frac{\sin t}{t}\,dt$. Use the Midpoint Rule to approximate Si (1) and Si (10). (Recall that $\lim_{x\to 0}(\sin x)/x = 1$.) Experiment with the number of subintervals until you obtain approximations that have an error less than 10^{-3}. A rule of thumb is that if two successive approximations differ by less than 10^{-3}, then the error is usually less than 10^{-3}.

51. Normal distribution of heights The heights of U.S. men are normally distributed with a mean of 69 in and a standard deviation of 3 in. This means that the fraction of men with a height between a and b (with $a < b$) inches is given by the integral

$$\frac{1}{3\sqrt{2\pi}}\int_a^b e^{-[(x-69)/3]^2/2}\,dx.$$

What percentage of American men are between 66 and 72 inches in height? Use the method of your choice and experiment with the number of subintervals until you obtain successive approximations that differ by less than 10^{-3}.

52. Normal distribution of movie lengths A recent study revealed that the lengths of U.S. movies are normally distributed with a mean of 110 min and a standard deviation of 22 min. This means that the fraction of movies with lengths between a and b minutes (with $a < b$) is given by the integral

$$\frac{1}{22\sqrt{2\pi}}\int_a^b e^{-[(x-110)/22]^2/2}\,dx.$$

What percentage of U.S. movies are between 1 hr and 1.5 hr long (60–90 min)?

53. U.S. oil produced and imported The figure shows the rate at which U.S. oil was produced and imported between 1920 and 2005 in units of millions of barrels per day. The total amount of oil produced or imported is given by the area of the region under the corresponding curve. Be careful with units because both days and years are used in this data set.

a. Use numerical integration to estimate the amount of U.S. oil produced between 1940 and 2000. Use the method of your choice and experiment with values of n.

b. Use numerical integration to estimate the amount of oil imported between 1940 and 2000. Use the method of your choice and experiment with values of n.

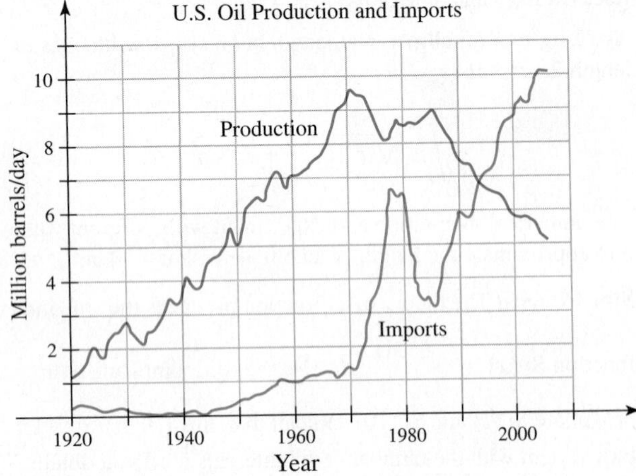

Source: U.S. Energy Information Administration

Additional Exercises

54. Estimating error Refer to Theorem 8.2 and let $f(x) = e^{x^2}$.

a. Find a Trapezoid Rule approximation to $\int_0^1 e^{x^2}\,dx$ using $n = 50$ subintervals.

b. Calculate $f''(x)$.

c. Explain why $|f''(x)| < 18$ on $[0, 1]$, given that $e < 3$.

d. Use Theorem 8.2 to find an upper bound on the absolute error in the estimate found in part (a).

55. Estimating error Refer to Theorem 8.2 and let $f(x) = \sin e^x$.

a. Find a Trapezoid Rule approximation to $\int_0^1 \sin(e^x)\,dx$ using $n = 40$ subintervals.

b. Calculate $f''(x)$.

c. Explain why $|f''(x)| < 6$ on $[0, 1]$, given that $e < 3$. (*Hint:* Graph f''.)

d. Find an upper bound on the absolute error in the estimate found in part (a) using Theorem 8.2.

56. Exact Trapezoid Rule Prove that the Trapezoid Rule is exact (no error) when approximating the definite integral of a linear function.

57. Exact Simpson's Rule Prove that Simpson's Rule is exact (no error) when approximating the definite integral of a linear function *and* a quadratic function.

58. Shortcut for the Trapezoid Rule Prove that if you have $M(n)$ and $T(n)$ (a Midpoint Rule approximation and a Trapezoid Rule approximation with n subintervals), then $T(2n) = (T(n) + M(n))/2$.

59. Trapezoid Rule and concavity Suppose f is positive and its first two derivatives are continuous on $[a, b]$. If f'' is positive on $[a, b]$, then is a Trapezoid Rule estimate of $\int_a^b f(x)\,dx$ an underestimate or overestimate of the integral? Justify your answer using Theorem 8.2 and an illustration.

60. Shortcut for Simpson's Rule Using the notation of the text, prove that $S(2n) = \dfrac{4T(2n) - T(n)}{3}$ for $n \geq 1$.

61. Another Simpson's Rule formula Another Simpson's Rule formula is $S(2n) = \dfrac{2M(n) + T(n)}{3}$ for $n \geq 1$. Use this rule to estimate $\int_1^e 1/x\,dx$ using $n = 10$ subintervals.

QUICK CHECK ANSWERS

1. 4, 6, 8, 10 **2.** Overestimates **3.** 4 and 4 **4.** 16 and 16

8.7 Improper Integrals

The definite integrals we have encountered so far involve finite-valued functions and finite intervals of integration. In this section, you will see that definite integrals can sometimes be evaluated when these conditions are not met. Here is an example. The energy required to launch a rocket from the surface of Earth ($R = 6370$ km from the center of Earth) to an altitude H is given by an integral of the form $\int_R^{R+H} k/x^2\,dx$, where k is a constant that includes the mass of the rocket, the mass of Earth, and the gravitational constant. This integral may be evaluated for any finite altitude $H > 0$. Now suppose that the aim is to launch the rocket to an arbitrarily large altitude H so that it escapes Earth's gravitational field. The energy required is given by the preceding integral as $H \to \infty$, which we write $\int_R^{\infty} k/x^2\,dx$. This integral is an example of an *improper integral*, and it has a finite value (which explains why it is possible to launch rockets to outer space). For historical reasons, the term *improper integral* is used for cases in which

- the interval of integration is infinite, or
- the integrand is unbounded on the interval of integration.

In this section, we explore improper integrals and their many uses.

Infinite Intervals

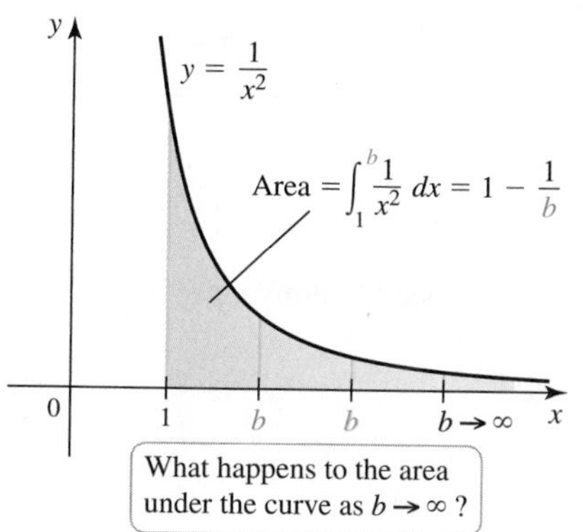

FIGURE 8.17

A simple example illustrates what can happen when integrating a function over an infinite interval. Consider the integral $\displaystyle\int_1^b \frac{1}{x^2}\,dx$, for any real number $b > 1$. As shown in Figure 8.17, this integral gives the area of the region bounded by the curve $y = x^{-2}$ and the x-axis between $x = 1$ and $x = b$. In fact, the value of the integral is

$$\int_1^b \frac{1}{x^2}\,dx = -\frac{1}{x}\bigg|_1^b = 1 - \frac{1}{b}.$$

For example, if $b = 2$, the area under the curve is $\frac{1}{2}$; if $b = 3$, the area under the curve is $\frac{2}{3}$. In general, as b increases, the area under the curve increases.

Now let's ask what happens to the area as b becomes arbitrarily large. Letting $b \to \infty$, the area of the region under the curve is

$$\lim_{b\to\infty}\left(1 - \frac{1}{b}\right) = 1.$$

We have discovered, surprising as it may seem, a curve of *infinite* length that bounds a region with *finite* area (1 square unit).

We express this result as

$$\int_1^{\infty} \frac{1}{x^2}\,dx = 1,$$

which is an improper integral because ∞ appears in the upper limit. In general, to evaluate $\int_a^{\infty} f(x)\,dx$, we first integrate over a finite interval $[a, b]$ and then let $b \to \infty$. A similar procedure is used to evaluate $\int_{-\infty}^{b} f(x)\,dx$ and $\int_{-\infty}^{\infty} f(x)\,dx$.

DEFINITIONS Improper Integrals over Infinite Intervals

1. If f is continuous on $[a, \infty)$, then

$$\int_a^\infty f(x)\,dx = \lim_{b\to\infty} \int_a^b f(x)\,dx,$$

provided the limit exists.

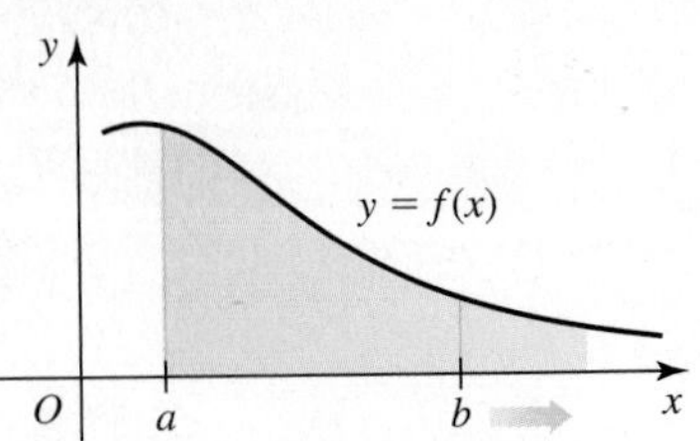

2. If f is continuous on $(-\infty, b]$, then

$$\int_{-\infty}^b f(x)\,dx = \lim_{a\to-\infty} \int_a^b f(x)\,dx,$$

provided the limit exists.

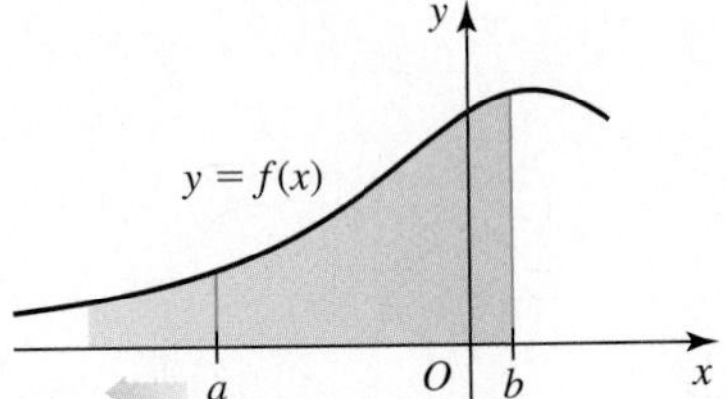

➤ Doubly infinite integrals (Case 3 in the definition) must be evaluated as two independent limits and not as

$$\int_{-\infty}^{\infty} f(x)\,dx = \lim_{b\to\infty} \int_{-b}^{b} f(x)\,dx.$$

3. If f is continuous on $(-\infty, \infty)$, then

$$\int_{-\infty}^\infty f(x)\,dx = \lim_{a\to-\infty} \int_a^c f(x)\,dx + \lim_{b\to\infty} \int_c^b f(x)\,dx$$

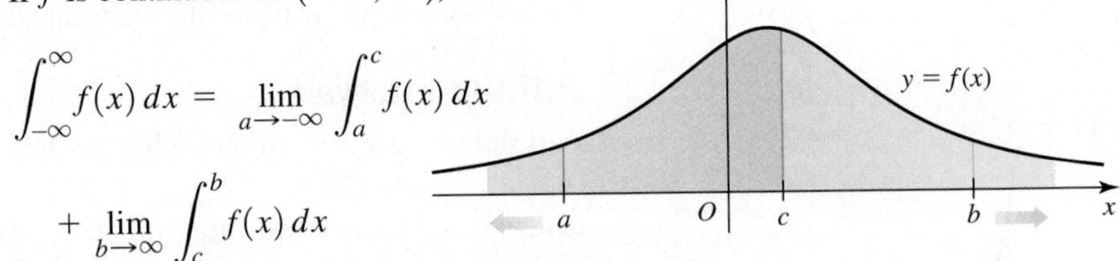

provided both limits exist, where c is any real number.

In each case, if the limit exists, the improper integral is said to **converge**; if it does not exist, the improper integral is said to **diverge**.

EXAMPLE 1 Infinite intervals Evaluate each integral.

a. $\displaystyle\int_0^\infty e^{-3x}\,dx$ **b.** $\displaystyle\int_0^\infty \frac{1}{1 + x^2}\,dx$

SOLUTION

a. Using the definition of the improper integral, we have

$$\begin{aligned}
\int_0^\infty e^{-3x}\,dx &= \lim_{b\to\infty} \int_0^b e^{-3x}\,dx && \text{Definition of improper integral}\\
&= \lim_{b\to\infty} \left(-\frac{1}{3}e^{-3x}\right)\Bigg|_0^b && \text{Evaluate the integral.}\\
&= \lim_{b\to\infty} \frac{1}{3}(1 - e^{-3b}) && \text{Simplify.}\\
&= \frac{1}{3}\Bigg(1 - \underbrace{\lim_{b\to\infty}\frac{1}{e^{3b}}}_{\text{equals } 0}\Bigg) = \frac{1}{3}. && e^{-3b} = \frac{1}{e^{3b}}
\end{aligned}$$

In this case the limit exists, so the integral converges and the region under the curve has a finite area of $\frac{1}{3}$ (Figure 8.18).

b. Using the definition of the improper integral, we have

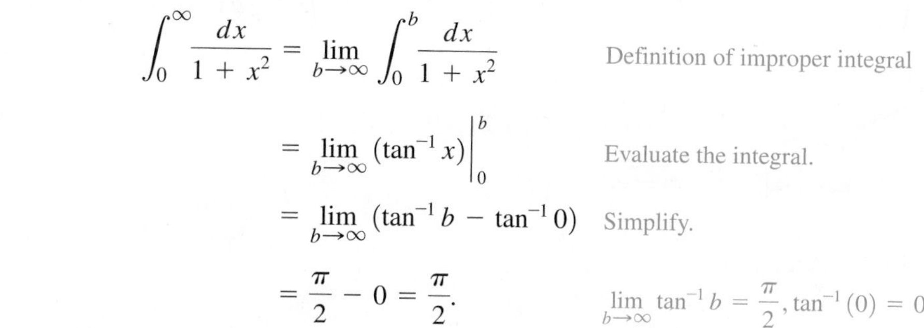

$$\int_0^\infty \frac{dx}{1+x^2} = \lim_{b\to\infty} \int_0^b \frac{dx}{1+x^2} \qquad \text{Definition of improper integral}$$

$$= \lim_{b\to\infty} \left(\tan^{-1} x\right)\Big|_0^b \qquad \text{Evaluate the integral.}$$

$$= \lim_{b\to\infty} \left(\tan^{-1} b - \tan^{-1} 0\right) \qquad \text{Simplify.}$$

$$= \frac{\pi}{2} - 0 = \frac{\pi}{2}. \qquad \lim_{b\to\infty} \tan^{-1} b = \frac{\pi}{2},\ \tan^{-1}(0) = 0$$

➤ Recall that

$$\int \frac{dx}{a^2+x^2} = \frac{1}{a}\tan^{-1}\left(\frac{x}{a}\right) + C$$

The graph of $y = \tan^{-1} x$ shows that

$$\lim_{x\to\infty} \tan^{-1} x = \frac{\pi}{2}.$$

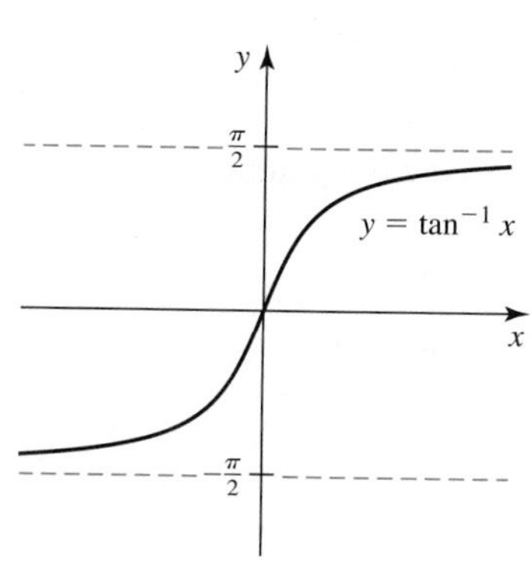

Figure 8.19 shows the region whose finite area is given by this integral.

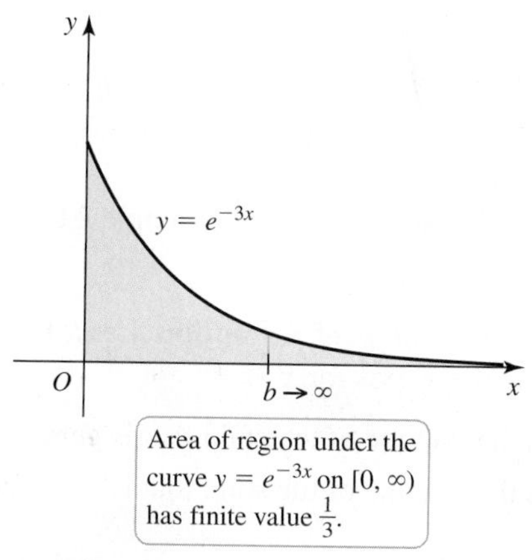

FIGURE 8.18

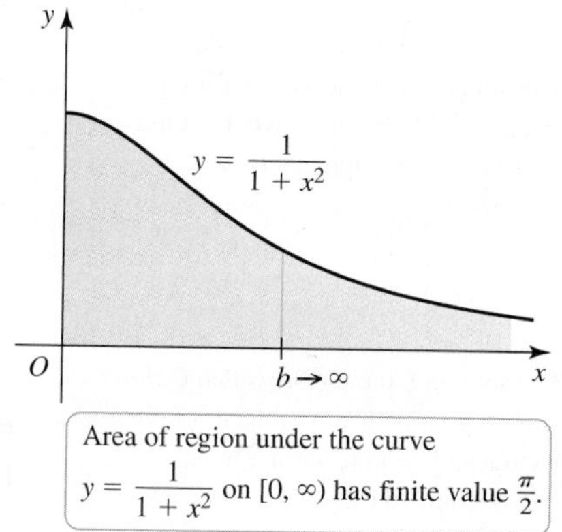

FIGURE 8.19

Related Exercises 5–20 ◀

QUICK CHECK 1 The function $f(x) = 1 + x^{-1}$ decreases to 1 as $x \to \infty$. Does $\int_1^\infty f(x)\,dx$ exist? ◀

EXAMPLE 2 **The family $f(x) = 1/x^p$** Consider the family of functions $f(x) = 1/x^p$, where p is a real number. For what values of p does $\int_1^\infty f(x)\,dx$ converge?

SOLUTION For $p > 0$, the functions $f(x) = 1/x^p$ approach zero as $x \to \infty$, with larger values of p giving greater rates of decrease (Figure 8.20). Assuming $p \neq 1$, the integral is evaluated as follows:

➤ Recall for $p \neq -1$,

$$\int \frac{1}{x^p}\,dx = \int x^{-p}\,dx = \frac{x^{-p+1}}{-p+1} + C = \frac{x^{1-p}}{1-p} + C$$

$$\int_1^\infty \frac{1}{x^p}\,dx = \lim_{b\to\infty} \int_1^b x^{-p}\,dx \qquad \text{Definition of improper integral}$$

$$= \frac{1}{1-p} \lim_{b\to\infty} \left(x^{1-p} \Big|_1^b \right) \qquad \text{Evaluate the integral on a finite interval.}$$

$$= \frac{1}{1-p} \lim_{b\to\infty} \left(b^{1-p} - 1\right) \qquad \text{Simplify.}$$

It is easiest to consider three cases.

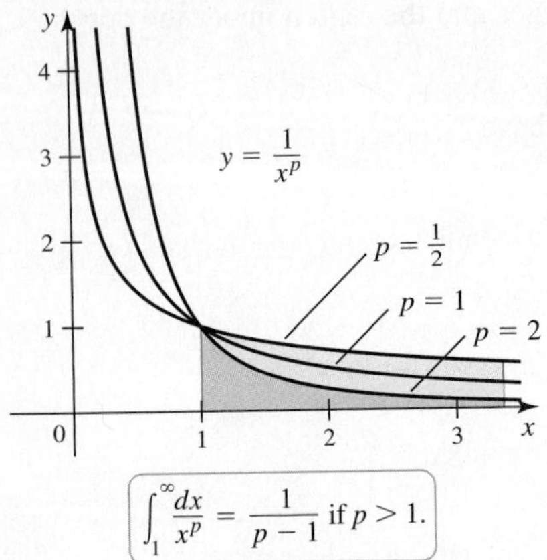

FIGURE 8.20

Case 1: If $p > 1$, then $p - 1 > 0$, and $b^{1-p} = 1/b^{p-1}$ approaches 0 as $b \to \infty$. Therefore,

$$\int_1^\infty \frac{1}{x^p}\,dx = \frac{1}{1-p} \lim_{b\to\infty} \underbrace{(b^{1-p} - 1)}_{\text{approaches } 0} = \frac{1}{p-1}.$$

Case 2: If $p < 1$, then $1 - p > 0$, and

$$\int_1^\infty \frac{1}{x^p}\,dx = \lim_{b\to\infty} \frac{1}{1-p} \underbrace{(b^{1-p} - 1)}_{\text{arbitrarily large}} = \infty.$$

Case 3: If $p = 1$, then $\int_1^\infty \frac{1}{x}\,dx = \lim_{b\to\infty} (\ln b) = \infty$; so the integral diverges.

In summary, $\int_1^\infty \frac{1}{x^p}\,dx = \frac{1}{p-1}$ if $p > 1$, and the integral diverges if $p \leq 1$.

Related Exercises 5–20 ◀

➤ Example 2 is important in the study of infinite series in Chapter 9. It shows that a continuous function f must do more than simply decrease to zero for its integral on $[a, \infty)$ to converge; it must decrease to zero *sufficiently fast*.

QUICK CHECK 2 Use the result of Example 2 to evaluate $\int_1^\infty \frac{1}{x^4}\,dx$. ◀

EXAMPLE 3 Solids of revolution Let R be the region bounded by the graph of $y = x^{-1}$ and the x-axis for $x \geq 1$.

a. What is the volume of the solid that is generated when R is revolved about the x-axis?

b. What is the volume of the solid that is generated when R is revolved about the y-axis?

➤ The solid in Example 3a, called *Gabriel's horn* or *Torricelli's trumpet*, has finite volume and infinite surface area (see Section 15.6).

SOLUTION

a. The region in question and the corresponding solid of revolution are shown in Figure 8.21. We use the disk method (Section 6.3) over the interval $[1, b]$ and then let $b \to \infty$:

$$\begin{aligned}\text{Volume} &= \pi \int_1^\infty \left(f(x)\right)^2 dx && \text{Disk method}\\ &= \pi \lim_{b\to\infty} \int_1^b \frac{1}{x^2}\,dx && \text{Definition of improper integral}\\ &= \pi \lim_{b\to\infty} \left(1 - \frac{1}{b}\right) = \pi && \text{Evaluate the integral.}\end{aligned}$$

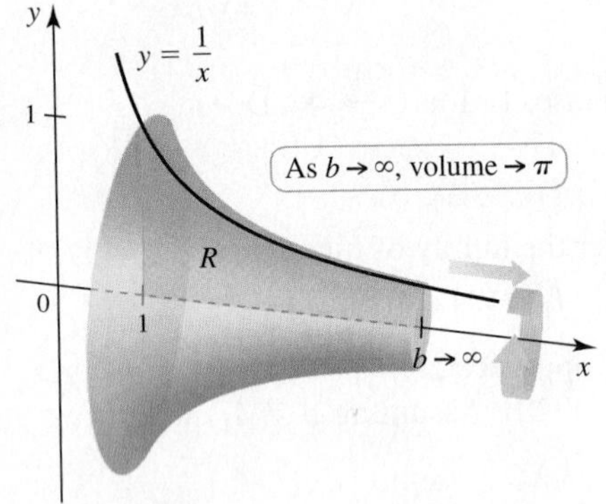

FIGURE 8.21

The improper integral exists and the solid has a volume of π cubic units.

b. The region in question and the corresponding solid of revolution are shown in Figure 8.22. Using the shell method (Section 6.4) on the interval $[1, b)$ and letting $b \to \infty$, the volume is given by

➤ Recall that if $f(x) > 0$ on $[a, b]$ and the region bounded by the graph of f and the x-axis on $[a, b]$ is revolved about the y-axis, the volume of the solid generated is

$$V = 2\pi \int_a^b x\,f(x)\,dx.$$

$$\begin{aligned}\text{volume} &= 2\pi \int_1^\infty x\,f(x)\,dx && \text{Shell method}\\ &= 2\pi \int_1^\infty 1\,dx && f(x) = x^{-1}\end{aligned}$$

$$= 2\pi \lim_{b\to\infty} \int_1^b 1\,dx \quad \text{Definition of improper integral}$$

$$= 2\pi \lim_{b\to\infty} (b - 1) \quad \text{Evaluate the integral over a finite interval.}$$

$$= \infty$$

In this case, the volume of the solid is infinite.

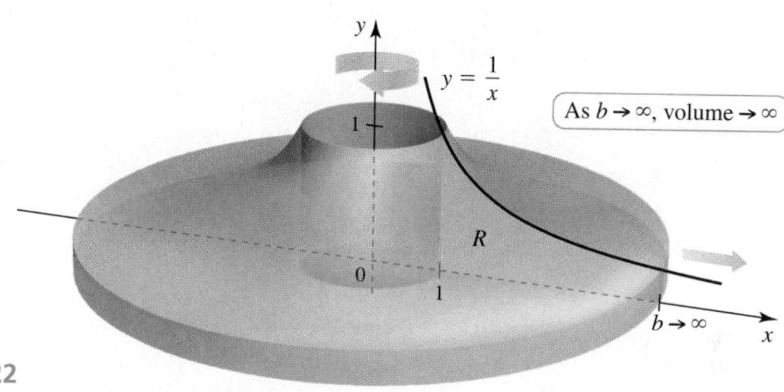

FIGURE 8.22

Related Exercises 21–26

Unbounded Integrands

Improper integrals also occur when the integrand becomes infinite somewhere on the interval of integration. Consider the function $f(x) = 1/\sqrt{x}$ (Figure 8.23). Let's examine the area of the region bounded by the graph of f between $x = 0$ and $x = 1$. Notice that f is not even defined at $x = 0$, and it increases without bound as $x \to 0^+$.

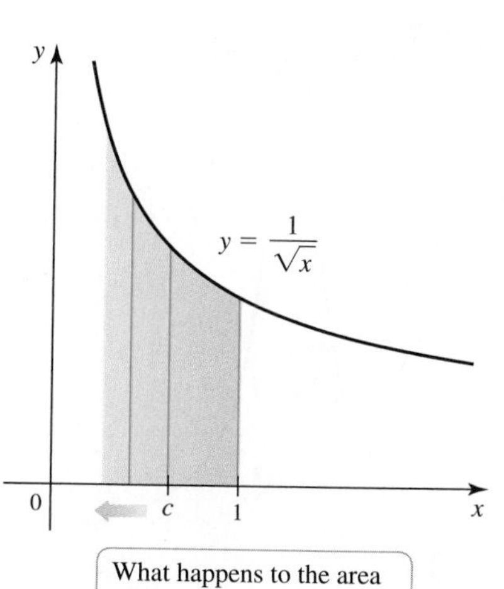

FIGURE 8.23

The idea here is to replace the lower limit 0 with a nearby positive number c and then consider the integral $\int_c^1 \frac{1}{\sqrt{x}}\,dx$, where $0 < c < 1$. We find that

$$\int_c^1 \frac{1}{\sqrt{x}}\,dx = 2\sqrt{x}\Big|_c^1 = 2(1 - \sqrt{c}).$$

To find the area of the region under the curve over the entire interval $[0, 1]$, we let $c \to 0^+$. The resulting area, which we denote $\int_0^1 \frac{dx}{\sqrt{x}}$, is

$$\lim_{c\to 0^+} \int_c^1 \frac{1}{\sqrt{x}}\,dx = \lim_{c\to 0^+} 2(1 - \sqrt{c}) = 2.$$

Once again we have a surprising result: Although the region in question has a boundary curve with infinite length, the area of the region is finite.

> The functions $f(x) = 1/x^p$ are unbounded at $x = 0$ for $p > 0$. It can be shown (Exercise 60) that
>
> $$\int_0^1 \frac{dx}{x^p} = \frac{1}{1 - p}$$
>
> provided $p < 1$. Otherwise, the integral diverges.

QUICK CHECK 3 Explain why the one-sided limit $c \to 0^+$ (instead of a two-sided limit) must be used in this example.

The preceding example shows that if a function is unbounded at a point c, it may be possible to integrate that function over an interval that contains c. The point c may occur at either endpoint or at an interior point of the interval of integration.

DEFINITIONS Improper Integrals with an Unbounded Integrand

1. Suppose f is continuous on $(a, b]$ with $\lim_{x \to a^+} f(x) = \pm\infty$. Then,

$$\int_a^b f(x)\,dx = \lim_{c \to a^+} \int_c^b f(x)\,dx,$$

provided the limit exists.

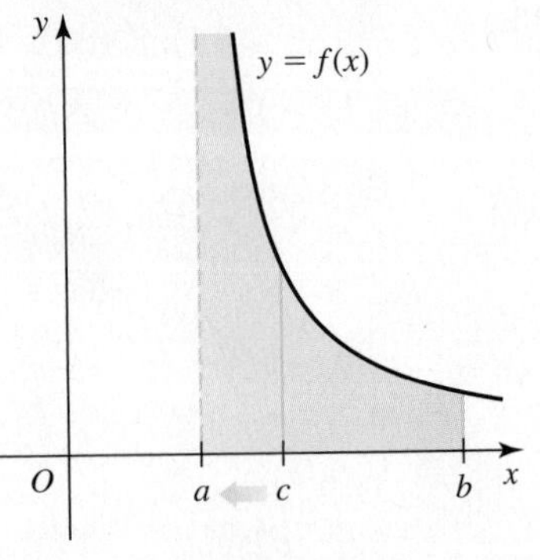

2. Suppose f is continuous on $[a, b)$ with $\lim_{x \to b^-} f(x) = \pm\infty$. Then,

$$\int_a^b f(x)\,dx = \lim_{c \to b^-} \int_a^c f(x)\,dx,$$

provided the limit exists.

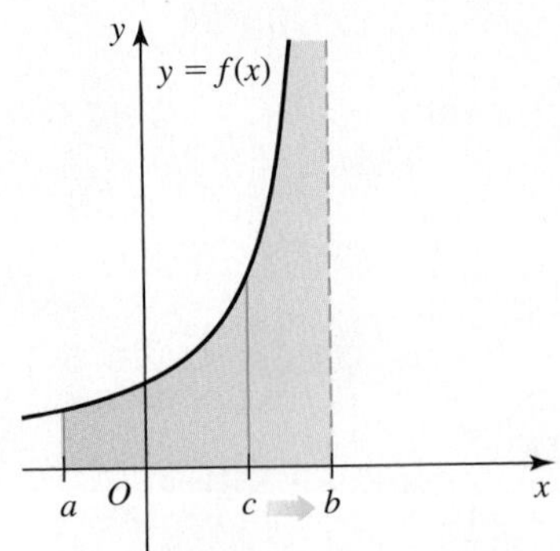

3. Suppose f is continuous on $[a, b]$ except at the interior point p where f is unbounded. Then,

$$\int_a^b f(x)\,dx = \int_a^p f(x)\,dx + \int_p^b f(x)\,dx$$

provided the improper integrals on the right side exist.

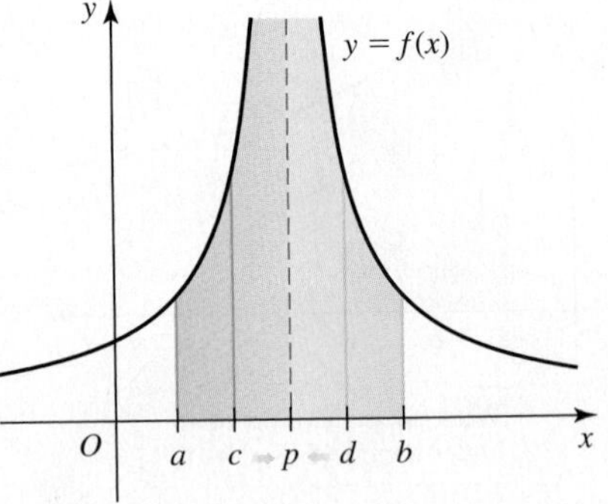

In each case, if the limit exists, the improper integral is said to **converge**; if it does not exist, the improper integral is said to **diverge**.

EXAMPLE 4 Infinite integrand Find the area of the region R between the graph of $f(x) = \dfrac{1}{\sqrt{9 - x^2}}$ and the x-axis on the interval $[-3, 3]$ (if it exists).

SOLUTION The integrand is even and has vertical asymptotes at $x = \pm 3$ (Figure 8.24). By symmetry, the area of R is given by

$$\int_{-3}^{3} \frac{1}{\sqrt{9 - x^2}}\,dx = 2\int_0^3 \frac{1}{\sqrt{9 - x^2}}\,dx,$$

➤ Recall that
$$\int \frac{dx}{\sqrt{a^2 - x^2}} = \sin^{-1}\left(\frac{x}{a}\right) + C.$$

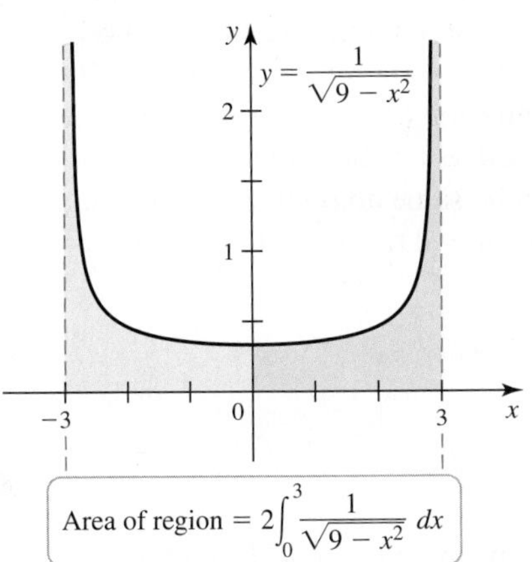

FIGURE 8.24

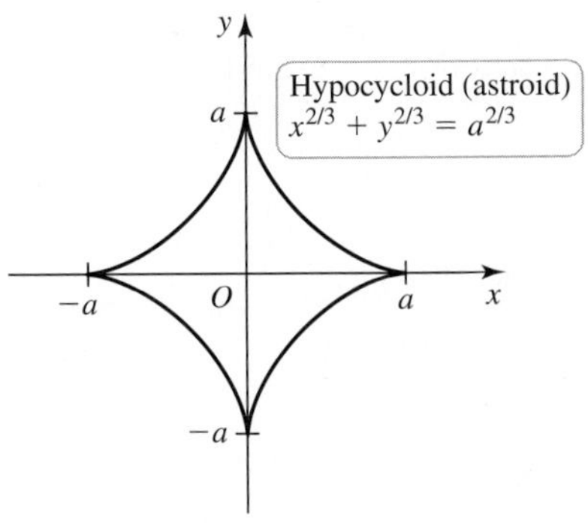

FIGURE 8.25

assuming these improper integrals exist. Because the integrand is unbounded at $x = 3$, we replace the upper limit with $x = c$, evaluate the resulting integral, and then let $c \to 3^-$:

$$\begin{aligned} 2\int_0^3 \frac{dx}{\sqrt{9 - x^2}} &= 2 \lim_{c \to 3^-} \int_0^c \frac{dx}{\sqrt{9 - x^2}} && \text{Definition of improper integral} \\ &= 2 \lim_{c \to 3^-} \sin^{-1}\left(\frac{x}{3}\right)\Big|_0^c && \text{Evaluate the integral.} \\ &= 2 \lim_{c \to 3^-} \Big(\underbrace{\sin^{-1}\left(\frac{c}{3}\right)}_{\text{approaches } \pi/2} - \underbrace{\sin^{-1} 0}_{\text{equals } 0}\Big) && \text{Simplify.} \end{aligned}$$

Note that as $c \to 3^-$, $\sin^{-1}(c/3) \to \sin^{-1} 1 = \pi/2$. Therefore, the area of R is

$$2\int_0^3 \frac{1}{\sqrt{9 - x^2}}\,dx = 2\left(\frac{\pi}{2} - 0\right) = \pi.$$

Related Exercises 27–40 ◄

EXAMPLE 5 Length of a hypocycloid Find the length L of the complete hypocycloid (or astroid; Figure 8.25) given by $x^{2/3} + y^{2/3} = a^{2/3}$, where $a > 0$.

SOLUTION Solving the equation $x^{2/3} + y^{2/3} = a^{2/3}$ for y, we find that the curve is described by the functions $f(x) = \pm(a^{2/3} - x^{2/3})^{3/2}$ (corresponding to the upper and lower halves of the curve). By symmetry, the length of the entire curve is four times the length of the curve in the first quadrant, which is given by $f(x) = (a^{2/3} - x^{2/3})^{3/2}$ for $0 \le x \le a$. We need the derivative f' for the arc length integral:

$$f'(x) = \frac{3}{2}(a^{2/3} - x^{2/3})^{1/2}\left(-\frac{2}{3}x^{-1/3}\right) = -x^{-1/3}(a^{2/3} - x^{2/3})^{1/2}$$

Now the arc length can be computed:

$$\begin{aligned} L &= 4\int_0^a \sqrt{1 + f'(x)^2}\,dx \\ &= 4\int_0^a \sqrt{1 + \left(-x^{-1/3}(a^{2/3} - x^{2/3})^{1/2}\right)^2}\,dx && \text{Substitute for } f'. \\ &= 4\int_0^a \sqrt{a^{2/3}x^{-2/3}}\,dx && \text{Simplify.} \\ &= 4a^{1/3}\int_0^a x^{-1/3}\,dx && \text{Simplify.} \end{aligned}$$

Because $x^{-1/3} \to \infty$ as $x \to 0^+$, the resulting integral is an improper integral, which is handled in the usual manner:

$$\begin{aligned} L &= 4a^{1/3} \lim_{c \to 0^+} \int_c^a x^{-1/3}\,dx && \text{Improper integral} \\ &= 4a^{1/3} \lim_{c \to 0^+} \left(\frac{3}{2}x^{2/3}\right)\Big|_c^a && \text{Integrate.} \\ &= 6a^{1/3} \lim_{c \to 0^+} (a^{2/3} - \underbrace{c^{2/3}}_{\to 0}) && \text{Simplify.} \\ &= 6a && \text{Evaluate limit.} \end{aligned}$$

The length of the entire hypocycloid is $6a$ units.

Related Exercises 41–42 ◄

EXAMPLE 6 **Bioavailability** The most efficient way to deliver a drug to its intended target site is to administer it intravenously (directly into the blood). If a drug is administered in any other way (for example, orally, nasal inhalant, or skin patch), then some of the drug is typically lost due to absorption before it gets to the blood. By definition, the bioavailability of a drug measures the effectiveness of a nonintravenous method compared to the intravenous method. The bioavailability of intravenous dosing is 100%.

Let the functions $C_i(t)$ and $C_o(t)$ give the concentration of a drug in the blood, for times $t \geq 0$, using intravenous and oral dosing, respectively. (These functions can be determined through clinical experiments.) Assuming the same amount of drug is initially administered by both methods, the bioavailability for an oral dose is defined to be

$$F = \frac{\text{AUC}_o}{\text{AUC}_i} = \frac{\int_0^\infty C_o(t)\,dt}{\int_0^\infty C_i(t)\,dt}$$

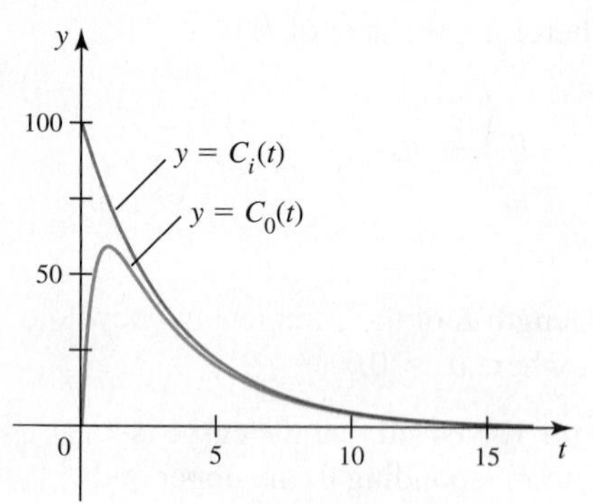

FIGURE 8.26

where AUC is used in the pharmacology literature to mean *area under the curve.*

Suppose the concentration of a certain drug in the blood in mg/L when given intravenously is $C_i(t) = 100e^{-0.3t}$, where $t \geq 0$ is measured in hours. Suppose also that concentration of the same drug when delivered orally is $C_o(t) = 90(e^{-0.3t} - e^{-2.5t})$ (Figure 8.26). Find the bioavailability of the drug.

SOLUTION Evaluating the integrals of the concentration functions, we find that

$$\begin{aligned}
\text{AUC}_i &= \int_0^\infty C_i(t)\,dt = \int_0^\infty 100e^{-0.3t}\,dt \\
&= \lim_{b\to\infty} \int_0^b 100e^{-0.3t}\,dt && \text{Improper integral} \\
&= \lim_{b\to\infty} \frac{1000}{3}(1 - \underbrace{e^{-0.3b}}_{\text{approaches zero}}) && \text{Evaluate the integral.} \\
&= \frac{1000}{3} && \text{Evaluate the limit.}
\end{aligned}$$

Similarly,

$$\begin{aligned}
\text{AUC}_o &= \int_0^\infty C_o(t)\,dt = \int_0^\infty 90(e^{-0.3t} - e^{-2.5t})\,dt \\
&= \lim_{b\to\infty} \int_0^b 90(e^{-0.3t} - e^{-2.5t})\,dt && \text{Improper integral} \\
&= \lim_{b\to\infty} [300(1 - \underbrace{e^{-0.3b}}_{\text{approaches zero}}) - 36(1 - \underbrace{e^{-2.5b}}_{\text{approaches zero}})] && \text{Evaluate the integral.} \\
&= 264 && \text{Evaluate the limt.}
\end{aligned}$$

Therefore, the bioavailability is $F = 264/(1000/3) = 0.792$, which means oral administration of the drug is roughly 80% as effective as intravenous dosing. Notice that F is the ratio of the areas under the two curves on the interval $[0, \infty)$. *Related Exercises 43–46* ◄

SECTION 8.7 EXERCISES

Review Questions

1. What are the two general ways in which an improper integral may occur?
2. Explain how to evaluate $\int_a^\infty f(x)\,dx$.
3. Explain how to evaluate $\int_0^1 x^{-1/2}\,dx$.
4. For what values of p does $\int_1^\infty x^{-p}\,dx$ converge?

Basic Skills

5–20. Infinite intervals of integration *Evaluate the following integrals or state that they diverge.*

5. $\displaystyle\int_1^\infty x^{-2}\,dx$
6. $\displaystyle\int_0^\infty \frac{dx}{(x+1)^3}$
7. $\displaystyle\int_2^\infty \frac{dx}{\sqrt{x}}$
8. $\displaystyle\int_0^\infty \frac{dx}{\sqrt[3]{x+2}}$
9. $\displaystyle\int_0^\infty e^{-2x}\,dx$
10. $\displaystyle\int_2^\infty \frac{dx}{x\ln x}$
11. $\displaystyle\int_{e^2}^\infty \frac{dx}{x\ln^p x},\ p>1$
12. $\displaystyle\int_0^\infty \frac{x}{\sqrt[5]{x^2+1}}\,dx$
13. $\displaystyle\int_0^\infty xe^{-x^2}\,dx$
14. $\displaystyle\int_0^\infty \cos x\,dx$
15. $\displaystyle\int_2^\infty \frac{\cos(\pi/x)}{x^2}\,dx$
16. $\displaystyle\int_0^\infty \frac{dx}{1+x^2}$
17. $\displaystyle\int_0^\infty \frac{x}{\sqrt{x^4+1}}\,dx$
18. $\displaystyle\int_a^\infty \sqrt{e^{-x}}\,dx$, for any finite constant a
19. $\displaystyle\int_2^\infty \frac{x}{(x+2)^2}\,dx$
20. $\displaystyle\int_1^\infty \frac{\tan^{-1} x}{x^2+1}\,dx$

21–26. Volumes on infinite intervals *Find the volume of the described solid of revolution or state that it does not exist.*

21. The region bounded by $f(x)=x^{-2}$ and the x-axis on the interval $[1,\infty)$ is revolved about the x-axis.
22. The region bounded by $f(x)=(x^2+1)^{-1/2}$ and the x-axis on the interval $[2,\infty)$ is revolved about the x-axis.
23. The region bounded by $f(x)=\sqrt{\dfrac{x+1}{x^3}}$ and the x-axis on the interval $[1,\infty)$ is revolved about the x-axis.
24. The region bounded by $f(x)=(x+1)^{-3}$ and the x-axis on the interval $[0,\infty)$ is revolved about the y-axis.
25. The region bounded by $f(x)=\dfrac{1}{\sqrt{x}\ln x}$ and the x-axis on the interval $[2,\infty)$ is revolved about the x-axis.
26. The region bounded by $f(x)=\dfrac{\sqrt{x}}{\sqrt[3]{x^2+1}}$ and the x-axis on the interval $[0,\infty)$ is revolved about the x-axis.

27–36. Integrals with unbounded integrands *Evaluate the following integrals or state that they diverge.*

27. $\displaystyle\int_0^8 \frac{dx}{\sqrt[3]{x}}$
28. $\displaystyle\int_0^{\pi/2} \tan\theta\,d\theta$
29. $\displaystyle\int_0^1 \frac{x^3}{x^4-1}\,dx$
30. $\displaystyle\int_1^\infty \frac{dx}{\sqrt[3]{x-1}}$
31. $\displaystyle\int_0^{10} \frac{dx}{\sqrt[4]{10-x}}$
32. $\displaystyle\int_1^{11} \frac{dx}{(x-3)^{2/3}}$
33. $\displaystyle\int_0^1 \ln x^2\,dx$
34. $\displaystyle\int_{-1}^1 \frac{x}{x^2+2x+1}\,dx$
35. $\displaystyle\int_{-2}^2 \frac{dx}{\sqrt{4-x^2}}$
36. $\displaystyle\int_0^{\pi/2} \sec\theta\,d\theta$

37–40. Volumes with infinite integrands *Find the volume of the described solid of revolution or state that it does not exist.*

37. The region bounded by $f(x)=(x-1)^{-1/4}$ and the x-axis on the interval $(1,2]$ is revolved about the x-axis.
38. The region bounded by $f(x)=(x^2-1)^{-1/4}$ and the x-axis on the interval $(1,2]$ is revolved about the y-axis.
39. The region bounded by $f(x)=(4-x)^{-1/3}$ and the x-axis on the interval $[0,4)$ is revolved about the y-axis.
40. The region bounded by $f(x)=(x+1)^{-3/2}$ and the y-axis on the interval $(-1,1]$ is revolved about the line $x=-1$.
41. **Arc length** Find the length of the hypocycloid (or astroid) $x^{2/3}+y^{2/3}=4$.
42. **Circumference of a circle** Use calculus to find the circumference of a circle with radius a.
43. **Bioavailability** When a drug is given intravenously, the concentration of the drug in the blood is $C_i(t)=250e^{-0.08t}$, for $t\ge 0$. When the same drug is given orally, the concentration of the drug in the blood is $C_o(t)=200(e^{-0.08t}-e^{-1.8t})$, for $t\ge 0$. Compute the bioavailability of the drug.
44. **Draining a pool** Water is drained from a swimming pool at a rate given by $R(t)=100e^{-0.05t}$ gal/hr. If the drain is left open indefinitely, how much water is drained from the pool?
45. **Maximum distance** An object moves on a line with velocity $v(t)=10/(t+1)^2$ mi/hr for $t\ge 0$. What is the maximum distance the object can travel?

46. Depletion of oil reserves Suppose that the rate at which a company extracts oil is given by $r(t) = r_0 e^{-kt}$, where $r_0 = 10^7$ barrels/yr and $k = 0.005\text{ yr}^{-1}$. Suppose also the estimate of the total oil reserve is 2×10^9 barrels. If the extraction continues indefinitely, will the reserve be exhausted?

Further Explorations

47. Explain why or why not Determine whether the following statements are true and give an explanation or counterexample.

a. If f is continuous and $0 < f(x) < g(x)$ on the interval $[0, \infty)$ and $\int_0^\infty g(x)\,dx = M < \infty$, then $\int_0^\infty f(x)\,dx$ exists.

b. If $\lim_{x\to\infty} f(x) = 1$, then $\int_0^\infty f(x)\,dx$ exists.

c. If $\int_0^1 x^{-p}\,dx$ exists, then $\int_0^1 x^{-q}\,dx$ exists, where $q > p$.

d. If $\int_1^\infty x^{-p}\,dx$ exists, then $\int_1^\infty x^{-q}\,dx$ exists, where $q > p$.

e. $\displaystyle\int_1^\infty \frac{dx}{x^{3p+2}}$ exists for $p > -\frac{1}{3}$.

48. Incorrect calculation What is wrong with this calculation?

$$\int_{-1}^{1} \frac{dx}{x} = \ln|x|\Big|_{-1}^{1} = \ln 1 - \ln 1 = 0$$

49. Using symmetry Use symmetry to evaluate the following integrals.

a. $\displaystyle\int_{-\infty}^{\infty} e^{-|x|}\,dx$ b. $\displaystyle\int_{-\infty}^{\infty} \frac{x^3}{1+x^8}\,dx$

50. Integral with a parameter For what values of p does the integral $\displaystyle\int_2^\infty \frac{dx}{x\ln^p x}$ exist and what is its value (in terms of p)?

T **51. Improper integrals by numerical methods** Use the Trapezoid Rule (Section 8.6) to approximate $\int_0^R e^{-x^2}\,dx$ with $R = 2, 4$, and 8. For each value of R, take $n = 4, 8, 16$, and 32, and compare approximations with successive values of n. Use these approximations to approximate $I = \int_0^\infty e^{-x^2}\,dx$.

52–54. Integration by parts *Use integration by parts to evaluate the following improper integrals.*

52. $\displaystyle\int_0^\infty xe^{-x}\,dx$ 53. $\displaystyle\int_0^1 x\ln x\,dx$ 54. $\displaystyle\int_1^\infty \frac{\ln x}{x^2}\,dx$

T **55. A close comparison** Graph the integrands; then evaluate and compare the values of $\int_0^\infty xe^{-x^2}\,dx$ and $\int_0^\infty x^2 e^{-x^2}\,dx$.

56. Area between curves Let R be the region bounded by the graphs of $y = x^{-p}$ and $y = x^{-q}$ for $x \ge 1$, where $q > p > 1$. Find the area of R.

57. Area between curves Let R be the region bounded by the graphs of $y = e^{-ax}$ and $y = e^{-bx}$ for $x \ge 0$, where $a > b > 0$. Find the area of R.

58. An area function Let $A(a)$ denote the area of the region bounded by $y = e^{-ax}$ and the x-axis on the interval $[0, \infty)$. Graph the function $A(a)$ for $0 < a < \infty$. Describe how the area of the region decreases as the parameter a increases.

T **59. Regions bounded by exponentials** Let $a > 0$ and let R be the region bounded by the graph of $y = e^{-ax}$ and the x-axis on the interval $[b, \infty)$.

a. Find $A(a, b)$, the area of R as a function of a and b.

b. Find the relationship $b = g(a)$ such that $A(a, b) = 2$.

c. What is the minimum value of b (call it b^*) such that when $b > b^*$, $A(a, b) = 2$ for some value of $a > 0$?

60. The family $f(x) = 1/x^p$ revisited Consider the family of functions $f(x) = 1/x^p$, where p is a real number. For what values of p does the integral $\int_0^1 f(x)\,dx$ exist? What is its value?

61. When is the volume finite? Let R be the region bounded by the graph of $f(x) = x^{-p}$ and the x-axis for $0 < x < 1$.

a. Let S be the solid generated when R is revolved about the x-axis. For what values of p is the volume of S finite?

b. Let S be the solid generated when R is revolved about the y-axis. For what values of p is the volume of S finite?

62. When is the volume finite? Let R be the region bounded by the graph of $f(x) = x^{-p}$ and the x-axis for $x \ge 1$.

a. Let S be the solid generated when R is revolved about the x-axis. For what values of p is the volume of S finite?

b. Let S be the solid generated when R is revolved about the y-axis. For what values of p is the volume of S finite?

T **63–66. By all means** *Use any means to verify (or approximate as closely as possible) the following integrals.*

63. $\displaystyle\int_0^{\pi/2} \ln(\sin x)\,dx = \int_0^{\pi/2} \ln(\cos x)\,dx = -\frac{\pi\ln 2}{2}$

64. $\displaystyle\int_0^\infty \frac{\sin^2 x}{x^2}\,dx = \frac{\pi}{2}$ 65. $\displaystyle\int_0^\infty \ln\left(\frac{e^x+1}{e^x-1}\right)dx = \frac{\pi^2}{4}$

66. $\displaystyle\int_0^1 \frac{\ln x}{1+x}\,dx = -\frac{\pi^2}{12}$

Applications

67. Perpetual annuity Imagine that today you deposit \$$B$ in a savings account that earns interest at a rate of $p\%$ per year compounded continuously (see Section 7.4). The goal is to draw an income of \$$I$ per year from the account forever. The amount of money that must be deposited is $B = I\int_0^\infty e^{-rt}\,dt$, where $r = p/100$. Suppose you find an account that earns 12% interest annually and you wish to have an income from the account of \$5000 per year. How much must you deposit today?

68. Draining a tank Water is drained from a 3000-gal tank at a rate that starts at 100 gal/hr and decreases continuously by 5%/hr. If the drain is left open indefinitely, how much water is drained from the tank? Can a full tank be emptied at this rate?

69. Decaying oscillations Let $a > 0$ and b be real numbers. Use integration to confirm the following identities.

a. $\displaystyle\int_0^\infty e^{-ax}\cos bx\,dx = \frac{a}{a^2+b^2}$

b. $\displaystyle\int_0^\infty e^{-ax}\sin bx\,dx = \frac{b}{a^2+b^2}$

70. **Electronic chips** Suppose the probability that a particular computer chip fails after $t = a$ hours of operation is $0.00005 \int_a^{\infty} e^{-0.00005t}\, dt$.

a. Find the probability that the computer chip fails after 15,000 hr of operation.

b. Of the chips that are still operating after 15,000 hr, what fraction of these will operate for at least another 15,000 hr?

c. Evaluate $0.00005 \int_0^{\infty} e^{-0.00005t}\, dt$ and interpret its meaning.

71. **Average lifetime** The average time until a computer chip fails (see Exercise 70) is $0.00005 \int_0^{\infty} te^{-0.00005t}\, dt$. Find this value.

72. **The Eiffel Tower property** Let R be the region between the curves $y = e^{-cx}$ and $y = -e^{-cx}$ on the interval $[a, \infty)$, where $a \geq 0$ and $c > 0$. The center of mass of R is located at $(\bar{x}, 0)$, where $\bar{x} = \dfrac{\int_a^{\infty} xe^{-cx}\, dx}{\int_a^{\infty} e^{-cx}\, dx}$. (The profile of the Eiffel Tower is modeled by the two exponential curves.)

a. For $a = 0$ and $c = 2$, sketch the curves that define R and find the center of mass of R. Indicate the location of the center of mass.

b. With $a = 0$ and $c = 2$, find equations of the tangent lines to the curves at the points corresponding to $x = 0$.

c. Show that the tangent lines intersect at the center of mass.

d. Show that this same property holds for any $a \geq 0$ and any $c > 0$; that is, the tangent lines to the curves $y = \pm e^{-cx}$ at $x = a$ intersect at the center of mass of R.

(*Source:* P. Weidman and I. Pinelis, *Comptes Rendu, Mechanique* 332 (2004): 571–584. Also see the Guided Projects.)

73. **Escape velocity and black holes** The work required to launch an object from the surface of Earth to outer space is given by $W = \int_R^{\infty} F(x)\, dx$, where $R = 6370$ km is the approximate radius of Earth, $F(x) = GMm/x^2$ is the gravitational force between Earth and the object, G is the gravitational constant, M is the mass of Earth, m is the mass of the object, and $GM = 4 \times 10^{14}\ \text{m}^3/\text{s}^2$.

a. Find the work required to launch an object in terms of m.

b. What escape velocity v_e is required to give the object a kinetic energy $\frac{1}{2}mv_e^2$ equal to W?

c. The French scientist Laplace anticipated the existence of black holes in the 18th century with the following argument: If a body has an escape velocity that equals or exceeds the speed of light, $c = 300{,}000$ km/s, then light cannot escape the body and it cannot be seen. Show that such a body has a radius $R \leq 2GM/c^2$. For Earth to be a black hole, what would its radius need to be?

74. **Adding a proton to a nucleus** The nucleus of an atom is positively charged because it consists of positively charged protons and uncharged neutrons. To bring a free proton toward a nucleus, a repulsive force $F(r) = kqQ/r^2$ must be overcome, where $q = 1.6 \times 10^{-19}$ C is the charge on the proton, $k = 9 \times 10^9\ \text{N-m}^2/\text{C}^2$, Q is the charge on the nucleus, and r is the distance between the center of the nucleus and the proton. Find the work required to bring a free proton (assumed to be a point mass) from a large distance $(r \to \infty)$ to the edge of a nucleus that has a charge $Q = 50q$ and a radius of 6×10^{-11} m.

T 75. **Gaussians** An important function in statistics is the Gaussian (or normal distribution, or bell-shaped curve), $f(x) = e^{-ax^2}$.

a. Graph the Gaussian for $a = 0.5, 1$, and 2.

b. Given that $\displaystyle\int_{-\infty}^{\infty} e^{-ax^2}\, dx = \sqrt{\frac{\pi}{a}}$, compute the area under the curves in part (a).

c. Complete the square to evaluate $\int_{-\infty}^{\infty} e^{-(ax^2+bx+c)}\, dx$, where $a > 0$, b, and c are real numbers.

76–80. Laplace transforms *A powerful tool in solving problems in engineering and physics is the Laplace transform. Given a function $f(t)$, the Laplace transform is a new function $F(s)$ defined by*

$$F(s) = \int_0^{\infty} e^{-st} f(t)\, dt,$$

where we assume that s is a positive real number. For example, to find the Laplace transform of $f(t) = e^{-t}$, the following improper integral is evaluated using integration by parts:

$$F(s) = \int_0^{\infty} e^{-st} e^{-t}\, dt = \int_0^{\infty} e^{-(s+1)t}\, dt = \frac{1}{s+1}$$

Verify the following Laplace transforms, where a is a real number.

76. $f(t) = 1 \quad \to \quad F(s) = \dfrac{1}{s}$

77. $f(t) = e^{at} \quad \to \quad F(s) = \dfrac{1}{s-a}$

78. $f(t) = t \quad \to \quad F(s) = \dfrac{1}{s^2}$

79. $f(t) = \sin at \quad \to \quad F(s) = \dfrac{a}{s^2 + a^2}$

80. $f(t) = \cos at \quad \to \quad F(s) = \dfrac{s}{s^2 + a^2}$

Additional Exercises

81. **Improper integrals** Evaluate the following improper integrals (Putnam Exam, 1939).

a. $\displaystyle\int_1^3 \frac{dx}{\sqrt{(x-1)(3-x)}}$ b. $\displaystyle\int_1^{\infty} \frac{dx}{e^{x+1} + e^{3-x}}$

82. **A better way** Compute $\int_0^1 \ln x\, dx$ using integration by parts. Then explain why $-\int_0^{\infty} e^{-x}\, dx$ (an easier integral) gives the same result.

83. **Competing powers** For what values of $p > 0$ is

$$\int_0^{\infty} \frac{dx}{x^p + x^{-p}} < \infty?$$

84. **Gamma function** The gamma function is defined by $\Gamma(p) = \int_0^{\infty} x^{p-1} e^{-x}\, dx$, for p not equal to zero or a negative integer.

a. Use the reduction formula

$$\int_0^{\infty} x^p e^{-x}\, dx = p \int_0^{\infty} x^{p-1} e^{-x}\, dx \quad \text{for } p = 1, 2, 3, \ldots$$

to show that $\Gamma(p + 1) = p!$ (p factorial).

b. Use the substitution $x = u^2$ and the fact that $\int_0^\infty e^{-u^2}\,du = \frac{\sqrt{\pi}}{2}$ to show that $\Gamma\left(\frac{1}{2}\right) = \sqrt{\pi}$.

85. Many methods needed Show that $\int_0^\infty \frac{\sqrt{x}\ln x}{(1+x)^2}\,dx = \pi$ in the following steps.

a. Integrate by parts with $u = \sqrt{x}\ln x$.
b. Change variables by letting $y = 1/x$.
c. Show that $\int_0^1 \frac{\ln x}{\sqrt{x}(1+x)}\,dx = -\int_1^\infty \frac{\ln x}{\sqrt{x}(1+x)}\,dx$ and conclude that $\int_0^\infty \frac{\ln x}{\sqrt{x}(1+x)}\,dx = 0$.
d. Evaluate the remaining integral using the change of variables $z = \sqrt{x}$.

(*Source: Mathematics Magazine* 59, no. 1, February 1986: 49)

86. Riemann sums to integrals Show that $L = \lim_{n\to\infty}\left(\frac{1}{n}\ln n! - \ln n\right) = -1$ in the following steps.

a. Note that $n! = n(n-1)(n-2)\cdots 1$ and use $\ln(ab) = \ln a + \ln b$ to show that

$$L = \lim_{n\to\infty}\left[\left(\frac{1}{n}\sum_{k=1}^{n}\ln k\right) - \ln n\right] = \lim_{n\to\infty}\frac{1}{n}\sum_{k=1}^{n}\ln\left(\frac{k}{n}\right)$$

b. Identify the limit of this sum as a Riemann sum for $\int_0^1 \ln x\,dx$. Integrate this improper integral by parts and reach the desired conclusion.

QUICK CHECK ANSWERS

1. The integral diverges. $\lim_{b\to\infty}\int_1^b (1 + x^{-1})\,dx = \lim_{b\to\infty}(x + \ln x)\big|_1^b$ does not exist. **2.** $\frac{1}{3}$ **3.** c must approach 0 through values in the interval of integration $(0, 1)$. Therefore, $c \to 0^+$.

8.8 Introduction to Differential Equations

> If you read Sections 4.8 and 6.1, then you have already encountered a preview of differential equations. Given the derivative of a function, these two sections show how to find the function itself by integration. This process amounts to solving a differential equation.

If you had to demonstrate the utility of mathematics to a skeptic, a convincing way would be to cite *differential equations*. This vast subject lies at the heart of mathematical modeling and is used in engineering, the natural and biological sciences, economics, management, and finance. Differential equations rely heavily on calculus, and they are usually studied in advanced courses that follow calculus. Nevertheless, you have now seen enough calculus to understand a brief survey of differential equations and appreciate their power.

An Overview

A differential equation involves an unknown function y and its derivatives. The unknown in a differential equation is not a number (as in an algebraic equation), but rather a function or a relationship. Here are some examples of differential equations:

$$\text{(A)}\ \frac{dy}{dx} + 4y = \cos x \qquad \text{(B)}\ \frac{d^2y}{dx^2} + 16y = 0 \qquad \text{(C)}\ y'(t) = 0.1y(100 - y)$$

In each case, the goal is to find a function y that satisfies the equation.

> Common choices for the independent variable in a differentiable equation are x and t, with t being used for time-dependent problems.

> A *linear* differential equation cannot have terms such as y^2, yy', or $\sin y$, where y is the unknown function. The most general first-order linear equation has the form $y' + py = q$, where p and q are functions of the independent variable.

The **order** of a differential equation is the order of the highest-order derivative that appears in the equation. Of the three differential equations just given, (A) and (C) are first order, and (B) is second order. A differential equation is **linear** if the unknown function and its derivatives appear only to the first power and are not composed with other functions. Of these equations, (A) and (B) are linear, but (C) is nonlinear (because the right side contains y^2).

Solving a first-order differential equation requires integration—you must "undo" the derivative $y'(t)$ in order to find $y(t)$. Integration introduces an arbitrary constant, so the **general solution** of a first-order differential equation involves one arbitrary constant. Similarly, the general solution of a second-order differential equation involves two arbitrary constants; with an nth-order differential equation, the general solution involves n arbitrary constants.

As discussed in Section 4.8, if a differential equation is accompanied by *initial conditions* then it is possible to determine specific values of the arbitrary constants. A differential equation together with the appropriate number of initial conditions is called an **initial value problem**. The solution of an initial value problem must satisfy both the differential equation and the initial conditions.

EXAMPLE 1 **An initial value problem** Solve the initial value problem

$$y'(t) = 10e^{-t/2}, \qquad y(0) = 4.$$

SOLUTION The solution is found by taking an indefinite integral of both sides of the differential equation with respect to t:

> The two integrals in this calculation both produce an arbitrary constant of integration. These two constants may be combined as one arbitrary constant.

$$\underbrace{\int y'(t)\,dt}_{y(t)} = \int 10e^{-t/2}\,dt \quad \text{Integrate both sides with respect to } t.$$

$$y(t) = -20e^{-t/2} + C \quad \text{Evaluate integrals; } y(t) \text{ is an antiderivative of } y'(t).$$

We have found the general solution, which involves one arbitrary constant. To determine its value, we use the initial condition by substituting $t = 0$ and $y = 4$ into the general solution:

$$y(0) = (-20e^{-t/2} + C)\big|_{t=0} = -20 + C = 4 \Rightarrow C = 24$$

Therefore, the solution of the initial value problem is $y(t) = -20e^{-t/2} + 24$ (Figure 8.27). You should check that this function satisfies both the differential equation and the initial condition.

Related Exercises 9–12 ◀

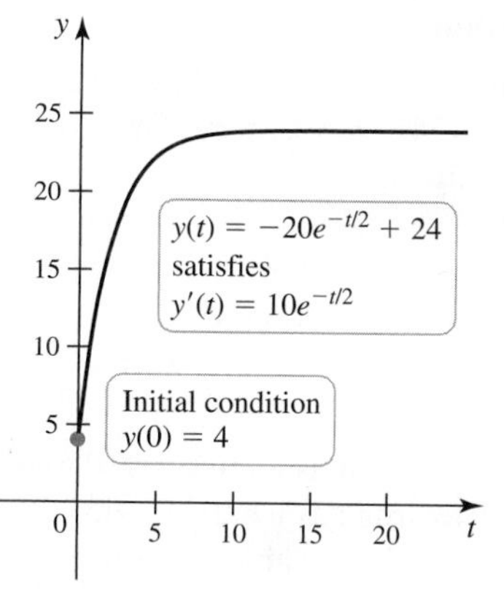

FIGURE 8.27

QUICK CHECK 1 What is the order of the equation in Example 1? Is it linear or nonlinear? ◀

A First-Order Linear Differential Equation

In Section 7.4 we studied functions that exhibit exponential growth or decay. Such functions have the property that their rate of change at a particular point is proportional to the function value at that point. In other words, these functions satisfy a first-order differential equation of the form $y'(t) = ky(t)$, where k is a real number. You should verify by substitution that the function $y(t) = Ce^{kt}$ is the general solution of this equation, where C is an arbitrary constant.

> The solution of the equation $y'(t) = ky(t)$ is $y(t) = Ce^{kt}$, so it models exponential growth when $k > 0$ and exponential decay when $k < 0$.

Now, let's generalize and consider the first-order linear equation $y'(t) = ky(t) + b$, where k and b are real numbers. Solutions of this equation have a wide range of behavior (depending on the values of k and b), and the equation itself has many modeling applications. Specifically, the terms of the equation have the following meaning:

$$\underbrace{y'(t)}_{\text{rate of change of } y} = \underbrace{ky(t)}_{\text{natural growth or decay rate of } y} + \underbrace{b}_{\text{growth or decay rate due to external effects}}$$

For example, if y represents the number of fish in a hatchery, then $ky(t)$ (with $k > 0$) models exponential growth in the fish population, in the absence of other factors, and $b < 0$ is the harvesting rate at which the population is depleted. As another example, if y represents the amount of a drug in the blood, then $ky(t)$ (with $k < 0$) models exponential decay of the drug through the kidneys, and $b > 0$ is the rate at which the drug is added to the blood intravenously. We can give an explicit solution for the equation $y'(t) = ky(t) + b$.

We begin by dividing both sides of the equation $y'(t) = ky + b$ by $ky + b$, which gives

$$\frac{y'(t)}{ky + b} = 1.$$

Because the goal is to determine $y(t)$ from $y'(t)$, we integrate both sides of this equation with respect to t:

$$\int \frac{y'(t)}{ky + b}\,dt = \int dt.$$

The factor $y'(t)\,dt$ on the left side is simply dy. Making this substitution and evaluating the integrals, we have

> The arbitrary constant of integration needs to be included in only one of the integrals.

$$\int \frac{dy}{ky + b} = \int dt \quad \text{or} \quad \frac{1}{k}\ln|ky + b| = t + C.$$

For the moment, we assume that $ky + b \geq 0$, or $y \geq -b/k$, so the absolute value may be removed. Multiplying through by k, exponentiating both sides of the equation, and solving for y gives the solution $y(t) = Ce^{kt} - b/k$. In the process of solving for y, we have successively redefined C; for example, if C is arbitrary, then kC and e^C are also arbitrary. You can also show that if $ky + b < 0$, or $y < -b/k$, then the same solution results.

> The equation $y'(t) = ky(t) + b$ is one of many first-order linear differential equations. If k and b are functions of t, the equation is still first-order linear.

Solution of a First-Order Linear Differential Equation

The general solution of the first-order linear equation $y'(t) = ky(t) + b$, where k and b are real numbers, is $y(t) = Ce^{kt} - b/k$, where C is an arbitrary constant. Given an initial condition, the value of C may be determined.

QUICK CHECK 2 Verify by substitution that $y(t) = Ce^{kt} - b/k$ is a solution of $y'(t) = ky(t) + b$. ◄

EXAMPLE 2 An initial value problem for drug dosing A drug is administered to a patient through an intravenous line at a rate of 6 mg/hr. The drug has a half-life that corresponds to a rate constant of 0.03/hr (Section 7.4). Let $y(t)$ be the amount of drug in the blood for $t \geq 0$. Solve the following initial value problem and interpret the solution.

$$\text{Differential equation:} \quad y'(t) = -0.03y(t) + 6$$
$$\text{Initial condition:} \quad y(0) = 0$$

SOLUTION The equation has the form $y'(t) = ky(t) + b$, where $k = -0.03$ and $b = 6$. Therefore, the general solution is $y(t) = Ce^{-0.03t} + 200$. To determine the value of C for this particular problem, we substitute $y(0) = 0$ into the general solution. We find that $y(0) = C + 200 = 0$, which implies that $C = -200$. Therefore, the solution of the initial value problem is

$$y(t) = -200e^{-0.03t} + 200 = 200(1 - e^{-0.03t}).$$

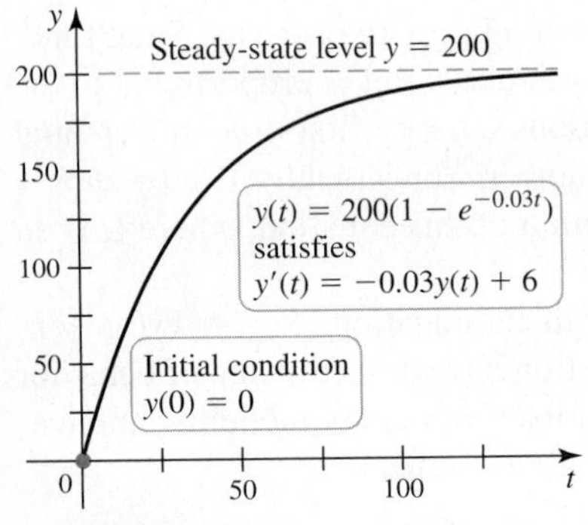

FIGURE 8.28

The graph of the solution (Figure 8.28) reveals an important fact: The amount of drug in the blood increases monotonically, but it approaches a steady-state level of

$$\lim_{t\to\infty} y(t) = \lim_{t\to\infty} [200(1 - e^{-0.03t})] = 200 \text{ mg}.$$

Related Exercises 13–22 ◄

QUICK CHECK 3 What is the solution of $y'(t) = 3y(t) + 6$ with the initial condition $y(0) = 14$? ◄

Separable First-Order Differential Equations

The most general first-order differential equation has the form $y'(t) = F(t, y)$, where F is a given function that may involve both variables. We have a *chance* of solving such an equation if it can be written in the form

$$g(y)\,y'(t) = h(t),$$

in which the terms that involve y appear on one side of the equation *separated* from the terms that involve t. An equation that can be written in this form is said to be **separable**.

The solution of the linear equation $y'(t) = ky(t) + b$ given above is a specific example of the method for solving separable differential equations. In general, we solve the separable equation $g(y)\,y'(t) = h(t)$ by integrating both sides of the equation with respect to t:

$$\int g(y)\underbrace{y'(t)\,dt}_{dy} = \int h(t)\,dt \quad \text{Integrate both sides.}$$

$$\int g(y)\,dy = \int h(t)\,dt \quad \text{Change of variables on the left side}$$

➤ The result of this change of variables is that the left side of the equation is integrated with respect to y and the right side is integrated with respect to t. With this justification, this shortcut is permissible and is often taken.

A change of variables on the left side of the equation leaves us with two integrals to evaluate, one with respect to y and one with respect to t. Finding a solution depends on evaluating these integrals.

QUICK CHECK 4 Write $y'(t) = (t^2 + 1)/y^3$ in separated form. ◄

EXAMPLE 3 **A separable equation** Find the function that satisfies the following initial value problem.

$$\frac{dy}{dx} = y^2 e^{-x}, \qquad y(0) = \frac{1}{2}$$

SOLUTION The equation can be written in separable form when we divide both sides of the equation by y^2 to give $y'(x)/y^2 = e^{-x}$. We now integrate both sides of the equation with respect to x and evaluate the resulting integrals:

$$\int \frac{1}{y^2}\underbrace{y'(x)\,dx}_{dy} = \int e^{-x}\,dx$$

$$\int \frac{dy}{y^2} = \int e^{-x}\,dx \quad \text{Change of variables on the left side}$$

$$-\frac{1}{y} = -e^{-x} + C \quad \text{Evaluate the integrals.}$$

Solving for y gives the general solution

$$y(x) = \frac{1}{e^{-x} - C}.$$

The initial condition $y(0) = \frac{1}{2}$ implies that

$$y(0) = \frac{1}{e^0 - C} = \frac{1}{1 - C} = \frac{1}{2}.$$

Solving for C gives $C = -1$, so the solution to the initial value problem is $y(x) = \dfrac{1}{e^{-x} + 1}$. The solution (Figure 8.29) has a graph that begins at $\left(0, \frac{1}{2}\right)$ and increases to approach the asymptote $y = 1$ because $\lim_{x\to\infty} \dfrac{1}{e^{-x} + 1} = 1$. *Related Exercises 23–32* ◄

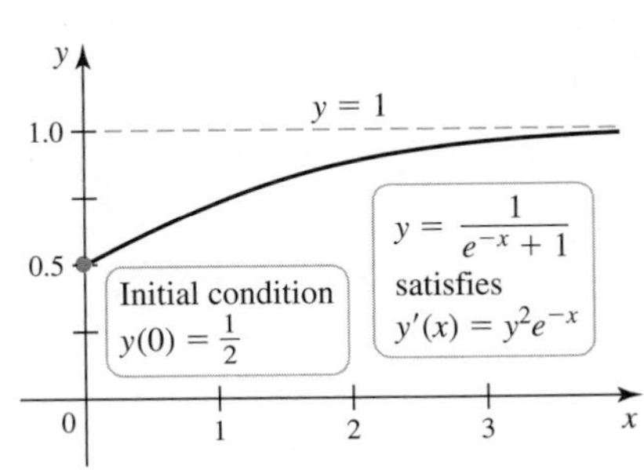

FIGURE 8.29

➤ The logistic equation is used to describe the population of many different species as well as the spread of rumors and epidemics (Exercises 33–34).

EXAMPLE 4 **Logistic population growth** Fifty fruit flies are in a large container at the beginning of an experiment. Let $P(t)$ be the number of fruit flies in the container t days later. At first, the population grows exponentially, but due to limited space and food supply, the growth rate decreases and the population is prevented from growing without bound. This experiment can be modeled by the *logistic equation*

$$\frac{dP}{dt} = 0.1P\left(1 - \frac{P}{300}\right)$$

together with the initial condition $P(0) = 50$. Solve this initial value problem.

SOLUTION We see that the equation is separable by writing it in the form

$$\frac{1}{P\left(1 - \frac{P}{300}\right)} \cdot \frac{dP}{dt} = 0.1.$$

Integrating both sides with respect to t leads to the equation

$$\int \frac{1}{P\left(1 - \frac{P}{300}\right)}\,dP = \underbrace{\int 0.1\,dt}_{0.1t + C} \qquad (1)$$

The integral on the right side of equation (1) is $\int 0.1\,dt = 0.1t + C$. Because the integrand on the left side is a rational function in P, we use partial fractions. You should verify that

$$\frac{1}{P\left(1 - \frac{P}{300}\right)} = \frac{300}{P(300 - P)} = \frac{1}{P} + \frac{1}{300 - P},$$

and therefore,

$$\int \frac{1}{P\left(1 - \frac{P}{300}\right)}\,dP = \int \left(\frac{1}{P} + \frac{1}{300 - P}\right) dP = \ln\left|\frac{P}{300 - P}\right| + C.$$

Equation (1) now becomes

➤ Notice again that two constants of integration have been combined into one.

$$\ln\left|\frac{P}{300 - P}\right| = 0.1t + C. \qquad (2)$$

The final step is to solve for P, which is tangled up inside the logarithm. To simplify matters, we assume that if the initial population $P(0)$ is between 0 and 300, then $0 < P(t) < 300$ for all $t > 0$. This assumption (which can be verified independently) allows us to remove the absolute value on the left side of equation (2).

Using the initial condition $P(0) = 50$ and solving for C (Exercise 60), we find that $C = \ln \frac{1}{5}$. It follows that the solution of the initial value problem is

➤ It is always a good idea to check that the final solution satisfies the initial condition. In this case, $P(0) = 50$.

$$P(t) = \frac{300}{1 + 5e^{-0.1t}}.$$

The graph of the solution shows that the population increases, but not without bound (Figure 8.30). Instead, it approaches a steady state value of

$$\lim_{t\to\infty} P(t) = \lim_{t\to\infty} \frac{300}{1 + 5e^{-0.1t}} = 300,$$

which is the maximum population that the environment (space and food supply) can sustain. This steady-state population is called the **carrying capacity**.

Related Exercises 33–34 ◄

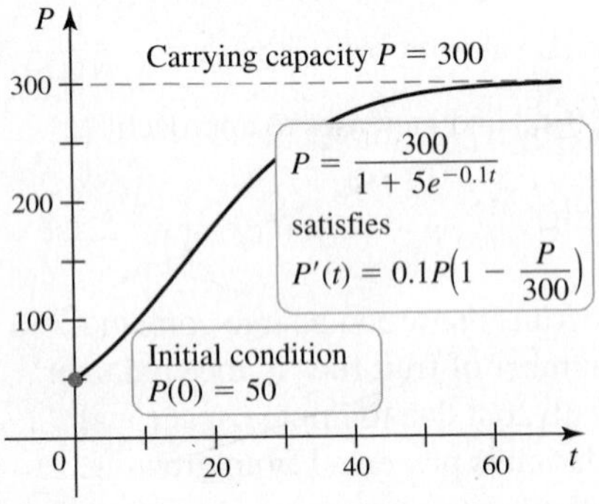

FIGURE 8.30

Direction Fields

The geometry of first-order differential equations is beautifully displayed using *direction fields*. Consider the general first-order differential equation $y'(t) = F(t, y)$, where F is a given function involving t and/or y. A solution of this equation has the property that at each point (t, y) of the solution curve, the slope of the curve is $F(t, y)$. A **direction field** is simply a picture that shows the slope of the solution at selected points of the ty-plane.

➤ Drawing direction fields by hand can be tedious. It's best to use a calculator or software.

For example, consider the equation $y'(t) = y^2e^{-t}$. We choose a regular grid of points in the ty-plane, and at each point (t, y) we make a small line segment with slope y^2e^{-t}. The line segment at a point P gives the slope of the solution curve that passes through P (Figure 8.31). For example, along the t-axis ($y = 0$), the slopes of the line segments are $F(t, 0) = 0$. And along the y-axis ($t = 0$), the slopes of the line segments are $F(0, y) = y^2$.

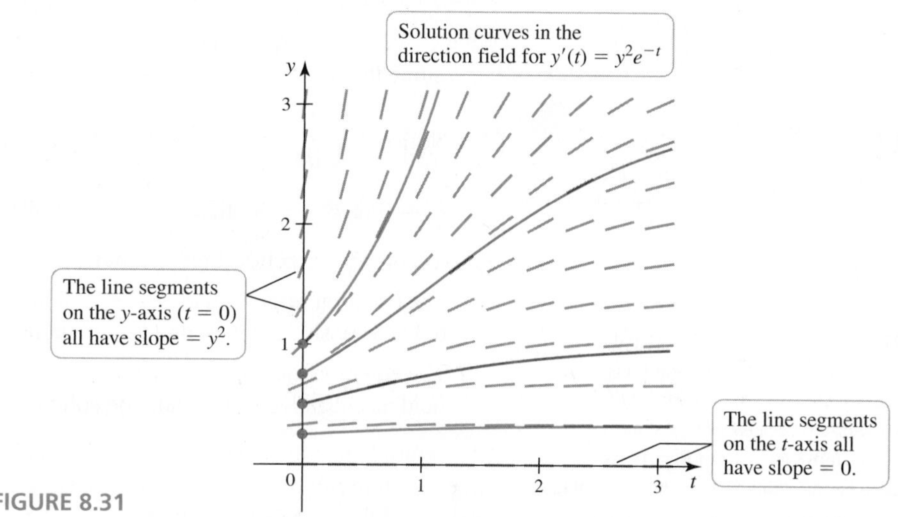

FIGURE 8.31

Now suppose an initial condition $y(a) = A$ is given. We start at the point (a, A) in the direction field and sketch a curve in the positive t-direction that follows the flow of the direction field. At each point of the solution curve, the slope matches the direction field. A different initial condition gives a different solution curve (Figure 8.31). The collection of solution curves for several different initial conditions is a representation of the general solution of the equation.

EXAMPLE 5 Direction field for a linear equation Sketch the direction field for the first-order linear equation $y'(t) = 3y - 6$. For what initial conditions at $t = 0$ are the solutions increasing?

SOLUTION Notice that $y'(t) = 0$ when $y = 2$. Therefore, the direction field has a horizontal line at $y = 2$. This line corresponds to an *equilibrium solution*, a solution that is constant in time: If the initial condition is $y(0) = 2$, then the solution is $y = 2$ for $t \geq 0$.

We also see that $y'(t) > 0$ when $y > 2$. Therefore, the direction field has small line segments with positive slopes above the line $y = 2$. When $y < 2$, $y'(t) < 0$, which means the direction field has small line segments with negative slopes below the line $y = 2$ (Figure 8.32).

Using the direction field, it now follows that if the initial condition satisfies $y(0) > 2$, the resulting solution increases for $t \geq 0$. If the initial condition satisfies $y(0) < 2$, the resulting solution decreases for $t \geq 0$. *Related Exercises 35–40* ◄

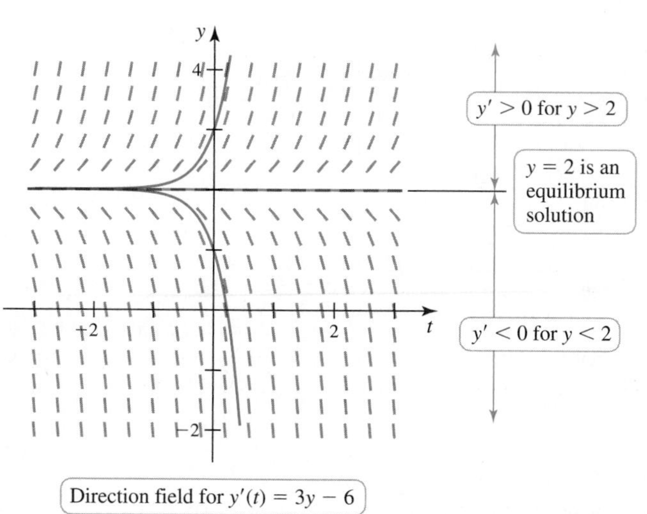

FIGURE 8.32

QUICK CHECK 5 In Example 5, describe the behavior of the solution that results from the initial condition (a) $y(-1) = 3$ and (b) $y(-2) = 0$. ◄

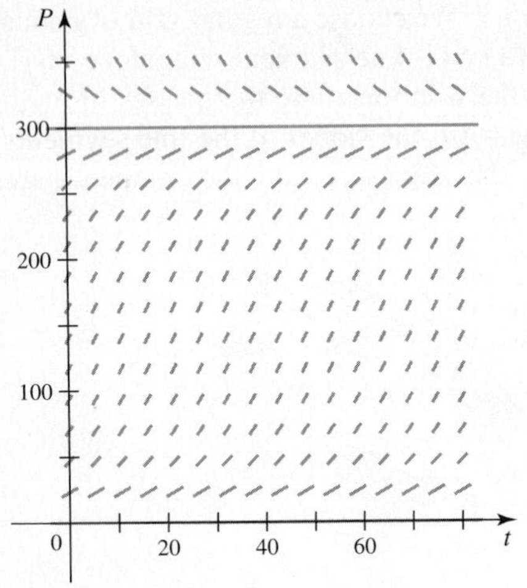

FIGURE 8.33

➤ The constant solutions $P = 0$ and $P = 300$ are equilibrium solutions. The solution $P = 0$ is an *unstable* equilibrium because nearby solution curves move away from $P = 0$. By contrast, the solution $P = 300$ is a stable equilibrium because nearby solution curves are attracted to $P = 300$.

EXAMPLE 6 Direction field for the logistic equation Consider the logistic equation of Example 4,

$$\frac{dP}{dt} = 0.1P\left(1 - \frac{P}{300}\right) \quad \text{for } t \geq 0$$

and its direction field (Figure 8.33). Sketch the solution curves corresponding to the initial conditions $P(0) = 50$, $P(0) = 150$, and $P(0) = 350$.

SOLUTION A few preliminary observations are useful. Because P represents a population, we assume that $P \geq 0$.

- Notice that $\frac{dP}{dt} = 0$ when $P = 0$ or $P = 300$. Therefore, if the initial population is $P = 0$ or $P = 300$, then $\frac{dP}{dt} = 0$ for all $t \geq 0$, and the solution is constant. For this reason, the direction field has horizontal line segments at $P = 0$ and $P = 300$.
- The equation implies that $dP/dt > 0$ provided $0 < P < 300$. Therefore, the direction field has positive slopes, and the solutions are increasing for $t \geq 0$ and $0 < P < 300$.
- The equation also implies that $dP/dt < 0$ provided $P > 300$. Therefore, the direction field has negative slopes, and the solutions are decreasing for $t \geq 0$ and $P > 300$.

Figure 8.34 shows the direction field with three solution curves corresponding to three different initial conditions. The horizontal line $P = 300$ corresponds to the carrying capacity of the population. We see that if the initial population is less than 300, the resulting solution increases to the carrying capacity from below. If the initial population is greater than 300, the resulting solution decreases to the carrying capacity from above.

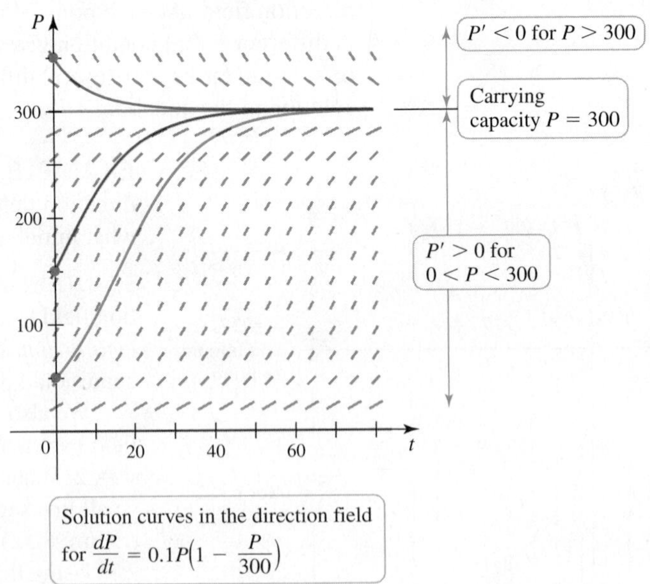

FIGURE 8.34

Related Exercises 35–40 ◀

Direction fields are useful for at least two reasons. As shown in Example 5, a direction field provides valuable qualitative information about the solutions of a differential equation *without solving the equation*. In addition, it turns out that direction fields are the basis for many computer-based methods for approximating solutions of a differential equation. The computer begins with the initial condition and advances the solution in small steps, always following the direction field at each time step.

SECTION 8.8 EXERCISES

Review Questions

1. What is the order of $y''(t) + 9y(t) = 10$?
2. Is $y''(t) + 9y(t) = 10$ linear or nonlinear?
3. How many arbitrary constants appear in the general solution of $y''(t) + 9y(t) = 10$?
4. If the general solution of a differential equation is $y(t) = Ce^{-3t} + 10$, what is the solution that satisfies the initial condition $y(0) = 5$?
5. What is a separable first-order differential equation?
6. Is the equation $t^2y'(t) = (t + 4)/y^2$ separable?
7. Explain how to solve a separable differential equation of the form $g(y)\,y'(t) = h(t)$.
8. Explain how to sketch the direction field of the equation $y'(t) = F(t, y)$, where F is given.

Basic Skills

9–12. Warm-up initial value problems *Solve the following problems.*

9. $y'(t) = 3t^2 - 4t + 10,\ y(0) = 20$
10. $\dfrac{dy}{dt} = 8e^{-4t} + 1,\ y(0) = 5$
11. $y'(t) = (2t^2 + 4)/t,\ y(1) = 2$
12. $\dfrac{dy}{dx} = 3\cos 2x + 2\sin 3x,\ y(\pi/2) = 8$

13–16. First-order linear equations *Find the general solution of the following equations.*

13. $y'(t) = 3y - 4$
14. $\dfrac{dy}{dx} = -y + 2$
15. $y'(x) = -2y - 4$
16. $\dfrac{dy}{dt} = 2y + 6$

17–20. Initial value problems *Solve the following problems.*

17. $y'(t) = 3y - 6,\ y(0) = 9$
18. $\dfrac{dy}{dx} = -y + 2,\ y(0) = -2$
19. $y'(t) = -2y - 4,\ y(0) = 0$
20. $\dfrac{du}{dx} = 2u + 6,\ u(1) = 6$

T 21. **Intravenous drug dosing** The amount of drug in the blood of a patient (in mg) due to an intravenous line is governed by the initial value problem

$$y'(t) = -0.02y + 3, \quad y(0) = 0 \qquad \text{for } t \geq 0$$

where t is measured in hours.

a. Find and graph the solution of the initial value problem.
b. What is the steady-state level of the drug?
c. When does the drug level reach 90% of the steady-state value?

T 22. **Fish harvesting** A fish hatchery has 500 fish at time $t = 0$, when harvesting begins at a rate of b fish/yr, where $b > 0$. The fish population is modeled by the initial value problem

$$y'(t) = 0.1y - b, \quad y(0) = 500 \qquad \text{for } t \geq 0$$

where t is measured in years.

a. Find the fish population for $t \geq 0$ in terms of the harvesting rate b.
b. Graph the solution in the case that $b = 40$ fish/yr. Describe the solution.
c. Graph the solution in the case that $b = 60$ fish/yr. Describe the solution.

23–26. Separable differential equations *Find the general solution of the following equations.*

23. $\dfrac{dy}{dt} = \dfrac{3t^2}{y}$
24. $\dfrac{dy}{dx} = y(x^2 + 1)$, where $y > 0$
25. $y'(t) = e^{y/2}\sin t$
26. $x^2\dfrac{dw}{dx} = \sqrt{w}(3x + 1)$

27–32. Separable differential equations *Determine whether the following equations are separable. If so, solve the given initial value problem.*

27. $\dfrac{dy}{dt} = ty + 2,\ y(1) = 2$
28. $y'(t) = y(4t^3 + 1),\ y(0) = 4$
29. $y'(t) = \dfrac{e^t}{2y},\ y(\ln 2) = 1$
30. $(\sec x)\,y'(x) = y^3,\ y(0) = 3$
31. $\dfrac{dy}{dx} = e^{x-y},\ y(0) = \ln 3$
32. $y'(t) = 2e^{3y-t},\ y(0) = 0$

T 33. **Logistic equation for a population** A community of hares on an island has a population of 50 when observations begin at $t = 0$. The population for $t \geq 0$ is modeled by the initial value problem

$$\frac{dP}{dt} = 0.08P\left(1 - \frac{P}{200}\right), \qquad P(0) = 50$$

a. Find and graph the solution of the initial value problem.
b. What is the steady-state population?

T 34. **Logistic equation for an epidemic** When an infected person is introduced into a closed and otherwise healthy community, the number of people who become infected with the disease (in the absence of any intervention) may be modeled by the logistic equation

$$\frac{dP}{dt} = kP\left(1 - \frac{P}{A}\right), \qquad P(0) = P_0$$

where k is a positive infection rate, A is the number of people in the community, and P_0 is the number of infected people at $t = 0$. The model assumes no recovery or intervention.

a. Find the solution of the initial value problem in terms of k, A, and P_0.

b. Graph the solution in the case that $k = 0.025$, $A = 300$, and $P_0 = 1$.

c. For fixed values of k and A, describe the long-term behavior of the solutions for any P_0 with $0 < P_0 < A$.

35–36. Direction fields *A differential equation and its direction field are given. Sketch a graph of the solution that results with each initial condition.*

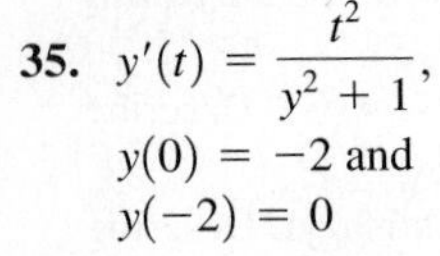

35. $y'(t) = \dfrac{t^2}{y^2 + 1}$, $y(0) = -2$ and $y(-2) = 0$

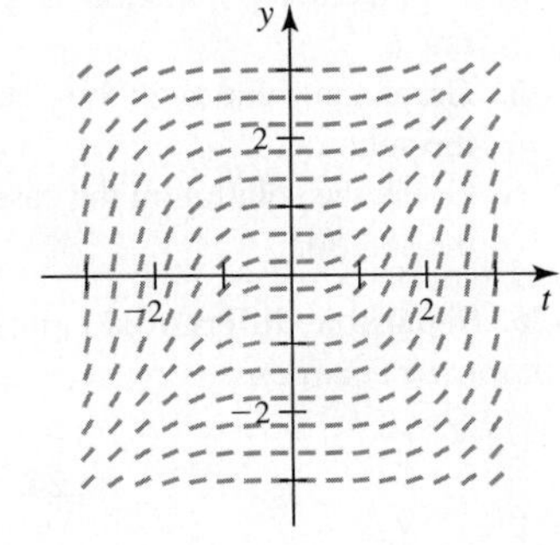

36. $y'(t) = \dfrac{\sin t}{y}$, $y(-2) = -2$ and $y(-2) = 2$

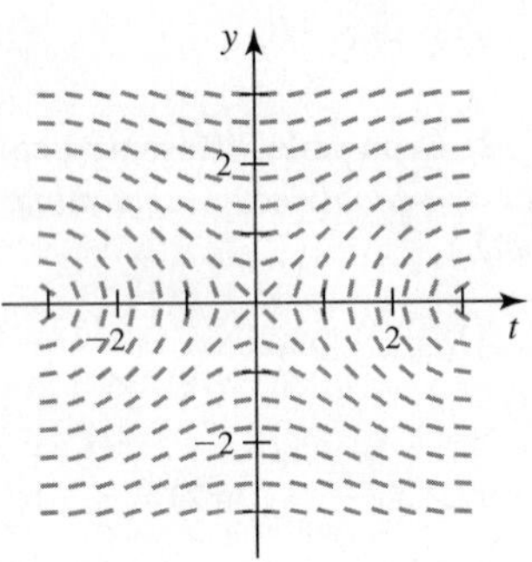

37. Matching direction fields Match equations (a)–(d) with the direction fields A–D.

(a) $y'(t) = t/2$ **(b)** $y'(t) = y/2$
(c) $y'(t) = (t^2 + y^2)/2$ **(d)** $y'(t) = y/t$

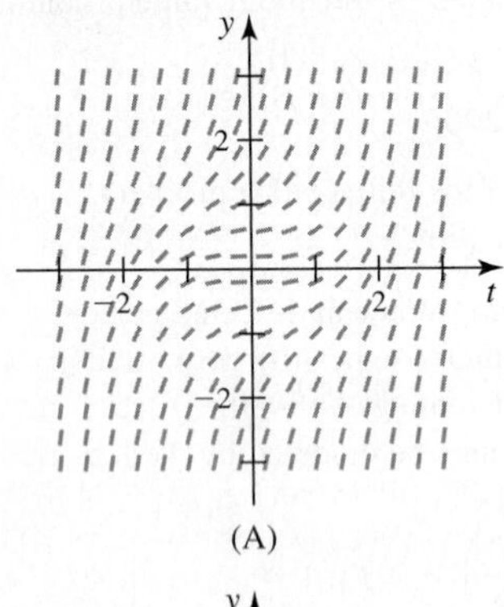

(A)

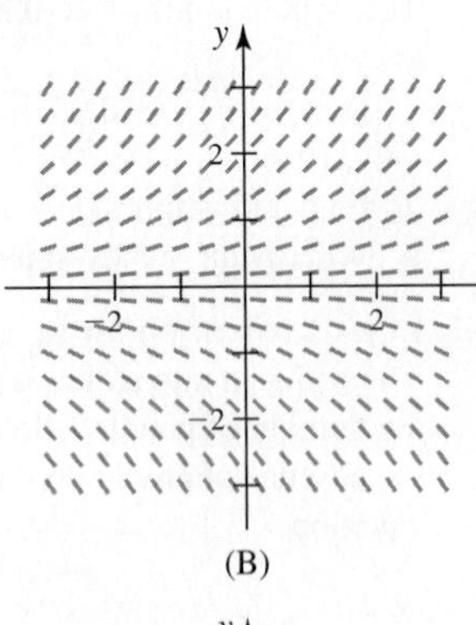

(B)

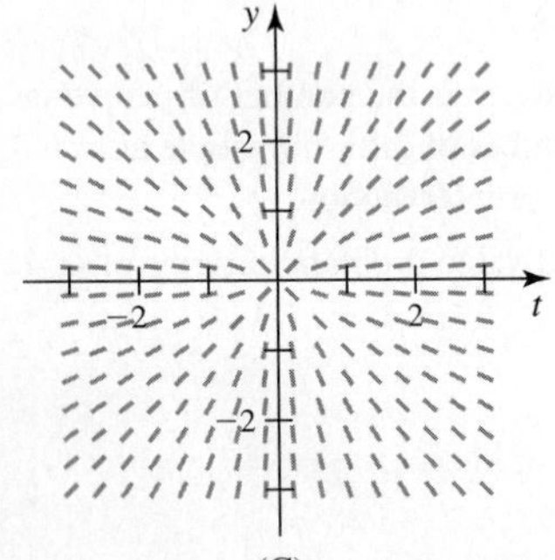

(C)

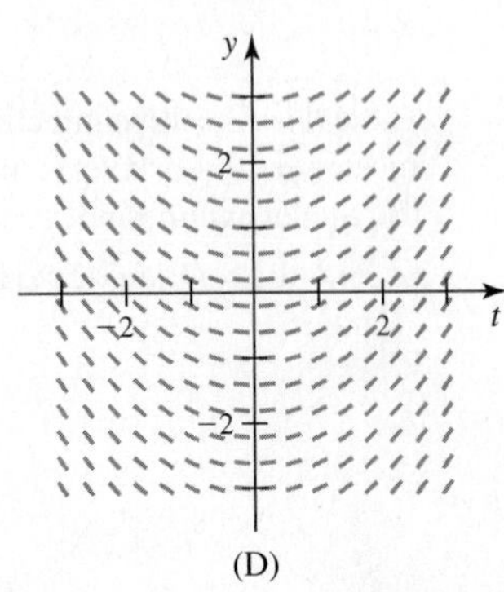

(D)

38–40. Sketching direction fields *Use the window $[-2, 2] \times [-2, 2]$ to sketch a direction field for the following equations. Then sketch the solution curve that corresponds to the given initial condition.*

38. $y'(t) = y - 3$, $y(0) = 1$

39. $y'(x) = \sin x$, $y(-2) = 2$

40. $y'(t) = \sin y$, $y(-2) = \frac{1}{2}$

Further Explorations

41. Explain why or why not Determine whether the following statements are true and give an explanation or counterexample.

a. The general solution of $y'(t) = 20y$ is $y = e^{20t}$.

b. The functions $y = 2e^{-2t}$ and $y = 10e^{-2t}$ do not both satisfy the differential equation $y' + 2y = 0$.

c. The equation $y'(t) = ty + 2y + 2t + 4$ is not separable.

d. A solution of $y'(t) = 2\sqrt{y}$ is $y = (t + 1)^2$.

42–47. Equilibrium solutions *A differential equation of the form $y'(t) = F(y)$ is said to be* ***autonomous*** *(the function F depends only on y). The constant function $y = y_0$ is an equilibrium solution of the equation provided $F(y_0) = 0$ (because then $y'(t) = 0$, and the solution remains constant for all t). Note that equilibrium solutions correspond to horizontal line segments in the direction field. Note also that for autonomous equations, the direction field is independent of t. Consider the following equations.*

a. *Find all equilibrium solutions.*

b. *Sketch the direction field on either side of the equilibrium solutions for $t \geq 0$.*

c. *Sketch the solution curve that corresponds to the initial condition $y(0) = 1$.*

42. $y'(t) = 2y + 4$

43. $y'(t) = y^2$

44. $y'(t) = y(2 - y)$

45. $y'(t) = y(y - 3)$

46. $y'(t) = \sin y$

47. $y'(t) = y(y - 3)(y + 2)$

48–51. Solving initial value problems *Solve the following problems using the method of your choice.*

48. $u'(t) = 4u - 2$, $u(0) = 4$

49. $\dfrac{dp}{dt} = \dfrac{p + 1}{t^2}$, $p(1) = 3$

50. $\dfrac{dz}{dx} = \dfrac{z^2}{1 + x^2}$, $z(0) = \dfrac{1}{6}$

51. $w'(t) = 2t \cos^2 w$, $w(0) = \pi/4$

52. Optimal harvesting rate Let $y(t)$ be the population of a species that is being harvested. Consider the harvesting model $y'(t) = 0.008y - h$, $y(0) = y_0$, where $h > 0$ is the annual harvesting rate and y_0 is the initial population of the species.

a. If $y_0 = 2000$, what harvesting rate should be used to maintain a constant population of $y = 2000$ for $t \geq 0$?

b. If the harvesting rate is $h = 200$/year, what initial population ensures a constant population for $t \geq 0$?

Applications

53. Logistic equation for spread of rumors Sociologists model the spread of rumors using logistic equations. The key assumption is that at any given time a fraction y of the population, where $0 \le y \le 1$, knows the rumor, while the remaining fraction $1 - y$ does not. Furthermore, the rumor spreads by interactions between those who know the rumor and those who do not. The number of such interactions is proportional to $y(1 - y)$. Therefore, the equation that describes the spread of the rumor is $y'(t) = ky(1 - y)$, where k is a positive real number. The fraction of people who initially know the rumor is $y(0) = y_0$, where $0 < y_0 < 1$.

a. Solve this initial value problem and give the solution in terms of k and y_0.
b. Assume $k = 0.3 \text{ weeks}^{-1}$ and graph the solution for $y_0 = 0.1$ and $y_0 = 0.7$.
c. Describe and interpret the long-term behavior of the rumor function for any $0 < y_0 < 1$.

54. Free fall An object in free fall may be modeled by assuming that the only forces at work are the gravitational force and resistance (friction due to the medium in which the object falls). By Newton's second law (mass × acceleration = the sum of the external forces), the velocity of the object satisfies the differential equation

$$\underbrace{m}_{\text{mass}} \cdot \underbrace{v'(t)}_{\text{acceleration}} = \underbrace{mg + f(v)}_{\text{external forces}},$$

where f is a function that models the resistance and the positive direction is downward. One common assumption (often used for motion in air) is that $f(v) = -kv^2$, where $k > 0$ is a drag coefficient.

a. Show that the equation can be written in the form $v'(t) = g - av^2$, where $a = k/m$.
b. For what (positive) value of v is $v'(t) = 0$? (This equilibrium solution is called the **terminal velocity**.)
c. Find the solution of this separable equation assuming $v(0) = 0$ and $0 < v(t)^2 < g/a$, for $t \ge 0$.
d. Graph the solution found in part (c) with $g = 9.8 \text{ m/s}^2$, $m = 1 \text{ kg}$, and $k = 0.1 \text{ kg/m}$, and verify that the terminal velocity agrees with the value found in part (b).

55. Free fall Using the background given in Exercise 54, assume the resistance is given by $f(v) = -Rv$, where $R > 0$ is a drag coefficient (an assumption often made for a heavy medium such as water or oil).

a. Show that the equation can be written in the form $v'(t) = g - bv$, where $b = R/m$.
b. For what (positive) value of v is $v'(t) = 0$? (This equilibrium solution is called the **terminal velocity**.)
c. Find the solution of this separable equation assuming $v(0) = 0$ and $0 < v < g/b$.
d. Graph the solution found in part (c) with $g = 9.8 \text{ m/s}^2$, $m = 1 \text{ kg}$, and $R = 0.1 \text{ kg/s}$, and verify that the terminal velocity agrees with the value found in part (b).

56. Torricelli's Law An open cylindrical tank initially filled with water drains through a hole in the bottom of the tank according to Torricelli's Law (see figure). If $h(t)$ is the depth of water in the tank for $t \ge 0$, then Torricelli's Law implies $h'(t) = -2k\sqrt{h}$, where $k > 0$ is a constant that includes the acceleration due to gravity, the radius of the tank, and the radius of the drain. Assume that the initial depth of the water is $h(0) = H$.

a. Find the general solution of the equation.
b. Find the solution in the case that $k = 0.1$ and $H = 0.5 \text{ m}$.
c. In general, how long does it take for the tank to drain in terms of k and H?

57. Chemical rate equations The reaction of chemical compounds can often be modeled by differential equations. Let $y(t)$ be the concentration of a substance in reaction for $t \ge 0$ (typical units of y are moles/L). The change in the concentration of the substance, under appropriate conditions, is $\frac{dy}{dt} = -ky^n$, where $k > 0$ is a rate constant and the positive integer n is the order of the reaction.

a. Show that for a first-order reaction $(n = 1)$, the concentration obeys an exponential decay law.
b. Solve the initial value problem for a second-order reaction $(n = 2)$ assuming $y(0) = y_0$.
c. Graph and compare the concentration for a first-order and second-order reaction with $k = 0.1$ and $y_0 = 1$.

58. Tumor growth The growth of cancer tumors may be modeled by the Gompertz growth equation. Let $M(t)$ be the mass of the tumor for $t \ge 0$. The relevant initial value problem is

$$\frac{dM}{dt} = -aM \ln\left(\frac{M}{K}\right), \qquad M(0) = M_0,$$

where a and K are positive constants and $0 < M_0 < K$.

a. Graph the growth rate function $R(M) = -aM \ln\left(\frac{M}{K}\right)$ assuming $a = 1$ and $K = 4$. For what values of M is the growth rate positive? For what value of M is the growth rate a maximum?
b. Solve the initial value problem and graph the solution for $a = 1$, $K = 4$, and $M_0 = 1$. Describe the growth pattern of the tumor. Is the growth unbounded? If not, what is the limiting size of the tumor?
c. In the general equation, what is the meaning of K?

59. Endowment model An endowment is an investment account in which the balance ideally remains constant and withdrawals are made on the interest earned by the account. Such an account may be modeled by the initial value problem $B'(t) = aB - m$ for $t \ge 0$, with $B(0) = B_0$. The constant a reflects the annual interest rate, m is the annual rate of withdrawal, and B_0 is the initial balance in the account.

a. Solve the initial value problem with $a = 0.05$, $m = \$1000/\text{yr}$, and $B_0 = \$15{,}000$. Does the balance in the account increase or decrease?
b. If $a = 0.05$ and $B_0 = \$50{,}000$, what is the annual withdrawal rate m that ensures a constant balance in the account? What is the constant balance?

Additional Exercises

60. Solution of the logistic equation Consider the solution of the logistic equation in Example 4.

a. From the general solution $\ln\left|\frac{P}{300 - P}\right| = 0.1t + C$, show that the initial condition $P(0) = 50$ implies that $C = \ln \frac{1}{5}$.

b. Solve for P and show that $P(t) = \frac{300}{1 + 5e^{-0.1t}}$.

61. Direction field analysis Consider the general first-order initial value problem $y'(t) = ay + b, y(0) = y_0$, for $t \geq 0$, where a, b, and y_0 are real numbers.

a. Explain why $y = -b/a$ is an equilibrium solution and corresponds to a horizontal line in the direction field.

b. Draw a representative direction field in the case that $a > 0$. Show that if $y_0 > -b/a$, then the solution increases for $t \geq 0$, and if $y_0 < -b/a$, then the solution decreases for $t \geq 0$.

c. Draw a representative direction field in the case that $a < 0$. Show that if $y_0 > -b/a$, then the solution decreases for $t \geq 0$, and if $y_0 < -b/a$, then the solution increases for $t \geq 0$.

QUICK CHECK ANSWERS

1. The equation is first order and linear. **3.** The solution is $y(t) = 16e^{3t} - 2$. **4.** $y^3 y'(t) = t^2 + 1$ **5. a.** Solution increases for $t \geq -1$. **b.** Solution decreases for $t \geq -2$. ◀

CHAPTER 8 REVIEW EXERCISES

1. Explain why or why not Determine whether the following statements are true and give an explanation or counterexample.

a. The integral $\int x^2 e^{2x}\,dx$ can be evaluated analytically using integration by parts.

b. To evaluate the integral $\int \frac{dx}{\sqrt{x^2 - 100}}$ analytically, it is best to use partial fractions.

c. One computer algebra system produces $\int 2 \sin x \cos x\,dx = \sin^2 x$. Another computer algebra system produces $\int 2 \sin x \cos x\,dx = -\cos^2 x$. One computer algebra system is wrong (apart from a missing constant of integration).

2–19. Integrals *Evaluate the following integrals analytically.*

2. $\int x^2 \cos x\,dx$

3. $\int e^x \sin x\,dx$

4. $\int_1^e x^2 \ln x\,dx$

5. $\int \cos^2 4\theta\,d\theta$

6. $\int \sin 3x \cos^6 3x\,dx$

7. $\int \sec^5 z \tan z\,dz$

8. $\int_0^{\pi/2} \cos^4 x\,dx$

9. $\int_0^{\pi/6} \sin^5 \theta\,d\theta$

10. $\int \tan^4 u\,du$

11. $\int \frac{dx}{\sqrt{4 - x^2}}$

12. $\int \frac{dx}{\sqrt{9x^2 - 25}}$ for $x > \frac{5}{3}$

13. $\int \frac{dy}{y^2\sqrt{9 - y^2}}$

14. $\int_0^{\sqrt{3}/2} \frac{x^2}{(1 - x^2)^{3/2}}\,dx$

15. $\int_0^{\sqrt{3}/2} \frac{4}{9 + 4x^2}\,dx$

16. $\int \frac{(1 - u^2)^{5/2}}{u^8}\,du$

17. $\int \frac{dx}{x^2 - 2x - 15}$

18. $\int \frac{dx}{x^3 - 2x^2}$

19. $\int_0^1 \frac{dy}{(y + 1)(y^2 + 1)}$

20–22. Table of integrals *Use a table of integrals to evaluate the following integrals.*

20. $\int x(2x + 3)^5\,dx$

21. $\int \frac{dx}{x\sqrt{4x - 6}}$

22. $\int_0^{\pi/2} \frac{d\theta}{1 + \sin 2\theta}$

T **23–24. Approximations** *Use a computer algebra system to approximate the value of the following integrals.*

23. $\int_{-1}^{1} e^{-2x^2}\,dx$

24. $\int_1^{\sqrt{e}} x^3 (\ln x)^3\,dx$

T **25. Numerical integration methods** Let $I = \int_0^3 x^2\,dx = 9$ and consider the Trapezoid Rule $T(n)$ and the Midpoint Rule $M(n)$ approximations to I.

a. Compute $T(6)$ and $M(6)$.

b. Compute $T(12)$ and $M(12)$.

26. Errors in numerical integration Let $I = \int_{-1}^{2}\left(x^7 - 3x^5 - x^2 + \frac{7}{8}\right) dx$ and note that $I = 0$.

a. Complete the following table with Trapezoid Rule $T(n)$ and Midpoint Rule $M(n)$ approximations to I for various values of n.

b. Fill in the error columns with the absolute errors in the approximations in part (a).

n	$T(n)$	$M(n)$	Abs error in $T(n)$	Abs error in $M(n)$
4				
8				
16				
32				
64				

c. How do the errors in $T(n)$ decrease as n doubles in size?

d. How do the errors in $M(n)$ decrease as n doubles in size?

27. Best approximation Let $I = \displaystyle\int_0^1 \frac{x^2 - x}{\ln x}\, dx$. Use any method you choose to find a good approximation to I. You may use the facts that $\displaystyle\lim_{x\to 0^+} \frac{x^2 - x}{\ln x} = 0$ and $\displaystyle\lim_{x\to 1} \frac{x^2 - x}{\ln x} = 1$.

28–31. Improper integrals *Evaluate the following integrals.*

28. $\displaystyle\int_1^{\infty} \frac{dx}{(x + 1)^9}$

29. $\displaystyle\int_0^{\infty} xe^{-x}\, dx$

30. $\displaystyle\int_0^{8} \frac{dx}{\sqrt{2x}}$

31. $\displaystyle\int_0^{3} \frac{dx}{\sqrt{9 - x^2}}$

32–37. Preliminary work *Make a change of variables or use an algebra step before evaluating the following integrals.*

32. $\displaystyle\int_{-1}^{1} \frac{dx}{x^2 + 2x + 5}$

33. $\displaystyle\int \frac{dx}{x^2 - x - 2}$

34. $\displaystyle\int \frac{3x^2 + x - 3}{x^2 - 1}\, dx$

35. $\displaystyle\int \frac{2x^2 - 4x}{x^2 - 4}\, dx$

36. $\displaystyle\int_{1/12}^{1/4} \frac{dx}{\sqrt{x}(1 + 4x)}$

37. $\displaystyle\int \frac{e^{2t}}{(1 + e^{4t})^{3/2}}\, dt$

38. Two ways Evaluate $\displaystyle\int \frac{dx}{4 - x^2}$ using partial fractions and a trigonometric substitution, and show that the results are consistent.

39–42. Volumes *The region R is bounded by the curve $y = \ln x$ and the x-axis on the interval $[1, e]$. Find the volume of the solid that is generated when R is revolved in the following ways.*

39. About the x-axis

40. About the y-axis

41. About the line $x = 1$

42. About the line $y = 1$

43. Comparing volumes Let R be the region bounded by the graph of $y = \sin x$ and the x-axis on the interval $[0, \pi]$. Which is greater, the volume of the solid generated when R is revolved about the x-axis or the y-axis?

44. Comparing areas Show that the area of the region bounded by the graph of $y = ae^{-ax}$ and the x-axis on the interval $[0, \infty)$ is the same for all values of $a > 0$.

45. Zero log integral It is evident from the graph of $y = \ln x$ that for every real number a with $0 < a < 1$, there is a unique real number $b = g(a)$ with $b > 1$, such that $\int_a^b \ln x\, dx = 0$ (the net area bounded by the graph of $y = \ln x$ on $[a, b]$ is 0).

a. Approximate $b = g\left(\frac{1}{2}\right)$.

b. Approximate $b = g\left(\frac{1}{3}\right)$.

c. Find the equation satisfied by all pairs of numbers (a, b) such that $b = g(a)$.

d. Is g an increasing or decreasing function of a? Explain.

46. Arc length Find the length of the curve $y = \ln x$ from $x = 1$ to $x = e^2$.

47. Average velocity Find the average velocity of a projectile whose velocity over the interval $0 \le t \le \pi$ is given by $v(t) = 10 \sin 3t$.

48. Comparing distances Starting at the same time and place ($t = 0$ and $s = 0$), the velocity of car A is given by $u(t) = 40/(t + 1)$ (mi/hr) and the velocity of car B is given by $v(t) = 40e^{-t/2}$ (mi/hr).

a. After $t = 2$ hr, which car has traveled the greater distance?

b. After $t = 3$ hr, which car has traveled the greater distance?

c. If allowed to travel indefinitely ($t \to \infty$), which car will travel a finite distance?

49. Traffic flow When data from a traffic study are fitted to a curve, the flow rate of cars past a point on a highway is approximated by $R(t) = 800te^{-t/2}$ cars/hr. How many cars pass the measuring site during the time interval $0 \le t \le 4$ hr?

50. Comparing integrals Graph the functions $f(x) = \pm 1/x^2$, $g(x) = (\cos x)/x^2$, and $h(x) = (\cos^2 x)/x^2$. Without evaluating integrals and knowing that $\int_1^{\infty} f(x)\, dx$ has a finite value, determine whether $\int_1^{\infty} g(x)\, dx$ and $\int_1^{\infty} h(x)\, dx$ have finite values.

51. A family of logarithm integrals Let $I(p) = \displaystyle\int_1^{e} \frac{\ln x}{x^p}\, dx$, where p is a real number.

a. Find an expression for $I(p)$ for all real values of p.

b. Evaluate $\displaystyle\lim_{p\to\infty} I(p)$ and $\displaystyle\lim_{p\to-\infty} I(p)$.

c. For what value of p is $I(p) = 1$?

52. CAS approximation Use a computer algebra system to determine the integer n that satisfies $\displaystyle\int_0^{1/2} \frac{\ln(1 + 2x)}{x}\, dx = \frac{\pi^2}{n}$.

53. CAS approximation Use a computer algebra system to determine the integer n that satisfies $\displaystyle\int_0^{1} \frac{\sin^{-1} x}{x}\, dx = \frac{\pi \ln 2}{n}$.

54. Two worthy integrals

a. Let $I(a) = \int_0^\infty \frac{dx}{(1 + x^a)(1 + x^2)}$, where a is a real number. Evaluate $I(a)$ and show that its value is independent of a. (*Hint:* Split the integral into two integrals over $[0, 1]$ and $[1, \infty)$; then, use a change of variables to convert the second integral into an integral over $[0, 1]$.)

b. Let f be a positive continuous function on $[0, \pi/2]$ and evaluate

$$\int_0^{\pi/2} \frac{f(\cos x)}{f(\cos x) + f(\sin x)}\,dx.$$

(*Hint:* Use the identity $\cos(\pi/2 - x) = \sin x$.)
(*Source: Mathematics Magazine*, 81, no. 2, April 2008: 152–154)

55–58. Initial value problems *Use the method of your choice to solve the following initial value problems.*

55. $y'(t) = 2y + 4,\ y(0) = 8$

56. $\frac{dy}{dt} = \frac{2ty}{\ln y},\ y(2) = e$

57. $y'(t) = \frac{t + 1}{2ty},\ y(1) = 4$

58. $\frac{dy}{dt} = \sqrt{y}\sin t,\ y(0) = 4$

59. Limit of a solution Evaluate $\lim_{t\to\infty} y(t)$, where y is the solution of the initial value problem $y'(t) = \frac{\sec y}{t^2}, y(1) = 0$.

60–62. Sketching direction fields *Use the window $[-2, 2] \times [-2, 2]$ to sketch a direction field for the given differential equation. Then, sketch the solution curve that corresponds to the given initial condition.*

60. $y'(t) = 3y - 6,\ y(0) = 1$

61. $y'(t) = t^2,\ y(-1) = -1$

62. $y'(t) = y - t,\ y(-2) = \frac{1}{2}$

T **63. Enzyme kinetics** The consumption of a substrate in a reaction involving an enzyme is often modeled using Michaelis-Menton kinetics, which involves the initial value problem $\frac{ds}{dt} = -\frac{Qs}{K + s}$, $s(0) = s_0$, where $s(t)$ is the amount of substrate present at time $t \geq 0$, and Q and K are positive constants. Solve the initial value problem with $Q = 10$, $K = 5$, and $s_0 = 50$. Notice that the solution can be expressed explicitly only with t as a function of s. Graph the solution and describe how s behaves as $t \to \infty$. (See the Guided Projects for more on enzyme kinetics.)

64. Investment model An investment account that earns interest and also has regular deposits can be modeled by the initial value problem $B'(t) = aB + m$ for $t \geq 0$, with $B(0) = B_0$. The constant a reflects the monthly interest rate, m is the rate of monthly deposits, and B_0 is the initial balance in the account. Solve the initial value problem with $a = 0.005$, $m = \$100/\text{month}$, and $B_0 = \$100$. After how many months does the account have a balance of \$7500?

T **65. Comparing volumes** Let R be the region bounded by $y = \ln x$, the x-axis, and the line $x = a$, where $a > 1$.

a. Find the volume $V_1(a)$ of the solid generated when R is revolved about the x-axis (as a function of a).

b. Find the volume $V_2(a)$ of the solid generated when R is revolved about the y-axis (as a function of a).

c. Graph V_1 and V_2. For what values of $a > 1$ is $V_1(a) > V_2(a)$?

66. Equal volumes

a. Let R be the region bounded by the graph of $f(x) = x^{-p}$ and the x-axis for $x \geq 1$. Let V_1 and V_2 be the volumes of the solids generated when R is revolved about the x-axis and the y-axis, respectively, if they exist. For what values of p (if any) is $V_1 = V_2$?

b. Repeat part (a) on the interval $(0, 1]$.

67. Equal volumes Let R_1 be the region bounded by the graph of $y = e^{-ax}$ and the x-axis on the interval $[0, b]$, where $a > 0$ and $b > 0$. Let R_2 be the region bounded by the graph of $y = e^{-ax}$ and the x-axis on the interval $[b, \infty)$. Let V_1 and V_2 be the volumes of the solids generated when R_1 and R_2 are revolved about the x-axis. Find and graph the relationship between a and b for which $V_1 = V_2$.

Chapter 8 Guided Projects

Applications of the material in this chapter and related topics can be found in the following Guided Projects. For additional information, see the Preface.

- Cooling coffee
- Euler's method for differential equations
- Terminal velocity
- A pursuit problem
- Simpson's rule
- Predator-prey models
- Period of the pendulum
- Logistic growth
- Mercator projections
- How long will your iPod last?

9

Sequences and Infinite Series

Chapter Preview This chapter covers topics that lie at the foundation of calculus—indeed, at the foundation of mathematics. The first task is to make a clear distinction between a *sequence* and an *infinite series*. A sequence is an ordered *list* of numbers, $a_1, a_2, \ldots$, while an infinite series is a *sum* of numbers, $a_1 + a_2 + \cdots$. The idea of convergence to a limit is important for both sequences and series, but convergence is analyzed differently in the two cases. To determine limits of sequences, we use the same tools used for limits at infinity of functions. Convergence of infinite series is a different matter, and we develop the required methods in this chapter. The study of infinite series begins with the ubiquitous *geometric series*; it has theoretical importance and it is used to answer many practical questions (When is your auto loan paid off? How much antibiotic do you have in your blood if you take three pills a day?). We then present several tests that are used to determine whether series with positive terms converge. Finally, alternating series, whose terms alternate in sign, are discussed in anticipation of power series in the next chapter.

9.1 An Overview

> Keeping with common practice, the terms *series* and *infinite series* are used interchangeably throughout this chapter.

To understand sequences and series, you must understand how they differ and how they are related. The purposes of this opening section are to introduce sequences and series in concrete terms and to illustrate their differences and their crucial relationships with each other.

Examples of Sequences

> The dots (...) after the last number (called an *ellipsis*) mean that the list goes on indefinitely.

Consider the following *list* of numbers:

$$\{1, 4, 7, 10, 13, 16, \ldots\}$$

Each number in the list is obtained by adding 3 to the previous number. With this rule, we could extend the list indefinitely.

This list is an example of a **sequence**, where each number in the sequence is called a **term** of the sequence. We denote sequences in any of the following forms:

$$\{a_1, a_2, a_3, \ldots, a_n, \ldots\} \qquad \{a_n\}_{n=1}^{\infty} \qquad \{a_n\}$$

The subscript n that appears in a_n is called an **index**, and it indicates the order of terms in the sequence. The choice of a starting index is arbitrary, but sequences usually begin with $n = 0$ or $n = 1$.

The sequence $\{1, 4, 7, 10, \ldots\}$ can be defined in two ways. First, we have the rule that each term of the sequence is 3 more than the previous term; that is, $a_2 = a_1 + 3$, $a_3 = a_2 + 3$, $a_4 = a_3 + 3$, and so forth. In general, we see that

$$a_1 = 1 \quad \text{and} \quad a_{n+1} = a_n + 3, \qquad \text{for } n = 1, 2, 3, \ldots.$$

This way of defining a sequence is called a **recurrence relation** (or an **implicit formula**). It specifies the initial term of the sequence (in this case, $a_1 = 1$) and gives a general rule for computing the next term of the sequence from previous terms. For example, if you know a_{100}, the recurrence relation can be used to find a_{101}.

Suppose instead you want to find a_{147} directly without computing the first 146 terms of the sequence. The first four terms of the sequence can be written

$$a_1 = 1 + (3 \cdot 0), \quad a_2 = 1 + (3 \cdot 1), \quad a_3 = 1 + (3 \cdot 2), \quad a_4 = 1 + (3 \cdot 3).$$

Observe the pattern: The nth term of the sequence is 1 plus 3 multiplied by $n - 1$, or

$$a_n = 1 + 3(n - 1) = 3n - 2, \qquad \text{for } n = 1, 2, 3, \ldots$$

QUICK CHECK 1 Find a_{10} for the sequence $\{1, 4, 7, 10, \ldots\}$ using the recurrence relation and then again using the explicit formula for the nth term.

With this **explicit formula**, the nth term of the sequence is determined directly from the value of n. For example, with $n = 147$,

$$\underbrace{a_{147}}_{n} = 3 \cdot \underbrace{147}_{n} - 2 = 439.$$

When defined by an explicit formula $a_n = f(n)$, it is evident that sequences are functions. The domain is the set of positive, or nonnegative, integers, and one real number a_n is assigned to each integer in the domain.

DEFINITION Sequence

A **sequence** $\{a_n\}$ is an ordered list of numbers of the form

$$\{a_1, a_2, a_3, \ldots, a_n, \ldots\}.$$

A sequence may be generated by a **recurrence relation** of the form $a_{n+1} = f(a_n)$, for $n = 1, 2, 3, \ldots$, where a_1 is given. A sequence may also be defined with an **explicit formula** for the nth term in the form $a_n = f(n)$, for $n = 1, 2, 3, \ldots$.

EXAMPLE 1 **Explicit formulas** Use the explicit formula for $\{a_n\}_{n=1}^{\infty}$ to write the first four terms of each sequence. Sketch a graph of the sequence.

a. $a_n = \dfrac{1}{2^n}$ **b.** $a_n = \dfrac{(-1)^n n}{n^2 + 1}$

SOLUTION

a. Substituting $n = 1, 2, 3, 4, \ldots$ into the explicit formula $a_n = \dfrac{1}{2^n}$, we find that the terms of the sequence are

$$\left\{\frac{1}{2}, \frac{1}{2^2}, \frac{1}{2^3}, \frac{1}{2^4}, \ldots\right\} = \left\{\frac{1}{2}, \frac{1}{4}, \frac{1}{8}, \frac{1}{16}, \ldots\right\}.$$

The graph of a sequence is like the graph of a function that is defined only on a set of integers. In this case, we plot the coordinate pairs (n, a_n) for $n = 1, 2, 3, \ldots$, resulting in a graph consisting of individual points. The graph of the sequence $a_n = \dfrac{1}{2^n}$ suggests that the terms of this sequence approach 0 as n increases (Figure 9.1).

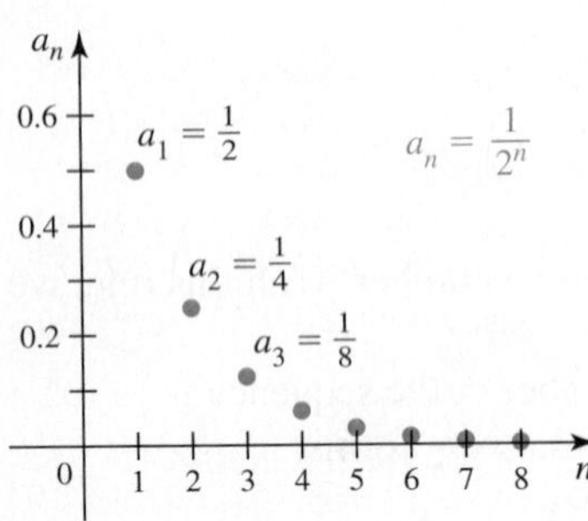

FIGURE 9.1

b. Substituting $n = 1, 2, 3, 4, \ldots$ into the explicit formula, the terms of the sequence are

$$\left\{\frac{(-1)^1(1)}{1^2 + 1}, \frac{(-1)^2 2}{2^2 + 1}, \frac{(-1)^3 3}{3^2 + 1}, \frac{(-1)^4 4}{4^2 + 1}, \ldots\right\} = \left\{-\frac{1}{2}, \frac{2}{5}, -\frac{3}{10}, \frac{4}{17}, \ldots\right\}.$$

The "switch" $(-1)^n$ is used frequently to alternate the signs of the terms of sequences and series.

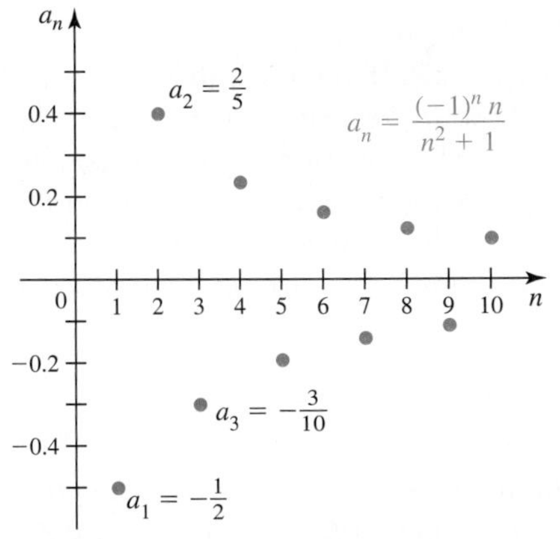

FIGURE 9.2

From the graph (Figure 9.2), we see that the terms of the sequence alternate in sign and appear to approach 0 as n increases. *Related Exercises 9–12*

EXAMPLE 2 **Recurrence relations** Use the recurrence relation for $\{a_n\}_{n=1}^{\infty}$ to write the first four terms of the sequences

$$a_{n+1} = 2a_n + 1, a_1 = 1 \quad \text{and} \quad a_{n+1} = 2a_n + 1, a_1 = -1.$$

SOLUTION Notice that the recurrence relation is the same for the two sequences; only the first term differs. The first four terms of the two sequences are as follows.

n	a_n with $a_1 = 1$	a_n with $a_1 = -1$
1	$a_1 = 1$ (given)	$a_1 = -1$ (given)
2	$a_2 = 2a_1 + 1 = 2 \cdot 1 + 1 = 3$	$a_2 = 2a_1 + 1 = 2(-1) + 1 = -1$
3	$a_3 = 2a_2 + 1 = 2 \cdot 3 + 1 = 7$	$a_3 = 2a_2 + 1 = 2(-1) + 1 = -1$
4	$a_4 = 2a_3 + 1 = 2 \cdot 7 + 1 = 15$	$a_4 = 2a_3 + 1 = 2(-1) + 1 = -1$

We see that the terms of the first sequence increase without bound, while all terms of the second sequence are -1. Clearly, the initial term of the sequence has a lot to say about the behavior of the entire sequence. *Related Exercises 13–16*

QUICK CHECK 2 Find an explicit formula for the sequence $\{1, 3, 7, 15, \ldots\}$ (Example 2).

EXAMPLE 3 **Working with sequences** Consider the following sequences.

a. $\{a_n\} = \{-2, 5, 12, 19, \ldots\}$ **b.** $\{b_n\} = \{3, 6, 12, 24, 48, \ldots\}$

(i) Find the next two terms of the sequence.
(ii) Find a recurrence relation that generates the sequence.
(iii) Find an explicit formula for the nth term of the sequence.

SOLUTION

a. (i) Each term is obtained by adding 7 to its predecessor. The next two terms are $19 + 7 = 26$ and $26 + 7 = 33$.

> In Example 3, we chose the starting index to be $n = 0$. Other choices are possible.

(ii) Because each term is seven more than its predecessor, the recurrence relation is

$$a_{n+1} = a_n + 7, a_0 = -2, \qquad \text{for } n = 0, 1, 2, \ldots$$

(iii) Notice that $a_0 = -2$, $a_1 = -2 + (1 \cdot 7)$, and $a_2 = -2 + (2 \cdot 7)$, so the explicit formula is

$$a_n = 7n - 2, \qquad \text{for } n = 0, 1, 2, \ldots.$$

b. (i) Each term is obtained by multiplying its predecessor by 2. The next two terms are $48 \cdot 2 = 96$ and $96 \cdot 2 = 192$.

(ii) Because each term is two times its predecessor, the recurrence relation is

$$a_{n+1} = 2a_n, a_0 = 3, \qquad \text{for } n = 0, 1, 2, \ldots$$

(iii) To obtain the explicit formula, note that $a_0 = 3$, $a_1 = 3(2^1)$, and $a_2 = 3(2^2)$. In general,

$$a_n = 3(2^n), \qquad \text{for } n = 0, 1, 2, \ldots.$$

Related Exercises 17–22

Limit of a Sequence

Perhaps the most important question about a sequence is this: If you go farther and farther out in the sequence, $a_{100}, \ldots, a_{10,000}, \ldots, a_{100,000}, \ldots$, how do the terms of the sequence behave? Do they approach a specific number, and if so, what is that number? Or do they grow in magnitude without bound? Or do they wander around with or without a pattern?

The long-term behavior of a sequence is described by its **limit**. The limit of a sequence is defined rigorously in the next section. For now, we work with an informal definition.

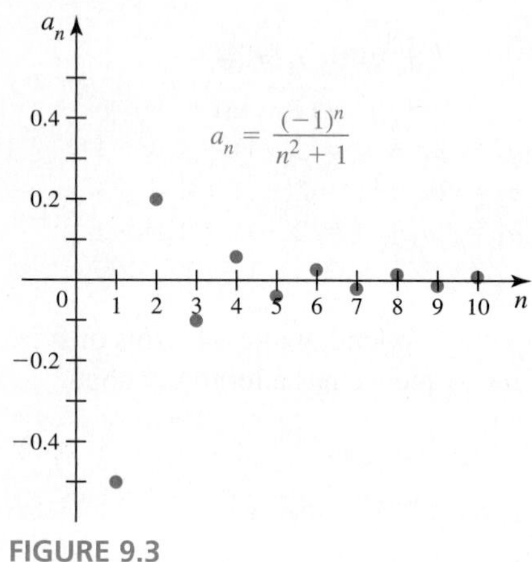

FIGURE 9.3

> **DEFINITION Limit of a Sequence**
>
> If the terms of a sequence $\{a_n\}$ approach a unique number L as n increases, then we say $\lim_{n\to\infty} a_n = L$ exists, and the sequence **converges** to L. If the terms of the sequence do not approach a single number as n increases, the sequence has no limit, and the sequence **diverges**.

EXAMPLE 4 Limit of a sequence Write the first four terms of each sequence. If you believe the sequence converges, make a conjecture about its limit. If the sequence appears to diverge, explain why.

a. $\left\{\frac{(-1)^n}{n^2+1}\right\}_{n=1}^{\infty}$ Explicit formula

b. $\{\cos(n\pi)\}_{n=1}^{\infty}$ Explicit formula

c. $\{a_n\}_{n=1}^{\infty}$, where $a_{n+1} = -2a_n$, $a_1 = 1$ Recurrence relation

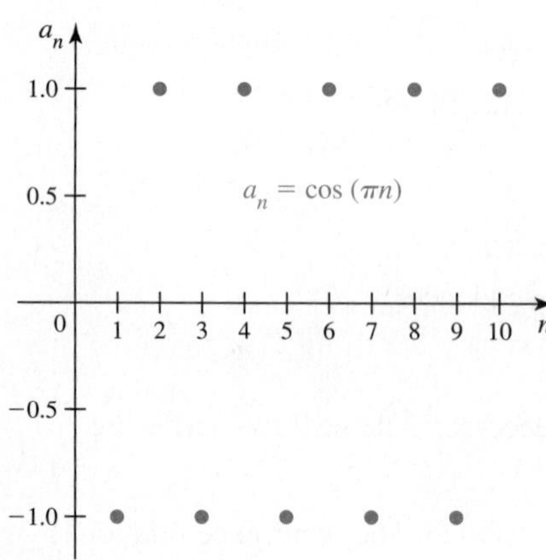

FIGURE 9.4

SOLUTION

a. Beginning with $n = 1$, the first four terms of the sequence are

$$\left\{\frac{(-1)^1}{1^2+1}, \frac{(-1)^2}{2^2+1}, \frac{(-1)^3}{3^2+1}, \frac{(-1)^4}{4^2+1}, \ldots\right\} = \left\{-\frac{1}{2}, \frac{1}{5}, -\frac{1}{10}, \frac{1}{17}, \ldots\right\}.$$

The terms decrease in magnitude and approach zero with alternating signs. The limit appears to be 0 (Figure 9.3).

b. The first four terms of the sequence are

$$\{\cos\pi, \cos 2\pi, \cos 3\pi, \cos 4\pi, \ldots\} = \{-1, 1, -1, 1, \ldots\}.$$

In this case, the terms of the sequence alternate between -1 and $+1$, and never approach a single value. Thus, the sequence diverges (Figure 9.4).

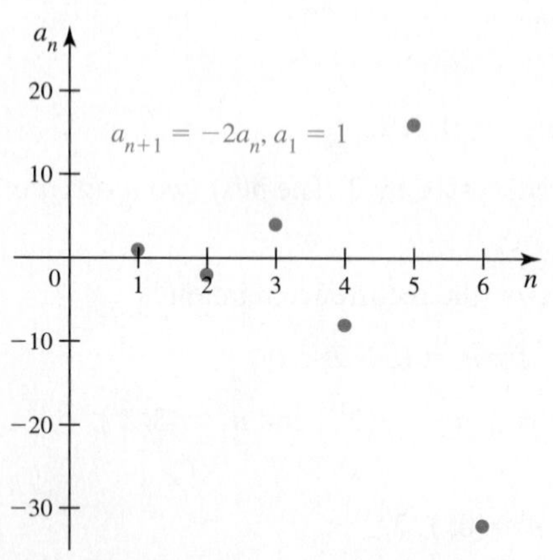

FIGURE 9.5

c. The first four terms of the sequence are

$$\{1, -2a_1, -2a_2, -2a_3, \ldots\} = \{1, -2, 4, -8, \ldots\}.$$

Because the magnitudes of the terms increase without bound, the sequence diverges (Figure 9.5).

Related Exercises 23–30 ◀

EXAMPLE 5 Limit of a sequence Enumerate and graph the terms of the following sequence and make a conjecture about its limit.

$$a_n = \frac{4n^3}{n^3+1}, \quad \text{for } n = 1, 2, 3, \ldots \quad \text{Explicit formula}$$

SOLUTION The first 14 terms of the sequence $\{a_n\}$ are tabulated in Table 9.1 and graphed in Figure 9.6. The terms appear to approach 4.

Table 9.1

n	a_n	n	a_n
1	2.000	8	3.992
2	3.556	9	3.995
3	3.857	10	3.996
4	3.938	11	3.997
5	3.968	12	3.998
6	3.982	13	3.998
7	3.988	14	3.999

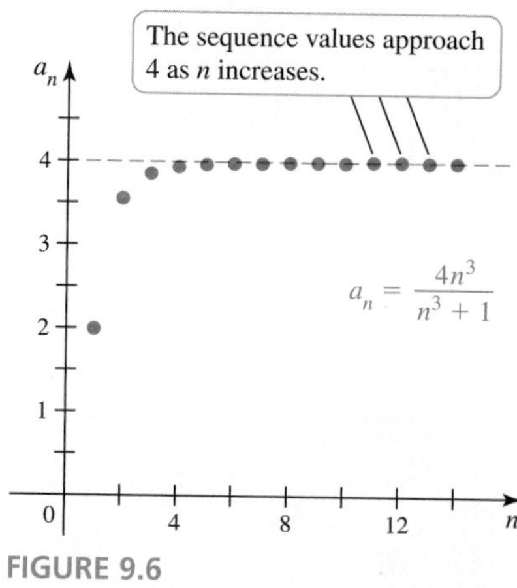

FIGURE 9.6

Related Exercises 31–44 ◄

EXAMPLE 6 **A bouncing ball** A basketball tossed straight up in the air reaches a high point and falls to the floor. Assume that each time the ball bounces on the floor it rebounds to 0.8 of its previous height. Let h_n be the high point after the nth bounce, with the initial height being $h_0 = 20$ ft.

a. Find a recurrence relation and an explicit formula for the sequence $\{h_n\}$.

b. What is the high point after the 10th bounce? after the 20th bounce?

c. Speculate on the limit of the sequence $\{h_n\}$.

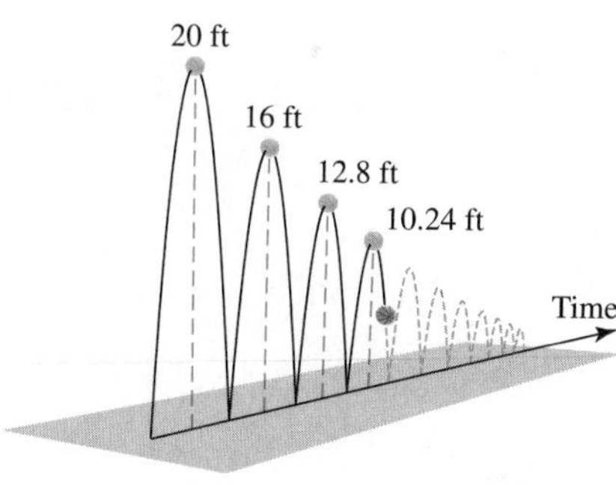

FIGURE 9.7

SOLUTION

a. We first write and graph the heights of the ball for several bounces using the rule that each height is 0.8 of the previous height (Figure 9.7). For example, we have

$$\begin{aligned} h_0 &= 20 \text{ ft} \\ h_1 &= 0.8\, h_0 = 16 \text{ ft} \\ h_2 &= 0.8\, h_1 = 0.8^2\, h_0 = 12.80 \text{ ft} \\ h_3 &= 0.8\, h_2 = 0.8^3\, h_0 = 10.24 \text{ ft} \\ h_4 &= 0.8\, h_3 = 0.8^4\, h_0 \approx 8.19 \text{ ft}. \end{aligned}$$

Each number in the list is 0.8 of the previous number. Therefore, the recurrence relation for the sequence of heights is

$$h_{n+1} = 0.8\, h_n, \qquad \text{for } n = 0, 1, 2, 3, \ldots, h_0 = 20 \text{ ft}.$$

To find an explicit formula for the nth term, note that

$$h_1 = h_0 \cdot 0.8, \qquad h_2 = h_0 \cdot 0.8^2, \qquad h_3 = h_0 \cdot 0.8^3, \qquad \text{and} \qquad h_4 = h_0 \cdot 0.8^4.$$

In general, we have

$$h_n = h_0 \cdot 0.8^n = 20 \cdot 0.8^n, \qquad \text{for } n = 0, 1, 2, 3, \ldots,$$

which is an explicit formula for the terms of the sequence.

b. Using the explicit formula for the sequence, we see that after $n = 10$ bounces, the next height is

$$h_{10} = 20 \cdot 0.8^{10} \approx 2.15 \text{ ft}.$$

After $n = 20$ bounces, the next height is

$$h_{20} = 20 \cdot 0.8^{20} \approx 0.23 \text{ ft}.$$

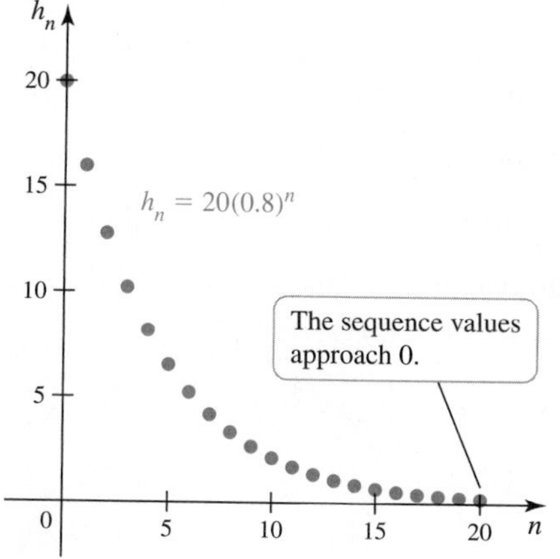

FIGURE 9.8

c. The terms of the sequence (Figure 9.8) appear to decrease and approach 0. A reasonable conjecture is that $\lim_{n\to\infty} h_n = 0$.

Related Exercises 45–48 ◄

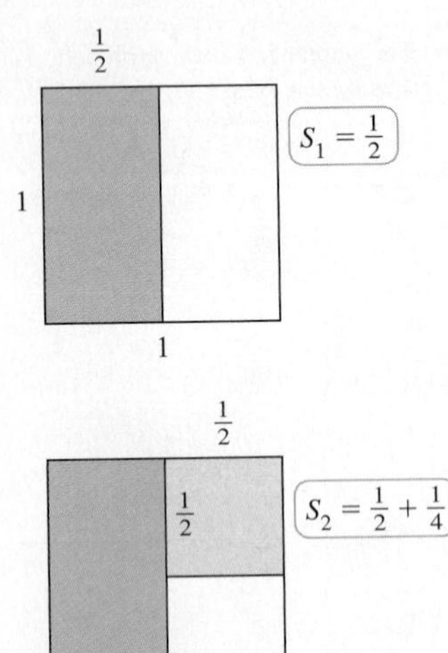

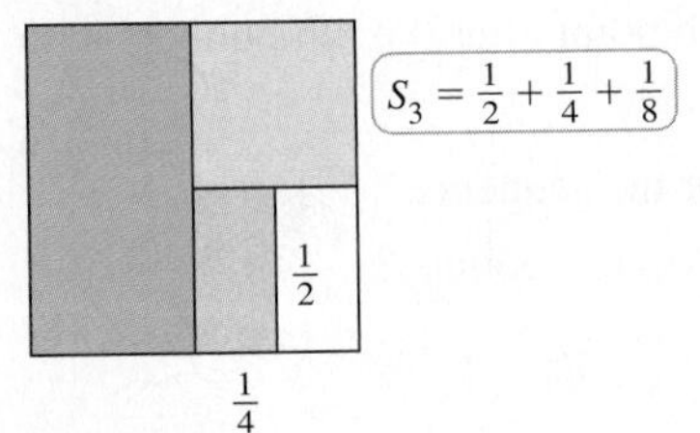

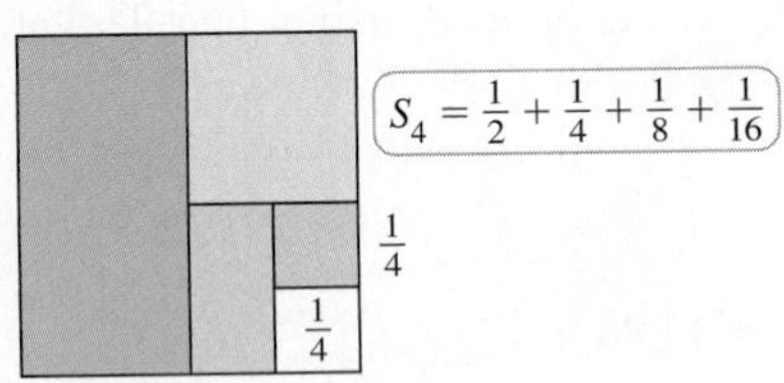

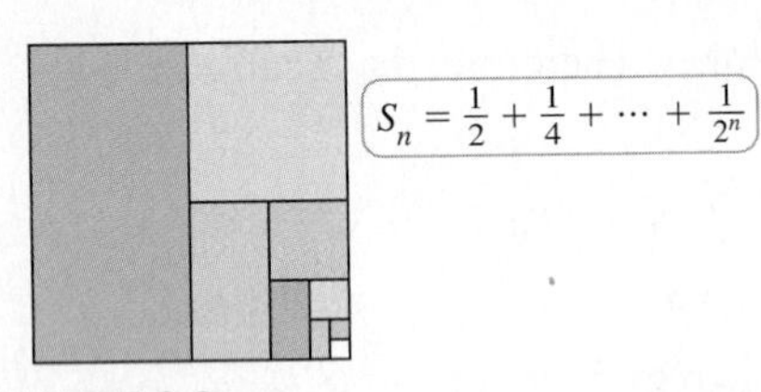

$S_n = \frac{1}{2} + \frac{1}{4} + \cdots + \frac{1}{2^n}$

FIGURE 9.9

Infinite Series and the Sequence of Partial Sums

An infinite series can be viewed as a sum of an infinite set of numbers; it has the form

$$a_1 + a_2 + \cdots + a_n + \cdots = \sum_{k=1}^{\infty} a_k,$$

where the terms of the series, $a_1, a_2, \ldots$, are real numbers. *An infinite series is quite distinct from a sequence.* We first answer the question: How is it possible to sum an infinite set of numbers and produce a finite number? Here is an informative example.

Consider a unit square (sides of length 1) that is subdivided as shown in Figure 9.9. We let S_n be the area of the colored region in the nth figure of the progression. The area of the colored region in the first figure is

$$S_1 = 1 \cdot \frac{1}{2} = \frac{1}{2}.$$

The area of the colored region in the second figure is S_1 plus the area of the smaller blue square, which is $\frac{1}{2} \cdot \frac{1}{2} = \frac{1}{4}$. Therefore,

$$S_2 = \frac{1}{2} + \frac{1}{4}.$$

The area of the colored region in the third figure is S_2 plus the area of the smaller green rectangle, which is $\frac{1}{2} \cdot \frac{1}{4} = \frac{1}{8}$. Therefore,

$$S_3 = \frac{1}{2} + \frac{1}{4} + \frac{1}{8}.$$

Continuing in this manner, we find that

$$S_n = \frac{1}{2} + \frac{1}{4} + \frac{1}{8} + \cdots + \frac{1}{2^n}.$$

If this process is continued indefinitely, the area of the colored region S_n approaches the area of the square, which is 1. So, it is plausible that

$$\lim_{n \to \infty} S_n = \underbrace{\frac{1}{2} + \frac{1}{4} + \frac{1}{8} + \cdots}_{\text{sum continues indefinitely}} = 1.$$

This example shows that it is possible to sum an infinite set of numbers and obtain a finite number—in this case, the sum is 1. The sequence $\{S_n\}$ generated in this example is extremely important. It is called a *sequence of partial sums*, and its limit is the value of the infinite series $\frac{1}{2} + \frac{1}{4} + \frac{1}{8} + \cdots$.

EXAMPLE 7 **Working with series** Consider the infinite series

$$0.9 + 0.09 + 0.009 + 0.0009 + \cdots,$$

where each term of the sum is $1/10$ of the previous term.

a. Find the sum of the first one, two, three, four, and five terms of the series.

b. What value would you assign to the infinite series $0.9 + 0.09 + 0.009 + \cdots$?

SOLUTION

a. Let S_n denote the sum of the first n terms of the given series. Then,

$$S_1 = 0.9$$
$$S_2 = 0.9 + 0.09 = 0.99$$
$$S_3 = 0.9 + 0.09 + 0.009 = 0.999$$
$$S_4 = 0.9 + 0.09 + 0.009 + 0.0009 = 0.9999$$
$$S_5 = 0.9 + 0.09 + 0.009 + 0.0009 + 0.00009 = 0.99999.$$

b. Notice that the sums $S_1, S_2, \ldots, S_n$ form a sequence $\{S_n\}$, which is a *sequence of partial sums*. As more and more terms are included, the values of S_n approach 1. Therefore, a reasonable conjecture for the value of the series is 1:

$$\underbrace{\underbrace{\underbrace{0.9}_{S_1 = 0.9} + 0.09}_{S_2 = 0.99} + 0.009}_{S_3 = 0.999} + 0.0009 + \cdots = 1$$

Related Exercises 49–52 ◀

QUICK CHECK 3 Reasoning as in Example 7, what is the value of $0.3 + 0.03 + 0.003 + \cdots$? ◀

The general nth term of the sequence in Example 7 can be written as

$$S_n = \underbrace{0.9 + 0.09 + 0.009 + \cdots + 0.0\ldots9}_{n \text{ terms}} = \sum_{k=1}^{n} 9 \cdot 0.1^k.$$

➤ Recall the summation notation introduced in Chapter 5: $\sum_{k=1}^{n} a_k$ means $a_1 + a_2 + \cdots + a_n$.

We observed that $\lim_{n\to\infty} S_n = 1$. For this reason, we write

$$\lim_{n\to\infty} S_n = \lim_{n\to\infty} \underbrace{\sum_{k=1}^{n} 9 \cdot 0.1^k}_{S_n} = \underbrace{\sum_{k=1}^{\infty} 9 \cdot 0.1^k}_{\text{new object}} = 1.$$

By letting $n \to \infty$ a new mathematical object $\sum_{k=1}^{\infty} 9 \cdot 0.1^k$ is created. It is an infinite series and it is the *limit of the sequence of partial sums*.

➤ The term *series* is used for historical reasons. When you see *series*, you should think *sum*.

DEFINITION **Infinite Series**

Given a set of numbers $\{a_1, a_2, a_3, \ldots\}$, the sum

$$a_1 + a_2 + a_3 + \cdots = \sum_{k=1}^{\infty} a_k$$

is called an **infinite series**. Its **sequence of partial sums** $\{S_n\}$ has the terms

$$S_1 = a_1$$
$$S_2 = a_1 + a_2$$
$$S_3 = a_1 + a_2 + a_3$$
$$\vdots$$
$$S_n = a_1 + a_2 + a_3 + \cdots + a_n = \sum_{k=1}^{n} a_k, \quad \text{for } n = 1, 2, 3, \ldots$$

If the sequence of partial sums $\{S_n\}$ has a limit L, the infinite series **converges** to that limit, and we write

$$\sum_{k=1}^{\infty} a_k = \lim_{n\to\infty} \underbrace{\sum_{k=1}^{n} a_k}_{S_n} = \lim_{n\to\infty} S_n = L.$$

If the sequence of partial sums diverges, the infinite series also **diverges**.

QUICK CHECK 4 Do the series $\sum_{k=1}^{\infty} 1$ and $\sum_{k=1}^{\infty} k$ converge or diverge? ◀

EXAMPLE 8 **Sequence of partial sums** Consider the infinite series

$$\sum_{k=1}^{\infty} \frac{1}{k(k+1)}.$$

a. Find the first four terms of the sequence of partial sums.

b. Find an expression for S_n and make a conjecture about the value of the series.

SOLUTION

a. The sequence of partial sums can be evaluated explicitly:

$$S_1 = \sum_{k=1}^{1} \frac{1}{k(k+1)} = \frac{1}{2}$$

$$S_2 = \sum_{k=1}^{2} \frac{1}{k(k+1)} = \frac{1}{2} + \frac{1}{6} = \frac{2}{3}$$

$$S_3 = \sum_{k=1}^{3} \frac{1}{k(k+1)} = \frac{1}{2} + \frac{1}{6} + \frac{1}{12} = \frac{3}{4}$$

$$S_4 = \sum_{k=1}^{4} \frac{1}{k(k+1)} = \frac{1}{2} + \frac{1}{6} + \frac{1}{12} + \frac{1}{20} = \frac{4}{5}$$

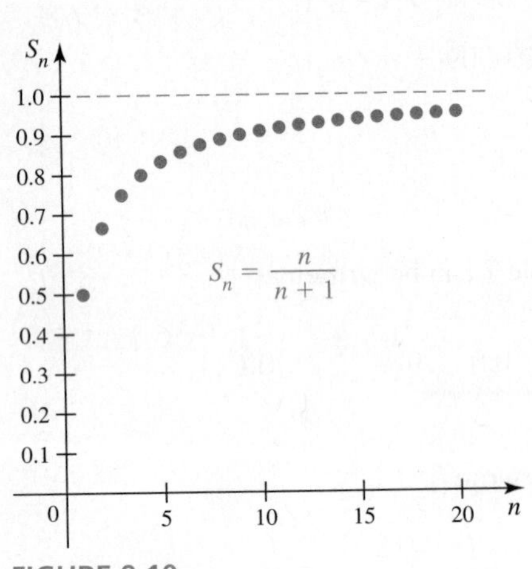

FIGURE 9.10

b. Based on the pattern in the sequence of partial sums, a reasonable conjecture is that $S_n = \frac{n}{n+1}$, for $n = 1, 2, 3, \ldots$, which produces the sequence $\left\{\frac{1}{2}, \frac{2}{3}, \frac{3}{4}, \frac{4}{5}, \frac{5}{6}, \ldots\right\}$ (Figure 9.10). Because $\lim_{n\to\infty} \frac{n}{n+1} = 1$, we conclude that

$$\lim_{n\to\infty} S_n = \sum_{k=1}^{\infty} \frac{1}{k(k+1)} = 1.$$

Related Exercises 53–56 ◀

QUICK CHECK 5 Find the first four terms of the sequence of partial sums for the series $\sum_{k=1}^{\infty} (-1)^k k$. Does the series converge or diverge? ◀

Summary

This section has shown that there are three key ideas to keep in mind.

- A *sequence* $\{a_1, a_2, \ldots, a_n, \ldots\}$ is an ordered *list* of numbers.
- An *infinite series* $\sum_{k=1}^{\infty} a_k = a_1 + a_2 + a_3 + \cdots$ is a *sum* of numbers.
- The *sequence of partial sums* $S_n = a_1 + a_2 + \cdots + a_n$ is used to evaluate the series $\sum_{k=1}^{\infty} a_k$.

For sequences, we ask about the behavior of the individual terms as we go out farther and farther in the list; that is, we ask about $\lim_{n\to\infty} a_n$. For infinite series, we examine the sequence of partial sums related to the series. If the sequence of partial sums $\{S_n\}$ has a limit, then the infinite series $\sum_{k=1}^{\infty} a_k$ converges to that limit. If the sequence of partial sums does not have a limit, the infinite series diverges.

Table 9.2 shows the correspondences between sequences/series and functions, and between summing and integration. For a sequence, the index n plays the role of the independent variable and takes on integer values; the terms of the sequence $\{a_n\}$ correspond to the dependent variable.

With sequences $\{a_n\}$, the idea of accumulation corresponds to summation, whereas with functions, accumulation corresponds to integration. A finite sum is analogous to integrating a function over a finite interval. An infinite series is analogous to integrating a function over an infinite interval.

Table 9.2

	Sequences/Series	Functions
Independent variable	n	x
Dependent variable	a_n	$f(x)$
Domain	Integers e.g., $n = 0, 1, 2, 3, \ldots$	Real numbers e.g., $\{x: x \geq 0\}$
Accumulation	Sums	Integrals
Accumulation over a finite interval	$\sum_{k=0}^{n} a_k$	$\int_0^n f(x)\,dx$
Accumulation over an infinite interval	$\sum_{k=0}^{\infty} a_k$	$\int_0^{\infty} f(x)\,dx$

SECTION 9.1 EXERCISES

Review Questions

1. Define *sequence* and give an example.

2. Suppose the sequence $\{a_n\}$ is defined by the explicit formula $a_n = 1/n$, for $n = 1, 2, 3, \ldots$. Write out the first five terms of the sequence.

3. Suppose the sequence $\{a_n\}$ is defined by the recurrence relation $a_{n+1} = na_n$, for $n = 1, 2, 3, \ldots$, where $a_1 = 1$. Write out the first five terms of the sequence.

4. Define *finite sum* and give an example.

5. Define *infinite series* and give an example.

6. Given the series $\sum_{k=1}^{\infty} k$, evaluate the first four terms of its sequence of partial sums $S_n = \sum_{k=1}^{n} k$.

7. The terms of a sequence of partial sums are defined by $S_n = \sum_{k=1}^{n} k^2$, for $n = 1, 2, 3, \ldots$. Evaluate the first four terms of the sequence.

8. Consider the infinite series $\sum_{k=1}^{\infty} \frac{1}{k}$. Evaluate the first four terms of the sequence of partial sums.

Basic Skills

9–12. Explicit formulas *Write the first four terms of the sequence* $\{a_n\}_{n=1}^{\infty}$.

9. $a_n = 1/10^n$

10. $a_n = n + 1/n$

11. $a_n = 1 + \sin(\pi n/2)$

12. $a_n = 2n^2 - 3n + 1$

13–16. Recurrence relations *Write the first four terms of the sequence $\{a_n\}$ defined by the following recurrence relations.*

13. $a_{n+1} = 3a_n - 12;\ a_1 = 10$

14. $a_{n+1} = a_n^2 - 1;\ a_1 = 1$

15. $a_{n+1} = 3a_n^2 + n + 1;\ a_1 = 0$

16. $a_{n+1} = a_n + a_{n-1};\ a_1 = 1, a_0 = 1$

17–22. Enumerated sequences *Several terms of a sequence $\{a_n\}_{n=1}^{\infty}$ are given.*

a. *Find the next two terms of the sequence.*
b. *Find a recurrence relation that generates the sequence (supply the initial value of the index and the first term of the sequence).*
c. *Find an explicit formula for the general nth term of the sequence.*

17. $\{1, \frac{1}{2}, \frac{1}{4}, \frac{1}{8}, \frac{1}{16}, \ldots\}$

18. $\{1, -2, 3, -4, 5, \ldots\}$

19. $\{1, 2, 4, 8, 16, \ldots\}$

20. $\{1, 4, 9, 16, 25, \ldots\}$

21. $\{1, 3, 9, 27, 81, \ldots\}$

22. $\{64, 32, 16, 8, 4, \ldots\}$

23–30. Limits of sequences *Write the terms a_1, a_2, a_3, and a_4 of the following sequences. If the sequence appears to converge, make a conjecture about its limit. If the sequence diverges, explain why.*

23. $a_n = 10^n - 1;\ n = 1, 2, 3, \ldots$

24. $a_n = n^8 + 1;\ n = 1, 2, 3, \ldots$

25. $a_n = \dfrac{(-1)^n}{n};\ n = 1, 2, 3, \ldots$

26. $a_n = 1 - 10^{-n};\ n = 1, 2, 3, \ldots$

27. $a_{n+1} = \dfrac{a_n^2}{10};\ a_0 = 1$

28. $a_{n+1} = 0.5a_n(1 - a_n);\ a_0 = 0.8$

29. $a_{n+1} = 0.5a_n + 50;\ a_0 = 100$

30. $a_{n+1} = 0.9a_n + 100;\ a_0 = 50$

T **31–36. Explicit formulas for sequences** *Consider the explicit formulas for the following sequences.*

a. *Find the first four terms of the sequence.*
b. *Using a calculator, make a table with at least 10 terms and determine a plausible value for the limit of the sequence or state that it does not exist.*

31. $a_n = n + 1;\ n = 0, 1, 2, \ldots$

32. $a_n = 2\tan^{-1}(1000n);\ n = 1, 2, 3, \ldots$

33. $a_n = n^2 - n;\ n = 1, 2, 3, \ldots$

34. $a_n = \dfrac{2n - 3}{n};\ n = 1, 2, 3, \ldots$

35. $a_n = \dfrac{(n-1)^2}{(n^2 - 1)};\ n = 2, 3, 4, \ldots$

36. $a_n = \sin(n\pi/2);\ n = 0, 1, 2, \ldots$

37–38. Limits from graphs *Consider the following sequences.*

a. *Find the first four terms of the sequence.*
b. *Based on part (a) and the figure, determine a plausible limit of the sequence.*

37. $a_n = 2 + 2^{-n};\ n = 1, 2, 3, \ldots$

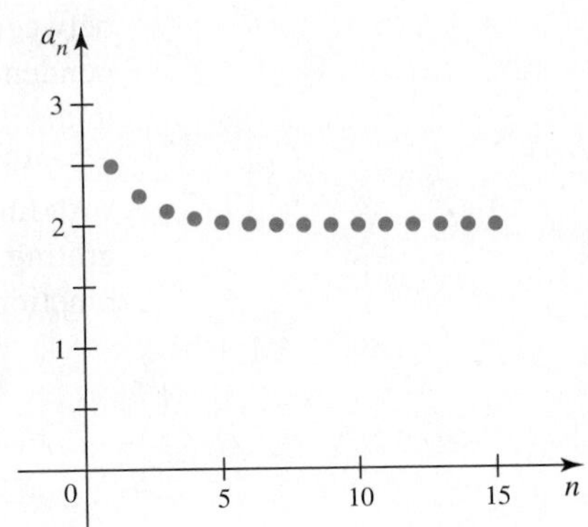

38. $a_n = \dfrac{n^2}{n^2 - 1};\ n = 2, 3, 4, \ldots$

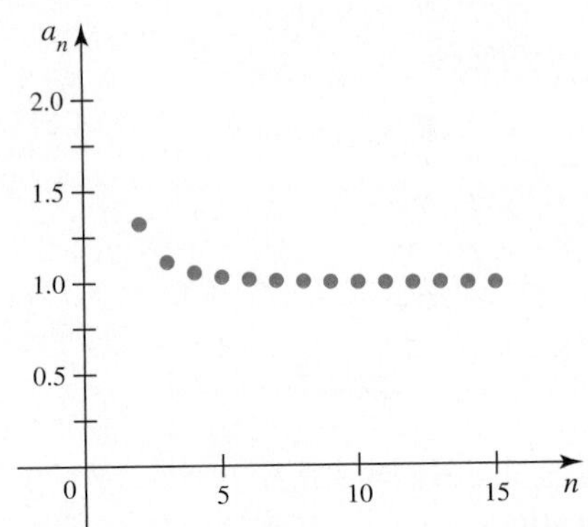

T **39–44. Recurrence relations to formulas** *Consider the following recurrence relations.*

a. *Find the terms a_0, a_1, a_2, a_3 of the sequence.*
b. *If possible, find an explicit formula for the nth term of the sequence.*
c. *Using a calculator, make a table with at least 10 terms and determine a plausible value for the limit of the sequence or state that it does not exist.*

39. $a_{n+1} = a_n + 2;\ a_0 = 3$

40. $a_{n+1} = a_n - 4;\ a_0 = 36$

41. $a_{n+1} = 2a_n + 1;\ a_0 = 0$

42. $a_{n+1} = \dfrac{a_n}{2};\ a_0 = 32$

43. $a_{n+1} = \frac{1}{2}a_n + 1;\ a_0 = 1$

44. $a_{n+1} = \sqrt{1 + a_n};\ a_0 = 1$

45–48. Heights of bouncing balls *Suppose a ball is thrown upward to a height of h_0 meters. Each time the ball bounces, it rebounds to a fraction r of its previous height. Let h_n be the height after the nth bounce. Consider the following values of h_0 and r.*

a. *Find the first four terms of the sequence of heights $\{h_n\}$.*
b. *Find a general expression for the nth term of the sequence $\{h_n\}$.*

45. $h_0 = 20,\ r = 0.5$

46. $h_0 = 10,\ r = 0.9$

47. $h_0 = 30,\ r = 0.25$

48. $h_0 = 20,\ r = 0.75$

49–52. Sequences of partial sums *For the following infinite series, find the first four terms of the sequence of partial sums. Then make a conjecture about the value of the infinite series.*

49. $0.3 + 0.03 + 0.003 + \cdots$

50. $0.6 + 0.06 + 0.006 + \cdots$

51. $4 + 0.9 + 0.09 + 0.009 + \cdots$

52. $1 + \frac{1}{2} + \frac{1}{4} + \frac{1}{8} + \cdots$

T 53–56. Formulas for sequences of partial sums *Consider the following infinite series.*

a. Find the first four terms of the sequence of partial sums.
b. Use the results of part (a) to propose a formula for S_n.
c. Propose a value of the series.

53. $\sum_{k=1}^{\infty} \frac{2}{(2k-1)(2k+1)}$

54. $\sum_{k=1}^{\infty} \frac{1}{2^k}$

55. $\sum_{k=1}^{\infty} \frac{1}{4k^2 - 1}$

56. $\sum_{k=1}^{\infty} \frac{2}{3^k}$

Further Explorations

57. Explain why or why not Determine whether the following statements are true and give an explanation or counterexample.

a. The sequence of partial sums for the series $1 + 2 + 3 + \cdots$ is $\{1, 3, 6, 10, \ldots\}$.

b. If a sequence of positive numbers converges, then the terms of the sequence must decrease in size.

c. If the positive terms of the sequence $\{a_n\}$ increase in size, then the sequence of partial sums for the series $\sum_{k=1}^{\infty} a_k$ diverges.

T 58–59. Distance traveled by bouncing balls *Suppose a ball is thrown upward to a height of h_0 meters. Each time the ball bounces, it rebounds to a fraction r of its previous height. Let h_n be the height after the nth bounce and let S_n be the total distance the ball has traveled at the moment of the nth bounce.*

a. Find the first four terms of the sequence $\{S_n\}$.
b. Make a table of 20 terms of the sequence $\{S_n\}$ and determine a plausible value for the limit of $\{S_n\}$.

58. $h_0 = 20, r = 0.5$

59. $h_0 = 20, r = 0.75$

60–67. Sequences of partial sums *Consider the following infinite series.*

a. Write out the first four terms of the sequence of partial sums.

b. Estimate the limit of $\{S_n\}$ or state that it does not exist.

60. $\sum_{k=1}^{\infty} \cos\left(\frac{\pi k}{2}\right)$

61. $\sum_{k=1}^{\infty} 0.5^k$

62. $\sum_{k=1}^{\infty} 1.5^k$

63. $\sum_{k=1}^{\infty} 3^{-k}$

64. $\sum_{k=1}^{\infty} k$

65. $\sum_{k=1}^{\infty} (-1)^k$

66. $\sum_{k=1}^{\infty} (-1)^k k$

67. $\sum_{k=1}^{\infty} \frac{3}{10^k}$

Applications

T 68–71. Practical sequences *Consider the following situations that generate a sequence.*

a. Write out the first five terms of the sequence.
b. Find an explicit formula for the terms of the sequence.
c. Find a recurrence relation that generates the sequence.
d. Using a calculator or a graphing utility, estimate the limit of the sequence or state that it does not exist.

68. Population growth When a biologist begins a study, a colony of prairie dogs has a population of 250. Regular measurements reveal that each month the prairie dog population increases by 3%. Let p_n be the population (rounded to whole numbers) at the end of the nth month, where the initial population is $p_0 = 250$.

69. Radioactive decay A material transmutes 50% of its mass to another element every 10 years due to radioactive decay. Let M_n be the mass of the radioactive material at the end of the nth decade, where the initial mass of the material is $M_0 = 20$ g.

70. Consumer Price Index The Consumer Price Index (the CPI is a measure of the U.S. cost of living) is given a base value of 100 in the year 1984. Assume the CPI has increased by an average of 3% per year since 1984. Let c_n be the CPI n years after 1984, where $c_0 = 100$.

71. Drug elimination Jack took a 200-mg dose of a strong pain killer at midnight. Every hour, 5% of the drug is washed out of his bloodstream. Let d_n be the amount of drug in Jack's blood n hours after the drug was taken, where $d_0 = 200$ mg.

T 72. A square root finder A well-known method for approximating $\sqrt{c}$ for positive real numbers c consists of the following recurrence relation (based on Newton's method; see Guided Projects). Let $a_0 = c$ and

$$a_{n+1} = \frac{1}{2}\left(a_n + \frac{c}{a_n}\right), \quad \text{for } n = 0, 1, 2, 3, \ldots.$$

a. Use this recurrence relation to approximate $\sqrt{10}$. How many terms of the sequence are needed to approximate $\sqrt{10}$ with an error less than 0.01? How many terms of the sequence are needed to approximate $\sqrt{10}$ with an error less than 0.0001? (To compute the error, assume a calculator gives the exact value.)

b. Use this recurrence relation to approximate $\sqrt{c}$ for $c = 2, 3, \ldots, 10$. Make a table showing how many terms of the sequence are needed to approximate $\sqrt{c}$ with an error less than 0.01.

Additional Exercises

73–80. Repeating decimals

a. Write the following repeating decimals as an infinite series. For example, $0.9999\ldots = \sum_{k=1}^{\infty} 9(0.1^k)$.

b. Find the limit of the sequence of partial sums for the infinite series and express it as a fraction.

73. $0.\overline{3} = 0.333\ldots$

74. $0.\overline{6} = 0.666\ldots$

75. $0.\overline{1} = 0.111\ldots$

76. $0.\overline{5} = 0.555\ldots$

77. $0.\overline{09} = 0.090909\ldots$

78. $0.\overline{27} = 0.272727\ldots$

79. $0.\overline{037} = 0.037037\ldots$

80. $0.\overline{027} = 0.027027\ldots$

QUICK CHECK ANSWERS

1. $a_{10} = 28$ **2.** $a_n = 2^n - 1,\ n = 1, 2, 3, \ldots$ **3.** $0.33333\ldots = \frac{1}{3}$ **4.** Both diverge **5.** $S_1 = -1, S_2 = 1, S_3 = -2, S_4 = 2$; the series diverges.

9.2 Sequences

The overview of the previous section sets the stage for an in-depth investigation of sequences and infinite series. This section is devoted to sequences, and the remainder of the chapter deals with series.

Limit of a Sequence

A fundamental question about sequences concerns the behavior of the terms as we go out farther and farther in the sequence. For example, in the sequence

$$\{a_n\}_{n=0}^{\infty} = \left\{\frac{1}{n^2+1}\right\}_{n=0}^{\infty} = \left\{1, \frac{1}{2}, \frac{1}{5}, \frac{1}{10}, \ldots\right\},$$

the terms remain positive and decrease to 0. We say that this sequence **converges** and its **limit** is 0, written $\lim_{n\to\infty} a_n = 0$. Similarly, the terms of the sequence

$$\{b_n\}_{n=1}^{\infty} = \left\{(-1)^n \frac{n(n+1)}{2}\right\}_{n=1}^{\infty} = \{-1, 3, -6, 10, \ldots\}$$

increase in magnitude and do not approach a unique value as n increases. In this case, we say that the sequence **diverges**.

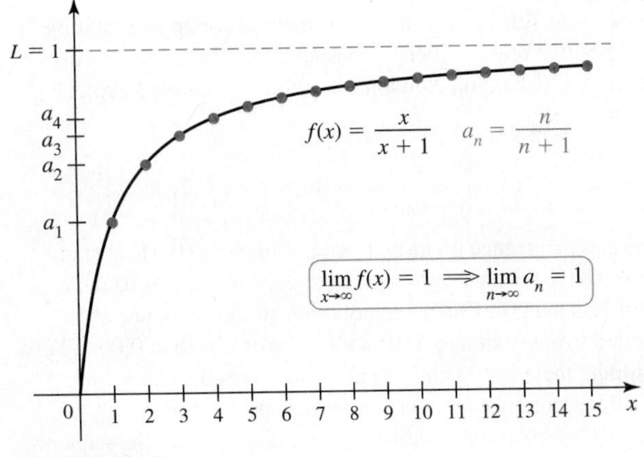

FIGURE 9.11

Limits of sequences are really no different from limits at infinity of functions except that the variable n assumes only integer values as $n \to \infty$. This idea works as follows.

Given a sequence $\{a_n\}$, we define a function f such that $f(n) = a_n$ for all indices n. For example, if $\{a_n\} = \{n/(n+1)\}$, then we let $f(x) = x/(x+1)$. By the methods of Section 2.5, we know that $\lim_{x\to\infty} f(x) = 1$; because the terms of the sequence lie on the graph of f, it follows that $\lim_{n\to\infty} a_n = 1$ (Figure 9.11). This reasoning is the basis of the following theorem.

> The converse of Theorem 9.1 is not true. For example, if $a_n = \cos 2\pi n$, then $\lim_{n\to\infty} a_n = 1$, but $\lim_{x\to\infty} \cos 2\pi x$ does not exist.

THEOREM 9.1 Limits of Sequences from Limits of Functions
Suppose f is a function such that $f(n) = a_n$ for all positive integers n. If $\lim_{x\to\infty} f(x) = L$, then the limit of the sequence $\{a_n\}$ is also L.

Because of the correspondence between limits of sequences and limits at infinity of functions, we have the following properties that are analogous to those for functions given in Theorem 2.3.

> The limit of a sequence $\{a_n\}$ is determined by the terms in the *tail* of the sequence—the terms with large values of n. If the sequences $\{a_n\}$ and $\{b_n\}$ differ in their first 100 terms but have identical terms for $n > 100$, then they have the same limit. For this reason, the initial index of a sequence (for example, $n = 0$ or $n = 1$) is often not specified.

THEOREM 9.2 Properties of Limits of Sequences

Assume that the sequences $\{a_n\}$ and $\{b_n\}$ have limits A and B, respectively. Then,

1. $\lim_{n\to\infty} (a_n \pm b_n) = A \pm B$
2. $\lim_{n\to\infty} ca_n = cA,$ where c is a real number
3. $\lim_{n\to\infty} a_n b_n = AB$
4. $\lim_{n\to\infty} \frac{a_n}{b_n} = \frac{A}{B},$ provided $B \neq 0$.

EXAMPLE 1 Limits of sequences Determine the limits of the following sequences.

a. $\{a_n\}_{n=0}^{\infty} = \left\{\frac{3n^3}{n^3+1}\right\}_{n=0}^{\infty}$ **b.** $\{b_n\}_{n=1}^{\infty} = \left\{\left(\frac{5+n}{n}\right)^n\right\}_{n=1}^{\infty}$

c. $\{c_n\}_{n=1}^{\infty} = \{e^{-n}n^{10}\}_{n=1}^{\infty}$

SOLUTION

a. A function with the property that $f(n) = a_n$ is $f(x) = \frac{3x^3}{x^3+1}$. Dividing numerator and denominator by x^3 (Section 2.5), we find that $\lim_{x\to\infty} f(x) = 3$. (Alternatively, we can apply l'Hôpital's Rule and obtain the same result.) Either way, we conclude that $\lim_{n\to\infty} a_n = 3$.

b. The limit

$$\lim_{n\to\infty} b_n = \lim_{n\to\infty}\left(\frac{5+n}{n}\right)^n = \lim_{n\to\infty}\left(1+\frac{5}{n}\right)^n$$

> For a review of l'Hôpital's Rule, see Section 7.6, where we showed that $\lim_{x\to\infty}\left(1+\frac{a}{x}\right)^x = e^a$.

has the indeterminate form 1^{∞}. Recall that for this limit (Section 4.7), we first evaluate

$$L = \lim_{n\to\infty} \ln\left(1+\frac{5}{n}\right)^n = \lim_{n\to\infty} n\ln\left(1+\frac{5}{n}\right)$$

and then, if L exists, $\lim_{n\to\infty} b_n = e^L$. Using l'Hôpital's Rule for the indeterminate form $0/0$, we have

> It is not necessary to convert the terms of a sequence to a function of x, as we did in Example 1a. You can take the limit as $n \to \infty$ of the terms of the sequence directly.

$$L = \lim_{n\to\infty} n\ln\left(1+\frac{5}{n}\right) = \lim_{n\to\infty}\frac{\ln(1+(5/n))}{1/n} \quad \text{Indeterminate form } 0/0$$

$$= \lim_{n\to\infty}\frac{\frac{1}{1+(5/n)}\left(-\frac{5}{n^2}\right)}{-1/n^2} \quad \text{L'Hôpital's Rule}$$

$$= \lim_{n\to\infty}\frac{5}{1+(5/n)} = 5 \quad \text{Simplify; } 5/n \to 0 \text{ as } n\to\infty.$$

Because $\lim_{n\to\infty} b_n = e^L = e^5$, we have $\lim_{n\to\infty}\left(\frac{5+n}{n}\right)^n = e^5$.

c. Computing the limit $\lim_{n\to\infty}\frac{n^{10}}{e^n}$ requires ten applications of l'Hôpital's Rule. Instead, we appeal to the relative growth rates of functions (Section 7.6) and recall that an exponential function grows faster than any power of n as $n \to \infty$. Therefore,

$$\lim_{n\to\infty}\frac{n^{10}}{e^n} = 0.$$

Related Exercises 9–26 ◀

Terminology for Sequences

We now introduce some terminology similar to that used for functions. A sequence $\{a_n\}$ in which each term is greater than or equal to its predecessor ($a_{n+1} \geq a_n$) is said to be **nondecreasing**. For example, the sequence

$$\left\{1 - \frac{1}{n}\right\}_{n=1}^{\infty} = \left\{0, \frac{1}{2}, \frac{2}{3}, \frac{3}{4}, \ldots\right\}$$

is nondecreasing (Figure 9.12). A sequence $\{a_n\}$ is **nonincreasing** if each term is less than or equal to its predecessor ($a_{n+1} \leq a_n$). For example, the sequence

$$\left\{1 + \frac{1}{n}\right\}_{n=1}^{\infty} = \left\{2, \frac{3}{2}, \frac{4}{3}, \frac{5}{4}, \ldots\right\}$$

is nonincreasing (Figure 9.12). A sequence that is either nonincreasing or nondecreasing is said to be **monotonic**; it progresses in only one direction. Finally, a sequence whose terms are all less than or equal to some finite number in magnitude ($|a_n| \leq M$, for some real number M) is said to be **bounded**. For example, the terms of $\left\{1 - \frac{1}{n}\right\}_{n=1}^{\infty}$ satisfy $|a_n| < 1$, and the terms of $\left\{1 + \frac{1}{n}\right\}_{n=1}^{\infty}$ satisfy $|a_n| \leq 2$ (Figure 9.12); so these sequences are bounded.

➤ Nondecreasing sequences include increasing sequences, which satisfy $a_{n+1} > a_n$ (strict inequality). Similarly, nonincreasing sequences include decreasing sequences, which satisfy $a_{n+1} < a_n$. For example, the sequence $\{1, 1, 2, 2, 3, 3, 4, 4, \ldots\}$ is nondecreasing but not increasing.

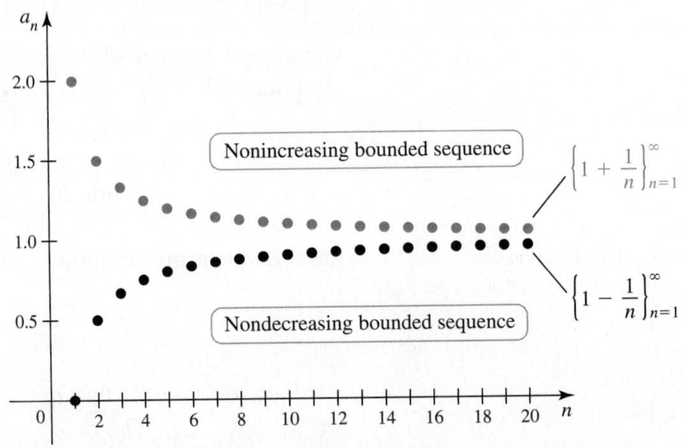

FIGURE 9.12

QUICK CHECK 1 Classify the following sequences as bounded, monotonic, or neither.

a. $\left\{\frac{1}{2}, \frac{3}{4}, \frac{7}{8}, \frac{15}{16}, \ldots\right\}$

b. $\left\{1, -\frac{1}{2}, \frac{1}{4}, -\frac{1}{8}, \frac{1}{16}, \ldots\right\}$

c. $\{1, -2, 3, -4, 5, \ldots\}$

d. $\{1, 1, 1, 1, \ldots\}$ ◄

EXAMPLE 2 Limits of sequences and graphing Compare and contrast the behavior of $\{a_n\}$ and $\{b_n\}$ as $n \to \infty$.

a. $a_n = \dfrac{n^{3/2}}{n^{3/2} + 1}$ **b.** $b_n = \dfrac{(-1)^n n^{3/2}}{n^{3/2} + 1}$

SOLUTION

a. The sequence $\{a_n\}$ consists of positive terms. Dividing the numerator and denominator of a_n by $n^{3/2}$, we see that

$$\lim_{n\to\infty} a_n = \lim_{n\to\infty} \frac{n^{3/2}}{n^{3/2} + 1} = \lim_{n\to\infty} \frac{1}{1 + \underbrace{\frac{1}{n^{3/2}}}_{\text{approaches 0 as } n \to \infty}} = 1.$$

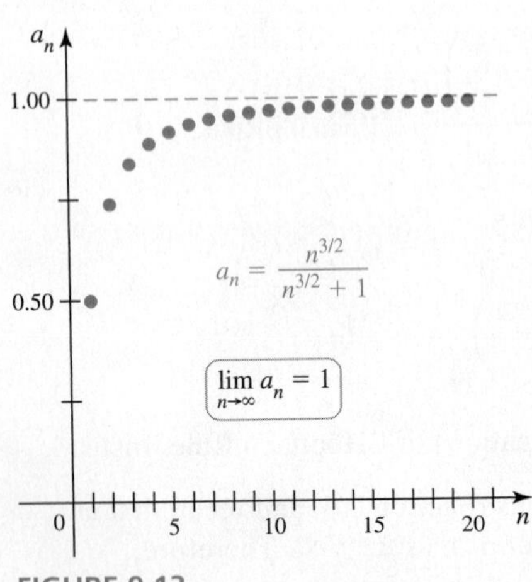

FIGURE 9.13

The terms of this sequence are nondecreasing and bounded (Figure 9.13).

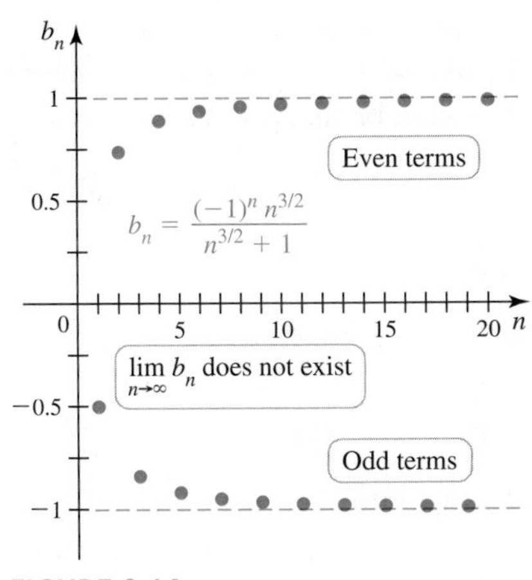

FIGURE 9.14

b. The terms of the bounded sequence $\{b_n\}$ alternate in sign. Using the result of part (a), it follows that the even terms of the sequence approach $+1$ and the odd terms approach -1 (Figure 9.14). Therefore, the sequence diverges, illustrating the fact that the presence of $(-1)^n$ may significantly alter the behavior of the sequence.

Related Exercises 27–34

Geometric Sequences

Geometric sequences have the property that each term is obtained by multiplying the previous term by a fixed constant, called the **ratio**. They have the form $\{r^n\}$, where the ratio r is a real number.

EXAMPLE 3 **Geometric sequences** Graph the following sequences and discuss their behavior.

a. $\{0.75^n\}$ **b.** $\{(-0.75)^n\}$ **c.** $\{1.15^n\}$ **d.** $\{(-1.15)^n\}$

SOLUTION

a. When a number less than 1 in magnitude is raised to increasing powers, the resulting numbers decrease to zero. The sequence $\{0.75^n\}$ converges monotonically to zero (Figure 9.15).

b. Note that $\{(-0.75)^n\} = \{(-1)^n\, 0.75^n\}$. Observe also that $(-1)^n$ oscillates between $+1$ and -1, while 0.75^n decreases to zero as n increases. Therefore, the sequence oscillates and converges to zero (Figure 9.16).

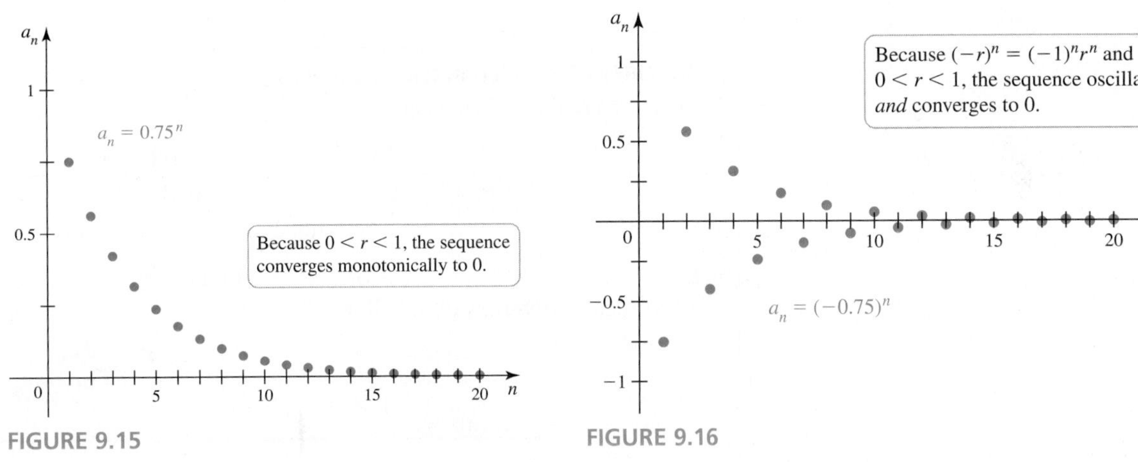

FIGURE 9.15

FIGURE 9.16

c. When a number greater than 1 in magnitude is raised to increasing powers, the resulting numbers increase in magnitude. The terms of the sequence $\{1.15^n\}$ are positive and increase without bound. In this case, the sequence diverges monotonically (Figure 9.17).

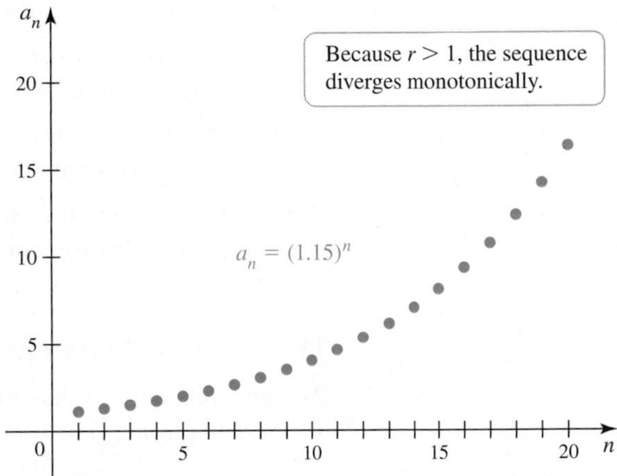

FIGURE 9.17

d. We write $\{(-1.15)^n\} = \{(-1)^n 1.15^n\}$ and observe that $(-1)^n$ oscillates between $+1$ and -1, while 1.15^n increases without bound as n increases. The terms of the sequence increase in magnitude without bound and alternate in sign. In this case, the sequence oscillates and diverges (Figure 9.18).

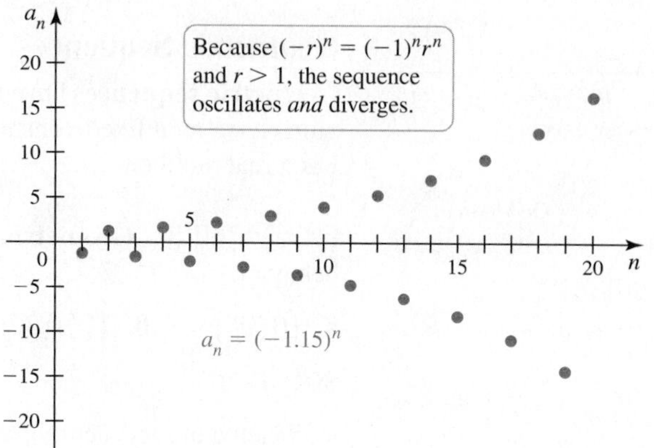

FIGURE 9.18

Related Exercises 35–42 ◀

QUICK CHECK 2 Describe the behavior of $\{r^n\}$ in the cases $r = -1$ and $r = 1$. ◀

The results of Example 3 and Quick Check 2 are summarized in the following theorem.

> **THEOREM 9.3 Geometric Sequences**
> Let r be a real number. Then,
>
> $$\lim_{n\to\infty} r^n = \begin{cases} 0 & \text{if } |r| < 1 \\ 1 & \text{if } r = 1 \\ \text{does not exist} & \text{if } r \le -1 \text{ or } r > 1 \end{cases}$$
>
> If $r > 0$, then $\{r^n\}$ converges or diverges monotonically. If $r < 0$, then $\{r^n\}$ converges or diverges by oscillation.
>
> 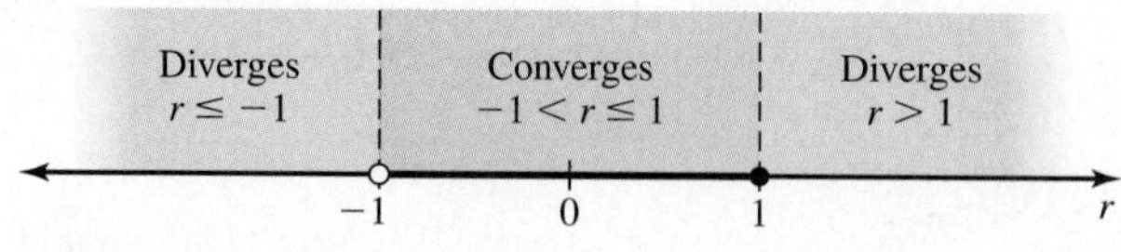
>

The previous examples show that a sequence may display any of the following behaviors:

- It may converge to a single value, which is the limit of the sequence.
- Its terms may increase in magnitude without bound (either with one sign or with mixed signs), in which case the sequence diverges.
- Its terms may remain bounded but settle into an oscillating pattern in which the terms approach two or more values; in this case, the sequence diverges.
- Not illustrated in the preceding examples is one other type of behavior: The terms of a sequence may remain bounded, but wander chaotically forever without a pattern. In this case, the sequence also diverges.

The Squeeze Theorem

We cite two theorems that are often useful in either establishing that a sequence has a limit or in finding limits. The first is a direct analog of Theorem 2.5 (the Squeeze Theorem).

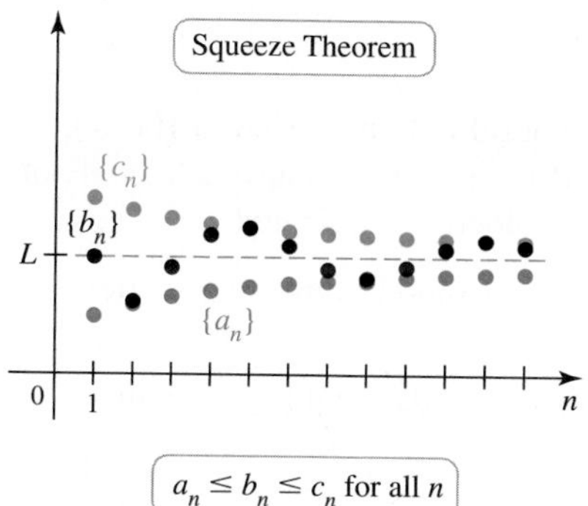

FIGURE 9.19

> **THEOREM 9.4 Squeeze Theorem for Sequences**
> Let $\{a_n\}$, $\{b_n\}$, and $\{c_n\}$ be sequences with $a_n \le b_n \le c_n$ for all integers n greater than some index N. If $\lim_{n\to\infty} a_n = \lim_{n\to\infty} c_n = L$, then $\lim_{n\to\infty} b_n = L$ (Figure 9.19).

EXAMPLE 4 Squeeze Theorem Find the limit of the sequence $b_n = \dfrac{\cos n}{n^2+1}$.

SOLUTION The goal is to find two sequences $\{a_n\}$ and $\{c_n\}$ whose terms lie below and above the terms of the given sequence $\{b_n\}$. Note that $-1 \le \cos \pi n \le 1$ for all n. Therefore,

$$\underbrace{-\frac{1}{n^2+1}}_{a_n} \le \underbrace{\frac{\cos n}{n^2+1}}_{b_n} \le \underbrace{\frac{1}{n^2+1}}_{c_n}.$$

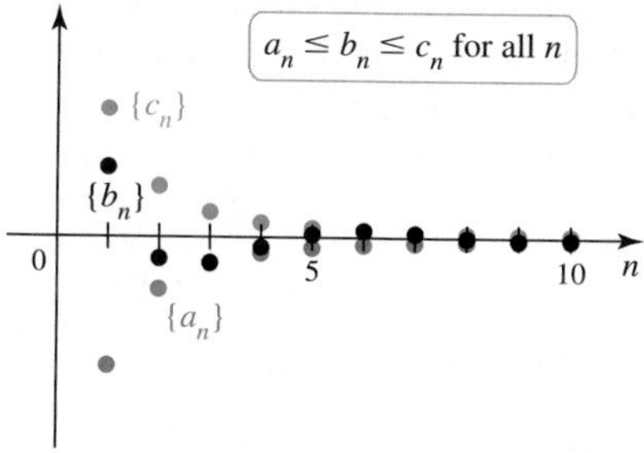

FIGURE 9.20

Letting $a_n = -\dfrac{1}{n^2+1}$ and $c_n = \dfrac{1}{n^2+1}$, we have $a_n \le b_n \le c_n$ for $n \ge 1$. Furthermore, $\lim_{n\to\infty} a_n = \lim_{n\to\infty} c_n = 0$. By the Squeeze Theorem, $\lim_{n\to\infty} b_n = 0$ (Figure 9.20).

Related Exercises 43–46 ◀

Bounded Monotonic Sequence Theorem

Suppose a basketball player improves her shooting percentage in every game she plays. Her shooting percentages for each game form an increasing and bounded sequence (the shooting percentage must always be less than or equal to 100%). Therefore, if she plays a *very* large number of games, her sequence of shooting percentages approaches a limit that is less than or equal to 100%. This example illustrates another important theorem that characterizes convergent series in terms of boundedness and monotonicity. This result is easy to believe, but its proof goes beyond the scope of this text and is omitted.

> **THEOREM 9.5 Bounded Monotonic Sequences**
> A bounded monotonic sequence converges.

➤ M is called an *upper bound* of the sequence, and N is a *lower bound* of the sequence. If M^* is the smallest of all the upper bounds of an increasing sequence, then a result from advanced calculus tells us that the sequence converges to M^*. Similarly, if N^* is the greatest of all the lower bounds of a decreasing sequence, then the sequence converges to N^*.

Figure 9.21 shows the two cases of this theorem. In the first case, we see a nondecreasing sequence, all of whose terms are less than M. It must converge to a limit less than or equal to M. Similarly, a nonincreasing sequence, all of whose terms are greater than N, must converge to a limit greater than or equal to N.

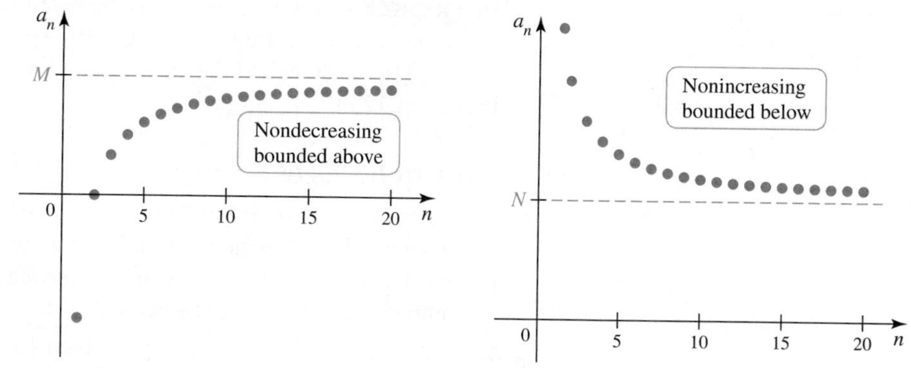

FIGURE 9.21

An Application: Recurrence Relations

➤ Most drugs decay exponentially in the bloodstream and have a characteristic half-life assuming that the drug is absorbed quickly into the blood.

EXAMPLE 5 Sequences for drug doses Suppose your doctor prescribes a 100-mg dose of an antibiotic every 12 hours. Furthermore, the drug is known to have a half-life of 12 hours; that is, every 12 hours half of the drug in your blood is eliminated.

a. Find the sequence that gives the amount of drug in your blood immediately after each dose.

b. Use a graph to propose the limit of this sequence; that is, in the long run, how much drug do you have in your blood?

c. Find the limit of the sequence directly.

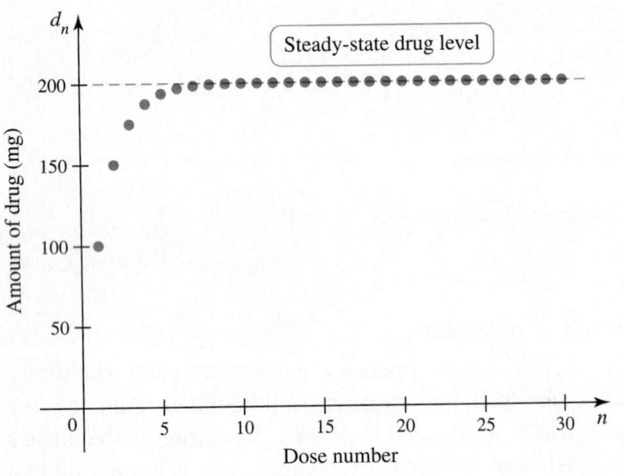

FIGURE 9.22

SOLUTION

a. Let d_n be the amount of drug in the blood immediately following the nth dose, where $n = 1, 2, 3, \ldots$ and $d_1 = 100$ mg. We want to write a recurrence relation that gives the amount of drug in the blood after the $(n + 1)$st dose (d_{n+1}) in terms of the amount of drug after the nth dose (d_n). In the 12 hr between the nth dose and the $(n + 1)$st dose, half of the drug in the blood is eliminated, *and* another 100 mg of drug is added. So, we have

$$d_{n+1} = 0.5\, d_n + 100, \qquad \text{for } n = 1, 2, 3, \ldots \text{ with } d_1 = 100,$$

which is the recurrence relation for the sequence $\{d_n\}$.

b. We see from Figure 9.22 that after about 10 doses (5 days) the amount of antibiotic in the blood is close to 200 mg, and—importantly for your body—it never exceeds 200 mg.

c. The graph of part (b) gives evidence that the terms of the sequence are increasing and bounded (Exercise 80). By the Bounded Monotonic Sequence Theorem, the sequence has a limit; therefore, $\lim_{n\to\infty} d_n = L$, and $\lim_{n\to\infty} d_{n+1} = L$. We now take the limit of both sides of the recurrence relation:

$$\begin{aligned} d_{n+1} &= 0.5\, d_n + 100 \\ \underbrace{\lim_{n\to\infty} d_{n+1}}_{L} &= 0.5 \underbrace{\lim_{n\to\infty} d_n}_{L} + \lim_{n\to\infty} 100 \\ L &= 0.5L + 100 \end{aligned}$$

Solving for L, the steady-state drug level is $L = 200$. *Related Exercises 47–50* ◀

QUICK CHECK 3 If a drug had the same half-life as in Example 5, (i) how would the steady-state level of drug in the blood change if the regular dose were 150 mg instead of 100 mg? (ii) How would the steady-state level change if the dosing interval were 6 hr instead of 12 hr? ◀

Growth Rates of Sequences

All the hard work we did in Section 7.6 to establish the relative growth rates of functions is now applied to sequences. Here is the question: Given two nondecreasing sequences of positive terms $\{a_n\}$ and $\{b_n\}$, which sequence grows faster as $n \to \infty$? As with functions, to compare growth rates, we evaluate $\lim_{n\to\infty} a_n/b_n$. If $\lim_{n\to\infty} a_n/b_n = 0$, then $\{b_n\}$ grows faster than $\{a_n\}$. If $\lim_{n\to\infty} a_n/b_n = \infty$, then $\{a_n\}$ grows faster than $\{b_n\}$.

Using the results of Section 7.6, we immediately arrive at the following ranking of growth rates of sequences as $n \to \infty$, with positive real numbers p, q, r, and s and $b > 1$:

$$\{\ln^q n\} \ll \{n^p\} \ll \{n^p \ln^r n\} \ll \{n^{p+s}\} \ll \{b^n\} \ll \{n^n\}.$$

As before, the notation $\{a_n\} \ll \{b_n\}$ means $\{b_n\}$ *grows faster than* $\{a_n\}$ as $n \to \infty$. Another important sequence that should be added to the list is the **factorial sequence** $\{n!\}$, where $n! = n(n-1)(n-2)\cdots 2 \cdot 1$.

> $0! = 1$ (by definition)
> $1! = 1$
> $2! = 2 \cdot 1! = 2$
> $3! = 3 \cdot 2! = 6$
> $4! = 4 \cdot 3! = 24$
> $5! = 5 \cdot 4! = 120$
> $6! = 6 \cdot 5! = 720$

Where does the factorial sequence $\{n!\}$ appear in the list? The following argument provides some intuition. Notice that

$$n^n = \underbrace{n \cdot n \cdot n \cdots n}_{n \text{ factors}} \quad \text{whereas}$$

$$n! = \underbrace{n \cdot (n-1) \cdot (n-2) \cdots 2 \cdot 1.}_{n \text{ factors}}$$

The nth term of both sequences involves the product of n factors; however, the factors of $n!$ decrease, while the factors of n^n are the same. Based on this observation, a reasonable conjecture is that $\{n^n\}$ grows faster than $\{n!\}$.

Therefore, we have the ordering $\{n!\} \ll \{n^n\}$. But where does $\{n!\}$ appear in the list relative to $\{b^n\}$? Again some intuition is gained by noting that

$$b^n = \underbrace{b \cdot b \cdot b \cdots b,}_{n \text{ factors}} \quad \text{whereas}$$

$$n! = \underbrace{n \cdot (n-1) \cdot (n-2) \cdots 2 \cdot 1.}_{n \text{ factors}}$$

The nth term of both sequences involves the product of n factors; however, the factors of b^n remain constant as n increases, while the factors of $n!$ increase with n. So we claim that $\{n!\}$ grows faster than $\{b^n\}$. This conjecture is supported by computation, although the outcome of the race may not be immediately evident if b is large (Exercise 75).

THEOREM 9.6 Growth Rates of Sequences

The following sequences are ordered according to increasing growth rates as $n \to \infty$; that is, if $\{a_n\}$ appears before $\{b_n\}$ in the list, then $\lim_{n\to\infty} a_n/b_n = 0$:

$$\{\ln^q n\} \ll \{n^p\} \ll \{n^p \ln^r n\} \ll \{n^{p+s}\} \ll \{b^n\} \ll \{n!\} \ll \{n^n\}$$

The ordering applies for positive real numbers p, q, r, and s and $b > 1$.

QUICK CHECK 4 Which sequence grows faster: $\{\ln n\}$ or $\{n^{1.1}\}$? What is $\lim_{n\to\infty} \dfrac{n^{1{,}000{,}000}}{e^n}$?

It is worth noting that the rankings in Theorem 9.6 do not change if a sequence is multiplied by a positive constant (Exercise 88).

EXAMPLE 6 Competing sequences Compare the growth rates of the following pairs of sequences as $n \to \infty$.

a. $\{\ln n^{10}\}$ and $\{0.00001n\}$ **b.** $\{n^8 \ln n\}$ and $\{n^{8.001}\}$ **c.** $\{n!\}$ and $\{10^n\}$

SOLUTION

a. Because $\ln n^{10} = 10 \ln n$, the first sequence is a constant multiple of the sequence $\{\ln n\}$ that appears in Theorem 9.6. Similarly, the second sequence is a constant multiple of the sequence $\{n\}$ that also appears in Theorem 9.6. By Theorem 9.6, $\{n\}$ grows faster than $\{\ln n\}$ as $n \to \infty$; therefore, $\{0.00001n\}$ grows faster than $\{\ln n^{10}\}$ as $n \to \infty$.

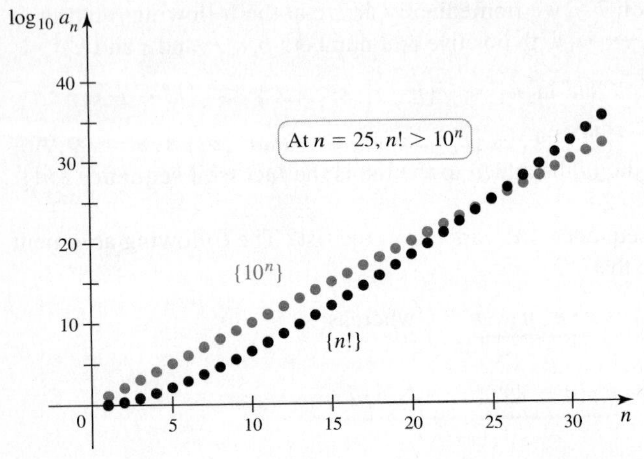

FIGURE 9.23

b. The sequence $\{n^8 \ln n\}$ is the sequence $\{n^p \ln^r n\}$ of Theorem 9.6 with $p = 8$ and $r = 1$. The sequence $\{n^{8.001}\}$ is the sequence $\{n^{p+s}\}$ of Theorem 9.6 with $p = 8$ and $s = 0.001$. Because $\{n^{p+s}\}$ grows faster than $\{n^p \ln^r n\}$, we conclude that $\{n^{8.001}\}$ grows faster than $\{n^8 \ln n\}$ as $n \to \infty$.

c. Using Theorem 9.6, we see that $n!$ grows faster than any exponential function; therefore, the sequence $\{n!\}$ grows faster than the sequence $\{10^n\}$ (Figure 9.23). Because these sequences grow so quickly, we plot the logarithm of the terms. The exponential sequence $\{10^n\}$ dominates the factorial sequence $\{n!\}$ until $n = 25$ terms. At that point, the factorial sequence overtakes the exponential sequence.

Related Exercises 51–56 ◀

Formal Definition of a Limit of a Sequence

As with limits of functions, there is a formal definition of the limit of a sequence.

> **DEFINITION Limit of a Sequence**
>
> The sequence $\{a_n\}$ converges to L provided the terms of a_n can be made arbitrarily close to L by taking n sufficiently large. More precisely, $\{a_n\}$ has the unique limit L if given any tolerance $\varepsilon > 0$, it is possible to find a positive integer N (depending only on ε) such that
>
> $$|a_n - L| < \varepsilon \qquad \text{whenever } n > N.$$
>
> If the **limit of a sequence** is L, we say the sequence **converges** to L, written
>
> $$\lim_{n\to\infty} a_n = L.$$
>
> A sequence that does not converge is said to **diverge**.

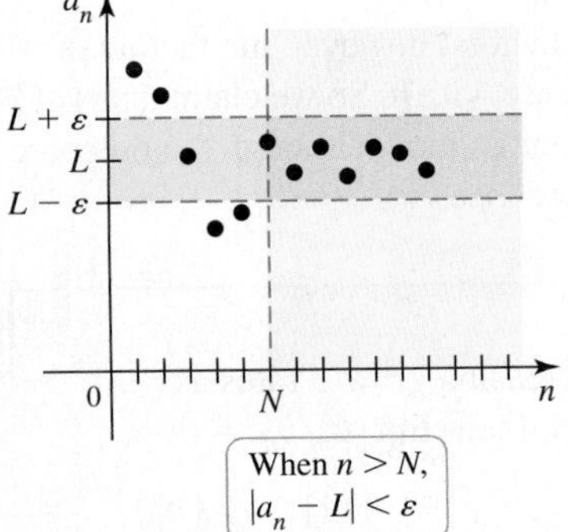

FIGURE 9.24

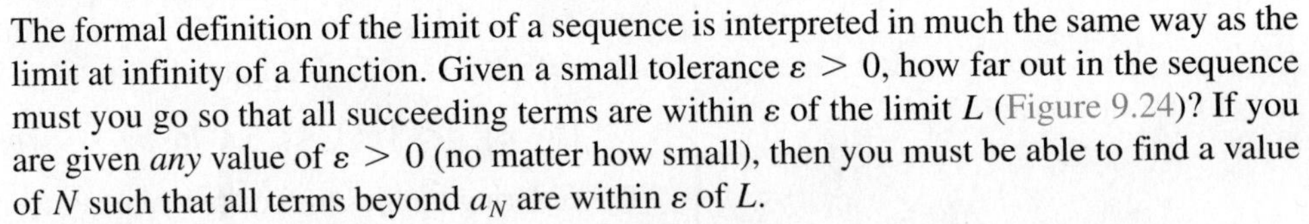
The formal definition of the limit of a sequence is interpreted in much the same way as the limit at infinity of a function. Given a small tolerance $\varepsilon > 0$, how far out in the sequence must you go so that all succeeding terms are within ε of the limit L (Figure 9.24)? If you are given *any* value of $\varepsilon > 0$ (no matter how small), then you must be able to find a value of N such that all terms beyond a_N are within ε of L.

EXAMPLE 7 Limits using the formal definition Consider the claim that

$$\lim_{n\to\infty} a_n = \lim_{n\to\infty} \frac{n}{n-1} = 1.$$

a. Given $\varepsilon = 0.01$, find a value of N that satisfies the conditions of the limit definition.

b. Prove that $\lim_{n\to\infty} a_n = 1$.

SOLUTION

a. We must find an integer N such that $|a_n - 1| < \varepsilon = 0.01$, whenever $n > N$. This condition can be written

$$|a_n - 1| = \left|\frac{n}{n-1} - 1\right| = \left|\frac{1}{n-1}\right| < 0.01.$$

Noting that $n > 1$, the absolute value can be removed. The condition on n becomes $n - 1 > 1/0.01 = 100$, or $n > 101$. Thus, we take $N = 101$ or any larger number. This means that $|a_n - 1| < 0.01$ whenever $n > 101$.

b. Given *any* $\varepsilon > 0$, we must find a value of N (depending on ε) that guarantees that $|a_n - 1| = \left|\frac{n}{n-1} - 1\right| < \varepsilon$ whenever $n > N$. For $n > 1$ the inequality $\left|\frac{n}{n-1} - 1\right| < \varepsilon$ implies that

$$\left|\frac{n}{n-1} - 1\right| = \frac{1}{n-1} < \varepsilon.$$

Solving for n, we find that $\frac{1}{n-1} < \varepsilon$ or $n - 1 > \frac{1}{\varepsilon}$ or $n > \frac{1}{\varepsilon} + 1$. Therefore, given a tolerance $\varepsilon > 0$, we must look beyond a_N in the sequence, where $N \geq \frac{1}{\varepsilon} + 1$, to be sure that the terms of the sequence are within ε of the limit 1. Because we can provide a value of N for *any* $\varepsilon > 0$, the limit exists and equals 1. *Related Exercises 57–62* ◀

➤ In general, $1/\varepsilon + 1$ is not an integer, so N should be the least integer greater than $1/\varepsilon + 1$ or any larger integer.

SECTION 9.2 EXERCISES

Review Questions

1. Give an example of a nonincreasing sequence with a limit.
2. Give an example of a nondecreasing sequence without a limit.
3. Give an example of a bounded sequence that has a limit.
4. Give an example of a bounded sequence without a limit.
5. For what values of r does the sequence $\{r^n\}$ converge? Diverge?
6. Explain how the methods used to find the limit of a function as $x \to \infty$ are used to find the limit of a sequence.
7. Explain with a picture the formal definition of the limit of a sequence.
8. Explain how two sequences that differ only in their first ten terms can have the same limit.

Basic Skills

9–26. Limits of sequences *Find the limit of the following sequences or determine that the limit does not exist.*

9. $\left\{\frac{n^3}{n^4 + 1}\right\}$
10. $\left\{\frac{n^{12}}{3n^{12} + 4}\right\}$
11. $\left\{\frac{3n^3 - 1}{2n^3 + 1}\right\}$
12. $\left\{\frac{2e^{n+1}}{e^n}\right\}$
13. $\left\{\frac{\tan^{-1} n}{n}\right\}$
14. $\{n^{1/n}\}$
15. $\left\{\left(1 + \frac{2}{n}\right)^n\right\}$
16. $\left\{\left(\frac{n}{n+5}\right)^n\right\}$
17. $\left\{\sqrt{\left(1 + \frac{1}{2n}\right)^n}\right\}$
18. $\left\{\frac{\ln(1/n)}{n}\right\}$
19. $\left\{\left(\frac{1}{n}\right)^{1/n}\right\}$
20. $\left\{\left(1 - \frac{4}{n}\right)^n\right\}$
21. $\{b_n\}$ if $b_n = \begin{cases} n/(n+1) & \text{if } n \leq 5000 \\ ne^{-n} & \text{if } n > 5000 \end{cases}$
22. $\{\ln(n^3 + 1) - \ln(3n^3 + 10n)\}$
23. $\{\ln \sin(1/n) + \ln n\}$
24. $\left\{\frac{\sin 6n}{5n}\right\}$
25. $\{n \sin(6/n)\}$
26. $\left\{\frac{n!}{n^n}\right\}$

T **27–34. Limits of sequences and graphing** *Find the limit of the following sequences or determine that the limit does not exist. Verify your result with a graphing utility.*

27. $a_n = \sin\left(\frac{n\pi}{2}\right)$
28. $a_n = \frac{(-1)^n n}{n + 1}$
29. $a_n = \frac{\sin(n\pi/3)}{\sqrt{n}}$
30. $a_n = \frac{3^n}{3^n + 4^n}$
31. $a_n = e^{-n} \cos n$
32. $a_n = \frac{\ln n}{n^{1.1}}$
33. $a_n = (-1)^n \sqrt[n]{n}$
34. $a_n = \cot\left(\frac{n\pi}{2n + 2}\right)$

35–42. Geometric sequences *Determine whether the following sequences converge or diverge and describe whether they do so monotonically or by oscillation. Give the limit when the sequence converges.*

35. $\{0.2^n\}$
36. $\{1.2^n\}$
37. $\{(-0.7)^n\}$
38. $\{(-1.01)^n\}$
39. $\{1.00001^n\}$
40. $\{2^n 3^{-n}\}$
41. $\{(-2.5)^n\}$
42. $\{(-0.003)^n\}$

43–46. Squeeze Theorem *Find the limit of the following sequences or state that they diverge.*

43. $\left\{\frac{\sin n}{2^n}\right\}$
44. $\left\{\frac{\cos(n\pi/2)}{\sqrt{n}}\right\}$
45. $\left\{\frac{2 \tan^{-1} n}{n^3 + 4}\right\}$
46. $\left\{\frac{n \sin^3 n}{n + 1}\right\}$

T 47. **Periodic dosing** Many people take aspirin on a regular basis as a preventive measure for heart disease. Suppose a person takes

80 mg of aspirin every 24 hr. Assume also that aspirin has a half-life of 24 hr; that is, every 24 hr half of the drug in the blood is eliminated.

a. Find a recurrence relation for the sequence $\{d_n\}$ that gives the amount of drug in the blood after the nth dose, where $d_1 = 80$.
b. Using a calculator, determine the limit of the sequence. In the long run, how much drug is in the person's blood?
c. Confirm the result of part (b) by finding the limit of $\{d_n\}$ directly.

T **48. A car loan** Marie takes out a \$20,000 loan for a new car. The loan has an annual interest rate of 6% or, equivalently, a monthly interest rate of 0.5%. Each month, the bank adds interest to the loan balance (the interest is always 0.5% of the current balance), and then Marie makes a \$200 payment to reduce the loan balance. Let B_n be the loan balance immediately after the nth payment, where $B_0 = \$20{,}000$.

a. Write the first five terms of the sequence $\{B_n\}$.
b. Find a recurrence relation that generates the sequence $\{B_n\}$.
c. Determine how many months are needed to reduce the loan balance to zero.

T **49. A savings plan** James begins a savings plan in which he deposits \$100 at the beginning of each month into an account that earns 9% interest annually or, equivalently, 0.75% per month. To be clear, on the first day of each month, the bank adds 0.75% of the current balance as interest, and then James deposits \$100. Let B_n be the balance in the account after the nth payment, where $B_0 = \$0$.

a. Write the first five terms of the sequence $\{B_n\}$.
b. Find a recurrence relation that generates the sequence $\{B_n\}$.
c. Determine how many months are needed to reach a balance of \$5000.

T **50. Diluting a solution** Suppose a tank is filled with 100 L of a 40% alcohol solution (by volume). You repeatedly perform the following operation: Remove 2 L of the solution from the tank and replace them with 2 L of 10% alcohol solution.

a. Let C_n be the concentration of the solution in the tank after the nth replacement, where $C_0 = 40\%$. Write the first five terms of the sequence $\{C_n\}$.
b. After how many replacements does the alcohol concentration reach 15%?
c. Determine the limiting (steady-state) concentration of the solution that is approached after many replacements.

51–56. Comparing growth rates of sequences *Determine which sequence has the greater growth rate as $n \to \infty$. Be sure to justify and explain your work.*

51. $a_n = n^2$; $b_n = n^2 \ln n$

52. $a_n = 3^n$; $b_n = n!$

53. $a_n = 3n^n$; $b_n = 100n!$

54. $a_n = \ln(n^{12})$; $b_n = n^{1/2}$

55. $a_n = n^{1/10}$; $b_n = n^{1/2}$

56. $a_n = e^{n/10}$; $b_n = 2^n$

57–62. Formal proofs of limits *Use the formal definition of the limit of a sequence to prove the following limits.*

57. $\lim_{n\to\infty} \frac{1}{n} = 0$

58. $\lim_{n\to\infty} \frac{1}{n^2} = 0$

59. $\lim_{n\to\infty} \frac{3n^2}{4n^2+1} = \frac{3}{4}$

60. $\lim_{n\to\infty} b^{-n} = 0$, for $b > 1$

61. $\lim_{n\to\infty} \frac{cn}{bn+1} = \frac{c}{b}$, for real numbers $c > 0$ and $b > 0$

62. $\lim_{n\to\infty} \frac{n}{n^2+1} = 0$

Further Explorations

63. Explain why or why not Determine whether the following statements are true and give an explanation or counterexample.

a. If $\lim_{n\to\infty} a_n = 1$ and $\lim_{n\to\infty} b_n = 3$; then $\lim_{n\to\infty} \frac{b_n}{a_n} = 3$.
b. If $\lim_{n\to\infty} a_n = 0$ and $\lim_{n\to\infty} b_n = \infty$; then $\lim_{n\to\infty} a_n b_n = 0$.
c. The convergent sequences $\{a_n\}$ and $\{b_n\}$ differ in their first 100 terms, but $a_n = b_n$ for $n > 100$. It follows that $\lim_{n\to\infty} a_n = \lim_{n\to\infty} b_n$.
d. If $\{a_n\} = \left\{1, \frac{1}{2}, \frac{1}{3}, \frac{1}{4}, \frac{1}{5}, \ldots\right\}$ and $\{b_n\} = \left\{1, 0, \frac{1}{2}, 0, \frac{1}{3}, 0, \frac{1}{4}, 0, \ldots\right\}$, then $\lim_{n\to\infty} a_n = \lim_{n\to\infty} b_n$.
e. If the sequence $\{a_n\}$ converges, then the sequence $\{(-1)^n a_n\}$ converges.
f. If the sequence $\{a_n\}$ diverges, then the sequence $\{0.000001\, a_n\}$ diverges.

64–65. Reindexing *Express each sequence $\{a_n\}_{n=1}^{\infty}$ as an equivalent sequence of the form $\{b_n\}_{n=3}^{\infty}$.*

64. $\{2n + 1\}_{n=1}^{\infty}$

65. $\{n^2 + 6n - 9\}_{n=1}^{\infty}$

66–69. More sequences *Evaluate the limit of the following sequences.*

66. $a_n = \int_1^n x^{-2}\, dx$

67. $a_n = \frac{75^{n-1}}{99^n} + \frac{5^n \sin n}{8^n}$

68. $a_n = \tan^{-1}\left(\frac{10n}{10n+4}\right)$

69. $a_n = \cos(0.99^n) + \frac{7^n + 9^n}{63^n}$

T **70–74. Sequences by recurrence relations** *Consider the following sequences defined by a recurrence relation. Use a calculator, analytical methods, and/or graphing to make a conjecture about the value of the limit or determine that the limit does not exist.*

70. $a_{n+1} = \frac{1}{2}a_n + 2$; $a_0 = 5$, $n = 0, 1, 2, \ldots$.

71. $a_{n+1} = 2a_n(1 - a_n)$; $a_0 = 0.3$, $n = 0, 1, 2, \ldots$.

72. $a_{n+1} = \frac{1}{2}(a_n + 2/a_n)$; $a_0 = 2$, $n = 0, 1, 2, \ldots$.

73. $a_{n+1} = 4a_n(1 - a_n)$; $a_0 = 0.5$, $n = 0, 1, 2, \ldots$.

74. $a_{n+1} = \sqrt{2 + a_n}$; $a_0 = 1$, $n = 0, 1, 2, \ldots$.

T **75. Crossover point** The sequence $\{n!\}$ ultimately grows faster than the sequence $\{b^n\}$ for any $b > 1$ as $n \to \infty$. However, b^n is generally greater than $n!$ for small values of n. Use a calculator to determine the smallest value of n such that $n! > b^n$ for each of the cases $b = 2$, $b = e$, and $b = 10$.

Applications

T **76. Fish harvesting** A fishery manager knows that her fish population naturally increases at a rate of 1.5% per month while 80 fish are harvested each month. Let F_n be the fish population after the nth month, where $F_0 = 4000$ fish.

a. Write out the first five terms of the sequence $\{F_n\}$.
b. Find a recurrence relation that generates the sequence $\{F_n\}$.

c. Does the fish population decrease or increase in the long run?

d. Determine whether the fish population decreases or increases in the long run if the initial population is 5500 fish.

e. Determine the initial fish population F_0 below which the population decreases.

T 77. The hungry hippo problem A pet hippopotamus weighing 200 lb today gains 5 lb per day with a food cost of 45¢/day. The price for hippos is 65¢/lb today but is falling 1¢/day.

a. Let h_n be the profit in selling the hippo on the nth day, where $h_0 = (200\text{ lb}) \times (\$0.65) = \$130$. Write out the first ten terms of the sequence $\{h_n\}$.

b. How many days after today should the hippo be sold to maximize the profit?

T 78. Sleep model After many nights of observation, you notice that if you oversleep one night you tend to undersleep the following night and vice versa. This pattern of compensation is described by the relationship

$$x_{n+1} = \frac{1}{2}(x_n + x_{n-1}) \quad \text{for } n = 1, 2, 3, \ldots,$$

where x_n is the number of hours of sleep you get on the nth night and $x_0 = 7$ and $x_1 = 6$ are the number of hours of sleep on the first two nights, respectively.

a. Write out the first six terms of the sequence $\{x_n\}$ and confirm that the terms alternately increase and decrease.

b. Show that the explicit formula

$$x_n = \tfrac{19}{3} + \tfrac{2}{3}\left(-\tfrac{1}{2}\right)^n, \text{ for } n \geq 0,$$

generates the terms of the sequence in part (a).

c. What is the limit of the sequence?

T 79. Calculator algorithm The CORDIC (COordinate Rotation DIgital Calculation) algorithm is used by most calculators to evaluate trigonometric and logarithmic functions. An important number in the CORDIC algorithm, called the *aggregate constant*, is

$$\prod_{n=0}^{\infty} \frac{2^n}{\sqrt{1 + 2^{2n}}}, \text{ where } \prod_{n=0}^{k} a_n \text{ represents the product } a_0 \cdot a_1 \cdots a_k.$$

This infinite product is the limit of the sequence

$$\left\{\prod_{n=0}^{0} \frac{2^n}{\sqrt{1 + 2^{2n}}}, \prod_{n=0}^{1} \frac{2^n}{\sqrt{1 + 2^{2n}}}, \prod_{n=0}^{2} \frac{2^n}{\sqrt{1 + 2^{2n}}}, \ldots\right\}.$$

(See the Guided Projects.) Estimate the value of the aggregate constant.

Additional Exercises

80. Bounded monotonic proof Prove that the drug dose sequence in Example 5,

$$d_{n+1} = 0.5d_n + 100, \qquad \text{for } n = 1, 2, 3, \ldots, d_1 = 100,$$

is bounded and monotonic.

T 81. Repeated square roots Consider the expression $\sqrt{1 + \sqrt{1 + \sqrt{1 + \sqrt{1 + \cdots}}}}$, where the process continues indefinitely.

a. Show that this expression can be built in steps using the recurrence relation $a_0 = 1, a_{n+1} = \sqrt{1 + a_n}$ for $n = 0, 1, 2, 3, \ldots$. Explain why the value of the expression can be interpreted as $\lim_{n\to\infty} a_n$.

b. Evaluate the first five terms of the sequence $\{a_n\}$.

c. Estimate the limit of the sequence. Compare your estimate with $(1 + \sqrt{5})/2$, a number known as the *golden mean.*

d. Assuming the limit exists, use the method of Example 5 to determine the limit exactly.

e. Repeat the above analysis for the expression $\sqrt{p + \sqrt{p + \sqrt{p + \sqrt{p + \cdots}}}}$, where $p > 0$. Make a table showing the approximate value of this expression for various values of p. Does the expression seem to have a limit for all positive values of p?

T 82. A sequence of products Find the limit of the sequence

$$\{a_n\}_{n=2}^{\infty} = \left\{\left(1 - \frac{1}{2}\right)\left(1 - \frac{1}{3}\right)\cdots\left(1 - \frac{1}{n}\right)\right\}.$$

T 83. Continued fractions The expression

$$1 + \cfrac{1}{1 + \cfrac{1}{1 + \cfrac{1}{1 + \cfrac{1}{1 + \ddots}}}}$$

where the process continues indefinitely, is called a *continued fraction.*

a. Show that this expression can be built in steps using the recurrence relation $a_0 = 1, a_{n+1} = 1 + 1/a_n$ for $n = 0, 1, 2, 3, \ldots$. Explain why the value of the expression can be interpreted as $\lim_{n\to\infty} a_n$.

b. Evaluate the first five terms of the sequence $\{a_n\}$.

c. Using computation and/or graphing, estimate the limit of the sequence.

d. Assuming the limit exists, use the method of Example 5 to determine the limit exactly. Compare your estimate with $(1 + \sqrt{5})/2$, a number known as the *golden mean.*

e. Assuming the limit exists, use the same ideas to determine the value of

$$a + \cfrac{b}{a + \cfrac{b}{a + \cfrac{b}{a + \cfrac{b}{a + \ddots}}}}$$

where a and b are positive real numbers.

T 84. Towers of powers For a positive real number p, how do you interpret $p^{p^{p^{p}}}$, where the tower of exponents continues indefinitely? As it stands, the expression is ambiguous. The tower could be built from the top or from the bottom; that is, it could be evaluated by the recurrence relations

(1) $a_{n+1} = p^{a_n}$ (building from the bottom) or

(2) $a_{n+1} = a_n^p$ (building from the top),

where $a_0 = p$ in either case. The two recurrence relations have very different behaviors that depend on the value of p.

a. Use computations with various values of $p > 0$ to find the values of p such that the recurrence relation (2) has a limit. Find the maximum value of p for which the recurrence relation has a limit.
b. Show that recurrence relation (1) has a limit for certain values of p. Make a table showing the approximate value of the tower for various values of p. Estimate the maximum value of p for which the recurrence relation has a value.

T **85. Fibonacci sequence** The famous Fibonacci sequence was proposed by Leonardo Pisano, also known as Fibonacci, in about A.D. 1200 as a model for the growth of rabbit populations. It is given by the recurrence relation $f_{n+1} = f_n + f_{n-1}$, for $n = 1, 2, 3, \ldots$, where $f_0 = f_1 = 1$. Each term of the sequence is the sum of its two predecessors.

a. Write out the first ten terms of the sequence.
b. Is the sequence bounded?
c. Estimate or determine $\varphi = \lim_{n\to\infty} \frac{f_{n+1}}{f_n}$, the ratio of successive terms of the sequence. Provide evidence that $\varphi = (1 + \sqrt{5})/2$, a number known as the *golden mean.*
d. Verify the remarkable result that

$$f_n = \frac{1}{\sqrt{5}}(\varphi^n - (-1)^n\varphi^{-n})$$

86. Arithmetic-geometric mean Pick two positive numbers a_0 and b_0 with $a_0 > b_0$ and write out the first few terms of the two sequences $\{a_n\}$ and $\{b_n\}$:

$$a_{n+1} = \frac{a_n + b_n}{2}, \qquad b_{n+1} = \sqrt{a_n b_n}, \qquad \text{for } n = 0, 1, 2 \ldots$$

(Recall that the arithmetic mean $A = (p + q)/2$ and the geometric mean $G = \sqrt{pq}$ of two positive numbers p and q satisfy $A \geq G$.)

a. Show that $a_n > b_n$ for all n.
b. Show that $\{a_n\}$ is a decreasing sequence and $\{b_n\}$ is an increasing sequence.
c. Conclude that $\{a_n\}$ and $\{b_n\}$ converge.
d. Show that $a_{n+1} - b_{n+1} < (a_n - b_n)/2$ and conclude that $\lim_{n\to\infty} a_n = \lim_{n\to\infty} b_n$. The common value of these limits is called the arithmetic-geometric mean of a_0 and b_0, denoted $\text{AGM}(a_0, b_0)$.
e. Estimate AGM(12, 20). Estimate Gauss' constant $1/\text{AGM}(1, \sqrt{2})$.

87. The hailstone sequence Here is a fascinating (unsolved) problem known as the hailstone problem (or the Ulam Conjecture or the Collatz Conjecture). It involves sequences in two different ways. First, choose a positive integer N and call it a_0. This is the *seed* of a sequence. The rest of the sequence is generated as follows: For $n = 0, 1, 2, \ldots$

$$a_{n+1} = \begin{cases} a_n/2 & \text{if } a_n \text{ is even} \\ 3a_n + 1 & \text{if } a_n \text{ is odd} \end{cases}$$

However, if $a_n = 1$ for any n, then the sequence terminates.

a. Compute the sequence that results from the seeds $N = 2, 3, 4, \ldots, 10$. You should verify that in all these cases, the sequence eventually terminates. The hailstone conjecture (still unproved) states that for all positive integers N, the sequence terminates after a finite number of terms.
b. Now define the hailstone sequence $\{H_k\}$, which is the number of terms needed for the sequence $\{a_n\}$ to terminate starting with a seed of k. Verify that $H_2 = 1, H_3 = 7$, and $H_4 = 2$.
c. Plot as many terms of the hailstone sequence as is feasible. How did the sequence get its name? Does the conjecture appear to be true?

88. Prove that if $\{a_n\} \ll \{b_n\}$ (as used in Theorem 9.6), then $\{ca_n\} \ll \{db_n\}$, where c and d are positive real numbers.

QUICK CHECK ANSWERS

1. (a) bounded, monotonic; (b) bounded, not monotonic; (c) not bounded, not monotonic; (d) bounded, monotonic (both nonincreasing and nondecreasing). **2.** If $r = -1$, the sequence is $\{-1, 1, -1, 1, \ldots\}$, the terms alternate in sign, and the sequence diverges. If $r = 1$, the sequence is $\{1, 1, 1, 1, \ldots\}$, the terms are constant, and the sequence converges. **3.** Both changes would increase the steady-state level of drug. **4.** $\{n^{1.1}\}$ grows faster; the limit is 0.

9.3 Infinite Series

We begin our discussion of infinite series with *geometric series.* These series arise more frequently than any other infinite series, they are used in many practical problems, and they illustrate all the essential features of infinite series in general. First let's summarize some important ideas from Section 9.1.

➤ The sequence of partial sums may be visualized nicely as follows:

$$\underbrace{\underbrace{\underbrace{a_1}_{S_1} + a_2}_{S_2} + a_3}_{S_3} + a_4 + \cdots$$

Recall that every infinite series $\sum_{k=1}^{\infty} a_k$ has a sequence of partial sums

$$S_1 = a_1, \qquad S_2 = a_1 + a_2, \qquad S_3 = a_1 + a_2 + a_3,$$

where in general $S_n = \sum_{k=1}^{n} a_k$, for $n = 1, 2, 3, \ldots$.

If the sequence of partial sums $\{S_n\}$ converges—that is, if $\lim_{n\to\infty} S_n = L$—then the value of the infinite series is also L. If the sequence of partial sums diverges, then the infinite series also diverges.

In summary, to evaluate an infinite series, it is necessary to determine a formula for the sequence of partial sums $\{S_n\}$ and then find its limit. This procedure can be carried out with the series that we discuss in this section: geometric series and telescoping series.

Geometric Series

➤ Geometric *sequences* have the form $\{r^k\}$. Geometric *sums* and *series* have the form $\sum_k r^k$ or $\sum_k ar^k$.

As a preliminary step to geometric series, we study **geometric sums**, which are *finite sums* in which each term is a constant multiple of the previous term. A geometric sum with n terms has the form

$$S_n = a + ar + ar^2 + \cdots + ar^{n-1} = \sum_{k=0}^{n-1} ar^k,$$

where a and r are real numbers; r is called the **ratio** of the sum and a is the first term of the series. For example, the geometric sum with $r = 0.1$, $a = 0.9$, and $n = 4$ is

$$0.9 + 0.09 + 0.009 + 0.0009 = 0.9(1 + 0.1 + 0.01 + 0.001)$$
$$= \sum_{k=0}^{3} 0.9(0.1^k).$$

QUICK CHECK 1 Which of the following sums are not geometric sums?

a. $\sum_{k=0}^{10} \left(\frac{1}{2}\right)^k$ b. $\sum_{k=0}^{20} \frac{1}{k}$

c. $\sum_{k=0}^{30} (2k + 1)$ ◄

Our goal is to find a formula for the value of the geometric sum

$$S_n = a + ar + ar^2 + \cdots + ar^{n-1} \quad (1)$$

for any values of a, r, and the positive integer n. Doing so requires a clever maneuver: We multiply both sides of equation (1) by the ratio r:

$$rS_n = r(a + ar + ar^2 + ar^3 + \cdots + ar^{n-1})$$
$$= ar + ar^2 + ar^3 + \cdots + ar^{n-1} + ar^n \quad (2)$$

We now subtract equation (2) from equation (1). Notice how most of the terms on the right sides of these equations cancel, leaving

$$S_n - rS_n = a - ar^n.$$

QUICK CHECK 2 Verify that the geometric sum formula gives the correct result for the sums $1 + \frac{1}{2}$ and $\frac{1}{2} + \frac{1}{4} + \frac{1}{8}$. ◄

Solving for S_n gives the formula

$$S_n = a \cdot \frac{1 - r^n}{1 - r}. \quad (3)$$

Having dealt with geometric *sums*, it is a short step to geometric *series*. We simply let the number of terms in the geometric sum $S_n = \sum_{k=0}^{n-1} ar^k$ increase without bound, which results in the geometric series $\sum_{k=0}^{\infty} ar^k$. The value of a geometric series is the limit of its sequence of partial sums (provided it exists). Using equation (3), we have

$$\underbrace{\sum_{k=0}^{\infty} ar^k}_{\text{geometric series}} = \lim_{n\to\infty} \underbrace{\sum_{k=0}^{n-1} ar^k}_{\text{geometric sum } S_n} = \lim_{n\to\infty} a\frac{1 - r^n}{1 - r}.$$

To compute this limit we must examine the behavior of r^n as $n \to \infty$. Recall from our work with geometric sequences (Section 9.2) that

$$\lim_{n\to\infty} r^n = \begin{cases} 0 & \text{if } |r| < 1 \\ 1 & \text{if } r = 1 \\ \text{does not exist} & \text{if } r \le -1 \text{ or } r > 1 \end{cases}$$

Case 1: $|r| < 1$ Because $\lim_{n\to\infty} r^n = 0$, we have

$$\lim_{n\to\infty} S_n = \lim_{n\to\infty} a\frac{1 - r^n}{1 - r} = a\frac{1 - \overbrace{\lim_{n\to\infty} r^n}^{0}}{1 - r} = \frac{a}{1 - r}.$$

In the case that $|r| < 1$, the geometric series *converges* to $\dfrac{a}{1 - r}$.

Case 2: $|r| > 1$ In this case, $\lim_{n\to\infty} r^n$ does not exist, so $\lim_{n\to\infty} S_n$ does not exist and the series *diverges*.

Case 3: $|r| = 1$ If $r = 1$, then the geometric series is $\sum_{k=0}^{\infty} 1 = 1 + 1 + 1 + \cdots$, which diverges. If $r = -1$, the geometric series is $\sum_{k=0}^{\infty} (-1)^k = 1 - 1 + 1 - \cdots$, which also diverges (because the sequence of partial sums oscillates between 0 and 1). So if $r = \pm 1$, then the geometric series *diverges*.

QUICK CHECK 3 Evaluate $1/2 + 1/4 + 1/8 + 1/16 + \cdots$. ◄

THEOREM 9.7 Geometric Series

Let r and a be real numbers. If $|r| < 1$, then $\sum_{k=0}^{\infty} ar^k = \dfrac{a}{1 - r}$. If $|r| \ge 1$, then the series diverges.

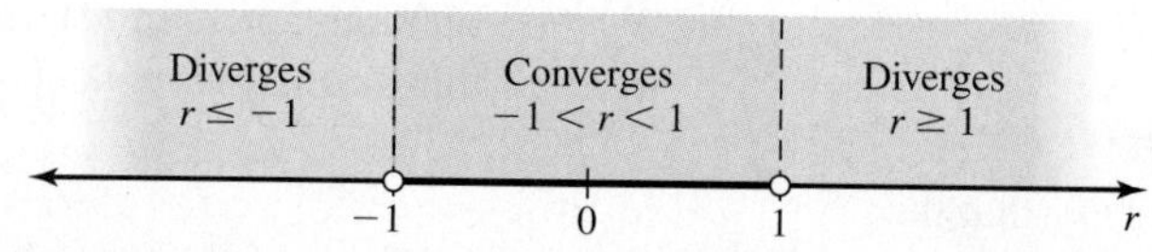

QUICK CHECK 4 Explain why $\sum_{k=0}^{\infty} 0.2^k$ converges and why $\sum_{k=0}^{\infty} 2^k$ diverges. ◄

EXAMPLE 1 Geometric series Evaluate the following geometric series or state that the series diverges.

a. $\sum_{k=0}^{\infty} 1.1^k$ **b.** $\sum_{k=0}^{\infty} e^{-k}$ **c.** $\sum_{k=2}^{\infty} 3(-0.75)^k$

SOLUTION

a. The ratio of this geometric series is $r = 1.1$. Because $|r| \ge 1$, the series diverges.

b. Note that $e^{-k} = \dfrac{1}{e^k} = \left(\dfrac{1}{e}\right)^k$. Therefore, the ratio of the series is $r = \dfrac{1}{e}$, and its first term is $a = 1$. Because $|r| < 1$, the series converges and its value is

$$\sum_{k=0}^{\infty} e^{-k} = \sum_{k=0}^{\infty} \left(\frac{1}{e}\right)^k = \frac{1}{1 - (1/e)} = \frac{e}{e - 1} \approx 1.582.$$

> The series in Example 1c is called an *alternating series* because the terms alternate in sign. Such series are discussed in detail in Section 9.6.

c. Writing out the first few terms of the series is helpful:

$$\sum_{k=2}^{\infty} 3(-0.75)^k = \underbrace{3(-0.75)^2}_{a} + \underbrace{3(-0.75)^3}_{ar} + \underbrace{3(-0.75)^4}_{ar^2} + \cdots.$$

We see that the first term of the series is $a = 3(-0.75)^2$, and the ratio of the series is $r = -0.75$. Because $|r| < 1$, the series converges, and its value is

$$\sum_{k=2}^{\infty} 3(-0.75)^k = \frac{3(-0.75)^2}{1 - (-0.75)} = \frac{27}{28}.$$

Related Exercises 7–40 ◀

EXAMPLE 2 **Decimal expansions** Write $1.0\overline{35} = 1.0353535\ldots$ as a geometric series and express its value as a fraction.

SOLUTION Notice that the decimal part of this number is a convergent geometric series with $a = 0.035$ and $r = 0.01$:

$$1.0353535\ldots = 1 + \underbrace{0.035 + 0.00035 + 0.0000035 + \cdots}_{\text{geometric series with } a = 0.035 \text{ and } r = 0.01}$$

Evaluating the series, we have

$$1.0353535\ldots = 1 + \frac{a}{1-r} = 1 + \frac{0.035}{1 - 0.01} = 1 + \frac{35}{990} = \frac{205}{198}.$$

Related Exercises 41–46 ◀

Telescoping Series

With geometric series, we carried out the entire evaluation process by finding a formula for the sequence of partial sums and evaluating the limit of the sequence. Not many infinite series can be subjected to this sort of analysis. With another class of series, called **telescoping series**, it can be done. Here is an example.

EXAMPLE 3 **Telescoping series** Evaluate the following series.

a. $\displaystyle\sum_{k=1}^{\infty}\left(\frac{1}{3^k} - \frac{1}{3^{k+1}}\right)$ **b.** $\displaystyle\sum_{k=1}^{\infty}\frac{1}{k(k+1)}$

SOLUTION

a. The nth term of the sequence of partial sums is

$$\begin{aligned} S_n &= \sum_{k=1}^{n}\left(\frac{1}{3^k} - \frac{1}{3^{k+1}}\right) = \left(\frac{1}{3} - \frac{1}{3^2}\right) + \left(\frac{1}{3^2} - \frac{1}{3^3}\right) + \cdots + \left(\frac{1}{3^n} - \frac{1}{3^{n+1}}\right) \\ &= \frac{1}{3} + \underbrace{\left(-\frac{1}{3^2} + \frac{1}{3^2}\right)}_{0} + \cdots + \underbrace{\left(-\frac{1}{3^n} + \frac{1}{3^n}\right)}_{0} - \frac{1}{3^{n+1}} \qquad \text{Regroup terms.} \\ &= \frac{1}{3} - \frac{1}{3^{n+1}} \qquad \text{Simplify.} \end{aligned}$$

> The series in Example 3a is also a geometric series and its value can be found using Theorem 9.7.

Observe that the interior terms of the sum cancel (or telescope) leaving a simple expression for S_n. Taking the limit, we find that

$$\sum_{k=1}^{\infty}\left(\frac{1}{3^k} - \frac{1}{3^{k+1}}\right) = \lim_{n\to\infty} S_n = \lim_{n\to\infty}\left(\frac{1}{3} - \underbrace{\frac{1}{3^{n+1}}}_{\to 0}\right) = \frac{1}{3}.$$

➤ See Section 8.4 for a review of partial fractions.

b. Using the method of partial fractions, the sequence of partial sums is

$$S_n = \sum_{k=1}^{n} \frac{1}{k(k+1)} = \sum_{k=1}^{n} \left(\frac{1}{k} - \frac{1}{k+1}\right).$$

Writing out this sum, we see that

$$\begin{aligned} S_n &= \left(1 - \frac{1}{2}\right) + \left(\frac{1}{2} - \frac{1}{3}\right) + \left(\frac{1}{3} - \frac{1}{4}\right) + \cdots + \left(\frac{1}{n} - \frac{1}{n+1}\right) \\ &= 1 + \underbrace{\left(-\frac{1}{2} + \frac{1}{2}\right)}_{0} + \underbrace{\left(-\frac{1}{3} + \frac{1}{3}\right)}_{0} + \cdots + \underbrace{\left(-\frac{1}{n} + \frac{1}{n}\right)}_{0} - \frac{1}{n+1} \\ &= 1 - \frac{1}{n+1}. \end{aligned}$$

Again, the sum telescopes and all the interior terms cancel. The result is a simple formula for the nth term of the sequence of partial sums. The value of the series is

$$\sum_{k=1}^{\infty} \frac{1}{k(k+1)} = \lim_{n\to\infty} S_n = \lim_{n\to\infty} \left(1 - \frac{1}{n+1}\right) = 1.$$

Related Exercises 47–58 ◀

SECTION 9.3 EXERCISES

Review Questions

1. What is the defining characteristic of a geometric series? Give an example.
2. What is the difference between a geometric sum and a geometric series?
3. What is meant by the *ratio* of a geometric series?
4. Does a geometric sum always have a finite value?
5. Does a geometric series always have a finite value?
6. What is the condition for convergence of the geometric series $\sum_{k=0}^{\infty} ar^k$?

Basic Skills

7–18. Geometric sums *Evaluate the following geometric sums.*

7. $\sum_{k=0}^{8} 3^k$
8. $\sum_{k=0}^{10} \left(\frac{1}{4}\right)^k$
9. $\sum_{k=0}^{20} \left(\frac{2}{5}\right)^{2k}$
10. $\sum_{k=4}^{12} 2^k$
11. $\sum_{k=0}^{9} \left(-\frac{3}{4}\right)^k$
12. $\sum_{k=1}^{5} (-2.5)^k$
13. $\sum_{k=0}^{6} \pi^k$
14. $\sum_{k=1}^{10} \left(\frac{4}{7}\right)^k$
15. $\sum_{k=0}^{20} (-1)^k$
16. $1 + \frac{2}{3} + \frac{4}{9} + \frac{8}{27}$
17. $\frac{1}{4} + \frac{1}{12} + \frac{1}{36} + \frac{1}{108} + \cdots + \frac{1}{2916}$
18. $\frac{1}{3} + \frac{1}{5} + \frac{3}{25} + \frac{9}{125} + \cdots + \frac{243}{15{,}625}$

19–34. Geometric series *Evaluate the geometric series or state that it diverges.*

19. $\sum_{k=0}^{\infty} \left(\frac{1}{4}\right)^k$
20. $\sum_{k=0}^{\infty} \left(\frac{3}{5}\right)^k$
21. $\sum_{k=0}^{\infty} 0.9^k$
22. $\sum_{k=0}^{\infty} \frac{2^k}{7^k}$
23. $\sum_{k=0}^{\infty} 1.01^k$
24. $\sum_{j=0}^{\infty} \left(\frac{1}{\pi}\right)^j$
25. $\sum_{k=1}^{\infty} e^{-2k}$
26. $\sum_{m=2}^{\infty} \frac{5}{2^m}$
27. $\sum_{k=1}^{\infty} 2^{-3k}$
28. $\sum_{k=3}^{\infty} \frac{3 \cdot 4^k}{7^k}$
29. $\sum_{k=4}^{\infty} \frac{1}{5^k}$
30. $\sum_{k=0}^{\infty} \left(\frac{4}{3}\right)^{-k}$
31. $\sum_{k=0}^{\infty} \left(\frac{e}{\pi}\right)^k$
32. $\sum_{k=1}^{\infty} \frac{3^{k-1}}{4^{k+1}}$
33. $\sum_{k=0}^{\infty} \left(\frac{1}{4}\right)^k 5^{6-k}$
34. $\sum_{k=2}^{\infty} \left(\frac{3}{8}\right)^{3k}$

35–40. Geometric series with alternating signs *Evaluate the geometric series or state that it diverges.*

35. $\sum_{k=0}^{\infty} \left(-\frac{9}{10}\right)^k$
36. $\sum_{k=1}^{\infty} \left(-\frac{2}{3}\right)^k$
37. $3\sum_{k=0}^{\infty} \frac{(-1)^k}{\pi^k}$
38. $\sum_{k=1}^{\infty} (-e)^{-k}$
39. $\sum_{k=2}^{\infty} (-0.15)^k$
40. $\sum_{k=1}^{\infty} 3\left(-\frac{1}{8}\right)^{3k}$

41–46. Decimal expansions *Write each repeating decimal first as a geometric series, then as a fraction (a ratio of two integers).*

41. 0.121212... **42.** 1.252525... **43.** 0.456456...

44. 1.00393939... **45.** 0.00952952... **46.** 5.12838383...

47–58. Telescoping series *For the following telescoping series, find a formula for the nth term of the sequence of partial sums* $\{S_n\}$. *Then evaluate* $\lim_{n\to\infty} S_n$ *to obtain the value of the series or state that the series diverges.*

47. $\sum_{k=1}^{\infty}\left(\frac{1}{k+1}-\frac{1}{k+2}\right)$ **48.** $\sum_{k=1}^{\infty}\left(\frac{1}{k+2}-\frac{1}{k+3}\right)$

49. $\sum_{k=1}^{\infty}\frac{1}{(k+1)(k+2)}$ **50.** $\sum_{k=0}^{\infty}\frac{1}{(3k+1)(3k+4)}$

51. $\sum_{k=1}^{\infty}\ln\left(\frac{k+1}{k}\right)$ **52.** $\sum_{k=1}^{\infty}\left(\sqrt{k+1}-\sqrt{k}\right)$

53. $\sum_{k=1}^{\infty}\frac{1}{(k+p)(k+p+1)}$, where p is a positive integer

54. $\sum_{k=1}^{\infty}\frac{1}{(ak+1)(ak+a+1)}$, where a is a positive integer

55. $\sum_{k=1}^{\infty}\left(\frac{1}{\sqrt{k+1}}-\frac{1}{\sqrt{k+3}}\right)$

56. $\sum_{k=0}^{\infty}\left[\sin\left(\frac{(k+1)\pi}{2k+1}\right)-\sin\left(\frac{k\pi}{2k-1}\right)\right]$

57. $\sum_{k=0}^{\infty}\frac{1}{16k^2+8k-3}$ **58.** $\sum_{k=1}^{\infty}\left[\tan^{-1}(k+1)-\tan^{-1}k\right]$

Further Explorations

59. Explain why or why not Determine whether the following statements are true and give an explanation or counterexample.

a. $\sum_{k=1}^{\infty}\left(\frac{\pi}{e}\right)^{-k}$ is a convergent geometric series.

b. If a is a real number and $\sum_{k=12}^{\infty}a^k$ converges, then $\sum_{k=1}^{\infty}a^k$ converges.

c. If the series $\sum_{k=1}^{\infty}a^k$ converges and $|a|<|b|$, then the series $\sum_{k=1}^{\infty}b^k$ converges.

60. Zeno's paradox The Greek philosopher Zeno of Elea (who lived about 450 B.C.) invented many paradoxes, the most famous of which tells of a race between the swift warrior Achilles and a tortoise. Zeno argued

The slower when running will never be overtaken by the quicker; for that which is pursuing must first reach the point from which that which is fleeing started, so that the slower must necessarily always be some distance ahead.

In other words, giving the tortoise a head start, Achilles will never overtake the tortoise because every time Achilles reaches the point where the tortoise was, the tortoise has moved ahead. Resolve this paradox by assuming that Achilles gives the tortoise a 1-mi head start and runs 5 mi/hr to the tortoise's 1 mi/hr. How far does Achilles run before he overtakes the tortoise, and how long does it take?

61. Archimedes' quadrature of the parabola The Greeks solved several calculus problems almost 2000 years before the discovery of calculus. One example is Archimedes' calculation of the area of the region R bounded by a segment of a parabola, which he did using the "method of exhaustion." As shown in the figure, the idea was to fill R with an infinite sequence of triangles. Archimedes began with one triangle inscribed in the parabola, with area A_1, and proceeded in stages, with the number of new triangles doubling at each stage. He was able to show (the key to the solution) that at each stage, the area of a new triangle is $\frac{1}{8}$ of the area of a triangle at the previous stage; for example, $A_2=\frac{1}{8}A_1$, and so forth. Show, as Archimedes did, that the area of R is $\frac{4}{3}$ times the area of A_1.

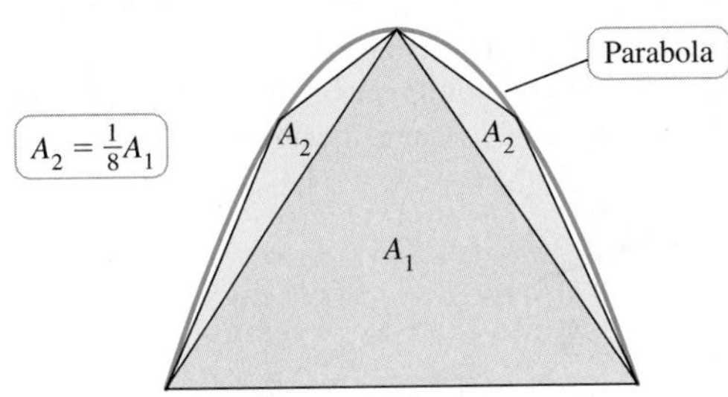

62. Value of a series

a. Find the value of the series

$$\sum_{k=1}^{\infty}\frac{3^k}{(3^{k+1}-1)(3^k-1)}.$$

b. For what value of a does the series

$$\sum_{k=1}^{\infty}\frac{a^k}{(a^{k+1}-1)(a^k-1)}$$

converge, and in those cases, what is its value?

Applications

T **63. House loan** Suppose you take out a home mortgage for \$180,000 at a monthly interest rate of 0.5%. If you make payments of \$1000 per month, after how many months will the loan balance be zero? Estimate the answer by graphing the sequence of loan balances and then obtain an exact answer.

T **64. Car loan** Suppose you borrow \$20,000 for a new car at a monthly interest rate of 0.75%. If you make payments of \$600 per month, after how many months will the loan balance be zero? Estimate the answer by graphing the sequence of loan balances and then obtain an exact answer.

65. Fish harvesting A fishery manager knows that her fish population naturally increases at a rate of 1.5% per month. At the end of each month, 120 fish are harvested. Let F_n be the fish population after the nth month, where $F_0 = 4000$ fish. Assuming that this process continues indefinitely, what is the long-term (steady-state) population of the fish?

66. Periodic doses Suppose that you take 200 mg of an antibiotic every 6 hr. The half-life of the drug is 6 hr (the time it takes for half of the drug to be eliminated from your blood). If you continue this regimen indefinitely, what is the long-term (steady-state) amount of antibiotic in your blood?

67. China's one-son policy In 1978, in an effort to reduce population growth, China instituted a policy that allows only one child per family. One unintended consequence has been that, because of a cultural bias toward sons, China now has many more young boys than girls. To solve this problem, some people have suggested replacing the one-child policy with a one-son policy: A family may have children until a boy is born. Suppose that the one-son policy were implemented and that natural birth rates remained the same (half boys and half girls). Using geometric series, compare the total number of children under the two policies.

68. Double glass An insulated window consists of two parallel panes of glass with a small spacing between them. Suppose that each pane reflects a fraction p of the incoming light and transmits the remaining light. Considering all reflections of light between the panes, what fraction of the incoming light is ultimately transmitted by the window? Assume the amount of incoming light is 1.

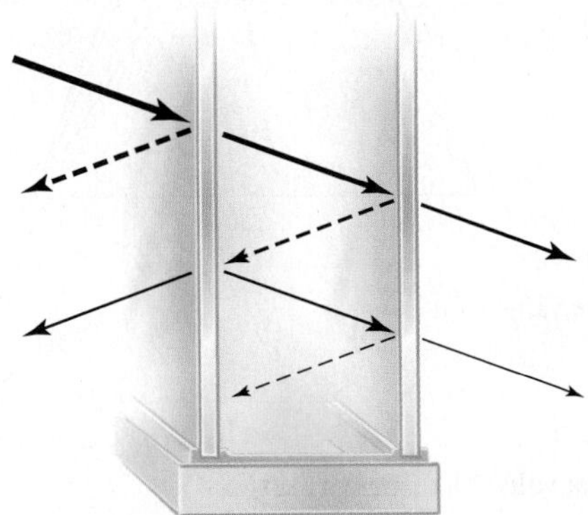

69. Bouncing ball for time Suppose a rubber ball, when dropped from a given height, returns to a fraction p of that height. How long does it take for a ball dropped from 10 m to come to rest? In the absence of air resistance, a ball dropped from a height h requires $\sqrt{2h/g}$ seconds to fall to the ground, where $g \approx 9.8\text{ m/s}^2$ is the acceleration due to gravity. The time taken to bounce *up* to a given height equals the time to fall from that height to the ground.

70. Multiplier effect Imagine that the government of a small community decides to give a total of $\$W$, distributed equally, to all of its citizens. Suppose that each month each citizen saves a fraction p of his or her new wealth and spends the remaining $1 - p$ in the community. Assume no money leaves or enters the community, and all of the spent money is redistributed throughout the community.

a. If this cycle of saving and spending continues for many months, how much money is ultimately spent? Specifically, by what factor is the initial investment of $\$W$ increased? (Economists refer to this increase in the investment as the multiplier effect.)

b. Evaluate the limits $p \to 0$ and $p \to 1$ and interpret their meanings.

(See Guided Projects for more on economic stimulus packages.)

71. Snowflake island fractal The fractal called the *snowflake island* (or *Koch island*) is constructed as follows: Let I_0 be an equilateral triangle with sides of length 1. The figure I_1 is obtained by replacing the middle third of each side of I_0 by a new outward equilateral triangle with sides of length $1/3$ (see figure). The process is repeated where I_{n+1} is obtained by replacing the middle third of each side of I_n by a new outward equilateral triangle with sides of length $1/3^{n+1}$. The limiting figure as $n \to \infty$ is called the snowflake island.

a. Let L_n be the perimeter of I_n. Show that $\lim_{n\to\infty} L_n = \infty$.

b. Let A_n be the area of I_n. Find $\lim_{n\to\infty} A_n$. It exists!

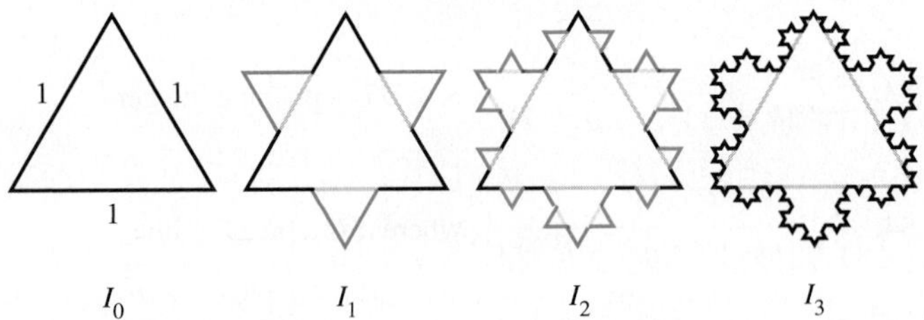

Additional Exercises

72. Decimal expansions

a. Consider the number 0.555555..., which can be viewed as the series $5\sum_{k=1}^{\infty} 10^{-k}$. Evaluate the geometric series to obtain a rational value of 0.555555...

b. Consider the number 0.54545454..., which can be represented by the series $54\sum_{k=1}^{\infty} 10^{-2k}$. Evaluate the geometric series to obtain a rational value of the number.

c. Now generalize parts (a) and (b). Suppose you are given a number with a decimal expansion that repeats in cycles of length p, say, $n_1, n_2, \ldots, n_p$, where $n_1, \ldots, n_p$ are integers between 0 and 9. Explain how to use geometric series to obtain a rational form of the number.

d. Try the method of part (c) on the number 0.123456789123456789....

e. Prove that $0.\overline{9} = 1$.

73. Remainder term Consider the geometric series $S = \sum_{k=0}^{\infty} r^k$, which has the value $1/(1 - r)$ provided $|r| < 1$, and let $S_n = \sum_{k=0}^{n-1} r^k = \frac{1 - r^n}{1 - r}$ be the sum of the first n terms. The remainder R_n is the error in approximating S by S_n. Show that

$$R_n = |S - S_n| = \left|\frac{r^n}{1 - r}\right|.$$

74–77. Comparing remainder terms *Use Exercise 73 to determine how many terms of each series are needed so that the partial sum is within 10^{-6} of the value of the series (that is, to ensure $R_n < 10^{-6}$).*

74. **a.** $\sum_{k=0}^{\infty} 0.6^k$ **b.** $\sum_{k=0}^{\infty} 0.15^k$

75. **a.** $\sum_{k=0}^{\infty} (-0.8)^k$ **b.** $\sum_{k=0}^{\infty} 0.2^k$

76. **a.** $\sum_{k=0}^{\infty} 0.72^k$ **b.** $\sum_{k=0}^{\infty} (-0.25)^k$

77. **a.** $\sum_{k=0}^{\infty} \left(\frac{1}{\pi}\right)^k$ **b.** $\sum_{k=0}^{\infty} \left(\frac{1}{e}\right)^k$

78. Functions defined as series Suppose a function f is defined by the geometric series $f(x) = \sum_{k=0}^{\infty} x^k$.

a. Evaluate $f(0), f(0.2), f(0.5), f(1)$, and $f(1.5)$, if possible.
b. What is the domain of f?

79. Functions defined as series Suppose a function f is defined by the geometric series $f(x) = \sum_{k=0}^{\infty} (-1)^k x^k$.

a. Evaluate $f(0), f(0.2), f(0.5), f(1)$, and $f(1.5)$.
b. What is the domain of f?

80. Functions defined as series Suppose a function f is defined by the geometric series $f(x) = \sum_{k=0}^{\infty} x^{2k}$.

a. Evaluate $f(0), f(0.2), f(0.5), f(1)$, and $f(1.5)$.
b. What is the domain of f?

81. Series in an equation For what values of x does the geometric series

$$f(x) = \sum_{k=0}^{\infty} \left(\frac{1}{1+x}\right)^k$$

converge? Solve $f(x) = 3$.

82. Bubbles Imagine a stack of hemispherical soap bubbles with decreasing radii $r_1 = 1, r_2, r_3, \ldots$ (see figure). Let h_n be the distance between the diameters of bubble n and bubble $n + 1$, and let H_n be the total height of the stack with n bubbles.

a. Use the Pythagorean theorem to show that in a stack with n bubbles, $h_1^2 = r_1^2 - r_2^2$, $h_2^2 = r_2^2 - r_3^2$, and so forth. Note that $h_n = r_n$.
b. Use part (a) to show that the height of a stack with n bubbles is

$$H_n = \sqrt{r_1^2 - r_2^2} + \sqrt{r_2^2 - r_3^2} + \cdots + \sqrt{r_{n-1}^2 - r_n^2} + r_n.$$

c. The height of a stack of bubbles depends on how the radii decrease. Suppose that $r_1 = 1, r_2 = a, r_3 = a^2, \ldots, r_n = a^n$, where $0 < a < 1$ is a fixed real number. In terms of a, find the height H_n of a stack with n bubbles.
d. Suppose the stack in part (c) is extended indefinitely ($n \to \infty$). In terms of a, how high would the stack be?
e. Challenge problem: Fix n and determine the sequence of radii $r_1, r_2, r_3, \ldots, r_n$ that maximizes H_n, the height of the stack with n bubbles.

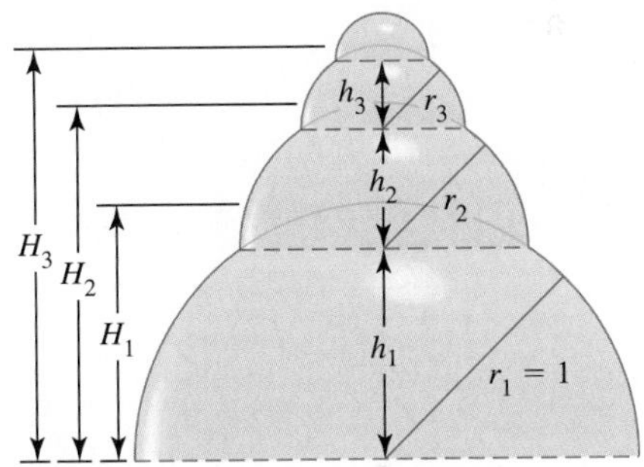

QUICK CHECK ANSWERS

1. b and c 2. Using the formula, the values are $\frac{3}{2}$ and $\frac{7}{8}$. 3. 1 4. The first converges because $|r| = 0.2 < 1$; the second diverges because $|r| = 2 > 1$.

9.4 The Divergence and Integral Tests

With geometric series and telescoping series, the sequence of partial sums can be found and its limit can be evaluated (when it exists). Unfortunately, it is difficult or impossible to find an explicit formula for the sequence of partial sums for most infinite series. Therefore, it is difficult to obtain the exact value of most convergent series.

In this section, we explore methods to determine whether or not a given infinite series converges, which is simply a *yes/no* question. If the answer is *no*, the series diverges, and there are no more questions to ask. If the answer is *yes*, the series converges and it may be possible to estimate its value.

The Harmonic Series

We begin with an example that has a surprising result. Consider the infinite series

$$\sum_{k=1}^{\infty} \frac{1}{k} = 1 + \frac{1}{2} + \frac{1}{3} + \frac{1}{4} + \frac{1}{5} + \cdots,$$

a famous series known as the **harmonic series**. Does it converge? Suppose you try to answer this question by writing out the terms of the sequence of partial sums:

> We analyze S_n numerically because an explicit formula for S_n does not exist.

$$S_1 = 1 \qquad S_2 = 1 + \frac{1}{2} = \frac{3}{2}$$

$$S_3 = 1 + \frac{1}{2} + \frac{1}{3} = \frac{11}{6} \qquad S_4 = 1 + \frac{1}{2} + \frac{1}{3} + \frac{1}{4} = \frac{25}{12}$$

$$\vdots \quad \vdots \quad \vdots$$

$$S_n = \sum_{k=1}^{n} \frac{1}{k} = 1 + \frac{1}{2} + \frac{1}{3} + \frac{1}{4} + \cdots + \frac{1}{n}$$

$$\vdots \quad \vdots \quad \vdots$$

Have a look at the first 200 terms of the sequence of partial sums shown in Figure 9.25. What do you think—does the series converge? The terms of the sequence of partial sums increase, but at a decreasing rate. They could approach a limit or they could increase without bound.

Computing additional terms of the sequence of partial sums does not provide conclusive evidence. Table 9.3 shows that the sum of the first million terms is less than 15; the sum of the first 10^{40} terms—an unimaginably large number of terms—is less than 100. This is a case in which computation alone is not sufficient to determine whether a series converges. We return to this example later with more refined methods.

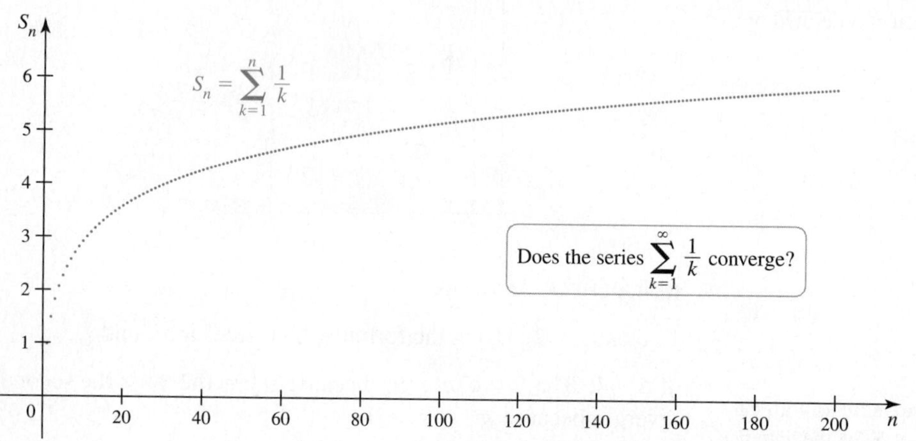

FIGURE 9.25

Table 9.3

n	S_n	n	S_n
10^3	≈ 7.49	10^{10}	≈ 23.60
10^4	≈ 9.79	10^{20}	≈ 46.63
10^5	≈ 12.09	10^{30}	≈ 69.65
10^6	≈ 14.39	10^{40}	≈ 92.68

Properties of Convergent Series

For now, we restrict our attention to series with positive terms; that is, series of the form $\sum a_k$, where $a_k > 0$. The notation $\sum a_k$, without initial and final values of k, is used to refer to a general infinite series.

THEOREM 9.8 Properties of Convergent Series

1. Suppose $\sum a_k$ converges to A and let c be a real number. The series $\sum ca_k$ converges and $\sum ca_k = c\sum a_k = cA$.
2. Suppose $\sum a_k$ converges to A and $\sum b_k$ converges to B. The series $\sum(a_k \pm b_k)$ converges and $\sum(a_k \pm b_k) = \sum a_k \pm \sum b_k = A \pm B$.
3. *Whether* a series converges does not depend on a finite number of terms added to or removed from the series. Specifically, if M is a positive integer, then $\sum_{k=1}^{\infty} a_k$ and $\sum_{k=M}^{\infty} a_k$ both converge or both diverge. However, the *value* of a convergent series does change if nonzero terms are added or deleted.

> The **leading terms** of an infinite series are those at the beginning with a small index. The **tail** of an infinite series consists of the terms at the "end" of the series with a large and increasing index. The convergence or divergence of an infinite series depends on the tail of the series, while the value of a convergent series is determined primarily by the leading terms.

Proof These properties are proved using properties of finite sums and limits of sequences. To prove Property 1, assume that $\sum_{k=1}^{\infty} a_k$ converges and note that

$$\begin{aligned}
\sum_{k=1}^{\infty} ca_k &= \lim_{n\to\infty} \sum_{k=1}^{n} ca_k && \text{Definition of infinite series} \\
&= \lim_{n\to\infty} c\sum_{k=1}^{n} a_k && \text{Property of finite sums} \\
&= c \lim_{n\to\infty} \sum_{k=1}^{n} a_k && \text{Property of limits} \\
&= c\sum_{k=1}^{\infty} a_k && \text{Definition of infinite series} \\
&= cA && \text{Value of the series}
\end{aligned}$$

Property 2 is proved in a similar way (Exercise 54).

Property 3 follows by noting that for finite sums with $1 < M < n$,

$$\sum_{k=M}^{n} a_k = \sum_{k=1}^{n} a_k - \sum_{k=1}^{M-1} a_k.$$

Letting $n \to \infty$ in this equation and assuming that $\sum_{k=0}^{\infty} a_k = A$, it follows that

$$\sum_{k=M}^{\infty} a_k = \underbrace{\sum_{k=1}^{\infty} a_k}_{A} - \underbrace{\sum_{k=1}^{M-1} a_k}_{\text{finite number}}.$$

QUICK CHECK 1 Explain why if $\sum_{k=1}^{\infty} a_k$ converges, then the series $\sum_{k=5}^{\infty} a_k$ (with a different starting index) also converges. Do the two series have the same value?

Because the right side has a finite value, $\sum_{k=M}^{\infty} a_k$ converges. Similarly, if $\sum_{k=M}^{\infty} a_k$ converges, then $\sum_{k=1}^{\infty} a_k$ converges. By an analogous argument, if one of these series diverges, then the other series diverges.

EXAMPLE 1 **Using properties of series** Evaluate the infinite series

$$S = \sum_{k=1}^{\infty}\left[5\left(\frac{2}{3}\right)^k - \frac{2^{k-1}}{7^k}\right].$$

SOLUTION We examine the two series $\sum_{k=1}^{\infty} 5\left(\frac{2}{3}\right)^k$ and $\sum_{k=1}^{\infty} \frac{2^{k-1}}{7^k}$ individually. The first series is a geometric series and is evaluated using the methods of Section 9.3. Its first few terms are

$$\sum_{k=1}^{\infty} 5\left(\frac{2}{3}\right)^k = 5\left(\frac{2}{3}\right) + 5\left(\frac{2}{3}\right)^2 + 5\left(\frac{2}{3}\right)^3 + \cdots.$$

The first term of the series is $a = 5\left(\frac{2}{3}\right)$ and the ratio is $r = \frac{2}{3} < 1$; therefore,

$$\sum_{k=1}^{\infty} 5\left(\frac{2}{3}\right)^k = \frac{a}{1-r} = \left[\frac{5\left(\frac{2}{3}\right)}{1-\frac{2}{3}}\right] = 10.$$

Writing out the first few terms of the second series, we see that it, too, is geometric:

$$\sum_{k=1}^{\infty} \frac{2^{k-1}}{7^k} = \frac{1}{7} + \frac{2}{7^2} + \frac{2^2}{7^3} + \cdots$$

The first term is $a = \frac{1}{7}$ and the ratio is $r = \frac{2}{7} < 1$; therefore,

$$\sum_{k=1}^{\infty} \frac{2^{k-1}}{7^k} = \frac{a}{1-r} = \frac{\frac{1}{7}}{1 - \frac{2}{7}} = \frac{1}{5}.$$

Both series converge. By Property 2 of Theorem 9.8, we combine them and have $S = 10 - \frac{1}{5} = \frac{49}{5}$.

Related Exercises 9–14 ◀

QUICK CHECK 2 For a series with positive terms, explain why the sequence of partial sums $\{S_n\}$ is an increasing sequence. ◀

The Divergence Test

The goal of this section is to develop tests to determine whether or not an infinite series converges. One of the simplest and most useful tests determines whether an infinite series *diverges*.

> **THEOREM 9.9 Divergence Test**
> If $\sum a_k$ converges, then $\lim_{k\to\infty} a_k = 0$. Equivalently, if $\lim_{k\to\infty} a_k \neq 0$, then the series diverges.

Important note: Theorem 9.9 cannot be used to determine convergence.

Proof Let $\{S_k\}$ be the sequence of partial sums for the series $\sum a_k$. Assuming the series converges, it has a finite value, call it S, where

$$S = \lim_{k\to\infty} S_k = \lim_{k\to\infty} S_{k-1}.$$

Note that $S_k - S_{k-1} = a_k$. Therefore,

$$\lim_{k\to\infty} a_k = \lim_{k\to\infty} (S_k - S_{k-1}) = S - S = 0;$$

that is, $\lim_{k\to\infty} a_k = 0$ (Figure 9.26). The second part of the test follows immediately because it is the *contrapositive* of the first part (see margin note). ◀

➤ If the statement *if p, then q* is true, then its contrapositive, *if (not q), then (not p)*, is also true. However its converse, *if q, then p*, is not necessarily true. Try it out on the true statement, *if I live in Paris, then I live in France.*

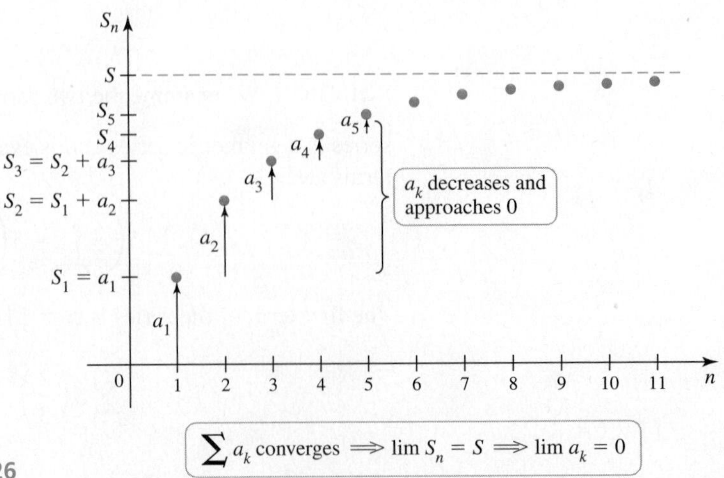

FIGURE 9.26

To summarize: If the terms a_k of a given series do *not* tend to zero as $k \to \infty$, then the series diverges. Unfortunately, the test is easy to misuse. It's tempting to conclude that if the terms of the series tend to zero, then the series converges. This is often not true, as illustrated by the harmonic series—to which we now return.

Recall that the harmonic series is

$$\sum_{k=1}^{\infty} \frac{1}{k} = 1 + \frac{1}{2} + \frac{1}{3} + \frac{1}{4} + \frac{1}{5} + \cdots.$$

With $a_k = 1/k$, we have $\lim_{k\to\infty} a_k = 0$, which does *not* imply convergence. We now determine whether the series converges.

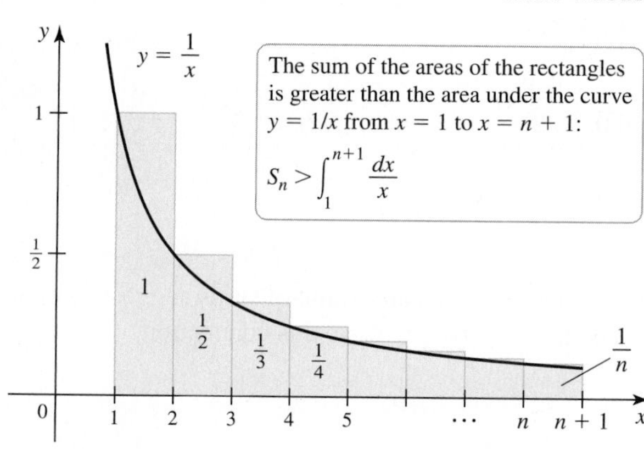

FIGURE 9.27

The nth term of the sequence of partial sums,

$$S_n = \sum_{k=1}^{n} \frac{1}{k} = 1 + \frac{1}{2} + \frac{1}{3} + \frac{1}{4} + \cdots + \frac{1}{n},$$

is represented geometrically by a left Riemann sum of the function $y = \frac{1}{x}$ on the interval $[1, n + 1]$ (Figure 9.27). This fact follows by observing that the areas of the rectangles, from left to right, are $1, \frac{1}{2}, \ldots, \frac{1}{n}$. By comparing the sum of the areas of these n rectangles with the area under the curve, which is $\int_1^{n+1} \frac{dx}{x}$, we see that $S_n > \int_1^{n+1} \frac{dx}{x}$.

➤ Recall that $\int \frac{dx}{x} = \ln |x| + C$.

In Section 8.7, we showed that $\int_1^{\infty} \frac{dx}{x^p}$ diverges for $p \leq 1$. Therefore, $\int_1^{\infty} \frac{dx}{x}$ diverges.

We know that $\int_1^{n+1} \frac{dx}{x} = \ln (n + 1)$ increases without bound as n increases. Because S_n exceeds $\int_1^{n+1} \frac{dx}{x}$, S_n also increases without bound; therefore, $\lim_{n\to\infty} S_n = \infty$ and the harmonic series $\sum_{k=1}^{\infty} \frac{1}{k}$ diverges. This argument justifies the following theorem.

THEOREM 9.10 Harmonic Series

The harmonic series $\sum_{k=1}^{\infty} \frac{1}{k} = 1 + \frac{1}{2} + \frac{1}{3} + \frac{1}{4} + \frac{1}{5} + \cdots$ diverges—even though the terms of the series tend to zero.

EXAMPLE 2 Using the Divergence Test Determine whether the following series diverge or state that the test is inconclusive.

a. $\sum_{k=0}^{\infty} \frac{k}{k + 1}$ **b.** $\sum_{k=1}^{\infty} \frac{1}{\sqrt{k}}$ **c.** $\sum_{k=1}^{\infty} \frac{1 + 3^k}{2^k}$

SOLUTION Recall that if $\lim_{k\to\infty} a_k \neq 0$, then the series diverges.

a. $\lim_{k\to\infty} a_k = \lim_{k\to\infty} \frac{k}{k + 1} = 1 \neq 0.$

The terms of the series do not tend to zero, so the series diverges by the Divergence Test.

b. $\lim_{k\to\infty} a_k = \lim_{k\to\infty} \frac{1}{\sqrt{k}} = 0.$

The terms of the series approach zero, so the Divergence Test is inconclusive. (Remember, the Divergence Test cannot be used to prove that a series converges.)

c. $\lim_{k\to\infty} a_k = \lim_{k\to\infty} \frac{1 + 3^k}{2^k}$

$= \lim_{k\to\infty} \Big[\underbrace{2^{-k}}_{\to 0} + \underbrace{\left(\frac{3}{2}\right)^k}_{\to\infty}\Big]$ Simplify.

$= \infty$

QUICK CHECK 3 Apply the Divergence Test to the geometric series Σr^k. For what values of r does the series diverge?

In this case, $\lim_{k\to\infty} a_k$ does not equal 0, so the corresponding series $\sum_{k=1}^{\infty} \frac{1 + 3^k}{2^k}$ diverges by the Divergence Test.

Related Exercises 15–22

The Integral Test

The fact that infinite series are sums and that integrals are limits of sums suggests a connection between series and integrals. The Integral Test exploits this connection.

THEOREM 9.11 Integral Test

Suppose f is a continuous, positive, decreasing function for $x \geq 1$ and let $a_k = f(k)$ for $k = 1, 2, 3, \ldots$. Then

$$\sum_{k=1}^{\infty} a_k \quad \text{and} \quad \int_1^{\infty} f(x)\,dx$$

either both converge or both diverge. In the case of convergence, the value of the integral is *not*, in general, equal to the value of the series.

The Integral Test also applies if the terms of the series a_k are decreasing for $k > N$ for some finite $N > 1$. The proof can be modified to account for this situation.

Proof By comparing the shaded regions in Figure 9.28, it follows that

$$\sum_{k=2}^{n} a_k \leq \int_1^n f(x)\,dx \leq \sum_{k=1}^{n-1} a_k. \tag{1}$$

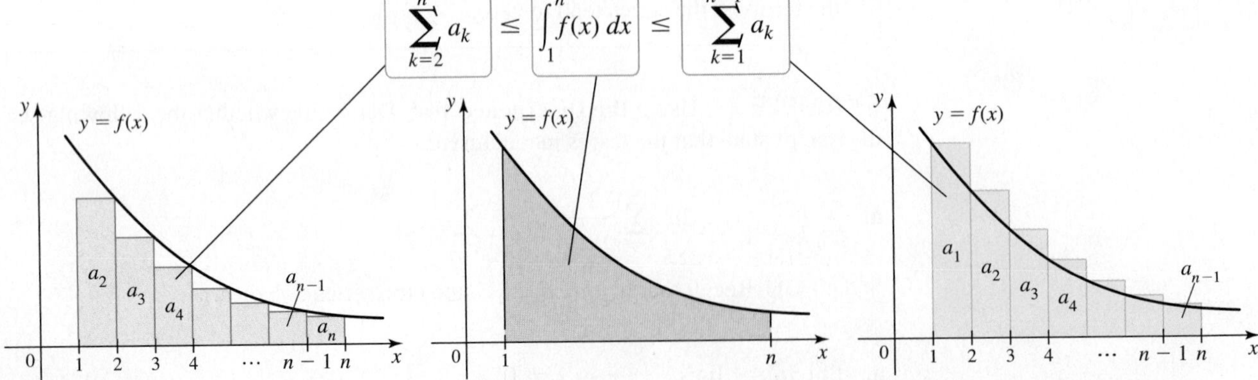

FIGURE 9.28

The proof must demonstrate two results: If the improper integral $\int_1^{\infty} f(x)\,dx$ has a finite value, then the infinite series converges, *and* if the infinite series converges, then the improper integral has a finite value. First suppose that the improper integral $\int_1^\infty f(x)\,dx$ has a finite value, say, I. We have

$$\begin{aligned}
\sum_{k=1}^{n} a_k &= a_1 + \sum_{k=2}^{n} a_k && \text{Separate the first term of the series.}\\
&\le a_1 + \int_1^n f(x)\,dx && \text{Left inequality in expression (1)}\\
&< a_1 + \int_1^\infty f(x)\,dx && f \text{ is positive, so } \int_1^n f(x)\,dx < \int_1^\infty f(x)\,dx.\\
&= a_1 + I.
\end{aligned}$$

In this proof, we rely twice on the Bounded Monotonic Sequence Theorem of Section 9.2: A bounded monotonic sequence converges.

This argument implies that the terms of the sequence of partial sums $S_n = \sum_{k=1}^{n} a_k$ are bounded above by $a_1 + I$. Because $\{S_n\}$ is also increasing (the series consists of positive terms), the sequence of partial sums converges, which means the series $\sum_{k=1}^{\infty} a_k$ converges (to a value less than or equal to $a_1 + I$).

Now suppose the infinite series $\sum_{k=1}^{\infty} a_k$ converges and has a value S. We have

$$\begin{aligned}
\int_1^n f(x)\,dx &\le \sum_{k=1}^{n-1} a_k && \text{Right inequality in expression (1)}\\
&< \sum_{k=1}^{\infty} a_k && \text{Terms } a_k \text{ are positive.}\\
&= S. && \text{Value of infinite series}
\end{aligned}$$

We see that the sequence $\left\{\int_1^n f(x)\,dx\right\}$ is increasing (because $f(x) > 0$) and bounded above by a fixed number S. Thus, the improper integral $\int_1^\infty f(x)\,dx = \lim_{n\to\infty} \int_1^n f(x)\,dx$ has a finite value (less than or equal to S).

We have shown that if $\int_1^\infty f(x)\,dx$ is finite, then Σa_k converges and vice versa. The same inequalities imply that $\int_1^\infty f(x)\,dx$ and Σa_k also diverge together. ◀

The Integral Test is used to determine *whether* a series converges or diverges. For this reason, adding or subtracting a few terms in the series *or* changing the lower limit of integration to another finite point does not change the outcome of the test. Therefore, the test does not depend on the lower index in the series or the lower limit of the integral.

EXAMPLE 3 Applying the Integral Test Determine whether the following series converge.

a. $\displaystyle\sum_{k=1}^{\infty} \frac{k}{k^2 + 1}$ **b.** $\displaystyle\sum_{k=3}^{\infty} \frac{1}{\sqrt{2k - 5}}$

SOLUTION

a. The function associated with this series is $f(x) = x/(x^2 + 1)$, which is positive for $x \ge 1$. We must also show that the terms of the series are decreasing beyond some fixed term of the series. The first few terms of the series are $\left\{\frac{1}{2}, \frac{2}{5}, \frac{3}{10}, \frac{4}{17}, \ldots\right\}$, and it appears that the terms are decreasing. When the decreasing property is difficult to confirm, one approach is to use derivatives to show that the associated function is decreasing. In this case, we have

$$f'(x) = \frac{d}{dx}\left(\frac{x}{x^2 + 1}\right) = \underbrace{\frac{x^2 + 1 - 2x^2}{(x^2 + 1)^2}}_{\text{Quotient Rule}} = \frac{1 - x^2}{(x^2 + 1)^2}.$$

For $x > 1, f'(x) < 0$, which implies that the function and the terms of the series are decreasing. The integral that determines convergence is

$$\int_1^\infty \frac{x}{x^2+1}\,dx = \lim_{b\to\infty}\int_1^b \frac{x}{x^2+1}\,dx \quad \text{Definition of improper integral}$$

$$= \lim_{b\to\infty}\frac{1}{2}\ln(x^2+1)\Big|_1^b \quad \text{Evaluate integral.}$$

$$= \frac{1}{2}\lim_{b\to\infty}(\ln(b^2+1) - \ln 2) \quad \text{Simplify.}$$

$$= \infty. \quad \lim_{b\to\infty}\ln(b^2+1) = \infty$$

Because the integral diverges, the series diverges.

b. The Integral Test may be modified to accommodate initial indices other than $k = 1$. The terms of this series decrease for $k \geq 3$. In this case, the relevant integral is

$$\int_3^\infty \frac{dx}{\sqrt{2x-5}} = \lim_{b\to\infty}\int_3^b \frac{dx}{\sqrt{2x-5}} \quad \text{Definition of improper integral}$$

$$= \lim_{b\to\infty}\sqrt{2x-5}\Big|_3^b \quad \text{Evaluate integral.}$$

$$= \infty \quad \lim_{b\to\infty}\sqrt{2b-5} = \infty$$

Because the integral diverges, the series also diverges. *Related Exercises 23–30* ◀

The *p*-Series

The Integral Test is used to analyze the convergence of an entire family of infinite series $\sum_{k=1}^{\infty}\frac{1}{k^p}$ known as the *p-series*. For what values of the real number p does the p-series converge?

EXAMPLE 4 **The *p*-series** For what values of p does the p-series $\sum_{k=1}^{\infty}\frac{1}{k^p}$ converge?

SOLUTION Notice that $p = 1$ corresponds to the harmonic series, which diverges. To apply the Integral Test, observe that the terms of the given series are positive and decreasing for $p > 0$. The function associated with the series is $f(x) = \frac{1}{x^p}$. The relevant integral is $\int_1^\infty x^{-p}\,dx = \int_1^\infty \frac{dx}{x^p}$. Appealing again to Section 8.7, recall that this integral converges when $p > 1$ and diverges when $p \leq 1$. Therefore, by the Integral Test, the p-series $\sum_{k=1}^{\infty}\frac{1}{k^p}$ converges when $p > 1$ and diverges when $0 < p \leq 1$. For example, the series

$$\sum_{k=1}^{\infty}\frac{1}{k^3} \quad \text{and} \quad \sum_{k=1}^{\infty}\frac{1}{\sqrt{k}}$$

converge and diverge, respectively. For $p < 0$, the series diverges by the Divergence Test. This argument justifies the following theorem. *Related Exercises 31–34* ◀

QUICK CHECK 4 Which of the following series are p-series, and which series converge?

a. $\sum_{k=1}^{\infty} k^{-0.8}$ **b.** $\sum_{k=1}^{\infty} 2^{-k}$ **c.** $\sum_{k=10}^{\infty} k^{-4}$

THEOREM 9.12 Convergence of the p-Series

The p-series $\sum_{k=1}^{\infty} \frac{1}{k^p}$ converges when $p > 1$ and diverges when $p \leq 1$.

EXAMPLE 5 Using the p-series test Determine whether the following series converge or diverge.

a. $\sum_{k=1}^{\infty} \frac{1}{\sqrt[4]{k^3}}$ **b.** $\sum_{k=4}^{\infty} \frac{1}{(k-1)^2}$

SOLUTION

a. This series is a p-series with $p = \frac{3}{4}$. By Theorem 9.12, it diverges.

b. The series

$$\sum_{k=4}^{\infty} \frac{1}{(k-1)^2} = \sum_{k=3}^{\infty} \frac{1}{k^2} = \frac{1}{3^2} + \frac{1}{4^2} + \frac{1}{5^2} + \cdots$$

is a convergent p-series ($p = 2$) without the first two terms. By property 3 of Theorem 9.8, adding or removing a finite number of terms does not affect the convergence of a series. Therefore, the given series converges.

Related Exercises 31–34

Estimating the Value of Infinite Series

The Integral Test is powerful in its own right, but it comes with an added bonus. In some cases, it is used to estimate the value of a series. We define the **remainder** to be the error in approximating a convergent infinite series by the sum of its first n terms; that is,

$$R_n = \underbrace{\sum_{k=1}^{\infty} a_k}_{\text{value of series}} - \underbrace{\sum_{k=1}^{n} a_k}_{\text{approximation based on first } n \text{ terms}} = a_{n+1} + a_{n+2} + a_{n+3} + \cdots.$$

QUICK CHECK 5 If $\sum a_k$ is a convergent series of positive terms, why is $R_n \geq 0$?

The remainder consists of the *tail* of the series—those terms beyond a_n.

We now argue much as we did in the proof of the Integral Test. Let f be a continuous, positive, decreasing function such that $f(k) = a_k$ for all relevant k. From Figure 9.29, we see that $\int_{n+1}^{\infty} f(x)\,dx \leq R_n$.

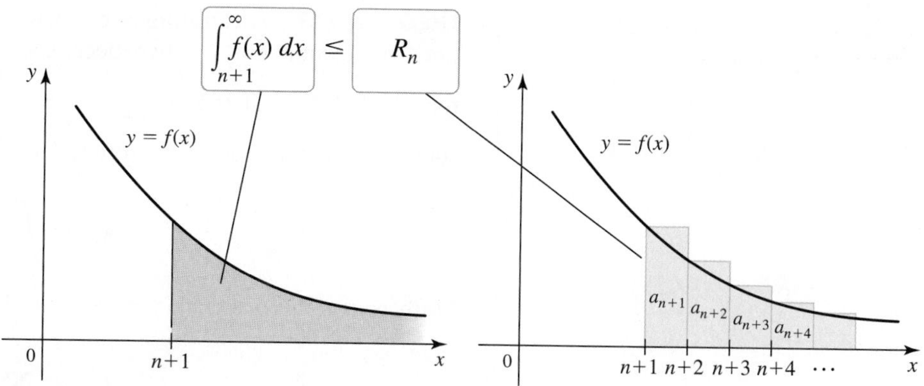

FIGURE 9.29

Similarly, Figure 9.30 shows that $R_n \le \int_n^\infty f(x)\,dx$.

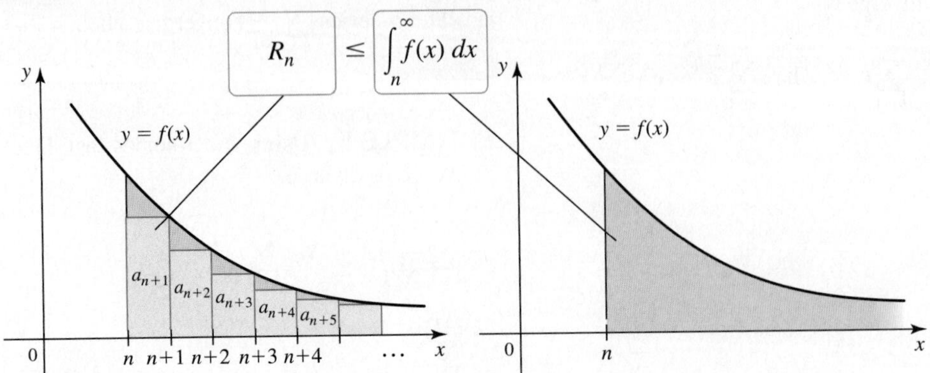

FIGURE 9.30

Combining these two inequalities, the remainder is squeezed between two integrals:

$$\int_{n+1}^{\infty} f(x)\,dx \le R_n \le \int_{n}^{\infty} f(x)\,dx \tag{2}$$

If the integrals can be evaluated, this result provides an estimate of the remainder.

There is, however, another equally useful way to express this result. Notice that the value of the series is

$$S = \sum_{k=1}^{\infty} a_k = \underbrace{\sum_{k=1}^{n} a_k}_{S_n} + R_n,$$

which is the sum of the first n terms S_n and the remainder R_n. Adding S_n to each term of (2), we have

$$\underbrace{S_n + \int_{n+1}^{\infty} f(x)\,dx}_{L_n} \le \underbrace{\sum_{k=1}^{\infty} a_k}_{S_n + R_n = S} \le \underbrace{S_n + \int_{n}^{\infty} f(x)\,dx}_{U_n}.$$

These inequalities can be abbreviated as $L_n \le S \le U_n$, where S is the exact value of the series, and L_n and U_n are lower and upper bounds for S, respectively. If the integrals can be evaluated, it is straightforward to compute S_n (by summing the first n terms of the series) and to compute both L_n and U_n.

THEOREM 9.13 Estimating Series with Positive Terms

Let f be a continuous, positive, decreasing function for $x \ge 1$ and let $a_k = f(k)$ for $k = 1, 2, 3, \ldots$. Let $S = \sum_{k=1}^{\infty} a_k$ be a convergent series and let $S_n = \sum_{k=1}^{n} a_k$ be the sum of the first n terms of the series. The remainder $R_n = S - S_n$ satisfies

$$R_n \le \int_n^\infty f(x)\,dx.$$

Furthermore, the exact value of the series is bounded as follows:

$$S_n + \int_{n+1}^{\infty} f(x)\,dx \le \sum_{k=1}^{\infty} a_k \le S_n + \int_{n}^{\infty} f(x)\,dx$$

EXAMPLE 6 Approximating a p-series

a. How many terms of the series $\sum_{k=1}^{\infty} \frac{1}{k^2}$ must be summed to obtain an approximation that is within 10^{-3} of the exact value of the series?

b. Find an approximation to the series using 50 terms of the series.

SOLUTION The function associated with this series is $f(x) = 1/x^2$.

a. Using the bound on the remainder, we have

$$R_n \le \int_n^{\infty} f(x)\,dx = \int_n^{\infty} \frac{dx}{x^2} = \frac{1}{n}.$$

To ensure that $R_n \le 10^{-3}$, we must choose n so that $1/n \le 10^{-3}$, which implies that $n \ge 1000$. In other words, we must sum at least 1000 terms of the series to be sure that the remainder is less than 10^{-3}.

b. Using the bounds on the series itself, we have $L_n \le S \le U_n$, where S is the exact value of the series, and

$$L_n = S_n + \int_{n+1}^{\infty} \frac{dx}{x^2} = S_n + \frac{1}{n+1} \quad \text{and} \quad U_n = S_n + \int_n^{\infty} \frac{dx}{x^2} = S_n + \frac{1}{n}.$$

Therefore, the series is bounded as follows:

$$S_n + \frac{1}{n+1} \le S \le S_n + \frac{1}{n},$$

where S_n is the sum of the first n terms. Using a calculator to sum the first 50 terms of the series, we find that $S_{50} \approx 1.625133$. The exact value of the series is in the interval

$$S_{50} + \frac{1}{50+1} \le S \le S_{50} + \frac{1}{50},$$

or $1.644741 < S < 1.645133$. Taking the average of these two bounds as our approximation of S, we find that $S \approx 1.644937$. This estimate is better than simply using S_{50}. Figure 9.31a shows the lower and upper bounds, L_n and U_n, respectively, for $n = 1, 2, \ldots, 50$. Figure 9.31b shows these bounds on an enlarged scale for $n = 50, 51, \ldots, 100$. These figures illustrate how the exact value of the series is squeezed into a narrowing interval as n increases.

➤ The values of p-series with even values of p are generally known. For example, with $p = 2$ the series converges to $\pi^2/6$ (a proof is outlined in Exercise 58); with $p = 4$, the series converges to $\pi^4/90$. The values of p-series with odd values of p are not known.

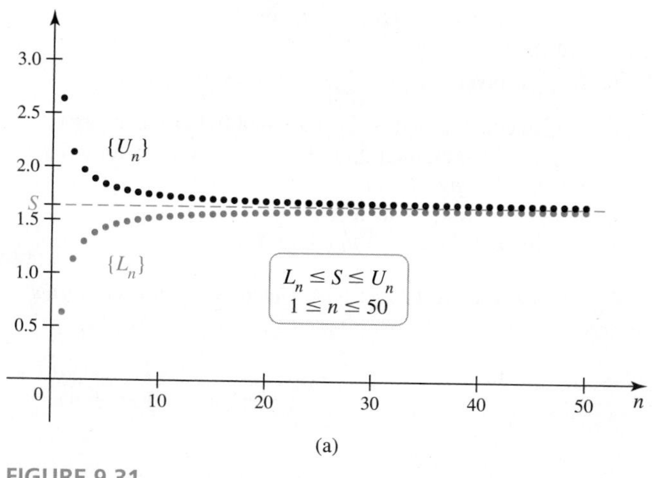

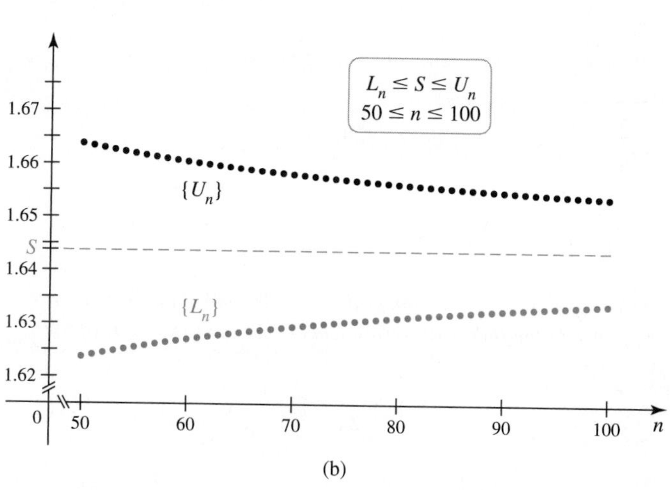

FIGURE 9.31

Related Exercises 35–42 ◄

SECTION 9.4 EXERCISES

Review Questions

1. Explain why computation alone may not determine whether a series converges.

2. Is it true that if the terms of a series of positive terms decrease to zero, then the series converges? Explain using an example.

3. Can the Integral Test be used to determine whether a series diverges?

4. For what values of p does the series $\sum_{k=1}^{\infty} \frac{1}{k^p}$ converge? For what values of p does it diverge?

5. For what values of p does the series $\sum_{k=10}^{\infty} \frac{1}{k^p}$ converge (initial index is 10)? For what values of p does it diverge?

6. Explain why the sequence of partial sums for a series with positive terms is an increasing sequence.

7. Define the remainder of an infinite series.

8. If a series of positive terms converges, does it follow that the remainder R_n must decrease to zero as $n \to \infty$? Explain.

Basic Skills

9–14. Properties of series *Use the properties of infinite series to evaluate the following series.*

9. $\sum_{k=0}^{\infty} \left[3\left(\frac{2}{5}\right)^k - 2\left(\frac{5}{7}\right)^k\right]$

10. $\sum_{k=1}^{\infty} \left[2\left(\frac{3}{5}\right)^k + 3\left(\frac{4}{9}\right)^k\right]$

11. $\sum_{k=1}^{\infty} \left[\frac{1}{3}\left(\frac{5}{6}\right)^k + \frac{3}{5}\left(\frac{7}{9}\right)^k\right]$

12. $\sum_{k=0}^{\infty} \left[\frac{1}{2}(0.2)^k + \frac{3}{2}(0.8)^k\right]$

13. $\sum_{k=1}^{\infty} \left[\left(\frac{1}{6}\right)^k + \left(\frac{1}{3}\right)^{k-1}\right]$

14. $\sum_{k=0}^{\infty} \frac{2 - 3^k}{6^k}$

15–22. Divergence Test *Use the Divergence Test to determine whether the following series diverge or state that the test is inconclusive.*

15. $\sum_{k=0}^{\infty} \frac{k}{2k + 1}$

16. $\sum_{k=1}^{\infty} \frac{k}{k^2 + 1}$

17. $\sum_{k=2}^{\infty} \frac{k}{\ln k}$

18. $\sum_{k=1}^{\infty} \frac{k^2}{2^k}$

19. $\sum_{k=0}^{\infty} \frac{1}{1000 + k}$

20. $\sum_{k=1}^{\infty} \frac{k^3}{k^3 + 1}$

21. $\sum_{k=2}^{\infty} \frac{\sqrt{k}}{\ln^{10} k}$

22. $\sum_{k=1}^{\infty} \frac{\sqrt{k^2 + 1}}{k}$

23–30. Integral Test *Use the Integral Test to determine the convergence or divergence of the following series. Check that the conditions of the test are satisfied.*

23. $\sum_{k=2}^{\infty} \frac{1}{k \ln k}$

24. $\sum_{k=1}^{\infty} \frac{k}{\sqrt{k^2 + 4}}$

25. $\sum_{k=1}^{\infty} k e^{-2k^2}$

26. $\sum_{k=1}^{\infty} \frac{1}{\sqrt[3]{k + 10}}$

27. $\sum_{k=0}^{\infty} \frac{1}{\sqrt{k + 8}}$

28. $\sum_{k=2}^{\infty} \frac{1}{k(\ln k)^2}$

29. $\sum_{k=1}^{\infty} \frac{k}{e^k}$

30. $\sum_{k=2}^{\infty} \frac{1}{k \ln k \ln (\ln k)}$

31–34. *p*-series *Determine the convergence or divergence of the following series.*

31. $\sum_{k=1}^{\infty} \frac{1}{k^{10}}$

32. $\sum_{k=2}^{\infty} \frac{k^e}{k^{\pi}}$

33. $\sum_{k=3}^{\infty} \frac{1}{(k - 2)^4}$

34. $\sum_{k=1}^{\infty} 2k^{-3/2}$

T **35–42. Remainders and estimates** *Consider the following convergent series.*

a. Find an upper bound for the remainder in terms of n.
b. Find how many terms are needed to ensure that the remainder is less than 10^{-3}.
c. Find lower and upper bounds (L_n and U_n, respectively) on the exact value of the series.
d. Find an interval in which the value of the series must lie if you approximate it using ten terms of the series.

35. $\sum_{k=1}^{\infty} \frac{1}{k^6}$

36. $\sum_{k=1}^{\infty} \frac{1}{k^8}$

37. $\sum_{k=1}^{\infty} \frac{1}{3^k}$

38. $\sum_{k=2}^{\infty} \frac{1}{k(\ln k)^2}$

39. $\sum_{k=1}^{\infty} \frac{1}{k^{3/2}}$

40. $\sum_{k=1}^{\infty} e^{-k}$

41. $\sum_{k=1}^{\infty} \frac{1}{k^3}$

42. $\sum_{k=1}^{\infty} k e^{-k^2}$

Further Explorations

43. **Explain why or why not** Determine whether the following statements are true and give an explanation or counterexample.

a. If $\sum_{k=1}^{\infty} a_k$ converges, then $\sum_{k=10}^{\infty} a_k$ converges.
b. If $\sum_{k=1}^{\infty} a_k$ diverges, then $\sum_{k=10}^{\infty} a_k$ diverges.
c. If $\sum a_k$ converges, then $\sum (a_k + 0.0001)$ also converges.
d. If $\sum p^k$ diverges, then $\sum (p + 0.001)^k$ diverges, for a fixed real number p.
e. If $\sum k^{-p}$ converges, then $\sum k^{-p+0.001}$ converges.
f. If $\lim_{k \to \infty} a_k = 0$, then $\sum a_k$ converges.

44–49. Choose your test *Determine whether the following series converge or diverge.*

44. $\sum_{k=1}^{\infty} \sqrt{\frac{k + 1}{k}}$

45. $\sum_{k=1}^{\infty} \frac{1}{(3k + 1)(3k + 4)}$

46. $\sum_{k=0}^{\infty} \frac{10}{k^2 + 9}$

47. $\sum_{k=0}^{\infty} \frac{k}{\sqrt{k^2 + 4}}$

48. $\sum_{k=1}^{\infty} \frac{2^k + 3^k}{4^k}$

49. $\sum_{k=2}^{\infty} \frac{4}{k \ln^2 k}$

50. Log *p*-series Consider the series $\sum_{k=2}^{\infty} \frac{1}{k(\ln k)^p}$, where p is a real number.

a. Use the Integral Test to determine the values of p for which this series converges.
b. Does this series converge faster for $p = 2$ or $p = 3$? Explain.

51. Loglog *p*-series Consider the series $\sum_{k=2}^{\infty} \frac{1}{k \ln k (\ln \ln k)^p}$, where p is a real number.

a. For what values of p does this series converge?
b. Which of the following series converges faster? Explain.

$$\sum_{k=2}^{\infty} \frac{1}{k(\ln k)^2} \quad \text{or} \quad \sum_{k=2}^{\infty} \frac{1}{k \ln k(\ln \ln k)^2}?$$

52. Find a series Find a series that . . .

a. converges faster than $\sum \frac{1}{k^2}$ but slower than $\sum \frac{1}{k^3}$.
b. diverges faster than $\sum \frac{1}{k}$ but slower than $\sum \frac{1}{\sqrt{k}}$.
c. converges faster than $\sum \frac{1}{k \ln^2 k}$ but slower than $\sum \frac{1}{k^2}$.

Additional Exercises

53. A divergence proof Give an argument, similar to that given in the text for the harmonic series, to show that $\sum_{k=1}^{\infty} \frac{1}{\sqrt{k}}$ diverges.

54. Properties proof Use the ideas in the proof of Property 1 of Theorem 9.8 to prove Property 2 of Theorem 9.8.

55. Property of divergent series Prove that if $\sum a_k$ diverges, then $\sum ca_k$ also diverges, where $c \neq 0$ is a constant.

56. Prime numbers The prime numbers are those positive integers that are divisible by only 1 and themselves (for example, 2, 3, 5, 7, 11, 13, . . .). A celebrated theorem states that the sequence of prime numbers $\{p_k\}$ satisfies $\lim_{k\to\infty} p_k/(k \ln k) = 1$. Show that $\sum_{k=2}^{\infty} \frac{1}{k \ln k}$ diverges, which implies that the series $\sum_{k=1}^{\infty} 1/p_k$ diverges.

T **57. The zeta function** The Riemann zeta function is the subject of extensive research and is associated with several renowned unsolved problems. It is defined by $\zeta(x) = \sum_{k=1}^{\infty} \frac{1}{k^x}$. When x is a real number, the zeta function becomes a p-series. For even positive integers p, the value of $\zeta(p)$ is known exactly. For example,

$$\sum_{k=1}^{\infty} \frac{1}{k^2} = \frac{\pi^2}{6}, \quad \sum_{k=1}^{\infty} \frac{1}{k^4} = \frac{\pi^4}{90}, \quad \sum_{k=1}^{\infty} \frac{1}{k^6} = \frac{\pi^6}{945}, \ldots.$$

Use the estimation techniques described in the text to approximate $\zeta(3)$ and $\zeta(5)$ (whose values are not known exactly) with a remainder less than 10^{-3}.

58. Showing that $\sum_{k=1}^{\infty} \frac{1}{k^2} = \frac{\pi^2}{6}$ In 1734, Leonhard Euler informally proved that $\sum_{k=1}^{\infty} \frac{1}{k^2} = \frac{\pi^2}{6}$. An elegant proof is outlined here that uses the inequality

$$\cot^2 x < \frac{1}{x^2} < 1 + \cot^2 x \quad (\text{provided that } 0 < x < \pi/2)$$

and the identity

$$\sum_{k=1}^{n} \cot^2(k\theta) = \frac{n(2n-1)}{3}, \text{ for } n = 1, 2, 3 \ldots, \text{where } \theta = \frac{\pi}{2n+1}.$$

a. Show that $\sum_{k=1}^{n} \cot^2(k\theta) < \frac{1}{\theta^2} \sum_{k=1}^{n} \frac{1}{k^2} < n + \sum_{k=1}^{n} \cot^2(k\theta)$.
b. Use the inequality in part (a) to show that

$$\frac{n(2n-1)\pi^2}{3(2n+1)^2} < \sum_{k=1}^{n} \frac{1}{k^2} < \frac{n(2n+2)\pi^2}{3(2n+1)^2}.$$

c. Use the Squeeze Theorem to conclude that $\sum_{k=1}^{\infty} \frac{1}{k^2} = \frac{\pi^2}{6}$.

[*Source: The College Mathematics Journal,* **24**, No. 5 (November, 1993).]

59. Reciprocals of odd squares Given that $\sum_{k=1}^{\infty} \frac{1}{k^2} = \frac{\pi^2}{6}$ (Exercises 57 and 58) and that the terms of this series may be rearranged without changing the value of the series. Determine the sum of the reciprocals of the squares of the odd positive integers.

T **60. Shifted *p*-series** Consider the sequence $\{F_n\}$ defined by

$$F_n = \sum_{k=1}^{\infty} \frac{1}{k(k+n)},$$

for $n = 0, 1, 2, \ldots$. When $n = 0$, the series is a p-series, and we have $F_0 = \pi^2/6$ (Exercises 57 and 58).

a. Explain why $\{F_n\}$ is a decreasing sequence.
b. Plot approximations to $\{F_n\}$ for $n = 1, 2, \ldots, 20$.
c. Based on your experiments, make a conjecture about $\lim_{n\to\infty} F_n$.

61. A sequence of sums Consider the sequence $\{x_n\}$ defined for $n = 1, 2, 3, \ldots$ by

$$x_n = \sum_{k=n+1}^{2n} \frac{1}{k} = \frac{1}{n+1} + \frac{1}{n+2} + \cdots + \frac{1}{2n}.$$

a. Write out the terms x_1, x_2, x_3.
b. Show that $\frac{1}{2} \leq x_n < 1$ for $n = 1, 2, 3, \ldots$.
c. Show that x_n is the right Riemann sum for $\int_1^2 \frac{dx}{x}$ using n subintervals.
d. Conclude that $\lim_{n\to\infty} x_n = \ln 2$.

T **62. The harmonic series and Euler's constant**

a. Sketch the function $f(x) = 1/x$ on the interval $[1, n+1]$, where n is a positive integer. Use this graph to verify that

$$\ln(n+1) < 1 + \frac{1}{2} + \frac{1}{3} + \cdots + \frac{1}{n} < 1 + \ln n.$$

b. Let S_n be the sum of the first n terms of the harmonic series, so part (a) says $\ln(n+1) < S_n < 1 + \ln n$. Define the new sequence $\{E_n\}$, where

$$E_n = S_n - \ln(n+1), \quad \text{for } n = 1, 2, 3, \ldots.$$

Show that $E_n > 0$ for $n = 1, 2, 3, \ldots$.

c. Using a figure similar to that used in part (a), show that

$$\frac{1}{n+1} > \ln(n+2) - \ln(n+1).$$

d. Use parts (a) and (c) to show that $\{E_n\}$ is an increasing sequence $(E_{n+1} > E_n)$.

e. Use part (a) to show that $\{E_n\}$ is bounded above by 1.

f. Conclude from parts (d) and (e) that $\{E_n\}$ has a limit less than or equal to 1. This limit is known as **Euler's constant** and is denoted γ (the Greek lowercase letter gamma).

g. By computing terms of $\{E_n\}$, estimate the value of γ and compare it to the value $\gamma \approx 0.5772$. (It has been conjectured, but not proved, that γ is irrational.)

h. The preceding arguments show that the sum of the first n terms of the harmonic series satisfy $S_n \approx 0.5772 + \ln(n+1)$. How many terms must be summed for the sum to exceed 10?

63. Stacking dominoes Consider a set of identical dominoes that are 2 in long. The dominoes are stacked on top of each other with their long edges aligned so that each domino overhangs the one beneath it *as far as possible* (see figure).

a. If there are n dominoes in the stack, what is the *greatest* distance that the top domino can be made to overhang the bottom domino? (*Hint:* Put the nth domino beneath the previous $n - 1$ dominoes.)

b. If we allow for infinitely many dominoes in the stack, what is the greatest distance that the top domino can be made to overhang the bottom domino?

QUICK CHECK ANSWERS

1. Adding a finite number of nonzero terms does not change whether the series converges. It does, however, change the value of the series. **2.** Given the nth term of the sequence of partial sums S_n, the next term is obtained by adding a positive number. So $S_{n+1} > S_n$, which means the sequence is increasing. **3.** The series diverges for $|r| \geq 1$. **4. a.** Divergent p-series **b.** Convergent geometric series **c.** Convergent p-series **5.** The remainder is $R_n = a_{n+1} + a_{n+2} + \cdots$, which consists of positive numbers.

9.5 The Ratio, Root, and Comparison Tests

We now consider several more convergence tests: the Ratio Test, the Root Test, and two comparison tests. The Ratio Test will be used frequently throughout the next chapter, and comparison tests are valuable when no other test works. Again, these tests determine *whether* an infinite series converges, but they do not establish the value of the series.

The Ratio Test

The Integral Test is powerful, but limited, because it requires evaluating integrals. For example, the series $\Sigma 1/k!$, with a factorial term, cannot be handled by the Integral Test. The next test significantly enlarges the set of infinite series that we can analyze.

> In words, the Ratio Test says the limit of the ratio of successive terms of the series must be less than 1 for convergence of the series.

THEOREM 9.14 The Ratio Test

Let Σa_k be an infinite series with positive terms and let $r = \lim_{k\to\infty} \frac{a_{k+1}}{a_k}$.

1. If $0 \leq r < 1$, the series converges.
2. If $r > 1$ (including $r = \infty$), the series diverges.
3. If $r = 1$, the test is inconclusive.

Proof (outline) We omit the details of the proof, but the idea behind the proof provides insight. Let's assume that the limit r exists. Then, as k gets large and the ratio a_{k+1}/a_k approaches r, we have $a_{k+1} \approx ra_k$. Therefore, as one goes farther and farther out in the series, it behaves like

$$\begin{aligned} a_k + a_{k+1} + a_{k+2} + \cdots &\approx a_k + ra_k + r^2a_k + r^3a_k + \cdots \\ &= a_k(1 + r + r^2 + r^3 + \cdots) \end{aligned}$$

The tail of the series, which determines whether the series converges, behaves like a geometric series with ratio r. We know that if $0 \le r < 1$, the geometric series converges, and if $r > 1$, the series diverges, which is the conclusion of the Ratio Test. ◄

EXAMPLE 1 **Using the Ratio Test** Use the Ratio Test to determine whether the following series converge.

a. $\displaystyle\sum_{k=1}^{\infty} \frac{10^k}{k!}$ **b.** $\displaystyle\sum_{k=1}^{\infty} \frac{k^k}{k!}$

SOLUTION In each case, the limit of the ratio of successive terms is determined.

➤ Recall that

$$k! = k \cdot (k-1) \cdots 2 \cdot 1.$$

Therefore,

$$(k+1)! = (k+1)k!.$$

a. $$\begin{aligned} r = \lim_{k\to\infty} \frac{a_{k+1}}{a_k} &= \lim_{k\to\infty} \frac{10^{k+1}/(k+1)!}{10^k/k!} && \text{Substitute } a_{k+1} \text{ and } a_k. \\ &= \lim_{k\to\infty} \frac{10^{k+1}}{10^k} \cdot \frac{k!}{(k+1)k!} && \text{Invert and multiply.} \\ &= \lim_{k\to\infty} \frac{10}{k+1} = 0 && \text{Simplify and evaluate the limit.} \end{aligned}$$

Because $r = 0$, the series converges by the Ratio Test.

b. $$\begin{aligned} r = \lim_{k\to\infty} \frac{a_{k+1}}{a_k} &= \lim_{k\to\infty} \frac{(k+1)^{k+1}/(k+1)!}{k^k/k!} && \text{Substitute } a_{k+1} \text{ and } a_k. \\ &= \lim_{k\to\infty} \left(\frac{k+1}{k}\right)^k && \text{Simplify.} \\ &= \lim_{k\to\infty} \left(1 + \frac{1}{k}\right)^k = e && \text{Simplify and evaluate the limit.} \end{aligned}$$

➤ Recall from Section 7.6 that $\displaystyle\lim_{k\to\infty}\left(1 + \frac{1}{k}\right)^k = e \approx 2.718.$

Because $r = e > 1$, the series diverges by the Ratio Test. Alternatively, we could have noted that $\lim_{k\to\infty} k^k/k! = \infty$ (Section 9.2) and used the Divergence Test to reach the same conclusion.

Related Exercises 9–18 ◄

QUICK CHECK 1 Evaluate $10!/9!$, $(k+2)!/k!$, and $k!/(k+1)!$ ◄

The Root Test

Occasionally a series arises for which none of the preceding tests gives a conclusive result. In these situations, the Root Test may be the tool that is needed.

THEOREM 9.15 **The Root Test**

Let $\sum a_k$ be an infinite series with nonnegative terms and let $\rho = \lim_{k\to\infty} \sqrt[k]{a_k}$.

1. If $0 \le \rho < 1$, the series converges.
2. If $\rho > 1$ (including $\rho = \infty$), the series diverges.
3. If $\rho = 1$, the test is inconclusive.

Proof (outline) Assume that the limit ρ exists. If k is large, we have $\rho \approx \sqrt[k]{a_k}$ or $a_k \approx \rho^k$. For large values of k, the tail of the series, which determines whether a series converges, behaves as

$$a_k + a_{k+1} + a_{k+2} + \cdots \approx \rho^k + \rho^{k+1} + \rho^{k+2} + \cdots$$

Therefore, the tail of the series is approximately a geometric series with ratio ρ. If $0 \leq \rho < 1$, the geometric series converges, and if $\rho > 1$, the series diverges, which is the conclusion of the Root Test. ◀

EXAMPLE 2 **Using the Root Test** Use the Root Test to determine whether the following series converge.

a. $\displaystyle\sum_{k=1}^{\infty}\left(\frac{4k^2-3}{7k^2+6}\right)^k$ **b.** $\displaystyle\sum_{k=1}^{\infty}\frac{2^k}{k^{10}}$

SOLUTION

a. The required limit is

$$\rho = \lim_{k\to\infty}\sqrt[k]{\left(\frac{4k^2-3}{7k^2+6}\right)^k} = \lim_{k\to\infty}\frac{4k^2-3}{7k^2+6} = \frac{4}{7}$$

Because $0 \leq \rho < 1$, the series converges by the Root Test.

b. In this case,

$$\rho = \lim_{k\to\infty}\sqrt[k]{\frac{2^k}{k^{10}}} = \lim_{k\to\infty}\frac{2}{k^{10/k}} = \lim_{k\to\infty}\frac{2}{(k^{1/k})^{10}} = 2 \qquad \lim_{k\to\infty} k^{1/k} = 1$$

Because $\rho > 1$, the series diverges by the Root Test.

We could have used the Ratio Test for both series in this example, but the Root Test is easier to apply in each case. In part (b), the Divergence Test leads to the same conclusion.

Related Exercises 19–26 ◀

The Comparison Test

Tests that use known series to test unknown series are called *comparison tests*. The first test is the Basic Comparison Test or simply the Comparison Test.

➤ Whether a series converges depends on the behavior of terms in the tail (large values of the index). So the inequalities $0 < a_k \leq b_k$ and $0 < b_k \leq a_k$ need not hold for all terms of the series. They must hold for all $k > N$ for some positive integer N.

THEOREM 9.16 Comparison Test

Let Σa_k and Σb_k be series with positive terms.

1. If $0 < a_k \leq b_k$ and Σb_k converges, then Σa_k converges.
2. If $0 < b_k \leq a_k$ and Σb_k diverges, then Σa_k diverges.

Proof Assume that Σb_k converges, which means that Σb_k has a finite value B. The sequence of partial sums for Σa_k satisfies

$$S_n = \sum_{k=1}^{n} a_k \leq \sum_{k=1}^{n} b_k \qquad a_k \leq b_k$$

$$< \sum_{k=1}^{\infty} b_k \qquad \text{Positive terms are added to a finite sum.}$$

$$= B \qquad \text{Value of series}$$

Therefore, the sequence of partial sums for Σa_k is increasing and bounded above by B. By the Bounded Monotonic Sequence Theorem (Theorem 9.5), the sequence of partial sums of $\sum a_k$ has a limit, which implies that $\sum a_k$ converges. The second case of the theorem is proved in a similar way. ◄

The Comparison Test is illustrated with graphs of sequences of partial sums. Consider the series

$$\sum_{k=1}^{\infty} a_k = \sum_{k=1}^{\infty} \frac{1}{k^2 + 10} \quad \text{and} \quad \sum_{k=1}^{\infty} b_k = \sum_{k=1}^{\infty} \frac{1}{k^2}.$$

Because $\frac{1}{k^2 + 10} < \frac{1}{k^2}$, it follows that $a_k < b_k$ for $k \geq 1$. Furthermore, $\sum b_k$ is a convergent p-series. By the Comparison Test, we conclude that $\sum a_k$ also converges (Figure 9.32). The second case of the Comparison Test is illustrated with the series

$$\sum_{k=4}^{\infty} a_k = \sum_{k=4}^{\infty} \frac{1}{\sqrt{k} - 3} \quad \text{and} \quad \sum_{k=4}^{\infty} b_k = \sum_{k=4}^{\infty} \frac{1}{\sqrt{k}}.$$

Now $\frac{1}{\sqrt{k}} < \frac{1}{\sqrt{k} - 3}$ for $k \geq 4$. Therefore, $b_k < a_k$ for $k \geq 4$. Because $\sum b_k$ is a divergent p-series, by the Comparison Test, $\sum a_k$ also diverges. Figure 9.33 shows that the sequence of partial sums for $\sum a_k$ lies above the sequence of partial sums for $\sum b_k$. Because the sequence of partial sums for $\sum b_k$ diverges, the sequence of partial sums for $\sum a_k$ also diverges.

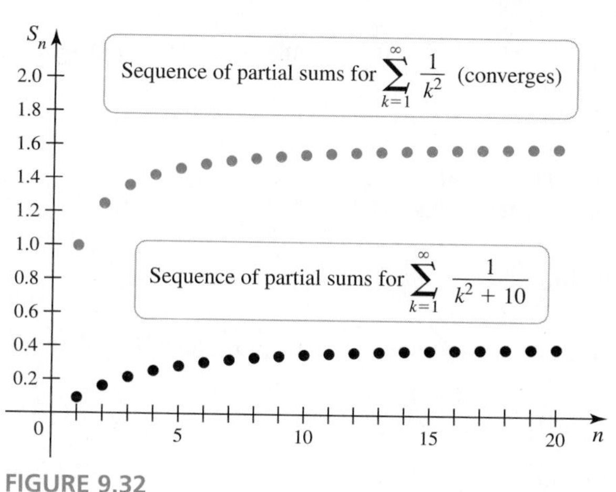

FIGURE 9.32

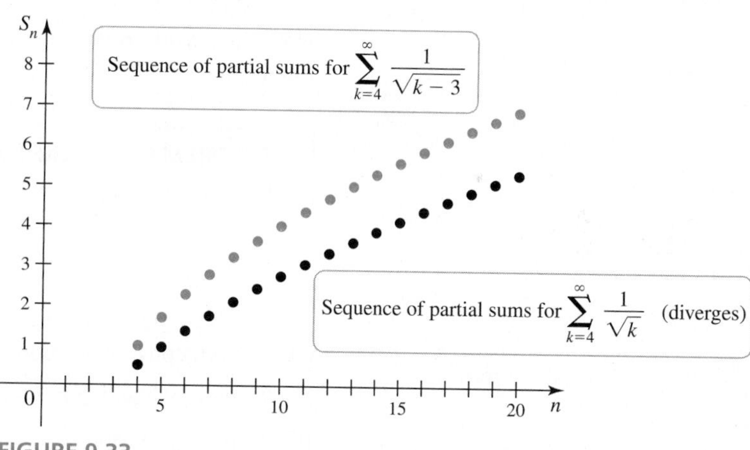

FIGURE 9.33

The key in using the Comparison Test is finding an appropriate comparison series. Plenty of practice will enable you to spot patterns and choose good comparison series.

EXAMPLE 3 **Using the Comparison Test** Determine whether the following series converge.

a. $\sum_{k=1}^{\infty} \frac{k^3}{2k^4 - 1}$ **b.** $\sum_{k=2}^{\infty} \frac{\ln k}{k^3}$

SOLUTION In using comparison tests, it's helpful to get a feel for how the terms of the given series are decreasing (if they are not decreasing, the series diverges).

a. As we go farther and farther out in this series ($k \to \infty$), the terms behave like

$$\frac{k^3}{2k^4 - 1} \approx \frac{k^3}{2k^4} = \frac{1}{2k}.$$

So a reasonable choice for a comparison series is the divergent series $\sum \frac{1}{2k}$. We must now show that the terms of the given series are *greater* than the terms of the comparison

➤ If $\sum a_k$ diverges, then $\sum ca_k$ also diverges for any constant $c \neq 0$ (Exercise 55 of Section 9.4). In Example 3a, one could use either $\sum \frac{1}{2k}$ or $\sum \frac{1}{k}$, both of which diverge, for the comparison series. The first choice makes the required inequality easier to prove.

series. It is done by noting that $2k^4 - 1 < 2k^4$. Inverting both sides, we have

$$\frac{1}{2k^4 - 1} > \frac{1}{2k^4}, \quad \text{which implies that} \quad \frac{k^3}{2k^4 - 1} > \frac{k^3}{2k^4} = \frac{1}{2k}.$$

Because $\sum \frac{1}{2k}$ diverges, case (2) of the Comparison Test implies that the given series also diverges.

b. We note that $\ln k < k$ for $k \geq 1$ and then divide by k^3:

$$\frac{\ln k}{k^3} < \frac{k}{k^3} = \frac{1}{k^2}.$$

Therefore, the appropriate comparison series is the convergent p-series $\sum \frac{1}{k^2}$. Because $\sum \frac{1}{k^2}$ converges, the given series converges.

Related Exercises 27–38 ◄

QUICK CHECK 2 Explain why it is difficult to use the divergent series $\Sigma 1/k$ as a comparison series to test $\Sigma 1/(k + 1)$. ◄

The Limit Comparison Test

The Comparison Test should be tried if there is an obvious comparison series and the necessary inequality is easily established. Notice, however, that if the series in Example 3a were $\sum_{k=1}^{\infty} \frac{k^3}{2k^4 + 10}$ instead of $\sum_{k=1}^{\infty} \frac{k^3}{2k^4 - 1}$, then the comparison to the harmonic series would not work. Rather than fiddling with inequalities, it is often easier to use a more refined test called the *Limit Comparison Test.*

> **THEOREM 9.17 The Limit Comparison Test**
> Let Σa_k and Σb_k be series with positive terms and let
>
> $$\lim_{k \to \infty} \frac{a_k}{b_k} = L.$$
>
> **1.** If $0 < L < \infty$ (that is, L is a finite positive number), then Σa_k and Σb_k either both converge or both diverge.
> **2.** If $L = 0$ and Σb_k converges, then Σa_k converges.
> **3.** If $L = \infty$ and Σb_k diverges, then Σa_k diverges.

Proof Recall the definition of $\lim_{k \to \infty} \frac{a_k}{b_k} = L$: Given any $\varepsilon > 0$, $\left| \frac{a_k}{b_k} - L \right| < \varepsilon$ provided k is sufficiently large. In this case, let's take $\varepsilon = L/2$. It then follows that for sufficiently large k, $\left| \frac{a_k}{b_k} - L \right| < \frac{L}{2}$, or (removing the absolute value) $-\frac{L}{2} < \frac{a_k}{b_k} - L < \frac{L}{2}$. Adding L to all terms in these inequalities, we have

$$\frac{L}{2} < \frac{a_k}{b_k} < \frac{3L}{2}.$$

➤ Recall that $|x| < a$ is equivalent to $-a < x < a$.

These inequalities imply that, for sufficiently large k,

$$\frac{Lb_k}{2} < a_k < \frac{3Lb_k}{2}.$$

We see that the terms of Σa_k are sandwiched between multiples of the terms of Σb_k. By the Comparison Test, it follows that the two series converge or diverge together. Cases (2) and (3) ($L = 0$ or $L = \infty$, respectively) are treated in Exercise 69. ◄

QUICK CHECK 3 For case (1) of the Limit Comparison Test, we must have $0 < L < \infty$. Why can either a_k or b_k be chosen as the known comparison series? That is, why can L be the limit of a_k/b_k or b_k/a_k? ◄

EXAMPLE 4 **Using the Limit Comparison Test** Determine whether the following series converge.

a. $\displaystyle\sum_{k=1}^{\infty} \frac{k^4 - 2k^2 + 3}{2k^6 - k + 5}$ **b.** $\displaystyle\sum_{k=1}^{\infty} \frac{\ln k}{k^2}$

SOLUTION In both cases, we must find a comparison series whose terms behave like the terms of the given series as $k \to \infty$.

a. As $k \to \infty$, a rational function behaves like the ratio of the leading (highest-power) terms. In this case, as $k \to \infty$,

$$\frac{k^4 - 2k^2 + 3}{2k^6 - k + 5} \approx \frac{k^4}{2k^6} = \frac{1}{2k^2}.$$

Therefore, a reasonable comparison series is the convergent p-series $\displaystyle\sum_{k=1}^{\infty} \frac{1}{k^2}$ (the factor of 2 does not affect whether the given series converges). Having chosen a comparison series, we compute the limit L:

$$\begin{aligned} L &= \lim_{k\to\infty} \frac{(k^4 - 2k^2 + 3)/(2k^6 - k + 5)}{1/k^2} && \text{Ratio of terms of series} \\ &= \lim_{k\to\infty} \frac{k^2(k^4 - 2k^2 + 3)}{2k^6 - k + 5} && \text{Simplify.} \\ &= \lim_{k\to\infty} \frac{k^6 - 2k^4 + 3k^2}{2k^6 - k + 5} = \frac{1}{2} && \text{Simplify and evaluate the limit.} \end{aligned}$$

We see that $0 < L < \infty$; therefore, the given series converges.

b. Why is this series interesting? We know that $\displaystyle\sum_{k=1}^{\infty} \frac{1}{k^2}$ converges and that $\displaystyle\sum_{k=1}^{\infty} \frac{1}{k}$ diverges. The given series $\displaystyle\sum_{k=1}^{\infty} \frac{\ln k}{k^2}$ is "between" these two series. This observation suggests that we use either $\displaystyle\sum_{k=1}^{\infty} \frac{1}{k^2}$ or $\displaystyle\sum_{k=1}^{\infty} \frac{1}{k}$ as a comparison series. In the first case, letting $a_k = \ln k/k^2$ and $b_k = 1/k^2$, we find that

$$L = \lim_{k\to\infty} \frac{a_k}{b_k} = \lim_{k\to\infty} \frac{\ln k/k^2}{1/k^2} = \lim_{k\to\infty} \ln k = \infty.$$

Case (3) of the Limit Comparison Test does not apply here because the comparison series $\displaystyle\sum_{k=1}^{\infty} \frac{1}{k^2}$ converges. So the test is inconclusive.

If, instead, we use the comparison series $\sum b_k = \sum \frac{1}{k}$, then

$$L = \lim_{k\to\infty} \frac{a_k}{b_k} = \lim_{k\to\infty} \frac{\ln k/k^2}{1/k} = \lim_{k\to\infty} \frac{\ln k}{k} = 0.$$

Case (2) of the Limit Comparison Test does not apply here because the comparison series $\displaystyle\sum_{k=1}^{\infty} \frac{1}{k}$ diverges. Again, the test is inconclusive.

With a bit more cunning, the Limit Comparison Test becomes conclusive. A series that lies "between" $\sum_{k=1}^{\infty} \frac{1}{k^2}$ and $\sum_{k=1}^{\infty} \frac{1}{k}$ is the convergent p-series $\sum_{k=1}^{\infty} \frac{1}{k^{3/2}}$; we try it as a comparison series. Letting $a_k = \ln k/k^2$ and $b_k = 1/k^{3/2}$, we find that

$$L = \lim_{k\to\infty} \frac{a_k}{b_k} = \lim_{k\to\infty} \frac{\ln k/k^2}{1/k^{3/2}} = \lim_{k\to\infty} \frac{\ln k}{\sqrt{k}} = 0.$$

(This limit is evaluated using l'Hôpital's Rule or by recalling that $\ln k$ grows more slowly than any positive power of k.) Now case (2) of the limit comparison test applies; the comparison series $\sum \frac{1}{k^{3/2}}$ converges, so the given series converges.

Related Exercises 27–38 ◀

Guidelines

We close by outlining a procedure that puts the various convergence tests in perspective. Here is a reasonable course of action when testing a series of positive terms $\sum a_k$ for convergence.

1. Begin with the Divergence Test. If you show that $\lim_{k\to\infty} a_k \neq 0$, then the series diverges and your work is finished. The order of growth rates of sequences given in Section 9.2 is useful for evaluating $\lim_{k\to\infty} a_k$.
2. Is the series a special series? Recall the convergence properties for the following series.
   - Geometric series: $\sum ar^k$ converges if $|r| < 1$ and diverges for $|r| \geq 1$.
   - p-series: $\sum \frac{1}{k^p}$ converges for $p > 1$ and diverges for $p \leq 1$.
   - Check also for a telescoping series.
3. If the general kth term of the series looks like a function you can integrate, then try the Integral Test.
4. If the general kth term of the series involves $k!$, k^k, or a^k, where a is a constant, the Ratio Test is advisable. Series with k in an exponent may yield to the Root Test.
5. If the general kth term of the series is a rational function of k (or a root of a rational function), use the Comparison or the Limit Comparison Test. Use the families of series given in Step 2 as comparison series.

These guidelines will help, but in the end, convergence tests are mastered through practice. It's your turn.

SECTION 9.5 EXERCISES

Review Questions

1. Explain how the Ratio Test works.
2. Explain how the Root Test works.
3. Explain how the Limit Comparison Test works.
4. What is the first test you should use in analyzing the convergence of a series?
5. What tests are advisable if the series involves a factorial term?
6. What tests are best for the series $\sum a_k$ when a_k is a rational function of k?
7. Explain why, with a series of positive terms, the sequence of partial sums is an increasing sequence.
8. Do the tests discussed in this section tell you the value of the series? Explain.

Basic Skills

9–18. The Ratio Test *Use the Ratio Test to determine whether the following series converge.*

9. $\sum_{k=1}^{\infty} \frac{1}{k!}$
10. $\sum_{k=1}^{\infty} \frac{2^k}{k!}$
11. $\sum_{k=1}^{\infty} \frac{k^2}{4^k}$
12. $\sum_{k=1}^{\infty} \frac{2^k}{k^k}$
13. $\sum_{k=1}^{\infty} ke^{-k}$
14. $\sum_{k=1}^{\infty} \frac{k!}{k^k}$
15. $\sum_{k=1}^{\infty} \frac{2^k}{k^{99}}$
16. $\sum_{k=1}^{\infty} \frac{k^6}{k!}$
17. $\sum_{k=1}^{\infty} \frac{(k!)^2}{(2k)!}$
18. $\sum_{k=1}^{\infty} k^4 2^{-k}$

19–26. The Root Test *Use the Root Test to determine whether the following series converge.*

19. $\sum_{k=1}^{\infty} \left(\frac{4k^3 + k}{9k^3 + k + 1}\right)^k$
20. $\sum_{k=1}^{\infty} \left(\frac{k + 1}{2k}\right)^k$
21. $\sum_{k=1}^{\infty} \frac{k^2}{2^k}$
22. $\sum_{k=1}^{\infty} \left(1 + \frac{3}{k}\right)^{k^2}$
23. $\sum_{k=1}^{\infty} \left(\frac{k}{k + 1}\right)^{2k^2}$
24. $\sum_{k=1}^{\infty} \left(\frac{1}{\ln (k + 1)}\right)^k$
25. $1 + \left(\frac{1}{2}\right)^2 + \left(\frac{1}{3}\right)^3 + \left(\frac{1}{4}\right)^4 + \cdots$
26. $\left(\frac{1}{2}\right)^2 + \left(\frac{2}{3}\right)^3 + \left(\frac{3}{4}\right)^4 + \cdots$

27–38. Comparison tests *Use the Comparison Test or Limit Comparison Test to determine whether the following series converge.*

27. $\sum_{k=1}^{\infty} \frac{1}{k^2 + 4}$
28. $\sum_{k=1}^{\infty} \frac{k^2 + k - 1}{k^4 + 4k^2 - 3}$
29. $\sum_{k=1}^{\infty} \frac{k^2 - 1}{k^3 + 4}$
30. $\sum_{k=1}^{\infty} \frac{0.0001}{k + 4}$
31. $\sum_{k=1}^{\infty} \frac{1}{k^{3/2} + 1}$
32. $\sum_{k=1}^{\infty} \sqrt{\frac{k}{k^3 + 1}}$
33. $\sum_{k=1}^{\infty} \frac{\sin (1/k)}{k^2}$
34. $\sum_{k=1}^{\infty} \frac{1}{3^k - 2^k}$
35. $\sum_{k=1}^{\infty} \frac{1}{2k - \sqrt{k}}$
36. $\sum_{k=1}^{\infty} \frac{1}{k\sqrt{k + 2}}$
37. $\sum_{k=1}^{\infty} \frac{\sqrt[3]{k^2 + 1}}{\sqrt{k^3 + 2}}$
38. $\sum_{k=2}^{\infty} \frac{1}{(k \ln k)^2}$

Further Explorations

39. **Explain why or why not** Determine whether the following statements are true and give an explanation or counterexample.
    a. Suppose that $0 < a_k < b_k$. If $\sum a_k$ converges, then $\sum b_k$ converges.
    b. Suppose that $0 < a_k < b_k$. If $\sum a_k$ diverges, then $\sum b_k$ diverges.
    c. Suppose $0 < b_k < c_k < a_k$. If $\sum a_k$ converges, then $\sum b_k$ and $\sum c_k$ converge.

40–57. Choose your test *Use the test of your choice to determine whether the following series converge.*

40. $\sum_{k=1}^{\infty} \frac{(k!)^3}{(3k)!}$
41. $\sum_{k=1}^{\infty} \left(\frac{1}{k} + 2^{-k}\right)$
42. $\sum_{k=2}^{\infty} \frac{5 \ln k}{k}$
43. $\sum_{k=1}^{\infty} \frac{2^k k!}{k^k}$
44. $\sum_{k=1}^{\infty} \left(1 - \frac{1}{k}\right)^{k^2}$
45. $\sum_{k=1}^{\infty} \frac{k^8}{k^{11} + 3}$
46. $\sum_{k=1}^{\infty} \frac{1}{(1 + p)^k},\ p > 0$
47. $\sum_{k=1}^{\infty} \frac{1}{k^{1+p}},\ p > 0$
48. $\sum_{k=2}^{\infty} \frac{1}{k^2 \ln k}$
49. $\sum_{k=1}^{\infty} \ln \left(\frac{k + 2}{k + 1}\right)$
50. $\sum_{k=1}^{\infty} k^{-1/k}$
51. $\sum_{k=2}^{\infty} \frac{1}{k^{\ln k}}$
52. $\sum_{k=1}^{\infty} \sin^2 \left(\frac{1}{k}\right)$
53. $\sum_{k=1}^{\infty} \tan \left(\frac{1}{k}\right)$
54. $\sum_{k=2}^{\infty} 100k^{-k}$
55. $\frac{1}{1 \cdot 3} + \frac{1}{3 \cdot 5} + \frac{1}{5 \cdot 7} + \cdots$
56. $\frac{1}{2^2} + \frac{2}{3^2} + \frac{3}{4^2} + \cdots$
57. $\frac{1}{1!} + \frac{4}{2!} + \frac{9}{3!} + \frac{16}{4!} + \cdots$

58–65. Convergence parameter *Find the values of the parameter p for which the following series converge.*

58. $\sum_{k=2}^{\infty} \frac{1}{(\ln k)^p}$
59. $\sum_{k=2}^{\infty} \frac{\ln k}{k^p}$
60. $\sum_{k=2}^{\infty} \frac{1}{k \ln k (\ln \ln k)^p}$
61. $\sum_{k=2}^{\infty} \left(\frac{\ln k}{k}\right)^p$
62. $\sum_{k=0}^{\infty} \frac{k! p^k}{(k + 1)^k}$
63. $\sum_{k=1}^{\infty} \frac{1 \cdot 3 \cdot 5 \cdots (2k - 1)}{kp^{k+1} k!}$
64. $\sum_{k=1}^{\infty} \ln \left(\frac{k}{k + 1}\right)^p$
65. $\sum_{k=1}^{\infty} \left(1 - \frac{p}{k}\right)^k$

66. **Series of squares** Prove that if $\sum a_k$ is a convergent series of positive terms, then the series $\sum a_k^2$ also converges.
67. **Geometric series revisited** We know from Section 9.3 that the geometric series $\sum r^k$ converges if $|r| < 1$ and diverges if $|r| > 1$. Prove these facts using the Integral Test, the Ratio Test, and the Root Test. What can be determined about the geometric series using the Divergence Test?
68. **Two sine series** Determine whether the following series converge.
    a. $\sum_{k=1}^{\infty} \sin \left(\frac{1}{k}\right)$
    b. $\sum_{k=1}^{\infty} \frac{1}{k} \sin \left(\frac{1}{k}\right)$

Additional Exercises

69. **Limit Comparison Test proof** Use the proof of case (1) of the Limit Comparison Test to prove cases (2) and (3).

70–75. A glimpse ahead to power series *Use the Ratio Test to determine the values of $x \geq 0$ for which each series converges.*

70. $\sum_{k=1}^{\infty} \frac{x^k}{k!}$ **71.** $\sum_{k=0}^{\infty} x^k$ **72.** $\sum_{k=1}^{\infty} \frac{x^k}{k}$

73. $\sum_{k=1}^{\infty} \frac{x^k}{k^2}$ **74.** $\sum_{k=1}^{\infty} \frac{x^{2k}}{k^2}$ **75.** $\sum_{k=1}^{\infty} \frac{x^k}{2^k}$

76. Infinite products An infinite product $P = a_1 a_2 a_3 \ldots$, which is denoted $\prod_{k=1}^{\infty} a_k$, is the limit of the *sequence of partial products* $\{a_1, a_1 a_2, a_1 a_2 a_3, \ldots\}$.

a. Show that the infinite product converges (which means its sequence of partial products converges) provided the series $\sum_{k=1}^{\infty} \ln a_k$ converges.

b. Consider the infinite product

$$P = \prod_{k=2}^{\infty}\left(1 - \frac{1}{k^2}\right) = \frac{3}{4} \cdot \frac{8}{9} \cdot \frac{15}{16} \cdot \frac{24}{25} \cdots.$$

Write out the first few terms of the sequence of partial products,

$$P_n = \prod_{k=2}^{n}\left(1 - \frac{1}{k^2}\right)$$

(for example, $P_2 = \frac{3}{4}, P_3 = \frac{2}{3}$). Write out enough terms to determine the value of the product, which is $\lim_{n\to\infty} P_n$.

c. Use the results of parts (a) and (b) to evaluate the series

$$\sum_{k=2}^{\infty} \ln\left(1 - \frac{1}{k^2}\right).$$

77. Infinite products Use the ideas of Exercise 76 to evaluate the following infinite products.

a. $\prod_{k=0}^{\infty} e^{1/2^k} = 1 \cdot e^{1/2} \cdot e^{1/4} \cdot e^{1/8} \cdots$

b. $\prod_{k=2}^{\infty}\left(1 - \frac{1}{k}\right) = \frac{1}{2} \cdot \frac{2}{3} \cdot \frac{3}{4} \cdot \frac{4}{5} \cdots$

78. An early limit Working in the early 1600s, the mathematicians Wallis, Pascal, and Fermat were attempting to determine the area of the region under the curve $y = x^p$ between $x = 0$ and $x = 1$, where p is a positive integer. Using arguments that predated the Fundamental Theorem of Calculus, they were able to prove that

$$\lim_{n\to\infty} \frac{1}{n} \sum_{k=0}^{n-1} \left(\frac{k}{n}\right)^p = \frac{1}{p+1}.$$

Use what you know about Riemann sums and integrals to verify this limit.

QUICK CHECK ANSWERS

1. 10; $(k + 2)(k + 1)$; $1/(k + 1)$ **2.** To use the Comparison Test, we would need to show that $1/(k + 1) > 1/k$, which is not true. **3.** If $\lim_{k\to\infty} \frac{a_k}{b_k} = L$ for $0 < L < \infty$, then $\lim_{k\to\infty} \frac{b_k}{a_k} = \frac{1}{L}$ where $0 < 1/L < \infty$.

9.6 Alternating Series

Our previous discussion focused on infinite series with positive terms, which is certainly an important part of the entire subject. But there are many interesting series with terms of mixed sign. For example, the series

$$1 + \frac{1}{2} - \frac{1}{3} - \frac{1}{4} + \frac{1}{5} + \frac{1}{6} - \frac{1}{7} - \frac{1}{8} + \cdots$$

has the pattern that two positive terms are followed by two negative terms and vice versa. Clearly, infinite series could have a variety of sign patterns, so we need to restrict our attention.

Fortunately, the simplest sign pattern is also the most important. We consider **alternating series** in which the signs strictly alternate, as in the series

$$\sum_{k=1}^{\infty} \frac{(-1)^{k+1}}{k} = 1 - \frac{1}{2} + \frac{1}{3} - \frac{1}{4} + \frac{1}{5} - \frac{1}{6} + \frac{1}{7} - \frac{1}{8} + \cdots.$$

The factor $(-1)^{k+1}$ (or $(-1)^k$) has the pattern $\{\ldots, 1, -1, 1, -1, \ldots\}$ and provides the alternating signs.

Alternating Harmonic Series

Let's see what is different about alternating series by working with the series $\sum_{k=1}^{\infty} \frac{(-1)^{k+1}}{k}$, which is called the **alternating harmonic series**. Recall that this series *without* the alternating signs, $\sum_{k=1}^{\infty} \frac{1}{k}$, is the *divergent* harmonic series. So an immediate question is whether alternating signs change the convergence or divergence of a series.

We investigate this question by looking at the sequence of partial sums for the series. In this case, the first four terms of the sequence of partial sums are

$$S_1 = 1$$

$$S_2 = 1 - \frac{1}{2} = \frac{1}{2}$$

$$S_3 = 1 - \frac{1}{2} + \frac{1}{3} = \frac{5}{6}$$

$$S_4 = 1 - \frac{1}{2} + \frac{1}{3} - \frac{1}{4} = \frac{7}{12}$$

$$\vdots$$

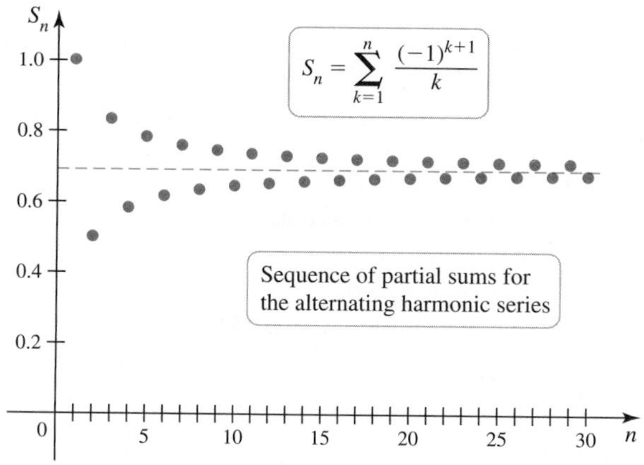

FIGURE 9.34

Plotting the first 30 terms of the sequence of partial sums results in Figure 9.34, which has several noteworthy features.

- The terms of the sequence of partial sums appear to converge to a limit; if they do, it means that, while the harmonic series diverges, the *alternating* harmonic series converges. We will soon learn that taking a divergent series with positive terms and making it an alternating series *may* turn it into a convergent series.
- For series with *positive* terms, the sequence of partial sums is necessarily an increasing sequence. Because the terms of an alternating series alternate in sign, the sequence of partial sums is not increasing.
- Because the sequence of partial sums oscillates, its limit (when it exists) lies between any two consecutive terms.

QUICK CHECK 1 Write out the first few terms of the sequence of partial sums for the alternating series $1 - 2 + 3 - 4 + 5 - 6 + \cdots$. Does this series appear to converge or diverge?

Alternating Series Test

The alternating harmonic series displays many of the properties of all alternating series. We now consider alternating series in general, which are written $\Sigma(-1)^{k+1}a_k$, where $a_k > 0$. The alternating signs are provided by $(-1)^{k+1}$.

With the exception of the Divergence Test, none of the convergence tests for series with positive terms applies to alternating series. The fortunate news is that only one test needs to be used for alternating series—and it is easy to use.

> Depending on the sign of the first term of the series, an alternating series may be written with $(-1)^k$ or $(-1)^{k+1}$.

> Recall that the Divergence Test of Section 9.4 applies to all series: If the terms of *any* series (including an alternating series) do not tend to zero, then the series diverges.

THEOREM 9.18 The Alternating Series Test
The alternating series $\Sigma(-1)^{k+1}a_k$ converges provided

1. the terms of the series are nonincreasing in magnitude ($0 < a_{k+1} \le a_k$ for k greater than some index N) and
2. $\lim_{k \to \infty} a_k = 0$.

The first condition is met by most series of interest, so the main job is to show that the terms approach zero. *There is potential for confusion here. For series of positive terms,*

$\lim_{k\to\infty} a_k = 0$ ***does not*** *imply convergence. For alternating series with nonincreasing terms,* $\lim_{k\to\infty} a_k = 0$ ***does*** *imply convergence.*

Proof The proof is short and instructive; it relies on Figure 9.35. We consider the series in the form

$$\sum_{k=1}^{\infty}(-1)^{k+1}a_k = a_1 - a_2 + a_3 - a_4 + \cdots.$$

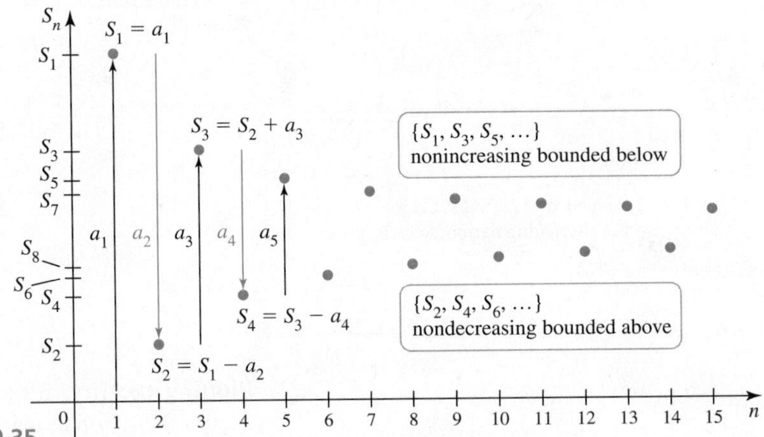

FIGURE 9.35

Because the terms of the series are nonincreasing in magnitude, the even terms of the sequence of partial sums $\{S_{2k}\} = \{S_2, S_4, \ldots\}$ form a nondecreasing sequence that is bounded above by S_1. By the Bounded Monotonic Sequence Theorem (Section 9.2), this sequence must have a limit; call it L. Similarly, the odd terms of the sequence of partial sums $\{S_{2k-1}\} = \{S_1, S_3, \ldots\}$ form a nonincreasing sequence that is bounded below by S_2. By the Bounded Monotonic Sequence Theorem, this sequence has a limit; call it L'. At the moment, we cannot conclude that $L = L'$. However, notice that $S_{2k} = S_{2k-1} + a_{2k}$. By the condition that $\lim_{k\to\infty} a_k = 0$, it follows that

$$\underbrace{\lim_{k\to\infty} S_{2k}}_{L} = \underbrace{\lim_{k\to\infty} S_{2k-1}}_{L'} + \underbrace{\lim_{k\to\infty} a_{2k}}_{0},$$

or $L = L'$. Thus, the sequence of partial sums converges to a (unique) limit and the corresponding alternating series converges to that limit. ◄

Now we can confirm that the alternating harmonic series $\sum_{k=1}^{\infty}\frac{(-1)^{k+1}}{k}$ converges. This fact follows immediately from the Alternating Series Test because the terms $a_k = \frac{1}{k}$ decrease and $\lim_{k\to\infty} a_k = 0$.

➤ $\sum_{k=1}^{\infty}\frac{1}{k}$
- Diverges
- Partial sums increase

$\sum_{k=1}^{\infty}\frac{(-1)^{k+1}}{k}$
- Converges
- Partial sums oscillate

THEOREM 9.19 Alternating Harmonic Series

The alternating harmonic series $\sum_{k=1}^{\infty}\frac{(-1)^{k+1}}{k} = 1 - \frac{1}{2} + \frac{1}{3} - \frac{1}{4} + \frac{1}{5} - \cdots$ converges (even though the harmonic series $\sum_{k=1}^{\infty}\frac{1}{k} = 1 + \frac{1}{2} + \frac{1}{3} + \frac{1}{4} + \frac{1}{5} + \cdots$ diverges).

QUICK CHECK 2 Explain why the value of a convergent alternating series is trapped between successive terms of the sequence of partial sums. ◀

EXAMPLE 1 Alternating Series Test Determine whether the following series converge or diverge.

a. $\sum_{k=1}^{\infty} \frac{(-1)^{k+1}}{k^2}$ **b.** $2 - \frac{3}{2} + \frac{4}{3} - \frac{5}{4} + \cdots$ **c.** $\sum_{k=2}^{\infty} \frac{(-1)^k \ln k}{k}$

SOLUTION

a. The terms of this series decrease in magnitude for $k \geq 1$. Furthermore,

$$\lim_{k\to\infty} a_k = \lim_{k\to\infty} \frac{1}{k^2} = 0.$$

Therefore, the series converges.

b. The magnitudes of the terms of this series are $a_k = \frac{k+1}{k} = 1 + \frac{1}{k}$. While these terms decrease, they approach 1, not 0, as $k \to \infty$. By the Divergence Test, the series diverges.

c. The first step is to show that the terms decrease in magnitude after some fixed term of the series. One way to proceed is to look at the function $f(x) = \frac{\ln x}{x}$, which generates the terms of the series. By the Quotient Rule, $f'(x) = \frac{1 - \ln x}{x^2}$. The fact that $f'(x) < 0$ for $x > e$ implies that the terms $\frac{\ln k}{k}$ decrease for $k \geq 3$. As long as the terms of the series decrease for all k greater than some fixed integer, the first condition of the test is met. Furthermore, using l'Hôpital's Rule or the fact that $\{\ln k\}$ increases more slowly than $\{k\}$ (Section 9.2), we see that

$$\lim_{k\to\infty} a_k = \lim_{k\to\infty} \frac{\ln k}{k} = 0.$$

The conditions of the Alternating Series Test are met and the series converges.

Related Exercises 11–24 ◀

➤ The absolute value is included in the remainder because with alternating series we have $S > S_n$ for some values of n and $S < S_n$ for other values of n (unlike series with positive terms, in which $S > S_n$ for all n).

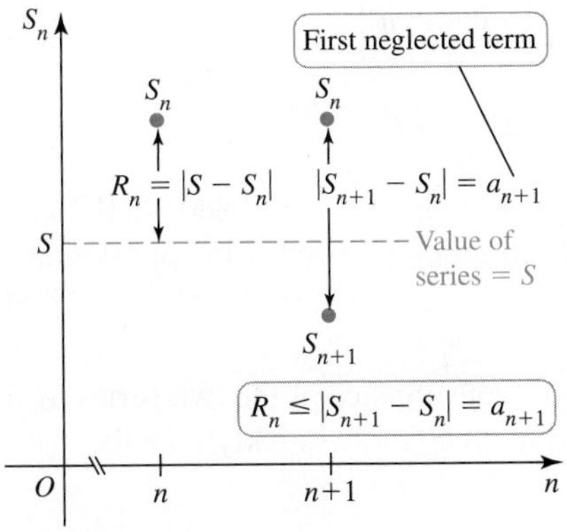

Remainders in Alternating Series

Recall that if a series converges to a value S, then the remainder is $R_n = |S - S_n|$, where S_n is the sum of the first n terms of the series. The remainder is the *absolute error* in approximating S by S_n.

An upper bound on the remainder in an alternating series is found by observing that the value of the series is always trapped between successive terms of the sequence of partial sums. Therefore, as shown in Figure 9.36,

$$R_n = |S - S_n| \leq |S_{n+1} - S_n| = a_{n+1}.$$

This argument is a proof of the following theorem.

FIGURE 9.36

THEOREM 9.20 Remainder in Alternating Series
Let $R_n = |S - S_n|$ be the remainder in approximating the value of a convergent alternating series $\sum_{k=1}^{\infty}(-1)^{k+1}a_k$ by the sum of its first n terms. Then $R_n \leq a_{n+1}$.
In other words, the remainder is less than or equal to the magnitude of the first neglected term.

EXAMPLE 2 **Remainder in an alternating series** How many terms of the following series are required to approximate the value of the series with a remainder less than 10^{-6}? The exact values of the series are given but are not needed to answer the question (these values are confirmed in Chapter 10).

a. $\ln 2 = 1 - \frac{1}{2} + \frac{1}{3} - \frac{1}{4} + \cdots = \sum_{k=1}^{\infty} \frac{(-1)^{k+1}}{k}$

b. $e^{-1} - 1 = -1 + \frac{1}{2!} - \frac{1}{3!} + \frac{1}{4!} - \cdots = \sum_{k=1}^{\infty} \frac{(-1)^k}{k!}$

SOLUTION

a. The series is expressed as the sum of the first n terms plus the remainder:

$$\sum_{k=1}^{\infty} \frac{(-1)^{k+1}}{k} = \underbrace{1 - \frac{1}{2} + \frac{1}{3} - \frac{1}{4} + \cdots + \frac{(-1)^{n+1}}{n}}_{S_n = \text{ the sum of the first } n \text{ terms}} + \underbrace{\frac{(-1)^{n+2}}{n+1}}_{R_n = |S - S_n| \text{ is less than the magnitude of this term}} + \cdots.$$

The remainder is less than or equal to the magnitude of the $(n + 1)$st term:

$$R_n = |S - S_n| \le a_{n+1} = \frac{1}{n+1}.$$

To ensure that the remainder is less than 10^{-6}, we require that

$$a_{n+1} = \frac{1}{n+1} < 10^{-6}, \quad \text{or} \quad n + 1 > 10^6.$$

Therefore, it takes 1 million terms of the series to approximate ln 2 with a remainder less than 10^{-6}.

b. The series is expressed as the sum of the first n terms plus the remainder:

$$\sum_{k=1}^{\infty} \frac{(-1)^k}{k!} = \underbrace{-1 + \frac{1}{2!} - \frac{1}{3!} + \frac{1}{4!} - \cdots + \frac{(-1)^n}{n!}}_{S_n = \text{ the sum of the first } n \text{ terms}} + \underbrace{\frac{(-1)^{n+1}}{(n+1)!}}_{R_n = |S - S_n| \text{ is less than the magnitude of this term}} + \cdots.$$

➤ The sum of the first nine terms of $\sum_{k=1}^{\infty} \frac{(-1)^k}{k!}$ is $S_9 = \sum_{k=1}^{9} \frac{(-1)^k}{k!} \approx -0.632120811$. A calculator gives $S = e^{-1} - 1 \approx -0.632120559$. Note that the remainder satisfies $R_n = |S - S_n| = 0.000000252$, which is less than 10^{-6}, as claimed in Example 2b.

The remainder satisfies

$$R_n = |S - S_n| \le a_{n+1} = \frac{1}{(n+1)!}.$$

To ensure that the remainder is less than 10^{-6}, we require that

$$a_{n+1} = \frac{1}{(n+1)!} < 10^{-6}, \quad \text{or} \quad (n+1)! > 10^6.$$

A bit of experimentation (or a table of factorials) reveals that $9! = 362{,}880 < 10^6$ and $10! = 3{,}628{,}800 > 10^6$. Therefore, nine terms of the series are needed to approximate $e^{-1} - 1$ with a remainder less than 10^{-6}.

Related Exercises 25–38 ◀

QUICK CHECK 3 Compare and comment on the speed of convergence of the two series in the previous example. Why does one series converge so much more quickly than the other? ◀

Absolute and Conditional Convergence

In this final segment, some terminology is introduced that is needed in Chapter 10. We now let the notation Σa_k denote any series—a series of positive terms, an alternating series, or even a more general infinite series.

Look again at the alternating harmonic series $\Sigma(-1)^{k+1}/k$, which converges. The corresponding series of positive terms, $\Sigma 1/k$, is the harmonic series, which diverges. We also saw in Example 1a that the alternating series $\Sigma(-1)^{k+1}/k^2$ converges, and the corresponding p-series of positive terms $\Sigma 1/k^2$ also converges. These examples illustrate that removing the alternating signs in a convergent series may or may not result in a convergent series. The terminology that we now introduce distinguishes these cases.

DEFINITION Absolute and Conditional Convergence

Assume the infinite series Σa_k converges. The series Σa_k **converges absolutely** if the series $\Sigma |a_k|$ converges. Otherwise, the series Σa_k **converges conditionally**.

The series $\Sigma(-1)^{k+1}/k^2$ is an example of an absolutely convergent series because the series of absolute values,

$$\sum_{k=1}^{\infty} \left| \frac{(-1)^{k+1}}{k^2} \right| = \sum_{k=1}^{\infty} \frac{1}{k^2},$$

is a convergent p-series. In this case, removing the alternating signs in the series does *not* affect its convergence.

On the other hand, the convergent alternating harmonic series $\Sigma(-1)^{k+1}/k$ has the property that the corresponding series of absolute values,

$$\sum_{k=1}^{\infty} \left| \frac{(-1)^{k+1}}{k} \right| = \sum_{k=1}^{\infty} \frac{1}{k},$$

does *not* converge. In this case, removing the alternating signs in the series *does* affect convergence, so this series does not converge absolutely. Instead, we say it converges conditionally. A convergent series (such as $\Sigma(-1)^{k+1}/k$) may not converge absolutely. It is, however, true that if a series converges absolutely, then it converges.

THEOREM 9.21 Absolute Convergence Implies Convergence

If $\Sigma |a_k|$ converges, then Σa_k converges (absolute convergence implies convergence). If Σa_k diverges, then $\Sigma |a_k|$ diverges.

Proof Because $|a_k| = a_k$ or $|a_k| = -a_k$, it follows that $0 \le |a_k| + a_k \le 2|a_k|$. By assumption $\Sigma |a_k|$ converges, which, in turn, implies that $2\Sigma |a_k|$ converges. Using the Comparison Test and the inequality $0 \le |a_k| + a_k \le 2|a_k|$, it follows that $\Sigma(a_k + |a_k|)$ converges. Now note that

$$\sum a_k = \sum (a_k + |a_k| - |a_k|) = \underbrace{\sum (a_k + |a_k|)}_{\text{converges}} - \underbrace{\sum |a_k|}_{\text{converges}}.$$

We see that Σa_k is the sum of two convergent series, so it also converges. The second statement of the theorem is logically equivalent to the first statement. ◄

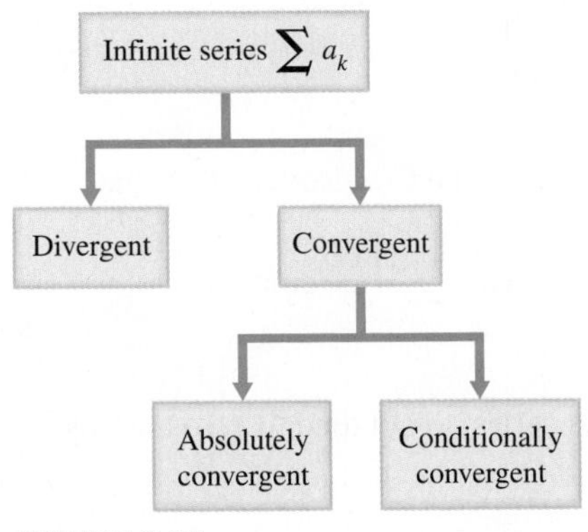

FIGURE 9.37

Figure 9.37 gives an overview of absolute and conditional convergence. It shows the universe of all infinite series, split first according to whether they converge or diverge.

Convergent series are further divided between absolutely and conditionally convergent series.

Here are a few more consequences of these definitions.

- The distinction between absolute and conditional convergence is relevant only for series of mixed sign, which includes alternating series. If a series of positive terms converges, it converges absolutely; conditional convergence does not apply.
- To test for absolute convergence, we test the series $\sum |a_k|$, which is a series of positive terms. Therefore, the convergence tests of Sections 9.4 and 9.5 (for positive-term series) are used to determine absolute convergence.

QUICK CHECK 4 Explain why a convergent series of positive terms converges absolutely.

EXAMPLE 3 **Absolute and conditional convergence** Determine whether the following series diverge, converge absolutely, or converge conditionally.

a. $\displaystyle\sum_{k=1}^{\infty} \frac{(-1)^{k+1}}{\sqrt{k}}$ **b.** $\displaystyle\sum_{k=1}^{\infty} \frac{(-1)^{k+1}}{\sqrt{k^3}}$ **c.** $\displaystyle\sum_{k=1}^{\infty} \frac{\sin k}{k^2}$ **d.** $\displaystyle\sum_{k=1}^{\infty} \frac{(-1)^k k}{k+1}$

SOLUTION

a. We examine the series of absolute values,

$$\sum_{k=1}^{\infty} \left| \frac{(-1)^{k+1}}{\sqrt{k}} \right| = \sum_{k=1}^{\infty} \frac{1}{\sqrt{k}},$$

which is a divergent p-series (with $p = \frac{1}{2} < 1$). Therefore, the given alternating series does not converge absolutely. To determine whether the series converges conditionally we look at the original series—with alternating signs. The magnitude of the terms of this series decrease with $\lim_{k\to\infty} 1/\sqrt{k} = 0$, so by the Alternating Series Test, the series converges. Because this series converges, but not absolutely, it converges conditionally.

b. To assess absolute convergence, we look at the series of absolute values,

$$\sum_{k=1}^{\infty} \left| \frac{(-1)^{k+1}}{\sqrt{k^3}} \right| = \sum_{k=1}^{\infty} \frac{1}{k^{3/2}},$$

which is a convergent p-series (with $p = \frac{3}{2} > 1$). Therefore, the original alternating series converges absolutely (and by Theorem 9.21 it converges).

c. The terms of this series do not strictly alternate sign (the first few signs are $+++---$), so the Alternating Series Test does not apply. Because $|\sin k| \le 1$, the terms of the series of absolute values satisfy

$$\left| \frac{\sin k}{k^2} \right| = \frac{|\sin k|}{k^2} \le \frac{1}{k^2}.$$

The series $\sum \frac{1}{k^2}$ is a convergent p-series. Therefore, by the Comparison Test, the series $\sum \left| \frac{\sin k}{k^2} \right|$ converges, which implies that the series $\sum \frac{\sin k}{k^2}$ converges absolutely.

d. Notice that $\lim_{k\to\infty} k/(k+1) = 1$. The terms of the series do not tend to zero and, by the Divergence Test, the series diverges.

Related Exercises 39–46

We close the chapter with the summary of tests and series shown in Table 9.4.

Table 9.4 **Special Series and Convergence Tests**

Series or test	Form of series	Condition for convergence	Condition for divergence	Comments
Geometric series	$\sum_{k=0}^{\infty} ar^k$	$\lvert r\rvert < 1$	$\lvert r\rvert \geq 1$	If $\lvert r\rvert < 1$, then $\sum_{k=0}^{\infty} ar^k = \frac{a}{1-r}$.
Divergence Test	$\sum_{k=1}^{\infty} a_k$	Does not apply	$\lim_{k\to\infty} a_k \neq 0$	Cannot be used to prove convergence
Integral Test	$\sum_{k=1}^{\infty} a_k$, where $a_k = f(k)$ and f is continuous, positive, and decreasing	$\int_1^{\infty} f(x)\,dx < \infty$	$\int_1^{\infty} f(x)\,dx$ does not exist.	The value of the integral is not the value of the series.
p-series	$\sum_{k=1}^{\infty} \frac{1}{k^p}$	$p > 1$	$p \leq 1$	Useful for comparison tests
Ratio Test	$\sum_{k=1}^{\infty} a_k$, where $a_k > 0$	$\lim_{k\to\infty} \frac{a_{k+1}}{a_k} < 1$	$\lim_{k\to\infty} \frac{a_{k+1}}{a_k} > 1$	Inconclusive if $\lim_{k\to\infty} \frac{a_{k+1}}{a_k} = 1$
Root Test	$\sum_{k=1}^{\infty} a_k$, where $a_k \geq 0$	$\lim_{k\to\infty} \sqrt[k]{a_k} < 1$	$\lim_{k\to\infty} \sqrt[k]{a_k} > 1$	Inconclusive if $\lim_{k\to\infty} \sqrt[k]{a_k} = 1$
Comparison Test	$\sum_{k=1}^{\infty} a_k$, where $a_k > 0$	$0 < a_k \leq b_k$ and $\sum_{k=1}^{\infty} b_k$ converges	$0 < b_k \leq a_k$ and $\sum_{k=1}^{\infty} b_k$ diverges	$\sum_{k=1}^{\infty} a_k$ is given; you supply $\sum_{k=1}^{\infty} b_k$.
Limit Comparison Test	$\sum_{k=1}^{\infty} a_k$, where $a_k > 0, b_k > 0$	$0 \leq \lim_{k\to\infty} \frac{a_k}{b_k} < \infty$ and $\sum_{k=1}^{\infty} b_k$ converges.	$\lim_{k\to\infty} \frac{a_k}{b_k} > 0$ and $\sum_{k=1}^{\infty} b_k$ diverges.	$\sum_{k=1}^{\infty} a_k$ is given; you supply $\sum_{k=1}^{\infty} b_k$.
Alternating Series Test	$\sum_{k=1}^{\infty} (-1)^k a_k$, where $a_k > 0, 0 < a_{k+1} \leq a_k$	$\lim_{k\to\infty} a_k = 0$	$\lim_{k\to\infty} a_k \neq 0$	Remainder R_n satisfies $R_n < a_{n+1}$

SECTION 9.6 EXERCISES

Review Questions

1. Explain why the sequence of partial sums for an alternating series is not an increasing sequence.
2. Describe how to apply the Alternating Series Test.
3. Why does the value of a converging alternating series lie between any two consecutive terms of its sequence of partial sums?
4. Suppose an alternating series converges to a value L. Explain how to estimate the remainder that occurs when the series is terminated after n terms.
5. Explain why the remainder in terminating an alternating series is less than the first neglected term.
6. Give an example of a convergent alternating series that fails to converge absolutely.
7. Is it possible for a series of positive terms to converge conditionally? Explain.
8. Why does absolute convergence imply convergence?
9. Is it possible for an alternating series to converge absolutely, but not conditionally?

10. Give an example of a series that converges conditionally but not absolutely.

Basic Skills

11–24. Alternating Series Test *Determine whether the following series converge.*

11. $\sum_{k=1}^{\infty} \frac{(-1)^{k+1}}{k^3}$

12. $\sum_{k=0}^{\infty} \frac{(-1)^k}{k^2 + 10}$

13. $\sum_{k=1}^{\infty} (-1)^{k+1} \frac{k^2}{k^3 + 1}$

14. $\sum_{k=2}^{\infty} (-1)^k \frac{\ln k}{k^2}$

15. $\sum_{k=2}^{\infty} (-1)^k \frac{k^2 - 1}{k^2 + 3}$

16. $\sum_{k=0}^{\infty} \left(-\frac{1}{5}\right)^k$

17. $\sum_{k=2}^{\infty} (-1)^k \left(1 + \frac{1}{k}\right)$

18. $\sum_{k=1}^{\infty} \frac{\cos \pi k}{k^2}$

19. $\sum_{k=1}^{\infty} (-1)^{k+1} \frac{k^{10} + 2k^5 + 1}{k(k^{10} + 1)}$

20. $\sum_{k=2}^{\infty} \frac{(-1)^k}{k \ln^2 k}$

21. $\sum_{k=1}^{\infty} (-1)^{k+1} k^{1/k}$

22. $\sum_{k=1}^{\infty} (-1)^{k+1} \frac{k!}{k^k}$

23. $\sum_{k=0}^{\infty} \frac{(-1)^k}{\sqrt{k^2 + 4}}$

24. $\sum_{k=1}^{\infty} (-1)^k k \sin\left(\frac{1}{k}\right)$

T **25–34. Remainders in alternating series** *Determine how many terms of the following convergent series must be summed to be sure that the remainder is less than 10^{-4}. Although you do not need it, the exact value of the series is given in each case.*

25. $\ln 2 = \sum_{k=1}^{\infty} \frac{(-1)^{k+1}}{k}$

26. $\frac{1}{e} = \sum_{k=0}^{\infty} \frac{(-1)^k}{k!}$

27. $\frac{\pi}{4} = \sum_{k=0}^{\infty} \frac{(-1)^k}{2k + 1}$

28. $\frac{\pi^2}{12} = \sum_{k=1}^{\infty} \frac{(-1)^{k+1}}{k^2}$

29. $\frac{7\pi^4}{720} = \sum_{k=1}^{\infty} \frac{(-1)^{k+1}}{k^4}$

30. $\frac{\pi^3}{32} = \sum_{k=0}^{\infty} \frac{(-1)^k}{(2k + 1)^3}$

31. $\frac{\pi\sqrt{3}}{9} + \frac{\ln 2}{3} = \sum_{k=0}^{\infty} \frac{(-1)^k}{3k + 1}$

32. $\frac{31\pi^6}{30{,}240} = \sum_{k=1}^{\infty} \frac{(-1)^{k+1}}{k^6}$

33. $\pi = \sum_{k=0}^{\infty} \frac{(-1)^k}{4^k}\left(\frac{2}{4k + 1} + \frac{2}{4k + 2} + \frac{1}{4k + 3}\right)$

34. $\frac{\pi\sqrt{3}}{9} - \frac{\ln 2}{3} = \sum_{k=0}^{\infty} \frac{(-1)^k}{3k + 2}$

T **35–38. Estimating infinite sums** *Estimate the value of the following convergent series with an absolute error less than 10^{-3}.*

35. $\sum_{k=1}^{\infty} \frac{(-1)^k}{k^5}$

36. $\sum_{k=1}^{\infty} \frac{(-1)^k}{(2k + 1)^3}$

37. $\sum_{k=1}^{\infty} \frac{(-1)^k}{k^k}$

38. $\sum_{k=1}^{\infty} \frac{(-1)^{k+1}}{(2k + 1)!}$

39–46. Absolute and conditional convergence *Determine whether the following series converge absolutely or conditionally.*

39. $\sum_{k=1}^{\infty} \frac{(-1)^{k+1}}{k^{3/2}}$

40. $\sum_{k=1}^{\infty} \left(-\frac{1}{3}\right)^k$

41. $\sum_{k=1}^{\infty} \frac{\cos k}{k^3}$

42. $\sum_{k=1}^{\infty} \frac{(-1)^k k^2}{\sqrt{k^6 + 1}}$

43. $\sum_{k=1}^{\infty} \frac{(-1)^k k}{2k + 1}$

44. $\sum_{k=2}^{\infty} \frac{(-1)^k}{\ln k}$

45. $\sum_{k=1}^{\infty} \frac{(-1)^k \tan^{-1} k}{k^3}$

46. $\sum_{k=1}^{\infty} \frac{(-1)^{k+1} e^k}{(k + 1)!}$

Further Explorations

47. Explain why or why not Determine whether the following statements are true and give an explanation or counterexample.

a. A series that converges must converge absolutely.
b. A series that converges absolutely must converge.
c. A series that converges conditionally must converge.
d. If $\sum a_k$ diverges, then $\sum |a_k|$ diverges.
e. If $\sum a_k^2$ converges, then $\sum a_k$ converges.
f. If $a_k > 0$ and $\sum a_k$ converges, then $\sum a_k^2$ converges.
g. If $\sum a_k$ converges conditionally, then $\sum |a_k|$ diverges.

48. Alternating Series Test Show that the series

$$\frac{1}{3} - \frac{2}{5} + \frac{3}{7} - \frac{4}{9} + \cdots = \sum_{k=1}^{\infty} (-1)^{k+1} \frac{k}{2k + 1}$$

diverges. Which condition of the Alternating Series Test is not satisfied?

49. Alternating *p*-series Given that $\sum_{k=1}^{\infty} \frac{1}{k^2} = \frac{\pi^2}{6}$, show that $\sum_{k=1}^{\infty} \frac{(-1)^{k+1}}{k^2} = \frac{\pi^2}{12}$. (Assume the result of Exercise 53.)

50. Alternating *p*-series Given that $\sum_{k=1}^{\infty} \frac{1}{k^4} = \frac{\pi^4}{90}$, show that $\sum_{k=1}^{\infty} \frac{(-1)^{k+1}}{k^4} = \frac{7\pi^4}{720}$. (Assume the result of Exercise 53.)

51. Geometric series In Section 9.3, we established that the geometric series $\sum r^k$ converges provided $|r| < 1$. Notice that if $-1 < r < 0$, the geometric series is also an alternating series. Use the Alternating Series Test to show that for $-1 < r < 0$, the series $\sum r^k$ converges.

T **52. Remainders in alternating series** Given any infinite series $\sum a_k$, let $N(r)$ be the number of terms of the series that must be summed to guarantee that the remainder is less than 10^{-r}, where r is a positive integer.

a. Graph the function $N(r)$ for the three alternating p-series $\sum_{k=1}^{\infty} \frac{(-1)^{k+1}}{k^p}$, for $p = 1, 2$, and 3. Compare the three graphs and discuss what they mean about the rates of convergence of the three series.

b. Carry out the procedure of part (a) for the series $\sum_{k=1}^{\infty} \frac{(-1)^{k+1}}{k!}$ and compare the rates of convergence of all four series.

Additional Exercises

53. Rearranging series It can be proved that if a series converges absolutely, then its terms may be summed in any order without changing the value of the series. However, if a series converges conditionally, then the value of the series depends on the order of summation. For example, the (conditionally convergent) alternating harmonic series has the value

$$1 - \frac{1}{2} + \frac{1}{3} - \frac{1}{4} + \cdots = \ln 2.$$

Show that by rearranging the terms (so the sign pattern is $++-$),

$$1 + \frac{1}{3} - \frac{1}{2} + \frac{1}{5} + \frac{1}{7} - \frac{1}{4} + \cdots = \frac{3}{2}\ln 2.$$

54. A better remainder Suppose an alternating series $\sum_{k=1}^{\infty} (-1)^k a_k$ converges to S and the sum of the first n terms of the series is S_n. Suppose also that the difference between the magnitudes of consecutive terms decreases with k. Then it can be shown that

$$\left| S - \left(S_n + \frac{(-1)^{n+1} a_{n+1}}{2} \right) \right| \le \frac{1}{2} |a_{n+1} - a_{n+2}|, \quad \text{for } n \ge 1.$$

a. Interpret this inequality and explain why it gives a better approximation to S than simply using S_n to approximate S.

b. For the following series, determine how many terms of the series are needed to approximate its exact value with an error less than 10^{-6} using both S_n and the method explained in part (a).

(i) $\sum_{k=1}^{\infty} \frac{(-1)^k}{k}$ **(ii)** $\sum_{k=2}^{\infty} \frac{(-1)^k}{k \ln k}$ **(iii)** $\sum_{k=2}^{\infty} \frac{(-1)^k}{\sqrt{k}}$

55. A fallacy Explain the fallacy in the following argument. Let $x = \frac{1}{1} + \frac{1}{3} + \frac{1}{5} + \frac{1}{7} + \cdots$ and $y = \frac{1}{2} + \frac{1}{4} + \frac{1}{6} + \frac{1}{8} + \cdots$. It follows that $2y = x + y$, which implies that $x = y$. On the other hand,

$$x - y = \underbrace{\left(1 - \frac{1}{2}\right)}_{>0} + \underbrace{\left(\frac{1}{3} - \frac{1}{4}\right)}_{>0} + \underbrace{\left(\frac{1}{5} - \frac{1}{6}\right)}_{>0} + \cdots > 0$$

is a sum of positive terms, so $x > y$. Thus, we have shown that $x = y$ and $x > y$.

QUICK CHECK ANSWERS

1. $1, -1, 2, -2, 3, -3, \ldots$; series diverges. **2.** The even terms of the sequence of partial sums approach the value of the series from one side; the odd terms of the sequence of partial sums approach the value of the series from the other side. **3.** The second series with $k!$ in the denominators converges much more quickly than the first series because $k!$ increases much faster than k as $k \to \infty$. **4.** If a series has positive terms, the series of absolute values is the same as the series itself.

CHAPTER 9 REVIEW EXERCISES

1. Explain why or why not Determine whether the following statements are true and give an explanation or counterexample.

a. The terms of the sequence $\{a_n\}$ increase in magnitude, so the limit of the sequence does not exist.

b. The terms of the series $\sum 1/\sqrt{k}$ approach zero, so the series converges.

c. The terms of the sequence of partial sums of the series $\sum a_k$ approach 5/2, so the infinite series converges to 5/2.

d. An alternating series that converges absolutely must converge conditionally.

2–10. Limits of sequences *Evaluate the limit of the sequence or state that it does not exist.*

2. $a_n = \frac{n^2 + 4}{\sqrt{4n^4 + 1}}$

3. $a_n = \frac{8^n}{n!}$

4. $a_n = \left(1 + \frac{3}{n}\right)^{2n}$

5. $a_n = \sqrt[n]{n}$

6. $a_n = n - \sqrt{n^2 - 1}$

7. $a_n = \left(\frac{1}{n}\right)^{1/\ln n}$

8. $a_n = \sin\left(\frac{\pi n}{6}\right)$

9. $a_n = \frac{(-1)^n}{0.9^n}$

10. $a_n = \tan^{-1} n$

11. Sequence of partial sums Consider the series

$$\sum_{k=1}^{\infty} \frac{1}{k(k+2)} = \frac{1}{2} \sum_{k=1}^{\infty} \left(\frac{1}{k} - \frac{1}{k+2} \right).$$

a. Write the first four terms of the sequence of partial sums $S_1, \ldots, S_4$.

b. Write the nth term of the sequence of partial sums S_n.

c. Find $\lim_{n\to\infty} S_n$ and evaluate the series.

12–20. Evaluating series *Evaluate the following infinite series or state that the series diverges.*

12. $\sum_{k=1}^{\infty} \left(\frac{9}{10}\right)^k$

13. $\sum_{k=1}^{\infty} 3(1.001)^k$

14. $\sum_{k=0}^{\infty}\left(-\frac{1}{5}\right)^k$

15. $\sum_{k=1}^{\infty}\frac{1}{k(k+1)}$

16. $\sum_{k=2}^{\infty}\left(\frac{1}{\sqrt{k}}-\frac{1}{\sqrt{k-1}}\right)$

17. $\sum_{k=1}^{\infty}\left(\frac{3}{3k-2}-\frac{3}{3k+1}\right)$

18. $\sum_{k=1}^{\infty}4^{-3k}$

19. $\sum_{k=1}^{\infty}\frac{2^k}{3^{k+2}}$

20. $\sum_{k=0}^{\infty}\left[\left(\frac{1}{3}\right)^k-\left(\frac{2}{3}\right)^{k+1}\right]$

21. **Sequences of partial sums** The sequences of partial sums for three series are shown in the figures below. Assume that the pattern in the sequences continues as $n \to \infty$.

a. Does it appear that series A converges? If so, what is its (approximate) value?

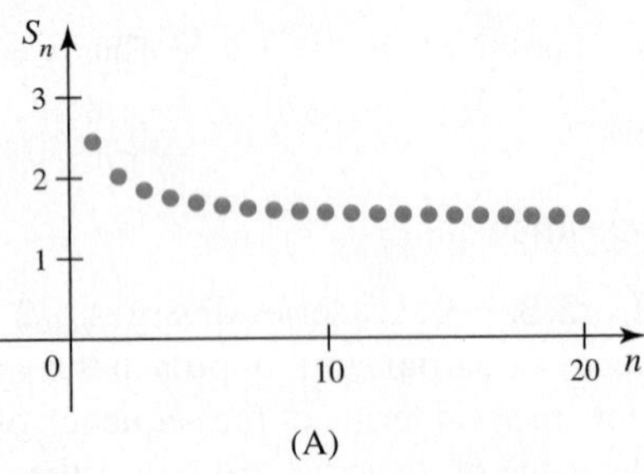

(A)

b. What can you conclude about the convergence or divergence of series B?

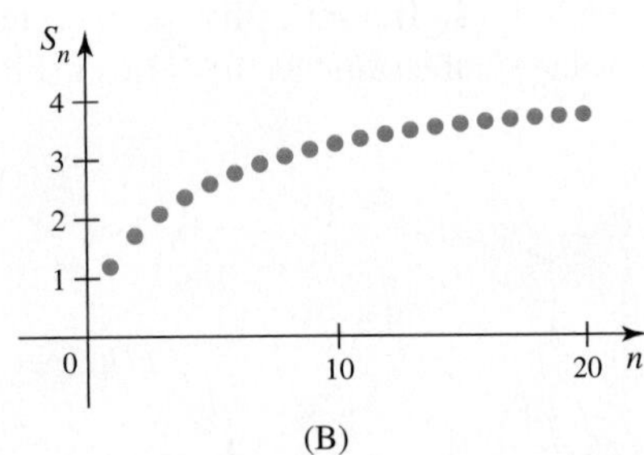

(B)

c. Does it appear that series C converges? If so, what is its (approximate) value?

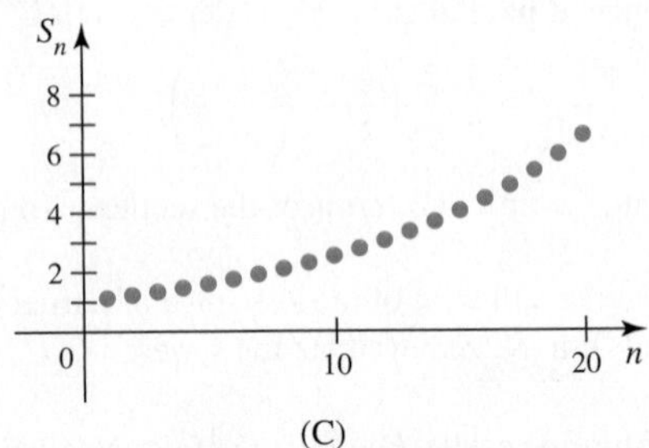

(C)

22–36. Convergence or divergence *Use a convergence test of your choice to determine whether the following series converge or diverge.*

22. $\sum_{k=1}^{\infty}\frac{2}{k^{3/2}}$

23. $\sum_{k=1}^{\infty}k^{-2/3}$

24. $\sum_{k=1}^{\infty}\frac{2k^2+1}{\sqrt{k^3+2}}$

25. $\sum_{k=1}^{\infty}\frac{2^k}{e^k}$

26. $\sum_{k=1}^{\infty}\left(\frac{k}{k+3}\right)^{2k}$

27. $\sum_{k=1}^{\infty}\frac{2^k k!}{k^k}$

28. $\sum_{k=1}^{\infty}\frac{1}{\sqrt{k}\sqrt{k+1}}$

29. $\sum_{k=1}^{\infty}\frac{3}{2+e^k}$

30. $\sum_{k=1}^{\infty}k\sin\left(\frac{1}{k}\right)$

31. $\sum_{k=1}^{\infty}\frac{\sqrt[3]{k}}{k^3}$

32. $\sum_{k=1}^{\infty}\frac{1}{1+\ln k}$

33. $\sum_{k=1}^{\infty}k^5e^{-k}$

34. $\sum_{k=4}^{\infty}\frac{2}{k^2-10}$

35. $\sum_{k=1}^{\infty}\frac{\ln k^2}{k^2}$

36. $\sum_{k=1}^{\infty}ke^{-k}$

37–42. Alternating series *Determine whether the following series converge or diverge. In the case of convergence, state whether the convergence is conditional or absolute.*

37. $\sum_{k=2}^{\infty}\frac{(-1)^k}{k^2-1}$

38. $\sum_{k=1}^{\infty}\frac{(-1)^{k+1}(k^2+4)}{2k^2+1}$

39. $\sum_{k=1}^{\infty}(-1)^k ke^{-k}$

40. $\sum_{k=1}^{\infty}\frac{(-1)^k}{\sqrt{k^2+1}}$

41. $\sum_{k=1}^{\infty}\frac{(-1)^{k+1}10^k}{k!}$

42. $\sum_{k=2}^{\infty}\frac{(-1)^k}{k\ln k}$

43. **Sequences vs. series**

a. Find the limit of $\left\{\left(-\frac{4}{5}\right)^k\right\}$.

b. Evaluate $\sum_{k=0}^{\infty}\left(-\frac{4}{5}\right)^k$.

44. **Sequences vs. series**

a. Find the limit of $\left\{\frac{1}{k}-\frac{1}{k+1}\right\}$.

b. Evaluate $\sum_{k=1}^{\infty}\left(\frac{1}{k}-\frac{1}{k+1}\right)$.

45. **Partial sums** Let S_n be the nth partial sum of $\sum_{k=1}^{\infty}a_k = 8$. Find $\lim_{k\to\infty}a_k$ and $\lim_{n\to\infty}S_n$.

T 46. **Remainder term** Let R_n be the remainder associated with $\sum_{k=1}^{\infty}\frac{1}{k^5}$. Find an upper bound for R_n (in terms of n). How many terms of the series must be summed to approximate the series with an error less than 10^{-4}?

47. **Conditional *p*-series** Find the values of p for which $\sum_{k=1}^{\infty}\frac{(-1)^k}{k^p}$ converges conditionally.

48. **Logarithmic *p*-series** Show that the series $\sum_{k=2}^{\infty}\frac{1}{k(\ln k)^p}$ converges provided $p > 1$.

T 49. Error in a finite sum Approximate the series $\sum_{k=1}^{\infty} \frac{1}{5^k}$ by evaluating the first 20 terms. Compute the maximum error in the approximation.

T 50. Error in a finite sum Approximate the series $\sum_{k=1}^{\infty} \frac{1}{k^5}$ by evaluating the first 20 terms. Compute the maximum error in the approximation.

T 51. Error in a finite alternating sum How many terms of the series $\sum_{k=1}^{\infty} \frac{(-1)^{k+1}}{k^4}$ must be summed to ensure that the remainder is less than 10^{-8}?

52. Equations involving series Solve the following equations for x.

a. $\sum_{k=0}^{\infty} e^{kx} = 2$ **b.** $\sum_{k=0}^{\infty} (3x)^k = 4$

c. $\sum_{k=1}^{\infty} \left(\frac{x}{kx - \frac{x}{2}} - \frac{x}{kx + \frac{x}{2}} \right) = 6$

53. Building a tunnel—first scenario A crew of workers is constructing a tunnel through a mountain. Understandably, the rate of construction decreases because rocks and earth must be removed a greater distance as the tunnel gets longer. Suppose that each week the crew digs 0.95 of the distance it dug the previous week. In the first week, the crew constructed 100 meters of tunnel.

a. How far does the crew dig in 10 weeks? 20 weeks? N weeks?
b. What is the longest tunnel the crew can build at this rate?

54. Building a tunnel—second scenario As in Exercise 53, a crew of workers is constructing a tunnel. The time required to dig 100 m increases by 10% each week, starting with 1 week to dig the first 100 m. Can the crew complete a 1.5-km (1500-m) tunnel in 30 weeks? Explain.

55. Pages of circles On page 1 of a book, there is one circle of radius 1. On page 2, there are two circles of radius $\frac{1}{2}$. On page n there are 2^{n-1} circles of radius 2^{-n+1}.

a. What is the sum of the areas of the circles on page n of the book?
b. Assuming the book continues indefinitely ($n \to \infty$), what is the sum of the areas of all the circles in the book?

T 56. Sequence on a calculator Let $\{x_n\}$ be generated by the recurrence relation $x_0 = 1$ and $x_{n+1} = x_n + \cos x_n$, for $n = 0, 1, 2, \ldots$. Use a calculator (in radian mode) to generate as many terms of the sequence $\{x_n\}$ needed to find the integer p such that $\lim_{n\to\infty} x_n = \pi/p$.

57. A savings plan Suppose that you open a savings account by depositing \$100. The account earns interest at an annual rate of 3% per year (0.25% per month). At the end of each month, you earn interest on the current balance, and then you deposit \$100. Let B_n be the balance at the beginning of the nth month, where $B_0 = \$100$.

a. Find a recurrence relation for the sequence $\{B_n\}$.
b. Find an explicit formula that gives B_n for $n = 0, 1, 2, 3, \ldots$.

58. Sequences of integrals Find the limits of the sequences $\{a_n\}$ and $\{b_n\}$.

a. $a_n = \int_0^1 x^n\,dx,\ n \ge 1$ **b.** $b_n = \int_1^n \frac{dx}{x^p},\ p > 1, n \ge 1$

59. Sierpinski triangle The fractal called the *Sierpinski triangle* is the limit of a sequence of figures. Starting with the equilateral triangle with sides of length 1, an inverted equilateral triangle with sides of length $\frac{1}{2}$ is removed. Then, three inverted equilateral triangles with sides of length $\frac{1}{4}$ are removed from this figure (see figure). The process continues in this way. Let T_n be the total area of the removed triangles after stage n of the process. The area of an equilateral triangle with side length L is $A = \sqrt{3}L^2/4$.

a. Find T_1 and T_2, the total area of the removed triangles after stages 1 and 2, respectively.
b. Find T_n for $n = 1, 2, 3, \ldots$.
c. Find $\lim_{n\to\infty} T_n$.
d. What is the area of the original triangle that remains as $n \to \infty$?

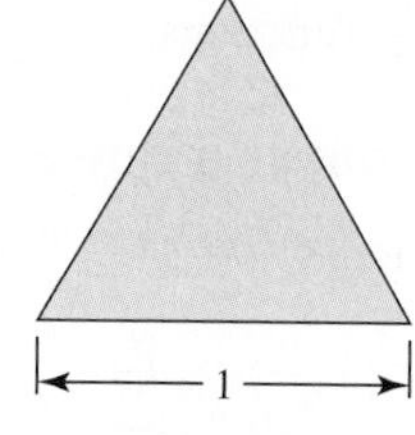

Initial stage

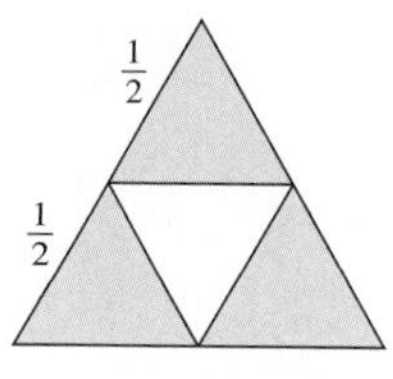

First stage

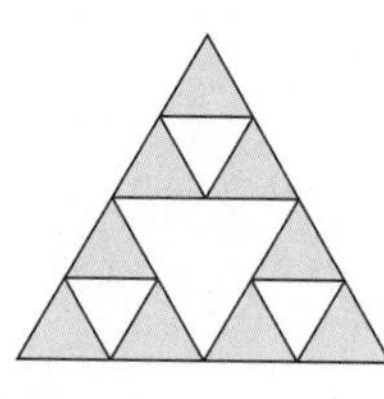
Second stage

60. Max sine sequence Let $a_n = \max\{\sin 1, \sin 2, \ldots, \sin n\}$, for $n = 1, 2, 3, \ldots$, where max $\{\ldots\}$ denotes the maximum element of the set. Does $\{a_n\}$ converge? If so, make a conjecture about the limit.

Chapter 9 Guided Projects

Applications of the material in this chapter and related topics can be found in the following Guided Projects. For additional information, see the Preface.

- Chaos!
- Periodic drug dosing
- The mathematics of loans
- Financial matters
- Economic stimulus packages
- Archimedes' approximation to π
- Exact values of infinite series
- Conditional convergence in a crystal lattice

10 Power Series

Chapter Preview Until now we have worked with infinite series consisting of real numbers. In this chapter a seemingly small, but significant change is made by considering infinite series whose terms include a variable. With this change, an infinite series becomes a *power series*. Surely one of the most significant ideas in all of calculus is that functions can be represented by power series. As a first step toward this result, we look at approximating functions using polynomials. The transition from polynomials to power series is then straightforward. With these tools, it is possible to represent the familiar functions of mathematics in terms of power series called *Taylor series*. The remainder of the chapter is devoted to the properties and many uses of these series.

10.1 Approximating Functions with Polynomials

Power series—like sets and functions—are among the most fundamental entities of mathematics because they provide a way to represent familiar functions and to define new functions.

What Is a Power Series?

A *power series* is an infinite series of the form

$$\sum_{k=0}^{\infty} c_k x^k = \underbrace{c_0 + c_1 x + c_2 x^2 + \cdots + c_n x^n}_{n\text{th degree polynomial}} + \underbrace{c_{n+1} x^{n+1} + \cdots}_{\text{terms continue}},$$

or, more generally,

$$\sum_{k=0}^{\infty} c_k (x-a)^k = \underbrace{c_0 + c_1 (x-a) + \cdots + c_n (x-a)^n}_{n\text{th degree polynomial}} + \underbrace{c_{n+1}(x-a)^{n+1} + \cdots}_{\text{terms continue}},$$

where the coefficients c_k and the **center** of the series a are constants. This type of series is called a power series because it consists of powers of x or $(x-a)$.

Viewed in another way, a power series is built up from polynomials of increasing degree, as shown in the following progression:

$$\left.\begin{array}{ll} \text{Degree 0:} & c_0 \\ \text{Degree 1:} & c_0 + c_1 x \\ \text{Degree 2:} & c_0 + c_1 x + c_2 x^2 \\ \vdots & \vdots \\ \text{Degree } n\text{:} & c_0 + c_1 x + c_2 x^2 + \cdots + c_n x^n = \displaystyle\sum_{k=0}^{n} c_k x^k \end{array}\right\} \text{Polynomials}$$

$$\vdots \quad \vdots \quad \vdots$$

$$c_0 + c_1 x + c_2 x^2 + \cdots + c_n x^n + \cdots = \sum_{k=0}^{\infty} c_k x^k \Big\} \text{ Power series}$$

We begin our exploration of power series by using polynomials to approximate functions.

Polynomial Approximation

An important observation motivates our work. To evaluate a polynomial $\left(\text{say, } f(x) = x^8 - 4x^5 + \frac{1}{2}\right)$, all we need is arithmetic—addition, subtraction, multiplication, and division. However, algebraic functions $\left(\text{say, } f(x) = \sqrt[3]{x^4 - 1}\right)$ or trigonometric, logarithmic, or exponential functions usually cannot be evaluated exactly using arithmetic. Therefore, it makes practical sense to use the simplest of functions, polynomials, to approximate more complicated functions.

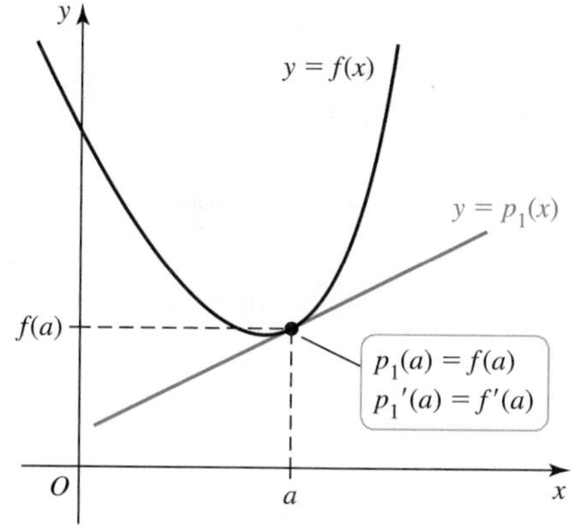

FIGURE 10.1

Linear and Quadratic Approximation

Recall that if a function f is differentiable at a point a, it can be approximated near a by its tangent line (Section 4.5); the tangent line provides the linear approximation to f at the point a. The equation of the tangent line at the point $(a, f(a))$ is

$$y - f(a) = f'(a)(x - a) \quad \text{or} \quad y = f(a) + f'(a)(x - a).$$

Because the linear approximation function is a first-degree polynomial, we name it p_1:

$$p_1(x) = f(a) + f'(a)(x - a)$$

This polynomial has some important properties: it matches f in *value* and in *slope* at a. In other words (Figure 10.1),

$$p_1(a) = f(a) \quad \text{and} \quad p_1'(a) = f'(a).$$

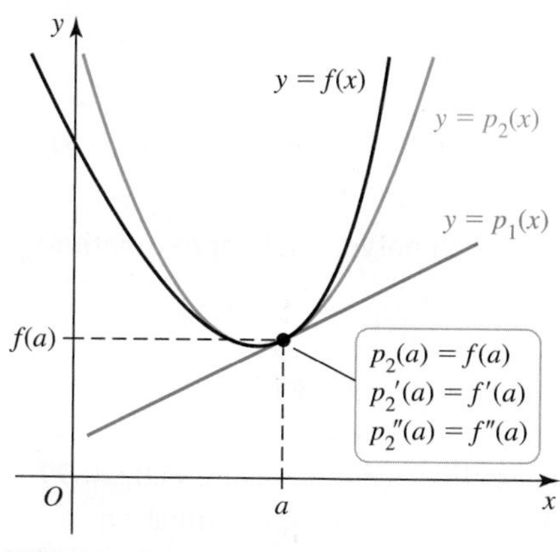

FIGURE 10.2

Linear approximation works well if f has a fairly constant slope near the point a. However if f has a lot of curvature near a, then the tangent line may not provide a good approximation. To remedy this situation, we create a quadratic approximating polynomial by adding a single term to the linear polynomial. Denoting this new polynomial p_2, we have

$$p_2(x) = \underbrace{f(a) + f'(a)(x - a)}_{p_1(x)} + \underbrace{c_2(x - a)^2}_{\text{quadratic term}}.$$

The new term consists of a coefficient c_2 that must be determined and a quadratic factor $(x - a)^2$.

To determine c_2 and to ensure that p_2 is a good approximation to f near the point a, we require that p_2 agree with f in value, slope, and concavity at a; that is, p_2 must satisfy the matching conditions

$$p_2(a) = f(a) \qquad p_2'(a) = f'(a) \qquad p_2''(a) = f''(a),$$

where we assume that f and its first and second derivatives exist at a (Figure 10.2).

➤ Matching concavity (second derivatives) ensures that the graph of p_2 bends in the same direction as the graph of f at a.

Substituting $x = a$ into p_2, we see immediately that $p_2(a) = f(a)$, so the first matching condition is met. Differentiating p_2 once, we have

$$p_2'(x) = f'(a) + 2c_2(x - a).$$

So, $p_2'(a) = f'(a)$, and the second matching condition is also met. Because $p_2''(a) = 2c_2$, the third matching condition is

$$p_2''(a) = 2c_2 = f''(a).$$

It follows that $c_2 = \frac{1}{2} f''(a)$; therefore, the quadratic approximating polynomial is

$$p_2(x) = \underbrace{f(a) + f'(a)(x - a)}_{p_1(x)} + \frac{1}{2} f''(a)(x - a)^2.$$

EXAMPLE 1 Approximations for $\ln x$

a. Find the linear approximation for $f(x) = \ln x$ at $x = 1$.

b. Find the quadratic approximation for $f(x) = \ln x$ at $x = 1$.

c. Use these approximations to estimate the value of $\ln 1.05$.

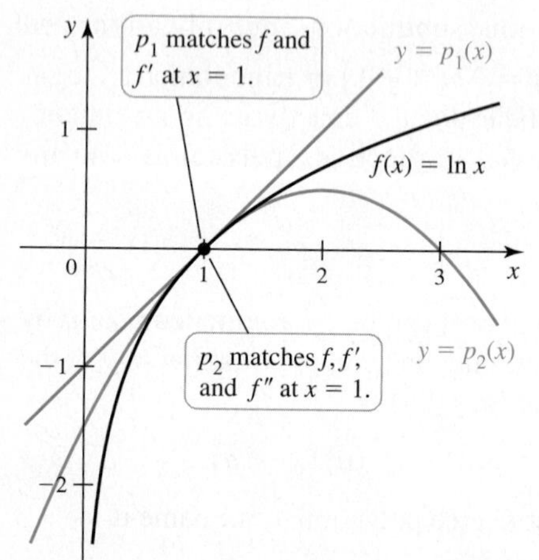

FIGURE 10.3

SOLUTION

a. Note that $f(1) = 0$, $f'(x) = 1/x$, and $f'(1) = 1$. Therefore, the linear approximation to $f(x) = \ln x$ at $x = 1$ is

$$p_1(x) = f(1) + f'(1)(x - 1) = 0 + 1(x - 1) = x - 1.$$

As shown in Figure 10.3, p_1 matches f in value ($p_1(1) = f(1)$) and in slope ($p_1'(1) = f'(1)$) at $x = 1$.

b. We first compute $f''(x) = -1/x^2$ and $f''(1) = -1$. Building on the linear approximation found in part (a), the quadratic approximation is

$$p_2(x) = \underbrace{x - 1}_{p_1(x)} + \underbrace{\frac{1}{2} f''(1)}_{c_2}(x - 1)^2$$

$$= (x - 1) + \frac{1}{2}(-1)(x - 1)^2$$

$$= (x - 1) - \frac{1}{2}(x - 1)^2.$$

Because p_2 matches f in value, slope, and concavity at $x = 1$, it provides a better approximation to f near $x = 1$ (Figure 10.3).

c. To approximate $\ln 1.05$, we substitute $x = 1.05$ into each polynomial approximation:

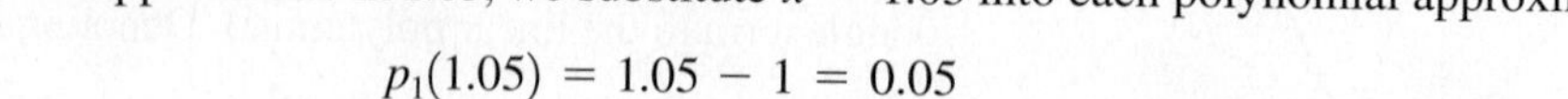

$$p_1(1.05) = 1.05 - 1 = 0.05$$

$$p_2(1.05) = (1.05 - 1) - \frac{1}{2}(1.05 - 1)^2 = 0.04875$$

The value of $\ln 1.05$ given by a calculator, rounded to five decimal places, is 0.04879, showing the improvement in quadratic approximation over linear approximation.

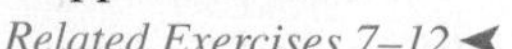

Related Exercises 7–12 ◄

Taylor Polynomials

The process used to find the approximating polynomial p_2 can be extended to obtain approximating polynomials of higher degree. Assuming that f and its first n derivatives exist at a, we can use p_2 to obtain a cubic polynomial p_3 of the form

> Building on ideas that were already circulating in the early 18th century, Brooke Taylor (1685–1731) published Taylor's Theorem in 1715. He is also credited with discovering integration by parts.

$$p_3(x) = p_2(x) + c_3(x - a)^3$$

that satisfies the four matching conditions

$$p_3(a) = f(a), \quad p_3'(a) = f'(a), \quad p_3''(a) = f''(a), \text{ and } p_3'''(a) = f'''(a).$$

> Recall that $2! = 2 \cdot 1$, $3! = 3 \cdot 2 \cdot 1$, $k! = k \cdot (k - 1)!$, and by definition $0! = 1$.

Because p_3 is built "on top of" p_2, the first three matching conditions are met. The last condition, $p_3'''(a) = f'''(a)$, is used to determine c_3. A short calculation shows that $p_3'''(x) = 3 \cdot 2c_3 = 3!c_3$, and so the last matching condition becomes $p_3'''(a) = 3!c_3 = f'''(a)$. Solving for c_3, we have $c_3 = \dfrac{f'''(a)}{3!}$. Therefore, the cubic approximating polynomial is

$$p_3(x) = \underbrace{f(a) + f'(a)(x - a) + \frac{f''(a)}{2!}(x - a)^2}_{p_2(x)} + \frac{f'''(a)}{3!}(x - a)^3.$$

QUICK CHECK 1 Verify that p_3 satisfies $p_3^{(k)}(a) = f^{(k)}(a)$, for $k = 0, 1, 2, 3$. ◂

Continuing in this fashion (Exercise 66), building each new polynomial on the previous polynomial, the nth approximating polynomial for f at a is

> Recall that $f^{(n)}$ denotes the nth derivative of f. By convention the zeroth derivative $f^{(0)}$ is f itself.

$$p_n(x) = f(a) + f'(a)(x - a) + \frac{f''(a)}{2!}(x - a)^2 + \cdots + \frac{f^{(n)}(a)}{n!}(x - a)^n.$$

It satisfies the $n + 1$ matching conditions

$$p_n(a) = f(a), \quad p_n'(a) = f'(a), \quad p_n''(a) = f''(a), \ldots, p_n^{(n)}(a) = f^{(n)}(a).$$

These conditions ensure that the graph of p_n conforms as closely as possible to the graph of f near a (Figure 10.4).

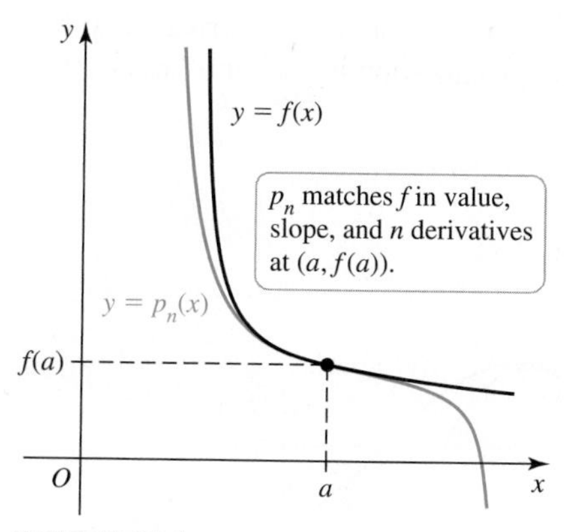

FIGURE 10.4

DEFINITION Taylor Polynomials

Let f be a function with $f', f'', \ldots, f^{(n)}$ defined at a. The ***n*th-order Taylor polynomial** for f with its **center** at a, denoted p_n, has the property that it matches f in value, slope, and all derivatives up to the nth derivative at a; that is,

$$p_n(a) = f(a), \quad p_n'(a) = f'(a), \ldots, p_n^{(n)}(a) = f^{(n)}(a).$$

The nth-order Taylor polynomial centered at a is

$$p_n(x) = f(a) + f'(a)(x - a) + \frac{f''(a)}{2!}(x - a)^2 + \cdots + \frac{f^{(n)}(a)}{n!}(x - a)^n.$$

More compactly, $p_n(x) = \sum_{k=0}^{n} c_k(x - a)^k$, where the **coefficients** are

$$c_k = \frac{f^{(k)}(a)}{k!}, \qquad \text{for } k = 0, 1, 2, \ldots, n.$$

EXAMPLE 2 Taylor polynomials for sin x Find the Taylor polynomials $p_1, \ldots, p_7$ centered at $x = 0$ for $f(x) = \sin x$.

SOLUTION Differentiating f repeatedly and evaluating the derivatives at 0, a pattern emerges:

$$\begin{aligned} f(x) &= \sin x \Rightarrow f(0) = 0 \\ f'(x) &= \cos x \Rightarrow f'(0) = 1 \\ f''(x) &= -\sin x \Rightarrow f''(0) = 0 \\ f'''(x) &= -\cos x \Rightarrow f'''(0) = -1 \\ f^{(4)}(x) &= \sin x \Rightarrow f^{(4)}(0) = 0 \end{aligned}$$

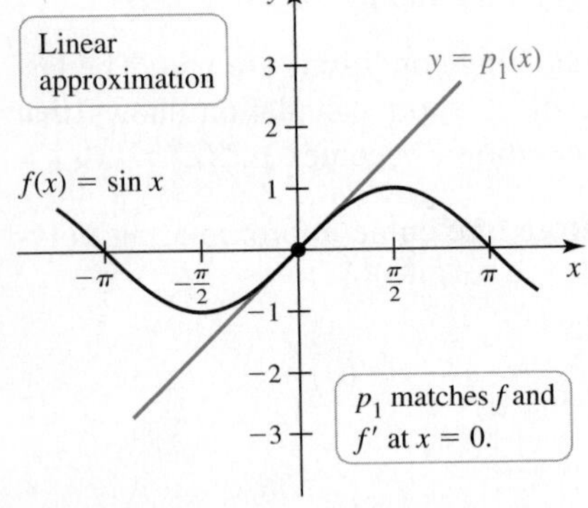

FIGURE 10.5

The derivatives of sin x at 0 cycle through the values $\{0, 1, 0, -1\}$. Therefore, $f^{(5)}(0) = 1$, $f^{(6)}(0) = 0$, and $f^{(7)}(0) = -1$.

We now construct the polynomials that approximate $f(x) = \sin x$ near 0, beginning with the linear polynomial. The polynomial of order 1 ($n = 1$) is

$$p_1(x) = f(0) + f'(0)x = x,$$

whose graph is the line through the origin with slope 1 (Figure 10.5). Notice that f and p_1 agree in value ($f(0) = p_1(0) = 0$) and in slope ($f'(0) = p_1'(0) = 1$) at 0. We see that p_1 provides a good fit to f near 0, but the graphs diverge visibly for $|x| > 0.5$.

The polynomial of order 2 ($n = 2$) is

$$p_2(x) = \underbrace{f(0)}_{0} + \underbrace{f'(0)}_{1}x + \underbrace{\frac{f''(0)}{2!}}_{0}x^2 = x,$$

so p_2 is the same as p_1.

The polynomial of order 3 that approximates f near 0 is

$$p_3(x) = \underbrace{f(0) + f'(0)x + \frac{f''(0)}{2!}x^2}_{p_2(x) = x} + \underbrace{\frac{f'''(0)}{3!}}_{-1/3!}x^3 = x - \frac{x^3}{6}.$$

➤ It is worth repeating that the next polynomial in the sequence is obtained by adding one new term to the previous polynomial. For example,

$$p_3(x) = p_2(x) + \frac{f'''(a)}{3!}(x - a)^3.$$

We have designed p_3 to agree with f in value, slope, concavity, and third derivative at 0 (Figure 10.6).The result is that p_3 provides a better approximation to f over a larger interval than p_1.

QUICK CHECK 2 Verify that $f(0) = p_3(0)$, $f'(0) = p_3'(0)$, $f''(0) = p_3''(0)$, and $f'''(0) = p_3'''(0)$ for $f(x) = \sin x$ and $p_3(x) = x - x^3/6$. ◄

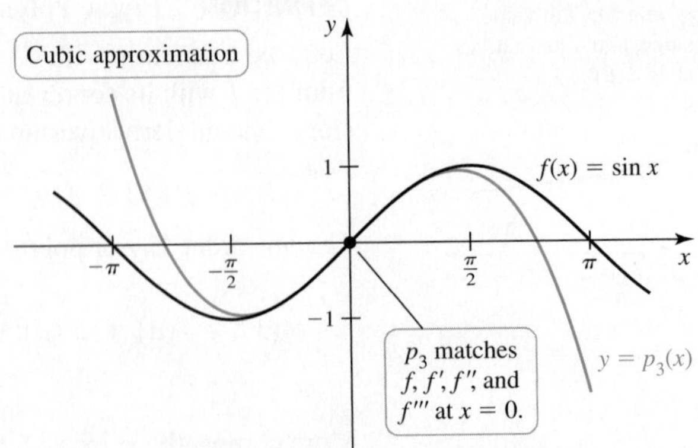

FIGURE 10.6

The procedure for finding Taylor polynomials may be extended to polynomials of any order. Because the even derivatives of $f(x) = \sin x$ are zero, $p_4(x) = p_3(x)$. For the same reason, $p_6(x) = p_5(x)$:

$$p_6(x) = p_5(x) = x - \frac{x^3}{3!} + \frac{x^5}{5!}$$

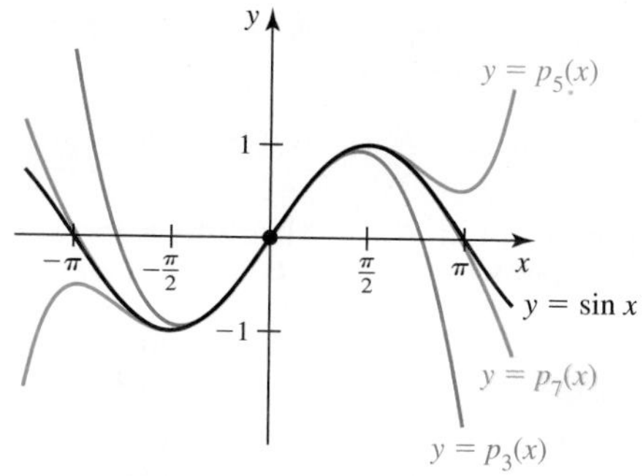

FIGURE 10.7

Finally, it can be shown that the Taylor polynomial of order 7 is

$$p_7(x) = x - \frac{x^3}{3!} + \frac{x^5}{5!} - \frac{x^7}{7!}.$$

In Figure 10.7 we see that as the order of the Taylor polynomials increases, better and better approximations to $f(x) = \sin x$ are obtained over larger and larger intervals centered at 0. For example, p_7 is a good fit to $f(x) = \sin x$ over the interval $[-\pi, \pi]$.

Related Exercises 13–20

QUICK CHECK 3 Given that $f(x) = \sin x$ is an odd function, why do the Taylor polynomials centered at 0 for f consist only of odd powers of x?

Approximations with Taylor Polynomials

Taylor polynomials find widespread use in approximating functions, as illustrated in the following examples.

EXAMPLE 3 Taylor polynomials for e^x

Recall that if c is an approximation to x, the absolute error in c is $|c - x|$ and the relative error in c is $|c - x|/|x|$. We use *error* to refer to *absolute error.*

a. Find the Taylor polynomials of order $n = 0, 1, 2$, and 3 for $f(x) = e^x$ centered at $x = 0$. Graph f and the polynomials.

b. Use the polynomials in part (a) to approximate $e^{0.1}$ and $e^{-0.25}$. Find the absolute errors, $|f(x) - p_n(x)|$, in the approximations. Use calculator values for the exact values of f.

SOLUTION

a. We use the formula for the coefficients in the Taylor polynomials:

$$c_k = \frac{f^{(k)}(0)}{k!}, \qquad \text{for } k = 0, 1, 2, \ldots, n$$

With $f(x) = e^x$, we have $f^{(k)}(x) = e^x$. Therefore, $f^{(k)}(0) = 1$ and $c_k = 1/k!$, for $k = 0, 1, 2, 3, \ldots$. The first four polynomials are

$$p_0(x) = f(0) = 1$$

$$p_1(x) = \underbrace{f(0)}_{p_0(x)=1} + \underbrace{f'(0)}_{1}x = 1 + x$$

$$p_2(x) = \underbrace{f(0) + f'(0)x}_{p_1(x)=1+x} + \underbrace{\frac{f''(0)}{2!}}_{1/2}x^2 = 1 + x + \frac{x^2}{2}$$

$$p_3(x) = \underbrace{f(0) + f'(0)x + \frac{f''(0)}{2!}x^2}_{p_2(x)=1+x+x^2/2} + \underbrace{\frac{f^{(3)}(0)}{3!}}_{1/6}x^3 = 1 + x + \frac{x^2}{2} + \frac{x^3}{6}.$$

Taylor polynomials for $f(x) = e^x$ centered at $x = 0$. Approximations improve as n increases.

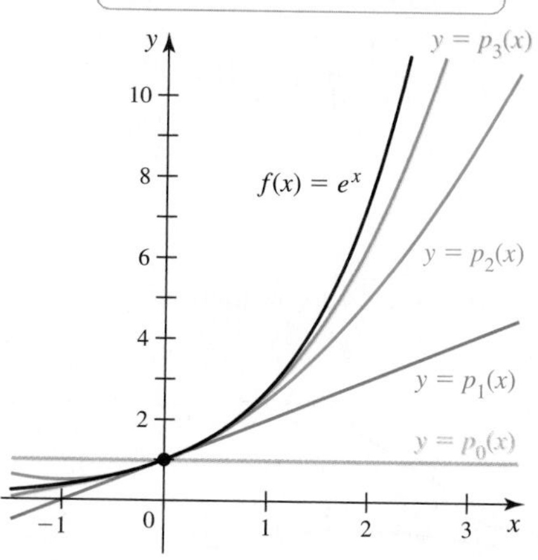

FIGURE 10.8

Notice that each successive polynomial provides a better fit to $f(x) = e^x$ near 0 (Figure 10.8). Better approximations are obtained with higher-order polynomials. If the pattern in these polynomials is continued, the nth-order Taylor polynomial for e^x centered at 0 is

$$p_n(x) = 1 + x + \frac{x^2}{2!} + \frac{x^3}{3!} + \cdots + \frac{x^n}{n!} = \sum_{k=0}^{n} \frac{x^k}{k!}.$$

b. We evaluate $p_n(0.1)$ and $p_n(-0.25)$ for $n = 0, 1, 2, 3$ and compare these values to the calculator values of $e^{0.1} \approx 1.1051709$ and $e^{-0.25} \approx 0.77880078$. The results are shown in Table 10.1. Observe that the errors in the approximations decrease as n increases. In addition, the errors in approximating $e^{0.1}$ are smaller in magnitude than the errors in approximating $e^{-0.25}$ because $x = 0.1$ is closer to the center of the polynomials than $x = -0.25$. Reasonable approximations based on these calculations are $e^{0.1} \approx 1.105$ and $e^{-0.25} \approx 0.78$.

Table 10.1

n	Approximations to $e^{0.1}$	Absolute error $\lvert e^{0.1} - p_n(0.1)\rvert$	Approximations to $e^{-0.25}$	Absolute error $\lvert e^{-0.25} - p_n(-0.25)\rvert$
0	1	1.05×10^{-1}	1	2.21×10^{-1}
1	1.1	5.17×10^{-3}	0.75	2.89×10^{-2}
2	1.105	1.71×10^{-4}	0.78125	2.45×10^{-3}
3	1.105167	4.25×10^{-6}	0.778646	1.55×10^{-4}

➤ A rule of thumb in finding estimates based on several approximations: Keep all of the digits that are common to the last two approximations after rounding.

QUICK CHECK 4 Write out the next two polynomials p_4 and p_5 for $f(x) = e^x$ in Example 3. ◂

Related Exercises 21–26 ◂

EXAMPLE 4 Approximating a real number using Taylor polynomials Use polynomials of order $n = 0, 1, 2,$ and 3 to approximate $\sqrt{18}$.

SOLUTION Letting $f(x) = \sqrt{x}$, we choose the center $a = 16$ because it is near 18, and f and its derivatives are easy to evaluate at 16. The Taylor polynomials have the form

$$p_n(x) = f(16) + f'(16)(x - 16) + \frac{f''(16)}{2!}(x - 16)^2 + \cdots + \frac{f^{(n)}(16)}{n!}(x - 16)^n.$$

We now evaluate the required derivatives:

$$f(x) = \sqrt{x} \Rightarrow f(16) = 4$$

$$f'(x) = \frac{1}{2}x^{-1/2} \Rightarrow f'(16) = \frac{1}{8}$$

$$f''(x) = -\frac{1}{4}x^{-3/2} \Rightarrow f''(16) = -\frac{1}{256}$$

$$f'''(x) = \frac{3}{8}x^{-5/2} \Rightarrow f'''(16) = \frac{3}{8192}$$

Therefore, the polynomial p_3 (which includes p_0, p_1, and p_2) is

$$p_3(x) = \underbrace{\underbrace{\underbrace{4}_{p_0} + \frac{1}{8}(x - 16)}_{p_1} - \frac{1}{512}(x - 16)^2}_{p_2} + \frac{1}{16{,}384}(x - 16)^3.$$

The graphs of the Taylor polynomials (Figure 10.9) show better approximations to f as the order of the approximation increases.

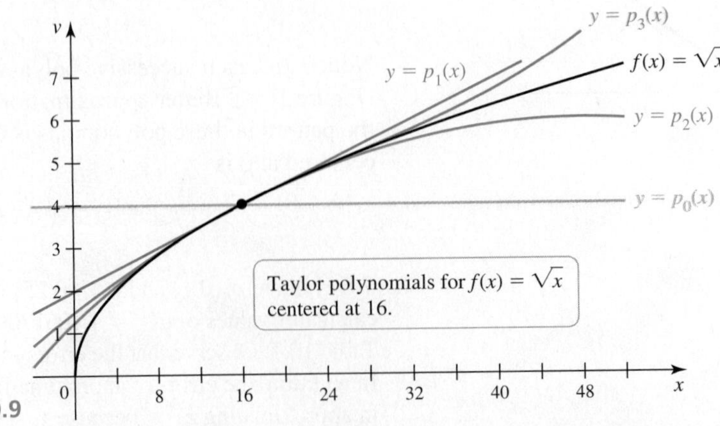

FIGURE 10.9

Letting $x = 18$, we obtain the approximations to $\sqrt{18}$ and the associated absolute errors shown in Table 10.2. (A calculator is used for the value of $\sqrt{18}$.) As expected, the errors decrease as n increases. Based on these calculations, a reasonable approximation is $\sqrt{18} \approx 4.24$.

QUICK CHECK 5 At what point would you center the Taylor polynomials for $\sqrt{x}$ and $\sqrt[4]{x}$ to approximate $\sqrt{51}$ and $\sqrt[4]{15}$, respectively?

Table 10.2

n	Approximations $p_n(18)$	Absolute Error $\lvert\sqrt{18} - p_n(18)\rvert$
0	4	2.43×10^{-1}
1	4.25	7.36×10^{-3}
2	4.242188	4.53×10^{-4}
3	4.242676	3.51×10^{-5}

Related Exercises 27–40

Remainder in a Taylor Polynomial

Taylor polynomials provide good approximations to functions near a specific point. But *how* good are the approximations? To answer this question we define the **remainder** in a Taylor polynomial. If p_n is the Taylor polynomial of order n for f, then the remainder at the point x is

$$R_n(x) = f(x) - p_n(x).$$

The absolute value of the remainder is the error made in approximating $f(x)$ by $p_n(x)$. Equivalently, we have $f(x) = p_n(x) + R_n(x)$, which says that f consists of two components: the polynomial approximation and the associated remainder.

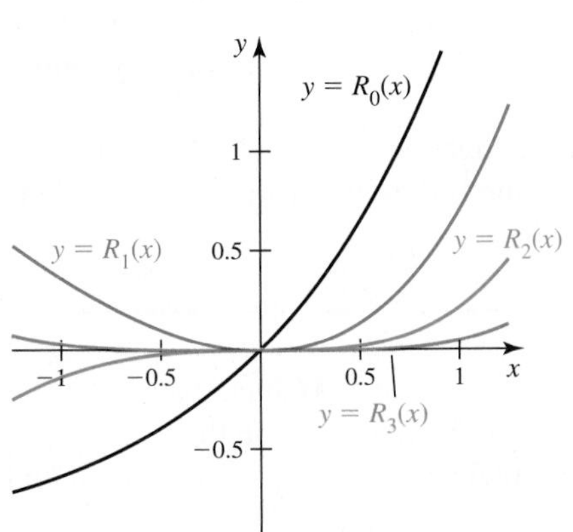

FIGURE 10.10

DEFINITION Remainder in a Taylor Polynomial

Let p_n be the Taylor polynomial of order n for f. The **remainder** in using p_n to approximate f at the point x is

$$R_n(x) = f(x) - p_n(x).$$

The idea of a remainder is illustrated in Figure 10.10, where we see the remainder terms associated with the Taylor polynomials for $f(x) = e^x$ centered at 0. For fixed order n, the remainders tend to increase in magnitude as x moves farther from the center of the polynomials (in this case 0). And for fixed x, remainders decrease in magnitude to zero with increasing n.

The remainder term for Taylor polynomials may be written quite concisely, which enables us to estimate remainders. The following result is known as **Taylor's Theorem** (or the **Remainder Theorem**).

> The remainder term for a Taylor polynomial can be expressed in several different forms. The form in Theorem 10.1 is called the *Lagrange form* of the remainder.

THEOREM 10.1 Taylor's Theorem

Let f have continuous derivatives up to $f^{(n+1)}$ on an open interval I containing a. For all x in I,

$$f(x) = p_n(x) + R_n(x),$$

where p_n is the nth-order Taylor polynomial for f centered at a, and the remainder is

$$R_n(x) = \frac{f^{(n+1)}(c)}{(n+1)!}(x - a)^{n+1},$$

for some point c between x and a.

Discussion We make two observations here and outline a proof in Exercise 84. First, the case $n = 0$ is the Mean Value Theorem (Section 4.6). This theorem states that the average slope of the curve $y = f(x)$ over an interval equals the slope of the line tangent to the curve at some point on the interval:

$$\frac{f(x) - f(a)}{x - a} = f'(c),$$

where c is between x and a. Rearranging this expression we have

$$\begin{aligned} f(x) &= \underbrace{f(a)}_{p_0(x)} + \underbrace{f'(c)(x - a)}_{R_0(x)} \\ &= p_0(x) + R_0(x), \end{aligned}$$

which is Taylor's Theorem with $n = 0$. Not surprisingly, the term $f^{(n+1)}(c)$ in Taylor's Theorem comes from a Mean Value Theorem argument.

The second observation makes the remainder term easier to remember. If you write the $(n + 1)$st Taylor polynomial p_{n+1}, the highest-degree term is $\dfrac{f^{(n+1)}(a)}{(n + 1)!}(x - a)^{n+1}$. Replacing $f^{(n+1)}(a)$ by $f^{(n+1)}(c)$ results in the remainder term for p_n.

Estimating the Remainder

The remainder has both practical and theoretical importance. We deal with practical matters now and theoretical matters in Section 10.3. The remainder term is used to estimate errors in approximations and to determine the number of terms of a Taylor polynomial needed to achieve a prescribed accuracy.

Because c is generally unknown, the difficulty in estimating of the remainder is finding a bound for $|f^{(n+1)}(c)|$. Assuming this can be done, the following theorem gives a standard estimate for the remainder term.

THEOREM 10.2 Estimate of the Remainder
Let n be a fixed positive integer. Suppose there exists a number M such that $|f^{(n+1)}(c)| \le M$ for all c between a and x inclusive. The remainder in the nth-order Taylor polynomial for f centered at a satisfies

$$|R_n(x)| = |f(x) - p_n(x)| \le M\frac{|x - a|^{n+1}}{(n + 1)!}.$$

Proof The proof requires taking the absolute value of the remainder term in Theorem 10.1, replacing $|f^{(n+1)}(c)|$ by a larger quantity M, and forming an inequality. ◄

EXAMPLE 5 Estimating the remainder for cos *x* Find a bound for the magnitude of the remainder term for the Taylor polynomials of $f(x) = \cos x$ centered at 0.

SOLUTION According to Theorem 10.1 with $a = 0$, we have

$$R_n(x) = \frac{f^{(n+1)}(c)}{(n + 1)!}x^{n+1},$$

where c is between 0 and x. Notice that $f^{(n+1)}(c) = \pm \sin c$ or $f^{(n+1)}(c) = \pm \cos c$. In all cases, $|f^{(n+1)}(c)| \le 1$. Therefore, we take $M = 1$ in Theorem 10.2, and the absolute value of the remainder term can be bounded as

$$|R_n(x)| = \left|\frac{f^{(n+1)}(c)}{(n + 1)!}x^{n+1}\right| \le \frac{|x|^{n+1}}{(n + 1)!}.$$

For example, if we approximate cos (0.1) using the Taylor polynomial p_{10}, the maximum error satisfies

$$|R_{10}(0.1)| \leq \frac{0.1^{11}}{11!} \approx 2.5 \times 10^{-19}.$$

Related Exercises 41–46

EXAMPLE 6 Estimating the remainder for e^x Estimate the error in approximating $e^{0.45}$ using the Taylor polynomial of order $n = 6$ for $f(x) = e^x$ centered at 0.

SOLUTION By Taylor's Theorem with $a = 0$, we have

$$R_n(x) = \frac{f^{(n+1)}(c)}{(n+1)!}x^{n+1},$$

where c is between 0 and x. Because $f^{(k)}(x) = e^x$, for $k = 0, 1, 2, \ldots$, $f^{(n+1)}(c) = e^c$ and the remainder term is

$$R_n(x) = \frac{e^c}{(n+1)!}x^{n+1}.$$

If we wish to approximate e^x for $x = 0.45$, then $0 < c < x = 0.45$. Because e^c is an increasing function, $e^c < e^{0.45}$. Assuming that $e^{0.45}$ cannot be evaluated exactly (it is the number we are approximating), it must be bounded above by a number M. A conservative bound is obtained by noting that $e^{0.45} < e^{1/2} < 4^{1/2} = 2$. So, if we take $M = 2$, the maximum error satisfies

$$|R_6(0.45)| < 2\frac{0.45^7}{7!} \approx 1.5 \times 10^{-6}.$$

Recall that if $f(x) = e^x$, then $p_n(x) = \sum_{k=0}^{n} \frac{x^k}{k!}$.

Using the Taylor polynomial derived in Example 3 with $n = 6$, the resulting approximation to $e^{0.45}$ is

$$p_6(0.45) = \sum_{k=0}^{6} \frac{0.45^k}{k!} \approx 1.5683114;$$

it has an error that does not exceed 1.5×10^{-6}. *Related Exercises 47–52*

QUICK CHECK 6 In Example 6, give an approximate upper bound for $R_7(0.45)$.

EXAMPLE 7 Maximum error The nth-order Taylor polynomial for $f(x) = \ln(1 - x)$ centered at 0 is

$$p_n(x) = -\sum_{k=1}^{n} \frac{x^k}{k} = -x - \frac{x^2}{2} - \frac{x^3}{3} - \cdots - \frac{x^n}{n}.$$

a. What is the maximum error in approximating $\ln(1 - x)$ by $p_3(x)$ for values of x in the interval $\left[-\frac{1}{2}, \frac{1}{2}\right]$?

b. How many terms of the Taylor polynomial are needed to approximate values of $f(x) = \ln(1 - x)$ with an error less than 10^{-3} on the interval $\left[-\frac{1}{2}, \frac{1}{2}\right]$?

SOLUTION

a. The remainder for the Taylor polynomial p_3 is $R_3(x) = \frac{f^{(4)}(c)}{4!}x^4$, where c is between 0 and x. Computing four derivatives of f, we find that $f^{(4)}(x) = -\frac{6}{(1-x)^4}$. On the interval $\left[-\frac{1}{2}, \frac{1}{2}\right]$, the maximum magnitude of this derivative occurs at $x = \frac{1}{2}$ (because the denominator is smallest at $x = \frac{1}{2}$) and is $6/\left(\frac{1}{2}\right)^4 = 96$. Similarly, the factor x^4 has its maximum magnitude at $x = \pm\frac{1}{2}$ and it is $\left(\frac{1}{2}\right)^4 = \frac{1}{16}$. Therefore, $|R_3(x)| \leq \frac{96}{4!} \cdot \left(\frac{1}{16}\right) = 0.25$ on the interval $\left[-\frac{1}{2}, \frac{1}{2}\right]$. The error in approximating $f(x)$ by $p_3(x)$ for $-\frac{1}{2} \leq x \leq \frac{1}{2}$ does not exceed 0.25.

b. For any positive integer n, the remainder is $R_n(x) = \dfrac{f^{(n+1)}(c)}{(n+1)!}x^{n+1}$. Differentiating f several times reveals that

$$f^{(n+1)}(x) = -\frac{n!}{(1-x)^{n+1}}.$$

On the interval $\left[-\frac{1}{2}, \frac{1}{2}\right]$, the maximum magnitude of this derivative occurs at $x = \frac{1}{2}$ and is $n!/\left(\frac{1}{2}\right)^{n+1}$. Similarly, x^{n+1} has its maximum magnitude at $x = \pm\frac{1}{2}$, and it is $\left(\frac{1}{2}\right)^{n+1}$. Therefore, a bound on the remainder is

$$|R_n(x)| \le \frac{n!2^{n+1}}{(n+1)!}\frac{1}{2^{n+1}} = \frac{1}{n+1}.$$

To ensure that the error is less than 10^{-3} on the entire interval $\left[-\frac{1}{2}, \frac{1}{2}\right]$, n must satisfy $|R_n| \le \dfrac{1}{n+1} < 10^{-3}$ or $n > 999$. This error is likely to be significantly less than 10^{-3} if x is near 0.

Related Exercises 53–64 ◀

SECTION 10.1 EXERCISES

Review Questions

1. Suppose you use a Taylor polynomial with $n = 2$ centered at 0 to approximate a function f. What matching conditions are satisfied by the polynomial?

2. Does the accuracy of a Taylor polynomial generally increase or decrease with the order of the polynomial? Explain.

3. The first three Taylor polynomials for $f(x) = \sqrt{1+x}$ centered at 0 are $p_0 = 1$, $p_1 = 1 + \dfrac{x}{2}$, and $p_2 = 1 + \dfrac{x}{2} - \dfrac{x^2}{8}$. Find three approximations to $\sqrt{1.1}$.

4. In general, how many terms do the Taylor polynomials p_2 and p_3 have in common?

5. How is the remainder in a Taylor polynomial defined?

6. Explain how to estimate the remainder in an approximation given by a Taylor polynomial.

Basic Skills

T 7–12. Linear and quadratic approximation

a. Find the linear approximating polynomial for the following functions centered at the given point a.

b. Find the quadratic approximating polynomial for the following functions centered at the given point a.

c. Use the polynomials obtained in parts (a) and (b) to approximate the given quantity.

7. $f(x) = e^{-x}$, $a = 0$; approximate $e^{-0.2}$.

8. $f(x) = \sqrt{x}$, $a = 4$; approximate $\sqrt{3.9}$.

9. $f(x) = (1+x)^{-1}$, $a = 0$; approximate $1/1.05$.

10. $f(x) = \cos x$, $a = \pi/4$; approximate $\cos(0.24\pi)$.

11. $f(x) = x^{1/3}$, $a = 8$; approximate $7.5^{1/3}$.

12. $f(x) = \tan^{-1} x$, $a = 0$; approximate $\tan^{-1} 0.1$.

T 13–20. Taylor polynomials

a. Find the nth-order Taylor polynomials of the given function centered at 0 for n = 0, 1, and 2.

b. Graph the Taylor polynomials and the function.

13. $f(x) = \cos x$

14. $f(x) = e^{-x}$

15. $f(x) = \ln(1-x)$

16. $f(x) = (1+x)^{-1/2}$

17. $f(x) = \tan x$

18. $f(x) = (1+x)^{-2}$

19. $f(x) = (1+x)^{-3}$

20. $f(x) = \sin^{-1} x$

T 21–26. Approximations with Taylor polynomials

a. Use the given Taylor polynomial p_2 to approximate the given quantity.

b. Compute the absolute error in the approximation assuming the exact value is given by a calculator.

21. Approximate $\sqrt{1.05}$ using $f(x) = \sqrt{1+x}$ and $p_2(x) = 1 + x/2 - x^2/8$.

22. Approximate $\sqrt[3]{1.1}$ using $f(x) = \sqrt[3]{1+x}$ and $p_2(x) = 1 + x/3 - x^2/9$.

23. Approximate $\dfrac{1}{\sqrt{1.08}}$ using $f(x) = \dfrac{1}{\sqrt{1+x}}$ and $p_2(x) = 1 - x/2 + 3x^2/8$.

24. Approximate $\ln 1.06$ using $f(x) = \ln(1+x)$ and $p_2(x) = x - x^2/2$.

25. Approximate $e^{-0.15}$ using $f(x) = e^{-x}$ and $p_2(x) = 1 - x + x^2/2$.

26. Approximate $\dfrac{1}{1.12^3}$ using $f(x) = \dfrac{1}{(1+x)^3}$ and $p_2(x) = 1 - 3x + 6x^2$.

27–32. Taylor polynomials centered at $a \neq 0$

a. Find the nth-order Taylor polynomials for the given function centered at the given point a for $n = 0$, 1, and 2.

b. Graph the Taylor polynomials and the function.

27. $f(x) = \sin x, a = \pi/4$
28. $f(x) = \cos x, a = \pi/6$
29. $f(x) = \sqrt{x}, a = 9$
30. $f(x) = \sqrt[3]{x}, a = 8$
31. $f(x) = \ln x, a = e$
32. $f(x) = \sqrt[4]{x}, a = 16$

33–40. Approximations with Taylor polynomials

a. Approximate the given quantities using Taylor polynomials with $n = 3$.

b. Compute the absolute error in the approximation assuming the exact value is given by a calculator.

33. $e^{0.12}$
34. $\cos(-0.2)$
35. $\tan(-0.1)$
36. $\ln(1.05)$
37. $\sqrt{1.06}$
38. $\sqrt[4]{79}$
39. $\sqrt{101}$
40. $\sqrt[3]{126}$

41–46. Remainder terms *Find the remainder term R_n in the nth-order Taylor polynomial centered at a for the given functions. Express the result for a general value of n.*

41. $f(x) = \sin x;\ a = 0$
42. $f(x) = \cos 2x;\ a = 0$
43. $f(x) = e^{-x};\ a = 0$
44. $f(x) = \cos x;\ a = \pi/2$
45. $f(x) = \sin x;\ a = \pi/2$
46. $f(x) = 1/(1 - x);\ a = 0$

47–52. Estimating errors *Use the remainder term to estimate the absolute error in approximating the following quantities with the nth-order Taylor polynomial centered at 0. Estimates are not unique.*

47. $\sin 0.3;\ n = 4$
48. $\cos 0.45;\ n = 3$
49. $e^{0.25};\ n = 4$
50. $\tan 0.3;\ n = 2$
51. $e^{-0.5};\ n = 4$
52. $\ln 1.04;\ n = 3$

53–58. Maximum error *Use the remainder term to estimate the maximum error in the following approximations on the given interval. Error bounds are not unique.*

53. $\sin x \approx x - x^3/6;\ [-\pi/4, \pi/4]$
54. $\cos x \approx 1 - x^2/2;\ [-\pi/4, \pi/4]$
55. $e^x \approx 1 + x + x^2/2;\ \left[-\frac{1}{2}, \frac{1}{2}\right]$
56. $\tan x \approx x;\ [-\pi/6, \pi/6]$
57. $\ln(1 + x) \approx x - x^2/2;\ [-0.2, 0.2]$
58. $\sqrt{1 + x} \approx 1 + x/2;\ [-0.1, 0.1]$

59–64. Number of terms *What is the minimum order of the Taylor polynomial required to approximate the following quantities with an absolute error no greater than 10^{-3}? (The answer depends on your choice of a center.)*

59. $e^{-0.5}$
60. $\sin 0.2$
61. $\cos(-0.25)$
62. $\ln 0.85$
63. $\sqrt{1.06}$
64. $1/\sqrt{0.85}$

Further Explorations

65. **Explain why or why not** Determine whether the following statements are true and give an explanation or counterexample.
    a. The Taylor polynomials for $f(x) = e^{-2x}$ consist of even powers only.
    b. For $f(x) = x^5 - 1$, the Taylor polynomial of order 10 centered at $x = 0$ is f itself.
    c. The nth-order Taylor polynomial for $f(x) = \sqrt{1 + x^2}$ centered at 0 consists of even powers of x only.

66. **Taylor coefficients for $x = a$** Follow the procedure in the text to show that the nth-order Taylor polynomial that matches f and its derivatives up to order n at a has coefficients

$$c_k = \frac{f^{(k)}(a)}{k!}, \text{ for } k = 0, 1, 2, \ldots, n.$$

67. **Matching functions with polynomials** Match the following six functions with the given six Taylor polynomials of order 2. Give reasons for your choices.

a. $\sqrt{1 + 2x}$	A. $p_2(x) = 1 + 2x + 2x^2$
b. $\dfrac{1}{\sqrt{1 + 2x}}$	B. $p_2(x) = 1 - 6x + 24x^2$
c. e^{2x}	C. $p_2(x) = 1 + x - \dfrac{x^2}{2}$
d. $\dfrac{1}{1 + 2x}$	D. $p_2(x) = 1 - 2x + 4x^2$
e. $\dfrac{1}{(1 + 2x)^3}$	E. $p_2(x) = 1 - x + \dfrac{3}{2}x^2$
f. e^{-2x}	F. $p_2(x) = 1 - 2x + 2x^2$

68. **Dependence of errors on x** Consider $f(x) = \ln(1 - x)$ and its Taylor polynomials given in Example 7.
    a. Graph $y = |f(x) - p_2(x)|$ and $y = |f(x) - p_3(x)|$ on the interval $\left[-\frac{1}{2}, \frac{1}{2}\right]$ (two curves).
    b. At what points of $\left[-\frac{1}{2}, \frac{1}{2}\right]$ is the error largest? Smallest?
    c. Are these results consistent with the theoretical error bounds obtained in Example 7?

Applications

69–76. Small argument approximations *Consider the following common approximations when x is near zero.*

a. Estimate $f(0.1)$ and give the maximum error in the approximation.

b. Estimate $f(0.2)$ and give the maximum error in the approximation.

69. $f(x) = \sin x \approx x$
70. $f(x) = \tan x \approx x$
71. $f(x) = \cos x \approx 1 - x^2/2$
72. $f(x) = \tan^{-1} x \approx x$
73. $f(x) = \sqrt{1 + x} \approx 1 + x/2$
74. $f(x) = \ln(1 + x) \approx x - x^2/2$
75. $f(x) = e^x \approx 1 + x$
76. $f(x) = \sin^{-1} x \approx x$

77. Errors in approximations Suppose you approximate $\sin x$ at the points $x = -0.2, -0.1, 0.0, 0.1, 0.2$ using the Taylor polynomials $p_3 = x - x^3/6$ and $p_5 = x - x^3/6 + x^5/120$. Assume that the exact value of $\sin x$ is given by a calculator.

a. Complete the table showing the absolute errors in the approximations at each point. Show two significant digits.

x	Error $= \lvert \sin x - p_3(x) \rvert$	Error $= \lvert \sin x - p_5(x) \rvert$
-0.2		
-0.1		
0.0		
0.1		
0.2		

b. In each error column, how do the errors vary with x? For what values of x are the errors the largest and smallest in magnitude?

78–81. Errors in approximations *Carry out the procedure described in Exercise 77 with the following functions and approximations.*

78. $f(x) = \cos x,\ p_2(x) = 1 - \dfrac{x^2}{2},\ p_4(x) = 1 - \dfrac{x^2}{2} + \dfrac{x^4}{24}$

79. $f(x) = e^{-x},\ p_1(x) = 1 - x,\ p_2(x) = 1 - x + \dfrac{x^2}{2}$

80. $f(x) = \ln(1 + x),\ p_1(x) = x,\ p_2(x) = x - \dfrac{x^2}{2}$

81. $f(x) = \tan x,\ p_1(x) = x,\ p_3(x) = x + \dfrac{x^3}{3}$

82. Best expansion point Suppose you wish to approximate $\cos(\pi/12)$ using Taylor polynomials. Is the approximation more accurate if you use Taylor polynomials centered at 0 or $\pi/6$? Use a calculator for numerical experiments and check for consistency with Theorem 10.2. Does the answer depend on the order of the polynomial?

83. Best expansion point Suppose you wish to approximate $e^{0.35}$ using Taylor polynomials. Is the approximation more accurate if you use Taylor polynomials centered at 0 or $\ln 2$? Use a calculator for numerical experiments and check for consistency with Theorem 10.2. Does the answer depend on the order of the polynomial?

Additional Exercises

84. Proof of Taylor's Theorem There are several proofs of Taylor's Theorem, which lead to various forms of the remainder. The following proof is instructive because it leads to two different forms of the remainder and it relies on the Fundamental Theorem of Calculus, integration by parts, and the Mean Value Theorem for Integrals. Assume that f has at least $n + 1$ continuous derivatives on an interval containing a.

a. Show that the Fundamental Theorem of Calculus can be written in the form

$$f(x) = f(a) + \int_a^x f'(t)\,dt.$$

b. Use integration by parts ($u = f'(t)$, $dv = dt$) to show that

$$f(x) = f(a) + (x - a)f'(a) + \int_a^x (x - t)f''(t)\,dt.$$

c. Show that n integrations by parts gives

$$f(x) = f(a) + \frac{f'(a)}{1!}(x - a) + \frac{f''(a)}{2!}(x - a)^2 + \cdots + \frac{f^{(n)}(a)}{n!}(x - a)^n + \underbrace{\int_a^x \frac{f^{(n+1)}(t)}{n!}(x - t)^n\,dt}_{R_n(x)}.$$

d. Challenge: The result in part (c) looks like $f(x) = p_n(x) + R_n(x)$, where p_n is the nth-order Taylor polynomial and R_n is a new form of the remainder term, known as the integral form of the remainder term. Use a general form of the Mean Value Theorem for Integrals (see margin note on p.298) to show that R_n can be expressed in the form

$$R_n(x) = \frac{f^{(n+1)}(c)}{(n + 1)!}(x - a)^{n+1},$$

where c is between a and x.

85. Tangent line is p_1 Let f be differentiable at $x = a$.

a. Find the equation of the line tangent to the curve $y = f(x)$ at $(a, f(a))$.

b. Find the Taylor polynomial p_1 centered at a and confirm that it describes the tangent line found in part (a).

86. Local extreme points and inflection points Suppose that f has two continuous derivatives at a.

a. Show that if f has a local maximum at a, then the Taylor polynomial p_2 centered at a also has a local maximum at a.

b. Show that if f has a local minimum at a, then the Taylor polynomial p_2 centered at a also has a local minimum at a.

c. Is it true that if f has an inflection point at a, then the Taylor polynomial p_2 centered at a also has an inflection point at a?

d. Are the converses to parts (a) and (b) true? If p_2 has a local extreme point at a, does f have the same type of point at a?

QUICK CHECK ANSWERS

3. $f(x) = \sin x$ is an odd function, and its even-ordered derivatives are zero at 0, so its Taylor polynomials are also odd functions. **4.** $p_4(x) = p_3(x) + \dfrac{x^4}{4!}$; $p_5(x) = p_4(x) + \dfrac{x^5}{5!}$ **5.** $x = 49$ and $x = 16$ are good choices. **6.** Because $e^{0.45} < 2$, $\lvert R_7(0.45) \rvert < 2\dfrac{0.45^8}{8!} \approx 8.3 \times 10^{-8}$.

10.2 Properties of Power Series

The preceding section demonstrated that Taylor polynomials provide accurate approximations to many functions and that, in general, the approximations improve as we let the degree of the polynomials increase. In this section, we take the next step and let the degree of the Taylor polynomials increase without bound to produce a *power series.*

Geometric Series as Power Series

A good way to become familiar with power series is to return to *geometric series*, first encountered in Section 9.3. Recall that for a fixed number r,

$$\sum_{k=0}^{\infty} r^k = 1 + r + r^2 + \cdots = \frac{1}{1-r}, \qquad \text{provided } |r| < 1.$$

It's a small change to replace the real number r by the variable x. In doing so, the geometric series becomes a new representation of a familiar function:

$$\sum_{k=0}^{\infty} x^k = 1 + x + x^2 + \cdots = \frac{1}{1-x}, \qquad \text{provided } |x| < 1$$

This infinite series is a *power series*. Notice that while $1/(1-x)$ is defined for $\{x: x \neq 1\}$, its power series converges only for $|x| < 1$. The set of values for which a power series converges is called its *interval of convergence.*

Figure 10.11 shows an approximation to the graph of g made by summing the first 500 terms of the power series at selected values of x on the interval $(-2, 2)$.

Power series are used to represent familiar functions such as trigonometric, exponential, and logarithmic functions. They are also used to define new functions. For example, consider the function defined by

$$g(x) = \sum_{k=1}^{\infty} \frac{(-1)^k\, k}{4^k} x^{2k}.$$

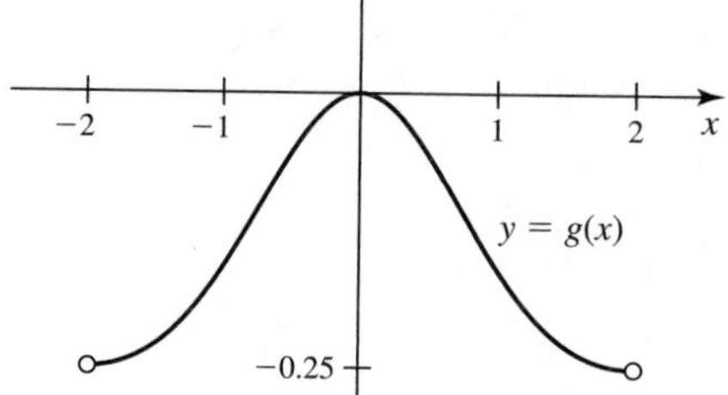

FIGURE 10.11

The term *function* is used advisedly because it's not yet clear whether g really is a function. If so, is it a continuous function? Does it have a derivative? Judging by its graph (Figure 10.11), g appears to be a rather ordinary continuous function (which is identified at the end of the chapter).

In fact, power series satisfy the defining property of all functions: For each value of x, a power series has at most one value. For this reason we refer to a power series as a function, although the domain, properties, and identity of the function may need to be discovered.

QUICK CHECK 1 By substituting $x = 0$ in the power series for g, evaluate $g(0)$ for the function in Figure 10.11.

Convergence of Power Series

We begin by establishing the terminology of power series.

DEFINITION Power Series

A **power series** has the general form

$$\sum_{k=0}^{\infty} c_k (x-a)^k,$$

where a and c_k are real numbers, and x is a variable. The c_k's are the **coefficients** of the power series and a is the **center** of the power series. The set of values of x for which the series converges is the **interval of convergence**. The **radius of convergence** of the power series, denoted R, is the distance from the center of the series to the boundary of the interval of convergence (Figure 10.12).

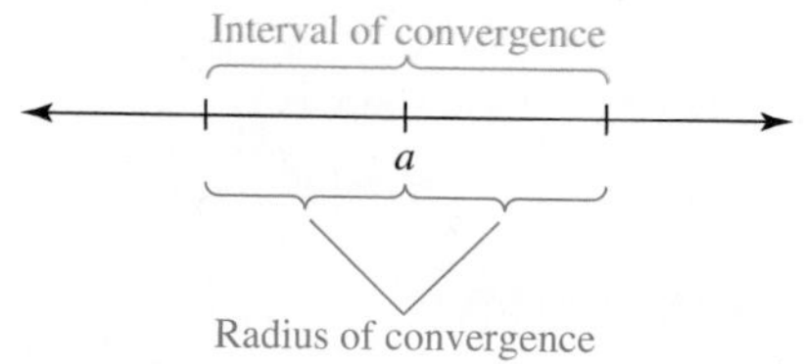

FIGURE 10.12

➤ By the Ratio Test, $\sum |a_k|$ converges if $r = \lim_{k\to\infty} \left|\frac{a_{k+1}}{a_k}\right| < 1$, it diverges if $r > 1$, and the test is inconclusive if $r = 1$.

➤ By the Root Test, $\sum |a_k|$ converges if $\rho = \lim_{k\to\infty} \sqrt[k]{|a_k|} < 1$, it diverges if $\rho > 1$, and the test is inconclusive if $\rho = 1$.

How do we determine the interval of convergence? The presence of the terms x^k or $(x - a)^k$ in a power series suggests using the Ratio Test or the Root Test. Furthermore, because these terms could be positive or negative, we test a power series for absolute convergence. By Theorem 9.21, if we determine the values of x for which the series converges absolutely, we have a set of values for which the series converges.

Recall that a series $\sum a_k$ converges absolutely if the series $\sum |a_k|$ converges. The following examples illustrate how the Ratio and Root Tests are used to determine the interval and radius of convergence.

EXAMPLE 1 **Interval and radius of convergence** Find the interval and radius of convergence for each power series.

a. $\displaystyle\sum_{k=0}^{\infty} \frac{x^k}{k!}$ **b.** $\displaystyle\sum_{k=0}^{\infty} \frac{(-1)^k(x-2)^k}{4^k}$ **c.** $\displaystyle\sum_{k=1}^{\infty} k!\, x^k$

SOLUTION

a. The center of the power series is 0 and the terms of the series are $x^k/k!$. We test the series for absolute convergence using the Ratio Test:

$$r = \lim_{k\to\infty} \frac{|x^{k+1}/(k+1)!|}{|x^k/k!|} \quad \text{Ratio Test}$$

$$= \lim_{k\to\infty} \frac{|x|^{k+1}}{|x|^k} \cdot \frac{k!}{(k+1)!} \quad \text{Invert and multiply.}$$

$$= |x| \lim_{k\to\infty} \frac{1}{k+1} = 0 \quad \text{Simplify and take the limit with } x \text{ fixed.}$$

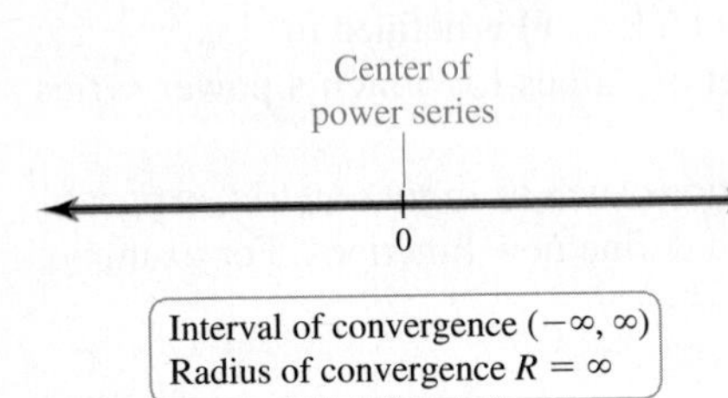

FIGURE 10.13

Notice that in taking the limit as $k \to \infty$, x is held fixed. Therefore, $r = 0$ for all values of x, which implies that the interval of convergence of the power series is $-\infty < x < \infty$ (Figure 10.13) and the radius of convergence is $R = \infty$.

b. We test for absolute convergence using the Root Test:

$$\rho = \lim_{k\to\infty} \sqrt[k]{\left|\frac{(-1)^k(x-2)^k}{4^k}\right|} = \frac{|x-2|}{4}$$

In this case, ρ depends on the value of x. For absolute convergence, x must satisfy

$$\rho = \frac{|x-2|}{4} < 1,$$

which implies that $|x - 2| < 4$. Using standard techniques for solving inequalities, the solution set is $-4 < x - 2 < 4$, or $-2 < x < 6$. Thus, the interval of convergence includes $(-2, 6)$.

The Root Test does not give information about convergence at the endpoints, $x = -2$ and $x = 6$, because at these points, the Root Test results in $\rho = 1$. To test for convergence at the endpoints, we must substitute each endpoint into the series and carry out separate tests. At $x = -2$, the power series becomes

$$\sum_{k=0}^{\infty} \frac{(-1)^k(x-2)^k}{4^k} = \sum_{k=0}^{\infty} \frac{4^k}{4^k} \quad \text{Substitute } x = -2 \text{ and simplify.}$$

$$= \sum_{k=0}^{\infty} 1. \quad \text{Diverges by Divergence Test.}$$

> The Ratio and Root Tests determine the radius of convergence conclusively. However, the interval of convergence is not determined until the endpoints are tested.

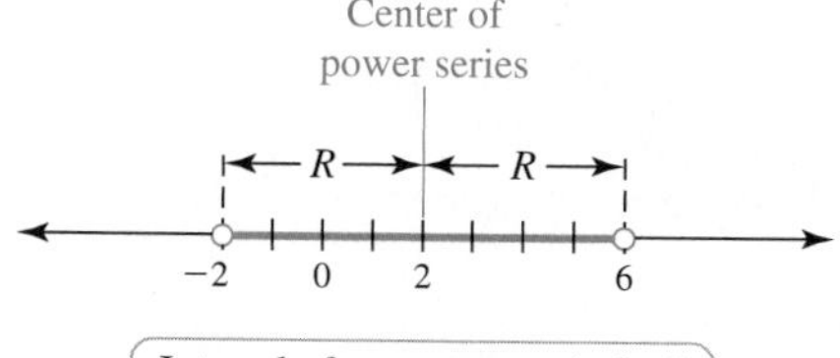

Interval of convergence $(-2, 6)$
Radius of convergence $R = 4$

FIGURE 10.14

The series clearly diverges at the left endpoint. At $x = 6$, the power series is

$$\sum_{k=0}^{\infty} \frac{(-1)^k (x-2)^k}{4^k} = \sum_{k=0}^{\infty} (-1)^k \frac{4^k}{4^k} \quad \text{Substitute } x = 6 \text{ and simplify.}$$

$$= \sum_{k=0}^{\infty} (-1)^k. \quad \text{Diverges by Divergence Test.}$$

This series also diverges at the right endpoint. Therefore, the interval of convergence is $(-2, 6)$, excluding the endpoints (Figure 10.14) and the radius of convergence is $R = 4$.

QUICK CHECK 2 Explain why the power series in Example 1b diverges if $x > 6$ or $x < -2$. ◀

c. To test for absolute convergence we use the Ratio Test:

$$r = \lim_{k\to\infty} \frac{|(k+1)!\, x^{k+1}|}{|k!\, x^k|} \quad \text{Ratio Test}$$

$$= |x| \lim_{k\to\infty} \frac{(k+1)!}{k!} \quad \text{Simplify.}$$

$$= |x| \lim_{k\to\infty} (k+1) \quad \text{Simplify.}$$

$$= \infty \quad \text{If } x \neq 0$$

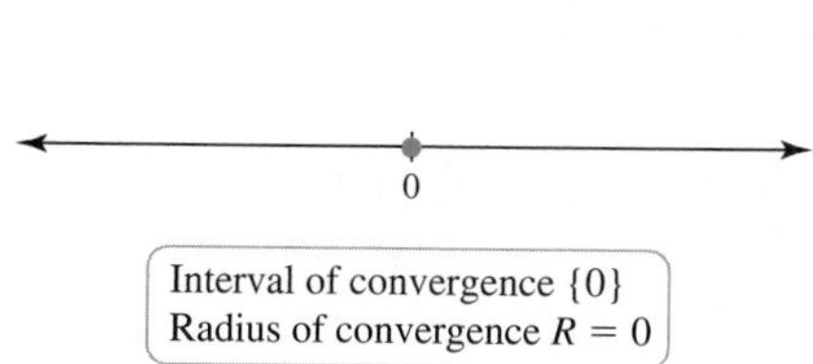

Interval of convergence $\{0\}$
Radius of convergence $R = 0$

FIGURE 10.15

The only way to satisfy $r < 1$ is to take $x = 0$, in which case the power series has a value of 0. The interval of convergence of the power series consists of the single point $x = 0$ (Figure 10.15) and the radius of convergence is $R = 0$. *Related Exercises 9–20* ◀

Example 1 illustrates the three common types of intervals of convergence, which are summarized in the following theorem (see Appendix B for a proof).

> Theorem 10.3 says nothing about convergence at the endpoints. For example, the radius of convergence is 2 for the intervals of convergence $(2, 6)$, $(2, 6]$, $[2, 6)$, or $[2, 6]$.

THEOREM 10.3 Convergence of Power Series

A power series $\sum_{k=0}^{\infty} c_k (x-a)^k$ centered at a converges in one of three ways:

1. The series coverges absolutely for all x, in which case the interval of convergence is $(-\infty, \infty)$ and the radius of convergence is $R = \infty$.
2. There is a real number $R > 0$ such that the series converges absolutely for $|x - a| < R$ and diverges for $|x - a| > R$, in which case the radius of convergence is R.
3. The series converges only at a, in which case the radius of convergence is $R = 0$.

QUICK CHECK 3 What are the interval and radius of convergence of the geometric series $\sum x^k$? ◀

EXAMPLE 2 Interval and radius of convergence Use the Ratio Test to find the radius and interval of convergence of $\sum_{k=1}^{\infty} \frac{(x-2)^k}{\sqrt{k}}$.

SOLUTION

$$r = \lim_{k\to\infty} \frac{|(x-2)^{k+1}/\sqrt{k+1}|}{|(x-2)^k/\sqrt{k}|} \quad \text{Ratio Test}$$

$$= |x-2| \lim_{k\to\infty} \sqrt{\frac{k}{k+1}} \quad \text{Simplify.}$$

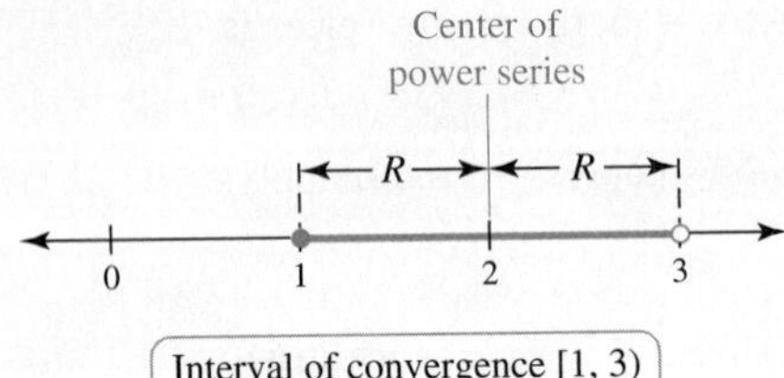

FIGURE 10.16

$$= |x - 2|\sqrt{\underbrace{\lim_{k\to\infty} \frac{k}{k+1}}_{1}} \qquad \text{Limit Law}$$

$$= |x - 2| \qquad \text{Limit equals 1.}$$

The series converges absolutely for all x such that $r < 1$, which implies $|x - 2| < 1$, or $1 < x < 3$. Therefore, the radius of convergence is 1 (Figure 10.16).

We now test the endpoints. Substituting $x = 1$ into the power series, we have

$$\sum_{k=1}^{\infty} \frac{(x-2)^k}{\sqrt{k}} = \sum_{k=1}^{\infty} \frac{(-1)^k}{\sqrt{k}}.$$

This series converges by the Alternating Series Test (the terms of the series decrease in magnitude and approach 0 as $k \to \infty$). Substituting $x = 3$ into the power series, we have

$$\sum_{k=1}^{\infty} \frac{(x-2)^k}{\sqrt{k}} = \sum_{k=1}^{\infty} \frac{1}{\sqrt{k}},$$

which is a divergent p-series. We conclude that the interval of convergence is $1 \le x < 3$ (Figure 10.16).

Related Exercises 9–20 ◂

Combining Power Series

A power series defines a function on its interval of convergence. When power series are combined algebraically, new functions are defined. The following theorem, stated without proof, gives three common ways to combine power series.

➤ New power series can also be defined as the product and quotient of power series. The calculation of the coefficients of such series is more challenging (Exercise 65).

➤ Theorem 10.4 also applies to power series centered at points other than $x = 0$. Property 1 applies directly; Properties 2 and 3 apply with slight modifications.

THEOREM 10.4 Combining Power Series

Suppose the power series $\sum c_k x^k$ and $\sum d_k x^k$ converge absolutely to $f(x)$ and $g(x)$, respectively, on an interval I.

1. **Sum and difference:** The power series $\sum (c_k \pm d_k)x^k$ converges absolutely to $f(x) \pm g(x)$ on I.
2. **Multiplication by a power:** The power series $x^m \sum c_k x^k = \sum c_k x^{k+m}$ converges absolutely to $x^m f(x)$ on I, provided m is an integer such that $k + m \ge 0$ for all terms of the series.
3. **Composition:** If $h(x) = bx^m$, where m is a positive integer and b is a real number, the power series $\sum c_k (h(x))^k$ converges absolutely to the composite function $f(h(x))$ for all x such that $h(x)$ is in I.

EXAMPLE 3 Combining power series Given the geometric series

$$\frac{1}{1-x} = \sum_{k=0}^{\infty} x^k = 1 + x + x^2 + x^3 + \cdots \qquad \text{for } |x| < 1,$$

find the power series and interval of convergence for the following functions.

a. $\frac{x^5}{1-x}$ **b.** $\frac{1}{1-2x}$ **c.** $\frac{1}{1+x^2}$

SOLUTION

a. $$\frac{x^5}{1-x} = x^5(1 + x + x^2 + \cdots) \quad \text{Theorem 10.4, Property 2}$$
$$= x^5 + x^6 + x^7 + \cdots$$
$$= \sum_{k=0}^{\infty} x^{k+5}$$

This geometric series has a ratio $r = x$ and converges when $|r| = |x| < 1$. The interval of convergence is $|x| < 1$.

b. We substitute $2x$ for x in the power series for $\frac{1}{1-x}$:

$$\frac{1}{1-2x} = 1 + (2x) + (2x)^2 + \cdots \quad \text{Theorem 10.4, Property 3}$$
$$= 1 + 2x + 4x^2 + \cdots$$
$$= \sum_{k=0}^{\infty} (2x)^k$$

This geometric series has a ratio $r = 2x$ and converges provided $|r| = |2x| < 1$ or $|x| < \frac{1}{2}$. The interval of convergence is $|x| < \frac{1}{2}$.

c. We substitute $-x^2$ for x in the power series for $\frac{1}{1-x}$:

$$\frac{1}{1+x^2} = 1 + (-x^2) + (-x^2)^2 + \cdots \quad \text{Theorem 10.4, Property 3}$$
$$= 1 - x^2 + x^4 - \cdots$$
$$= \sum_{k=0}^{\infty} (-1)^k x^{2k}$$

This geometric series has a ratio of $r = -x^2$ and converges provided $|r| = |-x^2| = |x^2| < 1$ or $|x| < 1$. *Related Exercises 21–32* ◀

Differentiating and Integrating Power Series

Some properties of polynomials carry over to power series, but others do not. For example, a polynomial is defined for all values of x, whereas a power series is defined only on its interval of convergence. In general, the properties of polynomials carry over to power series when the power series is restricted to its interval of convergence. The following result illustrates this principle.

➤ Theorem 10.5 makes no claim about the convergence of the differentiated or integrated series at the endpoints of the interval of convergence.

THEOREM 10.5 Differentiating and Integrating Power Series
Let the function f be defined by the power series $\sum c_k (x - a)^k$ on its interval of convergence I.

1. f is a continuous function on I.
2. The power series may be differentiated or integrated term by term, and the resulting power series converges to $f'(x)$ or $\int f(x)\,dx + C$, respectively, at all points in the interior of I, where C is an arbitrary constant.

These results are powerful and also deep mathematically. Their proofs require advanced ideas and are omitted. However, some discussion is in order before turning to examples.

The statements in Theorem 10.5 about term-by-term differentiation and integration say two things: The differentiated and integrated power series converge, provided x belongs to the interior of the interval of convergence. But the theorem claims more than convergence. According to the theorem, the differentiated and integrated power series converge to the derivative and indefinite integral of f, respectively, on the interior of the interval of convergence.

EXAMPLE 4 **Differentiating and integrating power series** Consider the geometric series

$$f(x) = \frac{1}{1-x} = \sum_{k=0}^{\infty} x^k = 1 + x + x^2 + x^3 + \cdots \quad \text{for } |x| < 1.$$

a. Differentiate this series term by term to find the power series for f', and identify the function it represents.

b. Integrate this series term by term and identify the function it represents.

SOLUTION

a. We know that $f'(x) = (1-x)^{-2}$. Differentiating the series, we find that

$$\begin{aligned} f'(x) &= \frac{d}{dx}(1 + x + x^2 + x^3 + \cdots) && \text{Differentiate the power series for } f. \\ &= 1 + 2x + 3x^2 + \cdots && \text{Differentiate term by term.} \\ &= \sum_{k=0}^{\infty} (k+1)\, x^k. && \text{Summation notation} \end{aligned}$$

Therefore, on the interval $|x| < 1$,

$$f'(x) = (1-x)^{-2} = \sum_{k=0}^{\infty} (k+1)\, x^k.$$

Substituting $x = \pm 1$ into the power series for f' reveals that the series diverges at both endpoints.

b. Integrating f and integrating the power series term by term, we have

$$\int \frac{dx}{1-x} = \int (1 + x + x^2 + x^3 + \cdots)\, dx,$$

which implies that

$$-\ln|1-x| = x + \frac{x^2}{2} + \frac{x^3}{3} + \frac{x^4}{4} + \cdots + C,$$

where C is an arbitrary constant. Notice that the left side is 0 when $x = 0$. The right side is 0 when $x = 0$ provided we choose $C = 0$. Because $|x| < 1$, the absolute value sign on the left side may be removed. Multiplying both sides by -1, we have a representation for $\ln(1-x)$:

$$\ln(1-x) = -x - \frac{x^2}{2} - \frac{x^3}{3} - \frac{x^4}{4} - \cdots = -\sum_{k=1}^{\infty} \frac{x^k}{k}$$

It is interesting to test the endpoints of the interval $|x| < 1$. When $x = 1$, the series is (a multiple of) the divergent harmonic series, and when $x = -1$, the series is the convergent alternating harmonic series (Section 9.6). So the interval of convergence is $-1 \le x < 1$. Here is a subtle point: Although we know the series converges at $x = -1$, Theorem 10.5 guarantees convergence to $\ln(1 - x)$ only at the interior points. So we cannot use Theorem 10.5 to claim that the series converges to $\ln 2$ at $x = -1$. In fact, it does, as shown in Section 10.3. *Related Exercises 33–38* ◀

QUICK CHECK 4 Use the result of Example 4 to write a power series representation for $\ln\frac{1}{2} = -\ln 2$. ◀

EXAMPLE 5 Functions to power series Find power series representations centered at 0 for the following functions and give their intervals of convergence.

a. $\tan^{-1} x$ **b.** $\ln\left(\frac{1 + x}{1 - x}\right)$

SOLUTION In both cases, we work with known power series and use differentiation, integration, and other combinations.

a. The key is to recall that

$$\int \frac{dx}{1 + x^2} = \tan^{-1} x + C$$

and that, by Example 3c,

$$\frac{1}{1 + x^2} = 1 - x^2 + x^4 - \cdots, \qquad \text{provided } |x| < 1.$$

We now integrate both sides of this last expression; we find that

$$\int \frac{dx}{1 + x^2} = \int (1 - x^2 + x^4 - \cdots)\, dx,$$

which implies that

$$\tan^{-1} x = x - \frac{x^3}{3} + \frac{x^5}{5} - \cdots + C.$$

Substituting $x = 0$ and noting that $\tan^{-1} 0 = 0$, the two sides of this equation agree provided we choose $C = 0$. Therefore,

▶ Again, Theorem 10.5 does not guarantee that the power series in part (a) converges to $\tan^{-1} x$ at $x = \pm 1$. In fact, it does.

$$\tan^{-1} x = x - \frac{x^3}{3} + \frac{x^5}{5} - \cdots = \sum_{k=0}^{\infty} \frac{(-1)^k x^{2k+1}}{2k + 1}.$$

By Theorem 10.5, this power series converges for $|x| < 1$. Testing the endpoints separately, we find that it also converges at $x = \pm 1$. Therefore, the interval of convergence is $[-1, 1]$.

b. We have already seen (Example 4) that

$$\ln(1 - x) = -x - \frac{x^2}{2} - \frac{x^3}{3} - \cdots.$$

Replacing x by $-x$, we have

▶ Nicolaus Mercator (1620–1687) and Sir Isaac Newton (1642–1727) independently derived the power series for $\ln(1 + x)$, which is called the *Mercator series*.

$$\ln(1 - (-x)) = \ln(1 + x) = x - \frac{x^2}{2} + \frac{x^3}{3} - \cdots.$$

Subtracting these two power series gives

$$\begin{aligned}\ln\left(\frac{1+x}{1-x}\right) &= \ln(1+x) - \ln(1-x) && \text{Properties of logarithms}\\ &= \underbrace{\left(x - \frac{x^2}{2} + \frac{x^3}{3} - \cdots\right)}_{\ln(1+x)} - \underbrace{\left(-x - \frac{x^2}{2} - \frac{x^3}{3} - \cdots\right)}_{\ln(1-x)}, \quad \text{for } |x| < 1\\ &= 2\left(x + \frac{x^3}{3} + \frac{x^5}{5} + \cdots\right) && \text{Combine, Theorem 10.4.}\\ &= 2\sum_{k=0}^{\infty} \frac{x^{2k+1}}{2k+1} && \text{Summation notation}\end{aligned}$$

QUICK CHECK 5 Verify that the power series in Example 5b does not converge at the endpoints $x = \pm 1$.◀

This power series is the difference of two power series, both of which converge on the interval $|x| < 1$. Therefore, by Theorem 10.4, the new series also converges on $|x| < 1$.

Related Exercises 39–44 ◀

If you look carefully, every example in this section is ultimately based on the geometric series. Using this single series, we were able to develop power series for many other functions. Imagine what we could do with a few more basic power series. The following section accomplishes precisely that end. There, we discover basic power series for all the standard functions of calculus.

SECTION 10.2 EXERCISES

Review Questions

1. Write the first four terms of a power series with coefficients c_0, c_1, c_2, c_3 centered at 0.
2. Write the first four terms of a power series with coefficients c_0, c_1, c_2, c_3 centered at 3.
3. What tests are used to determine the radius of convergence of a power series?
4. Explain why a power series is tested for *absolute* convergence.
5. Do the interval and radius of convergence of a power series change when the series is differentiated or integrated? Explain.
6. What is the radius of convergence of the power series $\sum c_k (x/2)^k$ if the radius of convergence of $\sum c_k x^k$ is R?
7. What is the interval of convergence of the power series $\sum (4x)^k$?
8. How are the radii of convergence of the power series $\sum c_k x^k$ and $\sum (-1)^k c_k x^k$ related?

Basic Skills

9–20. Interval and radius of convergence *Determine the radius of convergence of the following power series. Then test the endpoints to determine the interval of convergence.*

9. $\sum \left(\frac{x}{3}\right)^k$
10. $\sum (-1)^k \frac{x^k}{5^k}$
11. $\sum \frac{x^k}{k^k}$
12. $\sum (-1)^k \frac{k(x-4)^k}{2^k}$
13. $\sum \frac{k^2 x^{2k}}{k!}$
14. $\sum \frac{k^k x^k}{(k+1)!}$
15. $\sum \frac{x^{2k+1}}{3^{k-1}}$
16. $\sum \left(-\frac{x}{10}\right)^{2k}$
17. $\sum \frac{(x-1)^k k^k}{(k+1)^k}$
18. $\sum \frac{(-2)^k (x+3)^k}{3^{k+1}}$
19. $\sum \frac{k^{20} x^k}{(2k+1)!}$
20. $\sum (-1)^k \frac{x^{3k}}{27^k}$

21–26. Combining power series *Use the geometric series*

$$f(x) = \frac{1}{1-x} = \sum_{k=0}^{\infty} x^k, \quad \text{for } |x| < 1,$$

to find the power series representation for the following functions (centered at 0). Give the interval of convergence of the new series.

21. $f(3x) = \frac{1}{1-3x}$
22. $g(x) = \frac{x^3}{1-x}$
23. $h(x) = \frac{2x^3}{1-x}$
24. $f(x^3) = \frac{1}{1-x^3}$
25. $p(x) = \frac{4x^{12}}{1-x}$
26. $f(-4x) = \frac{1}{1+4x}$

27–32. Combining power series *Use the power series representation*

$$f(x) = \ln(1-x) = -\sum_{k=1}^{\infty} \frac{x^k}{k}, \quad \text{for } -1 \le x < 1,$$

to find the power series for the following functions (centered at 0). Give the interval of convergence of the new series.

27. $f(3x) = \ln(1-3x)$
28. $g(x) = x^3 \ln(1-x)$

29. $h(x) = x \ln(1 - x)$

30. $f(x^3) = \ln(1 - x^3)$

31. $p(x) = 2x^6 \ln(1 - x)$

32. $f(-4x) = \ln(1 + 4x)$

33–38. Differentiating and integrating power series *Find the power series representation for g centered at 0 by differentiating or integrating the power series for f (perhaps more than once). Give the interval of convergence for the resulting series.*

33. $g(x) = \dfrac{1}{(1 - x)^2}$ using $f(x) = \dfrac{1}{1 - x}$

34. $g(x) = \dfrac{1}{(1 - x)^3}$ using $f(x) = \dfrac{1}{1 - x}$

35. $g(x) = \dfrac{1}{(1 - x)^4}$ using $f(x) = \dfrac{1}{1 - x}$

36. $g(x) = \dfrac{x}{(1 + x^2)^2}$ using $f(x) = \dfrac{1}{1 + x^2}$

37. $g(x) = \ln(1 - 3x)$ using $f(x) = \dfrac{1}{1 - 3x}$

38. $g(x) = \ln(1 + x^2)$ using $f(x) = \dfrac{x}{1 + x^2}$

39–44. Functions to power series *Find power series representations centered at 0 for the following functions using known power series. Give the interval of convergence for the resulting series.*

39. $f(x) = \dfrac{1}{1 + x^2}$

40. $f(x) = \dfrac{1}{1 - x^4}$

41. $f(x) = \dfrac{3}{3 + x}$

42. $f(x) = \ln\sqrt{1 - x^2}$

43. $f(x) = \ln\sqrt{4 - x^2}$

44. $f(x) = \tan^{-1}(4x^2)$

Further Explorations

45. Explain why or why not Determine whether the following statements are true and give an explanation or counterexample.

a. The interval of convergence of the power series $\Sigma c_k (x - 3)^k$ could be $(-2, 8)$.

b. $\Sigma(-2x)^k$ converges for $-1/2 < x < 1/2$.

c. If $f(x) = \Sigma c_k x^k$ on the interval $|x| < 1$, then $f(x^2) = \Sigma c_k x^{2k}$ on the interval $|x| < 1$.

d. If $f(x) = \Sigma c_k x^k = 0$ for all x on an interval $(-a, a)$, then $c_k = 0$ for all k.

46–49. Summation notation *Write the following power series in summation (sigma) notation.*

46. $1 + \dfrac{x}{2} + \dfrac{x^2}{4} + \dfrac{x^3}{6} + \cdots$

47. $1 - \dfrac{x}{2} + \dfrac{x^2}{3} - \dfrac{x^3}{4} + \cdots$

48. $x - \dfrac{x^3}{4} + \dfrac{x^5}{9} - \dfrac{x^7}{16} + \cdots$

49. $-\dfrac{x^2}{1!} + \dfrac{x^4}{2!} - \dfrac{x^6}{3!} + \dfrac{x^8}{4!} - \cdots$

50. Scaling power series If the power series $f(x) = \Sigma c_k x^k$ has an interval of convergence of $|x| < R$, what is the interval of convergence of the power series for $f(ax)$, where $a \neq 0$ is a real number?

51. Shifting power series If the power series $f(x) = \Sigma c_k x^k$ has an interval of convergence of $|x| < R$, what is the interval of convergence of the power series for $f(x - a)$, where $a \neq 0$ is a real number?

52–57. Series to functions *Find the function represented by the following series and find the interval of convergence of the series.*

52. $\displaystyle\sum_{k=0}^{\infty} (x^2 + 1)^{2k}$

53. $\displaystyle\sum_{k=0}^{\infty} (\sqrt{x} - 2)^k$

54. $\displaystyle\sum_{k=1}^{\infty} \frac{x^{2k}}{4k}$

55. $\displaystyle\sum_{k=0}^{\infty} e^{-kx}$

56. $\displaystyle\sum_{k=1}^{\infty} \frac{(x - 2)^k}{3^{2k}}$

57. $\displaystyle\sum_{k=0}^{\infty} \left(\frac{x^2 - 1}{3}\right)^k$

58. A useful substitution Replace x by $x - 1$ in the series $\ln(1 + x) = \displaystyle\sum_{k=1}^{\infty} \frac{(-1)^{k+1} x^k}{k}$ to obtain a power series for $\ln x$ centered at $x = 1$. What is the interval of convergence for the new power series?

59–62. Exponential function *In Section 10.3, we show that the power series for the exponential function centered at 0 is*

$$e^x = \sum_{k=0}^{\infty} \frac{x^k}{k!}, \qquad \text{for } -\infty < x < \infty.$$

Use the methods of this section to find the power series for the following functions. Give the interval of convergence for the resulting series.

59. $f(x) = e^{-x}$

60. $f(x) = e^{2x}$

61. $f(x) = e^{-3x}$

62. $f(x) = x^2 e^x$

Additional Exercises

63. Powers of x multiplied by a power series Prove that if $f(x) = \displaystyle\sum_{k=0}^{\infty} c_k x^k$ converges on the interval I, then the power series for $x^m f(x)$ also converges on I for positive integers m.

T **64. Remainders** Let

$$f(x) = \sum_{k=0}^{\infty} x^k = \frac{1}{1 - x} \quad \text{and} \quad S_n(x) = \sum_{k=0}^{n-1} x^k.$$

Then, the remainder in truncating the power series after n terms is $R_n = f(x) - S_n(x)$, which now depends on x.

a. Show that $R_n(x) = x^n/(1 - x)$.

b. Graph the remainder function on the interval $|x| < 1$ for $n = 1, 2, 3$. Discuss and interpret the graph. Where on the interval is $|R_n(x)|$ largest? Smallest?

c. For fixed n, minimize $|R_n(x)|$ with respect to x. Does the result agree with the observations in part (b)?

d. Let $N(x)$ be the number of terms required to reduce $|R_n(x)|$ to less than 10^{-6}. Graph the function $N(x)$ on the interval $|x| < 1$. Discuss and interpret the graph.

65. Product of power series Let

$$f(x) = \sum_{k=0}^{\infty} c_k x^k \quad \text{and} \quad g(x) = \sum_{k=0}^{\infty} d_k x^k.$$

a. Multiply the power series together as if they were polynomials, collecting all terms that are multiples of 1, x, and x^2. Write the first three terms of the product $f(x)g(x)$.

b. Find a general expression for the coefficient of x^n in the product series, for $n = 0, 1, 2, \ldots$.

66. Inverse sine Given the power series

$$\frac{1}{\sqrt{1 - x^2}} = 1 + \frac{1}{2}x^2 + \frac{1 \cdot 3}{2 \cdot 4}x^4 + \frac{1 \cdot 3 \cdot 5}{2 \cdot 4 \cdot 6}x^6 + \cdots$$

for $-1 < x < 1$, find the power series for $f(x) = \sin^{-1} x$ centered at 0.

T **67. Computing with power series** Consider the following function and its power series:

$$f(x) = \frac{1}{(1 - x)^2} = \sum_{k=1}^{\infty} k x^{k-1}, \quad \text{for } -1 < x < 1$$

a. Let $S_n(x)$ be the first n terms of the series. With $n = 5$ and $n = 10$, graph $f(x)$ and $S_n(x)$ at the sample points $x = -0.9, -0.8, \ldots, -0.1, 0, 0.1, \ldots, 0.8, 0.9$ (two graphs). Where is the difference in the graphs the greatest?

b. What value of n is needed to guarantee that $|f(x) - S_n(x)| < 0.01$ at all of the sample points?

QUICK CHECK ANSWERS

1. $g(0) = 0$ **2.** For any value of x with $x > 6$ or $x < -2$, the series diverges by the Divergence Test. The Root or Ratio Test gives the same result. **3.** $|x| < 1, R = 1$ **4.** Substituting $x = 1/2$, $\ln(1/2) = -\ln 2 = -\sum_{k=1}^{\infty} \frac{1}{2^k k}$.

10.3 Taylor Series

In the preceding section we saw that a power series represents a function on its interval of convergence. This section explores the opposite question: Given a function, what is its power series representation? We have already made significant progress in answering this question because we know how Taylor polynomials are used to approximate functions. We now extend Taylor polynomials to produce power series—called *Taylor series*—that provide series representations of functions.

Taylor Series for a Function

Suppose a function f has derivatives $f^{(k)}(a)$ of *all* orders at the point a. If we write the Taylor polynomial of degree n for f centered at a and allow n to increase indefinitely, a power series is obtained. The power series consists of a Taylor polynomial of order n plus terms of higher degree called the *remainder*:

$$\underbrace{c_0 + c_1(x - a) + c_2(x - a)^2 + \cdots + c_n(x - a)^n}_{\text{Taylor polynomial of order } n} + \underbrace{c_{n+1}(x - a)^{n+1} + \cdots}_{\text{remainder}}$$

$$= \sum_{k=0}^{\infty} c_k (x - a)^k$$

The coefficients of the Taylor polynomial are given by

$$c_k = \frac{f^{(k)}(a)}{k!}, \quad \text{for } k = 0, 1, 2, \ldots.$$

These coefficients are also the coefficients of the power series. Furthermore, this power series has the same matching properties as the Taylor polynomials; that is, the function f and the power series agree in *all* of their derivatives at a. This power series is called the *Taylor series for f centered at a*. It is the natural extension of the set of Taylor polynomials for f at a. The special case of a Taylor series centered at 0 is called a *Maclaurin series*.

➤ Maclaurin series are named after the Scottish mathematician Colin Maclaurin (1698–1746), who described them (with credit to Taylor) in a textbook in 1742.

DEFINITION Taylor/Maclaurin Series for a Function

Suppose the function f has derivatives of all orders on an interval containing the point a. The **Taylor series for f centered at a** is

$$f(a) + f'(a)(x - a) + \frac{f''(a)}{2!}(x - a)^2 + \frac{f^{(3)}(a)}{3!}(x - a)^3 + \cdots$$
$$= \sum_{k=0}^{\infty} \frac{f^{(k)}(a)}{k!}(x - a)^k.$$

A Taylor series centered at 0 is called a **Maclaurin series.**

For the Taylor series to be useful, we need to know two things:

- The values of x for which the power series converges, which comprise the interval of convergence.
- The values of x for which the power series for f *equals* f. This question is more subtle and is postponed for a few pages. For now, we find the Taylor series for f at a point, but we refrain from saying $f(x)$ equals the power series.

➤ There are unusual cases in which the Taylor series for a function converges to a different function (Exercise 80).

QUICK CHECK 1 Verify that if the Taylor series for f centered at a is evaluated at $x = a$, then the Taylor series equals $f(a)$. ◄

EXAMPLE 1 **Maclaurin series and convergence** Find the Maclaurin series (which is the Taylor series centered at 0) for the following functions. Give the interval of convergence.

a. $f(x) = \cos x$ **b.** $f(x) = \dfrac{1}{1 - x}$

SOLUTION The procedure for finding the coefficients of a Taylor series is the same as for Taylor polynomials; most of the work is computing the derivatives of f.

a. The Maclaurin series (centered at 0) has the form

$$\sum_{k=0}^{\infty} c_k x^k, \qquad \text{where } c_k = \frac{f^{(k)}(0)}{k!}, \qquad \text{for } k = 0, 1, 2, \ldots.$$

We evaluate derivatives of $f(x) = \cos x$ at $x = 0$:

$$\begin{aligned} f(x) &= \cos x \Rightarrow f(0) = 1 \\ f'(x) &= -\sin x \Rightarrow f'(0) = 0 \\ f''(x) &= -\cos x \Rightarrow f''(0) = -1 \\ f'''(x) &= \sin x \Rightarrow f'''(0) = 0 \\ f^{(4)}(x) &= \cos x \Rightarrow f^{(4)}(0) = 1 \\ &\vdots \qquad\qquad\qquad \vdots \end{aligned}$$

Because the odd-order derivatives are zero, $c_k = \dfrac{f^{(k)}(0)}{k!} = 0$ when k is odd. Using the even-order derivatives, we have

$$c_0 = f(0) = 1 \qquad c_2 = \frac{f^{(2)}(0)}{2!} = -\frac{1}{2!}$$
$$c_4 = \frac{f^{(4)}(0)}{4!} = \frac{1}{4!} \qquad c_6 = \frac{f^{(6)}(0)}{6!} = -\frac{1}{6!}$$

and, in general, $c_{2k} = \dfrac{(-1)^k}{(2k)!}$. Therefore, the Maclaurin series for f is

$$1 - \frac{x^2}{2!} + \frac{x^4}{4!} - \frac{x^6}{6!} + \cdots = \sum_{k=0}^{\infty} \frac{(-1)^k}{(2k)!} x^{2k}.$$

Notice that this series contains all the Taylor polynomials. In this case, it consists only of even powers of x, reflecting the fact that $\cos x$ is an even function.

For what values of x does the series converge? As discussed in Section 10.2, we apply the Ratio Test to $\sum_{k=0}^{\infty} \left| \dfrac{(-1)^k}{(2k)!} x^{2k} \right|$ to test for absolute convergence:

➤ Recall that

$(2k + 2)! = (2k + 2)(2k + 1)(2k)!$

Therefore, $\dfrac{(2k)!}{(2k + 2)!} = \dfrac{1}{(2k + 2)(2k + 1)}$

$$r = \lim_{k \to \infty} \left| \frac{(-1)^{k+1} x^{2(k+1)}/(2(k+1))!}{(-1)^k x^{2k}/(2k)!} \right| \qquad \lim_{k \to \infty} \left| \frac{a_{k+1}}{a_k} \right|$$

$$= \lim_{k \to \infty} \left| \frac{x^2}{(2k + 2)(2k + 1)} \right| = 0 \qquad \text{Simplify and take the limit with } x \text{ fixed.}$$

In this case, $r < 1$ for all x, so the Maclaurin series converges absolutely for all x and the interval of convergence is $-\infty < x < \infty$.

b. We proceed in a similar way with $f(x) = 1/(1 - x)$ by evaluating the derivatives of f at 0:

$$f(x) = \frac{1}{1 - x} \Rightarrow f(0) = 1$$

$$f'(x) = \frac{1}{(1 - x)^2} \Rightarrow f'(0) = 1$$

$$f''(x) = \frac{2}{(1 - x)^3} \Rightarrow f''(0) = 2!$$

$$f'''(x) = \frac{3 \cdot 2}{(1 - x)^4} \Rightarrow f'''(0) = 3!$$

$$f^{(4)}(x) = \frac{4 \cdot 3 \cdot 2}{(1 - x)^5} \Rightarrow f^{(4)}(0) = 4!$$

and, in general, $f^{(k)}(0) = k!$. Therefore, the Maclaurin series coefficients are $c_k = \dfrac{f^{(k)}(0)}{k!} = \dfrac{k!}{k!} = 1$, for $k = 0, 1, 2, \ldots$. The series for f centered at 0 is

$$1 + x + x^2 + x^3 + \cdots = \sum_{k=0}^{\infty} x^k.$$

This power series is familiar! The Maclaurin series for $f(x) = 1/(1 - x)$ is a geometric series. We could apply the Ratio Test, but we have already demonstrated that this series converges for $|x| < 1$.

Related Exercises 9–22 ◄

QUICK CHECK 2 Based on Example 1b, what is the Taylor series for $f(x) = (1 + x)^{-1}$? ◄

The preceding example has an important lesson. *There is only one power series representation for a given function about a given point; however, there may be several ways to find it.*

EXAMPLE 2 **Manipulating Maclaurin series** Let $f(x) = e^x$.

a. Find the Maclaurin series for f (by definition centered at 0).

b. Find its interval of convergence.

c. Use the Maclaurin series for e^x to find the Maclaurin series for the functions $x^4 e^x$, e^{-2x}, and e^{-x^2}.

SOLUTION

a. The coefficients of the Taylor polynomials for $f(x) = e^x$ centered at 0 are $c_k = 1/k!$ (Example 3, Section 10.1). They are also the coefficients of the Maclaurin series. Therefore, the Maclaurin series for f is

$$1 + \frac{x}{1!} + \frac{x^2}{2!} + \cdots + \frac{x^n}{n!} + \cdots = \sum_{k=0}^{\infty} \frac{x^k}{k!}.$$

b. By the Ratio Test,

$$\begin{aligned} r &= \lim_{k\to\infty} \left| \frac{x^{k+1}/(k+1)!}{x^k/k!} \right| && \text{Substitute } (k+1)\text{st and } k\text{th terms.} \\ &= \lim_{k\to\infty} \left| \frac{x}{k+1} \right| = 0. && \text{Simplify; take the limit with } x \text{ fixed.} \end{aligned}$$

Because $r < 1$ for all x, the interval of convergence is $-\infty < x < \infty$.

c. As stated in Theorem 10.4, power series may be added, multiplied by powers of x, or composed with functions on their intervals of convergence. Therefore, the Maclaurin series for $x^4 e^x$ is

$$x^4 \sum_{k=0}^{\infty} \frac{x^k}{k!} = \sum_{k=0}^{\infty} \frac{x^{k+4}}{k!} = x^4 + \frac{x^5}{1!} + \frac{x^6}{2!} + \cdots + \frac{x^{k+4}}{k!} + \cdots.$$

Similarly, e^{-2x} is the composition $f(-2x)$. Replacing x by $-2x$ in the Maclaurin series for f, the series representation for e^{-2x} is

$$\sum_{k=0}^{\infty} \frac{(-2x)^k}{k!} = \sum_{k=0}^{\infty} \frac{(-1)^k (2x)^k}{k!} = 1 - 2x + 2x^2 - \frac{4}{3}x^3 + \cdots.$$

The Maclaurin series for e^{-x^2} is obtained by replacing x by $-x^2$ in the power series for f. The resulting series is

$$\sum_{k=0}^{\infty} \frac{(-x^2)^k}{k!} = \sum_{k=0}^{\infty} \frac{(-1)^k x^{2k}}{k!} = 1 - x^2 + \frac{x^4}{2!} - \frac{x^6}{3!} + \cdots.$$

Because the interval of convergence of $f(x) = e^x$ is $-\infty < x < \infty$, the manipulations used to obtain the series for $x^4 e^x$, e^{-2x}, or e^{-x^2} do not change the interval of convergence. If in doubt about the interval of convergence of a new series, apply the Ratio Test.

Related Exercises 23–28 ◀

QUICK CHECK 3 Find the first three terms of the Taylor series for $2xe^x$ and e^{-x}. ◀

The Binomial Series

We know from algebra that if p is a positive integer then $(1 + x)^p$ is a polynomial of degree p. In fact,

$$(1 + x)^p = \binom{p}{0} + \binom{p}{1}x + \binom{p}{2}x^2 + \cdots + \binom{p}{p}x^p,$$

where the binomial coefficients $\binom{p}{k}$ are defined as follows.

For nonnegative integers p, the binomial coefficients may also be defined as $\binom{p}{k} = \frac{p!}{k!(p-k)!}$, where $0! = 1$. The coefficients form the rows of Pascal's triangle. The coefficients of $(1 + x)^5$ form the sixth row of the triangle.

1
1 1
1 2 1
1 3 3 1
1 4 6 4 1
1 5 10 10 5 1

DEFINITION Binomial Coefficients

For real numbers p and integers $k \geq 1$,

$$\binom{p}{k} = \frac{p(p-1)(p-2)\cdots(p-k+1)}{k!}, \qquad \binom{p}{0} = 1.$$

For example,

$$(1+x)^5 = \underbrace{\binom{5}{0}}_{1} + \underbrace{\binom{5}{1}}_{5}x + \underbrace{\binom{5}{2}}_{10}x^2 + \underbrace{\binom{5}{3}}_{10}x^3 + \underbrace{\binom{5}{4}}_{5}x^4 + \underbrace{\binom{5}{5}}_{1}x^5$$

$$= 1 + 5x + 10x^2 + 10x^3 + 5x^4 + x^5$$

QUICK CHECK 4 Evaluate the binomial coefficients $\binom{-3}{2}$ and $\binom{\frac{1}{2}}{3}$.

Our goal is to extend this idea to the functions $f(x) = (1 + x)^p$, where p is a real number other than a nonnegative integer. The result is a Taylor series called the *binomial series*.

THEOREM 10.6 Binomial Series

For real numbers p, the Taylor series for $f(x) = (1 + x)^p$ centered at 0 is the **binomial series**

$$\sum_{k=0}^{\infty} \binom{p}{k} x^k = \sum_{k=0}^{\infty} \frac{p(p-1)(p-2)\cdots(p-k+1)}{k!} x^k$$

$$= 1 + px + \frac{p(p-1)}{2!}x^2 + \frac{p(p-1)(p-2)}{3!}x^3 + \cdots.$$

The series converges for $|x| < 1$ (and possibly at the endpoints depending on p). If p is a nonnegative integer, the series terminates and results in a polynomial of degree p.

Proof We seek a power series centered at 0 of the form

$$\sum_{k=0}^{\infty} c_k x^k, \qquad \text{where } c_k = \frac{f^{(k)}(0)}{k!}, \qquad \text{for } k = 0, 1, 2, \ldots.$$

The job is to evaluate the derivatives of f at 0:

$$f(x) = (1+x)^p \Rightarrow f(0) = 1$$
$$f'(x) = p(1+x)^{p-1} \Rightarrow f'(0) = p$$
$$f''(x) = p(p-1)(1+x)^{p-2} \Rightarrow f''(0) = p(p-1)$$
$$f'''(x) = p(p-1)(p-2)(1+x)^{p-3} \Rightarrow f'''(0) = p(p-1)(p-2)$$

To evaluate $\binom{p}{k}$, start with p, successively subtract 1 until k factors are obtained; then take the product of these k factors and divide by $k!$. Recall that $\binom{p}{0} = 1$.

A pattern emerges: The kth derivative $f^{(k)}(0)$ involves the k factors $p(p-1)(p-2)\cdots(p-k+1)$. In general, we have

$$f^{(k)}(0) = p(p-1)(p-2)\cdots(p-k+1).$$

Therefore,

$$c_k = \frac{f^{(k)}(0)}{k!} = \frac{p(p-1)(p-2)\cdots(p-k+1)}{k!} = \binom{p}{k} \quad \text{for } k = 0, 1, 2, \ldots.$$

The Taylor series for $f(x) = (1 + x)^p$ centered at 0 is

$$\binom{p}{0} + \binom{p}{1}x + \binom{p}{2}x^2 + \binom{p}{3}x^3 + \cdots = \sum_{k=0}^{\infty}\binom{p}{k}x^k.$$

This series has the same general form for all values of p. When p is a nonnegative integer, the series terminates and it is a polynomial of degree p.

The interval of convergence for the binomial series is determined by the Ratio Test. Holding p and x fixed, the relevant limit is

$$r = \lim_{k\to\infty}\left|\frac{x^{k+1}p(p-1)\cdots(p-k+1)(p-k)/(k+1)!}{x^k\, p(p-1)\cdots(p-k+1)/k!}\right| \quad \text{Ratio of } (k+1)\text{st to } k\text{th term}$$

$$= |x| \underbrace{\lim_{k\to\infty}\left|\frac{p-k}{k+1}\right|}_{\text{approaches } 1} \quad \text{Cancel terms and simplify.}$$

$$= |x|. \quad \text{With } p \text{ fixed, } \lim_{k\to\infty}\left|\frac{(p-k)}{k+1}\right| = 1.$$

Absolute convergence requires that $r = |x| < 1$. Therefore, the series converges absolutely for $|x| < 1$. (Depending on the value of p, the interval of convergence may include the endpoints; they should be tested on a case-by-case basis.) ◄

EXAMPLE 3 **Binomial series** Consider the function $f(x) = \sqrt{1 + x}$.

➤ A binomial series is a Taylor series. Because the series in Example 3 is centered at 0, it is also a Maclaurin series.

a. Find the binomial series for f centered at 0.

b. Approximate $\sqrt{1.15}$ to three decimal places. Assume the series for f converges to f on the interval of convergence.

SOLUTION

a. We use the formula for the binomial coefficients with $p = \frac{1}{2}$ to compute the first four coefficients:

$$c_0 = 1 \qquad c_1 = \binom{\frac{1}{2}}{1} = \frac{\left(\frac{1}{2}\right)}{1!} = \frac{1}{2}$$

$$c_2 = \binom{\frac{1}{2}}{2} = \frac{\frac{1}{2}\left(-\frac{1}{2}\right)}{2!} = -\frac{1}{8} \qquad c_3 = \binom{\frac{1}{2}}{3} = \frac{\frac{1}{2}\left(-\frac{1}{2}\right)\left(-\frac{3}{2}\right)}{3!} = \frac{1}{16}$$

The leading terms of the binomial series are

$$1 + \frac{1}{2}x - \frac{1}{8}x^2 + \frac{1}{16}x^3 - \cdots.$$

Table 10.3

n	Approximations: $p_n(0.15)$
0	1.0
1	1.075
2	1.0721875
3	1.072398438

➤ The remainder theorem for alternating series (Section 9.6) could be used to estimate the number of terms of the Taylor series needed to achieve a desired accuracy.

b. Truncating the binomial series in part (a) produces Taylor polynomials that may be used to approximate $f(0.15) = \sqrt{1.15}$. With $x = 0.15$, we find the polynomial approximations shown in Table 10.3. Four terms of the power series ($n = 3$) give $\sqrt{1.15} \approx 1.072$, which is accurate to three decimal places.

Related Exercises 29–34 ◄

QUICK CHECK 5 Use two and three terms of the binomial series in Example 3 to approximate $\sqrt{1.1}$.

EXAMPLE 4 **Working with binomial series** Consider the functions

$$f(x) = \sqrt[3]{1 + x} \quad \text{and} \quad g(x) = \sqrt[3]{c + x}, \qquad \text{where } c > 0 \text{ is a constant.}$$

a. Find the first four terms of the binomial series for f centered at 0.

b. Use part (a) to find the first four terms of the binomial series for g centered at 0.

c. Use part (b) to approximate $\sqrt[3]{23}, \sqrt[3]{24}, \ldots, \sqrt[3]{31}$. Assume the series for g converges to g on the interval of convergence.

SOLUTION

a. Because $f(x) = (1 + x)^{1/3}$, we find the binomial coefficients with $p = \frac{1}{3}$:

$$c_0 = \binom{\frac{1}{3}}{0} = 1 \qquad c_1 = \binom{\frac{1}{3}}{1} = \frac{\left(\frac{1}{3}\right)}{1!} = \frac{1}{3}$$

$$c_2 = \binom{\frac{1}{3}}{2} = \frac{\left(\frac{1}{3}\right)\left(\frac{1}{3} - 1\right)}{2!} = -\frac{1}{9} \qquad c_3 = \binom{\frac{1}{3}}{3} = \frac{\left(\frac{1}{3}\right)\left(\frac{1}{3} - 1\right)\left(\frac{1}{3} - 2\right)}{3!} = \frac{5}{81} \cdots$$

The first four terms of the binomial series are

$$1 + \frac{1}{3}x - \frac{1}{9}x^2 + \frac{5}{81}x^3 - \cdots.$$

b. To avoid deriving a new series for $g(x) = \sqrt[3]{c + x}$, a few steps of algebra allow us to use part (a). Note that

$$g(x) = \sqrt[3]{c + x} = \sqrt[3]{c\left(1 + \frac{x}{c}\right)} = \sqrt[3]{c} \cdot \sqrt[3]{1 + \frac{x}{c}} = \sqrt[3]{c} \cdot f\left(\frac{x}{c}\right).$$

In other words, g can be expressed in terms of f, for which we already have a binomial series. The binomial series for g is obtained by substituting x/c into the binomial series for f and multiplying by $\sqrt[3]{c}$:

$$g(x) = \sqrt[3]{c}\underbrace{\left[1 + \frac{1}{3}\left(\frac{x}{c}\right) - \frac{1}{9}\left(\frac{x}{c}\right)^2 + \frac{5}{81}\left(\frac{x}{c}\right)^3 - \cdots\right]}_{f(x/c)}$$

The series for $f(x/c)$ converges provided $|x/c| < 1$, or, equivalently, for $|x| < c$.

c. The series of part (b) may be truncated (forming a polynomial p_3) to approximate cube roots. For example, note that $\sqrt[3]{29} = \sqrt[3]{\underbrace{27}_{c} + \underbrace{2}_{x}}$, so we take $c = 27$ and $x = 2$. The choice $c = 27$ is made because 29 is near 27 and $\sqrt[3]{c} = \sqrt[3]{27} = 3$ is easy to evaluate. Substituting $c = 27$ and $x = 2$, we find that

$$\sqrt[3]{29} \approx \sqrt[3]{27}\left[1 + \frac{1}{3}\left(\frac{2}{27}\right) - \frac{1}{9}\left(\frac{2}{27}\right)^2 + \frac{5}{81}\left(\frac{2}{27}\right)^3\right] \approx 3.0723.$$

The same method is used to approximate the cube roots of 23, 24, …, 30, 31 (Table 10.4). The absolute error is the difference between p_3 and the value given by a calculator. Notice that the errors increase as we move away from 27.

Table 10.4

	Approximation p_3	Absolute error
$\sqrt[3]{23}$	2.8439	6.7×10^{-5}
$\sqrt[3]{24}$	2.8845	2.0×10^{-5}
$\sqrt[3]{25}$	2.9240	3.9×10^{-6}
$\sqrt[3]{26}$	2.9625	2.4×10^{-7}
$\sqrt[3]{27}$	3	0
$\sqrt[3]{28}$	3.0366	2.3×10^{-7}
$\sqrt[3]{29}$	3.0723	3.5×10^{-6}
$\sqrt[3]{30}$	3.1072	1.7×10^{-5}
$\sqrt[3]{31}$	3.1414	5.4×10^{-5}

Related Exercises 35–46 ◀

Convergence of Taylor Series

It may seem that the story of Taylor series is over. But there is a technical point that is easily overlooked. Given a function f, we know how to write its Taylor series centered at a point a. And we know how to find its interval of convergence. We still do not know that the power series actually converges to f. The remaining task is to determine when the Taylor series for f actually converges to f on its interval of convergence. Fortunately, the necessary tools have already been presented in Taylor's Theorem (Theorem 10.1), which gives the remainder for Taylor polynomials.

Assume f has derivatives $f^{(n)}$ of *all* orders on an open interval containing the point a. Taylor's Theorem tells us that

$$f(x) = p_n(x) + R_n(x),$$

where p_n is the nth-order Taylor polynomial for f centered at a,

$$R_n(x) = \frac{f^{(n+1)}(c)}{(n + 1)!}(x - a)^{n+1},$$

and c is a point between x and a. We see that the remainder, $R_n(x) = f(x) - p_n(x)$, measures the difference between f and the approximating polynomial p_n. For the Taylor series to converge to f on an interval, the remainder must approach zero at each point of the interval as the order of the Taylor polynomials increases. The following theorem makes these ideas precise.

THEOREM 10.7 Convergence of Taylor Series
Let f have derivatives of all orders on an open interval I containing a. The Taylor series for f centered at a converges to f for all x in I if and only if $\lim_{n\to\infty} R_n(x) = 0$ for all x in I, where

$$R_n(x) = \frac{f^{(n+1)}(c)}{(n + 1)!}(x - a)^{n+1}$$

is the remainder at x (with c between x and a).

Proof The theorem requires derivatives of *all* orders. Therefore, by Taylor's Theorem (Theorem 10.1), the remainder term exists in the given form for all n. Let p_n denote the nth-order Taylor polynomial and note that $\lim_{n\to\infty} p_n(x)$ is the Taylor series for f centered at a, evaluated at a point x in I.

First assume that $\lim_{n\to\infty} R_n(x) = 0$ on the interval I and recall that $p_n(x) = f(x) - R_n(x)$. Taking limits of both sides, we have

$$\underbrace{\lim_{n\to\infty} p_n(x)}_{\text{Taylor series}} = \lim_{n\to\infty} (f(x) - R_n(x)) = \underbrace{\lim_{n\to\infty} f(x)}_{f(x)} - \underbrace{\lim_{n\to\infty} R_n(x)}_{0} = f(x).$$

We conclude that the Taylor series $\lim_{n\to\infty} p_n(x)$ equals $f(x)$, for all x in I.

Conversely, if the Taylor series converges to f, then $f(x) = \lim_{n\to\infty} p_n(x)$ and

$$0 = f(x) - \lim_{n\to\infty} p_n(x) = \lim_{n\to\infty} \underbrace{(f(x) - p_n(x))}_{R_n(x)} = \lim_{n\to\infty} R_n(x).$$

It follows that $\lim_{n\to\infty} R_n(x) = 0$ for all x in I. ◀

Even with an expression for the remainder, it may be difficult to show that $\lim_{n\to\infty} R_n(x) = 0$. The following examples illustrate cases in which it is possible.

EXAMPLE 5 **Remainder term in the Maclaurin series for e^x** Show that the Maclaurin series for $f(x) = e^x$ converges to f for $-\infty < x < \infty$.

SOLUTION As shown in Example 2, the Maclaurin series for $f(x) = e^x$ is

$$\sum_{k=0}^{\infty} \frac{x^k}{k!} = 1 + x + \frac{x^2}{2!} + \cdots + \frac{x^n}{n!} + \cdots,$$

which converges for $-\infty < x < \infty$. In Example 6 of Section 10.1 it was shown that the remainder term is

$$R_n(x) = \frac{e^c}{(n+1)!} x^{n+1},$$

where c is between 0 and x. Notice that the intermediate point c varies with n, but it is always between 0 and x. Therefore, e^c is between $e^0 = 1$ and e^x; in fact, $e^c \le e^{|x|}$ for all n. It follows that

$$|R_n(x)| \le \frac{e^{|x|}}{(n+1)!} |x|^{n+1}.$$

Holding x fixed, we have

$$\lim_{n\to\infty} |R_n(x)| = \lim_{n\to\infty} \frac{e^{|x|}}{(n+1)!} |x|^{n+1} = e^{|x|} \lim_{n\to\infty} \frac{|x|^{n+1}}{(n+1)!} = 0,$$

where we used the fact that $\lim_{n\to\infty} x^n/n! = 0$ for $-\infty < x < \infty$ (Section 9.2). Because $\lim_{n\to\infty} |R_n(x)| = 0$, it follows that for all real numbers x the Taylor series converges to e^x, or

$$e^x = \sum_{k=0}^{\infty} \frac{x^k}{k!} = 1 + x + \frac{x^2}{2!} + \cdots + \frac{x^n}{n!} + \cdots.$$

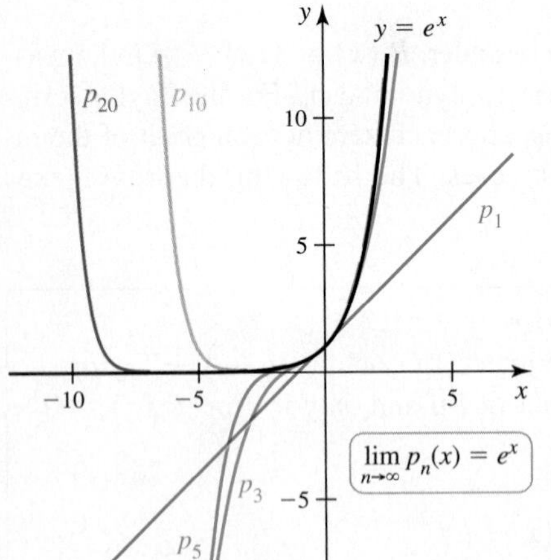

FIGURE 10.17

The convergence of the Taylor series to e^x is illustrated in Figure 10.17, where Taylor polynomials of increasing degree are graphed together with e^x. *Related Exercises 47–50* ◀

EXAMPLE 6 **Maclaurin series convergence for cos x** Show that the Maclaurin series for $\cos x$,

$$1 - \frac{x^2}{2!} + \frac{x^4}{4!} - \frac{x^6}{6!} + \cdots = \sum_{k=0}^{\infty} (-1)^k \frac{x^{2k}}{(2k)!},$$

converges to $f(x) = \cos x$, for $-\infty < x < \infty$.

SOLUTION To show that the power series converges to f, we must show that $\lim_{n\to\infty} |R_n(x)| = 0$ for $-\infty < x < \infty$. According to Taylor's Theorem with $a = 0$,

$$R_n(x) = \frac{f^{(n+1)}(c)}{(n+1)!}x^{n+1},$$

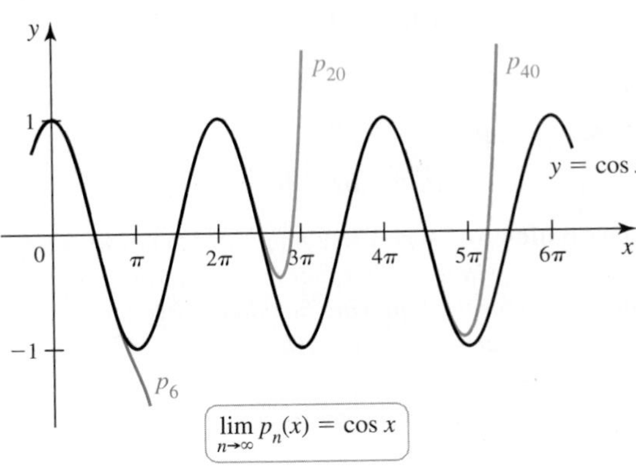

FIGURE 10.18

where c is between 0 and x. Notice that $f^{(n+1)}(c) = \pm\sin c$ or $f^{(n+1)}(c) = \pm\cos c$. In all cases, $|f^{(n+1)}(c)| \le 1$. Therefore, the absolute value of the remainder term is bounded as

$$|R_n(x)| = \left|\frac{f^{(n+1)}(c)}{(n+1)!}x^{n+1}\right| \le \frac{|x|^{n+1}}{(n+1)!}.$$

Holding x fixed and using $\lim_{n\to\infty} x^n/n! = 0$, we see that $\lim_{n\to\infty} R_n(x) = 0$ for all x. Therefore, the given power series converges to $f(x) = \cos x$ for all x; that is, $\cos x = \sum_{k=0}^{\infty} \frac{(-1)^k x^{2k}}{(2k)!}$. The convergence of the Taylor series to $\cos x$ is illustrated in Figure 10.18. *Related Exercises 47–50* ◀

The procedure used in Examples 5 and 6 can be carried out for all of the Taylor series we have worked with so far (with varying degrees of difficulty). In each case, the Taylor series converges to the function it represents on the interval of convergence. Table 10.5 summarizes commonly used Taylor series centered at 0 and the functions to which they converge.

➤ Table 10.5 asserts, without proof, that in several cases the Taylor series for f converges to f at the endpoints of the interval of convergence. Proving convergence at the endpoints generally requires advanced techniques. It may also be done using the following theorem:

Suppose the Taylor series for f centered at 0 converges to f on the interval $(-R, R)$. If the series converges at $x = R$, then it converges to $\lim_{x\to R^-} f(x)$. If the series converges at $x = -R$, then it converges to $\lim_{x\to -R^+} f(x)$.

For example, this theorem would allow us to conclude that the series for $\ln(1 + x)$ converges to $\ln 2$ at $x = 1$.

Table 10.5

$$\frac{1}{1-x} = 1 + x + x^2 + \cdots + x^k + \cdots = \sum_{k=0}^{\infty} x^k, \quad \text{for } |x| < 1$$

$$\frac{1}{1+x} = 1 - x + x^2 - \cdots + (-1)^k x^k + \cdots = \sum_{k=0}^{\infty} (-1)^k x^k, \quad \text{for } |x| < 1$$

$$e^x = 1 + x + \frac{x^2}{2!} + \cdots + \frac{x^k}{k!} + \cdots = \sum_{k=0}^{\infty} \frac{x^k}{k!}, \quad \text{for } |x| < \infty$$

$$\sin x = x - \frac{x^3}{3!} + \frac{x^5}{5!} - \cdots + \frac{(-1)^k x^{2k+1}}{(2k+1)!} + \cdots = \sum_{k=0}^{\infty} \frac{(-1)^k x^{2k+1}}{(2k+1)!}, \quad \text{for } |x| < \infty$$

$$\cos x = 1 - \frac{x^2}{2!} + \frac{x^4}{4!} - \cdots + \frac{(-1)^k x^{2k}}{(2k)!} + \cdots = \sum_{k=0}^{\infty} \frac{(-1)^k x^{2k}}{(2k)!}, \quad \text{for } |x| < \infty$$

$$\ln(1+x) = x - \frac{x^2}{2} + \frac{x^3}{3} - \cdots + \frac{(-1)^{k+1} x^k}{k} + \cdots = \sum_{k=1}^{\infty} \frac{(-1)^{k+1} x^k}{k}, \quad \text{for } -1 < x \le 1$$

$$-\ln(1-x) = x + \frac{x^2}{2} + \frac{x^3}{3} + \cdots + \frac{x^k}{k} + \cdots = \sum_{k=1}^{\infty} \frac{x^k}{k}, \quad \text{for } -1 \le x < 1$$

$$\tan^{-1} x = x - \frac{x^3}{3} + \frac{x^5}{5} - \cdots + \frac{(-1)^k x^{2k+1}}{2k+1} + \cdots = \sum_{k=0}^{\infty} \frac{(-1)^k x^{2k+1}}{2k+1}, \quad \text{for } |x| \le 1$$

$$(1+x)^p = \sum_{k=0}^{\infty} \binom{p}{k} x^k, \quad \text{for } |x| < 1 \quad \text{and} \quad \binom{p}{k} = \frac{p(p-1)(p-2)\cdots(p-k+1)}{k!}, \binom{p}{0} = 1$$

SECTION 10.3 EXERCISES

Review Questions

1. How are the Taylor polynomials for a function f centered at a related to the Taylor series of the function f centered at a?

2. What conditions must be satisfied by a function f to have a Taylor series centered at a?

3. How do you find the coefficients of the Taylor series for f centered at a?

4. How do you find the interval of convergence of a Taylor series?

5. Suppose you know the Maclaurin series for f and it converges for $|x| < 1$. How do you find the Maclaurin series for $f(x^2)$ and where does it converge?

6. For what values of p does the Taylor series for $f(x) = (1 + x)^p$ centered at 0 terminate?

7. In terms of the remainder, what does it mean for a Taylor series for a function f to converge to f?

8. Write the Maclaurin series for e^{2x}.

Basic Skills

9–16. Maclaurin series

a. *Find the first four nonzero terms of the Maclaurin series for the given function.*
b. *Write the power series using summation notation.*
c. *Determine the interval of convergence of the series.*

9. $f(x) = e^{-x}$
10. $f(x) = \cos 2x$
11. $f(x) = (1 + x^2)^{-1}$
12. $f(x) = \ln (1 + x)$
13. $f(x) = e^{2x}$
14. $f(x) = (1 + 2x)^{-1}$
15. $f(x) = \tan^{-1} x$
16. $f(x) = \sin 3x$

17–22. Taylor series centered at $a \neq 0$

a. *Find the first four nonzero terms of the Taylor series for the given function centered at a.*
b. *Write the power series using summation notation.*

17. $f(x) = \sin x,\ a = \pi/2$
18. $f(x) = \cos x,\ a = \pi$
19. $f(x) = 1/x,\ a = 1$
20. $f(x) = 1/x,\ a = 2$
21. $f(x) = \ln x,\ a = 3$
22. $f(x) = e^x,\ a = \ln 2$

23–28. Manipulating Taylor series *Use the Taylor series in Table 10.5 to find the first four nonzero terms of the Taylor series for the following functions centered at 0.*

23. $\ln (1 + x^2)$
24. $\sin x^2$
25. $\dfrac{e^x - 1}{x}$
26. $\cos \sqrt{x}$
27. $(1 + x^4)^{-1}$
28. $x \tan^{-1} x^2$

T 29–34. Binomial series

a. *Find the first four nonzero terms of the Taylor series centered at 0 for the given function.*
b. *Use the first four terms of the series to approximate the given quantity.*

29. $f(x) = (1 + x)^{-2}$; approximate $1/1.21 = 1/1.1^2$.
30. $f(x) = \sqrt{1 + x}$; approximate $\sqrt{1.06}$.
31. $f(x) = \sqrt[4]{1 + x}$; approximate $\sqrt[4]{1.12}$.
32. $f(x) = (1 + x)^{-3}$; approximate $1/1.331 = 1/1.1^3$.
33. $f(x) = (1 + x)^{-2/3}$; approximate $1.18^{-2/3}$.
34. $f(x) = (1 + x)^{2/3}$; approximate $1.02^{2/3}$.

35–40. Working with binomial series *Use properties of power series, substitution, and factoring to find the first four nonzero terms of the Taylor series centered at 0 for the following functions. Give the interval of convergence for the new series. Use the Taylor series*

$$\sqrt{1 + x} = 1 + \frac{x}{2} - \frac{x^2}{8} + \frac{x^3}{16} - \cdots, \qquad \text{for } -1 < x \leq 1.$$

35. $\sqrt{1 + x^2}$
36. $\sqrt{4 + x}$
37. $\sqrt{9 - 9x}$
38. $\sqrt{1 - 4x}$
39. $\sqrt{a^2 + x^2},\ a > 0$
40. $\sqrt{4 - 16x^2}$

41–46. Working with binomial series *Use properties of power series, substitution, and factoring of constants to find the first four nonzero terms of the Taylor series centered at 0 for the following functions. Use the Taylor series*

$$(1 + x)^{-2} = 1 - 2x + 3x^2 - 4x^3 + \cdots, \qquad \text{for } -1 < x < 1.$$

41. $(1 + 4x)^{-2}$
42. $\dfrac{1}{(1 - 4x)^2}$
43. $\dfrac{1}{(4 + x^2)^2}$
44. $(x^2 - 4x + 5)^{-2}$
45. $\dfrac{1}{(3 + 4x)^2}$
46. $\dfrac{1}{(1 + 4x^2)^2}$

47–50. Remainder terms *Find the remainder in the Taylor series centered at the point a for the following functions. Then show that $\lim_{n\to\infty} R_n(x) = 0$ for all x in the interval of convergence.*

47. $f(x) = \sin x,\ a = 0$
48. $f(x) = \cos 2x,\ a = 0$
49. $f(x) = e^{-x},\ a = 0$
50. $f(x) = \cos x,\ a = \pi/2$

Further Explorations

51. **Explain why or why not** Determine whether the following statements are true and give an explanation or counterexample.
    a. The function $f(x) = \sqrt{x}$ has a Taylor series centered at 0.
    b. The function $f(x) = \csc x$ has a Taylor series centered at $\pi/2$.
    c. If f has a Taylor series that converges only on $(-2, 2)$, then $f(x^2)$ has a Taylor series that also converges only on $(-2, 2)$.
    d. If p is the Taylor series for f centered at 0, then $p(x - 1)$ is the Taylor series for f centered at 1.
    e. The Taylor series for an even function about 0 has only even powers of x.

52–59. Any method

a. *Use any analytical method to find the first four nonzero terms of the Taylor series centered at 0 for the following functions. In most cases you do not need to use the definition of the Taylor series coefficients.*

b. *If possible, determine the radius of convergence of the series.*

52. $f(x) = \cos 2x + 2 \sin x$

53. $f(x) = \dfrac{e^x + e^{-x}}{2}$

54. $f(x) = \sec x$

55. $f(x) = (1 + x^2)^{-2/3}$

56. $f(x) = \tan x$

57. $f(x) = \sqrt{1 - x^2}$

58. $f(x) = b^x$, for $b > 0$

59. $f(x) = \dfrac{1}{x^4 + 2x^2 + 1}$

T 60–63. Alternative approach *Compute the coefficients for the Taylor series for the following functions about the given point a and then use the first four terms of the series to approximate the given number.*

60. $f(x) = \sqrt{x}$ with $a = 36$; approximate $\sqrt{39}$.

61. $f(x) = \sqrt[3]{x}$ with $a = 64$; approximate $\sqrt[3]{60}$.

62. $f(x) = 1/\sqrt{x}$ with $a = 4$; approximate $1/\sqrt{3}$.

63. $f(x) = \sqrt[4]{x}$ with $a = 16$; approximate $\sqrt[4]{13}$.

64. Geometric/binomial series Recall that the Taylor series for $f(x) = 1/(1 - x)$ about 0 is the geometric series $\sum_{k=0}^{\infty} x^k$. Show that this series can also be found as a case of the binomial series.

65. Integer coefficients Show that the coefficients in the Taylor series (binomial series) for $f(x) = \sqrt{1 + 4x}$ about 0 are integers.

66. Choosing a good center Suppose you want to approximate $\sqrt{72}$ using four terms of a Taylor series. Compare the accuracy of the approximations obtained using the Taylor series for $\sqrt{x}$ centered at 64 and 81.

67. Alternative means By comparing the first four terms, show that the Maclaurin series for $\sin^2 x$ can be found (a) by squaring the Maclaurin series for $\sin x$ or (b) by using the identity $\sin^2 x = (1 - \cos 2x)/2$.

68. Alternative means By comparing the first four terms, show that the Maclaurin series for $\cos^2 x$ can be found (a) by squaring the Maclaurin series for $\cos x$ or (b) by using the identity $\cos^2 x = (1 + \cos 2x)/2$.

69. Designer series Find a power series that has (2, 6) as an interval of convergence.

70–71. Patterns in coefficients *Find the next two terms of the following Taylor series.*

70. $\sqrt{1 + x}$: $1 + \dfrac{1}{2}x - \dfrac{1}{2 \cdot 4}x^2 + \dfrac{1 \cdot 3}{2 \cdot 4 \cdot 6}x^3 - \cdots$.

71. $\dfrac{1}{\sqrt{1 + x}}$: $1 - \dfrac{1}{2}x + \dfrac{1 \cdot 3}{2 \cdot 4}x^2 - \dfrac{1 \cdot 3 \cdot 5}{2 \cdot 4 \cdot 6}x^3 + \cdots$.

72. Composition of series Use composition of series to find the first three terms of the Maclaurin series for the following functions.

a. $e^{\sin x}$ **b.** $e^{\tan x}$ **c.** $\sqrt{1 + \sin^2 x}$

Applications

T 73–76. Approximations *Choose a Taylor series and a center point a to approximate the following quantities with an accuracy of at least* 10^{-4}.

73. $\cos 40°$

74. $\sin (0.98\pi)$

75. $\sqrt[3]{83}$

76. $1/\sqrt[4]{17}$

77. Different approximation strategies Suppose you want to approximate $\sqrt[3]{128}$ to within 10^{-4} of the exact value.

a. Use a Taylor polynomial centered at 0.

b. Use a Taylor polynomial centered at 125.

c. Compare the two approaches. Are they equivalent?

Additional Exercises

78. Mean Value Theorem Explain why the Mean Value Theorem (Theorem 4.9 of Section 4.6) is a special case of Taylor's Theorem.

79. Version of the Second Derivative Test Assume that f has at least two continuous derivatives on an interval containing a with $f'(a) = 0$. Use Taylor's Theorem to prove the following version of the Second Derivative Test:

a. If $f''(x) > 0$ on some interval containing a, then f has a local minimum at a.

b. If $f''(x) < 0$ on some interval containing a, then f has a local maximum at a.

80. Nonconvergence to *f* Consider the function

$$f(x) = \begin{cases} e^{-1/x^2} & \text{if } x \neq 0 \\ 0 & \text{if } x = 0 \end{cases}$$

a. Use the definition of the derivative to show that $f'(0) = 0$.

b. Assume the fact that $f^{(k)}(0) = 0$, for $k = 1, 2, 3, \ldots$. (You can write a proof using the definition of the derivative.) Write the Taylor series for f centered at 0.

c. Explain why the Taylor series for f does not converge to f for $x \neq 0$.

QUICK CHECK ANSWERS

1. When evaluated at $x = a$, all terms of the series are zero except for the first term, which is $f(a)$. Therefore the series equals $f(a)$ at this point.
2. $1 - x + x^2 - x^3 + x^4 - \cdots$ **3.** $2x + 2x^2 + x^3$; $1 - x + x^2/2$ **4.** 6, 1/16 **5.** 1.05, 1.04875 ◀

10.4 Working with Taylor Series

We now know the Taylor series for many familiar functions and we have tools for working with power series. The goal of this final section is to illustrate additional techniques associated with power series. As you will see, power series cover the entire landscape of calculus from limits and derivatives to integrals and approximation.

Limits by Taylor Series

An important use of Taylor series is evaluating limits. A couple of examples illustrate the essential ideas.

EXAMPLE 1 **A limit by Taylor series** Evaluate $\lim_{x\to 0} \frac{x^2 + 2\cos x - 2}{3x^4}$.

➤ L'Hôpital's Rule may be impractical when it must be used more than once on the same limit or when derivatives are difficult to compute.

SOLUTION Because the limit has the indeterminate form $0/0$, l'Hôpital's Rule can be used, which requires four applications of the rule. Alternatively, because the limit involves values of x near 0, we substitute the Maclaurin series for $\cos x$. Recalling that

$$\cos x = 1 - \frac{x^2}{2} + \frac{x^4}{24} - \frac{x^6}{720} + \cdots, \quad \text{Table 10.5, page 609}$$

we have

➤ In using a series approach to evaluating limits, it is often not obvious how many terms of the Taylor series to use. When in doubt, include extra (higher-power) terms. The dots in the calculation stand for powers of x greater than the last power that appears.

$$\begin{aligned}
\lim_{x\to 0} \frac{x^2 + 2\cos x - 2}{3x^4} &= \lim_{x\to 0} \frac{x^2 + 2\left(1 - \frac{x^2}{2} + \frac{x^4}{24} - \frac{x^6}{720} + \cdots\right) - 2}{3x^4} && \text{Substitute for } \cos x. \\
&= \lim_{x\to 0} \frac{x^2 + \left(2 - x^2 + \frac{x^4}{12} - \frac{x^6}{360} + \cdots\right) - 2}{3x^4} && \text{Simplify.} \\
&= \lim_{x\to 0} \frac{\frac{x^4}{12} - \frac{x^6}{360} + \cdots}{3x^4} && \text{Simplify.} \\
&= \lim_{x\to 0} \left(\frac{1}{36} - \frac{x^2}{1080} + \cdots\right) = \frac{1}{36}. && \text{Simplify; evaluate limit.}
\end{aligned}$$

Related Exercises 7–20 ◀

QUICK CHECK 1 Use the Taylor series $\sin x = x - x^3/6 + \cdots$ to verify that $\lim_{x\to 0} (\sin x)/x = 1$. ◀

EXAMPLE 2 **A limit by Taylor series** Evaluate

$$\lim_{x\to\infty} \left[6x^5 \sin\left(\frac{1}{x}\right) - 6x^4 + x^2\right].$$

SOLUTION A Taylor series may be centered at any finite point in the domain of the function, but we don't have the tools needed to expand a function about $x = \infty$. Using a technique introduced earlier, we replace x by $1/t$ and note that as $x \to \infty$, $t \to 0^+$. The new limit becomes

$$\begin{aligned}
\lim_{x\to\infty} \left[6x^5 \sin\left(\frac{1}{x}\right) - 6x^4 + x^2\right] &= \lim_{t\to 0^+} \left(\frac{6\sin t}{t^5} - \frac{6}{t^4} + \frac{1}{t^2}\right) && \text{Replace } x \text{ by } 1/t. \\
&= \lim_{t\to 0^+} \left(\frac{6\sin t - 6t + t^3}{t^5}\right). && \text{Common denominator}
\end{aligned}$$

This limit has the indeterminate form $0/0$. We now expand $\sin t$ in a Taylor series centered at $t = 0$. Because

$$\sin t = t - \frac{t^3}{6} + \frac{t^5}{120} - \frac{t^7}{5040} + \cdots, \quad \text{Table 10.5, page 609}$$

the value of the original limit is

$$\lim_{t\to 0^+}\left(\frac{6\sin t - 6t + t^3}{t^5}\right)$$

$$= \lim_{t\to 0^+}\left(\frac{6\left(t - \frac{t^3}{6} + \frac{t^5}{120} - \frac{t^7}{5040} + \cdots\right) - 6t + t^3}{t^5}\right) \quad \text{Substitute for } \sin t.$$

$$= \lim_{t\to 0^+}\left(\frac{\frac{t^5}{20} - \frac{t^7}{840} + \cdots}{t^5}\right) \quad \text{Simplify.}$$

$$= \lim_{t\to 0^+}\left(\frac{1}{20} - \frac{t^2}{840} + \cdots\right) = \frac{1}{20}. \quad \text{Simplify; evaluate limit.}$$

Related Exercises 7–20 ◀

Differentiating Power Series

The following examples illustrate the ways in which term-by-term differentiation (Theorem 10.5) may be used.

EXAMPLE 3 **Power series for derivatives** Differentiate the Maclaurin series for $f(x) = \sin x$ to verify that $\frac{d}{dx}(\sin x) = \cos x$.

SOLUTION The Maclaurin series for $f(x) = \sin x$ is

$$\sin x = x - \frac{x^3}{3!} + \frac{x^5}{5!} - \frac{x^7}{7!} + \cdots,$$

and it converges for $-\infty < x < \infty$. By Theorem 10.5, the differentiated series also converges for $-\infty < x < \infty$ and it converges to $f'(x)$. On differentiating, we have

$$\frac{d}{dx}\left(x - \frac{x^3}{3!} + \frac{x^5}{5!} - \frac{x^7}{7!} + \cdots\right) = 1 - \frac{x^2}{2!} + \frac{x^4}{4!} - \frac{x^6}{6!} + \cdots = \cos x.$$

The differentiated series is the Maclaurin series for $\cos x$, confirming that $f'(x) = \cos x$.

Related Exercises 21–26 ◀

QUICK CHECK 2 Differentiate the power series for $\cos x$ (given in Example 3) and identify the result. ◀

EXAMPLE 4 **A differential equation** Find a power series solution of the differential equation $y'(t) = y(t) + 2$, subject to the initial condition $y(0) = 6$. Identify the function represented by the power series.

SOLUTION Because the initial condition is given at $t = 0$, we expand the solution in a Taylor series about 0 of the form $y(t) = \sum_{k=0}^{\infty} c_k t^k$, where the coefficients c_k must be determined. Recall that the coefficients of the Taylor series are given by

$$c_k = \frac{y^{(k)}(0)}{k!}, \qquad \text{for } k = 0, 1, 2, \ldots.$$

If we can determine $y^{(k)}(0)$, for $k = 0, 1, 2, \ldots$, the coefficients of the series are also determined. The assumption that y has a Taylor series means that y has derivatives of all orders at 0.

Substituting the initial condition $t = 0$ and $y = 6$ into the power series

$$y(t) = c_0 + c_1 t + c_2 t^2 + \cdots,$$

we find that

$$6 = c_0 + c_1(0) + c_2(0)^2 + \cdots.$$

It follows that $c_0 = 6$. To determine $y'(0)$, we substitute $t = 0$ into the differential equation; the result is $y'(0) = y(0) + 2 = 6 + 2 = 8$. Therefore, $c_1 = y'(0)/1! = 8$.

The remaining derivatives are obtained by successively differentiating the differential equation and substituting $t = 0$. We find that $y''(0) = y'(0) = 8$, $y'''(0) = y''(0) = 8$, and, in general, $y^{(k)}(0) = 8$ for $k = 2, 3, 4, \ldots$. Therefore, $c_k = \dfrac{y^{(k)}(0)}{k!} = \dfrac{8}{k!}$, for $k = 1, 2, 3, \ldots$, and the Taylor series for the solution is

$$\begin{aligned} y(t) &= c_0 + c_1 t + c_2 t^2 + \cdots \\ &= 6 + \frac{8}{1!}t + \frac{8}{2!}t^2 + \frac{8}{3!}t^3 + \cdots. \end{aligned}$$

To identify the function represented by this series we write

$$\begin{aligned} y(t) &= \underbrace{-2 + 8}_{6} + \frac{8}{1!}t + \frac{8}{2!}t^2 + \frac{8}{3!}t^3 + \cdots \\ &= -2 + 8\underbrace{\left(1 + t + \frac{t^2}{2!} + \frac{t^3}{3!} + \cdots\right)}_{e^t}. \end{aligned}$$

➤ You should check that $y(t) = -2 + 8e^t$ satisfies $y'(t) = y(t) + 2$ and $y(0) = 6$.

The power series that appears is the Taylor series for e^t. Therefore, the solution is $y(t) = -2 + 8e^t$. *Related Exercises 27–30* ◀

Integrating Power Series

The following example illustrates the use of power series in approximating integrals that cannot be evaluated by analytical methods.

EXAMPLE 5 Approximating a definite integral Approximate the value of the integral $\int_0^1 e^{-x^2}\,dx$ with an error no greater than 5×10^{-4}.

SOLUTION The antiderivative of e^{-x^2} cannot be expressed in terms of familiar functions. The strategy is to write the Maclaurin series for e^{-x^2} and integrate it term by term. Recall that integration of a power series is valid within its interval of convergence (Theorem 10.5). Beginning with the Maclaurin series

$$e^x = 1 + x + \frac{x^2}{2!} + \frac{x^3}{3!} + \cdots + \frac{x^n}{n!} + \cdots,$$

which converges for $-\infty < x < \infty$, we replace x by $-x^2$ to obtain

$$e^{-x^2} = 1 - x^2 + \frac{x^4}{2!} - \frac{x^6}{3!} + \cdots + \frac{(-1)^n x^{2n}}{n!} + \cdots,$$

which also converges for $-\infty < x < \infty$. By the Fundamental Theorem of Calculus,

$$\begin{aligned} \int_0^1 e^{-x^2}\,dx &= \left(x - \frac{x^3}{3} + \frac{x^5}{5\cdot 2!} - \frac{x^7}{7\cdot 3!} + \cdots + \frac{(-1)^n x^{2n+1}}{(2n+1)n!} + \cdots\right)\Bigg|_0^1 \\ &= 1 - \frac{1}{3} + \frac{1}{5\cdot 2!} - \frac{1}{7\cdot 3!} + \cdots + \frac{(-1)^n}{(2n+1)n!} + \cdots. \end{aligned}$$

Because the definite integral is expressed as an alternating series, the remainder in truncating the series is less than the first neglected term, which is $\frac{(-1)^{n+1}}{(2n+3)(n+1)!}$. By trial and error, we find that the magnitude of this term is less than 5×10^{-4} if $n \geq 5$ (with $n = 5$, we have $\frac{1}{13 \cdot 6!} \approx 1.07 \times 10^{-4}$). The sum of the terms of the series up to $n = 5$ gives the approximation

> The integral in Example 5 is important in statistics and probability theory because of its relationship to the *normal distribution*.

$$\int_0^1 e^{-x^2}\,dx \approx 1 - \frac{1}{3} + \frac{1}{5 \cdot 2!} - \frac{1}{7 \cdot 3!} + \frac{1}{9 \cdot 4!} - \frac{1}{11 \cdot 5!} \approx 0.747.$$

Related Exercises 31–38 ◀

Representing Real Numbers

When values of x are substituted into a convergent power series, the result may be a series representation of a familiar real number. The following example illustrates some techniques.

EXAMPLE 6 Evaluating infinite series

a. Use the Maclaurin series for $f(x) = \tan^{-1} x$ to evaluate

$$1 - \frac{1}{3} + \frac{1}{5} - \cdots = \sum_{k=0}^{\infty} \frac{(-1)^k}{2k+1}.$$

b. Let $f(x) = (e^x - 1)/x$ for $x \neq 0$ and $f(0) = 1$. Use the Maclaurin series for f to evaluate $f'(1)$ and $\sum_{k=1}^{\infty} \frac{k}{(k+1)!}$.

SOLUTION

a. From Table 10.5 (page 609), we see that for $|x| \leq 1$,

$$\tan^{-1} x = x - \frac{x^3}{3} + \frac{x^5}{5} - \cdots + \frac{(-1)^k x^{2k+1}}{2k+1} + \cdots = \sum_{k=0}^{\infty} \frac{(-1)^k x^{2k+1}}{2k+1}.$$

Substituting $x = 1$, we have

> This series (known as the *Gregory series*) is one of a multitude of series representations of π. Because this series converges slowly, it does not provide an efficient way to approximate π.

$$\tan^{-1} 1 = 1 - \frac{1^3}{3} + \frac{1^5}{5} - \cdots = \sum_{k=0}^{\infty} \frac{(-1)^k}{2k+1}.$$

Because $\tan^{-1} 1 = \pi/4$, the value of the series is $\pi/4$.

b. Using the Maclaurin series for e^x, the series for $f(x) = (e^x - 1)/x$ is

$$f(x) = \frac{e^x - 1}{x} = \frac{1}{x}\left[\left(1 + x + \frac{x^2}{2!} + \frac{x^3}{3!} + \cdots\right) - 1\right] \quad \text{Substitute series for } e^x.$$

$$= 1 + \frac{x}{2!} + \frac{x^2}{3!} + \frac{x^3}{4!} + \cdots = \sum_{k=1}^{\infty} \frac{x^{k-1}}{k!}, \quad \text{Simplify.}$$

which converges for $-\infty < x < \infty$. By the Quotient Rule,

$$f'(x) = \frac{xe^x - (e^x - 1)}{x^2}.$$

Differentiating the series for f term by term (Theorem 10.5), we find that

$$f'(x) = \frac{d}{dx}\left(1 + \frac{x}{2!} + \frac{x^2}{3!} + \frac{x^3}{4!} + \cdots\right)$$

$$= \frac{1}{2!} + \frac{2x}{3!} + \frac{3x^2}{4!} + \cdots = \sum_{k=1}^{\infty} \frac{kx^{k-1}}{(k+1)!}.$$

We now have two expressions for f'; they are evaluated at $x = 1$ to show that

$$f'(1) = 1 = \sum_{k=1}^{\infty} \frac{k}{(k+1)!}.$$

Related Exercises 39–48 ◀

QUICK CHECK 3 What value of x would you substitute into the Maclaurin series for $\tan^{-1} x$ to obtain a series representation for $\pi/6$? ◀

Representing Functions as Power Series

Power series have a fundamental role in mathematics in defining functions and providing alternative representations of familiar functions. As an overall review, we close this chapter with two illustrations of the many techniques for working with power series.

EXAMPLE 7 Identify the series Identify the function represented by the power series $\sum_{k=0}^{\infty} \frac{(1-2x)^k}{k!}$ and give its interval of convergence.

SOLUTION The Taylor series for the exponential function,

$$e^x = \sum_{k=0}^{\infty} \frac{x^k}{k!},$$

converges for $-\infty < x < \infty$. Replacing x by $1 - 2x$ produces the given series:

$$\sum_{k=0}^{\infty} \frac{(1-2x)^k}{k!} = e^{1-2x}.$$

This replacement is allowed because $1 - 2x$ is within the interval of convergence of the series for e^x; that is, $-\infty < 2x - 1 < \infty$ for all x. Therefore, the given series represents e^{1-2x} for $-\infty < x < \infty$.

Related Exercises 49–58 ◀

EXAMPLE 8 Mystery series The power series $\sum_{k=1}^{\infty} \frac{(-1)^k k}{4^k} x^{2k}$ appeared in the opening of Section 10.2. Determine the interval of convergence of the power series and find the function it represents on this interval.

SOLUTION Applying the Ratio Test to the series, we determine that it converges when $|x^2/4| < 1$, which implies that $|x| < 2$. A quick check of the endpoints of the original series confirms that it diverges at $x = \pm 2$. Therefore, the interval of convergence is $|x| < 2$.

To find the function represented by the series, we apply several maneuvers until we obtain a geometric series. First note that

$$\sum_{k=1}^{\infty} \frac{(-1)^k k}{4^k} x^{2k} = \sum_{k=1}^{\infty} k\left(-\frac{1}{4}\right)^k x^{2k}.$$

The series on the right is not a geometric series because of the presence of the factor k. The key is to realize that k could appear in this way through differentiation; specifically, something like $\frac{d}{dx}(x^{2k}) = 2kx^{2k-1}$. To achieve terms of this form, we write

$$\underbrace{\sum_{k=1}^{\infty} \frac{(-1)^k k}{4^k} x^{2k}}_{\text{original series}} = \sum_{k=1}^{\infty} k\left(-\frac{1}{4}\right)^k x^{2k}$$

$$= \frac{1}{2} \sum_{k=1}^{\infty} 2k\left(-\frac{1}{4}\right)^k x^{2k} \quad \text{Multiply and divide by 2.}$$

$$= \frac{x}{2} \sum_{k=1}^{\infty} 2k\left(-\frac{1}{4}\right)^k x^{2k-1}. \quad \text{Remove } x \text{ from the series.}$$

Now we identify the last series as the derivative of another series:

$$\underbrace{\sum_{k=1}^{\infty} \frac{(-1)^k k}{4^k} x^{2k}}_{\text{original series}} = \frac{x}{2} \sum_{k=1}^{\infty} \left(-\frac{1}{4}\right)^k 2kx^{2k-1}$$

$$= \frac{x}{2} \sum_{k=1}^{\infty} \left(-\frac{1}{4}\right)^k \frac{d}{dx}(x^{2k}) \quad \text{Identify a derivative.}$$

$$= \frac{x}{2} \frac{d}{dx} \sum_{k=1}^{\infty} \left(-\frac{x^2}{4}\right)^k \quad \text{Combine factors; term by term differentiation.}$$

This last series is a geometric series with a ratio $r = -x^2/4$ and first term $-x^2/4$; therefore, its value is $\frac{-x^2/4}{1 + (x^2/4)}$, provided $\left|\frac{x^2}{4}\right| < 1$. We now have

$$\underbrace{\sum_{k=1}^{\infty} \frac{(-1)^k k}{4^k} x^{2k}}_{\text{original series}} = \frac{x}{2} \frac{d}{dx} \sum_{k=1}^{\infty} \left(-\frac{x^2}{4}\right)^k$$

$$= \frac{x}{2} \frac{d}{dx} \left(\frac{-x^2/4}{1 + (x^2/4)}\right) \quad \text{Sum of geometric series}$$

$$= \frac{x}{2} \frac{d}{dx} \left(\frac{-x^2}{4 + x^2}\right) \quad \text{Simplify.}$$

$$= -\frac{4x^2}{(4 + x^2)^2}. \quad \text{Differentiate and simplify.}$$

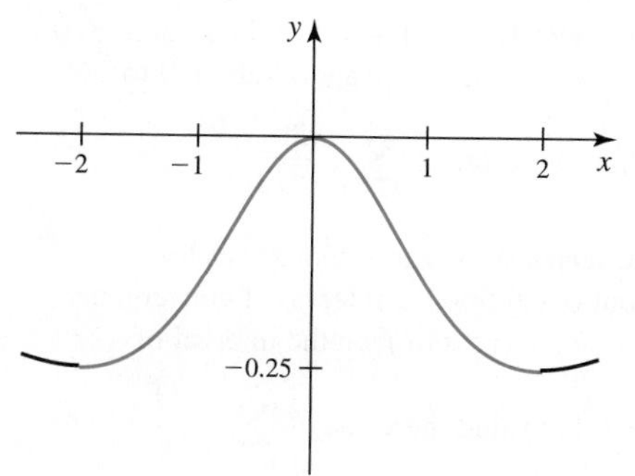

$$\sum_{k=1}^{\infty} \frac{(-1)^k k}{4^k} x^{2k} = -\frac{4x^2}{(4 + x^2)^2} \text{ on } (-2, 2)$$

FIGURE 10.19

Therefore, the function represented by the power series on $(-2, 2)$ has been uncovered; it is

$$f(x) = -\frac{4x^2}{(4 + x^2)^2}.$$

Notice that f is defined for $-\infty < x < \infty$ (Figure 10.19), but its power series centered at 0 converges to f only on $(-2, 2)$.

Related Exercises 49–58 ◀

SECTION 10.4 EXERCISES

Review Questions

1. Explain the strategy presented in this section for evaluating a limit of the form $\lim_{x\to a} f(x)/g(x)$, where f and g have Taylor series centered at a.

2. Explain the method presented in this section for evaluating $\int_a^b f(x)\,dx$, where f has a Taylor series with an interval of convergence centered at a that includes b.

3. How would you approximate $e^{-0.6}$ using the Taylor series for e^x?

4. Suggest a Taylor series and a method for approximating π.

5. If $f(x) = \sum_{k=0}^{\infty} c_k x^k$ and the series converges for $|x| < b$, what is the power series for $f'(x)$?

6. What condition must be met by a function f for it to have a Taylor series centered at a?

Basic Skills

7–20. Limits *Evaluate the following limits using Taylor series.*

7. $\displaystyle\lim_{x\to 0} \frac{e^x - e^{-x}}{x}$

8. $\displaystyle\lim_{x\to 0} \frac{1 + x - e^{-x}}{4x^2}$

9. $\displaystyle\lim_{x\to 0} \frac{2\cos 2x - 2 + 4x^2}{2x^4}$

10. $\displaystyle\lim_{x\to \infty} x \sin\left(\frac{1}{x}\right)$

11. $\displaystyle\lim_{x\to 0} \frac{3\tan x - 3x - x^3}{x^5}$

12. $\displaystyle\lim_{x\to 4} \frac{x^2 - 16}{\ln(x - 3)}$

13. $\displaystyle\lim_{x\to 0} \frac{3\tan^{-1} x - 3x + x^3}{x^5}$

14. $\displaystyle\lim_{x\to 0} \frac{\sqrt{1 + x} - 1 - (x/2)}{4x^2}$

15. $\displaystyle\lim_{x\to 0} \frac{\sin x - \tan x}{3x^3 \cos x}$

16. $\displaystyle\lim_{x\to 1} \frac{x - 1}{\ln x}$

17. $\displaystyle\lim_{x\to 2} \frac{x - 2}{\ln(x - 1)}$

18. $\displaystyle\lim_{x\to \infty} (x^4(e^{1/x} - 1) - x^3)$

19. $\displaystyle\lim_{x\to 0^+} \frac{(1 + x)^{-2} - 4\cos\sqrt{x} + 3}{2x^2}$

20. $\displaystyle\lim_{x\to 0} \frac{(1 - 2x)^{-1/2} - e^x}{8x^2}$

21–26. Power series for derivatives

a. Differentiate the Taylor series about 0 for the following functions.

b. Identify the function represented by the differentiated series.

c. Give the interval of convergence of the power series for the derivative.

21. $f(x) = e^x$

22. $f(x) = \cos x$

23. $f(x) = \ln(1 + x)$

24. $f(x) = \sin(x^2)$

25. $f(x) = e^{-2x}$

26. $f(x) = \sqrt{1 + x}$

27–30. Differential equations

a. Find a power series for the solution of the following differential equations.

b. Identify the function represented by the power series.

27. $y'(t) - y(t) = 0,\ y(0) = 2$

28. $y'(t) + 4y(t) = 8,\ y(0) = 0$

29. $y'(t) - 3y(t) = 10,\ y(0) = 2$

30. $y'(t) = 6y(t) + 9,\ y(0) = 2$

T **31–38. Approximating definite integrals** *Use a Taylor series to approximate the following definite integrals. Retain as many terms as needed to ensure the error is less than* 10^{-4}.

31. $\displaystyle\int_0^{0.25} e^{-x^2}\,dx$

32. $\displaystyle\int_0^{0.2} \sin x^2\,dx$

33. $\displaystyle\int_{-0.35}^{0.35} \cos 2x^2\,dx$

34. $\displaystyle\int_0^{0.2} \sqrt{1 + x^4}\,dx$

35. $\displaystyle\int_0^{0.15} \frac{\sin x}{x}\,dx$

36. $\displaystyle\int_0^{0.1} \cos\sqrt{x}\,dx$

37. $\displaystyle\int_0^{0.5} \frac{dx}{\sqrt{1 + x^6}}$

38. $\displaystyle\int_0^{0.2} \frac{\ln(1 + t)}{t}\,dt$

39–44. Approximating real numbers *Use an appropriate Taylor series to find the first four nonzero terms of an infinite series that is equal to the following numbers.*

39. e^2

40. $\sqrt{e}$

41. $\cos 2$

42. $\sin 1$

43. $\ln\left(\frac{3}{2}\right)$

44. $\tan^{-1}\left(\frac{1}{2}\right)$

45. **Evaluating an infinite series** Let $f(x) = (e^x - 1)/x$ for $x \neq 0$ and $f(0) = 1$. Use the Taylor series for f about 0 and evaluate $f(1)$ to find the value of $\displaystyle\sum_{k=0}^{\infty} \frac{1}{(k + 1)!}$.

46. **Evaluating an infinite series** Let $f(x) = (e^x - 1)/x$ for $x \neq 0$ and $f(0) = 1$. Use the Taylor series for f and f' about 0 to evaluate $f'(2)$ and to find the value of $\displaystyle\sum_{k=1}^{\infty} \frac{k2^{k-1}}{(k + 1)!}$.

47. **Evaluating an infinite series** Write the Taylor series for $f(x) = \ln(1 + x)$ about 0 and find the interval of convergence. Assume the Taylor series converges to f on the interval of convergence. Evaluate $f(1)$ to find the value of $\displaystyle\sum_{k=1}^{\infty} \frac{(-1)^{k+1}}{k}$ (the alternating harmonic series).

48. **Evaluating an infinite series** Write the Taylor series for $f(x) = \ln(1 + x)$ about 0 and find the interval of convergence. Evaluate $f\left(-\frac{1}{2}\right)$ to find the value of $\displaystyle\sum_{k=1}^{\infty} \frac{1}{k \cdot 2^k}$.

49–58. Representing functions by power series *Identify the functions represented by the following power series.*

49. $\sum_{k=0}^{\infty} \frac{x^k}{2^k}$

50. $\sum_{k=0}^{\infty} (-1)^k \frac{x^k}{3^k}$

51. $\sum_{k=0}^{\infty} (-1)^k \frac{x^{2k}}{4^k}$

52. $\sum_{k=0}^{\infty} 2^k x^{2k+1}$

53. $\sum_{k=1}^{\infty} \frac{x^k}{k}$

54. $\sum_{k=0}^{\infty} \frac{(-1)^k x^{k+1}}{4^k}$

55. $\sum_{k=1}^{\infty} (-1)^k \frac{kx^{k+1}}{3^k}$

56. $\sum_{k=1}^{\infty} \frac{x^{2k}}{k}$

57. $\sum_{k=2}^{\infty} \frac{k(k-1)x^k}{3^k}$

58. $\sum_{k=2}^{\infty} \frac{x^k}{k(k-1)}$

Further Explorations

59. Explain why or why not Determine whether the following statements are true and give an explanation or counterexample.

a. To evaluate $\int_0^2 \frac{dx}{1-x}$, one could expand the integrand in a Taylor series and integrate term by term.

b. To approximate $\pi/3$, one could substitute $x = \sqrt{3}$ into the Taylor series for $\tan^{-1} x$.

c. $\sum_{k=0}^{\infty} \frac{(\ln 2)^k}{k!} = 2.$

60–62. Limits with a parameter *Use Taylor series to evaluate the following limits. Express the result in terms of the parameter(s).*

60. $\lim_{x \to 0} \frac{e^{ax} - 1}{x}$

61. $\lim_{x \to 0} \frac{\sin ax}{\sin bx}$

62. $\lim_{x \to 0} \frac{\sin ax - \tan ax}{bx^3}$

63. A limit by Taylor series Use Taylor series to evaluate $\lim_{x \to 0} \left(\frac{\sin x}{x} \right)^{1/x^2}$.

64. Inverse hyperbolic sine A function known as the *inverse of the hyperbolic sine* is defined in several ways; among them are

$$\sinh^{-1} x = \ln\left(x + \sqrt{x^2 + 1}\right) = \int_0^x \frac{dt}{\sqrt{1 + t^2}}.$$

Find the first four terms of the Taylor series for $\sinh^{-1} x$ using these two definitions (and be sure they agree).

65–68. Derivative trick *Here is an alternative way to evaluate higher derivatives of a function f that may save time. Suppose you can find the Taylor series for f centered at the point a without evaluating derivatives (for example, from a known series). Explain why $f^{(k)}(a) = k!$ multiplied by the coefficient of $(x - a)^k$. Use this idea to evaluate $f^{(3)}(0)$ and $f^{(4)}(0)$ for the following functions. Use known series and do not evaluate derivatives.*

65. $f(x) = e^{\cos x}$

66. $f(x) = \frac{x^2 + 1}{\sqrt[3]{1 + x}}$

67. $f(x) = \int_0^x \sin(t^2)\, dt$

68. $f(x) = \int_0^x \frac{1}{1 + t^4}\, dt$

Applications

69. Probability: tossing for a head The expected (average) number of tosses of a fair coin required to obtain the first head is $\sum_{k=1}^{\infty} k\left(\frac{1}{2}\right)^k$. Evaluate this series and determine the expected number of tosses. (*Hint:* Differentiate a geometric series.)

70. Probability: sudden death playoff Teams A and B go into sudden death overtime after playing to a tie. The teams alternate possession of the ball and the first team to score wins. Each team has a $\frac{1}{6}$ chance of scoring when it has the ball, with Team A having the ball first.

a. The probability that Team A ultimately wins is $\sum_{k=0}^{\infty} \frac{1}{6}\left(\frac{5}{6}\right)^{2k}$. Evaluate this series.

b. The expected number of rounds (possessions by either team) required for the overtime to end is $\frac{1}{6}\sum_{k=1}^{\infty} k\left(\frac{5}{6}\right)^{k-1}$. Evaluate this series.

T **71. Elliptic integrals** The period of a pendulum is given by

$$T = 4\sqrt{\frac{\ell}{g}} \int_0^{\pi/2} \frac{d\theta}{\sqrt{1 - k^2 \sin^2 \theta}} \equiv 4\sqrt{\frac{\ell}{g}} F(k),$$

where ℓ is the length of the pendulum, $g \approx 9.8$ m/s^2 is the acceleration due to gravity, $k = \sin(\theta_0/2)$, and θ_0 is the initial angular displacement of the pendulum (in radians). The integral in this formula $F(k)$ is called an **elliptic integral** and it cannot be evaluated analytically.

a. Approximate $F(0.1)$ by expanding the integrand in a Taylor (binomial) series and integrating term by term.

b. How many terms of the Taylor series do you suggest using to obtain an approximation to $F(0.1)$ with an error less than 10^{-3}?

c. Would you expect to use fewer or more terms (than in part (b)) to approximate $F(0.2)$ to the same accuracy? Explain.

T **72. Sine integral function** The function $\text{Si}(x) = \int_0^x \frac{\sin t}{t}\, dt$ is called the **sine integral function**.

a. Expand the integrand in a Taylor series about 0.

b. Integrate the series to find a Taylor series for Si.

c. Approximate Si (0.5) and Si (1). Use enough terms of the series so the error in the approximation does not exceed 10^{-3}.

T 73. Fresnel integrals The theory of optics gives rise to the two **Fresnel integrals**

$$S(x) = \int_0^x \sin(t^2)\,dt \quad \text{and} \quad C(x) = \int_0^x \cos(t^2)\,dt.$$

a. Compute $S'(x)$ and $C'(x)$.
b. Expand $\sin(t^2)$ and $\cos(t^2)$ in a Maclaurin series and then integrate to find the first four nonzero terms of the Maclaurin series for S and C.
c. Use the polynomials in part (b) to approximate $S(0.05)$ and $C(-0.25)$.
d. How many terms of the Maclaurin series are required to approximate $S(0.05)$ with an error no greater than 10^{-4}?
e. How many terms of the Maclaurin series are required to approximate $C(-0.25)$ with an error no greater than 10^{-6}?

T 74. Error function An essential function in statistics and the study of the normal distribution is the **error function**

$$\text{erf}(x) = \frac{2}{\sqrt{\pi}} \int_0^x e^{-t^2}\,dt.$$

a. Compute the derivative of erf (x).
b. Expand e^{-t^2} in a Maclaurin series, then integrate to find the first four nonzero terms of the Maclaurin series for erf.
c. Use the polynomial in part (b) to approximate erf (0.15) and erf (-0.09).
d. Estimate the error in the approximations of part (c).

T 75. Bessel functions Bessel functions arise in the study of wave propagation in circular geometries (for example, waves on a circular drum head). They are conveniently defined as power series. One of an infinite family of Bessel functions is

$$J_0(x) = \sum_{k=0}^{\infty} \frac{(-1)^k}{2^{2k}(k!)^2} x^{2k}.$$

a. Write out the first four terms of J_0.
b. Find the radius and interval of convergence of the power series for J_0.
c. Differentiate J_0 twice and show (by keeping terms through x^6) that J_0 satisfies the equation $x^2y''(x) + xy'(x) + x^2y(x) = 0$.

Additional Exercises

76. Power series for sec *x* Use the identity $\sec x = \dfrac{1}{\cos x}$ and long division to find the first three terms of the Maclaurin series for $\sec x$.

77. Symmetry

a. Use infinite series to show that $\cos x$ is an even function. That is, show $\cos x = \cos(-x)$.
b. Use infinite series to show that $\sin x$ is an odd function. That is, show $\sin x = -\sin(-x)$.

78. Behavior of csc *x* We know that $\lim_{x \to 0^+} \csc x = \infty$. Use long division to determine exactly how $\csc x$ grows as $x \to 0^+$. Specifically, find a, b, and c (all positive) in the following sentence:

As $x \to 0^+$, $\csc x \approx \dfrac{a}{x^b} + cx$.

79. L'Hôpital's Rule by Taylor series Suppose f and g have Taylor series about the point a.

a. If $f(a) = g(a) = 0$ and $g'(a) \neq 0$, evaluate $\lim_{x \to a} f(x)/g(x)$ by expanding f and g in their Taylor series. Show that the result is consistent with l'Hôpital's Rule.
b. If $f(a) = g(a) = f'(a) = g'(a) = 0$ and $g''(a) \neq 0$, evaluate $\lim_{x \to a} \dfrac{f(x)}{g(x)}$ by expanding f and g in their Taylor series. Show that the result is consistent with two applications of l'Hôpital's Rule.

T 80. Newton's derivation of the sine and arcsine series Newton discovered the binomial series and then used it ingeniously to obtain many more results. Here is a case in point.

a. Referring to the figure, show that $x = \sin y$ or $y = \sin^{-1} x$.
b. The area of a circular sector of radius r subtended by an angle θ is $\frac{1}{2}r^2\theta$. Show that the area of the circular sector APE is $y/2$, which implies that

$$y = 2\int_0^x \sqrt{1 - t^2}\,dt - x\sqrt{1 - x^2}.$$

c. Use the binomial series for $f(x) = \sqrt{1 - x^2}$ to obtain the first few terms of the Taylor series for $y = \sin^{-1} x$.
d. Newton next inverted the series in part (c) to obtain the Taylor series for $x = \sin y$. He did this by assuming that $\sin y = \sum a_k y^k$ and solving $x = \sin(\sin^{-1} x)$ for the coefficients a_k. Find the first few terms of the Taylor series for $\sin y$ using this idea (a computer algebra system might be helpful as well).

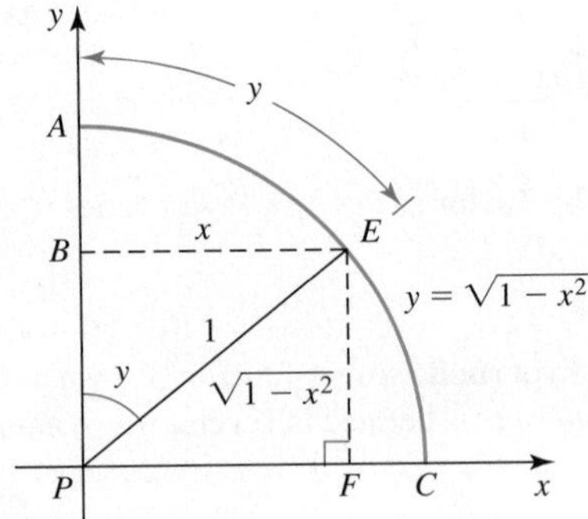

QUICK CHECK ANSWERS

1. $\dfrac{\sin x}{x} = \dfrac{x - x^3/3! + \cdots}{x} = 1 - \dfrac{x^2}{3!} + \cdots \to 1$ as $x \to 0$.
2. The result is the power series for $-\sin x$. 3. $x = 1/\sqrt{3}$ (which lies in the interval of convergence)

CHAPTER 10 REVIEW EXERCISES

1. **Explain why or why not** Determine whether the following statements are true and give an explanation or counterexample.
   a. Let p_n be the nth-order Taylor polynomial for f centered at 2. The approximation $p_3(2.1) \approx f(2.1)$ is likely to be more accurate than the approximation $p_2(2.2) \approx f(2.2)$.
   b. If the Taylor series for f centered at 3 has a radius of convergence of 6, then the interval of convergence is $[-3, 9]$.
   c. The interval of convergence of the power series $\sum c_k x^k$ could be $\left(-\frac{7}{3}, \frac{7}{3}\right)$
   d. The Taylor series for $f(x) = (1 + x)^{12}$ centered at 0 has a finite number of terms.

2–7. Taylor polynomials *Find the nth-order Taylor polynomial for the following functions with the given center point a.*

2. $f(x) = \sin 2x,\ n = 3,\ a = 0$
3. $f(x) = \cos x^2,\ n = 2,\ a = 0$
4. $f(x) = e^{-x},\ n = 2,\ a = 0$
5. $f(x) = \ln(1 + x),\ n = 3,\ a = 0$
6. $f(x) = \cos x,\ n = 2,\ a = \pi/4$
7. $f(x) = \ln x,\ n = 2,\ a = 1$

T **8–11. Approximations**
   a. *Find the Taylor polynomials of order $n = 0, 1,$ and 2 for the given functions centered at the given point a.*
   b. *Make a table showing the approximations and the absolute error in these approximations using a calculator for the exact function value.*

8. $f(x) = \cos x,\ a = 0$; approximate $\cos(-0.08)$.
9. $f(x) = e^x,\ a = 0$; approximate $e^{-0.08}$.
10. $f(x) = \sqrt{1 + x},\ a = 0$; approximate $\sqrt{1.08}$.
11. $f(x) = \sin x,\ a = \pi/4$; approximate $\sin(\pi/5)$.

12–14. Estimating remainders *Find the remainder term $R_n(x)$ for the Taylor series centered at 0 for the following functions. Find an upper bound for the magnitude of the remainder on the given interval for the given value of n. (The bound is not unique.)*

12. $f(x) = e^x$; bound $R_3(x)$ for $|x| < 1$.
13. $f(x) = \sin x$; bound $R_3(x)$ for $|x| < \pi$.
14. $f(x) = \ln(1 - x)$; bound $R_3(x)$ for $|x| < 1/2$.

15–20. Radius and interval of convergence *Use the Ratio or Root Test to determine the radius of convergence of the following power series. Test the endpoints to determine the interval of convergence, when appropriate.*

15. $\sum \frac{k^2 x^k}{k!}$
16. $\sum \frac{x^{4k}}{k^2}$
17. $\sum (-1)^k \frac{(x + 1)^{2k}}{k!}$
18. $\sum \frac{(x - 1)^k}{k \cdot 5^k}$
19. $\sum \left(\frac{x}{9}\right)^{3k}$
20. $\sum \frac{(x + 2)^k}{\sqrt{k}}$

21–26. Power series from the geometric series *Use the geometric series $\sum_{k=0}^{\infty} x^k = \frac{1}{1 - x}$, for $|x| < 1$ to determine the Maclaurin series and the interval of convergence for the following functions.*

21. $f(x) = \frac{1}{1 - x^2}$
22. $f(x) = \frac{1}{1 + x^3}$
23. $f(x) = \frac{1}{1 - 3x}$
24. $f(x) = \frac{10x}{1 + x}$
25. $f(x) = \frac{1}{(1 - x)^2}$
26. $f(x) = \ln(1 + x^2)$

27–32. Taylor series *Write out the first three terms of the Taylor series for the following functions centered at the given point a. Then write the series using summation notation.*

27. $f(x) = e^{3x},\ a = 0$
28. $f(x) = \frac{1}{x},\ a = 1$
29. $f(x) = \cos x,\ a = \pi/2$
30. $f(x) = -\ln(1 - x),\ a = 0$
31. $f(x) = \tan^{-1} x,\ a = 0$
32. $f(x) = \sin 2x,\ a = -\pi/2$

33–36. Binomial series *Write out the first three terms of the Maclaurin series for the following functions.*

33. $f(x) = (1 + x)^{1/3}$
34. $f(x) = (1 + x)^{-1/2}$
35. $f(x) = (1 + x/2)^{-3}$
36. $f(x) = (1 + 2x)^{-5}$

37–40. Convergence *Write the remainder term $R_n(x)$ for the Taylor series for the following functions centered at the given point a. Then show that $\lim_{n\to\infty} R_n(x) = 0$ for all x in the given interval.*

37. $f(x) = e^{-x},\ a = 0,\ -\infty < x < \infty$
38. $f(x) = \sin x,\ a = 0,\ -\infty < x < \infty$
39. $f(x) = \ln(1 + x),\ a = 0,\ -\frac{1}{2} \le x \le \frac{1}{2}$
40. $f(x) = \sqrt{1 + x},\ a = 0,\ -\frac{1}{2} \le x \le \frac{1}{2}$

41–46. Limits by power series *Use Taylor series to evaluate the following limits.*

41. $\lim_{x\to 0} \frac{x^2/2 - 1 + \cos x}{x^4}$
42. $\lim_{x\to 0} \frac{2 \sin x - \tan^{-1} x - x}{2x^5}$
43. $\lim_{x\to 4} \frac{\ln(x - 3)}{x^2 - 16}$
44. $\lim_{x\to 0} \frac{\sqrt{1 + 2x} - 1 - x}{x^2}$
45. $\lim_{x\to 0} \frac{\sec x - \cos x - x^2}{x^4}$
46. $\lim_{x\to 0} \frac{(1 + x)^{-2} - \sqrt[3]{1 - 6x}}{2x^2}$

47. **A differential equation** Find a power series solution of the differential equation $y'(x) - 4y(x) + 12 = 0$, subject to the condition $y(0) = 4$. Identify the solution in terms of known functions.

T **48. Rejected quarters** The probability that a random quarter is *not* rejected by a vending machine is given by the integral $11.4 \int_0^{0.14} e^{-102x^2}\,dx$ (assuming that the weights of quarters are normally distributed with a mean of 5.670 g and a standard deviation of 0.07 g). Expand the integrand in $n = 2$ and $n = 3$ terms of a Taylor series and integrate to find two estimates of the probability. Check for agreement between the two estimates.

T **49. Approximating ln 2** Consider the following three ways to approximate ln 2.

a. Use the Taylor series for $\ln(1 + x)$ centered at 0 and evaluate it at $x = 1$ (convergence was asserted in Table 10.5). Write the resulting infinite series.

b. Use the Taylor series for $\ln(1 - x)$ centered at 0 and the identity $\ln 2 = -\ln\left(\frac{1}{2}\right)$. Write the resulting infinite series.

c. Use the property $\ln(a/b) = \ln a - \ln b$ and the series of parts (a) and (b) to find the Taylor series for $f(x) = \ln\left(\frac{1 + x}{1 - x}\right)$ centered at 0.

d. At what value of x should the series in part (c) be evaluated to approximate ln 2? Write the resulting infinite series for ln 2.

e. Using four terms of the series, which of the three series derived in parts (a)–(d) gives the best approximation to ln 2? Which series gives the worst approximation? Can you explain why?

T **50. Graphing Taylor polynomials** Consider the function $f(x) = (1 + x)^{-4}$.

a. Find the Taylor polynomials p_0, p_1, p_2, and p_3 centered at 0.

b. Use a graphing utility to plot the Taylor polynomials and f for $-1 < x < 1$.

c. For each Taylor polynomial, give the interval on which its graph appears indistinguishable from the graph of f.

Chapter 10 Guided Projects

Applications of the material in this chapter and related topics can be found in the following Guided Projects. For additional information, see the Preface.

- Euler's formula (Taylor series with complex numbers)
- Fourier Series
- Three-sigma quality control
- Series approximations to π
- Stirling's formula and $n!$

11

Parametric and Polar Curves

Chapter Preview Until now, all our work has been done in the Cartesian coordinate system with functions of the form $y = f(x)$. There are, however, alternative ways to generate curves and represent functions. We begin by introducing parametric equations, which are featured prominently in Chapter 12 to represent curves and trajectories in three-dimensional space. When working with objects that have circular, cylindrical, or spherical shapes, other coordinate systems are often advantageous. In this chapter, we introduce the polar coordinate system for circular geometries. Cylindrical and spherical coordinate systems appear in Chapter 14. After working with parametric equations and polar coordinates, the next step is to investigate calculus in these settings. How do we find slopes of tangent lines and rates of changes? How are areas of regions bounded by curves in polar coordinates computed? The chapter ends with the related topic of *conic sections.* Ellipses, parabolas, and hyperbolas (all of which are conic sections) can be represented in both Cartesian and polar coordinates. These important families of curves have many fascinating properties and appear throughout the remainder of the book.

11.1 Parametric Equations

So far, we have used functions of the form $y = f(x)$ to describe curves in the xy-plane. In this section we look at another way to define curves, known as *parametric equations.* As you will see, parametric curves enable us to describe both common and exotic curves; they are also indispensable for modeling the trajectories of moving objects.

Basic Ideas

A motor boat speeds counterclockwise around a circular course with a radius of 4 mi, completing one lap every hour at a constant speed. Suppose we wish to describe the points on the path of the boat $(x(t), y(t))$ at any time $t \geq 0$, where t is measured in hours. We assume that the boat starts on the positive x-axis at the point $(4, 0)$ (Figure 11.1). Note that the angle θ corresponding to the position of the boat increases by 2π radians every hour beginning with $\theta = 0$ when $t = 0$; therefore, $\theta = 2\pi t$, for $t \geq 0$. As we show in Example 2, the x- and y-coordinates of the boat are

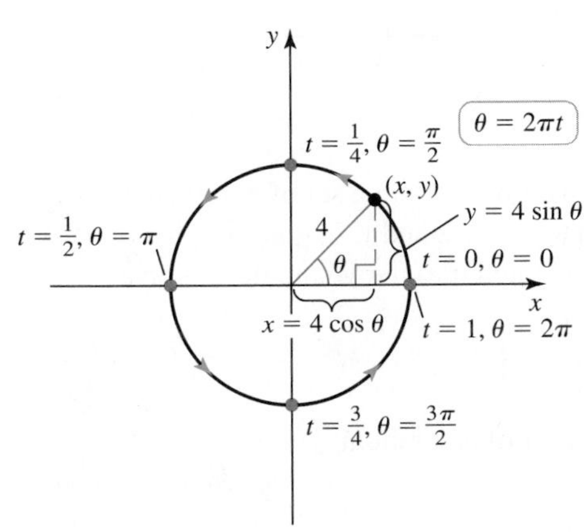

FIGURE 11.1

$$x = 4\cos\theta = 4\cos 2\pi t \quad \text{and} \quad y = 4\sin\theta = 4\sin 2\pi t,$$

where $t \geq 0$. You can confirm that when $t = 0$, the boat is at the starting point $(4, 0)$; when $t = 1$, it returns to the starting point.

The equations $x = 4\cos 2\pi t$ and $y = 4\sin 2\pi t$ are examples of **parametric equations**. They specify x and y in terms of a third variable t called a **parameter**, which often represents time (Figure 11.2).

➤ You can think of the parameter t as the independent variable. There are two dependent variables, x and y.

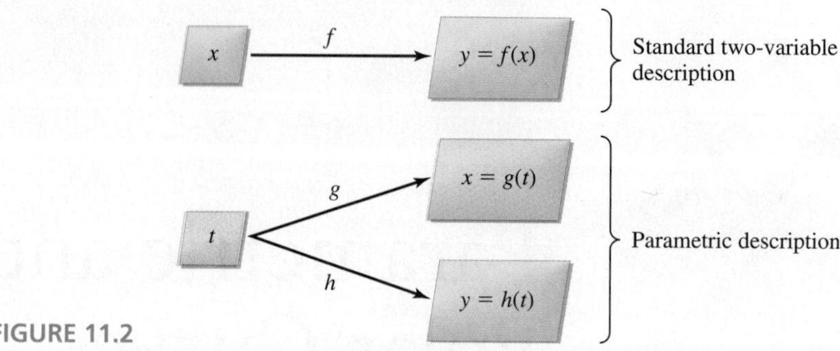

FIGURE 11.2

In general, parametric equations have the form

$$x = g(t), \qquad y = h(t),$$

where g and h are given functions and the parameter t typically varies over a specified interval, such as $a \le t \le b$. The **parametric curve** described by these equations consists of the points in the plane that satisfy

$$(x, y) = (g(t), h(t)), \qquad \text{for } a \le t \le b.$$

EXAMPLE 1 **Parametric parabola** Graph and analyze the parametric equations

$$x = g(t) = 2t, \qquad y = h(t) = \frac{1}{2}t^2 - 4, \qquad \text{for } 0 \le t \le 8.$$

Table 11.1

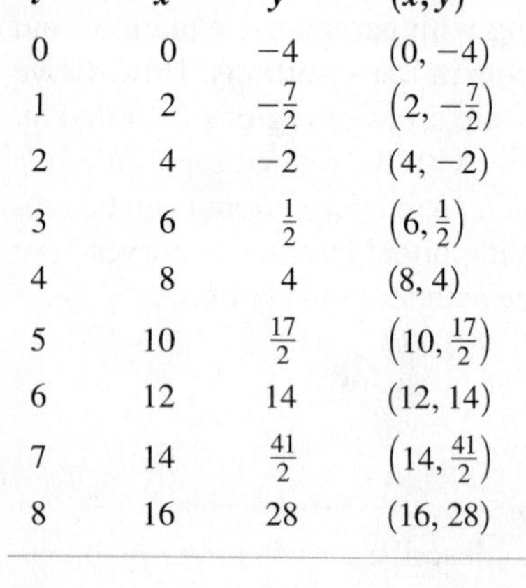

t	x	y	(x, y)
0	0	-4	$(0, -4)$
1	2	$-\frac{7}{2}$	$\left(2, -\frac{7}{2}\right)$
2	4	-2	$(4, -2)$
3	6	$\frac{1}{2}$	$\left(6, \frac{1}{2}\right)$
4	8	4	$(8, 4)$
5	10	$\frac{17}{2}$	$\left(10, \frac{17}{2}\right)$
6	12	14	$(12, 14)$
7	14	$\frac{41}{2}$	$\left(14, \frac{41}{2}\right)$
8	16	28	$(16, 28)$

SOLUTION Plotting individual points often helps visualize a parametric curve. Table 11.1 shows the values of x and y corresponding to several values of t on the interval $[0, 8]$. By plotting the (x, y) pairs in Table 11.1 and connecting them with a smooth curve, we obtain the graph shown in Figure 11.3. We see that as t increases from its initial value of $t = 0$ to its final value of $t = 8$, the curve is generated from the initial point $(0, -4)$ to the final point $(16, 28)$. Notice that the values of the parameter do not appear in the graph. The only signature of the parameter is the direction in which the curve is generated: In this case, it unfolds upward and to the right.

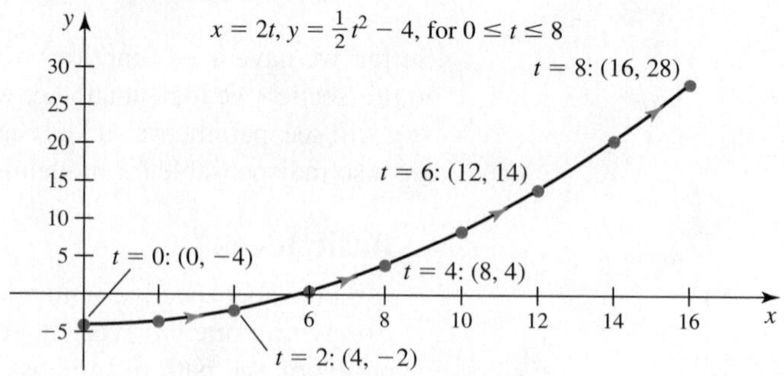

FIGURE 11.3

Occasionally, it is possible to eliminate the parameter from a set of parametric equations and obtain a description of the curve in terms of x and y. In this case, from the x-equation, we have $t = x/2$, which may be substituted into the y-equation to give

$$y = \frac{1}{2}t^2 - 4 = \frac{1}{2}\left(\frac{x}{2}\right)^2 - 4 = \frac{x^2}{8} - 4.$$

Expressed in this form, we identify the graph as part of a parabola.

Related Exercises 7–14 ◀

QUICK CHECK 1 Identify the graph that is generated by the parametric equations $x = t^2$, $y = t$, for $-10 \le t \le 10$. ◀

EXAMPLE 2 **Parametric circle** Graph and analyze the parametric equations

$$x = 4 \cos 2\pi t, \quad y = 4 \sin 2\pi t, \quad \text{for } 0 \le t \le 1$$

used to describe the path of the motor boat in the opening paragraphs.

SOLUTION For each value of t in Table 11.2, the corresponding ordered pairs (x, y) are recorded. Plotting these points as t increases from $t = 0$ to $t = 1$ results in a graph that appears to be a circle of radius 4; it is generated in a counterclockwise direction, beginning and ending at $(4, 0)$ (Figure 11.4). Letting t increase beyond $t = 1$ would simply retrace the same curve.

Table 11.2

t	(x, y)
0	$(4, 0)$
$\frac{1}{8}$	$(2\sqrt{2}, 2\sqrt{2})$
$\frac{1}{4}$	$(0, 4)$
$\frac{3}{8}$	$(-2\sqrt{2}, 2\sqrt{2})$
$\frac{1}{2}$	$(-4, 0)$
$\frac{3}{4}$	$(0, -4)$
1	$(4, 0)$

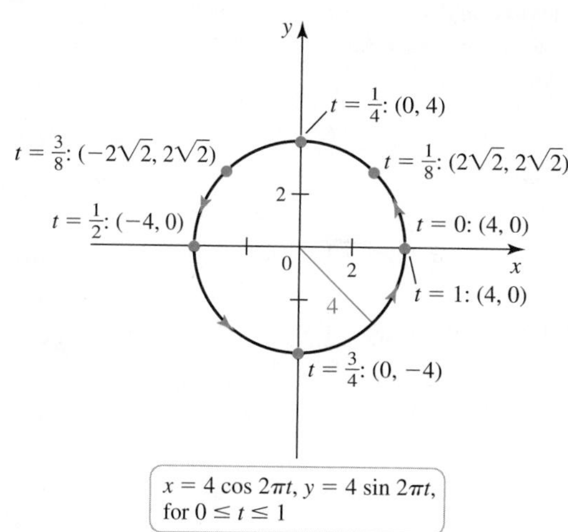

FIGURE 11.4

To identify the curve conclusively, the parameter t is eliminated by writing

$$\begin{aligned} x^2 + y^2 &= (4 \cos 2\pi t)^2 + (4 \sin 2\pi t)^2 \\ &= 16\underbrace{(\cos^2 2\pi t + \sin^2 2\pi t)}_{1} = 16. \end{aligned}$$

We see that the parametric equations are equivalent to $x^2 + y^2 = 16$, whose graph is a circle of radius 4.

Related Exercises 15–22 ◀

Generalizing Example 2 for nonzero real numbers a and b in the parametric equations $x = a \cos bt$, $y = a \sin bt$, notice that

$$\begin{aligned} x^2 + y^2 &= (a \cos bt)^2 + (a \sin bt)^2 \\ &= a^2 \underbrace{(\cos^2 bt + \sin^2 bt)}_{1} = a^2. \end{aligned}$$

➤ Recall that the functions $\sin bt$ and $\cos bt$ have period $2\pi/|b|$. The equations $x = a \cos bt$, $y = -a \sin bt$ also describe a circle of radius $|a|$, as do the equations $x = a \sin bt$, $y = \pm a \cos bt$.

Therefore, the parametric equations $x = a \cos bt$, $y = a \sin bt$ describe the circle $x^2 + y^2 = a^2$, centered at the origin with radius $|a|$, for any nonzero value of b. The circle is traversed once as t varies over any interval of length $2\pi/|b|$. If t represents time, the circle is traversed in $2\pi/|b|$ time units, which means we can vary the speed at which the curve unfolds by varying b. If $b > 0$, the curve is generated in the counterclockwise direction. If $b < 0$, the curve has a clockwise direction.

More generally, the parametric equations

$$x = x_0 + a \cos bt, \quad y = y_0 + a \sin bt$$

describe the circle $(x - x_0)^2 + (y - y_0)^2 = a^2$, centered at (x_0, y_0) with radius $|a|$. If $b > 0$, then the circle is generated in the counterclockwise direction.

➤ Example 3 shows that a single curve—for example, a circle of radius 4—may be parameterized in many different ways.

EXAMPLE 3 **Circular path** A turtle walks with constant speed in the counterclockwise direction on a circular track of radius 4 ft centered at the origin. Starting from the point $(4, 0)$, the turtle completes one lap in 30 minutes. Find a parametric description of the path of the turtle at any time $t \geq 0$.

➤ The constant $|b|$ is called the *angular frequency* because it is the number of radians the object moves per unit time. The turtle travels 2π rad every 30 min, so the angular frequency is $2\pi/30 = \pi/15$ rad/min. Because radians have no units, the angular frequency in this case has units *per minute*, sometimes written as min^{-1}.

SOLUTION Example 2 showed that a circle of radius of 4 may be described by the parametric equations

$$x = 4 \cos bt, \qquad y = 4 \sin bt.$$

The *angular frequency* b must be chosen so that, as t varies from 0 to 30, the product bt varies from 0 to 2π. Specifically, when $t = 30$, we must have $30b = 2\pi$, or $b = \pi/15$ rad/min. Therefore, the parametric equations for the turtle's motion are

$$x = 4 \cos\left(\frac{\pi t}{15}\right), \qquad y = 4 \sin\left(\frac{\pi t}{15}\right), \qquad \text{for } 0 \leq t \leq 30.$$

You should check that as t varies from 0 to 30, the points (x, y) make one complete circuit of a circle of radius 4 (Figure 11.5). *Related Exercises 23–26* ◄

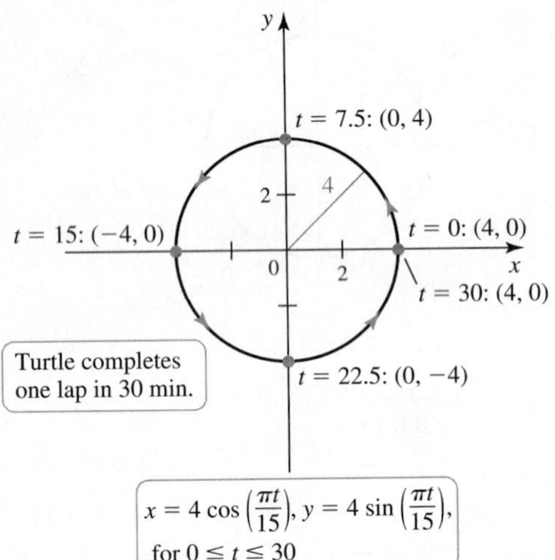

FIGURE 11.5

QUICK CHECK 2 Give the center and radius of the circle generated by the equations $x = 3 \sin t$, $y = -3 \cos t$, for $0 \leq t \leq 2\pi$. Specify the direction in which the curve is generated. ◄

EXAMPLE 4 **Parametric lines** Express the curve described by the equations $x = x_0 + at$, $y = y_0 + bt$ in the form $y = f(x)$. Assume that x_0, y_0, a, and b are constants with $a \neq 0$, and $-\infty < t < \infty$.

SOLUTION The parameter t may be eliminated by solving the x-equation for t, resulting in $t = (x - x_0)/a$. Substituting t into the y-equation, we have

$$y = y_0 + bt = y_0 + b\left(\frac{x - x_0}{a}\right) \quad \text{or} \quad y - y_0 = \frac{b}{a}(x - x_0).$$

This equation describes the line with slope b/a passing through the point (x_0, y_0). Figure 11.6 illustrates the line $x = 2 + 3t$, $y = 1 + t$, which passes through the point $(2, 1)$ at $t = 0$ with slope $\frac{1}{3}$.

➤ We can also vary the point on the line that corresponds to $t = 0$. For example, the equations

$$x = -1 + 6t, \qquad y = 2t$$

produce the same line shown in Figure 11.6. However, the point corresponding to $t = 0$ is $(-1, 0)$.

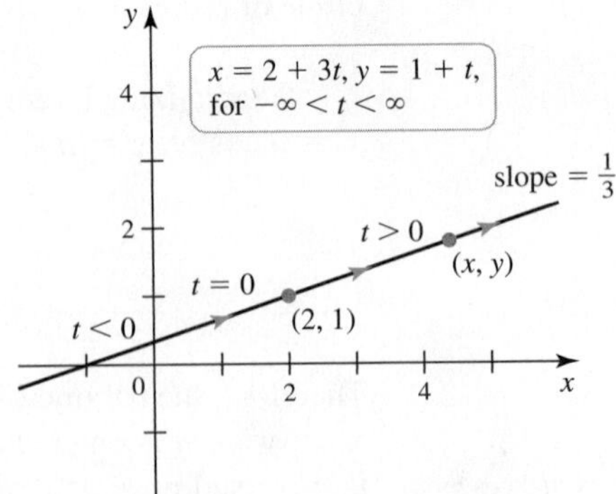

FIGURE 11.6

Notice that the parametric description of a given line is not unique: If k is any nonzero constant, the numbers a and b may be replaced by ka and kb, respectively, and the resulting equations describe the same line (although it is traversed at a different speed). If $b = 0$ and $a \neq 0$, the line has zero slope and is horizontal. If $a = 0$ and $b \neq 0$, the line is vertical. *Related Exercises 27–34* ◄

QUICK CHECK 3 Describe the curve generated by $x = 3 + 2t$, $y = -12 - 6t$, for $-\infty < t < \infty$. ◄

EXAMPLE 5 **Parametric equations of curves** A common task (particularly in upcoming chapters) is to parameterize curves given either by Cartesian equations or by graphs. Find a parametric representation of the following curves.

a. The segment of the parabola $y = 9 - x^2$, for $-1 \le x \le 3$

b. The complete curve $x = (y - 5)^2 + \sqrt{y}$

c. The piecewise linear path that connects $P(-2, 0)$ to $Q(0, 3)$ to $R(4, 0)$ (in that order), where the parameter varies over the interval $0 \le t \le 2$.

SOLUTION

a. The simplest way to represent the curve $y = f(x)$ parametrically is to let $x = t$ and $y = f(t)$, where t is the parameter. We must then find the appropriate interval for the parameter. Using this approach, the curve $y = 9 - x^2$ has the parametric representation

$$x = t, \qquad y = 9 - t^2, \qquad \text{for } -1 \le t \le 3.$$

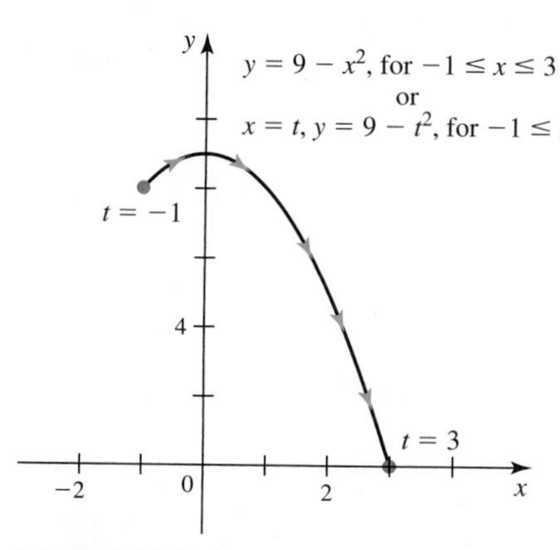

FIGURE 11.7

This representation is not unique. You should check that the parametric equations

$$x = 1 - t, \qquad y = 9 - (1 - t)^2, \qquad \text{for } -2 \le t \le 2$$

also do the job, although these equations trace the parabola from right to left, while the original equations trace the curve from left to right (Figure 11.7).

b. In this case, it is easier to let $y = t$. Then, a parametric description of the curve is

$$x = (t - 5)^2 + \sqrt{t}, \qquad y = t.$$

Notice that t can take values only in the interval $[0, \infty)$. As $t \to \infty$, we see that $x \to \infty$ and $y \to \infty$ (Figure 11.8).

c. The path consists of two line segments (Figure 11.9) that can be parameterized separately in the form $x = x_0 + at$ and $y = y_0 + bt$. The line segment PQ originates at $(-2, 0)$ and unfolds in the positive x-direction with slope $\frac{3}{2}$. It can be represented as

$$x = -2 + 2t, \qquad y = 3t, \qquad \text{for } 0 \le t \le 1.$$

> In moving from P to Q, y increases as x increases. In moving from Q to R, y decreases as x increases. The parametric equations must reflect these changes. Recall that the line $x = x_0 + at$, $y = y_0 + bt$ has slope b/a.

The line segment QR originates at $(0, 3)$ and unfolds in the positive x-direction with slope $-\frac{3}{4}$. On the interval $1 \le t \le 2$, the point $(0, 3)$ corresponds to $t = 1$. Therefore, the line segment has the representation

$$x = -4 + 4t, \qquad y = 6 - 3t, \qquad \text{for } 1 \le t \le 2.$$

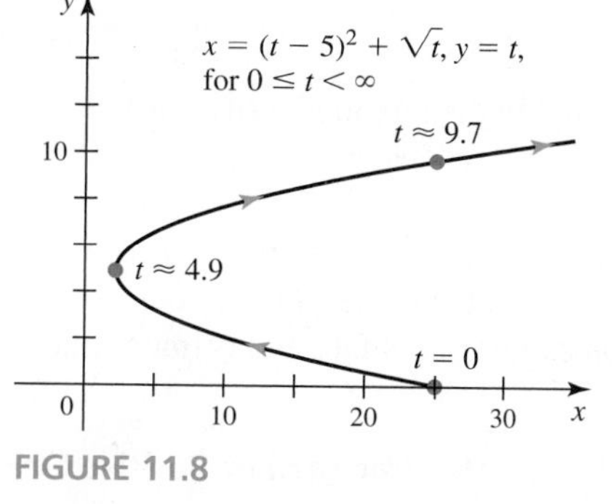

FIGURE 11.8

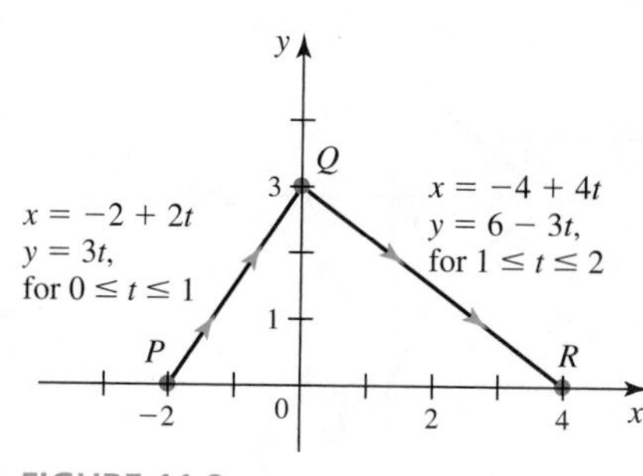

FIGURE 11.9

It is always wise to check the endpoints of the line segments for consistency. As before, this representation is not unique. *Related Exercises 35–38* ◀

QUICK CHECK 4 Find parametric equations for the line segment that goes from $Q(0, 3)$ to $P(-2, 0)$.

EXAMPLE 6 Rolling wheels Many fascinating curves are generated by points on rolling wheels. The path of a light on the rim of a rolling wheel (Figure 11.10) is a **cycloid**, which has the parametric equations

$$x = a(t - \sin t), \quad y = a(1 - \cos t), \quad \text{for } t \geq 0,$$

where $a > 0$. Use a graphing utility to graph the cycloid with $a = 1$. On what interval does the parameter generate one arch of the cycloid?

SOLUTION The graph of the cycloid for $0 \leq t \leq 3\pi$ is shown in Figure 11.11. The wheel completes one full revolution on the interval $0 \leq t \leq 2\pi$, which gives one arch of the cycloid.

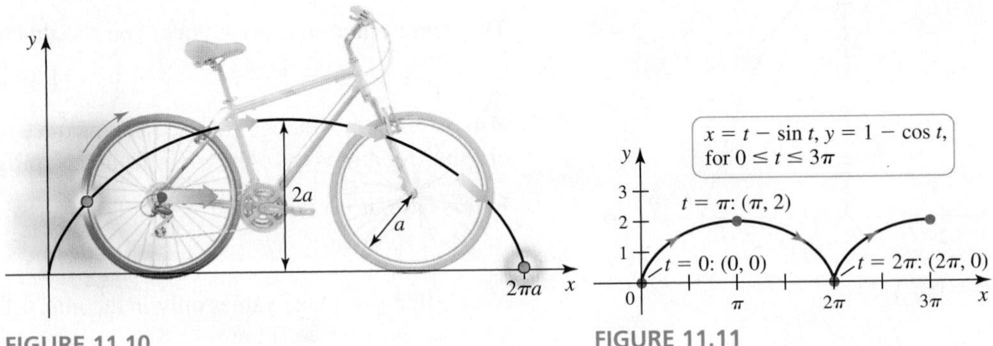

FIGURE 11.10

FIGURE 11.11

Related Exercises 39–44

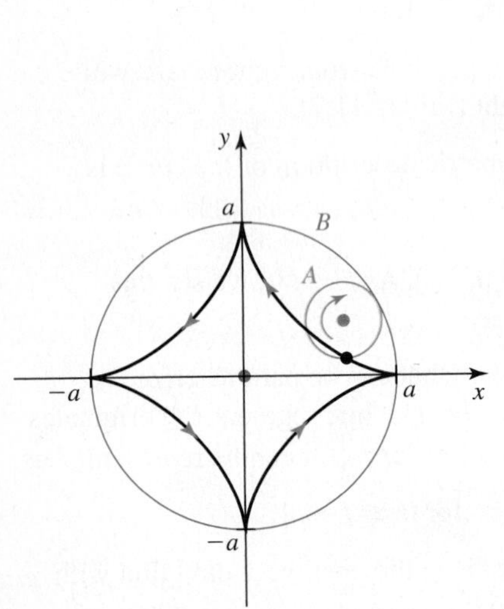

FIGURE 11.12

EXAMPLE 7 More rolling wheels The path of a point on circle A with radius $a/4$ that rolls on the inside of circle B with radius a (Figure 11.12) is an **astroid** or **hypocycloid**. Its parametric equations are

$$x = a \cos^3 t, \quad y = a \sin^3 t, \quad \text{for } 0 \leq t \leq 2\pi.$$

Graph the astroid with $a = 1$ and find its equation in terms of x and y.

SOLUTION Because both $\cos^3 t$ and $\sin^3 t$ have a period of 2π, the complete curve is generated on the interval $0 \leq t \leq 2\pi$ (Figure 11.13). To eliminate t from the parametric equations, note that $x^{2/3} = \cos^2 t$ and $y^{2/3} = \sin^2 t$. Therefore,

$$x^{2/3} + y^{2/3} = \cos^2 t + \sin^2 t = 1,$$

where the Pythagorean identity has been used. We see that an alternative description of the astroid is $x^{2/3} + y^{2/3} = 1$.

Related Exercises 39–44

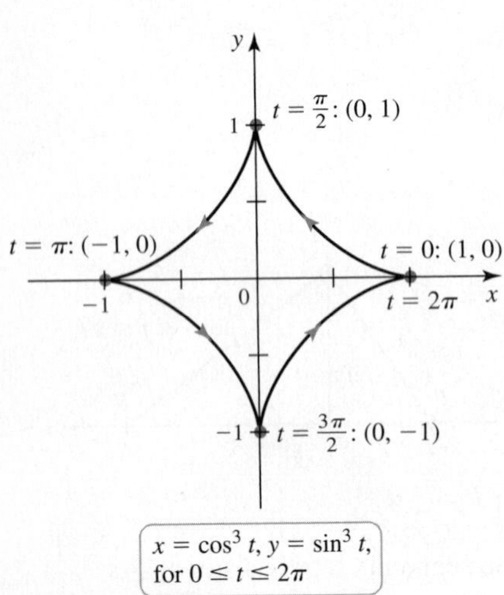

FIGURE 11.13

Given a set of parametric equations, the preceding examples show that as the parameter increases, the corresponding curve unfolds in a particular direction. The following definition captures this fact and is important in upcoming work.

> **DEFINITION Forward or Positive Orientation**
>
> The direction in which a parametric curve is generated as the parameter increases is called the **forward** or **positive orientation** of the curve.

Derivatives and Parametric Equations

Parametric equations express a relationship between the variables x and y. Therefore, it makes sense to ask about dy/dx, the rate of change of y with respect to x at a point on a parametric curve. Once we know how to compute dy/dx, it can be used to determine slopes of lines tangent to parametric curves.

Consider the parametric equations $x = g(t)$, $y = h(t)$ on an interval on which both g and h are differentiable. The Chain Rule relates the derivatives dy/dt, dx/dt, and dy/dx:

$$\frac{dy}{dt} = \frac{dy}{dx}\frac{dx}{dt}$$

Provided that $dx/dt \neq 0$, we divide both sides of this equation by dx/dt and solve for dy/dx to obtain the following result.

➤ We will soon interpret $x'(t)$ and $y'(t)$ as the horizontal and vertical velocities, respectively, of an object moving along a curve. The slope of the curve at a point is the ratio of the velocity components at that point.

THEOREM 11.1 Derivative for Parametric Curves
Let $x = g(t)$ and $y = h(t)$, where g and h are differentiable on an interval $[a, b]$. Then

$$\frac{dy}{dx} = \frac{dy/dt}{dx/dt} = \frac{h'(t)}{g'(t)},$$

provided $dx/dt \neq 0$.

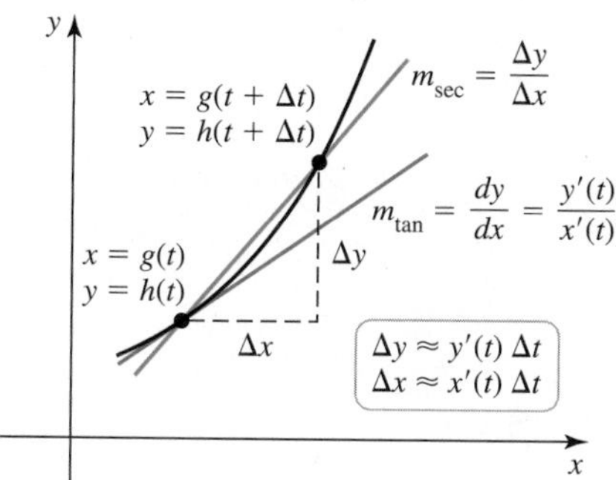

FIGURE 11.14

Figure 11.14 gives a geometric explanation of Theorem 11.1. The slope of the line tangent to a curve at a point is $\frac{dy}{dx} = \lim_{\Delta x \to 0} \frac{\Delta y}{\Delta x}$. Using linear approximation (Section 4.5), we have $\Delta x \approx x'(t)\Delta t$ and $\Delta y \approx y'(t)\Delta t$, with these approximations improving as $\Delta t \to 0$. Notice also that $\Delta t \to 0$ as $\Delta x \to 0$. Therefore, the slope of the tangent line is

$$\frac{dy}{dx} = \lim_{\Delta x \to 0} \frac{\Delta y}{\Delta x} = \lim_{\Delta t \to 0} \frac{y'(t)\Delta t}{x'(t)\Delta t} = \frac{y'(t)}{x'(t)}.$$

EXAMPLE 8 Slopes of tangent lines Find dy/dx for the following curves. Interpret the result and determine the points (if any) at which the curve has a horizontal or a vertical tangent line.

a. $x = t$, $y = 2\sqrt{t}$, for $t \geq 0$

b. $x = 4 \cos t$, $y = 16 \sin t$, for $0 \leq t \leq 2\pi$

SOLUTION

a. We find that $x'(t) = 1$ and $y'(t) = 1/\sqrt{t}$. Therefore,

$$\frac{dy}{dx} = \frac{y'(t)}{x'(t)} = \frac{1/\sqrt{t}}{1} = \frac{1}{\sqrt{t}},$$

provided $t \neq 0$. Notice that $dy/dx \neq 0$, for $t > 0$, so the curve has no horizontal tangent lines. On the other hand, as $t \to 0^+$, we see that $dy/dx \to \infty$. Therefore, the curve has a vertical tangent line at the point $(0, 0)$. To eliminate t from the parametric equations, we substitute $t = x$ into the y-equation to find that $y = 2\sqrt{x}$, or $x = y^2/4$. Because $y \geq 0$, the curve is the upper half of a parabola (Figure 11.15). Slopes of tangent lines at other points on the curve are found by substituting the corresponding values of t. For example, the point $(4, 4)$ corresponds to $t = 4$ and the slope of the tangent line at that point is $1/\sqrt{4} = \frac{1}{2}$.

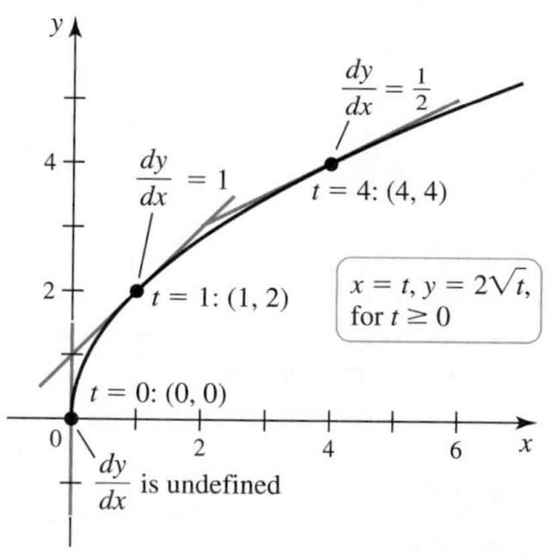

FIGURE 11.15

b. These parametric equations describe an **ellipse** with a long axis of length 32 on the y-axis and a short axis of length 8 on the x-axis (Figure 11.16). In this case, $x'(t) = -4 \sin t$ and $y'(t) = 16 \cos t$. Therefore,

$$\frac{dy}{dx} = \frac{y'(t)}{x'(t)} = \frac{16 \cos t}{-4 \sin t} = -4 \cot t.$$

➤ In general, the equations $x = a \cos t$, $y = b \sin t$, for $0 \le t \le 2\pi$, describe an ellipse. The constants a and b can be seen as horizontal and vertical scalings of the unit circle $x = \cos t$, $y = \sin t$. Ellipses are explored in Exercises 57–62 and in Section 11.4.

At $t = 0$ and $t = \pi$, $\cot t$ is undefined, and vertical tangent lines occur at the corresponding points $(\pm 4, 0)$. At $t = \pi/2$ and $t = 3\pi/2$, $\cot t = 0$ and the curve has horizontal tangent lines at the corresponding points $(0, \pm 16)$. Slopes of tangent lines at other points on the curve may be found. For example, the point $(2\sqrt{2}, 8\sqrt{2})$ corresponds to $t = \pi/4$; the slope of the tangent line at that point is $-4 \cot \pi/4 = -4$.

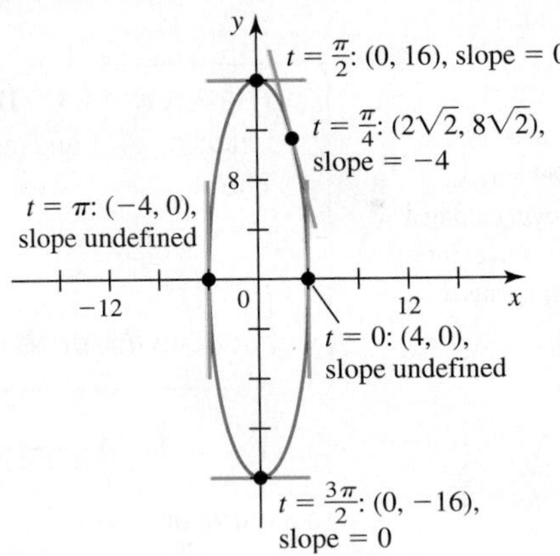

FIGURE 11.16

Related Exercises 45–50 ◄

SECTION 11.1 EXERCISES

Review Questions

1. Explain how a set of parametric equations generates a curve in the xy-plane.

2. Give two sets of parametric equations that generate a circle centered at the origin with radius 6.

3. Give a set of parametric equations that describes a full circle of radius R, where the parameter varies over the interval $[0, 10]$.

4. Give a set of parametric equations that generates the line with slope -2 passing through $(1, 3)$.

5. Find a set of parametric equations for the parabola $y = x^2$.

6. Describe the similarities and differences between the parametric equations $x = t, y = t^2$ and $x = -t, y = t^2$, where $t \ge 0$ in each case.

Basic Skills

7–10. Working with parametric equations *Consider the following parametric equations.*

a. Make a brief table of values of t, x, and y.
b. Plot the points in the table and the full parametric curve, indicating the positive orientation (the direction of increasing t).
c. Eliminate the parameter to obtain an equation in x and y.
d. Describe the curve.

7. $x = 2t, y = 3t - 4;\ -10 \le t \le 10$

8. $x = t^2 + 2, y = 4t;\ -4 \le t \le 4$

9. $x = -t + 6, y = 3t - 3;\ -5 \le t \le 5$

10. $x = \ln 5t, y = \ln t^2;\ 1 \le t \le e$

11–14. Working with parametric equations *Consider the following parametric equations.*

a. Eliminate the parameter to obtain an equation in x and y.
b. Describe the curve and indicate the positive orientation.

11. $x = \sqrt{t} + 4, y = 3\sqrt{t};\ 0 \le t \le 16$

12. $x = (t + 1)^2, y = t + 2;\ -10 \le t \le 10$

13. $x = t - 1, y = t^3;\ -4 \le t \le 4$

14. $x = e^{2t}, y = e^t + 1;\ 0 \le t \le 25$

15–18. Circles and arcs *Eliminate the parameter to find a description of the following circles or circular arcs in terms of x and y. Give the center and radius, and indicate the positive orientation.*

15. $x = 3 \cos t, y = 3 \sin t;\ \pi \le t \le 2\pi$

16. $x = 3 \cos t, y = 3 \sin t;\ 0 \le t \le \pi/2$

17. $x = -7 \cos 2t, y = -7 \sin 2t;\ 0 \le t \le \pi$

18. $x = 1 - 3 \sin 4\pi t, y = 2 + 3 \cos 4\pi t;\ 0 \le t \le \frac{1}{2}$

19–22. Parametric equations of circles *Find parametric equations (not unique) for the following circles (give an interval for the parameter values). Graph the circle and find a description in terms of x and y.*

19. A circle centered at the origin with radius 4, generated counterclockwise

20. A circle centered at the origin with radius 12, generated clockwise with initial point $(0, 12)$

21. A circle centered at $(-2, -3)$ with radius 8, generated clockwise

22. A circle centered at $(2, -4)$ with radius $3/2$, generated counterclockwise with initial point $\left(\frac{7}{2}, -4\right)$

23–26. Circular motion *Find parametric equations that describe the circular path of the following objects. Assume (x, y) denotes the position of the object relative to the origin at the center of the circle. Use the units of time specified in the problem. There is more than one way to describe any circle.*

23. A go-cart moves counterclockwise with constant speed around a circular track of radius 400 m, completing a lap in 1.5 min.

24. The tip of the 15-in second hand of a clock completes one revolution in 60 s.

25. A bicyclist rides counterclockwise with constant speed around a circular velodrome track with a radius of 50 m, completing one lap in 24 s.

26. A Ferris wheel has a radius of 20 m and completes a revolution in the clockwise direction at constant speed in 3 min. Assume that x and y measure the horizontal and vertical positions of a seat on the Ferris wheel relative to a coordinate system whose origin is at the low point of the wheel. Assume the seat begins moving at the origin.

27–30. Parametric lines *Find the slope of each line and a point on the line. Then graph the line.*

27. $x = 3 + t, y = 1 - t$

28. $x = 4 - 3t, y = -2 + 6t$

29. $x = 8 + 2t, y = 1$

30. $x = 1 + 2t/3, y = -4 - 5t/2$

31–34. Line segments *Find a parametric description of the line segment from the point P to the point Q. The solution is not unique.*

31. $P(0, 0), Q(2, 8)$

32. $P(1, 3), Q(-2, 6)$

33. $P(-1, -3), Q(6, -16)$

34. $P(-8, 2), Q(1, 2)$

35–38. Curves to parametric equations *Give a set of parametric equations that describes the following curves. Graph the curve and indicate the positive orientation. Be sure to specify the interval over which the parameter varies.*

35. The segment of the parabola $y = 2x^2 - 4$, where $-1 \le x \le 5$

36. The complete curve $x = y^3 - 3y$

37. The piecewise linear path from $P(-2, 3)$ to $Q(2, -3)$ to $R(3, 5)$

38. The path consisting of the line segment from $(-4, 4)$ to $(0, 8)$, followed by the segment of the parabola $y = 8 - 2x^2$ from $(0, 8)$ to $(2, 0)$

T **39–44. More parametric curves** *Use a graphing utility to graph the following curves. Be sure to choose an interval for the parameter that generates all features of interest.*

39. Spiral $x = t \cos t, y = t \sin t;\ t \ge 0$

40. Witch of Agnesi $x = 2 \cot t, y = 1 - \cos 2t$

41. Folium of Descartes $x = \dfrac{3t}{1 + t^3}, y = \dfrac{3t^2}{1 + t^3}$

42. Involute of a circle $x = \cos t + t \sin t, y = \sin t - t \cos t$

43. Evolute of an ellipse $x = (a^2 - b^2)\cos^3 t, y = (a^2 - b^2)\sin^3 t;$ $a = 4$ and $b = 3$

44. Cissoid of Diocles $x = 2 \sin 2t, y = \dfrac{2 \sin^3 t}{\cos t}$

45–50. Derivatives *Consider the following parametric curves.*

a. *Determine dy/dx in terms of t and evaluate it at the given value of t.*

b. *Make a sketch of the curve showing the tangent line at the point corresponding to the given value of t.*

45. $x = 2 + 4t, y = 4 - 8t;\ t = 2$

46. $x = 3 \sin t, y = 3 \cos t;\ t = \pi/2$

47. $x = \cos t, y = 8 \sin t;\ t = \pi/2$

48. $x = 2t, y = t^3;\ t = -1$

49. $x = t + 1/t, y = t - 1/t;\ t = 1$

50. $x = \sqrt{t}, y = 2t;\ t = 4$

Further Explorations

51. Explain why or why not Determine whether the following statements are true and give an explanation or counterexample.

a. The equations $x = -\cos t, y = -\sin t$, for $0 \le t \le 2\pi$, generate a circle in the clockwise direction.

b. An object following the parametric curve $x = 2 \cos 2\pi t$, $y = 2 \sin 2\pi t$ circles the origin once every 1 time unit.

c. The parametric equations $x = t, y = t^2$, for $t \ge 0$, describe the complete parabola $y = x^2$.

d. The parametric equations $x = \cos t, y = \sin t$, for $-\pi/2 \le t \le \pi/2$, describe a semicircle.

52–55. Words to curves *Find parametric equations for the following curves. Include an interval for the parameter values.*

52. The left half of the parabola $y = x^2 + 1$, originating at $(0, 1)$

53. The line that passes through the points $(1, 1)$ and $(3, 5)$, oriented in the direction of increasing x

54. The lower half of the circle centered at $(-2, 2)$ with radius 6, oriented in the counterclockwise direction

55. The upper half of the parabola $x = y^2$, originating at $(0, 0)$

56. Matching curves and equations Match the following four equations with the four graphs in the accompanying figures. Explain your reasoning.

a. $x = t^2 - 2, y = t^3 - t$

b. $x = \cos(t + \sin 50t), y = \sin(t + \cos 50t)$

c. $x = t + \cos 2t, y = t - \sin 4t$
d. $x = 2\cos t + \cos 20t, y = 2\sin t + \sin 20t$

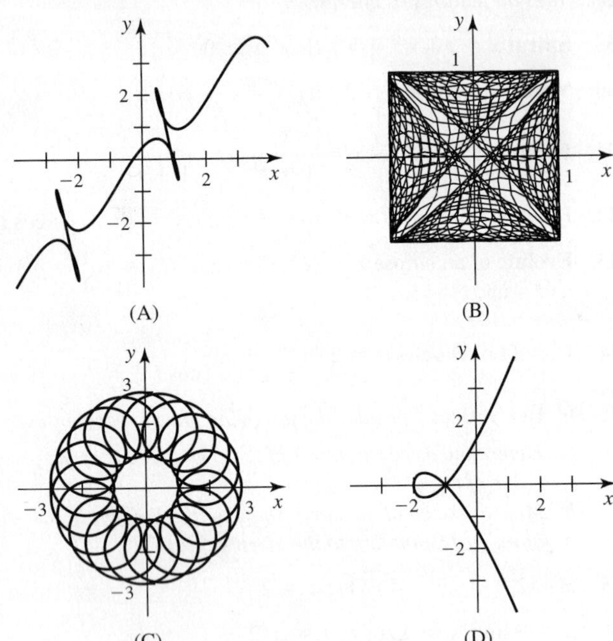

57–58. Ellipses *An **ellipse** (discussed in detail in Section 11.4) is generated by the parametric equations $x = a\cos t, y = b\sin t$. If $0 < a < b$, then the long axis (or **major axis**) lies on the y-axis and the short axis (or **minor axis**) lies on the x-axis. If $0 < b < a$, the axes are reversed. The lengths of the axes in the x- and y-directions are 2a and 2b, respectively. Sketch the graph of the following ellipses. Specify an interval in t over which the entire curve is generated.*

57. $x = 4\cos t, y = 9\sin t$. **58.** $x = 12\sin 2t, y = 3\cos 2t$

59–62. Parametric equations of ellipses *Find parametric equations of the following ellipses (see Exercises 57–58). Solutions are not unique. Graph the ellipse and find a description in terms of x and y.*

59. An ellipse centered at the origin with major axis of length 6 on the x-axis and minor axis of length 3 on the y-axis, generated counterclockwise

60. An ellipse centered at the origin with major and minor axes of length 12 and 2, on the x- and y-axes, respectively, generated clockwise

61. An ellipse centered at $(-2, -3)$ with major and minor axes of length 30 and 20, on the x- and y-axes, respectively, generated counterclockwise (Shift the parametric equations.)

62. An ellipse centered at $(0, -4)$ with major and minor axes of length 10 and 3, on the x- and y-axes, respectively, generated clockwise (Shift the parametric equations.)

63. Multiple descriptions Which of the following parametric equations describe the same line?

a. $x = 3 + t, y = 4 - 2t;\ -\infty < t < \infty$
b. $x = 3 + 4t, y = 4 - 8t;\ -\infty < t < \infty$
c. $x = 3 + t^3, y = 4 - t^3;\ -\infty < t < \infty$

64. Multiple descriptions Which of the following parametric equations describe the same curve?

a. $x = 2t^2, y = 4 + t;\ -4 < t < 4$
b. $x = 2t^4, y = 4 + t^2;\ -2 < t < 2$
c. $x = 2t^{2/3}, y = 4 + t^{1/3};\ -64 < t < 64$

65–70. Eliminating the parameter *Eliminate the parameter to express the following parametric equations as a single equation in x and y.*

65. $x = 2\sin 8t, y = 2\cos 8t$ **66.** $x = 3 - t, y = 3 + t$

67. $x = t, y = \sqrt{4 - t^2}$ **68.** $x = \sqrt{t + 1}, y = \dfrac{1}{t + 1}$

69. $x = \tan t, y = \sec^2 t - 1$

70. $x = a\sin^n t, y = b\cos^n t$, where a and b are real numbers and n is a positive integer

71–74. Slopes of tangent lines *Find all the points on the following curves that have the given slope.*

71. $x = 4\cos t, y = 4\sin t$; slope $= \frac{1}{2}$

72. $x = 2\cos t, y = 8\sin t$; slope $= -1$

73. $x = t + 1/t, y = t - 1/t$; slope $= 1$

74. $x = 2 + \sqrt{t}, y = 2 - 4t$; slope $= 0$

75–76. Equivalent descriptions *Find real numbers a and b such that equations A and B describe the same curve.*

75. $A\colon x = 10\sin t, y = 10\cos t;\ 0 \le t \le 2\pi$
$B\colon x = 10\sin 3t, y = 10\cos 3t;\ a \le t \le b$

76. $A\colon x = t + t^3, y = 3 + t^2;\ -2 \le t \le 2$
$B\colon x = t^{1/3} + t, y = 3 + t^{2/3};\ a \le t \le b$

77–78. Lissajous curves *Consider the following Lissajous curves. Find all points on the curve at which there is (a) a horizontal tangent line and (b) a vertical tangent line. (See the Guided Projects for more on Lissajous curves.)*

77. $x = \sin 2t, y = 2\sin t$; $0 \le t \le 2\pi$

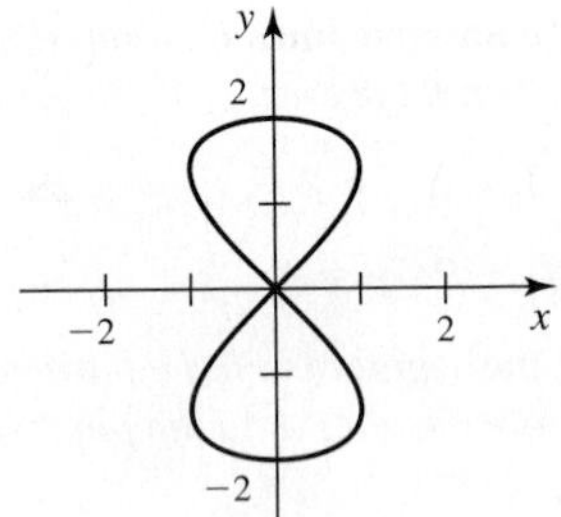

78. $x = \sin 4t, y = \sin 3t$; $0 \le t \le 2\pi$

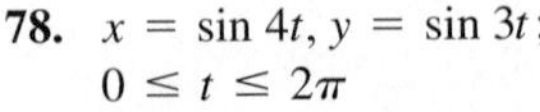

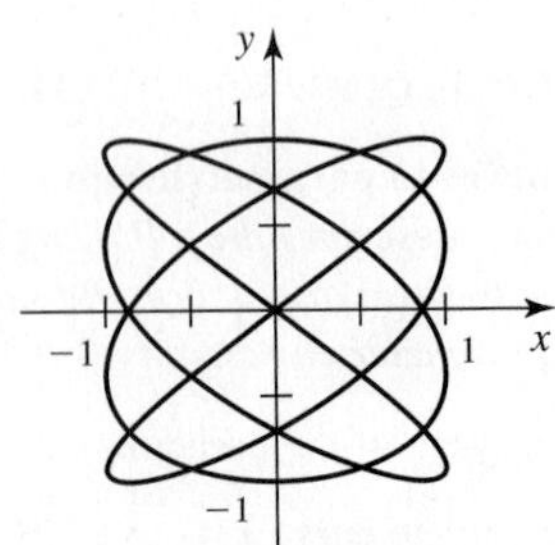

79. Lamé curves The *Lamé curve* described by $\left|\dfrac{x}{a}\right|^n + \left|\dfrac{y}{b}\right|^n = 1$, where a, b, and n are positive real numbers, is a generalization of an ellipse.

a. Express this equation in parametric form (four sets of equations are needed).
b. Graph the curve for $a = 4$ and $b = 2$, for various values of n.
c. Describe how the curves change as n increases.

T **80. Hyperbolas** A family of curves called *hyperbolas* (discussed in Section 11.4) has the parametric equations $x = a \tan t$, $y = b \sec t$, for $-\pi < t < \pi$ and $|t| \neq \pi/2$, where a and b are nonzero real numbers. Graph the hyperbola with $a = b = 1$. Indicate clearly the direction in which the curve is generated as t increases from $t = -\pi$ to $t = \pi$.

T **81. Trochoid explorations** A *trochoid* is the path followed by a point b units from the center of a wheel of radius a as the wheel rolls along the x-axis. Its parametric description is $x = at - b \sin t$, $y = a - b \cos t$. Choose specific values of a and b, and use a graphing utility to plot different trochoids. In particular, explore the difference between the cases $a > b$ and $a < b$.

T **82. Epitrochoid** An *epitrochoid* is the path of a point on a circle of radius b as it rolls on the outside of a circle of radius a. It is described by the equations

$$x = (a + b) \cos t - c \cos\left[\frac{(a + b)t}{b}\right]$$

$$y = (a + b) \sin t - c \sin\left[\frac{(a + b)t}{b}\right]$$

Use a graphing utility to explore the dependence of the curve on the parameters a, b, and c.

T **83. Hypocycloid** A general *hypocycloid* is described by the equations

$$x = (a - b) \cos t + b \cos\left[\frac{(a - b)t}{b}\right]$$

$$y = (a - b) \sin t - b \sin\left[\frac{(a - b)t}{b}\right]$$

Use a graphing utility to explore the dependence of the curve on the parameters a, b, and c.

Applications

84. Air drop A plane traveling horizontally at 80 m/s over flat ground at an elevation of 3000 m releases an emergency packet. The trajectory of the packet is given by

$$x = 80t, y = -4.9t^2 + 3000, \quad \text{for } t \geq 0,$$

where the origin is the point on the ground directly beneath the plane at the moment of the release. Graph the trajectory of the packet and find the coordinates of the point where the packet lands.

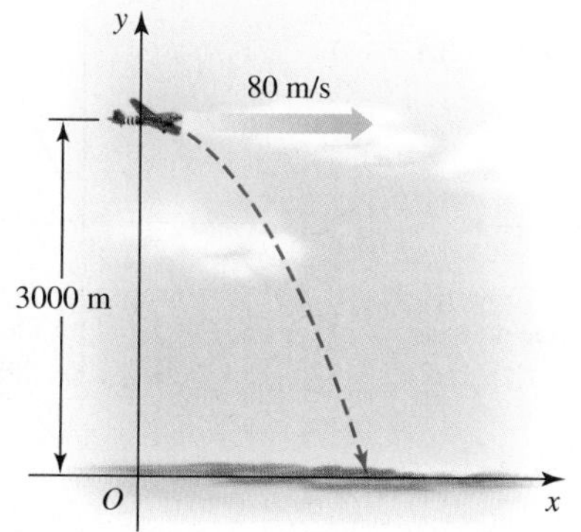

85. Air drop—inverse problem A plane traveling horizontally at 100 m/s over flat ground at an elevation of 4000 m must drop an emergency packet on a target on the ground. The trajectory of the packet is given by

$$x = 100t, \quad y = -4.9t^2 + 4000, \quad \text{for } t \geq 0,$$

where the origin is the point on the ground directly beneath the plane at the moment of the release. How many horizontal meters before the target should the packet be released in order to hit the target?

86. Projectile explorations A projectile launched from the ground with an initial speed of 20 m/s and a launch angle θ follows a trajectory approximated by

$$x = (20 \cos \theta)t, \quad y = -4.9t^2 + (20 \sin \theta)t,$$

where x and y are the horizontal and vertical positions of the projectile relative to the launch point $(0, 0)$.

a. Graph the trajectory for various values of θ in the range $0 < \theta < \pi/2$.
b. Based on your observations, what value of θ gives the greatest range (the horizontal distance between the launch and landing points)?

Additional Exercises

T **87. Implicit function graph** Explain and carry out a method for graphing the curve $x = 1 + \cos^2 y - \sin^2 y$ using parametric equations and a graphing utility.

88. Second derivative Assume a curve is given by the parametric equations $x = g(t)$ and $y = h(t)$, where g and h are twice differentiable. Use the Chain Rule to show that

$$y''(x) = \frac{x'(t)y''(t) - y'(t)x''(t)}{[x'(t)]^3}.$$

89. General equations for a circle Prove that the equations

$$x = a \cos t + b \sin t, \quad y = c \cos t + d \sin t$$

where a, b, c, and d are real numbers, describe a circle of radius R provided $a^2 + c^2 = b^2 + d^2 = R^2$ and $ab + cd = 0$.

90. x^y versus y^x Consider positive real numbers x and y. Notice that $4^3 < 3^4$, while $3^2 > 2^3$, and $4^2 = 2^4$. Describe the regions in the first quadrant of the xy-plane in which $x^y > y^x$ and $x^y < y^x$. (*Hint:* Find a parametric description of the curve that separates the two regions.)

QUICK CHECK ANSWERS

1. A segment of the parabola $x = y^2$ opening to the right with vertex at the origin **2.** The circle has center $(0, 0)$ and radius 3; it is generated in the counterclockwise direction starting at $(0, -3)$. **3.** The line $y = -3x - 3$ with slope -3 passing through $(3, -12)$ (when $t = 0$) **4.** One possibility is $x = -2t$, $y = 3 - 3t$, for $0 \leq t \leq 1$.

11.2 Polar Coordinates

Suppose you work for a company that designs heat shields for space shuttles. The shields are thin plates that are either rectangular or circular in shape. To solve the heat transfer equations for these two shields, you must choose a coordinate system that best fits the geometry of the problem. A Cartesian (rectangular) coordinate system is a natural choice for the rectangular shields (Figure 11.17a). However, it does not provide a good fit for the circular shields (Figure 11.17b). On the other hand, a **polar coordinate** system, in which the coordinates are constant on circles and rays, is much better suited for the circular shields (Figure 11.17c).

➤ Recall that the terms *Cartesian* coordinate system and *rectangular* coordinate system both describe the usual xy-coordinate system.

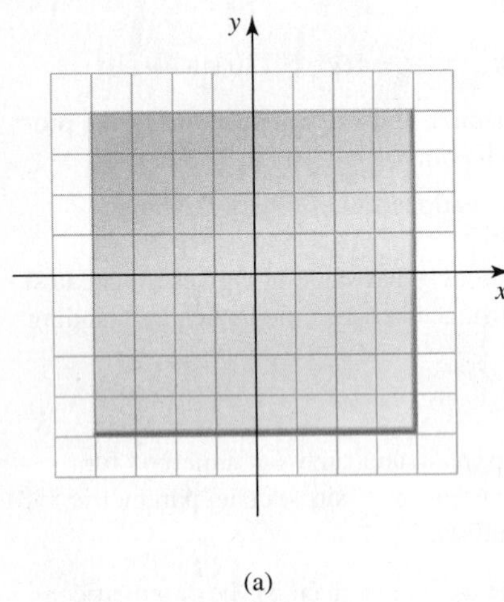

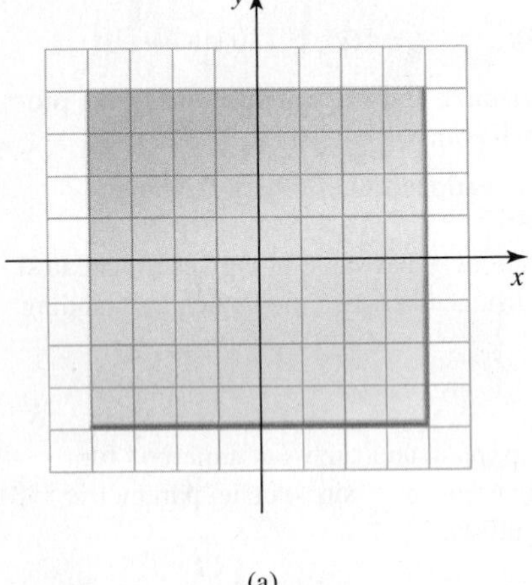

(a) (b) (c)

$\theta = \frac{\pi}{2}$ $\theta = \pi$ $\theta = 0$ $\theta = \frac{3\pi}{2}$

FIGURE 11.17

Defining Polar Coordinates

Like Cartesian coordinates, polar coordinates are used to locate points in the plane. When working in polar coordinates, the origin of the coordinate system is also called the **pole**, and the x-axis is called the **polar axis**. The polar coordinates for a point P have the form (r, θ). **The radial coordinate** r describes the *signed*, or *directed*, distance from the origin to P. The **angular coordinate** θ describes an angle whose initial side is the positive x-axis and whose terminal side lies on the ray passing through the origin and P (Figure 11.18a). Positive angles are measured counterclockwise from the positive x-axis.

With polar coordinates, points have more than one representation for two reasons. First, angles are determined up to multiples of 2π radians, so the coordinates (r, θ) and $(r, \theta \pm 2\pi)$ refer to the same point (Figure 11.18b). Second, the radial coordinate may be negative, which is interpreted as follows: The points (r, θ) and $(-r, \theta)$ are reflections of each other through the origin (Figure 11.18c). This means that (r, θ), $(-r, \theta + \pi)$, and $(-r, \theta - \pi)$ all refer to the same point. The origin is specified as $(0, \theta)$ in polar coordinates, where θ is any angle.

➤ Polar points and curves are usually sketched on a rectangular coordinate system, with standard "x" and "y" labels attached to the axes. However, plotting polar points and curves is often easier using polar graph paper, which has concentric circles centered at the origin and rays emanating from the origin (Figure 11.19).

QUICK CHECK 1 Which of the following coordinates represent the same point: $(3, \pi/2)$, $(3, 3\pi/2)$, $(3, 5\pi/2)$, $(-3, -\pi/2)$, and $(-3, 3\pi/2)$? ◄

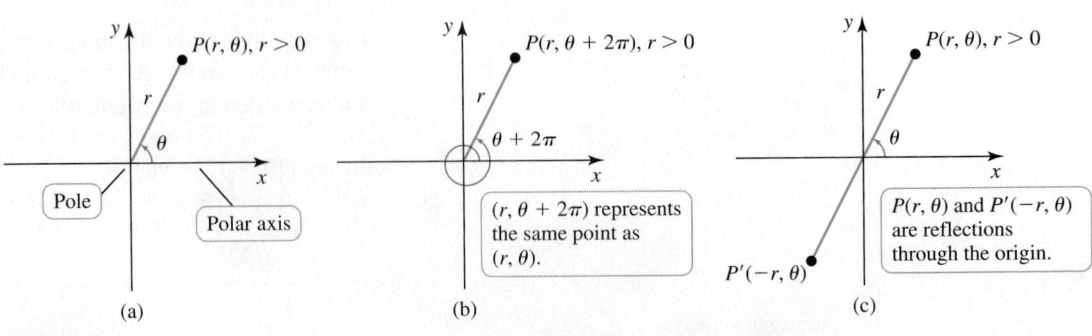

FIGURE 11.18

EXAMPLE 1 **Points in polar coordinates** Graph the following points in polar coordinates: $Q\left(1, \frac{5\pi}{4}\right)$, $R\left(-1, \frac{7\pi}{4}\right)$, and $S\left(2, -\frac{3\pi}{2}\right)$. Give two alternative representations for each point.

SOLUTION The point $Q\left(1, \frac{5\pi}{4}\right)$ is one unit from the origin on a line OQ that makes an angle of $\frac{5\pi}{4}$ with the positive x-axis (Figure 11.19a). Subtracting 2π from the angle, the point Q can be represented as $\left(1, -\frac{3\pi}{4}\right)$. Subtracting π from the angle and negating the radial coordinate means Q also has the coordinates $\left(-1, \frac{\pi}{4}\right)$.

To locate the point $R\left(-1, \frac{7\pi}{4}\right)$, it is easiest first to find the point $R'\left(1, \frac{7\pi}{4}\right)$ in the fourth quadrant. Then, $R\left(-1, \frac{7\pi}{4}\right)$ is the reflection of R' through the origin (Figure 11.19b). Other representations of R include $\left(-1, -\frac{\pi}{4}\right)$ and $\left(1, \frac{3\pi}{4}\right)$.

The point $S\left(2, -\frac{3\pi}{2}\right)$ is two units from the origin, found by rotating *clockwise* through an angle of $\frac{3\pi}{2}$ (Figure 11.19c). The point S can also be represented as $\left(2, \frac{\pi}{2}\right)$ or $\left(-2, -\frac{\pi}{2}\right)$.

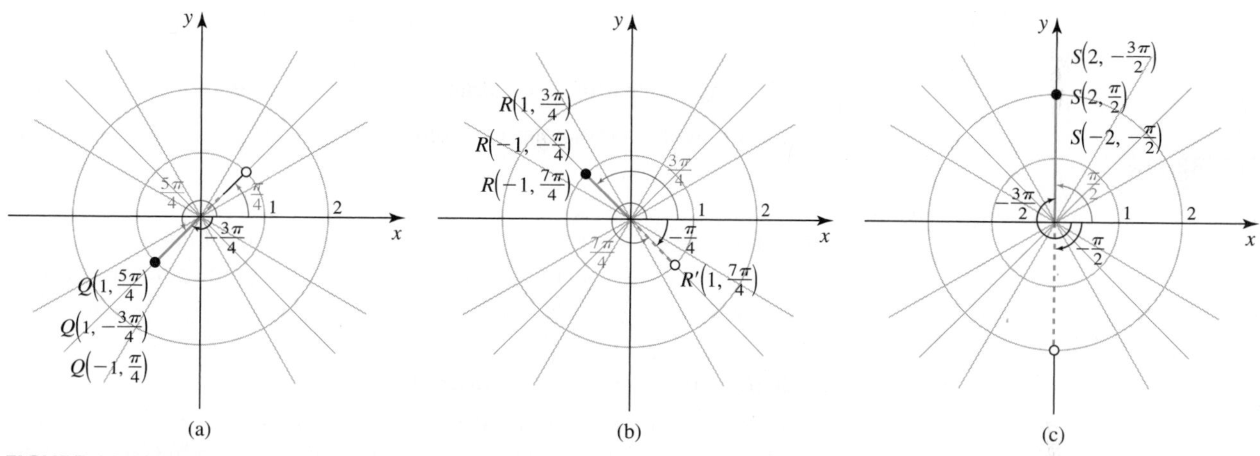

FIGURE 11.19

Related Exercises 9–14

Converting Between Cartesian and Polar Coordinates

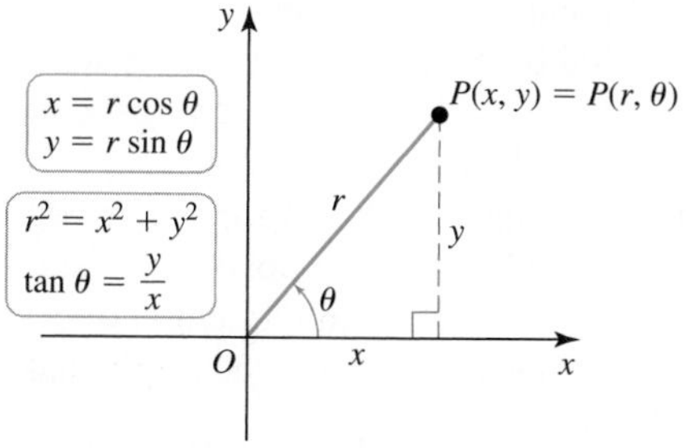

We often need to convert between Cartesian and polar coordinates. The conversion equations emerge when we look at a right triangle (Figure 11.20) in which

$$\cos \theta = \frac{x}{r} \quad \text{and} \quad \sin \theta = \frac{y}{r}.$$

$x = r\cos\theta$, $y = r\sin\theta$

$r^2 = x^2 + y^2$, $\tan\theta = \frac{y}{x}$

$P(x, y) = P(r, \theta)$

FIGURE 11.20

Given a point with polar coordinates (r, θ), we see that its Cartesian coordinates are $x = r\cos\theta$ and $y = r\sin\theta$. Conversely, given a point with Cartesian coordinates (x, y), its radial polar coordinate satisfies $r^2 = x^2 + y^2$. The coordinate θ is determined using the relation $\tan\theta = y/x$, where the quadrant in which θ lies is determined by the signs of x and y. Figure 11.20 illustrates the conversion formulas for a point P in the first quadrant. The same relationships hold if P is in any of the other three quadrants.

QUICK CHECK 2 Draw versions of Figure 11.20 with P in the second, third, and fourth quadrants. Verify that the same conversion formulas hold in all cases.

> To determine θ, you may also use the relationships $\cos\theta = x/r$ and $\sin\theta = y/r$. Either method requires checking the signs of x and y to be sure that θ is in the correct quadrant.

PROCEDURE **Converting Coordinates**

A point with polar coordinates (r, θ) has Cartesian coordinates (x, y), where

$$x = r\cos\theta \quad \text{and} \quad y = r\sin\theta.$$

A point with Cartesian coordinates (x, y) has polar coordinates (r, θ), where

$$r^2 = x^2 + y^2 \quad \text{and} \quad \tan\theta = y/x.$$

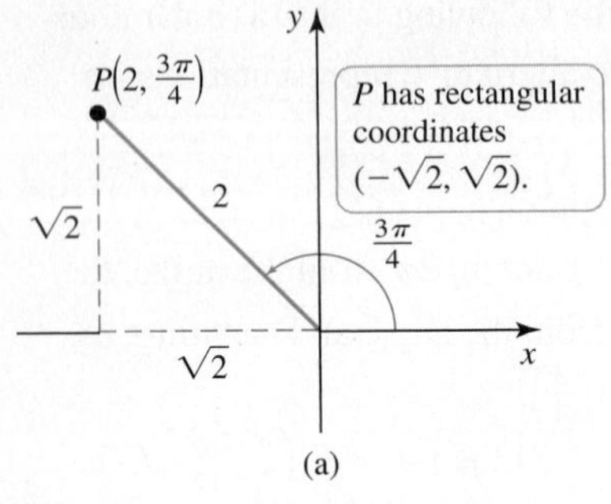

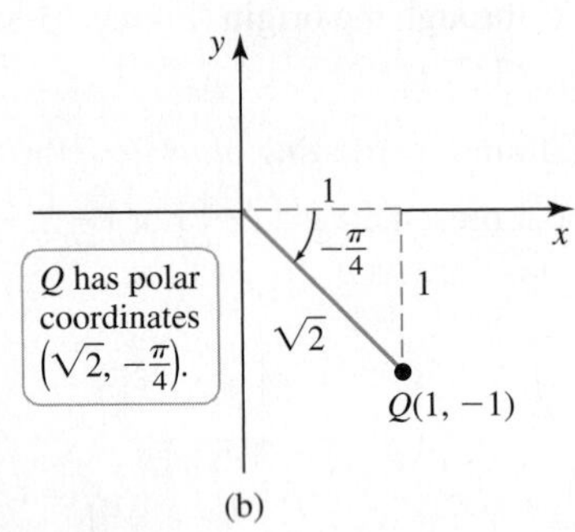

FIGURE 11.21

EXAMPLE 2 Converting coordinates

a. Express the point with polar coordinates $P\left(2, \frac{3\pi}{4}\right)$ in Cartesian coordinates.

b. Express the point with Cartesian coordinates $Q(1, -1)$ in polar coordinates.

SOLUTION

a. The point P has Cartesian coordinates

$$x = r\cos\theta = 2\cos\left(\frac{3\pi}{4}\right) = -\sqrt{2}$$

$$y = r\sin\theta = 2\sin\left(\frac{3\pi}{4}\right) = \sqrt{2}$$

As shown in Figure 11.21a, P is in the second quadrant.

b. It's best to locate this point first to be sure that the angle θ is chosen correctly. As shown in Figure 11.21b, the point $Q(1, -1)$ is in the fourth quadrant at a distance $r = \sqrt{1^2 + (-1)^2} = \sqrt{2}$ from the origin. The coordinate θ satisfies

$$\tan\theta = \frac{y}{x} = \frac{-1}{1} = -1.$$

The angle in the fourth quadrant with $\tan\theta = -1$ is $\theta = -\frac{\pi}{4}$ or $\frac{7\pi}{4}$. Therefore, two (of infinitely many) polar representations of Q are $\left(\sqrt{2}, -\frac{\pi}{4}\right)$ and $\left(\sqrt{2}, \frac{7\pi}{4}\right)$.

Related Exercises 15–26 ◀

QUICK CHECK 3 Give two polar coordinate descriptions of the point with Cartesian coordinates $(1, 0)$. What are the Cartesian coordinates of the point with polar coordinates $\left(2, \frac{\pi}{2}\right)$? ◀

Basic Curves in Polar Coordinates

A curve in polar coordinates is the set of points that satisfy an equation in r and θ. Some sets of points are easier to describe in polar coordinates than in Cartesian coordinates. Let's begin with two simple curves.

The polar equation $r = 3$ is satisfied by the set of points whose distance from the origin is 3. The angle θ is arbitrary because it is not specified by the equation, so the graph of $r = 3$ is the circle of radius 3 centered at the origin. In general, the equation $r = a$ describes a circle of radius $|a|$ centered at the origin (Figure 11.22a).

The equation $\theta = \pi/3$ is satisfied by the points whose angle with respect to the positive x-axis is $\pi/3$. Because r is unspecified, it is arbitrary (and can be positive or negative). Therefore, $\theta = \pi/3$ describes the line through the origin making an angle of $\pi/3$ with the positive x-axis. More generally, $\theta = \theta_0$ describes the line through the origin making an angle of θ_0 with the positive x-axis (Figure 11.22b).

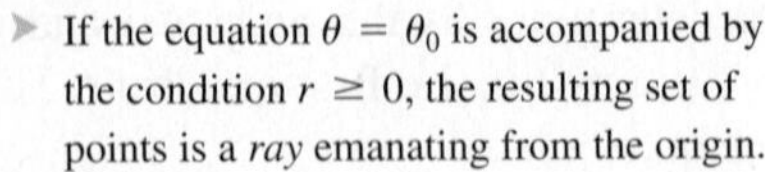
➤ If the equation $\theta = \theta_0$ is accompanied by the condition $r \geq 0$, the resulting set of points is a *ray* emanating from the origin.

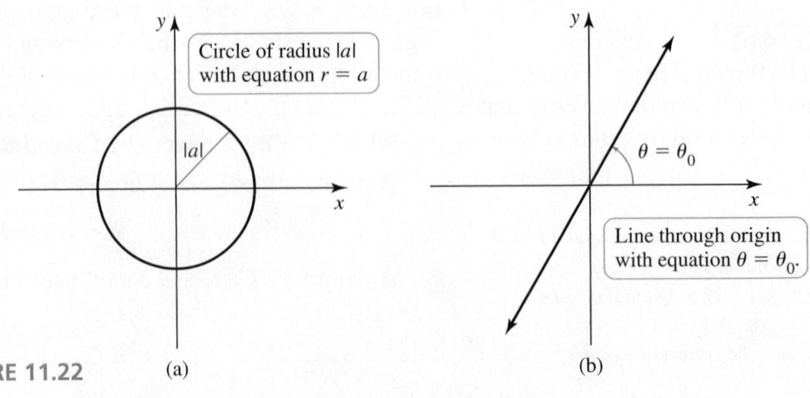

FIGURE 11.22

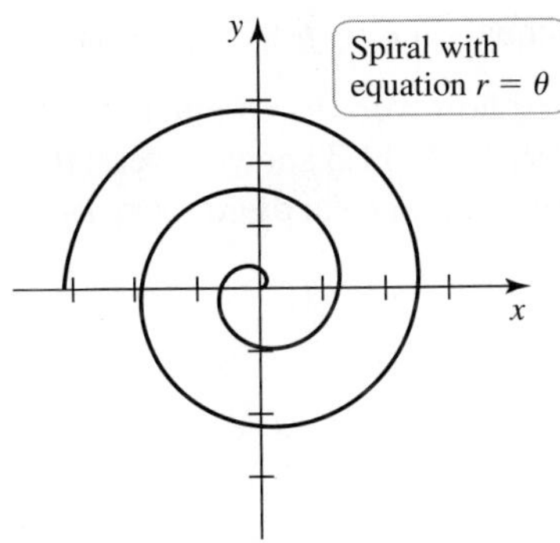

FIGURE 11.23

The simplest polar equation that involves both r and θ is $r = \theta$. Restricting θ to the interval $\theta \geq 0$, we see that as θ increases, r increases. Therefore, as θ increases, the points on the curve move away from the origin as they circle the origin in a counterclockwise direction, generating a spiral (Figure 11.23).

QUICK CHECK 4 Describe the polar curves $r = 12$, $r = 6\theta$, and $r \sin\theta = 10$. ◂

EXAMPLE 3 Polar to Cartesian coordinates Convert the polar equation $r = 6 \sin\theta$ to Cartesian coordinates and describe the corresponding graph.

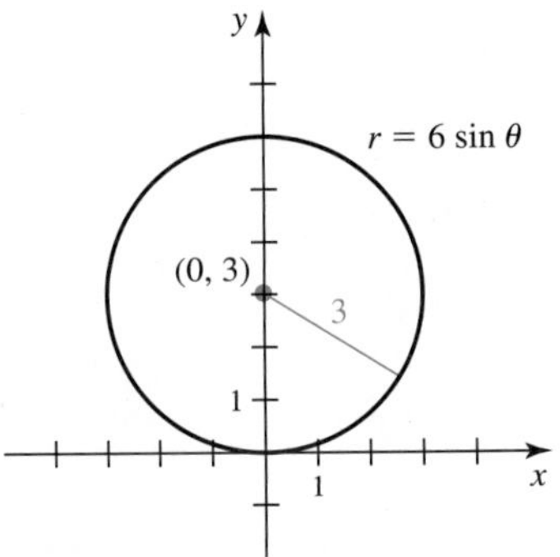

FIGURE 11.24

SOLUTION We first assume that $r \neq 0$ and multiply both sides of the equation by r, which produces the equation $r^2 = 6r \sin\theta$. Using the conversion relations $r^2 = x^2 + y^2$ and $y = r \sin\theta$, the equation

$$\underbrace{r^2}_{x^2 + y^2} = \underbrace{6r \sin\theta}_{6y}$$

becomes $x^2 + y^2 - 6y = 0$. Completing the square gives the equation

$$x^2 + \underbrace{y^2 - 6y + 9}_{(y-3)^2} - 9 = x^2 + (y - 3)^2 - 9 = 0.$$

We recognize $x^2 + (y - 3)^2 = 9$ as the equation of a circle of radius 3 centered at $(0, 3)$ (Figure 11.24). *Related Exercises 27–36* ◂

Calculations similar to those in Example 3 lead to the following equations of circles in polar coordinates.

SUMMARY Circles in Polar Coordinates

The equation $r = a$ describes a circle of radius $|a|$ centered at $(0, 0)$.

The equation $r = 2a \sin\theta$ describes a circle of radius $|a|$ centered at $(0, a)$.

The equation $r = 2a \cos\theta$ describes a circle of radius $|a|$ centered at $(a, 0)$.

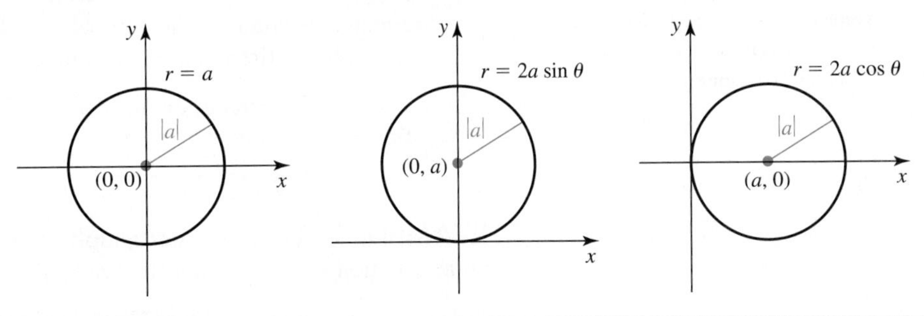

Graphing in Polar Coordinates

Equations in polar coordinates often describe curves that are difficult to represent in Cartesian coordinates. Partly for this reason, curve-sketching methods for polar coordinates differ from those used for curves in Cartesian coordinates. Conceptually, the easiest graphing method is to choose several values of θ, calculate the corresponding r-values, and tabulate the coordinates. The points are then plotted and connected with a smooth curve.

➤ When a curve is described as $r = f(\theta)$, it is natural to tabulate points in θ-r format, just as we list points in x-y format for $y = f(x)$. Despite this fact, the standard form for writing an ordered pair in polar coordinates is (r, θ).

EXAMPLE 4 **Plotting a polar curve** Graph the polar equation $r = f(\theta) = 1 + \sin\theta$.

SOLUTION The domain of f consists of all real values of θ; however, the complete curve is generated by letting θ vary over any interval of length 2π. Table 11.3 shows several θ-r pairs, which are plotted in Figure 11.25. The resulting curve, called a **cardioid**, is symmetric about the y-axis.

Table 11.3

θ	$r = 1 + \sin\theta$
0	1
$\pi/6$	3/2
$\pi/2$	2
$5\pi/6$	3/2
π	1
$7\pi/6$	1/2
$3\pi/2$	0
$11\pi/6$	1/2
2π	1

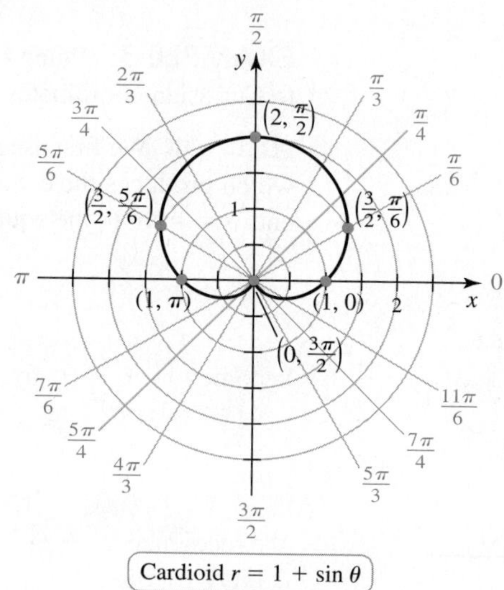

Cardioid $r = 1 + \sin\theta$

FIGURE 11.25

Related Exercises 27–36 ◀

Cartesian-to-Polar Method Plotting polar curves point by point is time consuming, and important details may not be revealed. Here is an alternative procedure for graphing polar curves that is usually quicker and more reliable.

➤ For some (but not all) curves, it suffices to graph $r = f(\theta)$ over any interval in θ whose length is the period of f. See Examples 6 and 9 for exceptions.

PROCEDURE **Cartesian-to-Polar Method for Graphing $r = f(\theta)$**

1. Graph $r = f(\theta)$ *as if r and θ were Cartesian coordinates* with θ on the horizontal axis and r on the vertical axis. Be sure to choose an interval in θ on which the entire polar curve is produced.
2. Use the Cartesian graph in Step 1 as a guide to sketch the points (r, θ) on the final *polar* curve.

EXAMPLE 5 **Plotting polar graphs** Use the Cartesian-to-polar method to graph the polar equation $r = 1 + \sin\theta$ (Example 4).

SOLUTION Viewing r and θ as Cartesian coordinates, the graph of $r = 1 + \sin\theta$ on the interval $[0, 2\pi]$ is a standard sine curve with amplitude 1 shifted up 1 unit (Figure 11.26). Notice that the graph begins with $r = 1$ at $\theta = 0$, increases to $r = 2$ at $\theta = \pi/2$, decreases to $r = 0$ at $\theta = 3\pi/2$ (which indicates an intersection with the origin on the polar graph), and increases to $r = 1$ at $\theta = 2\pi$. The second row of Figure 11.26 shows the final polar curve (a cardioid) as it is transferred from the Cartesian curve.

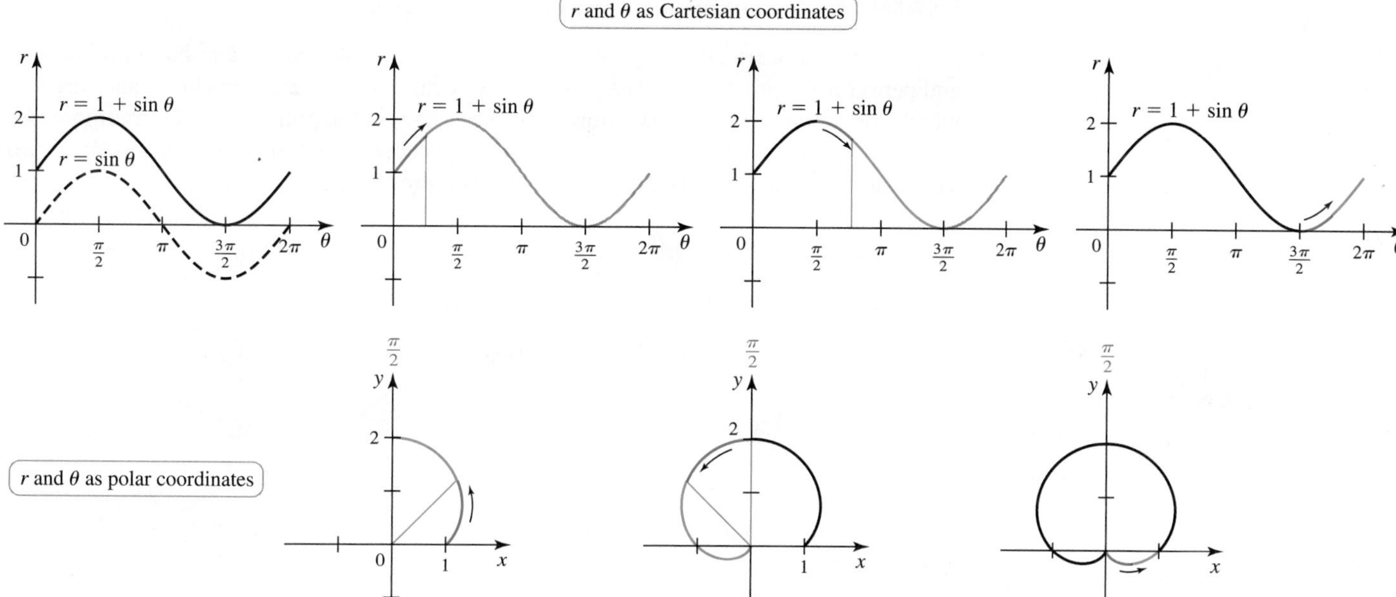

FIGURE 11.26

Related Exercises 37–44

Symmetry Given a polar equation in r and θ, three types of symmetry are easy to spot (Figure 11.27).

> Any two of these three symmetries implies the third. For example, if a graph is symmetric about both the x- and y-axes, then it must be symmetric about the origin.

SUMMARY Symmetry in Polar Equations

Symmetry about the *x*-axis occurs if the point (r, θ) is on the graph whenever $(r, -\theta)$ is on the graph.

Symmetry about the *y*-axis occurs if the point (r, θ) is on the graph whenever $(r, \pi - \theta) = (-r, -\theta)$ is on the graph.

Symmetry about the origin occurs if the point (r, θ) is on the graph whenever $(-r, \theta) = (r, \theta + \pi)$ is on the graph.

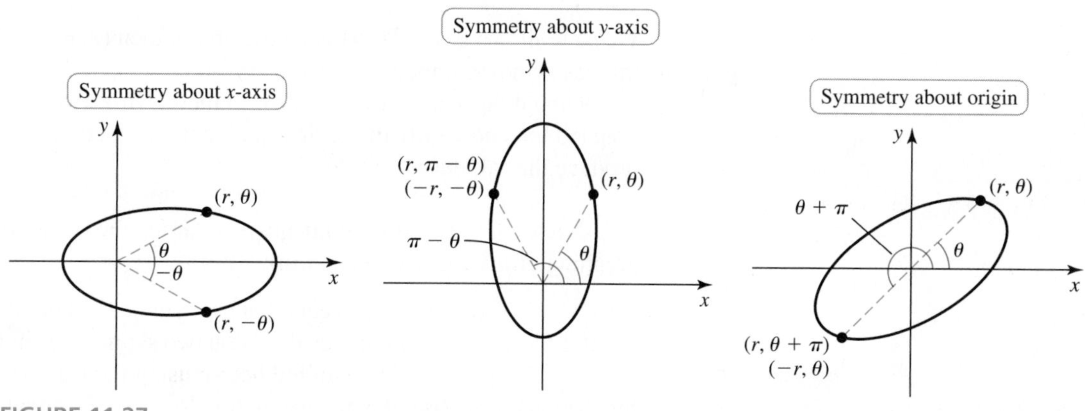

FIGURE 11.27

QUICK CHECK 5 Identify the symmetry in the graph of (a) $r = 4 + 4\cos\theta$ and (b) $r = 4\sin\theta$.

For instance, consider the polar equation $r = 1 + \sin\theta$ in Example 5. If (r, θ) satisfies the equation, then $(r, \pi - \theta)$ also satisfies the equation because $\sin\theta = \sin(\pi - \theta)$. Therefore, the graph is symmetric about the y-axis, as shown in Figure 11.26. Testing for symmetry produces a more accurate graph and often simplifies the task of graphing polar equations.

EXAMPLE 6 **Plotting polar graphs** Graph the polar equation $r = 3 \sin 2\theta$.

SOLUTION The Cartesian graph of $r = 3 \sin 2\theta$ on the interval $[0, 2\pi]$ has amplitude 3 and period π (Figure 11.28). The θ-intercepts occur at $\theta = 0, \pi/2, \pi, 3\pi/2$, and 2π, which correspond to the intersections with the origin on the polar graph. Furthermore, the arches of the Cartesian curve between θ-intercepts correspond to loops in the polar curve. The resulting polar curve is a **four-leaf rose** (Figure 11.28).

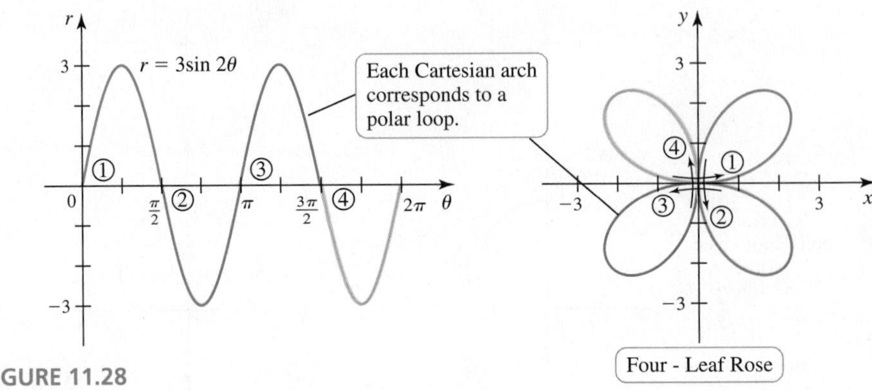

FIGURE 11.28

> **Subtle Point**
>
> The fact that one point has several representations in polar coordinates presents potential pitfalls. In Example 6, you can show that $(-r, \theta)$ does *not* satisfy the equation $r = 3 \sin 2\theta$ when (r, θ) satisfies the equation. And yet, as shown, the graph is symmetric about the origin because $(r, \theta + \pi)$ satisfies the equation whenever (r, θ) satisfies the equation. Note that $(-r, \theta)$ and $(r, \theta + \pi)$ are the same point.

The graph is symmetric about the x-axis, the y-axis, and the origin. It is instructive to see how these symmetries are justified. To prove symmetry about the y-axis, notice that

$$
\begin{aligned}
(r, \theta) \text{ on the graph} &\Rightarrow r = 3 \sin 2\theta \\
&\Rightarrow r = -3 \sin 2(-\theta) && \sin(-\theta) = -\sin\theta \\
&\Rightarrow -r = 3 \sin 2(-\theta) && \text{Simplify.} \\
&\Rightarrow (-r, -\theta) \text{ on the graph.}
\end{aligned}
$$

We see that if (r, θ) is on the graph, then $(-r, -\theta)$ is also on the graph, which implies symmetry about the y-axis. Similarly, to prove symmetry about the origin, notice that

$$
\begin{aligned}
(r, \theta) \text{ on the graph} &\Rightarrow r = 3 \sin 2\theta \\
&\Rightarrow r = 3 \sin(2\theta + 2\pi) && \sin(\theta + 2\pi) = \sin\theta \\
&\Rightarrow r = 3 \sin[2(\theta + \pi)] && \text{Simplify.} \\
&\Rightarrow (r, \theta + \pi) \text{ on the graph.}
\end{aligned}
$$

We have shown that if (r, θ) is on the graph, then $(r, \theta + \pi)$ is also on the graph, which implies symmetry about the origin. Symmetry about the y-axis and the origin imply symmetry about the x-axis. Had we proved these symmetries in advance, we could have graphed the curve only in the first quadrant—reflections about the x- and y-axes would produce the full curve. *Related Exercises 37–44* ◀

EXAMPLE 7 **Plotting polar graphs** Graph the polar equation $r^2 = 9 \cos\theta$. Use a graphing utility to check your work.

SOLUTION The graph of this equation has symmetry about the origin (because of the r^2) and about the x-axis (because of $\cos\theta$). These two symmetries imply symmetry about the y-axis.

A preliminary step is required before using the Cartesian-to-polar method for graphing the curve. Solving the given equation for r, we find that $r = \pm 3\sqrt{\cos\theta}$. Notice that $\cos\theta < 0$ for $\pi/2 < \theta < 3\pi/2$, so the curve does not exist on that interval. Therefore, we plot the curve on the intervals $0 \le \theta \le \pi/2$ and $3\pi/2 \le \theta \le 2\pi$ (the interval $[-\pi/2, \pi/2]$ would also work). Both the positive and negative values of r are included in the Cartesian graph (Figure 11.29a).

Now we are ready to transfer points from the Cartesian graph to the final polar graph (Figure 11.29b). The resulting curve is called a **lemniscate**.

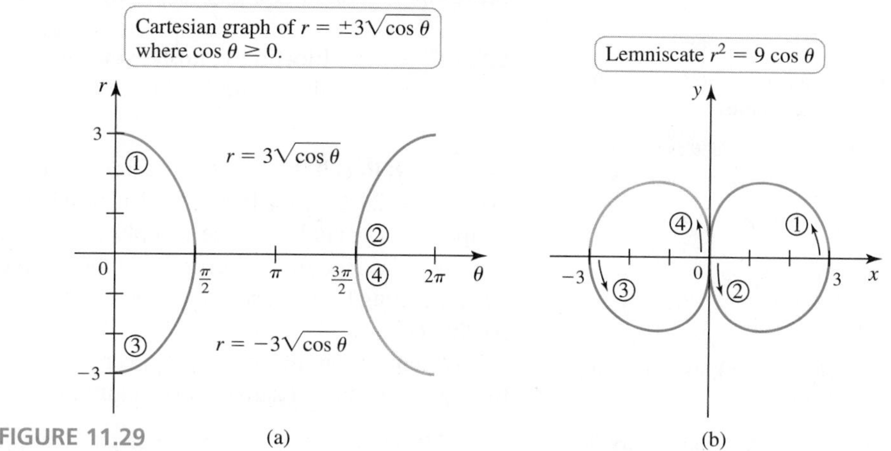

FIGURE 11.29 (a) (b)

Related Exercises 37–44

EXAMPLE 8 Matching polar and Cartesian graphs The butterfly curve

$$r = e^{\sin\theta} - 2\cos 4\theta, \qquad \text{for } 0 \leq \theta \leq 2\pi,$$

is plotted in polar coordinates in Figure 11.30b. The same function, $r = e^{\sin\theta} - 2\cos 4\theta$, is plotted in a Cartesian coordinate system with θ on the horizontal axis and r on the vertical axis (Figure 11.30a). Follow the Cartesian graph through the points $A, B, C, \ldots, N, O$ and mark the corresponding points on the polar curve.

➤ See Exercise 99 for a spectacular enhancement of the butterfly curve.

SOLUTION Point A in Figure 11.30a has the Cartesian coordinates $(\theta = 0, r = -1)$. The corresponding point in the polar plot (Figure 11.30b) with polar coordinates $(-1, 0)$ is marked A. Point B in the Cartesian plot is on the θ-axis; therefore, $r = 0$. The corresponding point in the polar plot is the origin. The same argument used to locate B applies to F, H, J, L, and N, all of which appear at the origin in the polar plot. In general, the local and endpoint maxima and minima in the Cartesian graph $(A, C, D, E, G, I, K, M,$ and $O)$ correspond to the extreme points of the loops of the polar plot and are marked accordingly in Figure 11.30b.

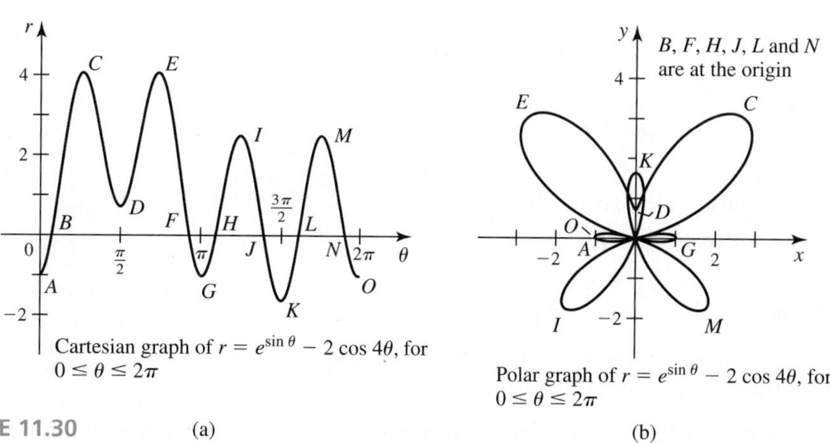

FIGURE 11.30 (a) (b)

Source: The butterfly curve is due to T. H. Fay *Amer. Math. Monthly* **96** (1989), revived in Wagon and Packel, *Animating Calculus*, Freeman, 1994.

Related Exercises 45–48

Using Graphing Utilities

With many graphing utilities, it is necessary to specify an interval in θ that generates the entire curve. In some cases, this problem is a challenge in itself.

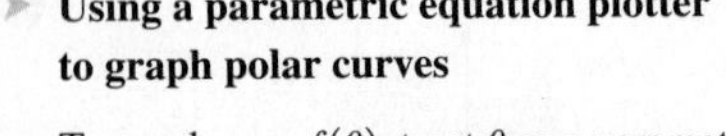

> **Using a parametric equation plotter to graph polar curves**
>
> To graph $r = f(\theta)$, treat θ as a parameter and define the parametric equations
>
> $$x = r\cos\theta = \underbrace{f(\theta)}_{r}\cos\theta$$
>
> $$y = r\sin\theta = \underbrace{f(\theta)}_{r}\sin\theta$$
>
> Then graph $(x(\theta), y(\theta))$ as a parametric curve with θ as the parameter.

> Once P is found, the complete curve is generated as θ varies over any interval of length P. This choice of P described here ensures that the complete curve is generated. Smaller values of P work in some cases.

EXAMPLE 9 **Plotting complete curves** Consider the curve described by $r = \cos(2\theta/5)$. Give an interval in θ that generates the entire curve and then graph the curve.

SOLUTION Recall that $\cos\theta$ has a period of 2π. Therefore, $\cos(2\theta/5)$ completes one cycle when $2\theta/5$ varies from 0 to 2π, or when θ varies from 0 to 5π. Therefore, it is tempting to conclude that the complete curve $r = \cos(2\theta/5)$ is generated as θ varies from 0 to 5π. But you can check that the point corresponding to $\theta = 0$ is *not* the point corresponding to $\theta = 5\pi$, which means the curve does not close on itself over the interval $[0, 5\pi]$ (Figure 11.31a).

In general, an interval $[0, P]$ over which the complete curve $r = f(\theta)$ is guaranteed to be generated must satisfy two conditions: P is the smallest positive number such that

- P is a multiple of the period of f (so that $f(0) = f(P)$), and
- P is a multiple of 2π (so that the points $(0, f(0))$ and $(P, f(P))$ are the same).

To graph the *complete* curve $r = \cos(2\theta/5)$, we must find an interval $[0, P]$, where P is a multiple of 5π and a multiple of 2π. The smallest number satisfying these conditions is 10π. Graphing $r = \cos(2\theta/5)$ over the interval $[0, 10\pi]$ produces the complete curve (Figure 11.31b).

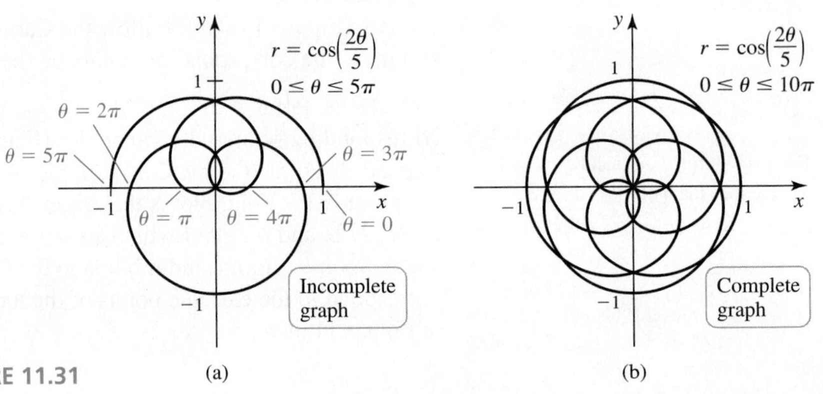

FIGURE 11.31 (a) (b)

Related Exercises 49–56 ◀

SECTION 11.2 EXERCISES

Review Questions

1. Plot the points with polar coordinates $\left(2, \frac{\pi}{6}\right)$ and $\left(-3, -\frac{\pi}{2}\right)$. Give two alternative sets of coordinate pairs for both points.
2. Write the equations that are used to express a point with polar coordinates (r, θ) in Cartesian coordinates.
3. Write the equations that are used to express a point with Cartesian coordinates (x, y) in polar coordinates.
4. What is the polar equation of a circle of radius $|a|$ centered at the origin?
5. What is the polar equation of the vertical line $x = 5$?
6. What is the polar equation of the horizontal line $y = 5$?
7. Explain three symmetries in polar graphs and how they are detected in equations.
8. Explain the Cartesian-to-polar method for graphing polar curves.

Basic Skills

9–13. *Graph the points with the following polar coordinates. Give two alternative representations of the points in polar coordinates.*

9. $\left(2, \frac{\pi}{4}\right)$ **10.** $\left(3, \frac{2\pi}{3}\right)$ **11.** $\left(-1, -\frac{\pi}{3}\right)$

12. $\left(2, \frac{7\pi}{4}\right)$ **13.** $\left(-4, \frac{3\pi}{2}\right)$

14. **Points in polar coordinates** Give two sets of polar coordinates for each of the points A–F in the figure.

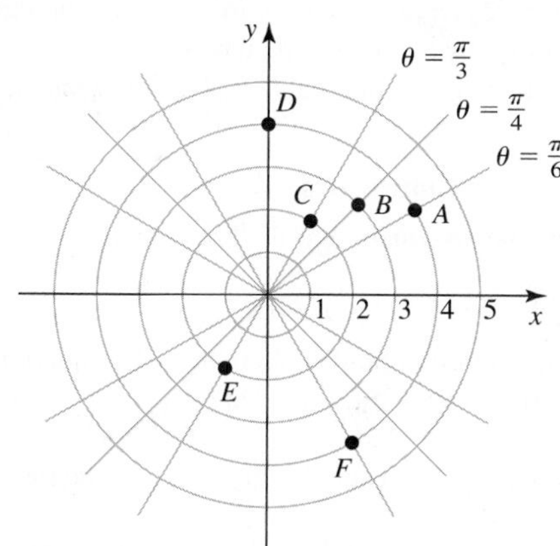

15–20. Converting coordinates *Express the following polar coordinates in Cartesian coordinates.*

15. $\left(3, \frac{\pi}{4}\right)$ 16. $\left(1, \frac{2\pi}{3}\right)$ 17. $\left(1, -\frac{\pi}{3}\right)$

18. $\left(2, \frac{7\pi}{4}\right)$ 19. $\left(-4, \frac{3\pi}{4}\right)$ 20. $(4, 5\pi)$

21–26. Converting coordinates *Express the following Cartesian coordinates in polar coordinates in at least two different ways. Make approximations when necessary.*

21. $(2, 2)$ 22. $(-1, 0)$ 23. $(1, \sqrt{3})$

24. $(-9, 0)$ 25. $(-4, 4\sqrt{3})$ 26. $(4, 4\sqrt{2})$

27–30. Simple curves *Tabulate and plot enough points to sketch a rough graph of the following equations.*

27. $r = 8 \cos \theta$

28. $r = 4 + 4 \cos \theta$

29. $r(\sin \theta - 2 \cos \theta) = 0$

30. $r = 1 - \cos \theta$

31–36. Polar to Cartesian coordinates *Convert the following equations to Cartesian coordinates. Describe the resulting curve.*

31. $r \cos \theta = -4$ 32. $r = \cot \theta \csc \theta$

33. $r \cos \theta = \sin 2\theta$ 34. $r = \sin \theta \sec^2 \theta$

35. $r = 8 \sin \theta$ 36. $r = \dfrac{1}{2 \cos \theta + 3 \sin \theta}$

37–44. Graphing polar curves *Graph the following equations. Use a graphing utility to check your work and produce a final graph.*

37. $r = 1 + \sin \theta$ 38. $r = 2 - 2 \sin \theta$ 39. $r = \sin^2 (\theta/2)$

40. $r^2 = 4 \sin \theta$ 41. $r^2 = 16 \cos \theta$ 42. $r^2 = 16 \sin 2\theta$

43. $r = \sin 3\theta$ 44. $r = 2 \sin 5\theta$

45–48. Matching polar and Cartesian curves *A Cartesian and a polar graph of $r = f(\theta)$ are given in the figures. Mark the points on the polar graph that correspond to the points shown on the Cartesian graph.*

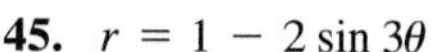
45. $r = 1 - 2 \sin 3\theta$

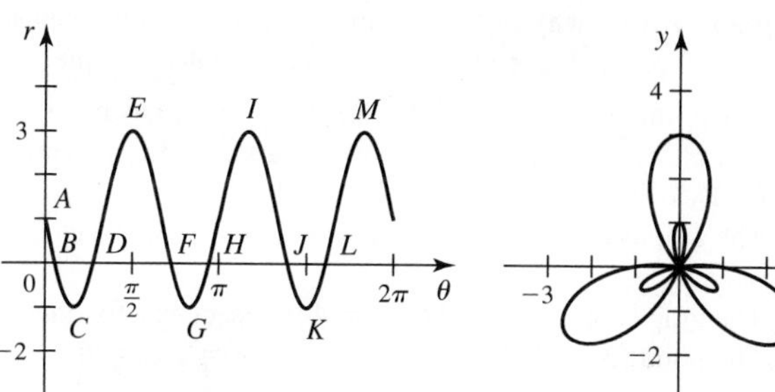

46. $r = \sin (1 + 3 \cos \theta)$

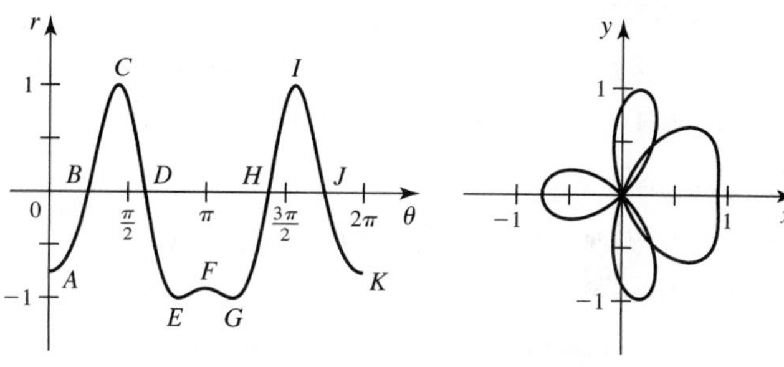

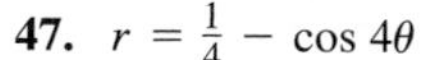
47. $r = \frac{1}{4} - \cos 4\theta$

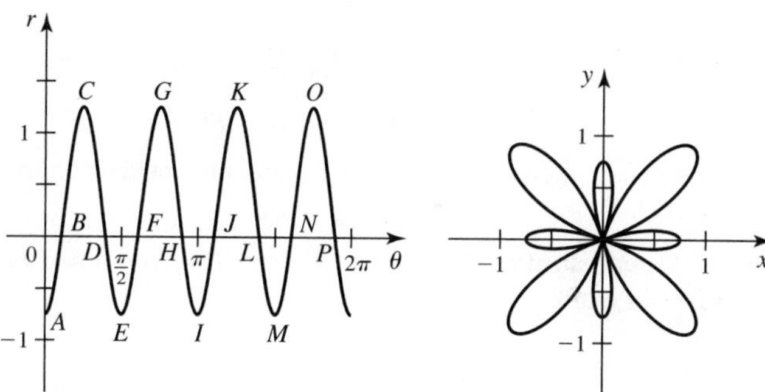

48. $r = \cos \theta + \sin 2\theta$

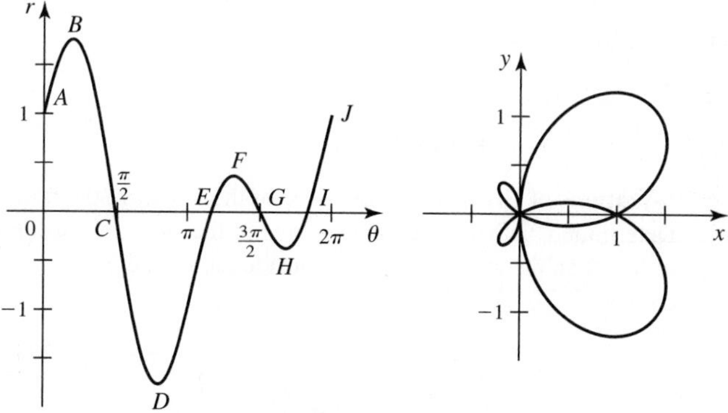

49–56. Using a graphing utility *Use a graphing utility to graph the following equations. In each case, give the smallest interval $[0, P]$ that generates the entire curve (if possible).*

49. $r = \theta \sin \theta$ 50. $r = 2 - 4 \cos 5\theta$

51. $r = \cos 3\theta + \cos^2 2\theta$ 52. $r = \sin^2 2\theta + 2 \sin 2\theta$

53. $r = \cos (3\theta/5)$ 54. $r = \sin (3\theta/7)$

55. $r = 1 - 3 \cos 2\theta$ 56. $r = 1 - 2 \sin 5\theta$

Further Explorations

57. **Explain why or why not** Determine whether the following statements are true and give an explanation or counterexample.
   a. The point with Cartesian coordinates $(-2, 2)$ has polar coordinates $(2\sqrt{2}, 3\pi/4)$, $(2\sqrt{2}, 11\pi/4)$, $(2\sqrt{2}, -5\pi/4)$, and $(-2\sqrt{2}, -\pi/4)$.
   b. The graphs of $r\cos\theta = 4$ and $r\sin\theta = -2$ intersect exactly once.
   c. The graphs of $r = 2$ and $\theta = \pi/4$ intersect exactly once.
   d. The point $(3, \pi/2)$ lies on the graph of $r = 3\cos 2\theta$.

58–65. Sets in polar coordinates *Sketch the following sets of points.*

58. $\{(r, \theta): r = 3\}$
59. $\{(r, \theta): \theta = 2\pi/3\}$
60. $\{(r, \theta): 2 \le r \le 8\}$
61. $\{(r, \theta): \pi/2 \le \theta \le 3\pi/4\}$
62. $\{(r, \theta): 1 < r < 2 \text{ and } \pi/6 \le \theta \le \pi/3\}$
63. $\{(r, \theta): |\theta| \le \pi/3\}$
64. $\{(r, \theta): |r| < 3 \text{ and } 0 \le \theta \le \pi\}$
65. $\{(r, \theta): r \ge 2\}$

66. **Circles in general** Show that the polar equation
$$r^2 - 2r(a\cos\theta + b\sin\theta) = R^2 - a^2 - b^2$$
describes a circle of radius R centered at (a, b).

67. **Circles in general** Show that the polar equation
$$r^2 - 2rr_0\cos(\theta - \theta_0) = R^2 - r_0^2$$
describes a circle of radius R whose center has polar coordinates (r_0, θ_0).

68–73. Equations of circles *Use the results of Exercises 66–67 to describe and graph the following circles.*

68. $r^2 - 6r\cos\theta = 16$
69. $r^2 - 4r\cos(\theta - \pi/3) = 12$
70. $r^2 - 8r\cos(\theta - \pi/2) = 9$
71. $r^2 - 2r(2\cos\theta + 3\sin\theta) = 3$
72. $r^2 + 2r(\cos\theta - 3\sin\theta) = 4$
73. $r^2 - 2r(-\cos\theta + 2\sin\theta) = 4$

74. **Equations of circles** Find equations of the circles in the figure. Determine whether the combined area of the circles is greater than or less than the area of the region inside the square but outside the circles.

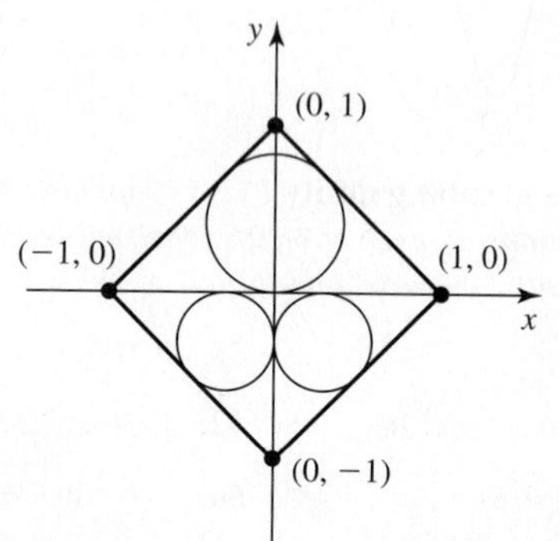

75. **Vertical lines** Consider the polar curve $r = 2\sec\theta$.
   a. Graph the curve on the intervals $(\pi/2, 3\pi/2)$, $(3\pi/2, 5\pi/2)$, and $(5\pi/2, 7\pi/2)$. In each case, state the direction in which the curve is generated as θ increases.
   b. Show that on any interval $(n\pi/2, (n + 2)\pi/2)$, where n is an odd integer, the graph is the vertical line $x = 2$.

76. **Lines in polar coordinates**
   a. Show that an equation of the line $y = mx + b$ in polar coordinate is $r = \dfrac{b}{\sin\theta - m\cos\theta}$.
   b. Use the figure to find an alternate polar equation of a line, $r\cos(\theta_0 - \theta) = r_0$. Note that $Q(r_0, \theta_0)$ is a fixed point on the line such that OQ is perpendicular to the line and $r_0 \ge 0$; $P(r, \theta)$ is an arbitrary point on the line.

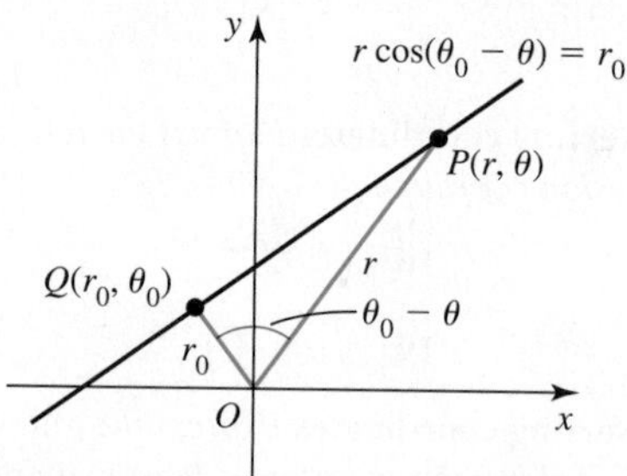

77–80. Equations of lines *Use the result of Exercise 76 to describe and graph the following lines.*

77. $r\cos(\theta - \pi/3) = 3$
78. $r\cos(\theta + \pi/6) = 4$
79. $r(\sin\theta - 4\cos\theta) - 3 = 0$
80. $r(4\sin\theta - 3\cos\theta) = 6$

81. **The limaçon family** The equations $r = a + b\cos\theta$ and $r = a + b\sin\theta$ describe curves known as *limaçons* (from Latin for *snail*). We have already encountered cardioids, which occur when $|a| = |b|$. The limaçon has an inner loop if $|a| < |b|$. The limaçon has a dent or dimple if $|b| < |a| < 2|b|$. And, the limaçon is oval-shaped if $|a| > 2|b|$. Match the limaçons in the figures A–F with the following equations.
   a. $r = -1 + \sin\theta$
   b. $r = -1 + 2\cos\theta$
   c. $r = 2 + \sin\theta$
   d. $r = 1 - 2\cos\theta$
   e. $r = 1 + 2\sin\theta$
   f. $r = 1 + (2/3)\sin\theta$

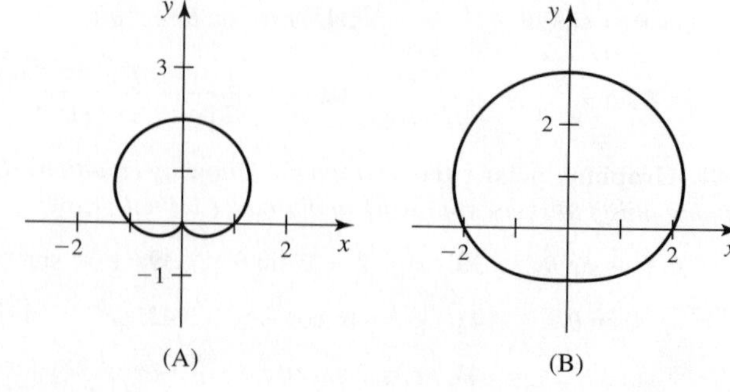

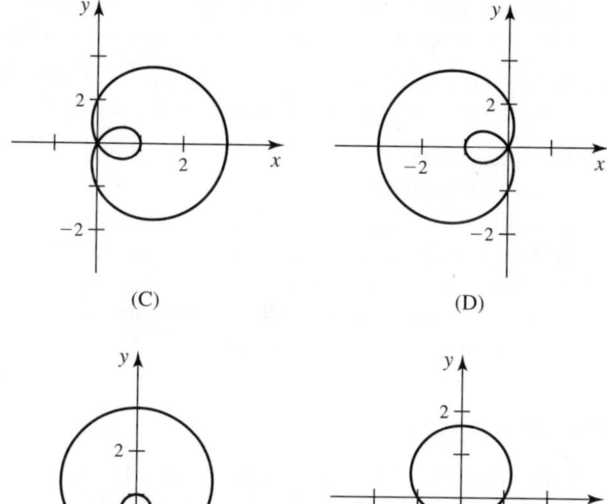

82. Limiting limaçon Consider the family of limaçons $r = 1 + b\cos\theta$. Describe the limiting curve as $b \to \infty$.

83–86. The lemniscate family *Equations of the form* $r^2 = a\sin 2\theta$ *and* $r^2 = a\cos 2\theta$ *describe lemniscates (see Example 7). Graph the following lemniscates.*

83. $r^2 = \cos 2\theta$

84. $r^2 = 4\sin 2\theta$

85. $r^2 = -2\sin 2\theta$

86. $r^2 = -8\cos 2\theta$

87–90. The rose family *Equations of the form* $r = a\sin m\theta$ *or* $r = a\cos m\theta$, *where a and b are real numbers and m is a positive integer, have graphs known as roses (see Example 6). Graph the following roses.*

87. $r = \sin 2\theta$

88. $r = 4\cos 3\theta$

89. $r = 2\sin 4\theta$

90. $r = 6\sin 5\theta$

91. Number of rose petals Show that the graph of $r = a\sin m\theta$ or $r = a\cos m\theta$ is a rose with m leaves if m is an odd integer and a rose with $2m$ leaves if m is an even integer.

92–94. Spirals *Graph the following spirals. Indicate the direction in which the spiral winds outward as* θ *increases, where* $\theta > 0$. *Let* $a = 1$ *and* $a = -1$.

92. Spiral of Archimedes: $r = a\theta$

93. Logarithmic spiral: $r = e^{a\theta}$

94. Hyperbolic spiral: $r = a/\theta$

95–98. Intersection points *Points at which the graphs of* $r = f(\theta)$ *and* $r = g(\theta)$ *intersect must be determined carefully. Solving* $f(\theta) = g(\theta)$ *identifies* some—*but perhaps not all—intersection points. The reason is that the curves may pass through the same point for different values of* θ. *Use analytical methods and a graphing utility to find all the intersection points between the following curves.*

95. $r = 2\cos\theta$ and $r = 1 + \cos\theta$

96. $r^2 = 4\cos\theta$ and $r = 1 + \cos\theta$

97. $r = 1 - \sin\theta$ and $r = 1 + \cos\theta$

98. $r^2 = \cos 2\theta$ and $r^2 = \sin 2\theta$

99. Enhanced butterfly curve The butterfly curve of Example 8 may be enhanced by adding a term:

$$r = e^{\sin\theta} - 2\cos 4\theta + \sin^5(\theta/12), \qquad \text{for } 0 \le \theta \le 24\pi.$$

a. Graph the curve.
b. Explain why the new term produces the observed effect.

(*Source:* S. Wagon and E. Packel, *Animating Calculus,* Freeman, New York, 1994)

100. Finger curves Consider the curve $r = f(\theta) = \cos(a^\theta) - 1.5$, where $a = (1 + 12\pi)^{1/2\pi} \approx 1.78933$ (see figure).

a. Show that $f(0) = f(2\pi)$ and find the points on the curve that correspond to $\theta = 0$ and $\theta = 2\pi$.
b. Is the same curve produced over the intervals $[-\pi, \pi]$ and $[0, 2\pi]$?
c. Let $f(\theta) = \cos(a^\theta) - b$, where $a = (1 + 2k\pi)^{1/2\pi}$, k is an integer, and b is a real number. Show that $f(0) = f(2\pi)$ and the curve closes on itself.
d. Plot the curve with various values of k. How many fingers can you produce?

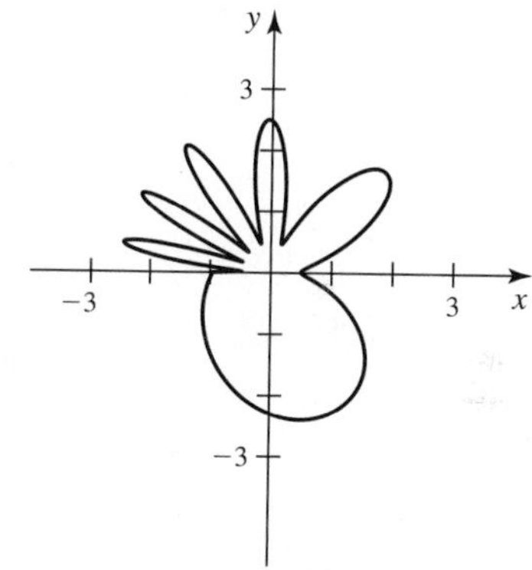

Applications

101. Earth–Mars system A simplified model assumes that the orbits of Earth and Mars are circular with radii of 2 and 3, respectively, and that Earth completes a complete orbit in one year while Mars takes two years. The position of Mars as seen from Earth is given by the parametric equations

$$x = (3 - 4\cos\pi t)\cos\pi t + 2, \qquad y = (3 - 4\cos\pi t)\sin\pi t.$$

a. Graph the parametric equations for $0 \le t \le 2$.
b. Letting $r = (3 - 4\cos\pi t)$, explain why the path of Mars as seen from Earth is a limaçon.

102. Channel flow Water flows in a shallow semicircular channel with inner and outer radii of 1 m and 2 m (see figure). At a point $P(r, \theta)$ in the channel, the flow is in the tangential direction (counterclockwise along circles), and it depends only on r, the distance from the center of the semicircles.

a. Express the region formed by the channel as a set in polar coordinates.
b. Express the inflow and outflow regions of the channel as sets in polar coordinates.
c. Suppose the tangential velocity of the water in m/s is given by $v(r) = 10r$, for $1 \le r \le 2$. Is the velocity greater at $\left(1.5, \frac{\pi}{4}\right)$ or $\left(1.2, \frac{3\pi}{4}\right)$? Explain.

d. Suppose the tangential velocity of the water is given by $v(r) = \frac{20}{r}$, for $1 \le r \le 2$. Is the velocity greater at $\left(1.8, \frac{\pi}{6}\right)$ or $\left(1.3, \frac{2\pi}{3}\right)$? Explain.

e. The total amount of water that flows through the channel (across a cross section of the channel $\theta = \theta_0$) is proportional to $\int_1^2 v(r)\,dr$. Is the total flow through the channel greater for the flow in part (c) or (d)?

Additional Exercises

103. Special circles Show that the equation $r = a\cos\theta + b\sin\theta$, where a and b are real numbers, describes a circle. Find the center and radius of the circle.

104. Cartesian lemniscate Find the equation in Cartesian coordinates of the lemniscate $r^2 = a^2\cos 2\theta$, where a is a real number.

105. Subtle symmetry Without using a graphing utility, determine the symmetries (if any) of the curve $r = 4 - \sin(\theta/2)$.

106. Complete curves Consider the polar curve $r = \cos(n\theta/m)$, where n and m are integers.

a. Graph the complete curve when $n = 2$ and $m = 3$.

b. Graph the complete curve when $n = 3$ and $m = 7$.

c. Find a general rule in terms of m and n for determining the least positive number P such that the complete curve is generated over the interval $[0, P]$.

QUICK CHECK ANSWERS

1. All the points are the same except $(3, 3\pi/2)$. **3.** Polar coordinates: $(1, 0)$, $(1, 2\pi)$; Cartesian coordinates: $(0, 2)$ **4.** A circle centered at the origin with radius 12; a double spiral; the horizontal line $y = 10$ **5.** (a) Symmetric about the x-axis; (b) symmetric about the y-axis

11.3 Calculus in Polar Coordinates

Having learned about the *geometry* of polar coordinates, we now have the groundwork needed to explore *calculus* in polar coordinates. Familiar topics, such as slopes of tangent lines and areas bounded by curves, are now revisited in a different setting.

Slopes of Tangent Lines

Given a function $y = f(x)$, the slope of the line tangent to the graph at a given point is dy/dx or $f'(x)$. So, it may be tempting to conclude that the slope of a curve described by the polar equation $r = f(\theta)$ is $dr/d\theta = f'(\theta)$. Unfortunately, it's not that simple.

➤ The slope is the change in the vertical coordinate divided by the change in the horizontal coordinate, independent of the coordinate system. In polar coordinates, neither r nor θ corresponds to a vertical or horizontal coordinate.

The key observation is that the slope of a tangent line—in any coordinate system—is the rate of change of the vertical coordinate y with respect to the horizontal coordinate x, which is dy/dx. We begin by writing the polar equation $r = f(\theta)$ in parametric form with θ as a parameter:

$$x = r\cos\theta = f(\theta)\cos\theta \quad \text{and} \quad y = r\sin\theta = f(\theta)\sin\theta \tag{1}$$

From Section 11.1, when x and y are defined parametrically as differentiable functions of θ, the derivative is $\frac{dy}{dx} = \frac{y'(\theta)}{x'(\theta)}$. Using the Product Rule to compute $y'(\theta)$ and $x'(\theta)$ in equation (1), we have

$$\frac{dy}{dx} = \frac{\overbrace{f'(\theta)\sin\theta + f(\theta)\cos\theta}^{y'(\theta)}}{\underbrace{f'(\theta)\cos\theta - f(\theta)\sin\theta}_{x'(\theta)}}. \tag{2}$$

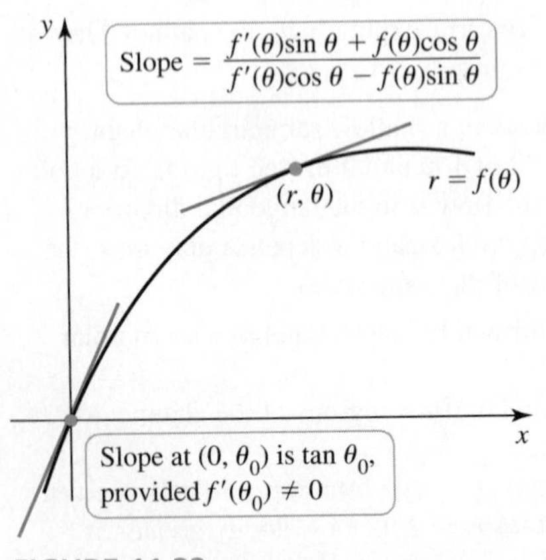

FIGURE 11.32

If the graph passes through the origin for some angle θ_0, then $f(\theta_0) = 0$, and equation (2) simplifies to

$$\frac{dy}{dx} = \frac{\sin\theta_0}{\cos\theta_0} = \tan\theta_0,$$

provided $f'(\theta_0) \ne 0$. However, $\tan\theta_0$ is the slope of the line $\theta = \theta_0$, which also passes through the origin. We conclude that if $f(\theta_0) = 0$, then the tangent line at $(0, \theta_0)$ is simply $\theta = \theta_0$ (Figure 11.32).

QUICK CHECK 1 Verify that if $y = f(\theta)\sin\theta$, then $y'(\theta) = f'(\theta)\sin\theta + f(\theta)\cos\theta$ (which was used earlier to find dy/dx).

THEOREM 11.2 Slope of a Tangent Line

Let f be a differentiable function at θ_0. The slope of the line tangent to the curve $r = f(\theta)$ at the point $(f(\theta_0), \theta_0)$ is

$$\frac{dy}{dx} = \frac{f'(\theta_0)\sin\theta_0 + f(\theta_0)\cos\theta_0}{f'(\theta_0)\cos\theta_0 - f(\theta_0)\sin\theta_0},$$

provided the denominator is nonzero at the point. At angles θ_0 for which $f(\theta_0) = 0$ and $f'(\theta_0) \neq 0$, the tangent line is $\theta = \theta_0$ with slope $\tan\theta_0$.

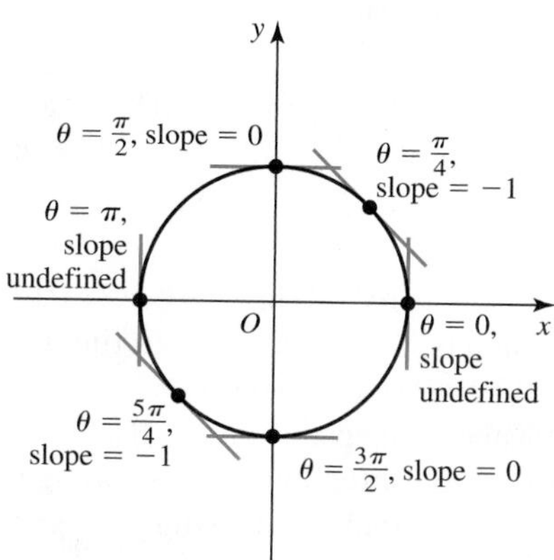

FIGURE 11.33

EXAMPLE 1 Slopes on a circle Find the slopes of the lines tangent to the circle $r = f(\theta) = 10$.

SOLUTION In this case, $f(\theta)$ is constant (independent of θ). Therefore, $f'(\theta) = 0$, $f(\theta) \neq 0$, and the slope formula becomes

$$\frac{dy}{dx} = \frac{f'(\theta)\sin\theta + f(\theta)\cos\theta}{f'(\theta)\cos\theta - f(\theta)\sin\theta} = -\frac{\cos\theta}{\sin\theta} = -\cot\theta.$$

We can check a few points to see that this result makes sense. With $\theta = 0$ and $\theta = \pi$, the slope $dy/dx = -\cot\theta$ is undefined, which is correct (Figure 11.33). With $\theta = \pi/2$ and $\theta = 3\pi/2$, the slope is zero; with $\theta = 3\pi/4$ and $\theta = 7\pi/4$, the slope is 1; and with $\theta = \pi/4$ and $\theta = 5\pi/4$, the slope is -1. At all points $P(r, \theta)$ on the circle, the slope of the line OP from the origin to P is $\tan\theta$, which is the negative reciprocal of $-\cot\theta$. Therefore, OP is perpendicular to the tangent line at all points P on the circle.

Related Exercises 5–20

EXAMPLE 2 Vertical and horizontal tangent lines Find the points on the interval $-\pi \le \theta \le \pi$ at which the cardioid $r = f(\theta) = 1 - \cos\theta$ has a vertical or horizontal tangent line.

SOLUTION Applying Theorem 11.2, we find that

$$\frac{dy}{dx} = \frac{f'(\theta)\sin\theta + f(\theta)\cos\theta}{f'(\theta)\cos\theta - f(\theta)\sin\theta}$$

$$= \frac{\overbrace{\sin\theta\sin\theta}^{\sin^2\theta = 1 - \cos^2\theta} + (1 - \cos\theta)\cos\theta}{\underbrace{\sin\theta\cos\theta - (1 - \cos\theta)\sin\theta}_{\sin\theta(2\cos\theta - 1)}} \quad \text{Substitute for } f(\theta) \text{ and } f'(\theta).$$

$$= -\frac{(2\cos^2\theta - \cos\theta - 1)}{\sin\theta(2\cos\theta - 1)} \quad \text{Simplify.}$$

$$= -\frac{(2\cos\theta + 1)(\cos\theta - 1)}{\sin\theta(2\cos\theta - 1)}. \quad \text{Factor the numerator.}$$

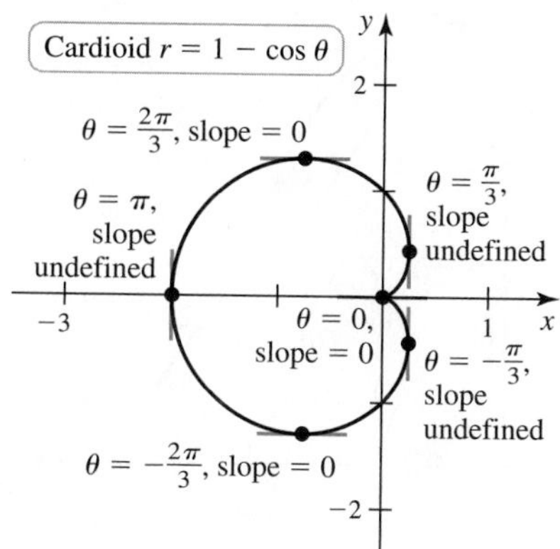

FIGURE 11.34

The points with a horizontal tangent line satisfy $dy/dx = 0$ and occur where the numerator is zero and the denominator is nonzero. The numerator is zero when $\theta = 0$ and $\pm 2\pi/3$. Because the denominator is *not* zero when $\theta = \pm 2\pi/3$, horizontal tangent lines occur at $\theta = \pm 2\pi/3$ (Figure 11.34).

Vertical tangent lines occur where the numerator of dy/dx is nonzero and the denominator is zero. The denominator is zero when $\theta = 0, \pm\pi$, and $\pm\pi/3$, and the numerator is not zero at $\theta = \pm\pi$ and $\pm\pi/3$. Therefore, vertical tangent lines occur at $\theta = \pm\pi$ and $\pm\pi/3$.

The point $(0, 0)$ on the curve must be handled carefully because both the numerator and denominator of dy/dx equal 0 at $\theta = 0$. Notice that with $f(\theta) = 1 - \cos\theta$, we have $f(0) = f'(0) = 0$. Therefore, dy/dx may be computed as a limit using l'Hôpital's Rule. As $\theta \to 0^+$, we find that

$$\begin{aligned} \frac{dy}{dx} &= \lim_{\theta\to 0^+}\left[-\frac{(2\cos\theta + 1)(\cos\theta - 1)}{\sin\theta\,(2\cos\theta - 1)}\right] \\ &= \lim_{\theta\to 0^+}\frac{4\cos\theta\sin\theta - \sin\theta}{-2\sin^2\theta + 2\cos^2\theta - \cos\theta} && \text{L'Hôpital's Rule} \\ &= \frac{0}{1} = 0. && \text{Evaluate the limit.} \end{aligned}$$

QUICK CHECK 2 What is the slope of the line tangent to the cardioid in Example 2 at the point corresponding to $\theta = \pi/4$?

A similar calculation using l'Hôpital's Rule shows that as $\theta \to 0^-$, $dy/dx \to 0$. Therefore, the curve has a slope of 0 at $(0, 0)$.

Related Exercises 5–20

Area of Regions Bounded by Polar Curves

The problem of finding the area of a region bounded by polar curves brings us back to the slice-and-sum strategy used extensively in Chapters 5 and 6. The objective is to find the area of the region R bounded by the graph of $r = f(\theta)$ between the two rays $\theta = \alpha$ and $\theta = \beta$ (Figure 11.35a). We assume that f is continuous and nonnegative on $[\alpha, \beta]$.

The area of R is found by slicing the region in the radial direction creating wedge-shaped slices. The interval $[\alpha, \beta]$ is partitioned into n subintervals by choosing the grid points

$$\alpha = \theta_0 < \theta_1 < \theta_2 < \cdots < \theta_k < \cdots < \theta_n = \beta.$$

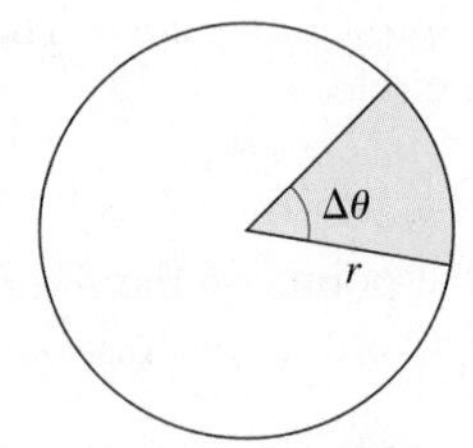

Area of circle $= \pi r^2$
Area of $\Delta\theta/(2\pi)$ of a circle
$= \left(\frac{\Delta\theta}{2\pi}\right)\pi r^2 = \frac{1}{2}r^2\Delta\theta$

We let $\Delta\theta_k = \theta_k - \theta_{k-1}$, for $k = 1, 2, \ldots, n$, and we let $\overline{\theta}_k$ be any point of the interval $[\theta_{k-1}, \theta_k]$. The kth slice is approximated by the sector of a circle swept out by an angle $\Delta\theta_k$ with radius $f(\overline{\theta}_k)$ (Figure 11.35b). Therefore, the area of the kth slice is approximately $\frac{1}{2}f(\overline{\theta}_k)^2\Delta\theta_k$, for $k = 1, 2, \ldots, n$ (Figure 11.35c). To find the approximate area of R, we sum the areas of these slices:

$$\text{area} \approx \sum_{k=1}^{n}\frac{1}{2}f(\overline{\theta}_k)^2\,\Delta\theta_k$$

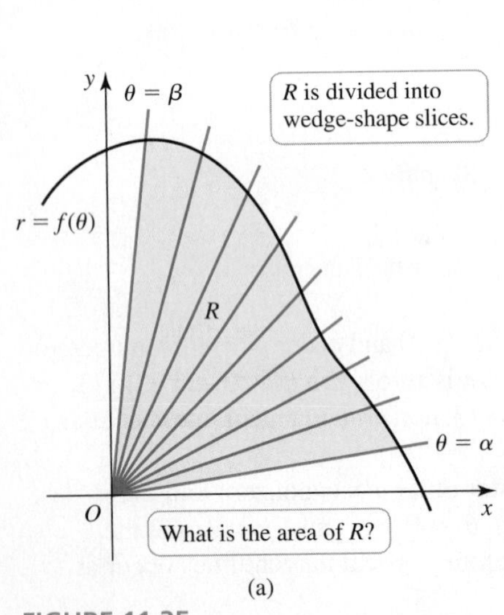

(a)

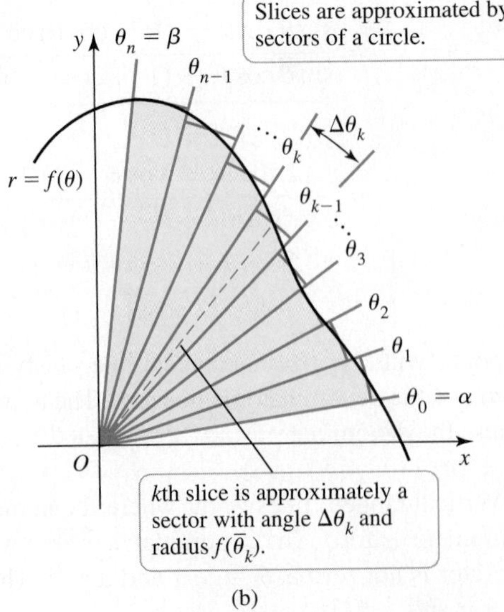

(b)

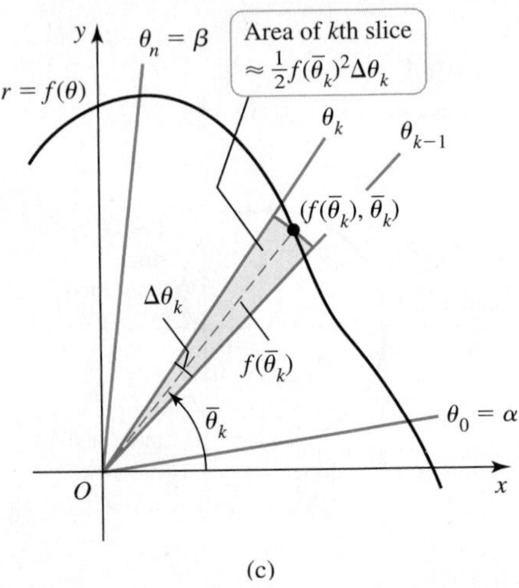

(c)

FIGURE 11.35

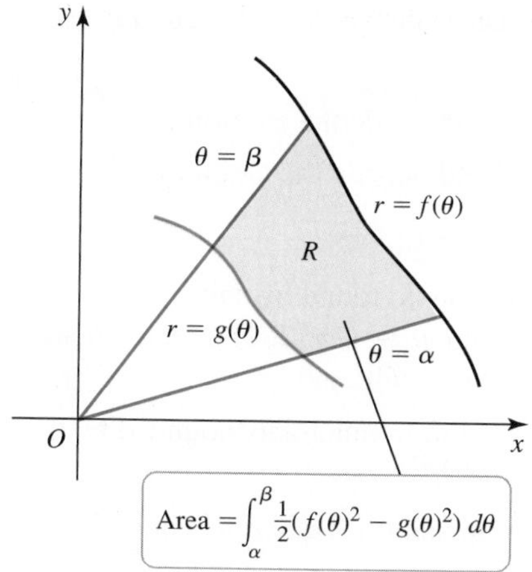

FIGURE 11.36

This approximation is a Riemann sum, and the approximation improves as we take more sectors ($n \to \infty$) and let $\Delta\theta_k \to 0$ for all k. The exact area is given by $\lim_{n\to\infty} \sum_{k=1}^{n} \frac{1}{2} f(\bar{\theta}_k)^2 \Delta\theta_k$, which we identify as the definite integral $\int_\alpha^\beta \frac{1}{2} f(\theta)^2\, d\theta$.

With a slight modification, a more general result is obtained for the area of a region R bounded by two curves, $r = f(\theta)$ and $r = g(\theta)$, between the rays $\theta = \alpha$ and $\theta = \beta$ (Figure 11.36). We assume that f and g are continuous and $f(\theta) \geq g(\theta) \geq 0$ on $[\alpha, \beta]$. To find the area of R, we subtract the area of the region bounded by $r = g(\theta)$ from the area of the entire region bounded by $r = f(\theta)$ (all between $\theta = \alpha$ and $\theta = \beta$); that is,

$$\text{area} = \int_\alpha^\beta \frac{1}{2} f(\theta)^2\, d\theta - \int_\alpha^\beta \frac{1}{2} g(\theta)^2\, d\theta = \int_\alpha^\beta \frac{1}{2}(f(\theta)^2 - g(\theta)^2)\, d\theta.$$

➤ If R is bounded by the graph of $r = f(\theta)$ between $\theta = \alpha$ and $\theta = \beta$, then $g(\theta) = 0$ and the area of R is $\int_\alpha^\beta \frac{1}{2} f(\theta)^2\, d\theta$.

DEFINITION Area of Regions in Polar Coordinates

Let R be the region bounded by the graphs of $r = f(\theta)$ and $r = g(\theta)$, between $\theta = \alpha$ and $\theta = \beta$, where f and g are continuous and $f(\theta) \geq g(\theta) \geq 0$ on $[\alpha, \beta]$. The area of R is

$$\int_\alpha^\beta \frac{1}{2}(f(\theta)^2 - g(\theta)^2)\, d\theta.$$

QUICK CHECK 3 Find the area of the circle $r = f(\theta) = 8$ (for $0 \leq \theta \leq 2\pi$). ◀

➤ The equation $r = 2\cos 2\theta$ is unchanged when θ is replaced by $-\theta$ (symmetry about the x-axis) and when θ is replaced by $\pi - \theta$ (symmetry about the y-axis).

EXAMPLE 3 Area of a polar region Find the area of the four-leaf rose $r = f(\theta) = 2\cos 2\theta$.

SOLUTION The graph of the rose (Figure 11.37) *appears* to be symmetric about the x- and y-axes; in fact, these symmetries can be proved. Appealing to this symmetry, we find the area of one-half of a leaf and then multiply the result by 8 to obtain the area of the full rose. The upper half of the rightmost leaf is generated as θ increases from $\theta = 0$ (when $r = 2$) to $\theta = \pi/4$ (when $r = 0$). Therefore, the area of the entire rose is

$$\begin{aligned}
8\int_0^{\pi/4} \frac{1}{2} f(\theta)^2\, d\theta &= 4\int_0^{\pi/4} (2\cos 2\theta)^2\, d\theta && f(\theta) = 2\cos 2\theta \\
&= 16\int_0^{\pi/4} \cos^2 2\theta\, d\theta && \text{Simplify.} \\
&= 16\int_0^{\pi/4} \frac{1 + \cos 4\theta}{2}\, d\theta && \text{Double-angle formula} \\
&= (8\theta + 2\sin 4\theta)\Big|_0^{\pi/4} && \text{Fundamental Theorem} \\
&= (2\pi - 0) - (0 - 0) = 2\pi. && \text{Simplify.}
\end{aligned}$$

Related Exercises 21–28 ◀

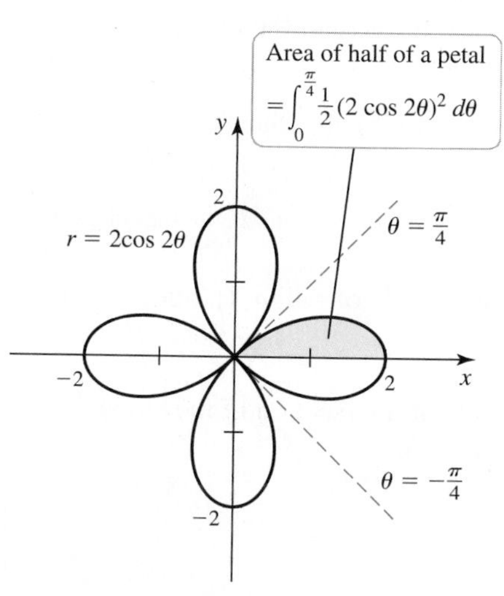

FIGURE 11.37

QUICK CHECK 4 Give an interval over which you could integrate to find the area of one leaf of the rose $r = 2\sin 3\theta$. ◀

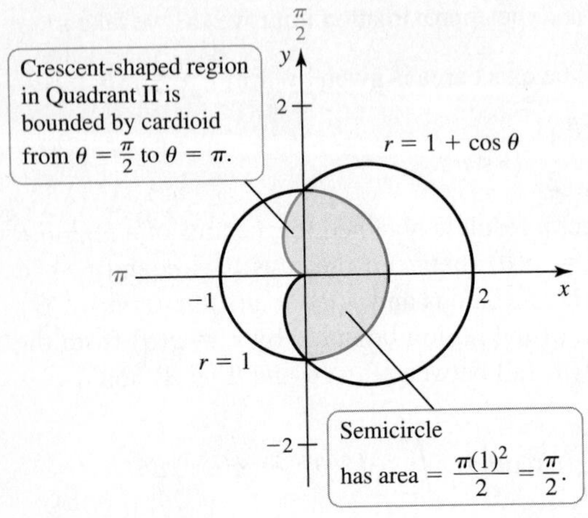
Crescent-shaped region in Quadrant II is bounded by cardioid from $\theta = \frac{\pi}{2}$ to $\theta = \pi$.
$\frac{\pi}{2}$
y
2
$r = 1 + \cos\theta$
π
−1
2
x
$r = 1$
−2
Semicircle has area $= \frac{\pi(1)^2}{2} = \frac{\pi}{2}$.

FIGURE 11.38

EXAMPLE 4 Areas of polar regions Consider the circle $r = 1$ and the cardioid $r = 1 + \cos\theta$ (Figure 11.38).

a. Find the area of the region inside the circle and inside the cardioid.

b. Find the area of the region inside the circle and outside the cardioid.

SOLUTION

a. The points of intersection of the two curves can be found by solving $1 + \cos\theta = 1$, or $\cos\theta = 0$. The solutions are $\theta = \pm\pi/2$. The region inside the circle and inside the cardioid consists of two subregions:

- A semicircle with radius 1 in the first and fourth quadrants bounded by the circle $r = 1$
- Two crescent-shaped regions in the second and third quadrants bounded by the cardioid $r = 1 + \cos\theta$ and the y-axis

The area of the semicircle is $\pi/2$. To find the area of the upper crescent-shaped region in the second quadrant, notice that it is bounded by $r = 1 + \cos\theta$, as θ varies from $\pi/2$ to π. Therefore, its area is

$$\int_{\pi/2}^{\pi} \frac{1}{2}(1 + \cos\theta)^2\, d\theta = \int_{\pi/2}^{\pi} \frac{1}{2}(1 + 2\cos\theta + \cos^2\theta)\, d\theta \quad \text{Expand.}$$

$$= \frac{1}{2}\int_{\pi/2}^{\pi}\left(1 + 2\cos\theta + \frac{1 + \cos 2\theta}{2}\right) d\theta \quad \text{Double-angle formula}$$

$$= \frac{1}{2}\left(\theta + 2\sin\theta + \frac{\theta}{2} + \frac{\sin 2\theta}{4}\right)\bigg|_{\pi/2}^{\pi} \quad \text{Fundamental Theorem}$$

$$= \frac{3\pi}{8} - 1. \quad \text{Simplify.}$$

The area of the entire region (two crescents and a semicircle) is

$$2\left(\frac{3\pi}{8} - 1\right) + \frac{\pi}{2} = \frac{5\pi}{4} - 2.$$

b. The region inside the circle and outside the cardioid is bounded by the outer curve $r = 1$ and the inner curve $r = 1 + \cos\theta$ on the interval $[\pi/2, 3\pi/2]$ (Figure 11.38). Using the symmetry about the x-axis, the area of the region is

$$2\int_{\pi/2}^{\pi} \frac{1}{2}(1^2 - (1 + \cos\theta)^2)\, d\theta = \int_{\pi/2}^{\pi}(-2\cos\theta - \cos^2\theta)\, d\theta \quad \text{Simplify the integrand.}$$

$$= 2 - \frac{\pi}{4}. \quad \text{Evaluate the integral.}$$

Note that the regions in parts (a) and (b) comprise a circle of radius 1; indeed, their areas have a sum of π.

Related Exercises 21–28 ◀

EXAMPLE 5 Final note of caution Find the points of intersection of the circle $r = 3\cos\theta$ and the cardioid $r = 1 + \cos\theta$ (Figure 11.39).

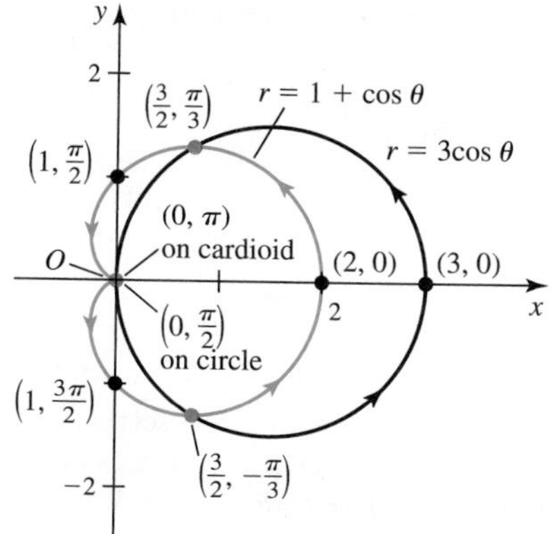

FIGURE 11.39

SOLUTION The fact that a point has multiple representations in polar coordinates may lead to subtle difficulties in finding intersection points. We first proceed algebraically. Equating the two expressions for r and solving for θ, we have

$$3\cos\theta = 1 + \cos\theta \quad \text{or} \quad \cos\theta = \frac{1}{2},$$

which has roots $\theta = \pm\pi/3$. Therefore, two intersection points are $(3/2, \pi/3)$ and $(3/2, -\pi/3)$ (Figure 11.39). Without graphs of the curves, we might be tempted to stop here. Yet, the figure shows another intersection point O that has not been detected. To find the third intersection point, we must investigate the way in which the two curves are generated. As θ increases from 0 to 2π, the cardioid is generated counterclockwise, beginning at $(2, 0)$. The cardioid passes through O when $\theta = \pi$. As θ increases from 0 to π, the circle is generated counterclockwise, beginning at $(3, 0)$. The circle passes through O when $\theta = \pi/2$. Therefore, the intersection point O is $(0, \pi)$ on the cardioid (and these coordinates do not satisfy the equation of the circle), while O is $(0, \pi/2)$ on the circle (and these coordinates do not satisfy the equation of the cardioid). There is no foolproof rule for detecting such "hidden" intersection points. Care must be used.

Related Exercises 29–32 ◄

SECTION 11.3 EXERCISES

Review Questions

1. Express the polar equation $r = f(\theta)$ in parametric form in Cartesian coordinates, where θ is the parameter.

2. How do you find the slope of the line tangent to the polar graph of $r = f(\theta)$ at a point?

3. Explain why the slope of the line tangent to the polar graph of $r = f(\theta)$ is not $dr/d\theta$.

4. What integral must be evaluated to find the area of the region bounded by the polar graphs of $r = f(\theta)$ and $r = g(\theta)$ on the interval $\alpha \le \theta \le \beta$, where $f(\theta) \ge g(\theta) \ge 0$?

Basic Skills

5–14. Slopes of tangent lines *Find the slope of the line tangent to the following polar curves at the given points. At the points where the curve intersects the origin (when this occurs), find the equation of the tangent line in polar coordinates.*

5. $r = 1 - \sin\theta$; $\left(\frac{1}{2}, \frac{\pi}{6}\right)$

6. $r = 4\cos\theta$; $\left(2, \frac{\pi}{3}\right)$

7. $r = 8\sin\theta$; $\left(4, \frac{5\pi}{6}\right)$

8. $r = 4 + \sin\theta$; $(4, 0)$ and $\left(3, \frac{3\pi}{2}\right)$

9. $r = 6 + 3\cos\theta$; $(3, \pi)$ and $(9, 0)$

10. $r = 2\sin 3\theta$; tips of the leaves

11. $r = 4\cos 2\theta$; tips of the leaves

12. $r^2 = 4\sin 2\theta$; tips of the lobes

13. $r^2 = 4\cos 2\theta$; $\left(0, \pm\frac{\pi}{4}\right)$

14. $r = 2\theta$; $\left(\frac{\pi}{2}, \frac{\pi}{4}\right)$

15–20. Horizontal and vertical tangents *Find the points at which the following polar curves have a horizontal or a vertical tangent line.*

15. $r = 4\cos\theta$

16. $r = 2 + 2\sin\theta$

17. $r = \sin 2\theta$

18. $r = 3 + 6\sin\theta$

19. $r^2 = 4\cos 2\theta$

20. $r = 2\sin 2\theta$

21–28. Areas of regions *Make a sketch of the region and its bounding curves. Find the area of the region.*

21. The region inside the circle $r = 8\sin\theta$

22. The region inside the cardioid $r = 4 + 4\sin\theta$

23. The region inside the limaçon $r = 2 + \cos\theta$

24. The region inside all the leaves of the rose $r = 3\sin 2\theta$

25. The region inside one leaf of the rose $r = \cos 5\theta$

26. The region inside the rose $r = 4\cos 2\theta$ and outside the circle $r = 2$

27. The region inside the rose $r = 4\sin 2\theta$ and inside the circle $r = 2$

28. The region inside the lemniscate $r^2 = 2\sin 2\theta$ and outside the circle $r = 1$

T **29–32. Intersection points** *Use algebraic methods to find as many intersection points of the following curves as possible. Use graphical methods to identify the remaining intersection points.*

29. $r = 3\sin\theta$ and $r = 3\cos\theta$

30. $r = 2 + 2\sin\theta$ and $r = 2 - 2\sin\theta$

31. $r^2 = 4\cos\theta$ and $r = 1 + \cos\theta$

32. $r = 1$ and $r = \sqrt{2}\cos 3\theta$

Further Explorations

33. **Explain why or why not** Determine whether the following statements are true and give an explanation or counterexample.
   a. The area of the region bounded by the polar graph of $r = f(\theta)$ on the interval $[\alpha, \beta]$ is $\int_\alpha^\beta f(\theta)\, d\theta$.
   b. The slope of the line tangent to the polar curve $r = f(\theta)$ at a point (r, θ) is $f'(\theta)$.

34. **Multiple identities** Explain why the point $(-1, 3\pi/2)$ is on the polar graph of $r = 1 + \cos\theta$ even though it does not satisfy the equation $r = 1 + \cos\theta$.

35–38. Area of plane regions *Find the area of the following regions.*

35. The region common to the circles $r = 2\sin\theta$ and $r = 1$.

36. The region inside the inner loop of the limaçon $r = 2 + 4\cos\theta$.

37. The region inside the outer loop but outside the inner loop of the limaçon $r = 3 - 6\sin\theta$.

38. The region common to the circle $r = 3\cos\theta$ and the cardioid $r = 1 + \cos\theta$.

T 39. **Spiral tangent lines** Use a graphing utility to determine the first three points with $\theta \geq 0$ at which the spiral $r = 2\theta$ has a horizontal tangent line. Find the first three points with $\theta \geq 0$ at which the spiral $r = 2\theta$ has a vertical tangent line.

40. **Area of roses**
   a. *Even number of leaves*: What is the relationship between the total area enclosed by the $4m$-leaf rose $r = \cos(2m\theta)$ and m?
   b. *Odd number of leaves*: What is the relationship between the total area enclosed by the $(2m + 1)$-leaf rose $r = \cos(2m + 1)\theta$ and m?

41. **Regions bounded by a spiral** Let R_n be the region bounded by the nth turn and the $(n + 1)$st turn of the spiral $r = e^{-\theta}$ in the first and second quadrants for $\theta \geq 0$ (see figure).
   a. Find the area A_n of R_n.
   b. Evaluate $\lim_{n\to\infty} A_n$.
   c. Evaluate $\lim_{n\to\infty} A_{n+1}/A_n$.

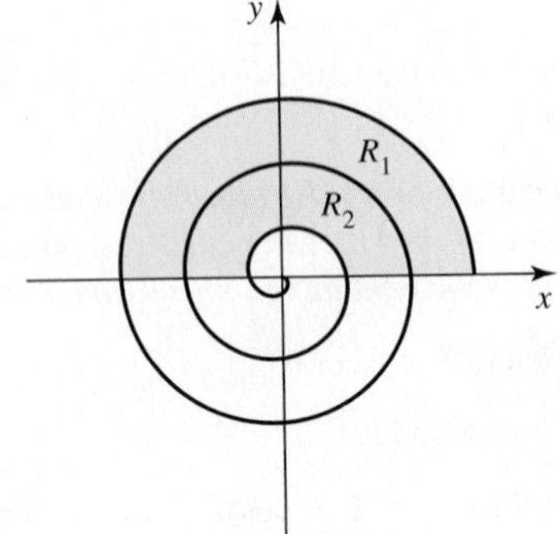

42–45. Area of polar regions *Find the area of the regions bounded by the following curves.*

42. The complete three-leaf rose $r = 2\cos 3\theta$

43. The lemniscate $r^2 = 6\sin 2\theta$

44. The limaçon $r = 2 - 4\sin\theta$

45. The limaçon $r = 4 - 2\cos\theta$

Applications

46. **Blood vessel flow** A blood vessel with a circular cross section of constant radius R carries blood that flows parallel to the axis of the vessel with a velocity of $v(r) = V(1 - r^2/R^2)$, where V is a constant and r is the distance from the axis of the vessel.
   a. Where is the velocity a maximum? A minimum?
   b. Find the average velocity of the blood over a cross section of the vessel.
   c. Suppose the velocity in the vessel is given by $v(r) = V(1 - r^2/R^2)^{1/p}$, where $p \geq 1$. Graph the velocity profiles for $p = 1, 2$, and 6 on the interval $0 \leq r \leq R$. Find the average velocity in the vessel as a function of p. How does the average velocity behave as $p \to \infty$?

47–49. Grazing goat problems. *Consider the following sequence of problems related to grazing goats tied to a rope. (See The Guided Projects for more grazing goat problems.)*

47. A circular corral of unit radius is enclosed by a fence. A goat inside the corral is tied to the fence with a rope of length $0 \leq a \leq 2$ (see figure). What is the area of the region (inside the corral) that the goat can graze? Check your answer with the special cases $a = 0$ and $a = 2$.

48. A circular concrete slab of unit radius is surrounded by grass. A goat is tied to the edge of the slab with a rope of length $0 \leq a \leq 2$ (see figure). What is the area of the grassy region that the goat can graze? Note that the rope can extend over the concrete slab. Check your answer with the special cases $a = 0$ and $a = 2$.

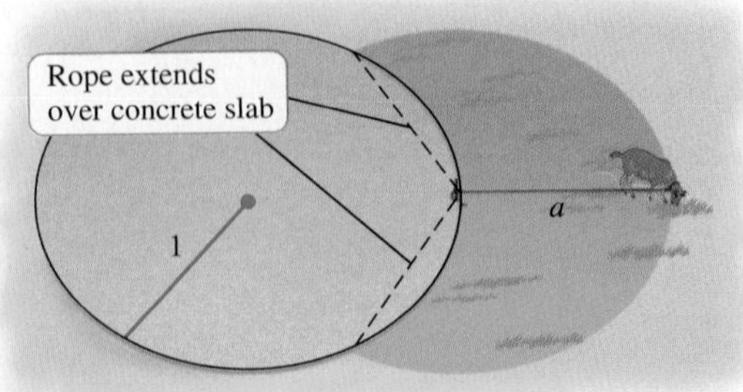

49. A circular corral of unit radius is enclosed by a fence. A goat is outside the corral and tied to the fence with a rope of length $a \geq 0$ (see figure). What is the area of the region (outside the corral) that the goat can reach?

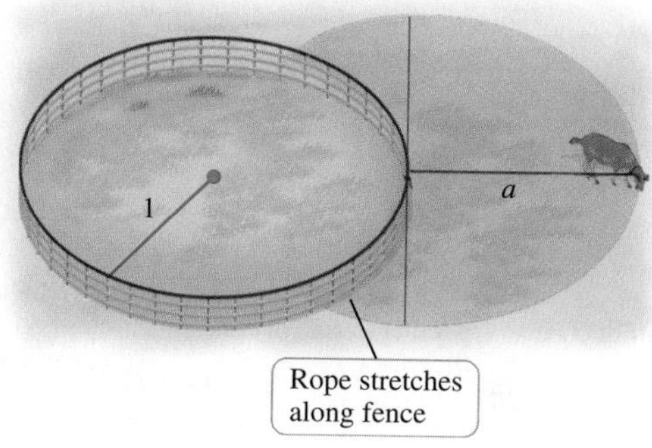

Additional Exercises

50. **Tangents and normals** Let a polar curve be described by $r = f(\theta)$ and let ℓ be the line tangent to the curve at the point $P(x, y) = P(r, \theta)$ (see figure).

a. Explain why $\tan \alpha = dy/dx$.
b. Explain why $\tan \theta = y/x$.
c. Let φ be the angle between ℓ and OP. Prove that $\tan \varphi = f(\theta)/f'(\theta)$.
d. Prove that the values of θ for which ℓ is parallel to the x-axis satisfy $\tan \theta = -f(\theta)/f'(\theta)$.
e. Prove that the values of θ for which ℓ is parallel to the y-axis satisfy $\tan \theta = f'(\theta)/f(\theta)$.

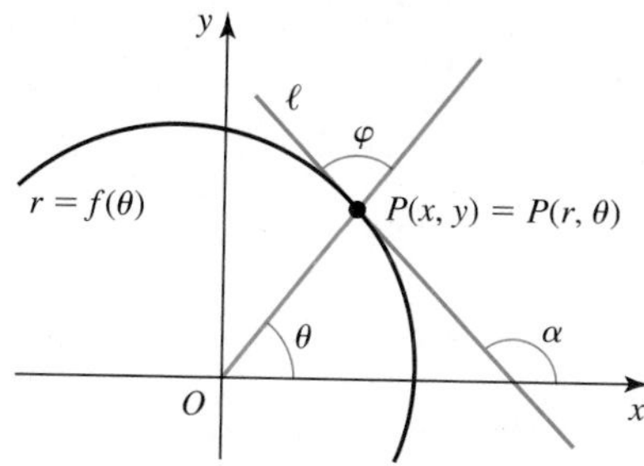

T 51. **Isogonal curves** Let a curve be described by $r = f(\theta)$, where $f(\theta) > 0$ on its domain. Referring to the figure of Exercise 50, a curve is **isogonal** provided the angle φ is constant for all θ.

a. Prove that φ is constant for all θ provided $\cot \varphi = f'(\theta)/f(\theta)$ is constant, which implies that $\frac{d}{d\theta}[\ln f(\theta)] = k$, where k is a constant.
b. Use part (a) to prove that the family of logarithmic spirals $r = Ce^{k\theta}$ consists of isogonal curves, where C and k are constants.
c. Graph the curve $r = 2e^{2\theta}$ and confirm the result of part (b).

QUICK CHECK ANSWERS

1. Apply the Product Rule. 2. $\sqrt{2} + 1$
3. Area $= \int_0^{2\pi} \frac{1}{2}(8)^2\, d\theta = 64\pi$
4. $\left[0, \frac{\pi}{3}\right]$ or $\left[\frac{\pi}{3}, \frac{2\pi}{3}\right]$ (among others) ◀

11.4 Conic Sections

Conic sections are best visualized as the Greeks did over 2000 years ago by slicing a double cone with a plane (Figure 11.40). Three of the seven different sets of points that arise in this way are *ellipses*, *parabolas*, and *hyperbolas*. These curves have practical applications and broad theoretical importance. For example, celestial bodies travel in orbits that are modeled by ellipses and hyperbolas. Mirrors for telescopes are designed using the properties of conic sections. And architectural structures, such as domes and arches, are sometimes based on these curves.

Parabolas

A **parabola** is the set of points in a plane that are equidistant from a fixed point F (called the **focus**) and a fixed line (called the **directrix**). In the four standard orientations, a parabola may open upward, downward, to the right, or to the left. We derive the equation of the parabola that opens upward.

Suppose the focus F is on the y-axis at $(0, p)$ and the directrix is the horizontal line $y = -p$, where $p > 0$. The parabola is the set of points P that satisfy the defining property

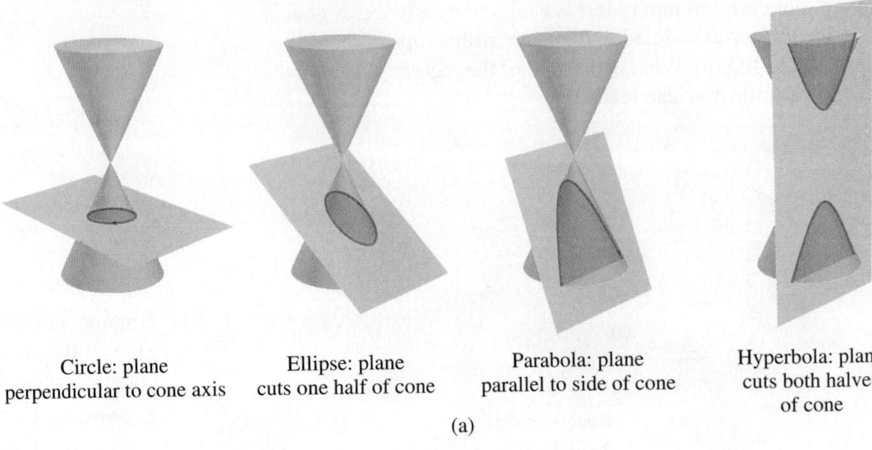

Point: plane through cone vertex only

Single line: plane tangent to cone

Pair of intersecting lines

(b)

FIGURE 11.40. The standard conic sections (a) are the intersection sets of a double cone and a plane that does not pass through the vertex of the cones. Degenerate conic sections (lines and points) are produced when a plane passes through the vertex of the cone (b).

$|PF| = |PL|$, where $L(x, -p)$ is the point on the directrix closest to P (Figure 11.41). Consider an arbitrary point $P(x, y)$ that satisfies this condition. Applying the distance formula, we have

$$\underbrace{\sqrt{x^2 + (y - p)^2}}_{|PF|} = \underbrace{y + p}_{|PL|}.$$

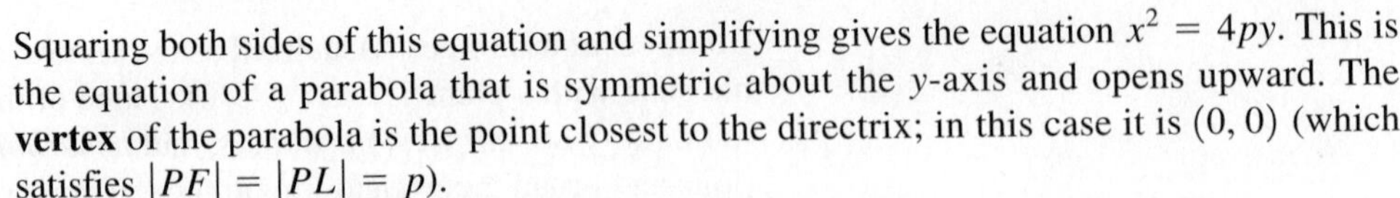

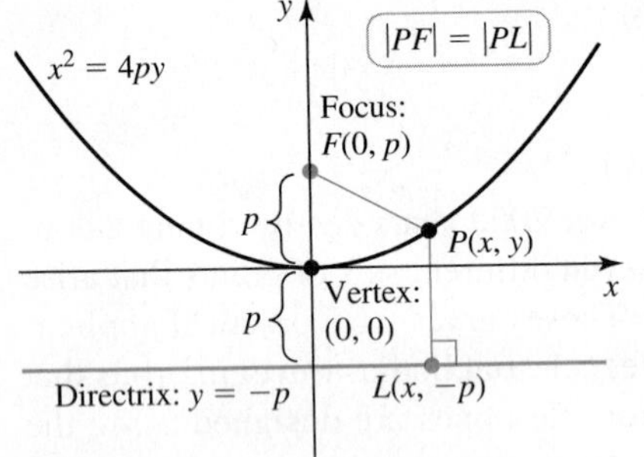

FIGURE 11.41

Squaring both sides of this equation and simplifying gives the equation $x^2 = 4py$. This is the equation of a parabola that is symmetric about the y-axis and opens upward. The **vertex** of the parabola is the point closest to the directrix; in this case it is $(0, 0)$ (which satisfies $|PF| = |PL| = p$).

The equations of the other three standard parabolas are derived in a similar way.

QUICK CHECK 1 Verify that $\sqrt{x^2 + (y - p)^2} = y + p$ is equivalent to $x^2 = 4py$.

Equations of Four Standard Parabolas

Let p be a real number. The parabola with focus at $(0, p)$ and directrix $y = -p$ is symmetric about the y-axis and has the equation $x^2 = 4py$. If $p > 0$, then the parabola opens *upward*; if $p < 0$, then the parabola opens *downward*.

The parabola with focus at $(p, 0)$ and directrix $x = -p$ is symmetric about the x-axis and has the equation $y^2 = 4px$. If $p > 0$, then the parabola opens *to the right*; if $p < 0$, then the parabola opens *to the left*.

Each of these parabolas has its vertex at the origin (Figure 11.42).

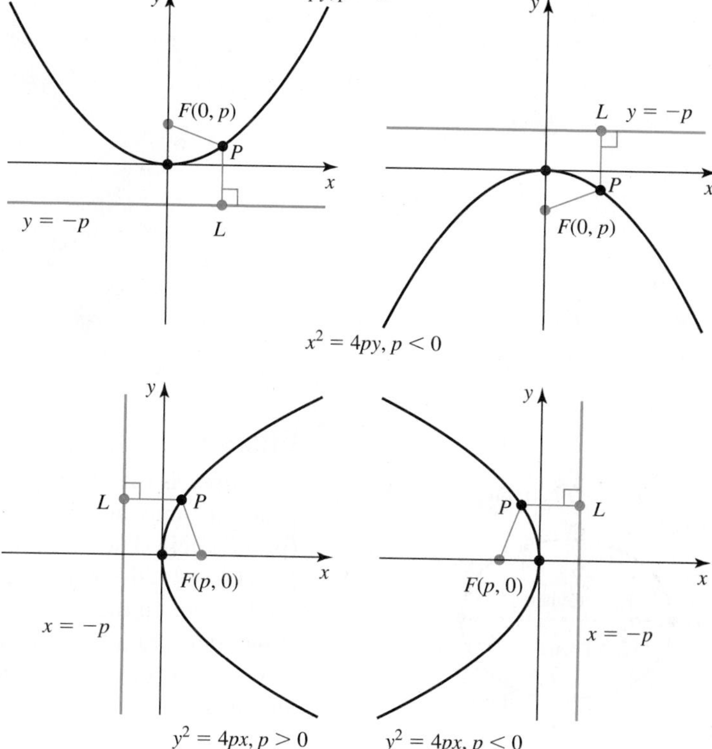

FIGURE 11.42

> Recall that a curve is symmetric with respect to the x-axis if $(x, -y)$ is on the curve whenever (x, y) is on the curve. So, a y^2-term indicates symmetry with respect to the x-axis. Similarly, an x^2-term indicates symmetry with respect to the y-axis.

QUICK CHECK 2 In which direction do the following parabolas open?
a. $y^2 = -4x$ **b.** $x^2 = 4y$

EXAMPLE 1 Graphing parabolas Find the focus and directrix of the parabola $y^2 = -12x$. Sketch its graph.

SOLUTION The y^2-term indicates that the parabola is symmetric with respect to the x-axis. Rewriting the equation as $x = -y^2/12$, we see that $x \le 0$ for all y, implying that the parabola opens to the left. Comparing $y^2 = -12x$ to the standard form $y^2 = 4px$, we see that $p = -3$; therefore, the focus is $(-3, 0)$, and the directrix is $x = 3$ (Figure 11.43).

Related Exercises 13–18

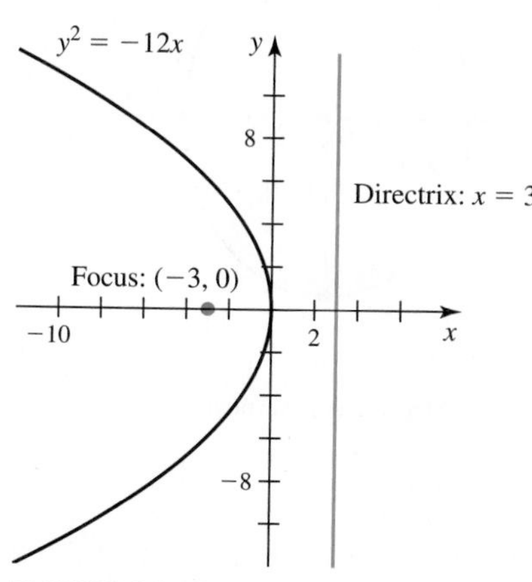

FIGURE 11.43

EXAMPLE 2 Equations of parabolas Find the equation of the parabola with vertex $(0, 0)$ that opens downward and passes through the point $(2, -3)$.

SOLUTION The standard parabola that opens downward has the equation $x^2 = 4py$. The point $(2, -3)$ must satisfy this equation. Substituting $x = 2$ and $y = -3$ into $x^2 = 4py$, we find that $p = -\frac{1}{3}$. Therefore, the focus is at $\left(0, -\frac{1}{3}\right)$, the directrix is $y = \frac{1}{3}$, and the equation of the parabola is $x^2 = -4y/3$, or $y = -3x^2/4$ (Figure 11.44).

Related Exercises 19–26

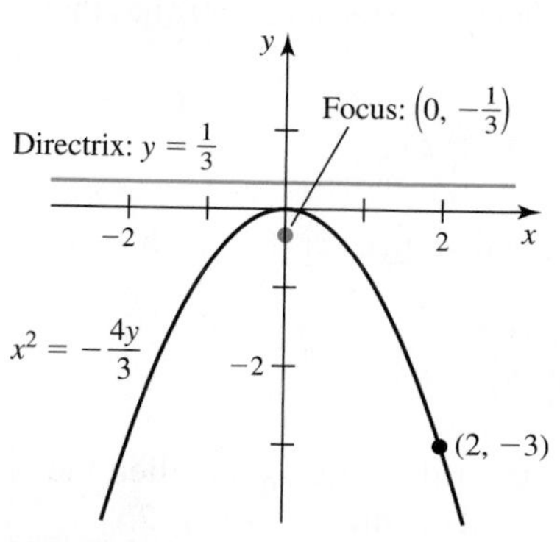

FIGURE 11.44

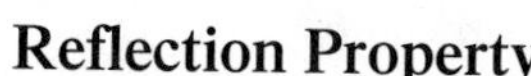

Reflection Property

Parabolas have a property that makes them useful in the design of reflectors and transmitters. A particle approaching a parabola on any line parallel to the axis of the parabola is reflected on a line that passes through the focus (Figure 11.45); this property is used to focus incoming light by a parabolic mirror on a telescope. Alternatively, signals emanating from the focus are reflected on lines parallel to the axis, a property used to design radio transmitters and headlights (Exercise 83).

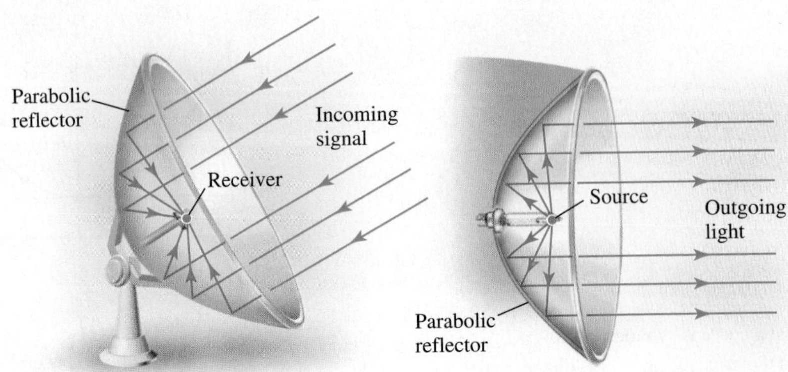

FIGURE 11.45

Ellipses

An **ellipse** is the set of points in a plane whose distances from two fixed points have a constant sum that we denote $2a$ (Figure 11.46). Each of the two fixed points is a **focus** (plural **foci**). The equation of an ellipse is simplest if the foci are on the x-axis at $(\pm c, 0)$ or on the y-axis at $(0, \pm c)$. In either case, the **center** of the ellipse is $(0, 0)$. If the foci are on the x-axis, the points $(\pm a, 0)$ lie on the ellipse and are called **vertices**. If the foci are on the y-axis, the vertices are $(0, \pm a)$ (Figure 11.47). A short calculation (Exercise 85) using the definition of the ellipse results in the following equations for an ellipse.

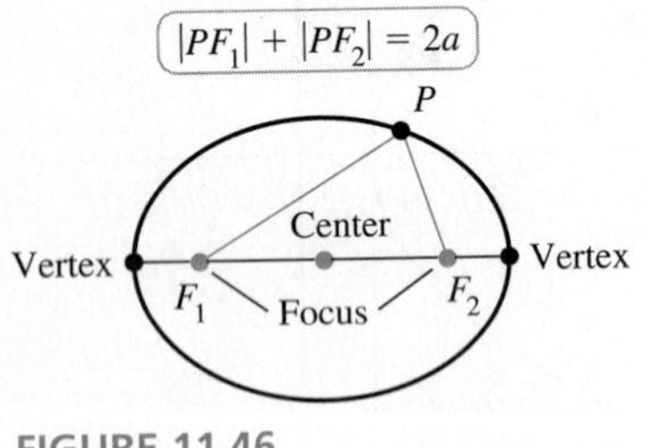

FIGURE 11.46

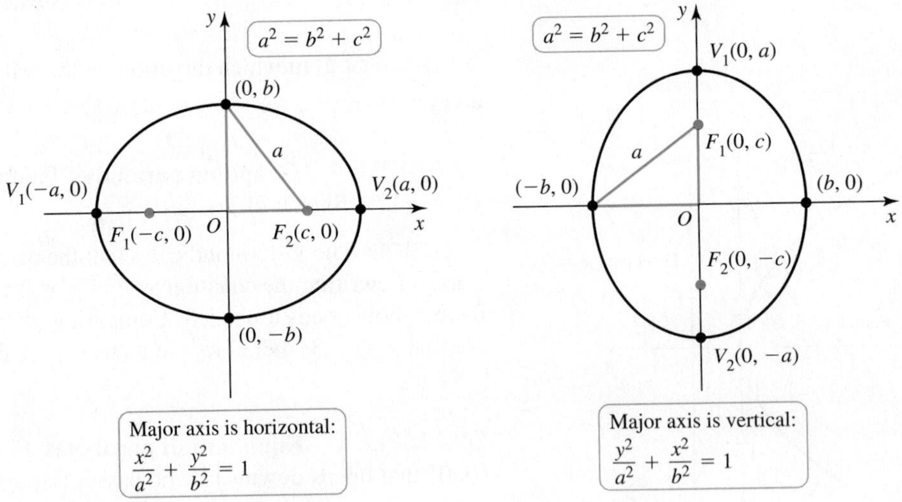

FIGURE 11.47

Equations of Standard Ellipses

An ellipse centered at the origin with foci at $(\pm c, 0)$ and vertices at $(\pm a, 0)$ has the equation

$$\frac{x^2}{a^2} + \frac{y^2}{b^2} = 1, \qquad \text{where } a^2 = b^2 + c^2.$$

An ellipse centered at the origin with foci at $(0, \pm c)$ and vertices at $(0, \pm a)$ has the equation

$$\frac{y^2}{a^2} + \frac{x^2}{b^2} = 1, \qquad \text{where } a^2 = b^2 + c^2.$$

In both cases, $a > b > 0$ and $a > c > 0$, the length of the long axis (called the **major axis**) is $2a$, and the length of the short axis (called the **minor axis**) is $2b$.

➤ When necessary, we may distinguish between the *major-axis vertices* $(\pm a, 0)$ or $(0, \pm a)$, and the *minor-axis vertices* $(\pm b, 0)$ or $(0, \pm b)$. The word *vertices* (without further description) is understood to mean *major-axis vertices*.

QUICK CHECK 3 In the case that the vertices and foci are on the x-axis, show that the length of the minor axis of an ellipse is $2b$. ◄

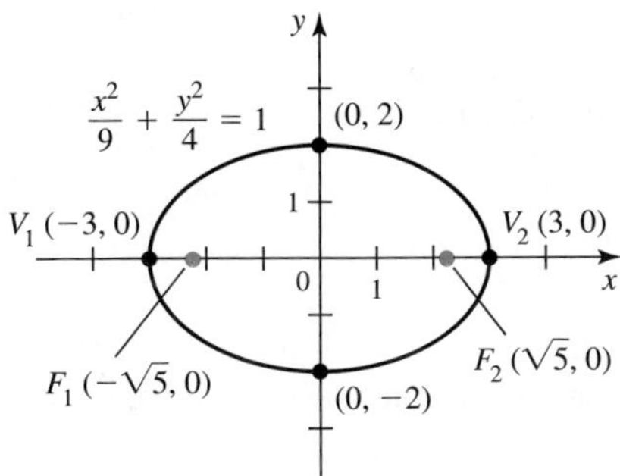

FIGURE 11.48

EXAMPLE 3 **Graphing ellipses** Find the vertices, foci, and the length of the major and minor axes of the ellipse $\frac{x^2}{9} + \frac{y^2}{4} = 1$. Graph the ellipse.

SOLUTION Because $9 > 4$, we identify $a^2 = 9$ and $b^2 = 4$. Therefore, $a = 3$ and $b = 2$. The lengths of the major and minor axes are $2a = 6$ and $2b = 4$, respectively. The vertices are $(\pm 3, 0)$ and lie on the x-axis, as do the foci. The relationship $c^2 = a^2 - b^2$ implies that $c^2 = 5$, or $c = \sqrt{5}$. Therefore, the foci are $(\pm\sqrt{5}, 0)$. The graph of the ellipse is shown in Figure 11.48. *Related Exercises 27–32*

EXAMPLE 4 **Equation of an ellipse** Find the equation of the ellipse centered at the origin with its foci on the y-axis, a major axis of length 8, and a minor axis of length 4. Graph the ellipse.

SOLUTION Because the length of the major axis is 8, the vertices are located at $(0, \pm 4)$, and $a = 4$. Because the length of the minor axis is 4, we have $b = 2$. Therefore, the equation of the ellipse is

$$\frac{y^2}{16} + \frac{x^2}{4} = 1.$$

Using the relation $c^2 = a^2 - b^2$, we find that $c = 2\sqrt{3}$ and the foci are at $(0, \pm 2\sqrt{3})$. The ellipse is shown in Figure 11.49. *Related Exercises 33–38*

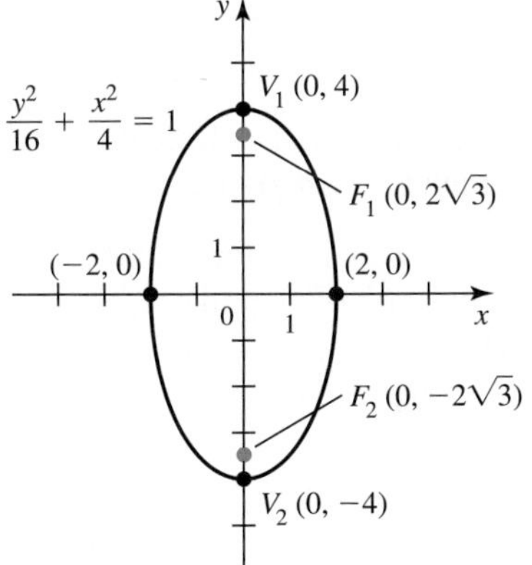

FIGURE 11.49

Hyperbolas

A **hyperbola** is the set of points in a plane whose distances from two fixed points have a constant difference, either $2a$ or $-2a$ (Figure 11.50). As with ellipses, the two fixed points are called **foci**. The equation of a hyperbola is simplest if the foci are on either the x-axis at $(\pm c, 0)$ or on the y-axis at $(0, \pm c)$. If the foci are on the x-axis, the points $(\pm a, 0)$ on the hyperbola are called the **vertices**. In this case, the hyperbola has no y-intercepts, but it has the **asymptotes** $y = \pm bx/a$, where $b^2 = c^2 - a^2$. Similarly, if the foci are on the y-axis, the vertices are $(0, \pm a)$, the hyperbola has no x-intercepts, and it has the asymptotes $y = \pm ax/b$ (Figure 11.51). A short calculation (Exercise 86) using the definition of the hyperbola results in the following equations for standard hyperbolas.

➤ Asymptotes that are not parallel to one of the coordinate axes, as in the case of the standard hyperbolas, are called **oblique**, or **slant**, **asymptotes**.

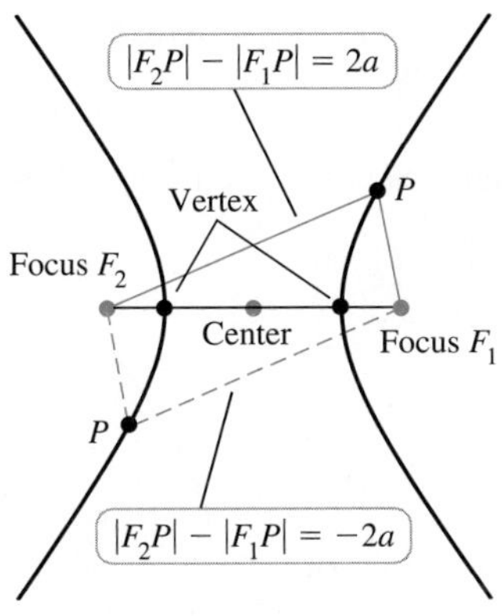

FIGURE 11.50

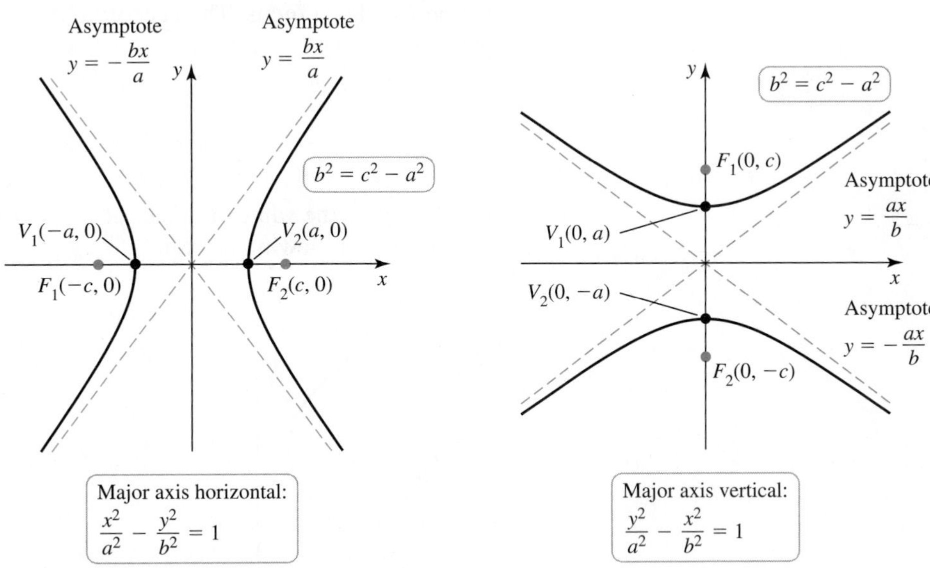

FIGURE 11.51

Equations of Standard Hyperbolas

A hyperbola centered at the origin with foci at $(\pm c, 0)$ and vertices at $(\pm a, 0)$ has the equation

$$\frac{x^2}{a^2} - \frac{y^2}{b^2} = 1, \quad \text{where} \quad b^2 = c^2 - a^2.$$

The hyperbola has **asymptotes** $y = \pm bx/a$.

A hyperbola centered at the origin with foci at $(0, \pm c)$ and vertices at $(0, \pm a)$ has the equation

$$\frac{y^2}{a^2} - \frac{x^2}{b^2} = 1, \quad \text{where} \quad b^2 = c^2 - a^2.$$

The hyperbola has **asymptotes** $y = \pm ax/b$.

In both cases, $c > a > 0$ and $c > b > 0$.

➤ Notice that the asymptotes for hyperbolas are $y = \pm bx/a$ when the vertices are on the x-axis and $y = \pm ax/b$ when the vertices are on the y-axis (the roles of a and b are reversed).

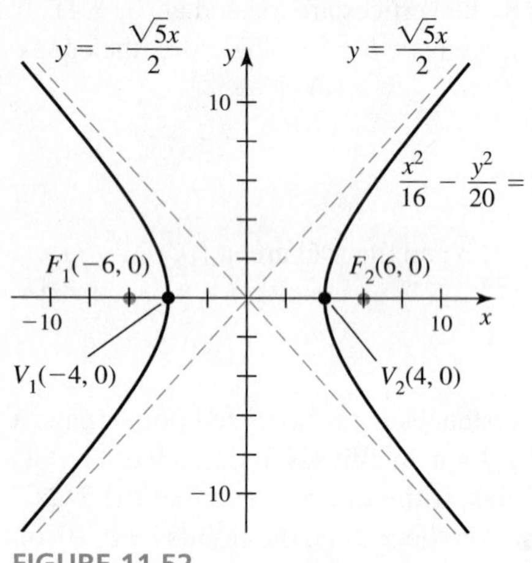

FIGURE 11.52

EXAMPLE 5 **Graphing hyperbolas** Find the equation of the hyperbola centered at the origin with vertices at $(\pm 4, 0)$ and foci at $(\pm 6, 0)$. Graph the hyperbola.

SOLUTION Because the foci are on the x-axis, the vertices are also on the x-axis, and there are no y-intercepts. With $a = 4$ and $c = 6$, we have $b^2 = c^2 - a^2 = 20$, or $b = 2\sqrt{5}$. Therefore, the equation of the hyperbola is

$$\frac{x^2}{16} - \frac{y^2}{20} = 1.$$

The asymptotes are $y = \pm bx/a = \pm\sqrt{5}x/2$ (Figure 11.52). *Related Exercises 39–50* ◀

QUICK CHECK 4 Identify the vertices and foci of the hyperbola $y^2 - x^2/4 = 1$. ◀

Eccentricity and Directrix

Parabolas, ellipses, and hyperbolas may also be developed in a single unified way called the *eccentricity-directrix* approach. We let ℓ be a line called the **directrix** and F be a point not on ℓ called a **focus**. The **eccentricity** is a real number $e > 0$. Consider the set C of points P in a plane with the property that the distance $|PF|$ equals e multiplied by the perpendicular distance $|PL|$ from P to ℓ (Figure 11.53); that is,

➤ The conic section lies in the plane formed by the directrix and the focus.

$$|PF| = e|PL| \quad \text{or} \quad \frac{|PF|}{|PL|} = e = \text{constant}.$$

Depending on the value of e, the set C is one of the three standard conic sections, as described in the following theorem.

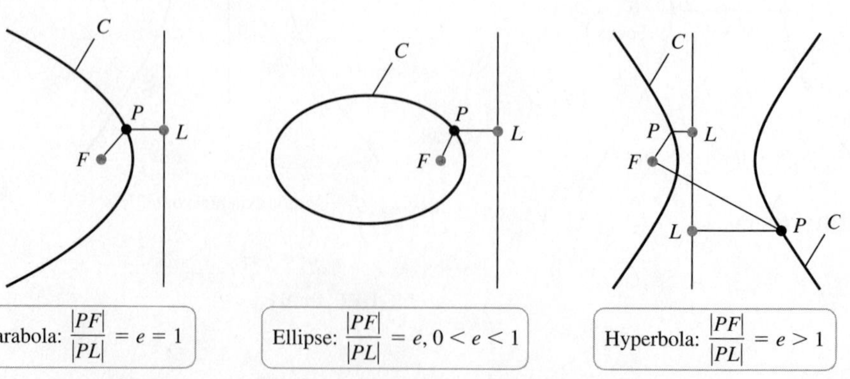

FIGURE 11.53

Theorem 11.3 for ellipses and hyperbolas describes how the entire curve is generated using just one focus and one directrix. Nevertheless, every ellipse or hyperbola has two foci and two directrices.

THEOREM 11.3 Eccentricity-Directrix Theorem
Let ℓ be a line, F be a point not on ℓ, and $e > 0$ be a real number. Let C be the set of points P in a plane with the property that $\frac{|PF|}{|PL|} = e$, where $|PL|$ is the perpendicular distance from P to ℓ.

1. If $e = 1$, C is a **parabola**.
2. If $0 < e < 1$, C is an **ellipse**.
3. If $e > 1$, C is a **hyperbola**.

The proof of the theorem is straightforward; it requires an algebraic calculation that can be found in Appendix B. The proof establishes relationships between five parameters a, b, c, d, and e that are characteristic of any ellipse or hyperbola. The relationships are given in the following summary.

SUMMARY Properties of Ellipses and Hyperbolas
An ellipse or hyperbola centered at the origin has the following properties.

	Foci on x-axis	Foci on y-axis
Major-axis vertices:	$(\pm a, 0)$	$(0, \pm a)$
Minor-axis vertices (for ellipses):	$(0, \pm b)$	$(\pm b, 0)$
Foci:	$(\pm c, 0)$	$(0, \pm c)$
Directrices:	$x = \pm d$	$y = \pm d$

Eccentricity: $0 < e < 1$ for ellipses, $e > 1$ for hyperbolas.

Given any two of the five parameters a, b, c, d, and e, the other three are found using the relations

$$c = ae \qquad d = \frac{a}{e}$$

$$b^2 = a^2 - c^2 \quad \text{(for ellipses)} \qquad b^2 = c^2 - a^2 \quad \text{(for hyperbolas)}$$

QUICK CHECK 5 Given an ellipse with $a = 3$ and $e = \frac{1}{2}$, what are the values of b, c, and d?

EXAMPLE 6 Equations of ellipses Find the equation of the ellipse centered at the origin with foci at $(0, \pm 4)$ and eccentricity $e = \frac{1}{2}$. Give the length of the major and minor axes, the location of the vertices, and the directrices. Graph the ellipse.

SOLUTION An ellipse with its major axis along the y-axis has the equation

$$\frac{y^2}{a^2} + \frac{x^2}{b^2} = 1,$$

where a and b must be determined (with $a > b$). Because the foci are at $(0, \pm 4)$, we have $c = 4$. Using $e = \frac{1}{2}$ and the relation $c = ae$, it follows that $a = c/e = 8$. So, the length of the major axis is $2a = 16$, and the major-axis vertices are $(0, \pm 8)$. Also $d = a/e = 16$, so the directrices are $y = \pm 16$. Finally, $b^2 = a^2 - c^2 = 48$, or $b = 4\sqrt{3}$. So, the length of the minor axis is $2b = 8\sqrt{3}$, and the minor-axis vertices are $(\pm 4\sqrt{3}, 0)$ (Figure 11.54). The equation of the ellipse is

$$\frac{y^2}{64} + \frac{x^2}{48} = 1.$$

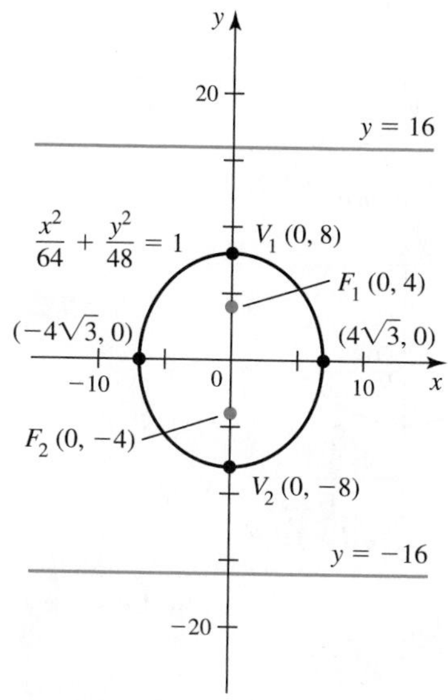

FIGURE 11.54

Related Exercises 51–54

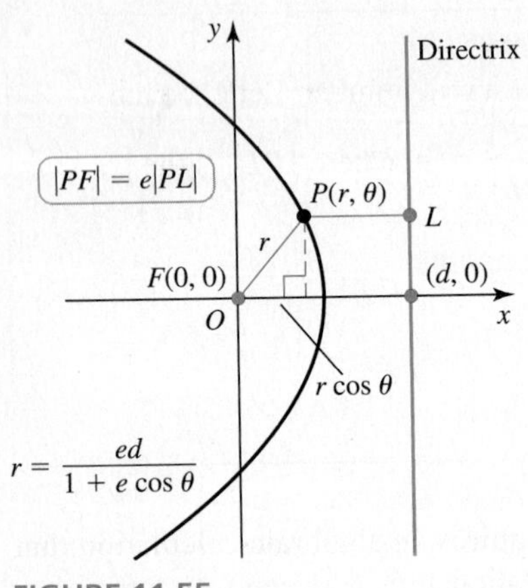

FIGURE 11.55

Polar Equations of Conic Sections

It turns out that conic sections have a natural representation in polar coordinates, provided we use the eccentricity-directrix approach given in Theorem 11.3. Furthermore, a single polar equation covers parabolas, ellipses, and hyperbolas.

When working in polar equations, the key is to place one focus of the conic section at the origin of the coordinate system. We begin by placing one focus F at the origin and taking a directrix perpendicular to the x-axis through $(d, 0)$, where $d > 0$ (Figure 11.55). We now use the definition $\frac{|PF|}{|PL|} = e$, where $P(r, \theta)$ is an arbitrary point on the conic. As shown in Figure 11.55, $|PF| = r$ and $|PL| = d - r\cos\theta$. The condition $\frac{|PF|}{|PL|} = e$ implies that $r = e(d - r\cos\theta)$. Solving for r, we have

$$r = \frac{ed}{1 + e\cos\theta}.$$

A similar derivation (Exercise 74) with the directrix at $x = -d$, where $d > 0$, results in the equation

$$r = \frac{ed}{1 - e\cos\theta}.$$

For horizontal directrices at $y = \pm d$ (Figure 11.56), a similar argument (Exercise 74) leads to the equations

$$r = \frac{ed}{1 \pm e\sin\theta}.$$

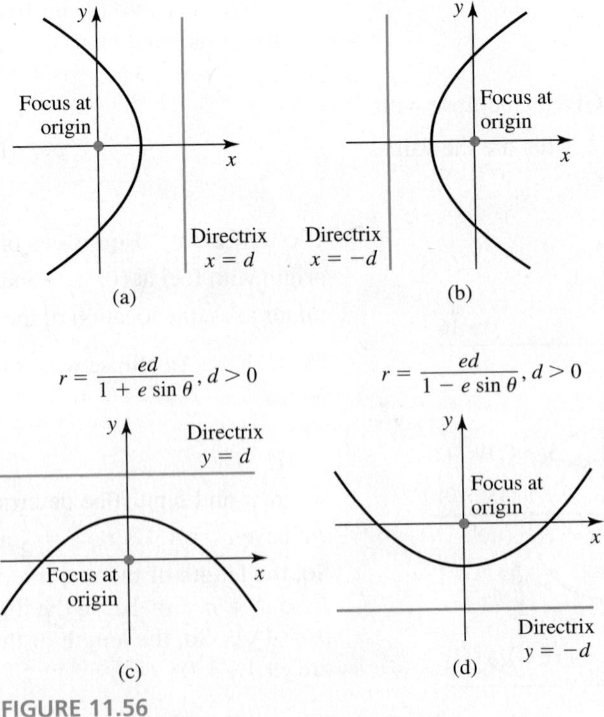

FIGURE 11.56

THEOREM 11.4 Polar Equations of Conic Sections
Let $d > 0$. The conic section with a focus at the origin and eccentricity e has the polar equation

$$\underbrace{r = \frac{ed}{1 + e\cos\theta}}_{\text{if one directrix is } x = d} \quad \text{or} \quad \underbrace{r = \frac{ed}{1 - e\cos\theta}}_{\text{if one directrix is } x = -d}.$$

The conic section with a focus at the origin and eccentricity e has the polar equation

$$\underbrace{r = \frac{ed}{1 + e\sin\theta}}_{\text{if one directrix is } y = d} \quad \text{or} \quad \underbrace{r = \frac{ed}{1 - e\sin\theta}}_{\text{if one directrix is } y = -d}.$$

If $0 < e < 1$, the conic section is an ellipse; if $e = 1$, it is a parabola; and if $e > 1$, it is a hyperbola. The curves are defined over any interval in θ of length 2π.

QUICK CHECK 6 On which axis do the vertices and foci of the conic section $r = 2/(1 - 2\sin\theta)$ lie?

EXAMPLE 7 Conic sections in polar coordinates Find the vertices, foci, and directrices of the following conic sections. Graph each curve and then check your work with a graphing utility.

a. $r = \dfrac{8}{2 + 3\cos\theta}$ **b.** $r = \dfrac{2}{1 + \sin\theta}$

SOLUTION

a. The equation must be put in the standard polar form for a conic section. Dividing numerator and denominator by 2, we have

$$r = \frac{4}{1 + \frac{3}{2}\cos\theta},$$

which allows us to identify $e = \frac{3}{2}$. Therefore, the equation describes a hyperbola (because $e > 1$) with one focus at the origin.

The directrices are vertical (because $\cos\theta$ appears in the equation). Knowing that $ed = 4$, we have $d = \frac{4}{e} = \frac{8}{3}$, and one directrix is $x = \frac{8}{3}$. Letting $\theta = 0$ and $\theta = \pi$, the polar coordinates of the vertices are $\left(\frac{8}{5}, 0\right)$ and $(-8, \pi)$; equivalently, the vertices are $\left(\frac{8}{5}, 0\right)$ and $(8, 0)$ in Cartesian coordinates (Figure 11.57). The center of the hyperbola is halfway between the vertices; therefore, its Cartesian coordinates are $\left(\frac{24}{5}, 0\right)$. The distance between the focus at $(0, 0)$ and the nearest vertex $\left(\frac{8}{5}, 0\right)$ is $\frac{8}{5}$. Therefore, the other focus is $\frac{8}{5}$ units to the right of the vertex $(8, 0)$. So, the Cartesian coordinates of the foci are $\left(\frac{48}{5}, 0\right)$ and $(0, 0)$. Because the directrices are symmetric about the center and the left directrix is $x = \frac{8}{3}$, the right directrix is $x = \frac{104}{15} \approx 6.9$. The graph of the hyperbola (Figure 11.57) is generated with $0 \le \theta \le 2\pi$ $\left(\text{with } \theta \neq \pm\cos^{-1}\left(-\frac{2}{3}\right)\right)$.

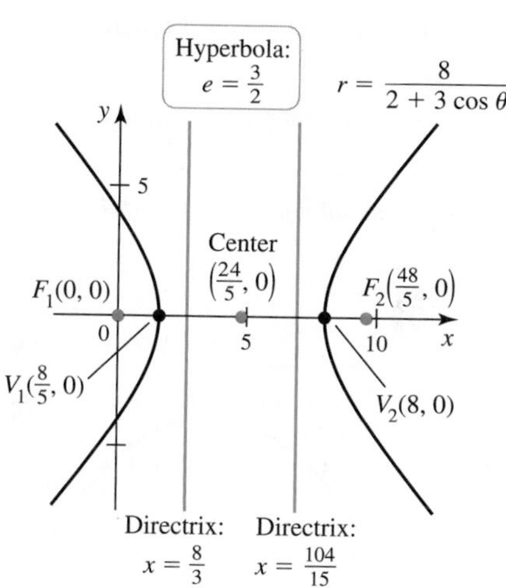

FIGURE 11.57

b. The equation is in standard form, and it describes a parabola because $e = 1$. The sole focus is at the origin. The directrix is horizontal (because of the $\sin\theta$ term); $ed = 1$ implies that $d = 2$ and the directrix is $y = 2$. The parabola opens downward because of the plus sign in the denominator. The vertex corresponds to $\theta = \frac{\pi}{2}$ and has polar coordinates $\left(1, \frac{\pi}{2}\right)$, or Cartesian coordinates $(0, 1)$. Setting $\theta = 0$ and $\theta = \pi$, the parabola crosses the x-axis at $(2, 0)$ and $(2, \pi)$ in polar coordinates, or $(\pm 2, 0)$ in Cartesian coordinates. As θ increases from $-\frac{\pi}{2}$ to $\frac{\pi}{2}$, the right branch of the parabola is generated and as θ increases from $\frac{\pi}{2}$ to $\frac{3\pi}{2}$, the left branch of the parabola is generated (Figure 11.58).

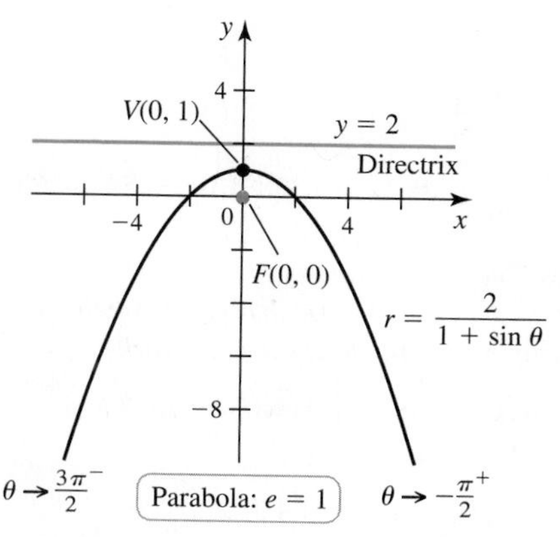

FIGURE 11.58

Related Exercises 55–64

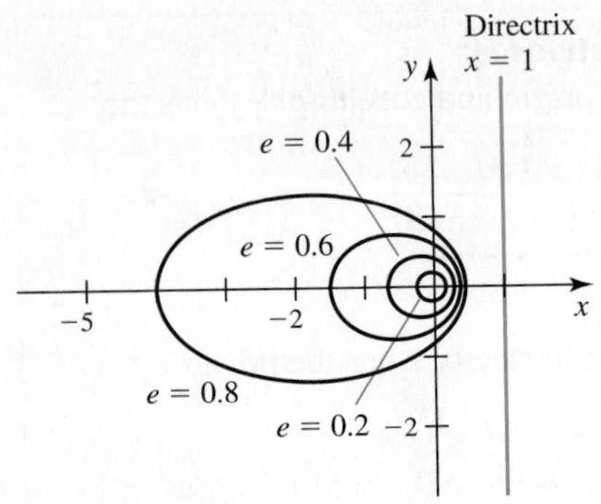

FIGURE 11.59

EXAMPLE 8 Conics in polar coordinates Use a graphing utility to plot the curves $r = \dfrac{e}{1 + e\cos\theta}$ with $e = 0.2, 0.4, 0.6$, and 0.8. Comment on the effect of varying the eccentricity, e.

SOLUTION Because $0 < e < 1$, all the curves are ellipses. Notice that the equation is in standard form with $d = 1$; therefore, the curves have the same directrix, $x = d = 1$. As the eccentricity increases, the ellipses become more elongated. Small values of e correspond to more circular ellipses (Figure 11.59). *Related Exercises 65–66* ◀

SECTION 11.4 EXERCISES

Review Questions

1. Give the property that defines all parabolas.
2. Give the property that defines all ellipses.
3. Give the property that defines all hyperbolas.
4. Sketch the three basic conic sections in standard position with vertices and foci on the x-axis.
5. Sketch the three basic conic sections in standard position with vertices and foci on the y-axis.
6. What is the equation of the standard parabola with its vertex at the origin that opens downward?
7. What is the equation of the standard ellipse with vertices at $(\pm a, 0)$ and foci at $(\pm c, 0)$?
8. What is the equation of the standard hyperbola with vertices at $(0, \pm a)$ and foci at $(0, \pm c)$?
9. Given the vertices $(\pm a, 0)$ and the eccentricity e, what are the coordinates of the foci of an ellipse and a hyperbola?
10. Give the equation in polar coordinates of a conic section with a focus at the origin, eccentricity e, and a directrix $x = d$, where $d > 0$.
11. What are the equations of the asymptotes of a standard hyperbola with vertices on the x-axis?
12. How does the eccentricity determine the type of conic section?

Basic Skills

13–18. Graphing parabolas *Sketch the graph of the following parabolas. Specify the location of the focus and the equation of the directrix. Use a graphing utility to check your work.*

13. $x^2 = 12y$
14. $y^2 = 20x$
15. $x = -y^2/16$
16. $4x = -y^2$
17. $8y = -3x^2$
18. $12x = 5y^2$

19–24. Equations of parabolas *Find an equation of the following parabolas, assuming the vertex is at the origin. Use a graphing utility to check your work.*

19. A parabola that opens to the right with directrix $x = -4$
20. A parabola that opens downward with directrix $y = 6$
21. A parabola with focus at $(3, 0)$
22. A parabola with focus at $(-4, 0)$
23. A parabola symmetric about the y-axis that passes through the point $(2, -6)$
24. A parabola symmetric about the x-axis that passes through the point $(1, -4)$

25–26. From graphs to equations *Write an equation of the following parabolas.*

25.

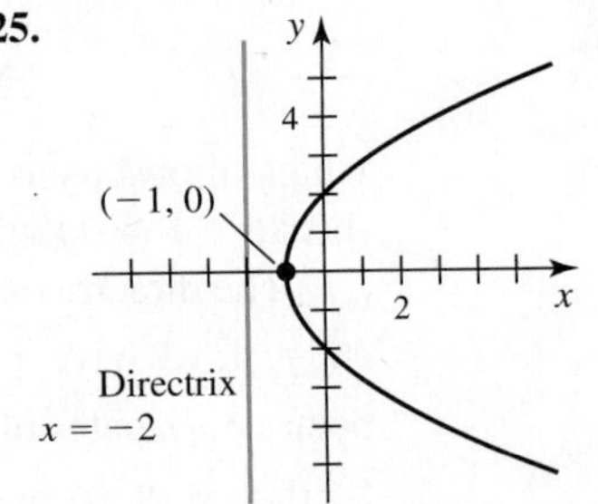

26.

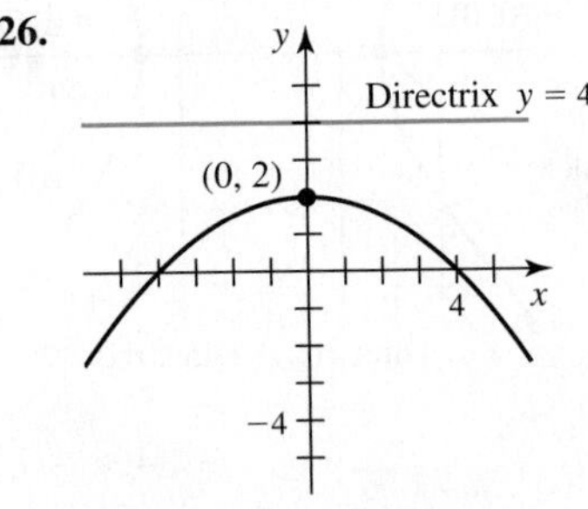

27–32. Graphing ellipses *Sketch the graph of the following ellipses. Plot and label the coordinates of the vertices and foci, and find the lengths of the major and minor axes. Use a graphing utility to check your work.*

27. $\dfrac{x^2}{4} + y^2 = 1$
28. $\dfrac{x^2}{9} + \dfrac{y^2}{4} = 1$
29. $\dfrac{x^2}{4} + \dfrac{y^2}{16} = 1$
30. $x^2 + \dfrac{y^2}{9} = 1$
31. $\dfrac{x^2}{5} + \dfrac{y^2}{7} = 1$
32. $12x^2 + 5y^2 = 60$

33–36. Equations of ellipses *Find an equation of the following ellipses, assuming the center is at the origin. Sketch a graph labeling the vertices and foci. Use a graphing utility to check your work.*

33. An ellipse whose major axis is on the x-axis with length 8 and whose minor axis has length 6
34. An ellipse with vertices $(\pm 6, 0)$ and foci $(\pm 4, 0)$

35. An ellipse with vertices $(\pm 5, 0)$, passing through the point $\left(4, \frac{3}{5}\right)$

36. An ellipse with vertices $(0, \pm 10)$, passing through the point $(\sqrt{3}/2, 5)$

37–38. From graphs to equations *Write an equation of the following ellipses.*

37.

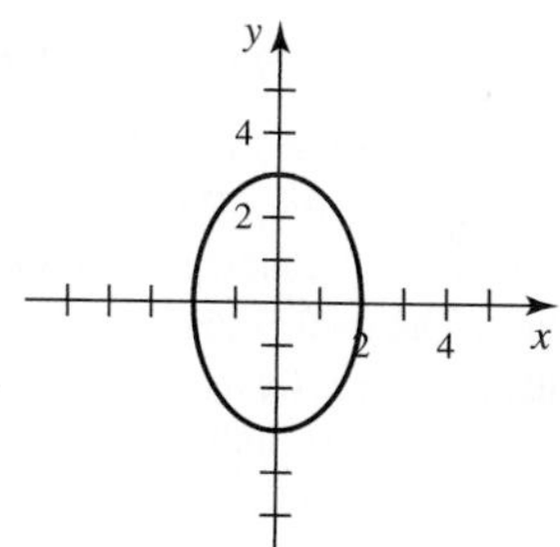

38.

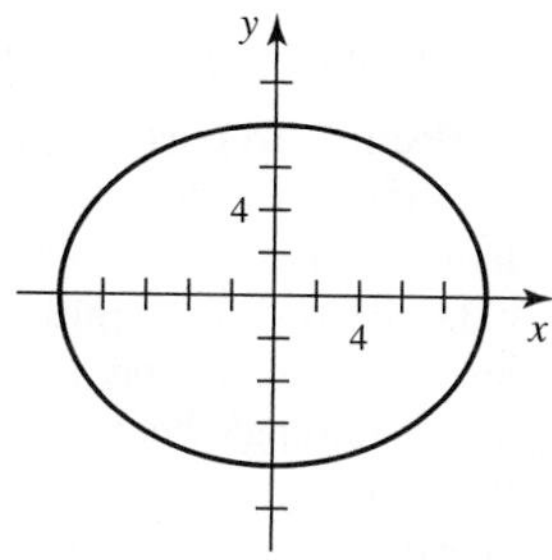

39–44. Graphing hyperbolas *Sketch the graph of the following hyperbolas. Specify the coordinates of the vertices and foci and find the equations of the asymptotes. Use a graphing utility to check your work.*

39. $\frac{x^2}{4} - y^2 = 1$

40. $\frac{y^2}{16} - \frac{x^2}{9} = 1$

41. $4x^2 - y^2 = 16$

42. $25y^2 - 4x^2 = 100$

43. $\frac{x^2}{3} - \frac{y^2}{5} = 1$

44. $10x^2 - 7y^2 = 140$

45–48. Equations of hyperbolas *Find an equation of the following hyperbolas, assuming the center is at the origin. Sketch a graph labeling the vertices, foci, and asymptotes. Use a graphing utility to check your work.*

45. A hyperbola with vertices $(\pm 4, 0)$ and foci $(\pm 6, 0)$

46. A hyperbola with vertices $(\pm 1, 0)$ that passes through $\left(\frac{5}{3}, 8\right)$

47. A hyperbola with vertices $(\pm 2, 0)$ and asymptotes $y = \pm 3x/2$

48. A hyperbola with vertices $(0, \pm 4)$ and asymptotes $y = \pm 2x$

49–50. From graphs to equations *Write an equation of the following hyperbolas.*

49. 50.

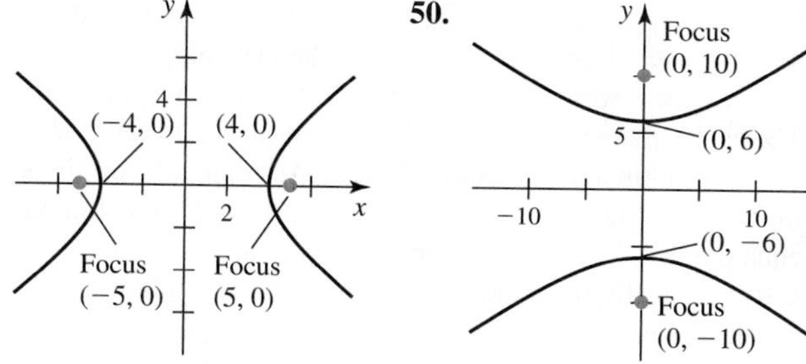

51–54. Eccentricity-directrix approach *Find an equation of the following curves, assuming the center is at the origin. Sketch a graph labeling the vertices, foci, asymptotes, and directrices. Use a graphing utility to check your work.*

51. An ellipse with vertices $(\pm 9, 0)$ and eccentricity $\frac{1}{3}$

52. An ellipse with vertices $(0, \pm 9)$ and eccentricity $\frac{1}{4}$

53. A hyperbola with vertices $(\pm 1, 0)$ and eccentricity 3

54. A hyperbola with vertices $(0, \pm 4)$ and eccentricity 2

55–60. Polar equations for conic sections *Graph the following conic sections, labeling the vertices, foci, directrices, and asymptotes (if they exist). Use a graphing utility to check your work.*

55. $r = \frac{4}{1 + \cos\theta}$

56. $r = \frac{4}{2 + \cos\theta}$

57. $r = \frac{1}{2 - \cos\theta}$

58. $r = \frac{6}{3 + 2\sin\theta}$

59. $r = \frac{1}{2 - 2\sin\theta}$

60. $r = \frac{12}{3 - \cos\theta}$

61–64. Tracing hyperbolas and parabolas *Graph the following equations. Then use arrows and labeled points to indicate how the curve is generated as θ increases from 0 to 2π.*

61. $r = \frac{1}{1 + \sin\theta}$

62. $r = \frac{1}{1 + 2\cos\theta}$

63. $r = \frac{3}{1 - \cos\theta}$

64. $r = \frac{1}{1 - 2\cos\theta}$

T 65. **Parabolas with a graphing utility** Use a graphing utility to graph the parabolas $y^2 = 4px$ for $p = -5, -2, -1, 1, 2$, and 5 on the same set of axes. Explain how the shapes of the curves vary as p changes.

T 66. **Hyperbolas with a graphing utility** Use a graphing utility to graph the hyperbolas $r = \frac{e}{1 + e\cos\theta}$ for $e = 1.1, 1.3, 1.5, 1.7$, and 2 on the same set of axes. Explain how the shapes of the curves vary as e changes.

Further Explorations

67. **Explain why or why not** Determine whether the following statements are true and give an explanation or counterexample.
   a. The hyperbola $x^2/4 - y^2/9 = 1$ has no y-intercepts.
   b. On every ellipse, there are exactly two points at which the curve has slope s, where s is any real number.
   c. Given the directrices and foci of a standard hyperbola, it is possible to find its vertices, eccentricity, and asymptotes.
   d. The point on a parabola closest to the focus is the vertex.

68–71. Tangent lines *Find an equation of the line tangent to the following curves at the given point.*

68. $y^2 = 8x;\ (8, -8)$

69. $x^2 = -6y;\ (-6, -6)$

70. $r = \frac{1}{1 + \sin\theta};\ \left(\frac{2}{3}, \frac{\pi}{6}\right)$

71. $y^2 - \frac{x^2}{64} = 1;\ \left(6, -\frac{5}{4}\right)$

72–73. Graphs to polar equations *Find a polar equation for each conic section.*

72.

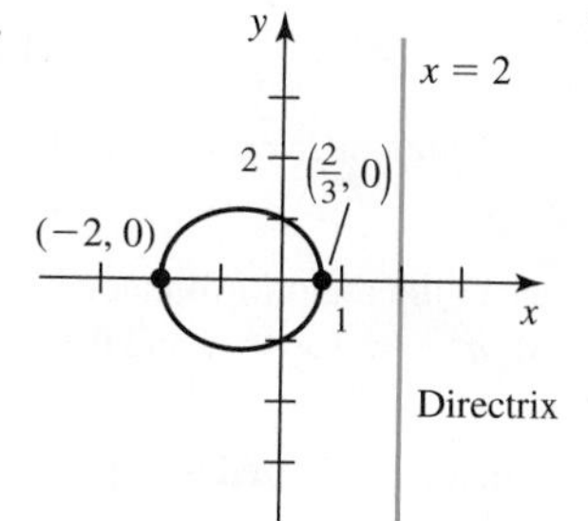

73.

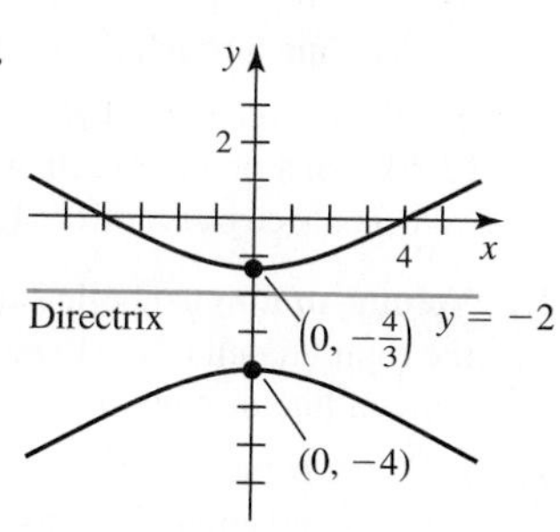

74. Deriving polar equations for conics Modify Figure 11.55 to derive the polar equation of a conic section with a focus at the origin in the following three cases.

a. Vertical directrix at $x = -d$, where $d > 0$
b. Horizontal directrix at $y = d$, where $d > 0$
c. Horizontal directrix at $y = -d$, where $d > 0$

75. Another construction for a hyperbola Suppose two circles are centered at F_1 and F_2, respectively, whose centers are at least $2a$ units apart (see figure). The radius of one circle is $2a + r$ and the radius of the other circle is r, where $r \geq 0$. Show that as r increases, the intersection point P of the two circles describes one branch of a hyperbola with foci at F_1 and F_2.

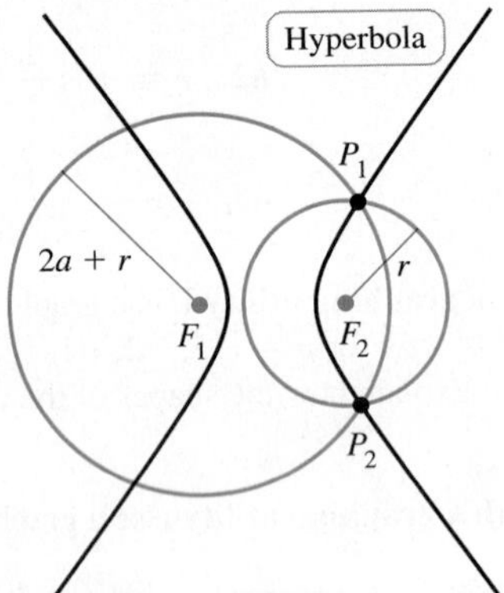

76. The ellipse and the parabola Let R be the region bounded by the upper half of the ellipse $x^2/2 + y^2 = 1$ and the parabola $y = x^2/\sqrt{2}$.

a. Find the area of R.
b. Which is greater, the volume of the solid generated when R is revolved about the x-axis or the volume of the solid generated when R is revolved about the y-axis?

77. Tangent lines for an ellipse Show that an equation of the line tangent to the ellipse $x^2/a^2 + y^2/b^2 = 1$ at the point (x_0, y_0) is

$$\frac{xx_0}{a^2} + \frac{yy_0}{b^2} = 1.$$

78. Tangent lines for a hyperbola Find an equation of the line tangent to the hyperbola $x^2/a^2 - y^2/b^2 = 1$ at the point (x_0, y_0).

79. Volume of an ellipsoid Suppose that the ellipse $x^2/a^2 + y^2/b^2 = 1$ is revolved about the x-axis. What is the volume of the *ellipsoid* that is generated? Is the volume different if the same ellipse is revolved about the y-axis?

80. Area of a sector of a hyperbola Consider the region R bounded by the right branch of the hyperbola $x^2/a^2 - y^2/b^2 = 1$ and the vertical line through the right focus.

a. What is the area of R?
b. Sketch a graph that shows how the area of R varies with the eccentricity e, for $e > 1$.

81. Volume of a hyperbolic cap Consider the region R bounded by the right branch of the hyperbola $x^2/a^2 - y^2/b^2 = 1$ and the vertical line through the right focus.

a. What is the volume of the solid that is generated when R is revolved about the x-axis?
b. What is the volume of the solid that is generated when R is revolved about the y-axis?

82. Volume of a paraboloid (Archimedes) The region bounded by the parabola $y = ax^2$ and the horizontal line $y = h$ is revolved about the y-axis to generate a solid bounded by a surface called a **paraboloid** (where $a > 0$ and $h > 0$). Show that the volume of the solid is $\frac{3}{2}$ the volume of the cone with the same base and vertex.

Applications

(See the Guided Projects for additional applications of conic sections.)

83. Reflection property of parabolas Consider the parabola $y = x^2/(4p)$ with its focus at $F(0, p)$ (see figure). We know that light is reflected from a surface in such a way that the angle of incidence equals the angle of reflection. The goal is to show that the angle between the ray ℓ and the tangent line L (α in the figure) equals the angle between the line PF and L (β in the figure). If these two angles are equal, then the reflection property is proved because ℓ is reflected through F.

a. Let $P(x_0, y_0)$ be a point on the parabola. Show that the slope of the line tangent to the curve at P is $\tan\theta = x_0/(2p)$.
b. Show that $\tan\varphi = (p - y_0)/x_0$.
c. Show that $\alpha = \pi/2 - \theta$; therefore, $\tan\alpha = \cot\theta$.
d. Note that $\beta = \theta + \varphi$. Use the tangent addition formula $\tan(\theta + \varphi) = \dfrac{\tan\theta + \tan\varphi}{1 - \tan\theta\tan\varphi}$ to show that $\tan\alpha = \tan\beta = 2p/x_0$.
e. Conclude that because α and β are acute angles, $\alpha = \beta$.

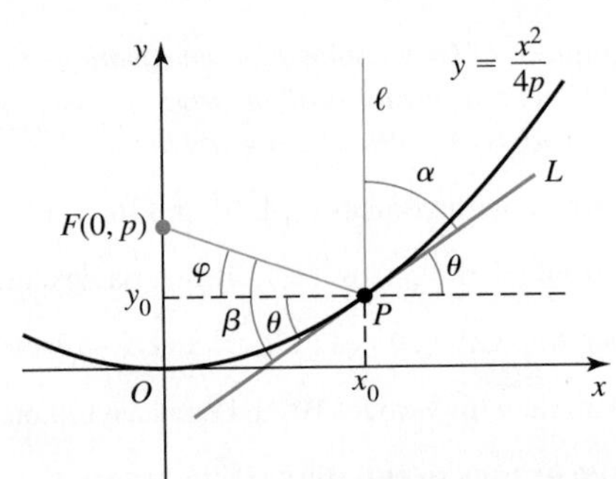

84. Golden Gate Bridge Completed in 1937, San Francisco's Golden Gate Bridge is 2.7 km long and weighs about 890,000 tons. The length of the span between the two central towers is 1280 m; the towers themselves extend 152 m above the roadway. The cables that support the deck of the bridge between the two towers hang in a parabola (see figure). Assuming the origin is midway between the towers on the deck of the bridge, find an equation that describes the cables. How long is a guy wire that hangs vertically from the cables to the roadway 500 m from the center of the bridge?

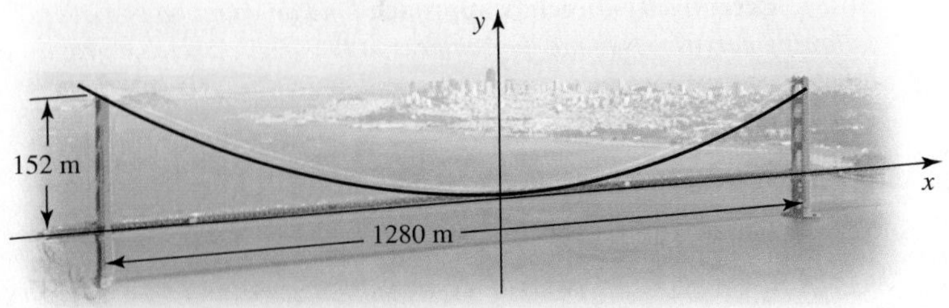

Additional Exercises

85. **Equation of an ellipse** Consider an ellipse to be the set of points in a plane whose distances from two fixed points have a constant sum $2a$. Derive the equation of an ellipse. Assume the two fixed points are on the x-axis equidistant from the origin.

86. **Equation of a hyperbola** Consider a hyperbola to be the set of points in a plane whose distances from two fixed points have a constant difference of $2a$ or $-2a$. Derive the equation of a hyperbola. Assume the two fixed points are on the x-axis equidistant from the origin.

87. **Equidistant set** Show that the set of points equidistant from a circle and a line not passing through the circle is a parabola.

88. **Polar equation of a conic** Show that the polar equation of an ellipse or hyperbola with one focus at the origin, major axis of length $2a$ on the x-axis, and eccentricity e is

$$r = \frac{a(1 - e^2)}{1 + e\cos\theta}.$$

89. **Shared asymptotes** Suppose that two hyperbolas with eccentricities e and E have perpendicular major axes and share a set of asymptotes. Show that $e^{-2} + E^{-2} = 1$.

90–94. Focal chords *A **focal chord** of a conic section is a line through a focus joining two points of the curve. The **latus rectum** is the focal chord perpendicular to the major axis of the conic. Prove the following properties.*

90. The lines tangent to the endpoints of any focal chord of a parabola $y^2 = 4px$ intersect on the directrix and are perpendicular.

91. Let L be the latus rectum of the parabola $y^2 = 4px$ for $p > 0$. Let F be the focus of the parabola, P be any point on the parabola to the left of L, and D be the (shortest) distance between P and L. Show that for all P, $D + |FP|$ is a constant. Find the constant.

92. The length of the latus rectum of the parabola $y^2 = 4px$ or $x^2 = 4py$ is $4|p|$.

93. The length of the latus rectum of an ellipse centered at the origin is $2b^2/a = 2b\sqrt{1 - e^2}$.

94. The length of the latus rectum of a hyperbola centered at the origin is $2b^2/a = 2b\sqrt{e^2 - 1}$.

95. **Confocal ellipse and hyperbola** Show that an ellipse and a hyperbola that have the same two foci intersect at right angles.

96. **Approach to asymptotes** Show that the vertical distance between a hyperbola $x^2/a^2 - y^2/b^2 = 1$ and its asymptote $y = bx/a$ approaches zero as $x \to \infty$, where $0 < b < a$.

97. **Sector of a hyperbola** Let H be the right branch of the hyperbola $x^2 - y^2 = 1$ and let ℓ be the line $y = m(x - 2)$ that passes through the point $(2, 0)$ with slope m, where $-\infty < m < \infty$. Let R be the region in the first quadrant bounded by H and ℓ (see figure). Let $A(m)$ be the area of R. Note that for some values of m, $A(m)$ is not defined.

 a. Find the x-coordinates of the intersection points between H and ℓ as functions of m; call them $u(m)$ and $v(m)$ where $v(m) > u(m) > 1$. For what values of m are there two intersection points?

 b. Evaluate $\lim\limits_{m\to 1^+} u(m)$ and $\lim\limits_{m\to 1^+} v(m)$.

 c. Evaluate $\lim\limits_{m\to\infty} u(m)$ and $\lim\limits_{m\to\infty} v(m)$.

 d. Evaluate and interpret $\lim\limits_{m\to\infty} A(m)$.

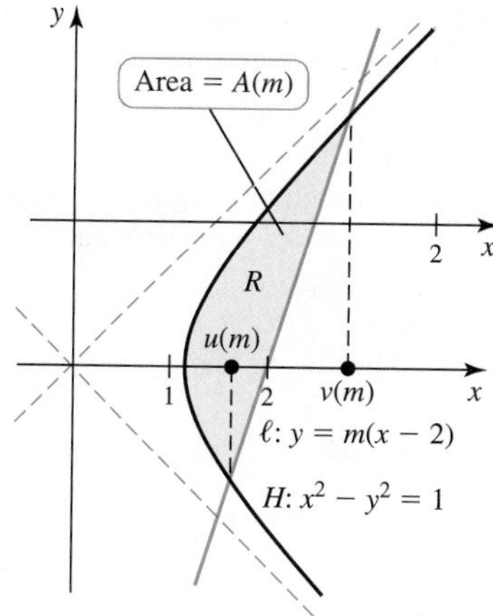

98. **The anvil of a hyperbola** Let H be the hyperbola $x^2 - y^2 = 1$ and let S be the 2-by-2 square bisected by the asymptotes of H. Let R be the anvil-shaped region bounded by the hyperbola and the horizontal lines $y = \pm p$ (see figure).

 a. For what value of p is the area of R equal to the area of S?

 b. For what value of p is the area of R twice the area of S?

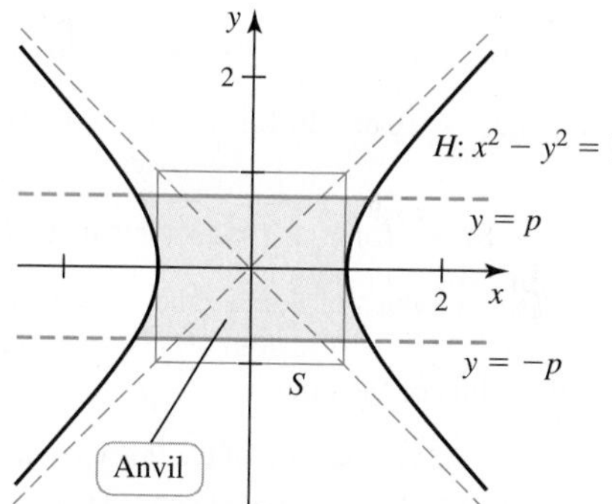

99. **Parametric equations for an ellipse** Consider the parametric equations

$$x = a\cos t + b\sin t, \qquad y = c\cos t + d\sin t,$$

where a, b, c, and d are real numbers.

 a. Show that (apart from a set of special cases) the equations describe an ellipse of the form $Ax^2 + Bxy + Cy^2 = K$, where A, B, C, and K are constants.

 b. Show that (apart from a set of special cases), the equations describe an ellipse with its axes aligned with the x- and y-axes provided $ab + cd = 0$.

 c. Show that the equations describe a circle provided $ab + cd = 0$ and $c^2 + d^2 = a^2 + b^2 \neq 0$.

QUICK CHECK ANSWERS

2. a. Left **b.** Up **3.** The minor-axis vertices are $(0, \pm b)$. The distance between them is $2b$, which is the length of the minor axis. **4.** Vertices: $(0, \pm 1)$; foci: $(0, \pm\sqrt{5})$ **5.** $b = 3\sqrt{3}/2$, $c = 3/2$, $d = 6$ **6.** y-axis

CHAPTER 11 REVIEW EXERCISES

1. **Explain why or why not** Determine whether the following statements are true and give an explanation or counterexample.
   a. A set of parametric equations for a given curve is always unique.
   b. The equations $x = e^t$, $y = 2e^t$ for $-\infty < t < \infty$ describe a line passing through the origin with slope 2.
   c. The polar coordinates $(3, -3\pi/4)$ and $(-3, \pi/4)$ describe the same point in the plane.
   d. The limaçon $r = f(\theta) = 1 - 4\cos\theta$ has an outer and inner loop. The area of the region between the two loops is $\frac{1}{2}\int_0^{2\pi}(f(\theta))^2\,d\theta$.
   e. The hyperbola $y^2/2 - x^2/4 = 1$ has no x-intercepts.
   f. The equation $x^2 + 4y^2 - 2x = 3$ describes an ellipse.

2–5. Parametric curves

a. Plot the following curves, indicating the positive orientation.
b. Eliminate the parameter to obtain an equation in x and y.
c. Identify or briefly describe the curve.
d. Evaluate dy/dx at the specified point.

2. $x = t^2 + 4$, $y = 6 - t$, for $-\infty < t < \infty$; evaluate dy/dx at $(5, 5)$.

3. $x = e^t$, $y = 3e^{-2t}$, for $-\infty < t < \infty$; evaluate dy/dx at $(1, 3)$.

4. $x = 10\sin 2t$, $y = 16\cos 2t$, for $0 \le t \le \pi$; evaluate dy/dx at $(5\sqrt{3}, 8)$.

5. $x = \ln t$, $y = 8\ln t^2$, for $1 \le t \le e^2$; evaluate dy/dx at $(1, 16)$.

6. **Circles** For what values of a, b, c, and d do the equations $x = a\cos t + b\sin t$, $y = c\cos t + d\sin t$ describe a circle? What is the radius of the circle?

T 7. **Tangent lines** Find an equation of the line tangent to the cycloid $x = t - \sin t$, $y = 1 - \cos t$ at the points corresponding to $t = \pi/6$ and $t = 2\pi/3$.

8–9. Sets in polar coordinates *Sketch the following sets of points.*

8. $\{(r, \theta): 4 \le r^2 \le 9\}$

9. $\{(r, \theta): 0 \le r \le 4, -\pi/2 \le \theta \le -\pi/3\}$

10. **Matching polar curves** Match equations a–f with graphs A–F.

a. $r = 3\sin 4\theta$ b. $r^2 = 4\cos\theta$
c. $r = 2 - 3\sin\theta$ d. $r = 1 + 2\cos\theta$
e. $r = 3\cos 3\theta$ f. $r = e^{-\theta/6}$

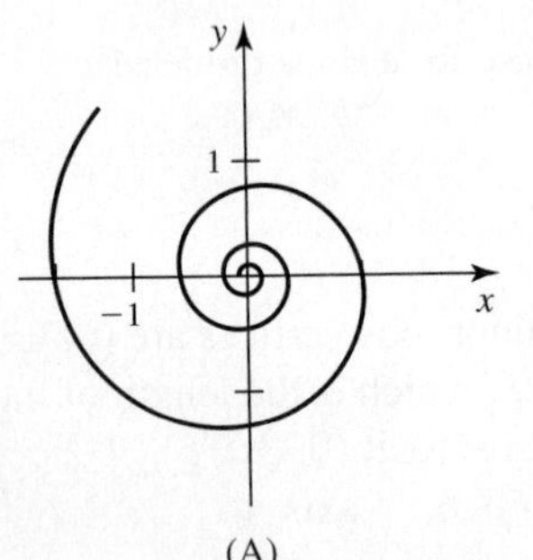

(A)

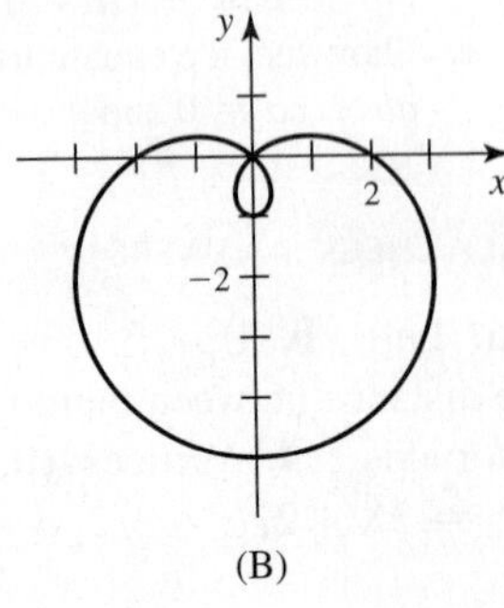

(B)

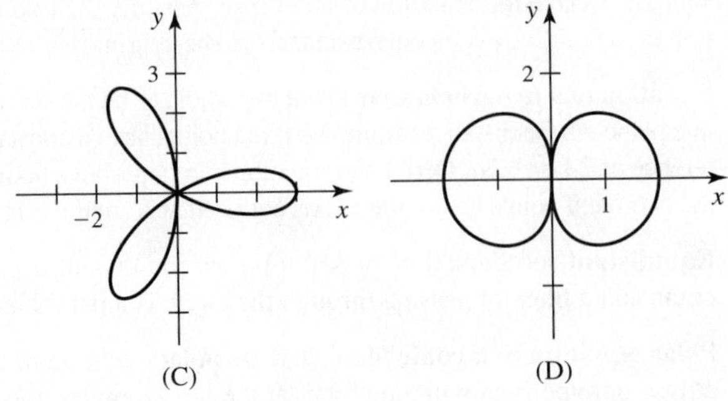

(C) (D)

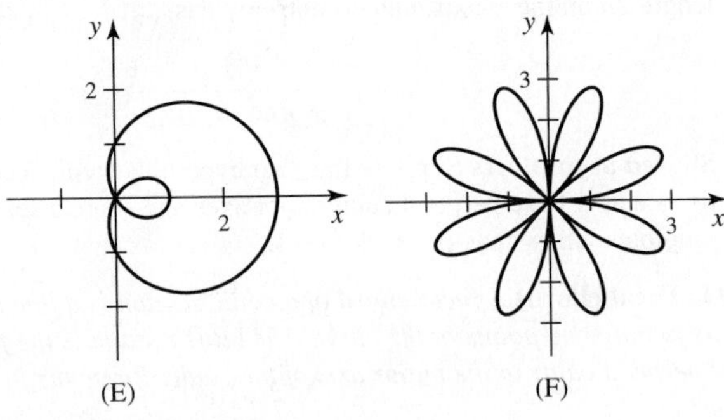

(E) (F)

11. **Polar conversion** Write the equation $r^2 + r(2\sin\theta - 6\cos\theta) = 0$ in Cartesian coordinates and identify the corresponding curve.

12. **Polar conversion** Consider the equation $r = 4/(\sin\theta - 6\cos\theta)$.
   a. Convert the equation to Cartesian coordinates and identify the curve it describes.
   b. Graph the curve and indicate the points that correspond to $\theta = 0, \pi/2$, and 2π.
   c. Give an interval in θ on which the entire curve is generated.

T 13. **Intersection points** Consider the equations $r = 1$ and $r = 2 - 4\cos\theta$.
   a. Graph the curves. How many intersection points do you observe?
   b. Give the approximate polar coordinates of the intersection points.

T **14–17. Slopes of tangent lines**

a. Find all points where the following curves have vertical and horizontal tangent lines.
b. Find the slope of the lines tangent to the curve at the origin (when relevant).
c. Sketch the curve and all the tangent lines identified in parts (a) and (b).

14. $r = 2\cos 2\theta$

15. $r = 4 + 2\sin\theta$

16. $r = 3 - 6\cos\theta$

17. $r^2 = 2\cos 2\theta$

18–21. Areas of regions *Find the area of the following regions. In each case, graph the curve(s) and shade the region in question.*

18. The region enclosed by all the leaves of the rose $r = 3\sin 4\theta$

19. The region enclosed by the limaçon $r = 3 - \cos\theta$

20. The region inside the limaçon $r = 2 + \cos\theta$ and outside the circle $r = 2$

21. The region inside the lemniscate $r^2 = 4\cos 2\theta$ and outside the circle $r = \frac{1}{2}$

22–27. Conic sections

a. Determine whether the following equations describe a parabola, an ellipse, or a hyperbola.
b. Use analytical methods to determine the location of the foci, vertices, and directrices.
c. Find the eccentricity of the curve.
d. Make an accurate graph of the curve

22. $x = 16y^2$
23. $x^2 - y^2/2 = 1$
24. $x^2/4 + y^2/25 = 1$
25. $y^2 - 4x^2 = 16$
26. $y = 8x^2 + 16x + 8$
27. $4x^2 + 8y^2 = 16$

28. **Matching equations and curves** Match equations a–f with graphs A–F.

a. $x^2 - y^2 = 4$
b. $x^2 + 4y^2 = 4$
c. $y^2 - 3x = 0$
d. $x^2 + 3y = 1$
e. $x^2/4 + y^2/8 = 1$
f. $y^2/8 - x^2/2 = 1$

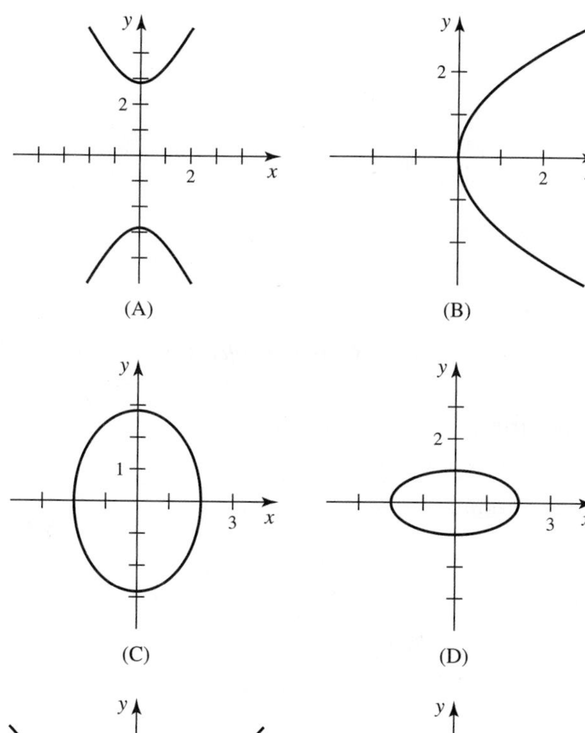

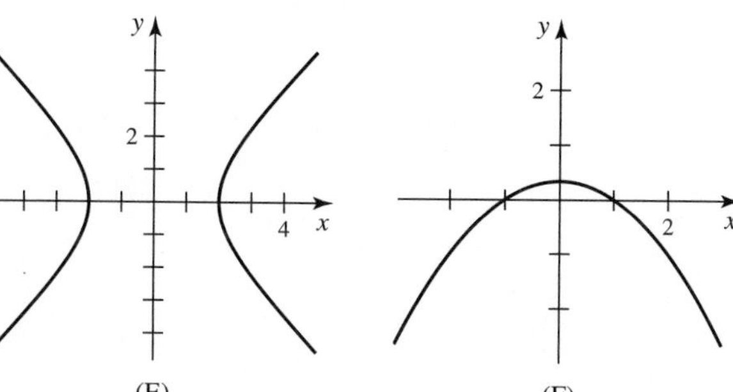

29–32. Tangent lines *Find an equation of the line tangent to the following curves at the given point. Check your work with a graphing utility.*

29. $y^2 = -12x;\ \left(-\frac{4}{3}, -4\right)$
30. $x^2 = 5y;\ \left(-2, \frac{4}{5}\right)$
31. $\frac{x^2}{100} + \frac{y^2}{64} = 1;\ \left(-6, -\frac{32}{5}\right)$
32. $\frac{x^2}{16} - \frac{y^2}{9} = 1;\ \left(\frac{20}{3}, -4\right)$

33–36. Polar equations for conic sections *Graph the following conic sections, labeling vertices, foci, directrices, and asymptotes (if they exist). Give the eccentricity of the curve. Use a graphing utility to check your work.*

33. $r = \frac{2}{1 + \sin\theta}$
34. $r = \frac{3}{1 - 2\cos\theta}$
35. $r = \frac{4}{2 + \cos\theta}$
36. $r = \frac{10}{5 + 2\cos\theta}$

37. **A polar conic section** Consider the equation $r^2 = \sec 2\theta$.
   a. Convert the equation to Cartesian coordinates and identify the curve.
   b. Find the vertices, foci, directrices, and eccentricity of the curve.
   c. Graph the curve. Explain why the polar equation does not have the form given in the text for conic sections in polar coordinates.

38–41. Eccentricity-directrix approach *Find an equation of the following curves, assuming the center is at the origin. Graph the curve, labeling vertices, foci, asymptotes (if they exist), and directrices.*

38. An ellipse with foci $(\pm 4, 0)$ and directrices $x = \pm 8$
39. An ellipse with vertices $(0, \pm 4)$ and directrices $y = \pm 10$
40. A hyperbola with vertices $(\pm 4, 0)$ and directrices $x = \pm 2$
41. A hyperbola with vertices $(0, \pm 2)$ and directrices $y = \pm 1$

42. **Conic parameters** A hyperbola has eccentricity $e = 2$ and foci $(0, \pm 2)$. Find the location of the vertices and directrices.

43. **Conic parameters** An ellipse has vertices $(0, \pm 6)$ and foci $(0, \pm 4)$. Find the eccentricity, the directrices and the minor axis vertices.

T **44–47. Intersection points** *Use analytical methods to find as many intersection points of the following curves as possible. Use methods of your choice to find the remaining intersection points.*

44. $r = 1 - \cos\theta$ and $r = \theta$
45. $r^2 = \sin 2\theta$ and $r = \theta$
46. $r^2 = \sin 2\theta$ and $r = 1 - 2\sin\theta$
47. $r = \theta/2$ and $r = -\theta$, for $\theta \geq 0$

48. **Area of an ellipse** Consider the polar equation of an ellipse $r = ed/(1 \pm e\cos\theta)$, where $0 < e < 1$. Evaluate an integral in polar coordinates to show that the area of the region enclosed by the ellipse is πab, where $2a$ and $2b$ are the lengths of the major and minor axes, respectively.

49. **Maximizing area** Among all rectangles centered at the origin with vertices on the ellipse $x^2/a^2 + y^2/b^2 = 1$, what are the dimensions of the rectangle with the maximum area (in terms of a and b)? What is that area?

50. Equidistant set Let S be the square centered at the origin with vertices $(\pm a, \pm a)$ and $(\pm a, \mp a)$. Describe and sketch the set of points that are equidistant from the square and the origin.

51. Bisecting an ellipse Let R be the region in the first quadrant bounded by the ellipse $x^2/a^2 + y^2/b^2 = 1$. Find the value of m (in terms of a and b) such that the line $y = mx$ divides R into two subregions of equal area.

52. Parabola-hyperbola tangency Let P be the parabola $y = px^2$ and H be the right half of the hyperbola $x^2 - y^2 = 1$.

a. For what value of p is P tangent to H?

b. At what point does the tangency occur?

c. Generalize your results for the hyperbola $x^2/a^2 - y^2/b^2 = 1$.

53. Another ellipse construction Start with two circles centered at the origin with radii $0 < a < b$ (see figure). Assume the line ℓ though the origin intersects the smaller circle at Q and the larger circle at R. Let $P(x, y)$ have the y-coordinate of Q and the x-coordinate of R. Show that the set of points $P(x, y)$ generated in this way for all lines ℓ through the origin is an ellipse.

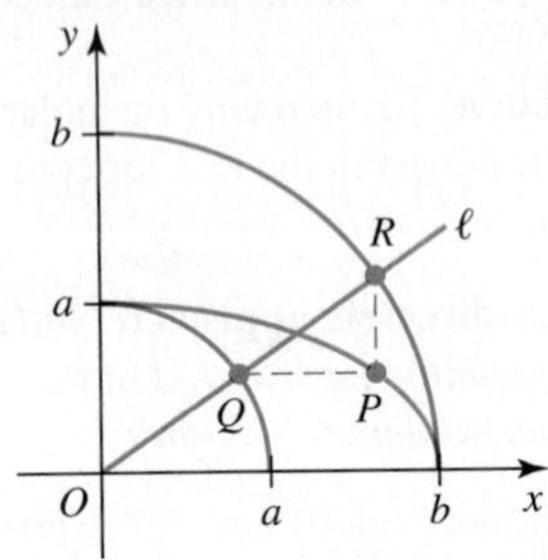

54–55. Graphs to polar equations *Find a polar equation for the coinc sections in the figures.*

54.

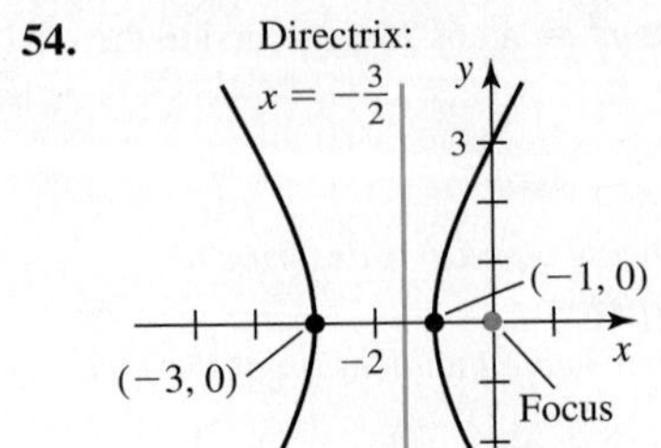

55.

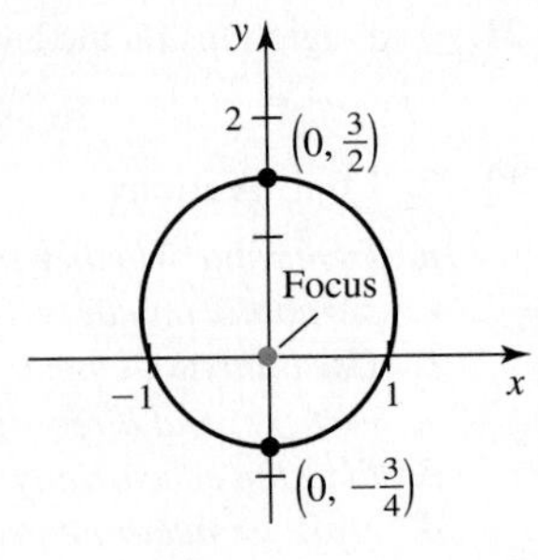

Chapter 11 Guided Projects

Applications of the material in this chapter and related topics can be found in the following Guided Projects. For additional information, see the Preface.

- The amazing cycloid
- Polar art
- Translations and rotations of axes
- Properties of conic sections
- Parametric art
- Grazing goat problems
- Celestial orbits

12

Vectors and Vector-Valued Functions

Chapter Preview We now make a significant departure from previous chapters by stepping out of the xy-plane into three-dimensional space. The fundamental concept of a *vector*—a quantity with magnitude and direction—is introduced in two and three dimensions. We then put vectors in motion by introducing *vector-valued functions,* or simply *vector functions.* The calculus of vector functions is a direct extension of everything you already know about limits, derivatives, and integrals. Also, with the calculus of vector functions, we can solve a wealth of practical problems involving the motion of objects in space. The chapter closes with an exploration of arc length, curvature, and tangent and normal vectors, all important features of space curves.

12.1 Vectors in the Plane

Imagine a raft drifting down a river, carried by the current. The speed and direction of the raft at a point may be represented by an arrow (Figure 12.1). The length of the arrow represents the speed of the raft at that point; longer arrows correspond to greater speeds. The orientation of the arrow gives the direction in which the raft is headed at that point. The arrows at points A and C in Figure 12.1 have the same length and direction indicating that the raft has the same speed and heading at these locations. The arrow at B is shorter and points to the left, indicating that the raft slows down as it nears the rock.

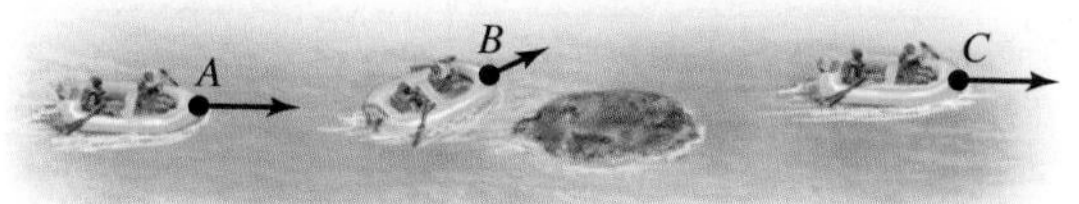

FIGURE 12.1

Basic Vector Operations

The arrows that describe the raft's motion are examples of **vectors**—quantities that have both **length** (or **magnitude**) and **direction**. Vectors arise naturally in many situations. For example, electric and magnetic fields, the flow of air over an airplane wing, and the velocity and acceleration of elementary particles are described by vectors (Figure 12.2). In this section we examine vectors in the xy-plane and then extend the concept to three dimensions in Section 12.2.

The vector whose *tail* is at the point P and whose *head* is at the point Q is denoted $\overrightarrow{PQ}$ (Figure 12.3). The vector $\overrightarrow{QP}$ has its tail at Q and its head at P. We also label vectors with single, boldfaced characters such as $\mathbf{u}$ and $\mathbf{v}$.

Two vectors $\mathbf{u}$ and $\mathbf{v}$ are **equal**, written $\mathbf{u} = \mathbf{v}$, if they have equal length and point in the same direction (Figure 12.4). An important fact is that equal vectors do not necessarily have the same location. *Any* two vectors with the same length and direction are equal.

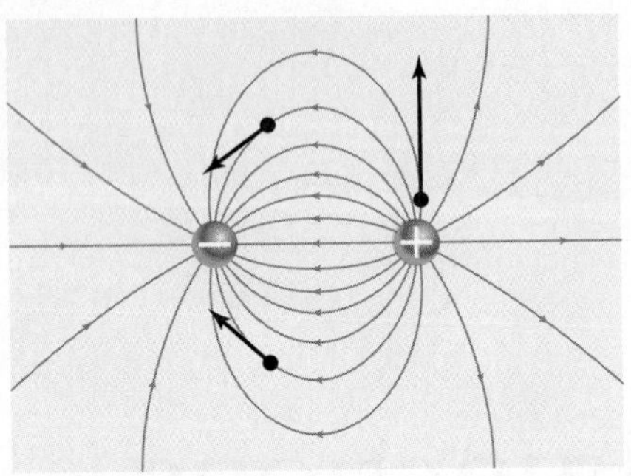

Electric field vectors due to two charges

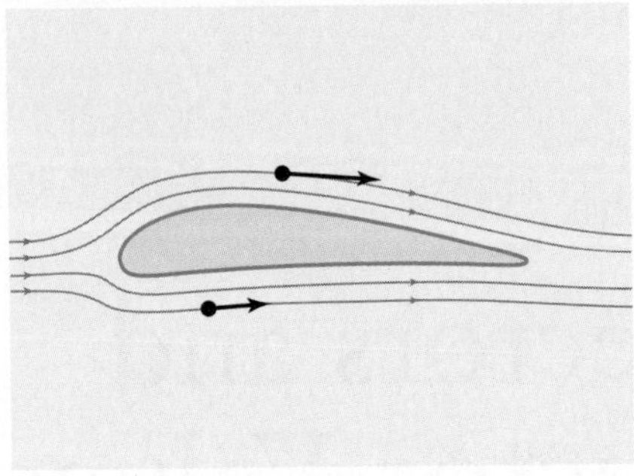

Velocity vectors of air flowing over an airplane wing

Tracks of elementary particles in a cloud chamber are aligned with the velocity vectors of the particles.

FIGURE 12.2

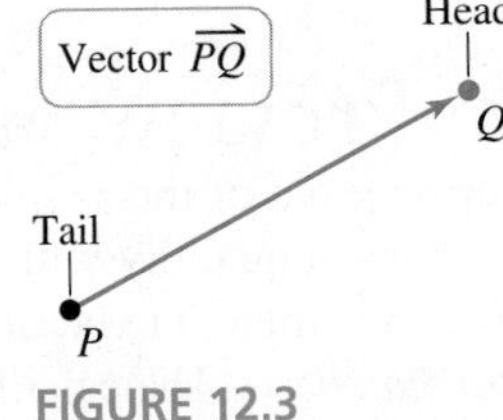
Vector $\overrightarrow{PQ}$
Head
Q
Tail
P

FIGURE 12.3

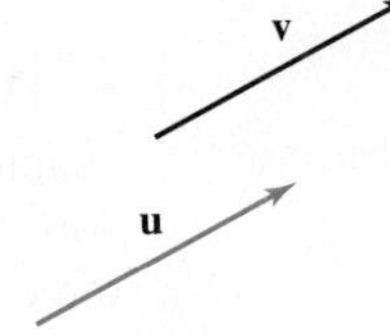
v
u
Vectors **u** and **v** are *equal* if they have the same length and direction.

FIGURE 12.4

➤ The vector **v** is commonly handwritten as $\vec{v}$.

Not all quantities are represented by vectors. For example, mass, temperature, and price have magnitude, but no direction. Such quantities are described by real numbers and are called *scalars*.

➤ In this book, *scalar* is another word for *real number*.

➤ The zero vector is handwritten $\vec{0}$.

Vectors, Equal Vectors, Scalars, Zero Vector

Vectors are quantities that have both length (or magnitude) and direction. Two vectors are **equal** if they have the same magnitude and direction. Quantities having magnitude but no direction are called **scalars**. One exception is the **zero vector**, denoted **0**: It has length 0 and no direction.

Scalar Multiplication

A scalar c and a vector **v** can be combined using **scalar-vector multiplication**, or simply **scalar multiplication**. The resulting vector, denoted $c\mathbf{v}$, is called a **scalar multiple** of **v**. The magnitude of $c\mathbf{v}$ is $|c|$ multiplied by the magnitude of **v**. The vector $c\mathbf{v}$ has the same direction as **v** if $c > 0$. If $c < 0$, then $c\mathbf{v}$ and **v** point in opposite directions. If $c = 0$, then $0 \cdot \mathbf{v} = \mathbf{0}$ (the zero vector).

For example, the vector $3\mathbf{v}$ is three times as long as **v** and has the same direction as **v**. The vector $-2\mathbf{v}$ is twice as long as **v**, but they point in opposite directions. The vector $\frac{1}{2}\mathbf{v}$ points in the same direction as **v** and has half the length of **v** (Figure 12.5). The vectors **v**, $3\mathbf{v}$, $-2\mathbf{v}$, and $\mathbf{v}/2$ (that is, $\frac{1}{2}\mathbf{v}$) are examples of *parallel vectors*: each one is a scalar multiple of the others.

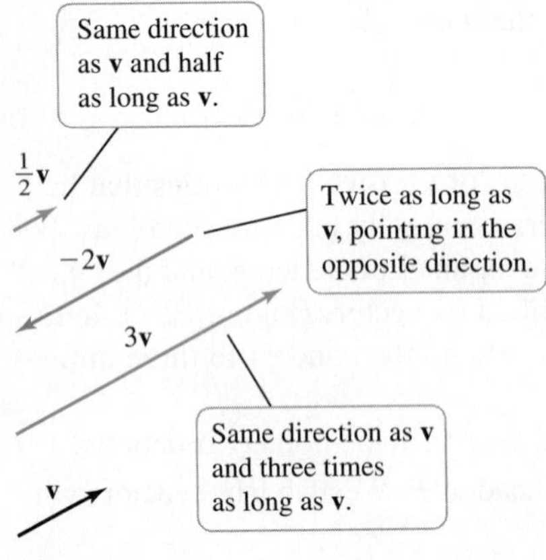
Same direction as **v** and half as long as **v**.
$\frac{1}{2}\mathbf{v}$
Twice as long as **v**, pointing in the opposite direction.
$-2\mathbf{v}$
$3\mathbf{v}$
Same direction as **v** and three times as long as **v**.
v

FIGURE 12.5

DEFINITION Scalar Multiples and Parallel Vectors

Given a scalar c and a vector **v**, the **scalar multiple** $c\mathbf{v}$ is a vector whose magnitude is $|c|$ multiplied by the magnitude of **v**. If $c > 0$, then $c\mathbf{v}$ has the same direction as **v**. If $c < 0$, then $c\mathbf{v}$ and **v** point in opposite directions. Two vectors are **parallel** if they are scalar multiples of each other.

➤ For convenience, we write $-\mathbf{u}$ for $(-1)\mathbf{u}$, $-c\mathbf{u}$ for $(-c)\mathbf{u}$, and $\mathbf{u}/c$ for $(1/c)\mathbf{u}$.

Notice that two vectors are parallel if they point in the same direction (for example, $\mathbf{v}$ and $12\mathbf{v}$) *or* if they point in opposite directions (for example, $\mathbf{v}$ and $-2\mathbf{v}$). Also, because $0\mathbf{v} = \mathbf{0}$ for all vectors $\mathbf{v}$, it follows that *the zero vector is parallel to all vectors*. While it may seem counterintuitive, this result turns out to be a useful convention.

QUICK CHECK 1 Describe the magnitude and direction of the vector $-5\mathbf{v}$ relative to $\mathbf{v}$. ◄

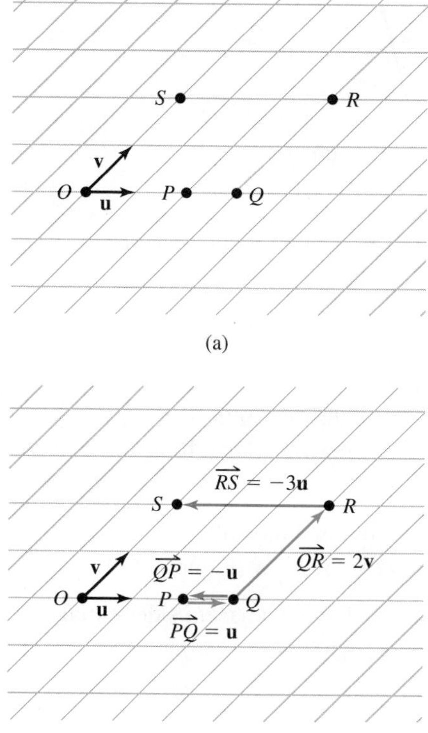

FIGURE 12.6

EXAMPLE 1 Parallel vectors Using Figure 12.6a, write the following vectors in terms of $\mathbf{u}$ or $\mathbf{v}$.

a. $\overrightarrow{PQ}$ **b.** $\overrightarrow{QP}$ **c.** $\overrightarrow{QR}$ **d.** $\overrightarrow{RS}$

SOLUTION

a. The vector $\overrightarrow{PQ}$ has the same direction and length as $\mathbf{u}$; therefore, $\overrightarrow{PQ} = \mathbf{u}$. These two vectors are equal even though they have different locations (Figure 12.6b).

b. Because $\overrightarrow{QP}$ and $\mathbf{u}$ have equal length, but opposite directions, $\overrightarrow{QP} = (-1)\mathbf{u} = -\mathbf{u}$.

c. $\overrightarrow{QR}$ points in the same direction as $\mathbf{v}$ and is twice as long as $\mathbf{v}$, so $\overrightarrow{QR} = 2\mathbf{v}$.

d. $\overrightarrow{RS}$ points in the direction opposite to that of $\mathbf{u}$ with three times the length of $\mathbf{u}$. Consequently, $\overrightarrow{RS} = -3\mathbf{u}$.

Related Exercises 17–18 ◄

Vector Addition and Subtraction

To illustrate the idea of vector addition, consider a plane flying horizontally at a constant speed in a crosswind (Figure 12.7). The length of vector $\mathbf{v}_a$ represents the plane's *airspeed*, which is the speed the plane would have in still air; $\mathbf{v}_a$ points in the direction of the nose of the plane. The wind vector $\mathbf{w}$ points in the direction of the crosswind and has a length equal to the speed of the crosswind. The combined effect of the motion of the plane and the wind is the *vector sum* $\mathbf{v}_g = \mathbf{v}_a + \mathbf{w}$, which is the velocity of the plane relative to the ground.

QUICK CHECK 2 Sketch the sum $\mathbf{v}_a + \mathbf{w}$ in Figure 12.7 if the direction of $\mathbf{w}$ is reversed. ◄

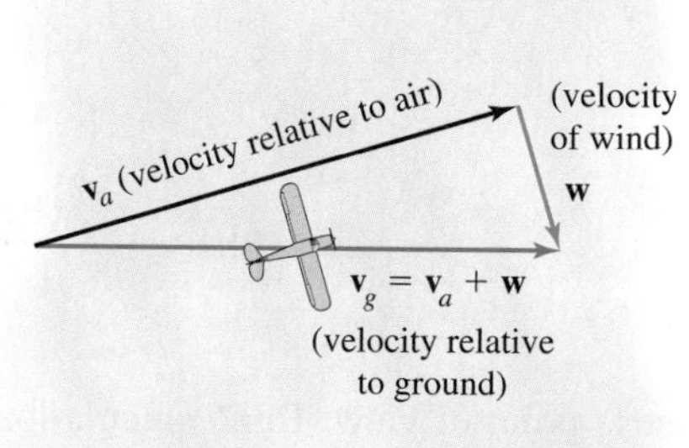

FIGURE 12.7

Figure 12.8 illustrates two ways to form the vector sum of two nonzero vectors $\mathbf{u}$ and $\mathbf{v}$ geometrically. The first method, called the **Triangle Rule**, places the tail of $\mathbf{v}$ at the head of $\mathbf{u}$. The sum $\mathbf{u} + \mathbf{v}$ is the vector that extends from the tail of $\mathbf{u}$ to the head of $\mathbf{v}$ (Figure 12.8b).

When $\mathbf{u}$ and $\mathbf{v}$ are not parallel, another way to form $\mathbf{u} + \mathbf{v}$ is to use the **Parallelogram Rule**. The *tails* of $\mathbf{u}$ and $\mathbf{v}$ are connected to form adjacent sides of a parallelogram; then, the remaining two sides of the parallelogram are sketched. The sum $\mathbf{u} + \mathbf{v}$ is the vector that coincides with the diagonal of the parallelogram, beginning at the tails of $\mathbf{u}$ and $\mathbf{v}$ (Figure 12.8c). The Triangle Rule and Parallelogram Rule each produce the same vector sum $\mathbf{u} + \mathbf{v}$.

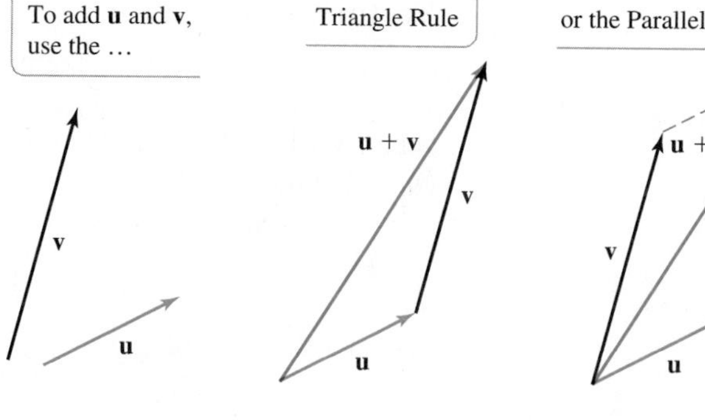

FIGURE 12.8

QUICK CHECK 3 Use the Triangle Rule to show that the vectors in Figure 12.8 satisfy $\mathbf{u} + \mathbf{v} = \mathbf{v} + \mathbf{u}$. ◄

The difference $\mathbf{u} - \mathbf{v}$ is defined to be the sum $\mathbf{u} + (-\mathbf{v})$. By the Triangle Rule, the tail of $-\mathbf{v}$ is placed at the head of $\mathbf{u}$; then, $\mathbf{u} - \mathbf{v}$ extends from the tail of $\mathbf{u}$ to the head of $-\mathbf{v}$ (Figure 12.9a). Equivalently, when the tails of $\mathbf{u}$ and $\mathbf{v}$ coincide, $\mathbf{u} - \mathbf{v}$ has its tail at the head of $\mathbf{v}$ and its head at the head of $\mathbf{u}$ (Figure 12.9b).

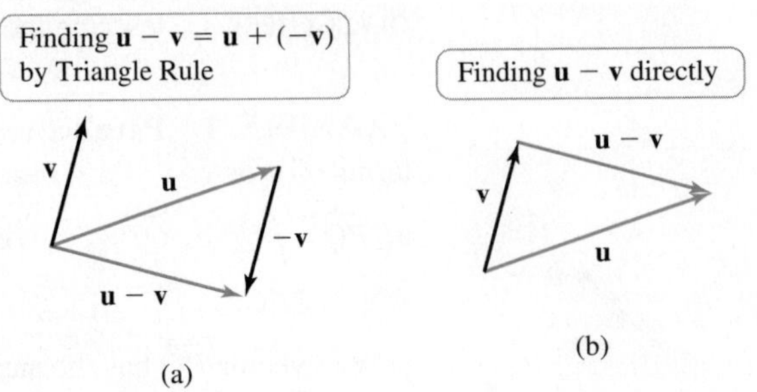

FIGURE 12.9

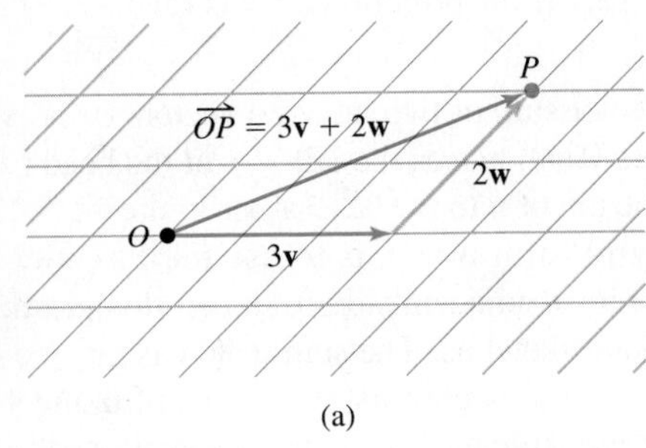

FIGURE 12.10

EXAMPLE 2 Vector operations Use Figure 12.10 to write the following vectors as sums of scalar multiples of $\mathbf{v}$ and $\mathbf{w}$.

a. $\overrightarrow{OP}$ **b.** $\overrightarrow{OQ}$ **c.** $\overrightarrow{QR}$

SOLUTION

a. Using the Triangle Rule, we start at O, move three lengths of $\mathbf{v}$ in the direction of $\mathbf{v}$ and then two lengths of $\mathbf{w}$ in the direction of $\mathbf{w}$ to reach P. Therefore, $\overrightarrow{OP} = 3\mathbf{v} + 2\mathbf{w}$ (Figure 12.11a).

b. The vector $\overrightarrow{OQ}$ coincides with the diagonal of a parallelogram having adjacent sides equal to $3\mathbf{v}$ and $-\mathbf{w}$. By the Parallelogram Rule, $\overrightarrow{OQ} = 3\mathbf{v} - \mathbf{w}$ (Figure 12.11b).

c. The vector $\overrightarrow{QR}$ lies on the diagonal of a parallelogram having adjacent sides equal to $\mathbf{v}$ and $2\mathbf{w}$. Therefore, $\overrightarrow{QR} = \mathbf{v} + 2\mathbf{w}$ (Figure 12.11c).

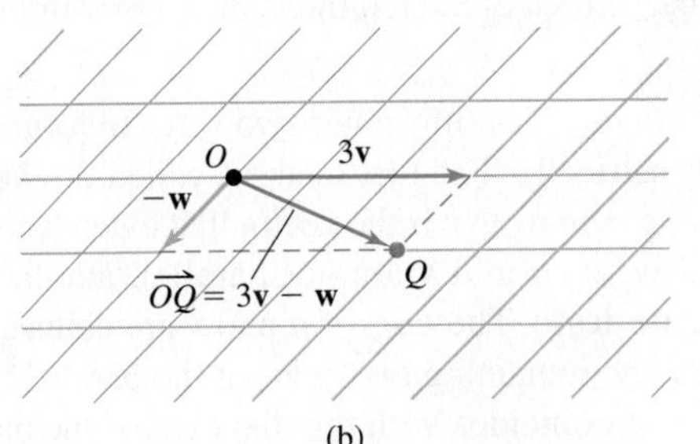

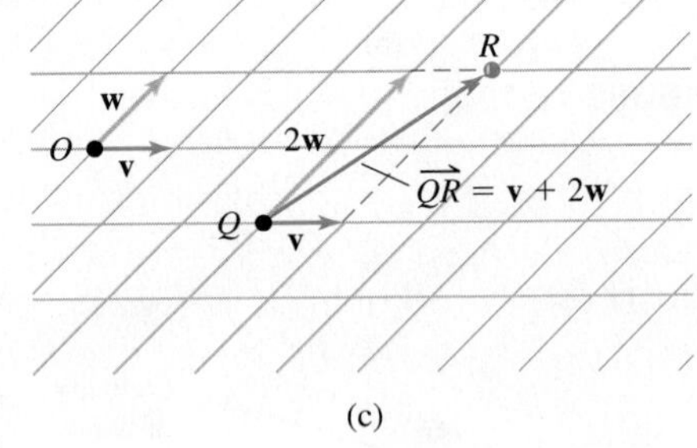

(a) $\overrightarrow{OP} = 3\mathbf{v} + 2\mathbf{w}$, P, 2w, O, 3v

FIGURE 12.11

Related Exercises 19–20 ◀

Vector Components

So far, vectors have been examined from a geometric point of view. To do calculations with vectors, it is necessary to introduce a coordinate system. We begin by considering a vector $\mathbf{v}$ whose tail is at the origin in the Cartesian plane and whose head is at the point (v_1, v_2) (Figure 12.12a).

> Round brackets (a, b) enclose the *coordinates* of a point, while angle brackets $\langle a, b \rangle$ enclose the *components* of a vector. Note that in component form, the zero vector is $\mathbf{0} = \langle 0, 0 \rangle$.

DEFINITION Position Vectors and Vector Components

A vector $\mathbf{v}$ with its tail at the origin and head at (v_1, v_2) is called a **position vector** (or is said to be in **standard position**) and is written $\langle v_1, v_2 \rangle$. The real numbers v_1 and v_2 are the x- and y-**components** of $\mathbf{v}$, respectively. The position vectors $\mathbf{u} = \langle u_1, u_2 \rangle$ and $\mathbf{v} = \langle v_1, v_2 \rangle$ are **equal** if and only if $u_1 = v_1$ and $u_2 = v_2$.

There are infinitely many vectors equal to the position vector $\mathbf{v}$, all with the same length and direction (Figure 12.12b). It is important to abide by the convention that $\mathbf{v} = \langle v_1, v_2 \rangle$ refers to the position vector $\mathbf{v}$ *or to any other vector equal to* $\mathbf{v}$.

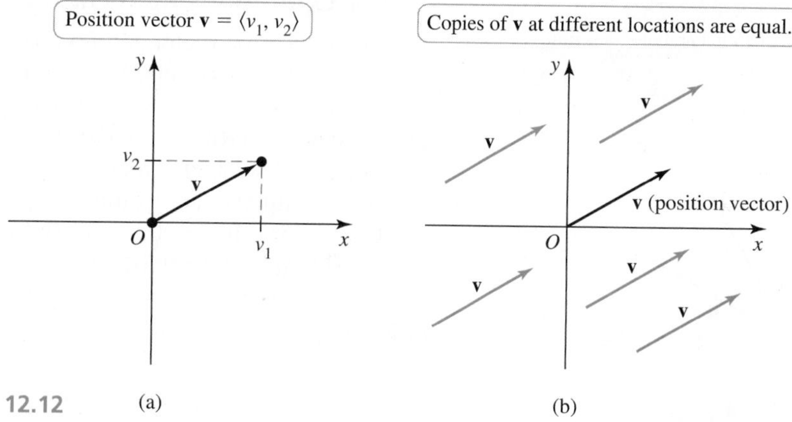

FIGURE 12.12 (a) (b)

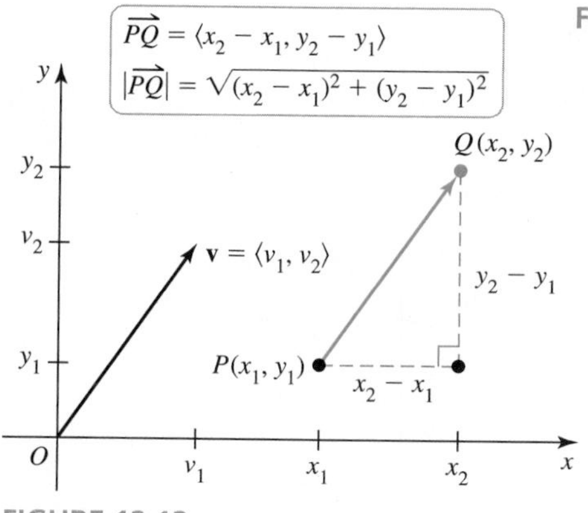

FIGURE 12.13

Now consider the vector $\overrightarrow{PQ}$, not in standard position, with its tail at the point $P(x_1, y_1)$ and its head at the point $Q(x_2, y_2)$. The x-component of $\overrightarrow{PQ}$ is the difference in the x-coordinates of Q and P, or $x_2 - x_1$. The y-component of $\overrightarrow{PQ}$ is the difference in the y-coordinates, $y_2 - y_1$ (Figure 12.13). Therefore, $\overrightarrow{PQ}$ has the same length and direction as the position vector $\langle v_1, v_2 \rangle = \langle x_2 - x_1, y_2 - y_1 \rangle$, and we write $\overrightarrow{PQ} = \langle x_2 - x_1, y_2 - y_1 \rangle$.

QUICK CHECK 4 Given the points $P(2, 3)$ and $Q(-4, 1)$, find the components of $\overrightarrow{PQ}$.

As already noted, there are infinitely many vectors equal to a given position vector. All these vectors have the same length and direction; therefore, they are all equal. In other words, two arbitrary vectors are **equal** if they are equal to the same position vector. For example, the vector $\overrightarrow{PQ}$ from $P(2, 5)$ to $Q(6, 3)$ and the vector $\overrightarrow{AB}$ from $A(7, 12)$ to $B(11, 10)$ are equal because they are both equal to the position vector $\langle 4, -2 \rangle$.

Magnitude

The magnitude of a vector is simply its length. By the Pythagorean Theorem and Figure 12.13, we have the following definition.

> Just as the absolute value $|p - q|$ gives the distance between two points on the number line, the magnitude $|\overrightarrow{PQ}|$ is the distance between the points P and Q. The magnitude of a vector is also called its **norm**.

DEFINITION Magnitude of a Vector

Given the points $P(x_1, y_1)$ and $Q(x_2, y_2)$, the **magnitude**, or **length**, of $\overrightarrow{PQ} = \langle x_2 - x_1, y_2 - y_1 \rangle$, denoted $|\overrightarrow{PQ}|$, is the distance between P and Q:

$$|\overrightarrow{PQ}| = \sqrt{(x_2 - x_1)^2 + (y_2 - y_1)^2}$$

The magnitude of the position vector $\mathbf{v} = \langle v_1, v_2 \rangle$ is $|\mathbf{v}| = \sqrt{v_1^2 + v_2^2}$.

EXAMPLE 3 **Calculating components and magnitude** Given the points $O(0,0)$, $P(-3,4)$, and $Q(6,5)$, find the components and magnitudes of the following vectors.

a. $\overrightarrow{OP}$ **b.** $\overrightarrow{PQ}$

SOLUTION

a. The vector $\overrightarrow{OP}$ is the position vector whose head is located at $P(-3,4)$. Therefore, $\overrightarrow{OP} = \langle -3, 4\rangle$ and $|\overrightarrow{OP}| = \sqrt{(-3)^2 + 4^2} = 5$.

b. $\overrightarrow{PQ} = \langle 6 - (-3), 5 - 4\rangle = \langle 9, 1\rangle$ and $|\overrightarrow{PQ}| = \sqrt{9^2 + 1^2} = \sqrt{82}$.

Related Exercises 21–25 ◀

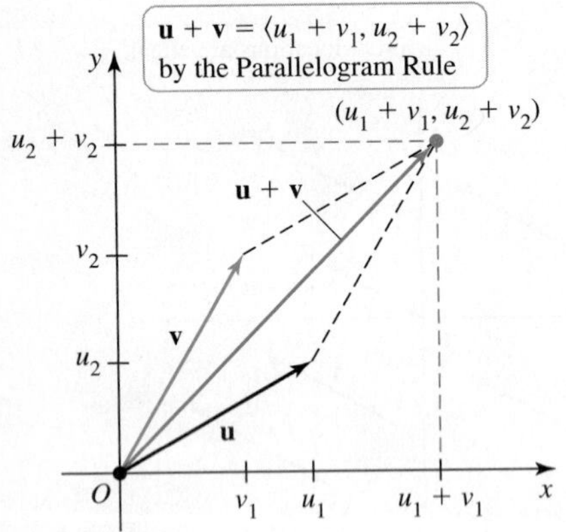

FIGURE 12.14

Vector Operations in Terms of Components

We now show how vector addition, vector subtraction, and scalar multiplication are performed using components. Suppose $\mathbf{u} = \langle u_1, u_2\rangle$ and $\mathbf{v} = \langle v_1, v_2\rangle$. The vector sum of $\mathbf{u}$ and $\mathbf{v}$ is $\mathbf{u} + \mathbf{v} = \langle u_1 + v_1, u_2 + v_2\rangle$. This definition of a vector sum is consistent with the Parallelogram Rule given earlier (Figure 12.14).

For a scalar c and a vector $\mathbf{u}$, the scalar multiple $c\mathbf{u}$ is $c\mathbf{u} = \langle cu_1, cu_2\rangle$; that is, the scalar c multiplies each component of $\mathbf{u}$. If $c > 0$, $\mathbf{u}$ and $c\mathbf{u}$ have the same direction (Figure 12.15a). If $c < 0$, $\mathbf{u}$ and $c\mathbf{u}$ have opposite directions (Figure 12.15b). In either case, $|c\mathbf{u}| = |c||\mathbf{u}|$ (Exercise 81).

Notice that $\mathbf{u} - \mathbf{v} = \mathbf{u} + (-\mathbf{v})$, where $-\mathbf{v} = \langle -v_1, -v_2\rangle$. Therefore, the vector difference of $\mathbf{u}$ and $\mathbf{v}$ is $\mathbf{u} - \mathbf{v} = \langle u_1 - v_1, u_2 - v_2\rangle$.

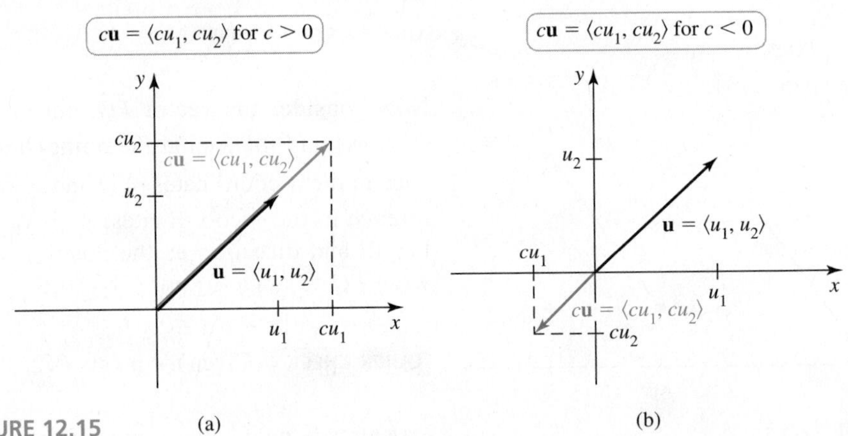

FIGURE 12.15

> **Vector Operations**
>
> Suppose c is a scalar, $\mathbf{u} = \langle u_1, u_2\rangle$, and $\mathbf{v} = \langle v_1, v_2\rangle$.
>
> $\mathbf{u} + \mathbf{v} = \langle u_1 + v_1, u_2 + v_2\rangle$ Vector addition
>
> $\mathbf{u} - \mathbf{v} = \langle u_1 - v_1, u_2 - v_2\rangle$ Vector subtraction
>
> $c\mathbf{u} = \langle cu_1, cu_2\rangle$ Scalar multiplication

EXAMPLE 4 **Vector operations** Let $\mathbf{u} = \langle -1, 2\rangle$ and $\mathbf{v} = \langle 2, 3\rangle$.

a. Evaluate $|\mathbf{u} + \mathbf{v}|$. **b.** Simplify $2\mathbf{u} - 3\mathbf{v}$.

c. Find two vectors half as long as $\mathbf{u}$ and parallel to $\mathbf{u}$.

SOLUTION

a. Because $\mathbf{u} + \mathbf{v} = \langle -1, 2\rangle + \langle 2, 3\rangle = \langle 1, 5\rangle$, we have $|\mathbf{u} + \mathbf{v}| = \sqrt{1^2 + 5^2} = \sqrt{26}$.

b. $2\mathbf{u} - 3\mathbf{v} = 2\langle -1, 2\rangle - 3\langle 2, 3\rangle = \langle -2, 4\rangle - \langle 6, 9\rangle = \langle -8, -5\rangle$.

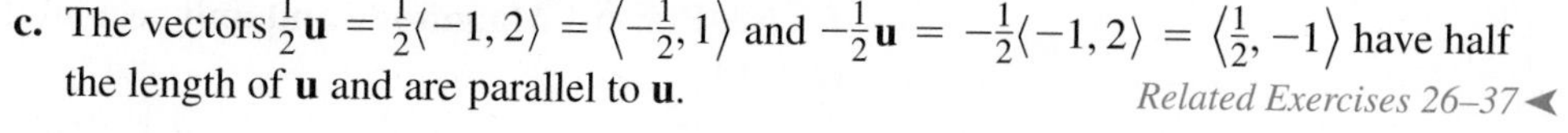

c. The vectors $\frac{1}{2}\mathbf{u} = \frac{1}{2}\langle -1, 2\rangle = \left\langle -\frac{1}{2}, 1\right\rangle$ and $-\frac{1}{2}\mathbf{u} = -\frac{1}{2}\langle -1, 2\rangle = \left\langle \frac{1}{2}, -1\right\rangle$ have half the length of $\mathbf{u}$ and are parallel to $\mathbf{u}$.

Related Exercises 26–37 ◀

Unit Vectors

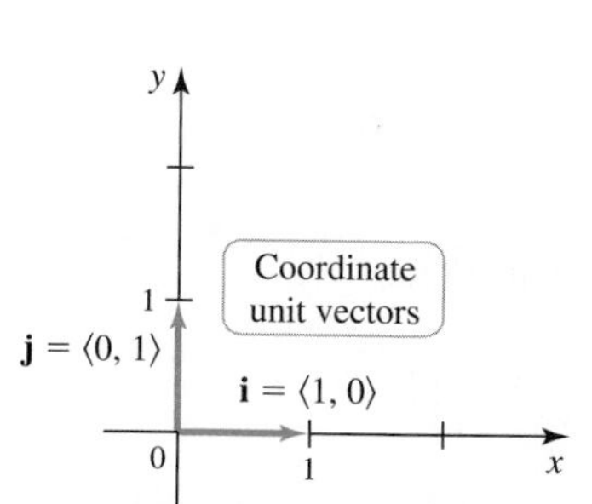

FIGURE 12.16

A **unit vector** is any vector with length 1. Two useful unit vectors are the **coordinate unit vectors** $\mathbf{i} = \langle 1, 0\rangle$ and $\mathbf{j} = \langle 0, 1\rangle$ (Figure 12.16). These vectors are directed along the coordinate axes and allow us to express all vectors in an alternate form. For example, by the Triangle Rule (Figure 12.17a),

$$\langle 3, 4\rangle = 3\langle 1, 0\rangle + 4\langle 0, 1\rangle = 3\mathbf{i} + 4\mathbf{j}.$$

In general, the vector $\mathbf{v} = \langle v_1, v_2\rangle$ (Figure 12.17b) is also written

$$\mathbf{v} = v_1\langle 1, 0\rangle + v_2\langle 0, 1\rangle = v_1\mathbf{i} + v_2\mathbf{j}.$$

➤ Coordinate unit vectors are also called **standard basis vectors**.

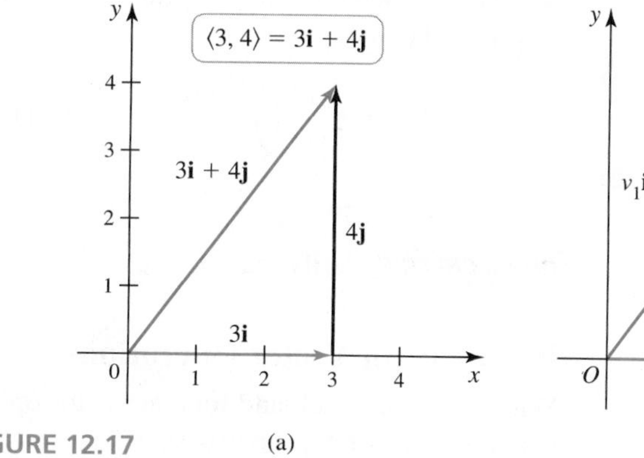
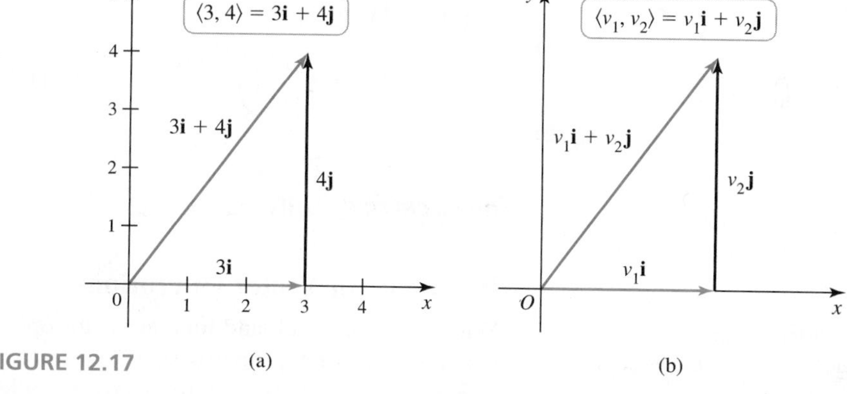
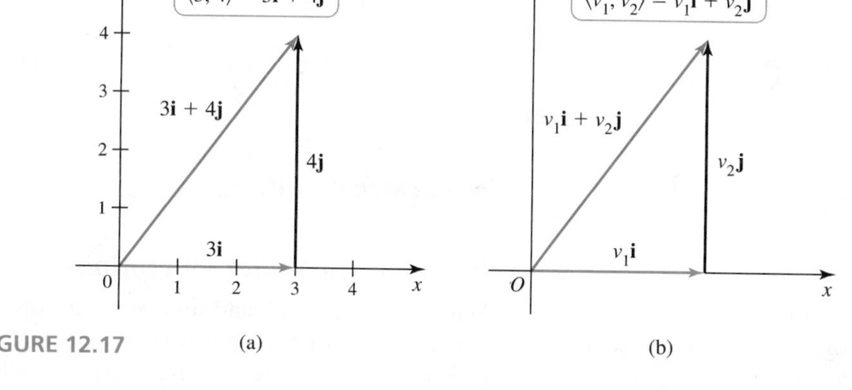

FIGURE 12.17 (a) (b)

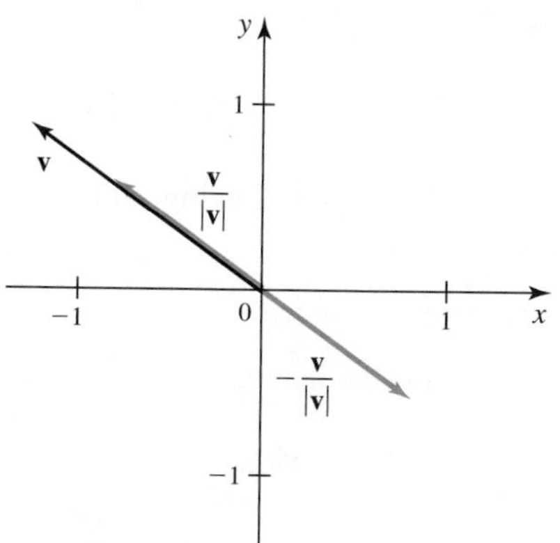

FIGURE 12.18

Given a nonzero vector $\mathbf{v}$, we sometimes need to construct a new vector parallel to $\mathbf{v}$ of a specified length. Dividing $\mathbf{v}$ by its length, we obtain the vector $\mathbf{u} = \frac{\mathbf{v}}{|\mathbf{v}|}$. Because $\mathbf{u}$ is a positive scalar multiple of $\mathbf{v}$, it follows that $\mathbf{u}$ has the same direction as $\mathbf{v}$. Furthermore, $\mathbf{u}$ is a unit vector because $|\mathbf{u}| = \frac{|\mathbf{v}|}{|\mathbf{v}|} = 1$. The vector $-\mathbf{u} = -\frac{\mathbf{v}}{|\mathbf{v}|}$ is also a unit vector (Figure 12.18). Therefore, $\pm\frac{\mathbf{v}}{|\mathbf{v}|}$ are unit vectors parallel to $\mathbf{v}$ that point in opposite directions.

To construct a vector that points in the direction of $\mathbf{v}$ and has a specified length $c > 0$, we form the vector $\frac{c\mathbf{v}}{|\mathbf{v}|}$: It is a positive scalar multiple of $\mathbf{v}$, so it points in the direction of $\mathbf{v}$, and its length is $\left|\frac{c\mathbf{v}}{|\mathbf{v}|}\right| = |c|\frac{|\mathbf{v}|}{|\mathbf{v}|} = c$. The vector $-\frac{c\mathbf{v}}{|\mathbf{v}|}$ points in the opposite direction and also has length c.

> **DEFINITION Unit Vectors and Vectors of a Specified Length**
>
> A **unit vector** is any vector with length 1. Given a nonzero vector $\mathbf{v}$, $\pm\frac{\mathbf{v}}{|\mathbf{v}|}$ are unit vectors parallel to $\mathbf{v}$. For a scalar $c > 0$, the vectors $\pm\frac{c\mathbf{v}}{|\mathbf{v}|}$ are vectors of length c parallel to $\mathbf{v}$.

QUICK CHECK 5 Find vectors of length 10 parallel to the unit vector $\mathbf{u} = \left\langle \frac{3}{5}, \frac{4}{5}\right\rangle$. ◀

EXAMPLE 5 **Magnitude and unit vectors** Consider the points $P(1, -2)$ and $Q(6, 10)$.

a. Find $\overrightarrow{PQ}$ and two unit vectors parallel to $\overrightarrow{PQ}$.

b. Find two vectors of length 2 parallel to $\overrightarrow{PQ}$.

SOLUTION

a. $\overrightarrow{PQ} = \langle 6 - 1, 10 - (-2) \rangle = \langle 5, 12 \rangle$, or $5\mathbf{i} + 12\mathbf{j}$. Because $|\overrightarrow{PQ}| = \sqrt{5^2 + 12^2} = \sqrt{169} = 13$, a unit vector parallel to $\overrightarrow{PQ}$ is

$$\frac{\overrightarrow{PQ}}{|\overrightarrow{PQ}|} = \frac{\langle 5, 12 \rangle}{13} = \left\langle \frac{5}{13}, \frac{12}{13} \right\rangle = \frac{5}{13}\mathbf{i} + \frac{12}{13}\mathbf{j}.$$

Another unit vector parallel to $\overrightarrow{PQ}$ but having the opposite direction is $\left\langle -\frac{5}{13}, -\frac{12}{13} \right\rangle$.

b. To obtain two vectors of length 2 that are parallel to $\overrightarrow{PQ}$, we multiply the unit vector $\frac{5}{13}\mathbf{i} + \frac{12}{13}\mathbf{j}$ by ± 2:

$$2\left(\frac{5}{13}\mathbf{i} + \frac{12}{13}\mathbf{j}\right) = \frac{10}{13}\mathbf{i} + \frac{24}{13}\mathbf{j} \quad \text{and} \quad -2\left(\frac{5}{13}\mathbf{i} + \frac{12}{13}\mathbf{j}\right) = -\frac{10}{13}\mathbf{i} - \frac{24}{13}\mathbf{j}$$

Related Exercises 38–43 ◀

QUICK CHECK 6 Verify that the vector $\left\langle \frac{5}{13}, \frac{12}{13} \right\rangle$ has length 1. ◀

Properties of Vector Operations

➤ The Parallelogram Rule illustrates the commutative property $\mathbf{u} + \mathbf{v} = \mathbf{v} + \mathbf{u}$.

When we stand back and look at vector operations, ten general properties emerge. For example, the first property says that vector addition is commutative, which means $\mathbf{u} + \mathbf{v} = \mathbf{v} + \mathbf{u}$. This property is proved by letting $\mathbf{u} = \langle u_1, u_2 \rangle$ and $\mathbf{v} = \langle v_1, v_2 \rangle$. By the commutative property of addition for real numbers,

$$\mathbf{u} + \mathbf{v} = \langle u_1 + v_1, u_2 + v_2 \rangle = \langle v_1 + u_1, v_2 + u_2 \rangle = \mathbf{v} + \mathbf{u}.$$

The proofs of other properties are outlined in Exercises 75–79.

SUMMARY **Properties of Vector Operations**

Suppose $\mathbf{u}$, $\mathbf{v}$, and $\mathbf{w}$ are vectors and a and c are scalars. Then the following properties hold (for vectors in any number of dimensions).

1. $\mathbf{u} + \mathbf{v} = \mathbf{v} + \mathbf{u}$	Commutative property of addition
2. $(\mathbf{u} + \mathbf{v}) + \mathbf{w} = \mathbf{u} + (\mathbf{v} + \mathbf{w})$	Associative property of addition
3. $\mathbf{v} + \mathbf{0} = \mathbf{v}$	Additive identity
4. $\mathbf{v} + (-\mathbf{v}) = \mathbf{0}$	Additive inverse
5. $c(\mathbf{u} + \mathbf{v}) = c\mathbf{u} + c\mathbf{v}$	Distributive property 1
6. $(a + c)\mathbf{v} = a\mathbf{v} + c\mathbf{v}$	Distributive property 2
7. $0\mathbf{v} = \mathbf{0}$	Multiplication by zero scalar
8. $c\mathbf{0} = \mathbf{0}$	Multiplication by zero vector
9. $1\mathbf{v} = \mathbf{v}$	Multiplicative identity
10. $a(c\mathbf{v}) = (ac)\mathbf{v}$	Associative property of scalar multiplication

These properties allow us to solve vector equations. For example, to solve the equation $\mathbf{u} + \mathbf{v} = \mathbf{w}$ for $\mathbf{u}$, we proceed as follows:

$$
\begin{aligned}
(\mathbf{u} + \mathbf{v}) + (-\mathbf{v}) &= \mathbf{w} + (-\mathbf{v}) && \text{Add } -\mathbf{v} \text{ to both sides.} \\
\mathbf{u} + \underbrace{[\mathbf{v} + (-\mathbf{v})]}_{\mathbf{0}} &= \mathbf{w} + (-\mathbf{v}) && \text{Property 2} \\
\mathbf{u} + \mathbf{0} &= \mathbf{w} - \mathbf{v} && \text{Property 4} \\
\mathbf{u} &= \mathbf{w} - \mathbf{v} && \text{Property 3}
\end{aligned}
$$

QUICK CHECK 7 Solve $3\mathbf{u} + 4\mathbf{v} = 12\mathbf{w}$ for $\mathbf{u}$.

Applications of Vectors

Vectors have countless practical applications, particularly in the physical sciences and engineering. These applications are explored throughout the remainder of the book. For now we present two common uses of vectors: to describe velocities and forces.

Velocity Vectors Consider a motorboat crossing a river whose current is everywhere represented by the constant vector $\mathbf{w}$ (Figure 12.19); this means that $|\mathbf{w}|$ is the speed of the moving water and $\mathbf{w}$ points in the direction of the moving water. Assume that the vector $\mathbf{v}_w$ gives the direction and speed of the boat relative to the water. The combined effect of $\mathbf{w}$ and $\mathbf{v}_w$ is the sum $\mathbf{v}_g = \mathbf{v}_w + \mathbf{w}$, which gives the speed and direction of the boat that would be observed by someone on the shore (or on the ground).

> *Speed of the boat relative to the water* means the speed the boat would have in still water (or relative to someone traveling with the current).

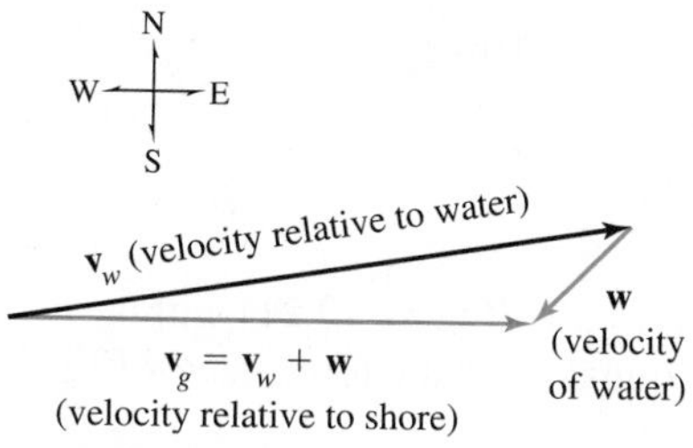

FIGURE 12.19

EXAMPLE 6 Speed of a boat in a current Assume the water in a river moves southwest (45° west of south) at 4 mi/hr. If a motorboat is traveling due east at 15 mi/hr relative to the shore, determine the speed of the boat and its heading relative to the moving water (Figure 12.19).

SOLUTION To solve this problem, the vectors are placed in a coordinate system (Figure 12.20). Because the boat is moving east at 15 mi/hr, $\mathbf{v}_g = \langle 15, 0 \rangle$. To obtain the components of $\mathbf{w} = \langle w_x, w_y \rangle$, observe that $|\mathbf{w}| = 4$ and the lengths of the sides of the 45–45–90 triangle in Figure 12.20 are

$$|w_x| = |w_y| = |\mathbf{w}| \cos 45° = \frac{4}{\sqrt{2}} = 2\sqrt{2}.$$

> Recall that the lengths of the legs of a 45–45–90 triangle are equal and are $(1/\sqrt{2})$ times the length of the hypotenuse.

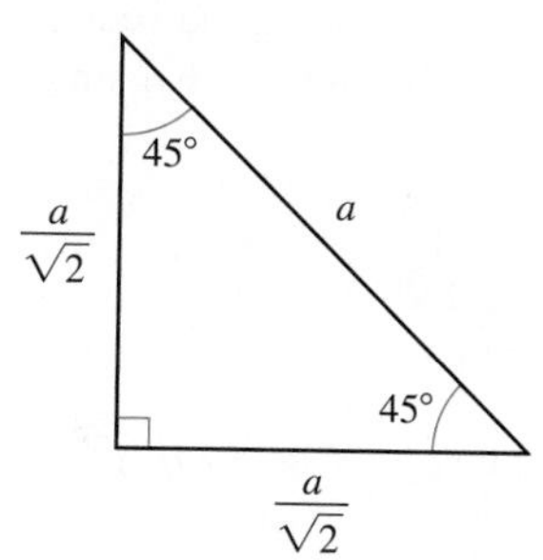

Given the orientation of $\mathbf{w}$ (southwest), $\mathbf{w} = \langle -2\sqrt{2}, -2\sqrt{2} \rangle$. Because $\mathbf{v}_g = \mathbf{v}_w + \mathbf{w}$ (Figure 12.19),

$$
\begin{aligned}
\mathbf{v}_w = \mathbf{v}_g - \mathbf{w} &= \langle 15, 0 \rangle - \langle -2\sqrt{2}, -2\sqrt{2} \rangle \\
&= \langle 15 + 2\sqrt{2}, 2\sqrt{2} \rangle.
\end{aligned}
$$

The magnitude of $\mathbf{v}_w$ is

$$|\mathbf{v}_w| = \sqrt{(15 + 2\sqrt{2})^2 + (2\sqrt{2})^2} \approx 18.$$

Therefore, the speed of the boat relative to the water is approximately 18 mi/hr.

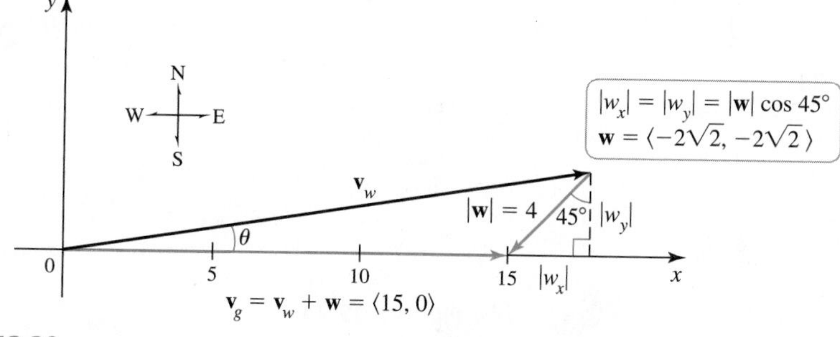

FIGURE 12.20

The heading of the boat is given by the angle θ between $\mathbf{v}_w$ and the positive x-axis. The x-component of $\mathbf{v}_w$ is $15 + 2\sqrt{2}$ and the y-component is $2\sqrt{2}$: therefore,

$$\theta = \tan^{-1}\left(\frac{2\sqrt{2}}{15 + 2\sqrt{2}}\right) \approx 9°.$$

The heading of the boat is approximately 9° north of east, and its speed relative to the water is approximately 18 mi/hr.

Related Exercises 44–47 ◀

➤ The magnitude of **F** is typically measured in pounds (lb) or newtons (N), where $1\text{N} = 1\text{ kg-m/s}^2$.

➤ The vector $\langle \cos\theta, \sin\theta \rangle$ is a unit vector. Therefore, any position vector **v** may be written $\mathbf{v} = \langle |\mathbf{v}|\cos\theta, |\mathbf{v}|\sin\theta \rangle$, where θ is the angle that **v** makes with the positive x-axis.

Force Vectors Suppose a child pulls on the handle of a wagon at an angle of θ with the horizontal (Figure 12.21a). The vector **F** represents the force exerted on the wagon; it has a magnitude $|\mathbf{F}|$ and a direction given by θ. We denote the horizontal and vertical components of **F** by F_x and F_y, respectively. Then, $F_x = |\mathbf{F}|\cos\theta$, $F_y = |\mathbf{F}|\sin\theta$, and the force vector is $\mathbf{F} = \langle |\mathbf{F}|\cos\theta, |\mathbf{F}|\sin\theta \rangle$ (Figure 12.21b).

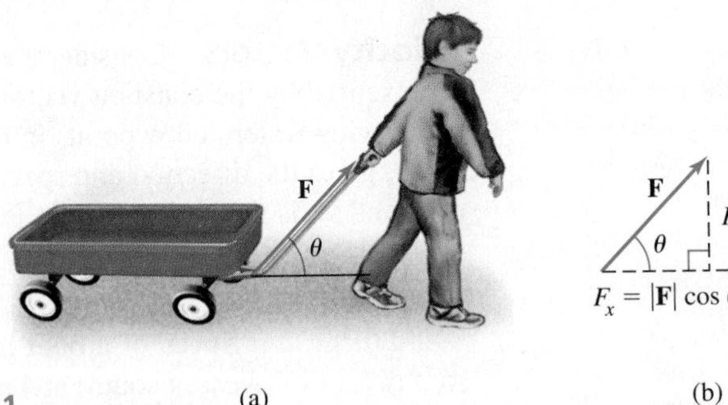

FIGURE 12.21

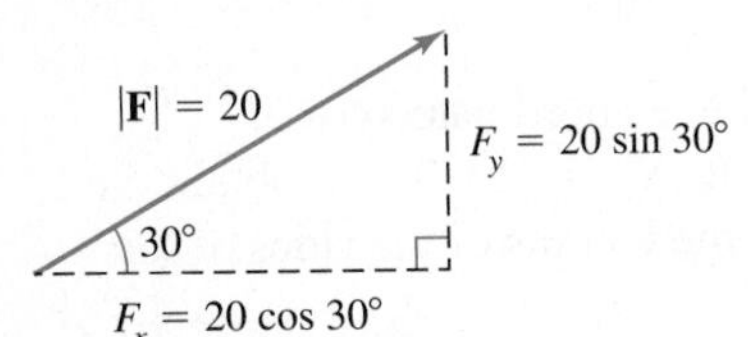

FIGURE 12.22

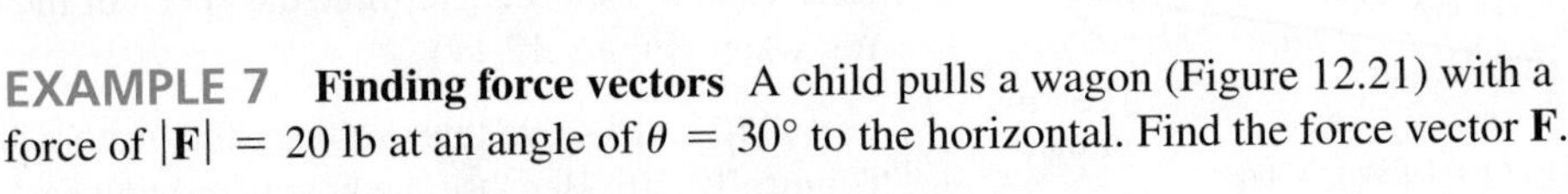

EXAMPLE 7 Finding force vectors A child pulls a wagon (Figure 12.21) with a force of $|\mathbf{F}| = 20$ lb at an angle of $\theta = 30°$ to the horizontal. Find the force vector **F**.

SOLUTION The force vector (Figure 12.22) is

$$\mathbf{F} = \langle |\mathbf{F}|\cos\theta, |\mathbf{F}|\sin\theta \rangle = \langle 20\cos 30°, 20\sin 30° \rangle = \langle 10\sqrt{3}, 10 \rangle.$$

Related Exercises 48–52 ◀

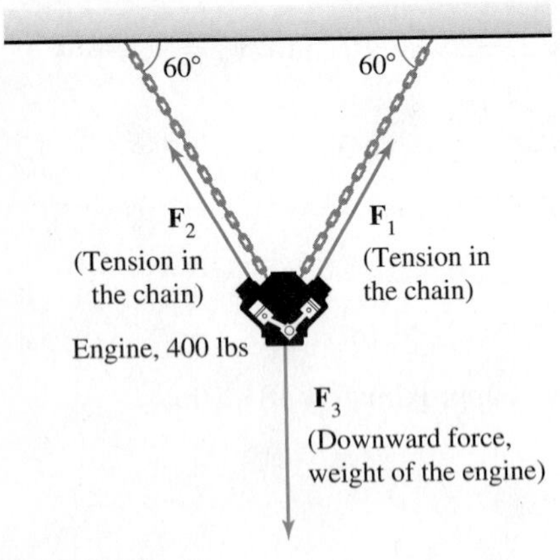

FIGURE 12.23

EXAMPLE 8 Balancing forces A 400-lb engine is suspended from two chains that form 60° angles with a horizontal ceiling (Figure 12.23). How much weight must each chain withstand?

SOLUTION Let $\mathbf{F}_1$ and $\mathbf{F}_2$ denote the forces exerted by the chains on the engine and let $\mathbf{F}_3$ be the downward force due to the weight of the engine (Figure 12.23). Placing the vectors in a standard coordinate system (Figure 12.24), we find that $\mathbf{F}_1 = \langle |\mathbf{F}_1|\cos 60°, |\mathbf{F}_1|\sin 60° \rangle$, $\mathbf{F}_2 = \langle -|\mathbf{F}_2|\cos 60°, |\mathbf{F}_2|\sin 60° \rangle$, and $\mathbf{F}_3 = \langle 0, -400 \rangle$.

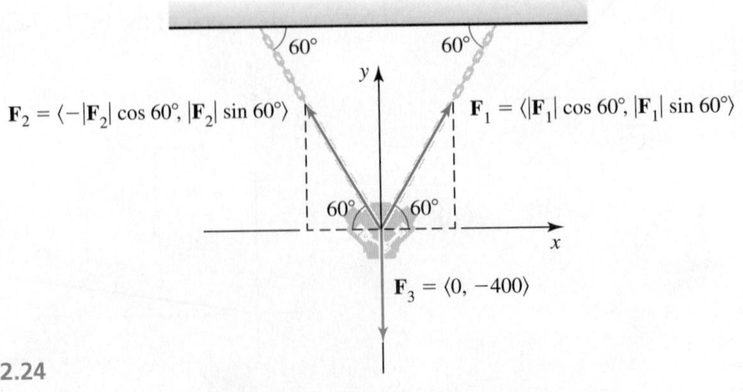

FIGURE 12.24

If the engine is in equilibrium (so the chains and engine are stationary), the sum of the forces must be zero; that is, $\mathbf{F}_1 + \mathbf{F}_2 + \mathbf{F}_3 = \mathbf{0}$ or $\mathbf{F}_1 + \mathbf{F}_2 = -\mathbf{F}_3$. Therefore,

$$\langle |\mathbf{F}_1| \cos 60° - |\mathbf{F}_2| \cos 60°, |\mathbf{F}_1| \sin 60° + |\mathbf{F}_2| \sin 60° \rangle = \langle 0, 400 \rangle.$$

Equating corresponding components, we obtain the following two equations to be solved for $|\mathbf{F}_1|$ and $|\mathbf{F}_2|$:

$$|\mathbf{F}_1| \cos 60° - |\mathbf{F}_2| \cos 60° = 0$$
$$|\mathbf{F}_1| \sin 60° + |\mathbf{F}_2| \sin 60° = 400$$

Factoring the first equation, we find that $(|\mathbf{F}_1| - |\mathbf{F}_2|) \cos 60° = 0$, which implies that $|\mathbf{F}_1| = |\mathbf{F}_2|$. Replacing $|\mathbf{F}_2|$ by $|\mathbf{F}_1|$ in the second equation gives $2|\mathbf{F}_1| \sin 60° = 400$. Noting that $\sin 60° = \sqrt{3}/2$ and solving for $|\mathbf{F}_1|$, we find that $|\mathbf{F}_1| = 400/\sqrt{3} \approx 231$. Each chain must be able to withstand a weight of approximately 231 lb.

Related Exercises 48–52 ◀

SECTION 12.1 EXERCISES

Review Questions

1. Interpret the following statement: Points have a location, but no size or direction; nonzero vectors have a size and direction, but no location.
2. What is a position vector?
3. Draw x- and y-axes on a page and mark two points P and Q. Then draw $\overrightarrow{PQ}$ and $\overrightarrow{QP}$.
4. On the diagram of Exercise 3, draw the position vector that is equal to $\overrightarrow{PQ}$.
5. Given a position vector **v**, why are there infinitely many vectors equal to **v**?
6. Explain how to add two vectors geometrically.
7. Explain how to find a scalar multiple of a vector geometrically.
8. Given two points P and Q, how are the components of $\overrightarrow{PQ}$ determined?
9. If $\mathbf{u} = \langle u_1, u_2 \rangle$ and $\mathbf{v} = \langle v_1, v_2 \rangle$, how do you find $\mathbf{u} + \mathbf{v}$?
10. If $\mathbf{v} = \langle v_1, v_2 \rangle$ and c is a scalar, how do you find $c\mathbf{v}$?
11. How do you compute the magnitude of $\mathbf{v} = \langle v_1, v_2 \rangle$?
12. Express the vector $\mathbf{v} = \langle v_1, v_2 \rangle$ in terms of the unit vectors **i** and **j**.
13. How do you compute $|\overrightarrow{PQ}|$ from the coordinates of the points P and Q?
14. Explain how to find two unit vectors parallel to a vector **v**.
15. How do you find a vector of length 10 in the direction of $\mathbf{v} = \langle 3, -2 \rangle$?
16. If a force has magnitude 100 and is directed 45° south of east, what are its components?

Basic Skills

17–20. Vector operations *Refer to the figure and carry out the following vector operations.*

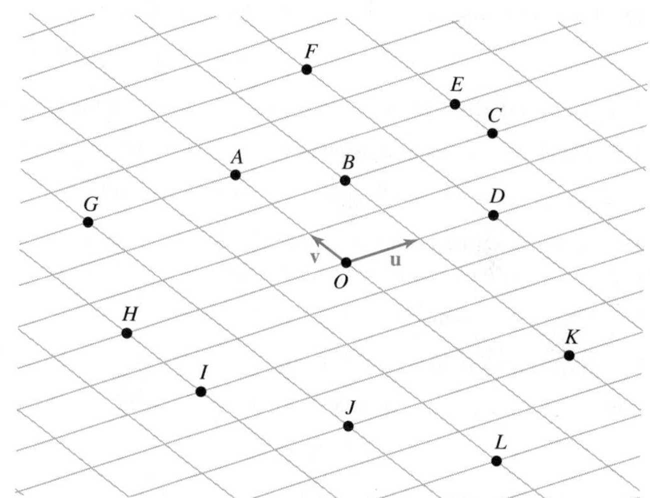

17. **Scalar multiples** Write the following vectors as scalar multiples of **u** or **v**.

    a. $\overrightarrow{OA}$ b. $\overrightarrow{OD}$ c. $\overrightarrow{OH}$ d. $\overrightarrow{AG}$ e. $\overrightarrow{CE}$

18. **Scalar multiples** Write the following vectors as scalar multiples of **u** or **v**.

    a. $\overrightarrow{IH}$ b. $\overrightarrow{HI}$ c. $\overrightarrow{JK}$ d. $\overrightarrow{FD}$ e. $\overrightarrow{EA}$

19. **Vector addition** Write the following vectors as sums of scalar multiples of **u** and **v**.

    a. $\overrightarrow{OE}$ b. $\overrightarrow{OB}$ c. $\overrightarrow{OF}$ d. $\overrightarrow{OG}$ e. $\overrightarrow{OC}$
    f. $\overrightarrow{OI}$ g. $\overrightarrow{OJ}$ h. $\overrightarrow{OK}$ i. $\overrightarrow{OL}$

20. **Vector addition** Write the following vectors as sums of scalar multiples of **u** and **v**.

    a. $\overrightarrow{BF}$ b. $\overrightarrow{DE}$ c. $\overrightarrow{AF}$ d. $\overrightarrow{AD}$ e. $\overrightarrow{CD}$
    f. $\overrightarrow{JD}$ g. $\overrightarrow{JI}$ h. $\overrightarrow{DB}$ i. $\overrightarrow{IL}$

21. **Components and magnitudes** Define the points $O(0,0)$, $P(3,2)$, $Q(4,2)$, and $R(-6,-1)$. For each vector, do the following.
   (i) Sketch the vector in an xy-coordinate system.
   (ii) Compute the magnitude of the vector.
   a. $\overrightarrow{OP}$ **b.** $\overrightarrow{QP}$ **c.** $\overrightarrow{RQ}$

22–25. Components and equality *Define the points* $P(-3,-1)$, $Q(-1,2)$, $R(1,2)$, $S(3,5)$, $T(4,2)$, *and* $U(6,4)$.

22. Sketch $\overrightarrow{PU}$, $\overrightarrow{TR}$, and $\overrightarrow{SQ}$ and the corresponding position vectors.

23. Sketch $\overrightarrow{QU}$, $\overrightarrow{PT}$, and $\overrightarrow{RS}$ and the corresponding position vectors.

24. Find the equal vectors among $\overrightarrow{PQ}$, $\overrightarrow{RS}$, and $\overrightarrow{TU}$.

25. Which of the vectors $\overrightarrow{QT}$ or $\overrightarrow{SU}$ is equal to $\langle 5,0\rangle$?

26–31. Vector operations *Let* $\mathbf{u} = \langle 4,-2\rangle$, $\mathbf{v} = \langle -4,6\rangle$, *and* $\mathbf{w} = \langle 0,8\rangle$. *Express the following vectors in the form* $\langle a,b\rangle$.

26. $\mathbf{u} + \mathbf{v}$ 27. $\mathbf{w} - \mathbf{u}$ 28. $2\mathbf{u} + 3\mathbf{v}$

29. $\mathbf{w} - 3\mathbf{v}$ 30. $10\mathbf{u} - 3\mathbf{v} + \mathbf{w}$ 31. $8\mathbf{w} + \mathbf{v} - 6\mathbf{u}$

32–37. Vector operations *Let* $\mathbf{u} = \langle 8,-4\rangle$, $\mathbf{v} = \langle 2,6\rangle$, *and* $\mathbf{w} = \langle 5,0\rangle$. *Carry out the following computations.*

32. Find $|\mathbf{u} + \mathbf{v} + \mathbf{w}|$. 33. Find $|2\mathbf{u} + 3\mathbf{v} - 4\mathbf{w}|$.

34. Find two vectors parallel to $\mathbf{u}$ with four times the magnitude of $\mathbf{u}$.

35. Find two vectors parallel to $\mathbf{v}$ with three times the magnitude of $\mathbf{v}$.

36. Which has the greatest magnitude, $\mathbf{u}$, $3\mathbf{v}/2$, or $2\mathbf{w}$?

37. Which has the greater magnitude, $\mathbf{u} - \mathbf{v}$ or $\mathbf{w} - \mathbf{u}$?

38–43. Unit vectors *Define the points* $P(-4,1)$, $Q(3,-4)$, *and* $R(2,6)$. *Carry out the following calculations.*

38. Express $\overrightarrow{PQ}$ in the form $a\mathbf{i} + b\mathbf{j}$.

39. Express $\overrightarrow{QR}$ in the form $a\mathbf{i} + b\mathbf{j}$.

40. Find the unit vector with the same direction as $\overrightarrow{QR}$.

41. Find a unit vector parallel to $\overrightarrow{PR}$.

42. Find two vectors parallel to $\overrightarrow{RP}$ with length 4.

43. Find two vectors parallel to $\overrightarrow{QP}$ with length 4.

44. **Parachute in a wind** In still air, a parachute with a payload would fall vertically at a terminal speed of 40 m/s. Find the direction and magnitude of its terminal velocity relative to the ground if it falls in a steady wind blowing horizontally from west to east at 10 m/s.

45. **Airplane in a wind** An airplane flies horizontally from east to west at 320 mi/hr relative to the air. If it flies in a steady 40-mi/hr wind that blows horizontally toward the southwest (45° south of west), find the speed and direction of the airplane relative to the ground.

46. **Canoe in a current** A woman in a canoe paddles due west at 4 mi/hr relative to the water in a current that flows northwest at 2 mi/hr. Find the speed and direction of the canoe relative to the shore.

47. **Boat in a wind** A sailboat floats in a current that flows due east at 4 m/s. Due to a wind, the boat's actual speed relative to the shore is $4\sqrt{3}$ m/s in a direction 30° north of east. Find the speed and direction of the wind.

48. **Towing a boat** A boat is towed with a force of 150 lb with a rope that makes an angle of 30° to the horizontal. Find the horizontal and vertical components of the force.

49. **Pulling a suitcase** Suppose you pull a suitcase with a strap that makes a 60° angle with the horizontal. The magnitude of the force you exert on the suitcase is 40 lb.
   a. Find the horizontal and vertical components of the force.
   b. Is the horizontal component of the force greater if the angle of the strap is 45° instead of 60°?
   c. Is the vertical component of the force greater if the angle of the strap is 45° instead of 60°?

50. **Which is greater?** Which has a greater horizontal component, a 100-N force directed at an angle of 60° above the horizontal or a 60-N force directed at an angle of 30° above the horizontal?

51. **Suspended load** If a 500-lb load is suspended by two chains (see figure), what is the magnitude of the force each chain must be able to withstand?

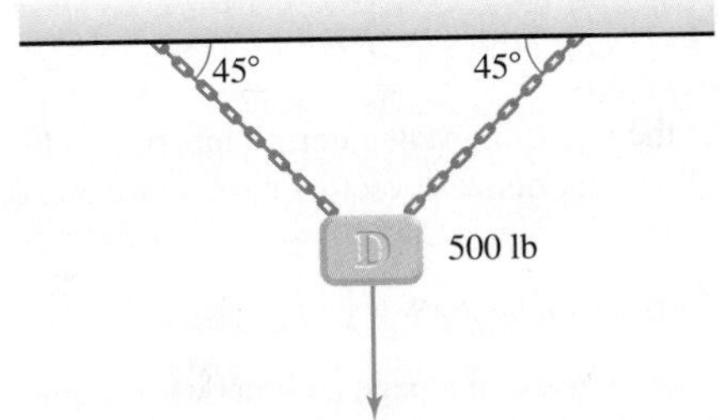

52. **Net force** Three forces are applied to an object, as shown in the figure. Find the magnitude and direction of the sum of the forces.

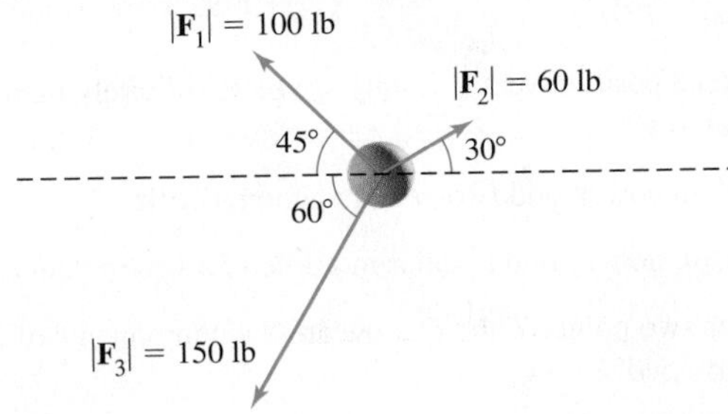

Further Explorations

53. **Explain why or why not** Determine whether the following statements are true and give an explanation or counterexample.
   a. José travels from point A to point B in the plane by following vector $\mathbf{u}$, then vector $\mathbf{v}$, and then vector $\mathbf{w}$. If he starts at A and follows $\mathbf{w}$, then $\mathbf{v}$, and then $\mathbf{u}$, he still arrives at B.
   b. Maria travels from A to B in the plane by following the vector $\mathbf{u}$. By following $-\mathbf{u}$, she returns from B to A.
   c. The magnitude of $\mathbf{u} + \mathbf{v}$ is at least the magnitude of $\mathbf{u}$.
   d. The magnitude of $\mathbf{u} + \mathbf{v}$ is at least the magnitude of $\mathbf{u}$ plus the magnitude of $\mathbf{v}$.
   e. Parallel vectors have the same length.
   f. If $\overrightarrow{AB} = \overrightarrow{CD}$, then $A = C$ and $B = D$.
   g. If $\mathbf{u}$ and $\mathbf{v}$ are perpendicular, then $|\mathbf{u} + \mathbf{v}| = |\mathbf{u}| + |\mathbf{v}|$.
   h. If $\mathbf{u}$ and $\mathbf{v}$ are parallel and have the same direction, then $|\mathbf{u} + \mathbf{v}| = |\mathbf{u}| + |\mathbf{v}|$.

54. **Finding vectors from two points** Given the points $A(-2,0)$, $B(6,16)$, $C(1,4)$, $D(5,4)$, $E(\sqrt{2},\sqrt{2})$, and $F(3\sqrt{2},-4\sqrt{2})$, find the position vector equal to the following vectors.
   a. $\overrightarrow{AB}$ **b.** $\overrightarrow{AC}$ **c.** $\overrightarrow{EF}$ **d.** $\overrightarrow{CD}$

55. Unit vectors

a. Find two unit vectors parallel to $\mathbf{v} = 6\mathbf{i} - 8\mathbf{j}$.
b. Find b if $\mathbf{v} = \langle 1/3, b \rangle$ is a unit vector.
c. Find all values of a such that $\mathbf{w} = a\mathbf{i} - \frac{a}{3}\mathbf{j}$ is a unit vector.

56. Equal vectors For the points $A(3, 4)$, $B(6, 10)$, $C(a + 2, b + 5)$, and $D(b + 4, a - 2)$, find the values of a and b such that $\overrightarrow{AB} = \overrightarrow{CD}$.

57–60. Vector equations *Use the properties of vectors to solve the following equations for the unknown vector* $\mathbf{x} = \langle a, b \rangle$. *Let* $\mathbf{u} = \langle 2, -3 \rangle$ *and* $\mathbf{v} = \langle -4, 1 \rangle$.

57. $10\mathbf{x} = \mathbf{u}$

58. $2\mathbf{x} + \mathbf{u} = \mathbf{v}$

59. $3\mathbf{x} - 4\mathbf{u} = \mathbf{v}$

60. $-4\mathbf{x} = \mathbf{u} - 8\mathbf{v}$

61–63. Linear combinations *A sum of scalar multiples of two or more vectors (such as* $c_1\mathbf{u} + c_2\mathbf{v} + c_3\mathbf{w}$, *where* c_i *are scalars) is called a* ***linear combination*** *of the vectors. Let* $\mathbf{i} = \langle 1, 0 \rangle$, $\mathbf{j} = \langle 0, 1 \rangle$, $\mathbf{u} = \langle 1, 1 \rangle$, *and* $\mathbf{v} = \langle -1, 1 \rangle$.

61. Express $\langle 4, -8 \rangle$ as a linear combination of **i** and **j** (that is, find scalars c_1 and c_2 such that $\langle 4, -8 \rangle = c_1\mathbf{i} + c_2\mathbf{j}$).

62. Express $\langle 4, -8 \rangle$ as a linear combination of **u** and **v**.

63. For arbitrary real numbers a and b, express $\langle a, b \rangle$ as a linear combination of **u** and **v**.

64–65. Solving vector equations *Solve the following pairs of equations for the vectors* **u** *and* **v**. *Assume* $\mathbf{i} = \langle 1, 0 \rangle$ *and* $\mathbf{j} = \langle 0, 1 \rangle$.

64. $2\mathbf{u} = \mathbf{i}$, $\mathbf{u} - 4\mathbf{v} = \mathbf{j}$

65. $2\mathbf{u} + 3\mathbf{v} = \mathbf{i}$, $\mathbf{u} - \mathbf{v} = \mathbf{j}$

66–69. Designer vectors *Find the following vectors.*

66. The vector that is 3 times $\langle 3, -5 \rangle$ plus -9 times $\langle 6, 0 \rangle$.

67. The vector in the direction of $\langle 5, -12 \rangle$ with length 3.

68. The vector in the direction opposite to that of $\langle 6, -8 \rangle$ with length 10.

69. The position vector for your final location if you start at the origin and walk along $\langle 4, -6 \rangle$ followed by $\langle 5, 9 \rangle$.

Applications

70. Ant on a page An ant is walking due east at a constant speed of 2 mi/hr on a sheet of paper that rests on a table. Suddenly the sheet of paper starts moving southeast at $\sqrt{2}$ mi/hr. Describe the motion of the ant relative to the table.

71. Clock vectors Consider the 12 vectors that have their tails at the center of a (circular) clock and their heads at the numbers on the edge of the clock.

a. What is the sum of these 12 vectors?
b. If the 12:00 vector is removed, what is the sum of the remaining 11 vectors?
c. By removing one or more of these 12 clock vectors, explain how to make the sum of the remaining vectors as large as possible in magnitude.
d. If the clock vectors originate at 12:00 and point to the other 11 numbers, what is the sum of the vectors?

(*Source: Calculus,* by Gilbert Strang. Wellesley-Cambridge Press, 1991.)

72. Three-way tug-of-war Three people located at A, B, and C pull on ropes tied to a ring. Find the magnitude and direction of the force with which C must pull so that no one moves (the system is at equilibrium).

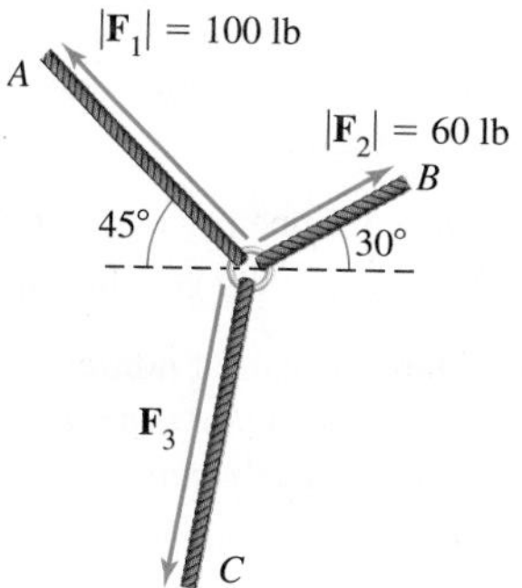

73. Net force Jack pulls east on a rope attached to a camel with a force of 40 lb. Jill pulls north on a rope attached to the same camel with a force of 30 lb. What is the magnitude and direction of the force on the camel? Assume the vectors lie in a horizontal plane.

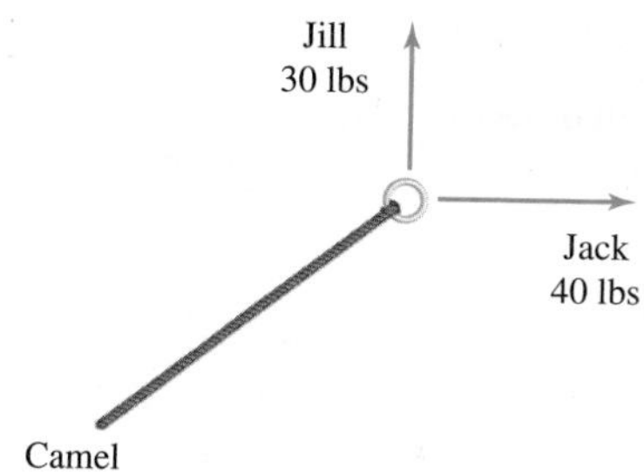

74. Mass on a plane A 100-kg object rests on an inclined plane at an angle of 30° to the floor. Find the components of the force perpendicular to and parallel to the plane. (The vertical component of the force exerted by an object of mass m is its weight, which is mg, where $g = 9.8\text{ m/s}^2$ is the acceleration due to gravity.)

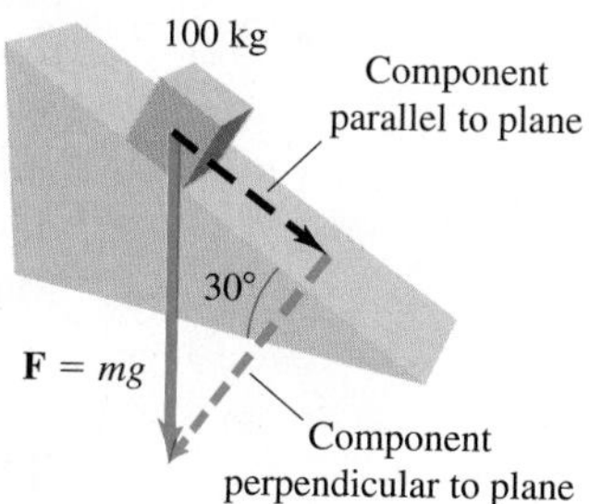

Additional Exercises

75–79. Vector properties *Prove the following vector properties using components. Then, make a sketch to illustrate the property geometrically. Suppose* **u**, **v**, *and* **w** *are vectors in the xy-plane and a and c are scalars.*

75. Commutative property: $\mathbf{u} + \mathbf{v} = \mathbf{v} + \mathbf{u}$

76. Associative property: $(\mathbf{u} + \mathbf{v}) + \mathbf{w} = \mathbf{u} + (\mathbf{v} + \mathbf{w})$

77. Associative property: $a(c\mathbf{v}) = (ac)\mathbf{v}$

78. Distributive property 1: $a(\mathbf{u} + \mathbf{v}) = a\mathbf{u} + a\mathbf{v}$

79. Distributive property 2: $(a + c)\mathbf{v} = a\mathbf{v} + c\mathbf{v}$

80. Midpoint of a line segment Use vectors to show that the midpoint of the line segment joining $P(x_1, y_1)$ and $Q(x_2, y_2)$ is the point $((x_1 + x_2)/2, (y_1 + y_2)/2)$. (*Hint:* Let O be the origin and let M be the midpoint of PQ. Draw a picture and show that $\overrightarrow{OM} = \overrightarrow{OP} + \frac{1}{2}\overrightarrow{PQ} = \overrightarrow{OP} + \frac{1}{2}(\overrightarrow{OQ} - \overrightarrow{OP})$.)

81. Magnitude of scalar multiple Prove that $|c\mathbf{v}| = |c||\mathbf{v}|$, where c is a scalar and $\mathbf{v}$ is a vector.

82. Equality of vectors Assume $\overrightarrow{PQ}$ equals $\overrightarrow{RS}$. Does it follow that $\overrightarrow{PR}$ is equal to $\overrightarrow{QS}$? Prove your conclusion.

83. Linear independence A pair of nonzero vectors in the plane is *linearly dependent* if one vector is a scalar multiple of the other. Otherwise, the pair is *linearly independent.*

a. Which pairs of the following vectors are linearly dependent and which are linearly independent: $\mathbf{u} = \langle 2, -3 \rangle$, $\mathbf{v} = \langle -12, 18 \rangle$, and $\mathbf{w} = \langle 4, 6 \rangle$?

b. Explain geometrically what it means for a pair of vectors in the plane to be linearly dependent and independent.

c. Prove that if a pair of vectors $\mathbf{u}$ and $\mathbf{v}$ is linearly independent, then given any vector $\mathbf{w}$, there are constants c_1 and c_2 such that $\mathbf{w} = c_1\mathbf{u} + c_2\mathbf{v}$.

84. Perpendicular vectors Show that two nonzero vectors $\mathbf{u} = \langle u_1, u_2 \rangle$ and $\mathbf{v} = \langle v_1, v_2 \rangle$ are perpendicular to each other if $u_1 v_1 + u_2 v_2 = 0$.

85. Parallel and perpendicular vectors Let $\mathbf{u} = \langle a, 5 \rangle$ and $\mathbf{v} = \langle 2, 6 \rangle$.

a. Find the value of a such that $\mathbf{u}$ is parallel to $\mathbf{v}$.

b. Find the value of a such that $\mathbf{u}$ is perpendicular to $\mathbf{v}$.

86. The Triangle Inequality Suppose $\mathbf{u}$ and $\mathbf{v}$ are vectors in the plane.

a. Use the Triangle Rule for adding vectors to explain why $|\mathbf{u} + \mathbf{v}| \le |\mathbf{u}| + |\mathbf{v}|$. This result is known as the *Triangle Inequality.*

b. Under what conditions is $|\mathbf{u} + \mathbf{v}| = |\mathbf{u}| + |\mathbf{v}|$?

QUICK CHECK ANSWERS

1. The vector $-5\mathbf{v}$ is five times as long as $\mathbf{v}$ and points in the opposite direction. **2.** $\mathbf{v}_a + \mathbf{w}$ points in a northeasterly direction. **3.** Constructing $\mathbf{u} + \mathbf{v}$ and $\mathbf{v} + \mathbf{u}$ using the Triangle Rule produces vectors having the same direction and magnitude. **4.** $\overrightarrow{PQ} = \langle -6, -2 \rangle$ **5.** $10\mathbf{u} = \langle 6, 8 \rangle$ and $-10\mathbf{u} = \langle -6, -8 \rangle$
6. $\left|\left\langle \frac{5}{13}, \frac{12}{13} \right\rangle\right| = \sqrt{\frac{25 + 144}{169}} = \sqrt{\frac{169}{169}} = 1$
7. $\mathbf{u} = -\frac{4}{3}\mathbf{v} + 4\mathbf{w}$ ◀

12.2 Vectors in Three Dimensions

Up to this point, our study of calculus has been limited to functions, curves, and vectors that can be plotted in the two-dimensional xy-plane. However, a two-dimensional coordinate system is insufficient for modeling many physical phenomena. For example, to describe the trajectory of a jet gaining altitude, we need two coordinates, say x and y, to measure east–west and north–south distances. In addition, another coordinate, say z, is needed to measure the altitude of the jet. By adding a third coordinate and creating an ordered triple (x, y, z), the location of the jet can be described. The set of all points described by the triples (x, y, z) is called *three-dimensional space*, *xyz*-space, or $\mathbf{R}^3$. Many of the properties of xyz-space are extensions of familiar ideas you have seen in the xy-plane.

The *xyz*-Coordinate System

➤ Recall that **R** is the notation for the real numbers and $\mathbf{R}^2$ (pronounced *R-two*) stands for all ordered pairs of real numbers. The notation $\mathbf{R}^3$ (pronounced *R-three*) means the set of all ordered triples of real numbers.

A three-dimensional coordinate system is created by adding a new axis, called the **z-axis**, to the familiar xy-coordinate system. The new z-axis is inserted through the origin perpendicular to the x- and y-axes (Figure 12.25). The result is a new coordinate system called the **three-dimensional rectangular coordinate system** or the ***xyz*-coordinate system**.

The coordinate system described here is a conventional **right-handed coordinate system**: If the curled fingers of the right hand are rotated from the positive x-axis to the positive y-axis, the thumb points in the direction of the positive z-axis (Figure 12.25).

The coordinate plane containing the x-axis and y-axis is still called the xy-plane. We now have two new coordinate planes: the ***xz*-plane** containing the x-axis and the z-axis, and the ***yz*-plane** containing the y-axis and the z-axis. Taken together, these three coordinate planes divide xyz-space into eight regions called **octants** (Figure 12.26).

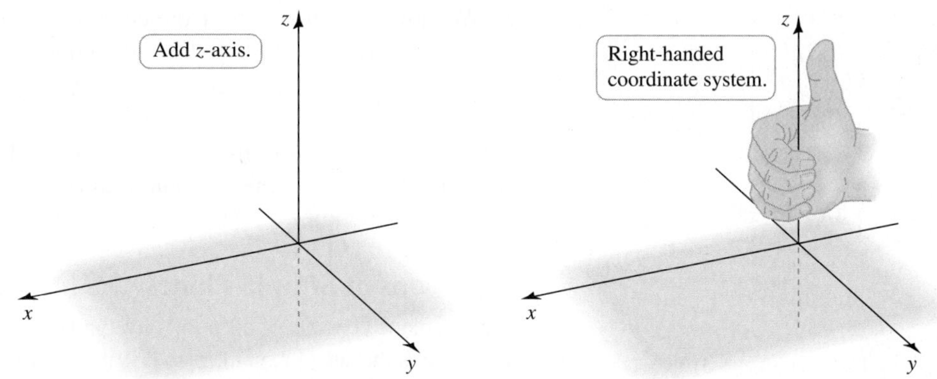

FIGURE 12.25

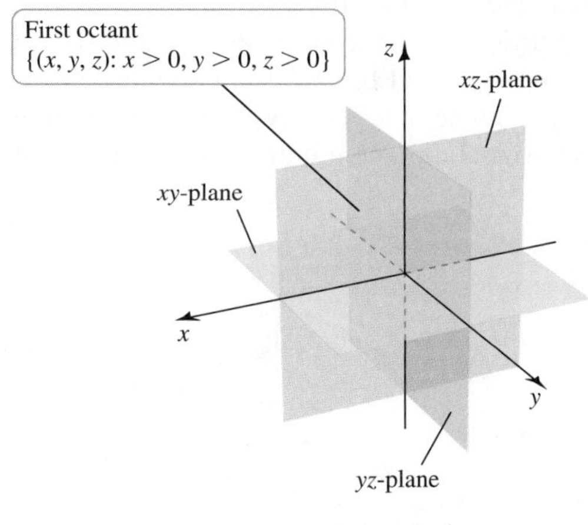

FIGURE 12.26

The point where all three axes intersect is the **origin**, which has coordinates $(0, 0, 0)$. An ordered triple (a, b, c) refers to a point in xyz-space that is found by starting at the origin, moving a units in the x-direction, b units in the y-direction, and c units in the z-direction. With a negative coordinate, you move in the negative direction along the corresponding coordinate axis. To visualize this point, it's helpful to construct a rectangular box with one vertex at the origin and the opposite vertex at the point (a, b, c) (Figure 12.27).

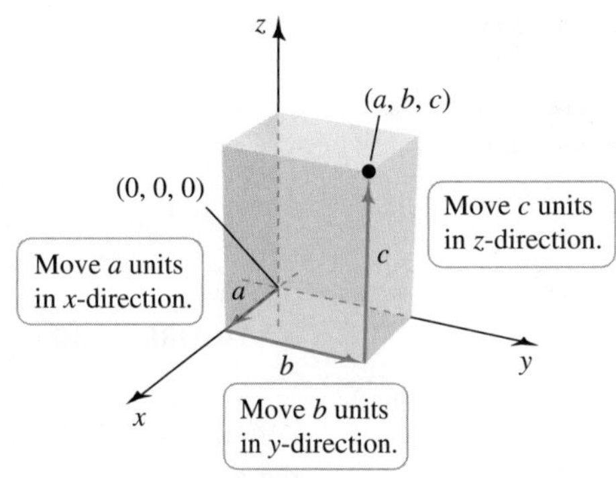

FIGURE 12.27

EXAMPLE 1 **Plotting points in *xyz*-space** Plot the following points.

a. $(3, 4, 5)$ **b.** $(-2, -3, 5)$

SOLUTION

a. Starting at $(0, 0, 0)$, we move 3 units in the x-direction to the point $(3, 0, 0)$, then 4 units in the y-direction to the point $(3, 4, 0)$, and finally, 5 units in the z-direction to reach the point $(3, 4, 5)$ (Figure 12.28).

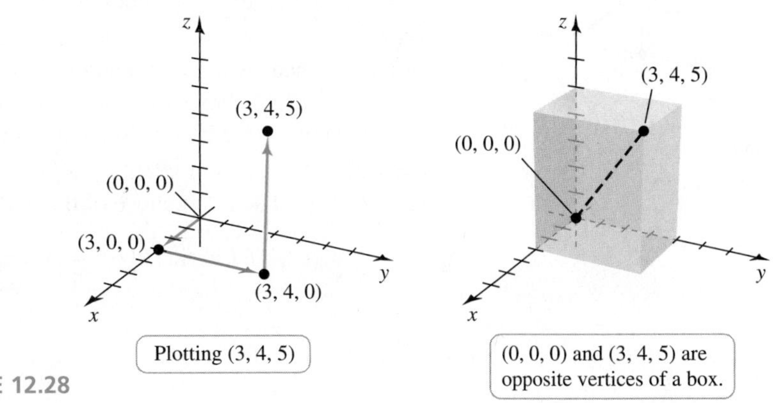

FIGURE 12.28

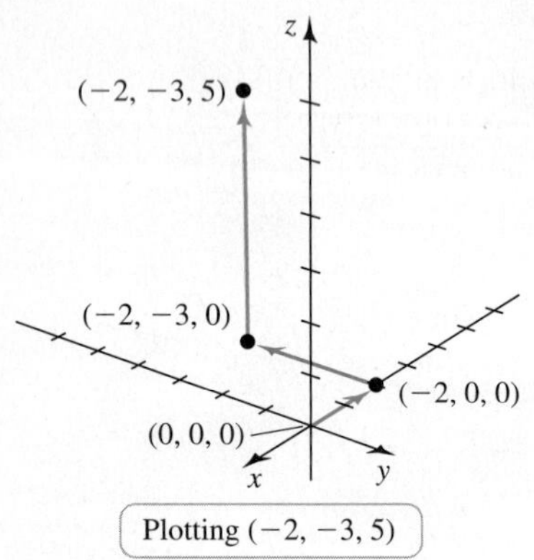

Plotting (−2, −3, 5)

FIGURE 12.29

b. We move −2 units in the x-direction to $(-2, 0, 0)$, −3 units in the y-direction to $(-2, -3, 0)$, and 5 units in the z-direction to reach $(-2, -3, 5)$ (Figure 12.29).

Related Exercises 9–14

QUICK CHECK 1 Suppose the positive x-, y-, and z-axes point east, north, and upward, respectively. Describe the location of the points $(-1, -1, 0)$, $(1, 0, 1)$, and $(-1, -1, -1)$ relative to the origin.

Equations of Simple Planes

The xy-plane consists of all points in xyz-space that have a z-coordinate of 0. Therefore, the xy-plane is the set $\{(x, y, z): z = 0\}$; it is represented by the equation $z = 0$. Similarly, the xz-plane has the equation $y = 0$, and the yz-plane has the equation $x = 0$.

Planes parallel to one of the coordinate planes are easy to describe. For example, the equation $x = 2$ describes the set of all points whose x-coordinate is 2 and whose y- and z-coordinates are arbitrary; this plane is parallel to and 2 units from the yz-plane. Similarly, the equation $y = a$ describes a plane that is everywhere a units from the xz-plane, and $z = a$ is the equation of a horizontal plane a units from the xy-plane (Figure 12.30).

Planes that are not parallel to the coordinate planes are extremely important in three-dimensional calculus. They are discussed in Section 13.1.

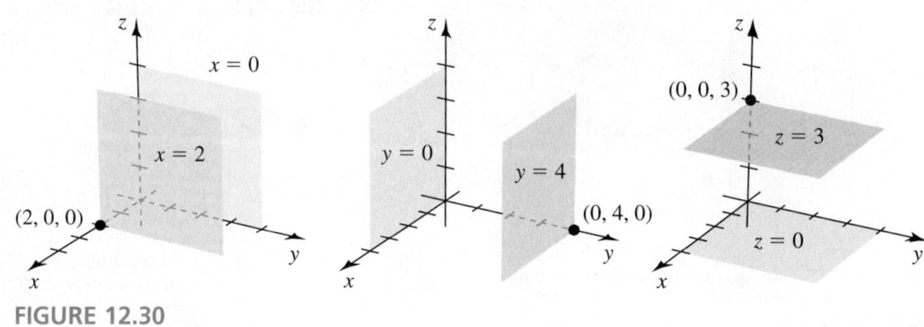

FIGURE 12.30

QUICK CHECK 2 To which coordinate planes are the planes $x = -2$ and $z = 16$ parallel?

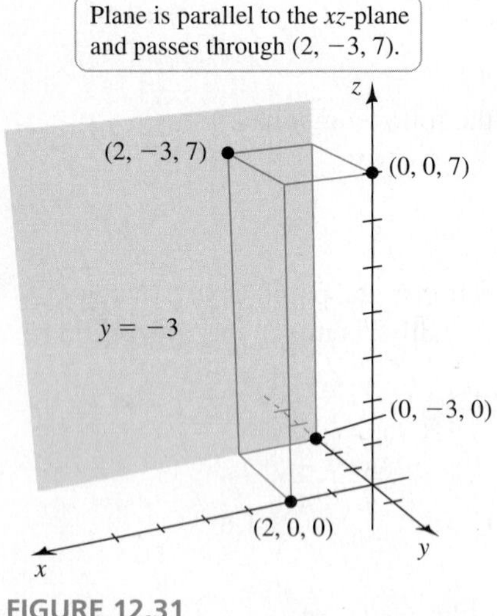

FIGURE 12.31

EXAMPLE 2 Parallel planes Determine the equation of the plane parallel to the xz-plane passing through the point $(2, -3, 7)$.

SOLUTION Points on a plane parallel to the xz-plane have the same y-coordinate. Therefore, the plane passing through the point $(2, -3, 7)$ with a y-coordinate of −3 has the equation $y = -3$ (Figure 12.31).

Related Exercises 15–22

Distances in *xyz*-Space

Recall that the distance between two points (x_1, y_1) and (x_2, y_2) in the xy-plane is $\sqrt{(x_2 - x_1)^2 + (y_2 - y_1)^2}$. This distance formula is useful in deriving a similar formula for the distance between two points $P(x_1, y_1, z_1)$ and $Q(x_2, y_2, z_2)$ in xyz-space.

Figure 12.32 shows the points P and Q, together with the auxiliary point $R(x_2, y_2, z_1)$, which has the same z-coordinate as P and the same x- and y-coordinates as Q. The line segment PR has length $|PR| = \sqrt{(x_2 - x_1)^2 + (y_2 - y_1)^2}$ and is one leg of the right triangle $\triangle PRQ$. The hypotenuse of that triangle is the distance between P and Q:

$$\sqrt{|PR|^2 + |RQ|^2} = \sqrt{\underbrace{(x_2 - x_1)^2 + (y_2 - y_1)^2}_{|PR|^2} + \underbrace{(z_2 - z_1)^2}_{|RQ|^2}}$$

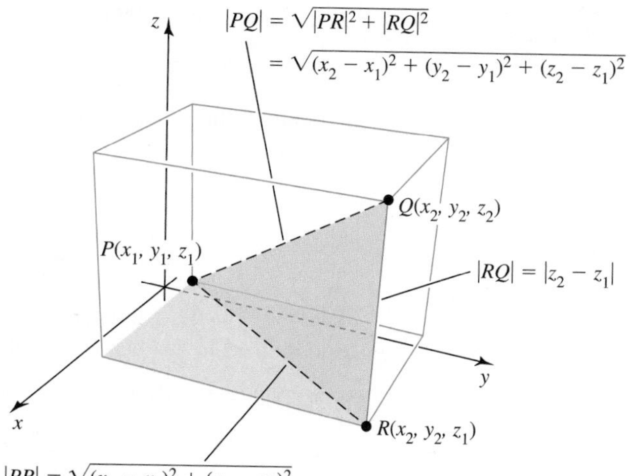

FIGURE 12.32 $|PR| = \sqrt{(x_2 - x_1)^2 + (y_2 - y_1)^2}$

Distance Formula in xyz-Space

The distance between the points $P(x_1, y_1, z_1)$ and $Q(x_2, y_2, z_2)$ is

$$\sqrt{(x_2 - x_1)^2 + (y_2 - y_1)^2 + (z_2 - z_1)^2}.$$

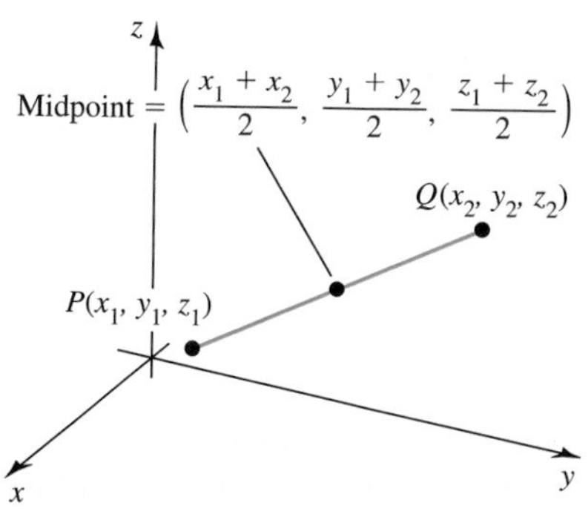

FIGURE 12.33

By using the distance formula, we can derive the formula (Exercise 65) for the **midpoint** of the line segment joining $P(x_1, y_1, z_1)$ and $Q(x_2, y_2, z_2)$, which is found by averaging the x-, y-, and z-coordinates (Figure 12.33):

$$\left(\frac{x_1 + x_2}{2}, \frac{y_1 + y_2}{2}, \frac{z_1 + z_2}{2}\right).$$

Equation of a Sphere

A *sphere* is the set of all points that are a fixed distance r from a point (a, b, c); r is the *radius* of the sphere and (a, b, c) is the *center* of the sphere. A *ball* centered at (a, b, c) with radius r consists of all the points inside and on the sphere centered at (a, b, c) with radius r (Figure 12.34). We now use the distance formula to translate these statements.

> Just as a circle is the boundary of a disk in two dimensions, a *sphere* is the boundary of a *ball* in three dimensions. We have defined a *closed ball*, which includes its boundary. An *open ball* does not contain its boundary.

Spheres and Balls

A **sphere** centered at (a, b, c) with radius r is the set of points satisfying the equation

$$(x - a)^2 + (y - b)^2 + (z - c)^2 = r^2.$$

A **ball** centered at (a, b, c) with radius r is the set of points satisfying the inequality

$$(x - a)^2 + (y - b)^2 + (z - c)^2 \le r^2.$$

Sphere: $(x - a)^2 + (y - b)^2 + (z - c)^2 = r^2$
Ball: $(x - a)^2 + (y - b)^2 + (z - c)^2 \le r^2$

FIGURE 12.34

EXAMPLE 3 **Equation of a sphere** Consider the points $P(1, -2, 5)$ and $Q(3, 4, -6)$. Find an equation of the sphere for which the line segment PQ is a diameter.

SOLUTION The center of the sphere is the midpoint of PQ:

$$\left(\frac{1 + 3}{2}, \frac{-2 + 4}{2}, \frac{5 - 6}{2}\right) = \left(2, 1, -\frac{1}{2}\right).$$

The diameter of the sphere is the distance $|PQ|$, which is

$$\sqrt{(3-1)^2 + (4+2)^2 + (-6-5)^2} = \sqrt{161}.$$

Therefore, the sphere's radius is $\frac{1}{2}\sqrt{161}$, its center is $\left(2, 1, -\frac{1}{2}\right)$, and it is described by the equation

$$(x-2)^2 + (y-1)^2 + \left(z + \frac{1}{2}\right)^2 = \left(\frac{1}{2}\sqrt{161}\right)^2 = \frac{161}{4}.$$

Related Exercises 23–28 ◄

EXAMPLE 4 Identifying equations Describe the set of points that satisfy the equation $x^2 + y^2 + z^2 - 2x + 6y - 8z = -1$.

SOLUTION We simplify the equation by completing the square and factoring:

$$\begin{aligned} (x^2 - 2x) + (y^2 + 6y) + (z^2 - 8z) &= -1 && \text{Group terms.} \\ (x^2 - 2x + 1) + (y^2 + 6y + 9) + (z^2 - 8z + 16) &= 25 && \text{Complete the square.} \\ (x-1)^2 + (y+3)^2 + (z-4)^2 &= 25 && \text{Factor.} \end{aligned}$$

The equation describes a sphere of radius 5 with center $(1, -3, 4)$.

Related Exercises 29–34 ◄

QUICK CHECK 3 Describe the solution set of the equation

$$(x-1)^2 + y^2 + (z+1)^2 + 4 = 0. ◄$$

Vectors in $\mathbf{R}^3$

Vectors in $\mathbf{R}^3$ are straightforward extensions of vectors in the xy-plane; we simply include a third component. The position vector $\mathbf{v} = \langle v_1, v_2, v_3 \rangle$ has its tail at the origin and its head at the point (v_1, v_2, v_3). Vectors having the same magnitude and direction are equal. Therefore, the vector from $P(x_1, y_1, z_1)$ to $Q(x_2, y_2, z_2)$ is denoted $\overrightarrow{PQ}$ and is equal to the position vector $\langle x_2 - x_1, y_2 - y_1, z_2 - z_1 \rangle$. It is also equal to all vectors such as $\overrightarrow{RS}$ that have the same length and direction as $\mathbf{v}$ (Figure 12.35).

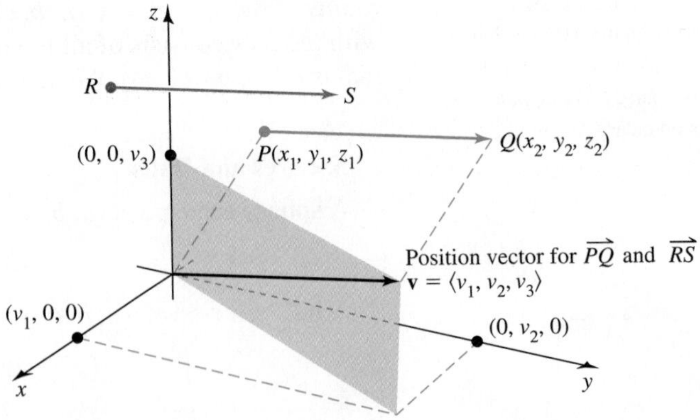

FIGURE 12.35

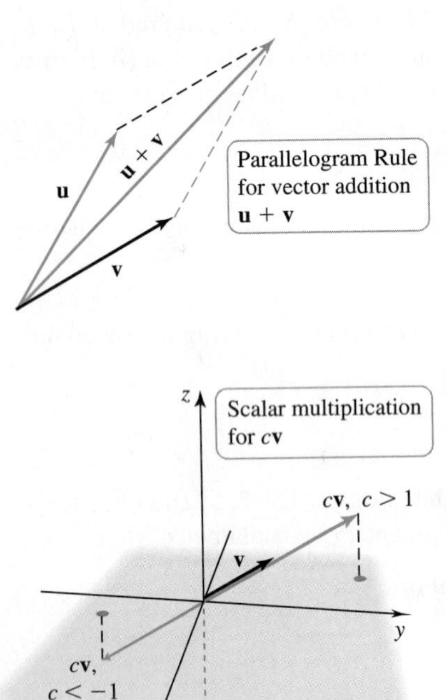

FIGURE 12.36

The operations of vector addition and scalar multiplication in $\mathbf{R}^2$ generalize in a natural way to three dimensions. For example, the sum of two vectors is found geometrically using the Triangle Rule or the Parallelogram Rule (Section 12.1). The sum is found analytically by adding the respective components of the two vectors. As with two-dimensional vectors, scalar multiplication corresponds to stretching or compressing a vector, possibly with a reversal of direction. Two nonzero vectors are parallel if one is a scalar multiple of the other (Figure 12.36).

QUICK CHECK 4 Which of the following vectors are parallel to each other?
a. $\mathbf{u} = \langle -2, 4, -6 \rangle$ **b.** $\mathbf{v} = \langle 4, -8, 12 \rangle$ **c.** $\mathbf{w} = \langle -1, 2, 3 \rangle$ ◄

> **DEFINITION Vector Operations in $\mathbf{R}^3$**
>
> Let c be a scalar, $\mathbf{u} = \langle u_1, u_2, u_3 \rangle$, and $\mathbf{v} = \langle v_1, v_2, v_3 \rangle$.
>
> $$\mathbf{u} + \mathbf{v} = \langle u_1 + v_1, u_2 + v_2, u_3 + v_3 \rangle \quad \text{Vector addition}$$
> $$\mathbf{u} - \mathbf{v} = \langle u_1 - v_1, u_2 - v_2, u_3 - v_3 \rangle \quad \text{Vector subtraction}$$
> $$c\mathbf{u} = \langle cu_1, cu_2, cu_3 \rangle \quad \text{Scalar multiplication}$$

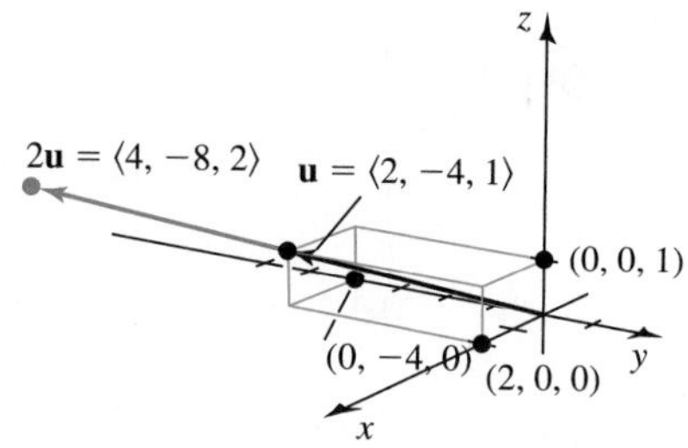

FIGURE 12.37

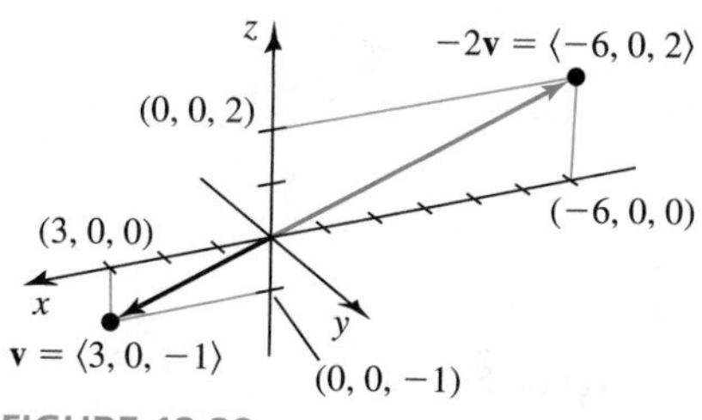

FIGURE 12.38

EXAMPLE 5 Vectors in $\mathbf{R}^3$ Let $\mathbf{u} = \langle 2, -4, 1 \rangle$ and $\mathbf{v} = \langle 3, 0, -1 \rangle$. Find the components of the following vectors and draw them in $\mathbf{R}^3$.

a. $2\mathbf{u}$ **b.** $-2\mathbf{v}$ **c.** $\mathbf{u} + 2\mathbf{v}$

SOLUTION

a. Using the definition of scalar multiplication, $2\mathbf{u} = 2\langle 2, -4, 1 \rangle = \langle 4, -8, 2 \rangle$. The vector $2\mathbf{u}$ has the same direction as $\mathbf{u}$ with twice the magnitude of $\mathbf{u}$ (Figure 12.37).

b. Using scalar multiplication, $-2\mathbf{v} = -2\langle 3, 0, -1 \rangle = \langle -6, 0, 2 \rangle$. The vector $-2\mathbf{v}$ has the opposite direction as $\mathbf{v}$ and twice the magnitude of $\mathbf{v}$ (Figure 12.38).

c. Using vector addition and scalar multiplication,

$$\mathbf{u} + 2\mathbf{v} = \langle 2, -4, 1 \rangle + 2\langle 3, 0, -1 \rangle = \langle 8, -4, -1 \rangle.$$

The vector $\mathbf{u} + 2\mathbf{v}$ is drawn by applying the Parallelogram Rule to $\mathbf{u}$ and $\mathbf{2v}$ (Figure 12.39).

Related Exercises 35–38 ◀

Magnitude and Unit Vectors

The magnitude of the vector $\overrightarrow{PQ}$ from $P(x_1, y_1, z_1)$ to $Q(x_2, y_2, z_2)$ is denoted $|\overrightarrow{PQ}|$; it is the distance between P and Q and is given by the distance formula (Figure 12.40).

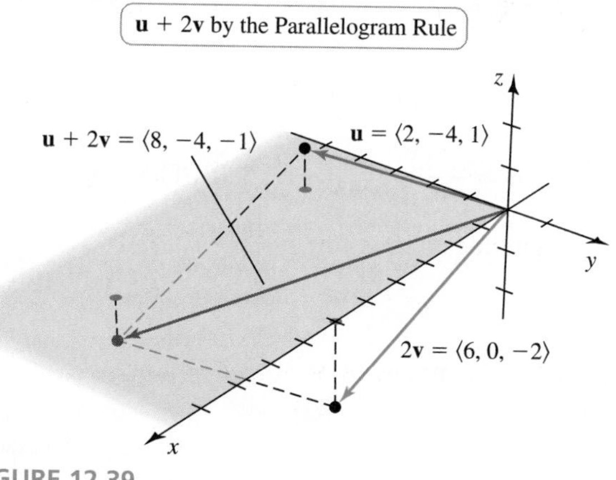

FIGURE 12.39

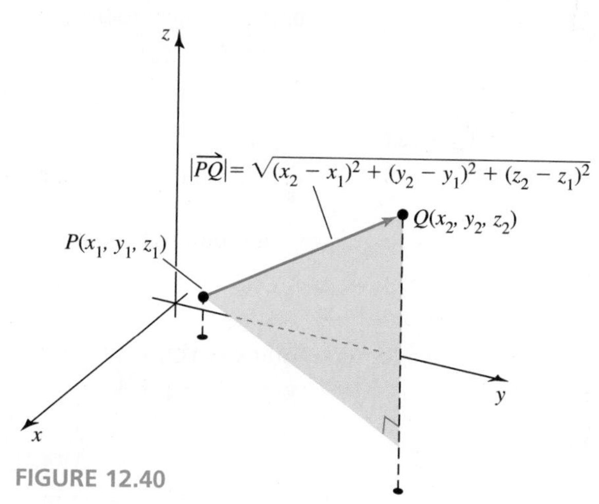

FIGURE 12.40

> **DEFINTION Magnitude of a Vector**
>
> The **magnitude** (or **length**) of the vector $\overrightarrow{PQ} = \langle x_2 - x_1, y_2 - y_1, z_2 - z_1 \rangle$ is the distance from $P(x_1, y_1, z_1)$ to $Q(x_2, y_2, z_2)$:
>
> $$|\overrightarrow{PQ}| = \sqrt{(x_2 - x_1)^2 + (y_2 - y_1)^2 + (z_2 - z_1)^2}$$

The coordinate unit vectors introduced in Section 12.1 extend naturally to three dimensions. The three coordinate unit vectors in $\mathbf{R}^3$ are (Figure 12.41)

$$\mathbf{i} = \langle 1, 0, 0 \rangle, \quad \mathbf{j} = \langle 0, 1, 0 \rangle, \quad \text{and} \quad \mathbf{k} = \langle 0, 0, 1 \rangle.$$

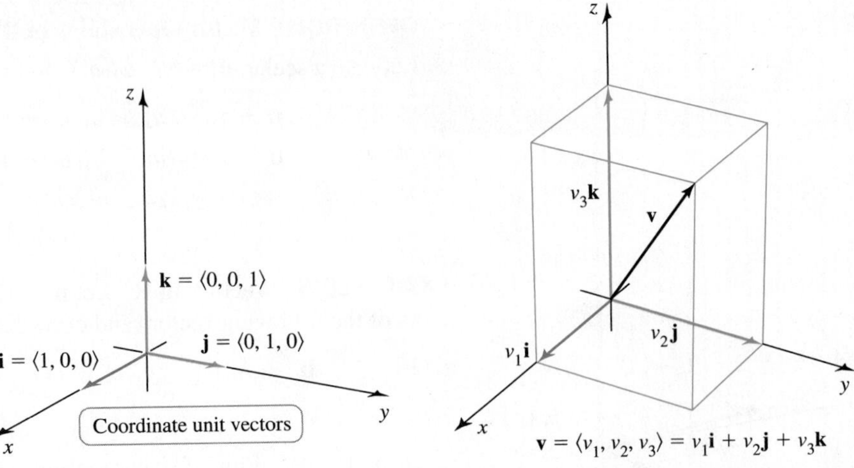

FIGURE 12.41

These unit vectors give an alternative way of expressing position vectors. If $\mathbf{v} = \langle v_1, v_2, v_3\rangle$, then we have

$$\mathbf{v} = v_1\langle 1, 0, 0\rangle + v_2\langle 0, 1, 0\rangle + v_3\langle 0, 0, 1\rangle = v_1\mathbf{i} + v_2\mathbf{j} + v_3\mathbf{k}.$$

EXAMPLE 6 **Magnitudes and unit vectors** Consider the points $P(5, 3, 1)$ and $Q(-7, 8, 1)$.

a. Express $\overrightarrow{PQ}$ in terms of the unit vectors **i**, **j**, and **k**.

b. Find the magnitude of $\overrightarrow{PQ}$.

c. Find the position vector of magnitude 10 in the direction of $\overrightarrow{PQ}$.

SOLUTION

a. $\overrightarrow{PQ}$ is equal to the position vector $\langle -7 - 5, 8 - 3, 1 - 1\rangle = \langle -12, 5, 0\rangle$. Thus, $\overrightarrow{PQ} = -12\mathbf{i} + 5\mathbf{j}$.

b. $|\overrightarrow{PQ}| = |-12\mathbf{i} + 5\mathbf{j}| = \sqrt{12^2 + 5^2} = \sqrt{169} = 13$

c. The unit vector in the direction of $\overrightarrow{PQ}$ is $\mathbf{u} = \dfrac{\overrightarrow{PQ}}{|\overrightarrow{PQ}|} = \frac{1}{13}\langle -12, 5, 0\rangle$. Therefore, a vector in the direction of **u** with a magnitude of 10 is $10\mathbf{u} = \frac{10}{13}\langle -12, 5, 0\rangle$.

Related Exercises 39–44 ◀

QUICK CHECK 5 Which vector has the smaller magnitude: $\mathbf{u} = 3\mathbf{i} - \mathbf{j} - \mathbf{k}$ or $\mathbf{v} = 2(\mathbf{i} + \mathbf{j} + \mathbf{k})$? ◀

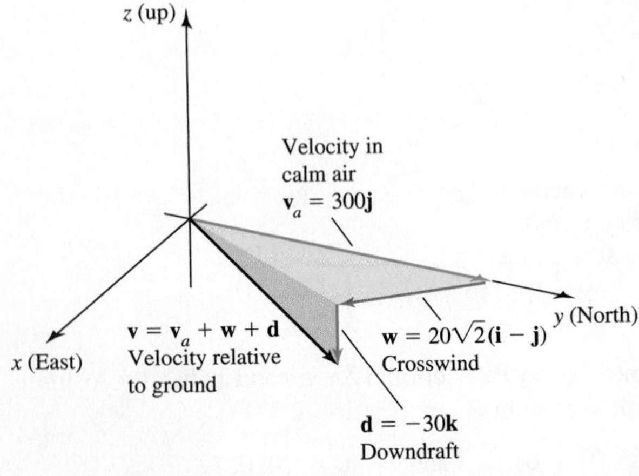

FIGURE 12.42

EXAMPLE 7 **Flight in crosswinds** A plane is flying horizontally due north in calm air at 300 mi/hr when it encounters a horizontal crosswind blowing southeast at 40 mi/hr and a downdraft blowing vertically downward at 30 mi/hr. What are the resulting speed and direction of the plane relative to the ground?

SOLUTION Let the unit vectors **i**, **j**, and **k** point east, north, and upward, respectively (Figure 12.42). The velocity of the plane relative to the air (300 mi/hr due north) is $\mathbf{v}_a = 300\mathbf{j}$. The crosswind blows 45° south of east, so its component to the east is $40\cos 45° = 20\sqrt{2}$ (in the **i** direction) and its component to the south is $40\cos 45° = 20\sqrt{2}$ (in the $-\mathbf{j}$ direction). Therefore, the crosswind may be expressed as $\mathbf{w} = 20\sqrt{2}\mathbf{i} - 20\sqrt{2}\mathbf{j}$. Finally, the downdraft in the negative **k** direction is $\mathbf{d} = -30\mathbf{k}$. The velocity of the plane relative to the ground is the sum of $\mathbf{v}_a$, $\mathbf{w}$, and $\mathbf{d}$:

$$\begin{aligned}\mathbf{v} &= \mathbf{v}_a + \mathbf{w} + \mathbf{d}\\ &= 300\mathbf{j} + (20\sqrt{2}\mathbf{i} - 20\sqrt{2}\mathbf{j}) - 30\mathbf{k}\\ &= 20\sqrt{2}\mathbf{i} + (300 - 20\sqrt{2})\mathbf{j} - 30\mathbf{k}\end{aligned}$$

Figure 12.42 shows the velocity vector of the plane. A quick calculation shows that the speed is $|\mathbf{v}| \approx 275$ mi/hr. The direction of the plane is slightly east of north and downward. (In the next section, we present methods for precisely determining the direction of the vector.)

Related Exercises 45–47

SECTION 12.2 EXERCISES

Review Questions

1. Explain how to plot the point $(3, -2, 1)$ in $\mathbf{R}^3$.
2. What is the y-coordinate of all points in the xz-plane?
3. Describe the plane $x = 4$.
4. What position vector is equal to the vector from $(3, 5, -2)$ to $(0, -6, 3)$?
5. Let $\mathbf{u} = \langle 3, 5, -7\rangle$ and $\mathbf{v} = \langle 6, -5, 1\rangle$. Evaluate $\mathbf{u} + \mathbf{v}$ and $3\mathbf{u} - \mathbf{v}$.
6. What is the magnitude of a vector joining two points $P(x_1, y_1, z_1)$ and $Q(x_2, y_2, z_2)$?
7. Which point is farther from the origin, $(3, -1, 2)$ or $(0, 0, -4)$?
8. Express the vector from $P(-1, -4, 6)$ to $Q(1, 3, -6)$ as a position vector in terms of $\mathbf{i}$, $\mathbf{j}$, and $\mathbf{k}$.

Basic Skills

9–12. Points in $\mathbf{R}^3$ *Find the coordinates of the vertices A, B, and C of the following rectangular boxes.*

9.

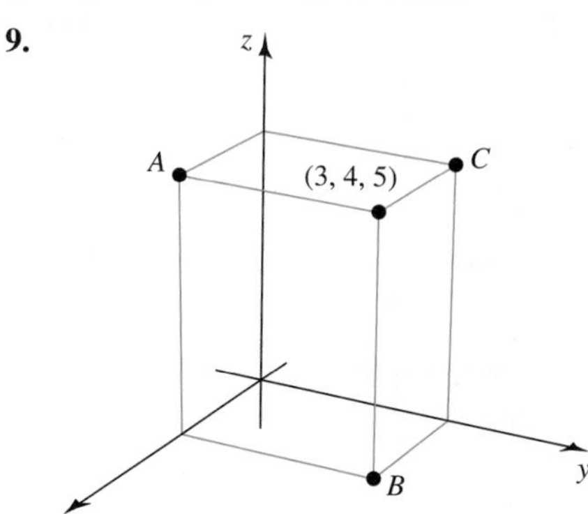

10.

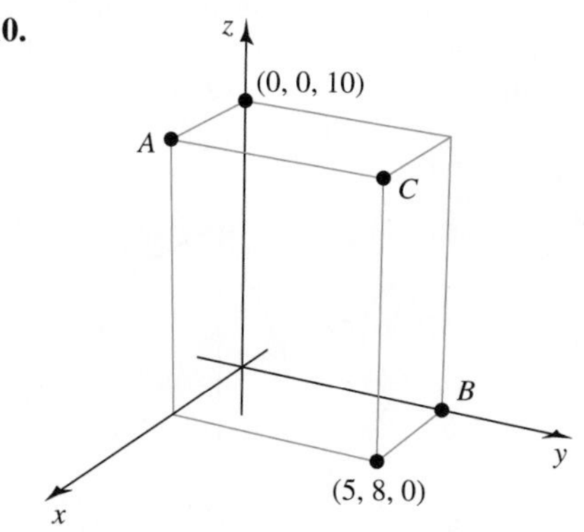

11.

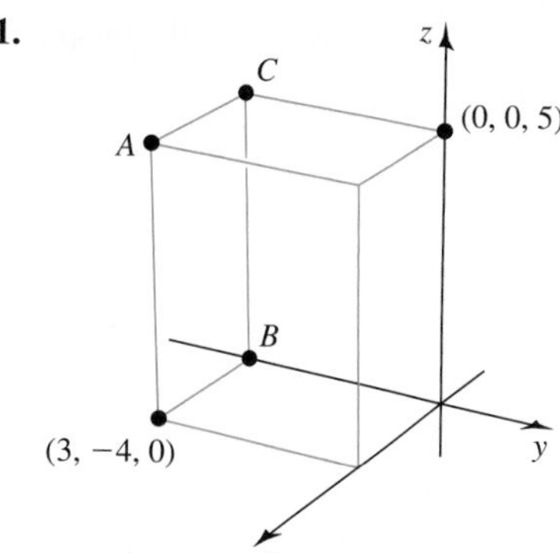

12. Assume all the edges have the same length.

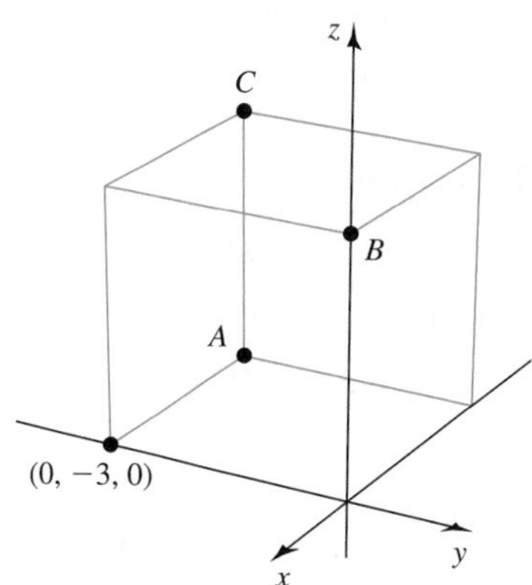

13–14. Plotting points in $\mathbf{R}^3$ *For each point $P(x, y, z)$ given below, let $A(x, y, 0)$, $B(x, 0, z)$, and $C(0, y, z)$ be points in the xy-, xz-, and yz-planes, respectively. Plot and label the points A, B, C, and P in $\mathbf{R}^3$.*

13. **a.** $P(2, 2, 4)$ **b.** $P(1, 2, 5)$ **c.** $P(-2, 0, 5)$

14. **a.** $P(-3, 2, 4)$ **b.** $P(4, -2, -3)$ **c.** $P(-2, -4, -3)$

15–20. Sketching planes *Sketch the following planes in the window $[0, 5] \times [0, 5] \times [0, 5]$.*

15. $x = 2$
16. $z = 3$
17. $y = 2$
18. $z = y$
19. The plane that passes through $(2, 0, 0)$, $(0, 3, 0)$, and $(0, 0, 4)$
20. The plane parallel to the xz-plane containing the point $(1, 2, 3)$
21. **Planes** Sketch the plane parallel to the xy-plane through $(2, 4, 2)$ and find its equation.
22. **Planes** Sketch the plane parallel to the yz-plane through $(2, 4, 2)$ and find its equation.

23–26. Spheres and balls *Find an equation or inequality that describes the following objects.*

23. A sphere with center $(1, 2, 3)$ and radius 4

24. A sphere with center $(1, 2, 0)$ passing through the point $(3, 4, 5)$

25. A ball with center $(-2, 0, 4)$ and radius 1

26. A ball with center $(0, -2, 6)$ with the point $(1, 4, 8)$ on its boundary

27. Midpoints and spheres Find an equation of the sphere passing through $P(1, 0, 5)$ and $Q(2, 3, 9)$ with its center at the midpoint of PQ.

28. Midpoints and spheres Find an equation of the sphere passing through $P(-4, 2, 3)$ and $Q(0, 2, 7)$ with its center at the midpoint of PQ.

29–34. Identifying sets *Give a geometric description of the following sets of points.*

29. $x^2 + y^2 + z^2 - 2y - 4z - 4 = 0$

30. $x^2 + y^2 + z^2 - 6x + 6y - 8z - 2 = 0$

31. $x^2 + y^2 - 14y + z^2 \geq -13$

32. $x^2 + y^2 - 14y + z^2 \leq -13$

33. $x^2 + y^2 + z^2 - 8x - 14y - 18z \leq 65$

34. $x^2 + y^2 + z^2 - 8x + 14y - 18z \geq 65$

35–38. Vector operations *For the given vectors* **u** *and* **v**, *evaluate the following expressions.*

a. $3\mathbf{u} + 2\mathbf{v}$ **b.** $4\mathbf{u} - \mathbf{v}$ **c.** $|\mathbf{u} + 3\mathbf{v}|$

35. $\mathbf{u} = \langle 1, 3, 0 \rangle, \mathbf{v} = \langle 3, 0, 2 \rangle$

36. $\mathbf{u} = \langle -1, 1, 0 \rangle, \mathbf{v} = \langle 2, -4, 1 \rangle$

37. $\mathbf{u} = \langle -7, 5, 1 \rangle, \mathbf{v} = \langle -2, 4, 0 \rangle$

38. $\mathbf{u} = \langle 5, 1, 3\sqrt{2} \rangle, \mathbf{v} = \langle 2, 0, 7\sqrt{2} \rangle$

39–44. Unit vectors and magnitude *Consider the following points P and Q.*

a. *Find $\overrightarrow{PQ}$ and state your answer in two forms: $\langle a, b, c \rangle$ and $a\mathbf{i} + b\mathbf{j} + c\mathbf{k}$.*

b. *Find the magnitude of $\overrightarrow{PQ}$.*

c. *Find two unit vectors parallel to $\overrightarrow{PQ}$.*

39. $P(1, 5, 0), Q(3, 11, 2)$

40. $P(5, 11, 12), Q(1, 14, 13)$

41. $P(-3, 1, 0), Q(-3, -4, 1)$

42. $P(3, 8, 12), Q(3, 9, 11)$

43. $P(0, 0, 2), Q(-2, 4, 0)$

44. $P(a, b, c), Q(1, 1, -1)$ (a, b, c are real numbers).

45. Crosswinds A small plane is flying horizontally due east in calm air at 250 mi/hr when it is hit by a horizontal crosswind blowing southwest at 50 mi/hr and a 30 mi/hr updraft. Find the resulting speed of the plane and describe with a sketch the approximate direction of the velocity relative to the ground.

46. Combined force An object at the origin is acted on by the forces $\mathbf{F}_1 = 20\mathbf{i} - 10\mathbf{j}$, $\mathbf{F}_2 = 30\mathbf{j} + 10\mathbf{k}$, and $\mathbf{F}_3 = 40\mathbf{j} + 20\mathbf{k}$. Find the magnitude of the combined force and describe the approximate direction of the force.

47. Submarine course A submarine climbs at an angle of 30° above the horizontal with a heading to the northeast. If its speed is 20 knots, find the components of the velocity in the east, north, and vertical directions.

48. Maintaining equilibrium An object is acted upon by the forces $\mathbf{F}_1 = \langle 10, 6, 3 \rangle$ and $\mathbf{F}_2 = \langle 0, 4, 9 \rangle$. Find the force $\mathbf{F}_3$ that must act on the object so that the sum of the forces is zero.

Further Explorations

49. Explain why or why not Determine whether the following statements are true and give an explanation or counterexample.

a. Suppose **u** and **v** both make a 45° angle with **w** in $\mathbf{R}^3$. Then, $\mathbf{u} + \mathbf{v}$ makes a 45° angle with **w**.

b. Suppose **u** and **v** both make a 90° angle with **w** in $\mathbf{R}^3$. Then, $\mathbf{u} + \mathbf{v}$ can never make a 90° angle with **w**.

c. $\mathbf{i} + \mathbf{j} + \mathbf{k} = \mathbf{0}$

d. The intersection of the planes $x = 1$, $y = 1$, and $z = 1$ is a point.

50–52. Sets of points *Describe with a sketch the sets of points (x, y, z) satisfying the following equations.*

50. $(x + 1)(y - 3) = 0$

51. $x^2y^2z^2 > 0$

52. $y - z = 0$

53–56. Parallel vectors of varying lengths *Find vectors parallel to* **v** *of the given length.*

53. $\mathbf{v} = \langle 6, -8, 0 \rangle$; length $= 20$

54. $\mathbf{v} = \langle 3, -2, 6 \rangle$; length $= 10$

55. $\mathbf{v} = \overrightarrow{PQ}$ with $P(3, 4, 0)$ and $Q(2, 3, 1)$; length $= 3$

56. $\mathbf{v} = \overrightarrow{PQ}$ with $P(1, 0, 1)$ and $Q(2, -1, 1)$; length $= 3$

57. Collinear points Determine whether the points P, Q, and R are collinear (lie on a line) by comparing $\overrightarrow{PQ}$ and $\overrightarrow{PR}$. If the points are collinear, determine which point lies between the other two points.

a. $P(1, 6, -5), Q(2, 5, -3), R(4, 3, 1)$

b. $P(1, 5, 7), Q(5, 13, -1), R(0, 3, 9)$

c. $P(1, 2, 3), Q(2, -3, 6), R(3, -1, 9)$

d. $P(9, 5, 1), Q(11, 18, 4), R(6, 3, 0)$

58. Collinear points Determine the values of x and y such that the points $(1, 2, 3)$, $(4, 7, 1)$, and $(x, y, 2)$ are collinear (lie on a line).

59. Lengths of the diagonals of a box A fisherman wants to know if his fly rod will fit in a rectangular 2 ft × 3 ft × 4 ft packing box. What is the longest rod that fits in this box?

Applications

T 60. Forces on an inclined plane An object on an inclined plane does not slide provided the component of the object's weight parallel to the plane $|\mathbf{W}_{\text{par}}|$ is less than or equal to the magnitude of the opposing frictional force $|\mathbf{F}_\text{f}|$. The magnitude of the frictional force, in turn, is proportional to the component of the object's weight perpendicular to the plane $|\mathbf{W}_{\text{perp}}|$ (see figure). The constant of proportionality is the coefficient of static friction, μ.

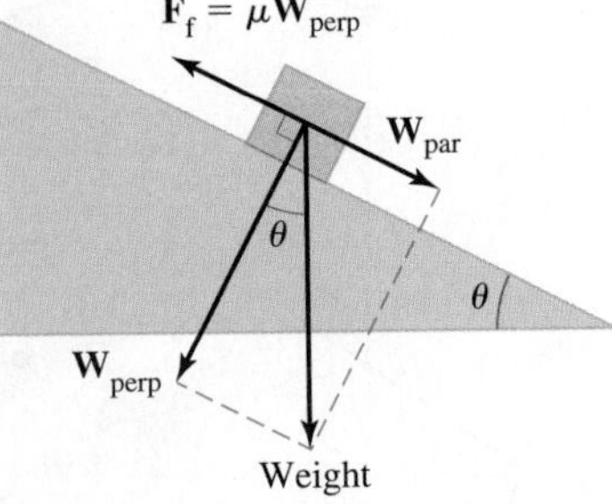

a. Suppose a 100-lb block rests in a plane that is tilted at an angle of $\theta = 20°$ to the horizontal. Find $|\mathbf{W}_{\text{par}}|$ and $|\mathbf{W}_{\text{perp}}|$.
b. The condition for the block not sliding is $|\mathbf{W}_{\text{par}}| \leq \mu|\mathbf{W}_{\text{perp}}|$. If $\mu = 0.65$, does the block slide?
c. What is the critical angle above which the block slides?

61. Three-cable load A 500-lb load hangs from three cables of equal length that are anchored at the points $(-2, 0, 0)$, $(1, \sqrt{3}, 0)$, and $(1, -\sqrt{3}, 0)$. The load is located at $(0, 0, -2\sqrt{3})$. Find the vectors describing the forces on the cables due to the load.

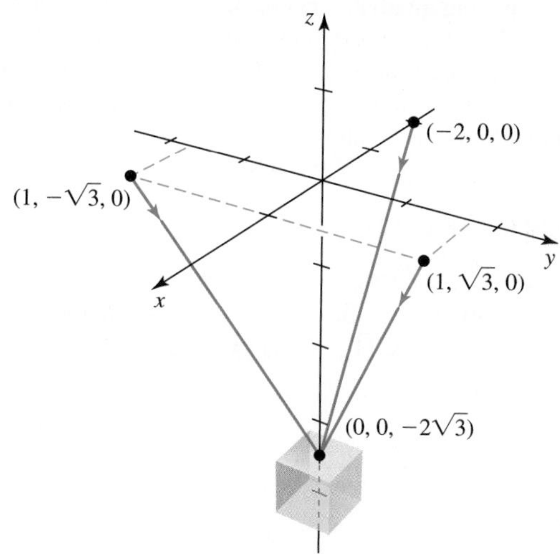

62. Four-cable load A 500-lb load hangs from four cables of equal length that are anchored at the points $(\pm 2, 0, 0)$ and $(0, \pm 2, 0)$. The load is located at $(0, 0, -4)$. Find the vectors describing the forces on the cables due to the load.

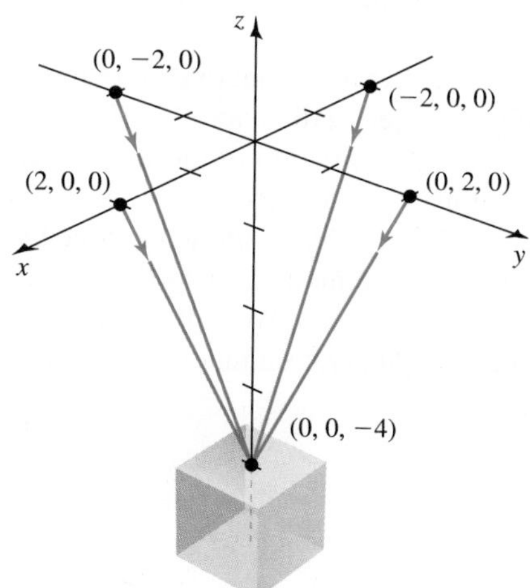

Additional Exercises

63. Possible parallelograms The points $O(0, 0, 0)$, $P(1, 4, 6)$, and $Q(2, 4, 3)$ lie at three vertices of a parallelogram. Find all possible locations of the fourth vertex.

64. Diagonals of parallelograms Two sides of a parallelogram are formed by the vectors $\mathbf{u}$ and $\mathbf{v}$. Prove that the diagonals of the parallelogram are $\mathbf{u} + \mathbf{v}$ and $\mathbf{u} - \mathbf{v}$.

65. Midpoint formula Prove that the midpoint of the line segment joining $P(x_1, y_1, z_1)$ and $Q(x_2, y_2, z_2)$ is

$$\left(\frac{x_1 + x_2}{2}, \frac{y_1 + y_2}{2}, \frac{z_1 + z_2}{2}\right).$$

66. Equation of a sphere For constants a, b, c, and d, show that the equation

$$x^2 + y^2 + z^2 - 2ax - 2by - 2cz = d$$

describes a sphere centered at (a, b, c) with radius r, where $r^2 = d + a^2 + b^2 + c^2$, provided $d + a^2 + b^2 + c^2 > 0$.

67. Medians of a triangle—coordinate free Assume that $\mathbf{u}$, $\mathbf{v}$, and $\mathbf{w}$ are vectors in $\mathbf{R}^3$ that form the sides of a triangle (see figure). Use the following steps to prove that the medians intersect at a point that divides each median in a 2:1 ratio. The proof does not use a coordinate system.

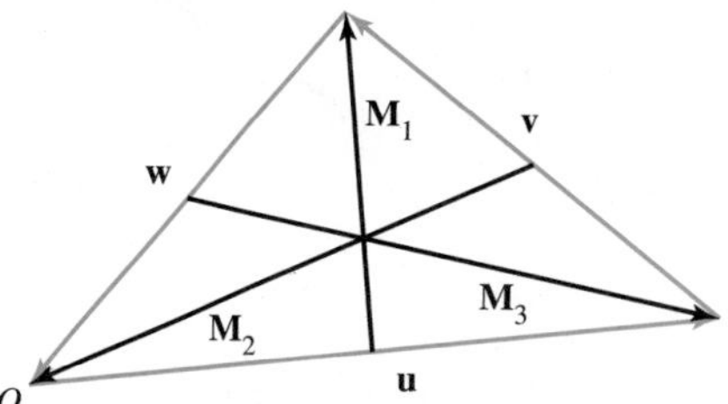

a. Show that $\mathbf{u} + \mathbf{v} + \mathbf{w} = 0$.
b. Let $\mathbf{M}_1$ be the median vector from the midpoint of $\mathbf{u}$ to the opposite vertex. Define $\mathbf{M}_2$ and $\mathbf{M}_3$ similarly. Using the geometry of vector addition show that $\mathbf{M}_1 = \mathbf{u}/2 + \mathbf{v}$. Find analogous expressions for $\mathbf{M}_2$ and $\mathbf{M}_3$.
c. Let $\mathbf{a}$, $\mathbf{b}$, and $\mathbf{c}$ be the vectors from O to the points one-third of the way along $\mathbf{M}_1$, $\mathbf{M}_2$, and $\mathbf{M}_3$, respectively. Show that $\mathbf{a} = \mathbf{b} = \mathbf{c} = (\mathbf{u} - \mathbf{w})/3$.
d. Conclude that the medians intersect at a point that divides each median in a 2:1 ratio.

68. Medians of a triangle—with coordinates In contrast to the proof in Exercise 67, we now use coordinates and position vectors to prove the same result. Without loss of generality, let $P(x_1, y_1, 0)$ and $Q(x_2, y_2, 0)$ be two points in the xy-plane and let $R(x_3, y_3, z_3)$ be a third point, such that P, Q, and R do not lie on a line. Consider $\triangle PQR$.

a. Let M_1 be the midpoint of the side PQ. Find the coordinates of M_1 and the components of the vector $\overrightarrow{RM_1}$.
b. Find the vector $\overrightarrow{OZ_1}$ from the origin to the point Z_1 two-thirds of the way along $\overrightarrow{RM_1}$.
c. Repeat the calculation of part (b) with the midpoint M_2 of RQ and the vector $\overrightarrow{PM_2}$ to obtain the vector $\overrightarrow{OZ_2}$.
d. Repeat the calculation of part (b) with the midpoint M_3 of PR and the vector $\overrightarrow{QM_3}$ to obtain the vector $\overrightarrow{OZ_3}$.

e. Conclude that the medians of $\triangle PQR$ intersect at a point. Give the coordinates of the point.

f. With $P(2, 4, 0)$, $Q(4, 1, 0)$, $R(6, 3, 4)$, find the point at which the medians of $\triangle PQR$ intersect.

69. The amazing quadrilateral property—coordinate free The points P, Q, R, and S, joined by the vectors **u**, **v**, **w**, **x**, are the vertices of a quadrilateral in $\mathbf{R}^3$. *The four points needn't lie in a plane* (see figure). Use the following steps to prove that the line segments joining the midpoints of the sides of the quadrilateral form a parallelogram. The proof does not use a coordinate system.

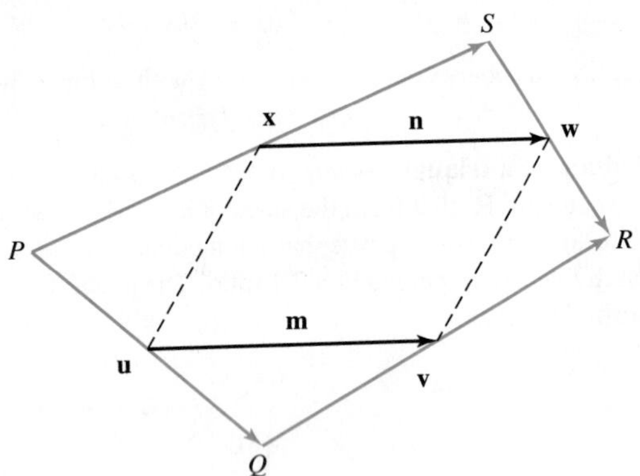

a. Use vector addition to show that $\mathbf{u} + \mathbf{v} = \mathbf{w} + \mathbf{x}$.

b. Let **m** be the vector that joins the midpoints of PQ and QR. Show that $\mathbf{m} = (\mathbf{u} + \mathbf{v})/2$.

c. Let **n** be the vector that joins the midpoints of PS and SR. Show that $\mathbf{n} = (\mathbf{x} + \mathbf{w})/2$.

d. Combine parts (a), (b), and (c) to conclude that $\mathbf{m} = \mathbf{n}$.

e. Explain why part (d) implies that the line segments joining the midpoints of the sides of the quadrilateral form a parallelogram.

70. The amazing quadrilateral property—with coordinates Prove the quadrilateral property in Exercise 69 assuming the coordinates of P, Q, R, and S are $P(x_1, y_1, 0)$, $Q(x_2, y_2, 0)$, $R(x_3, y_3, 0)$, and $S(x_4, y_4, z_4)$, where we assume that P, Q, and R lie in the xy-plane without loss of generality.

QUICK CHECK ANSWERS

1. Southwest; due east and upward; southwest and downward **2.** yz-plane; xy-plane **3.** No solution **4.** **u** and **v** are parallel. **5.** $|\mathbf{u}| = \sqrt{11}$ and $|\mathbf{v}| = \sqrt{12} = 2\sqrt{3}$; **u** has the smaller magnitude.

12.3 Dot Products

The dot product is also called the *scalar product*, a term we do not use in order to avoid confusion with *scalar multiplication*.

The *dot product* is used to determine the angle between two vectors. It is also a tool for calculating *projections*—the measure of how much of a given vector lies in the direction of another vector.

To see the usefulness of the dot product, consider an example. Recall that the work done by a constant force F in moving an object a distance d is $W = Fd$ (Section 6.6). This rule applies provided the force acts in the direction of motion (Figure 12.43a). Now assume the force is a vector **F** applied at an angle θ to the direction of motion; the resulting displacement of the object is a vector **d**. In this case, the work done by the force is the component of the force in the direction of motion multiplied by the distance moved by the object, which is $W = (|\mathbf{F}| \cos\theta)|\mathbf{d}|$ (Figure 12.43b). We call this product of the magnitudes of two vectors and the cosine of the angle between them the *dot product*.

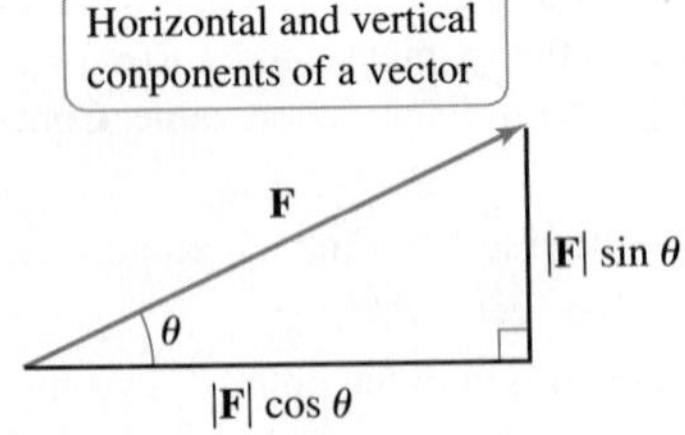

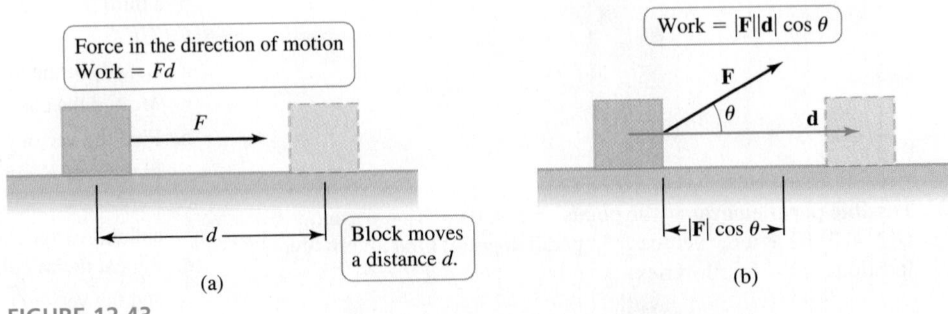

FIGURE 12.43

Two Forms of the Dot Product

Guided by the example of work done by a force, we give one definition of the dot product. Then, an equivalent definition is derived that is often better suited for computation.

> **DEFINITION Dot Product**
>
> Given two nonzero vectors $\mathbf{u}$ and $\mathbf{v}$ in two or three dimensions, their **dot product** is
>
> $$\mathbf{u} \cdot \mathbf{v} = |\mathbf{u}||\mathbf{v}| \cos \theta,$$
>
> where θ is the angle between $\mathbf{u}$ and $\mathbf{v}$ with $0 \leq \theta \leq \pi$ (Figure 12.44). If $\mathbf{u} = \mathbf{0}$ or $\mathbf{v} = \mathbf{0}$, then $\mathbf{u} \cdot \mathbf{v} = 0$, and θ is undefined.

The dot product of two vectors is itself a scalar. Two special cases immediately arise:

- $\mathbf{u}$ and $\mathbf{v}$ are parallel ($\theta = 0$ or $\theta = \pi$) if and only if $\mathbf{u} \cdot \mathbf{v} = \pm|\mathbf{u}||\mathbf{v}|$.
- $\mathbf{u}$ and $\mathbf{v}$ are perpendicular ($\theta = \pi/2$) if and only if $\mathbf{u} \cdot \mathbf{v} = 0$.

The second case gives rise to the important property of **orthogonality**.

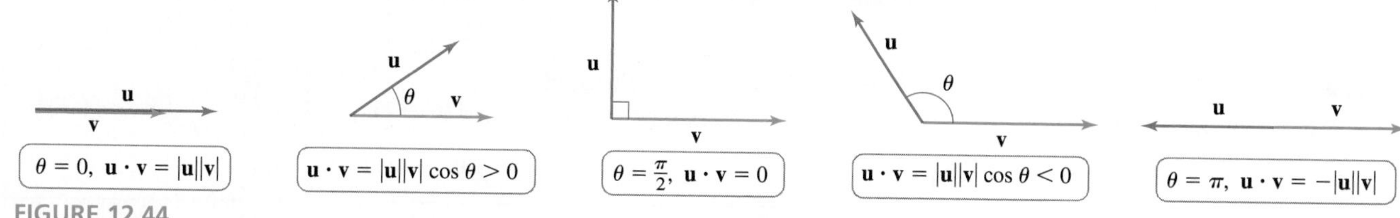

FIGURE 12.44

> In two and three dimensions, *orthogonal* and *perpendicular* are used interchangeably. *Orthogonal* is a more general term that also applies in more than three dimensions.

> **DEFINITION Orthogonal Vectors**
>
> Two vectors $\mathbf{u}$ and $\mathbf{v}$ are **orthogonal** if and only if $\mathbf{u} \cdot \mathbf{v} = 0$. The zero vector is orthogonal to all vectors. In two or three dimensions, two nonzero orthogonal vectors are perpendicular to each other.

QUICK CHECK 1 Sketch two vectors $\mathbf{u}$ and $\mathbf{v}$ with $\theta = 0$. Sketch two vectors $\mathbf{u}$ and $\mathbf{v}$ with $\theta = \pi$.

EXAMPLE 1 Dot products Compute the dot products of the following vectors.

a. $\mathbf{u} = 2\mathbf{i} - 6\mathbf{j}$ and $\mathbf{v} = 12\mathbf{k}$

b. $\mathbf{u} = \langle \sqrt{3}, 1 \rangle$ and $\mathbf{v} = \langle 0, 1 \rangle$

SOLUTION

a. The vector $\mathbf{u}$ lies in the xy-plane and the vector $\mathbf{v}$ is perpendicular to the xy-plane. Therefore, $\theta = \dfrac{\pi}{2}$, $\mathbf{u}$ and $\mathbf{v}$ are orthogonal, and $\mathbf{u} \cdot \mathbf{v} = 0$ (Figure 12.45a).

b. As shown in Figure 12.45b, $\mathbf{u}$ and $\mathbf{v}$ form two sides of a 30–60–90 triangle in the xy-plane, with an angle of $\pi/3$ between them. Because $|\mathbf{u}| = 2$, $|\mathbf{v}| = 1$, and $\cos \pi/3 = 1/2$, the dot product is

$$\mathbf{u} \cdot \mathbf{v} = |\mathbf{u}||\mathbf{v}| \cos \theta = 2 \cdot 1 \cdot \tfrac{1}{2} = 1.$$

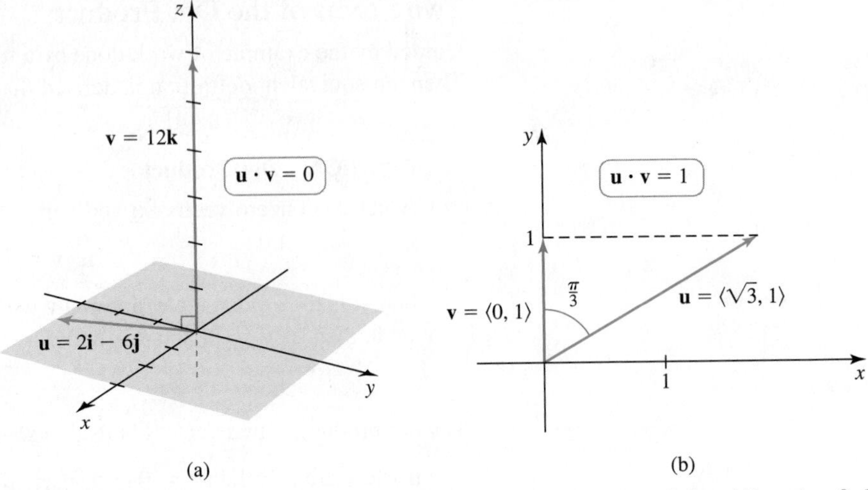

FIGURE 12.45

Related Exercises 9–12 ◀

The definition of the dot product requires knowing the angle θ between the vectors. Often the angle is not known; in fact, it may be exactly what we seek. For this reason, we present another method for computing the dot product that does not require knowing θ.

➤ In $\mathbf{R}^2$ with $\mathbf{u} = \langle u_1, u_2 \rangle$ and $\mathbf{v} = \langle v_1, v_2 \rangle$, $\mathbf{u} \cdot \mathbf{v} = u_1 v_1 + u_2 v_2$.

THEOREM 12.1 Dot Product
Given two vectors $\mathbf{u} = \langle u_1, u_2, u_3 \rangle$ and $\mathbf{v} = \langle v_1, v_2, v_3 \rangle$,

$$\mathbf{u} \cdot \mathbf{v} = u_1 v_1 + u_2 v_2 + u_3 v_3.$$

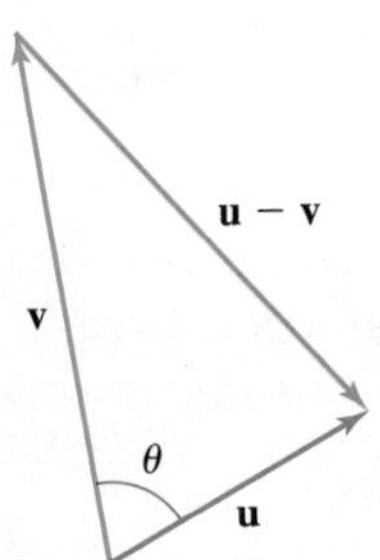

FIGURE 12.46

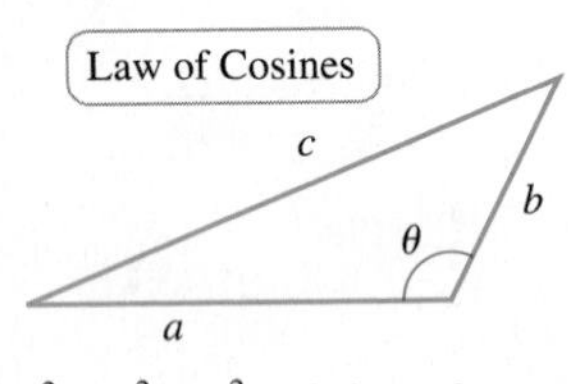

Proof Consider two position vectors $\mathbf{u} = \langle u_1, u_2, u_3 \rangle$ and $\mathbf{v} = \langle v_1, v_2, v_3 \rangle$, and suppose θ is the angle between them. The vector $\mathbf{u} - \mathbf{v}$ forms the third side of a triangle (Figure 12.46). By the Law of Cosines,

$$|\mathbf{u} - \mathbf{v}|^2 = |\mathbf{u}|^2 + |\mathbf{v}|^2 - 2\underbrace{|\mathbf{u}||\mathbf{v}| \cos \theta}_{\mathbf{u} \cdot \mathbf{v}}.$$

The definition of the dot product, $\mathbf{u} \cdot \mathbf{v} = |\mathbf{u}||\mathbf{v}| \cos \theta$, allows us to write

$$\mathbf{u} \cdot \mathbf{v} = |\mathbf{u}||\mathbf{v}| \cos \theta = \frac{1}{2}(|\mathbf{u}|^2 + |\mathbf{v}|^2 - |\mathbf{u} - \mathbf{v}|^2). \quad (1)$$

Using the definition of magnitude, we find that

$$|\mathbf{u}|^2 = u_1^2 + u_2^2 + u_3^2, \quad |\mathbf{v}|^2 = v_1^2 + v_2^2 + v_3^2,$$

and

$$|\mathbf{u} - \mathbf{v}|^2 = (u_1 - v_1)^2 + (u_2 - v_2)^2 + (u_3 - v_3)^2.$$

Expanding the terms in $|\mathbf{u} - \mathbf{v}|^2$ and simplifying yields

$$|\mathbf{u}|^2 + |\mathbf{v}|^2 - |\mathbf{u} - \mathbf{v}|^2 = 2(u_1 v_1 + u_2 v_2 + u_3 v_3).$$

Substituting into expression (1) gives a compact expression for the dot product:

$$\mathbf{u} \cdot \mathbf{v} = u_1 v_1 + u_2 v_2 + u_3 v_3.$$ ◀

This new representation of $\mathbf{u} \cdot \mathbf{v}$ has two immediate consequences.

1. Combining it with the definition of dot product gives

$$\mathbf{u} \cdot \mathbf{v} = u_1 v_1 + u_2 v_2 + u_3 v_3 = |\mathbf{u}||\mathbf{v}| \cos \theta.$$

If **u** and **v** are both nonzero, then

$$\cos\theta = \frac{u_1v_1 + u_2v_2 + u_3v_3}{|\mathbf{u}||\mathbf{v}|},$$

and we have a way to compute θ.

2. Notice that $\mathbf{u}\cdot\mathbf{u} = u_1^2 + u_2^2 + u_3^2 = |\mathbf{u}|^2$. Therefore, we have a relationship between the dot product and the magnitude of a vector: $|\mathbf{u}| = \sqrt{\mathbf{u}\cdot\mathbf{u}}$ or $|\mathbf{u}|^2 = \mathbf{u}\cdot\mathbf{u}$.

QUICK CHECK 2 Use Theorem 12.1 to compute the dot products $\mathbf{i}\cdot\mathbf{j}$, $\mathbf{i}\cdot\mathbf{k}$, and $\mathbf{j}\cdot\mathbf{k}$ for the unit coordinate vectors. What do you conclude about the angles between these vectors?

EXAMPLE 2 **Dot products and angles** Let $\mathbf{u} = \langle\sqrt{3}, 1, 0\rangle$, $\mathbf{v} = \langle 1, \sqrt{3}, 0\rangle$, and $\mathbf{w} = \langle 1, \sqrt{3}, 2\sqrt{3}\rangle$.

a. Compute $\mathbf{u}\cdot\mathbf{v}$.

b. Find the angle between **u** and **v**.

c. Find the angle between **u** and **w**.

SOLUTION

a. $\mathbf{u}\cdot\mathbf{v} = \langle\sqrt{3}, 1, 0\rangle\cdot\langle 1, \sqrt{3}, 0\rangle = \sqrt{3} + \sqrt{3} + 0 = 2\sqrt{3}$

b. Note that $|\mathbf{u}| = \sqrt{\mathbf{u}\cdot\mathbf{u}} = \sqrt{\langle\sqrt{3},1,0\rangle\cdot\langle\sqrt{3},1,0\rangle} = 2$ and similarly $|\mathbf{v}| = 2$. Therefore,

$$\cos\theta = \frac{\mathbf{u}\cdot\mathbf{v}}{|\mathbf{u}||\mathbf{v}|} = \frac{2\sqrt{3}}{2\cdot 2} = \frac{\sqrt{3}}{2}.$$

Because $0 \le \theta \le \pi$, it follows that $\theta = \pi/6$.

c. $\cos\theta = \dfrac{\mathbf{u}\cdot\mathbf{w}}{|\mathbf{u}||\mathbf{w}|} = \dfrac{\langle\sqrt{3},1,0\rangle\cdot\langle 1,\sqrt{3},2\sqrt{3}\rangle}{|\langle\sqrt{3},1,0\rangle||\langle 1,\sqrt{3},2\sqrt{3}\rangle|} = \dfrac{2\sqrt{3}}{2\cdot 4} = \dfrac{\sqrt{3}}{4}$

It follows that

$$\theta = \cos^{-1}\left(\frac{\sqrt{3}}{4}\right) \approx 1.12\text{ rad} \approx 64.3°.$$

Related Exercises 13–18

Properties of Dot Products The properties of the dot product in the following theorem are easily proved using vector components (Exercises 67–69).

Theorem 12.1 extends to vectors with any number of components. If $\mathbf{u} = \langle u_1, \ldots, u_n\rangle$ and $\mathbf{v} = \langle v_1, \ldots, v_n\rangle$, then

$$\mathbf{u}\cdot\mathbf{v} = u_1v_1 + \cdots + u_nv_n.$$

The properties in Theorem 12.2 also apply in two or more dimensions.

THEOREM 12.2 **Properties of the Dot Product**

Suppose **u**, **v**, and **w** are vectors and let c be a scalar.

1. $\mathbf{u}\cdot\mathbf{v} = \mathbf{v}\cdot\mathbf{u}$ Commutative property
2. $c(\mathbf{u}\cdot\mathbf{v}) = (c\mathbf{u})\cdot\mathbf{v} = \mathbf{u}\cdot(c\mathbf{v})$ Associative property
3. $\mathbf{u}\cdot(\mathbf{v} + \mathbf{w}) = \mathbf{u}\cdot\mathbf{v} + \mathbf{u}\cdot\mathbf{w}$ Distributive property

Orthogonal Projections

Given vectors **u** and **v**, how closely aligned are they? That is, how much of **u** points in the direction of **v**? This question is answered using *projections.* As shown in Figure 12.47a, the projection of the vector **u** onto a nonzero vector **v**, denoted $\text{proj}_{\mathbf{v}}\mathbf{u}$, is the "shadow" cast by **u** onto the line through **v**. The projection of **u** onto **v** is itself a vector; it points in the same direction as **v** if the angle between **u** and **v** lies in the interval $0 \le \theta < \pi/2$ (Figure 12.47b); it points in the direction opposite to that of **v** if the angle between **u** and **v** lies in the interval $\pi/2 < \theta \le \pi$ (Figure 12.47c).

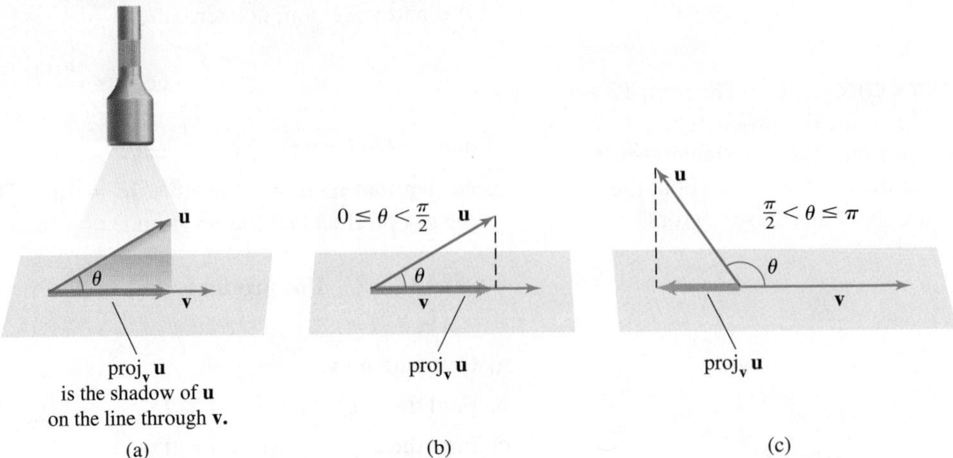

FIGURE 12.47 (a) (b) (c)

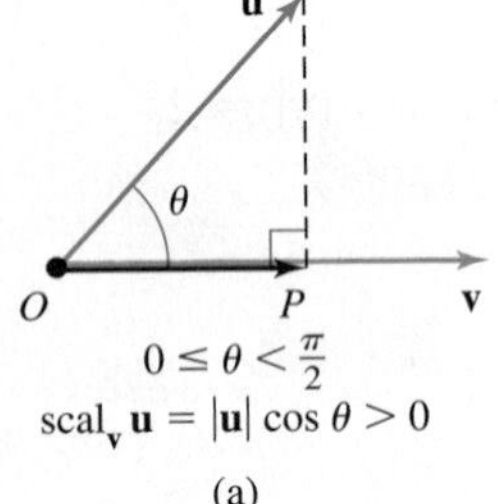

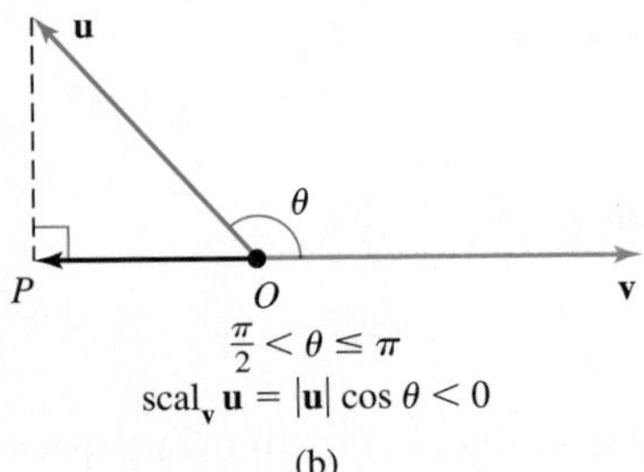

FIGURE 12.48

➤ Notice that $\text{scal}_{\mathbf{v}}\mathbf{u}$ may be positive, negative, or zero. However, $|\text{scal}_{\mathbf{v}}\mathbf{u}|$ is the length of $\text{proj}_{\mathbf{v}}\mathbf{u}$. The projection $\text{proj}_{\mathbf{v}}\mathbf{u}$ is defined for all vectors **u**, but only for nonzero vectors **v**.

To find the projection of **u** onto **v**, we proceed as follows: With the tails of **u** and **v** together, we drop a perpendicular line segment from the head of **u** to the point P on the line through **v** (Figure 12.48). The vector $\overrightarrow{OP}$ is the *orthogonal projection of* **u** *onto* **v**. An expression for $\text{proj}_{\mathbf{v}}\mathbf{u}$ is found using two observations:

- If $0 \le \theta < \pi/2$, then $\text{proj}_{\mathbf{v}}\mathbf{u}$ has length $|\mathbf{u}| \cos\theta$ and points in the direction of the unit vector $\mathbf{v}/|\mathbf{v}|$ (Figure 12.48a). Therefore,

$$\text{proj}_{\mathbf{v}}\mathbf{u} = \underbrace{|\mathbf{u}| \cos\theta}_{\text{length}} \underbrace{\left(\frac{\mathbf{v}}{|\mathbf{v}|}\right)}_{\text{direction}}.$$

We define the *scalar component of* **u** *in the direction of* **v** to be $\text{scal}_{\mathbf{v}}\mathbf{u} = |\mathbf{u}| \cos\theta$. In this case, $\text{scal}_{\mathbf{v}}\mathbf{u}$ is the length of $\text{proj}_{\mathbf{v}}\mathbf{u}$.

- If $\pi/2 < \theta \le \pi$, then $\text{proj}_{\mathbf{v}}\mathbf{u}$ has length $-|\mathbf{u}| \cos\theta$ (which is positive) and points in the direction of $-\mathbf{v}/|\mathbf{v}|$ (Figure 12.48b). Therefore,

$$\text{proj}_{\mathbf{v}}\mathbf{u} = \underbrace{-|\mathbf{u}| \cos\theta}_{\text{length}} \underbrace{\left(-\frac{\mathbf{v}}{|\mathbf{v}|}\right)}_{\text{direction}} = |\mathbf{u}| \cos\theta \left(\frac{\mathbf{v}}{|\mathbf{v}|}\right).$$

In this case, $\text{scal}_{\mathbf{v}}\mathbf{u} = |\mathbf{u}| \cos\theta < 0$.

We see that in both cases, the expression for $\text{proj}_{\mathbf{v}}\mathbf{u}$ is the same:

$$\text{proj}_{\mathbf{v}}\mathbf{u} = \underbrace{|\mathbf{u}| \cos\theta}_{\text{scal}_{\mathbf{v}}\mathbf{u}} \left(\frac{\mathbf{v}}{|\mathbf{v}|}\right) = \text{scal}_{\mathbf{v}}\mathbf{u}\left(\frac{\mathbf{v}}{|\mathbf{v}|}\right).$$

Using properties of the dot product, $\text{proj}_{\mathbf{v}}\mathbf{u}$ may be written in different ways:

$$\begin{aligned}
\text{proj}_{\mathbf{v}}\mathbf{u} &= |\mathbf{u}| \cos\theta \left(\frac{\mathbf{v}}{|\mathbf{v}|}\right) \\
&= \frac{\mathbf{u}\cdot\mathbf{v}}{|\mathbf{v}|}\left(\frac{\mathbf{v}}{|\mathbf{v}|}\right) && |\mathbf{u}| \cos\theta = \frac{|\mathbf{u}||\mathbf{v}| \cos\theta}{|\mathbf{v}|} = \frac{\mathbf{u}\cdot\mathbf{v}}{|\mathbf{v}|} \\
&= \underbrace{\left(\frac{\mathbf{u}\cdot\mathbf{v}}{\mathbf{v}\cdot\mathbf{v}}\right)}_{\text{scalar}}\mathbf{v} && \text{Regroup terms; } |\mathbf{v}|^2 = \mathbf{v}\cdot\mathbf{v}
\end{aligned}$$

QUICK CHECK 3 Let $\mathbf{u} = 4\mathbf{i} - 3\mathbf{j}$. By inspection (not calculations), find the orthogonal projection of $\mathbf{u}$ onto $\mathbf{i}$ and onto $\mathbf{j}$. Find the scalar component of $\mathbf{u}$ in the direction of $\mathbf{i}$ and in the direction of $\mathbf{j}$. ◂

The first two expressions show that $\text{proj}_{\mathbf{v}}\mathbf{u}$ is a scalar multiple of the unit vector $\frac{\mathbf{v}}{|\mathbf{v}|}$, whereas the last expression shows that $\text{proj}_{\mathbf{v}}\mathbf{u}$ is a scalar multiple of $\mathbf{v}$.

> **DEFINITION (Orthogonal) Projection of u onto v**
>
> The **orthogonal projection of u onto v**, denoted $\text{proj}_{\mathbf{v}}\mathbf{u}$, where $\mathbf{v} \neq \mathbf{0}$, is
>
> $$\text{proj}_{\mathbf{v}}\mathbf{u} = |\mathbf{u}| \cos\theta \left(\frac{\mathbf{v}}{|\mathbf{v}|}\right).$$
>
> The orthogonal projection may also be computed with the formulas
>
> $$\text{proj}_{\mathbf{v}}\mathbf{u} = \text{scal}_{\mathbf{v}}\mathbf{u}\left(\frac{\mathbf{v}}{|\mathbf{v}|}\right) = \left(\frac{\mathbf{u}\cdot\mathbf{v}}{\mathbf{v}\cdot\mathbf{v}}\right)\mathbf{v},$$
>
> where the **scalar component of u in the direction of v** is
>
> $$\text{scal}_{\mathbf{v}}\mathbf{u} = |\mathbf{u}| \cos\theta = \frac{\mathbf{u}\cdot\mathbf{v}}{|\mathbf{v}|}.$$

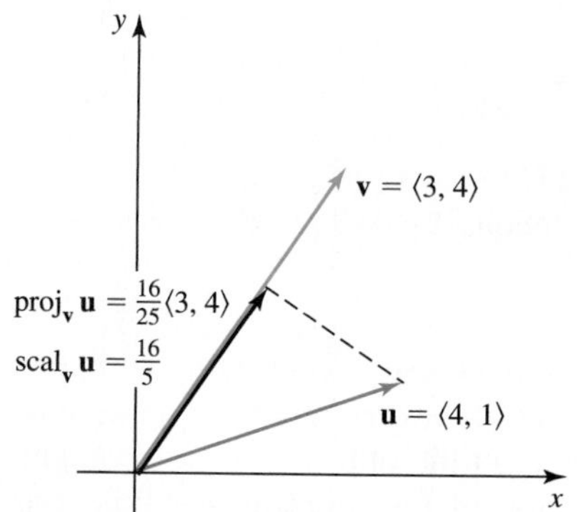

FIGURE 12.49

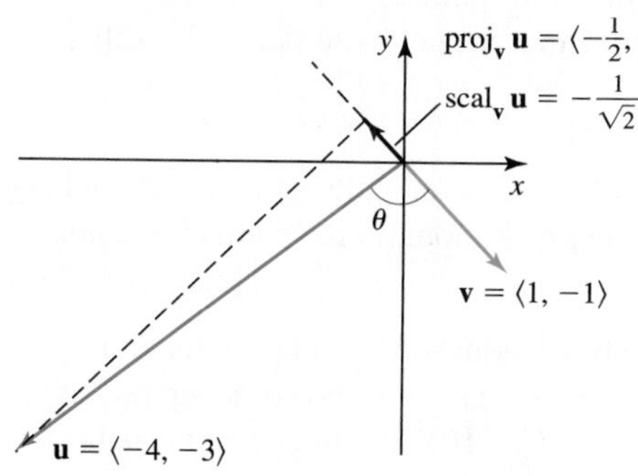

FIGURE 12.50

EXAMPLE 3 Orthogonal projections Find $\text{proj}_{\mathbf{v}}\mathbf{u}$ and $\text{scal}_{\mathbf{v}}\mathbf{u}$ for the following vectors and illustrate each result.

a. $\mathbf{u} = \langle 4, 1\rangle, \mathbf{v} = \langle 3, 4\rangle$ **b.** $\mathbf{u} = \langle -4, -3\rangle, \mathbf{v} = \langle 1, -1\rangle$

SOLUTION

a. The scalar component of $\mathbf{u}$ in the direction of $\mathbf{v}$ (Figure 12.49) is

$$\text{scal}_{\mathbf{v}}\mathbf{u} = \frac{\mathbf{u}\cdot\mathbf{v}}{|\mathbf{v}|} = \frac{\langle 4, 1\rangle \cdot \langle 3, 4\rangle}{|\langle 3, 4\rangle|} = \frac{16}{5}.$$

Because $\frac{\mathbf{v}}{|\mathbf{v}|} = \left\langle \frac{3}{5}, \frac{4}{5}\right\rangle$, we have

$$\text{proj}_{\mathbf{v}}\mathbf{u} = \text{scal}_{\mathbf{v}}\mathbf{u}\left(\frac{\mathbf{v}}{|\mathbf{v}|}\right) = \frac{16}{5}\left\langle \frac{3}{5}, \frac{4}{5}\right\rangle = \frac{16}{25}\langle 3, 4\rangle.$$

b. Using another formula for $\text{proj}_{\mathbf{v}}\mathbf{u}$, we have

$$\text{proj}_{\mathbf{v}}\mathbf{u} = \left(\frac{\mathbf{u}\cdot\mathbf{v}}{\mathbf{v}\cdot\mathbf{v}}\right)\mathbf{v} = \left(\frac{\langle -4, -3\rangle \cdot \langle 1, -1\rangle}{\langle 1, -1\rangle \cdot \langle 1, -1\rangle}\right)\langle 1, -1\rangle = -\frac{1}{2}\langle 1, -1\rangle.$$

The vectors $\mathbf{v}$ and $\text{proj}_{\mathbf{v}}\mathbf{u}$ point in opposite directions because $\pi/2 < \theta \leq \pi$ (Figure 12.50). This fact is reflected in the scalar component of $\mathbf{u}$ in the direction of $\mathbf{v}$, which is negative:

$$\text{scal}_{\mathbf{v}}\mathbf{u} = \frac{\langle -4, -3\rangle \cdot \langle 1, -1\rangle}{|\langle 1, -1\rangle|} = -\frac{1}{\sqrt{2}}.$$

Related Exercises 19–28 ◂

Direction of motion

F

θ

Only this component of **F** does work: $|\mathbf{F}| \cos\theta$

FIGURE 12.51

Applications of Dot Products

Work and Force In the opening of this section, we observed that if a constant force $\mathbf{F}$ acts at an angle θ to the direction of motion of an object (Figure 12.51), the work done by the force is

$$W = |\mathbf{F}| \cos\theta \, |\mathbf{d}| = \mathbf{F}\cdot\mathbf{d}.$$

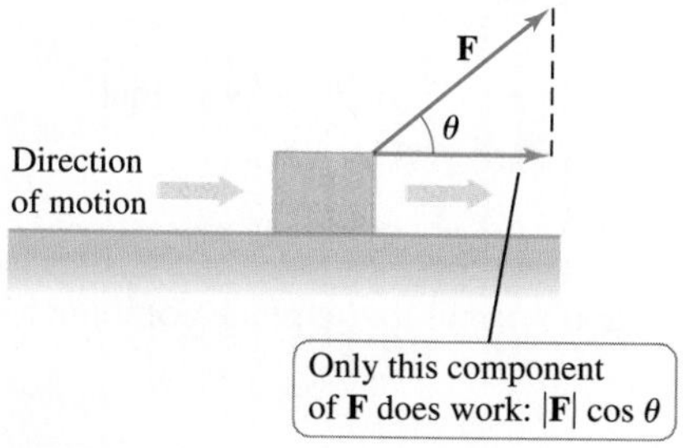

Notice that the work is a scalar, and if the force acts in a direction orthogonal to the motion ($\theta = \pi/2$), then no work is done by the force.

> **DEFINITION Work**
>
> Let a constant force $\mathbf{F}$ be applied to an object, producing a displacement $\mathbf{d}$. If the angle between $\mathbf{F}$ and $\mathbf{d}$ is θ, then the **work** done by the force is
>
> $$W = |\mathbf{F}||\mathbf{d}| \cos \theta = \mathbf{F} \cdot \mathbf{d}.$$

➤ If the unit of force is newtons (N) and the distance is measured in meters, then the unit of work is joules (J), where 1 J = 1 N-m. If force is measured in lb and distance is measured in ft, then work has units of ft-lb.

EXAMPLE 4 Calculating work A force $\mathbf{F} = \langle 3, 3, 2 \rangle$ (N) moves an object from $P(1, 1, 0)$ to $Q(6, 6, 0)$ (m). What is the work done by the force? Interpret the result.

SOLUTION The displacement of the object is $\mathbf{d} = \langle 6 - 1, 6 - 1, 0 - 0 \rangle = \langle 5, 5, 0 \rangle$. Therefore, the work done by the force is

$$W = \mathbf{F} \cdot \mathbf{d} = \langle 3, 3, 2 \rangle \cdot \langle 5, 5, 0 \rangle = 30 \text{ J}.$$

To interpret this result, notice that the angle between the force and the displacement vector satisfies

$$\cos \theta = \frac{\mathbf{F} \cdot \mathbf{d}}{|\mathbf{F}||\mathbf{d}|} = \frac{\langle 3, 3, 2 \rangle \cdot \langle 5, 5, 0 \rangle}{|\langle 3, 3, 2 \rangle||\langle 5, 5, 0 \rangle|} = \frac{30}{\sqrt{22}\sqrt{50}} \approx 0.905.$$

Therefore, $\theta \approx 0.44$ rad $\approx 25°$. The magnitude of the force is $|\mathbf{F}| = \sqrt{22} \approx 4.7$ N, but only the component of that force in the direction of motion, $|\mathbf{F}| \cos \theta \approx \sqrt{22} \cos 0.44 \approx 4.2$ N, contributes to the work (Figure 12.52). *Related Exercises 29–32* ◄

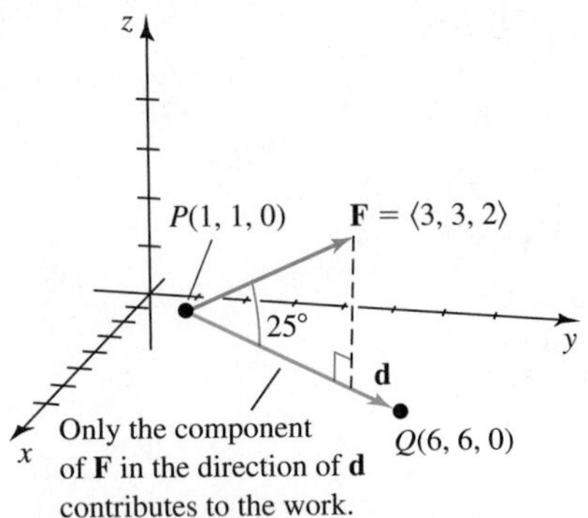

FIGURE 12.52

Parallel and Normal Forces Projections find frequent use in expressing a force in terms of orthogonal components. A common situation arises when an object rests on an inclined plane (Figure 12.53). The gravitational force on the object equals its weight, which is directed vertically downward. The projection of the force in the directions **parallel** to and **normal** (or perpendicular) to the plane are of interest. Specifically, the projection of the force parallel to the plane determines the tendency of the object to slide down the plane, while the projection of the force normal to the plane determines its tendency to "stick" to the plane.

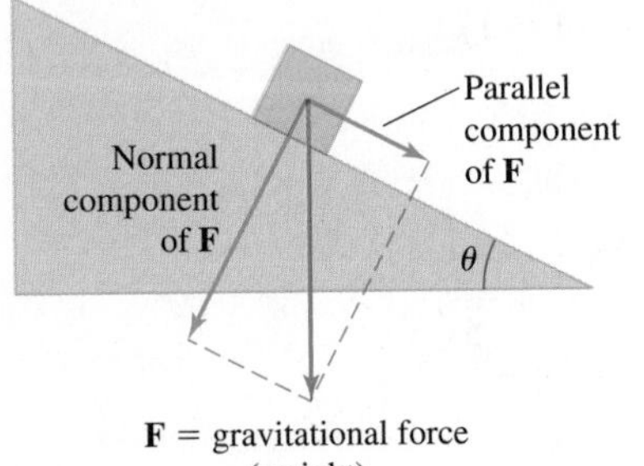

FIGURE 12.53

EXAMPLE 5 Components of a force A 10-lb block rests on a plane that is inclined at 30° below the horizontal. Find the components of the gravitational force parallel and normal (perpendicular) to the plane.

SOLUTION The gravitational force $\mathbf{F}$ acting on the block equals the weight of the block (10 lb), which we regard as a point mass. Using the coordinate system shown in Figure 12.54, the force acts in the negative y-direction; therefore, $\mathbf{F} = \langle 0, -10 \rangle$. The direction *down* the plane is given by the unit vector $\mathbf{v} = \langle \cos(-30°), \sin(-30°) \rangle = \left\langle \frac{\sqrt{3}}{2}, -\frac{1}{2} \right\rangle$ (check that $|\mathbf{v}| = 1$). The component of the force parallel to the plane is

$$\text{proj}_{\mathbf{v}}\mathbf{F} = \underbrace{\left(\frac{\mathbf{F} \cdot \mathbf{v}}{\mathbf{v} \cdot \mathbf{v}}\right)}_{\mathbf{v} \cdot \mathbf{v} = 1}\mathbf{v} = \left(\underbrace{\langle 0, -10 \rangle}_{\mathbf{F}} \cdot \underbrace{\left\langle \frac{\sqrt{3}}{2}, -\frac{1}{2} \right\rangle}_{\mathbf{v}}\right) \underbrace{\left\langle \frac{\sqrt{3}}{2}, -\frac{1}{2} \right\rangle}_{\mathbf{v}} = 5\left\langle \frac{\sqrt{3}}{2}, -\frac{1}{2} \right\rangle.$$

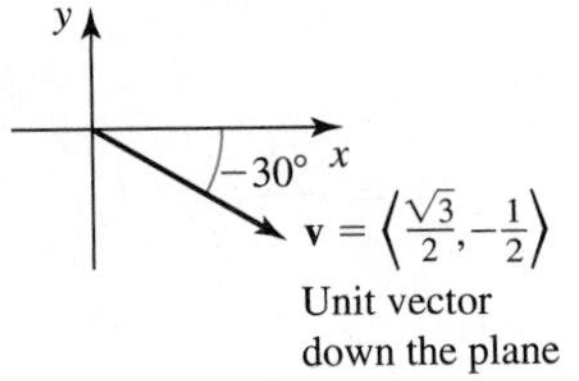

Let the component of $\mathbf{F}$ normal to the plane be $\mathbf{N}$. Note that $\mathbf{F} = \text{proj}_{\mathbf{v}}\mathbf{F} + \mathbf{N}$ so that

$$\mathbf{N} = \mathbf{F} - \text{proj}_{\mathbf{v}}\mathbf{F} = \langle 0, -10 \rangle - 5\left\langle \frac{\sqrt{3}}{2}, -\frac{1}{2} \right\rangle = \left\langle -\frac{5\sqrt{3}}{2}, -\frac{15}{2} \right\rangle.$$

Figure 12.54 shows how the components of $\mathbf{F}$ parallel and normal to the plane combine to form the total force $\mathbf{F}$. *Related Exercises 33–36* ◄

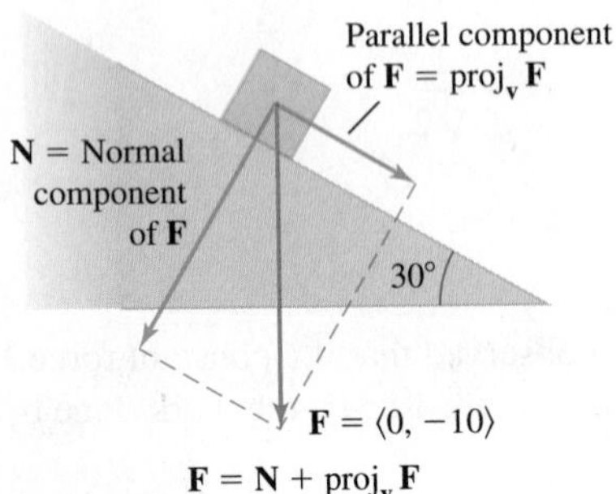

FIGURE 12.54

SECTION 12.3 EXERCISES

Review Questions

1. Define the dot product of **u** and **v** in terms of their magnitudes and the angle between them.

2. Define the dot product of **u** and **v** in terms of the components of the vectors.

3. Compute $\langle 2, 3, -6 \rangle \cdot \langle 1, -8, 3 \rangle$.

4. What is the dot product of two orthogonal vectors?

5. Explain how to find the angle between two nonzero vectors.

6. Use a sketch to illustrate the projection of **u** onto **v**.

7. Use a sketch to illustrate the scalar component of **u** in the direction of **v**.

8. Explain how the work done by a force in moving an object is computed using dot products.

Basic Skills

9–12. Dot product from the definition *Consider the following vectors* **u** *and* **v**. *Sketch the vectors, find the angle between the vectors, and compute the dot product using the definition* $\mathbf{u} \cdot \mathbf{v} = |\mathbf{u}||\mathbf{v}| \cos \theta$.

9. $\mathbf{u} = 4\mathbf{i}$ and $\mathbf{v} = 6\mathbf{j}$

10. $\mathbf{u} = \langle -3, 2, 0 \rangle$ and $\mathbf{v} = \langle 0, 0, 6 \rangle$

11. $\mathbf{u} = \langle 10, 0 \rangle$ and $\mathbf{v} = \langle 10, 10 \rangle$

12. $\mathbf{u} = \langle -\sqrt{3}, 1 \rangle$ and $\mathbf{v} = \langle \sqrt{3}, 1 \rangle$

13–18. Dot products and angles *Compute the dot product of the vectors* **u** *and* **v**, *and find the approximate angle between the vectors.*

13. $\mathbf{u} = 4\mathbf{i} + 3\mathbf{j}$ and $\mathbf{v} = 4\mathbf{i} - 6\mathbf{j}$

14. $\mathbf{u} = \langle 3, 4, 0 \rangle$ and $\mathbf{v} = \langle 0, 4, 5 \rangle$

15. $\mathbf{u} = \langle -10, 0, 4 \rangle$ and $\mathbf{v} = \langle 1, 2, 3 \rangle$

16. $\mathbf{u} = \langle 3, -5, 2 \rangle$ and $\mathbf{v} = \langle -9, 5, 1 \rangle$

17. $\mathbf{u} = 2\mathbf{i} - 3\mathbf{k}$ and $\mathbf{v} = \mathbf{i} + 4\mathbf{j} + 2\mathbf{k}$

18. $\mathbf{u} = \mathbf{i} - 4\mathbf{j} - 6\mathbf{k}$ and $\mathbf{v} = 2\mathbf{i} - 4\mathbf{j} + 2\mathbf{k}$

19–22. Sketching orthogonal projections *Find* $\text{proj}_{\mathbf{v}}\mathbf{u}$ *and* $\text{scal}_{\mathbf{v}}\mathbf{u}$ *by inspection without using formulas.*

19.

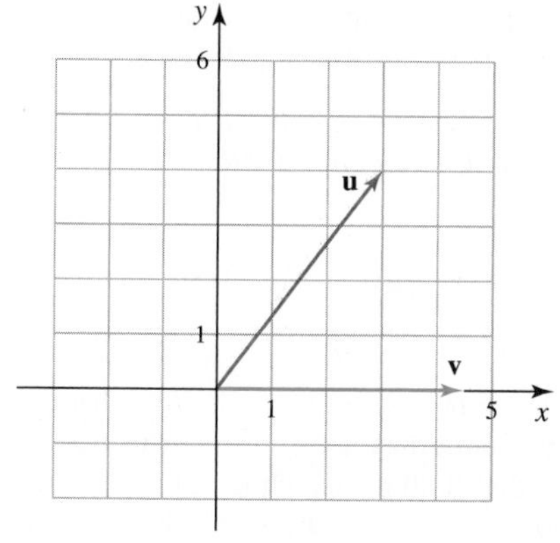

20.

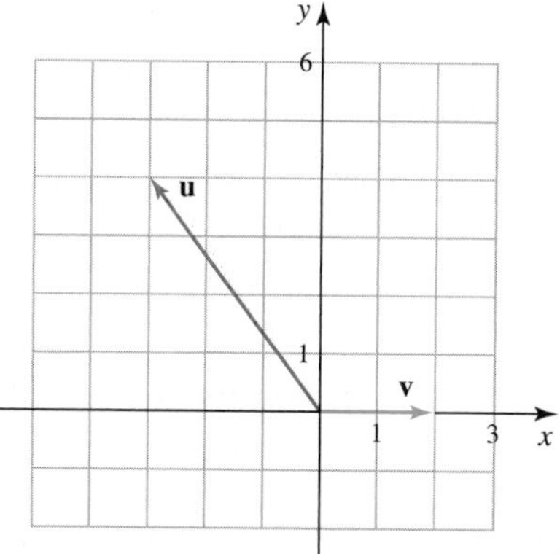

21.

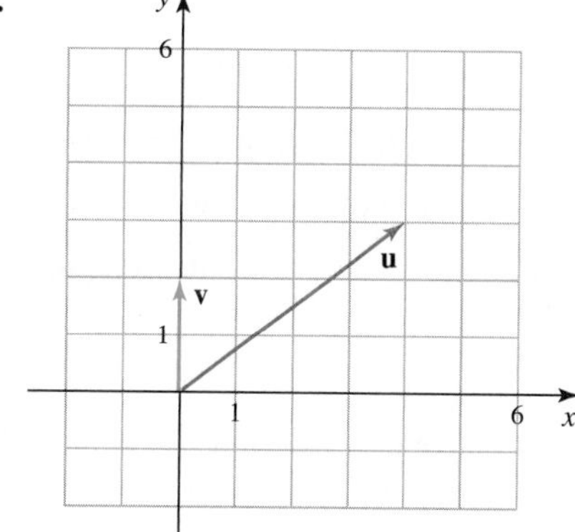

22.

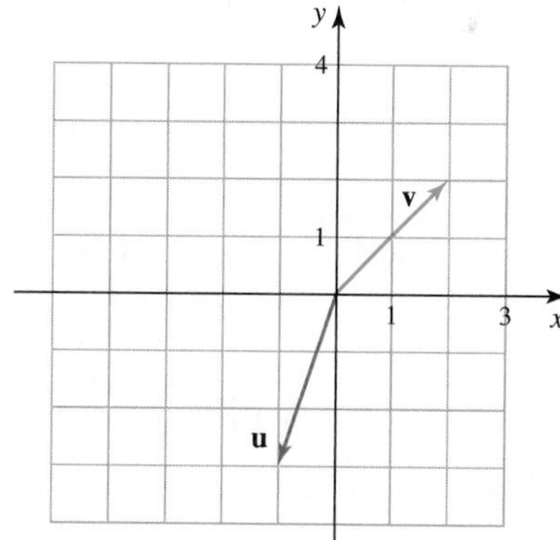

23–28. Calculating orthogonal projections *For the given vectors* **u** *and* **v**, *calculate* $\text{proj}_{\mathbf{v}}\mathbf{u}$ *and* $\text{scal}_{\mathbf{v}}\mathbf{u}$.

23. $\mathbf{u} = \langle -1, 4 \rangle$ and $\mathbf{v} = \langle -4, 2 \rangle$

24. $\mathbf{u} = \langle 10, 5 \rangle$ and $\mathbf{v} = \langle 2, 6 \rangle$

25. $\mathbf{u} = \langle -8, 0, 2 \rangle$ and $\mathbf{v} = \langle 1, 3, -3 \rangle$

26. $\mathbf{u} = \langle 3, -5, 2 \rangle$ and $\mathbf{v} = \langle -9, 5, 1 \rangle$

27. $\mathbf{u} = 2\mathbf{i} - 4\mathbf{k}$ and $\mathbf{v} = 9\mathbf{i} + 2\mathbf{k}$

28. $\mathbf{u} = \mathbf{i} + 4\mathbf{j} + 7\mathbf{k}$ and $\mathbf{v} = 2\mathbf{i} - 4\mathbf{j} + 2\mathbf{k}$

29–32. Computing work *Calculate the work done in the following situations.*

29. A suitcase is pulled 50 ft along a flat sidewalk with a constant force of 30 lb at an angle of 30° above the horizontal.

T 30. A stroller is pushed 20 m with a constant downward force of 10 N at an angle of 15° with the horizontal.

31. A constant force $\mathbf{F} = \langle 40, 30 \rangle$ is used to move a sled horizontally 10 m.

32. A constant force $\mathbf{F} = \langle 2, 4, 1 \rangle$ moves an object from $(0, 0, 0)$ to $(2, 4, 6)$.

33–36. Parallel and normal forces *Find the components of the vertical force $\mathbf{F} = \langle 0, -10 \rangle$ in the directions parallel to and normal to the following planes. Show that the total force is the sum of the two component forces.*

33. A plane that makes an angle of $\pi/4$ with the positive x-axis.

34. A plane that makes an angle of $\pi/6$ with the positive x-axis.

35. A plane that makes an angle of $\pi/3$ with the positive x-axis.

36. A plane that makes an angle of $\theta = \tan^{-1}\left(\frac{4}{5}\right)$ with the positive x-axis.

Further Explorations

37. **Explain why or why not** Determine whether the following statements are true and give an explanation or counterexample.
    a. $\text{proj}_{\mathbf{v}}\mathbf{u} = \text{proj}_{\mathbf{u}}\mathbf{v}$.
    b. If nonzero vectors $\mathbf{u}$ and $\mathbf{v}$ have the same magnitude they make equal angles with $\mathbf{u} + \mathbf{v}$.
    c. $(\mathbf{u} \cdot \mathbf{i})^2 + (\mathbf{u} \cdot \mathbf{j})^2 + (\mathbf{u} \cdot \mathbf{k})^2 = |\mathbf{u}|^2$.
    d. If $\mathbf{u}$ is orthogonal to $\mathbf{v}$ and $\mathbf{v}$ is orthogonal to $\mathbf{w}$, then $\mathbf{u}$ is orthogonal to $\mathbf{w}$.
    e. The vectors orthogonal to $\langle 1, 1, 1 \rangle$ lie on the same line.
    f. If $\text{proj}_{\mathbf{v}}\mathbf{u} = \mathbf{0}$, then vectors $\mathbf{u}$ and $\mathbf{v}$ (both nonzero) are orthogonal.

38–42. Orthogonal vectors *Let a and b be real numbers.*

38. Find all unit vectors orthogonal to $\mathbf{v} = \langle 3, 4, 0 \rangle$.

39. Find all vectors $\langle 1, a, b \rangle$ orthogonal to $\langle 4, -8, 2 \rangle$.

40. Describe all unit vectors orthogonal to $\mathbf{v} = \mathbf{i} + \mathbf{j} + \mathbf{k}$.

41. Find three mutually orthogonal unit vectors in $\mathbf{R}^3$ besides $\pm\mathbf{i}$, $\pm\mathbf{j}$, and $\pm\mathbf{k}$.

42. Find two vectors that are orthogonal to $\langle 0, 1, 1 \rangle$ and to each other.

43. **Equal angles** Consider all unit position vectors $\mathbf{u}$ in $\mathbf{R}^3$ that make a 60° angle with the unit vector $\mathbf{k}$ in $\mathbf{R}^3$.
    a. Prove that $\text{proj}_{\mathbf{k}}\mathbf{u}$ is the same for all vectors in this set.
    b. Is $\text{scal}_{\mathbf{k}}\mathbf{u}$ the same for all vectors in this set?

44–47. Vectors with equal projections *Given a fixed vector $\mathbf{v}$, there is an infinite set of vectors $\mathbf{u}$ with the same value of $\text{proj}_{\mathbf{v}}\mathbf{u}$.*

44. Find another vector that has the same projection onto $\mathbf{v} = \langle 1, 1 \rangle$ as $\mathbf{u} = \langle 1, 2 \rangle$. Draw a picture.

45. Let $\mathbf{v} = \langle 1, 1 \rangle$. Give a description of the position vectors $\mathbf{u}$ such that $\text{proj}_{\mathbf{v}}\mathbf{u} = \text{proj}_{\mathbf{v}}\langle 1, 2 \rangle$.

46. Find another vector that has the same projection onto $\mathbf{v} = \langle 1, 1, 1 \rangle$ as $\mathbf{u} = \langle 1, 2, 3 \rangle$.

47. Let $\mathbf{v} = \langle 0, 0, 1 \rangle$. Give a description of all position vectors $\mathbf{u}$ such that $\text{proj}_{\mathbf{v}}\mathbf{u} = \text{proj}_{\mathbf{v}}\langle 1, 2, 3 \rangle$.

48–51. Decomposing vectors *For the following vectors $\mathbf{u}$ and $\mathbf{v}$, express $\mathbf{u}$ as the sum $\mathbf{u} = \mathbf{p} + \mathbf{n}$, where $\mathbf{p}$ is parallel to $\mathbf{v}$ and $\mathbf{n}$ is orthogonal to $\mathbf{v}$.*

48. $\mathbf{u} = \langle 4, 3 \rangle, \mathbf{v} = \langle 1, 1 \rangle$

49. $\mathbf{u} = \langle -2, 2 \rangle, \mathbf{v} = \langle 2, 1 \rangle$

50. $\mathbf{u} = \langle 4, 3, 0 \rangle, \mathbf{v} = \langle 1, 1, 1 \rangle$

51. $\mathbf{u} = \langle -1, 2, 3 \rangle, \mathbf{v} = \langle 2, 1, 1 \rangle$

52–55. Distance between a point and a line *Carry out the following steps to determine the distance between the point P and the line ℓ through the origin.*

a. *Find any vector $\mathbf{v}$ in the direction of ℓ.*
b. *Find the position vector $\mathbf{u}$ corresponding to P.*
c. *Find $\text{proj}_{\mathbf{v}}\mathbf{u}$.*
d. *Show that $\mathbf{w} = \mathbf{u} - \text{proj}_{\mathbf{v}}\mathbf{u}$ is a vector orthogonal to $\mathbf{v}$ whose length is the distance between P and the line ℓ.*
e. *Find $\mathbf{w}$ and $|\mathbf{w}|$. Explain why $|\mathbf{w}|$ is the distance between P and ℓ.*

52. $P(2, -5)$; $\ell: y = 3x$

53. $P(-12, 4)$; $\ell: y = 2x$

54. $P(0, 2, 6)$; ℓ has the direction of $\langle 3, 0, -4 \rangle$.

55. $P(1, 1, -1)$; ℓ has the direction of $\langle -6, 8, 3 \rangle$.

56–58. Orthogonal unit vectors in the *xy*-plane *Consider the vectors $\mathbf{I} = \langle 1/\sqrt{2}, 1/\sqrt{2} \rangle$ and $\mathbf{J} = \langle -1/\sqrt{2}, 1/\sqrt{2} \rangle$.*

56. Show that $\mathbf{I}$ and $\mathbf{J}$ are orthogonal unit vectors.

57. Express $\mathbf{I}$ and $\mathbf{J}$ in terms of the usual unit coordinate vectors $\mathbf{i}$ and $\mathbf{j}$. Then write $\mathbf{i}$ and $\mathbf{j}$ in terms of $\mathbf{I}$ and $\mathbf{J}$.

58. Write the vector $\langle 2, -6 \rangle$ in terms of $\mathbf{I}$ and $\mathbf{J}$.

59. **Orthogonal unit vectors in $\mathbf{R}^3$** Consider the vectors $\mathbf{I} = \langle 1/2, 1/2, 1/\sqrt{2} \rangle, \mathbf{J} = \langle -1/\sqrt{2}, 1/\sqrt{2}, 0 \rangle$, and $\mathbf{K} = \langle 1/2, 1/2, -1/\sqrt{2} \rangle$.
    a. Sketch $\mathbf{I}$, $\mathbf{J}$, and $\mathbf{K}$ and show that they are unit vectors.
    b. Show that $\mathbf{I}$, $\mathbf{J}$, and $\mathbf{K}$ are mutually orthogonal.
    c. Express the vector $\langle 1, 0, 0 \rangle$ in terms of $\mathbf{I}$, $\mathbf{J}$, and $\mathbf{K}$.

T **60–61. Angles of a triangle** *For the given points P, Q, and R, find the approximate measurements of the angles of $\triangle PQR$.*

60. $P(1, -4), Q(2, 7), R(-2, 2)$

61. $P(0, -1, 3), Q(2, 2, 1), R(-2, 2, 4)$

Applications

62. **Flow through a circle** Suppose water flows in a thin sheet over the xy-plane with a uniform velocity given by the vector $\mathbf{v} = \langle 1, 2 \rangle$; this means that at all points of the plane, the velocity of the water has components 1 m/s in the x-direction and 2 m/s in the y-direction (see figure). Let C be an imaginary unit circle (that does not interfere with the flow).

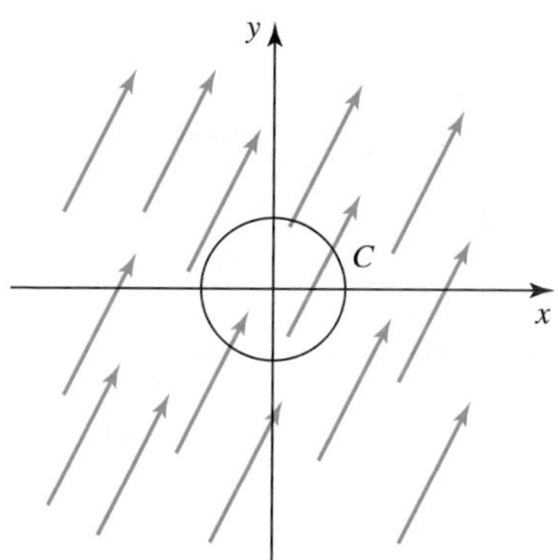

a. Show that at the point (x, y) on the circle C the outward-pointing unit vector normal to C is $\mathbf{n} = \langle x, y \rangle$.
b. Show that at the point $(\cos\theta, \sin\theta)$ on the circle C the outward-pointing unit vector normal to C is also $\mathbf{n} = \langle \cos\theta, \sin\theta \rangle$.
c. Find all points on C at which the velocity is normal to C.
d. Find all points on C at which the velocity is tangential to C.
e. At each point on C find the component of $\mathbf{v}$ normal to C. Express the answer as a function of (x, y) and as a function of θ.
f. What is the net flow through the circle? That is, does water accumulate inside the circle?

63. Heat flux Let D be a solid heat-conducting cube formed by the planes $x = 0$, $x = 1$, $y = 0$, $y = 1$, $z = 0$, $z = 1$. The heat flow at every point of D is given by the constant vector $\mathbf{Q} = \langle 0, 2, 1 \rangle$.

a. Through which faces of D does $\mathbf{Q}$ point into D?
b. Through which faces of D does $\mathbf{Q}$ point out of D?
c. On which faces of D is $\mathbf{Q}$ tangential to D (pointing neither in nor out of D)?
d. Find the scalar component of $\mathbf{Q}$ normal to the face $x = 0$.
e. Find the scalar component of $\mathbf{Q}$ normal to the face $z = 1$.
f. Find the scalar component of $\mathbf{Q}$ normal to the face $y = 0$.

64. Hexagonal circle packing The German mathematician Gauss proved that the densest way to pack circles with the same radius in the plane is to place the centers of the circles on a hexagonal grid (see figure). Some molecular structures use this packing or its three-dimensional analog. Assume all circles have a radius of 1 and let $\mathbf{r}_{ij}$ be the vector that extends from the center of circle i to the center of circle j for $i, j = 0, 1, \ldots, 6$.

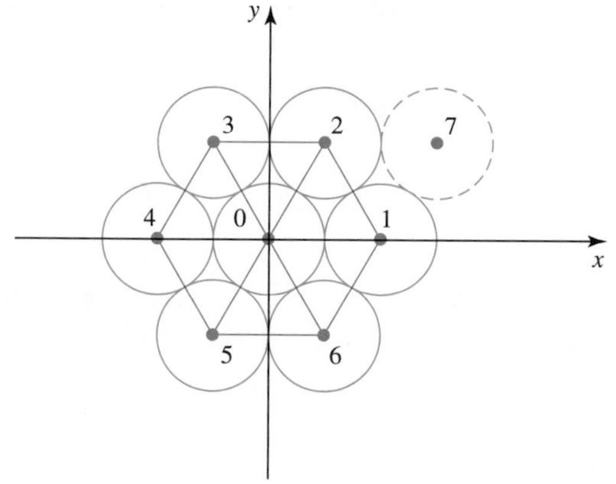

a. Find $\mathbf{r}_{0j}$ for $j = 1, 2, \ldots, 6$.
b. Find $\mathbf{r}_{12}$, $\mathbf{r}_{34}$, and $\mathbf{r}_{61}$.
c. Imagine circle 7 is added to the arrangement as shown in the figure. Find $\mathbf{r}_{07}$, $\mathbf{r}_{17}$, $\mathbf{r}_{47}$, and $\mathbf{r}_{75}$.

65. Hexagonal sphere packing Imagine three unit spheres (radius equal to 1) with centers at $O(0, 0, 0)$, $P(\sqrt{3}, -1, 0)$, and $Q(\sqrt{3}, 1, 0)$. Now place another unit sphere symmetrically on top of these spheres with its center at R (see figure).

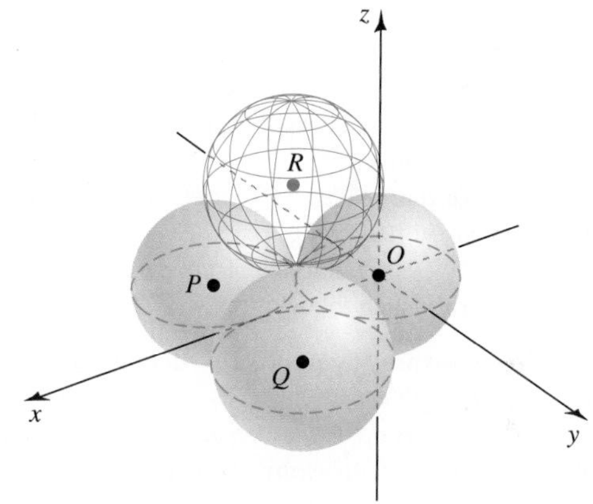

a. Find the coordinates of R. (*Hint:* The distance between the centers of any two spheres is 2.)
b. Let $\mathbf{r}_{ij}$ be the vector from the center of sphere i to the center of sphere j. Find $\mathbf{r}_{OP}$, $\mathbf{r}_{OQ}$, $\mathbf{r}_{PQ}$, $\mathbf{r}_{OR}$, and $\mathbf{r}_{PR}$.

Additional Exercises

66–70. Properties of dot products *Let* $\mathbf{u} = \langle u_1, u_2, u_3 \rangle$, $\mathbf{v} = \langle v_1, v_2, v_3 \rangle$, *and* $\mathbf{w} = \langle w_1, w_2, w_3 \rangle$. *Let c be a scalar. Prove the following vector properties.*

66. $|\mathbf{u} \cdot \mathbf{v}| \leq |\mathbf{u}||\mathbf{v}|$

67. $\mathbf{u} \cdot \mathbf{v} = \mathbf{v} \cdot \mathbf{u}$ Commutative property

68. $c(\mathbf{u} \cdot \mathbf{v}) = (c\mathbf{u}) \cdot \mathbf{v} = \mathbf{u} \cdot (c\mathbf{v})$ Associative property

69. $\mathbf{u} \cdot (\mathbf{v} + \mathbf{w}) = \mathbf{u} \cdot \mathbf{v} + \mathbf{u} \cdot \mathbf{w}$ Distributive property

70. Distributive properties

a. Show that $(\mathbf{u} + \mathbf{v}) \cdot (\mathbf{u} + \mathbf{v}) = |\mathbf{u}|^2 + 2\,\mathbf{u} \cdot \mathbf{v} + |\mathbf{v}|^2$.
b. Show that $(\mathbf{u} + \mathbf{v}) \cdot (\mathbf{u} + \mathbf{v}) = |\mathbf{u}|^2 + |\mathbf{v}|^2$ if $\mathbf{u}$ is perpendicular to $\mathbf{v}$.
c. Show that $(\mathbf{u} + \mathbf{v}) \cdot (\mathbf{u} - \mathbf{v}) = |\mathbf{u}|^2 - |\mathbf{v}|^2$.

71. Prove or disprove For fixed values of a, b, c, and d, the value of $\text{proj}_{\langle ka, kb \rangle} \langle c, d \rangle$ is constant for all nonzero values of k, for $\langle a, b \rangle \neq \langle 0, 0 \rangle$.

72. Orthogonal lines Recall that two lines $y = mx + b$ and $y = nx + c$ are orthogonal provided $mn = -1$ (the slopes are negative reciprocals of each other). Prove that the condition $mn = -1$ is equivalent to the orthogonality condition $\mathbf{u} \cdot \mathbf{v} = 0$, where $\mathbf{u}$ points in the direction of one line and $\mathbf{v}$ points in the direction of other line.

73. Direction angles and cosines Let $\mathbf{v} = \langle a, b, c \rangle$ and let α, β, and γ be the angles between $\mathbf{v}$ and the positive x-axis, the positive y-axis, and the positive z-axis, respectively (see figure).

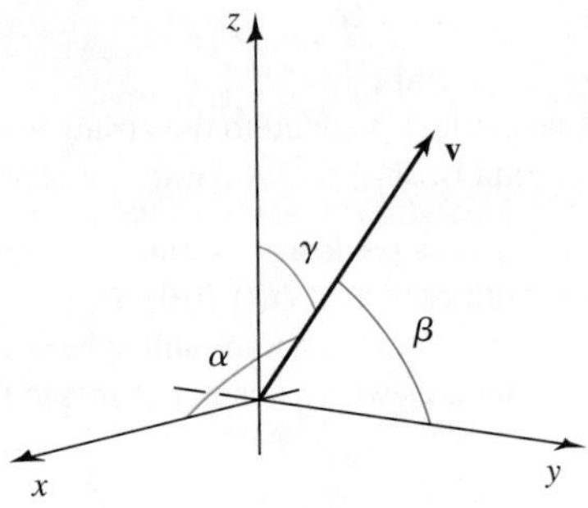

a. Prove that $\cos^2 \alpha + \cos^2 \beta + \cos^2 \gamma = 1$.
b. Find a vector that makes a 45° angle with **i** and **j**. What angle does it make with **k**?
c. Find a vector that makes a 60° angle with **i** and **j**. What angle does it make with **k**?
d. Is there a vector that makes a 30° angle with **i** and **j**? Explain.
e. Find a vector **v** such that $\alpha = \beta = \gamma$. What is the angle?

74–78. Cauchy–Schwarz Inequality *The definition* $\mathbf{u} \cdot \mathbf{v} = |\mathbf{u}||\mathbf{v}| \cos \theta$ *implies that* $|\mathbf{u} \cdot \mathbf{v}| \leq |\mathbf{u}||\mathbf{v}|$ *(because* $|\cos \theta| \leq 1$*). This inequality, known as the Cauchy-Schwarz Inequality, holds in any number of dimensions and has many consequences.*

74. What conditions on **u** and **v** lead to equality in the Cauchy–Schwarz Inequality?

75. Verify that the Cauchy–Schwarz Inequality holds for $\mathbf{u} = \langle 3, -5, 6 \rangle$ and $\mathbf{v} = \langle -8, 3, 1 \rangle$.

76. Geometric-arithmetic mean Use the vectors $\mathbf{u} = \langle \sqrt{a}, \sqrt{b} \rangle$ and $\mathbf{v} = \langle \sqrt{b}, \sqrt{a} \rangle$ to show that $\sqrt{ab} \leq (a + b)/2$, where $a \geq 0$ and $b \geq 0$.

77. Triangle Inequality Consider the vectors **u**, **v**, and **u** + **v** (in any number of dimensions). Use the following steps to prove that $|\mathbf{u} + \mathbf{v}| \leq |\mathbf{u}| + |\mathbf{v}|$.

a. Show that $|\mathbf{u} + \mathbf{v}|^2 = (\mathbf{u} + \mathbf{v}) \cdot (\mathbf{u} + \mathbf{v}) = |\mathbf{u}|^2 + 2\mathbf{u} \cdot \mathbf{v} + |\mathbf{v}|^2$.
b. Use the Cauchy–Schwarz Inequality to show that $|\mathbf{u} + \mathbf{v}|^2 \leq (|\mathbf{u}| + |\mathbf{v}|)^2$.
c. Conclude that $|\mathbf{u} + \mathbf{v}| \leq |\mathbf{u}| + |\mathbf{v}|$.
d. Interpret the Triangle Inequality geometrically in $\mathbf{R}^2$ or $\mathbf{R}^3$.

78. Algebra inequality Show that for real numbers u_1, u_2, and u_3, it is true that

$$(u_1 + u_2 + u_3)^2 \leq 3(u_1^2 + u_2^2 + u_3^2).$$

Use the Cauchy–Schwarz Inequality in three dimensions with $\mathbf{u} = \langle u_1, u_2, u_3 \rangle$ and choose **v** in the right way.

79. Diagonals of a parallelogram Consider the parallelogram with adjacent sides **u** and **v**.

a. Show that the diagonals of the parallelogram are **u** + **v** and **u** − **v**.
b. Prove that the diagonals have the same length if and only if $\mathbf{u} \cdot \mathbf{v} = 0$.
c. Show that the sum of the squares of the lengths of the diagonals equals the sum of the squares of the lengths of the sides.

80. Distance between a point and a line in the plane Use projections to find a general formula for the distance between the point $P(x_0, y_0)$ and the line $ax + by = c$. (See Exercises 52–55.)

QUICK CHECK ANSWERS

1. If $\theta = 0$, **u** and **v** are parallel and point in the same direction. If $\theta = \pi$, **u** and **v** are parallel and point in opposite directions. **2.** All these dot products are zero, and the unit vectors are mutually orthogonal. **3.** $\text{proj}_{\mathbf{i}}\mathbf{u} = 4\mathbf{i}$, $\text{proj}_{\mathbf{j}}\mathbf{u} = -3\mathbf{j}$, $\text{scal}_{\mathbf{i}}\mathbf{u} = 4$, $\text{scal}_{\mathbf{j}}\mathbf{u} = -3$. ◄

12.4 Cross Products

The dot product combines two vectors to produce a *scalar* result. There is an equally fundamental way to combine two vectors in $\mathbf{R}^3$ and obtain a *vector* result. This operation, known as the *cross product* (or *vector product*) may be motivated by a physical application.

Suppose you want to loosen a bolt with a wrench. As you apply force to the end of the wrench in the plane perpendicular to the bolt, the "twisting power" you generate depends on three variables:

- the magnitude of the force **F** applied to the wrench;
- the length $|\mathbf{r}|$ of the wrench;
- the angle at which the force is applied to the wrench.

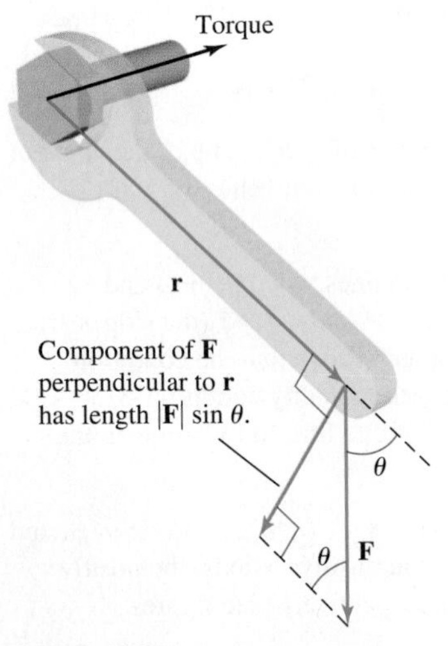

FIGURE 12.55

The twisting generated by a force acting at a distance from a pivot point is called **torque** (from the Latin *to twist*). The torque is a vector whose magnitude is proportional to $|\mathbf{F}|$, $|\mathbf{r}|$, and $\sin \theta$, where θ is the angle between **F** and **r** (Figure 12.55). If the force is applied parallel to the wrench—for example, if you pull the wrench ($\theta = 0$) or push the wrench ($\theta = \pi$)—there is no twisting effect; if the force is applied perpendicular to the wrench ($\theta = \pi/2$), the twisting effect is maximized. The direction of the torque vector is defined to be orthogonal to both **F** and **r**. As we will see shortly, the torque is expressed in terms of the cross product of **F** and **r**.

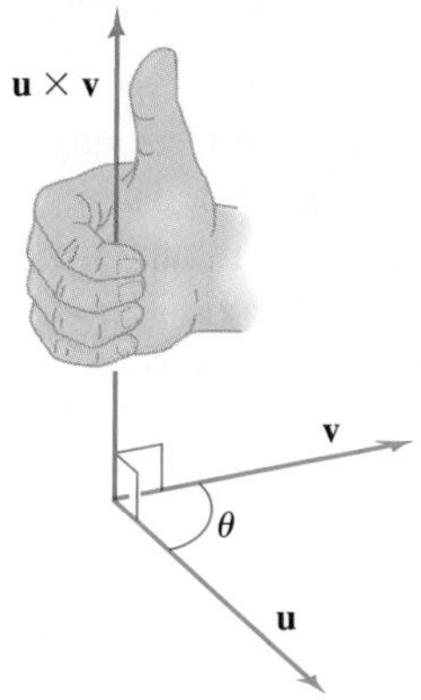

FIGURE 12.56

The Cross Product

The preceding physical example leads to the following definition of the cross product.

> **DEFINITION Cross Product**
> Given two nonzero vectors $\mathbf{u}$ and $\mathbf{v}$ in $\mathbf{R}^3$, the **cross product** $\mathbf{u} \times \mathbf{v}$ is a vector with magnitude
> $$|\mathbf{u} \times \mathbf{v}| = |\mathbf{u}||\mathbf{v}| \sin \theta,$$
> where $0 \leq \theta \leq \pi$ is the angle between $\mathbf{u}$ and $\mathbf{v}$. The direction of $\mathbf{u} \times \mathbf{v}$ is given by the **right-hand rule**: When you put the vectors tail to tail and let the fingers of your right hand curl from $\mathbf{u}$ to $\mathbf{v}$, the direction of $\mathbf{u} \times \mathbf{v}$ is the direction of your thumb, orthogonal to both $\mathbf{u}$ and $\mathbf{v}$ (Figure 12.56). When $\mathbf{u} \times \mathbf{v} = \mathbf{0}$, the direction of $\mathbf{u} \times \mathbf{v}$ is undefined.

QUICK CHECK 1 Sketch the vectors $\mathbf{u} = \langle 1, 2, 0 \rangle$ and $\mathbf{v} = \langle -1, 2, 0 \rangle$. Which way does $\mathbf{u} \times \mathbf{v}$ point? Which way does $\mathbf{v} \times \mathbf{u}$ point?

The following theorem is a consequence of the definition of the cross product.

> **THEOREM 12.3 Geometry of the Cross Product**
> Let $\mathbf{u}$ and $\mathbf{v}$ be two nonzero vectors in $\mathbf{R}^3$.
> 1. The vectors $\mathbf{u}$ and $\mathbf{v}$ are parallel ($\theta = 0$ or $\theta = \pi$) if and only if $\mathbf{u} \times \mathbf{v} = \mathbf{0}$.
> 2. If $\mathbf{u}$ and $\mathbf{v}$ are two sides of a parallelogram (Figure 12.57), then the area of the parallelogram is
> $$|\mathbf{u} \times \mathbf{v}| = |\mathbf{u}||\mathbf{v}| \sin \theta.$$

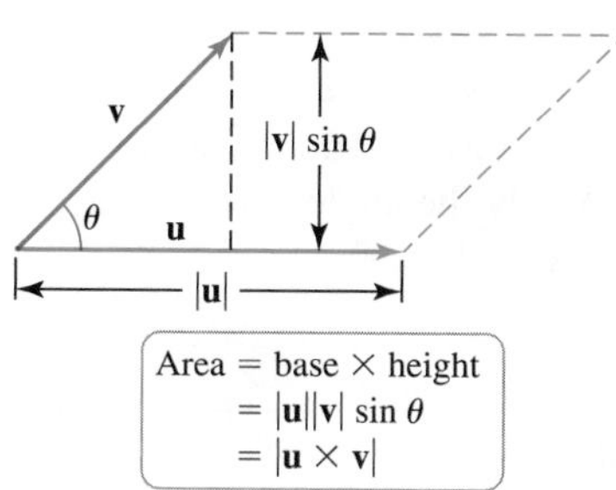

FIGURE 12.57

EXAMPLE 1 A cross product Find the magnitude and direction of $\mathbf{u} \times \mathbf{v}$, where $\mathbf{u} = \langle 1, 1, 0 \rangle$ and $\mathbf{v} = \langle 1, 1, \sqrt{2} \rangle$.

SOLUTION Because $\mathbf{u}$ is one side of a 45–45–90 triangle and $\mathbf{v}$ is the hypotenuse (Figure 12.58), we have $\theta = \pi/4$ and $\sin \theta = \frac{1}{\sqrt{2}}$. Also, $|\mathbf{u}| = \sqrt{2}$ and $|\mathbf{v}| = 2$, so the magnitude of $\mathbf{u} \times \mathbf{v}$ is
$$|\mathbf{u} \times \mathbf{v}| = |\mathbf{u}||\mathbf{v}| \sin \theta = \sqrt{2} \cdot 2 \cdot \frac{1}{\sqrt{2}} = 2.$$

The direction of $\mathbf{u} \times \mathbf{v}$ is given by the right-hand rule: $\mathbf{u} \times \mathbf{v}$ is orthogonal to $\mathbf{u}$ and $\mathbf{v}$ (Figure 12.58).

Related Exercises 7–12

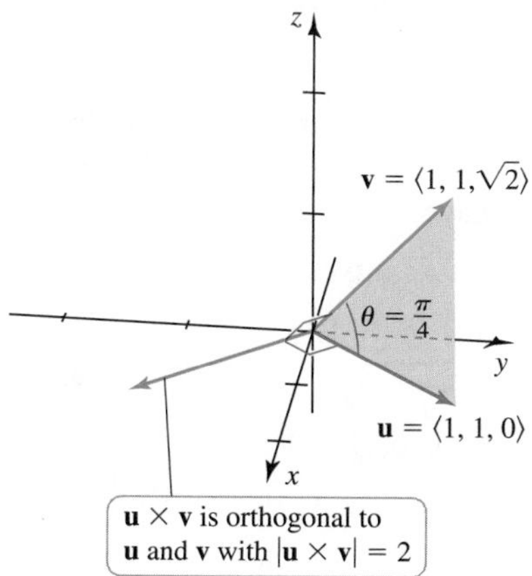

FIGURE 12.58

Properties of the Cross Product

The cross product has several algebraic properties that simplify calculations. For example, scalars factor out of a cross product; that is, if a and b are scalars, then (Exercise 61)
$$(a\mathbf{u}) \times (b\mathbf{v}) = ab(\mathbf{u} \times \mathbf{v}).$$

The order in which the cross product is performed is important. The magnitudes of $\mathbf{u} \times \mathbf{v}$ and $\mathbf{v} \times \mathbf{u}$ are equal. However, applying the right-hand rule shows that $\mathbf{u} \times \mathbf{v}$ and $\mathbf{v} \times \mathbf{u}$ point in opposite directions. Therefore, $\mathbf{u} \times \mathbf{v} = -(\mathbf{v} \times \mathbf{u})$. There are two distributive properties for the cross product, whose proofs are omitted.

> **THEOREM 12.4 Properties of the Cross Product**
> Let $\mathbf{u}$, $\mathbf{v}$, and $\mathbf{w}$ be nonzero vectors in $\mathbf{R}^3$, and let a and b be scalars.
> 1. $\mathbf{u} \times \mathbf{v} = -(\mathbf{v} \times \mathbf{u})$ — Anticommutative property
> 2. $(a\mathbf{u}) \times (b\mathbf{v}) = ab(\mathbf{u} \times \mathbf{v})$ — Associative property
> 3. $\mathbf{u} \times (\mathbf{v} + \mathbf{w}) = (\mathbf{u} \times \mathbf{v}) + (\mathbf{u} \times \mathbf{w})$ — Distributive property
> 4. $(\mathbf{u} + \mathbf{v}) \times \mathbf{w} = (\mathbf{u} \times \mathbf{w}) + (\mathbf{v} \times \mathbf{w})$ — Distributive property

QUICK CHECK 2 Explain why the vector $2\mathbf{u} \times 3\mathbf{v}$ points in the same direction as $\mathbf{u} \times \mathbf{v}$.

EXAMPLE 2 **Cross products of unit vectors** Evaluate all the cross products among the coordinate unit vectors **i**, **j**, and **k**.

SOLUTION These vectors are mutually orthogonal, which means the angle between any two distinct vectors is $\theta = \pi/2$ and $\sin\theta = 1$. Furthermore, $|\mathbf{i}| = |\mathbf{j}| = |\mathbf{k}| = 1$. Therefore, the cross product of any two distinct vectors has magnitude 1. By the right-hand rule, when the fingers of the right hand curl from **i** to **j**, the thumb points in the direction of the positive z-axis (Figure 12.59). The unit vector in the positive z-direction is **k**, so $\mathbf{i} \times \mathbf{j} = \mathbf{k}$. Similar calculations show that $\mathbf{j} \times \mathbf{k} = \mathbf{i}$ and $\mathbf{k} \times \mathbf{i} = \mathbf{j}$.

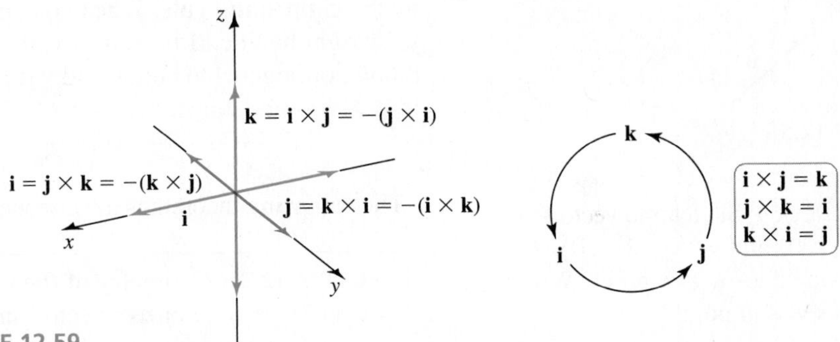

FIGURE 12.59

By property 1 of Theorem 12.4, $\mathbf{j} \times \mathbf{i} = -(\mathbf{i} \times \mathbf{j}) = -\mathbf{k}$, so $\mathbf{j} \times \mathbf{i}$ and $\mathbf{i} \times \mathbf{j}$ point in opposite directions. Similarly, $\mathbf{k} \times \mathbf{j} = -\mathbf{i}$ and $\mathbf{i} \times \mathbf{k} = -\mathbf{j}$. These relationships are easily remembered with a circle diagram (Figure 12.59). Finally the angle between any unit vector and itself is $\theta = 0$. Therefore, $\mathbf{i} \times \mathbf{i} = \mathbf{j} \times \mathbf{j} = \mathbf{k} \times \mathbf{k} = \mathbf{0}$.

Related Exercises 13–18 ◀

THEOREM 12.5 **Cross Products of Coordinate Unit Vectors**

$$\mathbf{i} \times \mathbf{j} = -(\mathbf{j} \times \mathbf{i}) = \mathbf{k} \qquad \mathbf{j} \times \mathbf{k} = -(\mathbf{k} \times \mathbf{j}) = \mathbf{i}$$
$$\mathbf{k} \times \mathbf{i} = -(\mathbf{i} \times \mathbf{k}) = \mathbf{j} \qquad \mathbf{i} \times \mathbf{i} = \mathbf{j} \times \mathbf{j} = \mathbf{k} \times \mathbf{k} = \mathbf{0}$$

What is missing so far is a method for finding the components of the cross product of two vectors in $\mathbf{R}^3$. Let $\mathbf{u} = u_1\mathbf{i} + u_2\mathbf{j} + u_3\mathbf{k}$ and $\mathbf{v} = v_1\mathbf{i} + v_2\mathbf{j} + v_3\mathbf{k}$. Using the distributive properties of the cross product (Theorem 12.4) we have

$$\begin{aligned} \mathbf{u} \times \mathbf{v} &= (u_1\mathbf{i} + u_2\mathbf{j} + u_3\mathbf{k}) \times (v_1\mathbf{i} + v_2\mathbf{j} + v_3\mathbf{k}) \\ &= u_1v_1\underbrace{(\mathbf{i} \times \mathbf{i})}_{\mathbf{0}} + u_1v_2\underbrace{(\mathbf{i} \times \mathbf{j})}_{\mathbf{k}} + u_1v_3\underbrace{(\mathbf{i} \times \mathbf{k})}_{-\mathbf{j}} \\ &\quad + u_2v_1\underbrace{(\mathbf{j} \times \mathbf{i})}_{-\mathbf{k}} + u_2v_2\underbrace{(\mathbf{j} \times \mathbf{j})}_{\mathbf{0}} + u_2v_3\underbrace{(\mathbf{j} \times \mathbf{k})}_{\mathbf{i}} \\ &\quad + u_3v_1\underbrace{(\mathbf{k} \times \mathbf{i})}_{\mathbf{j}} + u_3v_2\underbrace{(\mathbf{k} \times \mathbf{j})}_{-\mathbf{i}} + u_3v_3\underbrace{(\mathbf{k} \times \mathbf{k})}_{\mathbf{0}}. \end{aligned}$$

➤ The determinant of the matrix A is denoted both $|A|$ and $\det A$. The formula for the determinant of A is

$$\begin{vmatrix} a_1 & a_2 & a_3 \\ b_1 & b_2 & b_3 \\ c_1 & c_2 & c_3 \end{vmatrix} = a_1\begin{vmatrix} b_2 & b_3 \\ c_2 & c_3 \end{vmatrix} - a_2\begin{vmatrix} b_1 & b_3 \\ c_1 & c_3 \end{vmatrix} + a_3\begin{vmatrix} b_1 & b_2 \\ c_1 & c_2 \end{vmatrix},$$

where

$$\begin{vmatrix} a & b \\ c & d \end{vmatrix} = ad - bc.$$

This formula looks impossible to remember until we see that it fits the pattern used to evaluate 3×3 determinants. Specifically, if we compute the determinant of the matrix

$$\begin{matrix} \text{Unit vectors} & \rightarrow \\ \text{Components of } \mathbf{u} & \rightarrow \\ \text{Components of } \mathbf{v} & \rightarrow \end{matrix} \begin{pmatrix} \mathbf{i} & \mathbf{j} & \mathbf{k} \\ u_1 & u_2 & u_3 \\ v_1 & v_2 & v_3 \end{pmatrix}$$

(expanding about the first row), the following formula for the cross product emerges (see margin note).

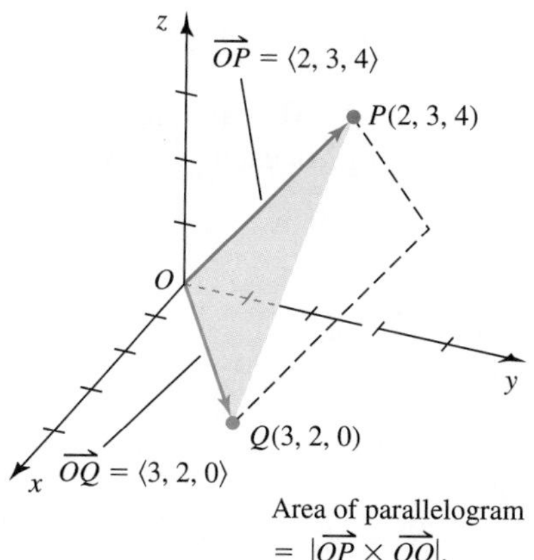

FIGURE 12.60

THEOREM 12.6 Evaluating the Cross Product
Let $\mathbf{u} = u_1\mathbf{i} + u_2\mathbf{j} + u_3\mathbf{k}$ and $\mathbf{v} = v_1\mathbf{i} + v_2\mathbf{j} + v_3\mathbf{k}$. Then,

$$\mathbf{u} \times \mathbf{v} = \begin{vmatrix} \mathbf{i} & \mathbf{j} & \mathbf{k} \\ u_1 & u_2 & u_3 \\ v_1 & v_2 & v_3 \end{vmatrix} = \begin{vmatrix} u_2 & u_3 \\ v_2 & v_3 \end{vmatrix}\mathbf{i} - \begin{vmatrix} u_1 & u_3 \\ v_1 & v_3 \end{vmatrix}\mathbf{j} + \begin{vmatrix} u_1 & u_2 \\ v_1 & v_2 \end{vmatrix}\mathbf{k}.$$

EXAMPLE 3 Area of a triangle Find the area of the triangle with vertices $O(0, 0, 0)$, $P(2, 3, 4)$, and $Q(3, 2, 0)$ (Figure 12.60).

SOLUTION First consider the parallelogram, two of whose sides are the vectors $\overrightarrow{OP}$ and $\overrightarrow{OQ}$. By Theorem 12.3, the area of this parallelogram is $|\overrightarrow{OP} \times \overrightarrow{OQ}|$. Computing the cross product, we find that

$$\overrightarrow{OP} \times \overrightarrow{OQ} = \begin{vmatrix} \mathbf{i} & \mathbf{j} & \mathbf{k} \\ 2 & 3 & 4 \\ 3 & 2 & 0 \end{vmatrix} = \begin{vmatrix} 3 & 4 \\ 2 & 0 \end{vmatrix}\mathbf{i} - \begin{vmatrix} 2 & 4 \\ 3 & 0 \end{vmatrix}\mathbf{j} + \begin{vmatrix} 2 & 3 \\ 3 & 2 \end{vmatrix}\mathbf{k}$$
$$= -8\mathbf{i} + 12\mathbf{j} - 5\mathbf{k}.$$

Therefore, the area of the parallelogram is

$$|\overrightarrow{OP} \times \overrightarrow{OQ}| = |-8\mathbf{i} + 12\mathbf{j} - 5\mathbf{k}| = \sqrt{233} \approx 15.26.$$

The triangle with vertices O, P, and Q comprises half of the parallelogram, so its area is $\sqrt{233}/2 \approx 7.63$.

Related Exercises 19–28 ◀

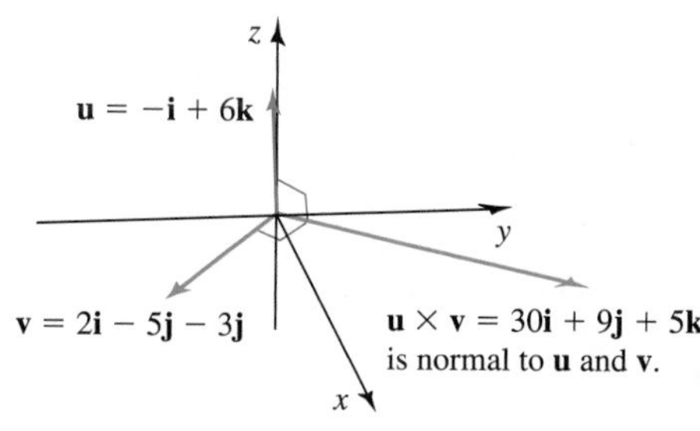

FIGURE 12.61

EXAMPLE 4 Vector normal to two vectors Find a vector normal (or orthogonal) to the two vectors $\mathbf{u} = -\mathbf{i} + 6\mathbf{k}$ and $\mathbf{v} = 2\mathbf{i} - 5\mathbf{j} - 3\mathbf{k}$.

SOLUTION A vector normal to **u** and **v** is parallel to $\mathbf{u} \times \mathbf{v}$ (Figure 12.61). One normal vector is

$$\mathbf{u} \times \mathbf{v} = \begin{vmatrix} \mathbf{i} & \mathbf{j} & \mathbf{k} \\ -1 & 0 & 6 \\ 2 & -5 & -3 \end{vmatrix}$$
$$= (0 + 30)\mathbf{i} - (3 - 12)\mathbf{j} + (5 - 0)\mathbf{k}$$
$$= 30\mathbf{i} + 9\mathbf{j} + 5\mathbf{k}.$$

Any scalar multiple of this vector is also orthogonal to **u** and **v**.

Related Exercises 29–32 ◀

QUICK CHECK 3 A good check on a cross product calculation is to verify that **u** and **v** are orthogonal to the computed $\mathbf{u} \times \mathbf{v}$. In Example 4, verify that $\mathbf{u} \cdot (\mathbf{u} \times \mathbf{v}) = 0$ and $\mathbf{v} \cdot (\mathbf{u} \times \mathbf{v}) = 0$. ◀

Applications of the Cross Product

We now investigate two physical applications of the cross product.

Torque Returning to the example of applying a force to a wrench, suppose a force **F** is applied to the point P at the head of a vector $\mathbf{r} = \overrightarrow{OP}$ (Figure 12.62). The **torque**, or twisting effect, produced by the force about the point O is given by $\boldsymbol{\tau} = \mathbf{r} \times \mathbf{F}$. The torque vector has a magnitude of

$$|\boldsymbol{\tau}| = |\mathbf{r} \times \mathbf{F}| = |\mathbf{r}||\mathbf{F}| \sin\theta,$$

where θ is the angle between **r** and **F**. The direction of the torque is given by the right-hand rule; it is orthogonal to both **r** and **F**. As noted earlier, if **r** and **F** are parallel then $\sin\theta = 0$ and the torque is the zero vector. For a given **r** and **F**, the maximum torque occurs when **F** is applied in a direction orthogonal to **r** ($\theta = \pi/2$).

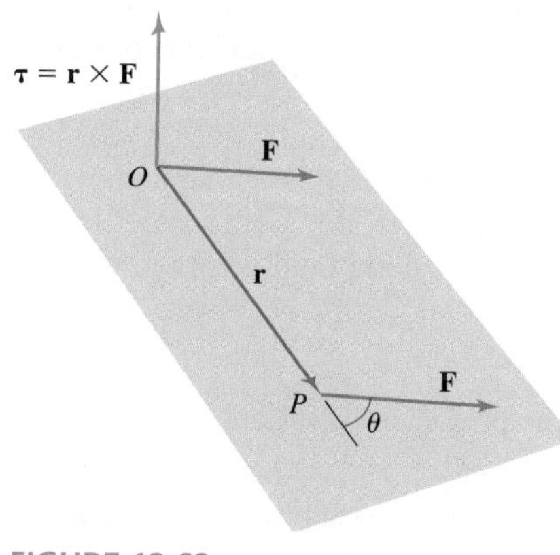

FIGURE 12.62

EXAMPLE 5 Tightening a bolt Suppose you apply a force of 20 N to a wrench attached to a bolt in a direction perpendicular to the bolt (Figure 12.63). Which produces more torque: applying the force at an angle of 60° on a wrench that is 0.15 m long or applying the force at an angle of 135° on a wrench that is 0.25 m long? In each case, what is the direction of the torque?

> When standard threads are added to the bolt in Figure 12.63, the forces used in Example 5 cause the bolt to move upward into a nut—in the direction of the torque.

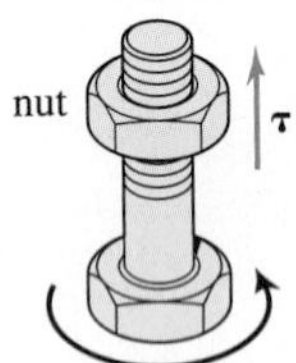

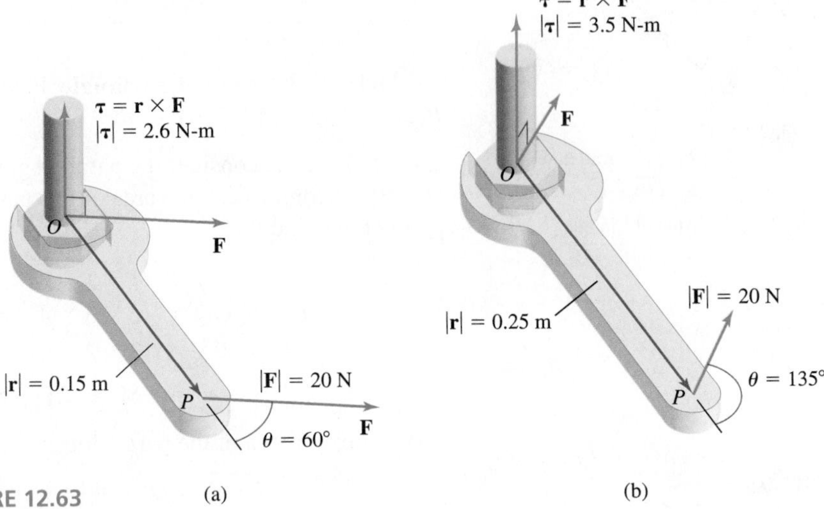

FIGURE 12.63

SOLUTION The magnitude of the torque in the first case is

$$|\boldsymbol{\tau}| = |\mathbf{r}||\mathbf{F}| \sin \theta = (0.15\,\text{m})(20\,\text{N}) \sin 60^\circ \approx 2.6\,\text{N}\cdot\text{m}.$$

In the second case, the magnitude of the torque is

$$|\boldsymbol{\tau}| = |\mathbf{r}||\mathbf{F}| \sin \theta = (0.25\,\text{m})(20\,\text{N}) \sin 135^\circ \approx 3.5\,\text{N}\cdot\text{m}.$$

The second instance gives the greater torque. In both cases, the torque is orthogonal to **r** and **F**, parallel to the shaft of the bolt (Figure 12.63). *Related Exercises 33–36* ◀

Magnetic Force on a Moving Charge Moving electric charges (either isolated charges or a current in a wire) experience a force when they pass through a magnetic field. For an isolated charge q, the force is given by $\mathbf{F} = q(\mathbf{v} \times \mathbf{B})$, where **v** is the velocity of the charge and **B** is the magnetic field. The magnitude of the force is

$$|\mathbf{F}| = |q||\mathbf{v} \times \mathbf{B}| = |q||\mathbf{v}||\mathbf{B}| \sin \theta,$$

where θ is the angle between **v** and **B** (Figure 12.64). Note that the sign of the charge also determines the direction of the force. If the velocity vector is parallel to the magnetic field, the charge experiences no force. The maximum force occurs when the velocity is orthogonal to the magnetic field.

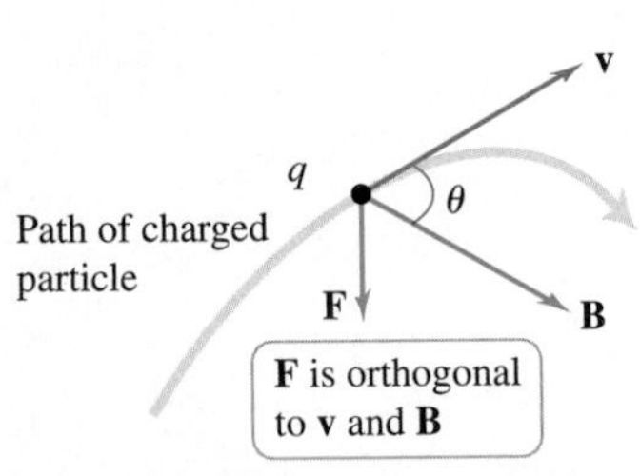

FIGURE 12.64

> The standard unit of magnetic field strength is the tesla (T, named after Nicola Tesla). A strong bar magnet has a strength of 1 T. In terms of other units, 1 T = 1 kg/C-s, where C is the unit of charge called the *coulomb*.

EXAMPLE 6 Force on a proton A proton with a mass of 1.7×10^{-27} kg and a charge of $q = +1.6 \times 10^{-19}$ coulombs (C) moves along the x-axis with a speed of $|\mathbf{v}| = 9 \times 10^5$ m/s. When it reaches (0, 0, 0) a uniform magnetic field is turned on. The field has a constant strength of 1 tesla and is directed along the negative z-axis (Figure 12.65).

a. Find the magnitude and direction of the force on the proton at the instant it enters the magnetic field.

b. Assume that the proton loses no energy and the force in part (a) acts as a *centripetal force* with magnitude $|\mathbf{F}| = m|\mathbf{v}|^2/R$ that keeps the proton in a circular orbit of radius R. Find the radius of the orbit.

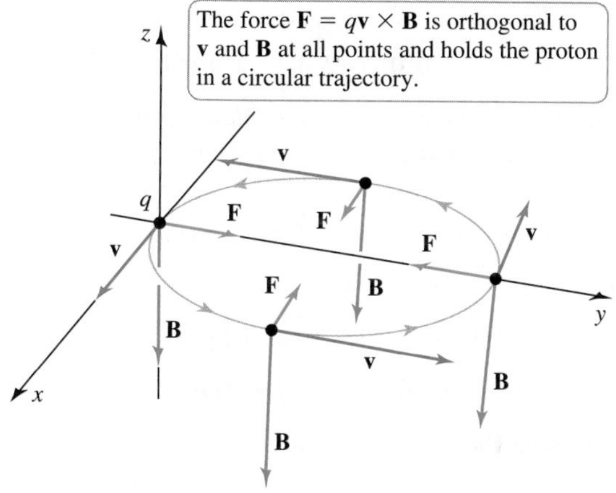
The force $\mathbf{F} = q\mathbf{v} \times \mathbf{B}$ is orthogonal to $\mathbf{v}$ and $\mathbf{B}$ at all points and holds the proton in a circular trajectory.
z
x
y
q
v
F
B

FIGURE 12.65

SOLUTION

a. Expressed as vectors, we have $\mathbf{v} = 9 \times 10^5\,\mathbf{i}$ and $\mathbf{B} = -\mathbf{k}$. Therefore, the force on the proton in newtons is

$$\begin{aligned}\mathbf{F} = q(\mathbf{v} \times \mathbf{B}) &= 1.6 \times 10^{-19}((9 \times 10^5\,\mathbf{i}) \times (-\mathbf{k})) \\ &= 1.44 \times 10^{-13}\mathbf{j}.\end{aligned}$$

As shown in Figure 12.65, when the proton enters the magnetic field in the positive x-direction, the force acts in the positive y-direction, which changes the path of the proton.

b. The magnitude of the force acting on the proton remains 1.44×10^{-13} N at all times (from part (a)). Equating this force to the centripetal force $|\mathbf{F}| = m|\mathbf{v}|^2/R$, we find that

$$R = \frac{m|\mathbf{v}|^2}{|\mathbf{F}|} = \frac{(1.7 \times 10^{-27}\,\text{kg})\,(9 \times 10^5\,\text{m/s})^2}{1.44 \times 10^{-13}\,\text{N}} \approx 0.01\text{ m}.$$

Assuming no energy loss, the proton moves in a circular orbit of radius 0.01 m.

Related Exercises 37–40 ◀

SECTION 12.4 EXERCISES

Review Questions

1. Explain how to find the magnitude of the cross product $\mathbf{u} \times \mathbf{v}$.
2. Explain how to find the direction of the cross product $\mathbf{u} \times \mathbf{v}$.
3. What is the magnitude of the cross product of two parallel vectors?
4. If $\mathbf{u}$ and $\mathbf{v}$ are orthogonal, what is the magnitude of $\mathbf{u} \times \mathbf{v}$?
5. Explain how to use a determinant to compute $\mathbf{u} \times \mathbf{v}$.
6. Explain how to find the torque produced by a force using cross products.

Basic Skills

7–8. Cross products from the definition *Find the magnitude of the cross product of the vectors* $\mathbf{u}$ *and* $\mathbf{v}$ *given in each figure.*

7.

z; x; y

$\mathbf{u} = \langle 3, 0, 0\rangle$

$\mathbf{v} = \langle 0, 5, 0\rangle$

8.

z; x; y

$\mathbf{v} = \langle 0, 0, 2\rangle$

$\mathbf{u} = \langle -4, 0, 0\rangle$

9–12. Cross products from the definition *Sketch the following vectors* $\mathbf{u}$ *and* $\mathbf{v}$*. Then compute* $|\mathbf{u} \times \mathbf{v}|$ *and show the cross product on your sketch.*

9. $\mathbf{u} = \langle 0, -2, 0\rangle, \mathbf{v} = \langle 0, 1, 0\rangle$

10. $\mathbf{u} = \langle 0, 4, 0\rangle, \mathbf{v} = \langle 0, 0, -8\rangle$

11. $\mathbf{u} = \langle 3, 3, 0\rangle, \mathbf{v} = \langle 3, 3, 3\sqrt{2}\rangle$

12. $\mathbf{u} = \langle 0, -2, -2\rangle, \mathbf{v} = \langle 0, 2, -2\rangle$

13–18. Coordinate unit vectors *Compute the following cross products. Then make a sketch showing the two vectors and their cross product.*

13. $\mathbf{j} \times \mathbf{k}$ **14.** $\mathbf{i} \times \mathbf{k}$ **15.** $-\mathbf{j} \times \mathbf{k}$

16. $3\mathbf{j} \times \mathbf{i}$ **17.** $-2\mathbf{i} \times 3\mathbf{k}$ **18.** $2\mathbf{j} \times (-5)\mathbf{i}$

19–22. Area of a parallelogram *Find the area of the parallelogram that has two adjacent sides* $\mathbf{u}$ *and* $\mathbf{v}$*.*

19. $\mathbf{u} = 3\mathbf{i} - \mathbf{j}, \mathbf{v} = 3\mathbf{j} + 2\mathbf{k}$

20. $\mathbf{u} = -3\mathbf{i} + 2\mathbf{k}, \mathbf{v} = \mathbf{i} + \mathbf{j} + \mathbf{k}$

21. $\mathbf{u} = 2\mathbf{i} - \mathbf{j} - 2\mathbf{k}, \mathbf{v} = 3\mathbf{i} + 2\mathbf{j} - \mathbf{k}$

22. $\mathbf{u} = 8\mathbf{i} + 2\mathbf{j} - 3\mathbf{k}, \mathbf{v} = 2\mathbf{i} + 4\mathbf{j} - 4\mathbf{k}$

23–28. Computing cross products *Find the cross products* $\mathbf{u} \times \mathbf{v}$ *and* $\mathbf{v} \times \mathbf{u}$ *for the following vectors* $\mathbf{u}$ *and* $\mathbf{v}$*.*

23. $\mathbf{u} = \langle 3, 5, 0\rangle, \mathbf{v} = \langle 0, 3, -6\rangle$

24. $\mathbf{u} = \langle -4, 1, 1\rangle, \mathbf{v} = \langle 0, 1, -1\rangle$

25. $\mathbf{u} = \langle 2, 3, -9\rangle, \mathbf{v} = \langle -1, 1, -1\rangle$

26. $\mathbf{u} = \langle 3, -4, 6\rangle, \mathbf{v} = \langle 1, 2, -1\rangle$

27. $\mathbf{u} = 3\mathbf{i} - \mathbf{j} - 2\mathbf{k}, \mathbf{v} = \mathbf{i} + 3\mathbf{j} - 2\mathbf{k}$

28. $\mathbf{u} = 2\mathbf{i} - 10\mathbf{j} + 15\mathbf{k}, \mathbf{v} = 0.5\mathbf{i} + \mathbf{j} - 0.6\mathbf{k}$

29–32. Normal vectors *Find a vector normal to the given vectors.*

29. $\langle 0, 1, 2\rangle$ and $\langle -2, 0, 3\rangle$ **30.** $\langle 1, 2, 3\rangle$ and $\langle -2, 4, -1\rangle$

31. $\langle 8, 0, 4\rangle$ and $\langle -8, 2, 1\rangle$ **32.** $\langle 6, -2, 4\rangle$ and $\langle 1, 2, 3\rangle$

33–36. Computing torque *Answer the following questions about torque.*

33. Let $\mathbf{r} = \overrightarrow{OP} = \mathbf{i} + \mathbf{j} + \mathbf{k}$. A force $\mathbf{F} = \langle 20, 0, 0\rangle$ is applied at P. Find the torque about O that is produced.

34. Let $\mathbf{r} = \overrightarrow{OP} = \mathbf{i} - \mathbf{j} + 2\mathbf{k}$. A force $\mathbf{F} = \langle 10, 10, 0\rangle$ is applied at P. Find the torque about O that is produced.

35. Let $\mathbf{r} = \overrightarrow{OP} = 10\mathbf{i}$. Which is greater (in magnitude): the torque about O when a force $\mathbf{F} = 5\mathbf{i} - 5\mathbf{k}$ is applied at P or the torque about O when a force $\mathbf{F} = 4\mathbf{i} - 3\mathbf{j}$ is applied at P?

36. A pump handle has a pivot at (0, 0, 0) and extends to $P(5, 0, -5)$. A force $\mathbf{F} = \langle 1, 0, -10\rangle$ is applied at P. Find the magnitude and direction of the torque about the pivot.

37–40. Force on a moving charge *Answer the following questions about force on a moving charge.*

37. A particle with unit charge ($q = 1$) enters a constant magnetic field $\mathbf{B} = \mathbf{i} + \mathbf{j}$ with a velocity $\mathbf{v} = 20\mathbf{k}$. Find the magnitude and direction of the force on the particle. Make a sketch of the magnetic field, the velocity, and the force.

38. A particle with unit negative charge ($q = -1$) enters a constant magnetic field $\mathbf{B} = 5\mathbf{k}$ with a velocity $\mathbf{v} = \mathbf{i} + 2\mathbf{j}$. Find the magnitude and direction of the force on the particle. Make a sketch of the magnetic field, the velocity, and the force.

39. An electron ($q = -1.6 \times 10^{-19}$ C) enters a constant 2-T magnetic field at an angle of 45° to the field with a speed of 2×10^5 m/s. Find the magnitude of the force on the electron.

40. A proton ($q = 1.6 \times 10^{-19}$ C) with velocity $2 \times 10^6\,\mathbf{j}$ m/s experiences a force in newtons of $\mathbf{F} = 5 \times 10^{-12}\,\mathbf{k}$ as it passes through the origin. Find the magnitude and direction of the magnetic field at that instant.

Further Explorations

41. Explain why or why not Determine whether the following statements are true and give an explanation or counterexample.

a. The cross product of two nonzero vectors is a nonzero vector.
b. $|\mathbf{u} \times \mathbf{v}|$ is less than both $|\mathbf{u}|$ and $|\mathbf{v}|$.
c. If $\mathbf{u}$ points east and $\mathbf{v}$ points south, then $\mathbf{u} \times \mathbf{v}$ points west.
d. If $\mathbf{u} \times \mathbf{v} = \mathbf{0}$ and $\mathbf{u} \cdot \mathbf{v} = 0$, then either $\mathbf{u} = \mathbf{0}$ or $\mathbf{v} = \mathbf{0}$ (or both).
e. Law of Cancellation? If $\mathbf{u} \times \mathbf{v} = \mathbf{u} \times \mathbf{w}$, then $\mathbf{v} = \mathbf{w}$.

42–45. Areas of parallelograms *Find the area of the following parallelograms P.*

42. Two of the adjacent sides of P are $\mathbf{u} = \langle 4, 0, 0\rangle$ and $\mathbf{v} = \langle 8, 8, 8\rangle$.

43. Two of the adjacent sides of P are $\mathbf{u} = \langle -1, 1, 1\rangle$ and $\mathbf{v} = \langle 0, -1, 1\rangle$.

44. Three vertices of P are $O(0, 0, 0)$, $Q(4, 4, 0)$, and $R(6, 6, 3)$.

45. Three vertices of P are $O(0, 0, 0)$, $Q(2, 4, 8)$, and $R(1, 4, 10)$.

46–49. Areas of triangles *Find the area of the following triangles T. (The area of a triangle is half the area of the corresponding parallelogram.)*

46. The sides of T are $\mathbf{u} = \langle 0, 6, 0\rangle$, $\mathbf{v} = \langle 4, 4, 4\rangle$, and $\mathbf{u} - \mathbf{v}$.

47. The sides of T are $\mathbf{u} = \langle 3, 3, 3\rangle$, $\mathbf{v} = \langle 6, 0, 6\rangle$, and $\mathbf{u} - \mathbf{v}$.

48. The vertices of T are $O(0, 0, 0)$, $P(2, 4, 6)$, and $Q(3, 5, 7)$.

49. The vertices of T are $O(0, 0, 0)$, $P(1, 2, 3)$, and $Q(6, 5, 4)$.

50. A unit cross product Under what conditions is $\mathbf{u} \times \mathbf{v}$ a unit vector?

51. Vector equation Find all vectors $\mathbf{u}$ that satisfy the equation

$$\langle 1, 1, 1\rangle \times \mathbf{u} = \langle -1, -1, 2\rangle.$$

52. Vector equation Find all vectors $\mathbf{u}$ that satisfy the equation

$$\langle 1, 1, 1\rangle \times \mathbf{u} = \langle 0, 0, 1\rangle.$$

53. Area of a triangle Find the area of the triangle with vertices on the coordinate axes at the points $(a, 0, 0)$, $(0, b, 0)$, and $(0, 0, c)$, in terms of a, b, and c.

54–56. Scalar triple product *Another operation with vectors is the* ***scalar triple product****, defined to be $\mathbf{u} \cdot (\mathbf{v} \times \mathbf{w})$, for vectors $\mathbf{u}$, $\mathbf{v}$, and $\mathbf{w}$ in $\mathbf{R}^3$.*

54. Express $\mathbf{u}$, $\mathbf{v}$, and $\mathbf{w}$ in terms of their components and show that $\mathbf{u} \cdot (\mathbf{v} \times \mathbf{w})$ equals the determinant

$$\begin{vmatrix} u_1 & u_2 & u_3 \\ v_1 & v_2 & v_3 \\ w_1 & w_2 & w_3 \end{vmatrix}.$$

55. Consider the parallelepiped (slanted box) determined by the position vectors $\mathbf{u}$, $\mathbf{v}$, and $\mathbf{w}$ (see figure). Show that the volume of the parallelepiped is $|\mathbf{u} \cdot (\mathbf{v} \times \mathbf{w})|$.

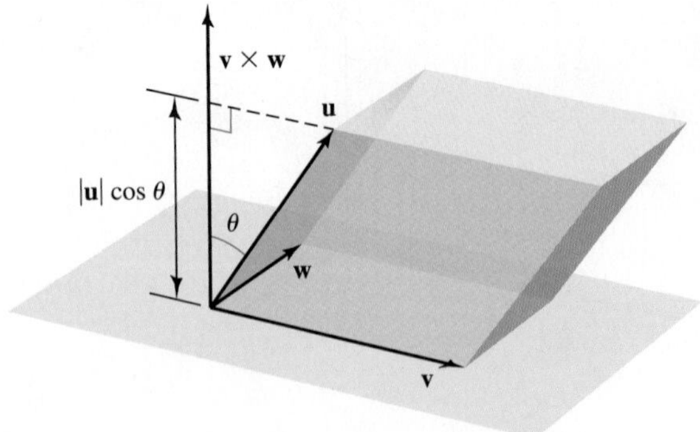

56. Prove that $\mathbf{u} \cdot (\mathbf{v} \times \mathbf{w}) = (\mathbf{u} \times \mathbf{v}) \cdot \mathbf{w}$.

Applications

57. Bicycle brakes A set of caliper brakes exerts a force on the rim of a bicycle wheel that creates a frictional force $\mathbf{F}$ of 40 N (see figure). Assuming the wheel has a radius of 66 cm, find the magnitude and direction of the torque about the axle of the wheel.

58. **Arm torque** A horizontally outstretched arm supports a weight of 20 lb in a hand (see figure). If the distance from the shoulder to the elbow is 1 ft and the distance from the elbow to the hand is 1 ft, find the magnitude and describe the direction of the torque about (a) the shoulder and (b) the elbow. (The units of torque in this case are ft-lb.)

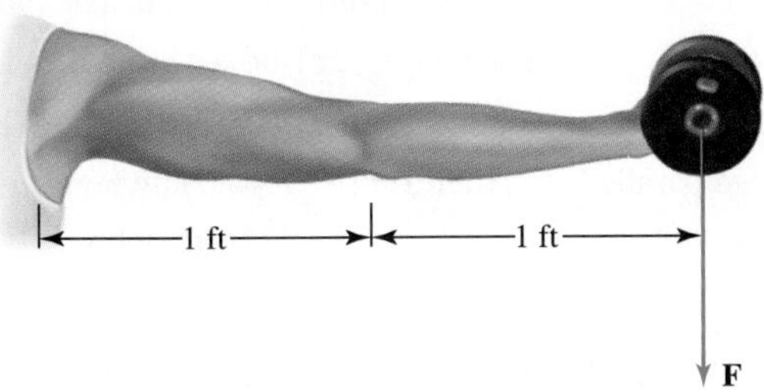

59. **Electron speed** An electron with a mass of 9.1×10^{-31} kg and a charge of -1.6×10^{-19} C travels in a circular path with no loss of energy in a magnetic field of 0.05 T that is orthogonal to the path of the electron (see figure). If the radius of the path is 0.002 m, what is the speed of the electron?

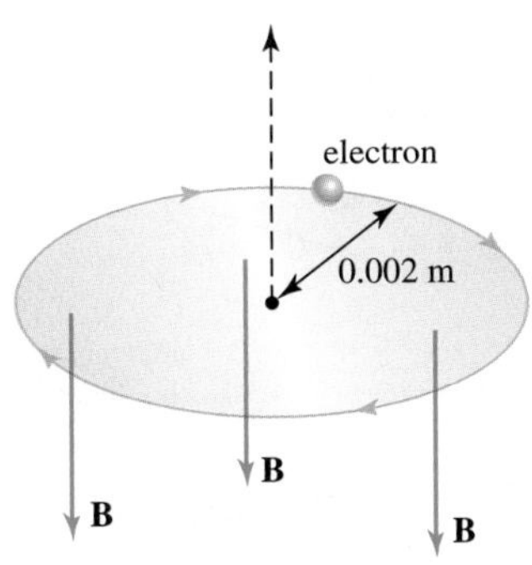

Additional Exercises

60. $\mathbf{u} \times \mathbf{u}$ Prove that $\mathbf{u} \times \mathbf{u} = \mathbf{0}$ in three ways.
    a. Use the definition of the cross product.
    b. Use the determinant formulation of the cross product.
    c. Use the property that $\mathbf{u} \times \mathbf{v} = -(\mathbf{v} \times \mathbf{u})$.

61. **Associative property** Prove in two ways that for scalars a and b, $(a\mathbf{u}) \times (b\mathbf{v}) = ab(\mathbf{u} \times \mathbf{v})$. Use the definition of the cross product and the determinant formula.

62–64. Possible identities *Determine whether the following statements are true using a proof or counterexample. Assume that* **u**, **v**, *and* **w** *are nonzero vectors in* $\mathbf{R}^3$.

62. $\mathbf{u} \times (\mathbf{u} \times \mathbf{v}) = \mathbf{0}$

63. $(\mathbf{u} - \mathbf{v}) \times (\mathbf{u} + \mathbf{v}) = 2\mathbf{u} \times \mathbf{v}$

64. $\mathbf{u} \cdot (\mathbf{v} \times \mathbf{w}) = \mathbf{w} \cdot (\mathbf{u} \times \mathbf{v})$

65–66. Identities *Prove the following identities. Assume that* **u**, **v**, **w**, *and* **x** *are nonzero vectors in* $\mathbf{R}^3$.

65. $\mathbf{u} \times (\mathbf{v} \times \mathbf{w}) = (\mathbf{u} \cdot \mathbf{w})\mathbf{v} - (\mathbf{u} \cdot \mathbf{v})\mathbf{w}$, $(\mathbf{u} \times (\mathbf{v} \times \mathbf{w})$ is called (the **vector triple product**)

66. $(\mathbf{u} \times \mathbf{v}) \cdot (\mathbf{w} \times \mathbf{x}) = (\mathbf{u} \cdot \mathbf{w})(\mathbf{v} \cdot \mathbf{x}) - (\mathbf{u} \cdot \mathbf{x})(\mathbf{v} \cdot \mathbf{w})$

67. **Cross product equations** Suppose **u** and **v** are nonzero vectors in $\mathbf{R}^3$.
    a. Prove that the equation $\mathbf{u} \times \mathbf{z} = \mathbf{v}$ has a nonzero solution **z** if and only if $\mathbf{u} \cdot \mathbf{v} = 0$. (*Hint:* Take the dot product of both sides with **v**.)
    b. Explain this result geometrically.

QUICK CHECK ANSWERS

1. $\mathbf{u} \times \mathbf{v}$ points in the positive z-direction; $\mathbf{v} \times \mathbf{u}$ points in the negative z-direction. **2.** The vector $2\mathbf{u}$ points in the same direction as **u** and the vector $3\mathbf{v}$ points in the same direction as **v**. So, the right-hand rule gives the same direction for $2\mathbf{u} \times 3\mathbf{v}$ as it does for $\mathbf{u} \times \mathbf{v}$. **3.** $\mathbf{u} \cdot (\mathbf{u} \times \mathbf{v}) = \langle -1, 0, 6\rangle \cdot \langle 30, 9, 5\rangle = -30 + 0 + 30 = 0$. A similar calculation shows that $\mathbf{v} \cdot (\mathbf{u} \times \mathbf{v}) = 0$.

12.5 Lines and Curves in Space

Imagine a projectile moving along a path in three-dimensional space; it could be an electron or a comet, a soccer ball or a rocket. If you take a snapshot of the object, its position is described by a static position vector $\mathbf{r} = \langle x, y, z\rangle$. However, if you want to describe the full trajectory of the object as it unfolds in time, you must use a position vector such as $\mathbf{r}(t) = \langle x(t), y(t), z(t)\rangle$ whose components change in time (Figure 12.66). The goal of this section is to describe continuous motion by using vector-valued functions.

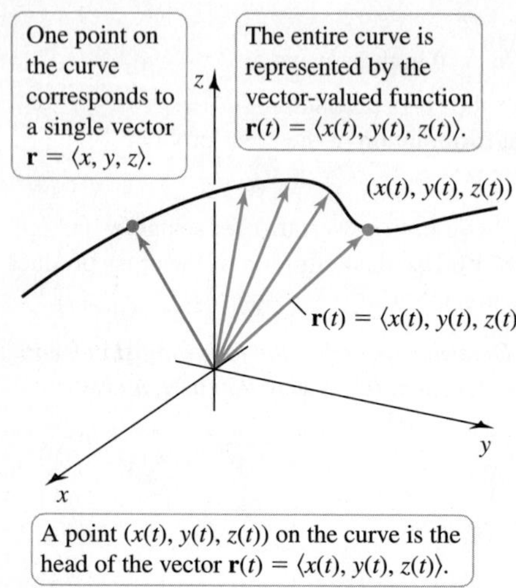
One point on the curve corresponds to a single vector $\mathbf{r} = \langle x, y, z\rangle$.
The entire curve is represented by the vector-valued function $\mathbf{r}(t) = \langle x(t), y(t), z(t)\rangle$.
z
$(x(t), y(t), z(t))$
$\mathbf{r}(t) = \langle x(t), y(t), z(t)\rangle$
y
x
A point $(x(t), y(t), z(t))$ on the curve is the head of the vector $\mathbf{r}(t) = \langle x(t), y(t), z(t)\rangle$.

FIGURE 12.66

Vector-Valued Functions

A function of the form $\mathbf{r}(t) = \langle x(t), y(t), z(t)\rangle$ may be viewed in two ways:

- It is a set of three parametric equations that describe a curve in space.
- It is also a **vector-valued function**, which means that the three dependent variables (x, y, and z) are the components of $\mathbf{r}$, and each component varies with respect to a single independent variable t (that often represents time).

Here is the connection between these two perspectives: As t varies, a point $(x(t), y(t), z(t))$ on a parametric curve is also the head of the position vector $\mathbf{r}(t) = \langle x(t), y(t), z(t)\rangle$. It is useful to keep both of these interpretations in mind as you work with vector-valued functions.

Lines in Space

Two distinct points in $\mathbf{R}^3$ determine a unique line. Alternatively, one point and a direction also determine a unique line. We use both of these properties to derive parametric equations for lines in space. The result is an example of a vector-valued function in $\mathbf{R}^3$.

Let ℓ be the line passing through the point $P_0(x_0, y_0, z_0)$ parallel to the nonzero vector $\mathbf{v} = \langle a, b, c\rangle$, where P_0 and $\mathbf{v}$ are given. The fixed point P_0 is associated with the position vector $\mathbf{r}_0 = \overrightarrow{OP_0} = \langle x_0, y_0, z_0\rangle$. We let $P(x, y, z)$ be a variable point on ℓ with $\mathbf{r} = \overrightarrow{OP} = \langle x, y, z\rangle$ the position vector associated with P (Figure 12.67). Because ℓ is parallel to $\mathbf{v}$, the vector $\overrightarrow{P_0P}$ is also parallel to $\mathbf{v}$; therefore $\overrightarrow{P_0P} = t\mathbf{v}$, where t is a real number. By vector addition, we see that $\overrightarrow{OP} = \overrightarrow{OP_0} + \overrightarrow{P_0P}$, from which it follows that $\overrightarrow{OP} = \overrightarrow{OP_0} + t\mathbf{v}$. This equation says that

$$\underbrace{\langle x, y, z\rangle}_{\mathbf{r} = \overrightarrow{OP}} = \underbrace{\langle x_0, y_0, z_0\rangle}_{\mathbf{r}_0 = \overrightarrow{OP_0}} + t\underbrace{\langle a, b, c\rangle}_{\mathbf{v}} \quad \text{or} \quad \mathbf{r} = \mathbf{r}_0 + t\mathbf{v}.$$

Equating the components, the line is described by the parametric equations

$$x = x_0 + at, \qquad y = y_0 + bt, \qquad z = z_0 + ct, \qquad \text{for } -\infty < t < \infty.$$

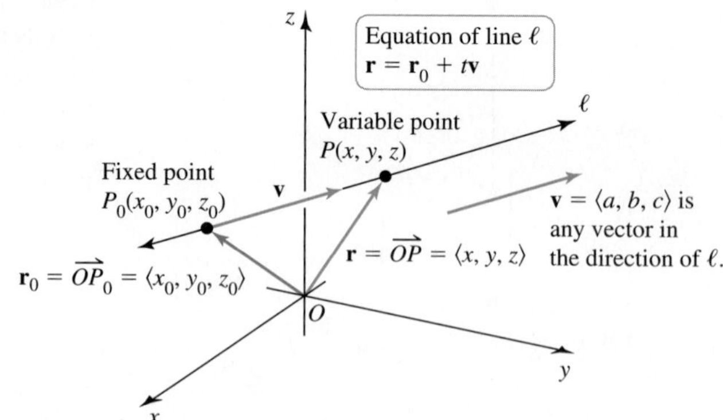
z
Equation of line ℓ
$\mathbf{r} = \mathbf{r}_0 + t\mathbf{v}$
ℓ
Variable point
$P(x, y, z)$
Fixed point
$P_0(x_0, y_0, z_0)$
$\mathbf{v}$
$\mathbf{v} = \langle a, b, c\rangle$ is any vector in the direction of ℓ.
$\mathbf{r} = \overrightarrow{OP} = \langle x, y, z\rangle$
$\mathbf{r}_0 = \overrightarrow{OP_0} = \langle x_0, y_0, z_0\rangle$
O
y
x

FIGURE 12.67

The parameter t determines the location of points on the line, where $t = 0$ corresponds to P_0. If t increases from 0, we move along the line in the direction of $\mathbf{v}$ and if t decreases from 0, we move along the line in the direction of $-\mathbf{v}$. As t varies over all real numbers ($-\infty < t < \infty$), the vector $\mathbf{r}$ sweeps out the entire line ℓ. If, instead of knowing the direction $\mathbf{v}$ of the line, we are given two points $P_0(x_0, y_0, z_0)$ and $P_1(x_1, y_1, z_1)$, then the direction of the line is $\mathbf{v} = \overrightarrow{P_0P_1} = \langle x_1 - x_0, y_1 - y_0, z_1 - z_0\rangle$.

QUICK CHECK 1 Describe the line $\mathbf{r}(t) = t\mathbf{k}$ for $-\infty < t < \infty$. Describe the line $\mathbf{r}(t) = t(\mathbf{i} + \mathbf{j} + 0\mathbf{k})$, for $-\infty < t < \infty$. ◄

➤ Although we may refer to *the* equation of a line, there are infinitely many equations for the same line. The direction vector is determined only up to a scalar multiple.

Equation of a Line

An **equation of the line** passing through the point $P_0(x_0, y_0, z_0)$ in the direction of the vector $\mathbf{v} = \langle a, b, c \rangle$ is $\mathbf{r} = \mathbf{r}_0 + t\mathbf{v}$, or

$$\langle x, y, z \rangle = \langle x_0, y_0, z_0 \rangle + t\langle a, b, c \rangle, \quad \text{for } -\infty < t < \infty.$$

Equivalently, the parametric equations of the line are

$$x = x_0 + at, \qquad y = y_0 + bt, \qquad z = z_0 + ct, \qquad \text{for } -\infty < t < \infty.$$

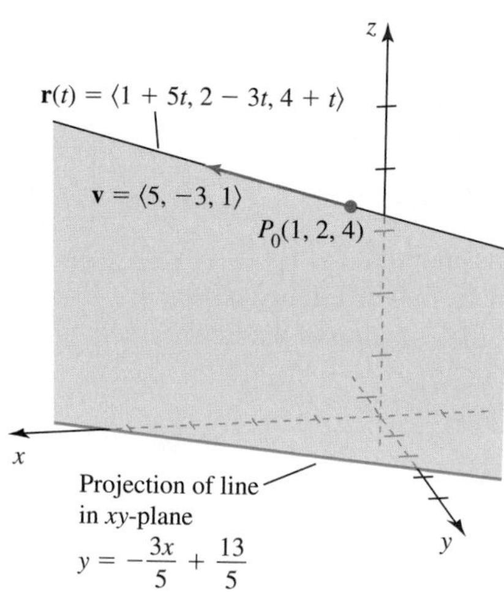

FIGURE 12.68

EXAMPLE 1 **Equations of lines** Find an equation of the line that passes through the point $P_0(1, 2, 4)$ in the direction of $\mathbf{v} = \langle 5, -3, 1 \rangle$.

SOLUTION We are given $\mathbf{r}_0 = \langle 1, 2, 4 \rangle$. Therefore, an equation of the line is

$$\mathbf{r}(t) = \mathbf{r}_0 + t\mathbf{v} = \langle 1, 2, 4 \rangle + t\langle 5, -3, 1 \rangle = \langle 1 + 5t, 2 - 3t, 4 + t \rangle,$$

where $-\infty < t < \infty$ (Figure 12.68). The corresponding parametric equations are

$$x = 1 + 5t \qquad y = 2 - 3t \qquad z = 4 + t.$$

The line is easier to visualize if it is plotted with its projection in the xy-plane. Setting $z = 0$ (the equation of the xy-plane), the parametric equations of the projection line are $x = 1 + 5t$, $y = 2 - 3t$, and $z = 0$. Eliminating t from these equations, an equation of the projection line is $y = -\frac{3}{5}x + \frac{13}{5}$ (Figure 12.68). *Related Exercises 9–16*

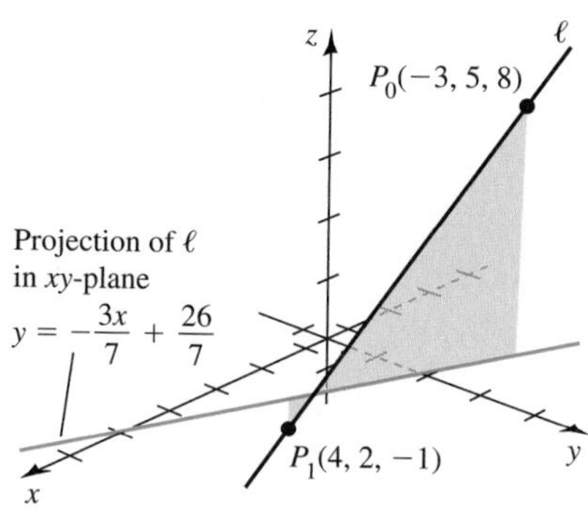

(a)

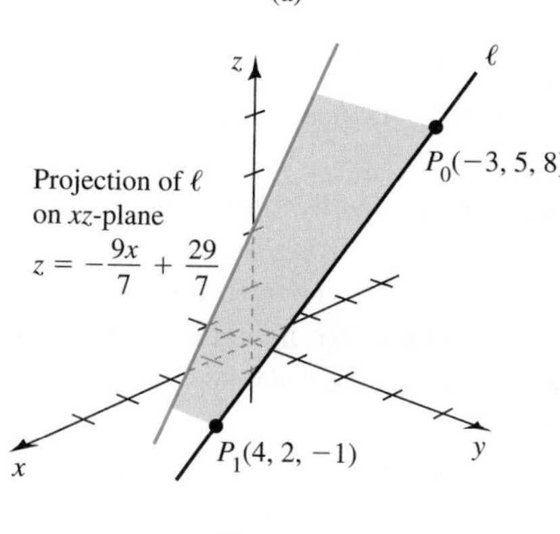

(b)

FIGURE 12.69

EXAMPLE 2 **Equations of lines** Let ℓ be the line that passes through the points $P_0(-3, 5, 8)$ and $P_1(4, 2, -1)$.

a. Find an equation of ℓ.

b. Find equations of the projections of ℓ on the xy- and xz-planes. Then graph those projection lines.

SOLUTION

a. The direction of the line is

$$\mathbf{v} = \overrightarrow{P_0P_1} = \langle 4 - (-3), 2 - 5, -1 - 8 \rangle = \langle 7, -3, -9 \rangle.$$

Therefore, with $\mathbf{r}_0 = \langle -3, 5, 8 \rangle$, the equation of ℓ is

$$\begin{aligned} \mathbf{r}(t) &= \mathbf{r}_0 + t\mathbf{v} \\ &= \langle -3, 5, 8 \rangle + t\langle 7, -3, -9 \rangle \\ &= \langle -3 + 7t, 5 - 3t, 8 - 9t \rangle. \end{aligned}$$

b. Setting the z-component of the equation of ℓ equal to zero, the parametric equations of the projection of ℓ on the xy-plane are $x = -3 + 7t$, $y = 5 - 3t$. Eliminating t from these equations gives the equation $y = -\frac{3}{7}x + \frac{26}{7}$ (Figure 12.69a). The projection of ℓ on the xz-plane (setting $y = 0$) is $x = -3 + 7t$, $z = 8 - 9t$. Eliminating t gives the equation $z = -\frac{9}{7}x + \frac{29}{7}$ (Figure 12.69b). *Related Exercises 9–16*

➤ A related problem: To find the point at which the line in Example 2 intersects the xy-plane, we set $z = 0$, solve for t, and find the corresponding x- and y-coordinates: $z = 0$ implies $t = \frac{8}{9}$, which implies $x = \frac{29}{9}$ and $y = \frac{7}{3}$.

QUICK CHECK 2 In the equation of the line

$$\mathbf{r}(t) = \langle x_0, y_0, z_0 \rangle + t\langle x_1 - x_0, y_1 - y_0, z_1 - z_0 \rangle,$$

what value of t corresponds to the point $P_0(x_0, y_0, z_0)$? What value of t corresponds to the point $P_1(x_1, y_1, z_1)$?

EXAMPLE 3 **Equation of a line segment** Find the equation of the line segment between $P_0(3, -1, 4)$ and $P_1(0, 5, 2)$.

SOLUTION The same ideas used to find an equation of an entire line work here. We just restrict the values of the parameter t, so that only the given line segment is generated. The direction of the line segment is

$$\mathbf{v} = \overrightarrow{P_0P_1} = \langle 0 - 3, 5 - (-1), 2 - 4 \rangle = \langle -3, 6, -2 \rangle.$$

Letting $\mathbf{r}_0 = \langle 3, -1, 4 \rangle$, the equation of the line through P_0 and P_1 is

$$\mathbf{r}(t) = \mathbf{r}_0 + t\mathbf{v} = \langle 3 - 3t, -1 + 6t, 4 - 2t \rangle.$$

Notice that if $t = 0$, then $\mathbf{r}(0) = \langle 3, -1, 4 \rangle$, which has endpoint P_0. If $t = 1$, then $\mathbf{r}(1) = \langle 0, 5, 2 \rangle$, which has endpoint P_1. Letting t vary from 0 to 1 generates the line segment between P_0 and P_1 (Figure 12.70). Therefore, the equation of the line segment is

$$\mathbf{r}(t) = \langle 3 - 3t, -1 + 6t, 4 - 2t \rangle, \qquad \text{for } 0 \le t \le 1.$$

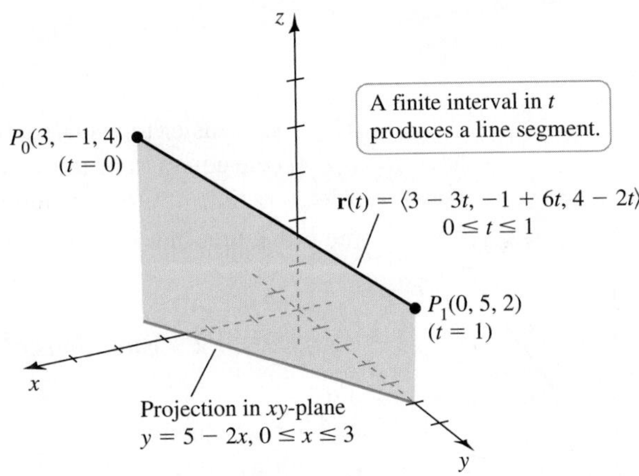

FIGURE 12.70

Related Exercises 17–20 ◄

Curves in Space

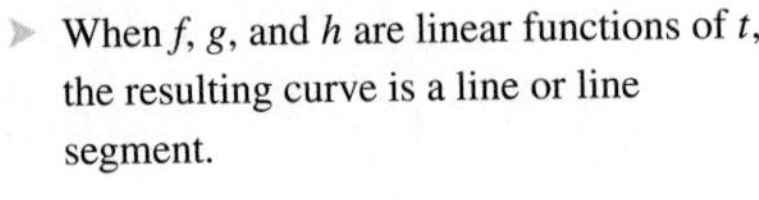
➤ When f, g, and h are linear functions of t, the resulting curve is a line or line segment.

We now explore general vector-valued functions of the form

$$\mathbf{r}(t) = \langle f(t), g(t), h(t) \rangle = f(t)\mathbf{i} + g(t)\mathbf{j} + h(t)\mathbf{k},$$

where f, g, and h are defined on an interval $a \le t \le b$. The **domain** of $\mathbf{r}$ is the largest set of values of t on which all of f, g, and h are defined.

Figure 12.71 illustrates how a parameterized curve is generated by such a function. As the parameter t varies over the interval $a \le t \le b$, each value of t produces a position vector that corresponds to a point on the curve, starting at the initial vector $\mathbf{r}(a)$ and ending at the terminal vector $\mathbf{r}(b)$. The resulting parameterized curve can either have finite length or extend indefinitely. The curve may also cross itself or close and retrace itself.

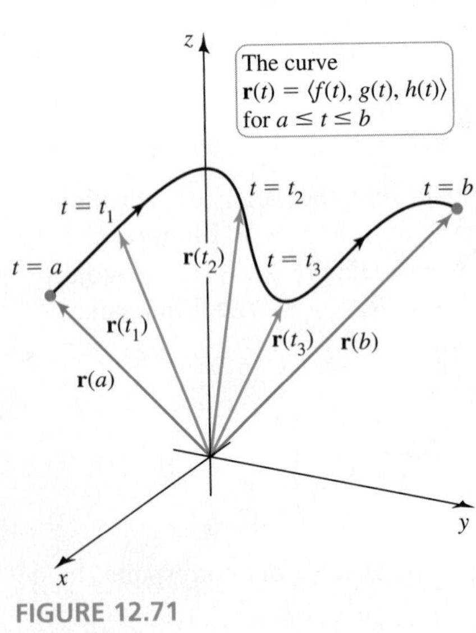

FIGURE 12.71

EXAMPLE 4 **A helix** Graph the curve described by the equation

$$\mathbf{r}(t) = 4 \cos t\,\mathbf{i} + \sin t\,\mathbf{j} + \frac{t}{2\pi}\mathbf{k},$$

where (a) $0 \le t \le 2\pi$ and (b) $-\infty < t < \infty$.

SOLUTION

a. We begin by setting $z = 0$ to determine the projection of the curve in the xy-plane. The resulting function $\mathbf{r}(t) = 4 \cos t\,\mathbf{i} + \sin t\,\mathbf{j}$ implies that $x = 4 \cos t$ and $y = \sin t$; these equations describe an ellipse in the xy-plane (Figure 12.72a). Because $z = t/2\pi$, the value of z increases from 0 to 1 as t increases from 0 to 2π. Therefore, the curve rises out of the xy-plane to create a helix (or coil). Over the interval $[0, 2\pi]$, the helix begins at $(4, 0, 0)$, circles the z-axis once, and ends at $(4, 0, 1)$ (Figure 12.72b).

b. Letting the parameter vary over the interval $-\infty < t < \infty$ generates a helix that winds around the z-axis endlessly in both directions (Figure 12.72c).

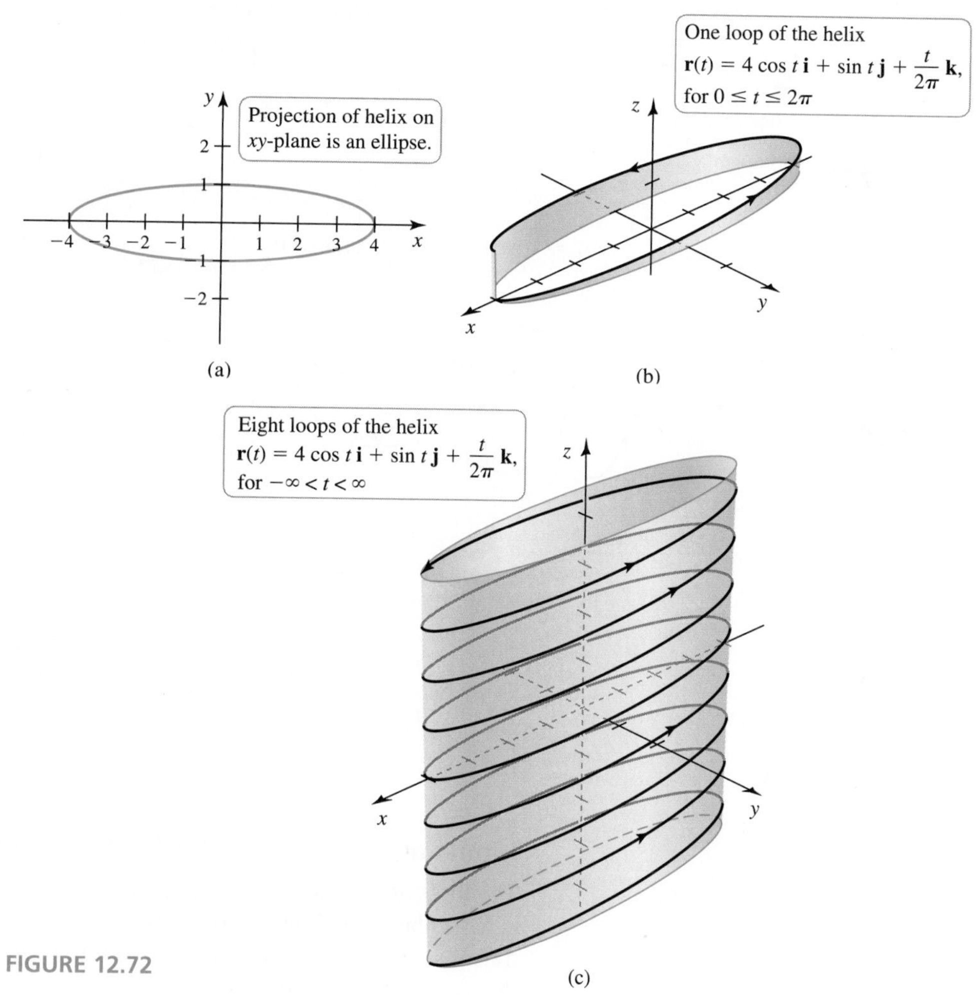
Projection of helix on xy-plane is an ellipse.
One loop of the helix $\mathbf{r}(t) = 4\cos t\,\mathbf{i} + \sin t\,\mathbf{j} + \frac{t}{2\pi}\mathbf{k}$, for $0 \le t \le 2\pi$
Eight loops of the helix $\mathbf{r}(t) = 4\cos t\,\mathbf{i} + \sin t\,\mathbf{j} + \frac{t}{2\pi}\mathbf{k}$, for $-\infty < t < \infty$
(a)
(b)
(c)

FIGURE 12.72

Related Exercises 21–28

Recall that the functions $\sin at$ and $\cos at$ oscillate a times over the interval $[0, 2\pi]$. Therefore, their period is $2\pi/a$.

EXAMPLE 5 Roller coaster curve Graph the curve

$$\mathbf{r}(t) = \cos t\,\mathbf{i} + \sin t\,\mathbf{j} + 0.4\sin 2t\,\mathbf{k}, \quad \text{for } 0 \le t \le 2\pi.$$

SOLUTION Without the z-component, the resulting function $\mathbf{r}(t) = \cos t\,\mathbf{i} + \sin t\,\mathbf{j}$ describes a circle of radius 1 in the xy-plane. The z-component of the function varies between -0.4 and 0.4 with a period of π units. Therefore, on the interval $[0, 2\pi]$ the z-coordinates of points on the curve oscillate twice between -0.4 and 0.4, while the x- and y-coordinates describe a circle. The result is a curve that circles the z-axis once with two peaks and two valleys (Figure 12.73).

Related Exercises 29–32

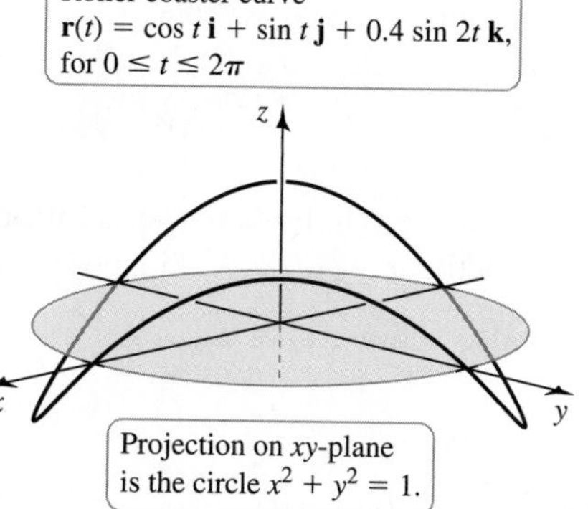
Roller coaster curve $\mathbf{r}(t) = \cos t\,\mathbf{i} + \sin t\,\mathbf{j} + 0.4\sin 2t\,\mathbf{k}$, for $0 \le t \le 2\pi$
Projection on xy-plane is the circle $x^2 + y^2 = 1$.

FIGURE 12.73

EXAMPLE 6 Slinky curve Graph the curve

$$\mathbf{r}(t) = (4 + \cos 20t)\cos t\,\mathbf{i} + (4 + \cos 20t)\sin t\,\mathbf{j} + 0.4\sin 20t\,\mathbf{k},$$

for $0 \le t \le 2\pi$.

SOLUTION The factor $A(t) = 4 + \cos 20t$ that appears in the x- and y-components is a varying amplitude for $\cos t\,\mathbf{i}$ and $\sin t\,\mathbf{j}$. Its effect is seen in the graph of the x-component

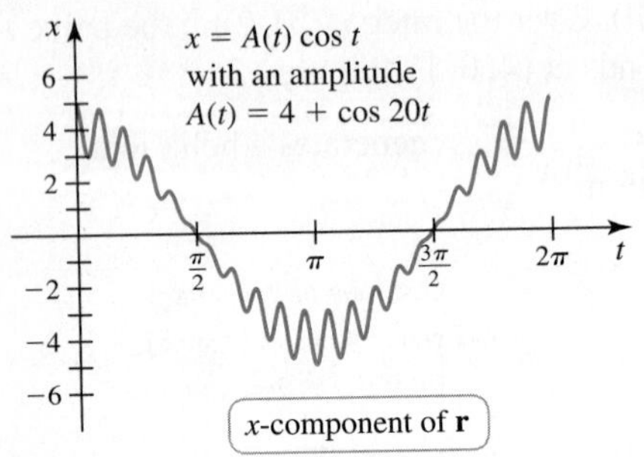

FIGURE 12.74

$A(t)\cos t$ (Figure 12.74). For $0 \le t \le 2\pi$, the curve consists of one period of $4\cos t$ with 20 small oscillations superimposed on it. As a result, the x-component of $\mathbf{r}$ varies from -5 to 5 with 20 small oscillations along the way. A similar behavior is seen in the y-component of $\mathbf{r}$. Finally, the z-component of $\mathbf{r}$, which is $0.4\sin 20t$, oscillates between -0.4 and 0.4 twenty times over $[0, 2\pi]$. Combining these effects, we discover a coil-shaped curve that circles the z-axis and closes on itself. Figure 12.75 shows two views, one looking along the xy-plane and the other from overhead on the z-axis.

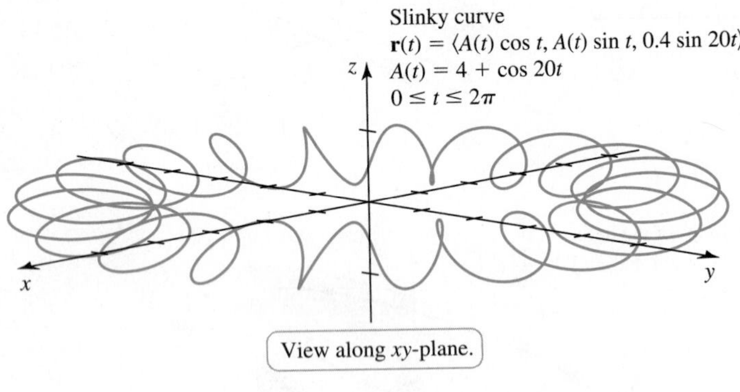

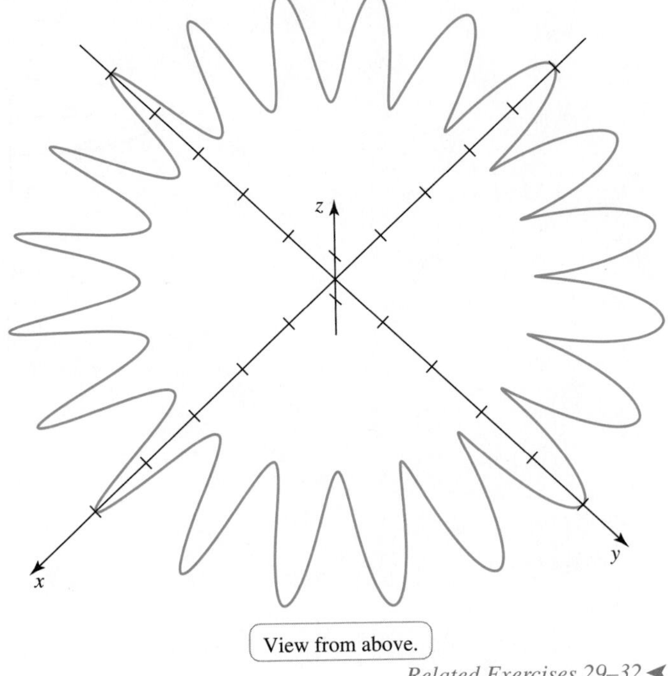

FIGURE 12.75

Related Exercises 29–32 ◀

Limits and Continuity for Vector-Valued Functions

The limit of a vector-valued function $\mathbf{r}(t) = f(t)\mathbf{i} + g(t)\mathbf{j} + h(t)\mathbf{k}$ is defined much as it is for scalar-valued functions. If there is a vector $\mathbf{L}$ such that $|\mathbf{r}(t) - \mathbf{L}|$ can be made arbitrarily small by taking t sufficiently close to a, then we write $\lim_{t\to a}\mathbf{r}(t) = \mathbf{L}$ and say that the limit of $\mathbf{r}$ as t approaches a is $\mathbf{L}$.

> **DEFINITION Limit of a Vector-Valued Function**
>
> A vector-valued function $\mathbf{r}$ approaches the limit $\mathbf{L}$ as t approaches a, written $\lim_{t\to a}\mathbf{r}(t) = \mathbf{L}$, provided $\lim_{t\to a}|\mathbf{r}(t) - \mathbf{L}| = 0$.

This definition, together with a short calculation (Exercise 60), leads to a straightforward method for computing limits of the vector-valued function $\mathbf{r} = \langle f, g, h\rangle$. Suppose that

$$\lim_{t\to a} f(t) = L_1, \qquad \lim_{t\to a} g(t) = L_2, \qquad \text{and} \qquad \lim_{t\to a} h(t) = L_3.$$

Then,

$$\lim_{t\to a}\mathbf{r}(t) = \left\langle \lim_{t\to a} f(t), \lim_{t\to a} g(t), \lim_{t\to a} h(t)\right\rangle = \langle L_1, L_2, L_3\rangle.$$

In other words, the limit of $\mathbf{r}$ is determined by computing the limits of its components.

The limit laws in Chapter 2 have analogs for vector-valued functions. For example, if $\lim_{t \to a} \mathbf{r}(t)$ and $\lim_{t \to a} \mathbf{s}(t)$ exist and c is a scalar, then

$$\lim_{t \to a} (\mathbf{r}(t) + \mathbf{s}(t)) = \lim_{t \to a} \mathbf{r}(t) + \lim_{t \to a} \mathbf{s}(t) \quad \text{and} \quad \lim_{t \to a} c\mathbf{r}(t) = c \lim_{t \to a} \mathbf{r}(t).$$

The idea of continuity also extends directly to vector-valued functions. A function $\mathbf{r}(t) = f(t)\mathbf{i} + g(t)\mathbf{j} + h(t)\mathbf{k}$ is continuous at a provided $\lim_{t \to a} \mathbf{r}(t) = \mathbf{r}(a)$. Specifically, if the component functions f, g, and h are continuous at a, then $\mathbf{r}$ is also continuous at a and vice versa. The function $\mathbf{r}$ is continuous on an interval I if it is continuous for all t in I.

➤ Continuity is often taken as part of the definition of a parameterized curve.

Continuity has the same intuitive meaning in this setting as it does for scalar-valued functions. If $\mathbf{r}$ is a continuous function, the curve it describes has no breaks or gaps, which is an important property when $\mathbf{r}$ describes the trajectory of an object.

EXAMPLE 7 **Limits and continuity** Consider the function

$$\mathbf{r}(t) = \cos \pi t\,\mathbf{i} + \sin \pi t\,\mathbf{j} + e^{-t}\mathbf{k}, \quad \text{for } t \ge 0.$$

a. Evaluate $\lim_{t \to 2} \mathbf{r}(t)$.

b. Evaluate $\lim_{t \to \infty} \mathbf{r}(t)$.

c. At what points is $\mathbf{r}$ continuous?

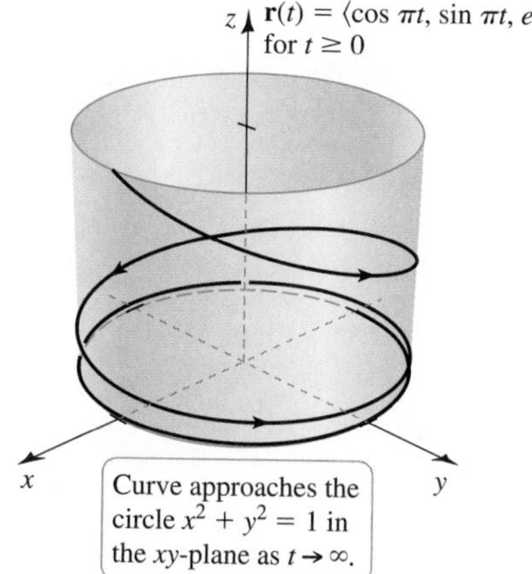
z
$\mathbf{r}(t) = \langle \cos \pi t, \sin \pi t, e^{-t} \rangle$, for $t \ge 0$
x
y
Curve approaches the circle $x^2 + y^2 = 1$ in the xy-plane as $t \to \infty$.

FIGURE 12.76

SOLUTION

a. We evaluate the limit of each component of $\mathbf{r}$:

$$\lim_{t \to 2} \mathbf{r}(t) = \lim_{t \to 2} (\underbrace{\cos \pi t}_{\to 1}\,\mathbf{i} + \underbrace{\sin \pi t}_{\to 0}\,\mathbf{j} + \underbrace{e^{-t}}_{\to e^{-2}}\mathbf{k}) = \mathbf{i} + e^{-2}\mathbf{k}.$$

b. Note that although $\lim_{t \to \infty} e^{-t} = 0$ exists, $\lim_{t \to \infty} \cos t$ and $\lim_{t \to \infty} \sin t$ do not exist. Therefore, $\lim_{t \to \infty} \mathbf{r}(t)$ does not exist. As shown in Figure 12.76, the curve is a coil that approaches the unit circle in the xy-plane.

c. Because the components of $\mathbf{r}$ are continuous for all t, $\mathbf{r}$ is also continuous for all t.

Related Exercises 33–36 ◀

SECTION 12.5 EXERCISES

Review Questions

1. How many independent variables does the function $\mathbf{r}(t) = \langle f(t), g(t), h(t) \rangle$ have?
2. How many dependent scalar variables does the function $\mathbf{r}(t) = \langle f(t), g(t), h(t) \rangle$ have?
3. Why is $\mathbf{r}(t) = \langle f(t), g(t), h(t) \rangle$ called a vector-valued function?
4. Explain how to find a vector in the direction of the line segment from $P_0(x_0, y_0, z_0)$ to $P_1(x_1, y_1, z_1)$.
5. How do you find an equation for the line through the points $P_0(x_0, y_0, z_0)$ and $P_1(x_1, y_1, z_1)$?
6. In what plane does the curve $\mathbf{r}(t) = t\mathbf{i} + t^2\mathbf{k}$ lie?
7. How do you evaluate $\lim_{t \to a} \mathbf{r}(t)$, where $\mathbf{r}(t) = \langle f(t), g(t), h(t) \rangle$?
8. How do you determine whether $\mathbf{r}(t) = f(t)\mathbf{i} + g(t)\mathbf{j} + h(t)\mathbf{k}$ is continuous at $t = a$?

Basic Skills

9–16. Equations of lines *Find an equation of the following lines. Make a sketch of the line.*

9. The line through $(0, 0, 1)$ parallel to the y-axis
10. The line through $(0, 0, 1)$ parallel to the x-axis
11. The line through $(0, 1, 1)$ parallel to $\langle 2, -2, 2 \rangle$
12. The line through $(0, 0, 1)$ and $(0, 1, 1)$
13. The line through $(0, 0, 0)$ and $(1, 2, 3)$
14. The line through $(1, 0, 1)$ and $(3, -3, 3)$
15. The line through $(-3, 4, 6)$ and $(5, -1, 0)$
16. The line through $(0, 4, 8)$ and $(10, -5, -4)$

17–20. Line segments *Find an equation of the line segment joining the given pairs of points.*

17. $(0, 0, 0)$ and $(1, 2, 3)$
18. $(1, 0, 1)$ and $(0, -2, 1)$
19. $(2, 4, 8)$ and $(7, 5, 3)$
20. $(-1, -8, 4)$ and $(-9, 5, -3)$

21–28. Curves in space *Graph the curves described by the following functions. Try to anticipate the shape of the curve before using a graphing utility.*

21. $\mathbf{r}(t) = \cos t\,\mathbf{i} + \sin t\,\mathbf{k}$, for $0 \le t \le 2\pi$

22. $\mathbf{r}(t) = 4\cos t\,\mathbf{j} + 16\sin t\,\mathbf{k}$, for $0 \le t \le 2\pi$

23. $\mathbf{r}(t) = \cos \pi t\,\mathbf{i} + 2t\,\mathbf{j} + \sin \pi t\,\mathbf{k}$, for $0 \le t \le 2$

24. $\mathbf{r}(t) = 2\cos t\,\mathbf{i} + 2\sin t\,\mathbf{j} + \sin t\,\mathbf{k}$, for $0 \le t \le 2\pi$

25. $\mathbf{r}(t) = 2t\,\mathbf{i} + t^2\mathbf{j} + 3t\,\mathbf{k}$, for $0 \le t \le 4$

26. $\mathbf{r}(t) = 4\sin t\,\mathbf{i} + 4\cos t\,\mathbf{j} + e^{-t}\mathbf{k}$, for $0 \le t < \infty$

27. $\mathbf{r}(t) = e^{-t}\sin t\,\mathbf{i} + e^{-t}\cos t\,\mathbf{j} + \mathbf{k}$, for $0 \le t < \infty$

28. $\mathbf{r}(t) = e^{-t}\mathbf{i} + 3\cos t\,\mathbf{j} + 3\sin t\,\mathbf{k}$, for $0 \le t < \infty$

T **29–32. Exotic curves** *Graph the curves described by the following functions. Use analysis to anticipate the shape of the curve before using a graphing utility.*

29. $\mathbf{r}(t) = 0.5\cos 15t\,\mathbf{i} + (8 + \sin 15t)\cos t\,\mathbf{j} + (8 + \sin 15t)\sin t\,\mathbf{k}$, for $0 \le t \le 2\pi$

30. $\mathbf{r}(t) = 2\cos t\,\mathbf{i} + 4\sin t\,\mathbf{j} + \cos 10t\,\mathbf{k}$, for $0 \le t \le 2\pi$

31. $\mathbf{r}(t) = \cos t^2\mathbf{i} + \sin t^2\mathbf{j} + t/(t+1)\mathbf{k}$, for $0 \le t < \infty$

32. $\mathbf{r}(t) = \cos t \sin 3t\,\mathbf{i} + \sin t \sin 3t\,\mathbf{j} + \sqrt{t}\,\mathbf{k}$, for $0 \le t \le 9$

33–36. Limits *Evaluate the following limits.*

33. $\lim_{t \to \pi/2} \left(\cos 2t\,\mathbf{i} - 4\sin t\,\mathbf{j} + \frac{2t}{\pi}\mathbf{k}\right)$

34. $\lim_{t \to \ln 2} (2e^t\mathbf{i} + 6e^{-t}\mathbf{j} - 4e^{-2t}\mathbf{k})$

35. $\lim_{t \to \infty} \left(e^{-t}\mathbf{i} - \frac{2t}{t+1}\mathbf{j} + \tan^{-1}t\,\mathbf{k}\right)$

36. $\lim_{t \to 2} \left(\frac{t}{t^2+1}\mathbf{i} - 4e^{-t}\sin \pi t\,\mathbf{j} + \frac{1}{\sqrt{4t+1}}\mathbf{k}\right)$

Further Explorations

37. Explain why or why not Determine whether the following statements are true and give an explanation or counterexample.

a. The line $\mathbf{r}(t) = \langle 3, -1, 4\rangle + t\langle 6, -2, 8\rangle$ passes through the origin.

b. Any two nonparallel lines in $\mathbf{R}^3$ intersect.

c. The curve $\mathbf{r}(t) = \langle e^{-t}, \sin t, -\cos t\rangle$ approaches a circle as $t \to \infty$.

d. If $\mathbf{r}(t) = e^{-t^2}\langle 1, 1, 1\rangle$ then $\lim_{t \to \infty} \mathbf{r}(t) = \lim_{t \to -\infty} \mathbf{r}(t)$.

38–41. Domains *Find the domain of the following vector-valued functions.*

38. $\mathbf{r}(t) = \frac{2}{t-1}\mathbf{i} + \frac{3}{t+2}\mathbf{j}$

39. $\mathbf{r}(t) = \sqrt{t+2}\,\mathbf{i} + \sqrt{2-t}\,\mathbf{j}$

40. $\mathbf{r}(t) = \cos 2t\,\mathbf{i} + e^{\sqrt{t}}\mathbf{j} + \frac{12}{t}\mathbf{k}$

41. $\mathbf{r}(t) = \sqrt{4-t^2}\,\mathbf{i} + \sqrt{t}\,\mathbf{j} - \frac{2}{\sqrt{1+t}}\mathbf{k}$

42–45. Line-plane intersections *Find the point (if it exists) at which the following planes and lines intersect.*

42. $x = 3$; $\mathbf{r}(t) = \langle t, t, t\rangle$, for $-\infty < t < \infty$

43. $z = 4$; $\mathbf{r}(t) = \langle 2t + 1, -t + 4, t - 6\rangle$, for $-\infty < t < \infty$

44. $y = -2$; $\mathbf{r}(t) = \langle 2t + 1, -t + 4, t - 6\rangle$, for $-\infty < t < \infty$

45. $z = -8$; $\mathbf{r}(t) = \langle 3t - 2, t - 6, -2t + 4\rangle$, for $-\infty < t < \infty$

46–48. Curve-plane intersections *Find the points (if they exist) at which the following planes and curves intersect.*

46. $y = 1$; $\mathbf{r}(t) = \langle 10\cos t, 2\sin t, 1\rangle$, for $0 \le t \le 2\pi$

47. $z = 16$; $\mathbf{r}(t) = \langle t, 2t, 4 + 3t\rangle$, for $-\infty < t < \infty$

48. $y + x = 0$; $\mathbf{r}(t) = \langle \cos t, \sin t, t\rangle$, for $0 \le t \le 4\pi$

49. Matching functions with graphs Match functions a–f with the appropriate graphs A–F.

a. $\mathbf{r}(t) = \langle t, -t, t\rangle$

b. $\mathbf{r}(t) = \langle t^2, t, t\rangle$

c. $\mathbf{r}(t) = \langle 4\cos t, 4\sin t, 2\rangle$

d. $\mathbf{r}(t) = \langle 2t, \sin t, \cos t\rangle$

e. $\mathbf{r}(t) = \langle \sin t, \cos t, \sin 2t\rangle$

f. $\mathbf{r}(t) = \langle \sin t, 2t, \cos t\rangle$

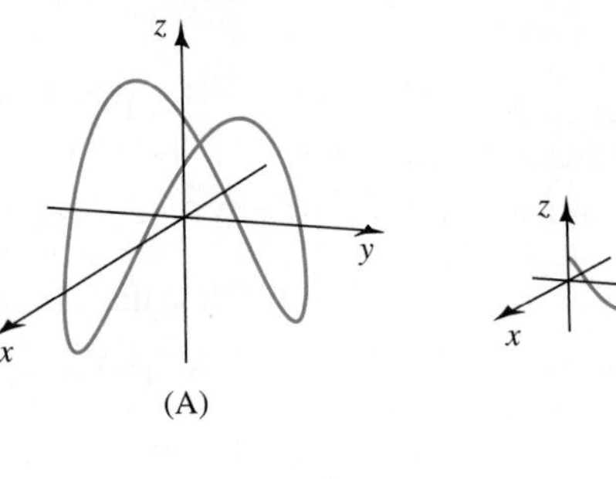

(A)

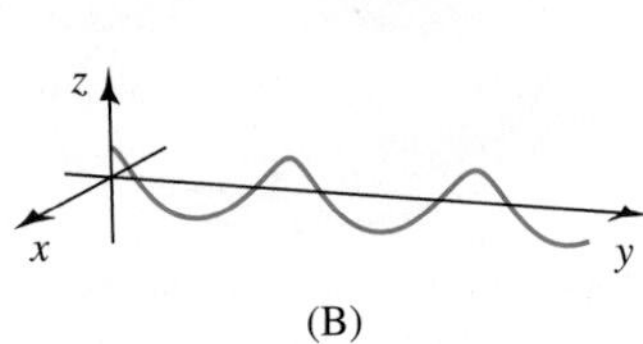

(B)

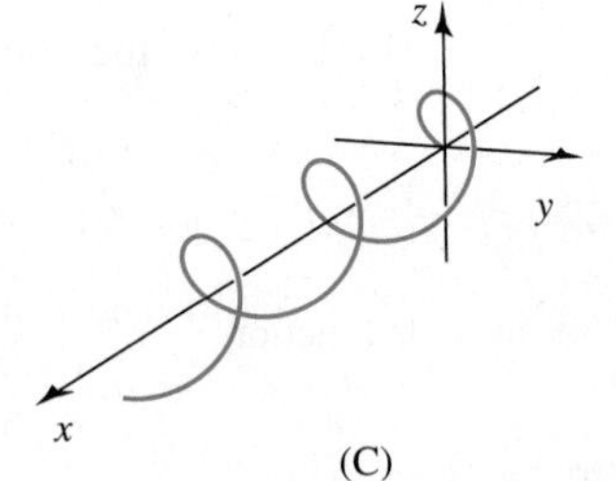

(C)

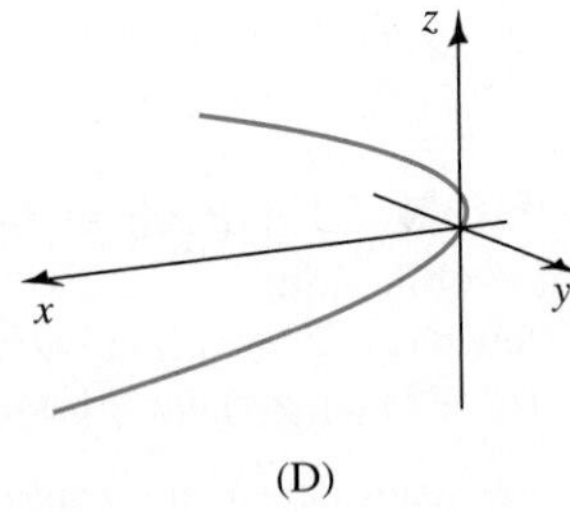

(D)

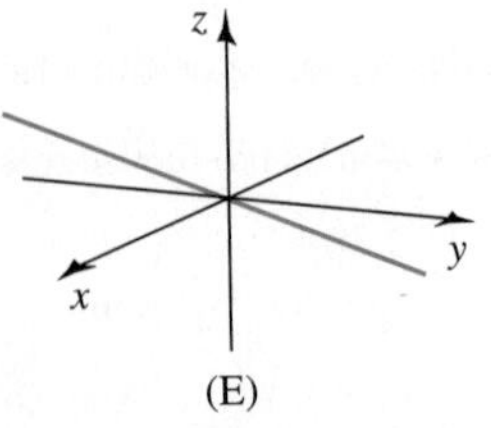

(E)

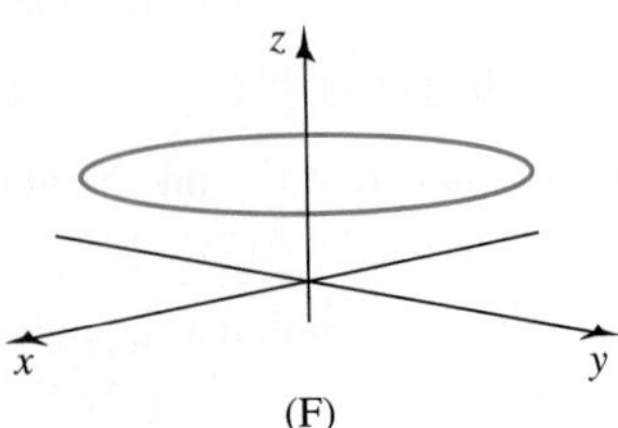

(F)

50. Intersecting lines and colliding particles Consider the lines

$$\mathbf{r}(t) = \langle 2 + 2t, 8 + t, 10 + 3t\rangle, \text{ for } -\infty < t < \infty$$
$$\mathbf{R}(s) = \langle 6 + s, 10 - 2s, 16 - s\rangle, \text{ for } -\infty < s < \infty.$$

a. Determine whether the lines intersect (have a common point) and if so, find the coordinates of that point.

b. If $\mathbf{r}$ and $\mathbf{R}$ describe the paths of two particles, do the particles collide? Assume $t \ge 0$ and $s \ge 0$ measure time in seconds.

51. Upward path Consider the curve described by the vector function $\mathbf{r}(t) = (50e^{-t}\cos t)\mathbf{i} + (50e^{-t}\sin t)\mathbf{j} + (5 - 5e^{-t})\mathbf{k}$, for $t \geq 0$.

a. What is the initial point of the path corresponding to $\mathbf{r}(0)$?

b. What is $\lim_{t\to\infty} \mathbf{r}(t)$?

c. Sketch the curve.

d. Eliminate the parameter t to show that $z = 5 - r/10$, where $r^2 = x^2 + y^2$.

52–55. Closed plane curves *Consider the curve* $\mathbf{r}(t) = (a\cos t + b\sin t)\mathbf{i} + (c\cos t + d\sin t)\mathbf{j} + (e\cos t + f\sin t)\mathbf{k}$, *where a, b, c, d, e, and f are real numbers. It can be shown that this curve lies in a plane.*

52. Assuming the curve lies in a plane, show that it is a circle centered at the origin with radius R provided $a^2 + c^2 + e^2 = b^2 + d^2 + f^2 = R^2$ and $ab + cd + ef = 0$.

T 53. Graph the following curve and describe it in words.

$$\mathbf{r}(t) = \left(\frac{1}{\sqrt{2}}\cos t + \frac{1}{\sqrt{3}}\sin t\right)\mathbf{i} + \left(-\frac{1}{\sqrt{2}}\cos t + \frac{1}{\sqrt{3}}\sin t\right)\mathbf{j} + \left(\frac{1}{\sqrt{3}}\sin t\right)\mathbf{k}$$

T 54. Graph the following curve and describe it in words.

$$\mathbf{r}(t) = (2\cos t + 2\sin t)\mathbf{i} + (-\cos t + 2\sin t)\mathbf{j} + (\cos t - 2\sin t)\mathbf{k}$$

55. Find a general expression for a nonzero vector orthogonal to the plane containing the curve.

$$\mathbf{r}(t) = (a\cos t + b\sin t)\mathbf{i} + (c\cos t + d\sin t)\mathbf{j} + (e\cos t + f\sin t)\mathbf{k},$$

where $\langle a, c, e\rangle \times \langle b, d, f\rangle \neq \mathbf{0}$.

Applications

Applications of parametric curves are considered in detail in Section 12.7.

T 56. Golf slice A golfer launches a tee shot down a horizontal fairway and it follows a path given by $\mathbf{r}(t) = \langle at, (75 - 0.1a)t, -5t^2 + 80t\rangle$, where $t \geq 0$ measures time in seconds and $\mathbf{r}$ has units of feet. The y-axis points straight down the fairway and the z-axis points vertically upward. The parameter a is the slice factor that determines how much the shot deviates from a straight path down the fairway.

a. With no slice ($a = 0$), sketch and describe the shot. How far does the ball travel horizontally (the distance between the point the ball leaves the ground and the point where it first strikes the ground)?

b. With a slice ($a = 0.2$), sketch and describe the shot. How far does the ball travel horizontally?

c. How far does the ball travel horizontally with $a = 2.5$?

Additional Exercises

57–59. Curves on spheres

T 57. Graph the curve $\mathbf{r}(t) = \left\langle \frac{1}{2}\sin 2t, \frac{1}{2}(1 - \cos 2t), \cos t\right\rangle$ and prove that it lies on the surface of a sphere centered at the origin.

58. Prove that for integers m and n, the curve

$$\mathbf{r}(t) = \langle a\sin mt\cos nt, b\sin mt\sin nt, c\cos mt\rangle$$

lies on the surface of a sphere provided $a^2 = b^2 = c^2$.

59. Find the period of the function in Exercise 58; that is find the smallest positive real number T such that $\mathbf{r}(t + T) = \mathbf{r}(t)$ for all t.

60. Limits of vector functions Let $\mathbf{r}(t) = \langle f(t), g(t), h(t)\rangle$.

a. Assume that $\lim_{t\to a} \mathbf{r}(t) = \mathbf{L} = \langle L_1, L_2, L_3\rangle$, which means that $\lim_{t\to a} |\mathbf{r}(t) - \mathbf{L}| = 0$. Prove that

$$\lim_{t\to a} f(t) = L_1, \quad \lim_{t\to a} g(t) = L_2, \quad \text{and} \quad \lim_{t\to a} h(t) = L_3.$$

b. Assume that $\lim_{t\to a} f(t) = L_1$, $\lim_{t\to a} g(t) = L_2$, and $\lim_{t\to a} h(t) = L_3$. Prove that $\lim_{t\to a} \mathbf{r}(t) = \mathbf{L} = \langle L_1, L_2, L_3\rangle$, which means that $\lim_{t\to a} |\mathbf{r}(t) - \mathbf{L}| = 0$.

QUICK CHECK ANSWERS

1. The z-axis; the line $y = x$ in the xy-plane. **2.** When $t = 0$, the point on the line is P_0; when $t = 1$, the point on the line is P_1. ◄

12.6 Calculus of Vector-Valued Functions

We now turn to the topic of ultimate interest in this chapter: the calculus of vector-valued functions. Everything you learned about differentiating and integrating functions of the form $y = f(x)$ carries over to vector-valued functions $\mathbf{r}(t)$; you simply apply the rules of differentiation and integration to the individual components of $\mathbf{r}$.

The Derivative and Tangent Vector

Consider the function $\mathbf{r}(t) = f(t)\mathbf{i} + g(t)\mathbf{j} + h(t)\mathbf{k}$, where f, g, and h are differentiable functions on an interval $a < t < b$. The first task is to explain the meaning of the *derivative* of a vector-valued function and to show how to compute it. We begin with the definition of the derivative—now with a vector perspective:

$$\mathbf{r}'(t) = \lim_{\Delta t\to 0} \frac{\Delta\mathbf{r}}{\Delta t} = \lim_{\Delta t\to 0} \frac{\mathbf{r}(t + \Delta t) - \mathbf{r}(t)}{\Delta t}$$

Before computing this limit, we look at its geometry. The function $\mathbf{r}(t) = f(t)\mathbf{i} + g(t)\mathbf{j} + h(t)\mathbf{k}$ describes a parameterized curve in space. Let P be a point on that curve, associated with position vector $\mathbf{r}(t)$ and let Q be a nearby point associated with the position vector $\mathbf{r}(t + \Delta t)$, where $\Delta t > 0$ is a small increment in t (Figure 12.77a). The difference $\Delta\mathbf{r} = \mathbf{r}(t + \Delta t) - \mathbf{r}(t)$ is the vector $\overrightarrow{PQ}$, where we assume $\Delta\mathbf{r} \neq \mathbf{0}$. Because Δt is a scalar, the direction of $\Delta\mathbf{r}/\Delta t$ is the same as the direction of $\overrightarrow{PQ}$.

➤ An analogous interpretation can be given for $\Delta t < 0$.

As Δt approaches 0, Q approaches P and the vector $\Delta\mathbf{r}/\Delta t$ approaches a limiting vector that we denote $\mathbf{r}'(t)$ (Figure 12.77b). This new vector $\mathbf{r}'(t)$ has two important interpretations:

- The vector $\mathbf{r}'(t)$ points in the direction of the curve at P. For this reason $\mathbf{r}'(t)$ is a **tangent vector** at P (provided it is not the zero vector).
- The vector $\mathbf{r}'(t)$ is the **derivative** of $\mathbf{r}$ with respect to t; it gives the rate of change of the function $\mathbf{r}(t)$ at the point P. In fact, if $\mathbf{r}(t)$ is the position function of a moving object, then $\mathbf{r}'(t)$ is the velocity vector of the object, which always points in the direction of motion, and $|\mathbf{r}'(t)|$ is the speed of the object.

➤ Section 12.7 is devoted to problems of motion in two and three dimensions.

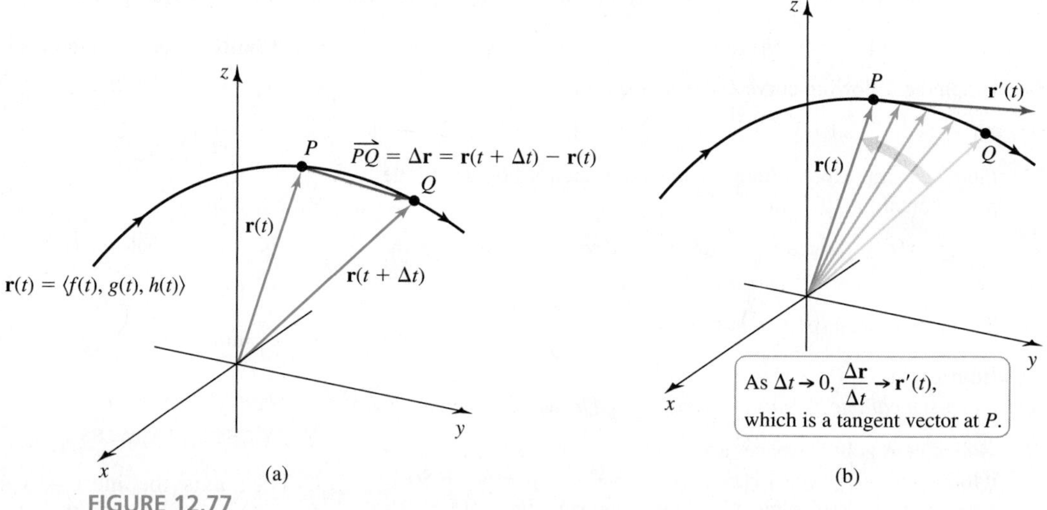

FIGURE 12.77

We now evaluate the limit that defines $\mathbf{r}'(t)$ by expressing $\mathbf{r}$ in terms of its components and using the properties of limits.

$$\begin{aligned}
\mathbf{r}'(t) &= \lim_{\Delta t \to 0} \frac{\mathbf{r}(t + \Delta t) - \mathbf{r}(t)}{\Delta t} \\
&= \lim_{\Delta t \to 0} \frac{(f(t + \Delta t)\mathbf{i} + g(t + \Delta t)\mathbf{j} + h(t + \Delta t)\mathbf{k}) - (f(t)\mathbf{i} + g(t)\mathbf{j} + h(t)\mathbf{k})}{\Delta t} && \text{Substitute components of } \mathbf{r}. \\
&= \lim_{\Delta t \to 0} \left[\frac{f(t + \Delta t) - f(t)}{\Delta t}\mathbf{i} + \frac{g(t + \Delta t) - g(t)}{\Delta t}\mathbf{j} + \frac{h(t + \Delta t) - h(t)}{\Delta t}\mathbf{k} \right] && \text{Rearrange terms inside of limit.} \\
&= \underbrace{\lim_{\Delta t \to 0} \frac{f(t + \Delta t) - f(t)}{\Delta t}}_{f'(t)}\mathbf{i} + \underbrace{\lim_{\Delta t \to 0} \frac{g(t + \Delta t) - g(t)}{\Delta t}}_{g'(t)}\mathbf{j} + \underbrace{\lim_{\Delta t \to 0} \frac{h(t + \Delta t) - h(t)}{\Delta t}}_{h'(t)}\mathbf{k} && \text{Limit of sum equals sum of limits.}
\end{aligned}$$

Because f, g, and h are differentiable scalar-valued functions of the variable t, the three limits in the last step are identified as the derivatives of f, g, and h, respectively. Therefore, there are no surprises:

$$\mathbf{r}'(t) = f'(t)\mathbf{i} + g'(t)\mathbf{j} + h'(t)\mathbf{k}.$$

In other words, to differentiate the vector-valued function $\mathbf{r}(t)$, we simply differentiate each of its components with respect to t.

DEFINITION Derivative and Tangent Vector

Let $\mathbf{r}(t) = f(t)\mathbf{i} + g(t)\mathbf{j} + h(t)\mathbf{k}$, where f, g, and h are differentiable functions on (a, b). Then $\mathbf{r}$ has a **derivative** (or is **differentiable**) on (a, b) and

$$\mathbf{r}'(t) = f'(t)\mathbf{i} + g'(t)\mathbf{j} + h'(t)\mathbf{k}.$$

Provided $\mathbf{r}'(t) \neq \mathbf{0}$, $\mathbf{r}'(t)$ is a **tangent vector** (or velocity vector) at the point corresponding to $\mathbf{r}(t)$.

EXAMPLE 1 Derivative of vector functions Compute the derivative of the following functions.

a. $\mathbf{r}(t) = \langle t^3, 3t^2, t^3/6 \rangle$ **b.** $\mathbf{r}(t) = e^{-t}\mathbf{i} + 10\sqrt{t}\,\mathbf{j} + 2\cos 3t\,\mathbf{k}$

SOLUTION

a. $\mathbf{r}'(t) = \langle 3t^2, 6t, t^2/2 \rangle$; note that $\mathbf{r}$ is differentiable for all t and $\mathbf{r}'(0) = \mathbf{0}$.

b. $\mathbf{r}'(t) = -e^{-t}\mathbf{i} + \dfrac{5}{\sqrt{t}}\mathbf{j} - 6\sin 3t\,\mathbf{k}$; the function $\mathbf{r}$ is differentiable for $t > 0$.

Related Exercises 7–16 ◀

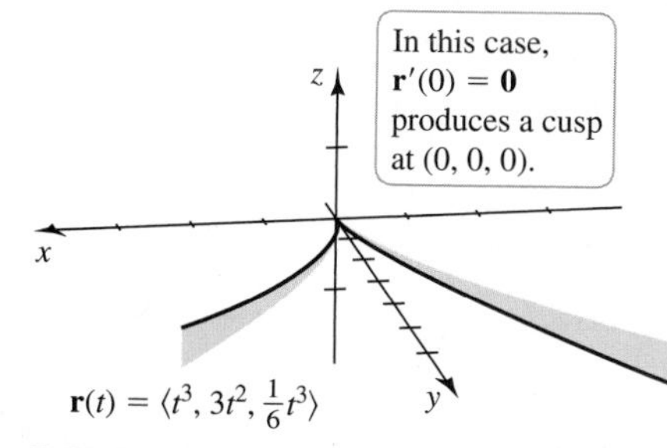
In this case, $\mathbf{r}'(0) = \mathbf{0}$ produces a cusp at (0, 0, 0).
z
x
y
$\mathbf{r}(t) = \langle t^3, 3t^2, \frac{1}{6}t^3 \rangle$

FIGURE 12.78

QUICK CHECK 1 Let $\mathbf{r}(t) = \langle t, t, t \rangle$. Compute $\mathbf{r}'(t)$ and interpret the result. ◀

▶ If a curve has a cusp at a point, then $\mathbf{r}'(t) = \mathbf{0}$ at that point. However, the converse is not true; it may happen that $\mathbf{r}'(t) = \mathbf{0}$ at a point that is not a cusp (Exercise 73).

The condition that $\mathbf{r}'(t) \neq \mathbf{0}$ in order for the tangent vector to be defined requires explanation. Consider the function $\mathbf{r}(t) = \langle t^3, 3t^2, t^3/6 \rangle$. As shown in Example 1a, $\mathbf{r}'(0) = \mathbf{0}$; that is, all three components of $\mathbf{r}'(t)$ are zero simultaneously when $t = 0$. We see in Figure 12.78 that an otherwise smooth curve has a *cusp* or a sharp point at the origin. If $\mathbf{r}$ describes the motion of an object, then $\mathbf{r}'(t) = \mathbf{0}$ means that the velocity (and speed) of the object is zero at a point. At such a stationary point the object *may* change direction abruptly creating a cusp in its trajectory. For this reason, we say a function $\mathbf{r}(t) = \langle f(t), g(t), h(t) \rangle$ is **smooth** on an interval if f, g, and h are differentiable *and* $\mathbf{r}'(t) \neq \mathbf{0}$ on that interval. Smooth curves have no cusps or corners.

Orientation of Curves

If a smooth curve C is viewed only as a set of points, then at any point of C it is possible to draw tangent vectors in two directions (Figure 12.79a). On the other hand, a parameterized curve described by the function $\mathbf{r}(t)$, where $a \leq t \leq b$, has a natural direction, or **orientation**. The *positive* or *forward* direction is the direction in which the curve is generated as the parameter increases from a to b. For example, the positive direction of the circle $\mathbf{r}(t) = \langle \cos t, \sin t \rangle$, for $0 \leq t \leq 2\pi$, is counterclockwise (Figure 12.79b). The orientation of a parameterized curve and its tangent vectors are consistent: The positive direction of the curve is also the direction in which the tangent vectors point along the curve.

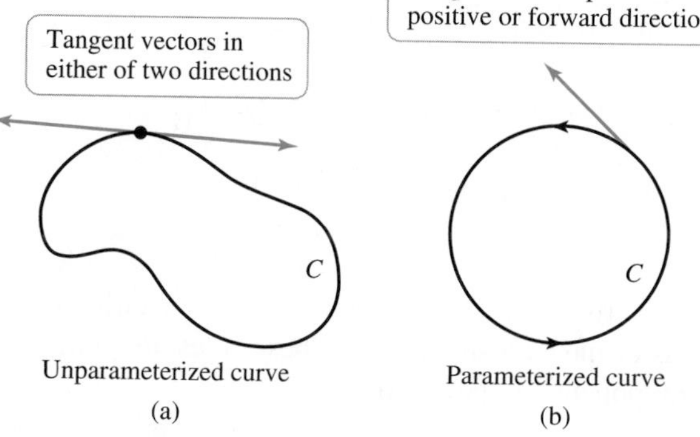
Tangent vectors in either of two directions
C
Unparameterized curve
(a)
Tangent vectors point in positive or forward direction.
C
Parameterized curve
(b)

FIGURE 12.79

Unit Tangent Vector In situations in which only the direction (but not the length) of the tangent vector is of interest, we work with the **unit tangent vector**. It is the vector with magnitude 1, formed by dividing $\mathbf{r}'(t)$ by its length.

> **DEFINITION Unit Tangent Vector**
> Let $\mathbf{r} = f(t)\mathbf{i} + g(t)\mathbf{j} + h(t)\mathbf{k}$ be a smooth parameterized curve, for $a \le t \le b$. The **unit tangent vector** for a particular value of t is
> $$\mathbf{T}(t) = \frac{\mathbf{r}'(t)}{|\mathbf{r}'(t)|}.$$

QUICK CHECK 2 Suppose $\mathbf{r}'(t)$ has units m/s. Explain why $\mathbf{T}(t) = \mathbf{r}'(t)/|\mathbf{r}'(t)|$ is dimensionless (has no units) and carries information only about direction. ◀

EXAMPLE 2 Unit tangent vectors Consider the following parameterized curves and find the unit tangent vectors.

a. $\mathbf{r}(t) = \langle t^2, 4t, 4\ln t\rangle$, for $t > 0$

b. $\mathbf{r}(t) = \langle 10, 3\cos t, 3\sin t\rangle$, for $0 \le t \le 2\pi$

SOLUTION

a. A tangent vector is $\mathbf{r}'(t) = \langle 2t, 4, 4/t\rangle$, which has a magnitude of

$$\begin{aligned} |\mathbf{r}'(t)| &= \sqrt{(2t)^2 + 4^2 + \left(\frac{4}{t}\right)^2} && \text{Definition of magnitude} \\ &= \sqrt{4t^2 + 16 + \frac{16}{t^2}} && \text{Expand.} \\ &= \sqrt{\left(2t + \frac{4}{t}\right)^2} && \text{Factor.} \\ &= 2t + \frac{4}{t}. && \text{Simplify.} \end{aligned}$$

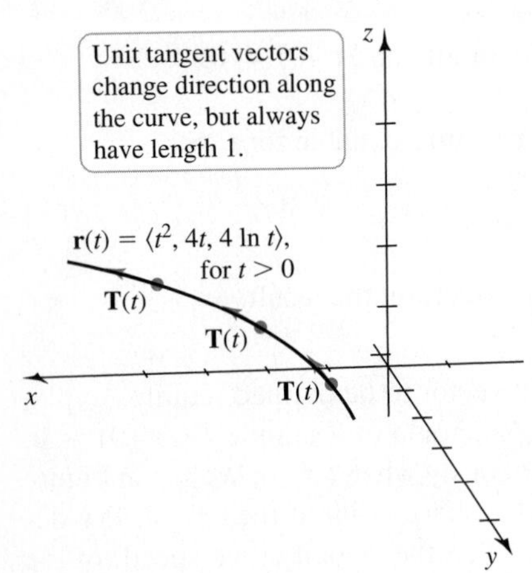
Unit tangent vectors change direction along the curve, but always have length 1.
r(t) = ⟨t², 4t, 4 ln t⟩, for t > 0
T(t)
T(t)
T(t)
x
y
z
FIGURE 12.80

Therefore, the unit tangent vector for a particular value of t is

$$\mathbf{T}(t) = \frac{\langle 2t, 4, 4/t\rangle}{2t + 4/t}.$$

As shown in Figure 12.80, the unit tangent vectors change direction along the curve but maintain unit length.

b. In this case, $\mathbf{r}'(t) = \langle 0, -3\sin t, 3\cos t\rangle$ and

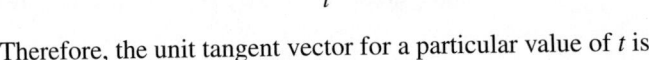

$$|\mathbf{r}'(t)| = \sqrt{0^2 + (-3\sin t)^2 + (3\cos t)^2} = \sqrt{9\underbrace{(\sin^2 t + \cos^2 t)}_{1}} = 3.$$

Therefore, the unit tangent vector for a particular value of t is

$$\mathbf{T}(t) = \frac{1}{3}\langle 0, -3\sin t, 3\cos t\rangle = \langle 0, -\sin t, \cos t\rangle.$$

The direction of $\mathbf{T}$ changes along the curve, but its length remains 1.

Related Exercises 17–24 ◀

Derivative Rules The rules for derivatives for single-variable functions either carry over directly to vector-valued functions or have close analogs. These rules are generally proved by working on the individual components of the vector function.

> With the exception of the Cross Product Rule, these rules apply to vector-valued functions with any number of components. Notice that we have three new product rules, all of which mimic the original Product Rule. In Rule 4, **u** must be differentiable at $f(t)$.

QUICK CHECK 3 Let $\mathbf{u}(t) = \langle t, t, t \rangle$ and $\mathbf{v}(t) = \langle 1, 1, 1 \rangle$. Compute $\frac{d}{dt}[\mathbf{u}(t) \cdot \mathbf{v}(t)]$ using Derivative Rule 5 and show that it agrees with the result obtained by first computing the dot product and differentiating directly.

THEOREM 12.7 Derivative Rules

Let **u** and **v** be differentiable vector-valued functions and let f be a differentiable scalar-valued function, all at a point t. Let **c** be a constant vector. The following rules apply.

1. $\frac{d}{dt}(\mathbf{c}) = \mathbf{0}$ Constant Rule
2. $\frac{d}{dt}(\mathbf{u}(t) + \mathbf{v}(t)) = \mathbf{u}'(t) + \mathbf{v}'(t)$ Sum Rule
3. $\frac{d}{dt}(f(t)\mathbf{u}(t)) = f'(t)\mathbf{u}(t) + f(t)\mathbf{u}'(t)$ Product Rule
4. $\frac{d}{dt}(\mathbf{u}(f(t))) = f'(t)\mathbf{u}'(f(t))$ Chain Rule
5. $\frac{d}{dt}(\mathbf{u}(t) \cdot \mathbf{v}(t)) = \mathbf{u}'(t) \cdot \mathbf{v}(t) + \mathbf{u}(t) \cdot \mathbf{v}'(t)$ Dot Product Rule
6. $\frac{d}{dt}(\mathbf{u}(t) \times \mathbf{v}(t)) = \mathbf{u}'(t) \times \mathbf{v}(t) + \mathbf{u}(t) \times \mathbf{v}'(t)$ Cross Product Rule

The proofs of these rules are assigned in Exercises 70–72 with the exception of the following representative proofs.

Proof of the Chain Rule Let $\mathbf{u}(t) = \langle u_1(t), u_2(t), u_3(t) \rangle$, which implies that

$$\mathbf{u}(f(t)) = u_1(f(t))\mathbf{i} + u_2(f(t))\mathbf{j} + u_3(f(t))\mathbf{k}.$$

We now apply the ordinary Chain Rule component-wise:

$$\begin{aligned}
\frac{d}{dt}\big(\mathbf{u}(f(t))\big) &= \frac{d}{dt}\big(u_1(f(t))\mathbf{i} + u_2(f(t))\mathbf{j} + u_3(f(t))\mathbf{k}\big) && \text{Components of } \mathbf{u} \\
&= \frac{d}{dt}\big(u_1(f(t))\big)\mathbf{i} + \frac{d}{dt}\big(u_2(f(t))\big)\mathbf{j} + \frac{d}{dt}\big(u_3(f(t))\big)\mathbf{k} && \text{Derivative of a sum} \\
&= u_1'(f(t))f'(t)\mathbf{i} + u_2'(f(t))f'(t)\mathbf{j} + u_3'(f(t))f'(t)\mathbf{k} && \text{Chain Rule} \\
&= \big(u_1'(f(t))\mathbf{i} + u_2'(f(t))\mathbf{j} + u_3'(f(t))\mathbf{k}\big)f'(t) && \text{Factor } f'(t). \\
&= \mathbf{u}'(f(t))f'(t) && \text{Definition of } \mathbf{u}'
\end{aligned}$$

Proof of the Dot Product Rule One proof of the Dot Product Rule uses the standard Product Rule on each component. Let $\mathbf{u}(t) = \langle u_1(t), u_2(t), u_3(t) \rangle$ and $\mathbf{v}(t) = \langle v_1(t), v_2(t), v_3(t) \rangle$. Then,

$$\begin{aligned}
\frac{d}{dt}(\mathbf{u} \cdot \mathbf{v}) &= \frac{d}{dt}(u_1 v_1 + u_2 v_2 + u_3 v_3) && \text{Definition of dot product} \\
&= u_1' v_1 + u_1 v_1' + u_2' v_2 + u_2 v_2' + u_3' v_3 + u_3 v_3' && \text{Product Rule} \\
&= \underbrace{u_1' v_1 + u_2' v_2 + u_3' v_3}_{u' \cdot v} + \underbrace{u_1 v_1' + u_2 v_2' + u_3 v_3'}_{u \cdot v'} && \text{Rearrange.} \\
&= \mathbf{u}' \cdot \mathbf{v} + \mathbf{u} \cdot \mathbf{v}'
\end{aligned}$$

EXAMPLE 3 Derivative rules Compute the following derivatives, where

$$\mathbf{u}(t) = t\mathbf{i} + t^2\mathbf{j} - t^3\mathbf{k} \quad \text{and} \quad \mathbf{v}(t) = \sin t\,\mathbf{i} + 2\cos t\,\mathbf{j} + \cos t\,\mathbf{k}.$$

a. $\frac{d}{dt}[\mathbf{v}(t^2)]$ **b.** $\frac{d}{dt}[t^2\,\mathbf{v}(t)]$ **c.** $\frac{d}{dt}[\mathbf{u}(t) \cdot \mathbf{v}(t)]$

SOLUTION

a. Note that $\mathbf{v}'(t) = \cos t\,\mathbf{i} - 2\sin t\,\mathbf{j} - \sin t\,\mathbf{k}$. Using the Chain Rule, we have

$$\frac{d}{dt}[\mathbf{v}(t^2)] = \mathbf{v}'(t^2)\frac{d}{dt}(t^2) = \underbrace{(\cos t^2\mathbf{i} - 2\sin t^2\mathbf{j} - \sin t^2\mathbf{k})}_{\mathbf{v}'(t^2)}(2t).$$

b.
$$\frac{d}{dt}(t^2\mathbf{v}(t)) = \frac{d}{dt}(t^2)\mathbf{v}(t) + t^2\frac{d}{dt}(\mathbf{v}(t)) \qquad \text{Product Rule}$$
$$= 2t\,\mathbf{v}(t) + t^2\mathbf{v}'(t)$$
$$= (2t)\underbrace{(\sin t\,\mathbf{i} + 2\cos t\,\mathbf{j} + \cos t\,\mathbf{k})}_{\mathbf{v}(t)} + t^2\underbrace{(\cos t\,\mathbf{i} - 2\sin t\,\mathbf{j} - \sin t\,\mathbf{k})}_{\mathbf{v}'(t)} \qquad \text{Differentiate.}$$
$$= (2t\sin t + t^2\cos t)\mathbf{i} + (4t\cos t - 2t^2\sin t)\mathbf{j} + (2t\cos t - t^2\sin t)\mathbf{k} \qquad \text{Collect terms.}$$

c.
$$\frac{d}{dt}(\mathbf{u}(t)\cdot\mathbf{v}(t)) = \mathbf{u}'(t)\cdot\mathbf{v}(t) + \mathbf{u}(t)\cdot\mathbf{v}'(t) \qquad \text{Dot Product Rule}$$
$$= (\mathbf{i} + 2t\mathbf{j} - 3t^2\mathbf{k})\cdot(\sin t\,\mathbf{i} + 2\cos t\,\mathbf{j} + \cos t\,\mathbf{k})$$
$$+ (t\mathbf{i} + t^2\mathbf{j} - t^3\mathbf{k})\cdot(\cos t\,\mathbf{i} - 2\sin t\,\mathbf{j} - \sin t\,\mathbf{k}) \qquad \text{Differentiate.}$$
$$= \sin t + 4t\cos t - 3t^2\cos t + t\cos t - 2t^2\sin t + t^3\sin t \qquad \text{Dot products}$$
$$= (1 - 2t^2 + t^3)\sin t + (5t - 3t^2)\cos t \qquad \text{Simplify.}$$

Note that the result is a scalar. The same result is obtained if you first compute $\mathbf{u}\cdot\mathbf{v}$ and then differentiate. *Related Exercises 25–34* ◀

Higher Derivatives Higher derivatives of vector-valued functions are computed in the expected way: We simply differentiate each component multiple times. Second derivatives feature prominently in the next section, playing the role of acceleration.

EXAMPLE 4 **Higher derivatives** Compute the first, second, and third derivative of $\mathbf{r}(t) = \langle t^2, 8\ln t, 3e^{-2t}\rangle$.

SOLUTION Differentiating once, we have $\mathbf{r}'(t) = \langle 2t, 8/t, -6e^{-2t}\rangle$. Differentiating again produces $\mathbf{r}''(t) = \langle 2, -8/t^2, 12e^{-2t}\rangle$. Differentiating once more we have $\mathbf{r}'''(t) = \langle 0, 16/t^3, -24e^{-2t}\rangle$. *Related Exercises 35–40* ◀

Integrals of Vector-Valued Functions

An **antiderivative** of the vector function $\mathbf{r}$ is a function $\mathbf{R}$ such that $\mathbf{R}' = \mathbf{r}$. If

$$\mathbf{r} = f\mathbf{i} + g\mathbf{j} + h\mathbf{k},$$

then an antiderivative of $\mathbf{r}$ is

$$\mathbf{R} = F\mathbf{i} + G\mathbf{j} + H\mathbf{k},$$

where F, G, and H are antiderivatives of f, g, and h, respectively. This fact follows by differentiating the components of $\mathbf{R}$ and verifying that $\mathbf{R}' = \mathbf{r}$. The collection of all antiderivatives of $\mathbf{r}$ is the **indefinite integral** of $\mathbf{r}$.

DEFINITION Indefinite Integral of a Vector-Valued Function

Let $\mathbf{r} = f\mathbf{i} + g\mathbf{j} + h\mathbf{k}$ be a vector function and let $\mathbf{R} = F\mathbf{i} + G\mathbf{j} + H\mathbf{k}$, where F, G, and H are antiderivatives of f, g, and h, respectively. The indefinite integral of $\mathbf{r}$ is

$$\int \mathbf{r}(t)\,dt = \mathbf{R}(t) + \mathbf{C},$$

where $\mathbf{C}$ is an arbitrary constant vector.

EXAMPLE 5 Indefinite integrals Compute

$$\int \left[\frac{t}{\sqrt{t^2+2}}\mathbf{i} + e^{-3t}\mathbf{j} + (\sin 4t + 1)\mathbf{k}\right] dt.$$

SOLUTION We compute the indefinite integral of each component:

➤ The substitution $u = t^2 + 2$ is used to evaluate the **i**-component of the integral.

$$\begin{aligned}\int &\left[\frac{t}{\sqrt{t^2+2}}\mathbf{i} + e^{-3t}\mathbf{j} + (\sin 4t + 1)\mathbf{k}\right] dt \\ &= \left(\sqrt{t^2+2} + C_1\right)\mathbf{i} + \left(-\frac{1}{3}e^{-3t} + C_2\right)\mathbf{j} + \left(-\frac{1}{4}\cos 4t + t + C_3\right)\mathbf{k} \\ &= \sqrt{t^2+2}\,\mathbf{i} - \frac{1}{3}e^{-3t}\mathbf{j} + \left(t - \frac{1}{4}\cos 4t\right)\mathbf{k} + \mathbf{C} \quad \text{where } \mathbf{C} = C_1\mathbf{i} + C_2\mathbf{j} + C_3\mathbf{k}\end{aligned}$$

In the last step, we combine the arbitrary constants for each component and use one constant vector $\mathbf{C}$. You may suppress C_1, C_2, and C_3 and append the vector constant $\mathbf{C}$ at the end of the calculation.

Related Exercises 41–44 ◄

QUICK CHECK 4 Let $\mathbf{r}(t) = \langle 1, 2t, 3t^2\rangle$. Compute $\int \mathbf{r}(t)\,dt$. ◄

EXAMPLE 6 Finding one antiderivative Find $\mathbf{r}(t)$ such that $\mathbf{r}'(t) = \langle e^2, \sin t, t\rangle$ and $\mathbf{r}(0) = \mathbf{j}$.

SOLUTION The required function $\mathbf{r}$ is an antiderivative of $\langle e^2, \sin t, t\rangle$:

$$\mathbf{r}(t) = \int \langle e^2, \sin t, t\rangle\,dt = \left\langle e^2 t, -\cos t, \frac{t^2}{2}\right\rangle + \mathbf{C},$$

where $\mathbf{C}$ is an arbitrary constant vector. The condition $\mathbf{r}(0) = \mathbf{j}$ allows us to determine $\mathbf{C}$; substituting $t = 0$ implies that $\mathbf{r}(0) = \langle 0, -1, 0\rangle + \mathbf{C} = \mathbf{j}$, where $\mathbf{j} = \langle 0, 1, 0\rangle$. Solving for $\mathbf{C}$, we have $\mathbf{C} = \langle 0, 1, 0\rangle - \langle 0, -1, 0\rangle = \langle 0, 2, 0\rangle$. Therefore,

$$\mathbf{r}(t) = \left\langle e^2 t, 2 - \cos t, \frac{t^2}{2}\right\rangle.$$

Related Exercises 45–48 ◄

Definite integrals are evaluated by applying the Fundamental Theorem of Calculus to each component of a vector-valued function.

DEFINITION Definite Integral of a Vector-Valued Function

Let $\mathbf{r}(t) = f(t)\mathbf{i} + g(t)\mathbf{j} + h(t)\mathbf{k}$, where f, g, and h are integrable on the interval $[a, b]$.

$$\int_a^b \mathbf{r}(t)\,dt = \left[\int_a^b f(t)\,dt\right]\mathbf{i} + \left[\int_a^b g(t)\,dt\right]\mathbf{j} + \left[\int_a^b h(t)\,dt\right]\mathbf{k}$$

EXAMPLE 7 Definite integrals Evaluate

$$\int_0^{\pi} \left[\mathbf{i} + 3\cos\left(\frac{t}{2}\right)\mathbf{j} - 4t\mathbf{k}\right] dt.$$

SOLUTION

$$\int_0^{\pi} \left[\mathbf{i} + 3\cos\left(\frac{t}{2}\right)\mathbf{j} - 4t\mathbf{k}\right] dt = t\mathbf{i}\Big|_0^{\pi} + 6\sin\left(\frac{t}{2}\right)\mathbf{j}\Big|_0^{\pi} - 2t^2\mathbf{k}\Big|_0^{\pi}$$ Evaluate integrals for each component.

$$= \pi\mathbf{i} + 6\mathbf{j} - 2\pi^2\mathbf{k}$$ Simplify.

Related Exercises 49–54 ◄

With the tools of differentiation and integration in hand, we are prepared to tackle some practical problems, notably the motion of objects in space.

SECTION 12.6 EXERCISES

Review Questions

1. Explain how to compute the derivative of $\mathbf{r}(t) = \langle f(t), g(t), h(t)\rangle$.
2. Explain the geometric meaning of $\mathbf{r}'(t)$.
3. Given a tangent vector on an oriented curve, how do you find the unit tangent vector?
4. Compute $\mathbf{r}''(t)$ when $\mathbf{r}(t) = \langle t^{10}, 8t, \cos t\rangle$.
5. How do you find the indefinite integral of $\mathbf{r}(t) = \langle f(t), g(t), h(t)\rangle$?
6. How do you evaluate $\int_a^b \mathbf{r}(t)\,dt$?

Basic Skills

7–12. Derivatives of vector-valued functions *Differentiate the following functions.*

7. $\mathbf{r}(t) = \langle 2t^3, 6\sqrt{t}, 3/t\rangle$
8. $\mathbf{r}(t) = \langle 4, 3\cos 2t, 2\sin 3t\rangle$
9. $\mathbf{r}(t) = \langle e^t, 2e^{-t}, -4e^{2t}\rangle$
10. $\mathbf{r}(t) = \langle \tan t, \sec t, \cos^2 t\rangle$
11. $\mathbf{r}(t) = \langle te^{-t}, t\ln t, t\cos t\rangle$
12. $\mathbf{r}(t) = \langle (t+1)^{-1}, \tan^{-1} t, \ln(t+1)\rangle$

13–16. Tangent vectors *For the following curves, find a tangent vector at the given value of t.*

13. $\mathbf{r}(t) = \langle t, \cos 2t, 2\sin t\rangle,\ t = \pi/2$
14. $\mathbf{r}(t) = \langle 2\sin t, 3\cos t, \sin(t/2)\rangle,\ t = \pi$
15. $\mathbf{r}(t) = \langle 2t^4, 6t^{3/2}, 10/t\rangle,\ t = 1$
16. $\mathbf{r}(t) = \langle 2e^t, e^{-2t}, 4e^{2t}\rangle,\ t = \ln 3$

17–20. Unit tangent vectors *For the following parameterized curves, find the unit tangent vector.*

17. $\mathbf{r}(t) = \langle 8, \cos 2t, 2\sin 2t\rangle$, for $0 \le t \le 2\pi$
18. $\mathbf{r}(t) = \langle \sin t, \cos t, \cos t\rangle$, for $0 \le t \le 2\pi$
19. $\mathbf{r}(t) = \langle t, 2, 2/t\rangle$, for $t \ge 1$
20. $\mathbf{r}(t) = \langle e^{2t}, 2e^{2t}, 2e^{-3t}\rangle$, for $t \ge 0$

21–24. Unit tangent vectors at a point *For the following parameterized curves, find the unit tangent vector at the given value of t.*

21. $\mathbf{r}(t) = \langle \cos 2t, 4, 3\sin 2t\rangle$, for $0 \le t \le \pi,\ t = \pi/2$
22. $\mathbf{r}(t) = \langle \sin t, \cos t, e^{-t}\rangle$, for $0 \le t \le \pi,\ t = 0$
23. $\mathbf{r}(t) = \langle 6t, 6, 3/t\rangle$, for $0 < t < 2,\ t = 1$
24. $\mathbf{r}(t) = \langle \sqrt{7}e^t, 3e^t, 3e^t\rangle$, for $0 \le t \le 1,\ t = \ln 2$

25–30. Derivative rules *Let*

$$\mathbf{u}(t) = 2t^3\mathbf{i} + (t^2 - 1)\mathbf{j} - 8\mathbf{k} \text{ and } \mathbf{v}(t) = e^t\mathbf{i} + 2e^{-t}\mathbf{j} - e^{2t}\mathbf{k}.$$

Compute the derivative of the following functions.

25. $(t^{12} + 3t)\mathbf{u}(t)$
26. $(4t^8 - 6t^3)\mathbf{v}(t)$
27. $\mathbf{u}(t^4 - 2t)$
28. $\mathbf{v}(\sqrt{t})$
29. $\mathbf{u}(t)\cdot\mathbf{v}(t)$
30. $\mathbf{u}(t)\times\mathbf{v}(t)$

31–34. Derivative rules *Compute the following derivatives.*

31. $\frac{d}{dt}[t^2(\mathbf{i} + 2\mathbf{j} - 2t\mathbf{k})\cdot(e^t\mathbf{i} + 2e^t\mathbf{j} - 3e^{-t}\mathbf{k})]$
32. $\frac{d}{dt}[(t^3\mathbf{i} - 2t\mathbf{j} - 2\mathbf{k})\times(t\mathbf{i} - t^2\mathbf{j} - t^3\mathbf{k})]$
33. $\frac{d}{dt}[(3t^2\mathbf{i} + \sqrt{t}\mathbf{j} - 2t^{-1}\mathbf{k})\cdot(\cos t\,\mathbf{i} + \sin 2t\,\mathbf{j} - 3t\,\mathbf{k})]$
34. $\frac{d}{dt}[(t^3\mathbf{i} + 6\mathbf{j} - 2\sqrt{t}\mathbf{k})\times(3t\mathbf{i} - 12t^2\mathbf{j} - 6t^{-2}\mathbf{k})]$

35–40. Higher derivatives *Compute $\mathbf{r}''(t)$ and $\mathbf{r}'''(t)$ for the following functions.*

35. $\mathbf{r}(t) = \langle t^2 + 1, t + 1, 1\rangle$
36. $\mathbf{r}(t) = \langle 3t^{12} - t^2, t^8 + t^3, t^{-4} - 2\rangle$
37. $\mathbf{r}(t) = \langle \cos 3t, \sin 4t, \cos 6t\rangle$
38. $\mathbf{r}(t) = \langle e^{4t}, 2e^{-4t} + 1, 2e^{-t}\rangle$

39. $\mathbf{r}(t) = \sqrt{t+4}\,\mathbf{i} + \dfrac{t}{t+1}\mathbf{j} - e^{-t^2}\mathbf{k}$

40. $\mathbf{r}(t) = \tan t\,\mathbf{i} + \left(t + \dfrac{1}{t}\right)\mathbf{j} - \ln(t+1)\mathbf{k}$

41–44. Indefinite integrals *Compute the indefinite integral of the following functions.*

41. $\mathbf{r}(t) = \langle t^4 - 3t, 2t - 1, 10\rangle$

42. $\mathbf{r}(t) = \langle 5t^{-4} - t^2, t^6 - 4t^3, 2/t\rangle$

43. $\mathbf{r}(t) = \langle 2\cos t, 2\sin 3t, 4\cos 8t\rangle$

44. $\mathbf{r}(t) = te^t\mathbf{i} + t\sin t^2\mathbf{j} - \dfrac{2t}{\sqrt{t^2+4}}\mathbf{k}$

45–48. Finding r from r′ *Find the function* **r** *that satisfies the following conditions.*

45. $\mathbf{r}'(t) = \langle 1, 2t, 3t^2\rangle$; $\mathbf{r}(1) = \langle 4, 3, -5\rangle$

46. $\mathbf{r}'(t) = \langle \sqrt{t}, \cos \pi t, 4/t\rangle$; $\mathbf{r}(1) = \langle 2, 3, 4\rangle$

47. $\mathbf{r}'(t) = \langle e^{2t}, 1 - 2e^{-t}, 1 - 2e^t\rangle$; $\mathbf{r}(0) = \langle 1, 1, 1\rangle$

48. $\mathbf{r}'(t) = \dfrac{t}{t^2+1}\mathbf{i} + te^{-t^2}\mathbf{j} - \dfrac{2t}{\sqrt{t^2+4}}\mathbf{k}$; $\mathbf{r}(0) = \mathbf{i} + \dfrac{3}{2}\mathbf{j} - 3\mathbf{k}$.

49–54. Definite integrals *Evaluate the following definite integrals.*

49. $\displaystyle\int_{-1}^{1} (\mathbf{i} + t\mathbf{j} + 3t^2\mathbf{k})\,dt$

50. $\displaystyle\int_{0}^{4} (\sqrt{t}\,\mathbf{i} + t^{-3}\mathbf{j} - 2t^2\mathbf{k})\,dt$

51. $\displaystyle\int_{-\pi}^{\pi} (\sin t\,\mathbf{i} + \cos t\,\mathbf{j} + 2t\,\mathbf{k})\,dt$

52. $\displaystyle\int_{0}^{\ln 2} (e^{-t}\mathbf{i} + 2e^{2t}\mathbf{j} - 4e^t\mathbf{k})\,dt$

53. $\displaystyle\int_{0}^{2} te^t(\mathbf{i} + 2\mathbf{j} - \mathbf{k})\,dt$

54. $\displaystyle\int_{0}^{\pi/4} (\sec^2 t\,\mathbf{i} - 2\cos t\,\mathbf{j} - \mathbf{k})\,dt$

Further Explorations

55. **Explain why or why not** Determine whether the following statements are true and give an explanation or counterexample.

a. The vectors $\mathbf{r}(t)$ and $\mathbf{r}'(t)$ are parallel for all values of t in the domain.

b. The curve described by the function $\mathbf{r}(t) = \langle 1, t^2 - 2t, \cos \pi t\rangle$ is smooth, for $-\infty < t < \infty$.

c. If f, g, and h are odd integrable functions and a is a real number, then

$$\int_{-a}^{a} (f(t)\mathbf{i} + g(t)\mathbf{j} + h(t)\mathbf{k})\,dt = \mathbf{0}.$$

56–61. Derivative rules *Let* $\mathbf{u}(t) = \langle 1, t, t^2\rangle$, $\mathbf{v}(t) = \langle t^2, -2t, 1\rangle$, *and* $g(t) = 2\sqrt{t}$. *Compute the derivatives of the following functions.*

56. $\mathbf{u}(t^3)$

57. $\mathbf{v}(e^t)$

58. $g(t)\mathbf{v}(t)$

59. $\mathbf{v}(g(t))$

60. $\mathbf{u}(t)\cdot\mathbf{v}(t)$

61. $\mathbf{u}(t)\times\mathbf{v}(t)$

62–67. Relationship between r and r′

62. Consider the circle $\mathbf{r}(t) = \langle a\cos t, a\sin t\rangle$, for $0 \le t \le 2\pi$, where a is a positive real number. Compute $\mathbf{r}'$ and show that it is orthogonal to $\mathbf{r}$ for all t.

63. Consider the parabola $\mathbf{r}(t) = \langle at^2 + 1, t\rangle$, for $-\infty < t < \infty$, where a is a positive real number. Find all points on the parabola at which $\mathbf{r}$ and $\mathbf{r}'$ are orthogonal.

64. Consider the curve $\mathbf{r}(t) = \langle \sqrt{t}, 1, t\rangle$, for $t > 0$. Find all points on the curve at which $\mathbf{r}$ and $\mathbf{r}'$ are orthogonal.

65. Consider the helix $\mathbf{r}(t) = \langle \cos t, \sin t, t\rangle$, for $-\infty < t < \infty$. Find all points on the helix at which $\mathbf{r}$ and $\mathbf{r}'$ are orthogonal.

66. Consider the ellipse $\mathbf{r}(t) = \langle 2\cos t, 8\sin t, 0\rangle$, for $0 \le t \le 2\pi$. Find all points on the ellipse at which $\mathbf{r}$ and $\mathbf{r}'$ are orthogonal.

67. For what curves in $\mathbf{R}^3$ is it true that $\mathbf{r}$ and $\mathbf{r}'$ are parallel for all t in the domain?

68. **Derivative rules** Suppose $\mathbf{u}$ and $\mathbf{v}$ are differentiable functions at $t = 0$ with $\mathbf{u}(0) = \langle 0, 1, 1\rangle$, $\mathbf{u}'(0) = \langle 0, 7, 1\rangle$, $\mathbf{v}(0) = \langle 0, 1, 1\rangle$, and $\mathbf{v}'(0) = \langle 1, 1, 2\rangle$. Evaluate the following expressions.

a. $\left.\dfrac{d}{dt}(\mathbf{u}\cdot\mathbf{v})\right|_{t=0}$ b. $\left.\dfrac{d}{dt}(\mathbf{u}\times\mathbf{v})\right|_{t=0}$ c. $\left.\dfrac{d}{dt}(\mathbf{u}(t)\cos t)\right|_{t=0}$

Additional Exercises

69. **Vectors r and r′ for lines**

a. If $\mathbf{r}(t) = \langle at, bt, ct\rangle$ with $\langle a, b, c\rangle \ne \langle 0, 0, 0\rangle$, show that the angle between $\mathbf{r}$ and $\mathbf{r}'$ is constant for all t.

b. If $\mathbf{r}(t) = \langle x_0 + at, y_0 + bt, z_0 + ct\rangle$, where x_0, y_0, and z_0 are not all zero, show that the angle between $\mathbf{r}$ and $\mathbf{r}'$ varies with t.

c. Explain the results of parts (a) and (b) geometrically.

70. **Proof of Sum Rule** By expressing $\mathbf{u}$ and $\mathbf{v}$ in terms of their components, prove that

$$\frac{d}{dt}(\mathbf{u}(t) + \mathbf{v}(t)) = \mathbf{u}'(t) + \mathbf{v}'(t).$$

71. **Proof of Product Rule** By expressing $\mathbf{u}$ in terms of its components, prove that

$$\frac{d}{dt}(f(t)\mathbf{u}(t)) = f'(t)\mathbf{u}(t) + f(t)\mathbf{u}'(t).$$

72. **Proof of Cross Product Rule** Prove that

$$\frac{d}{dt}(\mathbf{u}(t)\times\mathbf{v}(t)) = \mathbf{u}'(t)\times\mathbf{v}(t) + \mathbf{u}(t)\times\mathbf{v}'(t).$$

There are two ways to proceed: Either express $\mathbf{u}$ and $\mathbf{v}$ in terms of their three components or use the definition of the derivative.

T 73. **Cusps and noncusps**

a. Graph the curve $\mathbf{r}(t) = \langle t^3, t^3\rangle$. Show that $\mathbf{r}'(0) = \mathbf{0}$ and the curve does not have a cusp at $t = 0$. Explain.

b. Graph the curve $\mathbf{r}(t) = \langle t^3, t^2 \rangle$. Show that $\mathbf{r}'(0) = \mathbf{0}$ and the curve has a cusp at $t = 0$. Explain.

c. The functions $\mathbf{r}(t) = \langle t, t^2 \rangle$ and $\mathbf{p}(t) = \langle t^2, t^4 \rangle$ both satisfy $y = x^2$. Explain how the curves they parameterize are different.

d. Consider the curve $\mathbf{r}(t) = \langle t^m, t^n, t^p \rangle$, where m, n, and p are positive integers, not all equal. Is it true that the curve has a cusp at $t = 0$ if one or more of m, n, or p is even? Explain.

74. Motion on a sphere Prove that $\mathbf{r}$ describes a curve that lies on the surface of a sphere centered at the origin ($x^2 + y^2 + z^2 = a^2$ with $a \geq 0$) if and only if $\mathbf{r}$ and $\mathbf{r}'$ are orthogonal at all points of the curve.

QUICK CHECK ANSWERS

1. $\mathbf{r}(t)$ describes a line, so its tangent vector $\mathbf{r}'(t) = \langle 1, 1, 1 \rangle$ has constant direction and magnitude.
2. Both $\mathbf{r}'$ and $|\mathbf{r}'|$ have units of m/s. In forming $\mathbf{r}'/|\mathbf{r}'|$, the units cancel and $\mathbf{T}(t)$ is without units. **3.** $\frac{d}{dt}[\mathbf{u}(t) \cdot \mathbf{v}(t)] = \langle 1, 1, 1 \rangle \cdot \langle 1, 1, 1 \rangle + \langle t, t, t \rangle \cdot \langle 0, 0, 0 \rangle = 3$. $\frac{d}{dt}[\langle t, t, t \rangle \cdot \langle 1, 1, 1 \rangle] = \frac{d}{dt}[3t] = 3$. **4.** $\langle t, t^2, t^3 \rangle + \mathbf{C}$, where $\mathbf{C} = \langle a, b, c \rangle$ and a, b, and c are real numbers.

12.7 Motion in Space

It is a remarkable fact that given the forces acting on an object and its initial position and velocity, the motion of the object in three-dimensional space can be modeled for all future times. To be sure, the accuracy of the results depends on how well the various forces on the object are modeled. For example, it may be more difficult to predict the trajectory of a spinning soccer ball than the path of a space station orbiting Earth. Nevertheless, as shown in this section, by combining Newton's Second Law of Motion with everything we have learned about vectors, it is possible to solve a variety of moving body problems.

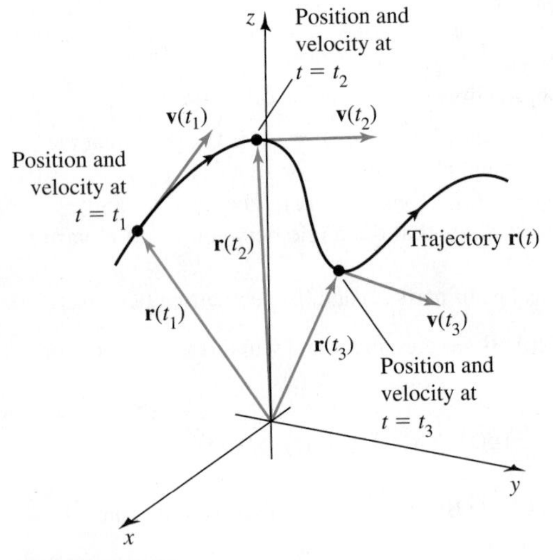

FIGURE 12.81

Position, Velocity, Speed, Acceleration

Until now we have studied objects that move in one dimension (along a line). The next step is to consider the motion of objects in two dimensions (in a plane) and three dimensions (in space).

We work in a three-dimensional coordinate system and let the vector-valued function $\mathbf{r}(t) = \langle x(t), y(t), z(t) \rangle$ describe the **position** of a moving object at times $t \geq 0$. The curve described by $\mathbf{r}$ is the **path** or **trajectory** of the object (Figure 12.81). Just as with one-dimensional motion, the rate of change of the position function with respect to time is the **instantaneous velocity** of the object—a vector with three components corresponding to the velocity in the x-, y-, and z-directions:

$$\mathbf{v}(t) = \mathbf{r}'(t) = \langle x'(t), y'(t), z'(t) \rangle$$

This expression should look familiar. The velocity vectors of a moving object are simply tangent vectors; that is, at any point the velocity vector is tangent to the trajectory (Figure 12.81).

As with one-dimensional motion, the speed of an object moving in three dimensions is the magnitude of its velocity vector:

$$|\mathbf{v}(t)| = |\langle x'(t), y'(t), z'(t) \rangle| = \sqrt{x'(t)^2 + y'(t)^2 + z'(t)^2}$$

The speed is a nonnegative scalar.

Finally, the **acceleration** of a moving object is the rate of change of the velocity:

$$\mathbf{a}(t) = \mathbf{v}'(t) = \mathbf{r}''(t)$$

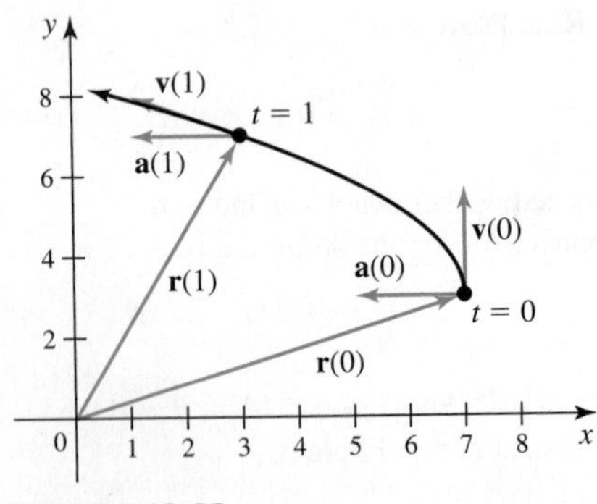

FIGURE 12.82

While the position vector gives the path of a moving object and the velocity vector is always tangent to the path, the acceleration vector is more difficult to visualize. Figure 12.82 shows one particular instance of two-dimensional motion. The trajectory is a piece of a parabola and is traced out by the position vectors (shown at $t = 0$ and 1). As expected, the velocity vectors are tangent to the trajectory. In this case, the acceleration is $\mathbf{a} = \langle -2, 0 \rangle$; it is constant in magnitude and direction for all times. The relationships among $\mathbf{r}$, $\mathbf{v}$, and $\mathbf{a}$ are explored in the coming examples.

> In the case of two-dimensional motion, $\mathbf{r}(t) = \langle x(t), y(t)\rangle$, $\mathbf{v}(t) = \mathbf{r}'(t)$, and $\mathbf{a}(t) = \mathbf{r}''(t)$.

QUICK CHECK 1 Given $\mathbf{r}(t) = \langle t, t^2, t^3\rangle$, find $\mathbf{v}(t)$ and $\mathbf{a}(t)$.

DEFINITION Position, Velocity, Speed, Acceleration

Let the **position** of an object moving in three-dimensional space be given by $\mathbf{r}(t) = \langle x(t), y(t), z(t)\rangle$, for $t \geq 0$. The **velocity** of the object is

$$\mathbf{v}(t) = \mathbf{r}'(t) = \langle x'(t), y'(t), z'(t)\rangle.$$

The **speed** of the object is the scalar function

$$|\mathbf{v}(t)| = \sqrt{x'(t)^2 + y'(t)^2 + z'(t)^2}.$$

The **acceleration** of the object is $\mathbf{a}(t) = \mathbf{v}'(t) = \mathbf{r}''(t)$.

EXAMPLE 1 Velocity and acceleration from position Consider the two-dimensional motion given by the position vector

$$\mathbf{r}(t) = \langle x(t), y(t)\rangle = \langle 3\cos t, 3\sin t\rangle, \qquad \text{for } 0 \leq t \leq 2\pi.$$

a. Sketch the trajectory of the object.

b. Find the velocity and speed of the object.

c. Find the acceleration of the object.

d. Sketch the position, velocity, and acceleration vectors for $t = 0, \pi/2, \pi, 3\pi/2$.

SOLUTION

a. Notice that for $0 \leq t \leq 2\pi$,

$$x(t)^2 + y(t)^2 = 9(\cos^2 t + \sin^2 t) = 9,$$

which is the equation of a circle centered at the origin with radius 3. Therefore, the object moves on this circle (Figure 12.83).

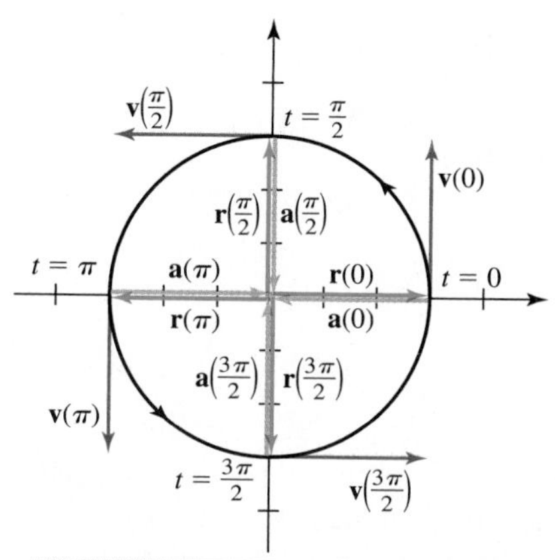

FIGURE 12.83

b.
$$\mathbf{v}(t) = \langle x'(t), y'(t)\rangle = \langle -3\sin t, 3\cos t\rangle \quad \text{Velocity vector}$$

$$\begin{aligned}|\mathbf{v}(t)| &= \sqrt{x'(t)^2 + y'(t)^2} \quad \text{Definition of speed}\\ &= \sqrt{(-3\sin t)^2 + (3\cos t)^2}\\ &= \sqrt{9\underbrace{(\sin^2 t + \cos^2 t)}_{1}} = 3\end{aligned}$$

The velocity vector has a constant magnitude and a continuously changing direction.

c. $\mathbf{a}(t) = \mathbf{v}'(t) = \langle -3\cos t, -3\sin t\rangle = -\mathbf{r}(t)$

In this case, the acceleration vector is the negative of the position vector at all times.

d. The relationships among **r**, **v**, and **a** at four points in time are shown in Figure 12.83. The velocity vector is always tangent to the trajectory and has length 3, while the acceleration vector and position vector have length 3 and point in opposite directions. At all times, **v** is orthogonal to **r** and **a**.

Related Exercises 7–14

EXAMPLE 2 Comparing trajectories Consider the trajectories described by the position functions

$$\mathbf{r}(t) = \left\langle t, t^2 - 4, \frac{t^3}{4} - 8\right\rangle, \quad \text{for } t \geq 0$$

$$\mathbf{R}(t) = \left\langle t^2, t^4 - 4, \frac{t^6}{4} - 8\right\rangle, \quad \text{for } t \geq 0,$$

where t is measured in the same time units for both functions.

a. Graph and compare the trajectories using a graphing utility.

b. Find the velocity vectors associated with the position functions.

SOLUTION

a. Plotting the position functions at selected values of t results in the trajectories shown in Figure 12.84. Because $\mathbf{r}(0) = \mathbf{R}(0) = \langle 0, -4, -8\rangle$, both curves have the same initial point. For $t \geq 0$, the two curves consist of the same points, but they are traced out differently. For example, both curves pass through the point (4, 12, 8), but that point corresponds to $\mathbf{r}(4)$ on the first curve and $\mathbf{R}(2)$ on the second curve. In general, $\mathbf{r}(t^2) = \mathbf{R}(t)$, for $t \geq 0$.

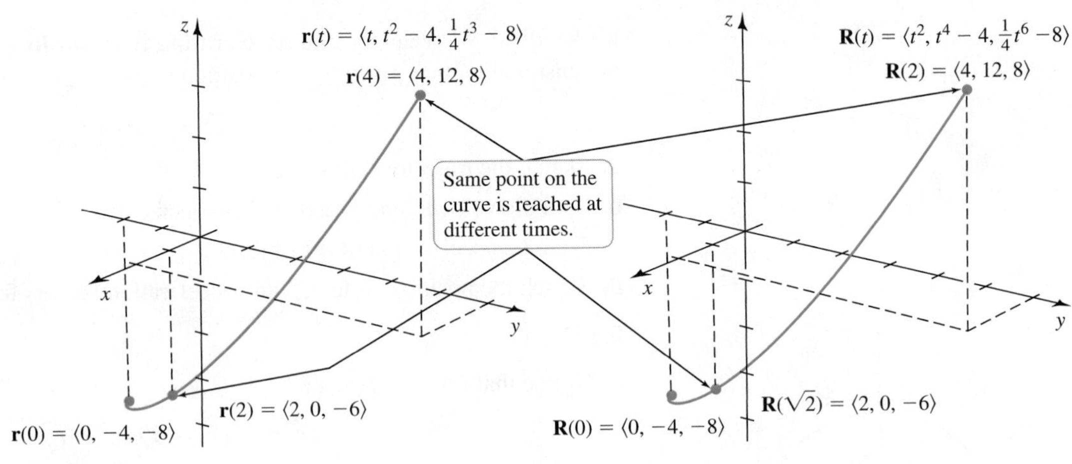

FIGURE 12.84

b. The velocity vectors are

$$\mathbf{r}'(t) = \left\langle 1, 2t, \frac{3t^2}{4}\right\rangle \quad \text{and} \quad \mathbf{R}'(t) = \left\langle 2t, 4t^3, \frac{3}{2}t^5\right\rangle.$$

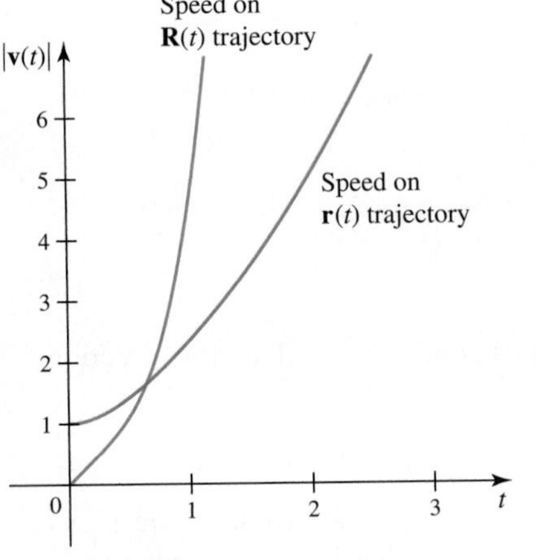

FIGURE 12.85

The difference in the motion on the two curves is revealed by the graphs of the speeds associated with the trajectories (Figure 12.85). The object on the first trajectory reaches the point (4, 12, 8) at $t = 4$ where its speed is $|\mathbf{r}'(4)| = |\langle 1, 8, 12\rangle| \approx 14.5$. The object on the second trajectory reaches the same point (4, 12, 8) at $t = 2$, where its speed is $|\mathbf{R}'(2)| = |\langle 4, 32, 48\rangle| \approx 57.8$. *Related Exercises 15–18* ◀

QUICK CHECK 2 Find the functions that give the speed of the two objects in Example 2 for all $t \geq 0$ (corresponding to the graphs in Figure 12.85). ◀

Straight-Line and Circular Motion

Two types of motion in space arise frequently and deserve to be singled out. First consider a trajectory described by the vector function

$$\mathbf{r}(t) = \langle x_0 + at, y_0 + bt, z_0 + ct\rangle, \qquad \text{for } t \geq 0,$$

where $x_0, y_0, z_0, a, b,$ and c are constants. This function describes a straight-line trajectory with an initial point $\langle x_0, y_0, z_0\rangle$ and a direction given by the vector $\langle a, b, c\rangle$ (Section 12.5). The velocity on this trajectory is the constant $\mathbf{v}(t) = \mathbf{r}'(t) = \langle a, b, c\rangle$ in the direction of the trajectory, and the acceleration is $\mathbf{a} = \langle 0, 0, 0\rangle$. The motion associated with this function is **uniform** (constant velocity) **straight-line motion**.

➤ See Exercise 49 for a discussion of nonuniform straight-line motion.

A different situation is **circular motion** (Example 1). Consider the two-dimensional circular path

$$\mathbf{r}(t) = \langle A\cos t, A\sin t\rangle, \qquad \text{for } 0 \leq t \leq 2\pi,$$

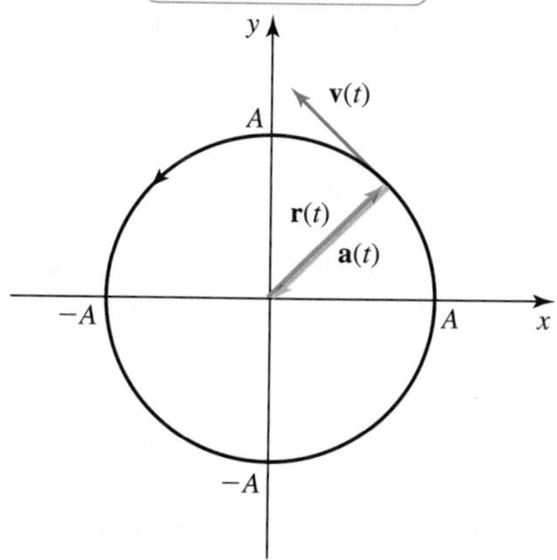

FIGURE 12.86

where A is a nonzero constant (Figure 12.86). The velocity and acceleration vectors are

$$\mathbf{v}(t) = \langle -A\sin t, A\cos t\rangle \quad \text{and}$$
$$\mathbf{a}(t) = \langle -A\cos t, -A\sin t\rangle = -\mathbf{r}(t).$$

Notice that $\mathbf{r}$ and $\mathbf{a}$ are parallel, but point in opposite directions. Furthermore, $\mathbf{r}\cdot\mathbf{v} = \mathbf{a}\cdot\mathbf{v} = 0$; thus, the position and acceleration vectors are both orthogonal to the velocity vectors (Figure 12.86). Finally, $\mathbf{r}$, $\mathbf{v}$, and $\mathbf{a}$ have constant magnitude A and variable directions. The conclusion that $\mathbf{r}\cdot\mathbf{v} = 0$ applies to any motion for which $|\mathbf{r}|$ is constant; that is, motion on a circle or motion on a sphere (Figure 12.87).

THEOREM 12.8 Motion with Constant $|\mathbf{r}|$
Let $\mathbf{r}$ describe a path on which $|\mathbf{r}|$ is constant (motion on a circle or a sphere centered at the origin). Then, $\mathbf{r}\cdot\mathbf{v} = 0$, which means the position vector and the velocity vector are orthogonal at all times for which the functions are defined.

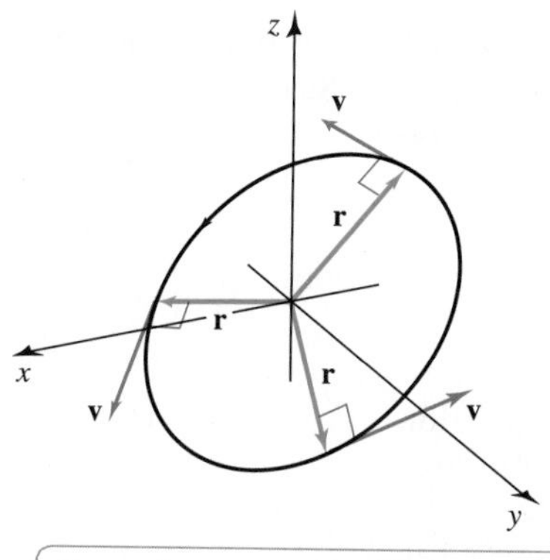

FIGURE 12.87

Proof If $\mathbf{r}$ has constant magnitude, then $|\mathbf{r}(t)|^2 = \mathbf{r}(t)\cdot\mathbf{r}(t) = c$ for some constant c. Differentiating the equation $\mathbf{r}(t)\cdot\mathbf{r}(t) = c$, we have

$$\begin{aligned} 0 &= \frac{d}{dt}(\mathbf{r}(t)\cdot\mathbf{r}(t)) && \text{Differentiate both sides of } |\mathbf{r}(t)|^2 = c \\ &= \mathbf{r}'(t)\cdot\mathbf{r}(t) + \mathbf{r}(t)\cdot\mathbf{r}'(t) && \text{Derivative of dot product (Theorem 12.7)} \\ &= 2\mathbf{r}'(t)\cdot\mathbf{r}(t) && \text{Simplify.} \\ &= 2\mathbf{v}(t)\cdot\mathbf{r}(t) && \mathbf{r}'(t) = \mathbf{v}(t) \end{aligned}$$

Because $\mathbf{r}(t)\cdot\mathbf{v}(t) = 0$ for all t, it follows that $\mathbf{r}$ and $\mathbf{v}$ are orthogonal for all t. ◄

EXAMPLE 3 Path on a sphere An object moves on a trajectory described by

$$\mathbf{r}(t) = \langle x(t), y(t), z(t)\rangle = \langle 3\cos t, 5\sin t, 4\cos t\rangle, \quad \text{for } 0 \le t \le 2\pi.$$

a. Show that the object moves on a sphere and find the radius of the sphere.

b. Find the velocity and speed of the object.

SOLUTION

a.
$$\begin{aligned} |\mathbf{r}(t)|^2 &= x(t)^2 + y(t)^2 + z(t)^2 && \text{Square of the distance from the origin} \\ &= (3\cos t)^2 + (5\sin t)^2 + (4\cos t)^2 && \text{Substitute.} \\ &= 25\cos^2 t + 25\sin^2 t && \text{Simplify.} \\ &= 25\underbrace{(\cos^2 t + \sin^2 t)}_{1} = 25 && \text{Factor.} \end{aligned}$$

Therefore, $|\mathbf{r}(t)| = 5$, for $0 \le t \le 2\pi$, and the curve lies on a sphere of radius 5 centered at the origin (Figure 12.88).

b.
$$\begin{aligned} \mathbf{v}(t) &= \mathbf{r}'(t) = \langle -3\sin t, 5\cos t, -4\sin t\rangle && \text{Velocity vector} \\ |\mathbf{v}(t)| &= \sqrt{\mathbf{v}(t)\cdot\mathbf{v}(t)} && \text{Speed of the object} \\ &= \sqrt{9\sin^2 t + 25\cos^2 t + 16\sin^2 t} && \text{Evaluate the dot product.} \\ &= \sqrt{25\underbrace{(\sin^2 t + \cos^2 t)}_{1}} && \text{Simplify.} \\ &= 5 && \text{Simplify.} \end{aligned}$$

➤ For generalizations of this example and explorations of trajectories that lie on spheres and ellipses, see Exercises 65, 68, and 69.

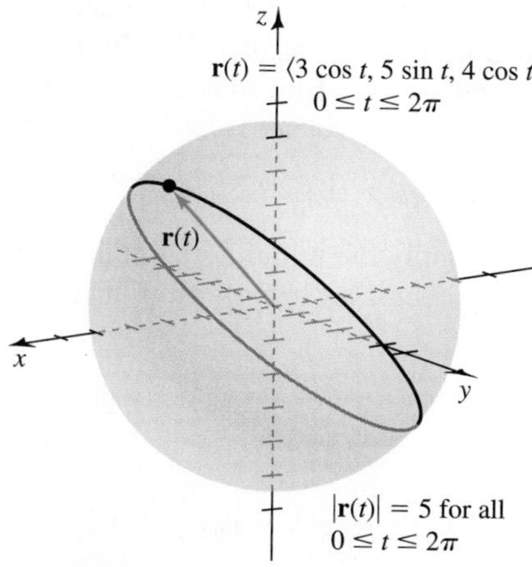

FIGURE 12.88

QUICK CHECK 3 Verify that $\mathbf{r}(t) \cdot \mathbf{v}(t) = 0$ in Example 3. ◀

The speed of the object is always 5. You should verify that $\mathbf{r}(t) \cdot \mathbf{v}(t) = 0$ for all t, implying that **r** and **v** are always orthogonal.

Related Exercises 19–24 ◀

Two-Dimensional Motion in a Gravitational Field

Newton's Second Law of Motion, which is used to model the motion of most objects, states that

$$\underbrace{\text{Mass}}_{m} \cdot \underbrace{\text{acceleration}}_{\mathbf{a}(t) = \mathbf{r}''(t)} = \underbrace{\text{sum of all forces.}}_{\sum \mathbf{F}_i}$$

In other words, the governing law says something about the *acceleration* of an object, and in order to describe the motion fully, we must find the velocity and position from the acceleration.

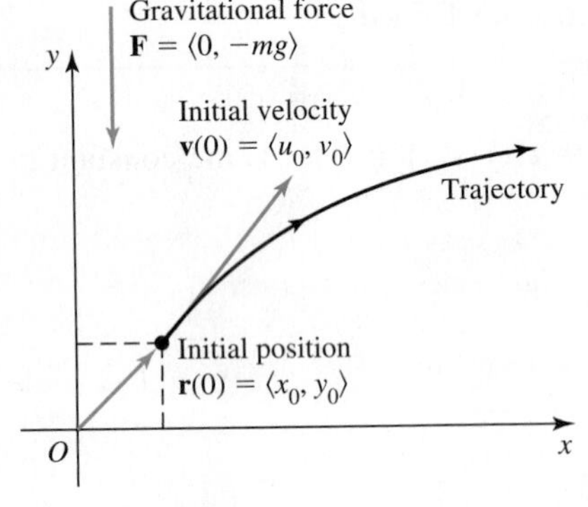

FIGURE 12.89

Finding Velocity and Position from Acceleration We begin with the case of two-dimensional projectile motion in which the only force acting on the object is the gravitational force; for the moment, air resistance and other possible external forces are neglected.

A convenient coordinate system uses a y-axis that points vertically upward and an x-axis that points in the direction of horizontal motion. The gravitational force is in the negative y-direction and is given by $\mathbf{F} = \langle 0, -mg \rangle$, where m is the mass of the object and $g \approx 9.8\ \text{m/s}^2 \approx 32\ \text{ft/s}^2$ is the acceleration due to gravity (Figure 12.89).

With these observations, Newton's Second Law takes the form

$$m\mathbf{a}(t) = \mathbf{F} = \langle 0, -mg \rangle.$$

Significantly, the mass of the object cancels, leaving the vector equation

$$\mathbf{a}(t) = \langle 0, -g \rangle. \tag{1}$$

In order to find the velocity $\mathbf{v}(t) = \langle x'(t), y'(t) \rangle$ and the position $\mathbf{r}(t) = \langle x(t), y(t) \rangle$ from this equation, we must be given the following **initial conditions**:

$$\text{Initial velocity at } t = 0\text{: } \mathbf{v}(0) = \langle u_0, v_0 \rangle$$
$$\text{Initial position at } t = 0\text{: } \mathbf{r}(0) = \langle x_0, y_0 \rangle$$

We now proceed in two steps.

▶ Recall that an antiderivative of 0 is a constant C and an antiderivative of $-g$ is $-gt + C$.

1. **Solve for the velocity** The velocity is an antiderivative of the acceleration in equation (1). Integrating the acceleration, we have

$$\mathbf{v}(t) = \int \mathbf{a}(t)\, dt = \int \langle 0, -g \rangle\, dt = \langle 0, -gt \rangle + \mathbf{C},$$

where $\mathbf{C}$ is an arbitrary constant vector. The arbitrary constant is determined by substituting $t = 0$ and using the initial condition $\mathbf{v}(0) = \langle u_0, v_0 \rangle$. We find that $\mathbf{v}(0) = \langle 0, 0 \rangle + \mathbf{C} = \langle u_0, v_0 \rangle$. Solving for the constant, we find that $\mathbf{C} = \langle u_0, v_0 \rangle$. Therefore, the velocity is

▶ You have a choice. You may do these calculations in vector notation as we have done here, or you may work with individual components.

$$\mathbf{v}(t) = \langle 0, -gt \rangle + \langle u_0, v_0 \rangle = \langle u_0, -gt + v_0 \rangle. \tag{2}$$

Notice that the horizontal component of velocity is simply the initial horizontal velocity u_0 for all time. The vertical component of velocity decreases linearly from its initial value of v_0.

2. **Solve for the position** The position vector is an antiderivative of the velocity given by equation (2):

$$\mathbf{r}(t) = \int \mathbf{v}(t)\, dt = \int \langle u_0, -gt + v_0 \rangle\, dt = \left\langle u_0 t, -\frac{1}{2}gt^2 + v_0 t \right\rangle + \mathbf{C},$$

where **C** is an arbitrary constant vector. Substituting $t = 0$, we have $\mathbf{r}(0) = \langle 0, 0 \rangle + \mathbf{C} = \langle x_0, y_0 \rangle$, which implies that $\mathbf{C} = \langle x_0, y_0 \rangle$. Therefore, the position of the object for $t \geq 0$ is

$$\mathbf{r}(t) = \left\langle u_0 t, -\frac{1}{2}gt^2 + v_0 t \right\rangle + \langle x_0, y_0 \rangle = \left\langle \underbrace{u_0 t + x_0}_{x(t)}, \underbrace{-\frac{1}{2}gt^2 + v_0 t + y_0}_{y(t)} \right\rangle$$

SUMMARY Two-Dimensional Motion in a Gravitational Field

Consider an object moving in a plane with a horizontal x-axis and a vertical y-axis, subject only to the force of gravity. Given the initial velocity $\mathbf{v}(0) = \langle u_0, v_0 \rangle$ and the initial position $\mathbf{r}(0) = \langle x_0, y_0 \rangle$, the velocity of the object for $t \geq 0$ is

$$\mathbf{v}(t) = \langle x'(t), y'(t) \rangle = \langle u_0, -gt + v_0 \rangle$$

and the position is

$$\mathbf{r}(t) = \langle x(t), y(t) \rangle = \left\langle u_0 t + x_0, -\frac{1}{2}gt^2 + v_0 t + y_0 \right\rangle.$$

EXAMPLE 4 Flight of a baseball A baseball is hit from 3 ft above home plate with an initial velocity in ft/s of $\mathbf{v}(0) = \langle u_0, v_0 \rangle = \langle 80, 80 \rangle$. Neglect all forces other than gravity.

a. Find the position and velocity of the ball between the time it is hit and the time it first hits the ground.

b. Show that the trajectory of the ball is a segment of a parabola.

c. Assuming a flat playing field, how far does the ball travel horizontally? Plot the trajectory of the ball.

d. What is the maximum height of the ball?

e. Does the ball clear a 20-ft fence that is 380 ft from home plate (directly under the path of the ball)?

SOLUTION Assume the origin is located at home plate. Because distances are measured in feet, we use $g = 32\text{ ft/s}^2$.

a. Substituting $x_0 = 0$ and $y_0 = 3$ into the equation for **r**, the position of the ball is

$$\mathbf{r}(t) = \langle x(t), y(t) \rangle = \langle 80t, -16t^2 + 80t + 3 \rangle, \qquad \text{for } t \geq 0. \tag{3}$$

We then compute $\mathbf{v}(t) = \mathbf{r}'(t) = \langle 80, -32t + 80 \rangle$.

b. Equation (3) says that $x = 80t$ and $y = -16t^2 + 80t + 3$. Substituting $t = x/80$ into the equation for y gives

$$y = -16\left(\frac{x}{80}\right)^2 + x + 3 = -\frac{x^2}{400} + x + 3,$$

which is the equation of a parabola.

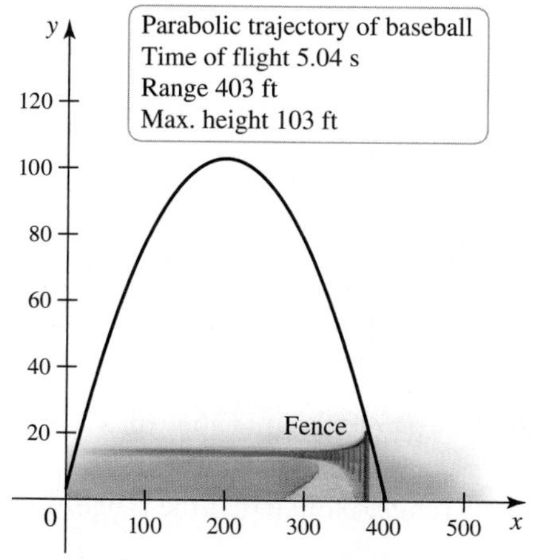

FIGURE 12.90

➤ The equation in part (c) can be solved using the quadratic formula or a root-finder on a calculator.

c. The ball lands on the ground at the value of $t > 0$ at which $y = 0$. Solving $y(t) = -16t^2 + 80t + 3 = 0$, we find that $t \approx -0.04$ and $t \approx 5.04$ s. The first root is not relevant for the problem at hand, so we conclude that the ball lands when $t \approx 5.04$ s. The horizontal distance traveled by the ball is $x(5.04) \approx 403$ ft. The path of the ball in the xy-coordinate system on the time interval $[0, 5.04]$ is shown in Figure 12.90.

d. The ball reaches its maximum height at the time its vertical velocity is zero. Solving $y'(t) = -32t + 80 = 0$, we find that $t = 2.5$ s. The height at that time is $y(2.5) = 103$ ft.

e. The ball reaches a horizontal distance of 380 ft (the distance to the fence) when $x(t) = 80t = 380$. Solving for t, we find that $t = 4.75$ s. The height of the ball at that time is $y(4.75) = 22$ ft. So, indeed, the ball clears a 20-ft fence.

Related Exercises 25–28

QUICK CHECK 4 Write the functions $x(t)$ and $y(t)$ in Example 4 in the case that $x_0 = 0$, $y_0 = 2$, $u_0 = 100$, $v_0 = 60$.

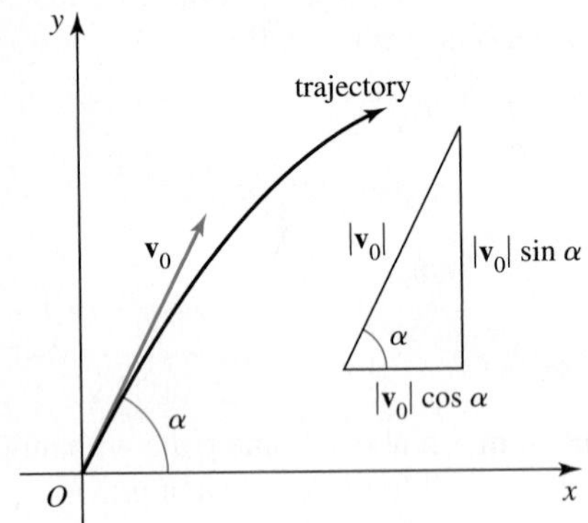

FIGURE 12.91

Range, Time of Flight, Maximum Height Having solved one specific motion problem, we can now make some general observations about two-dimensional projectile motion in a gravitational field. Assume that the motion of an object begins at the origin; that is, $x_0 = y_0 = 0$. Assume also that the object is launched at an angle of $\alpha\ (0 \le \alpha \le \pi/2)$ above the horizontal with an initial speed $|\mathbf{v}_0|$ (Figure 12.91). This means that the initial velocity is

$$\langle u_0, v_0 \rangle = \langle |\mathbf{v}_0| \cos \alpha, |\mathbf{v}_0| \sin \alpha \rangle.$$

Substituting these values into the general expressions for the velocity and position, we find that the velocity of the object for $t \ge 0$ is

$$\mathbf{v}(t) = \langle u_0, -gt + v_0 \rangle = \langle |\mathbf{v}_0| \cos \alpha, -gt + |\mathbf{v}_0| \sin \alpha \rangle.$$

The position of the object (with $x_0 = y_0 = 0$) for $t \ge 0$ is

$$\mathbf{r}(t) = \langle x(t), y(t) \rangle = \langle (|\mathbf{v}_0| \cos \alpha)t, -gt^2/2 + (|\mathbf{v}_0| \sin \alpha)t \rangle.$$

Notice that the motion is determined entirely by the parameters $|\mathbf{v}_0|$ and α. Several general conclusions now follow.

> The other root of the equation $y(t) = 0$ is $t = 0$, the time the object leaves the ground.

1. Assuming the object is launched from the origin over horizontal ground, it returns to the ground when $y(t) = -gt^2/2 + (|\mathbf{v}_0| \sin \alpha)t = 0$. Solving for t, the **time of flight** is $T = 2|\mathbf{v}_0| \sin \alpha / g$.
2. The **range** of the object, which is the horizontal distance it travels, is the x-coordinate of the trajectory at the time of flight:

$$\begin{aligned} x(T) &= (|\mathbf{v}_0| \cos \alpha)T \\ &= (|\mathbf{v}_0| \cos \alpha)\frac{2|\mathbf{v}_0| \sin \alpha}{g} && \text{Substitute for } T. \\ &= \frac{2|\mathbf{v}_0|^2 \sin \alpha \cos \alpha}{g} && \text{Simplify.} \\ &= \frac{|\mathbf{v}_0|^2 \sin 2\alpha}{g} && 2 \sin \alpha \cos \alpha = \sin 2\alpha \end{aligned}$$

Note that on the interval $0 \le \alpha \le \pi/2$, $\sin 2\alpha$ has a maximum value of 1 when $\alpha = \pi/4$, so the maximum range is $|\mathbf{v}_0|^2/g$. In other words, in an ideal world, firing an object from the ground at a 45° angle maximizes its range. Notice that the ranges obtained with the angles α and $\pi/2 - \alpha$ are equal (Figure 12.92).

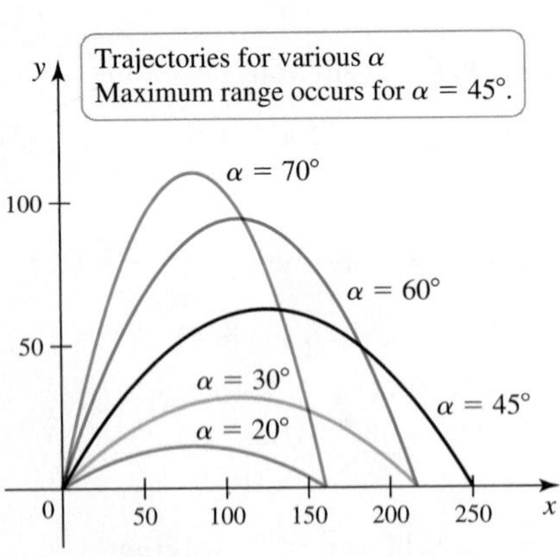

FIGURE 12.92

QUICK CHECK 5 Show that the range attained with an angle α equals the range attained with the angle $\pi/2 - \alpha$.

3. The maximum height of the object is reached when the vertical velocity is zero, or when $y'(t) = -gt + |\mathbf{v}_0| \sin \alpha = 0$. Solving for t, the maximum height is reached at $t = |\mathbf{v}_0|(\sin \alpha)/g = T/2$, which is half of the time of flight. The object spends equal amounts of time ascending and descending. The maximum height is

$$y\left(\frac{T}{2}\right) = \frac{(|\mathbf{v}_0| \sin \alpha)^2}{2g}.$$

4. Finally, by eliminating t from the equations for $x(t)$ and $y(t)$, it can be shown (Exercise 64) that the trajectory of the object is a segment of a parabola.

SUMMARY Two-Dimensional Motion

Assume an object traveling over horizontal ground, acted on only by the gravitational force, has an initial position $\langle x_0, y_0 \rangle = \langle 0, 0 \rangle$ and initial velocity $\langle u_0, v_0 \rangle = \langle |\mathbf{v}_0| \cos \alpha, |\mathbf{v}_0| \sin \alpha \rangle$. The trajectory, which is a segment of a parabola, has the following properties:

$$\text{time of flight} = T = \frac{2|\mathbf{v}_0| \sin \alpha}{g}$$

$$\text{range} = \frac{|\mathbf{v}_0|^2 \sin 2\alpha}{g}$$

$$\text{maximum height} = y\left(\frac{T}{2}\right) = \frac{(|\mathbf{v}_0| \sin \alpha)^2}{2g}$$

EXAMPLE 5 Flight of a golf ball A golf ball is driven down a horizontal fairway with an initial speed of 55 m/s at an initial angle of 25° (from a tee with negligible height). Neglect all forces except gravity and assume the ball's trajectory lies in a plane.

a. How far does the ball travel horizontally and when does it land?

b. What is the maximum height of the ball?

c. At what angles should the ball be hit to reach a green that is 300 m from the tee?

SOLUTION

a. Using the range formula with $\alpha = 25°$ and $|\mathbf{v}_0| = 55$ m/s, the ball travels

$$\frac{|\mathbf{v}_0|^2 \sin 2\alpha}{g} = \frac{(55 \text{ m/s})^2 \sin (50°)}{9.8 \text{ m/s}^2} \approx 236 \text{ m}.$$

The time of the flight is

$$T = \frac{2|\mathbf{v}_0| \sin \alpha}{g} = \frac{2(55 \text{ m/s}) \sin 25°}{9.8 \text{ m/s}^2} \approx 4.7 \text{ s}.$$

b. The maximum height of the ball is

$$\frac{(|\mathbf{v}_0| \sin \alpha)^2}{2g} = \frac{((55 \text{ m/s})(\sin 25°))^2}{2(9.8 \text{ m/s}^2)} \approx 27.6 \text{ m}.$$

c. Letting R denote the range and solving the range formula for $\sin 2\alpha$, we find that $\sin 2\alpha = Rg/|\mathbf{v}_0|^2$. For a range of $R = 300$ m and an initial speed of $|\mathbf{v}_0| = 55$ m/s, the required angle satisfies

$$\sin 2\alpha = \frac{Rg}{|\mathbf{v}_0|^2} = \frac{(300 \text{ m})(9.8 \text{ m/s}^2)}{(55 \text{ m/s})^2} \approx 0.972.$$

To travel a horizontal distance of exactly 300 m, the required angles are $\alpha = \frac{1}{2}\sin^{-1}(0.972) \approx 38.2°$ or $51.8°$.

Related Exercises 29–32 ◀

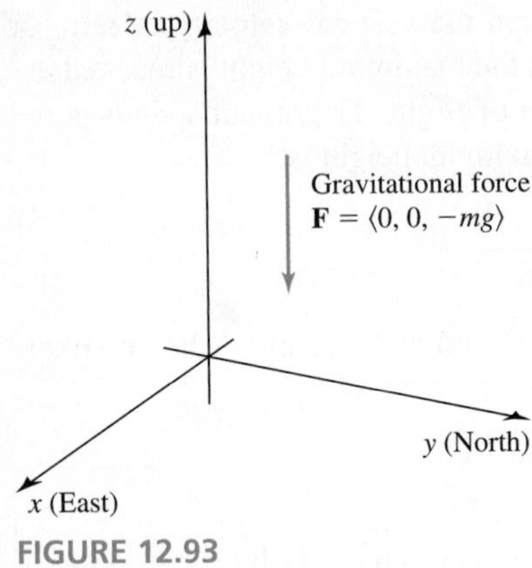

FIGURE 12.93

Three-Dimensional Motion

To solve three-dimensional motion problems, we adopt a coordinate system in which the x- and y-axes point in two perpendicular horizontal directions (for example, east and north), while the positive z-axis points vertically upward (Figure 12.93). Newton's Second Law now has three components and appears in the form

$$m\mathbf{a}(t) = \langle mx''(t), my''(t), mz''(t) \rangle = \mathbf{F}.$$

If only the gravitational force is present (now in the negative z-direction), then the force vector is $\mathbf{F} = \langle 0, 0, -mg \rangle$; the equation of motion is then $\mathbf{a}(t) = \langle 0, 0, -g \rangle$. Other effects, such as crosswinds, spins, or slices, can be modeled by including other force components.

EXAMPLE 6 Projectile motion A small projectile is fired over horizontal ground in an easterly direction with an initial speed of $|\mathbf{v}_0| = 300$ m/s at an angle of $\alpha = 30°$ above the horizontal. A crosswind blows from south to north producing an acceleration of the projectile of 0.36 m/s^2 to the north.

a. Where does the projectile land?

b. In order to correct for the crosswind and make the projectile land due east of the launch site, at what angle from due east must the projectile be fired? Assume the initial speed $|\mathbf{v}_0| = 300$ m/s and the angle of elevation $\alpha = 30°$ are the same as in part (a).

SOLUTION

a. Letting $g = 9.8\text{ m/s}^2$, the equations of motion are $\mathbf{a}(t) = \mathbf{v}'(t) = \langle 0, 0.36, -9.8 \rangle$. Proceeding as in the two-dimensional case, the indefinite integral of the acceleration is the velocity function

$$\mathbf{v}(t) = \langle 0, 0.36t, -9.8t \rangle + \mathbf{C},$$

where $\mathbf{C}$ is an arbitrary constant. With an initial speed $|\mathbf{v}_0| = 300$ m/s and an angle of elevation of $\alpha = 30°$ (Figure 12.94a), the initial velocity is

$$\mathbf{v}(0) = \langle 300 \cos 30°, 0, 300 \sin 30° \rangle = \langle 150\sqrt{3}, 0, 150 \rangle.$$

Substituting $t = 0$ and using the initial condition, we find that $\mathbf{C} = \langle 150\sqrt{3}, 0, 150 \rangle$. Therefore, the velocity function is

$$\mathbf{v}(t) = \langle 150\sqrt{3}, 0.36t, -9.8t + 150 \rangle.$$

Integrating the velocity function produces the position function

$$\mathbf{r}(t) = \langle 150\sqrt{3}t, 0.18t^2, -4.9t^2 + 150t \rangle + \mathbf{C}.$$

Using the initial condition $\mathbf{r}(0) = \langle 0, 0, 0 \rangle$, we find that $\mathbf{C} = \langle 0, 0, 0 \rangle$, and the position function is

$$\mathbf{r}(t) = \langle x(t), y(t), z(t) \rangle = \langle 150\sqrt{3}t, 0.18t^2, -4.9t^2 + 150t \rangle.$$

The projectile lands when $z(t) = -4.9t^2 + 150t = 0$. Solving for t, the positive root, which gives the time of flight, is $T = 150/4.9 \approx 30.6$ s. The x- and y-coordinates at that time are

$$x(T) \approx 7953\text{ m} \quad \text{and} \quad y(T) \approx 169\text{ m}.$$

Thus, the projectile lands approximately 7953 m east and 169 m north of the firing site (Figure 12.94a).

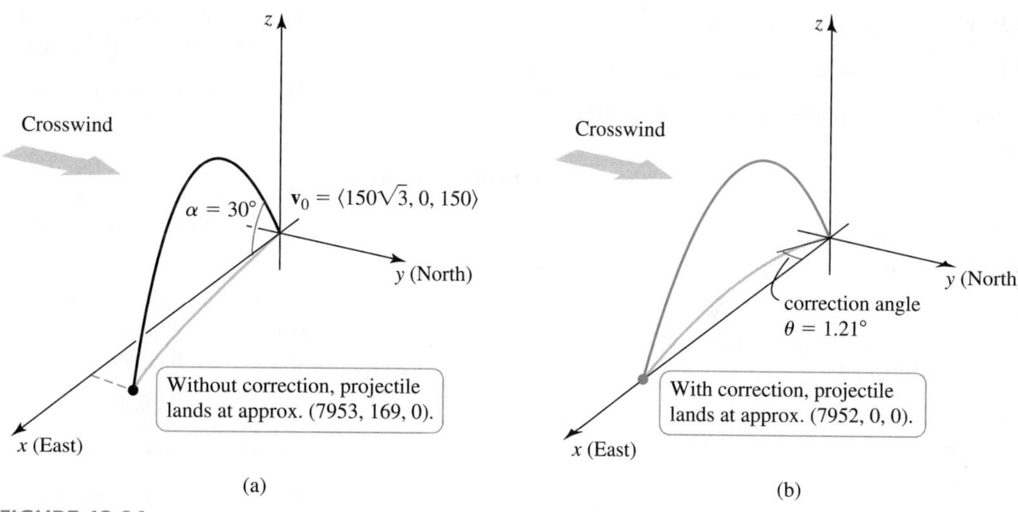

FIGURE 12.94

b. Keeping the initial speed of the projectile equal to $|\mathbf{v}_0| = 300$ m/s, we decompose the horizontal component of the speed, $150\sqrt{3}$ m/s, into an east component, $u_0 = 150\sqrt{3}\cos\theta$, and a north component, $v_0 = 150\sqrt{3}\sin\theta$, where θ is the angle relative to due east; we must determine the correction angle θ (Figure 12.94b). The x- and y-components of the position are

$$x(t) = (150\sqrt{3}\cos\theta)t \quad \text{and} \quad y(t) = 0.18t^2 + (150\sqrt{3}\sin\theta)t.$$

These changes in the initial velocity affect the x- and y-equations, but not the z-equation. Thus, the time of flight is still $T = 150/4.9 \approx 30.6$ s. The aim is to choose θ so that the projectile lands on the x-axis (due east from the launch site), which means $y(T) = 0$. Solving

$$y(T) = 0.18T^2 + (150\sqrt{3}\sin\theta)T = 0,$$

with $T = 150/4.9$, we find that $\sin\theta \approx -0.0212$; therefore, $\theta \approx -0.0212$ rad $\approx -1.21°$. In other words, the projectile must be fired at a horizontal angle of $1.21°$ to the *south* of east to correct for the northerly crosswind (Figure 12.94b). The landing location of the projectile is $x(T) \approx 7952$ m and $y(T) = 0$.

Related Exercises 33–40 ◀

SECTION 12.7 EXERCISES

Review Questions

1. Given the position function $\mathbf{r}$ of a moving object, explain how to find the velocity, speed, and acceleration of the object.
2. What is the relationship between the position and velocity vectors for motion on a circle?
3. State Newton's Second Law of Motion in vector form.
4. Write Newton's Second Law of Motion for three-dimensional motion with only the gravitational force (acting in the z-direction).
5. Given the acceleration of an object and its initial velocity, how do you find the velocity of the object for $t \geq 0$?
6. Given the velocity of an object and its initial position, how do you find the position of the object for $t \geq 0$?

Basic Skills

7–14. Velocity and acceleration from position *Consider the following position functions.*

a. Find the velocity and speed of the object.
b. Find the acceleration of the object.

7. $\mathbf{r}(t) = \langle 2 + 2t, 1 - 4t \rangle$, for $t \geq 0$
8. $\mathbf{r}(t) = \langle 1 - t^2, 3 + 2t^3 \rangle$, for $t \geq 0$
9. $\mathbf{r}(t) = \langle 8\sin t, 8\cos t \rangle$, for $0 \leq t \leq 2\pi$
10. $\mathbf{r}(t) = \langle 3\cos t, 4\sin t \rangle$, for $0 \leq t \leq 2\pi$
11. $\mathbf{r}(t) = \langle 3 + t, 2 - 4t, 1 + 6t \rangle$, for $t \geq 0$
12. $\mathbf{r}(t) = \langle 3\sin t, 5\cos t, 4\sin t \rangle$, for $0 \leq t \leq 2\pi$

13. $\mathbf{r}(t) = \langle 1, t^2, e^{-t} \rangle$, for $t \geq 0$

14. $\mathbf{r}(t) = \langle 13 \cos 2t, 12 \sin 2t, 5 \sin 2t \rangle$, for $0 \leq t \leq \pi$

T **15–18. Comparing trajectories** *Consider the following position functions* **r** *and* **R** *for two objects.*

a. Find the interval $[c, d]$ *over which the* **R** *trajectory is the same as the* **r** *trajectory over* $[a, b]$.
b. Find the velocity for both objects.
c. Graph the speed of the two objects over the intervals $[a, b]$ *and* $[c, d]$, *respectively.*

15. $\mathbf{r}(t) = \langle \cos t, 4 \sin t \rangle$, $[a, b] = [0, 2\pi]$,
$\mathbf{R}(t) = \langle \cos 3t, 4 \sin 3t \rangle$ on $[c, d]$

16. $\mathbf{r}(t) = \langle 2 - e^t, 4 - e^{-t} \rangle$, $[a, b] = [0, \ln 10]$,
$\mathbf{R}(t) = \langle 2 - t, 4 - 1/t \rangle$ on $[c, d]$

17. $\mathbf{r}(t) = \langle 4 + t^2, 3 - 2t^4, 1 + 3t^6 \rangle$, $[a, b] = [0, 6]$,
$\mathbf{R}(t) = \langle 4 + \ln t, 3 - 2 \ln^2 t, 1 + 3 \ln^3 t \rangle$ on $[c, d]$. For graphing, let $c = 1$ and $d = 20$.

18. $\mathbf{r}(t) = \langle 2 \cos 2t, \sqrt{2} \sin 2t, \sqrt{2} \sin 2t \rangle$, $[a, b] = [0, \pi]$,
$\mathbf{R}(t) = \langle 2 \cos 4t, \sqrt{2} \sin 4t, \sqrt{2} \sin 4t \rangle$ on $[c, d]$.

19–24. Trajectories on circles and spheres *Determine whether the following trajectories lie on a circle in* $\mathbf{R}^2$ *or a sphere in* $\mathbf{R}^3$ *centered at the origin. If so, find the radius of the circle or sphere and show that the position vector and the velocity vector are everywhere orthogonal.*

19. $\mathbf{r}(t) = \langle 8 \cos 2t, 8 \sin 2t \rangle$, for $0 \leq t \leq \pi$

20. $\mathbf{r}(t) = \langle 4 \sin t, 2 \cos t \rangle$, for $0 \leq t \leq 2\pi$

21. $\mathbf{r}(t) = \langle \sin t + \sqrt{3} \cos t, \sqrt{3} \sin t - \cos t \rangle$, for $0 \leq t \leq 2\pi$

22. $\mathbf{r}(t) = \langle 3 \sin t, 5 \cos t, 4 \sin t \rangle$, for $0 \leq t \leq 2\pi$

23. $\mathbf{r}(t) = \langle \sin t, \cos t, \cos t \rangle$, for $0 \leq t \leq 2\pi$

24. $\mathbf{r}(t) = \langle \sqrt{3} \cos t + \sqrt{2} \sin t, -\sqrt{3} \cos t + \sqrt{2} \sin t, \sqrt{2} \sin t \rangle$, for $0 \leq t \leq 2\pi$

25–28. Solving equations of motion *Given an acceleration vector, initial velocity* $\langle u_0, v_0 \rangle$, *and initial position* $\langle x_0, y_0 \rangle$, *find the velocity and position vectors for* $t \geq 0$.

25. $\mathbf{a}(t) = \langle 0, 10 \rangle, \langle u_0, v_0 \rangle = \langle 0, 5 \rangle, \langle x_0, y_0 \rangle = \langle 1, -1 \rangle$

26. $\mathbf{a}(t) = \langle 1, t \rangle, \langle u_0, v_0 \rangle = \langle 2, -1 \rangle, \langle x_0, y_0 \rangle = \langle 0, 8 \rangle$

27. $\mathbf{a}(t) = \langle \cos t, 2 \sin t \rangle, \langle u_0, v_0 \rangle = \langle 0, 1 \rangle, \langle x_0, y_0 \rangle = \langle 1, 0 \rangle$

28. $\mathbf{a}(t) = \langle e^{-t}, 1 \rangle, \langle u_0, v_0 \rangle = \langle 1, 0 \rangle, \langle x_0, y_0 \rangle = \langle 0, 0 \rangle$

T **29–32. Two-dimensional motion** *Consider the motion of the following objects. Assume the x-axis is horizontal, the positive y-axis is vertical (opposite g), the ground is horizontal, and only the gravitational force acts on the object.*

a. Find the velocity and position vectors for $t \geq 0$.
b. Graph the trajectory.
c. Determine the time of flight and range of the object.
d. Determine the maximum height of the object.

29. A soccer ball is kicked from the point $\langle x_0, y_0 \rangle = \langle 0, 0 \rangle$ with an initial velocity of $\langle u_0, v_0 \rangle = \langle 30, 6 \rangle$ m/s.

30. A golf ball is hit from the point $\langle x_0, y_0 \rangle = \langle 0, 0 \rangle$ at an angle of 30° with an initial speed of 150 ft/s.

31. A projectile is launched from a platform 20 ft above the ground at an angle of 60° with a speed of 250 ft/s. Assume the origin is at the base of the platform.

32. A rock is thrown from the edge of a vertical cliff 40 m above the ground at an angle of 45° with a speed of $10\sqrt{2}$ m/s. Assume the origin is at the foot of the cliff.

33–36. Solving equations of motion *Given an acceleration vector, initial velocity* $\langle u_0, v_0, w_0 \rangle$, *and initial position* $\langle x_0, y_0, z_0 \rangle$, *find the velocity and position vectors for* $t \geq 0$.

33. $\mathbf{a}(t) = \langle 0, 0, 10 \rangle, \langle u_0, v_0, w_0 \rangle = \langle 1, 5, 0 \rangle, \langle x_0, y_0, z_0 \rangle = \langle 0, 5, 0 \rangle$

34. $\mathbf{a}(t) = \langle 1, t, 4t \rangle, \langle u_0, v_0, w_0 \rangle = \langle 20, 0, 0 \rangle, \langle x_0, y_0, z_0 \rangle = \langle 0, 0, 0 \rangle$

35. $\mathbf{a}(t) = \langle \sin t, \cos t, 1 \rangle, \langle u_0, v_0, w_0 \rangle = \langle 0, 2, 0 \rangle,$
$\langle x_0, y_0, z_0 \rangle = \langle 0, 0, 0 \rangle$

36. $\mathbf{a}(t) = \langle t, e^{-t}, 1 \rangle, \langle u_0, v_0, w_0 \rangle = \langle 0, 0, 1 \rangle, \langle x_0, y_0, z_0 \rangle = \langle 4, 0, 0 \rangle$

T **37–40. Three-dimensional motion** *Consider the motion of the following objects. Assume the x-axis points east, the y-axis points north, the positive z-axis is vertical (opposite g), the ground is horizontal, and only the gravitational force acts on the object unless otherwise stated.*

a. Find the velocity and position vectors for $t \geq 0$.
b. Make a sketch of the trajectory.
c. Determine the time of flight and range of the object.
d. Determine the maximum height of the object.

37. A bullet is fired from a rifle 1 m above the ground in a northeast direction. The initial velocity of the bullet is $\langle 200, 200, 0 \rangle$ m/s.

38. A golf ball is hit east down a fairway with an initial velocity of $\langle 50, 0, 30 \rangle$ m/s. A crosswind blowing to the south produces an acceleration of the ball of -0.8 m/s^2.

39. A small rocket is fired from a launch pad 10 m above the ground with an initial velocity of $\langle 300, 400, 500 \rangle$ m/s. A crosswind blowing to the north produces an acceleration of the rocket of 2.5 m/s^2.

40. A soccer ball is kicked from the point $\langle 0, 0, 0 \rangle$ with an initial velocity of $\langle 0, 80, 80 \rangle$ ft/s. The spin on the ball produces an acceleration of $\langle 1.2, 0, 0 \rangle \text{ ft/s}^2$.

Further Explorations

41. Explain why or why not Determine whether the following statements are true and give an explanation or counterexample.

a. If the speed of an object is constant, then its velocity components are constant.
b. The functions $\mathbf{r}(t) = \langle \cos t, \sin t \rangle$ and $\mathbf{R}(t) = \langle \sin t^2, \cos t^2 \rangle$ generate the same set of points for $t \geq 0$.
c. It is not possible for a velocity vector to have a constant direction but a variable magnitude for all $t \geq 0$.
d. If the acceleration of an object is zero for all $t \geq 0$ ($\mathbf{a}(t) = \mathbf{0}$), then the velocity of the object is constant.
e. If you double the initial speed of a projectile, its range also doubles (assume no forces other than gravity act on the projectile).

f. If you double the initial speed of a projectile, its time of flight also doubles (assume no forces other than gravity).
g. A trajectory with $\mathbf{v}(t) = \mathbf{a}(t) \neq \mathbf{0}$ for all t is possible.

42–45. Trajectory properties *Find the time of flight, range, and maximum height of the following two-dimensional trajectories, assuming no forces other than gravity. In each case the initial position is $\langle 0, 0 \rangle$ and the initial velocity is $\mathbf{v}_0 = \langle u_0, v_0 \rangle$.*

42. $\langle u_0, v_0 \rangle = \langle 10, 20 \rangle$ ft/s

43. Initial speed $|\mathbf{v}_0| = 150$ m/s, launch angle $\alpha = 30°$

44. $\langle u_0, v_0 \rangle = \langle 40, 80 \rangle$ m/s

45. Initial speed $|\mathbf{v}_0| = 400$ ft/s, launch angle $\alpha = 60°$

46. Motion on the moon The acceleration due to gravity on the moon is approximately $g/6$ (one-sixth its value on Earth). Compare the time of flight, range, and maximum height of a projectile on the moon with the corresponding values on Earth.

47. Firing angles A projectile is fired over horizontal ground from the origin with an initial speed of 60 m/s. What firing angles will produce a range of 300 m?

T **48. Firing strategies** Suppose you wish to fire a projectile over horizontal ground from the origin and attain a range of 1000 m.

a. Make a graph of the initial speed required for all firing angles $0 < \alpha < \pi/2$.
b. What firing angle requires the least initial speed?
c. What firing angle requires the least flight time?

49. Nonuniform straight-line motion Consider the motion of an object given by the position function

$$\mathbf{r}(t) = f(t)\langle a, b, c \rangle + \langle x_0, y_0, z_0 \rangle, \quad \text{for } t \geq 0,$$

where a, b, c, x_0, y_0, and z_0 are constants and f is a differentiable scalar function for $t \geq 0$.

a. Explain why this function describes motion along a line.
b. Find the velocity function. In general, is the velocity constant in magnitude or direction along the path?

50. A race Two people travel from $P(4, 0)$ to $Q(-4, 0)$ along the paths given by

$$\mathbf{r}(t) = \langle 4\cos(\pi t/8), 4\sin(\pi t/8) \rangle \quad \text{and}$$
$$\mathbf{R}(t) = \langle 4 - t, (4 - t)^2 - 16 \rangle.$$

a. Graph both paths between P and Q.
b. Graph the speeds of both people between P and Q.
c. Who arrives at Q first?

51. Circular motion Consider an object moving along the circular trajectory $\mathbf{r}(t) = \langle A\cos\omega t, A\sin\omega t \rangle$, where A and ω are constants.

a. Over what time interval $[0, T]$ does the object traverse the circle once?
b. Find the velocity and speed of the object. Is the velocity constant in either direction or magnitude? Is the speed constant?
c. Find the acceleration of the object.
d. How are the position and velocity related? How are the position and acceleration related?
e. Sketch the position, velocity, and acceleration vectors at four different points on the trajectory with $A = \omega = 1$.

52. A linear trajectory An object moves along a straight line from the point $P(1, 2, 4)$ to the point $Q(-6, 8, 10)$.

a. Find a position function $\mathbf{r}$ that describes the motion if it occurs with a constant speed over the time interval $[0, 5]$.
b. Find a position function $\mathbf{r}$ that describes the motion if it occurs with speed e^t.

53. A circular trajectory An object moves clockwise around a circle centered at the origin with radius 5 m beginning at the point (0, 5).

a. Find a position function $\mathbf{r}$ that describes the motion if the object moves with a constant speed, completing 1 lap every 12 s.
b. Find a position function $\mathbf{r}$ that describes the motion if it occurs with speed e^{-t}.

54. A helical trajectory An object moves on the helix $\langle \cos t, \sin t, t \rangle$, for $t \geq 0$.

a. Find a position function $\mathbf{r}$ that describes the motion if it occurs with a constant speed of 10.
b. Find a position function $\mathbf{r}$ that describes the motion if it occurs with speed t.

T **55. Speed on an ellipse** An object moves along an ellipse given by the function $\mathbf{r}(t) = \langle a\cos t, b\sin t \rangle$, for $0 \leq t \leq 2\pi$, where $a > 0$ and $b > 0$.

a. Find the velocity and speed of the object in terms of a and b, for $0 \leq t \leq 2\pi$.
b. With $a = 1$ and $b = 6$, graph the speed function for $0 \leq t \leq 2\pi$. Mark the points on the trajectory at which the speed is a minimum and a maximum.
c. Is it true that the object speeds up along the flattest (straightest) parts of the trajectory and slows down where the curves are sharpest?
d. For general a and b, find the ratio of the maximum speed to the minimum speed on the ellipse (in terms of a and b).

T **56. Travel on a cycloid** Consider an object moving on the cycloid $\mathbf{r}(t) = \langle t - \sin t, 1 - \cos t \rangle$, for $0 \leq t \leq 4\pi$.

a. Graph the trajectory.
b. Find the velocity and speed of the object. At what point(s) on the trajectory does the object move fastest? Slowest?
c. Find the acceleration of the object and show that $|\mathbf{a}(t)|$ is constant.
d. Explain why the trajectory has a cusp at $t = 2\pi$.

57. Analyzing a trajectory Consider the trajectory given by the position function

$$\mathbf{r}(t) = \langle 50e^{-t}\cos t, 50e^{-t}\sin t, 5(1 - e^{-t}) \rangle, \quad \text{for } t \geq 0.$$

a. Find the initial point ($t = 0$) and the "terminal" point $\left(\lim_{t\to\infty} \mathbf{r}(t)\right)$ of the trajectory.
b. At what point on the trajectory is the speed the greatest?
c. Graph the trajectory.

Applications

58. Golf shot A golfer stands 390 ft (130 yd) horizontally from the hole and 40 ft below the hole (see figure). Assuming the ball is hit with an initial speed of 150 ft/s, at what angle should it be hit to land in the hole? Assume the path of the ball lies in a plane.

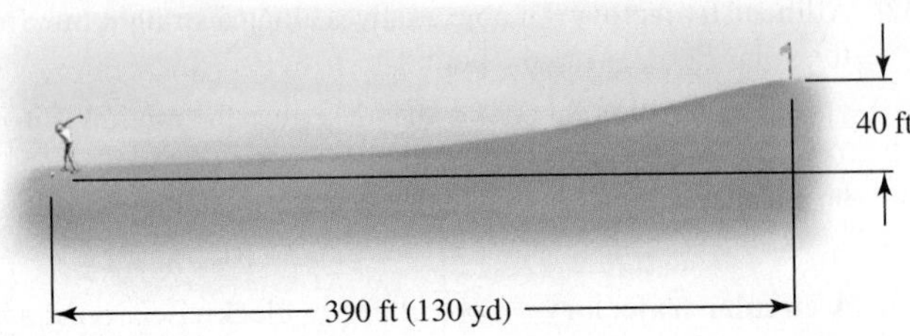

59. Another golf shot A golfer stands 420 ft (140 yd) horizontally from the hole and 50 ft above the hole (see figure). Assuming the ball is hit with an initial speed of 120 ft/s, at what angle should it be hit to land in the hole? Assume the path of the ball lies in a plane.

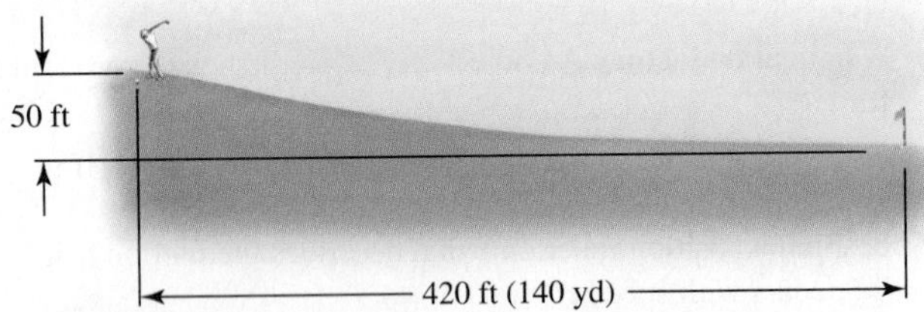

60. Ski jump The lip of a ski jump is 8 m above the outrun that is sloped at an angle of 30° to the horizontal (see figure).

a. If the initial velocity of a ski jumper at the lip of the jump is $\langle 40, 0\rangle$ m/s, how far down the outrun does he land? Assume only gravity affects the motion.

b. Assume that air resistance produces a constant horizontal acceleration of 0.15 m/s^2 opposing the motion. How far down the outrun does the ski jumper land?

c. Suppose that the takeoff ramp is tilted upward at an angle of $\theta°$, so that the skier's initial velocity is $40\langle \cos\theta, \sin\theta\rangle$ m/s. What value of θ maximizes the length of the jump? Express your answer in degrees and neglect air resistance.

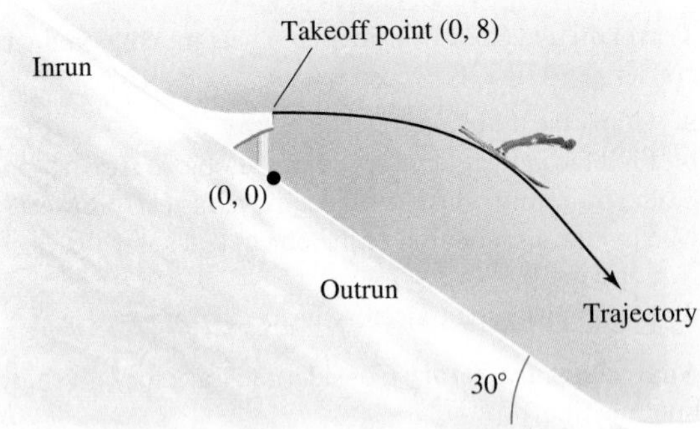

61. Designing a baseball pitch A baseball leaves the hand of a pitcher 6 vertical feet above home plate and 60 ft from home plate. Assume the coordinate axes are oriented as shown in the figure.

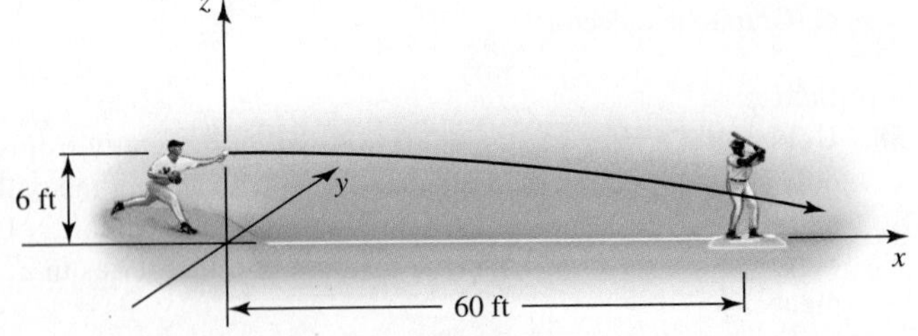

a. In the absence of all forces except gravity, assume that a pitch is thrown with an initial velocity of $\langle 130, 0, -3\rangle$ ft/s (about 90 mi/hr). How far above the ground is the ball when it crosses home plate and how long does it take for the pitch to arrive?

b. What vertical velocity component should the pitcher use so that the pitch crosses home plate exactly 3 ft above the ground?

c. A simple model to describe the curve of a baseball assumes that the spin of the ball produces a constant sideways acceleration (in the y-direction) of $c\text{ ft/s}^2$. Assume a pitcher throws a curve ball with $c = 8\text{ ft/s}^2$ (one fourth the acceleration of gravity). How far does the ball move in the y-direction by the time it reaches home plate, assuming an initial velocity of $\langle 130, 0, -3\rangle$ ft/s?

d. In part (c), does the ball curve more in the first half of its trip to the plate or in the second half? How does this fact affect the batter?

e. Suppose the pitcher releases the ball from an initial position of $\langle 0, -3, 6\rangle$ with initial velocity $\langle 130, 0, -3\rangle$. What value of the spin parameter c is needed to put the ball over home plate passing through the point $\langle 60, 0, 3\rangle$?

62. Trajectory with a sloped landing Assume an object is launched from the origin with an initial speed $|\mathbf{v}_0|$ at an angle α to the horizontal, where $0 < \alpha < \frac{\pi}{2}$.

a. Find the time of flight, range, and maximum height (relative to launch point) of the trajectory if the ground slopes *downward* at a constant angle of θ from the launch site where $0 < \theta < \frac{\pi}{2}$.

b. Find the time of flight, range, and maximum height of the trajectory if the ground slopes *upward* at a constant angle of θ from the launch site.

63. Time of flight, range, height Derive the formulas for time of flight, range, and maximum height in the case that an object is launched from the initial position $\langle 0, y_0\rangle$ with initial velocity $|\mathbf{v}_0|\langle \cos\alpha, \sin\alpha\rangle$.

Additional Exercises

64. Parabolic trajectories Show that the two-dimensional trajectory

$$x(t) = u_0 t + x_0 \quad\text{and}\quad y(t) = -\frac{gt^2}{2} + v_0 t + y_0, \text{ for } 0 \le t \le T$$

of an object moving in a gravitational field is a segment of a parabola for some value of $T > 0$. Find T such that $y(T) = 0$.

65. Tilted ellipse Consider the curve $\mathbf{r}(t) = \langle \cos t, \sin t, c\sin t\rangle$, for $0 \le t \le 2\pi$, where c is a real number. It can be shown that the curve lies in a plane. Prove that the curve is an ellipse in that plane.

66. Equal area property Consider the ellipse $\mathbf{r}(t) = \langle a\cos t, b\sin t\rangle$, for $0 \le t \le 2\pi$, where a and b are real numbers. Let θ be the angle between the position vector and the x-axis.

a. Show that $\tan\theta = (b/a)\tan t$.

b. Find $\theta'(t)$.

c. Recall that the area bounded by the polar curve $r = f(\theta)$ on the interval $[0, \theta]$ is $A(\theta) = \frac{1}{2}\int_0^\theta (f(u))^2\,du$. Letting $f(\theta(t)) = |\mathbf{r}(\theta(t))|$, show that $A'(t) = \frac{1}{2}ab$.

d. Conclude that as an object moves around the ellipse, it sweeps out equal areas in equal times.

67. Another property of constant $|\mathbf{r}|$ motion Suppose an object moves on the surface of a sphere with $|\mathbf{r}(t)|$ constant for all t. Show that $\mathbf{r}(t)$ and $\mathbf{a}(t) = \mathbf{r}''(t)$ satisfy $\mathbf{r}(t) \cdot \mathbf{a}(t) = -|\mathbf{v}(t)|^2$.

68. Conditions for a circular/elliptical trajectory in the plane An object moves along a path given by

$$\mathbf{r}(t) = \langle a \cos t + b \sin t, c \cos t + d \sin t \rangle, \quad \text{for } 0 \leq t \leq 2\pi.$$

a. What conditions on a, b, c and d guarantee that the path is a circle?

b. What conditions on a, b, c, and d guarantee that the path is an ellipse?

69. Conditions for a circular/elliptical trajectory in space An object moves along a path given by

$$\mathbf{r}(t) = \langle a \cos t + b \sin t, c \cos t + d \sin t, e \cos t + f \sin t \rangle,$$
for $0 \leq t \leq 2\pi$.

a. What conditions on a, b, c, d, e, and f guarantee that the path is a circle (in a plane)?

b. What conditions on a, b, c, d, e, and f guarantee that the path is an ellipse (in a plane)?

QUICK CHECK ANSWERS

1. $\mathbf{v}(t) = \langle 1, 2t, 3t^2 \rangle$, $\mathbf{a}(t) = \langle 0, 2, 6t \rangle$

2. $|\mathbf{r}'(t)| = \sqrt{1 + 4t^2 + 9t^4/16}$

$|\mathbf{R}'(t)| = \sqrt{4t^2 + 16t^6 + 9t^{10}/4}$

3. $\mathbf{r} \cdot \mathbf{v} = \langle 3 \cos t, 5 \sin t, 4 \cos t \rangle \cdot \langle -3 \sin t, 5 \cos t, -4 \sin t \rangle = 0$

4. $x(t) = 100t$, $y(t) = -16t^2 + 60t + 2$

5. $\sin [2(\pi/2 - \alpha)] = \sin (\pi - 2\alpha) = \sin 2\alpha$

12.8 Length of Curves

With the methods of Section 12.7, it is possible to model the trajectory of an object moving in three-dimensional space. Although we can predict the position of the object at all times, we still don't have the tools needed to answer a simple question: How far does the object travel along its flight path over a given interval of time? In this section we answer this question of *arc length*.

Arc Length

➤ Arc length for curves of the form $y = f(x)$ was discussed in Section 6.5. You should look for the parallels between that discussion and the one in this section.

Suppose that a parameterized curve C is given by the vector-valued function $\mathbf{r}(t) = \langle f(t), g(t), h(t) \rangle$, for $a \leq t \leq b$, where f', g', and h' are continuous on $[a, b]$. We first show how to find the length of the two-dimensional curve, $\mathbf{r}(t) = \langle f(t), g(t) \rangle$, for $a \leq t \leq b$. The modification for three-dimensional curves then follows.

To find the length of the curve between $(f(a), g(a))$ and $(f(b), g(b))$, we first subdivide the interval $[a, b]$ into n subintervals using the grid points

$$a = t_0 < t_1 < t_2 < \cdots < t_n = b.$$

We connect the corresponding points on the curve,

$$(f(t_0), g(t_0)), \ldots, (f(t_k), g(t_k)), \ldots, (f(t_n), g(t_n)),$$

by line segments (Figure 12.95a).

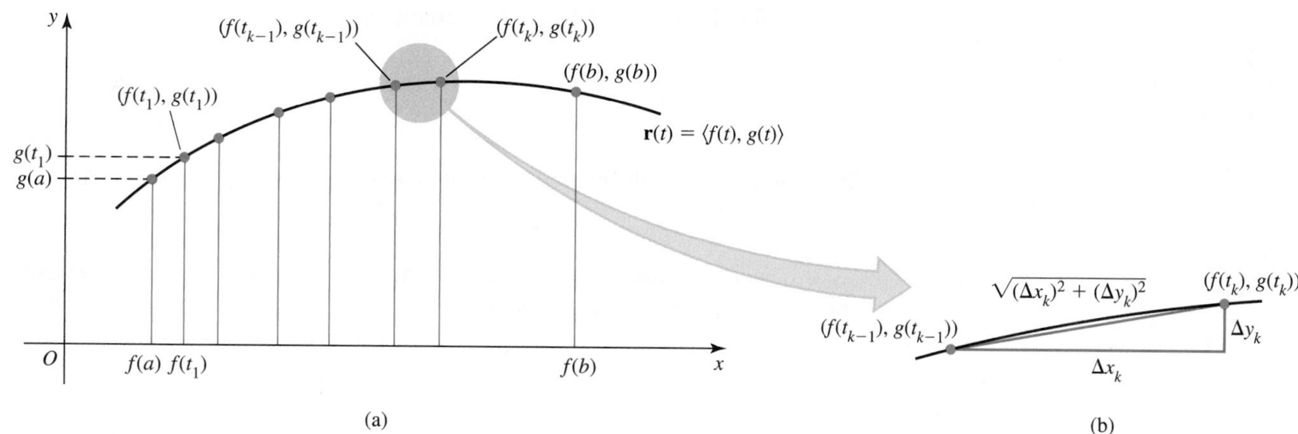

FIGURE 12.95

The kth line segment is the hypotenuse of a right triangle, for which we define

$$\Delta x_k = f(t_k) - f(t_{k-1}) \quad \text{and} \quad \Delta y_k = g(t_k) - g(t_{k-1}),$$

for $k = 1, 2, \ldots, n$ (Figure 12.95b). Therefore, the length of the kth line segment is

$$\sqrt{(\Delta x_k)^2 + (\Delta y_k)^2}.$$

The length of the entire curve L is approximated by the sum of the lengths of the line segments:

$$L \approx \sum_{k=1}^{n} \sqrt{(\Delta x_k)^2 + (\Delta y_k)^2} \qquad (1)$$

The goal is to express this sum as a Riemann sum.

The change in $x = f(t)$ over the kth subinterval is $\Delta x_k = f(t_k) - f(t_{k-1})$. By the Mean Value Theorem, there is a point $\bar{t}_k$ in (t_{k-1}, t_k) such that

$$\frac{\overbrace{f(t_k) - f(t_{k-1})}^{\Delta x_k}}{\underbrace{t_k - t_{k-1}}_{\Delta t_k}} = f'(\bar{t}_k).$$

So, the change in x as t changes by $\Delta t_k = t_k - t_{k-1}$ is

$$\Delta x_k = f(t_k) - f(t_{k-1}) = f'(\bar{t}_k)\Delta t_k.$$

Similarly, the change in y over the kth subinterval is

$$\Delta y_k = g(t_k) - g(t_{k-1}) = g'(\hat{t}_k)\Delta t_k,$$

where $\hat{t}_k$ is also a point in (t_{k-1}, t_k). We now substitute these expressions for Δx_k and Δy_k into equation (1):

$$\begin{aligned} L &\approx \sum_{k=1}^{n} \sqrt{(\Delta x_k)^2 + (\Delta y_k)^2} \\ &= \sum_{k=1}^{n} \sqrt{(f'(\bar{t}_k)\Delta t_k)^2 + (g'(\hat{t}_k)\Delta t_k)^2} && \text{Substitute for } \Delta x_k \text{ and } \Delta y_k. \\ &= \sum_{k=1}^{n} \sqrt{f'(\bar{t}_k)^2 + g'(\hat{t}_k)^2}\,\Delta t_k && \text{Factor } \Delta t_k \text{ out of square root.} \end{aligned}$$

The intermediate points $\bar{t}_k$ and $\hat{t}_k$ both approach t_k as n increases and as Δt_k approaches zero. Therefore, given the conditions on f' and g', the limit of this sum as $n \to \infty$ and $\Delta t_k \to 0$ for all k exists and equals a definite integral:

$$L = \lim_{n \to \infty} \sum_{k=1}^{n} \sqrt{f'(\bar{t}_k)^2 + g'(\hat{t}_k)^2}\,\Delta t_k = \int_a^b \sqrt{f'(t)^2 + g'(t)^2}\,dt$$

QUICK CHECK 1 Use the arc length formula to find the length of the line $\mathbf{r}(t) = \langle t, t \rangle$, for $0 \le t \le 1$.◄

An analogous arc length formula for three-dimensional curves follows using a similar argument. The length of the curve $\mathbf{r}(t) = \langle f(t), g(t), h(t) \rangle$ on the interval $[a, b]$ is

$$L = \int_a^b \sqrt{f'(t)^2 + g'(t)^2 + h'(t)^2}\,dt.$$

Noting that $\mathbf{r}'(t) = \langle f'(t), g'(t), h'(t) \rangle$, we state the following definition.

> Arc length integrals are usually difficult to evaluate exactly. The few easily evaluated integrals appear in the examples and exercises. Often numerical methods must be used to approximate the more challenging integrals (see Example 4).

DEFINITION Arc Length for Vector Functions

Consider the parameterized curve $\mathbf{r}(t) = \langle f(t), g(t), h(t) \rangle$, where f', g', and h' are continuous, and the curve is traversed once for $a \le t \le b$. The **arc length** of the curve between $(f(a), g(a), h(a))$ and $(f(b), g(b), h(b))$ is

$$L = \int_a^b \sqrt{f'(t)^2 + g'(t)^2 + h'(t)^2}\, dt = \int_a^b |\mathbf{r}'(t)|\, dt.$$

QUICK CHECK 2 What does the arc length formula give for the length of the line $\mathbf{r}(t) = \langle t, t, t \rangle$, for $0 \le t \le 1$?

EXAMPLE 1 Circumference of a circle Prove that the circumference of a circle of radius a is $2\pi a$.

SOLUTION A circle of radius a is described by

$$\mathbf{r}(t) = \langle f(t), g(t) \rangle = \langle a \cos t, a \sin t \rangle,$$

for $0 \le t \le 2\pi$. For curves in the xy-plane we set $h(t) = 0$ in the definition of arc length. Note that $f'(t) = -a \sin t$ and $g'(t) = a \cos t$. The circumference is

> An important fact is that the arc length of a smooth parameterized curve is independent of the choice of parameter (Exercise 52).

$$\begin{aligned} L &= \int_0^{2\pi} \sqrt{f'(t)^2 + g'(t)^2}\, dt && \text{Arc length formula} \\ &= \int_0^{2\pi} \sqrt{(-a \sin t)^2 + (a \cos t)^2}\, dt && \text{Substitute for } f' \text{ and } g'. \\ &= a \int_0^{2\pi} \sqrt{\sin^2 t + \cos^2 t}\, dt && \text{Factor } a > 0 \text{ out of square root.} \\ &= a \int_0^{2\pi} 1\, dt && \sin^2 t + \cos^2 t = 1 \\ &= 2\pi a. && \text{Integrate a constant.} \end{aligned}$$

Related Exercises 7–18

EXAMPLE 2 Length of a hypocycloid (or astroid) Find the length of the complete hypocycloid given by $\mathbf{r}(t) = \langle \cos^3 t, \sin^3 t \rangle$, where $0 \le t \le 2\pi$ (Figure 12.96).

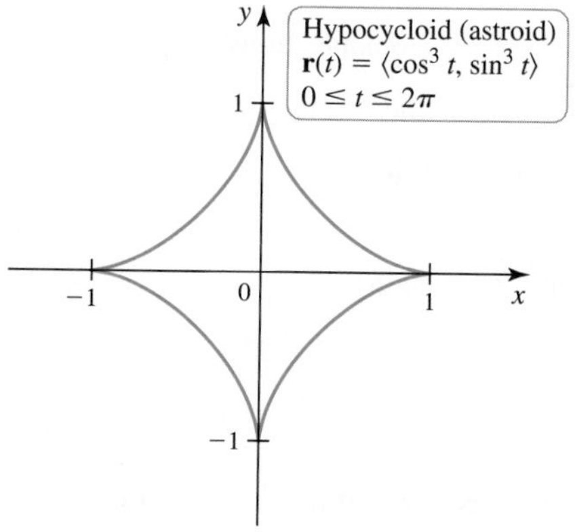

SOLUTION The length of the entire curve is four times the length of the curve in the first quadrant. You should verify that the curve in the first quadrant is generated as the parameter varies from $t = 0$ (corresponding to $(1, 0)$) to $t = \pi/2$ (corresponding to $(0, 1)$). Letting $f(t) = \cos^3 t$ and $g(t) = \sin^3 t$, we have

$$f'(t) = -3 \cos^2 t \sin t \quad \text{and} \quad g'(t) = 3 \sin^2 t \cos t.$$

Hypocycloid (astroid) $\mathbf{r}(t) = \langle \cos^3 t, \sin^3 t \rangle$, $0 \le t \le 2\pi$

FIGURE 12.96

The arc length of the full curve is

$$\begin{aligned} L &= 4 \int_0^{\pi/2} \sqrt{f'(t)^2 + g'(t)^2}\, dt && \text{Factor of 4 by symmetry} \\ &= 4 \int_0^{\pi/2} \sqrt{(-3 \cos^2 t \sin t)^2 + (3 \sin^2 t \cos t)^2}\, dt && \text{Substitute for } f' \text{ and } g'. \\ &= 4 \int_0^{\pi/2} \sqrt{9 \cos^4 t \sin^2 t + 9 \cos^2 t \sin^4 t}\, dt && \text{Simplify terms.} \end{aligned}$$

$$= 4\int_0^{\pi/2} 3\sqrt{\cos^2 t \sin^2 t \underbrace{(\cos^2 t + \sin^2 t)}_{1}}\, dt \quad \text{Factor.}$$

$$= 12\int_0^{\pi/2} \cos t \sin t \, dt. \qquad \cos t \sin t \geq 0 \text{ for } 0 \leq t \leq \frac{\pi}{2}$$

Letting $u = \sin t$ with $du = \cos t\, dt$, we have

$$L = 12\int_0^{\pi/2} \cos t \sin t\, dt = 12\int_0^1 u\, du = 6.$$

The length of the entire hypocycloid is 6 units. *Related Exercises 7–18*

➤ Recall from Chapter 6 that the distance traveled by an object in one dimension is $\int_a^b |v(t)|\, dt$. The arc length formula generalizes this formula to three dimensions.

Paths and Trajectories If the function $\mathbf{r}(t) = \langle x(t), y(t), z(t)\rangle$ is the position function for a moving object, then the arc length formula has a natural interpretation. Recall that $\mathbf{v}(t) = \mathbf{r}'(t)$ is the velocity of the object and $|\mathbf{v}(t)| = |\mathbf{r}'(t)|$ is the speed of the object. Therefore, the arc length formula becomes

$$L = \int_a^b |\mathbf{r}'(t)|\, dt = \int_a^b |\mathbf{v}(t)|\, dt.$$

This formula is the analog of the familiar *distance* = *speed* × *elapsed time* formula.

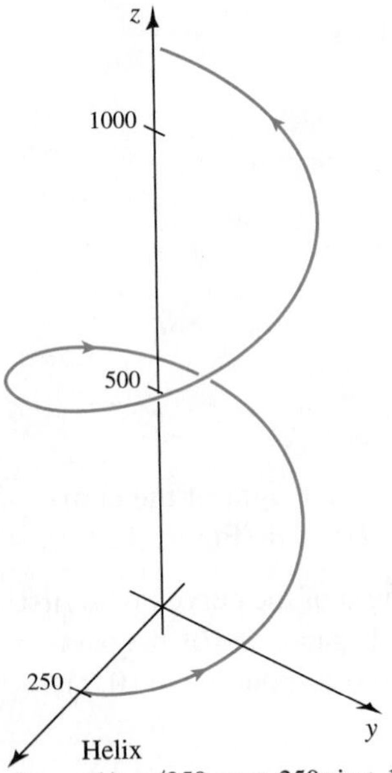

Helix $\mathbf{r}(t) = \langle 250 \cos t, 250 \sin t, 100t\rangle$

FIGURE 12.97

EXAMPLE 3 Flight of an eagle An eagle rises at a rate of 100 vertical ft/min on a helical path given by

$$\mathbf{r}(t) = \langle 250 \cos t, 250 \sin t, 100t\rangle$$

(Figure 12.97), where $\mathbf{r}$ is measured in feet and t is measured in minutes. How far does it travel in 10 min?

SOLUTION The speed of the eagle is

$$\begin{aligned} |\mathbf{v}(t)| &= \sqrt{x'(t)^2 + y'(t)^2 + z'(t)^2} \\ &= \sqrt{(-250 \sin t)^2 + (250 \cos t)^2 + 100^2} && \text{Substitute derivatives.} \\ &= \sqrt{250^2(\sin^2 t + \cos^2 t) + 100^2} && \text{Combine terms.} \\ &= \sqrt{250^2 + 100^2} \approx 269. && \sin^2 t + \cos^2 t = 1 \end{aligned}$$

The constant speed makes the arc length integral easy to evaluate:

$$L = \int_0^{10} |\mathbf{v}(t)|\, dt \approx \int_0^{10} 269\, dt = 2690.$$

The eagle travels approximately 2690 ft in 10 min. *Related Exercises 19–22*

QUICK CHECK 3 If the speed of an object is a constant S (as in Example 3), explain why the arc length on the interval $[a, b]$ is $S(b - a)$.

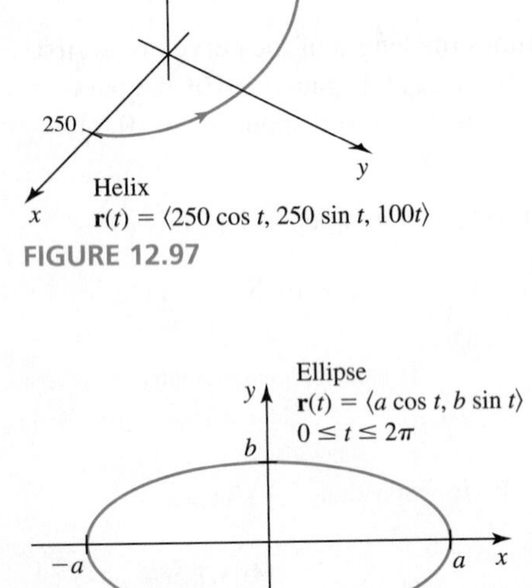

FIGURE 12.98

EXAMPLE 4 Lengths of planetary orbits According to Kepler's first law, the planets revolve about the sun in elliptical orbits. A vector function that describes an ellipse in the xy-plane is

$$\mathbf{r}(t) = \langle a \cos t, b \sin t\rangle, \qquad \text{where } 0 \leq t \leq 2\pi.$$

If $a > b$, then a is the length of the semimajor axis and b is the length of the semiminor axis (Figure 12.98). Verify the lengths of the planetary orbits given in Table 12.1. Distances are given in terms of the astronomical unit (AU), which is the length of the semimajor axis of Earth's orbit, or about 93 million miles.

➤ The German astronomer and mathematician Johannes Kepler (1571–1630) worked with the meticulously gathered data of Tycho Brahe to formulate three empirical laws obeyed by planets and comets orbiting the sun. The work of Kepler formed the foundation for Newton's laws of gravitation developed 50 years later.

➤ In September 2006, Pluto joined the ranks of Ceres, Haumea, Makemake, and Eris as one of five dwarf planets in our solar system.

Table 12.1

Planet	Semimajor axis, a (AU)	Semiminor axis, b (AU)	$\alpha = b/a$	Orbit length (AU)
Mercury	0.387	0.379	0.979	2.41
Venus	0.723	0.723	1.000	4.54
Earth	1.000	0.999	0.999	6.28
Mars	1.524	1.517	0.996	9.57
Jupiter	5.203	5.179	0.999	32.68
Saturn	9.539	9.524	0.998	59.91
Uranus	19.182	19.161	0.999	120.49
Neptune	30.058	30.057	1.000	189.56

SOLUTION Using the arc length formula, the length of a general elliptical orbit is

$$\begin{aligned} L &= \int_0^{2\pi} \sqrt{(x'(t))^2 + (y'(t))^2}\, dt \\ &= \int_0^{2\pi} \sqrt{(-a \sin t)^2 + (b \cos t)^2}\, dt && \text{Substitute for } x'(t) \text{ and } y'(t). \\ &= \int_0^{2\pi} \sqrt{a^2 \sin^2 t + b^2 \cos^2 t}\, dt. && \text{Simplify.} \end{aligned}$$

Factoring a^2 out of the square root and letting $\alpha = b/a$, we have

$$\begin{aligned} L &= \int_0^{2\pi} \sqrt{a^2 (\sin^2 t + (b/a)^2 \cos^2 t)}\, dt && \text{Factor out } a^2. \\ &= a \int_0^{2\pi} \sqrt{\sin^2 t + \alpha^2 \cos^2 t}\, dt && \text{Let } \alpha = b/a. \\ &= 4a \int_0^{\pi/2} \sqrt{\sin^2 t + \alpha^2 \cos^2 t}\, dt. && \text{Use symmetry.} \end{aligned}$$

➤ The integral that gives the length of the ellipse is a *complete elliptic integral of the second kind.* Many reference books and software packages provide approximate values of this integral.

In the last step we used the fact that the length of the full orbit is four times the length of a quarter of the orbit.

Unfortunately, an antiderivative for this integrand cannot be found in terms of elementary functions, so we have two options: This integral is well known and values have been tabulated for various values of α. Alternatively, we may use a calculator to approximate the integral numerically (see Section 8.6). Using numerical integration, the orbit lengths in Table 12.1 are obtained. For example, the length of Mercury's orbit with $a = 0.387$ and $\alpha = 0.979$ is

$$\begin{aligned} L &= 4a \int_0^{\pi/2} \sqrt{\sin^2 t + \alpha^2 \cos^2 t}\, dt \\ &= 1.548 \int_0^{\pi/2} \sqrt{\sin^2 t + 0.958 \cos^2 t}\, dt && \text{Simplify.} \\ &\approx 2.41. && \text{Approximate using calculator.} \end{aligned}$$

The fact that α is so close to 1 for all of the planets means that their orbits are very nearly circular. For this reason, the lengths of the orbits shown in the table are nearly equal to $2\pi a$, which is the length of a circular orbit with radius a. *Related Exercises 23–26* ◀

Arc Length of a Polar Curve

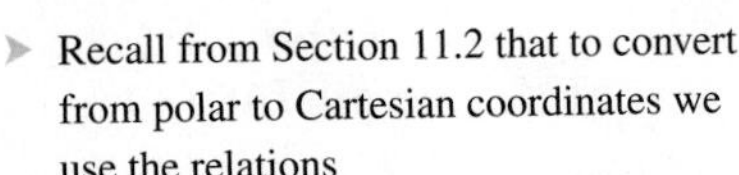

➤ Recall from Section 11.2 that to convert from polar to Cartesian coordinates we use the relations
$x = r\cos\theta$ and $y = r\sin\theta$.

We now return to polar coordinates and answer the arc length question for polar curves: Given the polar equation $r = f(\theta)$, what is the length of the corresponding curve for $\alpha \le \theta \le \beta$? The key idea is to express the polar equation as a set of parametric equations in Cartesian coordinates and then use the arc length formula derived above. Letting θ play the role of a parameter and using $r = f(\theta)$, the parametric equations for the polar curve are

$$x = r\cos\theta = f(\theta)\cos\theta \quad \text{and} \quad y = r\sin\theta = f(\theta)\sin\theta,$$

where $\alpha \le \theta \le \beta$. The arc length formula in terms of the parameter θ is

$$L = \int_\alpha^\beta \sqrt{\left(\frac{dx}{d\theta}\right)^2 + \left(\frac{dy}{d\theta}\right)^2}\, d\theta,$$

where

$$\frac{dx}{d\theta} = f'(\theta)\cos\theta - f(\theta)\sin\theta \quad \text{and} \quad \frac{dy}{d\theta} = f'(\theta)\sin\theta + f(\theta)\cos\theta.$$

When substituted into the arc length formula and simplified, the result is a new arc length integral (Exercise 50).

Arc Length of a Polar Curve

Let f have a continuous derivative on the interval $[\alpha, \beta]$. The **arc length** of the polar curve $r = f(\theta)$ on $[\alpha, \beta]$ is

$$L = \int_\alpha^\beta \sqrt{f(\theta)^2 + f'(\theta)^2}\, d\theta.$$

QUICK CHECK 4 Find the arc length of the circle $r = f(\theta) = 1$, for $0 \le \theta \le 2\pi$. ◀

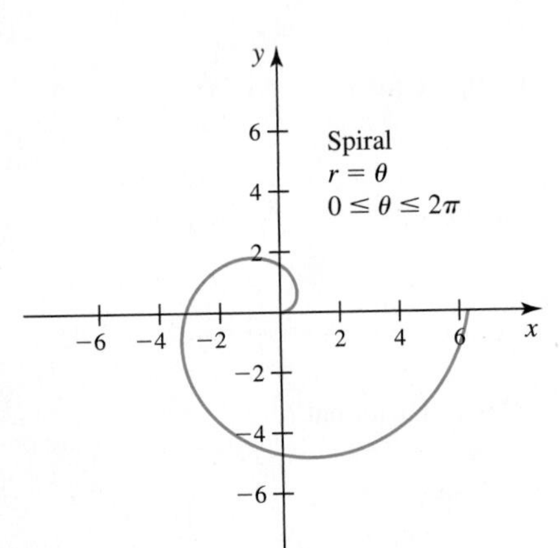

FIGURE 12.99

EXAMPLE 5 Arc length of polar curves

a. Find the arc length of the spiral $r = f(\theta) = \theta$, for $0 \le \theta \le 2\pi$ (Figure 12.99).

b. Find the arc length of the cardioid $r = 1 + \cos\theta$ (Figure 12.100).

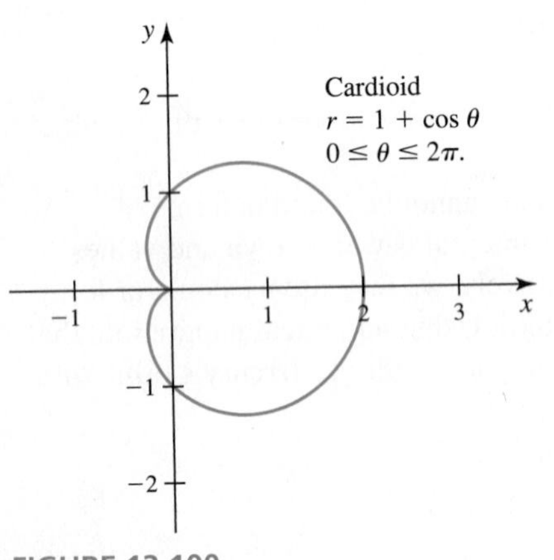

FIGURE 12.100

SOLUTION

a. $L = \int_0^{2\pi} \sqrt{\theta^2 + 1}\, d\theta$ $f(\theta) = \theta$ and $f'(\theta) = 1$

$= \left[\frac{\theta}{2}\sqrt{\theta^2 + 1} + \frac{1}{2}\ln\left(\theta + \sqrt{\theta^2 + 1}\right)\right]\Bigg|_0^{2\pi}$ Table of integrals or trigonometric substitution

$= \pi\sqrt{4\pi^2 + 1} + \frac{1}{2}\ln\left(2\pi + \sqrt{4\pi^2 + 1}\right)$ Substitute limits of integration.

≈ 21.26 Evaluate.

b. The cardioid is symmetric about the x-axis and its upper half is generated for $0 \le \theta \le \pi$. The length of the full curve is twice the length of its upper half:

$$L = 2\int_0^{\pi} \sqrt{(1 + \cos\theta)^2 + (-\sin\theta)^2}\, d\theta \qquad f(\theta) = 1 + \cos\theta;\ f'(\theta) = -\sin\theta$$

$$= 2\int_0^{\pi} \sqrt{2 + 2\cos\theta}\, d\theta \qquad \text{Simplify.}$$

$$= 2\int_0^{\pi} \sqrt{4\cos^2(\theta/2)}\, d\theta \qquad 1 + \cos\theta = 2\cos^2(\theta/2)$$

$$= 4\int_0^{\pi} \cos(\theta/2)\, d\theta \qquad \cos(\theta/2) \ge 0, \text{ for } 0 \le \theta \le \pi$$

$$= 8\sin(\theta/2)\Big|_0^{\pi} = 8 \qquad \text{Integrate and simplify.}$$

Related Exercises 27–34 ◀

SECTION 12.8 EXERCISES

Review Questions

1. Find the length of the line given by $\mathbf{r}(t) = \langle t, 2t\rangle$, for $a \le t \le b$.

2. Explain how to find the length of the curve $\mathbf{r}(t) = \langle f(t), g(t), h(t)\rangle$, for $a \le t \le b$.

3. Express the arc length of a curve in terms of the speed of an object moving along the curve.

4. Suppose an object moves in space with the position function $\mathbf{r}(t) = \langle x(t), y(t), z(t)\rangle$. Write the integral that gives the distance it travels between $t = a$ and $t = b$.

5. An object moves on a trajectory given by $\mathbf{r}(t) = \langle 10\cos 2t, 10\sin 2t\rangle$, for $0 \le t \le \pi$. How far does it travel?

6. How do you find the arc length of the polar curve $r = f(\theta)$, for $\alpha \le \theta \le \beta$?

Basic Skills

7–18. Arc length calculations *Find the length of the following two- and three-dimensional curves.*

7. $\mathbf{r}(t) = \langle 3\cos t, 3\sin t\rangle$, for $0 \le t \le \pi$

8. $\mathbf{r}(t) = \langle 4\cos 3t, 4\sin 3t\rangle$, for $0 \le t \le 2\pi/3$

9. $\mathbf{r}(t) = \langle \cos t + t\sin t, \sin t - t\cos t\rangle$, for $0 \le t \le \pi/2$

10. $\mathbf{r}(t) = \langle \cos t + \sin t, \cos t - \sin t\rangle$, for $0 \le t \le 2\pi$

11. $\mathbf{r}(t) = \langle 2 + 3t, 1 - 4t, -4 + 3t\rangle$, for $1 \le t \le 6$

12. $\mathbf{r}(t) = \langle 4\cos t, 4\sin t, 3t\rangle$, for $0 \le t \le 6\pi$

13. $\mathbf{r}(t) = \langle t, 8\sin t, 8\cos t\rangle$, for $0 \le t \le 4\pi$

14. $\mathbf{r}(t) = \langle t^2/2, (2t + 1)^{3/2}/3\rangle$, for $0 \le t \le 2$

15. $\mathbf{r}(t) = \langle t^2/2, 8(t + 1)^{3/2}/3\rangle$, for $0 \le t \le 2$

16. $\mathbf{r}(t) = \langle t^2, t^3\rangle$, for $0 \le t \le 4$

17. $\mathbf{r}(t) = \langle \cos^3 t, \sin^3 t\rangle$, for $0 \le t \le \pi/2$

18. $\mathbf{r}(t) = \langle 3\cos t, 4\cos t, 5\sin t\rangle$, for $0 \le t \le 2\pi$

19–22. Speed and arc length *For the following trajectories, find the speed associated with the trajectory and then find the length of the trajectory on the given interval.*

19. $\mathbf{r}(t) = \langle 2t^3, -t^3, 5t^3\rangle$, for $0 \le t \le 4$

20. $\mathbf{r}(t) = \langle t^2, 2t^2, t^3\rangle$, for $1 \le t \le 2$

21. $\mathbf{r}(t) = \langle 13\sin 2t, 12\cos 2t, 5\cos 2t\rangle$, for $0 \le t \le \pi$

22. $\mathbf{r}(t) = \langle e^t\sin t, e^t\cos t, e^t\rangle$, for $0 \le t \le \ln 2$

T **23–26. Arc length approximations** *Use a calculator to approximate the length of the following curves. In each case, simplify the arc length integral as much as possible before finding an approximation.*

23. $\mathbf{r}(t) = \langle 2\cos t, 4\sin t\rangle$, for $0 \le t \le 2\pi$

24. $\mathbf{r}(t) = \langle 2\cos t, 4\sin t, 6\cos t\rangle$, for $0 \le t \le 2\pi$

25. $\mathbf{r}(t) = \langle t, 4t^2, 10\rangle$, for $-2 \le t \le 2$

26. $\mathbf{r}(t) = \langle e^t, 2e^{-t}, t\rangle$, for $0 \le t \le \ln 3$

27–34. Arc length of polar curves *Find the length of the following polar curves.*

27. The complete circle $r = a\sin\theta$, where $a > 0$

28. The complete cardioid $r = 2 - 2\sin\theta$

29. The complete cardioid $r = 4 + 4\cos\theta$

30. The spiral $r = 4\theta^2$, for $0 \le \theta \le 6$

31. The spiral $r = 2e^{2\theta}$, for $0 \le \theta \le \ln 8$

32. The curve $r = \sin^2(\theta/2)$, for $0 \le \theta \le \pi$

33. The curve $r = \sin^3(\theta/3)$, for $0 \le \theta \le \pi/2$

34. The parabola $r = \sqrt{2}/(1 + \cos\theta)$, for $0 \le \theta \le \pi/2$

Further Explorations

35. **Explain why or why not** Determine whether the following statements are true and give an explanation or counterexample.
   a. If an object moves on a trajectory with constant speed S over a time interval $a \le t \le b$, then the length of the trajectory is $S(b - a)$.
   b. The curves defined by $\mathbf{r}(t) = \langle f(t), g(t) \rangle$ and $\mathbf{R}(t) = \langle g(t), f(t) \rangle$ have the same length over the interval $[a, b]$.
   c. The curve $\mathbf{r}(t) = \langle f(t), g(t) \rangle$, for $0 \le a \le t \le b$, and the curve $\mathbf{R}(t) = \langle f(t^2), g(t^2) \rangle$, for $\sqrt{a} \le t \le \sqrt{b}$, have the same length.

36. **Length of a line segment** Consider the line segment joining the points $P(x_0, y_0, z_0)$ and $Q(x_1, y_1, z_1)$.
   a. Find a parametric description of the line segment PQ.
   b. Use the arc length formula to find the length of PQ.
   c. Use geometry (distance formula) to verify the result of part (b).

37. **Tilted circles** Let the curve C be described by $\mathbf{r}(t) = \langle a \cos t, b \sin t, c \sin t \rangle$, where a, b, and c are real positive numbers.
   a. Assume that C lies in a plane and show that C is a circle centered at the origin provided $a^2 = b^2 + c^2$.
   b. Find the arc length of the circle.
   c. Assuming that the curve lies in a plane, find the conditions under which $\mathbf{r}(t) = \langle a \cos t + b \sin t, c \cos t + d \sin t, e \cos t + f \sin t \rangle$ describes a circle. Then find its arc length.

38. **A family of arc length integrals** Find the length of the curve $\mathbf{r}(t) = \langle t^m, t^m, t^{3m/2} \rangle$, for $0 \le a \le t \le b$, where m is a real number. Express the result in terms of m, a, and b.

39. **A special case** Suppose a curve is described by $\mathbf{r}(t) = \langle A\,h(t), B\,h(t) \rangle$, for $a \le t \le b$, where A and B are constants and h has a continuous derivative.
   a. Show that the length of the curve is
   $$\sqrt{A^2 + B^2} \int_a^b |h'(t)|\, dt.$$
   b. Use part (a) to find the length of the curve $x = 2t^3$, $y = 5t^3$, for $0 \le t \le 4$.
   c. Use part (a) to find the length of the curve $x = 4/t$, $y = 10/t$, for $1 \le t \le 8$.

40. **Spiral arc length** Consider the spiral $r = 4\theta$, for $\theta \ge 0$.
   a. Use a trigonometric substitution or a calculator to find the length of the spiral, for $0 \le \theta \le \sqrt{8}$.
   b. Find $L(\theta)$, the length of the spiral on the interval $[0, \theta]$, for any $\theta \ge 0$.
   c. Show that $L'(\theta) > 0$. Is $L''(\theta)$ positive or negative? Interpret your answers.

41. **Spiral arc length** Find the length of the entire spiral $r = e^{-a\theta}$, for $\theta \ge 0$ and $a > 0$.

T 42–45. **Arc length using technology** *Use a calculator to find the approximate length of the following curves.*

42. The three-leaf rose $r = 2 \cos 3\theta$

43. The lemniscate $r^2 = 6 \sin 2\theta$

44. The limaçon $r = 2 - 4 \sin \theta$

45. The limaçon $r = 4 - 2 \cos \theta$

Applications

46. **A cycloid** A cycloid is the path traced by a point on a rolling circle (think of a light on the rim of a moving bicycle wheel). The cycloid generated by a circle of radius a is given by the parametric equations
$$x = a(t - \sin t), \qquad y = a(1 - \cos t);$$
the parameter range $0 \le t \le 2\pi$ produces one arch of the cycloid (see figure). Show that the length of one arch of a cycloid is $8a$.

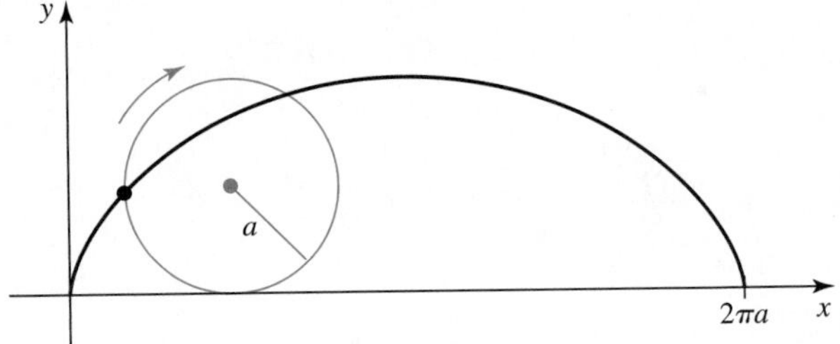

T 47. **Projectile trajectories** A projectile (such as a baseball or a cannonball) launched from the origin with an initial horizontal velocity u_0 and an initial vertical velocity v_0 moves in a parabolic trajectory given by
$$x = u_0 t, y = -\left(\frac{1}{2}\right)gt^2 + v_0 t, \qquad \text{for } t \ge 0,$$
where air resistance is neglected and $g \approx 9.8 \text{ m/s}^2$ is the acceleration due to gravity.
   a. Let $u_0 = 20$ m/s and $v_0 = 25$ m/s. Assuming the projectile is launched over horizontal ground, at what time does it return to Earth?
   b. Find the integral that gives the length of the trajectory from launch to landing.
   c. Evaluate the integral in part (b) by first making the change of variables $u = -gt + v_0$. The resulting integral is evaluated either by making a second change of variables or by using a calculator. What is the length of the trajectory?
   d. How far does the projectile land from its launch site?

48. **Variable speed on a circle** Consider a particle that moves in a plane according to the equations $x = \sin t^2$ and $y = \cos t^2$ with a starting position $(0, 1)$ at $t = 0$.
   a. Describe the path of the particle, including the time required to return to the starting position.
   b. What is the length of the path in part (a)?
   c. Describe how the motion of this particle differs from the motion described by the equations $x = \sin t$ and $y = \cos t$.
   d. Now consider the motion described by $x = \sin t^n$ and $y = \cos t^n$, where n is a positive integer. Describe the path of the particle, including the time required to return to the starting position.
   e. What is the length of the path in part (d) for any positive integer n?
   f. If you were watching a race on a circular path between two runners, one moving according to $x = \sin t$ and $y = \cos t$ and one according to $x = \sin t^2$ and $y = \cos t^2$, who would win and when would one runner pass the other?

Additional Exercises

49. **Lengths of related curves** Suppose a curve is given by $\mathbf{r}(t) = \langle f(t), g(t) \rangle$, where f' and g' are continuous for $a \leq t \leq b$. Assume the curve is traversed once for $a \leq t \leq b$ and the length of the curve between $(f(a), g(a))$ and $(f(b), g(b))$ is L. Prove that for any nonzero constant c the length of the curve defined by $\mathbf{r}(t) = \langle c\,f(t), c\,g(t) \rangle$, for $a \leq t \leq b$, is $|c|L$.

50. **Arc length for polar curves** Prove that the length of the curve $r = f(\theta)$, for $\alpha \leq \theta \leq \beta$, is

$$L = \int_{\alpha}^{\beta} \sqrt{f(\theta)^2 + f'(\theta)^2}\, d\theta.$$

51. **Arc length for $y = f(x)$** The arc length formula for functions of the form $y = f(x)$ on $[a, b]$ found in Section 6.5 is

$$L = \int_{a}^{b} \sqrt{1 + f'(x)^2}\, dx.$$

Derive this formula from the arc length formula for vector curves. (*Hint:* Let $x = t$ be the parameter.)

52. **Change of variables** Consider the parameterized curves $\mathbf{r}(t) = \langle f(t), g(t), h(t) \rangle$ and $\mathbf{R}(t) = \langle f(u(t)), g(u(t)), h(u(t)) \rangle$, where f, g, h, and u are continuously differentiable functions and u has an inverse on $[a, b]$.
    a. Show that the curve generated by $\mathbf{r}$ on the interval $a \leq t \leq b$ is the same as the curve generated by $\mathbf{R}$ on $u^{-1}(a) \leq t \leq u^{-1}(b)$ (or $u^{-1}(b) \leq t \leq u^{-1}(a)$).
    b. Show that the lengths of the two curves are equal. (*Hint:* Use the Chain Rule and a change of variables in the arc length integral for the curve generated by $\mathbf{R}$.)

QUICK CHECK ANSWERS

1. $\sqrt{2}$ **2.** $\sqrt{3}$

3. $L = \int_a^b |\mathbf{v}(t)|\, dt = \int_a^b S\, dt = S(b - a)$ **4.** 2π ◀

12.9 Curvature and Normal Vectors

We know how to find tangent vectors and lengths of curves in space, but much more can be said about the shape of such curves. In this section, we introduce two new concepts: *curvature* and *normal vectors. Curvature* measures how *fast* a curve turns at a point and the *normal vector* describes the *direction* in which a curve turns.

Arc Length as a Parameter

Until now the parameter t used to represent a curve $\mathbf{r}(t) = \langle f(t), g(t), h(t) \rangle$ has been chosen either for convenience or because it represents time in some specified unit. We now introduce the most natural parameter for describing curves; that parameter is *arc length.* Let's see what it means for a curve to be *parameterized by arc length.*

Consider the following two characterizations of the unit circle centered at the origin:

- $\langle \cos t, \sin t \rangle$, for $0 \leq t \leq 2\pi$
- $\langle \cos 2t, \sin 2t \rangle$, for $0 \leq t \leq \pi$

In the first description, as the parameter t increases from $t = 0$ to $t = 2\pi$, the full circle is generated and the arc length s of the curve also increases from $s = 0$ to $s = 2\pi$. In other words, as the parameter t increases, it measures the arc length of the curve that is generated. (Figure 12.101a).

In the second description, as t varies from $t = 0$ to $t = \pi$, the full circle is generated and the arc length increases from $s = 0$ to $s = 2\pi$. In this case, the length of the interval in t does not equal the length of the curve generated; therefore, the parameter t does not represent arc length. In general, there are infinitely many ways to parameterize a given curve; however, for a given initial point and orientation, arc length is the parameter for only one of them (Figure 12.101b).

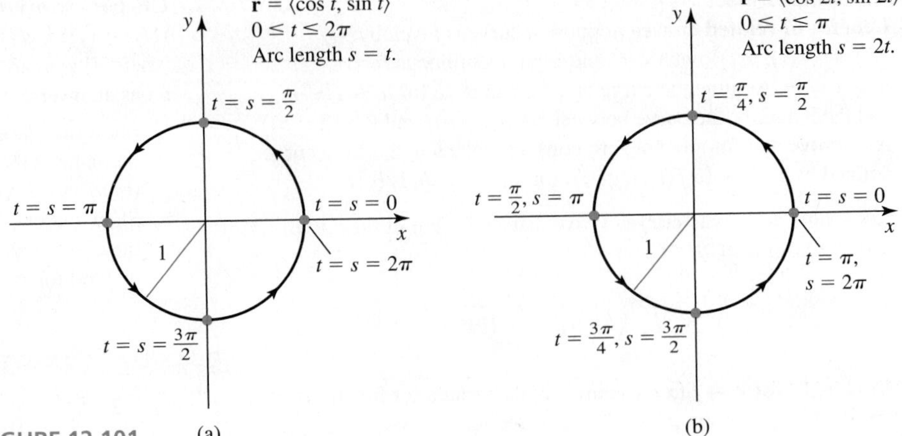

FIGURE 12.101

QUICK CHECK 1 Consider the portion of a circle $\mathbf{r}(t) = \langle \cos t, \sin t \rangle$, for $a \le t \le b$. Show that the arc length of the curve is $b - a$. ◀

The Arc Length Function Suppose that a smooth curve is represented by the function $\mathbf{r}(t) = \langle x(t), y(t), z(t) \rangle$, for $t \ge a$, where t is a parameter. Notice that as t increases, the length of the curve also increases. Using the arc length formula from the previous section, the length of the curve from $\mathbf{r}(a)$ to $\mathbf{r}(t)$ is

$$s(t) = \int_a^t \sqrt{x'(u)^2 + y'(u)^2 + z'(u)^2}\, du = \int_a^t |\mathbf{v}(u)|\, du.$$

➤ Notice that t is the independent variable of the function $s(t)$, so a different symbol u is used for the variable of integration. It is common to use s as the arc length function.

This equation gives the relationship between the arc length of a curve and any parameter t used to describe the curve.

An important consequence of this relationship arises if we differentiate both sides with respect to t using the Fundamental Theorem of Calculus:

$$\frac{ds}{dt} = \frac{d}{dt}\left(\int_a^t |\mathbf{v}(u)|\, du\right) = |\mathbf{v}(t)|$$

Specifically, if t represents time and $\mathbf{r}$ is the position of an object moving on the curve, then the rate of change of the arc length with respect to time is the speed of the object. Notice that if $\mathbf{r}(t)$ describes a smooth curve, then $|\mathbf{v}(t)| \ne 0$; hence $ds/dt > 0$, and s is an increasing function of t—as t increases, the arc length also increases. If $\mathbf{r}(t)$ is a curve on which $|\mathbf{v}(t)| = 1$ for all t, then

$$s(t) = \int_a^t |\mathbf{v}(u)|\, du = \int_a^t 1\, du = t - a,$$

which means the parameter t corresponds to arc length.

THEOREM 12.9 Arc Length as a Function of a Parameter
Let $\mathbf{r}(t)$ describe a smooth curve for $t \ge a$. The arc length is given by

$$s(t) = \int_a^t |\mathbf{v}(u)|\, du,$$

where $|\mathbf{v}| = |\mathbf{r}'|$. Equivalently, $\dfrac{ds}{dt} = |\mathbf{v}(t)| > 0$. If $|\mathbf{v}(t)| = 1$ for all $t \ge a$, then the parameter t corresponds to arc length.

EXAMPLE 1 **Arc length parameterization** Consider the helix $\mathbf{r}(t) = \langle 2\cos t, 2\sin t, 4t \rangle$, for $t \geq 0$.

a. Find the arc length function $s(t)$.

b. Find another description of the helix that uses arc length as the parameter.

SOLUTION

a. Note that $\mathbf{r}'(t) = \langle -2\sin t, 2\cos t, 4 \rangle$ and

$$\begin{aligned} |\mathbf{v}(t)| = |\mathbf{r}'(t)| &= \sqrt{(-2\sin t)^2 + (2\cos t)^2 + 4^2} \\ &= \sqrt{4(\sin^2 t + \cos^2 t) + 4^2} && \text{Simplify.} \\ &= \sqrt{4 + 4^2} && \sin^2 t + \cos^2 t = 1 \\ &= \sqrt{20} = 2\sqrt{5}. && \text{Simplify.} \end{aligned}$$

Therefore, the relationship between the arc length s and the parameter t is

$$s(t) = \int_a^t |\mathbf{v}(u)|\, du = \int_0^t 2\sqrt{5}\, du = 2\sqrt{5}\, t.$$

b. Substituting $t = s/(2\sqrt{5})$ into the original parametric description of the helix, we find that the description with arc length as a parameter is (using a different function name)

$$\mathbf{r}_1(s) = \left\langle 2\cos\left(\frac{s}{2\sqrt{5}}\right), 2\sin\left(\frac{s}{2\sqrt{5}}\right), \frac{2s}{\sqrt{5}} \right\rangle, \quad \text{for } s \geq 0.$$

This description has the property that an increment of Δs in the parameter corresponds to an increment of exactly Δs in the arc length. *Related Exercises 9–14* ◄

➤ It is difficult to parameterize most curves in terms of arc length. Arc length is used as a parameter for defining fundamental properties of curves, such as curvature and normal vectors, but then we develop formulas that work for any parametric description.

QUICK CHECK 2 Does the line $\mathbf{r}(t) = \langle t, t, t \rangle$ have arc length as a parameter? Explain. ◄

Curvature

Imagine driving a car along a winding mountain road. There are two ways to change the velocity of the car (that is, to accelerate). You can change the *speed* of the car or you can change the *direction* of the car. A change of speed is relatively easy to describe, so we postpone that discussion and focus on the change of direction. The rate at which the car changes direction is related to the notion of *curvature*.

Unit Tangent Vector Recall from Section 12.6 that if $\mathbf{r}(t) = \langle x(t), y(t), z(t) \rangle$ is a smooth oriented curve, then the unit tangent is the unit vector that points in the direction of the tangent vector $\mathbf{r}'(t)$; that is,

$$\mathbf{T}(t) = \frac{\mathbf{r}'(t)}{|\mathbf{r}'(t)|} = \frac{\mathbf{v}(t)}{|\mathbf{v}(t)|}.$$

Because $\mathbf{T}$ is a unit vector, its length does not change along the curve. The only way $\mathbf{T}$ can change is through a change in direction.

How quickly does $\mathbf{T}$ change (in direction) as we move along the curve? If a small increment in arc length Δs along the curve results in a large change in the direction of $\mathbf{T}$, the curve is turning quickly over that interval and we say it has a large *curvature* (Figure 12.102a). If a small increment Δs in arc length results in a small change in the direction of $\mathbf{T}$, the curve is turning slowly over that interval and it has a small curvature (Figure 12.102b). The magnitude of the rate at which the direction of $\mathbf{T}$ changes with respect to arc length is the curvature of the curve.

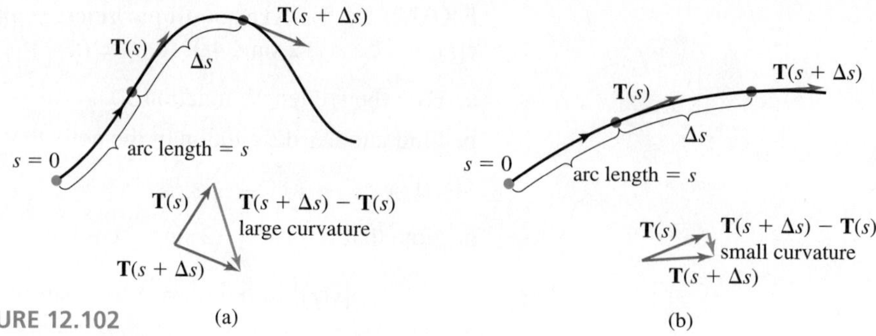

FIGURE 12.102

➤ Recall that the unit tangent vector at a point depends on the orientation of the curve. The curvature does not depend on the orientation of the curve, but it does depend on the shape of the curve. The Greek letter *kappa* κ is used to denote curvature.

DEFINITION Curvature

Let $\mathbf{r}$ describe a smooth parameterized curve. If s denotes arc length and $\mathbf{T} = \mathbf{r}'/|\mathbf{r}'|$ is the unit tangent vector, the **curvature** is $\kappa(s) = \left|\dfrac{d\mathbf{T}}{ds}\right|$.

Note that κ is a nonnegative scalar-valued function. A large value of κ at a point indicates a tight curve that changes direction quickly. If κ is small, then the curve is relatively flat and its direction changes slowly. The minimum curvature (zero) occurs on a straight line where the tangent never changes direction along the curve.

In order to evaluate $d\mathbf{T}/ds$, a description of the curve in terms of the arc length appears to be needed, but it may be difficult to obtain. A short calculation leads to the first of two practical curvature formulas.

We begin by using the Chain Rule and writing $\dfrac{d\mathbf{T}}{dt} = \dfrac{d\mathbf{T}}{ds} \cdot \dfrac{ds}{dt}$. Dividing by $ds/dt = |\mathbf{v}|$ and taking absolute values leads to

$$\kappa = \left|\frac{d\mathbf{T}}{ds}\right| = \frac{|d\mathbf{T}/dt|}{|ds/dt|} = \frac{1}{|\mathbf{v}|}\left|\frac{d\mathbf{T}}{dt}\right|.$$

This calculation is a proof of the following theorem.

THEOREM 12.10 Formula for Curvature

Let $\mathbf{r}(t)$ describe a smooth parameterized curve, where t is any parameter. If $\mathbf{v} = \mathbf{r}'$ is the velocity and $\mathbf{T}$ is the unit tangent vector, then the curvature is

$$\kappa(t) = \frac{1}{|\mathbf{v}|}\left|\frac{d\mathbf{T}}{dt}\right| = \frac{|\mathbf{T}'(t)|}{|\mathbf{r}'(t)|}.$$

EXAMPLE 2 Lines have zero curvature Consider the line $\mathbf{r}(t) = \langle x_0 + at, y_0 + bt, z_0 + ct\rangle$, for $-\infty < t < \infty$. Show that $\kappa = 0$ at all points on the line.

SOLUTION Note that $\mathbf{r}'(t) = \langle a, b, c\rangle$ and $|\mathbf{r}'(t)| = |\mathbf{v}(t)| = \sqrt{a^2 + b^2 + c^2}$. Therefore,

$$\mathbf{T}(t) = \frac{\mathbf{r}'(t)}{|\mathbf{r}'(t)|} = \frac{\langle a, b, c\rangle}{\sqrt{a^2 + b^2 + c^2}}.$$

Because $\mathbf{T}$ is a constant, $\dfrac{d\mathbf{T}}{dt} = \mathbf{0}$ and $\kappa = 0$ at all points of the line.

Related Exercises 15–22 ◄

EXAMPLE 3 **Circles have constant curvature** Consider the circle $\mathbf{r}(t) = \langle R\cos t, R\sin t\rangle$, for $0 \le t \le 2\pi$, where $R > 0$. Show that $\kappa = 1/R$.

SOLUTION We compute $\mathbf{r}'(t) = \langle -R\sin t, R\cos t\rangle$ and

$$\begin{aligned} |\mathbf{v}(t)| = |\mathbf{r}'(t)| &= \sqrt{(-R\sin t)^2 + (R\cos t)^2} \\ &= \sqrt{R^2(\sin^2 t + \cos^2 t)} && \text{Simplify.} \\ &= R. && \sin^2 t + \cos^2 t = 1, R > 0 \end{aligned}$$

Therefore,

$$\mathbf{T}(t) = \frac{\mathbf{r}'(t)}{|\mathbf{r}'(t)|} = \frac{\langle -R\sin t, R\cos t\rangle}{R} = \langle -\sin t, \cos t\rangle, \text{ and}$$

$$\frac{d\mathbf{T}}{dt} = \langle -\cos t, -\sin t\rangle.$$

Combining these observations, the curvature is

$$\kappa = \frac{1}{|\mathbf{v}|}\left|\frac{d\mathbf{T}}{dt}\right| = \frac{1}{R}|\langle -\cos t, -\sin t\rangle| = \frac{1}{R}\underbrace{\sqrt{\cos^2 t + \sin^2 t}}_{1} = \frac{1}{R}.$$

The curvature of a circle is constant; a circle with a small radius has a large curvature and vice versa. *Related Exercises 15–22* ◀

> The curvature of a curve at a point can also be visualized in terms of a **circle of curvature**, which is a circle of radius R that is tangent to the curve at that point. The curvature at the point is $\kappa = 1/R$. See Exercises 64–68.

QUICK CHECK 3 What is the curvature of the circle $\mathbf{r}(t) = \langle 3\sin t, 3\cos t\rangle$? ◀

An Alternative Curvature Formula A second curvature formula, which pertains specifically to trajectories of moving objects, is easier to use in some cases. The calculation is instructive because it relies on many properties of vector functions. In the end, a remarkably simple formula emerges.

Again consider a smooth curve $\mathbf{r}(t) = \langle x(t), y(t), z(t)\rangle$, where $\mathbf{v}(t) = \mathbf{r}'(t)$ and $\mathbf{a}(t) = \mathbf{v}'(t)$ are the velocity and acceleration of an object moving along that curve, respectively. We assume that $\mathbf{v}(t) \ne \mathbf{0}$ and $\mathbf{a}(t) \ne \mathbf{0}$. Because $\mathbf{T} = \mathbf{v}/|\mathbf{v}|$, we begin by writing $\mathbf{v} = |\mathbf{v}|\,\mathbf{T}$ and differentiating both sides with respect to t:

$$\mathbf{a} = \frac{d\mathbf{v}}{dt} = \frac{d}{dt}(|\mathbf{v}(t)|\,\mathbf{T}(t)) = \frac{d}{dt}(|\mathbf{v}(t)|)\mathbf{T}(t) + |\mathbf{v}(t)|\frac{d\mathbf{T}}{dt} \quad \text{Product Rule} \qquad (1)$$

We now form $\mathbf{a} \times \mathbf{v}$:

$$\begin{aligned} \mathbf{a} \times \mathbf{v} &= \underbrace{\left[\frac{d}{dt}(|\mathbf{v}(t)|)\mathbf{T} + |\mathbf{v}|\frac{d\mathbf{T}}{dt}\right]}_{\mathbf{a}} \times \underbrace{|\mathbf{v}|\mathbf{T}}_{\mathbf{v}} \\ &= \underbrace{\left(\frac{d}{dt}(|\mathbf{v}(t)|)\right)\mathbf{T} \times |\mathbf{v}|\mathbf{T}}_{\mathbf{0}} + |\mathbf{v}|\frac{d\mathbf{T}}{dt} \times |\mathbf{v}|\mathbf{T} \quad \text{Distributive law for cross products} \end{aligned}$$

> Distributive Law for cross products:
> $(\mathbf{u} + \mathbf{v}) \times \mathbf{w} = (\mathbf{u} \times \mathbf{w}) + (\mathbf{v} \times \mathbf{w})$

The first term in this expression has the form $a\mathbf{T} \times b\mathbf{T}$, where a and b are scalars. Therefore, $a\mathbf{T}$ and $b\mathbf{T}$ are parallel vectors and $a\mathbf{T} \times b\mathbf{T} = \mathbf{0}$. To simplify the second term, recall that a vector $\mathbf{u}(t)$ of constant length has the property that $\mathbf{u}$ and $d\mathbf{u}/dt$ are orthogonal (Section 12.7). Because $\mathbf{T}$ is a unit vector, it has constant length, and $\mathbf{T}$ and $d\mathbf{T}/dt$ are orthogonal. Furthermore, scalar multiples of $\mathbf{T}$ and $d\mathbf{T}/dt$ are orthogonal. Therefore, the magnitude of the second term simplifies as follows:

➤ Recall that the magnitude of the cross product of nonzero vectors is $|\mathbf{u} \times \mathbf{v}| = |\mathbf{u}||\mathbf{v}| \sin\theta$, where θ is the angle between the vectors. If the vectors are orthogonal, $\sin\theta = 1$ and $|\mathbf{u} \times \mathbf{v}| = |\mathbf{u}||\mathbf{v}|$.

$$\left||\mathbf{v}|\frac{d\mathbf{T}}{dt} \times |\mathbf{v}|\mathbf{T}\right| = \left||\mathbf{v}|\frac{d\mathbf{T}}{dt}\right||\mathbf{v}||\mathbf{T}| \underbrace{\sin\theta}_{1} \qquad |\mathbf{u} \times \mathbf{v}| = |\mathbf{u}||\mathbf{v}|\sin\theta$$

$$= |\mathbf{v}|^2\left|\frac{d\mathbf{T}}{dt}\right| \underbrace{|\mathbf{T}|}_{1} \qquad \text{Simplify, } \theta = \pi/2.$$

$$= |\mathbf{v}|^2\left|\frac{d\mathbf{T}}{dt}\right| \qquad |\mathbf{T}| = 1$$

The final step is to use Theorem 12.10 and substitute $\left|\frac{d\mathbf{T}}{dt}\right| = \kappa|\mathbf{v}|$. Putting these results together, we find that

$$|\mathbf{a} \times \mathbf{v}| = |\mathbf{v}|^2\left|\frac{d\mathbf{T}}{dt}\right| = |\mathbf{v}|^2\kappa|\mathbf{v}| = \kappa|\mathbf{v}|^3.$$

Solving for the curvature gives $\kappa = \dfrac{|\mathbf{a} \times \mathbf{v}|}{|\mathbf{v}|^3}$.

➤ Note that $\mathbf{a}(t) = \mathbf{0}$ corresponds to straight-line motion and $\kappa = 0$. If $\mathbf{v}(t) = \mathbf{0}$, the object is at rest and κ is undefined.

THEOREM 12.11 Alternative Curvature Formula

Let $\mathbf{r}$ be the position of an object moving on a smooth curve. The **curvature** at a point on the curve is

$$\kappa = \frac{|\mathbf{a} \times \mathbf{v}|}{|\mathbf{v}|^3},$$

where $\mathbf{v} = \mathbf{r}'$ is the velocity and $\mathbf{a} = \mathbf{v}'$ is the acceleration.

QUICK CHECK 4 Use the alternative curvature formula to compute the curvature of the curve $\mathbf{r}(t) = \langle t^2, 10, -10\rangle$. ◄

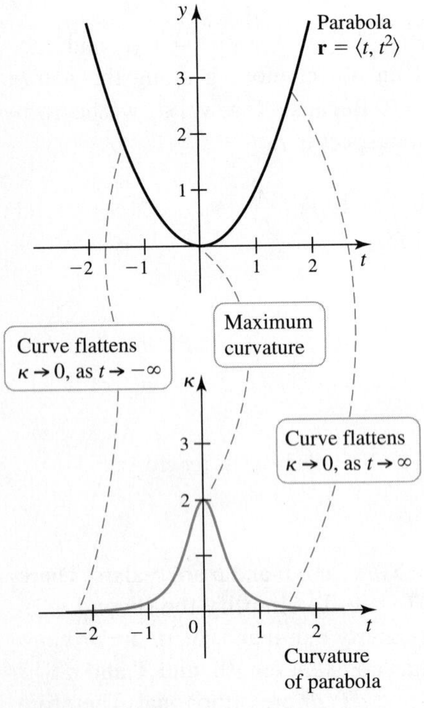

FIGURE 12.103

EXAMPLE 4 Curvature of a parabola Find the curvature of the parabola $\mathbf{r}(t) = \langle t, at^2\rangle$, for $-\infty < t < \infty$, where $a > 0$ is a real number.

SOLUTION The alternative formula works well in this case. We find that $\mathbf{v}(t) = \mathbf{r}'(t) = \langle 1, 2at\rangle$ and $\mathbf{a}(t) = \mathbf{v}'(t) = \langle 0, 2a\rangle$. To compute the cross product $\mathbf{a} \times \mathbf{v}$, we append a third component of 0 to each vector:

$$\mathbf{a} \times \mathbf{v} = \begin{vmatrix} \mathbf{i} & \mathbf{j} & \mathbf{k} \\ 0 & 2a & 0 \\ 1 & 2at & 0 \end{vmatrix} = -2a\,\mathbf{k}$$

Therefore, the curvature is

$$\kappa(t) = \frac{|\mathbf{a} \times \mathbf{v}|}{|\mathbf{v}|^3} = \frac{|-2a\mathbf{k}|}{|\langle 1, 2at\rangle|^3} = \frac{2a}{(1 + 4a^2t^2)^{3/2}}.$$

The curvature is a maximum at the vertex of the parabola where $t = 0$ and $\kappa = 2a$. The curvature decreases as one moves along the curve away from the vertex, as shown in Figure 12.103 with $a = 1$. *Related Exercises 23–28* ◄

EXAMPLE 5 Curvature of a helix Find the curvature of the helix $\mathbf{r}(t) = \langle a\cos t, a\sin t, bt\rangle$, for $-\infty < t < \infty$, where $a > 0$ and $b > 0$ are real numbers.

SOLUTION We use the alternative curvature formula, with

$$\mathbf{v}(t) = \mathbf{r}'(t) = \langle -a \sin t, a \cos t, b \rangle \quad \text{and}$$
$$\mathbf{a}(t) = \mathbf{v}'(t) = \langle -a \cos t, -a \sin t, 0 \rangle.$$

The cross product $\mathbf{a} \times \mathbf{v}$ is

$$\mathbf{a} \times \mathbf{v} = \begin{vmatrix} \mathbf{i} & \mathbf{j} & \mathbf{k} \\ -a \cos t & -a \sin t & 0 \\ -a \sin t & a \cos t & b \end{vmatrix} = -ab \sin t\, \mathbf{i} + ab \cos t\, \mathbf{j} - a^2\, \mathbf{k}.$$

Therefore,

$$\begin{aligned} |\mathbf{a} \times \mathbf{v}| &= |-ab \sin t\, \mathbf{i} + ab \cos t\, \mathbf{j} - a^2\, \mathbf{k}| \\ &= \sqrt{a^2 b^2 \underbrace{(\sin^2 t + \cos^2 t)}_{1} + a^4} \\ &= a\sqrt{a^2 + b^2}. \end{aligned}$$

> In the curvature formula for the helix, if $b = 0$, the helix becomes a circle of radius a with $\kappa = \frac{1}{a}$. At the other extreme, holding a fixed and letting $b \to \infty$ stretches and straightens the helix so that $\kappa \to 0$.

By a familiar calculation, $|\mathbf{v}| = |\langle -a \sin t, a \cos t, b \rangle| = \sqrt{a^2 + b^2}$. Therefore,

$$\kappa = \frac{|\mathbf{a} \times \mathbf{v}|}{|\mathbf{v}|^3} = \frac{a\sqrt{a^2 + b^2}}{\left(\sqrt{a^2 + b^2}\right)^3} = \frac{a}{a^2 + b^2}.$$

Related Exercises 23–28 ◀

Principal Unit Normal Vector

The curvature answers the question of how *fast* a curve turns. The *principal unit normal* vector determines the *direction* in which a curve turns. Specifically, the magnitude of $d\mathbf{T}/ds$ is the curvature: $\kappa = |d\mathbf{T}/ds|$. What about the direction of $d\mathbf{T}/ds$? If only the direction, but not the magnitude, of a vector is of interest, it is convenient to work with a unit vector that has the same direction as the original vector. We apply this idea to $d\mathbf{T}/ds$. The unit vector that points in the direction of $d\mathbf{T}/ds$ is the *principal unit normal vector*.

> The principal unit normal vector depends on the shape of the curve but not on the orientation of the curve.

DEFINITION Principal Unit Normal Vector

Let $\mathbf{r}$ describe a smooth parameterized curve. The **principal unit normal vector** at a point P on the curve at which $\kappa \neq 0$ is

$$\mathbf{N} = \frac{d\mathbf{T}/ds}{|d\mathbf{T}/ds|} = \frac{1}{\kappa}\frac{d\mathbf{T}}{ds}.$$

In practice, we use the equivalent formula

$$\mathbf{N} = \frac{d\mathbf{T}/dt}{|d\mathbf{T}/dt|},$$

evaluated at the value of t corresponding to P.

The practical formula $\mathbf{N} = \dfrac{d\mathbf{T}/dt}{|d\mathbf{T}/dt|}$ follows from the definition by using the Chain Rule to write $\dfrac{d\mathbf{T}}{ds} = \dfrac{d\mathbf{T}}{dt} \cdot \dfrac{dt}{ds}$ (Exercise 76). Two important properties of the principal unit normal vector follow from the definition.

THEOREM 12.12 Properties of the Principal Unit Normal Vector

Let $\mathbf{r}$ describe a smooth parameterized curve with unit tangent vector $\mathbf{T}$ and principal unit normal vector $\mathbf{N}$.

1. $\mathbf{T}$ and $\mathbf{N}$ are orthogonal at all points of the curve; that is, $\mathbf{T}(t) \cdot \mathbf{N}(t) = 0$ at all points where $\mathbf{N}$ is defined.
2. The principal unit normal vector points to the inside of the curve—in the direction that the curve is turning.

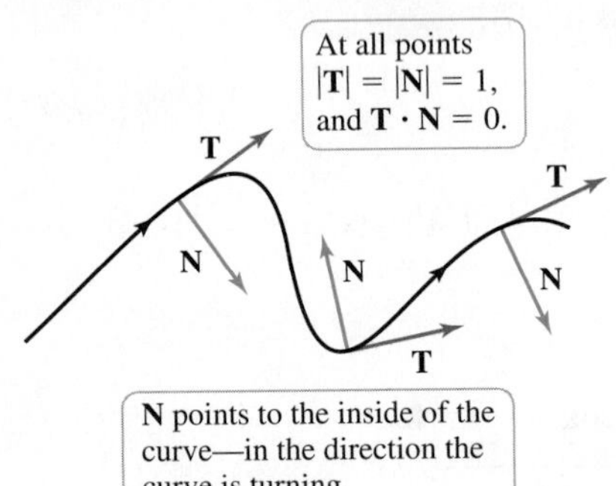
At all points
$|\mathbf{T}| = |\mathbf{N}| = 1$,
and $\mathbf{T} \cdot \mathbf{N} = 0$.
T
N
N
T
N
T
N points to the inside of the curve—in the direction the curve is turning.

FIGURE 12.104

Proof

1. As a unit vector, $\mathbf{T}$ has constant length. Therefore, by Theorem 12.8, $\mathbf{T}$ and $d\mathbf{T}/dt$ (or $\mathbf{T}$ and $d\mathbf{T}/ds$) are orthogonal. Because $\mathbf{N}$ is a scalar multiple of $d\mathbf{T}/ds$, $\mathbf{T}$ and $\mathbf{N}$ are orthogonal (Figure 12.104).
2. We motivate—but do not prove—this fact, by recalling that

$$\frac{d\mathbf{T}}{ds} = \lim_{\Delta s \to 0} \frac{\mathbf{T}(s + \Delta s) - \mathbf{T}(s)}{\Delta s}.$$

Therefore, $d\mathbf{T}/ds$ points in the approximate direction of $\mathbf{T}(s + \Delta s) - \mathbf{T}(s)$ when Δs is small. As shown in Figure 12.105, this difference points in the direction in which the curve is turning. Because $\mathbf{N}$ is a positive scalar multiple of $d\mathbf{T}/ds$, it points in the same direction. ◀

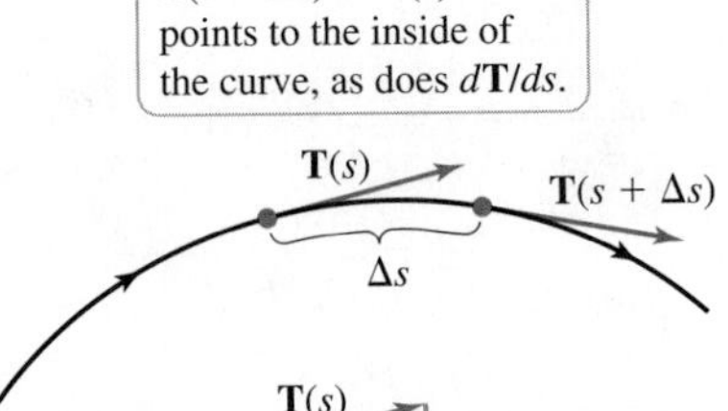
For small Δs
$\mathbf{T}(s + \Delta s) - \mathbf{T}(s)$
points to the inside of the curve, as does $d\mathbf{T}/ds$.
$\mathbf{T}(s)$
$\mathbf{T}(s + \Delta s)$
Δs
$\mathbf{T}(s)$
$\mathbf{T}(s + \Delta s) - \mathbf{T}(s)$
$\mathbf{T}(s + \Delta s)$

FIGURE 12.105

QUICK CHECK 5 Consider the parabola $\mathbf{r}(t) = \langle t, -t^2 \rangle$. Does the principal unit normal vector point in the positive y-direction or negative y-direction along the curve? ◀

EXAMPLE 6 Principal unit normal vector for a helix Find the principal unit normal vector for the helix $\mathbf{r}(t) = \langle a \cos t, a \sin t, bt \rangle$, for $-\infty < t < \infty$, where $a > 0$ and $b > 0$ are real numbers.

SOLUTION Several preliminary calculations are needed. First, we have $\mathbf{v}(t) = \mathbf{r}'(t) = \langle -a \sin t, a \cos t, b \rangle$. Therefore,

$$\begin{aligned} |\mathbf{v}(t)| = |\mathbf{r}'(t)| &= \sqrt{(-a \sin t)^2 + (a \cos t)^2 + b^2} \\ &= \sqrt{a^2(\sin^2 t + \cos^2 t) + b^2} && \text{Simplify.} \\ &= \sqrt{a^2 + b^2}. && \sin^2 t + \cos^2 t = 1 \end{aligned}$$

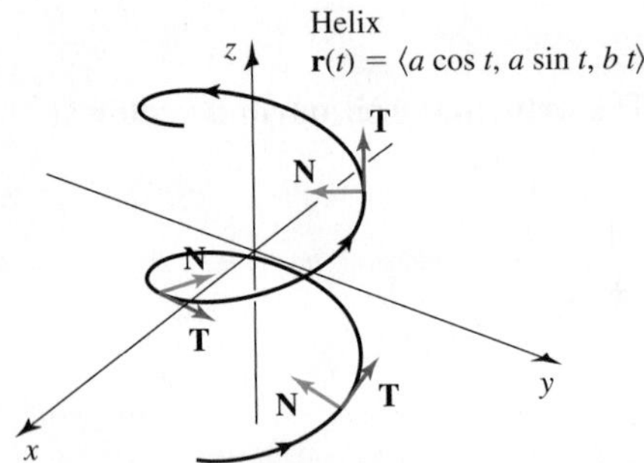
Helix
$\mathbf{r}(t) = \langle a \cos t, a \sin t, b\,t \rangle$
z
T
N
N
T
N
T
y
x
$\mathbf{T} \cdot \mathbf{N} = 0$ at all points of the curve.
T points in the direction of the curve.
N points to the inside of the curve.

FIGURE 12.106

The unit tangent vector is

$$\mathbf{T}(t) = \frac{\mathbf{r}'(t)}{|\mathbf{r}'(t)|} = \frac{\langle -a \sin t, a \cos t, b \rangle}{\sqrt{a^2 + b^2}}.$$

Notice that $\mathbf{T}$ points along the curve in an upward direction (at an angle to the horizontal that satisfies $\tan \theta = b/a$) (Figure 12.106). We can now calculate the principal unit normal vector. First, we determine that

$$\frac{d\mathbf{T}}{dt} = \frac{d}{dt}\left(\frac{\langle -a \sin t, a \cos t, b \rangle}{\sqrt{a^2 + b^2}}\right) = \frac{\langle -a \cos t, -a \sin t, 0 \rangle}{\sqrt{a^2 + b^2}}$$

and

$$\left|\frac{d\mathbf{T}}{dt}\right| = \frac{a}{\sqrt{a^2 + b^2}}.$$

The principal unit normal vector now follows:

$$\mathbf{N} = \frac{d\mathbf{T}/dt}{|d\mathbf{T}/dt|} = \frac{\dfrac{\langle -a\cos t, -a\sin t, 0\rangle}{\sqrt{a^2+b^2}}}{\dfrac{a}{\sqrt{a^2+b^2}}} = \langle -\cos t, -\sin t, 0\rangle.$$

Several important checks should be made. First note that $\mathbf{N}$ is a unit vector (that is, $|\mathbf{N}| = 1$). It should also be confirmed that $\mathbf{T} \cdot \mathbf{N} = 0$; that is, the unit tangent vector and the principal unit normal vector are everywhere orthogonal. Finally, $\mathbf{N}$ is parallel to the xy-plane and points inward toward the z-axis, in the direction the curve turns (Figure 12.106). Notice that in the special case $b = 0$, the trajectory is a circle, but the normal vector is still $\mathbf{N} = \langle -\cos t, -\sin t, 0\rangle$. *Related Exercises 29–36* ◀

QUICK CHECK 6 Explain why the principal unit vector for a straight line is undefined. ◀

Components of the Acceleration

We now use the vectors $\mathbf{T}$ and $\mathbf{N}$ to gain insight into how moving objects accelerate. Recall the observation made earlier that the two ways to change the velocity of an object (to accelerate) are to change its *speed* and change its *direction* of motion. We now show that changing the speed produces acceleration in the direction of $\mathbf{T}$ and changing the direction produces acceleration in the direction of $\mathbf{N}$.

We begin with the fact that

$$\mathbf{T} = \frac{\mathbf{v}}{|\mathbf{v}|} \quad \text{or} \quad \mathbf{v} = \mathbf{T}|\mathbf{v}| = \mathbf{T}\frac{ds}{dt}.$$

➤ Recall that the speed is $|\mathbf{v}| = ds/dt$, where s is arc length.

Differentiating both sides of $\mathbf{v} = \mathbf{T}\dfrac{ds}{dt}$ gives

$$\begin{aligned}\mathbf{a} = \frac{d\mathbf{v}}{dt} &= \frac{d}{dt}\left(\mathbf{T}\frac{ds}{dt}\right)\\ &= \frac{d\mathbf{T}}{dt}\frac{ds}{dt} + \mathbf{T}\frac{d^2s}{dt^2} && \text{Product Rule}\\ &= \frac{d\mathbf{T}}{ds}\frac{ds}{dt}\frac{ds}{dt} + \mathbf{T}\frac{d^2s}{dt^2} && \text{Chain Rule: } \frac{d\mathbf{T}}{dt} = \frac{d\mathbf{T}}{ds}\frac{ds}{dt}\end{aligned}$$

We now substitute $|\mathbf{v}| = ds/dt$ and $\kappa\mathbf{N} = d\mathbf{T}/ds$ to obtain the following useful result.

➤ Note that a_N and a_T are defined even at points where $\kappa = 0$ and $\mathbf{N}$ is undefined.

THEOREM 12.13 Tangential and Normal Components of the Acceleration
The acceleration vector of an object moving in space along a smooth curve has the following representation in terms of its **tangential component** a_T (in the direction of $\mathbf{T}$) and its **normal component** a_N (in the direction of $\mathbf{N}$):

$$\mathbf{a} = a_N\mathbf{N} + a_T\mathbf{T},$$

where $a_N = \kappa|\mathbf{v}|^2 = \dfrac{|\mathbf{a} \times \mathbf{v}|}{|\mathbf{v}|}$ and $a_T = \dfrac{d^2s}{dt^2}$.

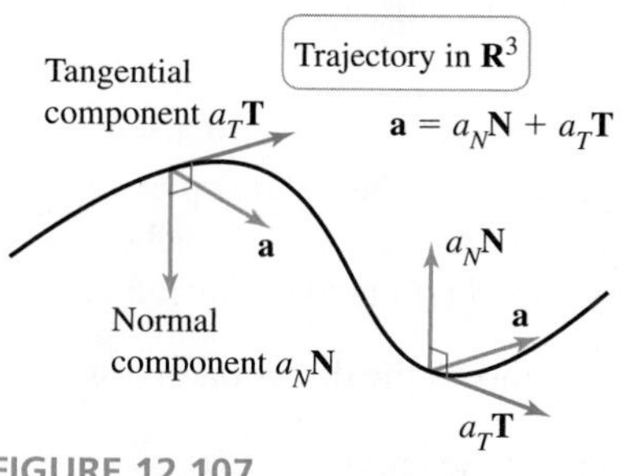

FIGURE 12.107

The tangential component of the acceleration, in the direction of $\mathbf{T}$, is the usual acceleration $a_T = d^2s/dt^2$ of an object moving along a straight line (Figure 12.107). The normal component, in the direction of $\mathbf{N}$, increases with the speed $|\mathbf{v}|$ and with the curvature. Higher speeds on tighter curves produce greater normal accelerations.

EXAMPLE 7 Acceleration on a circular path Find the components of the acceleration on the circular trajectory

$$\mathbf{r}(t) = \langle R\cos\omega t, R\sin\omega t\rangle,$$

where R and ω are positive real numbers.

SOLUTION We find that $\mathbf{r}'(t) = \langle -R\omega\sin\omega t, R\omega\cos\omega t\rangle$, $|\mathbf{v}(t)| = |\mathbf{r}'(t)| = R\omega$, and, by Example 3, $\kappa = 1/R$. Recall that $ds/dt = |\mathbf{v}(t)|$, which is constant; therefore, $d^2s/dt^2 = 0$ and the tangential component of the acceleration is zero. The acceleration is

$$\mathbf{a} = \kappa|\mathbf{v}|^2\,\mathbf{N} + \underbrace{\frac{d^2s}{dt^2}}_{0}\mathbf{T} = \frac{1}{R}(R\omega)^2\,\mathbf{N} = R\omega^2\,\mathbf{N}.$$

On a circular path (traversed at constant speed), the acceleration is entirely in the normal direction, orthogonal to the tangent vectors. The acceleration increases with the radius of the circle R and with the frequency of the motion ω. *Related Exercises 37–42* ◀

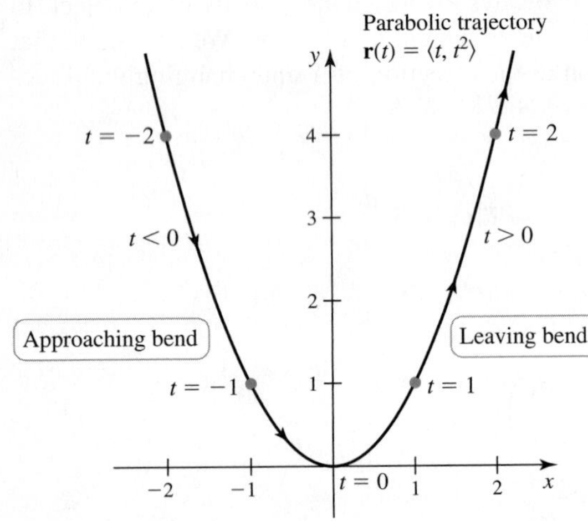

FIGURE 12.108

➤ Using the fact that $|\mathbf{T}| = |\mathbf{N}| = 1$, we have, from Section 12.3, that

$$a_N = \text{scal}_{\mathbf{N}}\mathbf{a} = \frac{\mathbf{a}\cdot\mathbf{N}}{|\mathbf{N}|} = \mathbf{a}\cdot\mathbf{N}$$

and

$$a_T = \text{scal}_{\mathbf{T}}\mathbf{a} = \frac{\mathbf{a}\cdot\mathbf{T}}{|\mathbf{T}|} = \mathbf{a}\cdot\mathbf{T} = \frac{\mathbf{a}\cdot\mathbf{v}}{|\mathbf{v}|}.$$

EXAMPLE 8 A bend in the road The driver of a car follows the parabolic trajectory $\mathbf{r}(t) = \langle t, t^2\rangle$, for $-2 \le t \le 2$, through a sharp bend (Figure 12.108). Find the tangential and normal components of the acceleration of the car.

SOLUTION The velocity and acceleration vectors are easily computed: $\mathbf{v}(t) = \mathbf{r}'(t) = \langle 1, 2t\rangle$ and $\mathbf{a}(t) = \mathbf{r}''(t) = \langle 0, 2\rangle$. The goal is to express $\mathbf{a} = \langle 0, 2\rangle$ in terms of $\mathbf{T}$ and $\mathbf{N}$. A short calculation reveals that

$$\mathbf{T} = \frac{\mathbf{v}}{|\mathbf{v}|} = \frac{\langle 1, 2t\rangle}{\sqrt{1+4t^2}} \quad\text{and}\quad \mathbf{N} = \frac{d\mathbf{T}/dt}{|d\mathbf{T}/dt|} = \frac{\langle -2t, 1\rangle}{\sqrt{1+4t^2}}.$$

We now have two ways to proceed. One is to compute the normal and tangential components of the acceleration directly using the definitions. More efficient is to note that $\mathbf{T}$ and $\mathbf{N}$ are orthogonal unit vectors, and then to compute the scalar projections of $\mathbf{a} = \langle 0, 2\rangle$ in the directions of $\mathbf{T}$ and $\mathbf{N}$. We find that

$$a_N = \mathbf{a}\cdot\mathbf{N} = \langle 0, 2\rangle\cdot\frac{\langle -2t, 1\rangle}{\sqrt{1+4t^2}} = \frac{2}{\sqrt{1+4t^2}}$$

and

$$a_T = \mathbf{a}\cdot\mathbf{T} = \langle 0, 2\rangle\cdot\frac{\langle 1, 2t\rangle}{\sqrt{1+4t^2}} = \frac{4t}{\sqrt{1+4t^2}}.$$

You should verify that at all times (Exercise 70),

$$\mathbf{a} = a_N\mathbf{N} + a_T\mathbf{T} = \frac{2}{\sqrt{1+4t^2}}(\mathbf{N} + 2t\mathbf{T}) = \langle 0, 2\rangle.$$

Let's interpret these results. First, notice that the driver negotiates the curve in a sensible way: The speed $|\mathbf{v}| = \sqrt{1+4t^2}$ decreases as the car approaches the tightest part of the curve and increases as it leaves the curve (Figure 12.109). As the car approaches the curve ($t < 0$), $\mathbf{T}$ points in the direction of the trajectory and $\mathbf{N}$ points to the inside of the curve. However $a_T = \dfrac{d^2s}{dt^2} < 0$ when $t < 0$, so $a_T\mathbf{T}$ points in the direction opposite to that of $\mathbf{T}$ (corresponding to a deceleration). As the car leaves the curve ($t > 0$), $a_T > 0$ (corresponding to an acceleration) and $a_T\mathbf{T}$ and $\mathbf{T}$ point in the direction of the trajectory, while $\mathbf{N}$ still points to the inside of the curve (Figure 12.109; Exercise 72).

Related Exercises 37–42 ◀

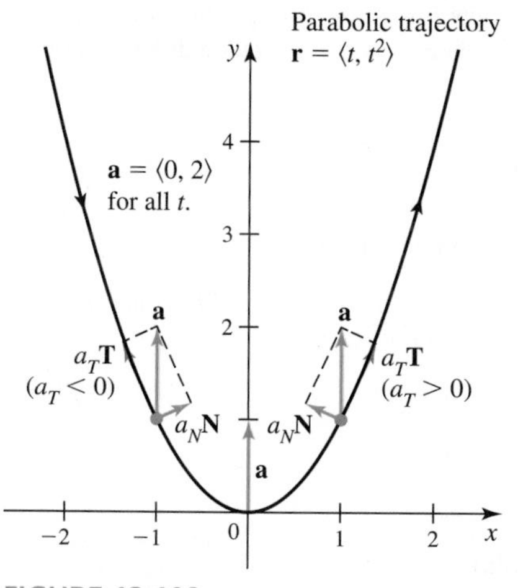

FIGURE 12.109

QUICK CHECK 7 Verify that **T** and **N** given in Example 8 satisfy $|\mathbf{T}| = |\mathbf{N}| = 1$ and that $\mathbf{T} \cdot \mathbf{N} = 0$.

SUMMARY Formulas for Curves in Space

Position function: $\mathbf{r}(t) = \langle x(t), y(t), z(t) \rangle$

Velocity: $\mathbf{v} = \mathbf{r}'$

Acceleration: $\mathbf{a} = \mathbf{v}'$

Unit tangent vector: $\mathbf{T} = \dfrac{\mathbf{v}}{|\mathbf{v}|}$

Principal unit normal vector: $\mathbf{N} = \dfrac{d\mathbf{T}/dt}{|d\mathbf{T}/dt|}$ (provided $d\mathbf{T}/dt \neq \mathbf{0}$)

Curvature: $\kappa = \left|\dfrac{d\mathbf{T}}{ds}\right| = \dfrac{1}{|\mathbf{v}|}\left|\dfrac{d\mathbf{T}}{dt}\right| = \dfrac{|\mathbf{a} \times \mathbf{v}|}{|\mathbf{v}|^3}$

Components of acceleration: $\mathbf{a} = a_N\mathbf{N} + a_T\mathbf{T}$, where $a_N = \kappa|\mathbf{v}|^2 = \dfrac{|\mathbf{a} \times \mathbf{v}|}{|\mathbf{v}|}$

and $a_T = \dfrac{d^2s}{dt^2} = \dfrac{\mathbf{a} \cdot \mathbf{v}}{|\mathbf{v}|}$

SECTION 12.9 EXERCISES

Review Questions

1. Explain what it means for a curve to be parameterized by its arc length.

2. Is the curve $\mathbf{r}(t) = \langle \cos t, \sin t \rangle$ parameterized by its arc length? Explain.

3. Is the curve $\mathbf{r}(t) = \langle t, t, t \rangle$ parameterized by its arc length? Explain.

4. Explain in words the meaning of *the curvature of a curve*. Is it a scalar function or a vector function?

5. Give a practical formula for computing the curvature.

6. Interpret *the principal unit normal vector of a curve*. Is it a scalar function or a vector function?

7. Give a practical formula for computing the principal unit normal vector.

8. Explain how to decompose the acceleration vector of a moving object into its tangential and normal components.

Basic Skills

9–14. Arc length parameterization *Determine whether the following curves use arc length as a parameter. If not, find a description that uses arc length as a parameter.*

9. $\mathbf{r}(t) = \langle t, 2t \rangle$, for $0 \leq t \leq 3$

10. $\mathbf{r}(t) = \langle t + 1, 2t - 3, 6t \rangle$, for $0 \leq t \leq 10$

11. $\mathbf{r}(t) = \langle 2\cos t, 2\sin t \rangle$, for $0 \leq t \leq 2\pi$

12. $\mathbf{r}(t) = \langle 5\cos t, 3\sin t, 4\sin t \rangle$, for $0 \leq t \leq \pi$

13. $\mathbf{r}(t) = \langle \cos t^2, \sin t^2 \rangle$, for $0 \leq t \leq \sqrt{\pi}$

14. $\mathbf{r}(t) = \langle t^2, 2t^2, 4t^2 \rangle$, for $1 \leq t \leq 4$

15–22. Curvature *Find the unit tangent vector* **T** *and the curvature* κ *for the following parameterized curves.*

15. $\mathbf{r}(t) = \langle 2t + 1, 4t - 5, 6t + 12 \rangle$

16. $\mathbf{r}(t) = \langle 2\cos t, -2\sin t \rangle$

17. $\mathbf{r}(t) = \langle 2t, 4\sin t, 4\cos t \rangle$

18. $\mathbf{r}(t) = \langle \cos t^2, \sin t^2 \rangle$

19. $\mathbf{r}(t) = \langle \sqrt{3}\sin t, \sin t, 2\cos t \rangle$

20. $\mathbf{r}(t) = \langle t, \ln(\cos t) \rangle$

21. $\mathbf{r}(t) = \langle t, 2t^2 \rangle$

22. $\mathbf{r}(t) = \langle \cos^3 t, \sin^3 t \rangle$

23–28. Alternative curvature formula *Use the alternative curvature formula* $\kappa = |\mathbf{a} \times \mathbf{v}|/|\mathbf{v}|^3$ *to find the curvature of the following parameterized curves.*

23. $\mathbf{r}(t) = \langle -3\cos t, 3\sin t, 0 \rangle$

24. $\mathbf{r}(t) = \langle t, 8 \sin t, 8 \cos t \rangle$

25. $\mathbf{r}(t) = \langle 4 + t^2, t, 0 \rangle$

26. $\mathbf{r}(t) = \langle \sqrt{3} \sin t, \sin t, 2 \cos t \rangle$

27. $\mathbf{r}(t) = \langle 7 \cos t, \sqrt{3} \sin t, 2 \cos t \rangle$

28. $\mathbf{r}(t) = \langle e^t \cos t, e^t \sin t, t \rangle$

29–36. Principal unit normal vector *Find the unit tangent vector* **T** *and the principal unit normal vector* **N** *for the following parameterized curves. In each case, verify that* $|\mathbf{T}| = |\mathbf{N}| = 1$ *and* $\mathbf{T} \cdot \mathbf{N} = 0$.

29. $\mathbf{r}(t) = \langle 2 \sin t, 2 \cos t \rangle$

30. $\mathbf{r}(t) = \langle 4 \sin t, 4 \cos t, 10t \rangle$

31. $\mathbf{r}(t) = \langle t^2/2, 4 - 3t, 1 \rangle$

32. $\mathbf{r}(t) = \langle t^2/2, t^3/3 \rangle$

33. $\mathbf{r}(t) = \langle \cos t^2, \sin t^2 \rangle$

34. $\mathbf{r}(t) = \langle \cos^3 t, \sin^3 t \rangle$

35. $\mathbf{r}(t) = \langle t^2, t \rangle$

36. $r(t) = \langle t, \ln(\cos t) \rangle$

37–42. Components of the acceleration *Consider the following trajectories of moving objects. Find the tangential and normal components of the acceleration.*

37. $\mathbf{r}(t) = \langle t, 1 + 4t, 2 - 6t \rangle$

38. $\mathbf{r}(t) = \langle 10 \cos t, -10 \sin t \rangle$

39. $\mathbf{r}(t) = \langle \cos t, 6 \sin t, \sqrt{5} \cos t \rangle$

40. $\mathbf{r}(t) = \langle t, t^2 + 1 \rangle$

41. $\mathbf{r}(t) = \langle t^3, t^2 \rangle$

42. $\mathbf{r}(t) = \langle 20 \cos t, 20 \sin t, 30t \rangle$

Further Explorations

43. **Explain why or why not** Determine whether the following statements are true and give an explanation or counterexample.
   a. The position, unit tangent, and principal unit normal vectors (**r**, **T**, and **N**) at a point lie in the same plane.
   b. The vectors **T** and **N** at a point depend on the orientation of a curve.
   c. The curvature at a point depends on the orientation of a curve.
   d. An object with unit speed ($|\mathbf{v}| = 1$) on a circle of radius R has an acceleration of $\mathbf{a} = \mathbf{N}/R$.
   e. If the speedometer of a car reads a constant 60 mi/hr, the car is not accelerating.

44. **Special formula: Curvature for $y = f(x)$** Assume that f is twice differentiable and prove that the curve $y = f(x)$ has curvature

$$\kappa(x) = \frac{|f''(x)|}{(1 + f'(x)^2)^{3/2}}.$$

(*Hint:* Use the parametric description $x = t, y = f(t)$.)

45–48. Curvature for $y = f(x)$ *Use the result of Exercise 44 to find the curvature function of the following curves.*

45. $f(x) = x^2$

46. $f(x) = \sqrt{a^2 - x^2}$

47. $f(x) = \ln x$

48. $f(x) = \ln(\cos x)$

49. **Special formula: Curvature for plane curves** Show that the curve $\mathbf{r}(t) = \langle f(t), g(t) \rangle$, where f and g are twice differentiable, has curvature

$$\kappa(t) = \frac{|f'g'' - f''g'|}{((f')^2 + (g')^2)^{3/2}},$$

where all derivatives are taken with respect to t.

50–53. Curvature for plane curves *Use the result of Exercise 49 to find the curvature function of the following curves.*

50. $\mathbf{r}(t) = \langle a \sin t, a \cos t \rangle$ (circle)

51. $\mathbf{r}(t) = \langle a \sin t, b \cos t \rangle$ (ellipse)

52. $\mathbf{r}(t) = \langle a \cos^3 t, a \sin^3 t \rangle$ (astroid)

53. $\mathbf{r}(t) = \langle t, at^2 \rangle$ (parabola)

When appropriate, consider using the special formulas derived in Exercises 44 and 49 in the remaining exercises.

54–57. Same paths, different velocity *The position functions of objects A and B describe different motion along the same path for* $t \ge 0$.

a. Sketch the path followed by both A and B.
b. Find the velocity and acceleration of A and B and discuss the differences.
c. Express the acceleration of A and B in terms of the tangential and normal components and discuss the differences.

54. A: $\mathbf{r}(t) = \langle 1 + 2t, 2 - 3t, 4t \rangle$, B: $\mathbf{r}(t) = \langle 1 + 6t, 2 - 9t, 12t \rangle$

55. A: $\mathbf{r}(t) = \langle t, 2t, 3t \rangle$, B: $\mathbf{r}(t) = \langle t^2, 2t^2, 3t^2 \rangle$

56. A: $\mathbf{r}(t) = \langle \cos t, \sin t \rangle$, B: $\mathbf{r}(t) = \langle \cos 3t, \sin 3t \rangle$

57. A: $\mathbf{r}(t) = \langle \cos t, \sin t \rangle$, B: $\mathbf{r}(t) = \langle \cos t^2, \sin t^2 \rangle$

T **58–61. Graphs of the curvature** *Consider the following curves.*

a. Graph the curve.
b. Compute the curvature (using either of the two formulas).
c. Graph the curvature as a function of the parameter.
d. Identify the points (if any) at which the curve has a minimum and maximum curvature.
e. Verify that the graph of the curvature is consistent with the graph of the curve.

58. $\mathbf{r}(t) = \langle t, t^2 \rangle$, for $-2 \le t \le 2$ (parabola)

59. $\mathbf{r}(t) = \langle t - \sin t, 1 - \cos t \rangle$, for $0 \le t \le 2\pi$ (cycloid)

60. $\mathbf{r}(t) = \langle t, \sin t \rangle$, for $0 \le t \le \pi$ (sine curve)

61. $\mathbf{r}(t) = \langle t^2/2, t^3/3 \rangle$, for $t > 0$

62. **Curvature of ln x** Find the curvature of $f(x) = \ln x$, for $x > 0$, and find the point at which it is a maximum. What is the value of the maximum curvature?

63. **Curvature of e^x** Find the curvature of $f(x) = e^x$ and find the point at which it is a maximum. What is the value of the maximum curvature?

64. Circle and radius of curvature Choose a point P on a smooth curve C in the plane. The **circle of curvature** (or **osculating circle**) at the point P is the circle that (a) is tangent to C at P, (b) has the same curvature as C at P, and (c) lies on the same side of C as the principal unit normal **N** (see figure). The **radius of curvature** is the radius of the circle of curvature. Show that the radius of curvature is $1/\kappa$, where κ is the curvature of C at P.

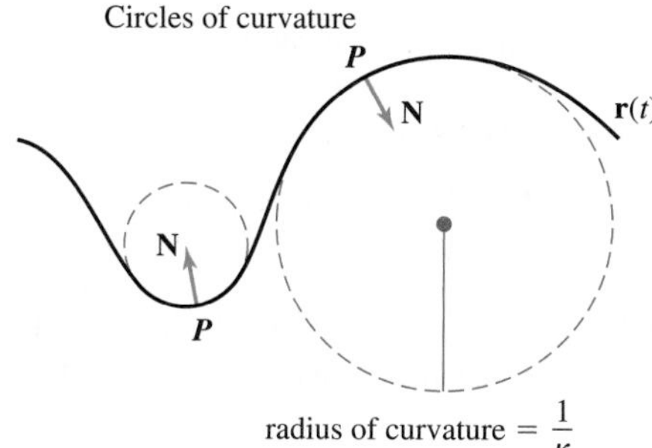

65–68. Finding radii of curvature *Find the radius of curvature (see Exercise 64) of the following curves at the given point. Then write the equation of the circle of curvature at the point.*

65. $\mathbf{r}(t) = \langle t, t^2 \rangle$ (parabola) at $t = 0$

66. $y = \ln x$ at $x = 1$

67. $\mathbf{r}(t) = \langle t - \sin t, 1 - \cos t \rangle$ (cycloid) at $t = \pi$

68. $y = \sin x$ at $x = \pi/2$

69. Curvature of the sine curve The function $f(x) = \sin nx$, where n is a positive real number, has a local maximum at $x = \pi/(2n)$. Compute the curvature κ of f at this point. How does κ vary (if at all) as n varies?

Applications

70. Parabolic trajectory In Example 8 it was shown that for the parabolic trajectory $\mathbf{r}(t) = \langle t, t^2 \rangle$, $\mathbf{a} = \langle 0, 2 \rangle$ and $\mathbf{a} = \dfrac{2}{\sqrt{1 + 4t^2}}(\mathbf{N} + 2t\,\mathbf{T})$. Show that the second equation for **a** reduces to the first equation.

T **71. Parabolic trajectory** Consider the parabolic trajectory

$$x = (V_0 \cos \alpha)t, y = (V_0 \sin \alpha)t - \tfrac{1}{2}gt^2,$$

where V_0 is the initial speed, α is the angle of launch, and g is the acceleration due to gravity. Consider all times $[0, T]$ for which $y \geq 0$.

a. Find and graph the speed for $0 \leq t \leq T$.
b. Find and graph the curvature for $0 \leq t \leq T$.
c. At what times (if any) do the speed and curvature have minimum and maximum values?

72. Relationship between T, N, and a Show that if an object accelerates in the sense that $d^2s/dt^2 > 0$ and $\kappa \neq 0$, then the acceleration vector lies between **T** and **N** in the plane of **T** and **N**. If an object decelerates in the sense that $d^2s/dt^2 < 0$, then the acceleration vector lies in the plane of **T** and **N**, but not between **T** and **N**.

Additional Exercises

73. Arc length parameterization Prove that the line $\mathbf{r}(t) = \langle x_0 + at, y_0 + bt, z_0 + ct \rangle$ is parameterized by arc length provided $a^2 + b^2 + c^2 = 1$.

74. Arc length parameterization Prove that the curve $\mathbf{r}(t) = \langle a \cos t, b \sin t, c \sin t \rangle$ is parameterized by arc length provided $a^2 = b^2 + c^2 = 1$.

75. Zero curvature Prove that the curve

$$\mathbf{r}(t) = \langle a + bt^p, c + dt^p, e + ft^p \rangle,$$

where a, b, c, d, e, f are real numbers and p is a positive integer, has zero curvature. Give an explanation.

76. Practical formula for N Show that the definition of the principal unit normal vector $\mathbf{N} = \dfrac{d\mathbf{T}/ds}{|d\mathbf{T}/ds|}$ implies the practical formula $\mathbf{N} = \dfrac{d\mathbf{T}/dt}{|d\mathbf{T}/dt|}$. Use the Chain Rule and recall that $|\mathbf{v}| = ds/dt > 0$.

T **77. Maximum curvature** Consider the "superparabolas" $f_n(x) = x^{2n}$, where n is a positive integer.

a. Find the curvature function of f_n, for $n = 1, 2, 3$.
b. Plot f_n and their curvature functions, for $n = 1, 2, 3$, and check for consistency.
c. At what points does the maximum curvature occur, for $n = 1, 2, 3$?
d. Let the maximum curvature for f_n occur at $x = \pm z_n$. Using either analytical methods or a calculator determine $\lim_{n \to \infty} z_n$. Interpret your result.

78. Descartes' four-circle solution Consider the four mutually tangent circles shown in the figure that have radii a, b, c, and d, and curvatures $A = 1/a$, $B = 1/b$, $C = 1/c$, and $D = 1/d$. Prove Descartes' result (1643) that

$$(A + B + C + D)^2 = 2(A^2 + B^2 + C^2 + D^2).$$

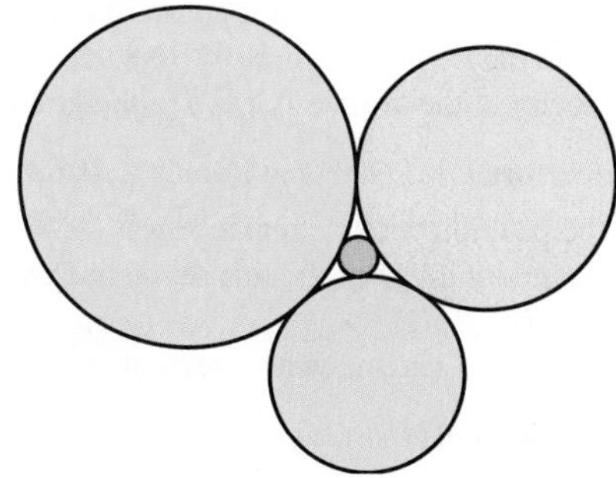

QUICK CHECK ANSWERS

1. For $a \leq t \leq b$, the curve C generated is $(b - a)/2\pi$ of a full circle. Because the full circle has a length of 2π, the curve C has a length of $b - a$. **2.** No. If t increases by one unit, the length of the curve increases by $\sqrt{3}$ units. **3.** $\kappa = \frac{1}{3}$ **4.** $\kappa = 0$ **5.** Negative y-direction **6.** $\kappa = 0$, so **N** is undefined.

CHAPTER 12 REVIEW EXERCISES

1. **Explain why or why not** Determine whether the following statements are true and give an explanation or counterexample.
   a. Given two vectors **u** and **v**, it is always true that $2\mathbf{u} + \mathbf{v} = \mathbf{v} + 2\mathbf{u}$.
   b. The vector in the direction of **u** with the length of **v** equals the vector in the direction of **v** with the length of **u**.
   c. If $\mathbf{u} \neq \mathbf{0}$, $\mathbf{u} + \mathbf{v} = \mathbf{0}$, then **u** and **v** are parallel.
   d. If $\mathbf{r}'(t) = \mathbf{0}$, then $\mathbf{r}(t) = \langle a, b, c \rangle$ where a, b, and c are real numbers.
   e. The curve $\mathbf{r}(t) = \langle 5\cos t, 12\cos t, 13\sin t \rangle$ uses arc length as a parameter.
   f. The position vector and the principal unit normal are always parallel on a smooth curve.

2–5. Drawing vectors *Let* $\mathbf{u} = \langle 3, -4 \rangle$ *and* $\mathbf{v} = \langle -1, 2 \rangle$. *Use geometry to sketch* **u**, **v**, *and the following vectors.*

2. $\mathbf{u} - \mathbf{v}$
3. $-3\mathbf{v}$
4. $\mathbf{u} + 2\mathbf{v}$
5. $2\mathbf{v} - \mathbf{u}$

6–9. Working with vectors *Let* $\mathbf{u} = \langle 2, 4, -5 \rangle$ *and* $\mathbf{v} = \langle -6, 10, 2 \rangle$.

6. Compute $\mathbf{u} - 3\mathbf{v}$.
7. Compute $|\mathbf{u} + \mathbf{v}|$.
8. Find the unit vector with the same direction as **u**.
9. Find a vector parallel to **v** with length 20.
10. **Scalar multiples** Find scalars a, b, and c such that
$$\langle 2, 2, 2 \rangle = a\langle 1, 1, 0 \rangle + b\langle 0, 1, 1 \rangle + c\langle 1, 0, 1 \rangle.$$
11. **Velocity vectors** Assume the positive x-axis points east and the positive y-axis points north.
    a. An airliner flies northwest at a constant altitude at 550 mi/hr in calm air. Find a and b such that its velocity may be expressed in the form $\mathbf{v} = a\mathbf{i} + b\mathbf{j}$.
    b. An airliner flies northwest at a constant altitude at 550 mi/hr relative to the air in a southerly crosswind $\mathbf{w} = \langle 0, 40 \rangle$. Find the velocity of the airliner relative to the ground.
12. **Position vectors** Let $\overrightarrow{PQ}$ extend from $P(2, 0, 6)$ to $Q(2, -8, 5)$.
    a. Find the position vector equal to $\overrightarrow{PQ}$.
    b. Find the midpoint M of the line segment PQ. Then find the magnitude of $\overrightarrow{PM}$.
    c. Find a vector of length 8 with direction opposite to that of $\overrightarrow{PQ}$.

13–15. Spheres and balls *Use set notation to describe the following sets.*

13. The sphere of radius 4 centered at $(1, 0, -1)$
14. The open ball of radius 10 centered at $(2, 4, -3)$
15. The points outside the sphere of radius 2 centered at $(0, 1, 0)$
16. **Combined force** An object at the origin is acted on by the forces $\mathbf{F}_1 = -10\mathbf{i} + 20\mathbf{k}$, $\mathbf{F}_2 = 40\mathbf{j} + 10\mathbf{k}$, and $\mathbf{F}_3 = -50\mathbf{i} + 20\mathbf{j}$. Find the magnitude of the combined force and describe with a sketch the direction of the force.
17. **Falling probe** A remote sensing probe falls vertically with a terminal velocity of 60 m/s when it encounters a horizontal crosswind blowing north at 4 m/s and an updraft blowing vertically at 10 m/s. Find the magnitude and direction of the resulting velocity relative to the ground.

18–19. Angles and projections

a. Find the angle between **u** *and* **v**.
b. Compute $\text{proj}_{\mathbf{v}}\mathbf{u}$ *and* $\text{scal}_{\mathbf{v}}\mathbf{u}$.
c. Compute $\text{proj}_{\mathbf{u}}\mathbf{v}$ *and* $\text{scal}_{\mathbf{u}}\mathbf{v}$.

18. $\mathbf{u} = -3\mathbf{j} + 4\mathbf{k}$, $\mathbf{v} = -4\mathbf{i} + \mathbf{j} + 5\mathbf{k}$
19. $\mathbf{u} = 6\mathbf{i} - \mathbf{k}$, $\mathbf{v} = 8\mathbf{i} + 2\mathbf{j} - 3\mathbf{k}$
20. **Work** A 180-lb man stands on a hillside that makes an angle of 30° with the horizontal, producing a force of $\mathbf{W} = \langle 0, -180 \rangle$ lb.

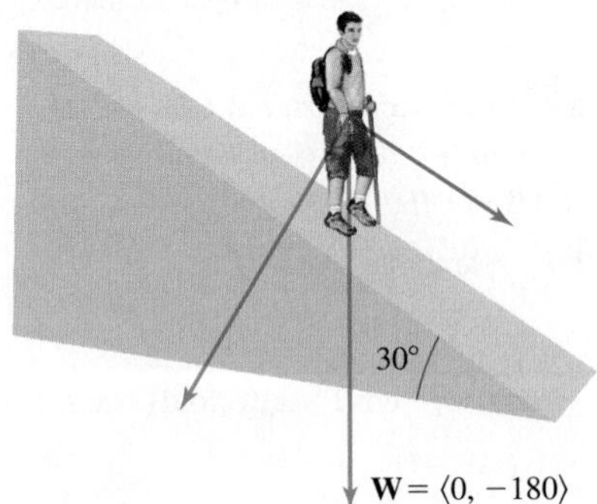

    a. Find the component of his weight in the downward direction perpendicular to the hillside and in the downward direction parallel to the hillside.
    b. How much work is done when the man moves 10 ft up the hillside?
21. **Normal vectors** Find a unit vector normal to the vectors $\langle 2, -6, 9 \rangle$ and $\langle -1, 0, 6 \rangle$.
22. **Angle in two ways** Find the angle between $\langle 2, 0, -2 \rangle$ and $\langle 2, 2, 0 \rangle$ using (a) the dot product and (b) the cross product.
23. **Knee torque** Jan does leg lifts with a 10-kg weight attached to her foot, so the resulting force is $mg \approx 98$ N directed vertically downward. If the distance from her knee to the weight is 0.4 m and her lower leg makes an angle of θ to the vertical, find the magnitude of the torque about her knee as her leg is lifted (as a function of θ). What is the minimum and maximum magnitude of the torque? Does the direction of the torque change as her leg is lifted?

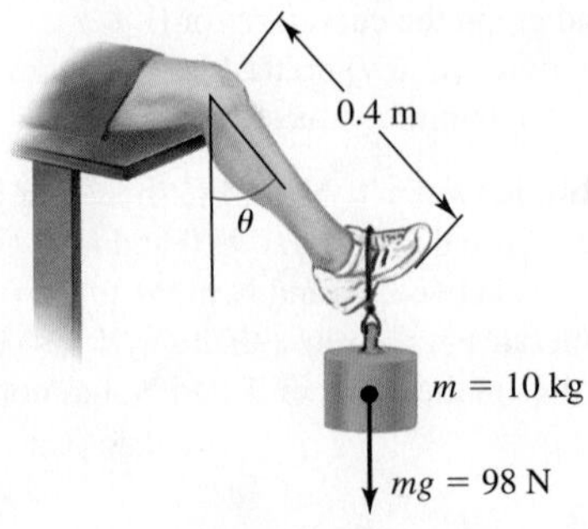

24–26. Lines in space *Find an equation of the following lines or line segments.*

24. The line that passes through the points $(2, 6, -1)$ and $(-6, 4, 0)$

25. The line segment that joins the points $(0, -3, 9)$ and $(2, -8, 1)$

26. The line through the point $(0, 1, 1)$ and normal to the vector $\langle 2, -1, 3 \rangle$.

T 27–29. Curves in space *Sketch the curves described by the following functions. Use analysis and describe the shape of the curve before using a graphing utility.*

27. $\mathbf{r}(t) = 4 \cos t\, \mathbf{i} + \mathbf{j} + 4 \sin t\, \mathbf{k}$, for $0 \le t \le 2\pi$

28. $\mathbf{r}(t) = e^t \mathbf{i} + 2e^t \mathbf{j} + \mathbf{k}$, for $t \ge 0$

29. $\mathbf{r}(t) = \sin t\, \mathbf{i} + \sqrt{2} \cos t\, \mathbf{j} + \sin t\, \mathbf{k}$, for $0 \le t \le 2\pi$

T 30. Orthogonal r and r′ Find all points on the ellipse $\mathbf{r}(t) = \langle 1, 8 \sin t, \cos t \rangle$, for $0 \le t \le 2\pi$, at which $\mathbf{r}(t)$ and $\mathbf{r}'(t)$ are orthogonal. Sketch the curve and the tangent vectors to verify your conclusion.

31. **Projectile motion** A projectile is launched from the origin, which is a point 50 ft from a 30-ft vertical cliff (see figure). It is launched at a speed of $50\sqrt{2}$ ft/s at an angle of 45° to the horizontal. Assume the ground is horizontal on top of the cliff and only the gravitational force affects the motion of the object.

a. Give the coordinates of the landing spot of the projectile on the top of the cliff.
b. What is the maximum height reached by the projectile?
c. What is the time of flight?
d. Write the integral that gives the length of the trajectory.
e. Approximate the length of the trajectory.
f. What is the range of launch angles needed to clear the edge of the cliff?

32–33. Arc length of polar curves *Find the approximate length of the following curves.*

32. The limaçon $r = 3 + 2 \cos \theta$

33. The limaçon $r = 3 - 6 \cos \theta$

34. **Tangents and normals to an ellipse** Consider the ellipse $\mathbf{r}(t) = \langle 3 \cos t, 4 \sin t \rangle$, for $0 \le t \le 2\pi$.

a. Find the tangent vector $\mathbf{r}'$, the unit tangent vector $\mathbf{T}$, and the principal unit normal vector $\mathbf{N}$ at all points on the curve.
b. At what points does $|\mathbf{r}'|$ have maximum and minimum values?
c. At what points does the curvature have maximum and minimum values? Interpret this result in light of part (b).
d. Find the points (if any) at which $\mathbf{r}$ and $\mathbf{N}$ are parallel.

T 35–38. Properties of space curves *Do the following calculations for all values of t for which the given curve is defined.*

a. Find the tangent vector and the unit tangent vector.
b. Find the curvature.
c. Find the principal unit normal vector.
d. Verify that $|\mathbf{N}| = 1$ *and* $\mathbf{T} \cdot \mathbf{N} = 0$.
e. Graph the curve and sketch $\mathbf{T}$ *and* $\mathbf{N}$ *at two points.*

35. $\mathbf{r}(t) = \langle 6 \cos t, 3 \sin t \rangle$, for $0 \le t \le 2\pi$

36. $\mathbf{r}(t) = \cos t\, \mathbf{i} + 2 \sin t\, \mathbf{j} + \mathbf{k}$, for $0 \le t \le 2\pi$

37. $\mathbf{r}(t) = \cos t\, \mathbf{i} + 2 \cos t\, \mathbf{j} + \sqrt{5} \sin t\, \mathbf{k}$, for $0 \le t \le 2\pi$

38. $\mathbf{r}(t) = t\, \mathbf{i} + 2 \cos t\, \mathbf{j} + 2 \sin t\, \mathbf{k}$, for $0 \le t \le 2\pi$

39–42. Analyzing motion *Consider the position vector of the following moving objects.*

a. Find the normal and tangential components of the acceleration.
b. Graph the trajectory and sketch the normal and tangential components of the acceleration at two points on the trajectory. Show that their sum gives the total acceleration.

39. $\mathbf{r}(t) = 2 \cos t\, \mathbf{i} + 2 \sin t\, \mathbf{j}$, for $0 \le t \le 2\pi$

40. $\mathbf{r}(t) = 3t\, \mathbf{i} + (4 - t)\mathbf{j} + t\, \mathbf{k}$, for $t \ge 0$

41. $\mathbf{r}(t) = (t^2 + 1)\mathbf{i} + 2t\, \mathbf{j}$, for $t \ge 0$

42. $\mathbf{r}(t) = 2 \cos t\, \mathbf{i} + 2 \sin t\, \mathbf{j} + 10t\, \mathbf{k}$, for $0 \le t \le 2\pi$

43. **Lines in the plane**

a. Use a dot product to find the equation of the line in the xy-plane passing through the point (x_0, y_0) perpendicular to the vector $\langle a, b \rangle$.
b. Given a point $(x_0, y_0, 0)$ and a vector $\mathbf{v} = \langle a, b, 0 \rangle$ in $\mathbf{R}^3$, describe the set of points that satisfy the equation

$$\langle a, b, 0 \rangle \times \langle x - x_0, y - y_0, 0 \rangle = \mathbf{0}.$$

Use this result to determine an equation of a line in $\mathbf{R}^2$ passing through (x_0, y_0) parallel to the vector $\langle a, b \rangle$.

44. **Length of a DVD groove** The capacity of a single-sided, single-layer digital versatile disc (DVD) is approximately 4.7 billion bytes—enough to store a two-hour movie. (Newer double-sided, double-layer DVDs have about four times that capacity, and Blu-ray discs are in the range of 50 gigabytes.) A DVD consists of a single "groove" that spirals outward from the inner edge to the outer edge of the storage region.

a. First consider the spiral given in polar coordinates by $r = t\theta/(2\pi)$, where $0 \le \theta \le 2\pi N$ and successive loops of the spiral are t units apart. Explain why this spiral has N loops and why the entire spiral has a radius of $R = Nt$ units. Sketch three loops of the spiral.
b. Write an integral for the length L of the spiral with N loops.
c. The integral in part (b) can be evaluated exactly, but a good approximation can also be made. Assuming N is large, explain

why $\theta^2 + 1 \approx \theta^2$. Use this approximation to simplify the integral in part (b) and show that $L \approx t\pi N^2 = \dfrac{\pi R^2}{t}$.

d. Now consider a DVD with an inner radius of $r = 2.5$ cm and an outer radius of $R = 5.9$ cm. Model the groove by a spiral with a thickness of $t = 1.5$ microns $= 1.5 \times 10^{-6}$ m. Because of the hole in the DVD, the lower limit in the arc length integral is not $\theta = 0$. What are the limits of integration?

e. Use the approximation in part (c) to find the length of the DVD groove. Express your answer in centimeters and miles.

Chapter 12 Guided Projects

Applications of the material in this chapter and related topics can be found in the following Guided Projects. For additional information, see the Preface.

- Designing a trajectory
- CORDIC algorithms: How your calculator works
- Kepler's laws
- Intercepting a UFO
- Bezier curves for graphic design

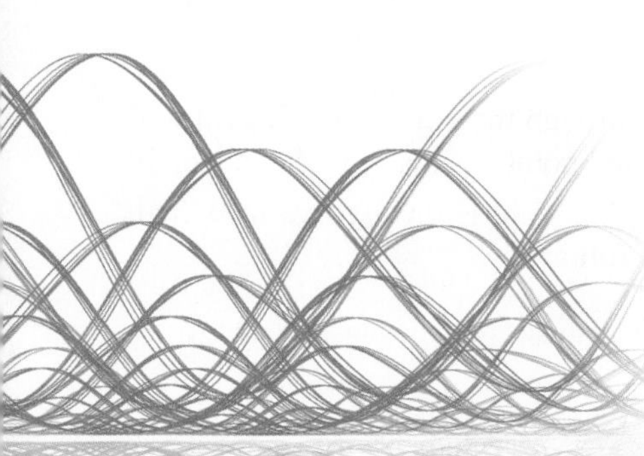

13

Functions of Several Variables

Chapter Preview Chapter 12 was devoted to vector-valued functions, which generally have one independent variable and two or more dependent variables. In this chapter, we step into three-dimensional space along a different path by considering functions with several independent variables and one dependent variable. All the familiar properties of single-variable functions—domains, graphs, limits, continuity, and derivatives—have generalizations for multivariable functions, although there are often subtle differences when compared to single-variable functions. With functions of several independent variables, we work with *partial derivatives*, which, in turn, give rise to directional derivatives and the *gradient*, a fundamental concept in calculus. Partial derivatives allow us to find maximum and minimum values of multivariable functions. We define tangent planes, rather than tangent lines, that allow us to make linear approximations. The chapter ends with a survey of optimization problems in several variables.

13.1 Planes and Surfaces

Functions with one independent variable, such as $f(x) = xe^{-x}$, or *equations* in two variables, such as $x^2 + y^2 = 4$, describe curves in $\mathbf{R}^2$. We now add a third variable to the picture and consider functions of two independent variables (for example, $f(x, y) = x^2 + 2y^2$) and equations in three variables (for example, $x^2 + y^2 + 2z^2 = 4$). We see in this chapter that such functions and equations describe *surfaces* that may be displayed in $\mathbf{R}^3$. Just as a line is the simplest curve in $\mathbf{R}^2$, a plane is the fundamental surface in $\mathbf{R}^3$.

Equations of Planes

Intuitively, a plane is a flat surface with infinite extent in all directions. Three noncollinear points (not all on the same line) determine a unique plane in $\mathbf{R}^3$. A plane in $\mathbf{R}^3$ is also uniquely determined by one point in the plane and any nonzero vector orthogonal (perpendicular) to the plane. Such a vector, called a **normal vector**, specifies the orientation of the plane.

> Just as the slope determines the orientation of a line, a normal vector determines the orientation of a plane.

DEFINITION Plane in $\mathbf{R}^3$

Given a fixed point P_0 and a nonzero vector $\mathbf{n}$, the set of points P in $\mathbf{R}^3$ for which $\overrightarrow{P_0P}$ is orthogonal to $\mathbf{n}$ is called a **plane** (Figure 13.1).

QUICK CHECK 1 Describe the plane that is orthogonal to the unit vector $\mathbf{i} = \langle 1, 0, 0 \rangle$ and passes through the point $(1, 2, 3)$.

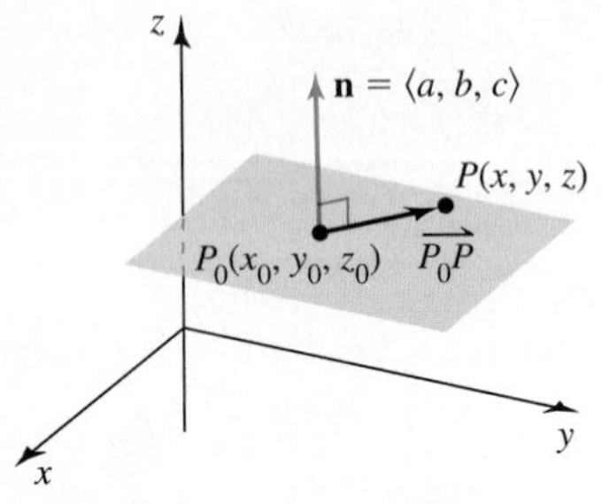

The orientation of a plane is specified by a normal vector **n**. All vectors $\overrightarrow{P_0P}$ in the plane are orthogonal to **n**.

FIGURE 13.1

We now derive an equation of the plane passing through the point $P_0(x_0, y_0, z_0)$ with nonzero normal vector $\mathbf{n} = \langle a, b, c \rangle$. Notice that for any point $P(x, y, z)$ in the plane, the vector $\overrightarrow{P_0P} = \langle x - x_0, y - y_0, z - z_0 \rangle$ lies in the plane and is orthogonal to **n**. This orthogonality relationship is written and simplified as follows:

$$\begin{aligned} \mathbf{n} \cdot \overrightarrow{P_0P} &= 0 && \text{Dot product of orthogonal vectors} \\ \langle a, b, c \rangle \cdot \langle x - x_0, y - y_0, z - z_0 \rangle &= 0 && \text{Substitute vector components.} \\ a(x - x_0) + b(y - y_0) + c(z - z_0) &= 0 && \text{Expand the dot product.} \\ ax + by + cz &= d && d = ax_0 + by_0 + cz_0 \end{aligned}$$

This important result states that the most general linear equation in three variables, $ax + by + cz = d$, describes a plane in $\mathbf{R}^3$.

> A vector $\mathbf{n} = \langle a, b, c \rangle$ is used to describe a *plane* by specifying a direction *orthogonal* to the plane. By contrast, a vector $\mathbf{v} = \langle a, b, c \rangle$ is used to describe a *line* by specifying a direction *parallel* to the line (Section 12.5).

General Equation of a Plane in $\mathbf{R}^3$

The plane passing through the point $P_0(x_0, y_0, z_0)$ with a normal vector $\mathbf{n} = \langle a, b, c \rangle$ is described by the equation

$$a(x - x_0) + b(y - y_0) + c(z - z_0) = 0 \quad \text{or} \quad ax + by + cz = d,$$

where $d = ax_0 + by_0 + cz_0$.

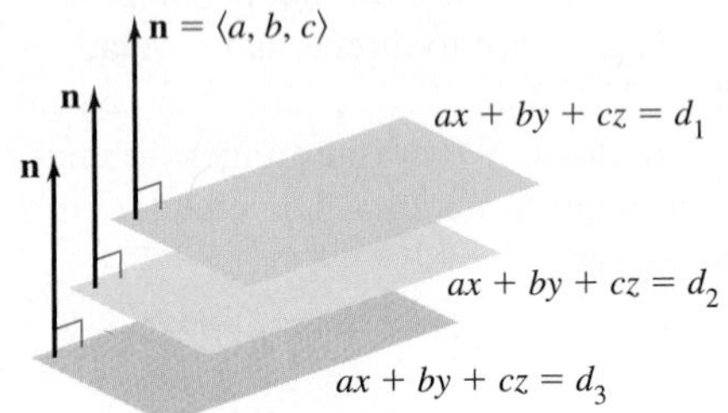

The normal vectors of parallel planes have the same direction.

FIGURE 13.2

The coefficients a, b, and c in the equation of a plane determine the *orientation* of the plane, while the constant term d determines the *location* of the plane. If a, b, and c are held constant and d is varied, a family of parallel planes is generated, all with the same orientation (Figure 13.2).

QUICK CHECK 2 Consider the equation of a plane in the form $\mathbf{n} \cdot \overrightarrow{P_0P} = 0$. Explain why the equation of the plane depends only on the direction, but not the length, of the normal vector **n**. ◀

EXAMPLE 1 **Equation of a plane** Find an equation of the plane passing through $P_0(2, -3, 4)$ with a normal vector $\mathbf{n} = \langle -1, 2, 3 \rangle$.

SOLUTION Substituting the components of **n** ($a = -1, b = 2$, and $c = 3$) and the coordinates of P_0 ($x_0 = 2, y_0 = -3$, and $z_0 = 4$) into the equation of a plane, we have

$$\begin{aligned} a(x - x_0) + b(y - y_0) + c(z - z_0) &= 0 && \text{General equation of a plane} \\ (-1)(x - 2) + 2(y - (-3)) + 3(z - 4) &= 0 && \text{Substitute.} \\ -x + 2y + 3z &= 4 && \text{Simplify.} \end{aligned}$$

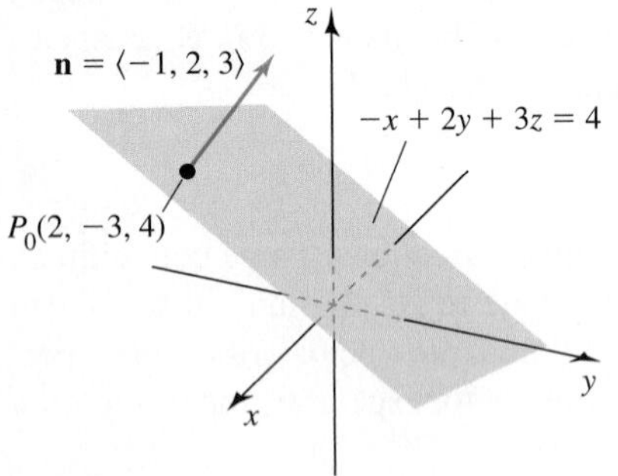

FIGURE 13.3

The plane is shown in Figure 13.3. *Related Exercises 11–14* ◀

EXAMPLE 2 **A plane through three points** Find an equation of the plane that passes through the (noncollinear) points $P(2, -1, 3)$, $Q(1, 4, 0)$, and $R(0, -1, 5)$.

SOLUTION To write an equation for the plane, we must find a normal vector. Because P, Q, and R lie in the plane, the vectors $\overrightarrow{PQ} = \langle -1, 5, -3 \rangle$ and $\overrightarrow{PR} = \langle -2, 0, 2 \rangle$ also lie in the plane. The cross product $\overrightarrow{PQ} \times \overrightarrow{PR}$ is perpendicular to both $\overrightarrow{PQ}$ and $\overrightarrow{PR}$; therefore a vector normal to the plane is

$$\mathbf{n} = \overrightarrow{PQ} \times \overrightarrow{PR} = \begin{vmatrix} \mathbf{i} & \mathbf{j} & \mathbf{k} \\ -1 & 5 & -3 \\ -2 & 0 & 2 \end{vmatrix} = 10\mathbf{i} + 8\mathbf{j} + 10\mathbf{k}.$$

> For three points P, Q, and R to determine a plane, they must not be collinear. If P, Q, and R *are* collinear, then the vectors $\overrightarrow{PQ}$ and $\overrightarrow{PR}$ are parallel, which implies that $\overrightarrow{PQ} \times \overrightarrow{PR} = \mathbf{0}$.

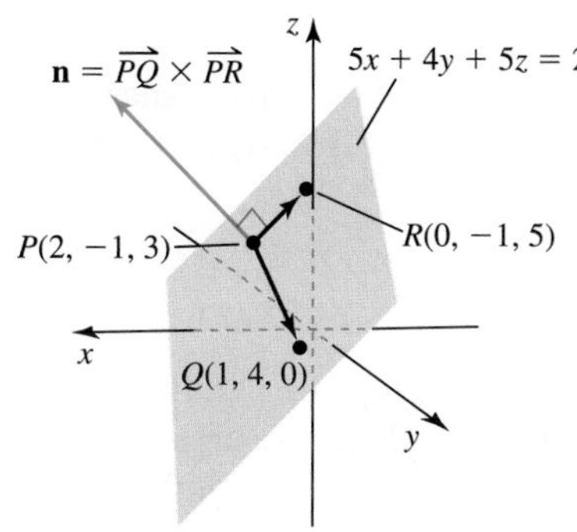

FIGURE 13.4

Any scalar multiple of $\mathbf{n}$ may be used as the normal vector. Choosing $\mathbf{n} = \langle 10, 8, 10 \rangle$ and $P_0(2, -1, 3)$ as the fixed point in the plane (Figure 13.4), an equation of the plane is

$$10(x - 2) + 8(y - (-1)) + 10(z - 3) = 0 \quad \text{or} \quad 5x + 4y + 5z = 21.$$

Using either Q or R as the fixed point in the plane leads to an equivalent equation of the plane.

Related Exercises 15–18

QUICK CHECK 3 Verify in Example 2 that the same equation for the plane results if either Q or R is used as the fixed point in the plane.

EXAMPLE 3 Properties of a plane Let Q be the plane described by the equation $2x - 3y - z = 6$.

a. Find a vector normal to Q.

b. Find the points at which Q intersects the coordinate axes and plot Q.

c. Describe the sets of points at which Q intersects the yz-plane, the xz-plane, and the xy-plane.

SOLUTION

a. The coefficients of x, y, and z in the equation of Q are the components of a vector normal to Q. Therefore, a normal vector is $\mathbf{n} = \langle 2, -3, -1 \rangle$ (or any nonzero multiple of $\mathbf{n}$).

b. The point (x, y, z) at which Q intersects the x-axis must have $y = z = 0$. Substituting $y = z = 0$ into the equation of Q gives $x = 3$, so Q intersects the x-axis at $(3, 0, 0)$. Similarly, Q intersects the y-axis at $(0, -2, 0)$, and Q intersects the z-axis at $(0, 0, -6)$. Connecting the three intercepts with straight lines allows us to visualize the plane (Figure 13.5).

➤ There is a possibility for confusion here. Working in $\mathbf{R}^3$ with no other restrictions, the equation $-3y - z = 6$ describes a plane that is parallel to the x-axis (because x is unspecified). To make it clear that $-3y - z = 6$ is a line in the yz-plane, the condition $x = 0$ is included.

c. All points in the yz-plane have $x = 0$. Setting $x = 0$ in the equation of Q gives the equation $-3y - z = 6$, which, with the condition $x = 0$, describes a line in the yz-plane. If we set $y = 0$, Q intersects the xz-plane in the line $2x - z = 6$, where $y = 0$. If $z = 0$, Q intersects the xy-plane in the line $2x - 3y = 6$, where $z = 0$ (Figure 13.5).

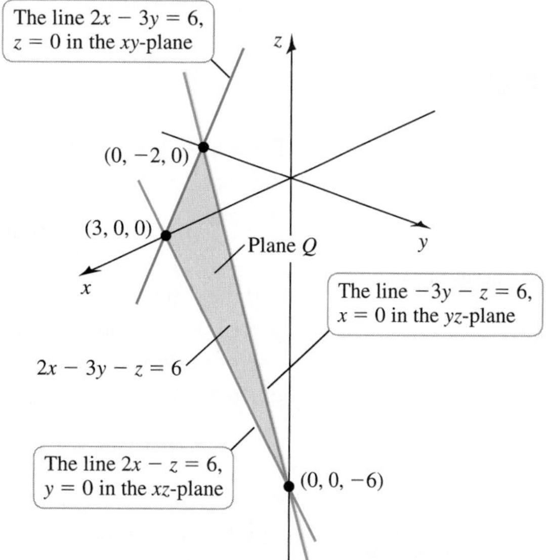

FIGURE 13.5

Related Exercises 19–22

Two distinct planes are parallel if $\mathbf{n}_1$ and $\mathbf{n}_2$ are parallel.

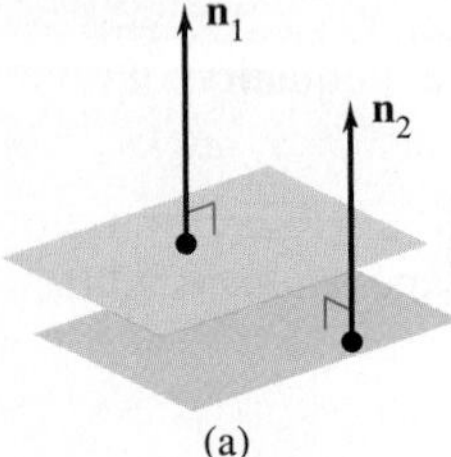

(a)

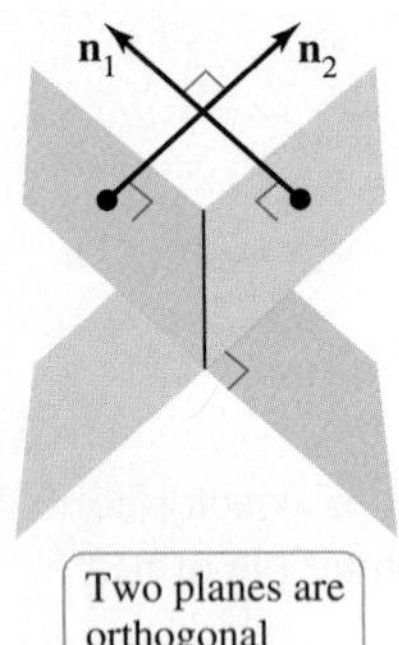

Two planes are orthogonal if $\mathbf{n}_1 \cdot \mathbf{n}_2 = 0$.

(b)

FIGURE 13.6

Parallel and Orthogonal Planes

The normal vectors of distinct planes tell us about the relative orientation of the planes. Two cases are of particular interest: two distinct planes may be **parallel** (Figure 13.6a) and two intersecting planes may be **orthogonal** (Figure 13.6b).

> DEFINITION **Parallel and Orthogonal Planes**
>
> Two distinct planes are **parallel** if their respective normal vectors are parallel (that is, the normal vectors are scalar multiples of each other). Two planes are **orthogonal** if their respective normal vectors are orthogonal (that is, the dot product of the normal vectors is zero).

EXAMPLE 4 **Parallel and orthogonal planes** Which of the following distinct planes are parallel and which are orthogonal?

$$Q\colon\ 2x - 3y + 6z = 12 \qquad R\colon\ -x + \tfrac{3}{2}y - 3z = 14$$
$$S\colon\ 6x + 8y + 2z = 1 \qquad T\colon\ -9x - 12y - 3z = 7$$

SOLUTION Let $\mathbf{n}_Q$, $\mathbf{n}_R$, $\mathbf{n}_S$, and $\mathbf{n}_T$ be vectors normal to Q, R, S, and T, respectively. Normal vectors may be read from the coefficients of x, y, and z in the equations of the planes:

$$\mathbf{n}_Q = \langle 2, -3, 6 \rangle \qquad \mathbf{n}_R = \left\langle -1, \tfrac{3}{2}, -3 \right\rangle$$
$$\mathbf{n}_S = \langle 6, 8, 2 \rangle \qquad \mathbf{n}_T = \langle -9, -12, -3 \rangle$$

Notice that $\mathbf{n}_Q = -2\mathbf{n}_R$, which implies that Q and R are parallel. Similarly, $\mathbf{n}_T = -\frac{3}{2}\mathbf{n}_S$, so S and T are parallel. Furthermore, $\mathbf{n}_Q \cdot \mathbf{n}_S = 0$ and $\mathbf{n}_Q \cdot \mathbf{n}_T = 0$, which implies that Q is orthogonal to both S and T. Because Q and R are parallel, it follows that R is also orthogonal to both S and T. *Related Exercises 23–24* ◀

QUICK CHECK 4 Verify in Example 4 that $\mathbf{n}_R \cdot \mathbf{n}_S = 0$ and $\mathbf{n}_R \cdot \mathbf{n}_T = 0$. ◀

EXAMPLE 5 **Parallel planes** Find an equation of the plane Q that passes through the point $(-2, 4, 1)$ and is parallel to the plane $R\colon 3x - 2y + z = 4$.

SOLUTION The vector $\mathbf{n} = \langle 3, -2, 1 \rangle$ is normal to R. Because Q and R are parallel, $\mathbf{n}$ is also normal to Q. Therefore, an equation of Q passing through $(-2, 4, 1)$ with normal vector $\langle 3, -2, 1 \rangle$ is

$$3(x + 2) - 2(y - 4) + (z - 1) = 0 \quad \text{or} \quad 3x - 2y + z = -13.$$

Related Exercises 25–28 ◀

EXAMPLE 6 **Intersecting planes** Find an equation of the line of intersection of the planes $Q\colon x + 2y + z = 5$ and $R\colon 2x + y - z = 7$.

SOLUTION First note that the vectors normal to the planes, $\mathbf{n}_Q = \langle 1, 2, 1 \rangle$ and $\mathbf{n}_R = \langle 2, 1, -1 \rangle$, are *not* multiples of each other. Therefore, the planes are not parallel and they must intersect in a line; call it ℓ. To find an equation of ℓ, we need two pieces of information: a point on ℓ and a vector pointing in the direction of ℓ. Here is one of several ways to find a point on ℓ. Setting $z = 0$ in the equations of the planes gives equations of the lines in which the planes intersect the xy-plane:

$$x + 2y = 5$$
$$2x + y = 7$$

Solving these equations simultaneously, we find that $x = 3$ and $y = 1$. Combining this result with $z = 0$, we see that $(3, 1, 0)$ is a point on ℓ (Figure 13.7).

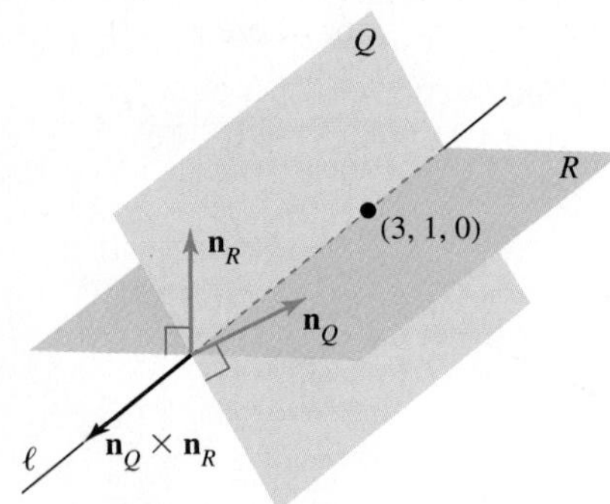

$\mathbf{n}_Q \times \mathbf{n}_R$ is a vector perpendicular to $\mathbf{n}_Q$ and $\mathbf{n}_R$.
Line ℓ is perpendicular to $\mathbf{n}_Q$ and $\mathbf{n}_R$.
Thus, ℓ and $\mathbf{n}_Q \times \mathbf{n}_R$ are parallel to each other.

FIGURE 13.7

➤ By setting $z = 0$ and solving these two equations, we find the point that lies on both planes *and* lies in the xy-plane ($z = 0$).

We next find a vector parallel to ℓ. Because ℓ lies in Q and R, it is orthogonal to the normal vectors $\mathbf{n}_Q$ and $\mathbf{n}_R$. Therefore, the cross product of $\mathbf{n}_Q$ and $\mathbf{n}_R$ is a vector parallel to ℓ (Figure 13.7). In this case, the cross product is

$$\mathbf{n}_Q \times \mathbf{n}_R = \begin{vmatrix} \mathbf{i} & \mathbf{j} & \mathbf{k} \\ 1 & 2 & 1 \\ 2 & 1 & -1 \end{vmatrix} = -3\mathbf{i} + 3\mathbf{j} - 3\mathbf{k} = \langle -3, 3, -3 \rangle.$$

> Another question related to Example 6 concerns the angle between two planes. See Exercise 79 for an example.

An equation of the line ℓ in the direction of the vector $\langle -3, 3, -3 \rangle$ passing through the point $(3, 1, 0)$ is

$$\begin{aligned} \mathbf{r}(t) &= \langle x_0, y_0, z_0 \rangle + t\langle a, b, c \rangle && \text{Equation of a line (Section 12.5)} \\ &= \langle 3, 1, 0 \rangle + t\langle -3, 3, -3 \rangle && \text{Substitute.} \\ &= \langle 3 - 3t, 1 + 3t, -3t \rangle, && \text{Simplify.} \end{aligned}$$

> Any nonzero scalar multiple of $\langle -3, 3, -3 \rangle$ can be used for the direction of ℓ. For example, another equation of ℓ is $\mathbf{r}(t) = \langle 3 + t, 1 - t, t \rangle$.

where $-\infty < t < \infty$. You can check that any point (x, y, z) with $x = 3 - 3t$, $y = 1 + 3t$, and $z = -3t$ satisfies the equations of both planes.

Related Exercises 29–32 ◄

Cylinders and Traces

In the context of three-dimensional surfaces, the term *cylinder* has a more general meaning than it does in everyday usage.

DEFINITION Cylinder

Given a curve C in a plane P and a line ℓ not in P, a **cylinder** is the surface consisting of all lines parallel to ℓ that pass through C (Figure 13.8).

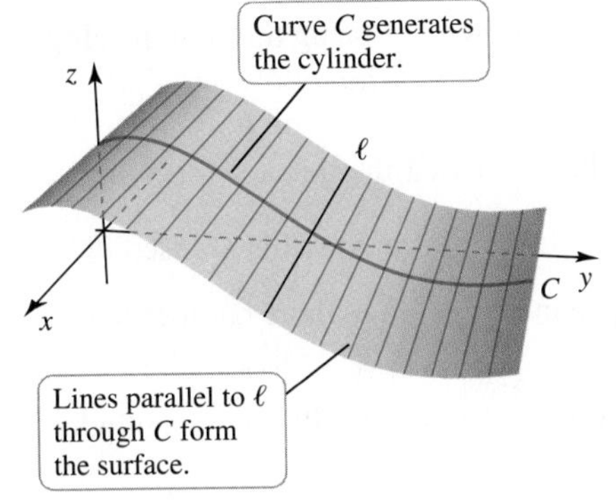
Curve C generates the cylinder.
z
ℓ
x
C
y
Lines parallel to ℓ through C form the surface.
FIGURE 13.8

A common situation arises when ℓ is parallel to one of the coordinate axes. In these cases, the cylinder is also parallel to one of the coordinate axes. Equations for such cylinders are easy to identify: The variable corresponding to the coordinate axis parallel to ℓ is missing.

For example, working in $\mathbf{R}^3$, the equation $y = x^2$ does not include z, which means that z is arbitrary and can take on all values. Therefore, $y = x^2$ describes the cylinder consisting of all lines parallel to the z-axis that pass through the parabola $y = x^2$ in the xy-plane (Figure 13.9a). In a similar way, the equation $z^2 = y$ in $\mathbf{R}^3$ is missing the variable x, so it describes a cylinder parallel to the x-axis. The cylinder consists of lines parallel to the x-axis that pass through the curve $z^2 = y$ in the yz-plane (Figure 13.9b).

QUICK CHECK 5 To which coordinate axis in $\mathbf{R}^3$ is the cylinder $z - 2 \ln x = 0$ parallel? To which coordinate axis in $\mathbf{R}^3$ is the cylinder $y = 4z^2 - 1$ parallel? ◄

Graphing surfaces—and cylinders in particular—is facilitated by identifying the *traces* of the surface.

DEFINITION Trace

A **trace** of a surface is the set of points at which the surface intersects a plane that is parallel to one of the coordinate planes. The traces in the coordinate planes are called the ***xy*-trace**, the ***xz*-trace**, and the ***yz*-trace** (Figure 13.10).

EXAMPLE 7 Graphing cylinders Sketch the graphs of the following cylinders in $\mathbf{R}^3$. Identify the axis to which each cylinder is parallel.

a. $x^2 + 4y^2 = 16$ **b.** $x - \sin z = 0$

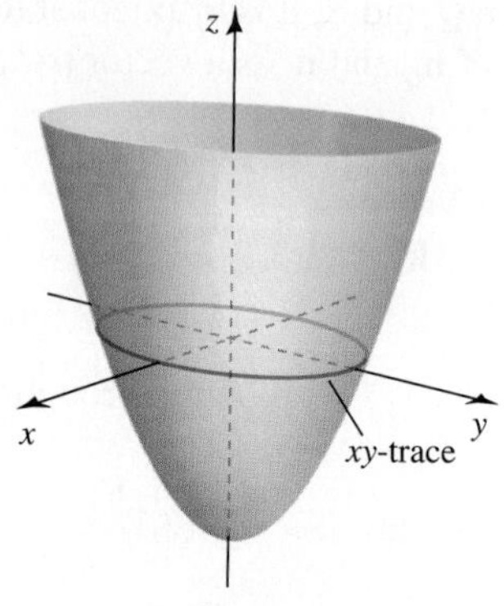
z
x
y
xy-trace

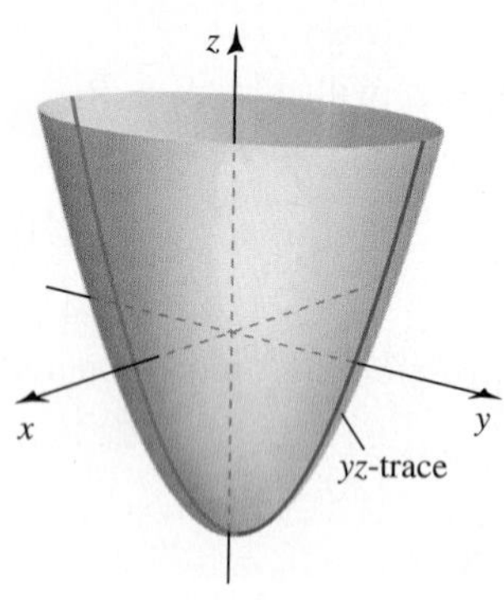
z
x
y
yz-trace

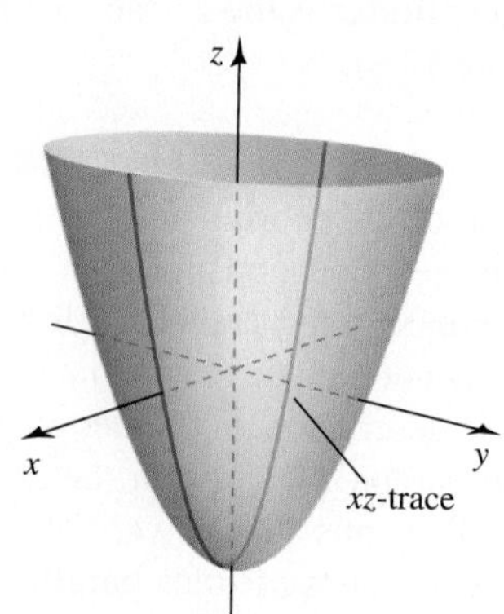
z
x
y
xz-trace

FIGURE 13.10

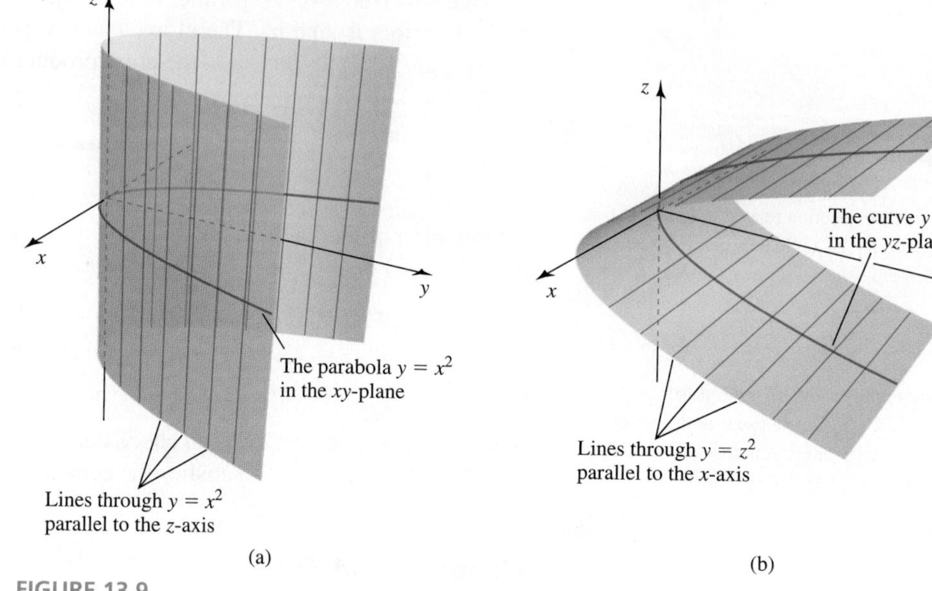
z
x
y
The parabola $y = x^2$ in the xy-plane
Lines through $y = x^2$ parallel to the z-axis
(a)
z
x
y
The curve $y = z^2$ in the yz-plane
Lines through $y = z^2$ parallel to the x-axis
(b)

FIGURE 13.9

SOLUTION

a. As an equation in $\mathbf{R}^3$, the variable z is absent. Therefore, z assumes all real values and the graph is a cylinder consisting of lines parallel to the z-axis passing through the ellipse $x^2 + 4y^2 = 16$ in the xy-plane. You can sketch the cylinder in the following steps:

1. Rewriting the given equation as $\frac{x^2}{4^2} + \frac{y^2}{2^2} = 1$, we see that the trace of the cylinder in the xy-plane (the xy-trace) is an ellipse. We begin by drawing this ellipse.

2. Next draw a second trace (a copy of the ellipse in Step 1) in a plane parallel to the xy-plane.

3. Now draw lines parallel to the z-axis through the two traces to fill out the cylinder (Figure 13.11a).

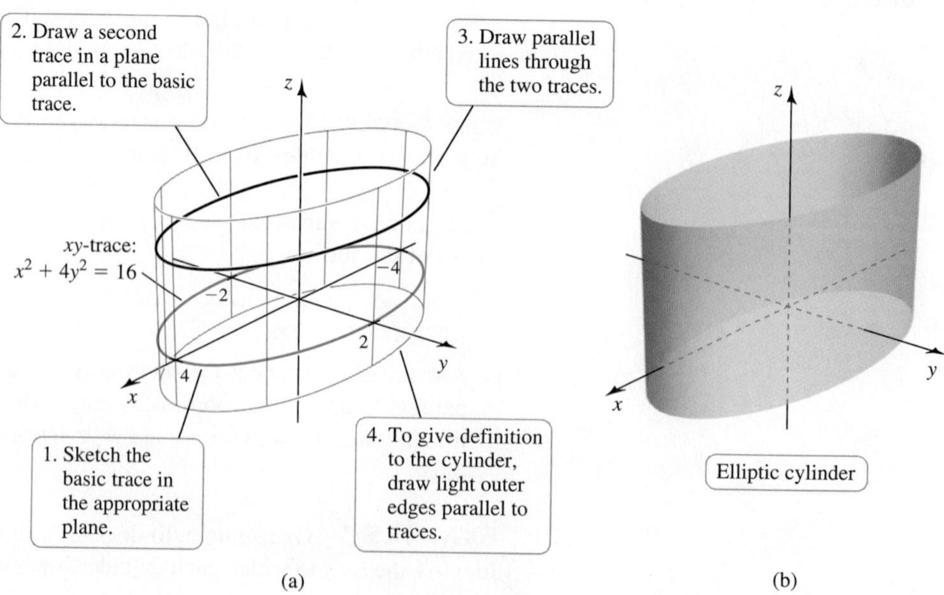
2. Draw a second trace in a plane parallel to the basic trace.
3. Draw parallel lines through the two traces.
z
xy-trace:
$x^2 + 4y^2 = 16$
−2
−4
2
4
x
y
1. Sketch the basic trace in the appropriate plane.
4. To give definition to the cylinder, draw light outer edges parallel to traces.
(a)
z
x
y
Elliptic cylinder
(b)

FIGURE 13.11

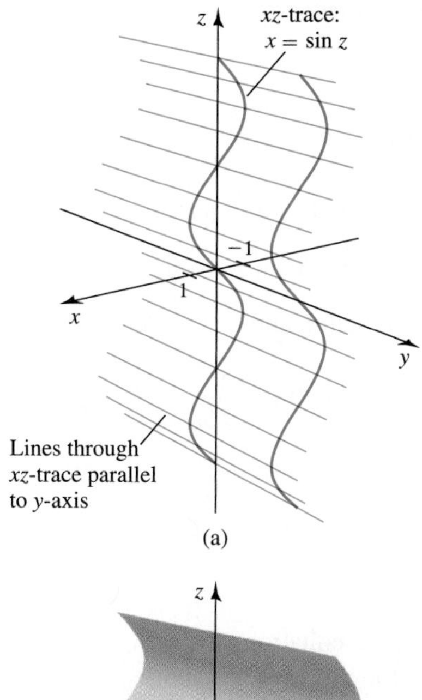

(b)

FIGURE 13.12

The resulting surface, called an *elliptic cylinder*, runs parallel to the z-axis (Figure 13.11b).

b. As an equation in $\mathbf{R}^3$, $x - \sin z = 0$ is missing the variable y. Therefore, y assumes all real values and the graph is a cylinder consisting of lines parallel to the y-axis passing through the curve $x = \sin z$ in the xz-plane. You can sketch the cylinder in the following steps:

1. Graph the curve $x = \sin z$ in the xz-plane, which is the xz-trace of the surface.
2. Draw a second trace (a copy of the curve in Step 1) in a plane parallel to the xz-plane.
3. Draw lines parallel to the y-axis passing through the two traces. (Figure 13.12a).

The result is a cylinder, running parallel to the y-axis, consisting of copies of the curve $x = \sin z$ (Figure 13.12b). *Related Exercises 33–36* ◀

Quadric Surfaces

Quadric surfaces are described by the general quadratic (second-degree) equation in three variables,

$$Ax^2 + By^2 + Cz^2 + Dxy + Exz + Fyz + Gx + Hy + Iz + J = 0,$$

where the coefficients $A, \ldots, J$ are constants and not all of A, B, C, D, E, and F are zero. We do not attempt a detailed study of this large family of surfaces. However, a few standard surfaces are worth investigating.

Apart from their mathematical interest, quadric surfaces have a variety of practical uses. Paraboloids (defined in Example 9) share the reflective properties of their two-dimensional counterparts (Section 11.4) and are used to design satellite dishes, headlamps, and mirrors in telescopes. Cooling towers for nuclear power plants have the shape of hyperboloids of one sheet. Ellipsoids appear in the design of water tanks and gears.

Making hand sketches of quadric surfaces can be challenging. Here are a few general features of quadric surfaces to keep in mind as you sketch their graphs.

➤ Working with quadric surfaces requires familiarity with conic sections (Section 11.4).

1. **Intercepts** Determine the points, if any, where the surface intersects the coordinate axes. To find these intercepts, set x, y, and z equal to zero in pairs in the equation of the surface and solve for the third coordinate.
2. **Traces** As illustrated in the following examples, finding traces of the surface helps visualize the surface. For example, setting $z = 0$ or $z = z_0$ (a constant) gives the traces in planes parallel to the xy-plane.
3. Sketch at least two traces in parallel planes (for example, traces with $z = 0$ and $z = \pm 1$). Then draw smooth curves that pass through the traces to fill out the surface.

QUICK CHECK 6 Explain why the elliptic cylinder discussed in Example 7a is a quadric surface. ◀

EXAMPLE 8 **An ellipsoid** The surface defined by the equation $\dfrac{x^2}{a^2} + \dfrac{y^2}{b^2} + \dfrac{z^2}{c^2} = 1$ is an *ellipsoid*. Graph the ellipsoid with $a = 3, b = 4$, and $c = 5$.

SOLUTION Setting x, y, and z to zero in pairs gives the intercepts $(\pm 3, 0, 0)$, $(0, \pm 4, 0)$, and $(0, 0, \pm 5)$. Note that points in $\mathbf{R}^3$ with $|x| > 3$ or $|y| > 4$ or $|z| > 5$ do not satisfy the equation of the surface (because the left side of the equation is the sum of nonnegative terms, which cannot exceed 1). Therefore, the entire surface is contained in the rectangular box defined by $|x| \le 3$, $|y| \le 4$, and $|z| \le 5$.

The name *ellipsoid* is used because all traces of this surface, when they exist, are ellipses.

The trace in the horizontal plane $z = z_0$ is found by substituting $z = z_0$ into the equation of the ellipsoid, which gives

$$\frac{x^2}{9} + \frac{y^2}{16} + \frac{z_0^2}{25} = 1 \quad \text{or} \quad \frac{x^2}{9} + \frac{y^2}{16} = 1 - \frac{z_0^2}{25}.$$

If $|z_0| < 5$, then $1 - \frac{z_0^2}{25} > 0$, and the equation describes an ellipse in the horizontal plane $z = z_0$. The largest ellipse parallel to the xy-plane occurs with $z_0 = 0$; it is the xy-trace, which is the ellipse $\frac{x^2}{9} + \frac{y^2}{16} = 1$ with axes of length 6 and 8 (Figure 13.13a).

You can check that the yz-trace, found by setting $x = 0$, is the ellipse $\frac{y^2}{16} + \frac{z^2}{25} = 1$.

The xz-trace (set $y = 0$) is the ellipse $\frac{x^2}{9} + \frac{z^2}{25} = 1$ (Figure 13.13b). By sketching the xy-, xz-, and yz-traces, an outline of the ellipsoid emerges (Figure 13.13c).

Related Exercises 37–40

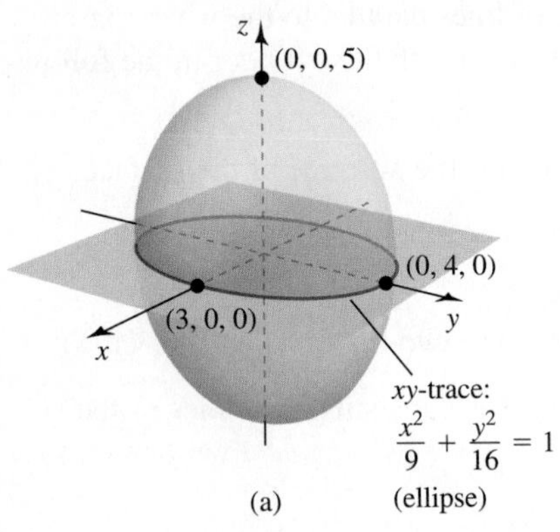

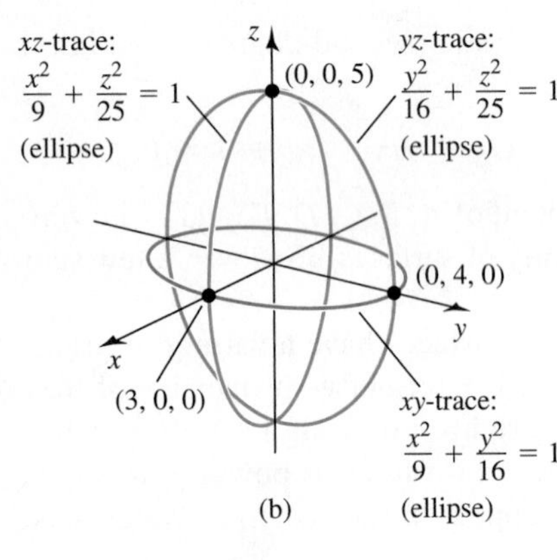

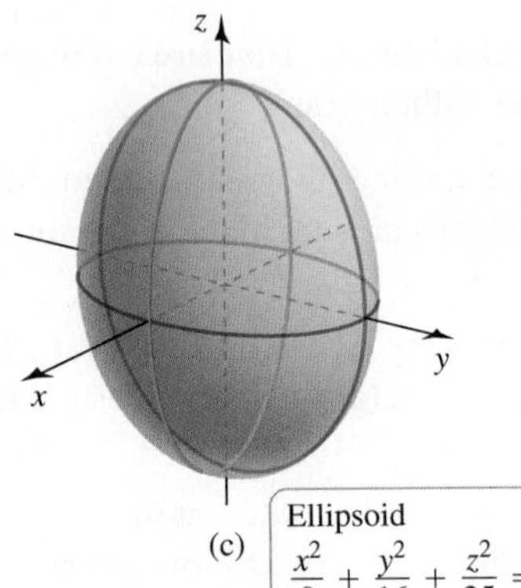

FIGURE 13.13

QUICK CHECK 7 Assume that $0 < c < b < a$ in the general equation of an ellipsoid. Along which coordinate axis does the ellipsoid have its longest axis? Its shortest axis?

EXAMPLE 9 An elliptic paraboloid The surface defined by the equation $z = \frac{x^2}{a^2} + \frac{y^2}{b^2}$ is an *elliptic paraboloid*. Graph the elliptic paraboloid with $a = 4$ and $b = 2$.

SOLUTION Note that the only intercept of the coordinate axes is $(0, 0, 0)$, which is the *vertex* of the paraboloid. The trace in the horizontal plane $z = z_0$, where $z_0 > 0$, satisfies the equation $\frac{x^2}{16} + \frac{y^2}{4} = z_0$, which describes an ellipse; there are no horizontal traces when $z_0 < 0$ (Figure 13.14a). The trace in the vertical plane $x = x_0$ is the parabola $z = \frac{x_0^2}{16} + \frac{y^2}{4}$ (Figure 13.14b); the trace in the vertical plane $y = y_0$ is the parabola $z = \frac{x^2}{16} + \frac{y_0^2}{4}$ (Figure 13.14c).

To graph the surface, we sketch the xz-trace $z = \frac{x^2}{16}$ (setting $y = 0$) and the yz-trace $z = \frac{y^2}{4}$ (setting $x = 0$). When these traces are combined with an elliptical trace $\frac{x^2}{16} + \frac{y^2}{4} = z_0$ in a plane $z = z_0$, an outline of the surface appears (Figure 13.14d).

The name *elliptic paraboloid* says that the traces of this surface are parabolas and ellipses. Two of the three traces in the coordinate planes are parabolas, so it is called a paraboloid rather than an ellipsoid.

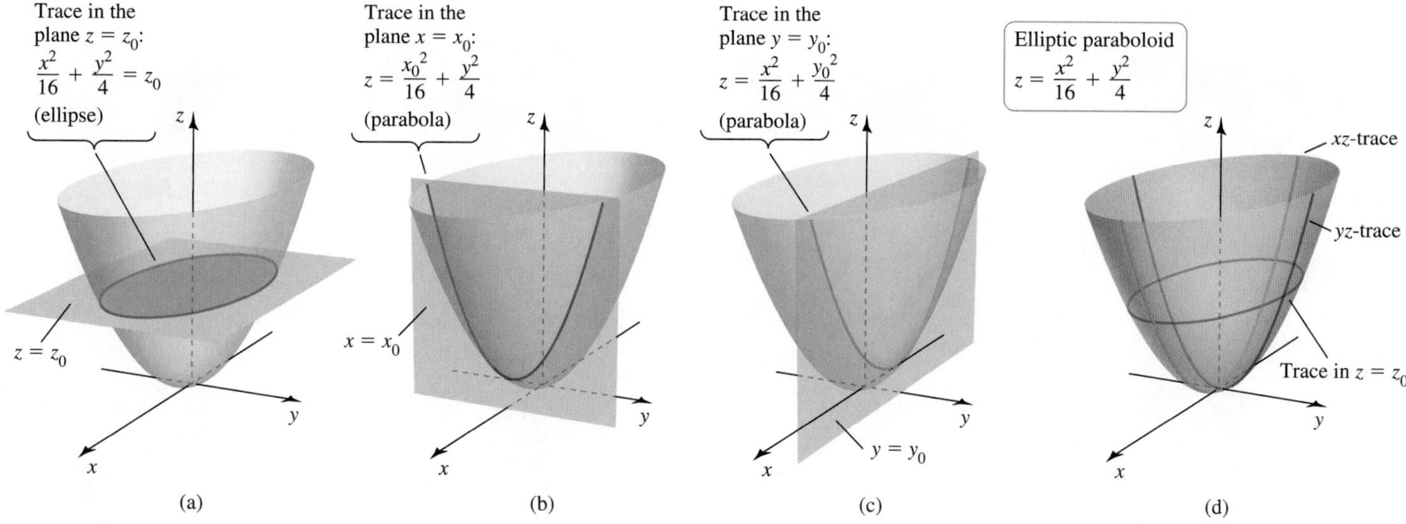

FIGURE 13.14

Related Exercises 41–44

QUICK CHECK 8 The elliptic paraboloid $x = \frac{y^2}{3} + \frac{z^2}{7}$ is a bowl-shaped surface. Along which axis does the bowl open?

EXAMPLE 10 **A hyperboloid of one sheet** Graph the surface defined by the equation $\frac{x^2}{4} + \frac{y^2}{9} - z^2 = 1$.

> To be completely accurate, this surface should be called an *elliptic hyperboloid of one sheet* because the traces are ellipses and hyperbolas.

SOLUTION The intercepts of the coordinate axes are $(0, \pm 3, 0)$ and $(\pm 2, 0, 0)$. Setting $z = z_0$, the traces in horizontal planes are ellipses of the form $\frac{x^2}{4} + \frac{y^2}{9} = 1 + z_0^2$. This equation has solutions for all choices of z_0, so the surface has traces in all horizontal planes. These elliptical traces increase in size as $|z_0|$ increases (Figure 13.15a), with the smallest trace being the ellipse $\frac{x^2}{4} + \frac{y^2}{9} = 1$ in the xy-plane. Setting $x = 0$, the yz-trace is the hyperbola $\frac{y^2}{9} - z^2 = 1$; with $y = 0$, the xz-trace is the hyperbola $\frac{x^2}{4} - z^2 = 1$ (Figure 13.15b,c). In fact, traces in all vertical planes are hyperbolas. The resulting surface is a *hyperboloid of one sheet* (Figure 13.15d).

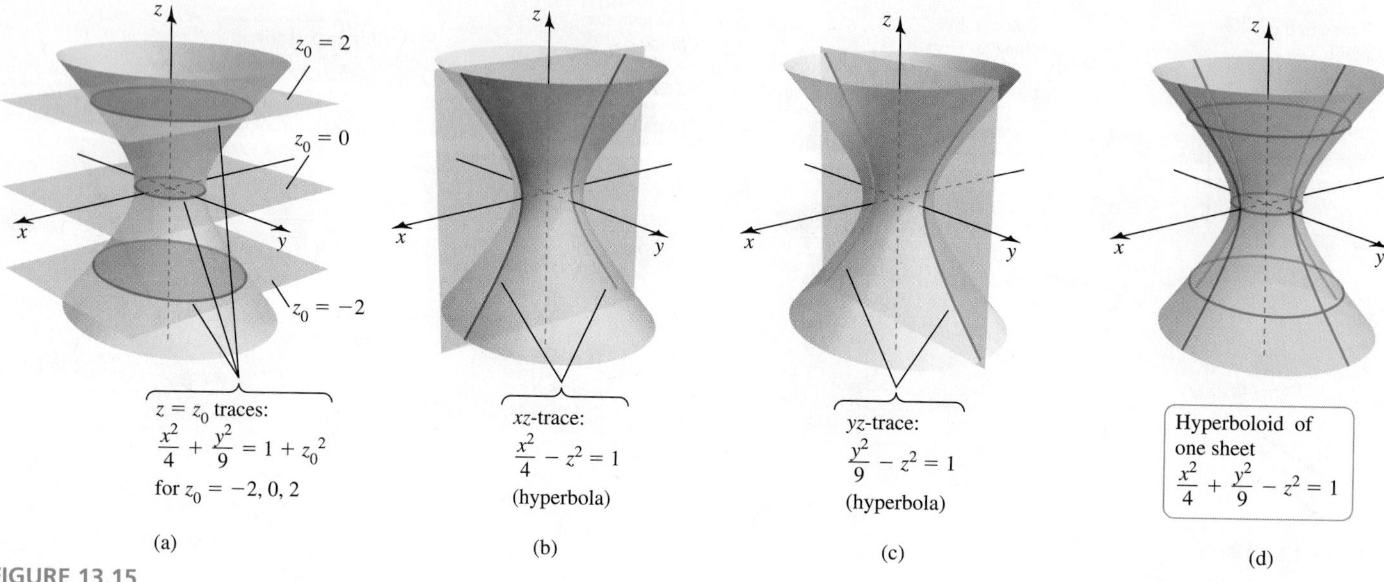

FIGURE 13.15

Related Exercises 45–48

QUICK CHECK 9 To which coordinate axis is the axis of the hyperboloid $\frac{y^2}{a^2} + \frac{z^2}{b^2} - \frac{x^2}{c^2} = 1$ parallel?

> The name *hyperbolic paraboloid* tells us that the traces are hyperbolas and parabolas. Two of the three traces in the coordinate planes are parabolas, so it is a paraboloid rather than a hyperboloid.

> The hyperbolic paraboloid has a feature called a *saddle point*. For the surface in Example 11, if you walk from the saddle point at the origin in the direction of the x-axis, you move uphill. If you walk from the saddle point in the direction of the y-axis, you move downhill. Saddle points are examined in detail in Section 13.8.

EXAMPLE 11 A hyperbolic paraboloid Graph the surface defined by the equation $z = x^2 - \frac{y^2}{4}$.

SOLUTION Setting $z = 0$ in the equation of the surface, we see that the xy-trace consists of the two lines $y = \pm 2x$. However, slicing the surface with any other horizontal plane $z = z_0$ produces a hyperbola $x^2 - \frac{y^2}{4} = z_0$. If $z_0 > 0$, then the axis of the hyperbola is parallel to the x-axis. On the other hand, if $z_0 < 0$, then the axis of the hyperbola is parallel to the y-axis (Figure 13.16a). Setting $x = x_0$, produces the trace $z = x_0^2 - \frac{y^2}{4}$, which

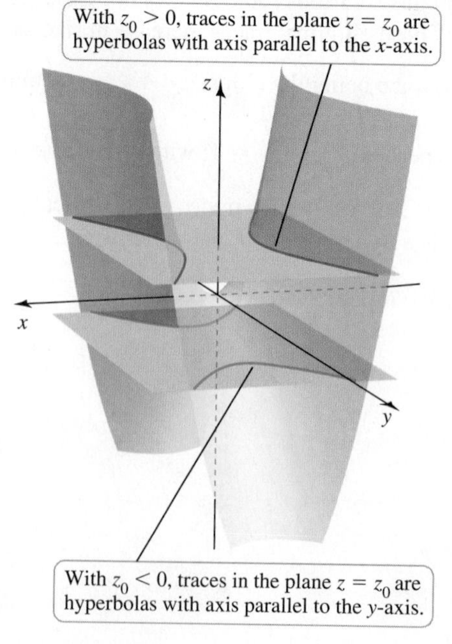

With $z_0 > 0$, traces in the plane $z = z_0$ are hyperbolas with axis parallel to the x-axis.
With $z_0 < 0$, traces in the plane $z = z_0$ are hyperbolas with axis parallel to the y-axis.

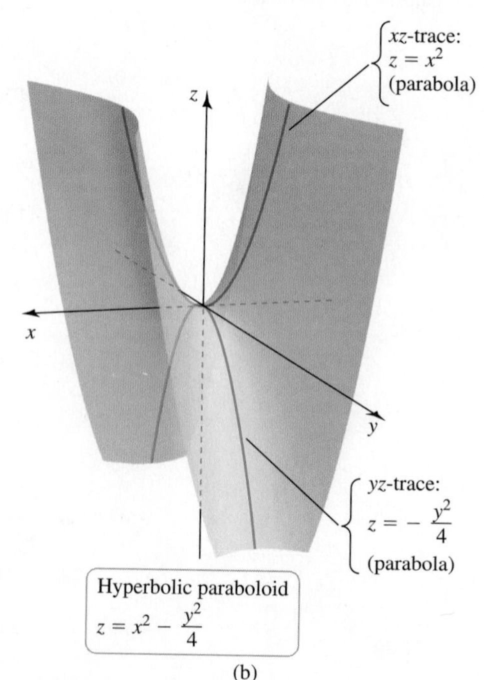

FIGURE 13.16 (a) (b)

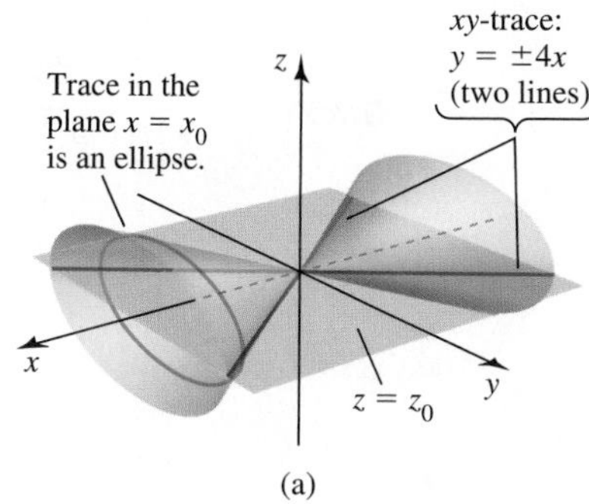

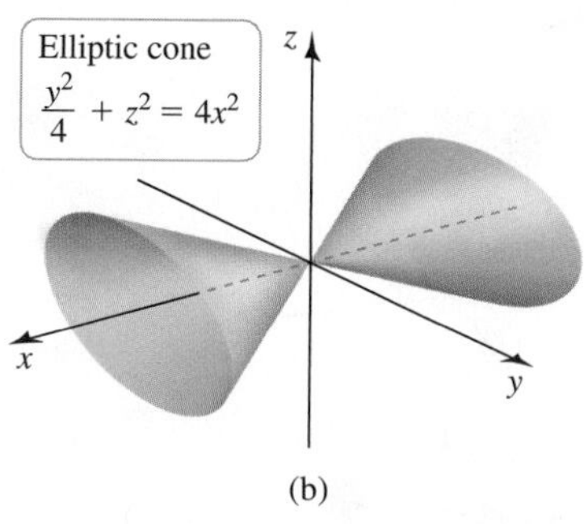

FIGURE 13.17

is the equation of a parabola that opens downward in a plane parallel to the yz-plane. You can check that traces in planes parallel to the xz-plane are parabolas that open upward. The resulting surface is a *hyperbolic paraboloid* (Figure 13.16b).

Related Exercises 49–52

EXAMPLE 12 **Elliptic cones** Graph the surface defined by the equation $\frac{y^2}{4} + z^2 = 4x^2$.

SOLUTION The only intercept of the coordinate axes is $(0, 0, 0)$. Traces in the planes $x = x_0$ are ellipses of the form $\frac{y^2}{4} + z^2 = 4x_0^2$ that shrink in size as x_0 approaches 0. Setting $y = 0$, the xz-trace satisfies the equation $z^2 = 4x^2$ or $z = \pm 2x$, which are equations of two lines in the xz-plane that intersect at the origin. Setting $z = 0$, the xy-trace satisfies $y^2 = 16x^2$ or $y = \pm 4x$, which describe two lines in the xy-plane that intersect at the origin (Figure 13.17a). The complete surface consists of two *cones* opening in opposite directions along the x-axis with a common vertex at the origin (Figure 13.17b).

Related Exercises 53–56

EXAMPLE 13 **A hyperboloid of two sheets** Graph the surface defined by the equation

$$-16x^2 - 4y^2 + z^2 + 64x - 80 = 0.$$

SOLUTION We first regroup terms, giving

$$-16\underbrace{(x^2 - 4x)}_{\text{complete the square}} - 4y^2 + z^2 - 80 = 0,$$

and then complete the square in x:

$$-16(\underbrace{x^2 - 4x + 4}_{(x-2)^2} - 4) - 4y^2 + z^2 - 80 = 0$$

Collecting terms and dividing by 16 gives the equation

$$-(x - 2)^2 - \frac{y^2}{4} + \frac{z^2}{16} = 1.$$

Notice that if $z = 0$, the equation has no solutions, so the surface does not intersect the xy-plane. The traces in planes parallel to the xz- and yz-planes are hyperbolas. If $|z_0| \geq 4$, the trace in the plane $z = z_0$ is an ellipse. This equation describes a *hyperboloid of two sheets*, with its axis parallel to the z-axis and shifted 2 units in the positive x-direction (Figure 13.18).

Related Exercises 57–60

➤ The equation $-x^2 - \frac{y^2}{4} + \frac{z^2}{16} = 1$ describes a hyperboloid of two sheets with its axis on the z-axis. Therefore, the equation in Example 13 describes the same surface shifted 2 units in the positive x-direction.

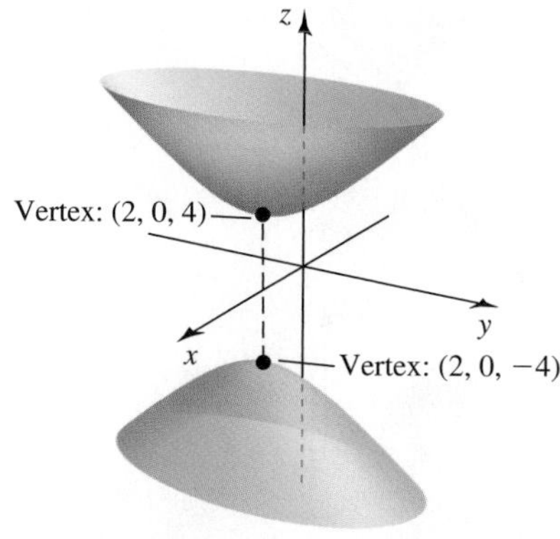

FIGURE 13.18

QUICK CHECK 10 In which variable(s) should you complete the square to identify the surface $x = y^2 + 2y + z^2 - 4z + 16$? Name and describe the surface.

Table 13.1 summarizes the standard quadric surfaces. It is important to note that the same surfaces with different orientations are obtained when the roles of the variables are interchanged. For this reason, Table 13.1 summarizes many more surfaces than those listed.

Table 13.1

Name	Standard Equation	Features	Graph
Ellipsoid	$\frac{x^2}{a^2} + \frac{y^2}{b^2} + \frac{z^2}{c^2} = 1$	All traces are ellipses.	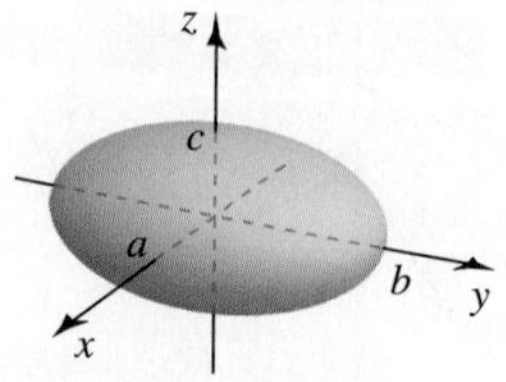
Elliptic paraboloid	$z = \frac{x^2}{a^2} + \frac{y^2}{b^2}$	Traces with $z = z_0 > 0$ are ellipses. Traces with $x = x_0$ or $y = y_0$ are parabolas.	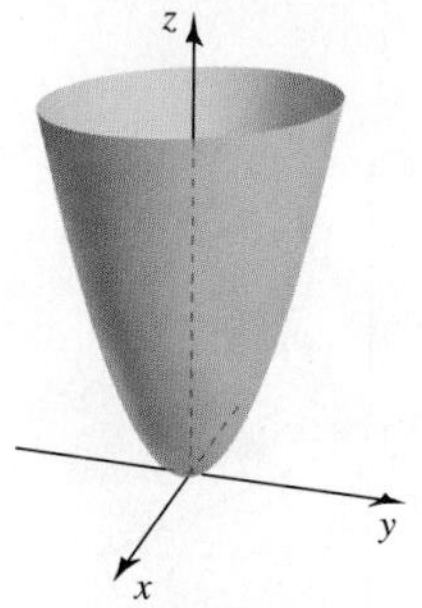
Hyperboloid of one sheet	$\frac{x^2}{a^2} + \frac{y^2}{b^2} - \frac{z^2}{c^2} = 1$	Traces with $z = z_0$ are ellipses for all z_0. Traces with $x = x_0$ or $y = y_0$ are hyperbolas.	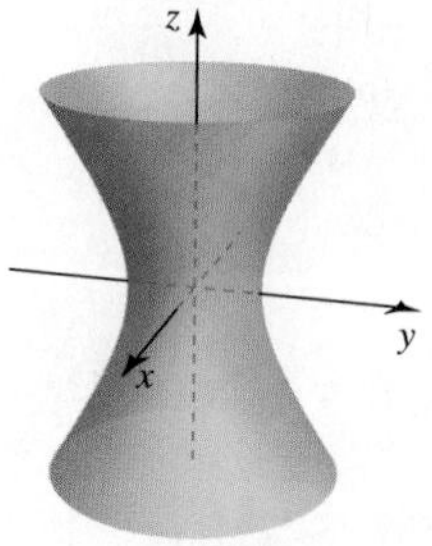
Hyperboloid of two sheets	$-\frac{x^2}{a^2} - \frac{y^2}{b^2} + \frac{z^2}{c^2} = 1$	Traces with $z = z_0$ with $\lvert z_0\rvert > \lvert c\rvert$ are ellipses. Traces with $x = x_0$ and $y = y_0$ are hyperbolas.	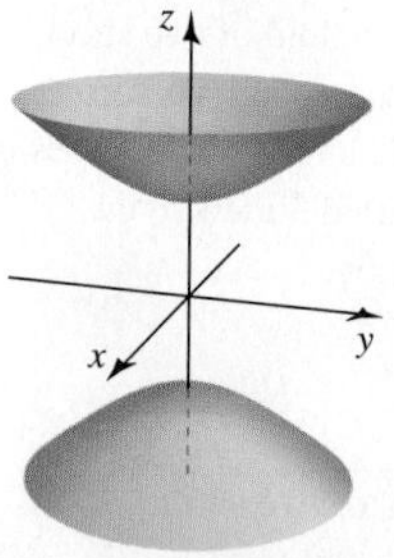
Elliptic cone	$\frac{x^2}{a^2} + \frac{y^2}{b^2} = \frac{z^2}{c^2}$	Traces with $z = z_0$ are ellipses. Traces with $x = x_0$ or $y = y_0$ are hyperbolas or intersecting lines.	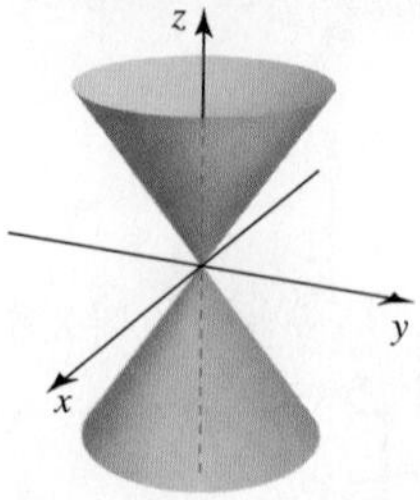
Hyperbolic paraboloid	$z = \frac{x^2}{a^2} - \frac{y^2}{b^2}$	Traces with $z = z_0 \neq 0$ are hyperbolas. Traces with $x = x_0$ or $y = y_0$ are parabolas.	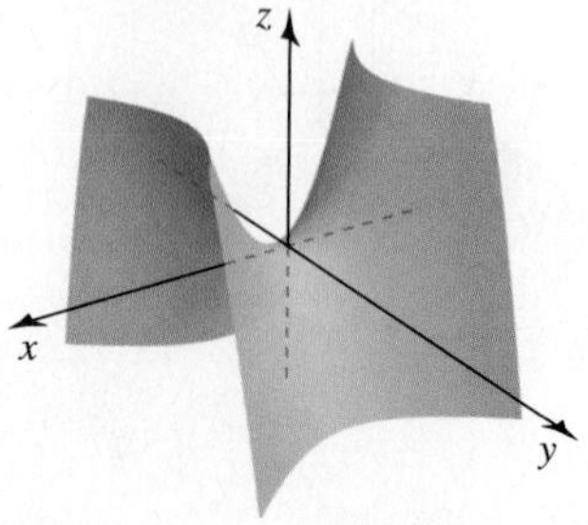

SECTION 13.1 EXERCISES

Review Questions

1. Give two pieces of information which, taken together, uniquely determine a plane.
2. Find a vector normal to the plane $-2x - 3y + 4z = 12$.
3. Where does the plane $-2x - 3y + 4z = 12$ intersect the coordinate axes?
4. Give an equation of the plane with a normal vector $\mathbf{n} = \langle 1, 1, 1 \rangle$ that passes through the point $(1, 0, 0)$.
5. To which coordinate axes are the following cylinders in $\mathbf{R}^3$ parallel: $x^2 + 2y^2 = 8$, $z^2 + 2y^2 = 8$, and $x^2 + 2z^2 = 8$?
6. Describe the graph of $x = z^2$ in $\mathbf{R}^3$.
7. What are the traces of a surface?
8. What is the name of the type of surface defined by the equation $y = \dfrac{x^2}{4} + \dfrac{z^2}{8}$?
9. What is the name of the type of surface defined by the equation $x^2 + \dfrac{y^2}{3} + 2z^2 = 1$?
10. What is the name of the type of surface defined by the equation $-y^2 - \dfrac{z^2}{2} + x^2 = 1$?

Basic Skills

11–14. Equations of planes *Find an equation of the plane that passes through the point P_0 with a normal vector* **n**.

11. $P_0(0, 2, -2)$; $\mathbf{n} = \langle 1, 1, -1 \rangle$
12. $P_0(1, 0, -3)$; $\mathbf{n} = \langle 1, -1, 2 \rangle$
13. $P_0(2, 3, 0)$; $\mathbf{n} = \langle -1, 2, -3 \rangle$
14. $P_0(1, 2, -3)$; $\mathbf{n} = \langle -1, 4, -3 \rangle$

15–18. Equations of planes *Find an equation of the following planes.*

15. The plane passing through the points $(1, 0, 3)$, $(0, 4, 2)$, and $(1, 1, 1)$
16. The plane passing through the points $(-1, 1, 1)$, $(0, 0, 2)$, and $(3, -1, -2)$
17. The plane passing through the points $(2, -1, 4)$, $(1, 1, -1)$, and $(-4, 1, 1)$
18. The plane passing through the points $(5, 3, 1)$, $(1, 3, -5)$, and $(-1, 3, 1)$

19–22. Properties of planes *Find the points at which the following planes intersect the coordinate axes and find equations of the lines where the planes intersect the coordinate planes. Sketch a graph of the plane.*

19. $3x - 2y + z = 6$
20. $-4x + 8z = 16$
21. $x + 3y - 5z - 30 = 0$
22. $12x - 9y + 4z + 72 = 0$

23–24. Equations of planes *For the following sets of planes, determine which pairs of planes in the set are parallel, orthogonal, or identical.*

23. $Q: 3x - 2y + z = 12$; $R: -x + 2y/3 - z/3 = 0$; $S: -x + 2y + 7z = 1$; $T: 3x/2 - y + z/2 = 6$
24. $Q: x + y - z = 0$; $R: y + z = 0$; $S: x - y = 0$; $T: x + y + z = 0$

25–28. Parallel planes *Find an equation of the plane parallel to the plane Q passing through the point P_0.*

25. $Q: -x + 2y - 4z = 1$; $P_0(1, 0, 4)$
26. $Q: 2x + y - z = 1$; $P_0(0, 2, -2)$
27. $Q: 4x + 3y - 2z = 12$; $P_0(1, -1, 3)$
28. $Q: x - 5y - 2z = 1$; $P_0(1, 2, 0)$

29–32. Intersecting planes *Find an equation of the line where the planes Q and R intersect.*

29. $Q: -x + 2y + z = 1$; $R: x + y + z = 0$
30. $Q: x + 2y - z = 1$; $R: x + y + z = 1$
31. $Q: 2x - y + 3z - 1 = 0$; $R: -x + 3y + z - 4 = 0$
32. $Q: x - y - 2z = 1$; $R: x + y + z = -1$

33–36. Cylinders in $\mathbf{R}^3$ *Consider the following cylinders in $\mathbf{R}^3$.*

- **a.** *Identify the coordinate axis to which the cylinder is parallel.*
- **b.** *Sketch the cylinder.*

33. $y - x^3 = 0$
34. $x - 2z^2 = 0$
35. $z - \ln y = 0$
36. $x - 1/y = 0$

37–60. Quadric surfaces *Consider the following equations of quadric surfaces.*

- **a.** *Find the intercepts with the three coordinate axes, when they exist.*
- **b.** *Find the equations of the xy-, xz-, and yz-traces, when they exist.*
- **c.** *Sketch a graph of the surface.*

Ellipsoids

37. $x^2 + \dfrac{y^2}{4} + \dfrac{z^2}{9} = 1$
38. $4x^2 + y^2 + \dfrac{z^2}{2} = 1$
39. $\dfrac{x^2}{3} + 3y^2 + \dfrac{z^2}{12} = 3$
40. $\dfrac{x^2}{6} + 24y^2 + \dfrac{z^2}{24} - 6 = 0$

Elliptic paraboloids

41. $x = y^2 + z^2$
42. $z = \dfrac{x^2}{4} + \dfrac{y^2}{9}$
43. $9x - 81y^2 - \dfrac{z^2}{4} = 0$
44. $2y - \dfrac{x^2}{8} - \dfrac{z^2}{18} = 0$

Hyperboloids of one sheet

45. $\frac{x^2}{25} + \frac{y^2}{9} - z^2 = 1$

46. $\frac{y^2}{2} + \frac{z^2}{36} - 4x^2 = 1$

47. $\frac{y^2}{16} + 36z^2 - \frac{x^2}{4} - 9 = 0$

48. $9z^2 + x^2 - \frac{y^2}{3} - 1 = 0$

Hyperbolic paraboloids

49. $z = \frac{x^2}{9} - y^2$

50. $y = \frac{x^2}{16} - 4z^2$

51. $5x - \frac{y^2}{5} + \frac{z^2}{20} = 0$

52. $6y + \frac{x^2}{6} - \frac{z^2}{24} = 0$

Elliptic cones

53. $x^2 + \frac{y^2}{4} = z^2$

54. $4y^2 + \frac{z^2}{4} = 9x^2$

55. $\frac{z^2}{32} + \frac{y^2}{18} = 2x^2$

56. $\frac{x^2}{3} + \frac{z^2}{12} = 3y^2$

Hyperboloids of two sheets

57. $-x^2 + \frac{y^2}{4} - \frac{z^2}{9} = 1$

58. $1 - 4x^2 + y^2 + \frac{z^2}{2} = 0$

59. $-\frac{x^2}{3} + 3y^2 - \frac{z^2}{12} = 1$

60. $-\frac{x^2}{6} - 24y^2 + \frac{z^2}{24} - 6 = 0$

Further Explorations

61. Explain why or why not Determine whether the following statements are true and give an explanation or counterexample.

a. The plane passing through the point $(1, 1, 1)$ with a normal vector $\mathbf{n} = \langle 1, 2, -3 \rangle$ is the same as the plane passing through the point $(3, 0, 1)$ with a normal vector $\mathbf{n} = \langle -2, -4, 6 \rangle$.

b. The equations $x + y - z = 1$ and $-x - y + z = 1$ describe the same plane.

c. Given a plane Q, there is exactly one plane orthogonal to Q.

d. Given a line ℓ and a point P_0 not on ℓ, there is exactly one plane that contains ℓ and passes through P_0.

e. Given a plane R and a point P_0, there is exactly one plane that is orthogonal to R and passes through P_0.

f. Any two distinct lines in $\mathbf{R}^3$ determine a unique plane.

g. If plane Q is orthogonal to plane R and plane R is orthogonal to plane S, then plane Q is orthogonal to plane S.

62. Plane containing a line and a point Find an equation of the plane that passes through the point P_0 and contains the line ℓ.

a. $P_0(1, -2, 3)$; ℓ: $\mathbf{r} = \langle t, -t, 2t \rangle, -\infty < t < \infty$

b. $P_0(-4, 1, 2)$; ℓ: $\mathbf{r} = \langle 2t, -2t, -4t \rangle, -\infty < t < \infty$

63. Matching graphs with equations Match equations a–f with surfaces A–F.

a. $y - z^2 = 0$

b. $2x + 3y - z = 5$

c. $4x^2 + \frac{y^2}{9} + z^2 = 1$

d. $x^2 + \frac{y^2}{9} - z^2 = 1$

e. $x^2 + \frac{y^2}{9} = z^2$

f. $y = |x|$

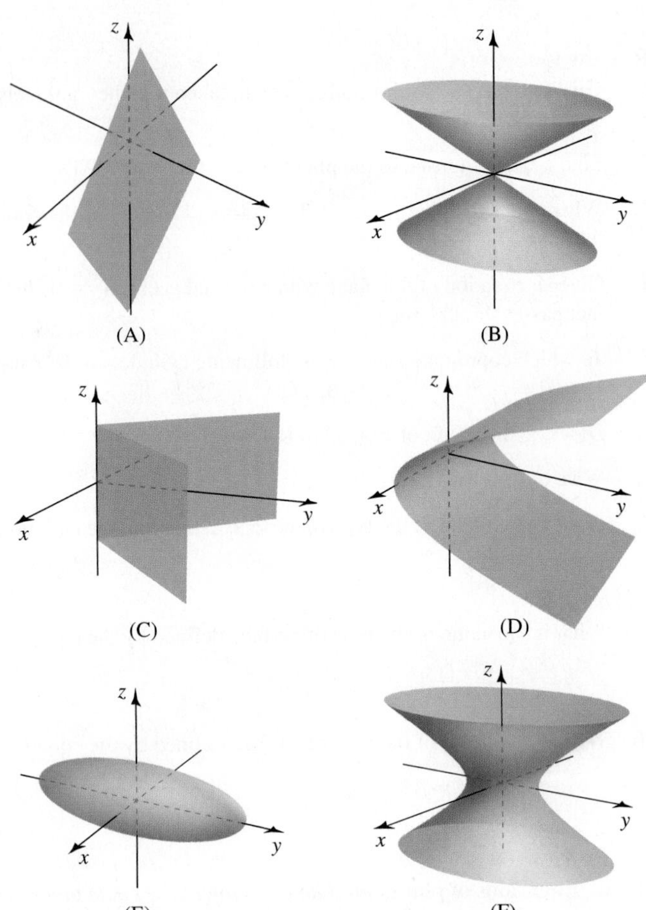

64–73. Identifying surfaces *Identify and briefly describe the surfaces defined by the following equations.*

64. $z^2 + 4y^2 - x^2 = 1$

65. $y = 4z^2 - x^2$

66. $-y^2 - 9z^2 + x^2/4 = 1$

67. $y = x^2/6 + z^2/16$

68. $x^2 + y^2 + 4z^2 + 2x = 0$

69. $9x^2 + y^2 - 4z^2 + 2y = 0$

70. $x^2 + 4y^2 = 1$

71. $y^2 - z^2 = 2$

72. $-x^2 - y^2 + z^2/9 + 6x - 8y = 26$

73. $x^2/4 + y^2 - 2x - 10y - z^2 + 41 = 0$

74–77. Curve-plane intersections *Find the points (if they exist) at which the following planes and curves intersect.*

74. $y = 2x + 1$; $\mathbf{r}(t) = \langle 10 \cos t, 2 \sin t, 1 \rangle$, for $0 \le t \le 2\pi$

75. $8x + y + z = 60$; $\mathbf{r}(t) = \langle t, t^2, 3t^2 \rangle$, for $-\infty < t < \infty$

76. $8x + 15y + 3z = 20$; $\mathbf{r}(t) = \langle 1, \sqrt{t}, -t \rangle$, for $t > 0$

77. $2x + 3y - 12z = 0$; $\mathbf{r}(t) = \langle 4 \cos t, 4 \sin t, \cos t \rangle$, for $0 \le t \le 2\pi$

78. Intercepts Let a, b, c, and d be constants. Find the points at which the plane $ax + by + cz = d$ intersects the x-, y-, and z-axes.

79. **Angle between planes** The angle between two planes is the angle θ between the normal vectors of the planes, where the directions of the normal vectors are chosen so that $0 \leq \theta \leq \pi$. Find the angle between the planes $5x + 2y - z = 0$ and $-3x + y + 2z = 0$.

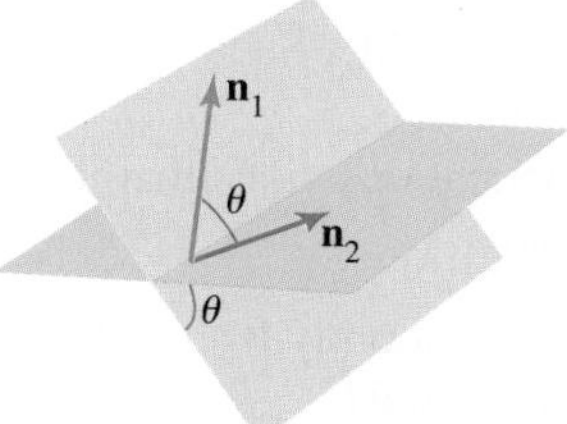

80. **Solids of revolution** Consider the ellipse $x^2 + 4y^2 = 1$ in the xy-plane.

    a. If this ellipse is revolved about the x-axis, what is the equation of the resulting ellipsoid?
    b. If this ellipse is revolved about the y-axis, what is the equation of the resulting ellipsoid?

81. **Solids of revolution** Which of the quadric surfaces in Table 13.1 can be generated by revolving a curve in one of the coordinate planes about a coordinate axis?

Applications

82. **Light cones** The idea of a *light cone* appears in the Special Theory of Relativity. The xy-plane (see figure) represents all of three-dimensional space, and the z-axis is the time axis (t-axis). If an event E occurs at the origin, the interior of the future light cone ($t > 0$) represents all events in the future that are affected by E, assuming that no signal travels faster than the speed of light. The interior of the past light cone ($t < 0$) represents all events in the past that could have affected E, again assuming that no signal travels faster than the speed of light.

    a. If time is measured in seconds and distance (x and y) is measured in light-seconds (the distance light travels in 1 s), the light cone makes a 45° angle with the xy-plane. Write the equation of the light cone in this case.
    b. Suppose distance is measured in meters and time is measured in seconds. Write the equation of the light cone in this case given that the speed of light is 3×10^8 m/s.

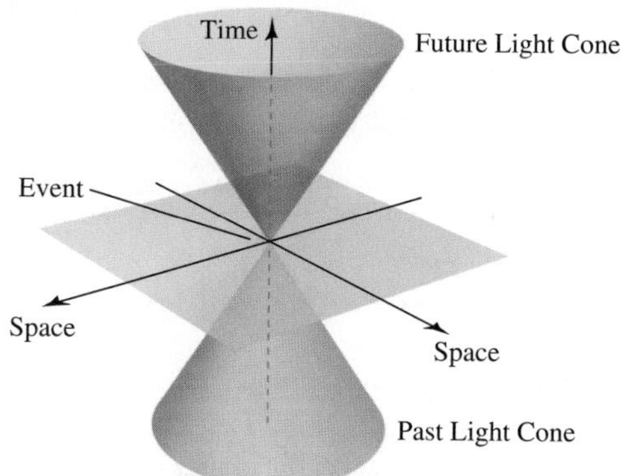

83. **T-shirt profits** A clothing company makes a profit of \$10 on its long-sleeved T-shirts and \$5 on its short-sleeved T-shirts. Assuming there is a \$200 setup cost, the profit on T-shirt sales is $z = 10x + 5y - 200$, where x is the number of long-sleeved T-shirts sold and y is the number of short-sleeved T-shirts sold. Assume x and y are nonnegative.

    a. Graph the plane that gives the profit using the window $[0, 40] \times [0, 40] \times [-400, 400]$.
    b. If $x = 20$ and $y = 10$, is the profit positive or negative?
    c. Describe the values of x and y for which the company breaks even (for which the profit is zero). Mark this set on your graph.

Additional Exercises

84. **Parallel line and plane** Show that the plane $ax + by + cz = d$ and the line $\mathbf{r}(t) = \mathbf{r}_0 + \mathbf{v}t$, not in the plane, have no points of intersection if and only if $\mathbf{v} \cdot \langle a, b, c \rangle = 0$. Give a geometric explanation of the result.

85. **Tilted ellipse** Consider the curve $\mathbf{r}(t) = \langle \cos t, \sin t, c \sin t \rangle$ for $0 \leq t \leq 2\pi$, where c is a real number.

    a. What is the equation of the plane P in which the curve lies?
    b. What is the angle between P and the xy-plane?
    c. Prove that the curve is an ellipse in P.

86. **Distance from a point to a plane**

    a. Show that the point in the plane $ax + by + cz = d$ nearest the origin is $P(ad/D^2, bd/D^2, cd/D^2)$, where $D^2 = a^2 + b^2 + c^2$. Conclude that the least distance from the plane to the origin is $|d|/D$. (*Hint:* The least distance is along a normal to the plane.)
    b. Show that the least distance from the point $P_0(x_0, y_0, z_0)$ to the plane $ax + by + cz = d$ is $|ax_0 + by_0 + cz_0 - d|/D$. (*Hint:* Find the point P on the plane closest to P_0.)

87. **Projections** Find the projection of the position vector $\langle 2, 3, -4 \rangle$ on the plane $3x + 2y - z = 0$.

88. **Ellipsoid-plane intersection** Let E be the ellipsoid $x^2/9 + y^2/4 + z^2 = 1$, P be the plane $z = Ax + By$, and C be the intersection of E and P.

    a. Is C an ellipse for all values of A and B? Explain.
    b. Sketch and interpret the situation in which $A = 0$ and $B \neq 0$.
    c. Find an equation of the projection of C on the xy-plane.
    d. Assume $A = \frac{1}{6}$ and $B = \frac{1}{2}$. Find a parametric description of C as a curve in $\mathbf{R}^3$. (*Hint:* Assume C is described by $\langle a \cos t + b \sin t, c \cos t + d \sin t, e \cos t + f \sin t \rangle$ and find a, b, c, d, e, and f.)

QUICK CHECK ANSWERS

1. The plane passes through $(1, 2, 3)$ and is parallel to the yz-plane; its equation is $x = 1$. **2.** Because the right side of the equation is 0, the equation can be multiplied by any nonzero constant (changing the length of $\mathbf{n}$) without changing the graph. **5.** y-axis; x-axis **6.** The equation $x^2 + 4y^2 = 16$ is a special case of the general equation for quadric surfaces; all the coefficients except A, B, and J are zero. **7.** x-axis; z-axis **8.** Positive x-axis **9.** x-axis **10.** Complete the square in y and z; elliptic paraboloid with its axis parallel to the x-axis.

13.2 Graphs and Level Curves

In Chapter 12 we discussed vector-valued functions with one independent variable and several dependent variables. We now reverse the situation and consider functions with several independent variables and one dependent variable. Such functions are aptly called *functions of several variables* or *multivariable functions*.

To set the stage, consider the following practical questions that illustrate a few of the many applications of functions of several variables.

- What is the probability that one man selected randomly from a large group of men weighs more than 200 pounds and is over 6 feet tall?
- Where on the wing of an airliner flying at a speed of 550 mi/hr is the pressure greatest?
- A physician knows the optimal blood concentration of an antibiotic needed by a patient. What dosage of antibiotic is needed and how often should it be given to reach this optimal level?

Although we don't answer these questions immediately, they provide an idea of the scope and importance of the topic. First, we must introduce the idea of a function of several variables.

Functions of Two Variables

The key concepts related to functions of several variables are most easily presented in the case of two independent variables; the extension to three or more variables is then straightforward. In general, functions of two variables are written *explicitly* in the form

$$z = f(x, y)$$

or in the form

$$F(x, y, z) = 0.$$

Both forms are important, but for now we consider explicitly defined functions.

The concepts of domain and range carry over directly from functions of a single variable.

> **DEFINITION Function, Domain, and Range with Two Independent Variables**
> A **function** $z = f(x, y)$ assigns to each point (x, y) in a set D in $\mathbf{R}^2$ a unique real number z in a subset of $\mathbf{R}$. The set D is the **domain** of f. The **range** of f is the set of real numbers z that are assumed as the points (x, y) vary over the domain (Figure 13.19).

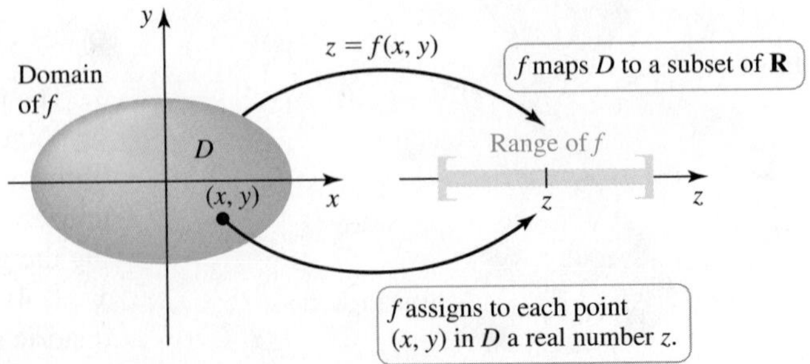

FIGURE 13.19

As with functions of one variable, a function of several variables may have a domain that is restricted by the context of the problem. For example, if the independent variables correspond to price or length or population, they take only nonnegative values, even though the associated function may be defined for negative values of the variables. If not stated otherwise, D is the set of points for which the function is defined.

A polynomial in x and y consists of sums and products of polynomials in x and polynomials in y; for example, $f(x, y) = x^2y - 2xy - xy^2$. Such polynomials are defined for all values of x and y, so their domain is $\mathbf{R}^2$. A quotient of two polynomials in x and y, such as $h(x, y) = \dfrac{xy}{x - y}$, is a rational function in x and y. The domain of a rational function must exclude points at which the denominator is zero, so the domain of h is $\{(x, y): x \neq y\}$.

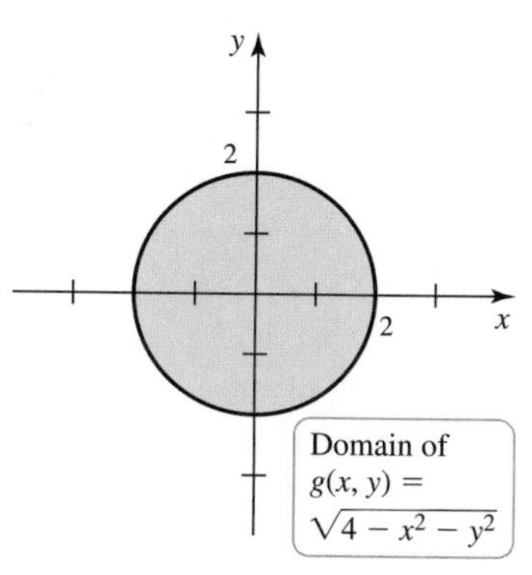

FIGURE 13.20

EXAMPLE 1 **Finding domains** Find the domain of the function $g(x, y) = \sqrt{4 - x^2 - y^2}$.

SOLUTION Because g involves a square root, its domain consists of ordered pairs (x, y) for which $4 - x^2 - y^2 \geq 0$ or $x^2 + y^2 \leq 4$. Therefore, the domain of g is $\{(x, y): x^2 + y^2 \leq 4\}$, which is the set of points on or within the circle of radius 2 centered at the origin in the xy-plane (a *disk* of radius 2) (Figure 13.20).

Related Exercises 11–18 ◄

QUICK CHECK 1 Find the domains of $f(x, y) = \sin xy$ and $g(x, y) = \sqrt{x^2y}$. ◄

Graphs of Functions of Two Variables

The **graph** of a function f of two variables is the set of points (x, y, z) that satisfy the equation $z = f(x, y)$. More specifically, for each point (x, y) in the domain of f, the point $(x, y, f(x, y))$ lies on the graph of f (Figure 13.21). A similar definition applies to relations of the form $F(x, y, z) = 0$.

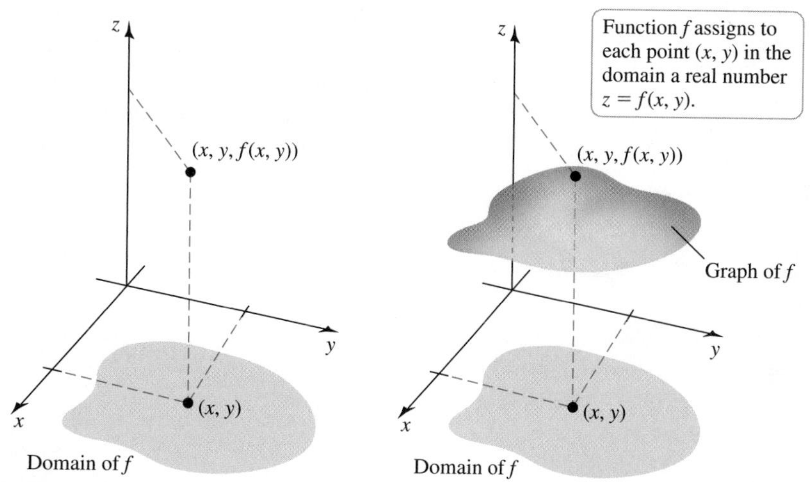

FIGURE 13.21

Like functions of one variable, functions of two variables must pass a **vertical line test**. A relation of the form $F(x, y, z) = 0$ is a function provided every line parallel to the z-axis intersects the graph of F at most once. For example, an ellipsoid (discussed in Section 13.1) is not the graph of a function because some vertical lines intersect the surface twice. On the other hand, an elliptic paraboloid of the form $z = ax^2 + by^2$ does represent a function (Figure 13.22).

QUICK CHECK 2 Does the graph of a hyperboloid of one sheet represent a function? Does the graph of a cone with its axis parallel to the x-axis represent a function? ◄

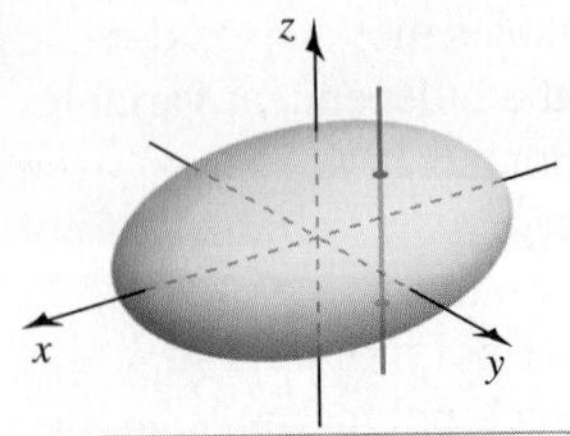

An ellipsoid does not pass the vertical line test: not the graph of a function.

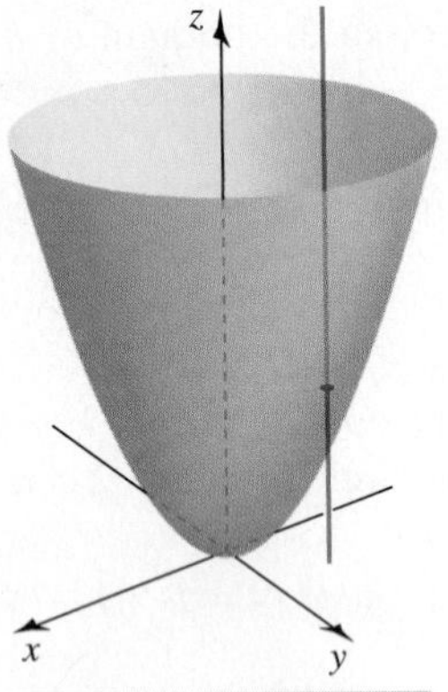

This elliptic paraboloid passes the vertical line test: graph of a function.

FIGURE 13.22

EXAMPLE 2 Graphing two-variable functions Find the domain and range of the following functions. Then sketch a graph.

a. $f(x, y) = 2x + 3y - 12$ **b.** $g(x, y) = x^2 + y^2$

c. $h(x, y) = \sqrt{1 + x^2 + y^2}$

SOLUTION

a. Letting $z = f(x, y)$, we have the equation $z = 2x + 3y - 12$, or $2x + 3y - z = 12$, which describes a plane with a normal vector $\langle 2, 3, -1 \rangle$ (Section 13.1). The domain consists of all points in $\mathbf{R}^2$, and the range is $\mathbf{R}$. We sketch the surface by noting that the x-intercept is $(6, 0, 0)$ (setting $y = z = 0$); the y-intercept is $(0, 4, 0)$ and the z-intercept is $(0, 0, -12)$ (Figure 13.23).

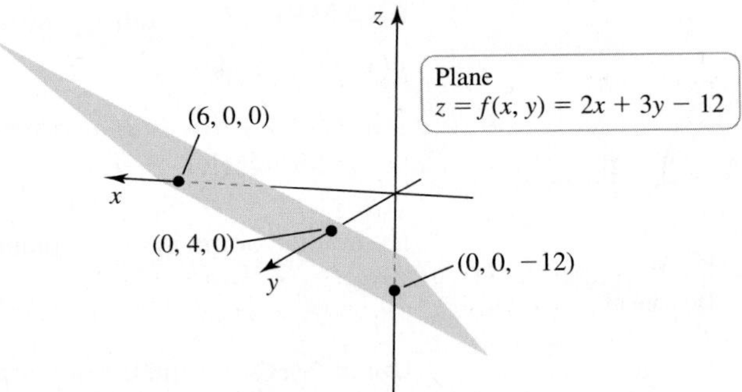

FIGURE 13.23

b. Letting $z = g(x, y)$, we have the equation $z = x^2 + y^2$, which describes an elliptic paraboloid that opens upward with vertex $(0, 0, 0)$. The domain is $\mathbf{R}^2$ and the range consists of all nonnegative real numbers (Figure 13.24).

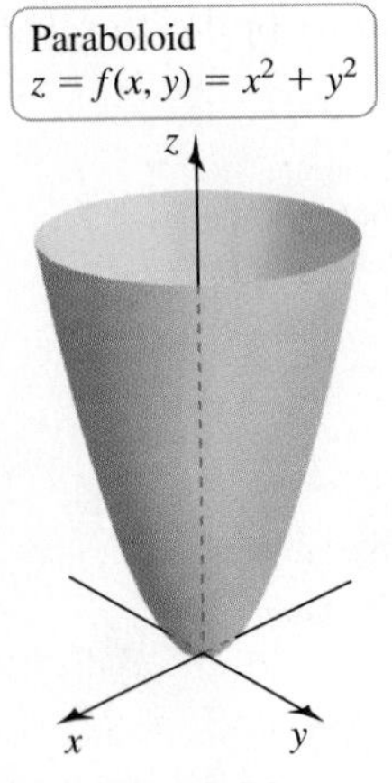

FIGURE 13.24

c. The domain of the function is $\mathbf{R}^2$ because the quantity under the square root is always positive. Note that $1 + x^2 + y^2 \geq 1$, so the range is $\{z: z \geq 1\}$. Squaring both sides of $z = \sqrt{1 + x^2 + y^2}$, we obtain $z^2 = 1 + x^2 + y^2$, or $-x^2 - y^2 + z^2 = 1$. This is the equation of a hyperboloid of two sheets that opens along the z-axis. Because the range is $\{z: z \geq 1\}$, the given function represents only the upper sheet of the hyperboloid (Figure 13.25; the lower sheet was introduced when we squared the original equation).

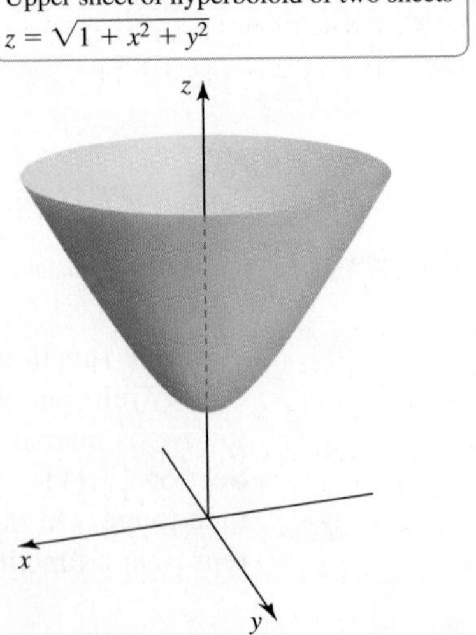

FIGURE 13.25

Related Exercises 19–27 ◄

QUICK CHECK 3 Find a function whose graph is the lower half of the hyperboloid $-x^2 - y^2 + z^2 = 1$.

Level Curves Functions of two variables are represented by surfaces in $\mathbf{R}^3$. However, such functions can be represented in another illuminating way, which is used to make topographic maps (Figure 13.26).

> To anticipate results that appear later in the chapter, notice how the streams in the topographic map—which flow downhill—cross the level curves roughly at right angles.

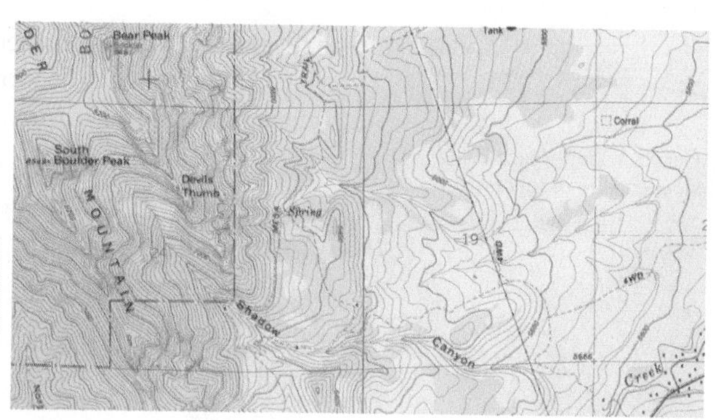

FIGURE 13.26

Consider a surface defined by the function $z = f(x, y)$ (Figure 13.27). Now imagine stepping onto the surface and walking along a path on which your elevation has the constant value $z = z_0$. The path you walk on the surface is part of a **contour curve**; the complete contour curve is the intersection of the surface and the horizontal plane $z = z_0$. When the contour curve is projected onto the xy-plane, the result is the curve $f(x, y) = z_0$. This curve in the xy-plane is called a **level curve**.

Imagine repeating this process with a different constant value of z, say, $z = z_1$. The path you walk this time when projected onto the xy-plane is part of another level curve $f(x, y) = z_1$. A collection of such level curves, corresponding to different values of z, provides a useful two-dimensional representation of the surface (Figure 13.28).

> A level curve may not always be a single curve. It might consist of a point ($x^2 + y^2 = 0$) or it might consist of several lines or curves ($xy = 0$).

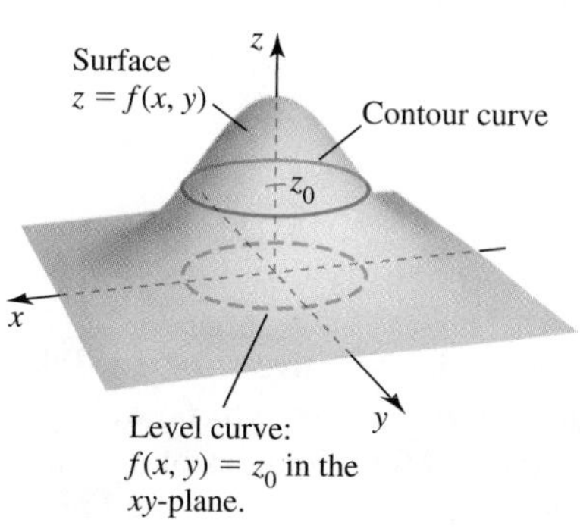

FIGURE 13.27

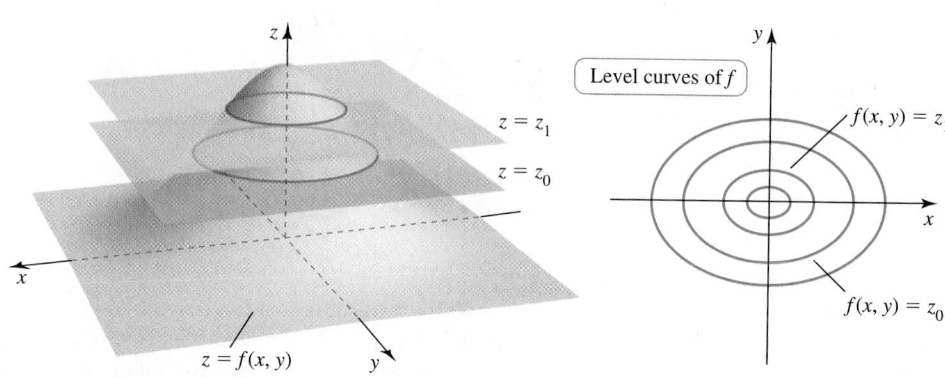

FIGURE 13.28

QUICK CHECK 4 Can two level curves of a function intersect? Explain.

Assuming that two adjacent level curves always correspond to the same change in z, widely spaced level curves indicate gradual changes in z-values, while closely spaced level curves indicate rapid changes in some directions (Figure 13.29). Concentric closed level curves indicate either a peak or a depression on the surface.

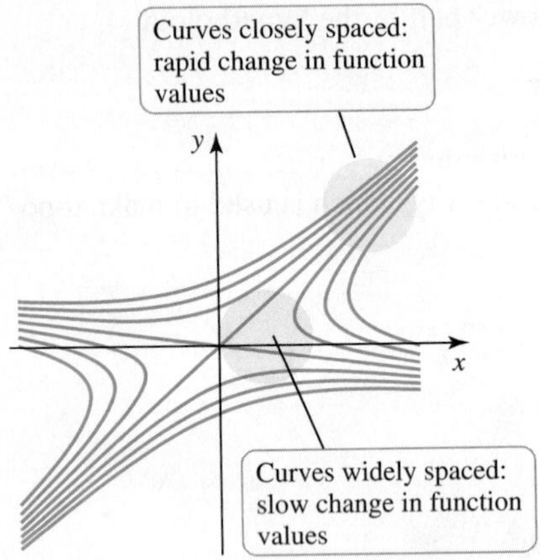

FIGURE 13.29

QUICK CHECK 5 Describe in words the level curves of the top half of the sphere $x^2 + y^2 + z^2 = 1$.

EXAMPLE 3 **Level curves** Find and sketch the level curves of the following surfaces.

a. $f(x, y) = y - x^2 - 1$ **b.** $f(x, y) = e^{-x^2-y^2}$

SOLUTION

a. The level curves are described by the equation $y - x^2 - 1 = z_0$, where z_0 is a constant in the range of f. For all values of z_0, these curves are parabolas in the xy-plane, as seen by writing the equation in the form $y = x^2 + z_0 + 1$. For example:

- With $z_0 = 0$, the level curve is the parabola $y = x^2 + 1$; along this curve, the surface has an elevation (z-coordinate) of 0.
- With $z_0 = -1$, the level curve is $y = x^2$; along this curve, the surface has an elevation of -1.
- With $z_0 = 1$, the level curve is $y = x^2 + 2$, along which the surface has an elevation of 1.

As shown in Figure 13.30a, the level curves form a family of shifted parabolas. When these level curves are labeled with their z-coordinates, the graph of the surface $z = f(x, y)$ can be visualized (Figure 13.30b).

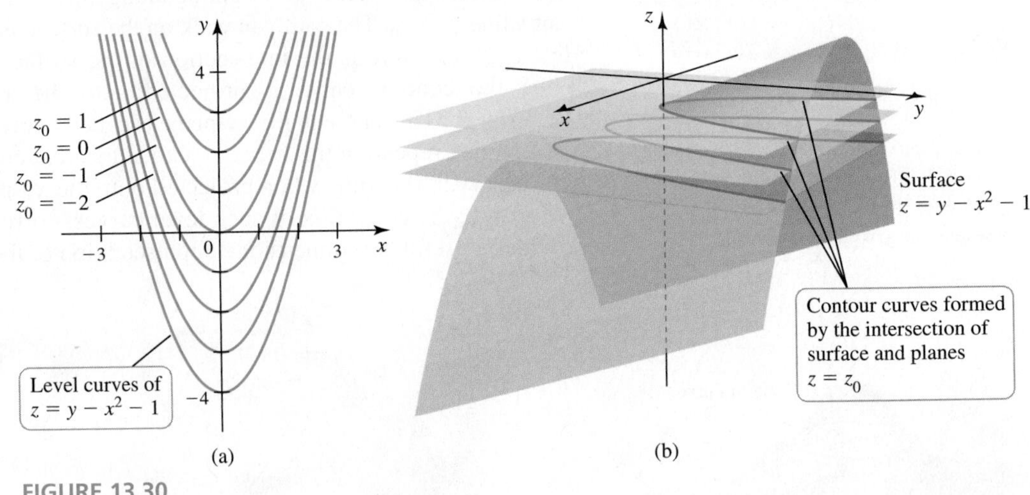

FIGURE 13.30

b. The level curves satisfy the equation $e^{-x^2-y^2} = z_0$, where z_0 is a positive constant. Taking the natural logarithm of both sides gives the equation $x^2 + y^2 = -\ln z_0$, which describes circular level curves. These curves can be sketched for all values of z_0 with $0 < z_0 \le 1$ (because the right side of $x^2 + y^2 = -\ln z_0$ must be nonnegative). For example:

- With $z_0 = 1$, the level curve satisfies the equation $x^2 + y^2 = 0$, whose solution is the single point $(0, 0)$; at this point, the surface has an elevation of 1.
- With $z_0 = e^{-1}$, the level curve is $x^2 + y^2 = -\ln e^{-1} = 1$, which is a circle centered at $(0, 0)$ with a radius of 1; along this curve the surface has an elevation of $e^{-1} \approx 0.37$.

In general, the level curves are circles centered at $(0, 0)$; as the radii of the circles increase, the corresponding z-values decrease. Figure 13.31a shows the level curves, with larger z-values corresponding to darker shades. From these labeled level curves, we can reconstruct the graph of the surface (Figure 13.31b).

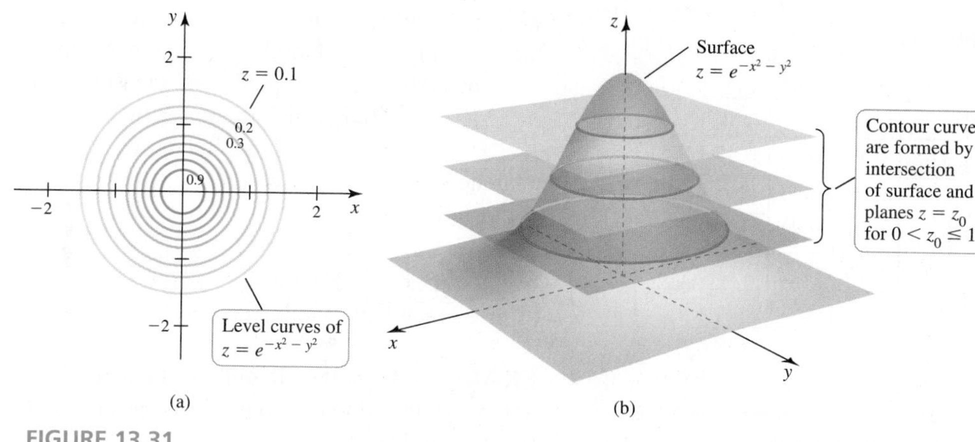

(a) (b)

FIGURE 13.31

Related Exercises 28–34

QUICK CHECK 6 Does the surface in Example 3b have a level curve for $z_0 = 0$? Explain.

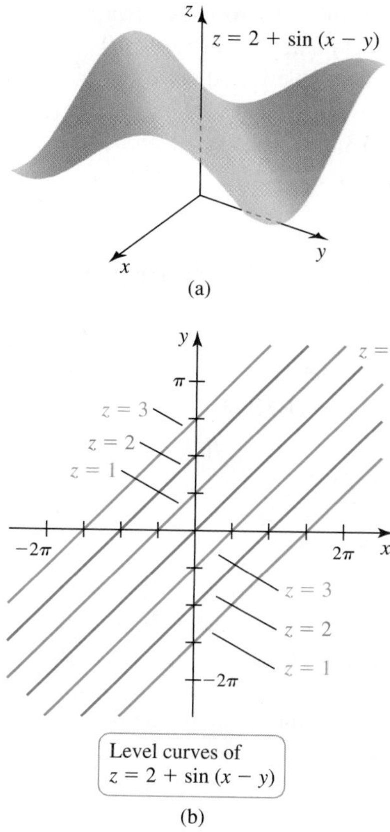

(a)

(b)

FIGURE 13.32

EXAMPLE 4 **Level curves** The graph of the function

$$f(x, y) = 2 + \sin(x - y)$$

is shown in Figure 13.32a. Sketch several level curves of the function.

SOLUTION The level curves are $f(x, y) = 2 + \sin(x - y) = z_0$, or $\sin(x - y) = z_0 - 2$. Because $-1 \le \sin(x - y) \le 1$, the admissible values of z_0 satisfy $-1 \le z_0 - 2 \le 1$, or, equivalently, $1 \le z_0 \le 3$. For example, when $z_0 = 2$, the level curves satisfy $\sin(x - y) = 0$. The solutions of this equation are $x - y = k\pi$, or $y = x - k\pi$, where k is an integer. Therefore, the surface has an elevation of 2 on this set of lines. With $z_0 = 1$ (the minimum value of z), the level curves satisfy $\sin(x - y) = -1$. The solutions are $x - y = -\pi/2 + 2k\pi$, where k is an integer; along these lines, the surface has an elevation of 1. Here we have an example in which each level curve is an infinite collection of lines of slope 1 (Figure 13.32b).

Related Exercises 28–34

Applications of Functions of Two Variables

The following examples offer two of many applications of functions of two variables.

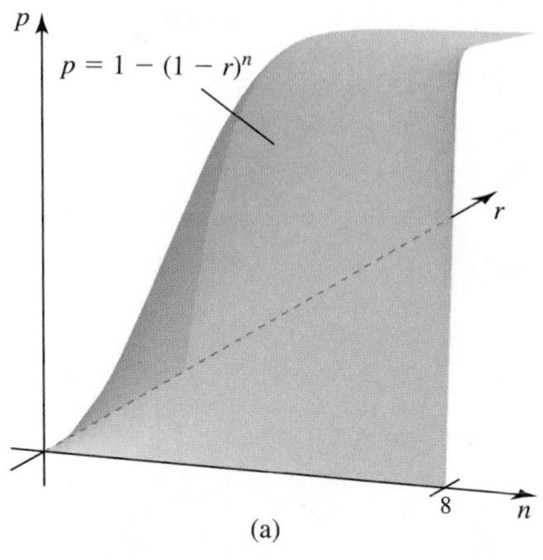

(a)

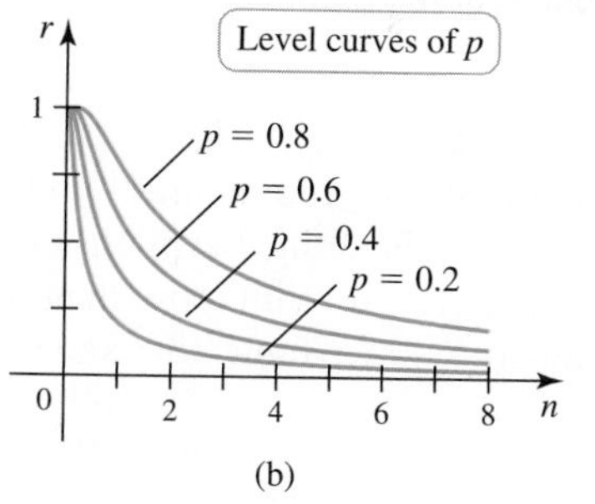

(b)

FIGURE 13.33

EXAMPLE 5 **A probability function of two variables** Suppose that on a particular day, the fraction of students on campus infected with flu is r, where $0 \le r \le 1$. If you have n random (possibly repeated) encounters with students during the day, the probability of meeting *at least* one infected person is $p(n, r) = 1 - (1 - r)^n$ (Figure 13.33a). Discuss this probability function.

SOLUTION The independent variable r is restricted to the interval $[0, 1]$ because it is a fraction of the population. The other independent variable n is any nonnegative integer; for the purposes of graphing, we treat n as a real number in the interval $[0, 8]$. With $0 \le r \le 1$, note that $0 \le 1 - r \le 1$. Because n is nonnegative, $0 \le (1 - r)^n \le 1$, and it follows that $0 \le p(n, r) \le 1$. Therefore, the range of the function is $[0, 1]$, which is consistent with the fact that p is a probability.

The level curves (Figure 13.33b) show that for a fixed value of n, the probability of at least one encounter increases with r; and for a fixed value of r, the probability increases

Table 13.2

		n				
		2	5	10	15	20
	0.05	0.10	0.23	0.40	0.54	0.64
	0.1	0.19	0.41	0.65	0.79	0.88
r	0.3	0.51	0.83	0.97	1	1
	0.5	0.75	0.97	1	1	1
	0.7	0.91	1	1	1	1

with n. Therefore, as r increases or as n increases, the probability approaches 1 (surprisingly quickly). If 10% of the population is infected ($r = 0.1$) and you have $n = 10$ encounters, then the probability of at least one encounter with an infected person is $p(0.1, 10) \approx 0.651$, which is about 2 in 3.

A numerical view of this function is given in Table 13.2, where we see probabilities tabulated for various values of n and r (rounded to two digits). The numerical values confirm the preceding observations.

Related Exercises 35–41 ◀

QUICK CHECK 7 In Example 5, if 50% of the population is infected, what is the probability of meeting at least one infected person in five encounters? ◀

➤ The electric potential function, often denoted φ (pronounced *fee* or *fie*), is a scalar-valued function from which the electric field can be computed. Potential functions are discussed in detail in Chapter 15.

EXAMPLE 6 Electric potential function in two variables The electric field at points in the xy-plane due to two point charges located at $(0, 0)$ and $(1, 0)$ is related to the electric potential function

$$\varphi(x, y) = \frac{2}{\sqrt{x^2 + y^2}} + \frac{2}{\sqrt{(x - 1)^2 + y^2}}.$$

Discuss the electric potential function.

SOLUTION The domain of the function contains all points of $\mathbf{R}^2$ except $(0, 0)$ and $(1, 0)$ where the charges are located. As these points are approached, the potential function becomes arbitrarily large (Figure 13.34a). The potential approaches zero as x or y increases in magnitude. These observations imply that the range of the potential function is all positive real numbers. The level curves of φ are closed curves, encircling either a single charge (at small distances) or both charges (at larger distances; Figure 13.34b).

➤ A function that grows without bound near a point, as in the case of the electric potential function, is said to have a *singularity* at that point. A singularity is analogous to a vertical asymptote in a function of one variable.

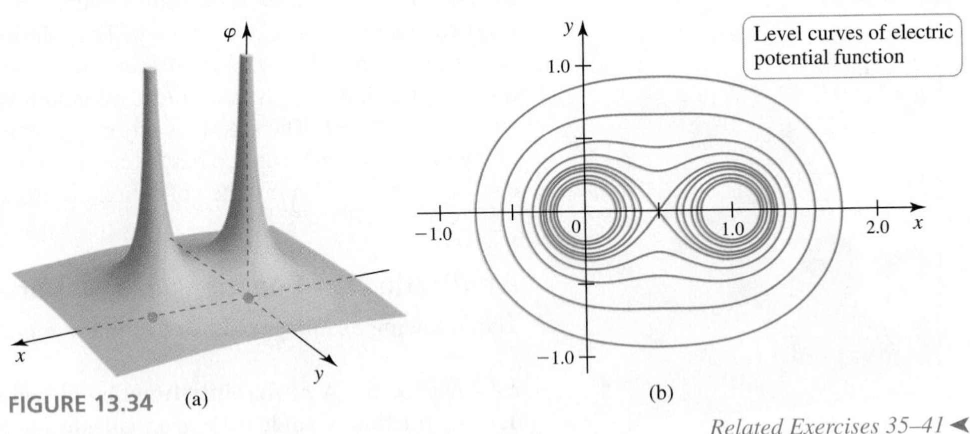

FIGURE 13.34 (a) (b)

Related Exercises 35–41 ◀

QUICK CHECK 8 In Example 6, what is the electric potential at the point $\left(\frac{1}{2}, 0\right)$? ◀

Functions of More Than Two Variables

The characteristics of functions of two independent variables extend naturally to functions of three or more variables. A function of three variables is defined explicitly in the form $w = f(x, y, z)$ and implicitly in the form $F(w, x, y, z) = 0$. With more than three independent variables, the variables are usually written $x_1, \ldots, x_n$. Table 13.3 shows the progression of functions of several variables.

Table 13.3

Number of *independent* variables	Explicit form	Implicit form	Graph resides in ...
1	$y = f(x)$	$F(x, y) = 0$	$\mathbf{R}^2$ (xy-plane)
2	$z = f(x, y)$	$F(x, y, z) = 0$	$\mathbf{R}^3$ (xyz-space)
3	$w = f(x, y, z)$	$F(w, x, y, z) = 0$	$\mathbf{R}^4$
n	$y = f(x_1, x_2, \ldots, x_n)$	$F(x_1, x_2, \ldots, x_n, x_{n+1}) = 0$	$\mathbf{R}^{n+1}$

The concepts of domain and range extend from the one- and two-variable cases in an obvious way.

> **DEFINITION Function, Domain, and Range with n Independent Variables**
>
> The **function** $y = f(x_1, x_2, \ldots, x_n)$ assigns a unique real number y to each point $(x_1, x_2, \ldots, x_n)$ in a set D in $\mathbf{R}^n$. The set D is the **domain** of f. The **range** is the set of real numbers y that are assumed as the points $(x_1, x_2, \ldots, x_n)$ vary over the domain.

EXAMPLE 7 Finding domains Find the domain of the following functions.

a. $g(x, y, z) = \sqrt{16 - x^2 - y^2 - z^2}$ **b.** $h(x, y, z) = \dfrac{12y^2}{z - y}$

SOLUTION

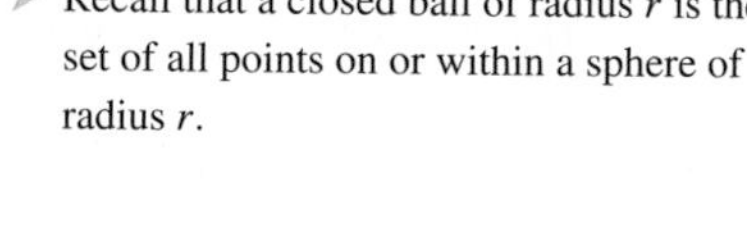

Recall that a closed ball of radius r is the set of all points on or within a sphere of radius r.

a. Values of the variables that make the argument of a square root negative must be excluded from the domain. In this case, the quantity under the square root is nonnegative provided

$$16 - x^2 - y^2 - z^2 \geq 0, \quad \text{or} \quad x^2 + y^2 + z^2 \leq 16.$$

Therefore, the domain of g is a closed ball in $\mathbf{R}^3$ of radius 4.

b. Values of the variables that make a denominator zero must be excluded from the domain. In this case, the denominator vanishes for all points in $\mathbf{R}^3$ that satisfy $z - y = 0$, or $y = z$. Therefore, the domain of h is the set $\{(x, y, z): y \neq z\}$. This set is $\mathbf{R}^3$ excluding the points on the plane $y = z$. *Related Exercises 42–48* ◀

QUICK CHECK 9 What is the domain of the function $w = f(x, y, z) = 1/xyz$? ◀

Graphs of Functions of More Than Two Variables

Graphing functions of *two* independent variables requires a three-dimensional coordinate system, which is the limit of ordinary graphing methods. Clearly, difficulties arise in graphing functions with three or more independent variables. For example, the graph of the function $w = f(x, y, z)$ resides in four dimensions. Here are two approaches to representing functions of three independent variables.

The idea of level curves can be extended. With the function $w = f(x, y, z)$, level curves become **level surfaces**, which are surfaces in $\mathbf{R}^3$ on which w is constant. For example, the level surfaces of the function

$$w = f(x, y, z) = \sqrt{z - x^2 - 2y^2}$$

satisfy $w = \sqrt{z - x^2 - 2y^2} = C$, where C is a nonnegative constant. This equation is satisfied when $z = x^2 + 2y^2 + C^2$. Therefore, the level surfaces are elliptic paraboloids, stacked one inside another (Figure 13.35).

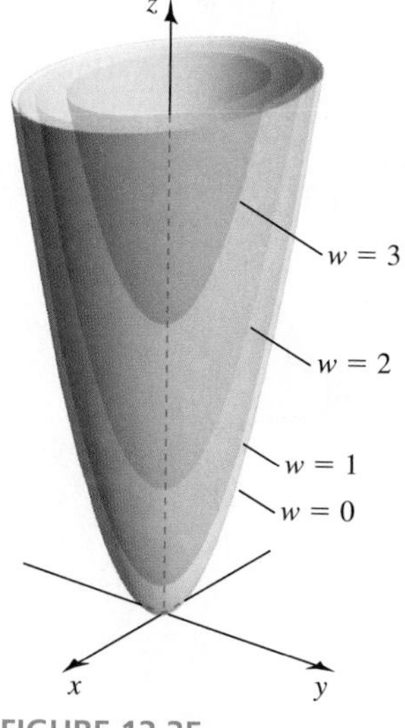

FIGURE 13.35

Another approach to displaying functions of three variables is to use colors to gain access to the fourth dimension. Figure 13.36a shows the electrical activity of the heart at one snapshot in time. The three independent variables correspond to locations in the heart. At each point, the value of the electrical activity, which is the dependent variable, is coded by colors.

In Figure 13.36b, the dependent variable is the switching speed in an integrated circuit, again represented by colors, as it varies over points of the domain. Software to produce such images, once expensive and inefficient, has become much more accessible.

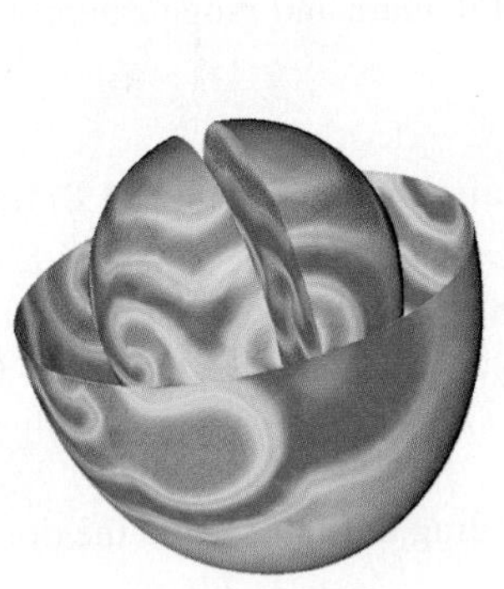

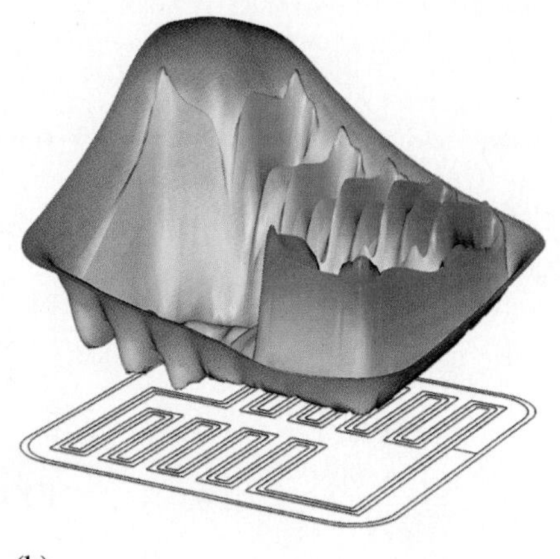

FIGURE 13.36 (a) (b)

SECTION 13.2 EXERCISES

Review Questions

1. A function is defined by $z = x^2y - xy^2$. Identify the independent and dependent variables.
2. What is the domain of $f(x, y) = x^2y - xy^2$?
3. What is the domain of $g(x, y) = 1/(xy)$?
4. What is the domain of $h(x, y) = \sqrt{x - y}$?
5. How many axes or how many dimensions are needed to graph the function $z = f(x, y)$? Explain.
6. Explain how to graph the level curves of a surface $z = f(x, y)$.
7. Describe in words the level curves of the paraboloid $z = x^2 + y^2$.
8. How many axes (or how many dimensions) are needed to graph the level surfaces of $w = f(x, y, z)$? Explain.
9. The domain of $Q = f(u, v, w, x, y, z)$ lies in $\mathbf{R}^n$ for what value of n? Explain.
10. Give two methods for graphically representing a function with three independent variables.

Basic Skills

11–18. Domains *Find the domain of the following functions.*

11. $f(x, y) = 2xy - 3x + 4y$
12. $f(x, y) = \cos(x^2 - y^2)$
13. $f(x, y) = \sin\left(\dfrac{x}{y}\right)$
14. $f(x, y) = \dfrac{12}{y^2 - x^2}$
15. $g(x, y) = \ln(x^2 - y)$
16. $f(x, y) = \tan^{-1}(x + y)$
17. $g(x, y) = \sqrt{\dfrac{xy}{x^2 + y^2}}$
18. $h(x, y) = \sqrt{x - 2y + 4}$

19–26. Graphs of familiar functions *Use what you learned about surfaces in Section 13.1 to sketch a graph of the following functions. In each case identify the surface, and state the domain and range of the function.*

19. $f(x, y) = 3x - 6y + 18$
20. $h(x, y) = 2x^2 + 3y^2$
21. $p(x, y) = x^2 - y^2$
22. $F(x, y) = \sqrt{1 - x^2 - y^2}$
23. $G(x, y) = -\sqrt{1 + x^2 + y^2}$
24. $H(x, y) = \sqrt{x^2 + y^2}$
25. $P(x, y) = \sqrt{x^2 + y^2 - 1}$
26. $g(x, y) = y^3 + 1$

27. **Matching surfaces** Match functions a–d with surfaces A–D in the figure.

 a. $f(x, y) = \cos xy$
 b. $g(x, y) = \ln(x^2 + y^2)$
 c. $h(x, y) = 1/(x - y)$
 d. $p(x, y) = 1/(1 + x^2 + y^2)$

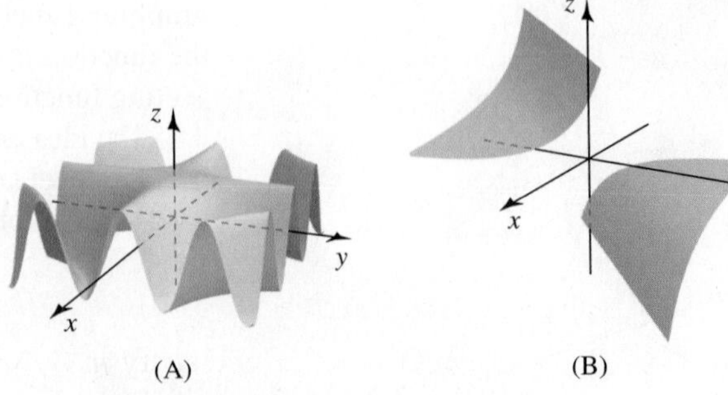

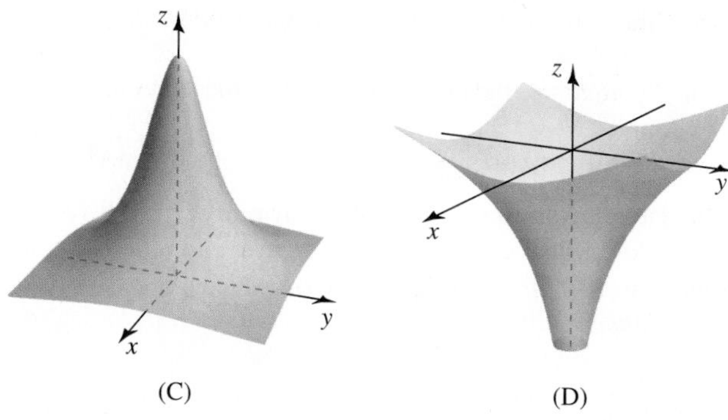

28–33. Level curves *Graph several level curves of the following functions using the given window. Label at least two level curves with their z-values.*

28. $z = 2x - y$; $[-2, 2] \times [-2, 2]$

29. $z = \sqrt{x^2 + 4y^2}$; $[-8, 8] \times [-8, 8]$

30. $z = e^{-x^2-2y^2}$; $[-2, 2] \times [-2, 2]$

31. $z = \sqrt{25 - x^2 - y^2}$; $[-6, 6] \times [-6, 6]$

32. $z = \sqrt{y - x^2 - 1}$; $[-5, 5] \times [-5, 5]$

33. $z = 3\cos(2x + y)$; $[-2, 2] \times [-2, 2]$

34. Matching level curves with surfaces Match surfaces a–f in the figure with level curves A–F.

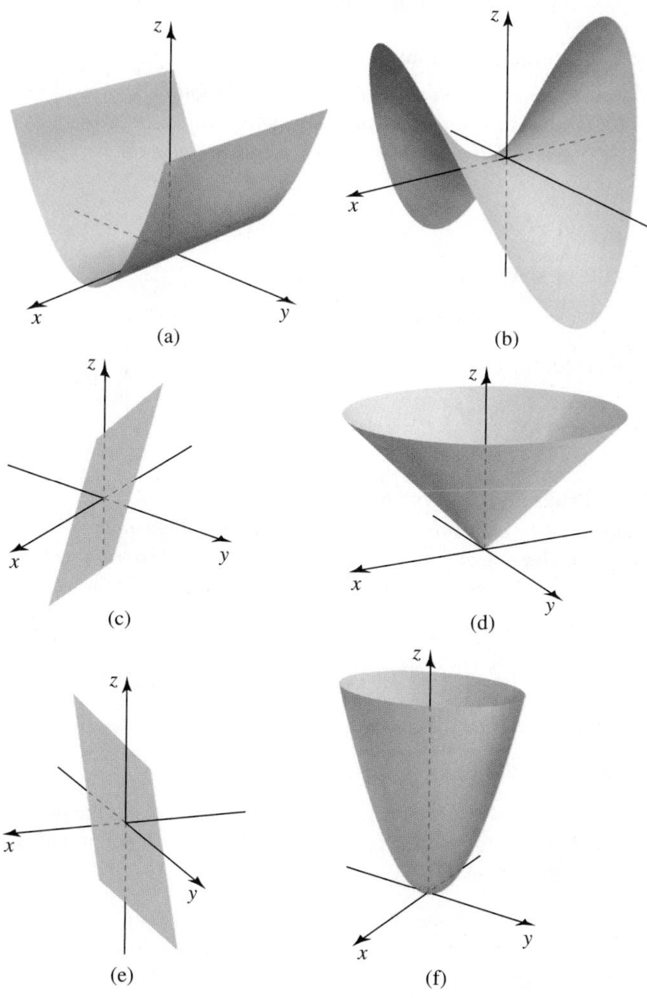

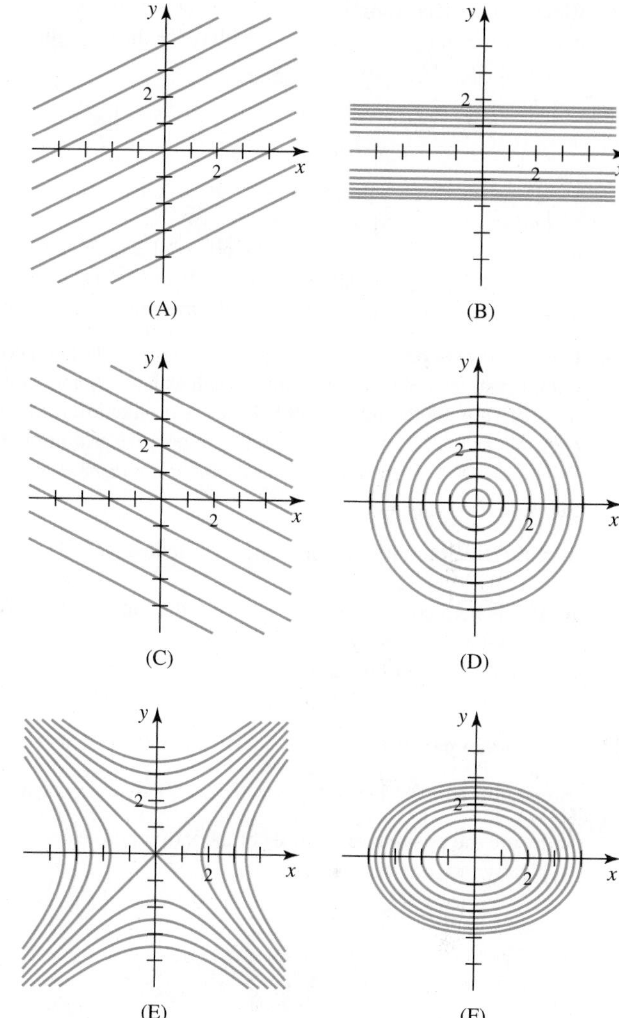

35. A volume function The volume of a right circular cone of radius r and height h is $V(r, h) = \pi r^2 h/3$.

a. Graph the function in the window $[0, 5] \times [0, 5] \times [0, 150]$.

b. What is the domain of the volume function?

c. What is the relationship between the values of r and h when $V = 100$?

36. Earned run average A baseball pitcher's earned run average (ERA) is $A(e, i) = 9e/i$, where e is the number of earned runs given up by the pitcher and i is the number of innings pitched. Good pitchers have low ERAs. Assume that $e \geq 0$ and $i > 0$ are real numbers.

a. The single-season major league record for the lowest ERA was set by Dutch Leonard of the Detroit Tigers in 1914. During that season, Dutch pitched a total of 224 innings and gave up just 24 earned runs. What was his ERA?

b. Determine the ERA of a relief pitcher who gives up 4 earned runs in one-third of an inning.

c. Graph the level curve $A(e, i) = 3$, and describe the relationship between e and i in this case.

37. Electric potential function The electric potential function for two positive charges, one at $(0, 1)$ with twice the strength as the charge at $(0, -1)$, is given by

$$\varphi(x, y) = \frac{2}{\sqrt{x^2 + (y - 1)^2}} + \frac{1}{\sqrt{x^2 + (y + 1)^2}}.$$

a. Graph the electric potential using the window $[-5, 5] \times [-5, 5] \times [0, 10]$.
b. For what values of x and y is the potential φ defined?
c. Is the electric potential greater at $(3, 2)$ or $(2, 3)$?
d. Describe how the electric potential varies along the line $y = x$.

38. Cobb-Douglas production function The output Q of an economic system subject to two inputs, such as labor L and capital K, is often modeled by the Cobb-Douglas production function $Q(L, K) = cL^aK^b$, where a, b, and c are positive real numbers. When $a + b = 1$, the case is called *constant returns to scale*. Suppose $a = \frac{1}{3}$, $b = \frac{2}{3}$, and $c = 40$.

a. Graph the output function using the window $[0, 20] \times [0, 20] \times [0, 500]$.
b. If L is held constant at $L = 10$, write the function that gives the dependence of Q on K.
c. If K is held constant at $K = 15$, write the function that gives the dependence of Q on L.

39. Resistors in parallel Two resistors wired in parallel in an electrical circuit give an effective resistance of $R(x, y) = \dfrac{xy}{x + y}$, where x and y are the positive resistances of the individual resistors (typically measured in ohms).

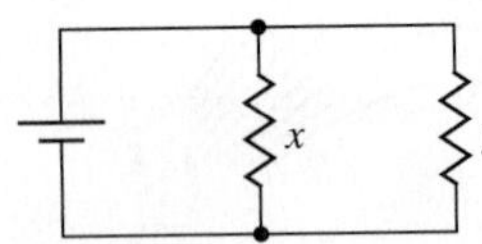

a. Graph the resistance function using the window $[0, 10] \times [0, 10] \times [0, 5]$.
b. Estimate the maximum value of R for $0 < x \leq 10$ and $0 < y \leq 10$.
c. Explain what it means to say that the resistance function is symmetric in x and y.

40. Water waves A snapshot of a water wave moving toward shore is described by the function $z = 10 \sin (2x - 3y)$, where z is the height of the water surface above (or below) the xy-plane, which is the level of undisturbed water.

a. Graph the height function using the window $[-5, 5] \times [-5, 5] \times [-15, 15]$.
b. For what values of x and y is z defined?
c. What are the maximum and minimum values of the water height?
d. Give a vector in the xy-plane that is orthogonal to the level curves of the crests and troughs of the wave (which also gives the direction of wave propagation).

41. Approximate mountains Suppose the elevation of Earth's surface over a 16-mi by 16-mi region is approximated by the function

$$z = 10e^{-(x^2+y^2)} + 5e^{-((x+5)^2+(y-3)^2)/10} + 4e^{-2((x-4)^2+(y+1)^2)}.$$

a. Graph the height function using the window $[-8, 8] \times [-8, 8] \times [0, 15]$.
b. Approximate the points (x, y) where the peaks in the landscape appear.
c. What are the approximate elevations of the peaks?

42–48. Domains of functions of three or more variables *Find the domain of the following functions. If possible, give a description of the domain in words (for example, all points outside a sphere of radius 1 centered at the origin).*

42. $f(x, y, z) = 2xyz - 3xz + 4yz$

43. $g(x, y, z) = \dfrac{1}{x - z}$

44. $p(x, y, z) = \sqrt{x^2 + y^2 + z^2 - 9}$

45. $f(x, y, z) = \sqrt{y - z}$

46. $Q(x, y, z) = \dfrac{10}{1 + x^2 + y^2 + 4z^2}$

47. $F(x, y, z) = \sqrt{y - x^2}$

48. $f(w, x, y, z) = \sqrt{1 - w^2 - x^2 - y^2 - z^2}$

Further Explorations

49. Explain why or why not Determine whether the following statements are true and give an explanation or counterexample.

a. The domain of the function $f(x, y) = 1 - |x - y|$ is $\{(x, y): x \geq y\}$.
b. The domain of the function $Q = g(w, x, y, z)$ is a region in $\mathbf{R}^3$.
c. All level curves of the plane $z = 2x - 3y$ are lines.

50–56. Graphing functions

a. Determine the domain and range of the following functions.
b. Graph each function using a graphing utility. Be sure to experiment with the window and orientation to give the best perspective on the surface.

50. $g(x, y) = e^{-xy}$

51. $f(x, y) = |xy|$

52. $p(x, y) = 1 - |x - 1| + |y + 1|$

53. $h(x, y) = (x + y)/(x - y)$

54. $G(x, y) = \ln (2 + \sin (x + y))$

55. $F(x, y) = \tan^2 (x - y)$

56. $P(x, y) = \cos x \sin 2y$

57–60. Peaks and valleys *The following functions have exactly one isolated peak or one isolated depression (one local maximum or minimum). Use a graphing utility to approximate the coordinates of the peak or depression.*

57. $f(x, y) = x^2y^2 - 8x^2 - y^2 + 6$

58. $g(x, y) = (x^2 - x - 2)(y^2 + 2y)$

59. $h(x, y) = 1 - e^{-(x^2+y^2-2x)}$

60. $p(x, y) = 2 + |x - 1| + |y - 1|$

61. Level curves of planes Prove that the level curves of the plane $ax + by + cz = d$ are parallel lines in the xy-plane, provided $a^2 + b^2 \neq 0$ and $c \neq 0$.

Applications

62. Level curves of a savings account Suppose you make a one-time deposit of P dollars into a savings account that earns interest at an annual rate of $p\%$ compounded continuously. The balance in the account after t years is $B(P, r, t) = Pe^{rt}$, where $r = p/100$ (for example, if the annual interest rate is 4%, then $r = 0.04$). Let the interest rate be fixed at $r = 0.04$.

a. With a target balance of \$2000, find the set of all points (P, t) that satisfy $B = 2000$. This curve gives all deposits P and times t that result in a balance of \$2000.

b. Repeat part (a) with $B = \$500, \$1000, \$1500$, and \$2500, and draw the resulting level curves of the balance function.

c. In general, on one level curve, if t increases, does P increase or decrease?

63. Level curves of a savings plan Suppose you make monthly deposits of P dollars into an account that earns interest at a *monthly* rate of $p\%$. The balance in the account after t years is $B(P, r, t) = P\left[\frac{(1 + r)^{12t} - 1}{r}\right]$, where $r = p/100$ (for example, if the annual interest rate is 9%, then $p = \frac{9}{12} = 0.75$ and $r = 0.0075$). Let the time of investment be fixed at $t = 20$ years.

a. With a target balance of \$20,000, find the set of all points (P, r) that satisfy $B = 20{,}000$. This curve gives all deposits P and monthly interest rates r that result in a balance of \$20,000 after 20 years.

b. Repeat part (a) with $B = \$5000, \$10{,}000, \$15{,}000$, and \$25,000, and draw the resulting level curves of the balance function.

64. Quarterback ratings One measurement of the quality of a quarterback in the National Football League is known as the *quarterback rating*. The rating formula is $R(c, t, i, y) = \frac{50 + 20c + 80t - 100i + 100y}{24}$, where c is the percentage of passes completed, t is the percentage of passes thrown for touchdowns, i is the percentage of intercepted passes, and y is the yards gained per attempted pass.

a. In his career, Hall of Fame quarterback Johnny Unitas completed 54.57% of his passes, 5.59% of his passes were thrown for touchdowns, 4.88% of his passes were intercepted, and he gained an average of 7.76 yards per attempted pass. What was his quarterback rating?

b. If c, t, and y remained fixed, what happens to the quarterback rating as i increases? Explain your answer with and without mathematics.

[*Source: The College Mathematics Journal* (November 1993).]

65. Ideal Gas Law Many gases can be modeled by the Ideal Gas Law, $PV = nRT$, which relates the temperature (T, measured in Kelvin (K)), pressure (P, measured in Pascals (Pa)), and volume (V, measured in m^3) of a gas. Assume that the quantity of gas in question is $n = 1$ mole (mol). The gas constant has a value of $R = 8.3\ m^3Pa/mol\text{-}K$.

a. Consider T to be the dependent variable and plot several level curves (called *isotherms*) of the temperature surface in the region $0 \le P \le 100{,}000$ and $0 \le V \le 0.5$.

b. Consider P to be the dependent variable and plot several level curves (called *isobars*) of the pressure surface in the region $0 \le T \le 900$ and $0 < V \le 0.5$.

c. Consider V to be the dependent variable and plot several level curves of the volume surface in the region $0 \le T \le 900$ and $0 < P \le 100{,}000$.

Additional Exercises

66–69. Challenge domains *Find the domains of the following functions. Specify the domain mathematically and then describe it in words or with a sketch.*

66. $g(x, y, z) = \frac{10}{x^2 - (y + z)x + yz}$

67. $f(x, y) = \sin^{-1}(x - y)^2$

68. $f(x, y, z) = \ln(z - x^2 - y^2 + 2x + 3)$

69. $h(x, y, z) = \sqrt[4]{z^2 - xz + yz - xy}$

70. Other balls The closed unit ball in $\mathbf{R}^3$ centered at the origin is the set $\{(x, y, z): x^2 + y^2 + z^2 \le 1\}$. Describe in words the following alternative unit balls.

a. $\{(x, y, z): |x| + |y| + |z| \le 1\}$

b. $\{(x, y, z): \max\{|x|, |y|, |z|\} \le 1\}$, where $\max\{a, b, c\}$ is the maximum value of a, b, and c.

QUICK CHECK ANSWERS

1. $\mathbf{R}^2$; $\{(x, y): y \ge 0\}$ **2.** No; no **3.** $z = -\sqrt{1 + x^2 + y^2}$ **4.** No, otherwise the function would have two values at a single point. **5.** Concentric circles **6.** No; $z = 0$ is not in the range of the function. **7.** 0.97 **8.** 8 **9.** $\{(x, y, z): x \ne 0 \text{ and } y \ne 0 \text{ and } z \ne 0\}$ (which is $\mathbf{R}^3$, excluding the coordinate planes)

13.3 Limits and Continuity

You have now seen examples of functions of several variables, but calculus has not yet entered the picture. In this section we revisit topics encountered in single-variable calculus and see how they apply to functions of several variables. We begin with the fundamental concepts of limits and continuity.

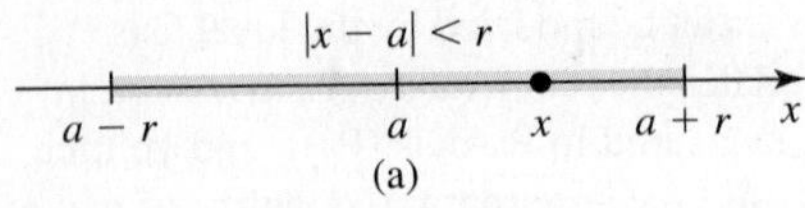

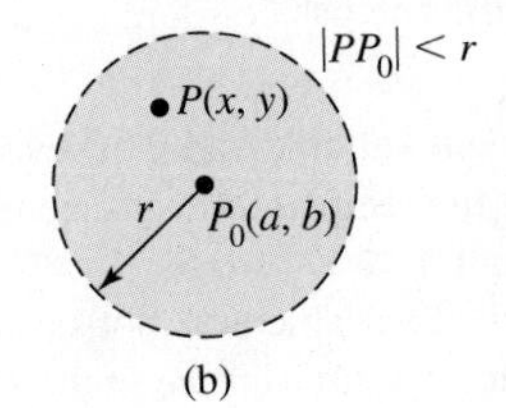

FIGURE 13.37

Limit of a Function of Two Variables

A function f of two variables has a limit L as $P(x, y)$ approaches a fixed point $P_0(a, b)$ if $|f(x, y) - L|$ can be made arbitrarily small for all P in the domain that are sufficiently close to P_0. If such a limit exists, we write

$$\lim_{(x,y)\to(a,b)} f(x, y) = \lim_{P\to P_0} f(x, y) = L.$$

To make this definition more precise, *close to* must be defined carefully.

A point x on the number line is close to another point a provided the distance $|x - a|$ is small (Figure 13.37a). In $\mathbf{R}^2$, a point $P(x, y)$ is close to another point $P_0(a, b)$ if the distance between them $|PP_0| = \sqrt{(x - a)^2 + (y - b)^2}$ is small (Figure 13.37b). When we say *for all P close to P_0*, it means that $|PP_0|$ is small for points P on all sides of P_0.

With this understanding of closeness, we can give a formal definition of a limit with two independent variables. This definition parallels the formal definition of a limit given in Section 2.7 (Figure 13.38).

➤ The formal definition extends naturally to any number of variables. With n variables, the limit point is $P_0(a_1, \ldots, a_n)$, the variable point is $P(x_1, \ldots, x_n)$, and $|PP_0| = \sqrt{(x_1 - a_1)^2 + \cdots + (x_n - a_n)^2}$.

> **DEFINITION Limit of a Function of Two Variables**
>
> The function f has the **limit** L as $P(x, y)$ approaches $P_0(a, b)$, written
>
> $$\lim_{(x,y)\to(a,b)} f(x, y) = \lim_{P\to P_0} f(x, y) = L,$$
>
> if, given any $\varepsilon > 0$, there exists a $\delta > 0$ such that
>
> $$|f(x, y) - L| < \varepsilon$$
>
> whenever (x, y) is in the domain of f and
>
> $$0 < |PP_0| = \sqrt{(x - a)^2 + (y - b)^2} < \delta.$$

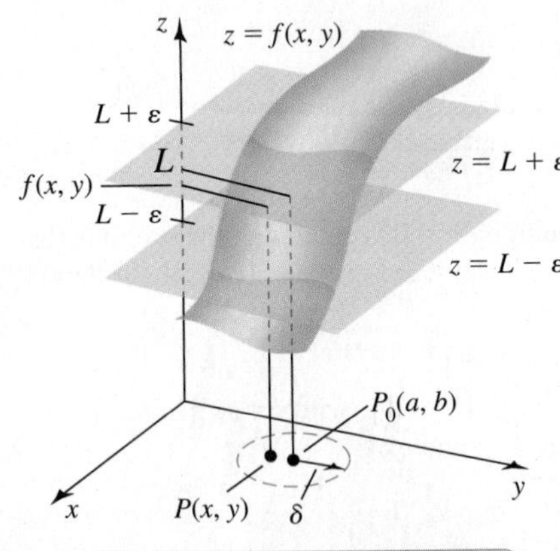

FIGURE 13.38

The condition $|PP_0| < \delta$ means that the distance between $P(x, y)$ and $P_0(a, b)$ is less than δ as P approaches P_0 from all possible directions (Figure 13.39). Therefore, the limit exists only if $f(x, y)$ approaches L as P approaches P_0 *along all possible paths* in the domain of f. As shown in upcoming examples, this interpretation is critical in determining whether or not a limit exists.

As with functions of one variable, we first establish limits of the simplest functions.

> **THEOREM 13.1 Limits of Constants and Linear Functions**
>
> Let a, b, and c be real numbers.
>
> 1. Constant functions $f(x, y) = c$: $\displaystyle\lim_{(x,y)\to(a,b)} c = c$
> 2. Linear function $f(x, y) = x$: $\displaystyle\lim_{(x,y)\to(a,b)} x = a$
> 3. Linear function $f(x, y) = y$: $\displaystyle\lim_{(x,y)\to(a,b)} y = b$

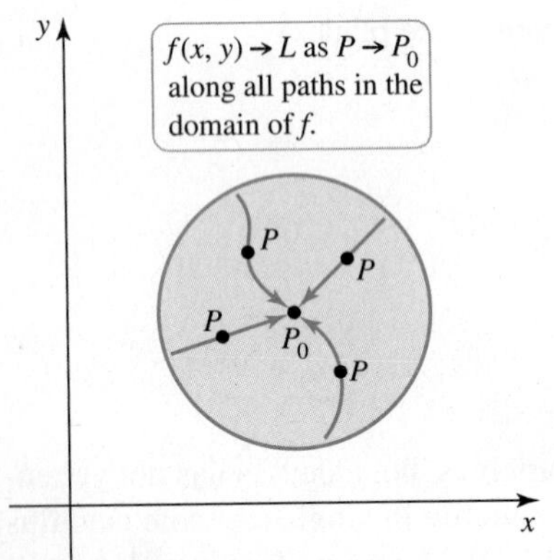

FIGURE 13.39

Proof

1. Consider the constant function $f(x, y) = c$ and assume $\varepsilon > 0$ is given. To prove that the value of the limit is $L = c$, we must produce a $\delta > 0$ such that $|f(x, y) - L| < \varepsilon$

whenever $\sqrt{(x-a)^2+(y-b)^2}<\delta$. For constant functions, we may use *any* constant $\delta>0$. Then, for every (x, y) in the domain of f,

$$|f(x,y)-L| = |f(x,y)-c| = |c-c| = 0 < \varepsilon$$

whenever $\sqrt{(x-a)^2+(y-b)^2}<\delta$.

2. Assume $\varepsilon>0$ is given and take $\delta=\varepsilon$. The condition $\sqrt{(x-a)^2+(y-b)^2}<\delta$ implies that

$$\begin{aligned} \sqrt{(x-a)^2+(y-b)^2} &< \varepsilon && \delta=\varepsilon \\ \sqrt{(x-a)^2} &< \varepsilon && (x-a)^2 \le (x-a)^2+(y-b)^2 \\ |x-a| &< \varepsilon. && \sqrt{x^2}=|x| \text{ for real numbers } x \end{aligned}$$

Because $f(x,y)=x$ and $a=L$, we have shown that $|f(x,y)-L|<\varepsilon$ whenever $\sqrt{(x-a)^2+(y-b)^2}<\delta$. Therefore, $\lim\limits_{(x,y)\to(a,b)} f(x,y)=L$, or $\lim\limits_{(x,y)\to(a,b)} x=a$. The proof that $\lim\limits_{(x,y)\to(a,b)} y=b$ is similar (Exercise 68). ◀

Using the three basic limits in Theorem 13.1, we can compute limits of more complicated functions. The only tools needed are limit laws analogous to those given in Theorem 2.3. The proofs of these laws are examined in Exercises 70–71.

> **THEOREM 13.2 Limit Laws for Functions of Two Variables**
> Let L and M be real numbers and suppose that $\lim\limits_{(x,y)\to(a,b)} f(x,y)=L$ and $\lim\limits_{(x,y)\to(a,b)} g(x,y)=M$. Assume c is a constant, and m and n are integers.
>
> 1. **Sum** $\lim\limits_{(x,y)\to(a,b)} [f(x,y)+g(x,y)] = L+M$
> 2. **Difference** $\lim\limits_{(x,y)\to(a,b)} [f(x,y)-g(x,y)] = L-M$
> 3. **Constant multiple** $\lim\limits_{(x,y)\to(a,b)} [cf(x,y)] = cL$
> 4. **Product** $\lim\limits_{(x,y)\to(a,b)} f(x,y)g(x,y) = LM$
> 5. **Quotient** $\lim\limits_{(x,y)\to(a,b)} \left[\dfrac{f(x,y)}{g(x,y)}\right] = \dfrac{L}{M}$, provided $M\neq 0$
> 6. **Power** $\lim\limits_{(x,y)\to(a,b)} [f(x,y)]^n = L^n$
> 7. ***m/n* power** If m and n have no common factors and $n\neq 0$, then $\lim\limits_{(x,y)\to(a,b)} [f(x,y)]^{m/n} = L^{m/n}$, where we assume $L>0$ if n is even.

Combining Theorems 13.1 and 13.2 allows us to find limits of polynomial, rational, and algebraic functions in two variables.

➤ Recall that a polynomial in two variables consists of sums and products of polynomials in x and polynomials in y. A rational function is the quotient of two polynomials.

EXAMPLE 1 Limits of two-variable functions Evaluate $\lim\limits_{(x,y)\to(2,8)} (3x^2y+\sqrt{xy})$.

SOLUTION All the operations in this function appear in Theorem 13.2. Therefore, we can apply the limit laws directly.

$$\begin{aligned}\lim_{(x,y)\to(2,8)} (3x^2y + \sqrt{xy}) &= \lim_{(x,y)\to(2,8)} 3x^2y + \lim_{(x,y)\to(2,8)} \sqrt{xy} && \text{Law 1}\\ &= 3\left[\lim_{(x,y)\to(2,8)} x\right]^2\left[\lim_{(x,y)\to(2,8)} y\right]\\ &\quad + \sqrt{\left[\lim_{(x,y)\to(2,8)} x\right]\left[\lim_{(x,y)\to(2,8)} y\right]} && \text{Laws 3, 4, 6, 7}\\ &= 3\cdot 2^2\cdot 8 + \sqrt{2\cdot 8} = 100 && \text{Theorem 13.1}\end{aligned}$$

Related Exercises 11–18 ◄

In Example 1, the value of the limit equals the value of the function; in other words $\lim_{(x,y)\to(a,b)} f(x, y) = f(a, b)$, and the limit can be evaluated by substitution. This is a property of *continuous* functions, discussed later in this section.

QUICK CHECK 1 Which of the following limits exist?

a. $\lim_{(x,y)\to(1,1)} 3x^{12}y^2$ **b.** $\lim_{(x,y)\to(0,0)} 3x^{-2}y^2$ **c.** $\lim_{(x,y)\to(1,2)} \sqrt{x - y^2}$ ◄

Q is a boundary point: Every disk centered at Q contains points in R and points not in R.

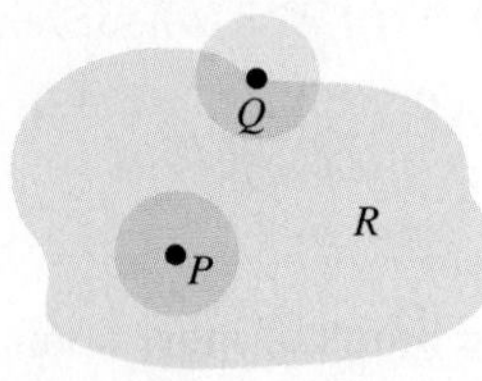

P is an interior point: There is a disk centered at P that lies entirely in R.

FIGURE 13.40

Limits at Boundary Points

This is an appropriate place to make some definitions that will be used in the remainder of the book.

> The definitions of interior point and boundary point apply to regions in $\mathbf{R}^3$ if we replace *disk* by *ball*.

DEFINITION Interior and Boundary Points

Let R be a region in $\mathbf{R}^2$. An **interior point** P of R lies entirely within R, which means it is possible to find a disk centered at P that contains only points of R (Figure 13.40).

A **boundary point** Q of R lies on the edge of R in the sense that *every* disk centered at Q contains at least one point in R and at least one point not in R.

For example, let R be the points in $\mathbf{R}^2$ satisfying $x^2 + y^2 < 9$. The boundary points of R lie on the circle $x^2 + y^2 = 9$. The interior points lie inside that circle and satisfy $x^2 + y^2 < 9$. Notice that the boundary points of a set need not lie in the set.

> Many sets, such as the annulus $\{(x, y): 2 \le x^2 + y^2 < 5\}$ are neither open nor closed.

DEFINITION Open and Closed Sets

A region is **open** if it consists entirely of interior points. A region is **closed** if it contains all its boundary points.

An example of an open region in $\mathbf{R}^2$ is the open disk $\{(x, y): x^2 + y^2 < 9\}$. An example of a closed region in $\mathbf{R}^2$ is the square $\{(x, y): |x| \le 1, |y| \le 1\}$. Later in the book, we encounter interior and boundary points of three-dimensional sets such as balls, boxes, and cubes.

QUICK CHECK 2 Give an example of a set that contains none of its boundary points. ◄

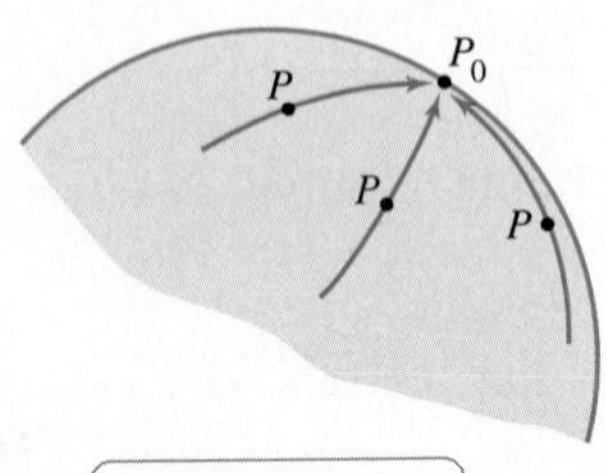

P must approach P_0 along all paths in the domain of f.

FIGURE 13.41

Suppose $P_0(a, b)$ is a boundary point of the domain of f. The limit $\lim_{(x,y)\to(a,b)} f(x, y)$ exists, even if P_0 is not in the domain of f, provided $f(x, y)$ approaches the same value as (x, y) approaches (a, b) *along all paths that lie in the domain* (Figure 13.41).

> Recall that this same method was used with functions of one variable. For example, after canceling the common term $x - 2$, the function
>
> $$g(x) = \frac{x^2 - 4}{x - 2}$$
>
> becomes $g(x) = x + 2$, provided $x \neq 2$. In this case, 2 plays the role of a boundary point.

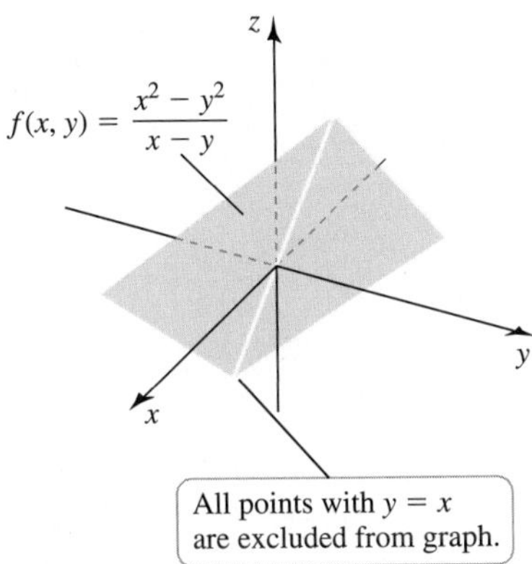

FIGURE 13.42

Consider the function $f(x, y) = \frac{x^2 - y^2}{x - y}$ whose domain is $\{(x, y): x \neq y\}$. Provided $x \neq y$, we may cancel the factor $(x - y)$ from the numerator and denominator and write

$$f(x, y) = \frac{x^2 - y^2}{x - y} = \frac{(x - y)(x + y)}{x - y} = x + y.$$

The graph of f (Figure 13.42) is the plane $z = x + y$, with points corresponding to the line $x = y$ removed.

Now, we examine $\lim_{(x,y)\to(4,4)} \frac{x^2 - y^2}{x - y}$, where $(4, 4)$ is a boundary point of the domain of f but does not lie in the domain. For this limit to exist, $f(x, y)$ must approach the same value along all paths to $(4, 4)$ that lie in the domain of f—that is, all paths approaching $(4, 4)$ except the path $x = y$. To evaluate the limit, we proceed as follows:

$$\begin{aligned} \lim_{(x,y)\to(4,4)} \frac{x^2 - y^2}{x - y} &= \lim_{(x,y)\to(4,4)} (x + y) && \text{Assume } x \neq y \text{, cancel } x - y. \\ &= 4 + 4 = 8 && \text{Same limit along all paths in the domain} \end{aligned}$$

To emphasize, we let $(x, y) \to (4, 4)$ along all paths except the path $x = y$, which lies outside the domain of f. Along all admissible paths, the function approaches 8.

QUICK CHECK 3 Can the limit $\lim_{(x,y)\to(0,0)} \frac{x^2 - xy}{x}$ be evaluated by direct substitution? ◂

EXAMPLE 2 Limits at boundary points

Evaluate $\lim_{(x,y)\to(4,1)} \frac{xy - 4y^2}{\sqrt{x} - 2\sqrt{y}}$.

SOLUTION Points in the domain of this function satisfy $x \geq 0$ and $y \geq 0$ (because of the square roots) and $x \neq 4y$ (to ensure the denominator is nonzero). We see that the point $(4, 1)$ lies on the boundary of the domain. Multiplying the numerator and denominator by the algebraic conjugate of the denominator, the limit is computed as follows:

$$\begin{aligned} \lim_{(x,y)\to(4,1)} \frac{xy - 4y^2}{\sqrt{x} - 2\sqrt{y}} &= \lim_{(x,y)\to(4,1)} \frac{(xy - 4y^2)(\sqrt{x} + 2\sqrt{y})}{(\sqrt{x} - 2\sqrt{y})(\sqrt{x} + 2\sqrt{y})} && \text{Multiply by conjugate.} \\ &= \lim_{(x,y)\to(4,1)} \frac{y(x - 4y)(\sqrt{x} + 2\sqrt{y})}{x - 4y} && \text{Simplify.} \\ &= \lim_{(x,y)\to(4,1)} y(\sqrt{x} + 2\sqrt{y}) && \text{Cancel } x - 4y \text{, assumed to be nonzero.} \\ &= 4 && \text{Evaluate limit.} \end{aligned}$$

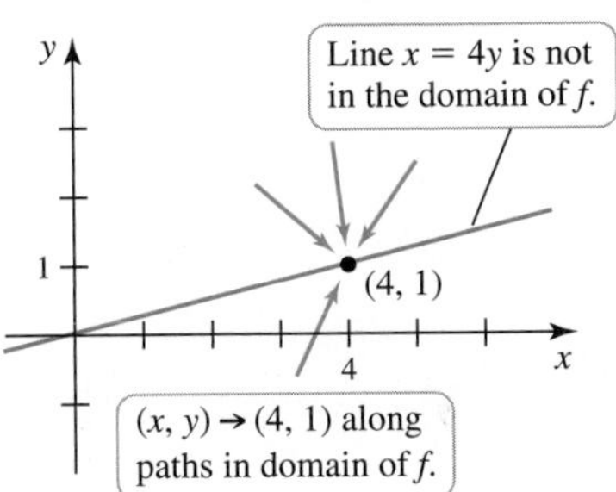

FIGURE 13.43

Because points on the line $x = 4y$ are outside the domain of the function, we assume that $x - 4y \neq 0$. Along all other paths to $(4, 1)$, the function values approach 4 (Figure 13.43).

Related Exercises 19–24 ◂

EXAMPLE 3 Nonexistence of a limit

Investigate the limit $\lim_{(x,y)\to(0,0)} \frac{(x + y)^2}{x^2 + y^2}$.

SOLUTION The domain of the function is $\{(x, y): (x, y) \neq (0, 0)\}$; therefore, the limit is at a boundary point outside the domain. Suppose we let (x, y) approach $(0, 0)$ along the line $y = mx$ for a fixed constant m. Substituting $y = mx$ and noting that $y \to 0$ as $x \to 0$, we have

$$\lim_{(x,y)\to(0,0)} \frac{(x + y)^2}{(x^2 + y^2)} = \lim_{x\to 0} \frac{(x + mx)^2}{(x^2 + m^2x^2)} = \lim_{x\to 0} \frac{x^2(1 + m)^2}{x^2(1 + m^2)} = \frac{(1 + m)^2}{1 + m^2}.$$

> Notice that if we choose any path of the form $y = mx$, then $y \to 0$ as $x \to 0$. Therefore, $\lim_{(x,y)\to(0,0)}$ can be replaced by $\lim_{x\to 0}$ along this path. A similar argument applies to paths of the form $y = mx^p$ for $p > 0$.

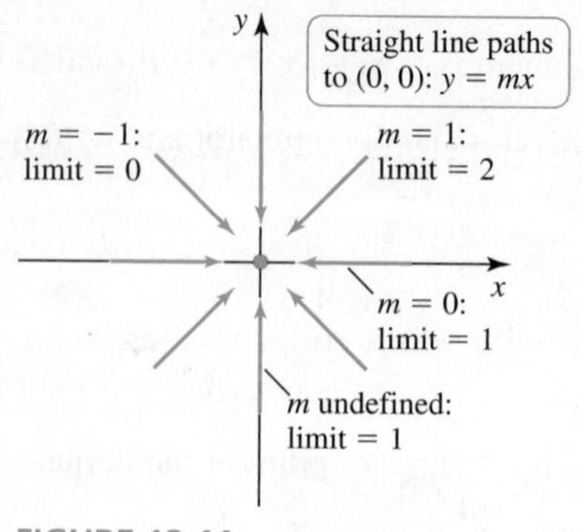

FIGURE 13.44

The constant m determines the direction of approach to $(0, 0)$. Therefore, depending on m, the function may approach any value in the interval $[0, 2]$ (which is the range of $(1 + m)^2/(1 + m^2)$) as (x, y) approaches $(0, 0)$ (Figure 13.44). For example, if $m = 0$, the corresponding limit is 1 and if $m = -1$, the limit is 0. Because the function approaches different values along different paths, we conclude that the *limit does not exist*. The reason for this behavior is revealed if we plot the surface and look at two level curves. We see that the level curves for function values 0 and 2 are straight lines that pass through the origin (Figure 13.45).

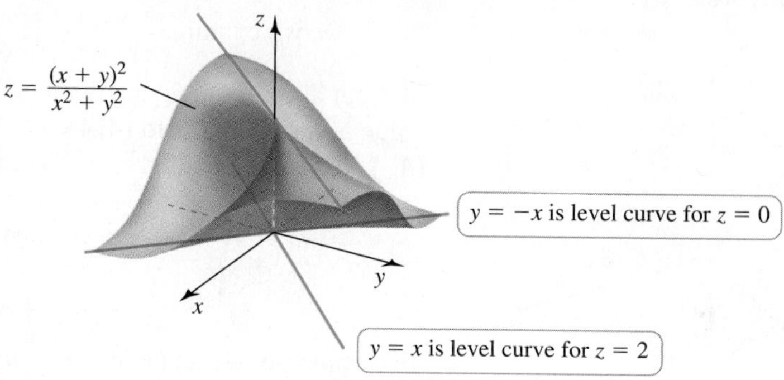

FIGURE 13.45

Related Exercises 25–30 ◂

The strategy used in Example 3 is one of the most effective ways to prove the nonexistence of a limit.

> **PROCEDURE Two-Path Test for Nonexistence of Limits**
>
> If $f(x, y)$ approaches two different values as (x, y) approaches (a, b) along two different paths in the domain of f, then $\lim_{(x,y)\to(a,b)} f(x, y)$ does not exist.

QUICK CHECK 4 What is the analog of the Two-Path Test for functions of a single variable? ◂

Continuity of Functions of Two Variables

The following definition of continuity for functions of two variables is analogous to the continuity definition for functions of one variable.

> **DEFINITION Continuity**
>
> The function f is continuous at the point (a, b) provided
>
> **1.** f is defined at (a, b).
>
> **2.** $\lim_{(x,y)\to(a,b)} f(x, y)$ exists.
>
> **3.** $\lim_{(x,y)\to(a,b)} f(x, y) = f(a, b)$

A function of two (or more) variables is continuous at a point, provided its limit equals its value at that point (which implies the limit and the value both exist). The definition of continuity applies at boundary points of the domain of f provided the limits in the definition are taken along paths that lie in the domain.

Because limits of polynomials and rational functions can be evaluated by substitution at points of their domains (that is, $\lim_{(x,y)\to(a,b)} f(x, y) = f(a, b)$), it follows that polynomials and rational functions are continuous at all points of their domains. Similarly, trigonometric, logarithmic, and exponential functions are continuous on their domains.

EXAMPLE 4 Checking continuity Determine the points at which the following function is continuous.

$$f(x, y) = \begin{cases} \dfrac{3xy^2}{x^2 + y^4} & \text{if } (x, y) \neq (0, 0) \\ 0 & \text{if } (x, y) = (0, 0) \end{cases}$$

SOLUTION The function $\dfrac{3xy^2}{x^2 + y^4}$ is a rational function, so it is continuous at all points of its domain, which consists of all points of $\mathbf{R}^2$ except $(0, 0)$. In order for f to be continuous at $(0, 0)$, we must show that

$$\lim_{(x,y)\to(0,0)} \frac{3xy^2}{x^2 + y^4} = f(0, 0) = 0.$$

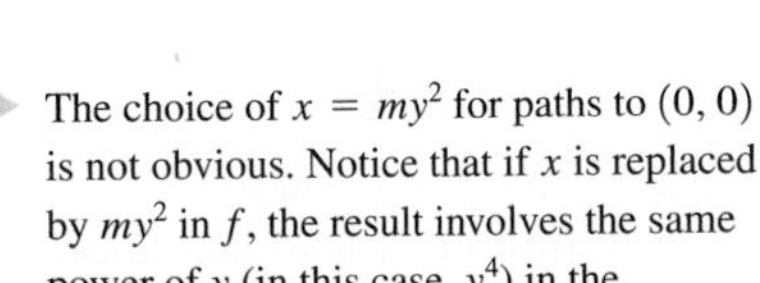

The choice of $x = my^2$ for paths to $(0, 0)$ is not obvious. Notice that if x is replaced by my^2 in f, the result involves the same power of y (in this case, y^4) in the numerator and denominator, which may be canceled.

You can verify that as (x, y) approaches $(0, 0)$ along paths of the form $y = mx$, where m is any constant, the function values approach $f(0, 0) = 0$. Now consider parabolic paths of the form $x = my^2$, where m is a nonzero constant (Figure 13.46). This time we substitute $x = my^2$ and note that $x \to 0$ as $y \to 0$:

$$\begin{aligned} \lim_{(x,y)\to(0,0)} \frac{3xy^2}{x^2 + y^4} &= \lim_{y\to 0} \frac{3(my^2)y^2}{(my^2)^2 + y^4} && \text{Subtitute } x = my^2. \\ &= \lim_{y\to 0} \frac{3my^4}{m^2y^4 + y^4} && \text{Simplify.} \\ &= \lim_{y\to 0} \frac{3m}{m^2 + 1} && \text{Cancel } y^4. \\ &= \frac{3m}{m^2 + 1} \end{aligned}$$

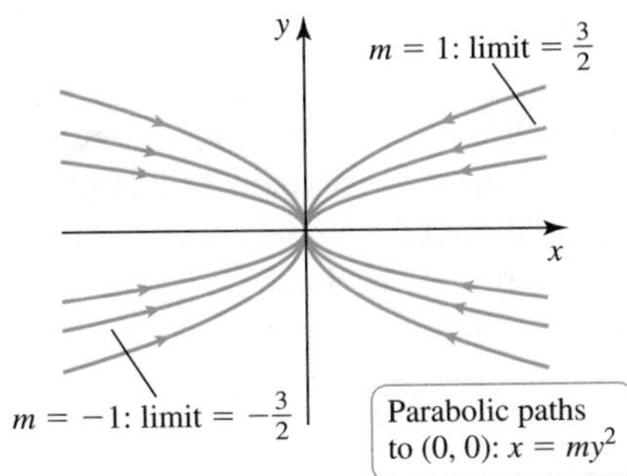

FIGURE 13.46

We see that along parabolic paths, the limit depends on the approach path. For example, with $m = 1$, along the path $x = y^2$, the function values approach $\frac{3}{2}$; with $m = -1$, along the path $x = -y^2$, the function values approach $-\frac{3}{2}$ (Figure 13.47). Because function values approach two different numbers along two different paths, the limit at $(0, 0)$ does not exist, and f is not continuous at $(0, 0)$.

$z = \dfrac{3xy^2}{x^2 + y^4}$

$x = y^2$ is a level curve for $z = \frac{3}{2}$.

$x = -y^2$ is a level curve for $z = -\frac{3}{2}$.

FIGURE 13.47

Related Exercises 31–34 ◀

QUICK CHECK 5 Which of the following functions are continuous at $(0, 0)$?

a. $f(x, y) = 2x^2y^5$

b. $f(x, y) = \dfrac{2x^2y^5}{x - 1}$

c. $f(x, y) = 2x^{-2}y^5$ ◄

Composite Functions Recall that for functions of a single variable, compositions of continuous functions are also continuous. The following theorem gives the analogous result for functions of two variables; it is proved in Appendix B.

> **THEOREM 13.3 Continuity of Composite Functions**
> If $u = g(x, y)$ is continuous at (a, b) and $z = f(u)$ is continuous at $g(a, b)$, then the composite function $z = f(g(x, y))$ is continuous at (a, b).

EXAMPLE 5 Continuity of composite functions. Determine the points at which the following functions are continuous.

a. $h(x, y) = \ln(x^2 + y^2 + 4)$ **b.** $h(x, y) = e^{x/y}$

SOLUTION

a. This function is the composition $f(g(x, y))$, where

$$f(u) = \ln u \quad \text{and} \quad u = g(x, y) = x^2 + y^2 + 4.$$

As a polynomial, g is continuous for all (x, y) in $\mathbf{R}^2$. The function f is continuous for $u > 0$. Because $u = x^2 + y^2 + 4 > 0$ for all (x, y), it follows that h is continuous at all points of $\mathbf{R}^2$.

b. Letting $f(u) = e^u$ and $u = g(x, y) = x/y$, we have $h(x, y) = f(g(x, y))$. Note that f is continuous at all points of $\mathbf{R}$ and g is continuous at all points of $\mathbf{R}^2$ provided $y \neq 0$. Therefore, h is continuous on the set $\{(x, y): y \neq 0\}$. *Related Exercises 35–42* ◄

Functions of Three Variables

The work we have done with limits and continuity of functions of two variables extends to functions of three or more variables. Specifically, the limit laws of Theorem 13.2 apply to functions of the form $w = f(x, y, z)$. Polynomials and rational functions are continuous at all points of their domains, and limits of these functions may be evaluated by direct substitution at all points of their domains. Compositions of continuous functions of the form $f(g(x, y, z))$ are also continuous.

EXAMPLE 6 Functions of three variables

a. Evaluate $\displaystyle\lim_{(x,y,z)\to(2,\pi/2,0)} \frac{x^2 \sin y}{z^2 + 4}$.

b. Find the points at which $h(x, y, z) = \sqrt{x^2 + y^2 + z^2 - 1}$ is continuous.

SOLUTION

a. This function consists of products and quotients of functions that are continuous at $(2, \pi/2, 0)$. Therefore, the limit is evaluated by direct substitution:

$$\lim_{(x,y,z)\to(2,\pi/2,0)} \frac{x^2 \sin y}{z^2 + 4} = \frac{2^2 \sin(\pi/2)}{0^2 + 4} = 1.$$

b. This function is a composition in which the outer function $f(u) = \sqrt{u}$ is continuous for $u \geq 0$. The inner function

$$g(x, y, z) = x^2 + y^2 + z^2 - 1$$

is nonnegative provided $x^2 + y^2 + z^2 \geq 1$. Therefore, the function is continuous at all points on or outside the unit sphere in $\mathbf{R}^3$. *Related Exercises 43–46* ◄

SECTION 13.3 EXERCISES

Review Questions

1. Describe in words what $\lim_{(x,y)\to(a,b)} f(x, y) = L$ means.
2. Explain why $f(x, y)$ must approach L as (x, y) approaches (a, b) along *all* paths in the domain in order for $\lim_{(x,y)\to(a,b)} f(x, y)$ to exist.
3. Explain what it means to say that limits of polynomials may be evaluated by direct substitution.
4. Suppose (a, b) is on the boundary of the domain of f. Explain how you would determine whether $\lim_{(x,y)\to(a,b)} f(x, y)$ exists.
5. Explain how examining limits along multiple paths may prove the nonexistence of a limit.
6. Explain why evaluating a limit along a finite number of paths does not prove the existence of a limit of a function of several variables.
7. What three conditions must be met for a function f to be continuous at the point (a, b)?
8. Let R be the unit disk $\{(x, y): x^2 + y^2 \leq 1\}$ with $(0, 0)$ removed. Is $(0, 0)$ a boundary point of R? Is R open or closed?
9. At what points of $\mathbf{R}^2$ is a rational function of two variables continuous?
10. Evaluate $\lim_{(x,y,z)\to(1,1,-1)} xy^2z^3$.

Basic Skills

11–18. Limits of functions *Evaluate the following limits.*

11. $\lim_{(x,y)\to(2,9)} 101$

12. $\lim_{(x,y)\to(1,-3)} (3x + 4y - 2)$

13. $\lim_{(x,y)\to(-3,3)} (4x^2 - y^2)$

14. $\lim_{(x,y)\to(2,-1)} (xy^8 - 3x^2y^3)$

15. $\lim_{(x,y)\to(0,\pi)} \dfrac{\cos xy + \sin xy}{2y}$

16. $\lim_{(x,y)\to(e^2,4)} \ln \sqrt{xy}$

17. $\lim_{(x,y)\to(2,0)} \dfrac{x^2 - 3xy^2}{x + y}$

18. $\lim_{(x,y)\to(1,-1)} \dfrac{10xy - 2y^2}{x^2 + y^2}$

19–24. Limits at boundary points *Evaluate the following limits.*

19. $\lim_{(x,y)\to(6,2)} \dfrac{x^2 - 3xy}{x - 3y}$

20. $\lim_{(x,y)\to(1,-2)} \dfrac{y^2 + 2xy}{y + 2x}$

21. $\lim_{(x,y)\to(2,2)} \dfrac{y^2 - 4}{xy - 2x}$

22. $\lim_{(x,y)\to(4,5)} \dfrac{\sqrt{x + y} - 3}{x + y - 9}$

23. $\lim_{(x,y)\to(1,2)} \dfrac{\sqrt{y} - \sqrt{x + 1}}{y - x - 1}$

24. $\lim_{(x,y)\to(8,8)} \dfrac{x^{1/3} - y^{1/3}}{x^{2/3} - y^{2/3}}$

25–30. Nonexistence of limits *Use the Two-Path Test to prove that the following limits do not exist.*

25. $\lim_{(x,y)\to(0,0)} \dfrac{x + 2y}{x - 2y}$

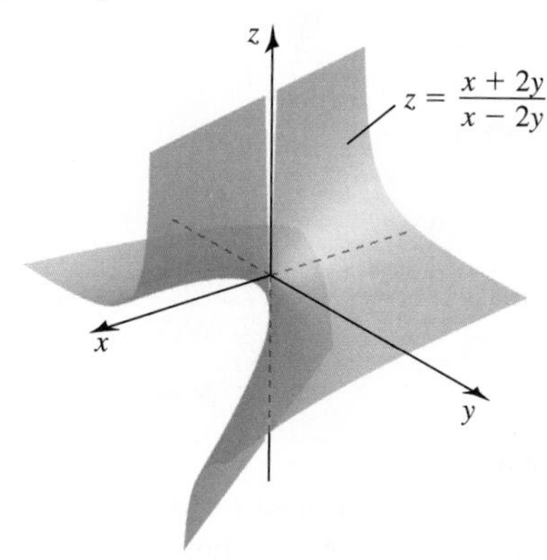

26. $\lim_{(x,y)\to(0,0)} \dfrac{4xy}{3x^2 + y^2}$

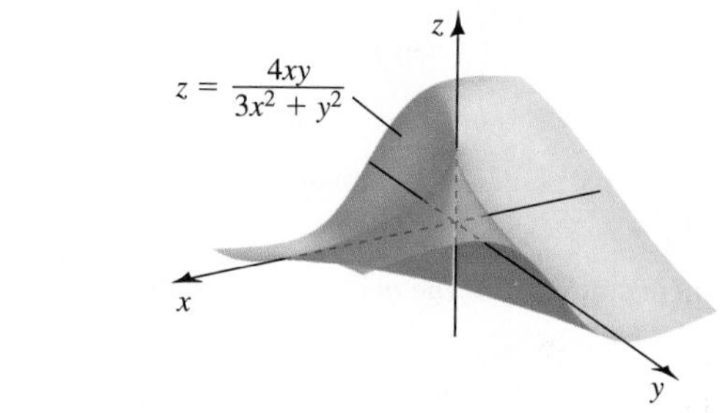

27. $\lim_{(x,y)\to(0,0)} \dfrac{y^4 - 2x^2}{y^4 + x^2}$

28. $\lim_{(x,y)\to(0,0)} \dfrac{x^3 - y^2}{x^3 + y^2}$

29. $\lim_{(x,y)\to(0,0)} \dfrac{y^3 + x^3}{xy^2}$

30. $\lim_{(x,y)\to(0,0)} \dfrac{y}{\sqrt{x^2 - y^2}}$

31–34. Continuity *At what points of $\mathbf{R}^2$ are the following functions continuous?*

31. $f(x, y) = x^2 + 2xy - y^3$

32. $f(x, y) = \dfrac{xy}{x^2y^2 + 1}$

33. $p(x, y) = \dfrac{4x^2y^2}{x^4 + y^2}$

34. $S(x, y) = \dfrac{4x^2y^2}{x^2 + y^2}$

35–42. Continuity of composite functions *At what points of $\mathbf{R}^2$ are the following functions continuous?*

35. $f(x, y) = \sin xy$

36. $g(x, y) = \ln (x - y)$

37. $h(x, y) = \cos (x + y)$

38. $p(x, y) = e^{x-y}$

39. $f(x, y) = \ln(x^2 + y^2)$

40. $f(x, y) = \sqrt{4 - x^2 - y^2}$

41. $g(x, y) = \sqrt[3]{x^2 + y^2 - 9}$

42. $h(x, y) = \dfrac{\sqrt{x - y}}{4}$

43–46. Limits of functions of three variables *Evaluate the following limits.*

43. $\lim_{(x,y,z)\to(1,\ln 2,3)} ze^{xy}$

44. $\lim_{(x,y,z)\to(0,1,0)} e^{xz}\ln(1 + y)$

45. $\lim_{(x,y,z)\to(1,1,1)} \dfrac{yz - xy - xz - x^2}{yz + xy + xz - y^2}$

46. $\lim_{(x,y,z)\to(1,1,1)} \dfrac{x - \sqrt{xz} - \sqrt{xy} + \sqrt{yz}}{x - \sqrt{xz} + \sqrt{xy} - \sqrt{yz}}$

Further Explorations

47. Explain why or why not Determine whether the following statements are true and give an explanation or counterexample.

a. If the limits $\lim_{(x,0)\to(0,0)} f(x, 0)$ and $\lim_{(0,y)\to(0,0)} f(0, y)$ exist and equal L, then $\lim_{(x,y)\to(0,0)} f(x, y) = L$.

b. If $\lim_{(x,y)\to(a,b)} f(x, y) = L$, then f is continuous at (a, b).

c. If f is continuous at (a, b), then $\lim_{(x,y)\to(a,b)} f(x, y)$ exists.

d. If P is a boundary point of the domain of f, then P is in the domain of f.

48–55. Miscellaneous limits *Use the method of your choice to evaluate the following limits.*

48. $\lim_{(x,y)\to(0,0)} \dfrac{y^2}{x^8 + y^2}$

49. $\lim_{(x,y)\to(0,1)} \dfrac{y \sin x}{x(y + 1)}$

50. $\lim_{(x,y)\to(1,1)} \dfrac{x^2 + xy - 2y^2}{2x^2 - xy - y^2}$

51. $\lim_{(x,y)\to(1,0)} \dfrac{y \ln y}{x}$

52. $\lim_{(x,y)\to(0,0)} \dfrac{|xy|}{xy}$

53. $\lim_{(x,y)\to(0,0)} \dfrac{|x - y|}{|x + y|}$

54. $\lim_{(x,y)\to(-1,0)} \dfrac{xye^{-y}}{x^2 + y^2}$

55. $\lim_{(x,y)\to(2,0)} \dfrac{1 - \cos y}{xy^2}$

56–59. Limits using polar coordinates *Limits at $(0, 0)$ may be easier to evaluate by converting to polar coordinates. Remember that the same limit must be obtained as $r \to 0$ along all paths to $(0, 0)$. Evaluate the following limits or state that they do not exist.*

56. $\lim_{(x,y)\to(0,0)} \dfrac{x - y}{\sqrt{x^2 + y^2}}$

57. $\lim_{(x,y)\to(0,0)} \dfrac{x^2}{x^2 + y^2}$

58. $\lim_{(x,y)\to(0,0)} \dfrac{(x - y)^2}{x^2 + xy + y^2}$

59. $\lim_{(x,y)\to(0,0)} \dfrac{(x - y)^2}{(x^2 + y^2)^{3/2}}$

Additional Exercises

60. Sine limits Evaluate the following limits.

a. $\lim_{(x,y)\to(0,0)} \dfrac{\sin(x + y)}{x + y}$

b. $\lim_{(x,y)\to(0,0)} \dfrac{\sin x + \sin y}{x + y}$

61. Nonexistence of limits Show that $\lim_{(x,y)\to(0,0)} \dfrac{ax^m y^n}{bx^{m+n} + cy^{m+n}}$ does not exist when a, b, and c are nonzero real numbers and m and n are positive integers.

62. Nonexistence of limits Show that $\lim_{(x,y)\to(0,0)} \dfrac{ax^{2(p-n)}y^n}{bx^{2p} + cy^p}$ does not exist when a, b, and c are nonzero real numbers and n and p are positive integers with $p \geq n$.

63–66. Limits of composite functions *Evaluate the following limits.*

63. $\lim_{(x,y)\to(1,0)} \dfrac{\sin xy}{xy}$

64. $\lim_{(x,y)\to(4,0)} x^2 y \ln xy$

65. $\lim_{(x,y)\to(0,2)} (2xy)^{xy}$

66. $\lim_{(x,y)\to(0,\pi/2)} \dfrac{1 - \cos xy}{4x^2y^3}$

67. Filling in a function value The domain of $f(x, y) = e^{-1/(x^2 + y^2)}$ excludes $(0, 0)$. How should f be defined at $(0, 0)$ to make it continuous there?

68. Limit proof Use the formal definition of a limit to prove that $\lim_{(x,y)\to(a,b)} y = b$ (*Hint:* Take $\delta = \varepsilon$.)

69. Limit proof Use the formal definition of a limit to prove that $\lim_{(x,y)\to(a,b)} (x + y) = a + b$. (*Hint:* Take $\delta = \varepsilon/2$.)

70. Proof of Limit Law 1 Use the formal definition of a limit to prove that $\lim_{(x,y)\to(a,b)} [f(x, y) + g(x, y)] = \lim_{(x,y)\to(a,b)} f(x, y) + \lim_{(x,y)\to(a,b)} g(x, y)$.

71. Proof of Limit Law 3 Use the formal definition of a limit to prove that $\lim_{(x,y)\to(a,b)} [cf(x, y)] = c \lim_{(x,y)\to(a,b)} f(x, y)$.

QUICK CHECK ANSWERS

1. The limit exists only for (a). **2.** $\{(x, y): x^2 + y^2 < 2\}$ **3.** If a factor of x is first canceled, then the limit may be evaluated by substitution. **4.** If the left and right limits at a point are not equal, then the two-sided limit does not exist. **5.** (a) and (b) are continuous at $(0, 0)$.

13.4 Partial Derivatives

The derivative of a function of one variable, $y = f(x)$, measures the rate of change of y with respect to x, and it gives slopes of tangent lines. The analogous idea for functions of several variables presents a new twist: Derivatives may be defined with respect to any of the independent variables. For example, we can compute the derivative of $f(x, y)$ with respect to x or y. The resulting derivatives are called *partial derivatives*; they still represent rates of change and they are associated with slopes of tangents. So, much of what you have learned about derivatives applies to functions of several variables. However, much is also different.

Derivatives with Two Variables

Consider a function f defined on a domain D in the xy-plane. Suppose that f represents the elevation of the land (above sea level) over D. Imagine that you are on the surface $z = f(x, y)$ at the point $(a, b, f(a, b))$ and you are asked to determine the slope of the surface where you are standing. Your answer should be, *it depends*!

Figure 13.48a shows a function that resembles the landscape in Figure 13.48b. Suppose you are standing at the point $P(0, 0, f(0, 0))$, which lies on the pass or the saddle. The surface behaves differently, depending on the direction in which you walk. If you walk east (positive x-direction), the elevation increases and your path takes you upward on the surface. If you walk north (positive y-direction), the elevation decreases and your path takes you downward on the surface. In fact, in every direction you walk from the point P, the function values change at different rates. So how should the slope or the rate of change at a given point be defined?

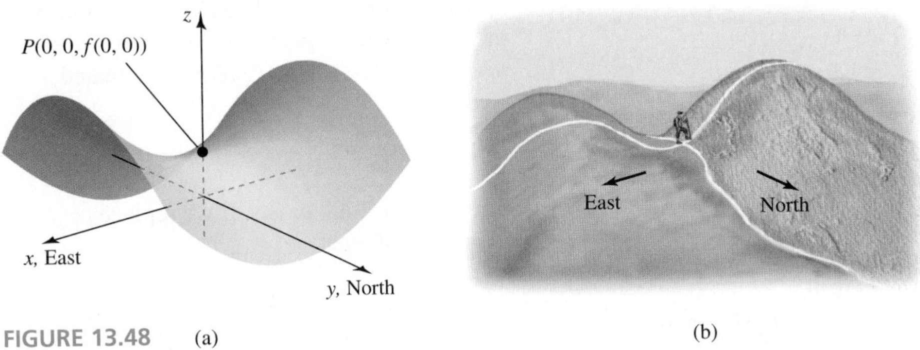

FIGURE 13.48 (a) (b)

The answer to this question involves *partial derivatives*, which arise when we hold all but one independent variable fixed and then compute an ordinary derivative with respect to the remaining variable. Suppose we move along the surface $z = f(x, y)$, starting at the point $(a, b, f(a, b))$ in such a way that $y = b$ is fixed and only x varies. The resulting path is a curve (a trace) on the surface that varies in the x-direction (Figure 13.49). This curve is the intersection of the surface with the vertical plane $y = b$; it is described by $z = f(x, b)$, which is a function of the single variable x. We know how to compute the slope of this curve: It is the ordinary derivative of $f(x, b)$ with respect to x. This derivative is called the *partial derivative of f with respect to x*, denoted $\partial f/\partial x$ or f_x. When evaluated at (a, b) its value is defined by the limit

$$f_x(a, b) = \lim_{h \to 0} \frac{f(a + h, b) - f(a, b)}{h},$$

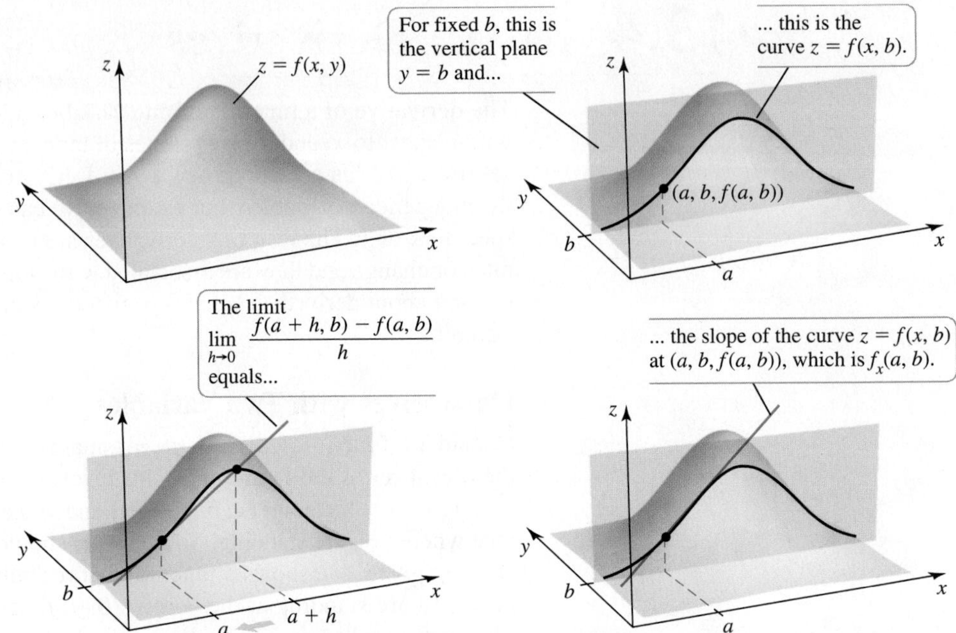

FIGURE 13.49

provided this limit exists. Notice that the y-coordinate is fixed at $y = b$ in this limit. If we replace (a, b) by the variable point (x, y), then f_x becomes a function of x and y.

In a similar way, we can move along the surface $z = f(x, y)$ from the point $(a, b, f(a, b))$ in such a way that $x = a$ is fixed and only y varies. Now, the result is a trace described by $z = f(a, y)$, which is the intersection of the surface and the plane $x = a$ (Figure 13.50). The slope of this curve at (a, b) is given by the ordinary derivative of $f(a, y)$ with respect to y. This derivative is called the *partial derivative of f with respect to y*, denoted $\partial f/\partial y$ or f_y. When evaluated at (a, b), it is defined by the limit

$$f_y(a, b) = \lim_{h \to 0} \frac{f(a, b + h) - f(a, b)}{h},$$

provided this limit exists. If we replace (a, b) by the variable point (x, y), then f_y becomes a function of x and y.

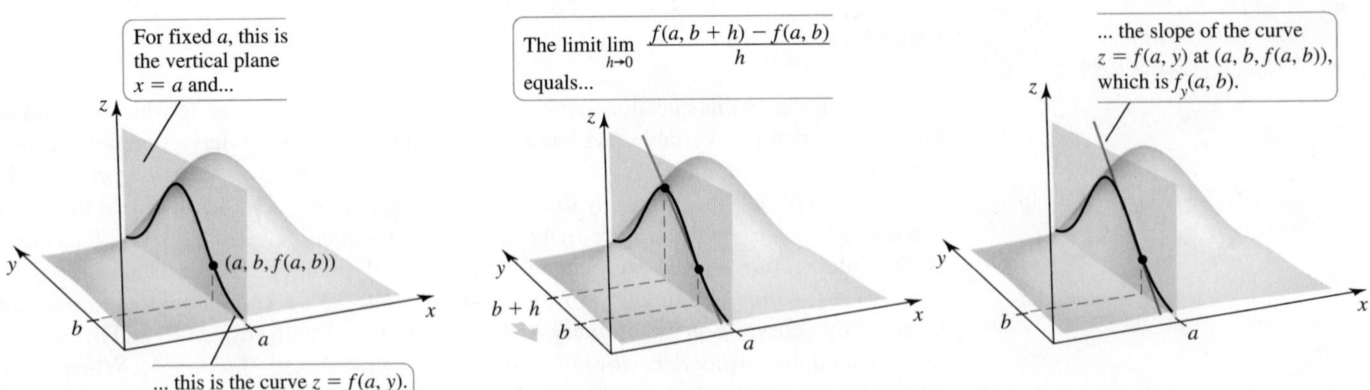

FIGURE 13.50

> **DEFINITION Partial Derivatives**
>
> The **partial derivative of f with respect to x at the point (a, b)** is
>
> $$f_x(a, b) = \lim_{h \to 0} \frac{f(a + h, b) - f(a, b)}{h}.$$
>
> The **partial derivative of f with respect to y at the point (a, b)** is
>
> $$f_y(a, b) = \lim_{h \to 0} \frac{f(a, b + h) - f(a, b)}{h},$$
>
> provided these limits exist.

➤ Recall that f' is a function, while $f'(a)$ is the value of the derivative at $x = a$. In the same way, f_x and f_y are functions of x and y, while $f_x(a, b)$ and $f_y(a, b)$ are their values at (a, b).

Notation The partial derivatives evaluated at a point (a, b) are denoted in any of the following ways:

$$\frac{\partial f}{\partial x}(a, b) = \left.\frac{\partial f}{\partial x}\right|_{(a,b)} = f_x(a, b) \quad \text{and} \quad \frac{\partial f}{\partial y}(a, b) = \left.\frac{\partial f}{\partial y}\right|_{(a,b)} = f_y(a, b).$$

Notice that the d in the ordinary derivative df/dx has been replaced by ∂ in the partial derivatives $\partial f/\partial x$ and $\partial f/\partial y$. The notation $\partial/\partial x$ is an instruction or operator: It says, "take the partial derivative with respect to x of the function that follows."

Calculating Partial Derivatives All the rules and results for ordinary derivatives can be used to compute partial derivatives. Specifically, to compute $f_x(x, y)$, we treat y as a constant and take an ordinary derivative with respect to x. Similarly, to compute $f_y(x, y)$, we treat x as a constant and differentiate with respect to y. Some examples illustrate the process.

EXAMPLE 1 Partial derivatives Let $f(x, y) = x^2 - y^2 + 4$.

a. Compute $\dfrac{\partial f}{\partial x}$ and $\dfrac{\partial f}{\partial y}$.

b. Evaluate each derivative at $(2, -4)$.

SOLUTION

a. We compute the partial derivative with respect to x assuming that y is a constant; the Power Rule gives

$$\frac{\partial f}{\partial x} = \frac{\partial}{\partial x}(\underbrace{x^2}_{\text{variable}} - \underbrace{y^2 + 4}_{\text{constant with respect to } x}) = 2x + 0 = 2x.$$

The partial derivative with respect to y is computed by treating x as a constant; using the Power Rule gives

$$\frac{\partial f}{\partial y} = \frac{\partial}{\partial y}(\underbrace{x^2}_{\text{constant with respect to } y} - \underbrace{y^2}_{\text{variable}} + \underbrace{4}_{\text{constant}}) = -2y.$$

QUICK CHECK 1 Compute f_x and f_y for $f(x, y) = 2xy$. ◄

b. It follows that $f_x(2, -4) = (2x)|_{(2,-4)} = 4$ and $f_y(2, -4) = (-2y)|_{(2,-4)} = 8$.

Related Exercises 7–16 ◄

EXAMPLE 2 **Partial derivatives** Compute the partial derivatives of the following functions.

a. $f(x, y) = \sin xy$ **b.** $g(x, y) = x^2e^{xy}$

SOLUTION

a. Treating y as a constant and differentiating with respect to x, we have

$$\frac{\partial f}{\partial x} = \frac{\partial}{\partial x}(\sin xy) = y \cos xy.$$

Holding x fixed and differentiating with respect to y, we have

$$\frac{\partial f}{\partial y} = \frac{\partial}{\partial y}(\sin xy) = x \cos xy.$$

➤ Recall that

$$\frac{d}{dx}(\sin 2x) = 2 \cos 2x.$$

Replacing 2 by the constant y, we have

$$\frac{\partial}{\partial x}(\sin xy) = y \cos (xy).$$

b. To compute the partial derivative with respect to x, we call on the Product Rule. Holding y fixed, we have

$$\begin{aligned}\frac{\partial g}{\partial x} &= \frac{\partial}{\partial x}(x^2e^{xy}) \\ &= x^2\frac{\partial}{\partial x}(e^{xy}) + e^{xy}\frac{\partial}{\partial x}(x^2) && \text{Product Rule} \\ &= x^2 \cdot ye^{xy} + e^{xy} \cdot 2x && \text{Evaluate partial derivatives.} \\ &= xe^{xy}(xy + 2) && \text{Simplify.}\end{aligned}$$

Treating x as a constant, the partial derivative with respect to y is

$$\frac{\partial g}{\partial y} = \frac{\partial}{\partial y}(x^2e^{xy}) = x^2\underbrace{\frac{\partial}{\partial y}(e^{xy})}_{xe^{xy}} = x^3e^{xy}.$$

➤ Because x and y are *independent* variables,

$$\frac{\partial}{\partial x}(y) = 0 \quad \text{and} \quad \frac{\partial}{\partial y}(x) = 0.$$

Related Exercises 7–16 ◄

Higher-Order Partial Derivatives

Just as we have second derivatives of functions of one variable, we also have higher-order partial derivatives. For example, given a function f and its partial derivative f_x, we can take the derivative of f_x with respect to x or with respect to y, which accounts for two of the four possible *second-order partial derivatives*. Table 13.4 summarizes the notation for second partial derivatives.

Table 13.4

Notation 1	Notation 2	What we say . . .
$\frac{\partial}{\partial x}\left(\frac{\partial f}{\partial x}\right) = \frac{\partial^2 f}{\partial x^2}$	$(f_x)_x = f_{xx}$	*d squared f dx squared* or *f-x-x*
$\frac{\partial}{\partial y}\left(\frac{\partial f}{\partial y}\right) = \frac{\partial^2 f}{\partial y^2}$	$(f_y)_y = f_{yy}$	*d squared f dy squared* or *f-y-y*
$\frac{\partial}{\partial x}\left(\frac{\partial f}{\partial y}\right) = \frac{\partial^2 f}{\partial x \partial y}$	$(f_y)_x = f_{yx}$	*f-y-x*
$\frac{\partial}{\partial y}\left(\frac{\partial f}{\partial x}\right) = \frac{\partial^2 f}{\partial y \partial x}$	$(f_x)_y = f_{xy}$	*f-x-y*

The order of differentiation can make a difference in the **mixed partial derivatives** f_{xy} and f_{yx}. So, it is important to use the correct notation to reflect the order in which derivatives are taken. For example, the notations $\dfrac{\partial^2 f}{\partial x \partial y}$ and f_{yx} both mean $\dfrac{\partial}{\partial x}\left(\dfrac{\partial f}{\partial y}\right)$; that is, differentiate first with respect to y, then with respect to x.

QUICK CHECK 2 Which of the following expressions are equivalent: (a) f_{xy}; (b) f_{yx}; (c) $\dfrac{\partial^2 f}{\partial y \partial x}$? Write $\dfrac{\partial^2 f}{\partial p \partial q}$ in subscript notation.

QUICK CHECK 3 Compute f_{xxx} and f_{xxy} for $f(x, y) = x^3 y$.

EXAMPLE 3 **Second partial derivatives** Find the four second partial derivatives of $f(x, y) = 3x^4 y - 2xy + 5xy^3$.

SOLUTION First, we compute

$$\frac{\partial f}{\partial x} = \frac{\partial}{\partial x}(3x^4 y - 2xy + 5xy^3) = 12x^3 y - 2y + 5y^3$$

and

$$\frac{\partial f}{\partial y} = \frac{\partial}{\partial y}(3x^4 y - 2xy + 5xy^3) = 3x^4 - 2x + 15xy^2.$$

For the second partial derivatives, we have

$$\frac{\partial^2 f}{\partial x^2} = \frac{\partial}{\partial x}\left(\frac{\partial f}{\partial x}\right) = \frac{\partial}{\partial x}(12x^3 y - 2y + 5y^3) = 36x^2 y$$

$$\frac{\partial^2 f}{\partial y^2} = \frac{\partial}{\partial y}\left(\frac{\partial f}{\partial y}\right) = \frac{\partial}{\partial y}(3x^4 - 2x + 15xy^2) = 30xy$$

$$\frac{\partial^2 f}{\partial x \partial y} = \frac{\partial}{\partial x}\left(\frac{\partial f}{\partial y}\right) = \frac{\partial}{\partial x}(3x^4 - 2x + 15xy^2) = 12x^3 - 2 + 15y^2$$

$$\frac{\partial^2 f}{\partial y \partial x} = \frac{\partial}{\partial y}\left(\frac{\partial f}{\partial x}\right) = \frac{\partial}{\partial y}(12x^3 y - 2y + 5y^3) = 12x^3 - 2 + 15y^2.$$

Related Exercises 17–30

Equality of Mixed Partial Derivatives

Notice that the two mixed partial derivatives in Example 3 are equal; that is, $f_{xy} = f_{yx}$. It turns out that most of the functions we encounter in this book have this property. Sufficient conditions for equality of mixed partial derivatives are given in a theorem attributed to the French mathematician Alexis Clairaut (1713–1765). The proof is found in advanced texts.

> THEOREM 13.4 (Clairaut) **Equality of Mixed Partial Derivatives**
> Assume that f is defined on an open set D of $\mathbf{R}^2$, and f_{xy} and f_{yx} are continuous throughout D. Then $f_{xy} = f_{yx}$ at all points of D.

Assuming sufficient continuity, Theorem 13.4 can be extended to higher derivatives of f. For example, $f_{xyx} = f_{xxy} = f_{yxx}$.

Functions of Three Variables

Everything we learned about partial derivatives of functions with two variables carries over to functions of three or more variables, as illustrated in Example 4.

EXAMPLE 4 Partial derivatives with more than two variables Find f_x, f_y, and f_z when $f(x, y, z) = e^{-xy} \cos z$.

SOLUTION To find f_x, we treat y and z as constants and differentiate with respect to x:

$$\frac{\partial f}{\partial x} = \frac{\partial}{\partial x}(\underbrace{e^{-xy}}_{y \text{ is constant}} \underbrace{\cos z}_{\text{constant}}) = -ye^{-xy} \cos z$$

Holding x and z constant and differentiating with respect to y, we have

$$\frac{\partial f}{\partial y} = \frac{\partial}{\partial y}(\underbrace{e^{-xy}}_{x \text{ is constant}} \underbrace{\cos z}_{\text{constant}}) = -xe^{-xy} \cos z.$$

To find f_z, we hold x and y constant and differentiate with respect to z:

$$\frac{\partial f}{\partial z} = \frac{\partial}{\partial z}(\underbrace{e^{-xy}}_{\text{constant}} \cos z) = -e^{-xy} \sin z$$

Related Exercises 31–40 ◄

QUICK CHECK 4 Compute f_{xz} and f_{zz} for $f(x, y, z) = xyz - x^2 z + yz^2$. ◄

Applications of Partial Derivatives When functions are used in realistic applications (for example, to describe velocity, pressure, investment fund balance, or population), they often involve more than one independent variable. For this reason, partial derivatives appear frequently in mathematical modeling.

EXAMPLE 5 Ideal Gas Law The pressure P, volume V, and temperature T of an ideal gas are related by the equation $PV = kT$, where $k > 0$ is a constant depending on the amount of gas.

a. Determine the rate of change of the pressure with respect to the volume at constant temperature. Interpret the result.

b. Determine the rate of change of the pressure with respect to the temperature at constant volume. Interpret the result.

c. Explain these results using level curves.

SOLUTION Expressing the pressure as a function of volume and temperature, we have $P = k\frac{T}{V}$.

➤ Implicit differentiation can also be used with partial derivatives. Instead of solving for P, we could differentiate both sides of $PV = kT$ with respect to V holding T fixed. Using the Product Rule, $P + VP_V = 0$, which implies that $P_V = -P/V$. Substituting $P = kT/V$, we have $P_V = -kT/V^2$.

a. We find the partial derivative $\partial P/\partial V$ by holding T constant and differentiating P with respect to V:

$$\frac{\partial P}{\partial V} = \frac{\partial}{\partial V}\left(k\frac{T}{V}\right) = kT\frac{\partial}{\partial V}(V^{-1}) = -\frac{kT}{V^2}$$

Recognizing that P, V, and T are always positive, we see that $\frac{\partial P}{\partial V} < 0$, which means that the pressure is a decreasing function of volume at a constant temperature.

➤ In the Ideal Gas Law, temperature is a positive variable because it is measured in Kelvins.

b. The partial derivative $\partial P/\partial T$ is found by holding V constant and differentiating P with respect to T:

$$\frac{\partial P}{\partial T} = \frac{\partial}{\partial T}\left(k\frac{T}{V}\right) = \frac{k}{V}$$

In this case $\partial P/\partial T > 0$, which says that the pressure is an increasing function of temperature at constant volume.

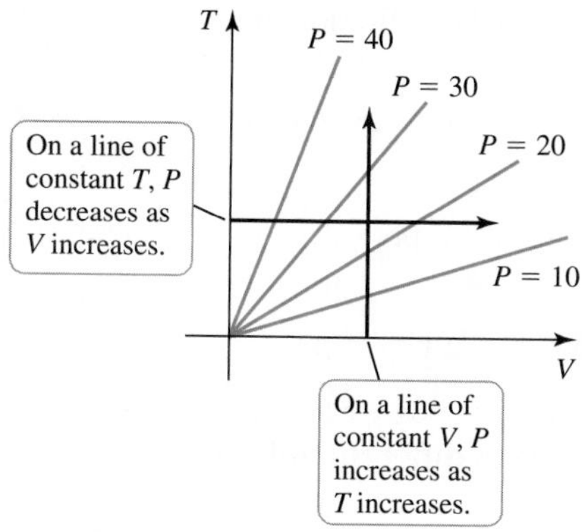
T
P = 40
P = 30
P = 20
P = 10
V
On a line of constant T, P decreases as V increases.
On a line of constant V, P increases as T increases.

FIGURE 13.51

c. The level curves (Section 13.2) of the pressure function are curves in the VT-plane that satisfy $k\frac{T}{V} = P_0$, where P_0 is a constant. Solving for T, the level curves are given by $T = \frac{1}{k}P_0V$. Because $\frac{P_0}{k}$ is a positive constant, the level curves are lines in the first quadrant passing through the origin (Figure 13.51) with slope P_0/k. The fact that $\frac{\partial P}{\partial V} < 0$ (from part (a)), means that if we hold $T > 0$ fixed and move in the direction of increasing V on a *horizontal* line, we cross level curves corresponding to decreasing pressures. Similarly, $\frac{\partial P}{\partial T} > 0$ (from part (b)) means that if we hold $V > 0$ fixed and move in the direction of increasing T on a *vertical* line, we cross level curves corresponding to increasing pressures. *Related Exercises 41–42* ◄

QUICK CHECK 5 Explain why, in Figure 13.51, the slopes of the level curves increase as the pressures increase. ◄

Differentiability

We close this section with a technical matter that bears on the remainder of the chapter. Although we know how to compute partial derivatives of a function of several variables, we have not said what it means for such a function to be *differentiable* at a point. It is tempting to conclude that if the partial derivatives f_x and f_y exist at a point, then f is differentiable there. However, it is not so simple.

Recall that a function f of one variable is differentiable at $x = a$ provided the limit

$$f'(a) = \lim_{\Delta x \to 0} \frac{f(a + \Delta x) - f(a)}{\Delta x}$$

exists. If f is differentiable at a, it means that the curve is smooth at the point $(a, f(a))$ (no jumps, corners, or cusps); furthermore, the curve has a unique tangent line at that point with slope $f'(a)$. Differentiability for a function of several variables should carry the same properties: The surface should be smooth at the point in question and something analogous to a unique tangent line should exist at the point.

We work by analogy with the one-variable case and define the quantity

$$\varepsilon = \underbrace{\frac{f(a + \Delta x) - f(a)}{\Delta x}}_{\text{slope of secant line}} - \underbrace{f'(a)}_{\substack{\text{slope of}\\ \text{tangent line}}},$$

where ε is viewed as a function of Δx. Notice that ε is the difference between the slopes of secant lines and the slope of the tangent line at the point $(a, f(a))$. If f is differentiable at a, then this difference approaches zero as $\Delta x \to 0$; therefore, $\lim_{\Delta x \to 0} \varepsilon = 0$. Multiplying both sides of this expression by Δx gives

$$\varepsilon\, \Delta x = \underbrace{f(a + \Delta x) - f(a)}_{\Delta y} - f'(a)\Delta x.$$

Rearranging, we have the change in the function $y = f(x)$:

$$\Delta y = f(a + \Delta x) - f(a) = f'(a)\Delta x + \underbrace{\varepsilon}_{\to 0 \text{ as } \Delta x \to 0} \Delta x$$

➤ Notice that $f'(a)\Delta x$ is the approximate change in the function given by a linear approximation.

This expression says that, in the one-variable case, if f is differentiable at a, then the change in f between a and a nearby point $a + \Delta x$ is represented by $f'(a)\Delta x$ plus a quantity $\varepsilon\, \Delta x$, where $\lim_{\Delta x \to 0} \varepsilon = 0$.

The analogous requirement with several variables is the definition of differentiability for functions or two (or more) variables.

DEFINITION Differentiability

The function $z = f(x, y)$ is **differentiable** at (a, b) provided $f_x(a, b)$ and $f_y(a, b)$ exist and the change $\Delta z = f(a + \Delta x, b + \Delta y) - f(a, b)$ equals

$$\Delta z = f_x(a, b)\Delta x + f_y(a, b)\Delta y + \varepsilon_1 \Delta x + \varepsilon_2 \Delta y,$$

where for fixed a and b, ε_1 and ε_2 are functions that depend only on Δx and Δy, with $(\varepsilon_1, \varepsilon_2) \to (0, 0)$ as $(\Delta x, \Delta y) \to (0, 0)$. A function is **differentiable** on an open region R if it is differentiable at every point of R.

Several observations are needed here. First, the definition extends to functions of more than two variables. Second, we show how differentiability is related to linear approximation and the existence of a *tangent plane* in Section 13.7. Finally, the conditions of the definition are generally difficult to verify. The following theorem may be useful in checking differentiability.

THEOREM 13.5 Conditions for Differentiability

Suppose the function f has partial derivatives f_x and f_y defined on an open region containing (a, b), with f_x and f_y continuous at (a, b). Then f is differentiable at (a, b).

This theorem states that existence of f_x and f_y at (a, b) is not enough to ensure differentiability of f at (a, b); we also need their continuity. Polynomials and rational functions are differentiable at all points of their domains, as are compositions of exponential, logarithmic, and trigonometric functions with other differentiable functions. The proof of this theorem is given in Appendix B.

We close with the analog of Theorem 3.1, which states that differentiability implies continuity.

THEOREM 13.6 Differentiability Implies Continuity

If a function f is differentiable at (a, b), then it is continuous at (a, b).

Proof By the definition of differentiability,

$$\Delta z = f_x(a, b)\Delta x + f_y(a, b)\Delta y + \varepsilon_1 \Delta x + \varepsilon_2 \Delta y,$$

where $(\varepsilon_1, \varepsilon_2) \to (0, 0)$ as $(\Delta x, \Delta y) \to (0, 0)$. Because f is assumed to be differentiable, as Δx and Δy approach 0, we see that

$$\lim_{(\Delta x, \Delta y) \to (0,0)} \Delta z = 0.$$

Also, because $\Delta z = f(a + \Delta x, b + \Delta y) - f(a, b)$, it follows that

$$\lim_{(\Delta x, \Delta y) \to (0,0)} f(a + \Delta x, b + \Delta y) = f(a, b),$$

which implies continuity of f at (a, b). ◀

➤ Recall that continuity requires that $\lim_{(x,y) \to (0,0)} f(x, y) = f(a, b)$, which is equivalent to $\lim_{(\Delta x, \Delta y) \to (0,0)} f(a + \Delta x, b + \Delta y) = f(a, b)$.

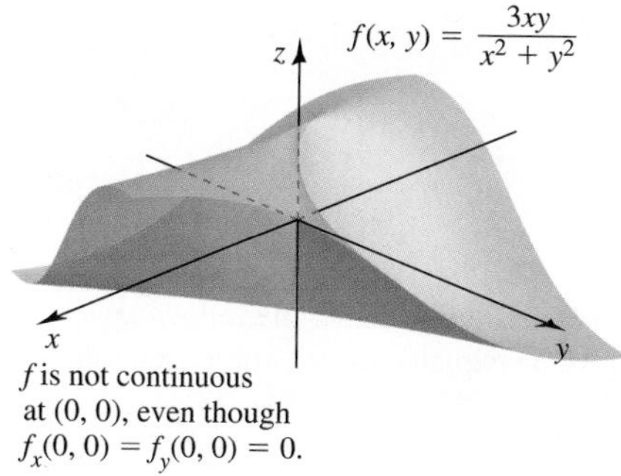

f is not continuous at (0, 0), even though $f_x(0, 0) = f_y(0, 0) = 0$.

FIGURE 13.52

EXAMPLE 6 A nondifferentiable function Discuss the differentiability and continuity of the function

$$f(x, y) = \begin{cases} \dfrac{3xy}{x^2 + y^2} & \text{if } (x, y) \neq (0, 0) \\ 0 & \text{if } (x, y) = (0, 0) \end{cases}.$$

SOLUTION As a rational function, f is continuous and differentiable at all points $(x, y) \neq (0, 0)$. The interesting behavior occurs at the origin. Using calculations similar to those in Example 4 in Section 13.3, it can be shown that if the origin is approached along the line $y = mx$, then

$$\lim_{(x,y)\to(0,0)} \frac{3xy}{x^2 + y^2} = \frac{3m}{m^2 + 1}.$$

Therefore, the value of the limit depends on the direction of approach, which implies that the limit does not exist, and f is not continuous at (0, 0). By Theorem 13.6, it follows that f is not differentiable at (0, 0). Figure 13.52 shows the discontinuity of f at the origin.

Let's look at the first partial derivatives of f at (0, 0). A short calculation shows that

$$f_x(0, 0) = \lim_{h\to 0} \frac{f(0 + h, 0) - f(0, 0)}{h} = \lim_{h\to 0} \frac{0 - 0}{h} = 0$$

$$f_y(0, 0) = \lim_{h\to 0} \frac{f(0, 0 + h) - f(0, 0)}{h} = \lim_{h\to 0} \frac{0 - 0}{h} = 0.$$

Despite the fact that f is not differentiable at (0, 0), its first partial derivatives exist at (0, 0). Existence of first partial derivatives at a point is not enough to ensure differentiability at that point. As expressed in Theorem 13.5, continuity of first partial derivatives is required for differentiability. It can be shown that f_x and f_y are not continuous at (0, 0).

Related Exercises 43–46 ◀

SECTION 13.4 EXERCISES

Review Questions

1. Suppose you are standing on the surface $z = f(x, y)$ at the point $(a, b, f(a, b))$. Interpret the meaning of $f_x(a, b)$ and $f_y(a, b)$ in terms of slopes or rates of change.
2. Find f_x and f_y when $f(x, y) = 3x^2y + xy^3$.
3. Find f_x and f_y when $f(x, y) = x \cos(xy)$.
4. Find the four second partial derivatives of $f(x, y) = 3x^2y + xy^3$.
5. Explain how you would evaluate f_z for the differentiable function $w = f(x, y, z)$.
6. The volume of a right circular cylinder with radius r and height h is $V = \pi r^2 h$. Is the volume an increasing or decreasing function of the radius at a fixed height (assume $r > 0$ and $h > 0$)?

Basic Skills

7–16. Partial derivatives *Find the first partial derivatives of the following functions.*

7. $f(x, y) = 3x^2y + 2$
8. $f(x, y) = y^8 + 2x^6 + 2xy$
9. $g(x, y) = \cos 2xy$
10. $h(x, y) = (y^2 + 1)\, e^x$
11. $f(w, z) = \dfrac{w}{w^2 + z^2}$
12. $g(x, z) = x \ln(z^2 + x^2)$
13. $s(y, z) = z^2 \tan yz$
14. $F(p, q) = \sqrt{p^2 + pq + q^2}$
15. $G(s, t) = \dfrac{\sqrt{st}}{s + t}$
16. $h(u, v) = \sqrt{\dfrac{uv}{u - v}}$

17–24. Second partial derivatives *Find the four second partial derivatives of the following functions.*

17. $h(x, y) = x^3 + xy^2 + 1$
18. $f(x, y) = 2x^5y^2 + x^2y$
19. $f(x, y) = y^3 \sin 4x$
20. $f(x, y) = \cos xy$
21. $p(u, v) = \ln(u^2 + v^2 + 4)$
22. $Q(r, s) = r/s$
23. $F(r, s) = r\, e^s$
24. $H(x, y) = \sqrt{4 + x^2 + y^2}$

25–30. Equality of mixed partial derivatives *Verify that* $f_{xy} = f_{yx}$ *for the following functions.*

25. $f(x, y) = 2x^3 + 3y^2 + 1$
26. $f(x, y) = xe^y$
27. $f(x, y) = \cos xy$
28. $f(x, y) = 3x^2y^{-1} - 2x^{-1}y^2$
29. $f(x, y) = e^{x+y}$
30. $f(x, y) = \sqrt{xy}$

31–40. Partial derivatives with more than two variables *Find the first partial derivatives of the following functions.*

31. $f(x, y, z) = xy + xz + yz$

32. $g(x, y, z) = 2x^2y - 3xz^4 + 10y^2z^2$

33. $h(x, y, z) = \cos(x + y + z)$

34. $Q(x, y, z) = \tan xyz$

35. $F(u, v, w) = \dfrac{u}{v + w}$

36. $G(r, s, t) = \sqrt{rs + rt + st}$

37. $f(w, x, y, z) = w^2xy^2 + xy^3z^2$

38. $g(w, x, y, z) = \cos(w + x)\sin(y - z)$

39. $h(w, x, y, z) = \dfrac{wz}{xy}$

40. $F(w, x, y, z) = w\sqrt{x + 2y + 3z}$

41. **Gas law calculations** Consider the Ideal Gas Law $PV = kT$, where $k > 0$ is a constant. Solve this equation for V in terms of P and T.
   a. Determine the rate of change of the volume with respect to the pressure at constant temperature. Interpret the result.
   b. Determine the rate of change of the volume with respect to the temperature at constant pressure. Interpret the result.
   c. Assuming $k = 1$, draw several level curves of the volume function and interpret the results as in Example 5.

42. **Volume of a box** A box with a square base of length x and height h has a volume $V = x^2h$.
   a. Compute the partial derivatives V_x and V_h.
   b. For a box with $h = 1.5$ m, use linear approximation to estimate the change in volume if x increases from $x = 0.5$ m to $x = 0.51$ m.
   c. For a box with $x = 0.5$ m, use linear approximation to estimate the change in volume if h decreases from $h = 1.5$ m to $h = 1.49$ m.
   d. For a fixed height, does a 10% change in x always produce (approximately) a 10% change in V? Explain.
   e. For a fixed base length, does a 10% change in h always produce (approximately) a 10% change in V? Explain.

43–46. Nondifferentiability? *Consider the following functions f.*
   a. Is f continuous at $(0, 0)$?
   b. Is f differentiable at $(0, 0)$?
   c. If possible, evaluate $f_x(0, 0)$ and $f_y(0, 0)$.
   d. Determine whether f_x and f_y are continuous at $(0, 0)$.
   e. Explain why Theorems 13.5 and 13.6 are consistent with the results in parts (a)–(d).

43. $f(x, y) = \begin{cases} -\dfrac{xy}{x^2 + y^2} & \text{if } (x, y) \neq (0, 0) \\ 0 & \text{if } (x, y) = (0, 0) \end{cases}$

44. $f(x, y) = \begin{cases} \dfrac{2xy^2}{x^2 + y^4} & \text{if } (x, y) \neq (0, 0) \\ 0 & \text{if } (x, y) = (0, 0) \end{cases}$

45. $f(x, y) = 1 - |xy|$

46. $f(x, y) = \sqrt{|xy|}$

Further Explorations

47. **Explain why or why not** Determine whether the following statements are true and give an explanation or counterexample.
   a. $\dfrac{\partial}{\partial x}\left(y^{10}\right) = 10y^9$
   b. $\dfrac{\partial^2}{\partial x \partial y}\left(\sqrt{xy}\right) = \dfrac{1}{\sqrt{xy}}$
   c. If f has continuous partial derivatives of all orders, then $f_{xxy} = f_{yxx}$.

48–52. Miscellaneous partial derivatives *Compute the first partial derivatives of the following functions.*

48. $f(x, y) = \ln(1 + e^{-xy})$

49. $f(x, y) = 1 - \tan^{-1}(x^2 + y^2)$

50. $f(x, y) = 1 - \cos(2(x + y)) + \cos^2(x + y)$

51. $h(x, y, z) = (1 + x + 2y)^z$

52. $g(x, y, z) = \dfrac{4x - 2y - 2z}{3y - 6x - 3z}$

53. **Partial derivatives and level curves** Consider the function $z = x/y^2$.
   a. Compute z_x and z_y.
   b. Sketch the level curves for $z = 1, 2, 3$, and 4.
   c. Move along the horizontal line $y = 1$ in the xy-plane and describe how the corresponding z-values change. Explain how this observation is consistent with z_x as computed in part (a).
   d. Move along the vertical line $x = 1$ in the xy-plane and describe how the corresponding z-values change. Explain how this observation is consistent with z_y as computed in part (a).

54. **Spherical caps** The volume of the cap of a sphere of radius r and thickness h is $V = \dfrac{\pi}{3}h^2(3r - h)$, for $0 \leq h \leq r$.

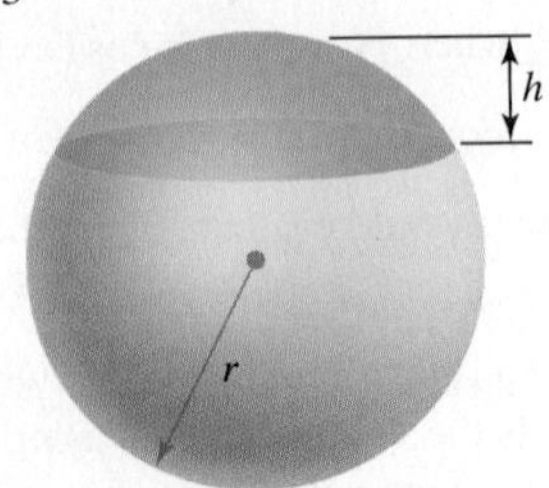

$V = \frac{\pi}{3}h^2(3r - h)$

   a. Compute the partial derivatives V_h and V_r.
   b. For a sphere of any radius, is the rate of change of volume with respect to r greater when $h = 0.2r$ or when $h = 0.8r$?
   c. For a sphere of any radius, for what value of h is the rate of change of volume with respect to r equal to 1?
   d. For a fixed radius r, for what value of h $(0 \leq h \leq r)$ is the rate of change of volume with respect to h the greatest?

55. Law of Cosines All triangles satisfy the Law of Cosines,

$$c^2 = a^2 + b^2 - 2ab\cos\theta$$

(see figure). Notice that when $\theta = \pi/2$, the Law of Cosines becomes the Pythagorean Theorem. Consider all triangles with a fixed angle $\theta = \pi/3$, in which case, c is a function of a and b, where $a > 0$ and $b > 0$.

a. Compute $\dfrac{\partial c}{\partial a}$ and $\dfrac{\partial c}{\partial b}$ by solving for c and differentiating.

b. Compute $\dfrac{\partial c}{\partial a}$ and $\dfrac{\partial c}{\partial b}$ by implicit differentiation. Check for agreement with part (a).

c. What relationship between a and b makes c an increasing function of a (for constant b)?

Applications

56. Body mass index The body mass index (BMI) for an adult human is given by the function $B = w/h^2$, where w is the weight measured in kilograms and h is the height measured in meters. (The BMI for units of pounds and inches is $B = 703w/h^2$.)

a. Find the rate of change of the BMI with respect to weight at a constant height.

b. For fixed h, is the BMI an increasing or decreasing function of w? Explain.

c. Find the rate of change of the BMI with respect to height at a constant weight.

d. For fixed w, is the BMI an increasing or decreasing function of h? Explain.

57. Electric potential function The electric potential in the xy-plane associated with two positive charges, one at $(0, 1)$ with twice the magnitude as the charge at $(0, -1)$, is

$$\varphi(x, y) = \frac{2}{\sqrt{x^2 + (y-1)^2}} + \frac{1}{\sqrt{x^2 + (y+1)^2}}.$$

a. Compute φ_x and φ_y.

b. Describe how φ_x and φ_y behave as $x, y \to \pm\infty$.

c. Evaluate $\varphi_x(0, y)$ for all $y \neq \pm 1$. Interpret this result.

d. Evaluate $\varphi_y(x, 0)$ for all x. Interpret this result.

58. Cobb-Douglas production function The output Q of an economic system subject to two inputs, such as labor L and capital K, is often modeled by the Cobb-Douglas production function $Q(L, K) = cL^aK^b$. Suppose $a = \frac{1}{3}$, $b = \frac{2}{3}$, and $c = 1$.

a. Evaluate the partial derivatives Q_L and Q_K.

b. If $L = 10$ is fixed and K increases from $K = 20$ to $K = 20.5$, use linear approximation to estimate the change in Q.

c. If $K = 20$ is fixed and L decreases from $L = 10$ to $L = 9.5$, use linear approximation to estimate the change in Q.

d. Graph the level curves of the production function in the first quadrant of the LK-plane for $Q = 1, 2, 3$.

e. If you move along the vertical line $L = 2$ in the positive K-direction, how does Q change? Is this consistent with Q_K computed in part (a)?

f. If you move along the horizontal line $K = 2$ in the positive L-direction, how does Q change? Is this consistent with Q_L computed in part (a)?

59. Resistors in parallel Two resistors in an electrical circuit with resistance R_1 and R_2 wired in parallel with a constant voltage give an effective resistance of R, where $\dfrac{1}{R} = \dfrac{1}{R_1} + \dfrac{1}{R_2}$.

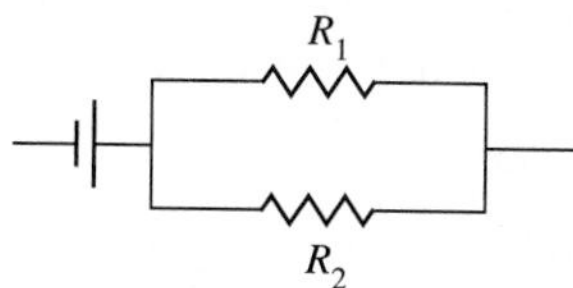

a. Find $\dfrac{\partial R}{\partial R_1}$ and $\dfrac{\partial R}{\partial R_2}$ by solving for R and differentiating.

b. Find $\dfrac{\partial R}{\partial R_1}$ and $\dfrac{\partial R}{\partial R_2}$ by differentiating implicitly.

c. Describe how an increase in R_1 with R_2 constant affects R.

d. Describe how a decrease in R_2 with R_1 constant affects R.

60. Wave on a string Imagine a string that is fixed at both ends (for example, a guitar string). When plucked, the string forms a standing wave. The displacement u of the string varies with position x and with time t. Suppose it is given by $u = f(x, t) = 2\sin(\pi x)\sin(\pi t/2)$, for $0 \le x \le 1$ and $t \ge 0$ (see figure). At a fixed point in time, the string forms a wave on $[0, 1]$. Alternatively, if you focus on a point on the string (fix a value of x), that point oscillates up and down in time.

a. What is the period of the motion in time?

b. Find the rate of change of the displacement with respect to time at a constant position (which is the vertical velocity of a point on the string).

c. At a fixed time, what point on the string is moving fastest?

d. At a fixed position on the string, when is the string moving fastest?

e. Find the rate of change of the displacement with respect to position at a constant time (which is the slope of the string).

f. At a fixed time, where is the slope of the string greatest?

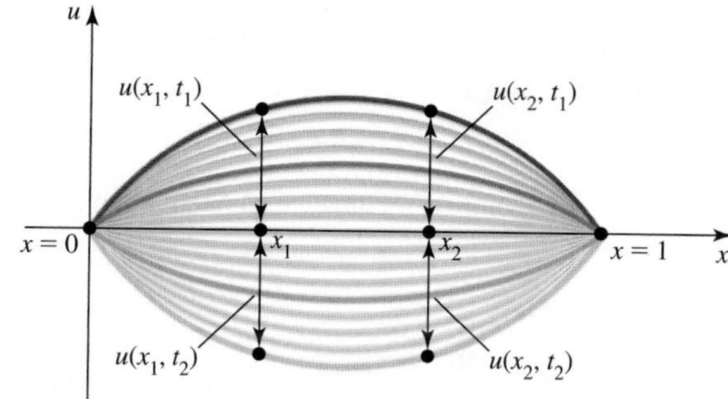

61–63. Wave equation *Traveling waves (for example, water waves or electromagnetic waves) exhibit periodic motion in both time and position. In one dimension (for example, a wave on a string) wave motion is governed by the one-dimensional wave equation*

$$\frac{\partial^2 u}{\partial t^2} = c^2 \frac{\partial^2 u}{\partial x^2},$$

where $u(x, t)$ is the height or displacement of the wave surface at position x and time t, and c is the constant speed of the wave. Show that the following functions are solutions of the wave equation.

61. $u(x, t) = \cos(2(x + ct))$

62. $u(x, t) = 5\cos(2(x + ct)) + 3\sin(x - ct)$

63. $u(x, t) = A\,f(x + ct) + B\,g(x - ct)$, where A and B are constants, and f and g are twice differentiable functions of one variable.

64–67. Laplace's equation *A classical equation of mathematics is Laplace's equation, which arises in both theory and applications. It governs ideal fluid flow, electrostatic potentials, and the steady-state distribution of heat in a conducting medium. In two dimensions, Laplace's equation is*

$$\frac{\partial^2 u}{\partial x^2} + \frac{\partial^2 u}{\partial y^2} = 0.$$

Show that the following functions are ***harmonic****; that is, they satisfy Laplace's equation.*

64. $u(x, y) = e^{-x}\sin y$

65. $u(x, y) = x(x^2 - 3y^2)$

66. $u(x, y) = e^{ax}\cos ay$, for any real number a

67. $u(x, y) = \tan^{-1}\left(\frac{y}{x - 1}\right) - \tan^{-1}\left(\frac{y}{x + 1}\right)$

68–71. Heat equation *The flow of heat along a thin conducting bar is governed by the one-dimensional heat equation (with analogs for thin plates in two dimensions and for solids in three dimensions)*

$$\frac{\partial u}{\partial t} = k\frac{\partial^2 u}{\partial x^2},$$

where u is a measure of the temperature at a location x on the bar at time t and the positive constant k is related to the conductivity of the material. Show that the following functions satisfy the heat equation with $k = 1$.

68. $u(x, t) = 10e^{-t}\sin x$

69. $u(x, t) = 4e^{-4t}\cos 2x$

70. $u(x, t) = e^{-t}(2\sin x + 3\cos x)$

71. $u(x, t) = Ae^{-a^2 t}\cos ax$, for any real numbers a and A

Additional Exercises

72–73. Differentiability *Use the definition of differentiability to prove that the following functions are differentiable at $(0, 0)$. You must produce functions ε_1 and ε_2 with the required properties.*

72. $f(x, y) = x + y$

73. $f(x, y) = xy$

74. Mixed partial derivatives

a. Consider the function $w = f(x, y, z)$. List all possible second partial derivatives that could be computed.
b. Let $f(x, y, z) = x^2y + 2xz^2 - 3y^2z$ and determine which second partial derivatives are equal.
c. How many second partial derivatives does $p = g(w, x, y, z)$ have?

75. Derivatives of an integral Let h be continuous for all real numbers.

a. Find f_x and f_y when $f(x, y) = \int_x^y h(s)\,ds$.
b. Find f_x and f_y when $f(x, y) = \int_1^{xy} h(s)\,ds$.

76. An identity Show that if $f(x, y) = \frac{ax + by}{cx + dy}$, where a, b, c, and d are real numbers with $ad - bc = 0$, then $f_x = f_y = 0$, for all x and y in the domain of f. Give an explanation.

77. Cauchy-Riemann equations In the advanced subject of complex variables, a function typically has the form $f(x, y) = u(x, y) + i\,v(x, y)$, where u and v are real-valued functions and $i = \sqrt{-1}$ is the imaginary unit. A function $f = u + iv$ is said to be *analytic* (analogous to differentiable) if it satisfies the Cauchy-Riemann equations: $u_x = v_y$ and $u_y = -v_x$.

a. Show that $f(x, y) = (x^2 - y^2) + i(2xy)$ is analytic.
b. Show that $f(x, y) = x(x^2 - 3y^2) + iy(3x^2 - y^2)$ is analytic.
c. Show that if $f = u + iv$ is analytic, then $u_{xx} + u_{yy} = 0$ and $v_{xx} + v_{yy} = 0$.

QUICK CHECK ANSWERS

1. $f_x = 2y$; $f_y = 2x$ **2.** (a) and (c) are the same; f_{qp} **3.** $f_{xxx} = 6y$; $f_{xxy} = 6x$ **4.** $f_{xz} = y - 2x$; $f_{zz} = 2y$ **5.** The equations of the level curves are $T = \frac{1}{k}P_0V$. As the pressure P_0 increases, the slope of the line increases.

13.5 The Chain Rule

In this section, we combine ideas based on the Chain Rule (Section 3.6) with what we know about partial derivatives (Section 13.4) to develop new methods for finding derivatives of functions of several variables. To illustrate the importance of these methods, consider the following situation.

An economist modeling the output of a manufacturing system often works with *production functions* that relate the productivity of the system (output) to all the variables on which it depends (input). A simplified production function might take the form $P = F(L, K, R)$, where L, K, and R represent the availability of labor, capital, and natural resources, respectively. However, the variables L, K, and R may be intermediate variables that depend on other variables. For example, it might be that L is a function of the unemployment rate u, K is a function of the prime interest rate i, and R is a function of time t (seasonal availability of resources). Even in this simplified model we see that productivity, which is the dependent variable, is ultimately related to many other variables (Figure 13.53). Of critical interest to an economist is how changes in one variable determine changes in other variables. For instance, if the unemployment rate increases by 0.1% and the interest rate decreases by 0.2%, what is the effect on productivity? In this section we develop the tools needed to answer such questions.

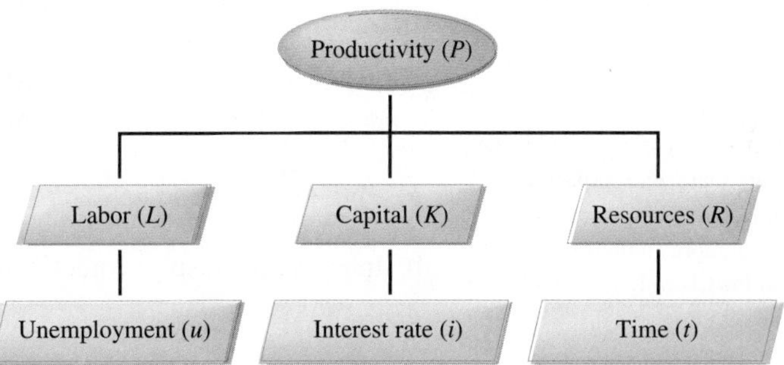

FIGURE 13.53

The Chain Rule with One Independent Variable

Recall the basic Chain Rule: If y is a function of u and u is a function of t, then $\frac{dy}{dt} = \frac{dy}{du}\frac{du}{dt}$. We first extend the Chain Rule to composite functions of the form $z = f(x, y)$, where x and y are functions of t. What is $\frac{dz}{dt}$?

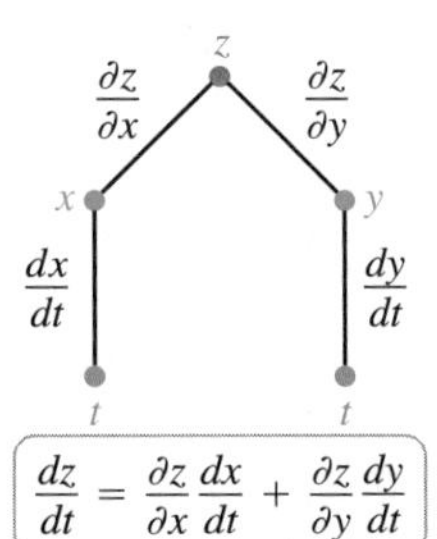

FIGURE 13.54

We illustrate the relationships among the variables t, x, y, and z using a *tree diagram* (Figure 13.54). To find dz/dt, first notice that z depends on x, which in turn depends on t. The change in z with respect to x is $\partial z/\partial x$, while the change in x with respect to t is the ordinary derivative dx/dt. These derivatives appear on the corresponding branches of the tree diagram. Using the Chain Rule idea, the product of these derivatives gives the change in z with respect to t through x.

Similarly, z also depends on y. The change in z with respect to y is $\partial z/\partial y$, while the change in y with respect to t is dy/dt. The product of these derivatives, which appear on the corresponding branches of the tree, gives the change in z with respect to t through y. Summing the contributions to dz/dt along each branch of the tree leads to the following theorem, whose proof is found in Appendix B.

> A subtle observation about notation should be made. If $z = f(x, y)$, where x and y are functions of another variable t, it is common to write $z = f(t)$ to show that z ultimately depends on t. However, the two functions denoted f are actually different. To be careful, we should write (or at least remember) that in fact $z = F(t)$, where F is a function other than f. This distinction is often overlooked for the sake of convenience.

THEOREM 13.7 Chain Rule (One Independent Variable)
Let z be a differentiable function of x and y on its domain, where x and y are differentiable functions of t on an interval I. Then,

$$\frac{dz}{dt} = \frac{\partial z}{\partial x}\frac{dx}{dt} + \frac{\partial z}{\partial y}\frac{dy}{dt}.$$

QUICK CHECK 1 Explain why Theorem 13.7 reduces to the Chain Rule for a function of one variable in the case that $z = f(x)$ and $x = g(t)$.

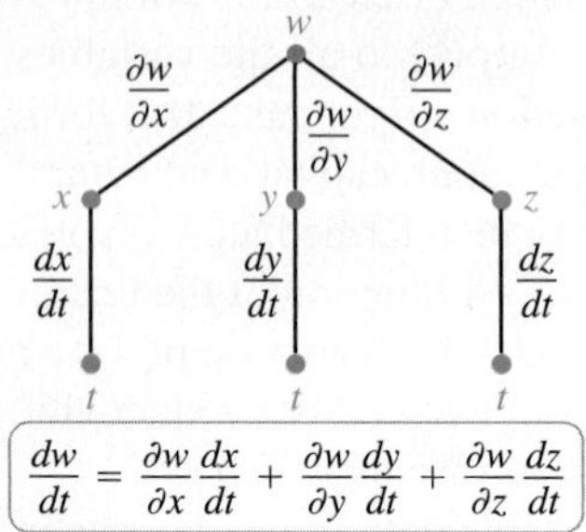

FIGURE 13.55

Before presenting examples, several comments are in order.

- With $z = f(x(t), y(t))$, the dependent variable is z and the sole independent variable is t. The variables x and y are **intermediate variables**.
- The choice of notation for partial and ordinary derivatives in the Chain Rule is important. We write ordinary derivatives dx/dt and dy/dt because x and y depend only on t. We write partial derivatives $\partial z/\partial x$ and $\partial z/\partial y$ because z is a function of both x and y. Finally, we write dz/dt as an ordinary derivative because z ultimately depends only on t.
- This theorem generalizes directly to functions of more than two intermediate variables (Figure 13.55). For example, if $w = f(x, y, z)$, where x, y, and z are functions of the single independent variable t, then

$$\frac{dw}{dt} = \frac{\partial w}{\partial x}\frac{dx}{dt} + \frac{\partial w}{\partial y}\frac{dy}{dt} + \frac{\partial w}{\partial z}\frac{dz}{dt}.$$

➤ If f, x, and y are simple, as in Example 1, it is possible to substitute $x(t)$ and $y(t)$ into f, producing a function of t only, and then differentiate with respect to t. But this approach quickly becomes impractical with more complicated functions and the Chain Rule offers a great advantage.

EXAMPLE 1 **Chain Rule with one independent variable** Let $z = x^2 - 3y^2 + 20$, where $x = 2\cos t$ and $y = 2\sin t$.

a. Find $\dfrac{dz}{dt}$ and evaluate it at $t = \pi/4$.

b. Interpret the result geometrically.

SOLUTION

a. Computing the intermediate derivatives and applying the Chain Rule (Theorem 13.7), we find that

$$\begin{aligned} \frac{dz}{dt} &= \frac{\partial z}{\partial x}\frac{dx}{dt} + \frac{\partial z}{\partial y}\frac{dy}{dt} \\ &= \underbrace{(2x)}_{\frac{\partial z}{\partial x}}\underbrace{(-2\sin t)}_{\frac{dx}{dt}} + \underbrace{(-6y)}_{\frac{\partial z}{\partial y}}\underbrace{(2\cos t)}_{\frac{dy}{dt}} && \text{Evaluate derivatives.} \\ &= -4x\sin t - 12y\cos t && \text{Simplify.} \\ &= -8\cos t\sin t - 24\sin t\cos t && \text{Substitute } x = 2\cos t,\ y = 2\sin t. \\ &= -16\sin 2t && \text{Simplify; } \sin 2t = 2\sin t\cos t. \end{aligned}$$

Substituting $t = \pi/4$ gives $\left.\dfrac{dz}{dt}\right|_{t=\pi/4} = -16$.

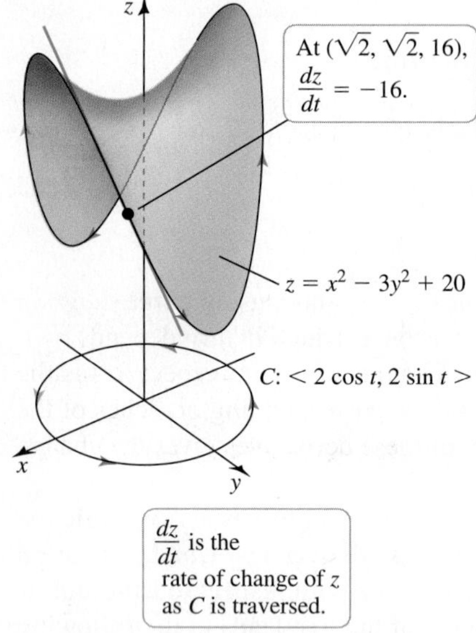

FIGURE 13.56

b. The parametric equations $x = 2\cos t$, $y = 2\sin t$, for $0 \le t \le 2\pi$, describe a circle C of radius 2 in the xy-plane. Imagine walking on the surface $z = x^2 - 3y^2 + 20$ while staying directly above the circle C in the xy-plane. Your path rises and falls as you walk (Figure 13.56); the rate of change of your elevation z with respect to t is given by dz/dt. For example, when $t = \pi/4$, the corresponding point on the surface is $(\sqrt{2}, \sqrt{2}, 16)$, and z changes with respect to t at a rate of -16 (by part (a)).

Related Exercises 7–16 ◀

The Chain Rule with Several Independent Variables

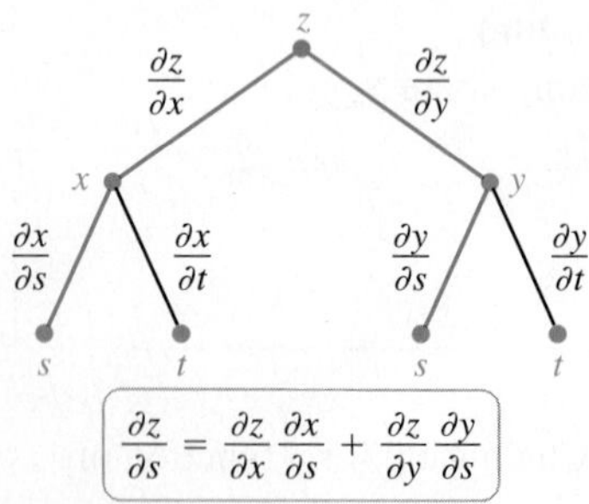

FIGURE 13.57

The ideas behind the Chain Rule of Theorem 13.7 can be modified to cover a variety of situations in which functions of several variables are composed with one another. For example, suppose z depends on two intermediate variables x and y, each of which depends on the independent variables s and t. Once again, a tree diagram (Figure 13.57) helps us organize the relationships among variables. The dependent variable z now ultimately depends on the two independent variables s and t, so it makes sense to ask about the rates of change of z with respect to either s or t, which are $\partial z/\partial s$ and $\partial z/\partial t$, respectively.

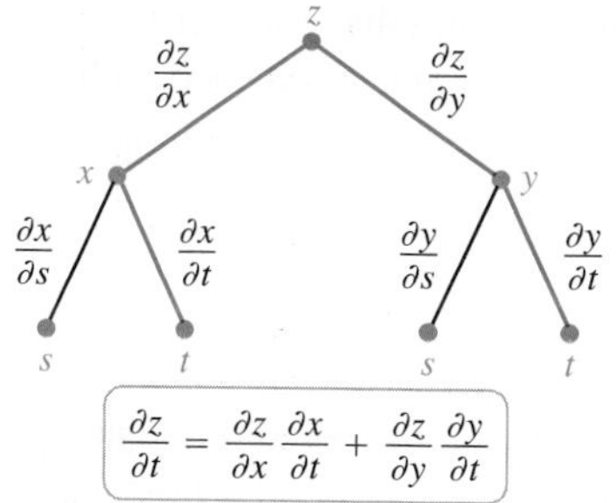

FIGURE 13.58

To compute $\partial z/\partial s$, we note that there are two paths in the tree (in red in Figure 13.57) that connect z to s and contribute to $\partial z/\partial s$. Along one path, z changes with respect to x (with rate of change $\partial z/\partial x$) and x changes with respect to s (with rate of change $\partial x/\partial s$). Along the other path, z changes with respect to y (with rate of change $\partial z/\partial y$) and y changes with respect to s (with rate of change $\partial y/\partial s$; Figure 13.57). We use a Chain Rule calculation along each path and combine the results. A similar argument leads to $\partial z/\partial t$ (Figure 13.58).

QUICK CHECK 2 Suppose that $w = f(x, y, z)$, where $x = g(s, t)$, $y = h(s, t)$, and $z = p(s, t)$. Extend Theorem 13.8 to write a formula for $\partial w/\partial t$. ◂

THEOREM 13.8 Chain Rule (Two Independent Variables)
Let z be a differentiable function of x and y, where x and y are differentiable functions of s and t. Then

$$\frac{\partial z}{\partial s} = \frac{\partial z}{\partial x}\frac{\partial x}{\partial s} + \frac{\partial z}{\partial y}\frac{\partial y}{\partial s} \quad \text{and} \quad \frac{\partial z}{\partial t} = \frac{\partial z}{\partial x}\frac{\partial x}{\partial t} + \frac{\partial z}{\partial y}\frac{\partial y}{\partial t}.$$

EXAMPLE 2 Chain Rule with two independent variables Let $z = \sin 2x \cos 3y$, where $x = s + t$ and $y = s - t$. Evaluate $\partial z/\partial s$ and $\partial z/\partial t$.

SOLUTION The tree diagram in Figure 13.57 gives the Chain Rule formula for $\partial z/\partial s$: We form products of the derivatives along the red branches connecting z to s and add the results. The partial derivative is

$$\begin{aligned}\frac{\partial z}{\partial s} &= \frac{\partial z}{\partial x}\frac{\partial x}{\partial s} + \frac{\partial z}{\partial y}\frac{\partial y}{\partial s}\\ &= \underbrace{2\cos 2x \cos 3y}_{\frac{\partial z}{\partial x}} \cdot \underbrace{1}_{\frac{\partial x}{\partial s}} + \underbrace{(-3\sin 2x \sin 3y)}_{\frac{\partial z}{\partial y}} \cdot \underbrace{1}_{\frac{\partial y}{\partial s}}\\ &= 2\cos(\underbrace{2(s+t)}_{x})\cos(\underbrace{3(s-t)}_{y}) - 3\sin(\underbrace{2(s+t)}_{x})\sin(\underbrace{3(s-t)}_{y}).\end{aligned}$$

Following the red branches of Figure 13.58 connecting z to t, we have

$$\begin{aligned}\frac{\partial z}{\partial t} &= \frac{\partial z}{\partial x}\frac{\partial x}{\partial t} + \frac{\partial z}{\partial y}\frac{\partial y}{\partial t}\\ &= \underbrace{2\cos 2x \cos 3y}_{\frac{\partial z}{\partial x}} \cdot \underbrace{1}_{\frac{\partial x}{\partial t}} + \underbrace{(-3\sin 2x \sin 3y)}_{\frac{\partial z}{\partial y}} \cdot \underbrace{-1}_{\frac{\partial y}{\partial t}}\\ &= 2\cos(\underbrace{2(s+t)}_{x})\cos(\underbrace{3(s-t)}_{y}) + 3\sin(\underbrace{2(s+t)}_{x})\sin(\underbrace{3(s-t)}_{y}).\end{aligned}$$

Related Exercises 17–22 ◂

EXAMPLE 3 More variables Let w be a function of x, y, and z, each of which is a function of s and t.

a. Draw a labeled tree diagram showing the relationships among the variables.

b. Write the Chain Rule formula for $\frac{\partial w}{\partial s}$.

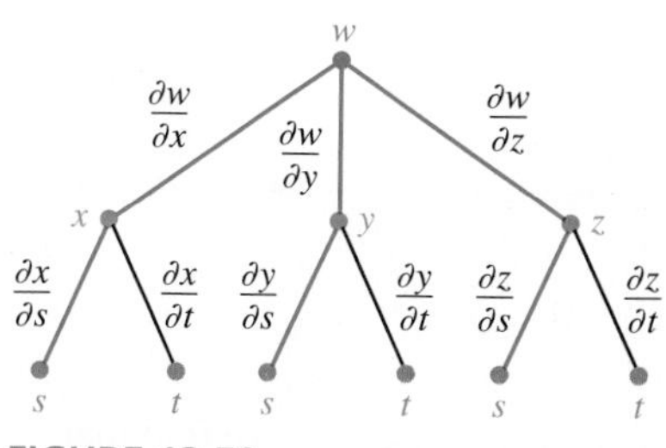

FIGURE 13.59

SOLUTION

a. Because w is a function of x, y, and z, the upper branches of the tree (Figure 13.59) are labeled with the partial derivatives w_x, w_y, and w_z. Each of x, y, and z is a function of two variables, so the lower branches of the tree also require partial derivative labels.

QUICK CHECK 3 If Q is a function of w, x, y, and z, each of which is a function of r, s, and t, how many dependent variables, intermediate variables, and independent variables are there?

b. Extending Theorem 13.8, we take the three paths through the tree that connect w to s (red branches in Figure 13.59). Multiplying the derivatives that appear on each path and adding gives the result

$$\frac{\partial w}{\partial s} = \frac{\partial w}{\partial x}\frac{\partial x}{\partial s} + \frac{\partial w}{\partial y}\frac{\partial y}{\partial s} + \frac{\partial w}{\partial z}\frac{\partial z}{\partial s}.$$

Related Exercises 17–22

It is probably clear by now that we can create a Chain Rule for any set of relationships among variables. The key is to draw an accurate tree diagram and label the branches of the tree with the appropriate derivatives.

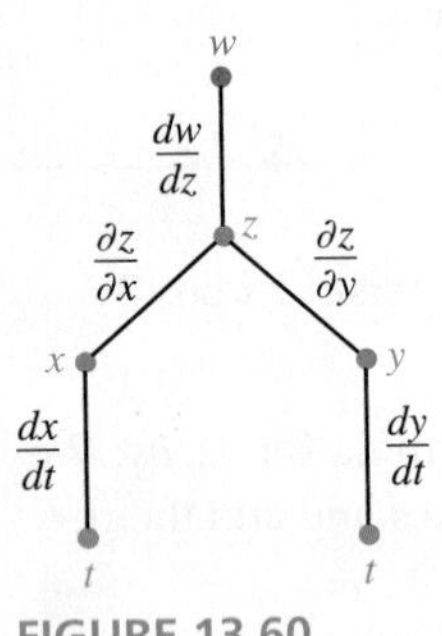

FIGURE 13.60

EXAMPLE 4 **A different kind of tree** Let w be a function of z, where z is a function of x and y, and each of x and y is a function of t. Draw a labeled tree diagram and write the Chain Rule formula for dw/dt.

SOLUTION The dependent variable w is related to the independent variable t through two paths in the tree: $w \to z \to x \to t$ and $w \to z \to y \to t$ (Figure 13.60). At the top of the tree, w is a function of the single variable z, so the rate of change is the ordinary derivative dw/dz. The tree below z looks like Figure 13.54. Multiplying the derivatives on each of the two branches connecting w to t, we have

$$\frac{dw}{dt} = \frac{dw}{dz}\frac{\partial z}{\partial x}\frac{dx}{dt} + \frac{dw}{dz}\frac{\partial z}{\partial y}\frac{dy}{dt} = \frac{dw}{dz}\left(\frac{\partial z}{\partial x}\frac{dx}{dt} + \frac{\partial z}{\partial y}\frac{dy}{dt}\right).$$

Related Exercises 23–26

Implicit Differentiation

Using the Chain Rule for partial derivatives, the technique of implicit differentiation can be put in a larger perspective. Recall that if x and y are related through an implicit relationship, such as $\sin xy + \pi y^2 = x$, then dy/dx is computed using implicit differentiation (Section 3.7). Another way to compute dy/dx is to define the function $F(x, y) = \sin xy + \pi y^2 - x$. Notice that the original equation $\sin xy + \pi y^2 = x$ is $F(x, y) = 0$.

To find dy/dx, we treat x as the independent variable and differentiate both sides of $F(x, y(x)) = 0$ with respect to x. The derivative of the right side is 0. On the left side, we use the Chain Rule of Theorem 13.7:

$$\frac{\partial F}{\partial x}\underbrace{\frac{dx}{dx}}_{1} + \frac{\partial F}{\partial y}\frac{dy}{dx} = 0.$$

Noting that $dx/dx = 1$ and solving for dy/dx, we obtain the following theorem.

➤ The question of whether a relationship of the form $F(x, y) = 0$ or $F(x, y, z) = 0$ determines a function is addressed by a theorem of advanced calculus called the Implicit Function Theorem.

THEOREM 13.9 **Implicit Differentiation**
Let F be differentiable on its domain and suppose that $F(x, y) = 0$ defines y as a differentiable function of x. Provided $F_y \neq 0$,

$$\frac{dy}{dx} = -\frac{F_x}{F_y}.$$

EXAMPLE 5 **Implicit differentiation** Find dy/dx when $F(x, y) = \sin xy + \pi y^2 - x = 0$.

SOLUTION Computing the partial derivatives of F with respect to x and y, we find that

$$F_x = y \cos xy - 1 \quad \text{and} \quad F_y = x \cos xy + 2\pi y.$$

➤ The preceding method generalizes to computing $\frac{\partial z}{\partial x}$ and $\frac{\partial z}{\partial y}$ with functions of the form $F(x, y, z) = 0$ (Exercise 44).

Therefore,

$$\frac{dy}{dx} = -\frac{F_x}{F_y} = -\frac{y \cos xy - 1}{x \cos xy + 2\pi y}.$$

As with many implicit differentiation calculations, the result is left in terms of both x and y. The same result is obtained using the methods of Section 3.7. *Related Exercises 27–32* ◄

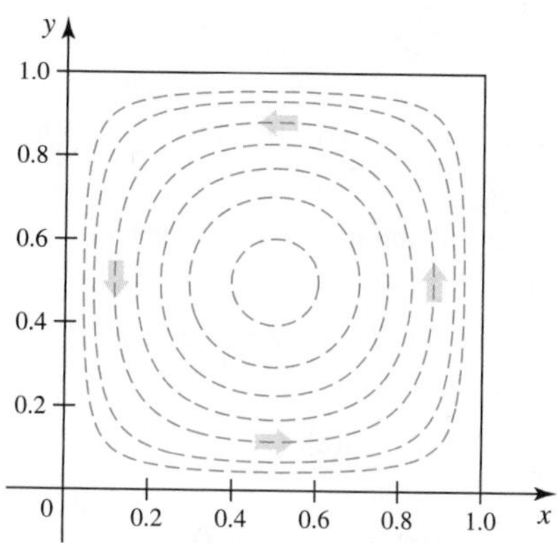

FIGURE 13.61

EXAMPLE 6 **Fluid flow** A basin of circulating water is represented by the square region $\{(x, y): 0 \le x \le 1, 0 \le y \le 1\}$, where x is positive in the eastward direction and y is positive in the northward direction. The velocity components of the water,

$$\text{East-west velocity: } u(x, y) = 2 \sin \pi x \cos \pi y$$
$$\text{North-south velocity: } v(x, y) = -2 \cos \pi x \sin \pi y,$$

produce the flow pattern shown in Figure 13.61. The *streamlines* shown in the figure are the paths followed by small parcels of water. The speed of the water at a point (x, y) is given by the function $s(x, y) = \sqrt{u(x, y)^2 + v(x, y)^2}$. Find $\partial s/\partial x$ and $\partial s/\partial y$, the rates of change of the water speed in the x- and y-directions, respectively.

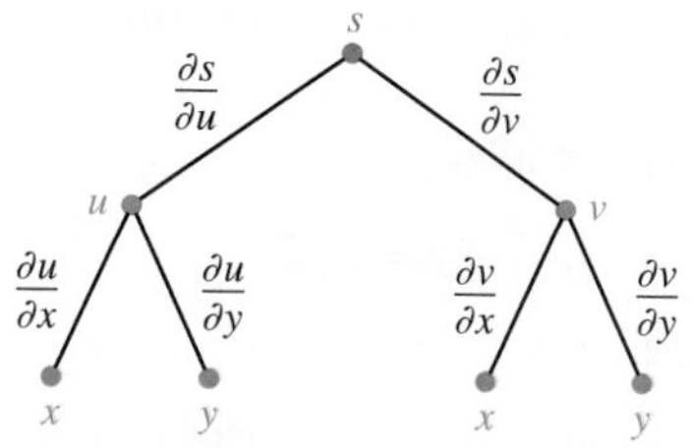

FIGURE 13.62

SOLUTION The dependent variable s depends on the independent variables x and y through the intermediate variables u and v (Figure 13.62). Theorem 13.8 applies here in the form

$$\frac{\partial s}{\partial x} = \frac{\partial s}{\partial u}\frac{\partial u}{\partial x} + \frac{\partial s}{\partial v}\frac{\partial v}{\partial x} \quad \text{and} \quad \frac{\partial s}{\partial y} = \frac{\partial s}{\partial u}\frac{\partial u}{\partial y} + \frac{\partial s}{\partial v}\frac{\partial v}{\partial y}.$$

The derivatives $\partial s/\partial u$ and $\partial s/\partial v$ are easier to find if we square the speed function to obtain $s^2 = u^2 + v^2$ and then use implicit differentiation. To compute $\partial s/\partial u$, we differentiate both sides of $s^2 = u^2 + v^2$ with respect to u:

$$2s\frac{\partial s}{\partial u} = 2u, \quad \text{which implies that} \quad \frac{\partial s}{\partial u} = \frac{u}{s}.$$

Similarly, differentiating $s^2 = u^2 + v^2$ with respect to v gives

$$2s\frac{\partial s}{\partial v} = 2v, \quad \text{which implies that} \quad \frac{\partial s}{\partial v} = \frac{v}{s}.$$

Now the Chain Rule leads to $\frac{\partial s}{\partial x}$:

$$\begin{aligned}\frac{\partial s}{\partial x} &= \frac{\partial s}{\partial u}\frac{\partial u}{\partial x} + \frac{\partial s}{\partial v}\frac{\partial v}{\partial x}\\ &= \underbrace{\frac{u}{s}}_{\frac{\partial s}{\partial u}}\underbrace{(2\pi \cos \pi x \cos \pi y)}_{\frac{\partial u}{\partial x}} + \underbrace{\frac{v}{s}}_{\frac{\partial s}{\partial v}}\underbrace{(2\pi \sin \pi x \sin \pi y)}_{\frac{\partial v}{\partial x}}\\ &= \frac{2\pi}{s}(u \cos \pi x \cos \pi y + v \sin \pi x \sin \pi y)\end{aligned}$$

A similar calculation shows that

$$\frac{\partial s}{\partial y} = -\frac{2\pi}{s}(u \sin \pi x \sin \pi y + v \cos \pi x \cos \pi y).$$

As a final step, you could replace s, u and v by their definitions in terms of x and y.

Related Exercises 33–34 ◄

SECTION 13.5 EXERCISES

Review Questions

1. Suppose $z = f(x, y)$, where x and y are functions of t. How many dependent, intermediate, and independent variables are there?
2. If z is a function of x and y, while x and y are functions of t, explain how to find $\frac{dz}{dt}$.
3. If w is a function of x, y, and z, which are each functions of t, explain how to find dw/dt.
4. If $z = f(x, y)$, $x = g(s, t)$, and $y = h(s, t)$, explain how to find $\partial z/\partial t$.
5. Given that $w = F(x, y, z)$, and x, y, and z are functions of r and s, sketch a tree diagram with branches labeled with the appropriate derivatives.
6. If $F(x, y) = 0$ and y is a differentiable function of x, explain how to find dy/dx.

Basic Skills

7–14. Chain Rule with one independent variable *Use Theorem 13.7 to find the following derivatives. When feasible, express your answer in terms of the independent variable.*

7. dz/dt, where $z = x \sin y$, $x = t^2$, and $y = 4t^3$
8. dz/dt, where $z = x^2y - xy^3$, $x = t^2$, and $y = t^{-2}$
9. dw/dt, where $w = \cos 2x \sin 3y$, $x = t/2$, and $y = t^4$
10. dz/dt, where $z = \sqrt{r^2 + s^2}$, $r = \cos 2t$, and $s = \sin 2t$
11. dw/dt, where $w = xy \sin z$, $x = t^2$, $y = 4t^3$, and $z = t + 1$
12. dQ/dt, where $Q = \sqrt{x^2 + y^2 + z^2}$, $x = \sin t$, $y = \cos t$, and $z = \cos t$
13. dU/dt, where $U = \ln (x + y + z)$, $x = t$, $y = t^2$, and $z = t^3$
14. dV/dt, where $V = \frac{x - y}{y + z}$, $x = t$, $y = 2t$, and $z = 3t$
15. **Changing cylinder** The volume of a right circular cylinder with radius r and height h is $V = \pi r^2 h$.
    a. Assume that r and h are functions of t. Find $V'(t)$.
    b. Suppose that $r = e^t$ and $h = e^{-2t}$, for $t \geq 0$. Use part (a) to find $V'(t)$.
    c. Does the volume of the cylinder in part (b) increase or decrease as t increases?
16. **Changing pyramid** The volume of a pyramid with a square base x units on a side and a height of h is $V = \frac{1}{3}x^2h$.
    a. Assume that x and h are functions of t. Find $V'(t)$.
    b. Suppose that $x = t/(t + 1)$ and $h = 1/(t + 1)$, for $t \geq 0$. Use part (a) to find $V'(t)$.
    c. Does the volume of the pyramid in part (b) increase or decrease as t increases?

17–22. Chain Rule with several independent variables *Find the following derivatives.*

17. z_s and z_t, where $z = xy - x^2 y$, $x = s + t$, and $y = s - t$
18. z_s and z_t, where $z = \sin x \cos 2y$, $x = s + t$, and $y = s - t$
19. z_s and z_t, where $z = e^{x+y}$, $x = st$, and $y = s + t$
20. z_s and z_t, where $z = xy - 2x + 3y$, $x = \cos s$, and $y = \sin t$
21. w_s and w_t, where $w = \frac{x - z}{y + z}$, $x = s + t$, $y = st$, and $z = s - t$
22. w_r, w_s and w_t, where $w = \sqrt{x^2 + y^2 + z^2}$, $x = st$, $y = rs$, and $z = rt$

23–26. Making trees *Use a tree diagram to write the required Chain Rule formula.*

23. w is a function of z, where z is a function of x and y, each of which is a function of t. Find dw/dt.
24. $w = f(x, y, z)$, where $x = g(t)$, $y = h(s, t)$, $z = p(r, s, t)$. Find $\partial w/\partial t$.
25. $u = f(v)$, where $v = g(w, x, y)$, $w = h(z)$, $x = p(t, z)$, $y = q(t, z)$. Find $\partial u/\partial z$.
26. $u = f(v, w, x)$, where $v = g(r, s, t)$, $w = h(r, s, t)$, $x = p(r, s, t)$, $r = F(z)$. Find $\partial u/\partial z$.

27–32. Implicit differentiation *Given the following equations, evaluate dy/dx. Assume that each equation implicitly defines y as a differentiable function of x.*

27. $x^2 - 2y^2 - 1 = 0$
28. $x^3 + 3xy^2 - y^5 = 0$
29. $2 \sin xy = 1$
30. $ye^{xy} - 2 = 0$
31. $\sqrt{x^2 + 2xy + y^4} = 3$
32. $y \ln (x^2 + y^2 + 4) = 3$

33–34. Fluid flow *The x- and y-components of a fluid moving in two dimensions are given by the following functions u and v. The speed of the fluid at (x, y) is $s(x, y) = \sqrt{u(x, y)^2 + v(x, y)^2}$. Use the Chain Rule to find $\partial s/\partial x$ and $\partial s/\partial y$.*

33. $u(x, y) = 2y$ and $v(x, y) = -2x$; $x \geq 0$ and $y \geq 0$
34. $u(x, y) = x(1 - x)(1 - 2y)$ and $v(x, y) = y(y - 1)(1 - 2x)$; $0 \leq x \leq 1, 0 \leq y \leq 1$

Further Explorations

35. **Explain why or why not** Determine whether the following statements are true and give an explanation or counterexample. Assume all partial derivatives exist.
    a. If $z = (x + y) \sin xy$, where x and y are functions of s, then $\frac{\partial z}{\partial s} = \frac{dz}{dx}\frac{dx}{ds}$.
    b. Given that $w = f(x(s, t), y(s, t), z(s, t))$, the rate of change of w with respect to t is dw/dt.

36–37. Derivative practice two ways *Find the indicated derivative in two ways:*

a. Replace x and y to write z as a function of t and differentiate.
b. Use the Chain Rule.

36. $z'(t)$, where $z = \ln (x + y)$, $x = te^t$, and $y = e^t$
37. $z'(t)$, where $z = \frac{1}{x} + \frac{1}{y}$, $x = t^2 + 2t$, and $y = t^3 - 2$

38–42. Derivative practice *Find the indicated derivative for the following functions.*

38. $\partial z/\partial p$, where $z = x/y$, $x = p + q$, and $y = p - q$

39. dw/dt, where $w = xyz$, $x = 2t^4$, $y = 3t^{-1}$, and $z = 4t^{-3}$

40. $\partial w/\partial x$, where $w = \cos z - \cos x \cos y + \sin x \sin y$, and $z = x + y$

41. $\dfrac{\partial z}{\partial x}$, where $\dfrac{1}{x} + \dfrac{1}{y} + \dfrac{1}{z} = 1$

42. $\partial z/\partial x$, where $xy - z = 1$

43. Change on a line Suppose $w = f(x, y, z)$ and ℓ is the line $\mathbf{r}(t) = \langle at, bt, ct \rangle$, for $-\infty < t < \infty$.

a. Find $w'(t)$ on ℓ (in terms of a, b, c, w_x, w_y, and w_z).
b. Apply part (a) to find $w'(t)$ when $f(x, y, z) = xyz$.
c. Apply part (a) to find $w'(t)$ when $f(x, y, z) = \sqrt{x^2 + y^2 + z^2}$.
d. For a general function $w = f(x, y, z)$, find $w''(t)$.

44. Implicit differentiation rule with three variables Assume that $F(x, y, z(x, y)) = 0$ implicitly defines z as a differentiable function of x and y. Extend Theorem 13.9 to show that

$$\frac{\partial z}{\partial x} = -\frac{F_x}{F_z} \quad \text{and} \quad \frac{\partial z}{\partial y} = -\frac{F_y}{F_z}$$

45–48. Implicit differentiation with three variables *Use the result of Exercise 44 to evaluate* $\dfrac{\partial z}{\partial x}$ *and* $\dfrac{\partial z}{\partial y}$ *for the following relations.*

45. $xy + xz + yz = 3$

46. $x^2 + 2y^2 - 3z^2 = 1$

47. $xyz + x + y - z = 0$

48. More than one way Let $e^{xyz} = 2$. Find z_x and z_y in three ways (and check for agreement).

a. Use the result of Exercise 44.
b. Take logarithms of both sides and differentiate $xyz = \ln 2$.
c. Solve for z and differentiate $z = \ln 2/(xy)$.

49–52. Walking on a surface *Consider the following surfaces specified in the form $z = f(x, y)$ and the curve C in the xy-plane given parametrically in the form $x = g(t)$, $y = h(t)$.*

a. In each case, find $z'(t)$.
b. Imagine that you are walking on the surface directly above the curve C in the direction of increasing t. Find the values of t for which you are walking uphill (that is, z is increasing).

49. $z = x^2 + 4y^2 + 1$, C: $x = \cos t$, $y = \sin t$; $0 \le t \le 2\pi$

50. $z = 4x^2 - y^2 + 1$, C: $x = \cos t$, $y = \sin t$; $0 \le t \le 2\pi$

51. $z = \sqrt{1 - x^2 - y^2}$, C: $x = e^{-t}$, $y = e^{-t}$; $t \ge \frac{1}{2}\ln 2$

52. $z = 2x^2 + y^2 + 1$, C: $x = 1 + \cos t$, $y = \sin t$; $0 \le t \le 2\pi$

Applications

53. Conservation of energy A projectile is launched into the air on a parabolic trajectory. For $t \ge 0$, its horizontal and vertical coordinates are $x(t) = u_0 t$ and $y(t) = -(1/2)gt^2 + v_0 t$, respectively, where u_0 is the initial horizontal velocity, v_0 is the initial vertical velocity, and g is the acceleration due to gravity. Recalling that $u(t) = x'(t)$ and $v(t) = y'(t)$ are the components of the velocity, the energy of the projectile (kinetic plus potential) is

$$E(t) = \frac{1}{2}m(u^2 + v^2) + mgy$$

Use the Chain Rule to compute $E'(t)$ and show that $E'(t) = 0$ for all $t \ge 0$. Interpret the result.

54. Utility functions in economics Economists use *utility functions* to describe consumers' relative preference for two or more commodities (for example, vanilla vs. chocolate ice cream or leisure time vs. material goods). The Cobb-Douglas family of utility functions has the form $U(x, y) = x^a y^{1-a}$, where x and y are the amounts of two commodities and $0 < a < 1$ is a parameter. Level curves on which the utility function is constant are called *indifference curves*; the preference is the same for all combinations of x and y along an indifference curve (see figure).

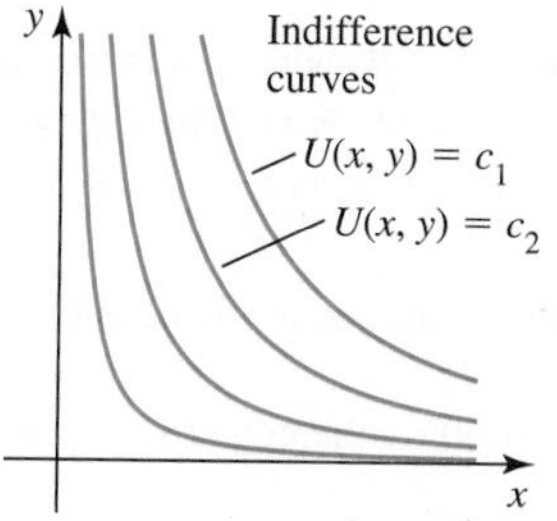

a. The marginal utilities of the commodities x and y are defined to be $\partial U/\partial x$ and $\partial U/\partial y$, respectively. Compute the marginal utilities for the utility function $U(x, y) = x^a y^{1-a}$.
b. The marginal rate of substitution (MRS) is the slope of the indifference curve at the point (x, y). Use the Chain Rule to show that for $U(x, y) = x^a y^{1-a}$, the MRS is $-\dfrac{a}{1-a}\dfrac{y}{x}$.
c. Find the MRS for the utility function $U(x, y) = x^{0.4}y^{0.6}$ at $(x, y) = (8, 12)$.

55. Constant volume tori The volume of a solid torus (a bagel or doughnut) is given by $V = (\pi^2/4)(R + r)(R - r)^2$, where r and R are the inner and outer radii and $R > r$ (see figure).

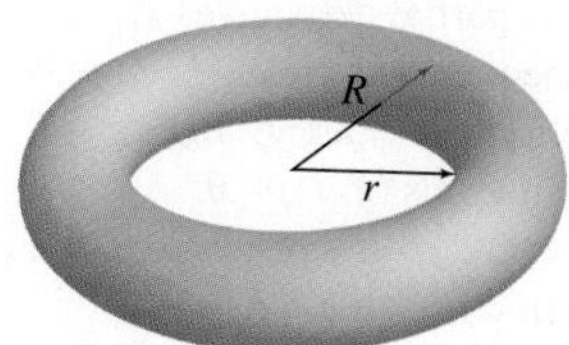

a. If R and r increase at the same rate, does the volume of the torus increase, decrease, or remain constant?
b. If R and r decrease at the same rate, does the volume of the torus increase, decrease, or remain constant?

56. Body surface area One of several empirical formulas that relates the surface area S of a human body to the height h and weight w of the body is the Mosteller formula $S(h, w) = \frac{1}{60}\sqrt{hw}$, where h

is measured in cm, w is measured in kg, and S is measured in m^2. Suppose that h and w are functions of t.

a. Find $S'(t)$.

b. Show that the condition that the surface area remains constant as h and w change is $wh'(t) + hw'(t) = 0$.

c. Show that part (b) implies that for constant surface area, h and w must be inversely related; that is, $h = C/w$, where C is a constant.

57. The Ideal Gas Law The pressure, temperature, and volume of an ideal gas are related by $PV = kT$, where $k > 0$ is a constant. Any two of the variables may be considered independent, which determines the third variable.

a. Use implicit differentiation to compute the partial derivatives $\frac{\partial P}{\partial V}, \frac{\partial T}{\partial P}$, and $\frac{\partial V}{\partial T}$.

b. Show that $\frac{\partial P}{\partial V}\frac{\partial T}{\partial P}\frac{\partial V}{\partial T} = -1$. (See Exercise 63 for a generalization.)

58. Variable density The density of a thin circular plate of radius 2 is given by $\rho(x, y) = 4 + xy$. The edge of the plate is described by the parametric equations $x = 2\cos t$, $y = 2\sin t$, for $0 \le t \le 2\pi$.

a. Find the rate of change of the density with respect to t on the edge of the plate.

b. At what point(s) on the edge of the plate is the density a maximum?

T **59. Spiral through a domain** Suppose you follow the spiral path $C: x = \cos t, y = \sin t, z = t$, for $t \ge 0$, through the domain of the function $w = f(x, y, z) = (xyz)/(z^2 + 1)$.

a. Find $w'(t)$ along C.

b. Estimate the point (x, y, z) on C at which w has its maximum value.

Additional Exercises

60. Change of coordinates Recall that Cartesian and polar coordinates are related through the transformation equations

$$\begin{cases} x = r\cos\theta \\ y = r\sin\theta \end{cases} \quad \text{or} \quad \begin{cases} r^2 = x^2 + y^2 \\ \tan\theta = y/x \end{cases}$$

a. Evaluate the partial derivatives x_r, y_r, x_θ, and y_θ.

b. Evaluate the partial derivatives r_x, r_y, θ_x, and θ_y.

c. For a function $z = f(x, y)$, find z_r and z_θ, where x and y are expressed in terms of r and θ.

d. For a function $z = g(r, \theta)$, find z_x and z_y, where r and θ are expressed in terms of x and y.

e. Show that

$$\left(\frac{\partial z}{\partial x}\right)^2 + \left(\frac{\partial z}{\partial y}\right)^2 = \left(\frac{\partial z}{\partial r}\right)^2 + \frac{1}{r^2}\left(\frac{\partial z}{\partial \theta}\right)^2.$$

61. Change of coordinates continued An important derivative operation in many applications is called the Laplacian; in Cartesian coordinates, for $z = f(x, y)$, the Laplacian is $z_{xx} + z_{yy}$. Determine the Laplacian in polar coordinates using the following steps.

a. Begin with $z = g(r, \theta)$ and write z_x and z_y in terms of polar coordinates (see Exercise 60).

b. Use the Chain Rule to find $z_{xx} = \frac{\partial}{\partial x}(z_x)$. There should be two major terms, which when expanded and simplified, result in five terms.

c. Use the Chain Rule to find $z_{yy} = \frac{\partial}{\partial y}(z_y)$. There should be two major terms, which when expanded and simplified, result in five terms.

d. Combine part (a) and (b) to show that

$$z_{xx} + z_{yy} = z_{rr} + \frac{1}{r}z_r + \frac{1}{r^2}z_{\theta\theta}.$$

62. Geometry of implicit differentiation Suppose x and y are related by the equation $F(x, y) = 0$. Interpret the solution of this equation as the set of points (x, y) that lie on the intersection of the surface $z = F(x, y)$ with the xy-plane ($z = 0$).

a. Make a sketch of a surface and its intersection with the xy-plane. Give a geometric interpretation of the result that $\frac{dy}{dx} = -\frac{F_x}{F_y}$.

b. Explain geometrically what happens at points where $F_y = 0$.

63. General three-variable relationship In the implicit relationship $F(x, y, z) = 0$, any two of the variables may be considered independent, which then determines the third variable. To avoid confusion, we may use a subscript to indicate which variable is held fixed in a derivative calculation; for example, $\left(\frac{\partial z}{\partial x}\right)_y$ means that y is held fixed in taking the partial derivative of z with respect to x. (In this context, the subscript does *not* mean a derivative.)

a. Differentiate $F(x, y, z) = 0$ with respect to x holding y fixed to show that $\left(\frac{\partial z}{\partial x}\right)_y = -\frac{F_x}{F_z}$.

b. As in part (a), find $\left(\frac{\partial y}{\partial z}\right)_x$ and $\left(\frac{\partial x}{\partial y}\right)_z$.

c. Show that $\left(\frac{\partial z}{\partial x}\right)_y\left(\frac{\partial y}{\partial z}\right)_x\left(\frac{\partial x}{\partial y}\right)_z = -1$.

d. Find the relationship analogous to part (c) for the case $F(w, x, y, z) = 0$.

64. Second derivative Let $f(x, y) = 0$ define y as a twice differentiable function of x.

a. Show that $y''(x) = -\frac{f_{xx}f_y^2 - 2f_xf_yf_{xy} + f_{yy}f_x^2}{f_y^3}$.

b. Verify part (a) using the function $f(x, y) = xy - 1$.

65. Subtleties of the Chain Rule Let $w = f(x, y, z) = 2x + 3y + 4z$, which is defined for all (x, y, z) in $\mathbf{R}^3$. Suppose that we are interested in the partial derivative w_x on a subset of $\mathbf{R}^3$, such as the plane P given by $z = 4x - 2y$. The point to be made is that the result is not unique unless we specify which variables are considered independent.

a. We could proceed as follows. On the plane P, consider x and y as the independent variables, which means z depends on x and y, so we write $w = f(x, y, z(x, y))$. Differentiate with respect to x holding y fixed to show that $\left(\frac{\partial w}{\partial x}\right)_y = 18$, where the subscript y indicates that y is held fixed.

b. Alternatively, on the plane P, we could consider x and z as the independent variables, which means y depends on x and z, so we write $w = f(x, y(x, z), z)$ and differentiate with respect to x holding z fixed. Show that $\left(\frac{\partial w}{\partial x}\right)_z = 8$, where the subscript z indicates that z is held fixed.

c. Make a sketch of the plane $z = 4x - 2y$ and interpret the results of parts (a) and (b) geometrically.

d. Repeat the arguments of parts (a) and (b) to find $\left(\frac{\partial w}{\partial y}\right)_x, \left(\frac{\partial w}{\partial y}\right)_z, \left(\frac{\partial w}{\partial z}\right)_x, \left(\frac{\partial w}{\partial z}\right)_y$.

QUICK CHECK ANSWERS

1. If $z = f(x(t))$, then $\frac{\partial z}{\partial y} = 0$, and the original Chain Rule results. **2.** $\frac{\partial w}{\partial t} = \frac{\partial w}{\partial x}\frac{\partial x}{\partial t} + \frac{\partial w}{\partial y}\frac{\partial y}{\partial t} + \frac{\partial w}{\partial z}\frac{\partial z}{\partial t}$ **3.** One dependent variable, four intermediate variables, and three independent variables ◄

13.6 Directional Derivatives and the Gradient

Partial derivatives tell us a lot about the rate of change of a function on its domain. However, they do not *directly* answer some important questions. For example, suppose you are standing at a point $(a, b, f(a, b))$ on the surface $z = f(x, y)$. The partial derivatives f_x and f_y tell you the rate of change (or slope) of the surface at that point in the directions parallel to the x-axis and y-axis, respectively. But you could walk in an infinite number of directions from that point and find a different rate of change in every direction. With this observation in mind, we pose several questions.

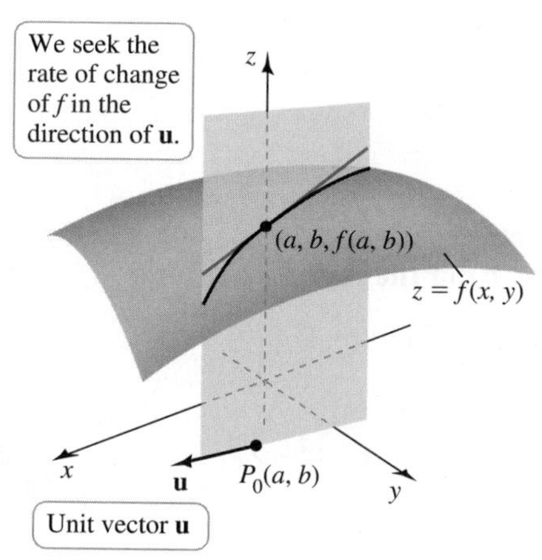

FIGURE 13.63

- Suppose you are standing on a surface and you walk in a direction *other* than a coordinate direction—say, northwest or south-southeast. What is the rate of change of the function in such a direction?
- Suppose you are standing on a surface and you release a ball at your feet and let it roll. In which direction will it roll?
- If you are hiking up a mountain, in what direction should you walk after each step if you want to follow the steepest path?

These questions will be answered in this section as we introduce the *directional derivative*, followed by one of the central concepts of calculus—the *gradient*.

Directional Derivatives

Let $(a, b, f(a, b))$ be a point on the surface $z = f(x, y)$ and let $\mathbf{u}$ be a unit vector in the xy-plane (Figure 13.63). Our aim is to find the rate of change of f in the direction $\mathbf{u}$ at $P_0(a, b)$. In general, this rate of change is neither $f_x(a, b)$ nor $f_y(a, b)$ (unless $\mathbf{u} = \langle 1, 0 \rangle$ or $\mathbf{u} = \langle 0, 1 \rangle$), but it turns out to be a combination of $f_x(a, b)$ and $f_y(a, b)$.

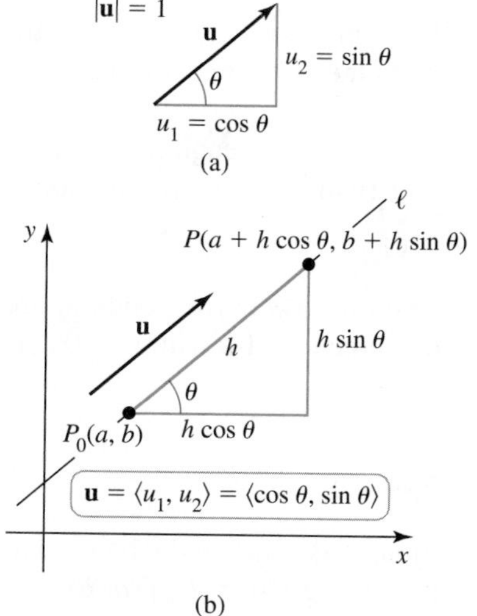

FIGURE 13.64

Figure 13.64a shows the unit vector $\mathbf{u}$ at an angle θ to the positive x-axis; its components are $\mathbf{u} = \langle u_1, u_2 \rangle = \langle \cos\theta, \sin\theta \rangle$. The derivative we seek must be computed along the line ℓ in the xy-plane through P_0 in the direction of $\mathbf{u}$. A neighboring point P, which is h units from P_0 along ℓ, has coordinates $P(a + h\cos\theta, b + h\sin\theta)$ (Figure 13.64b).

Now imagine the plane Q perpendicular to the xy-plane, containing ℓ. This plane cuts the surface $z = f(x, y)$ in a curve (a trace) C. Consider two points on C corresponding to P and P_0; they have z-coordinates $f(a, b)$ and $f(a + h\cos\theta, b + h\sin\theta)$ (Figure 13.65). The slope of the secant line between these points is

$$\frac{f(a + h\cos\theta, b + h\sin\theta) - f(a, b)}{h}.$$

The derivative of f in the direction of $\mathbf{u}$ is obtained by letting $h \to 0$; when the limit exists, it is called the ***directional derivative of f at (a, b) in the direction of* u**. It gives the slope of the line tangent to the curve C in the plane Q.

➤ The definition of the directional derivative looks like the definition of the ordinary derivative if we write it as

$$\lim_{P \to P_0} \frac{f(P) - f(P_0)}{|P - P_0|},$$

where P approaches P_0 along the line determined by the angle θ.

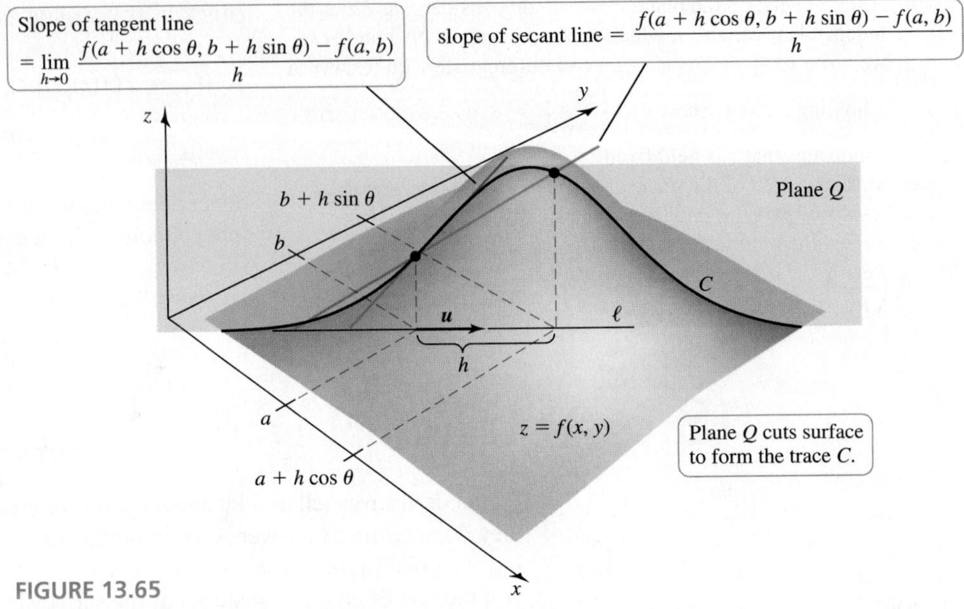

FIGURE 13.65

> **DEFINITION** **Directional Derivative**
>
> Let f be differentiable at (a, b) and let $\mathbf{u} = \langle \cos\theta, \sin\theta \rangle$ be a unit vector in the xy-plane. The **directional derivative of f at (a, b) in the direction of u** is
>
> $$D_{\mathbf{u}}f(a, b) = \lim_{h \to 0} \frac{f(a + h\cos\theta, b + h\sin\theta) - f(a, b)}{h},$$
>
> provided the limit exists.

QUICK CHECK 1 Explain why, when $\theta = 0$ in the definition of the directional derivative, the result is $f_x(a, b)$ and when $\theta = \pi/2$, the result is $f_y(a, b)$. ◄

As with ordinary derivatives, we would prefer to evaluate directional derivatives without taking limits. Fortunately, there is an easy way to express the directional derivative in terms of partial derivatives.

The key is to define a function that is equal to f along the line ℓ through (a, b) in the direction of the unit vector $\mathbf{u} = \langle u_1, u_2 \rangle$. The points on ℓ satisfy the parametric equations

$$x = a + su_1 \quad \text{and} \quad y = b + su_2,$$

where $-\infty < s < \infty$. Because $\mathbf{u}$ is a unit vector, the parameter s corresponds to arc length. As s increases, the points (x, y) move along ℓ in the direction of $\mathbf{u}$ with $s = 0$ corresponding to (a, b). Now we define the function

$$g(s) = f(\underbrace{a + su_1}_{x}, \underbrace{b + su_2}_{y}),$$

which gives the values of f along ℓ. The derivative of f along ℓ is $g'(s)$, and when evaluated at $s = 0$, it is the directional derivative of f at (a, b); that is, $g'(0) = D_{\mathbf{u}}f(a, b)$.

➤ To see that s is an arc length parameter, suppose that s changes from $s = 0$ to $s = \Delta s$. The resulting line segment extends from (a, b) to $(a + \Delta s u_1, b + \Delta s u_2)$, and has length Δs because $\mathbf{u}$ is a unit vector. Thus, any change in s produces the same change in the length of the line. Because the directional derivative is a derivative with respect to length along the line ℓ, it is essential that s be an arc length parameter, and this occurs only if $\mathbf{u}$ is a unit vector.

Noting that $\frac{dx}{ds} = u_1$ and $\frac{dy}{ds} = u_2$, we apply the Chain Rule to find that

$$D_{\mathbf{u}} f(a, b) = g'(0) = \left[\frac{\partial f}{\partial x}\underbrace{\frac{dx}{ds}}_{u_1} + \frac{\partial f}{\partial y}\underbrace{\frac{dy}{ds}}_{u_2}\right]\bigg|_{s=0} \qquad \text{Chain Rule}$$

$$= f_x(a, b)u_1 + f_y(a, b)u_2. \qquad s = 0 \text{ corresponds to } (a, b).$$

We see that the directional derivative is a weighted average of the partial derivatives $f_x(a, b)$ and $f_y(a, b)$, with the components of **u** serving as the weights. In other words, knowing the slope of the surface in the x- and y-directions allows us to find the slope in any direction. Notice that the directional derivative can be written as a dot product, which provides a practical formula for computing directional derivatives.

QUICK CHECK 2 In the parametric description $x = a + su_1$ and $y = b + su_2$, where $\mathbf{u} = \langle u_1, u_2 \rangle$ is a unit vector, show that any change Δs in s produces a line segment of length Δs. ◄

THEOREM 13.10 Directional Derivative

Let f be differentiable at (a, b) and let $\mathbf{u} = \langle u_1, u_2 \rangle$ be a unit vector in the xy-plane. The **directional derivative of f at (a, b) in the direction of u** is

$$D_{\mathbf{u}} f(a, b) = \langle f_x(a, b), f_y(a, b) \rangle \cdot \langle u_1, u_2 \rangle$$

EXAMPLE 1 Computing directional derivatives Consider the paraboloid $z = f(x, y) = \frac{1}{4}(x^2 + 2y^2) + 2$. Let P_0 be the point $(3, 2)$ and consider the unit vectors

$$\mathbf{u} = \left\langle \frac{1}{\sqrt{2}}, \frac{1}{\sqrt{2}} \right\rangle \quad \text{and} \quad \mathbf{v} = \left\langle \frac{1}{2}, -\frac{\sqrt{3}}{2} \right\rangle.$$

a. Find the directional derivative of f at P_0 in the directions of **u** and **v**.

b. Graph the surface and interpret the directional derivatives.

SOLUTION

a. We see that $f_x = x/2$ and $f_y = y$; evaluated at $(3, 2)$, we have $f_x(3, 2) = 3/2$ and $f_y(3, 2) = 2$. The directional derivatives in the directions **u** and **v** are

$$D_{\mathbf{u}} f(3, 2) = \langle f_x(3, 2), f_y(3, 2) \rangle \cdot \langle u_1, u_2 \rangle$$
$$= \frac{3}{2} \cdot \frac{1}{\sqrt{2}} + 2 \cdot \frac{1}{\sqrt{2}} = \frac{7}{2\sqrt{2}} \approx 2.47$$

$$D_{\mathbf{v}} f(3, 2) = \langle f_x(3, 2), f_y(3, 2) \rangle \cdot \langle v_1, v_2 \rangle$$
$$= \frac{3}{2} \cdot \frac{1}{2} + 2\left(-\frac{\sqrt{3}}{2}\right) = \frac{3}{4} - \sqrt{3} \approx -0.98.$$

➤ It is understood that the line tangent to the trace of the surface in the direction of **u** lies in the plane containing **u** perpendicular to the xy-plane.

b. In the direction of **u**, the directional derivative is approximately 2.47. Because it is positive, the function is increasing at $(3, 2)$ in this direction. Equivalently, the slope of the line tangent to the trace C in the direction of **u** is approximately 2.47 (Figure 13.66a). In the direction of **v**, the directional derivative is approximately -0.98. Because it is negative, the function is decreasing in this direction. In this case, the slope of the line tangent to the trace C in the direction of **v** is approximately -0.98 (Figure 13.66b).

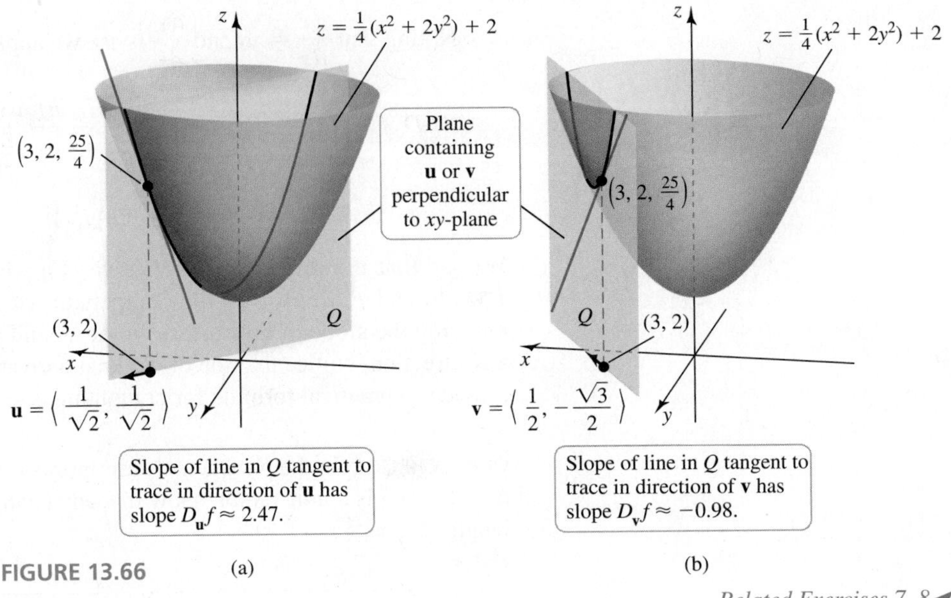

FIGURE 13.66 (a) (b)

Related Exercises 7–8

QUICK CHECK 3 In Example 1, evaluate $D_{-\mathbf{u}}f(a, b)$ and $D_{-\mathbf{v}}f(a, b)$.

The Gradient Vector

We have seen that the directional derivative can be written as a dot product: $D_{\mathbf{u}}f(a, b) = \langle f_x(a, b), f_y(a, b)\rangle \cdot \langle u_1, u_2\rangle$. The vector $\langle f_x(a, b), f_y(a, b)\rangle$ that appears in the dot product is important in its own right and is called the *gradient* of f.

> Recall that the unit coordinate vectors in $\mathbf{R}^2$ are $\mathbf{i} = \langle 1, 0\rangle$ and $\mathbf{j} = \langle 0, 1\rangle$. The gradient of f is also written grad f, read *grad* f.

DEFINITION Gradient (Two Dimensions)

Let f be differentiable at the point (x, y). The **gradient** of f at (x, y) is the vector-valued function

$$\nabla f(x, y) = \langle f_x(x, y), f_y(x, y)\rangle = f_x(x, y)\mathbf{i} + f_y(x, y)\mathbf{j}.$$

With the definition of the gradient, the directional derivative of f at (a, b) in the direction of the unit vector **u** can be written

$$D_{\mathbf{u}}f(a, b) = \nabla f(a, b) \cdot \mathbf{u}.$$

The gradient satisfies sum, product, and quotient rules analogous to those for ordinary derivatives (Exercise 75).

EXAMPLE 2 Computing gradients Find ∇f and $\nabla f(3, 2)$ for $f(x, y) = x^2 + 2xy - y^3$.

SOLUTION Computing $f_x = 2x + 2y$ and $f_y = 2x - 3y^2$, we have

$$\nabla f(x, y) = \langle 2(x + y), 2x - 3y^2\rangle = 2(x + y)\mathbf{i} + (2x - 3y^2)\mathbf{j}.$$

Substituting $x = 3$ and $y = 2$ gives

$$\nabla f(3, 2) = \langle 10, -6\rangle = 10\mathbf{i} - 6\mathbf{j}.$$

Related Exercises 9–14

EXAMPLE 3 Computing directional derivatives with gradients Let $f(x, y) = 3 - \dfrac{x^2}{10} + \dfrac{xy^2}{10}$.

a. Compute $\nabla f(3, -1)$.

b. Compute $D_{\mathbf{u}} f(3, -1)$, where $\mathbf{u} = \left\langle \dfrac{1}{\sqrt{2}}, -\dfrac{1}{\sqrt{2}} \right\rangle$.

c. Compute the directional derivative of f at $(3, -1)$ in the direction of the vector $\langle 3, 4 \rangle$.

SOLUTION

a. Note that $f_x = -x/5 + y^2/10$ and $f_y = xy/5$. Therefore,

$$\nabla f(3, -1) = \left\langle -\frac{x}{5} + \frac{y^2}{10}, \frac{xy}{5} \right\rangle \bigg|_{(3,-1)} = \left\langle -\frac{1}{2}, -\frac{3}{5} \right\rangle.$$

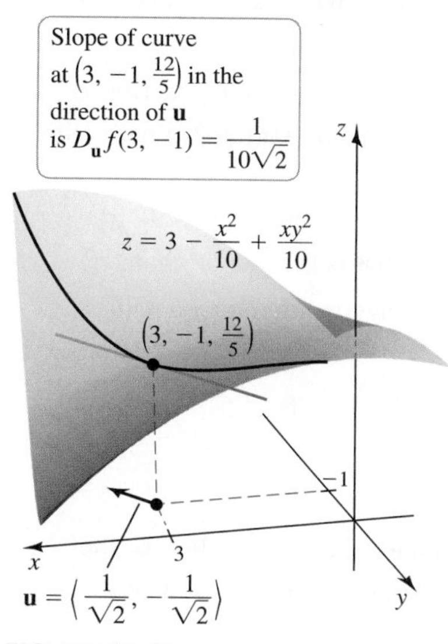

FIGURE 13.67

b. Before computing the directional derivative, it is important to verify that **u** is a unit vector (in this case, it is). The required directional derivative is

$$D_{\mathbf{u}} f(3, -1) = \nabla f(3, -1) \cdot \mathbf{u} = \left\langle -\frac{1}{2}, -\frac{3}{5} \right\rangle \cdot \left\langle \frac{1}{\sqrt{2}}, -\frac{1}{\sqrt{2}} \right\rangle = \frac{1}{10\sqrt{2}}.$$

Figure 13.67 shows the line tangent to the trace in the plane corresponding to **u** whose slope is $D_{\mathbf{u}} f(3, -1)$.

c. In this case, the direction is given in terms of a nonunit vector. The vector $\langle 3, 4 \rangle$ has length 5, so the unit vector in the direction of $\langle 3, 4 \rangle$ is $\mathbf{u} = \left\langle \frac{3}{5}, \frac{4}{5} \right\rangle$. The directional derivative at $(3, -1)$ in the direction of **u** is

$$D_{\mathbf{u}} f(3, -1) = \nabla f(3, -1) \cdot \mathbf{u} = \left\langle -\frac{1}{2}, -\frac{3}{5} \right\rangle \cdot \left\langle \frac{3}{5}, \frac{4}{5} \right\rangle = -\frac{39}{50},$$

which gives the slope of the surface in the direction of **u** at $(3, -1)$.

Related Exercises 15–20

Interpretations of the Gradient

The gradient is important not only in calculating directional derivatives; it plays many other roles in multivariable calculus. Our present goal is to develop some intuition about the meaning of the gradient.

➤ Recall that $\mathbf{u} \cdot \mathbf{v} = |\mathbf{u}||\mathbf{v}| \cos \theta$, where θ is the angle between **u** and **v**.

We have seen that the directional derivative of f at (a, b) in the direction of the unit vector **u** is $D_{\mathbf{u}} f(a, b) = \nabla f(a, b) \cdot \mathbf{u}$. Using properties of the dot product, we have

$$\begin{aligned} D_{\mathbf{u}} f(a, b) &= \nabla f(a, b) \cdot \mathbf{u} \\ &= |\nabla f(a, b)||\mathbf{u}| \cos \theta \\ &= |\nabla f(a, b)| \cos \theta, \qquad |\mathbf{u}| = 1 \end{aligned}$$

where θ is the angle between $\nabla f(a, b)$ and **u**. It follows that $D_{\mathbf{u}} f(a, b)$ has its maximum value when $\cos \theta = 1$, which corresponds to $\theta = 0$. Therefore, $D_{\mathbf{u}} f(a, b)$ has its maximum value and f has its greatest rate of *increase* when $\nabla f(a, b)$ and **u** point in the same direction. Notice that when $\cos \theta = 1$, the actual rate of increase is $D_{\mathbf{u}} f(a, b) = |\nabla f(a, b)|$ (Figure 13.68).

➤ It is important to remember and easy to forget that $\nabla f(a, b)$ lies in the same plane as the domain of f.

Similarly, when $\theta = \pi$, we have $\cos \theta = -1$, and f has its greatest rate of *decrease* when $\nabla f(a, b)$ and **u** point in opposite directions. The actual rate of decrease is $D_{\mathbf{u}} f(a, b) = -|\nabla f(a, b)|$. These observations are summarized as follows: The gradient $\nabla f(a, b)$ points in the *direction of steepest ascent* at (a, b), while $-\nabla f(a, b)$ points in the *direction of steepest descent*.

Notice that $D_{\mathbf{u}} f(a, b) = 0$ when the angle between $\nabla f(a, b)$ and **u** is $\pi/2$, which means $\nabla f(a, b)$ and **u** are orthogonal (Figure 13.68). These observations justify the following theorem.

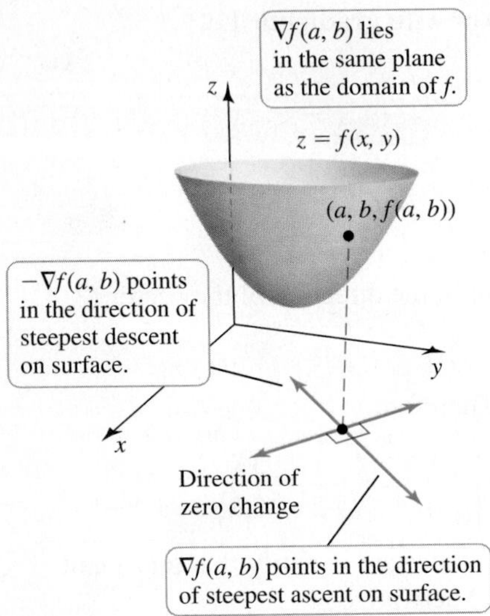

FIGURE 13.68

> **THEOREM 13.11 Directions of Change**
> Let f be differentiable at (a, b).
>
> **1.** f has its maximum rate of increase at (a, b) in the direction of the gradient $\nabla f(a, b)$. The rate of increase in this direction is $|\nabla f(a, b)|$.
>
> **2.** f has its maximum rate of decrease at (a, b) in the direction of $-\nabla f(a, b)$. The rate of decrease in this direction is $-|\nabla f(a, b)|$.
>
> **3.** The directional derivative is zero in any direction orthogonal to $\nabla f(a, b)$.

EXAMPLE 4 Steepest ascent and descent Consider the bowl-shaped paraboloid $z = f(x, y) = 4 + x^2 + 3y^2$.

a. If you are located on the paraboloid at the point $\left(2, -\frac{1}{2}, \frac{35}{4}\right)$, in which direction should you move in order to *ascend* on the surface at the maximum rate? What is the rate of change?

b. If you are located at the point $\left(2, -\frac{1}{2}, \frac{35}{4}\right)$, in which direction should you walk in order to *descend* on the surface at the maximum rate? What is the rate of change?

c. At the point $(3, 1, 16)$, in what direction(s) is there no change in the function values?

SOLUTION

a. At the point $\left(2, -\frac{1}{2}\right)$, the value of the gradient is

$$\nabla f\left(2, -\tfrac{1}{2}\right) = \langle 2x, 6y\rangle|_{(2,-1/2)} = \langle 4, -3\rangle.$$

Therefore, the direction of steepest ascent in the xy-plane is in the direction of the gradient vector $\langle 4,-3\rangle$ (or $\mathbf{u} = \frac{1}{5}\langle 4, -3\rangle$, as a unit vector). The rate of change is $\left|\nabla f\left(2, -\frac{1}{2}\right)\right| = |\langle 4, -3\rangle| = 5$ (Figure 13.69a).

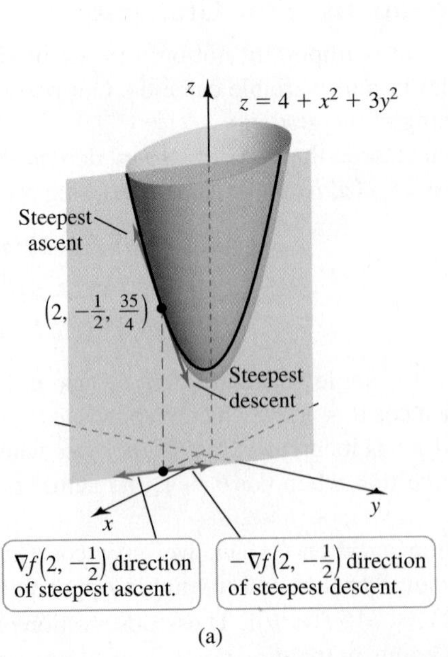

(a)

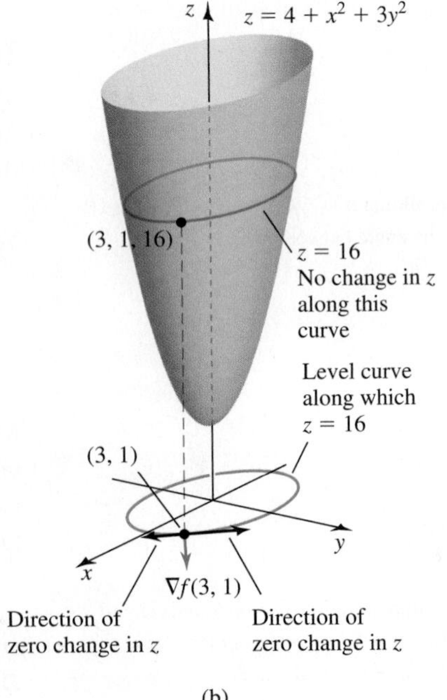

(b)

FIGURE 13.69

b. The direction of steepest *descent* is the direction of $-\nabla f\left(2, -\frac{1}{2}\right) = \langle -4, 3\rangle$ (or $\mathbf{u} = \frac{1}{5}\langle -4, 3\rangle$, as a unit vector). The rate of change is $-\left|\nabla f\left(2, -\frac{1}{2}\right)\right| = -5$.

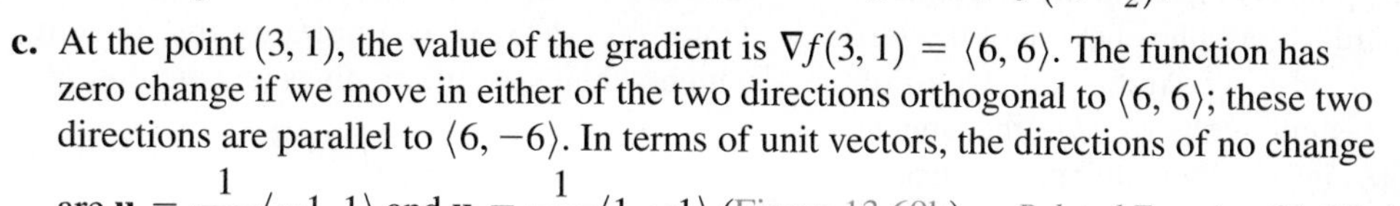

c. At the point $(3, 1)$, the value of the gradient is $\nabla f(3, 1) = \langle 6, 6\rangle$. The function has zero change if we move in either of the two directions orthogonal to $\langle 6, 6\rangle$; these two directions are parallel to $\langle 6, -6\rangle$. In terms of unit vectors, the directions of no change are $\mathbf{u} = \frac{1}{\sqrt{2}}\langle -1, 1\rangle$ and $\mathbf{u} = \frac{1}{\sqrt{2}}\langle 1, -1\rangle$ (Figure 13.69b). *Related Exercises 21–26*

➤ Note that $\langle 6, 6\rangle$ and $\langle 6, -6\rangle$ are orthogonal because $\langle 6, 6\rangle \cdot \langle 6, -6\rangle = 0$.

EXAMPLE 5 Interpreting directional derivatives Consider the function $f(x, y) = 3x^2 - 2y^2$.

a. Compute $\nabla f(x, y)$ and $\nabla f(2, 3)$.

b. Let $\mathbf{u} = \langle \cos\theta, \sin\theta\rangle$ be a unit vector. For what values of θ (measured relative to the positive x-axis), with $0 \le \theta < 2\pi$, does the directional derivative have its maximum and minimum values and what are those values?

SOLUTION

a. The gradient is $\nabla f(x, y) = \langle f_x, f_y\rangle = \langle 6x, -4y\rangle$, and at $(2, 3)$, we have $\nabla f(2, 3) = \langle 12, -12\rangle$.

b. The gradient $\nabla f(2, 3) = \langle 12, -12\rangle$ makes an angle of $7\pi/4$ with the positive x-axis. So, the maximum rate of change of f occurs in this direction, and that rate of change is $|\nabla f(2, 3)| = |\langle 12, -12\rangle| = 12\sqrt{2} \approx 17$. The direction of maximum decrease is opposite to the direction of the gradient, which corresponds to $\theta = 3\pi/4$. The maximum rate of decrease is the negative of the maximum rate of increase, or $-12\sqrt{2} \approx -17$. The function has zero change in the directions orthogonal to the gradient, which correspond to $\theta = \pi/4$ and $\theta = 5\pi/4$.

Figure 13.70 summarizes these conclusions. Notice that the gradient at $(2, 3)$ appears to be orthogonal to the level curve of f passing through $(2, 3)$. We next see that this is always the case. *Related Exercises 27–36*

FIGURE 13.70

The Gradient and Level Curves

Theorem 13.11 states that in any direction orthogonal to the gradient $\nabla f(a, b)$, the function f does not change at (a, b). Recall from Section 13.2 that the curve $f(x, y) = z_0$, where z_0 is a constant, is a *level curve*, on which function values are constant. Combining these two observations, we conclude that the gradient $\nabla f(a, b)$ is orthogonal to the line tangent to the level curve through (a, b).

THEOREM 13.12 The Gradient and Level Curves
Given a function f differentiable at (a, b), the line tangent to the level curve of f at (a, b) is orthogonal to the gradient $\nabla f(a, b)$.

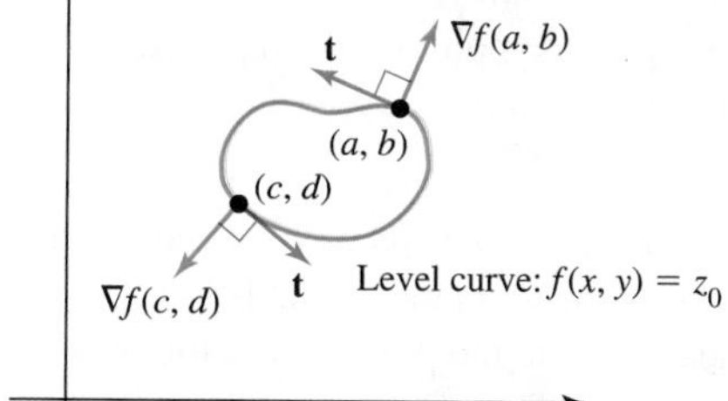

FIGURE 13.71

Proof A level curve of the function $z = f(x, y)$ is a curve in the xy-plane of the form $f(x, y) = z_0$, where z_0 is a constant. By Theorem 13.9, the slope of the line tangent to the level curve is $y'(x) = -f_x/f_y$.

It follows that any vector that points in the direction of the tangent line at the point (a, b) is a scalar multiple of the vector $\mathbf{t} = \langle -f_y(a, b), f_x(a, b)\rangle$ (Figure 13.71). At that same point, the gradient points in the direction $\nabla f(a, b) = \langle f_x(a, b), f_y(a, b)\rangle$. The dot product of $\mathbf{t}$ and $\nabla f(a, b)$ is

$$\mathbf{t} \cdot \nabla f(a, b) = \langle -f_y, f_x\rangle_{(a,b)} \cdot \langle f_x, f_y\rangle_{(a,b)} = (-f_x f_y + f_x f_y)_{(a,b)} = 0,$$

which implies that $\mathbf{t}$ and $\nabla f(a, b)$ are orthogonal.

➤ We have used the fact that the vector $\langle a, b\rangle$ has slope b/a.

QUICK CHECK 4 Draw a circle in the xy-plane centered at the origin and regard it is as a level curve of the surface $z = x^2 + y^2$. At the point (a, a) of the level curve, the slope of the tangent line is -1. Show that the gradient at (a, a) is orthogonal to the tangent line.

An immediate consequence of Theorem 13.12 is an alternative equation of the tangent line. The curve described by $f(x, y) = z_0$ can be viewed as a level curve for a surface. By Theorem 13.12, the line tangent to the curve at (a, b) is orthogonal to $\nabla f(a, b)$. Therefore, if (x, y) is a point on the tangent line, then $\nabla f(a, b) \cdot \langle x - a, y - b \rangle = 0$, which, when simplified, gives an equation of the line tangent to the curve $f(x, y) = z_0$:

$$f_x(a, b)(x - a) + f_y(a, b)(y - b) = 0$$

EXAMPLE 6 Gradients and level curves Consider the upper sheet $z = f(x, y) = \sqrt{1 + 2x^2 + y^2}$ of a hyperboloid of two sheets.

a. Verify that the gradient at $(1, 1)$ is orthogonal to the corresponding level curve at that point.

b. Find an equation of the line tangent to the level curve at $(1, 1)$.

SOLUTION

> The fact that $y' = -2x/y$ may also be obtained using Theorem 13.9: If $F(x, y) = 0$, then $y'(x) = -F_x/F_y$.

a. You can verify that $(1, 1, 2)$ is on the surface; therefore, $(1, 1)$ is on the level curve corresponding to $z = 2$. Setting $z = 2$ in the equation of the surface and squaring both sides, the equation of the level curve is $4 = 1 + 2x^2 + y^2$, or $2x^2 + y^2 = 3$, which is the equation of an ellipse (Figure 13.72). Differentiating $2x^2 + y^2 = 3$ with respect to x gives $4x + 2yy'(x) = 0$, which implies that the slope of the level curve is $y'(x) = -\dfrac{2x}{y}$. Therefore, at the point $(1, 1)$, the slope of the tangent line is -2. Any vector proportional to $\mathbf{t} = \langle 1, -2 \rangle$ has slope -2 and points in the direction of the tangent line.

We now compute the gradient:

$$\nabla f(x, y) = \langle f_x, f_y \rangle = \left\langle \frac{2x}{\sqrt{1 + 2x^2 + y^2}}, \frac{y}{\sqrt{1 + 2x^2 + y^2}} \right\rangle$$

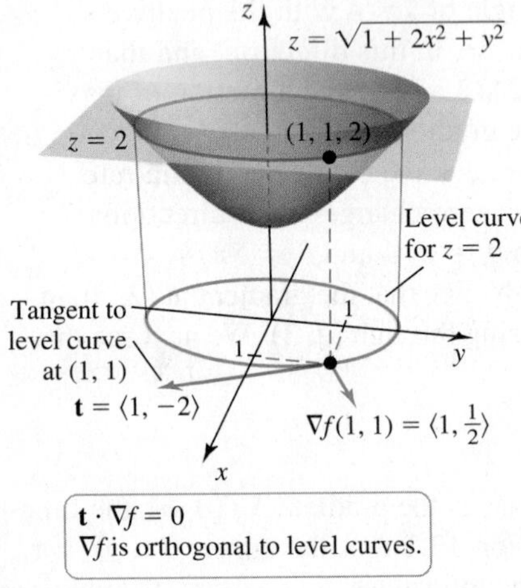

FIGURE 13.72

It follows that $\nabla f(1, 1) = \left\langle 1, \frac{1}{2} \right\rangle$ (Figure 13.72). The tangent vector $\mathbf{t}$ and the gradient are orthogonal because

$$\mathbf{t} \cdot \nabla f(1, 1) = \langle 1, -2 \rangle \cdot \left\langle 1, \tfrac{1}{2} \right\rangle = 0.$$

b. An equation of the line tangent to the level curve at $(1, 1)$ is

$$\underbrace{f_x(1, 1)}_{1}(x - 1) + \underbrace{f_y(1, 1)}_{\frac{1}{2}}(y - 1) = 0,$$

or $y = -2x + 3$.

Related Exercises 37–44

EXAMPLE 7 Path of steepest descent Consider the paraboloid $z = f(x, y) = 4 + x^2 + 3y^2$ (Figure 13.73). Beginning at the point $(3, 4, 61)$ on the surface, find the path in the xy-plane that points in the direction of steepest descent on the surface.

SOLUTION Imagine releasing a ball at $(3, 4, 61)$ and assume that it rolls in the direction of steepest descent at all points. The projection of this path in the xy-plane points is in the direction of $-\nabla f(x, y) = \langle -2x, -6y \rangle$, which means that at the point (x, y) the line tangent to the path has slope $y'(x) = (-6y)/(-2x) = 3y/x$. Therefore, the path in the xy-plane satisfies $y'(x) = 3y/x$ and passes through the initial point $(3, 4)$. You can verify that the solution to this equation is $y = 4x^3/27$ and the projection of the path of steepest descent

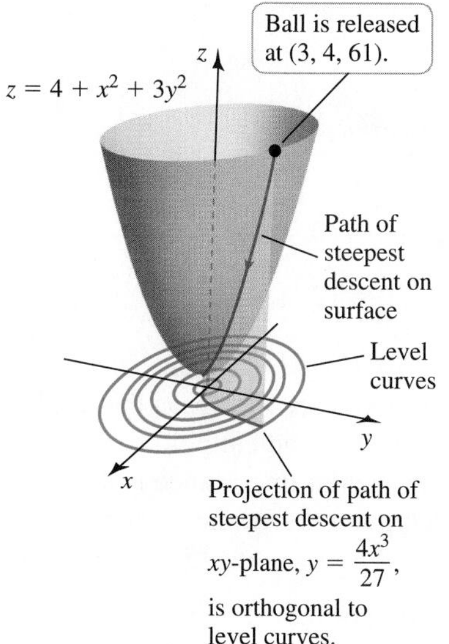
Ball is released at (3, 4, 61).
z
z = 4 + x² + 3y²
Path of steepest descent on surface
Level curves
y
x
Projection of path of steepest descent on xy-plane, y = 4x³/27, is orthogonal to level curves.

FIGURE 13.73

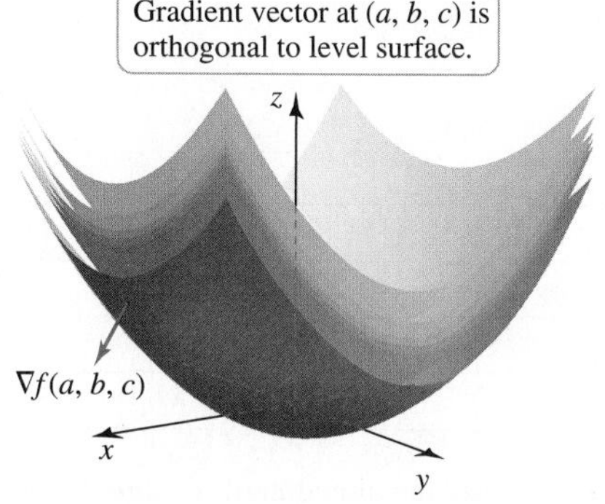
Gradient vector at (a, b, c) is orthogonal to level surface.
z
∇f(a, b, c)
x
y

FIGURE 13.74

➤ When we introduce the tangent plane in Section 13.7, we can also claim that $\nabla f(a, b, c)$ is orthogonal to the level surface that passes through (a, b, c).

in the xy-plane is the curve $y = 4x^3/27$. The descent ends at $(0, 0)$, which corresponds to the vertex of the paraboloid (Figure 13.73). At all points of the descent, the curve in the xy-plane is orthogonal to the level curves of the surface. *Related Exercises 45–48* ◀

QUICK CHECK 5 Verify that $y = 4x^3/27$ satisfies the equation $y'(x) = 3y/x$, with $y(3) = 4$. ◀

The Gradient in Three Dimensions

The directional derivative, the gradient, and the idea of a level curve extend immediately to functions of three variables of the form $w = f(x, y, z)$. The main differences are that the gradient is a vector in $\mathbf{R}^3$ and level curves become *level surfaces* (Section 13.2). Here is how the gradient looks when we step up one dimension.

The easiest way to visualize the surface $w = f(x, y, z)$ is to picture its level surfaces—the surfaces in $\mathbf{R}^3$ on which f has a constant value. The level surfaces are given by the equation $f(x, y, z) = C$, where C is a constant (Figure 13.74). The level surfaces *can* be graphed, and they may be viewed as layers of the full four-dimensional surface (like layers of an onion). With this image in mind, we now extend the concept of a gradient.

Given the function $w = f(x, y, z)$, we argue just as we did in the two-variable case and define the directional derivative. Given a unit vector $\mathbf{u} = \langle u_1, u_2, u_3 \rangle$, the directional derivative of f in the direction of $\mathbf{u}$ at the point (a, b, c) is

$$D_{\mathbf{u}}f(a, b, c) = f_x(a, b, c)u_1 + f_y(a, b, c)u_2 + f_z(a, b, c)u_3.$$

As before, we recognize this expression as a dot product of the vector $\mathbf{u}$ and the vector $\nabla f(x, y, z) = \left\langle \frac{\partial f}{\partial x}, \frac{\partial f}{\partial y}, \frac{\partial f}{\partial z} \right\rangle$, which is the *gradient* in three dimensions. Therefore, the directional derivative in the direction of $\mathbf{u}$ at the point (a, b, c) is

$$D_{\mathbf{u}}f(a, b, c) = \nabla f(a, b, c) \cdot \mathbf{u}.$$

Following the line of reasoning in the two-variable case, f has its maximum rate of *increase* in the direction of $\nabla f(a, b, c)$. The actual rate of increase is $|\nabla f(a, b, c)|$. Similarly, f has its maximum rate of *decrease* in the direction of $-\nabla f(a, b, c)$. Also, in all directions orthogonal to $\nabla f(a, b, c)$, the directional derivative at (a, b, c) is zero.

QUICK CHECK 6 Compute $\nabla f(-1, 2, 1)$ when $f(x, y, z) = xy/z$. ◀

> **DEFINITION Gradient and Directional Derivative in Three Dimensions**
>
> Let f be differentiable at the point (x, y, z). The **gradient** of f at (x, y, z) is the vector-valued function
>
> $$\begin{aligned}\nabla f(x, y, z) &= \langle f_x(x, y, z), f_y(x, y, z), f_z(x, y, z) \rangle \\ &= f_x(x, y, z)\mathbf{i} + f_y(x, y, z)\mathbf{j} + f_z(x, y, z)\mathbf{k}.\end{aligned}$$
>
> The **directional derivative** of f in the direction of the unit vector $\mathbf{u} = \langle u_1, u_2, u_3 \rangle$ at the point (a, b, c) is $D_{\mathbf{u}}f(a, b, c) = \nabla f(a, b, c) \cdot \mathbf{u}$.

EXAMPLE 8 Gradients in three dimensions Consider the function $f(x, y, z) = x^2 + 2y^2 + 4z^2 - 1$ and its level surface $f(x, y, z) = 3$.

a. Find and interpret the gradient at the points $P(2, 0, 0)$, $Q(0, \sqrt{2}, 0)$, $R(0, 0, 1)$, and $S\left(1, 1, \frac{1}{2}\right)$ on the level surface.

b. What are the actual rates of change of f in the directions of the gradients in part (a)?

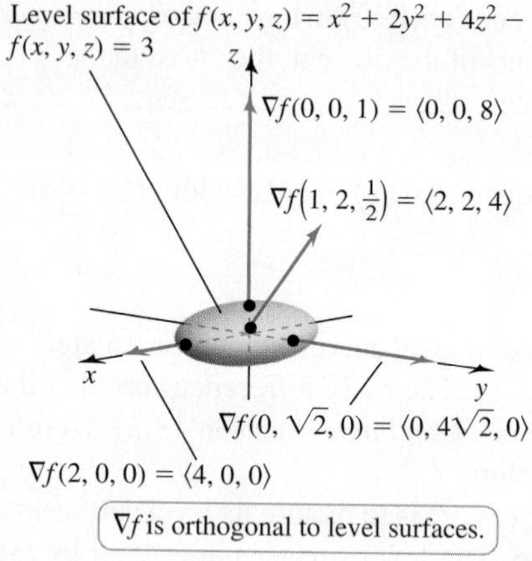

FIGURE 13.75

SOLUTION

a. The gradient is

$$\nabla f = \langle f_x, f_y, f_z\rangle = \langle 2x, 4y, 8z\rangle.$$

Evaluating the gradient at the four points we find that

$$\nabla f(2, 0, 0) = \langle 4, 0, 0\rangle, \qquad \nabla f(0, \sqrt{2}, 0) = \langle 0, 4\sqrt{2}, 0\rangle,$$
$$\nabla f(0, 0, 1) = \langle 0, 0, 8\rangle, \qquad \nabla f\left(1, 1, \tfrac{1}{2}\right) = \langle 2, 4, 4\rangle.$$

The level surface $f(x, y, z) = 3$ is an ellipsoid (Figure 13.75), which is one shell of a four-dimensional surface. The four points P, Q, R, and S are shown on the level surface with the respective gradient vectors. In each case, the gradient points in the direction that f has its maximum rate of increase. Of particular importance is the fact—to be made clear in the next section—that at each point the gradient is orthogonal to the level surface.

b. The actual rate of increase of f at (a, b, c) in the direction of the gradient is $|\nabla f(a, b, c)|$. At P, the rate of increase of f in the direction of the gradient is $|\langle 4, 0, 0\rangle| = 4$; at Q, the rate of increase is $|\langle 0, 4\sqrt{2}, 0\rangle| = 4\sqrt{2}$; at R the rate of increase is $|\langle 0, 0, 8\rangle| = 8$; and at S, the rate of increase is $|\langle 2, 4, 4\rangle| = 6$.

Related Exercises 49–56 ◀

SECTION 13.6 EXERCISES

Review Questions

1. Explain how a directional derivative is formed from the two partial derivatives f_x and f_y.

2. How do you compute the gradient of the functions $f(x, y)$ and $f(x, y, z)$?

3. Interpret the direction of the gradient vector at a point.

4. Interpret the magnitude of the gradient vector at a point.

5. Given a function f, explain the relationship between the gradient and the level curves of f.

6. The level curves of the surface $z = x^2 + y^2$ are circles in the xy-plane centered at the origin. Without computing the gradient, what is the direction of the gradient at $(1, 1)$ and $(-1, -1)$ (determined up to a scalar multiple)?

Basic Skills

7. **Directional derivatives** Consider the function $f(x, y) = 8 - x^2/2 - y^2$, whose graph is a paraboloid (see figure).

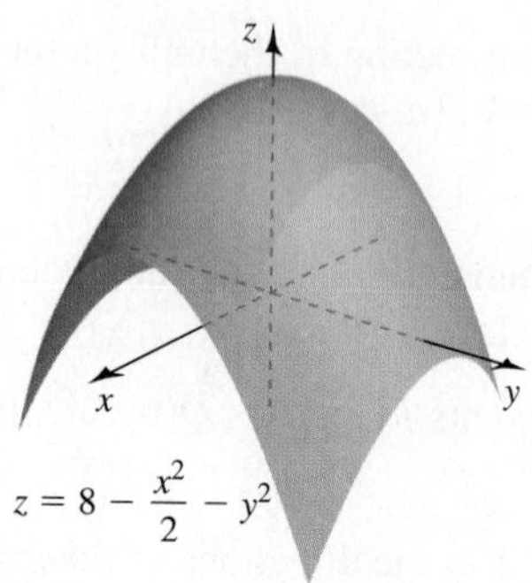

a. Fill in the table with the values of the directional derivative at the points (a, b) in the directions $\langle\cos\theta, \sin\theta\rangle$.

	$(a, b) = (2, 0)$	$(a, b) = (0, 2)$	$(a, b) = (1, 1)$
$\theta = \pi/4$			
$\theta = 3\pi/4$			
$\theta = 5\pi/4$			

b. Sketch the xy-plane and indicate the direction of the directional derivative for each of the table entries in part (a).

8. **Directional derivatives** Consider the function $f(x, y) = \sqrt{1 - \left(\frac{x}{4}\right)^2 - \left(\frac{y}{9}\right)^2}$, whose graph is the upper half of an ellipsoid (see figure).

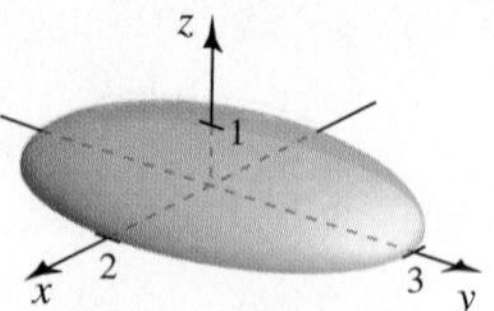

a. Fill in the table with the values of the directional derivative at the points (a, b) in the directions $\langle\cos\theta, \sin\theta\rangle$.

	$(a, b) = (1, 0)$	$(a, b) = (0, 2)$	$(a, b) = (1, 1)$
$\theta = \pi/4$			
$\theta = 3\pi/4$			
$\theta = 5\pi/4$			

b. Sketch the xy-plane and indicate the direction of the directional derivative for each of the table entries in part (a).

9–14. Computing gradients *Compute the gradient of the following functions and evaluate it at the given point P.*

9. $f(x, y) = 2 + 3x^2 - 5y^2$; $P(2, -1)$

10. $f(x, y) = 4x^2 - 2xy + y^2$; $P(-1, -5)$

11. $g(x, y) = x^2 - 4x^2y - 8xy^2$; $P(-1, 2)$

12. $p(x, y) = \sqrt{12 - 4x^2 - y^2}$; $P(-1, -1)$

13. $F(x, y) = e^{-x^2-2y^2}$; $P(-1, 2)$

14. $h(x, y) = \ln(1 + x^2 + 2y^2)$; $P(2, -3)$

15–20. Computing directional derivatives with the gradient *Compute the directional derivative of the following functions at the given point P in the direction of the given vector. Be sure to use a unit vector for the direction vector.*

15. $f(x, y) = 10 - 3x^2 + y^4/4$; $P(2, -3)$; $\left\langle \frac{\sqrt{3}}{2}, -\frac{1}{2} \right\rangle$

16. $g(x, y) = \sin \pi(2x - y)$; $P(-1, -1)$; $\left\langle \frac{5}{13}, -\frac{12}{13} \right\rangle$

17. $f(x, y) = \sqrt{4 - x^2 - 2y}$; $P(2, -2)$; $\left\langle \frac{1}{\sqrt{5}}, \frac{2}{\sqrt{5}} \right\rangle$

18. $h(x, y) = e^{-x-y}$; $P(\ln 2, \ln 3)$; $\langle 1, 1 \rangle$

19. $P(x, y) = \ln(4 + x^2 + y^2)$; $P(-1, 2)$; $\langle 2, 1 \rangle$

20. $f(x, y) = x/(x - y)$; $P(4, 1)$; $\langle -1, 2 \rangle$

21–26. Direction of steepest ascent and descent *Consider the following functions and points P.*

a. *Find the unit vectors that give the direction of steepest ascent and steepest descent at P.*

b. *Find a vector that points in a direction of no change in the function at P.*

21. $f(x, y) = x^2 - 4y^2 - 9$; $P(1, -2)$

22. $f(x, y) = 6x^2 + 4xy - 3y^2$; $P(6, -1)$

23. $f(x, y) = x^4 - x^2y + y^2 + 6$; $P(-1, 1)$

24. $p(x, y) = \sqrt{20 + x^2 + 2xy - y^2}$; $P(1, 2)$

25. $F(x, y) = e^{-x^2/2-y^2/2}$; $P(-1, 1)$

26. $f(x, y) = 2\sin(2x - 3y)$; $P(0, \pi)$

T **27–32. Interpreting directional derivatives** *A function f and a point P are given. Let θ correspond to the direction of the directional derivative.*

a. *Find the gradient and evaluate it at P.*

b. *Find the angles θ (with respect to the positive x-axis) associated with the directions of maximum increase, maximum decrease, and zero change.*

c. *Write the directional derivative at P as a function of θ; call this function g(θ).*

d. *Find the value of θ that maximizes g(θ) and find the maximum value.*

e. *Verify that the value of θ that maximizes g corresponds to the direction of the gradient. Verify that the maximum value of g equals the magnitude of the gradient.*

27. $f(x, y) = 10 - 2x^2 - 3y^2$; $P(3, 2)$

28. $f(x, y) = 8 + x^2 + 3y^2$; $P(-3, -1)$

29. $f(x, y) = \sqrt{2 + x^2 + y^2}$; $P(\sqrt{3}, 1)$

30. $f(x, y) = \sqrt{12 - x^2 - y^2}$; $P(-1, -1/\sqrt{3})$

31. $f(x, y) = e^{-x^2-2y^2}$; $P(-1, 0)$

32. $f(x, y) = \ln(1 + 2x^2 + 3y^2)$; $P\left(\frac{3}{4}, -\sqrt{3}\right)$

33–36. Directions of change *Consider the following functions f and points P. Sketch the xy-plane showing P and the level curve through P. Indicate (as in Figure 13.70) the directions of maximum increase, maximum decrease, and no change for f.*

33. $f(x, y) = 8 + 4x^2 + 2y^2$; $P(2, -4)$

34. $f(x, y) = -4 + 6x^2 + 3y^2$; $P(-1, -2)$

35. $f(x, y) = x^2 + xy + y^2 + 7$; $P(-3, 3)$

36. $f(x, y) = \tan(2x + 2y)$; $P(\pi/16, \pi/16)$

37–40. Level curves *Consider the paraboloid* $f(x, y) = 16 - x^2/4 - y^2/16$ *and the point P on the given level curve of f. Compute the slope of the line tangent to the level curve at P and verify that the tangent line is orthogonal to the gradient at that point.*

37. $f(x, y) = 0$; $P(0, 16)$

38. $f(x, y) = 0$; $P(8, 0)$

39. $f(x, y) = 12$; $P(4, 0)$

40. $f(x, y) = 12$; $P(2\sqrt{3}, 4)$

41–44. Level curves *Consider the ellipsoid* $f(x, y) = \sqrt{1 - \frac{x^2}{4} - \frac{y^2}{16}}$ *and the point P on the given level curve of f. Compute the slope of the line tangent to the level curve at P and verify that the tangent line is orthogonal to the gradient at that point.*

41. $f(x, y) = \sqrt{3}/2$; $P(1/2, \sqrt{3})$

42. $f(x, y) = 1/\sqrt{2}$; $P(0, \sqrt{8})$

43. $f(x, y) = 1/\sqrt{2}$; $P(\sqrt{2}, 0)$

44. $f(x, y) = 1/\sqrt{2}$; $P(1, 2)$

45–48. Path of steepest descent *Consider each of the following surfaces and the point P on the surface.*

a. *Find the gradient of f.*

b. *Let C′ be the path of steepest descent on the surface beginning at P and let C be the projection of C′ on the xy-plane. Find an equation of C in the xy-plane.*

45. $f(x, y) = 4 + x$ (a plane); $P(4, 4, 8)$

46. $f(x, y) = y + x$ (a plane); $P(2, 2, 4)$

47. $f(x, y) = 4 - x^2 - 2y^2$; $P(1, 1, 1)$

48. $f(x, y) = y + x^{-1}$; $P(1, 2, 3)$

49–56. Gradients in three dimensions *Consider the following functions f, points P, and unit vectors* **u**.

a. *Compute the gradient of f and evaluate it at P.*

b. *Find the unit vector in the direction of maximum increase of f at P.*

c. *Find the rate of change of the function in the direction of maximum increase at P.*

d. *Find the directional derivative at P in the direction of the given vector.*

49. $f(x, y, z) = x^2 + 2y^2 + 4z^2 + 10$; $P(1, 0, 4)$; $\langle \frac{1}{\sqrt{2}}, 0, \frac{1}{\sqrt{2}} \rangle$

50. $f(x, y, z) = 4 - x^2 + 3y^2 + z^2/2$; $P(0, 2, -1)$; $\langle 0, \frac{1}{\sqrt{2}}, -\frac{1}{\sqrt{2}} \rangle$

51. $f(x, y, z) = 1 + 4xyz$; $P(1, -1, -1)$; $\langle \frac{1}{\sqrt{3}}, \frac{1}{\sqrt{3}}, -\frac{1}{\sqrt{3}} \rangle$

52. $f(x, y, z) = xy + yz + xz + 4$; $P(2, -2, 1)$; $\langle 0, -\frac{1}{\sqrt{2}}, -\frac{1}{\sqrt{2}} \rangle$

53. $f(x, y, z) = 1 + \sin(x + 2y - z)$; $P\left(\frac{\pi}{6}, \frac{\pi}{6}, -\frac{\pi}{6}\right)$; $\langle \frac{1}{3}, \frac{2}{3}, \frac{2}{3} \rangle$

54. $f(x, y, z) = e^{xyz-1}$; $P(0, 1, -1)$; $\langle -\frac{2}{3}, \frac{2}{3}, -\frac{1}{3} \rangle$

55. $f(x, y, z) = \ln(1 + x^2 + y^2 + z^2)$; $P(1, 1, -1)$; $\langle \frac{2}{3}, \frac{2}{3}, -\frac{1}{3} \rangle$

56. $f(x, y, z) = \dfrac{x - z}{y - z}$; $P(3, 2, -1)$; $\langle \frac{1}{3}, \frac{2}{3}, -\frac{2}{3} \rangle$

Further Explorations

57. **Explain why or why not** Determine whether the following statements are true and give an explanation or counterexample.
   a. If $f(x, y) = x^2 + y^2 - 10$, then $\nabla f(x, y) = 2x + 2y$.
   b. Because the gradient gives the direction of maximum increase of a function, the gradient is always positive.
   c. The gradient of $f(x, y, z) = 1 + xyz$ has four components.
   d. If $f(x, y, z) = 4$, then $\nabla f = \mathbf{0}$.

58. **Gradient of a composite function** Consider the function $F(x, y, z) = e^{xyz}$.
   a. Write F as a composite function $f \circ g$, where f is a function of one variable and g is a function of three variables.
   b. Relate ∇F to ∇g.

59–63. Directions of zero change *Find the directions in the xy-plane in which the following functions have zero change at the given point. Express the directions in terms of unit vectors.*

59. $f(x, y) = 12 - 4x^2 - y^2$; $P(1, 2, 4)$

60. $f(x, y) = x^2 - 4y^2 - 8$; $P(4, 1, 4)$

61. $f(x, y) = \sqrt{3 + 2x^2 + y^2}$; $P(1, -2, 3)$

62. $f(x, y) = e^{1-xy}$; $P(1, 0, e)$

63. **Steepest ascent on a plane** Suppose a long sloping hillside is described by the plane $z = ax + by + c$, where a, b, and c are constants. Find the path in the xy-plane, beginning at (x_0, y_0), that corresponds to the path of steepest ascent on the hillside.

64. **Gradient of a distance function** Let (a, b) be a fixed point in $\mathbf{R}^2$ and let $d = f(x, y)$ be the distance between (a, b) and an arbitrary point (x, y).
   a. Show that the graph of f is a cone.
   b. Show that the gradient of f at any point other than (a, b) is a unit vector.
   c. Interpret the direction and magnitude of ∇f.

65–68. Looking ahead—tangent planes *Consider the following surfaces $f(x, y, z) = 0$, which may be regarded as a level surface of the function $w = f(x, y, z)$. A point $P(a, b, c)$ on the surface is also given.*
   a. Find the (three-dimensional) gradient of f and evaluate it at P.
   b. The heads of all vectors orthogonal to the gradient with their tails at P form a plane. Find an equation of that plane (soon to be called the tangent plane *to the surface at f).*

65. $f(x, y, z) = x^2 + y^2 + z^2 - 3 = 0$; $P(1, 1, 1)$

66. $f(x, y, z) = 8 - xyz = 0$; $P(2, 2, 2)$

67. $f(x, y, z) = e^{x+y-z} - 1 = 0$; $P(1, 1, 2)$

68. $f(x, y, z) = xy + xz - yz - 1$; $P(1, 1, 1)$

Applications

T 69. **A traveling wave** A snapshot (frozen in time) of a water wave is described by the function $z = 1 + \sin(x - y)$, where z gives the height of the wave relative to a reference point and (x, y) are coordinates in a horizontal plane.
   a. Use a graphing utility to graph $z = 1 + \sin(x - y)$.
   b. The crests and the troughs of the waves are aligned in the direction in which the height function has zero change. Find the direction in which the crests and troughs are aligned.
   c. If you were surfing on this wave and wanted the steepest descent from a crest to a trough, in which direction would you point your surfboard (given in terms of a unit vector in the xy-plane)?
   d. Check that your answers to parts (b) and (c) are consistent with the graph of part (a).

70. **Traveling waves in general** Generalize Exercise 69 by considering a wave described by the function $z = A + \sin(ax - by)$, where a, b, and A are real numbers.
   a. Find the direction in which the crests and troughs of the wave are aligned. Express your answer as a unit vector in terms of a and b.
   b. Find the surfer's direction—that is, the direction of steepest descent from a crest to a trough. Express your answer as a unit vector in terms of a and b.

71–73. Potential functions *Potential functions arise frequently in physics and engineering. A potential function has the property that a field of interest (for example, an electric field, a gravitational field, or a velocity field) is the gradient of the potential (or sometimes the negative of the gradient of the potential). (Potential functions are considered in depth in Chapter 15.)*

71. **Electric potential due to a point charge** The electric field due to a point charge of strength Q at the origin has a potential function $V = kQ/r$, where $r^2 = x^2 + y^2 + z^2$ is the square of the distance between a variable point $P(x, y, z)$ and the charge and $k > 0$ is a physical constant. The electric field is given by $\mathbf{E} = -\nabla V$, where ∇V is the gradient in three dimensions.
   a. Show that the three-dimensional electric field due to a point charge is given by
   $$\mathbf{E}(x, y, z) = kQ\left\langle \frac{x}{r^3}, \frac{y}{r^3}, \frac{z}{r^3} \right\rangle.$$
   b. Show that the electric field at a point has a magnitude $|\mathbf{E}| = kQ/r^2$. Explain why this relationship is called an inverse square law.

72. Gravitational potential The gravitational potential associated with two objects of mass M and m is $V = -GMm/r$, where G is the gravitational constant. If one of the objects is at the origin and the other object is at $P(x, y, z)$, then $r^2 = x^2 + y^2 + z^2$ is the square of the distance between the objects. The gravitational field at a point is given by $\mathbf{F} = -\nabla V$, where ∇V is the gradient in three dimensions. Show that the force has a magnitude $|\mathbf{F}| = GMm/r^2$. Explain why this relationship is called an inverse square law.

73. Velocity potential In two dimensions, the motion of an ideal fluid (an incompressible and irrotational fluid) is governed by a velocity potential φ. The velocity components of the fluid, u in the x-direction and v in the y-direction, are given by $\langle u, v \rangle = \nabla\varphi$. Find the velocity components associated with the velocity potential $\varphi(x, y) = \sin \pi x \sin 2\pi y$.

Additional Exercises

74. Gradients for planes Prove that for the plane described by $f(x, y) = Ax + By$, where A and B are nonzero constants, the gradient is constant (independent of (x, y)). Interpret this result.

75. Rules for gradients Use the definition of the gradient (in two or three dimensions), assume that f and g are differentiable functions on $\mathbf{R}^2$ or $\mathbf{R}^3$, and let c be a constant. Prove the following gradient rules.

a. Constants Rule: $\nabla(cf) = c\nabla f$

b. Sum Rule: $\nabla(f + g) = \nabla f + \nabla g$

c. Product Rule: $\nabla(fg) = (\nabla f)g + f\nabla g$

d. Quotient Rule: $\nabla\left(\dfrac{f}{g}\right) = \dfrac{g\nabla f - f\nabla g}{g^2}$

e. Chain Rule: $\nabla(f \circ g) = f'(g)\nabla g$, where f is a function of one variable

76–81. Using gradient rules *Use the gradient rules of Exercise 75 to find the gradient of the following functions.*

76. $f(x, y) = xy \cos(xy)$

77. $f(x, y) = \dfrac{x + y}{x^2 + y^2}$

78. $f(x, y) = \ln(1 + x^2 + y^2)$

79. $f(x, y, z) = \sqrt{25 - x^2 - y^2 - z^2}$

80. $f(x, y, z) = (x + y + z)\, e^{xyz}$

81. $f(x, y, z) = \dfrac{x + yz}{y + xz}$

QUICK CHECK ANSWERS

1. If $\theta = 0$ then

$$D_{\mathbf{u}}f(a, b) = \lim_{h\to 0} \frac{f(a + h\cos\theta, b + h\sin\theta) - f(a, b)}{h} = \lim_{h\to 0} \frac{f(a + h, b) - f(a, b)}{h} = f_x.$$

Similarly, when $\theta = \pi/2$, $\mathbf{u} = \langle 0, 1 \rangle$ is parallel to the y-axis, and the partial derivative f_y results. **2.** The vector from (a, b) to $(a + \Delta s u_1, b + \Delta s u_2)$ is $\langle \Delta s u_1, \Delta s u_2 \rangle = \Delta s \langle u_1, u_2 \rangle = \Delta s \mathbf{u}$. Its length is $|\Delta s \mathbf{u}| = \Delta s |\mathbf{u}| = \Delta s$. Therefore, s measures arc length. **3.** Reversing (negating) the direction vector negates the directional derivative. So, the respective values are -2.47 and 0.98. **4.** The gradient is $\langle 2x, 2y \rangle$, which, evaluated at (a, a), is $\langle 2a, 2a \rangle$. Taking the dot product of the gradient and the vector $\langle -1, 1 \rangle$ (a vector parallel to a line of slope -1), we see that $\langle 2a, 2a \rangle \cdot \langle -1, 1 \rangle = 0$. **6.** $\langle 2, -1, 2 \rangle$ ◄

13.7 Tangent Planes and Linear Approximation

In Section 4.5, we saw that if we zoom in on a point on a smooth curve (one described by a differentiable function), the curve looks more and more like the tangent line at that point. Once we have the tangent line at a point, it can be used to approximate function values and to estimate changes in the dependent variable. In this section, an analogous story is developed, elevated by one dimension. Now we see that differentiability at a point (as discussed in Section 13.4) implies the existence of a tangent *plane* at that point (Figure 13.76).

Consider a smooth surface described by a differentiable function f and focus on a single point on the surface. As we zoom in on that point (Figure 13.77), the surface appears more and more like a plane. The first step is to define this plane carefully; it is called the *tangent plane*. Once we have the tangent plane, we can use it to approximate function values and to estimate changes in the dependent variable.

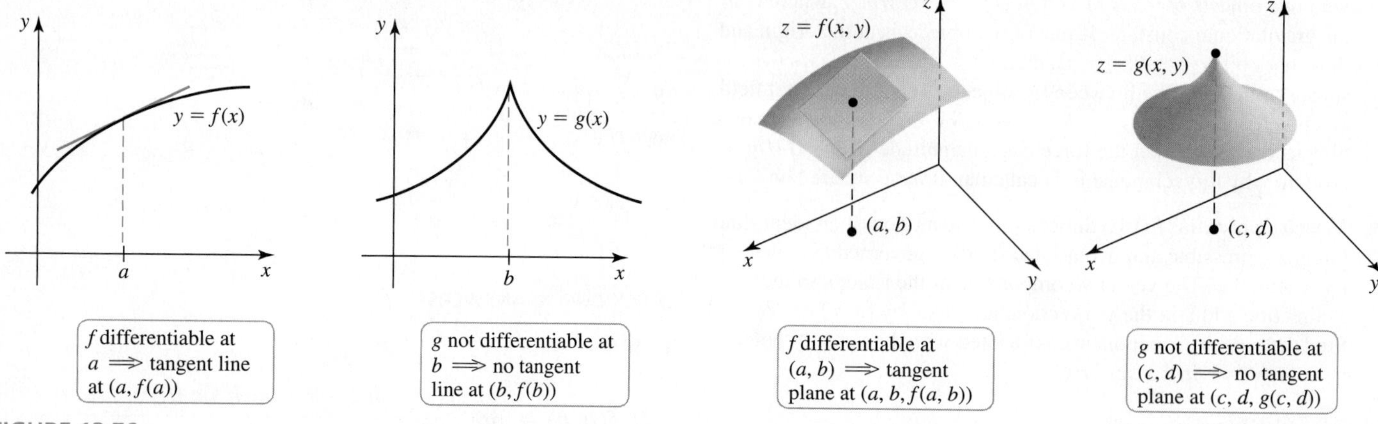

FIGURE 13.76

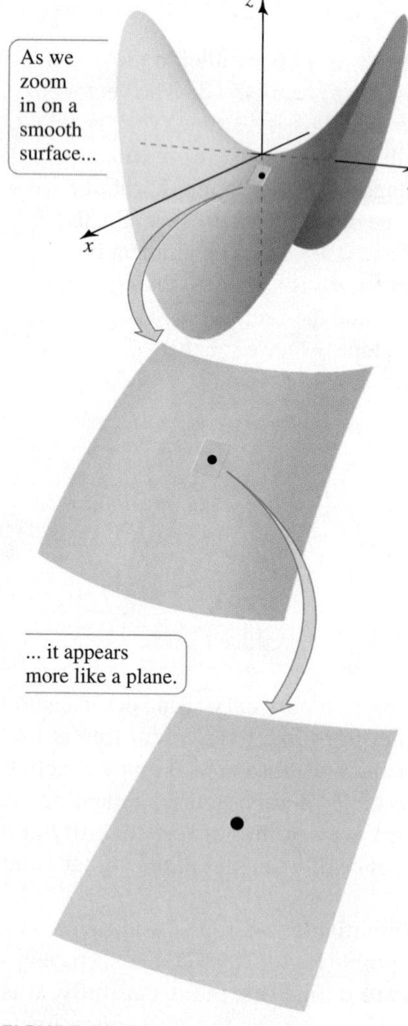

FIGURE 13.77

Tangent Planes

Recall that a surface in $\mathbf{R}^3$ may be defined in at least two different ways:

- **Explicitly** in the form $z = f(x, y)$
- **Implicitly** in the form $F(x, y, z) = 0$

It is easiest to begin by considering a surface defined implicitly by $F(x, y, z) = 0$, where F is differentiable at a particular point. Such a surface may be viewed as a level surface of a function $w = F(x, y, z)$; it is the level surface for $w = 0$.

QUICK CHECK 1 Write the function $z = xy + x - y$ in the form $F(x, y, z) = 0$.

Tangent Planes for $F(x, y, z) = 0$ To find an equation of the tangent plane, consider a smooth curve $C: \mathbf{r} = \langle x(t), y(t), z(t) \rangle$ that lies on the surface $F(x, y, z) = 0$ (Figure 13.78a). Because the points of C lie on the surface, we have $F(x(t), y(t), z(t)) = 0$. Differentiating both sides of this equation with respect to t, a useful relationship emerges. The derivative of the right side is 0. The Chain Rule applied to the left side yields

$$\begin{aligned}\frac{d}{dt}[F(x(t), y(t), z(t))] &= \frac{\partial F}{\partial x}\frac{dx}{dt} + \frac{\partial F}{\partial y}\frac{dy}{dt} + \frac{\partial F}{\partial z}\frac{dz}{dt} \\ &= \underbrace{\left\langle \frac{\partial F}{\partial x}, \frac{\partial F}{\partial y}, \frac{\partial F}{\partial z} \right\rangle}_{\nabla F(x,y,z)} \cdot \underbrace{\left\langle \frac{dx}{dt}, \frac{dy}{dt}, \frac{dz}{dt} \right\rangle}_{\mathbf{r}'(t)} \\ &= \nabla F(x, y, z) \cdot \mathbf{r}'(t).\end{aligned}$$

Therefore, $\nabla F(x, y, z) \cdot \mathbf{r}'(t) = 0$ and at any point on the curve, the tangent vector $\mathbf{r}'(t)$ is orthogonal to the gradient.

Now, fix a point $P_0(a, b, c)$ on the surface, assume that $\nabla F(a, b, c) \neq \mathbf{0}$, and let C be any smooth curve on the surface passing through P_0. We have shown that the vector tangent to C is orthogonal to $\nabla F(a, b, c)$ at P_0. Because this argument applies to *all* smooth curves on the surface passing through P_0, the tangent vectors for all these curves (with their tails at P_0) are orthogonal to $\nabla F(a, b, c)$, and thus they all lie in the same plane (Figure 13.78b). This plane is called the *tangent plane* at P_0. We can easily find an equation of the tangent plane because we know both a point on the plane $P_0(a, b, c)$ and a normal vector $\nabla F(a, b, c)$; an equation is simply

$$\nabla F(a, b, c) \cdot \langle x - a, y - b, z - c \rangle = 0.$$

➤ Recall that an equation of the plane passing though (a, b, c) with a normal vector $\mathbf{n} = \langle n_1, n_2, n_3 \rangle$ is $n_1(x - a) + n_2(y - b) + n_3(z - c) = 0$.

➤ If $\mathbf{r}$ is a position vector corresponding to an arbitrary point on the tangent plane and $\mathbf{r}_0$ is a position vector corresponding to a fixed point (a, b, c) on the plane, then an equation of the tangent plane may be written concisely as

$$\nabla F(a, b, c) \cdot (\mathbf{r} - \mathbf{r}_0) = 0.$$

Notice the analogy with tangent lines and level curves (Section 13.6). An equation of the line tangent to $f(x, y) = 0$ at (a, b) is

$$\nabla f(a, b) \cdot \langle x - a, y - b \rangle = 0.$$

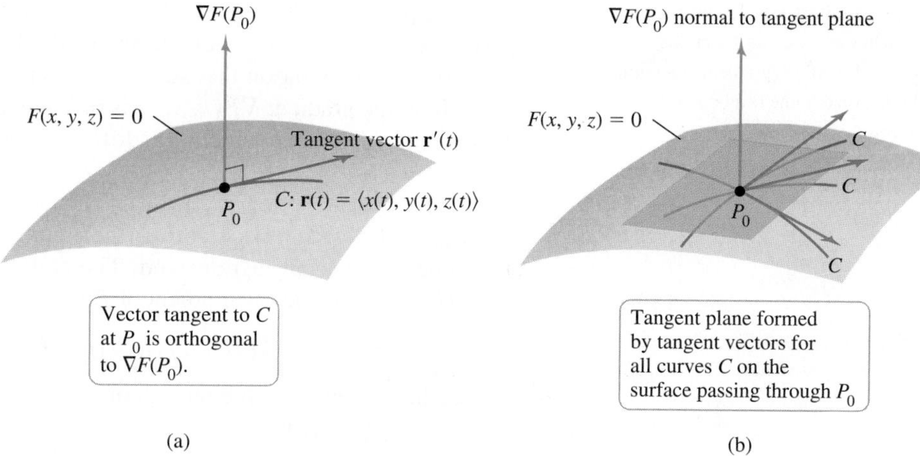

FIGURE 13.78

Equation of the Tangent Plane for $F(x, y, z) = 0$

Let F be differentiable at the point $P_0(a, b, c)$ with $\nabla F(a, b, c) \neq \mathbf{0}$. The plane tangent to the surface $F(x, y, z) = 0$ at P_0, called the **tangent plane**, is the plane passing through P_0 orthogonal to $\nabla F(a, b, c)$. An equation of the tangent plane is

$$F_x(a, b, c)(x - a) + F_y(a, b, c)(y - b) + F_z(a, b, c)(z - c) = 0.$$

EXAMPLE 1 **Equation of a tangent plane** Consider the ellipsoid $F(x, y, z) = \frac{x^2}{9} + \frac{y^2}{25} + z^2 - 1 = 0.$

a. Find the equation of the plane tangent to the ellipsoid at $\left(0, 4, \frac{3}{5}\right)$.

b. At what points on the ellipsoid is the tangent plane horizontal?

SOLUTION

a. Notice that we have written the equation of the ellipsoid in the implicit form $F(x, y, z) = 0$. The gradient of F is $\nabla F(x, y, z) = \left\langle \frac{2x}{9}, \frac{2y}{25}, 2z \right\rangle$. Evaluated at $\left(0, 4, \frac{3}{5}\right)$, we have

$$\nabla F\left(0, 4, \frac{3}{5}\right) = \left\langle 0, \frac{8}{25}, \frac{6}{5} \right\rangle.$$

An equation of the tangent plane at this point is

$$0 \cdot (x - 0) + \frac{8}{25}(y - 4) + \frac{6}{5}\left(z - \frac{3}{5}\right) = 0,$$

or $8y + 30z = 50$. The equation does not involve x, so the tangent plane is parallel to the x-axis (Figure 13.79).

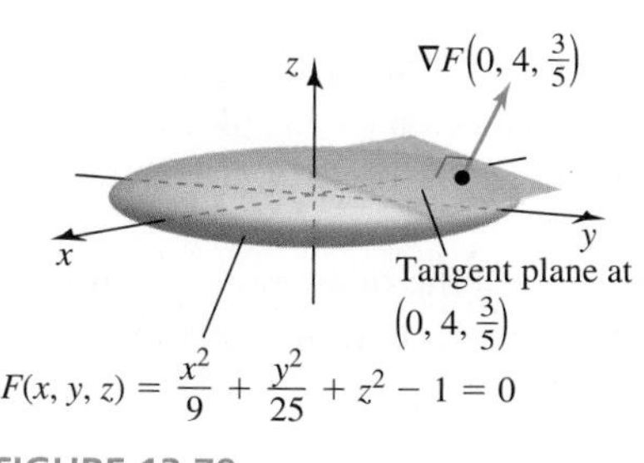

FIGURE 13.79

b. A horizontal plane has a normal vector of the form $\langle 0, 0, c \rangle$, where $c \neq 0$. A plane tangent to the ellipsoid has a normal vector $\nabla F(x, y, z) = \left\langle \frac{2x}{9}, \frac{2y}{25}, 2z \right\rangle$. Therefore, the ellipsoid has a horizontal tangent plane when $F_x = \frac{2x}{9} = 0$ and $F_y = \frac{2y}{25} = 0$, or when $x = 0$ and $y = 0$. Substituting these values into the original equation for the ellipsoid, we find that horizontal planes occur at $(0, 0, 1)$ and $(0, 0, -1)$.

Related Exercises 9–14 ◄

➤ This result extends Theorem 13.12, which states that for functions $f(x, y) = 0$, the gradient at a point is orthogonal to the level curve that passes through that point.

The preceding discussion allows us to confirm a claim made in Section 13.6. The surface $F(x, y, z) = 0$ is a level surface of the function $w = F(x, y, z)$ (corresponding to $w = 0$). At any point on that surface, the tangent plane has a normal vector $\nabla F(x, y, z)$. Therefore, the gradient $\nabla F(x, y, z)$ is orthogonal to the level surface $F(x, y, z) = 0$ at all points of the domain at which F is differentiable.

Tangent Planes for $z = f(x, y)$ Surfaces in $\mathbf{R}^3$ are often defined explicitly in the form $z = f(x, y)$. In this situation, the equation of the tangent plane is a special case of the general equation just derived. The equation $z = f(x, y)$ is written as $F(x, y, z) = z - f(x, y) = 0$, and the gradient of F at the point $(a, b, f(a, b))$ is

➤ To be clear, when $F(x, y, z) = z - f(x, y)$, we have $F_x = -f_x$, $F_y = -f_y$, and $F_z = 1$.

$$\nabla F(a, b, f(a, b)) = \langle -f_x(a, b), -f_y(a, b), 1 \rangle.$$

Proceeding as before, an equation of the plane tangent to the surface $z = f(x, y)$ at the point $(a, b, f(a, b))$ is

$$-f_x(a, b)(x - a) - f_y(a, b)(y - b) + 1(z - f(a, b)) = 0.$$

After some rearranging, we obtain an equation of the tangent plane.

Tangent Plane for $z = f(x, y)$

Let f be differentiable at the point (a, b). An equation of the plane tangent to the surface $z = f(x, y)$ at the point $(a, b, f(a, b))$ is

$$z = f_x(a, b)(x - a) + f_y(a, b)(y - b) + f(a, b).$$

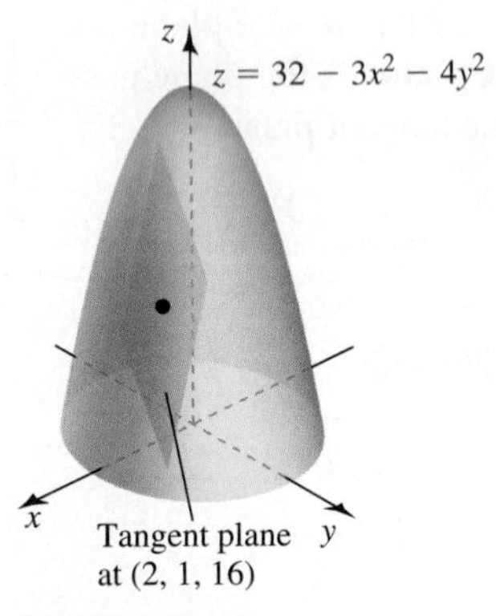

FIGURE 13.80

EXAMPLE 2 Tangent plane for $z = f(x, y)$ Find an equation of the plane tangent to the paraboloid $z = f(x, y) = 32 - 3x^2 - 4y^2$ at $(2, 1, 16)$.

SOLUTION The partial derivatives are $f_x = -6x$ and $f_y = -8y$. Evaluating the partial derivatives at $(2, 1)$, we have $f_x(2, 1) = -12$ and $f_y(2, 1) = -8$. Therefore, an equation of the tangent plane (Figure 13.80) is

$$\begin{aligned} z &= f_x(a, b)(x - a) + f_y(a, b)(y - b) + f(a, b) \\ &= -12(x - 2) - 8(y - 1) + 16 \\ &= -12x - 8y + 48. \end{aligned}$$

Related Exercises 15–20 ◄

Linear Approximation

With a function of the form $y = f(x)$, the tangent line at a point often gives good approximations to the function near that point. A straightforward extension of this idea applies to approximating functions of two variables with tangent planes. As before, the method is called *linear approximation*.

➤ The term *linear approximation* applies in both $\mathbf{R}^2$ and $\mathbf{R}^3$ because lines in $\mathbf{R}^2$ and planes in $\mathbf{R}^3$ are described by linear functions of the independent variables. In both cases, we call the linear approximation L.

Figure 13.81 shows the details of linear approximation in the one- and two-variable cases. In the one-variable case (Section 4.5), if f is differentiable at a, the equation of the line tangent to the curve $y = f(x)$ at the point $(a, f(a))$ is

$$L(x) = f(a) + f'(a)(x - a).$$

The tangent line gives an approximation to the function. At points near a, we have $f(x) \approx L(x)$.

The two-variable case is analogous. If f is differentiable at (a, b), an equation of the plane tangent to the surface $z = f(x, y)$ at the point $(a, b, f(a, b))$ is

$$L(x, y) = f_x(a, b)(x - a) + f_y(a, b)(y - b) + f(a, b).$$

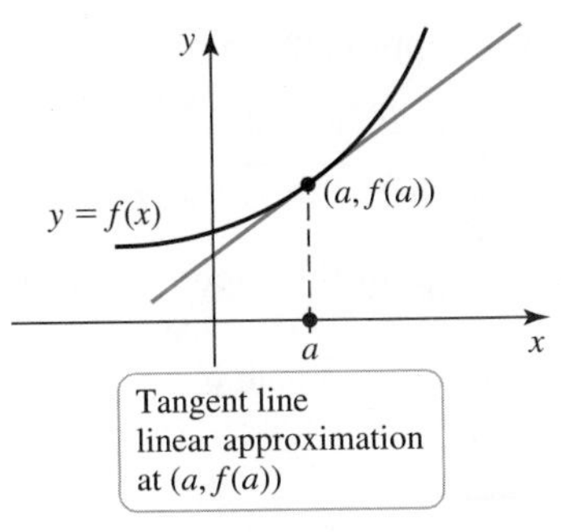

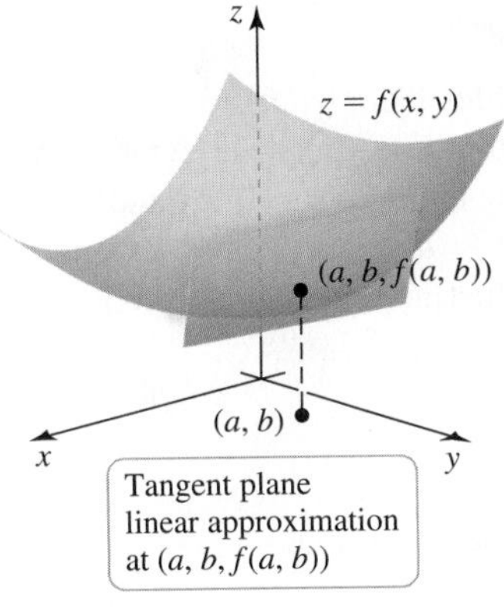

FIGURE 13.81

This tangent plane is the linear approximation to f at (a, b). At points near (a, b), we have $f(x, y) \approx L(x, y)$.

DEFINITION Linear Approximation

Let f be differentiable at (a, b). The linear approximation to the surface $z = f(x, y)$ at the point $(a, b, f(a, b))$ is the tangent plane at that point, given by the equation

$$L(x, y) = f_x(a, b)(x - a) + f_y(a, b)(y - b) + f(a, b).$$

➤ The approximation $f(x, y) \approx L(x, y)$ is made precise by the definition of differentiability (Section 13.4). If f is differentiable at (a, b), then $|f(x, y) - L(x, y)| \to 0$ as $x \to a$ and $y \to b$.

EXAMPLE 3 Linear approximation Let $f(x, y) = \dfrac{5}{x^2 + y^2}$.

a. Find the linear approximation to the function at the point $(-1, 2, 1)$.

b. Use the linear approximation to estimate the value of $f(-1.05, 2.1)$.

SOLUTION

a. The partial derivatives of f are

$$f_x = -\frac{10x}{(x^2 + y^2)^2} \quad \text{and} \quad f_y = -\frac{10y}{(x^2 + y^2)^2}.$$

Evaluated at $(-1, 2)$, we have $f_x(-1, 2) = \frac{2}{5} = 0.4$ and $f_y(-1, 2) = -\frac{4}{5} = -0.8$. Therefore, the linear approximation to the function at $(-1, 2, 1)$ is

$$\begin{aligned} L(x, y) &= f_x(-1, 2)(x - (-1)) + f_y(-1, 2)(y - 2) + f(-1, 2) \\ &= 0.4(x + 1) - 0.8(y - 2) + 1 \\ &= 0.4x - 0.8y + 3. \end{aligned}$$

The surface and the tangent plane are shown in Figure 13.82.

b. The value of the function at the point $(-1.05, 2.1)$ is approximated by the value of the linear approximation at that point, which is

$$L(-1.05, 2.1) = 0.4(-1.05) - 0.8(2.1) + 3 = 0.90.$$

➤ Relative error =

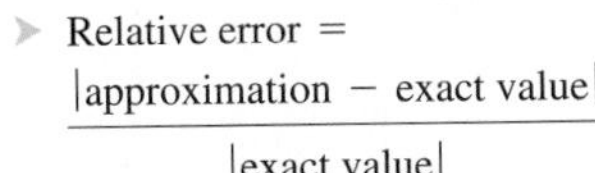

In this case, we can easily evaluate $f(-1.05, 2.1) \approx 0.907$ and compare the linear approximation with the exact value; the approximation has a relative error of about 0.8%.

Related Exercises 21–26 ◀

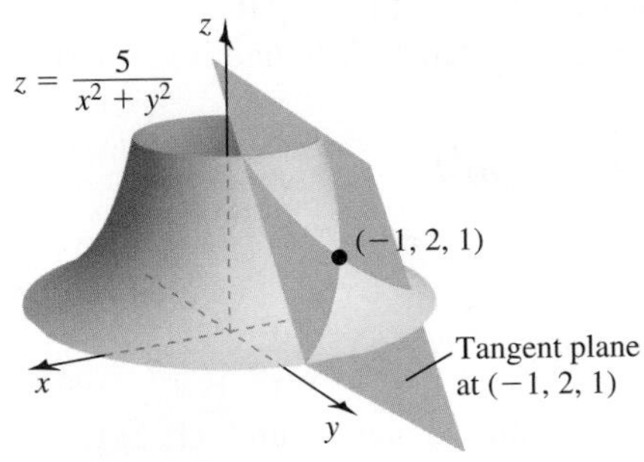

FIGURE 13.82

QUICK CHECK 2 Look at the graph of the surface in Example 3 (Figure 13.82) and explain why $f_x(-1, 2) > 0$ and $f_y(-1, 2) < 0$. ◀

Differentials and Change

Recall that for a function of the form $y = f(x)$, if the independent variable changes from x to $x + dx$, the corresponding change Δy in the dependent variable is approximated by the differential $dy = f'(x)\,dx$, which is the change in the linear approximation. Therefore, $\Delta y \approx dy$, with the approximation improving as dx approaches 0.

For functions of the form $z = f(x, y)$, we start with the linear approximation to the surface

$$f(x, y) \approx L(x, y) = f_x(a, b)(x - a) + f_y(a, b)(y - b) + f(a, b).$$

The exact change in the function between the points (a, b) and (x, y) is

$$\Delta z = f(x, y) - f(a, b).$$

Replacing $f(x, y)$ by its linear approximation, the change Δz is approximated by

$$\Delta z \approx \underbrace{L(x, y) - f(a, b)}_{dz} = f_x(a, b)\underbrace{(x - a)}_{dx} + f_y(a, b)\underbrace{(y - b)}_{dy}.$$

The change in the x-coordinate is $dx = x - a$ and the change in the y-coordinate is $dy = y - b$ (Figure 13.83). As before, we let the differential dz denote the change in the linear approximation. Therefore, the approximate change in the z-coordinate is

➤ Alternative notation for the differential at (a, b) is $dz|_{(a,b)}$ or $df|_{(a,b)}$.

$$\Delta z \approx dz = \underbrace{f_x(a, b)\, dx}_{\substack{\text{change in } z \text{ due} \\ \text{to change in } x}} + \underbrace{f_y(a, b)\, dy}_{\substack{\text{change in } z \text{ due} \\ \text{to change in } y}}.$$

This expression says that if we move the independent variables from (a, b) to $(a + dx, b + dy)$, the corresponding change in the dependent variable Δz has two contributions—one due to the change in x and one due to the change in y. If dx and dy are small in magnitude, then so is Δz. The approximation $\Delta z \approx dz$ improves as dx and dy approach 0. The relationships among the differentials are illustrated in Figure 13.83.

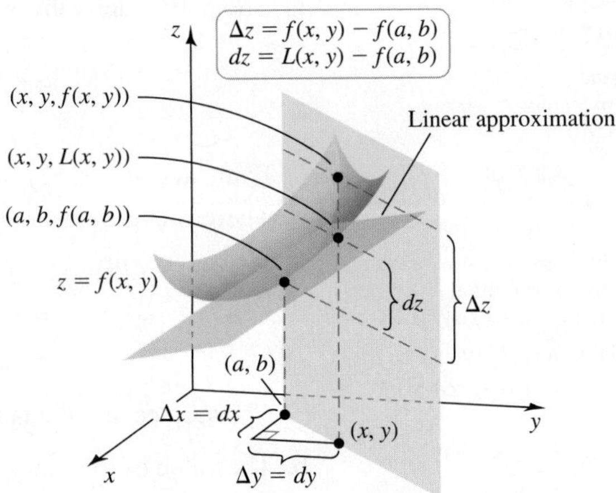

FIGURE 13.83

QUICK CHECK 3 Explain why, if $dx = 0$ or $dy = 0$ in the change formula for Δz, the result is the change formula for one variable. ◂

> **DEFINITION The differential dz**
>
> Let f be differentiable at the point (a, b). The change in $z = f(x, y)$ as the independent variables change from (a, b) to $(a + dx, b + dy)$ is denoted Δz and is approximated by the differential dz:
>
> $$\Delta z \approx dz = f_x(a, b)\, dx + f_y(a, b)\, dy$$

EXAMPLE 4 Approximating function change Let $z = f(x, y) = \dfrac{5}{x^2 + y^2}$. Approximate the change in z when the independent variables change from $(-1, 2)$ to $(-0.93, 1.94)$.

SOLUTION If the independent variables change from $(-1, 2)$ to $(-0.93, 1.94)$, then $dx = 0.07$ (an increase) and $dy = -0.06$ (a decrease). Using the values of the partial derivatives evaluated in Example 3, the corresponding change in z is approximately

$$\begin{aligned} dz &= f_x(-1, 2)\,dx + f_y(-1, 2)\,dy \\ &= 0.4(0.07) + (-0.8)(-0.06) \\ &= 0.076. \end{aligned}$$

Again, we can check the accuracy of the approximation. The actual change is $f(-0.93, 1.94) - f(-1, 2) \approx 0.080$, so the approximation has a 5% error.

Related Exercises 27–30 ◀

EXAMPLE 5 **Body mass index** The body mass index (BMI) for an adult human is given by the function $B(w, h) = w/h^2$, where w is weight measured in kilograms and h is height measured in meters.

a. Use differentials to approximate the change in the BMI when weight increases from 55 to 56.5 kg and height increases from 1.65 to 1.66 m.

b. Which produces a greater *percentage* change in the BMI, a 1% change in the weight (at a constant height) or a 1% change in the height (at a constant weight)?

SOLUTION

a. The approximate change in the BMI is $dB = B_w\,dw + B_h\,dh$, where the derivatives are evaluated at $w = 55$ and $h = 1.65$, and the changes in the independent variables are $dw = 1.5$ and $dh = 0.01$. Evaluating the partial derivatives, we find that

$$B_w(w, h) = \frac{1}{h^2} \qquad B_w(55, 1.65) \approx 0.37$$

$$B_h(w, h) = -\frac{2w}{h^3} \qquad B_h(55, 1.65) \approx -24.49.$$

Therefore, the approximate change in the BMI is

$$\begin{aligned} dB &= B_w(55, 1.65)\,dw + B_h(55, 1.65)\,dh \\ &\approx (0.37)(1.5) + (-24.49)(0.01) \\ &\approx 0.56 - 0.25 \\ &= 0.31. \end{aligned}$$

As expected, an increase in weight *increases* the BMI, while an increase in height *decreases* the BMI. In this case, the two contributions combine for a net increase in the BMI.

b. The changes dw, dh, and dB that appear in the differential change formula in part (a) are *absolute changes*. The corresponding *relative*, or *percentage*, changes are $\frac{dw}{w}$, $\frac{dh}{h}$, and $\frac{dB}{B}$. To introduce relative changes into the change formula, we divide both sides of $dB = B_w\,dw + B_h\,dh$ by $B = w/h^2 = wh^{-2}$. The result is

$$\begin{aligned} \frac{dB}{B} &= B_w\frac{dw}{wh^{-2}} + B_h\frac{dh}{wh^{-2}} \\ &= \frac{1}{h^2}\frac{dw}{wh^{-2}} - \frac{2w}{h^3}\frac{dh}{wh^{-2}} && \text{Substitute for } B_w \text{ and } B_h. \\ &= \underbrace{\frac{dw}{w}}_{\substack{\text{relative}\\ \text{change}\\ \text{in } w}} - 2\underbrace{\frac{dh}{h}}_{\substack{\text{relative}\\ \text{change}\\ \text{in } h}}. && \text{Simplify.} \end{aligned}$$

➤ See Exercises 60–61 for general results about relative or percentage changes in functions.

This expression relates the relative changes in w, h, and B. With h constant $(dh = 0)$, a 1% change in w $(dw/w = 0.01)$ produces approximately a 1% change of the same sign in B. With w constant $(dw = 0)$, a 1% change in h $(dh/h = 0.01)$ produces approximately a 2% change in B of the opposite sign. We see that the BMI formula is more sensitive to small changes in h than in w. *Related Exercises 31–34* ◀

QUICK CHECK 4 In Example 5, interpret the facts that $B_w > 0$ and $B_h < 0$ for $w, h > 0$. ◀

The differential for functions of two variables extends naturally to more variables. For example, if f is differentiable at (a, b, c) with $w = f(x, y, z)$, then

$$dw = f_x(a, b, c)\,dx + f_y(a, b, c)\,dy + f_z(a, b, c)\,dz.$$

The differential dw (or df) gives the approximate change in f at the point (a, b, c) due to changes of dx, dy, and dz in the independent variables.

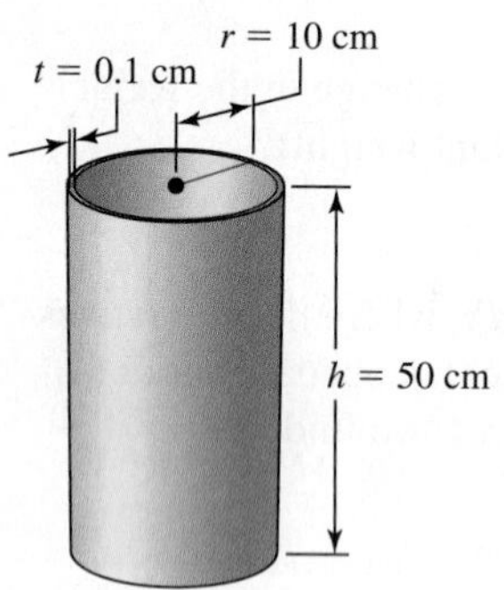

FIGURE 13.84

EXAMPLE 6 Manufacturing errors A company manufactures cylindrical aluminum tubes to rigid specifications. The tubes are designed to have an outside radius of $r = 10$ cm, a height of $h = 50$ cm, and a thickness of $t = 0.1$ cm (Figure 13.84). The manufacturing process produces tubes with a maximum error of ± 0.05 cm in the radius and height and a maximum error of ± 0.0005 cm in the thickness. The volume of the material used to construct a cylindrical tube is $V(r, h, t) = \pi ht(2r - t)$. Use differentials to estimate the maximum error in the volume of a tube.

SOLUTION The approximate change in the volume of a tube due to changes dr, dh, and dt in the radius, height, and thickness, respectively, is

$$dV = V_r\,dr + V_h\,dh + V_t\,dt.$$

The partial derivatives evaluated at $r = 10$, $h = 50$, and $t = 0.1$ are

$$\begin{aligned} V_r(r, h, t) &= 2\pi ht & V_r(10, 50, 0.1) &= 10\pi \\ V_h(r, h, t) &= \pi t(2r - t) & V_h(10, 50, 0.1) &= 1.99\pi \\ V_t(r, h, t) &= 2\pi h(r - t) & V_t(10, 50, 0.1) &= 990\pi. \end{aligned}$$

We let $dr = dh = 0.05$ and $dt = 0.0005$ be the maximum errors in the radius, height, and thickness, respectively. The maximum error in the volume is approximately

$$\begin{aligned} dV &= V_r(10, 50, 0.1)\,dr + V_h(10, 50, 0.1)\,dh + V_t(10, 50, 0.1)\,dt \\ &= 10\pi(0.05) + 1.99\pi(0.05) + 990\pi(0.0005) \\ &\approx 1.57 + 0.31 + 1.56 \\ &= 3.44. \end{aligned}$$

The maximum error in the volume is approximately 3.44 cm^3. Notice that the "magnification factor" for the thickness (990π) is roughly 100 and 500 times greater than the magnification factors for the radius and height, respectively. This means that for the same errors in r, h, and t, the volume is far more sensitive to errors in the thickness. The partial derivatives allow us to do a sensitivity analysis to determine which independent (input) variables are most critical in producing change in the dependent (output) variable.

Related Exercises 35–40 ◀

SECTION 13.7 EXERCISES

Review Questions

1. Suppose $\mathbf{n}$ is a vector normal to the tangent plane of the surface $F(x, y, z) = 0$ at a point. How is $\mathbf{n}$ related to the gradient of F at that point?

2. Write the explicit function $z = xy^2 + x^2y - 10$ in the implicit form $F(x, y, z) = 0$.

3. Write an equation for the plane tangent to the surface $F(x, y, z) = 0$ at the point (a, b, c).

4. Write an equation for the plane tangent to the surface $z = f(x, y)$ at the point $(a, b, f(a, b))$.

5. Explain how to approximate a function f at a point near (a, b) where the values of f, f_x, and f_y are known at (a, b).

6. Explain how to approximate the change in a function f when the independent variables change from (a, b) to $(a + \Delta x, b + \Delta y)$.

7. Write the approximate change formula for a function $z = f(x, y)$ at the point (a, b) in terms of differentials.

8. Write the differential dw for the function $w = f(x, y, z)$.

Basic Skills

9–14. Tangent planes for $F(x, y, z) = 0$ *Find an equation of the plane tangent to the following surfaces at the given points.*

9. $xy + xz + yz - 12 = 0$; $(2, 2, 2)$ and $\left(-1, -2, -\frac{10}{3}\right)$

10. $x^2 + y^2 - z^2 = 0$; $(3, 4, 5)$ and $(-4, -3, 5)$

11. $xy \sin z = 1$; $(1, 2, \pi/6)$ and $(-2, -1, 5\pi/6)$

12. $yze^{xz} - 8 = 0$; $(0, 2, 4)$ and $(0, -8, -1)$

13. $z^2 - x^2/16 - y^2/9 - 1 = 0$; $(4, 3, -\sqrt{3})$ and $(-8, 9, \sqrt{14})$

14. $2x + y^2 - z^2 = 0$; $(0, 1, 1)$ and $(4, 1, -3)$

15–20. Tangent planes for $z = f(x, y)$ *Find an equation of the plane tangent to the following surfaces at the given points.*

15. $z = 4 - 2x^2 - y^2$; $(2, 2, -8)$ and $(-1, -1, 1)$

16. $z = 2 + 2x^2 + y^2/2$; $\left(-\frac{1}{2}, 1, 3\right)$ and $(3, -2, 22)$

17. $z = x^2 e^{x-y}$; $(2, 2, 4)$ and $(-1, -1, 1)$

18. $z = \ln(1 + xy)$; $(1, 2, \ln 3)$ and $(-2, -1, \ln 3)$

19. $z = (x - y)/(x^2 + y^2)$; $\left(1, 2, -\frac{1}{5}\right)$ and $\left(2, -1, \frac{3}{5}\right)$

20. $z = 2\cos(x - y) + 2$; $(\pi/6, -\pi/6, 3)$ and $(\pi/3, \pi/3, 4)$

21–26. Linear approximation

a. Find the linear approximation for the following functions at the given point.

b. Use part (a) to estimate the given function value.

21. $f(x, y) = xy + x - y$; $(2, 3)$; estimate $f(2.1, 2.99)$.

22. $f(x, y) = 12 - 4x^2 - 8y^2$; $(-1, 4)$; estimate $f(-1.05, 3.95)$.

23. $f(x, y) = -x^2 + 2y^2$; $(3, -1)$; estimate $f(3.1, -1.04)$.

24. $f(x, y) = \sqrt{x^2 + y^2}$; $(3, -4)$; estimate $f(3.06, -3.92)$.

25. $f(x, y) = \ln(1 + x + y)$; $(0, 0)$; estimate $f(0.1, -0.2)$.

26. $f(x, y) = (x + y)/(x - y)$; $(3, 2)$; estimate $f(2.95, 2.05)$.

27–30. Approximate function change *Use differentials to approximate the change in z for the given changes in the independent variables.*

27. $z = 2x - 3y - 2xy$ when (x, y) changes from $(1, 4)$ to $(1.1, 3.9)$

28. $z = -x^2 + 3y^2 + 2$ when (x, y) changes from $(-1, 2)$ to $(-1.05, 1.9)$

29. $z = e^{x+y}$ when (x, y) changes from $(0, 0)$ to $(0.1, -0.05)$

30. $z = \ln(1 + x + y)$ when (x, y) changes from $(0, 0)$ to $(-0.1, 0.03)$

31. **Changes in torus surface area** The surface area of a torus (an ideal bagel or doughnut) with an inner radius r and an outer radius $R > r$ is $S = 4\pi^2(R^2 - r^2)$.
    a. If r increases and R decreases, does S increase or decrease, or is it impossible to say?
    b. If r increases and R increases, does S increase or decrease, or is it impossible to say?
    c. Estimate the change in the surface area of the torus when r changes from $r = 3.00$ to $r = 3.05$ and R changes from $R = 5.50$ to $R = 5.65$.
    d. Estimate the change in the surface area of the torus when r changes from $r = 3.00$ to $r = 2.95$ and R changes from $R = 7.00$ to $R = 7.04$.
    e. Find the relationship between the changes in r and R that leaves the surface area (approximately) unchanged.

32. **Changes in cone volume** The volume of a right circular cone with radius r and height h is $V = \pi r^2 h/3$.
    a. Approximate the change in the volume of the cone when the radius changes from $r = 6.5$ to $r = 6.6$ and the height changes from $h = 4.20$ to $h = 4.15$.
    b. Approximate the change in the volume of the cone when the radius changes from $r = 5.40$ to $r = 5.37$ and the height changes from $h = 12.0$ to $h = 11.96$.

33. **Area of an ellipse** The area of an ellipse with axes of length $2a$ and $2b$ is $A = \pi ab$. Approximate the percent change in the area when a increases by 2% and b increases by 1.5%.

34. **Volume of a paraboloid** The volume of a segment of a circular paraboloid (see figure) with radius r and height h is $V = \pi r^2 h/2$. Approximate the percent change in the volume when the radius decreases by 1.5% and the height increases by 2.2%.

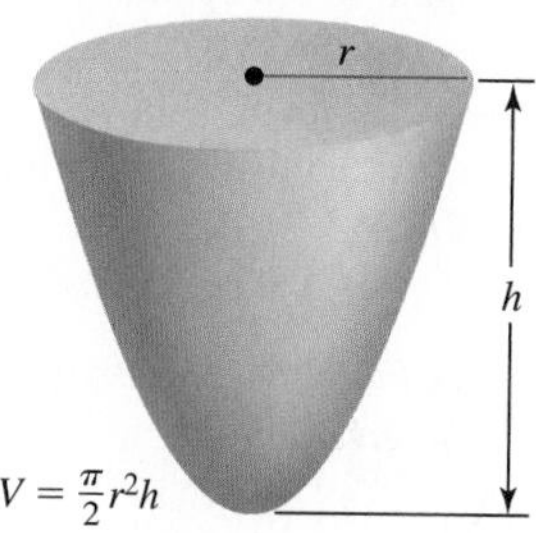

35–38. Differentials with more than two variables *Write the differential dw in terms of the differentials of the independent variables.*

35. $w = f(x, y, z) = xy^2 + zx^2 + yz^2$

36. $w = f(x, y, z) = \sin(x + y - z)$

37. $w = f(u, x, y, z) = (u + x)/(y + z)$

38. $w = f(p, q, r, s) = pq/(rs)$

T 39. **Law of Cosines** The side lengths of any triangle are related by the Law of Cosines,

$$c^2 = a^2 + b^2 - 2ab\cos\theta.$$

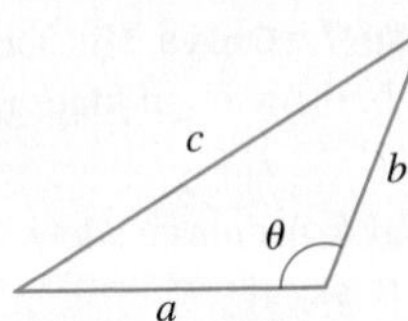

a. Estimate the change in the side length c when a changes from $a = 2$ to $a = 2.03$, b changes from $b = 4.00$ to $b = 3.96$ and θ changes from $\theta = \pi/3$ to $\theta = \pi/3 + \pi/90$.
b. If a changes from $a = 2$ to $a = 2.03$ and b changes from $b = 4.00$ to $b = 3.96$, is the resulting change in c greater in magnitude when $\theta = \pi/20$ (small angle) or when $\theta = 9\pi/20$ (close to a right angle)?

40. Travel cost The cost of a trip that is L miles long, driving a car that gets m miles per gallon, with gas costs of $\$p$/gal is $C = Lp/m$ dollars. Suppose you plan a trip of $L = 1500$ mi in a car that gets $m = 32$ mi/gal, with gas costs of $p = \$3.80$/gal.

a. Explain how the cost function is derived.
b. Compute the partial derivatives C_L, C_m, and C_p. Explain the meaning of the signs of the derivatives in the context of this problem.
c. Estimate the change in the total cost of the trip if L changes from $L = 1500$ to $L = 1520$, m changes from $m = 32$ to 31, and p changes from \$3.80 to $p = \$3.85$.
d. Is the total cost of the trip (with $L = 1500$ mi, $m = 32$ mi/gal, and $p = \$3.80$) more sensitive to a 1% change in L, m, or p (assuming the other two variables are fixed)? Explain.

Further Explorations

41. Explain why or why not Determine whether the following statements are true and give an explanation or counterexample.

a. The planes tangent to the cylinder $x^2 + z^2 = 1$ in $\mathbf{R}^3$ all have the form $ax + bz + c = 0$.
b. Suppose $w = xy/z$, for $x > 0$, $y > 0$, and $z > 0$. A decrease in z with x and y fixed results in an increase in w.
c. The gradient $\nabla F(a, b, c)$ lies in the plane tangent to the surface $F(x, y, z) = 0$ at (a, b, c).

42–45. Tangent planes *Find an equation of the plane tangent to the following surfaces at the given point.*

42. $z = \tan^{-1}(x + y)$; $(0, 0, 0)$

43. $z = \tan^{-1}(xy)$; $(1, 1, \pi/4)$

44. $(x + z)/(y - z) = 2$; $(4, 2, 0)$

45. $\sin xyz = \frac{1}{2}$; $\left(\pi, 1, \frac{1}{6}\right)$

46–49. Horizontal tangent planes *Find the points at which the following surfaces have horizontal tangent planes.*

46. $z = \sin(x - y)$, in the region $-2\pi \le x \le 2\pi$, $-2\pi \le y \le 2\pi$

47. $x^2 + y^2 - z^2 - 2x + 2y + 3 = 0$

48. $x^2 + 2y^2 + z^2 - 2x - 2z - 2 = 0$

49. $z = \cos 2x \sin y$, in the region $-\pi \le x \le \pi$, $-\pi \le y \le \pi$

50. Heron's formula The area of a triangle with sides of length a, b, and c is given by a formula from antiquity called Heron's formula:

$$A = \sqrt{s(s - a)(s - b)(s - c)},$$

where $s = (a + b + c)/2$ is the *semiperimeter* of the triangle.

a. Find the partial derivatives A_a, A_b, and A_c.
b. A triangle has sides of length $a = 2$, $b = 4$, $c = 5$. Estimate the change in the area when a increases by 0.03, b decreases by 0.08, and c increases by 0.6.
c. For an equilateral triangle with $a = b = c$, estimate the percent change in the area when all sides increase in length by p%.

51. Surface area of a cone A cone with height h and radius r has a lateral surface area (the curved surface only, excluding the base) of $S = \pi r\sqrt{r^2 + h^2}$.

a. Estimate the change in the surface area when r increases from $r = 2.50$ to $r = 2.55$ and h decreases from $h = 0.60$ to $h = 0.58$.
b. When $r = 100$ and $h = 200$, is the surface area more sensitive to a small change in r or a small change in h? Explain.

52. Line tangent to an intersection curve Consider the paraboloid $z = x^2 + 3y^2$ and the plane $z = x + y + 4$, which intersects the paraboloid in a curve C at $(2, 1, 7)$ (see figure). Find the equation of the line tangent to C at the point $(2, 1, 7)$. Proceed as follows.

a. Find a vector normal to the plane at $(2, 1, 7)$.
b. Find a vector normal to the plane tangent to the paraboloid at $(2, 1, 7)$.
c. Argue that the line tangent to C at $(2, 1, 7)$ is orthogonal to both normal vectors found in parts (a) and (b). Use this fact to find a direction vector for the tangent line.
d. Knowing a point on the tangent line and the direction of the tangent line, write an equation of the tangent line in parametric form.

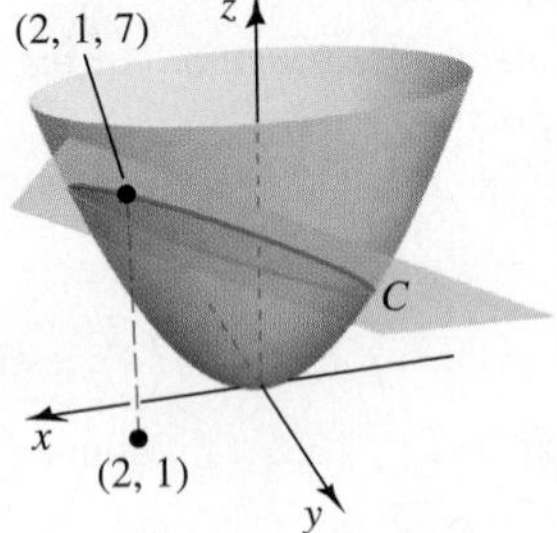

Applications

53. Batting averages Batting averages in baseball are defined by $A = x/y$, where $x \ge 0$ is the total number of hits and $y > 0$ is the total number of at-bats. Treat x and y as positive real numbers and note that $0 \le A \le 1$.

a. Use differentials to estimate the change in the batting average if the number of hits increases from 60 to 62 and the number of at-bats increases from 175 to 180.
b. If a batter currently has a batting average of $A = 0.350$, does the average decrease if the batter fails to get a hit more than it increases if the batter gets a hit?
c. Does the answer to part (b) depend on the current batting average? Explain.

54. **Water-level changes** A conical tank with radius 0.50 m and height 2.00 m is filled with water (see figure). Water is released from the tank, and the water level drops by 0.05 m (from 2.00 m to 1.95 m). Approximate the change in the volume of water in the tank. (*Hint:* When the water level drops, both the radius and height of the cone of water change.)

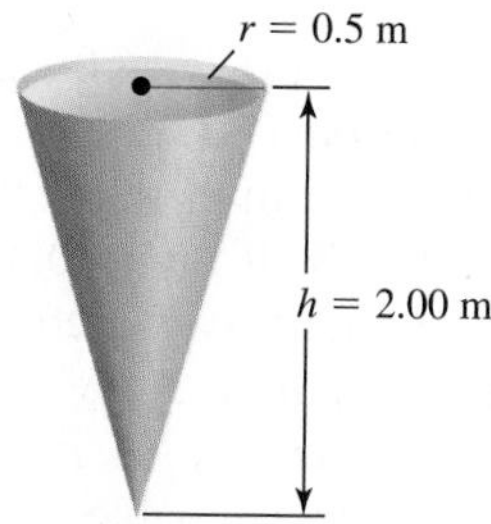

55. **Flow in a cylinder** Poiseuille's Law is a fundamental law of fluid dynamics that describes the flow velocity of a viscous incompressible fluid in a cylinder (it is used to model blood flow through veins and arteries). It says that in a cylinder of radius R and length L, the velocity of the fluid $r \leq R$ units from the center line of the cylinder is $V = \frac{P}{4L\nu}(R^2 - r^2)$, where P is the difference in the pressure between the ends of the cylinder and ν is the viscosity of the fluid (see figure). Assuming that P and ν are constant, the velocity V along the centerline of the cylinder $(r = 0)$ is $V = kR^2/L$, where k is a constant that we will take to be $k = 1$.

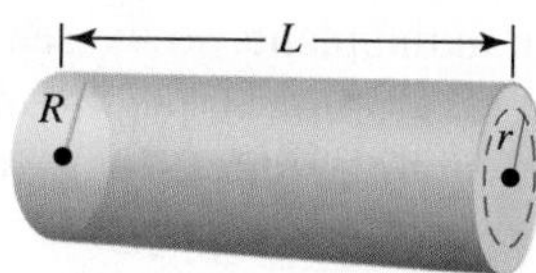

a. Estimate the change in the centerline velocity $(r = 0)$ if the radius of the flow cylinder increases from $R = 3$ cm to $R = 3.05$ cm and the length increases from $L = 50$ cm to $L = 50.5$ cm.
b. Estimate the percent change in the centerline velocity if the radius of the flow cylinder R decreases by 1% and the length L increases by 2%.
c. Complete the following sentence: If the radius of the cylinder increases by p%, then the length of the cylinder must decrease by approximately ____% in order for the velocity to remain constant.

56. **Floating-point operations** In general, real numbers (with infinite decimal expansions) cannot be represented exactly in a computer by floating-point numbers (with finite decimal expansions). Suppose that floating-point numbers on a particular computer carry an error of at most 10^{-16}. Estimate the maximum error that is committed in doing the following arithmetic operations. Express the error in absolute and relative (percent) terms.

a. $f(x, y) = xy$
b. $f(x, y) = x/y$
c. $F(x, y, z) = xyz$
d. $F(x, y, z) = (x/y)/z$

57. **Probability of at least one encounter** Suppose that in a large group of people a fraction $0 \leq r \leq 1$ of the people have flu. The probability that in n random encounters, you will meet at least one person with flu is $P = f(n, r) = 1 - (1 - r)^n$. Although n is a positive integer, regard it as a positive real number.

a. Compute f_r and f_n.
b. How sensitive is the probability P to the flu rate r? Suppose you meet $n = 20$ people. Approximately how much does the probability P increase if the flu rate increases from $r = 0.1$ to $r = 0.11$ (with n fixed)?
c. Approximately how much does the probability P increase if the flu rate increases from $r = 0.9$ to $r = 0.91$?
d. Interpret the results of parts (b) and (c).

58. **Two electrical resistors** When two electrical resistors with resistance $R_1 > 0$ and $R_2 > 0$ are wired in parallel in a circuit (see figure), the combined resistance R is given by $\frac{1}{R} = \frac{1}{R_1} + \frac{1}{R_2}$.

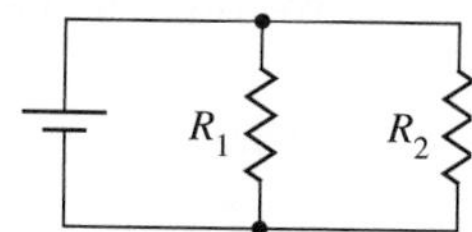

a. Estimate the change in R if R_1 increases from 2 ohms to 2.05 ohms and R_2 decreases from 3 ohms to 2.95 ohms.
b. Is it true that if $R_1 = R_2$ and R_1 increases by the same small amount as R_2 decreases, then R is approximately unchanged? Explain.
c. Is it true that if R_1 and R_2 increase, then R increases? Explain.
d. Suppose $R_1 > R_2$ and R_1 increases by the same small amount as R_2 decreases. Does R increase or decrease?

59. **Three electrical resistors** Extending Exercise 58, when three electrical resistors with resistance $R_1 > 0$, $R_2 > 0$, and $R_3 > 0$ are wired in parallel in a circuit (see figure), the combined resistance R is given by $\frac{1}{R} = \frac{1}{R_1} + \frac{1}{R_2} + \frac{1}{R_3}$. Estimate the change in R if R_1 increases from 2 ohms to 2.05 ohms, R_2 decreases from 3 ohms to 2.95 ohms, and R_3 increases from 1.5 ohms to 1.55 ohms.

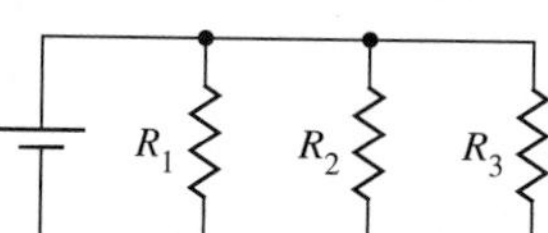

Additional Exercises

60. **Power functions and percent change** Suppose that $z = f(x, y) = x^a y^b$, where a and b are real numbers. Let dx/x, dy/y, and dz/z be the approximate relative (percent) changes in x, y, and z, respectively. Show that $(dz)/z = a(dx)/x + b(dy)/y$; that is, the relative changes are additive when weighted by the exponents a and b.

61. **Logarithmic differentials** Let f be a differentiable function of one or more variables that is positive on its domain.

a. Show that $d(\ln f) = \frac{df}{f}$.

b. Use part (a) to explain the statement that the absolute change in $\ln f$ is approximately equal to the relative change in f.

c. Let $f(x, y) = xy$, note that $\ln f = \ln x + \ln y$, and show that relative changes add; that is, $(df)/f = (dx)/x + (dy)/y$.

d. Let $f(x, y) = x/y$, note that $\ln f = \ln x - \ln y$, and show that relative changes subtract; that is, $(df)/f = (dx)/x - (dy)/y$.

e. Show that in a product of n numbers, $f = x_1 x_2 \cdots x_n$, the relative change in f is approximately equal to the sum of the relative changes in the variables.

62. Distance from a plane to an ellipsoid (Adapted from 1938 Putnam Exam.) Consider the ellipsoid $x^2/a^2 + y^2/b^2 + z^2/c^2 = 1$ and the plane P given by $Ax + By + Cz + 1 = 0$. Let $h = (A^2 + B^2 + C^2)^{-1/2}$ and $m = (a^2A^2 + b^2B^2 + c^2C^2)^{1/2}$.

a. Find the equation of the plane tangent to the ellipsoid at the point (p, q, r).

b. Find the two points on the ellipsoid at which the tangent plane is parallel to P and find equations of the tangent planes.

c. Show that the distance between the origin and the plane P is h.

d. Show that the distance between the origin and the tangent planes is hm.

e. Find a condition that guarantees the plane P does not intersect the ellipsoid.

QUICK CHECK ANSWERS

1. $F(x, y, z) = z - xy - x + y = 0$ **2.** If you walk in the positive x-direction from $(-1, 2, 1)$, then you walk uphill. If you walk in the positive y-direction from $(-1, 2, 1)$, then you walk downhill. **3.** If $\Delta x = 0$, then the change formula becomes $\Delta z \approx f_y(a, b)\,\Delta y$, which is the change formula for the single variable y. If $\Delta y = 0$, then the change formula becomes $\Delta z \approx f_x(a, b)\,\Delta x$, which is the change formula for the single variable x. **4.** The BMI increases with weight w and decreases with height h. ◀

13.8 Maximum/Minimum Problems

In Chapter 4 we showed how to use derivatives to find maximum and minimum values of functions of a single variable. When those techniques are extended to functions of two variables, we discover both similarities and differences. The landscape of a surface is far more complicated than the profile of a curve in the plane, so we see more interesting features when working with several variables. In addition to peaks (maximum values) and hollows (minimum values), we encounter winding ridges, long valleys, and mountain passes. Yet despite these complications, many of the ideas used for single-variable functions reappear in higher dimensions. For example, the Second Derivative Test, suitably adapted for two variables, plays a central role. As with single-variable functions, the techniques developed here are useful for solving practical optimization problems.

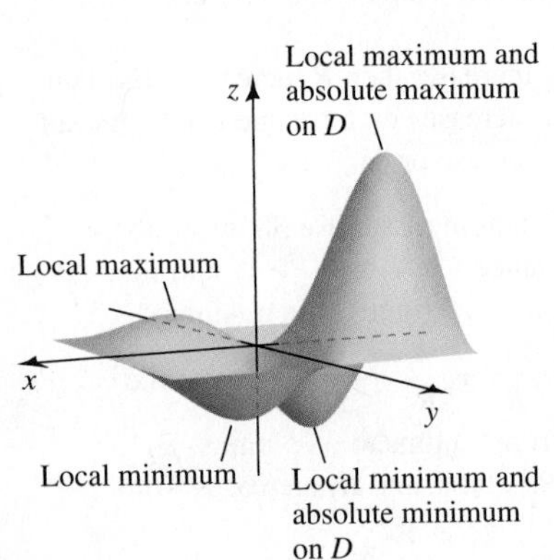

FIGURE 13.85

Local Maximum/Minimum Values

The concepts of local maximum and minimum values encountered in Chapter 4 extend readily to functions of two variables of the form $z = f(x, y)$. Figure 13.85 shows a general surface defined on a domain D, which is a subset of $\mathbf{R}^2$. The surface has peaks (local high points) and hollows (local low points) at points in the interior of D. The goal is to locate and classify these extreme points.

➤ We maintain the convention adopted in Chapter 4 that local maxima or minima occur at interior points of the domain. Recall that an open disk centered at (a, b) is the set of points within a circle centered at (a, b).

DEFINITIONS Local Maximum/Minimum Values

A function f has a **local maximum value** at (a, b) if $f(x, y) \le f(a, b)$ for all (x, y) in the domain of f in some open disk centered at (a, b). A function f has a **local minimum value** at (a, b) if $f(x, y) \ge f(a, b)$ for all (x, y) in the domain of f in some open disk centered at (a, b). Local maximum or local minimum values are also called **local extreme values** or **local extrema**.

In familiar terms, a local maximum is a point on a surface from which you cannot walk uphill. A local minimum is a point from which you cannot walk downhill. The following theorem is the analog of Theorem 4.2.

THEOREM 13.13 Derivatives and Local Maximum/Minimum Values
If f has a local maximum or minimum value at (a, b) and the partial derivatives f_x and f_y exist at (a, b), then $f_x(a, b) = f_y(a, b) = 0$.

Proof Suppose f has a local maximum value at (a, b). The function of one variable $g(x) = f(x, b)$, obtained by holding $y = b$ fixed, also has a local maximum at (a, b). By Theorem 4.2, $g'(a) = 0$. However, $g'(a) = f_x(a, b)$; therefore, $f_x(a, b) = 0$. Similarly, the function $h(y) = f(a, y)$, obtained by holding $x = a$ fixed, has a local maximum at (a, b), which implies that $f_y(a, b) = h'(b) = 0$. An analogous argument is used for the local minimum case. ◀

Suppose f is differentiable at (a, b) (ensuring the existence of a tangent plane) and f has a local extremum at (a, b). Then, $f_x(a, b) = f_y(a, b) = 0$, which, when substituted into the equation of the tangent plane, gives the equation $z = f(a, b)$ (a constant). Therefore, if the tangent plane exists at a local extremum, then it is horizontal there.

QUICK CHECK 1 The paraboloid $z = x^2 + y^2 - 4x + 2y + 5$ has a local minimum at $(2, -1)$. Verify the conclusion of Theorem 13.13 for this function. ◀

Recall that for a function of one variable the condition $f'(a) = 0$ does not guarantee a local extremum at a. A similar precaution must be taken with Theorem 13.13. The conditions $f_x(a, b) = f_y(a, b) = 0$ do not imply that f has a local extremum at (a, b), as we show momentarily. Theorem 13.13 provides *candidates* for local extrema. We call these candidates *critical points*, as we did for functions of one variable. Therefore, the procedure for locating local maximum and minimum values is to find the critical points and then determine whether these candidates correspond to genuine local maximum and minimum values.

DEFINITION Critical Point
An interior point (a, b) in the domain of f is a **critical point** of f if either

1. $f_x(a, b) = f_y(a, b) = 0$, or
2. one (or both) of f_x or f_y does not exist at (a, b).

Critical points are candidates for local maximum and minimum values.

EXAMPLE 1 Finding critical points Find the critical points of $f(x, y) = xy(x - 2)(y + 3)$.

SOLUTION This function is differentiable at all points of $\mathbf{R}^2$, so the critical points occur only at points where $f_x(x, y) = f_y(x, y) = 0$. Computing and simplifying the partial derivatives, these conditions become

$$f_x(x, y) = 2y(x - 1)(y + 3) = 0$$
$$f_y(x, y) = x(x - 2)(2y + 3) = 0.$$

We must now identify all (x, y) pairs that satisfy both equations. The first equation is satisfied if and only if $y = 0$, $x = 1$, or $y = -3$. We consider each of these cases.

- Substituting $y = 0$, the second equation is $3x(x - 2) = 0$, which has solutions $x = 0$ and $x = 2$. So, $(0, 0)$ and $(2, 0)$ are critical points.
- Substituting $x = 1$, the second equation is $-(2y + 3) = 0$, which has the solution $y = -\frac{3}{2}$. So, $\left(1, -\frac{3}{2}\right)$ is a critical point.
- Substituting $y = -3$, the second equation is $-3x(x - 2) = 0$, which has roots $x = 0$ and $x = 2$. So, $(0, -3)$ and $(2, -3)$ are critical points.

We find that there are five critical points: $(0, 0)$, $(2, 0)$, $\left(1, -\frac{3}{2}\right)$, $(0, -3)$, and $(2, -3)$. Some of these critical points may correspond to local maximum or minimum values. We return to this example and a complete analysis shortly.

Related Exercises 9–14

Second Derivative Test

Critical points are candidates for local extreme values. With functions of one variable, the Second Derivative Test may be used to determine whether critical points correspond to local maxima or minima (it can also be inconclusive). The analogous test for functions of two variables not only detects local maxima and minima, but also identifies another type of point known as a *saddle point*.

> The usual image of a saddle point is that of a mountain pass (or a horse saddle), where you can walk upward in some directions and downward in other directions. The definition of a saddle point we have given includes other less common situations. For example, with this definition, the cylinder $z = x^3$ has a line of saddle points along the y-axis.

DEFINITION Saddle Point

A function f has a **saddle point** at a critical point (a, b) if, in every open disk centered at (a, b), there are points (x, y) for which $f(x, y) > f(a, b)$ and points for which $f(x, y) < f(a, b)$.

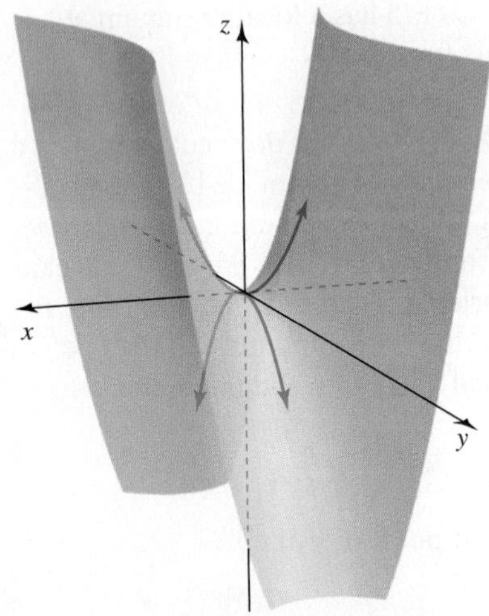

The hyperbolic paraboloid $z = x^2 - y^2$ has a saddle point at $(0, 0)$.

FIGURE 13.86

A saddle point on the surface $z = f(x, y)$ is a point $(a, b, f(a, b))$ from which it is possible to walk uphill in some directions and downhill in other directions. The function $f(x, y) = x^2 - y^2$ (a hyperbolic paraboloid) is a good example to remember. The surface *rises* from $(0, 0)$ along the x-axis and *falls* from $(0, 0)$ along the y-axis (Figure 13.86). We can easily check that $f_x(0, 0) = f_y(0, 0) = 0$, demonstrating that critical points do not necessarily correspond to local maxima or minima.

QUICK CHECK 2 Consider the plane tangent to a surface at a saddle point. In what direction does the normal to the plane point?

THEOREM 13.14 Second Derivative Test

Suppose that the second partial derivatives of f are continuous throughout an open disk centered at the point (a, b), where $f_x(a, b) = f_y(a, b) = 0$. Let $D(x, y) = f_{xx}f_{yy} - f_{xy}^2$.

1. If $D(a, b) > 0$ and $f_{xx}(a, b) < 0$, then f has a local maximum value at (a, b).
2. If $D(a, b) > 0$ and $f_{xx}(a, b) > 0$, then f has a local minimum value at (a, b).
3. If $D(a, b) < 0$, then f has a saddle point at (a, b).
4. If $D(a, b) = 0$, then the test is inconclusive.

> The Second Derivative Test for functions of a single variable states that if a is a critical point with $f'(a) = 0$, then $f''(a) > 0$ implies that f has a local minimum at a, $f''(a) < 0$ implies that f has a local maximum at a, and if $f''(a) = 0$, the test is inconclusive. Theorem 13.14 is easier to remember if you notice the parallels between the two second derivative tests.

The proof of this theorem is given in Appendix B, but a few comments are in order. The test relies on the quantity $D(x, y) = f_{xx} f_{yy} - f_{xy}^2$, which is called the **discriminant** of f. It can be remembered as the 2×2 determinant of the **Hessian** matrix $\begin{pmatrix} f_{xx} & f_{xy} \\ f_{yx} & f_{yy} \end{pmatrix}$, where $f_{xy} = f_{yx}$, provided these derivatives are continuous (Theorem 13.4). The condition $D(x, y) > 0$ means that the surface has the same general behavior in all directions near (a, b); either the surface rises in all directions, or it falls in all directions. In the case that $D(a, b) = 0$, the test is inconclusive: (a, b) could correspond to a local maximum, a local minimum, or a saddle point.

Finally, another useful characterization of a saddle point can be derived from Theorem 13.14: The tangent plane at a saddle point lies both above and below the surface.

QUICK CHECK 3 Compute the discriminant $D(x, y)$ of $f(x, y) = x^2y^2$.

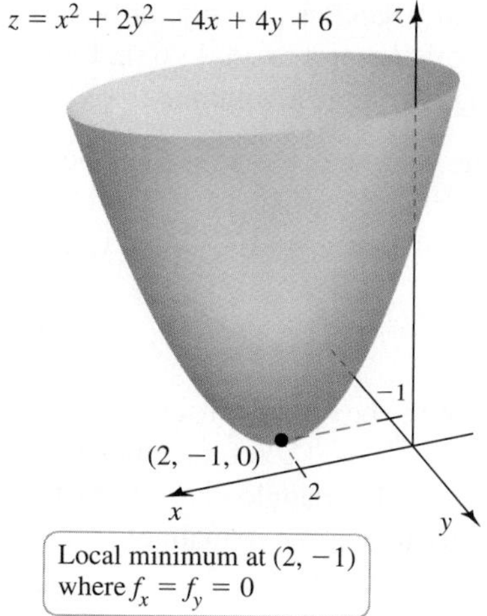

FIGURE 13.87

EXAMPLE 2 **Analyzing critical points** Use the Second Derivative Test to classify the critical points of $f(x, y) = x^2 + 2y^2 - 4x + 4y + 6$.

SOLUTION We begin with the following derivative calculations:

$$f_x = 2x - 4 \qquad f_y = 4y + 4$$
$$f_{xx} = 2 \qquad f_{xy} = f_{yx} = 0 \qquad f_{yy} = 4$$

Setting both f_x and f_y equal to zero yields the single critical point $(2, -1)$. The value of the discriminant at the critical point is $D(2, -1) = f_{xx}f_{yy} - f_{xy}^2 = 8 > 0$. Furthermore, $f_{xx}(2, -1) = 2 > 0$. By the Second Derivative Test, f has a local minimum at $(2, -1)$; the value of the function at that point is $f(2, -1) = 0$ (Figure 13.87).

Related Exercises 15–28 ◂

EXAMPLE 3 **Analyzing critical points** Use the Second Derivative Test to classify the critical points of $f(x, y) = xy(x - 2)(y + 3)$.

SOLUTION In Example 1, we determined that the critical points of f are $(0, 0)$, $(2, 0)$, $\left(1, -\frac{3}{2}\right)$, $(0, -3)$, and $(2, -3)$. The derivatives needed to evaluate the discriminant are

$$f_x = 2y(x - 1)(y + 3), \qquad f_y = x(x - 2)(2y + 3)$$
$$f_{xx} = 2y(y + 3), \qquad f_{xy} = 2(2y + 3)(x - 1), \qquad f_{yy} = 2x(x - 2)$$

The values of the discriminant at the critical points and the conclusions of the Second Derivative Test are shown in Table 13.5.

Table 13.5

(x, y)	$D(x, y)$	f_{xx}	Conclusion
$(0, 0)$	-36	0	Saddle point
$(2, 0)$	-36	0	Saddle point
$\left(1, -\frac{3}{2}\right)$	9	$-\frac{9}{2}$	Local maximum
$(0, -3)$	-36	0	Saddle point
$(2, -3)$	-36	0	Saddle point

The surface described by f has one local maximum at $\left(1, -\frac{3}{2}\right)$, surrounded by four saddle points (Figure 13.88a). The structure of the surface may also be visualized by plotting the level curves of f (Figure 13.88b).

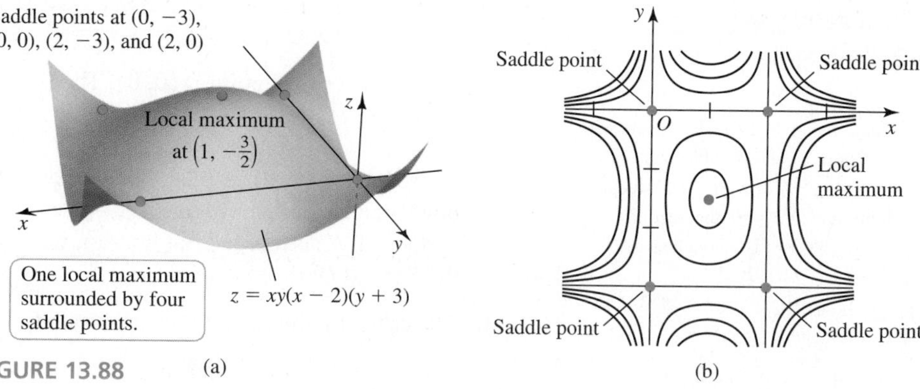

FIGURE 13.88

Related Exercises 15–28 ◂

➤ Example 4 is a *constrained optimization problem,* in which the goal is to maximize the volume subject to an additional condition called a *constraint.* We return to such problems in the next section and present another method of solution.

EXAMPLE 4 Shipping regulations A shipping company handles rectangular boxes provided the sum of the length, width, and height of the box does not exceed 96 in. Find the dimensions of the box that meets this condition and has the largest volume.

SOLUTION Let x, y, and z be the dimensions of the box; its volume is $V = xyz$. The box with the maximum volume satisfies the condition $x + y + z = 96$, which is used to eliminate any one of the variables from the volume function. Noting that $z = 96 - x - y$, the volume function becomes

$$V(x, y) = xy(96 - x - y).$$

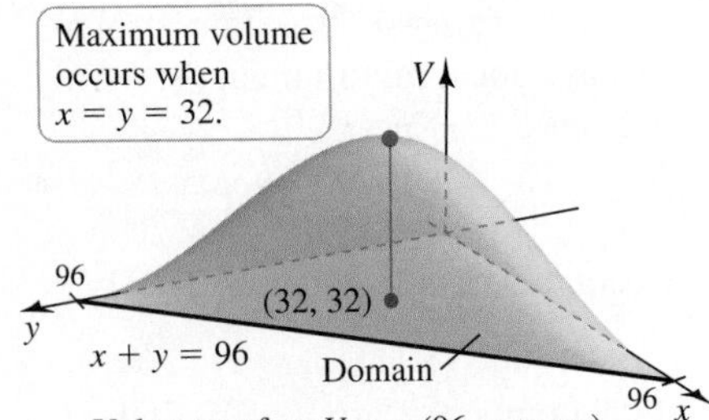
Maximum volume occurs when $x = y = 32$.
V
96
(32, 32)
y
$x + y = 96$
Domain
96
x
Volume surface $V = xy(96 - x - y)$
FIGURE 13.89

Notice that because x, y, and $96 - x - y$ are dimensions of the box, they must be nonnegative. The condition $96 - x - y \geq 0$ implies that $x + y \leq 96$. Therefore, among points in the xy-plane, the constraint is met only if (x, y) lies in the triangle bounded by the lines $x = 0$, $y = 0$, and $x + y = 96$ (Figure 13.89). This triangle is the domain of the problem and on its boundary, $V = 0$.

The goal is to find the maximum value of V. The critical points of V satisfy

$$V_x = 96y - 2xy - y^2 = y(96 - 2x - y) = 0$$
$$V_y = 96x - 2xy - x^2 = x(96 - 2y - x) = 0.$$

You can check that these two equations have four solutions: (0, 0), (96, 0), (0, 96), and (32, 32). The first three solutions lie on the boundary of the domain, where $V = 0$. Therefore, the only critical point is (32, 32). The required second derivatives are

$$V_{xx} = -2y, \qquad V_{xy} = 96 - 2x - 2y, \qquad V_{yy} = -2x.$$

The discriminant is

$$D(x, y) = V_{xx}V_{yy} - V_{xy}^2 = 4xy - (96 - 2x - 2y)^2,$$

which, when evaluated at (32, 32), has the value $D(32, 32) = 3072 > 0$. Therefore, the critical point corresponds to either a local maximum or minimum. Noting that $V_{xx}(32, 32) = -64 < 0$, we conclude that the critical point corresponds to a local maximum. The dimensions of the box with maximum volume are $x = 32$, $y = 32$, and $z = 96 - x - y = 32$ (it is a cube), and its volume is 32,768 in^3.

Related Exercises 29–32 ◀

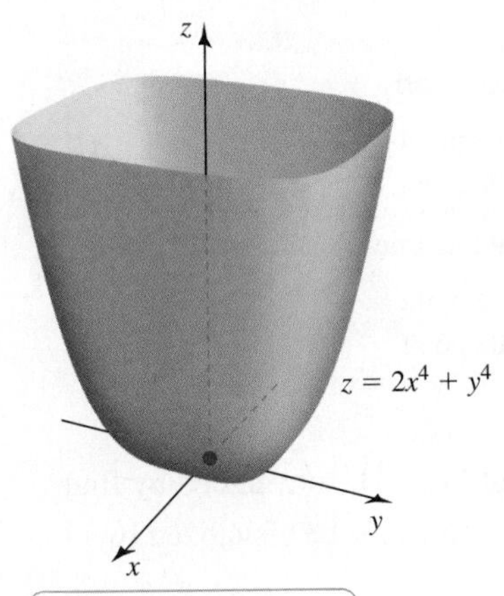
z
$z = 2x^4 + y^4$
y
x
Local minimum at (0, 0), but the Second Derivative Test is inconclusive.
FIGURE 13.90

EXAMPLE 5 Inconclusive tests Apply the Second Derivative Test to the following functions and interpret the results.

a. $f(x, y) = 2x^4 + y^4$ **b.** $f(x, y) = 2 - xy^2$

SOLUTION

a. The critical points of f satisfy the conditions

$$f_x = 8x^3 = 0 \quad \text{and} \quad f_y = 4y^3 = 0,$$

so the sole critical point is (0, 0). The second partial derivatives evaluated at (0, 0) are

$$f_{xx}(0, 0) = f_{xy}(0, 0) = f_{yy}(0, 0) = 0.$$

We see that $D(0, 0) = 0$, and the Second Derivative Test is inconclusive. While the bowl-shaped surface (Figure 13.90) described by f has a local minimum at (0, 0), the surface also has a broad flat bottom, which makes the local minimum "invisible" to the Second Derivative Test.

➤ The same "flat" behavior occurs with functions of one variable, such as $f(x) = x^4$. Although f has a local minimum at $x = 0$, the Second Derivative Test is inconclusive.

b. The critical points of this function satisfy

$$f_x(x, y) = -y^2 = 0 \quad \text{and} \quad f_y(x, y) = -2xy = 0.$$

The solutions of these equations have the form $(a, 0)$, where a is a real number. It is easy to check that the second partial derivatives evaluated at $(a, 0)$ are

$$f_{xx}(a, 0) = f_{xy}(a, 0) = 0 \quad \text{and} \quad f_{yy}(a, 0) = -2a.$$

Therefore, the discriminant is $D(a, 0) = 0$, and the Second Derivative Test is inconclusive. Figure 13.91 shows that f has a flat ridge above the x-axis that the Second Derivative Test is unable to classify. *Related Exercises 33–36* ◀

➤ It is not surprising that the Second Derivative Test is inconclusive in Example 5b. The function has a line of local maxima at $(a, 0)$ for $a > 0$, a line of local minima at $(a, 0)$ for $a < 0$, and a saddle point at $(0, 0)$.

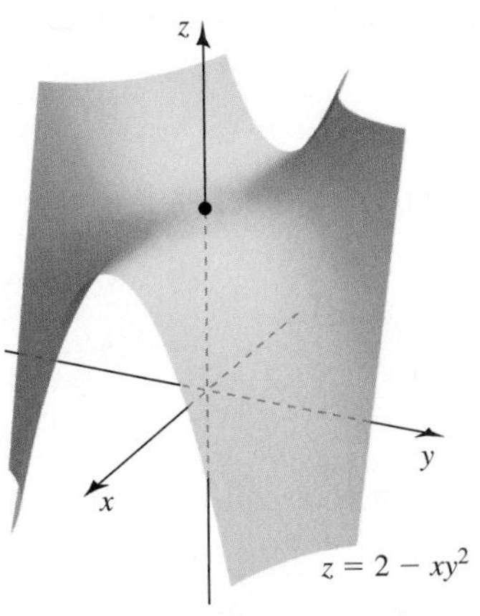
z
y
x
$z = 2 - xy^2$
Second derivative test fails to detect saddle point at (0, 0).

FIGURE 13.91

Absolute Maximum and Minimum Values

As in the one-variable case, we are often interested in knowing where a function of two or more variables attains its extreme values over its entire domain.

> **DEFINITIONS Absolute Maximum/Minimum Values**
>
> If $f(x, y) \le f(a, b)$ for all (x, y) in the domain of f, then f has an **absolute maximum value** at (a, b). If $f(x, y) \ge f(a, b)$ for all (x, y) in the domain of f, then f has an **absolute minimum value** at (a, b).

The concepts of absolute maximum and minimum values may also be applied to a specified subset of the domain, as shown in Example 6. It should be noted that the Extreme Value Theorem of Chapter 4 has an analog in $\mathbf{R}^2$ (or in higher dimensions): A continuous function on a closed bounded set in $\mathbf{R}^2$ attains its absolute maximum and absolute minimum values on that set. Absolute maximum and minimum values on a closed bounded set R occur in two ways:

➤ Recall that a *closed set* in $\mathbf{R}^2$ is a set that includes its boundary. A *bounded set* in $\mathbf{R}^2$ is a set that may be enclosed by a circle of finite radius.

- They may be local maximum or minimum values at interior points of R, where they are associated with critical points.
- They may occur on the boundary of R.

Therefore, the search for absolute maximum and minimum values on a closed bounded set is accomplished in the following three steps.

> **PROCEDURE Finding Absolute Maximum/Minimum Values on Closed, Bounded Sets**
>
> Let f be continuous on a closed bounded set R in $\mathbf{R}^2$. To find the absolute maximum and minimum values of f on R:
>
> 1. Determine the values of f at all critical points in R.
> 2. Find the maximum and minimum values of f on the boundary of R.
> 3. The greatest function value found in Steps 1 and 2 is the absolute maximum value of f on R, and the least function value found in Steps 1 and 2 is the absolute minimum value of f on R.

The techniques for carrying out Step 1 of this process have been presented. The challenge generally lies in locating extreme values on the boundary. For now, we restrict our attention to sets whose boundaries are described parametrically; then, finding extreme values on the boundary becomes a one-variable problem. In the next section, we discuss an alternative method for finding extreme values on boundaries.

EXAMPLE 6 Absolute maximum and minimum values Find the absolute maximum and minimum values of $f(x, y) = x^2 + y^2 - 2x + 2y + 5$ on the set $R = \{(x, y): x^2 + y^2 \le 4\}$ (the closed disk centered at $(0, 0)$ with radius 2).

SOLUTION We begin by locating the critical points and the local maxima and minima. The critical points satisfy the equations

$$f_x(x, y) = 2x - 2 = 0 \quad \text{and} \quad f_y(x, y) = 2y + 2 = 0,$$

which have the solution $x = 1$ and $y = -1$. The value of the function at this point is $f(1, -1) = 3$.

We now determine the maximum and minimum values of f on the boundary of R, which is a circle of radius 2 described by the parametric equations

➤ Recall that a parametric description of a circle of radius a centered at the origin is $x = a\cos\theta$, $y = a\sin\theta$, for $0 \le \theta \le 2\pi$.

$$x = 2\cos\theta, \qquad y = 2\sin\theta, \quad \text{for} \quad 0 \le \theta \le 2\pi.$$

Substituting x and y in terms of θ into the function f, we obtain a new function $g(\theta)$ that gives the values of f on the boundary of R:

$$\begin{aligned} g(\theta) &= (2\cos\theta)^2 + (2\sin\theta)^2 - 2(2\cos\theta) + 2(2\sin\theta) + 5 \\ &= 4(\cos^2\theta + \sin^2\theta) - 4\cos\theta + 4\sin\theta + 5 \\ &= -4\cos\theta + 4\sin\theta + 9 \end{aligned}$$

Finding the maximum and minimum boundary values is now a one-variable problem. The critical points of g satisfy

$$g'(\theta) = 4\sin\theta + 4\cos\theta = 0,$$

or $\tan\theta = -1$. Therefore, g has critical points $\theta = -\pi/4$ and $\theta = 3\pi/4$, which correspond to the points $(\sqrt{2}, -\sqrt{2})$ and $(-\sqrt{2}, \sqrt{2})$. The function values at these points are $f(\sqrt{2}, -\sqrt{2}) = 9 - 4\sqrt{2} \approx 3.3$ and $f(-\sqrt{2}, \sqrt{2}) = 9 + 4\sqrt{2} \approx 14.7$.

Having completed the first two steps of this procedure, we have three function values to consider:

- $f(1, -1) = 3$ (critical point)
- $f(\sqrt{2}, -\sqrt{2}) = 9 - 4\sqrt{2} \approx 3.3$ (boundary point)
- $f(-\sqrt{2}, \sqrt{2}) = 9 + 4\sqrt{2} \approx 14.7$ (boundary point)

The greatest value, $f(-\sqrt{2}, \sqrt{2}) = 9 + 4\sqrt{2}$, is the absolute maximum value, and it occurs at a boundary point. The least value, $f(1, -1) = 3$, is the absolute minimum value, and it occurs at an interior point (Figure 13.92a). Also revealing is the plot of the level curves of the surface with the boundary of R superimposed (Figure 13.92b). As the boundary of R is traversed, the values of f vary, reaching a maximum value at $\theta = 3\pi/4$, or $(-\sqrt{2}, \sqrt{2})$, and a minimum value at $\theta = -\pi/4$, or $(\sqrt{2}, -\sqrt{2})$.

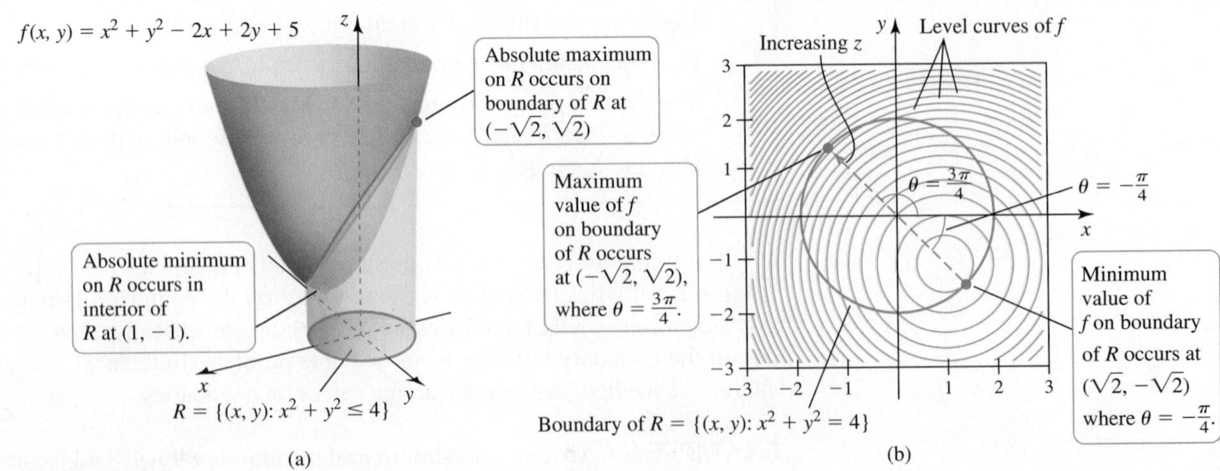

$f(x, y) = x^2 + y^2 - 2x + 2y + 5$
z
Absolute maximum on R occurs on boundary of R at $(-\sqrt{2}, \sqrt{2})$
Absolute minimum on R occurs in interior of R at $(1, -1)$.
x
y
$R = \{(x, y): x^2 + y^2 \le 4\}$
(a)
y
Level curves of f
Increasing z
3
2
1
-1
-2
-3
Maximum value of f on boundary of R occurs at $(-\sqrt{2}, \sqrt{2})$, where $\theta = \frac{3\pi}{4}$.
$\theta = \frac{3\pi}{4}$
$\theta = -\frac{\pi}{4}$
x
Minimum value of f on boundary of R occurs at $(\sqrt{2}, -\sqrt{2})$ where $\theta = -\frac{\pi}{4}$.
-3 -2 -1 1 2 3
Boundary of $R = \{(x, y): x^2 + y^2 = 4\}$
(b)

FIGURE 13.92

Related Exercises 37–44 ◀

Open and/or Unbounded Domains Finding absolute maximum and minimum values of a function on an open domain (for example, $R = \{(x, y) = x^2 + y^2 < 9\}$) or an unbounded domain (for example, $R = \{(x, y): x > 0, y > 0\}$) presents additional challenges. Because there is no systematic procedure for dealing with such problems, some ingenuity is generally needed.

EXAMPLE 7 **Absolute extreme values on an open set** Find the absolute maximum and minimum values of $f(x, y) = 4 - x^2 - y^2$ on the open disk $R = \{(x, y): x^2 + y^2 < 1\}$ (if they exist).

SOLUTION You should verify that f has a critical point at $(0, 0)$ and it corresponds to a local maximum (on an inverted paraboloid). Moving away from $(0, 0)$ in all directions, the function values decrease, so f also has an absolute maximum at $(0, 0)$. The boundary of R is the unit circle $\{(x, y): x^2 + y^2 = 1\}$, which is not contained in R. As (x, y) approaches any point on the unit circle along any path in R, the function values $f(x, y) = 4 - (x^2 + y^2)$ decrease and approach 3 but never reach 3. Therefore, f does not have an absolute minimum on R.

Related Exercises 45–52 ◀

QUICK CHECK 4 Does the linear function $f(x, y) = 2x + 3y$ have an absolute maximum or minimum value on the open unit square $\{(x, y): 0 < x < 1, 0 < y < 1\}$? ◀

EXAMPLE 8 **Absolute extreme values on an open set** Find the point(s) on the plane $x + 2y + z = 2$ closest to the point $P(2, 0, 4)$.

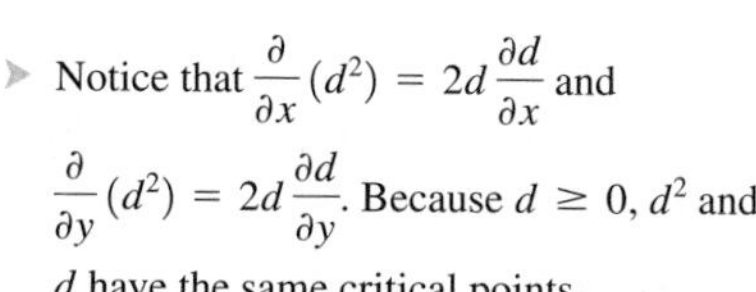
➤ Notice that $\frac{\partial}{\partial x}(d^2) = 2d\frac{\partial d}{\partial x}$ and $\frac{\partial}{\partial y}(d^2) = 2d\frac{\partial d}{\partial y}$. Because $d \geq 0$, d^2 and d have the same critical points.

SOLUTION Suppose that (x, y, z) is a point on the plane, which means that $z = 2 - x - 2y$. The distance between $P(2, 0, 4)$ and (x, y, z) that we seek to minimize is

$$d(x, y, z) = \sqrt{(x - 2)^2 + y^2 + (z - 4)^2}.$$

It is easier to minimize d^2, which has the same critical points as d. Squaring d and eliminating z using $z = 2 - x - 2y$, we have

$$\begin{aligned} f(x, y) = (d(x, y, z))^2 &= (x - 2)^2 + y^2 + (-x - 2y - 2)^2 \\ &= 2x^2 + 5y^2 + 4xy + 8y + 8. \end{aligned}$$

The critical points of f satisfy the equations

$$f_x = 4x + 4y = 0 \quad \text{and} \quad f_y = 4x + 10y + 8 = 0,$$

whose only solution is $x = \frac{4}{3}, y = -\frac{4}{3}$. The Second Derivative Test confirms that this point corresponds to a local minimum of f. We now ask: Does $\left(\frac{4}{3}, -\frac{4}{3}\right)$ correspond to the *absolute* minimum value of f over the entire domain of the problem, which is $\mathbf{R}^2$? Because the domain has no boundary, we cannot check values of f on the boundary. Instead, we argue geometrically that there is exactly one point on the plane that is closest to P. We have found a point that is closest to P among nearby points on the plane. As we move away from this point, the values of f increase without bound. Therefore, $\left(\frac{4}{3}, -\frac{4}{3}\right)$ corresponds to the absolute minimum value of f. A graph of f (Figure 13.93) confirms this reasoning, and we conclude that the point $\left(\frac{4}{3}, -\frac{4}{3}, \frac{10}{3}\right)$ is the point on the plane nearest P.

Related Exercises 45–52 ◀

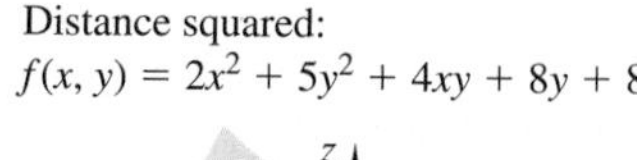
Distance squared:
$f(x, y) = 2x^2 + 5y^2 + 4xy + 8y + 8$

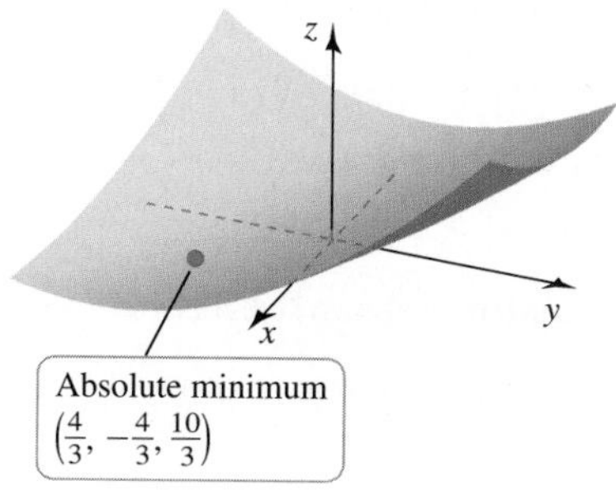

FIGURE 13.93

SECTION 13.8 EXERCISES

Review Exercises

1. Describe the appearance of a smooth surface with a local maximum at a point.
2. Describe the usual appearance of a smooth surface at a saddle point.
3. What are the conditions for a critical point of a function f?
4. If $f_x(a, b) = f_y(a, b) = 0$, does it follow that f has a local maximum or local minimum at (a, b)? Explain.
5. What is the discriminant and how do you compute it?

6. Explain how the Second Derivative Test is used.

7. What is an absolute minimum value of a function f on a set R in $\mathbf{R}^2$?

8. What is the procedure for locating absolute maximum and minimum values on a closed bounded domain?

Basic Skills

9–14. Critical points *Find all critical points of the following functions.*

9. $f(x, y) = 1 + x^2 + y^2$

10. $f(x, y) = x^2 - 6x + y^2 + 8y$

11. $f(x, y) = (3x - 2)^2 + (y - 4)^2$

12. $f(x, y) = 3x^2 - 4y^2$

13. $f(x, y) = x^4 + y^4 - 16xy$

14. $f(x, y) = x^3/3 - y^3/3 + 3xy$

15–28. Analyzing critical points *Find the critical points of the following functions. Use the Second Derivative Test to determine (if possible) whether each critical point corresponds to a local maximum, local minimum, or saddle point. Confirm your results using a graphing utility.*

15. $f(x, y) = 4 + 2x^2 + 3y^2$

16. $f(x, y) = (4x - 1)^2 + (2y + 4)^2 + 1$

17. $f(x, y) = -4x^2 + 8y^2 - 3$

18. $f(x, y) = x^4 + y^4 - 4x - 32y + 10$

19. $f(x, y) = x^4 + 2y^2 - 4xy$

20. $f(x, y) = xye^{-x-y}$

21. $f(x, y) = \sqrt{x^2 + y^2 - 4x + 5}$

22. $f(x, y) = \tan^{-1}(xy)$

23. $f(x, y) = 2xye^{-x^2-y^2}$

24. $f(x, y) = x^2 - x^4/2 - y^2 - xy$

25. $f(x, y) = \dfrac{x - y}{1 + x^2 + y^2}$

26. $f(x, y) = \dfrac{xy(x - y)}{x^2 + y^2}$

27. $f(x, y) = ye^x - e^y$

28. $f(x, y) = \sin(2\pi x)\cos(\pi y)$, for $|x| \le \frac{1}{2}$ and $|y| \le \frac{1}{2}$.

29. **Shipping regulations** A shipping company handles rectangular boxes provided the sum of the height and the girth of the box does not exceed 96 in. (The girth is the perimeter of the smallest base of the box.) Find the dimensions of the box that meets this condition and has the largest volume.

30. **Cardboard boxes** A lidless box is to be made using 2 m^2 of cardboard. Find the dimensions of the box with the largest possible volume.

31. **Cardboard boxes** A lidless cardboard box is to be made with a volume of 4 m^3. Find the dimensions of the box that requires the least amount of cardboard.

32. **Optimal box** Find the dimensions of the largest rectangular box in the first octant of the xyz-coordinate system that has one vertex at the origin and the opposite vertex on the plane $x + 2y + 3z = 6$.

33–36. Inconclusive tests *Show that the Second Derivative test is inconclusive when applied to the following functions at* $(0, 0)$. *Describe the behavior of the function at the critical point.*

33. $f(x, y) = 4 + x^4 + 3y^4$

34. $f(x, y) = x^2y - 3$

35. $f(x, y) = x^4y^2$

36. $f(x, y) = \sin(x^2y^2)$

37–44. Absolute maxima and minima *Find the absolute maximum and minimum values of the following functions on the given set R.*

37. $f(x, y) = x^2 + y^2 - 2y + 1$; $R = \{(x, y): x^2 + y^2 \le 4\}$

38. $f(x, y) = -x^2 - y^2 + \sqrt{3}x - y - 1$; $R = \{(x, y): x^2 + y^2 \le 6\}$

39. $f(x, y) = 4 + 2x^2 + y^2$; $R = \{(x, y): -1 \le x \le 1, -1 \le y \le 1\}$

40. $f(x, y) = 6 - x^2 - 4y^2$; $R = \{(x, y): -2 \le x \le 2, -1 \le y \le 1\}$

41. $f(x, y) = x^2 + y^2 + 4x - 2y$; $R = \{(x, y): x^2 + y^2 \le 16\}$

42. $f(x, y) = x^2 + y^2 - 2x - 2y$; R is the closed set bounded by the triangle with vertices $(0, 0)$, $(2, 0)$, and $(0, 2)$.

43. $f(x, y) = x^2 + 4y^2 + 2x + 4y$; R is the closed set bounded by the ellipse $\{(x, y): x = 4\cos\theta, y = \sin\theta, \text{ for } 0 \le \theta \le 2\pi\}$.

44. $f(x, y) = \sqrt{x^2 + y^2 - 2x + 2}$; R is the closed half disk $\{(x, y): x^2 + y^2 \le 4 \text{ with } y \ge 0\}$.

45–48. Absolute extrema on open and/or unbounded sets *If possible, find the absolute maximum and minimum values of the following functions on the set R.*

45. $f(x, y) = x^2 + y^2 - 4$; $R = \{(x, y): x^2 + y^2 < 4\}$

46. $f(x, y) = x + 3y$; $R = \{(x, y): |x| < 1, |y| < 2\}$

47. $f(x, y) = 2e^{-x-y}$; $R = \{(x, y): x \ge 0, y \ge 0\}$

48. $f(x, y) = x^2 - y^2$; $R = \{(x, y): |x| < 1, |y| < 1\}$

49–52. Absolute extrema on open and/or unbounded sets

49. Find the point on the plane $x + y + z = 4$ nearest the point $P(0, 3, 6)$.

50. Find the point(s) on the cone $z^2 = x^2 + y^2$ nearest the point $P(1, 4, 0)$.

51. Find the point on the surface $f(x, y) = x^2 + y^2 + 10$ nearest the plane $x + 2y - z = 0$. Identify the point on the plane.

52. Rectangular boxes with a volume of 10 m^3 are to be made of two materials. The material for the top and bottom of the box costs \$8/m^2 and the material for the sides of the box costs \$1/m^2. What are the dimensions of the box that minimizes the cost of the box?

Further Explorations

53. Explain why or why not Determine whether the following statements are true and give an explanation or counterexample. Assume that f is differentiable at the points in question.

a. The fact that $f_x(2, 2) = f_y(2, 2) = 0$ implies that f has a local maximum, local minimum, or saddle point at $(2, 2)$.

b. The function f could have a local maximum at (a, b) where $f_y(a, b) \neq 0$.

c. The function f could have both an absolute maximum and an absolute minimum at two different points that are not critical points.

d. The tangent plane is horizontal at a point on a surface corresponding to a critical point.

54–55. Extreme points from contour plots *Based on the level curves that are visible in the following graphs, identify the approximate locations of the local maxima, local minima, and saddle points.*

54.

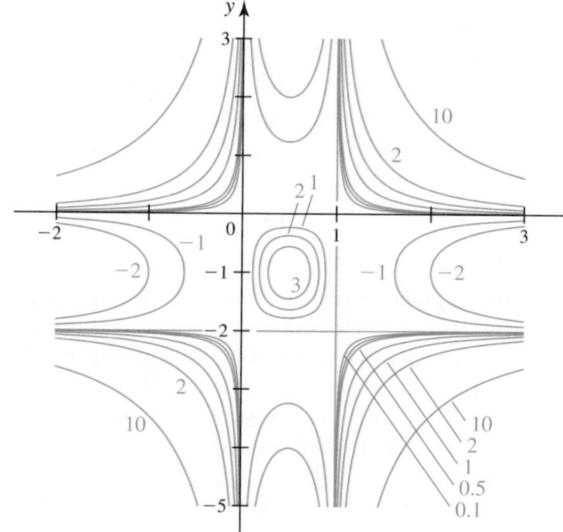

55.

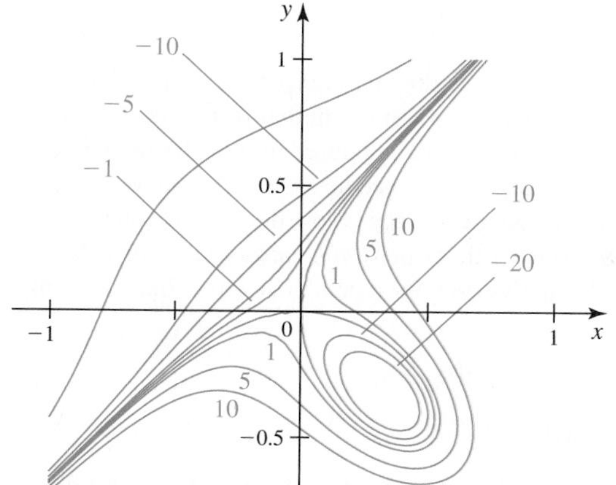

56. Optimal box Find the dimensions of the rectangular box with maximum volume in the first octant with one vertex at the origin and the opposite vertex on the ellipsoid $36x^2 + 4y^2 + 9z^2 = 36$.

57. Least distance What point on the plane $x - y + z = 2$ is closest to the point $(1, 1, 1)$?

58. Maximum/minimum of linear functions Let R be a closed bounded set in $\mathbf{R}^2$ and let $f(x, y) = ax + by + c$, where a, b, and c are real numbers, with a and b not both zero. Give a geometrical argument explaining why the absolute maximum and minimum values of f over R occur on the boundaries of R.

59. Magic triples Let x, y, and z be nonnegative numbers with $x + y + z = 200$.

a. Find the values of x, y, and z that minimize $x^2 + y^2 + z^2$.

b. Find the values of x, y, and z that minimize $\sqrt{x^2 + y^2 + z^2}$.

c. Find the values of x, y, and z that maximize xyz.

d. Find the values of x, y, and z that maximize $x^2y^2z^2$.

60. Powers and roots Assume that $x + y + z = 1$ with $x \geq 0$, $y \geq 0$, and $z \geq 0$.

a. Find the maximum and minimum values of $(1 + x^2)(1 + y^2)(1 + z^2)$.

b. Find the maximum and minimum values of $(1 + \sqrt{x})(1 + \sqrt{y})(1 + \sqrt{z})$.

Source: Math Horizons (April 2004).

Applications

61. Optimal locations Suppose n houses are located at the distinct points $(x_1, y_1), (x_2, y_2), \ldots, (x_n, y_n)$. A power substation must be located at a point such that the *sum of the squares* of the distances between the houses and the substation is minimized.

a. Find the optimal location of the substation in the case that $n = 3$ and the houses are located at $(0, 0)$, $(2, 0)$, and $(1, 1)$.

b. Find the optimal location of the substation in the case that $n = 3$ and the houses are located at distinct points (x_1, y_1), (x_2, y_2), and (x_3, y_3).

c. Find the optimal location of the substation in the general case of n houses located at distinct points $(x_1, y_1), (x_2, y_2), \ldots, (x_n, y_n)$.

d. You might argue that the locations found in parts (a), (b) and (c) are not optimal because they result from minimizing the sum of the *squares* of the distances, not the sum of the distances themselves. Use the locations in part (a) and write the function that gives the sum of the distances. Note that minimizing this function is much more difficult than in part (a). Then use a graphing utility to determine whether the optimal location is the same in the two cases. (Also see Exercise 69 about Steiner's problem.)

62–65. Least squares approximation *In its many guises, least squares approximation arises in numerous areas of mathematics and statistics. Suppose you collect data for two variables (for example, height and shoe size) in the form of pairs $(x_1, y_1), (x_2, y_2), \ldots, (x_n, y_n)$. The data may be plotted as a scatterplot in the xy-plane, as shown in the figure. The technique known as* linear regression *asks the question: What is the equation of the line that "best fits" the data? The least squares criterion for best fit requires that the sum of the squares of the vertical distances between the line and the data points is a minimum.*

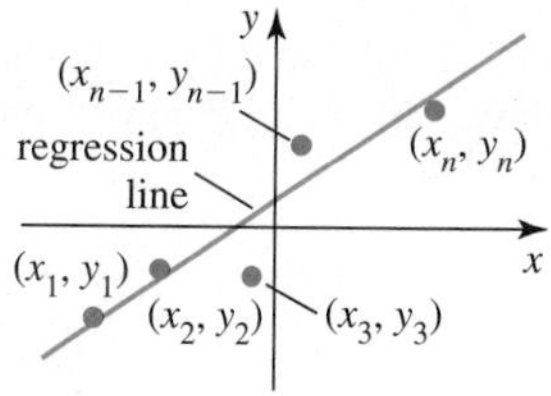

62. Let the equation of the best-fit line be $y = mx + b$, where the slope m and the y-intercept b must be determined using the least squares condition. First assume that there are three data points $(1, 2)$, $(3, 5)$, and $(4, 6)$. Show that the function of m and b that gives the sum of the squares of the vertical distances between the line and the three data points is

$$E(m, b) = [(m + b) - 2]^2 + [(3m + b) - 5]^2 + [(4m + b) - 6]^2.$$

Find the critical points of E and find the values of m and b that minimize E. Graph the three data points and the best-fit line.

T 63. Generalize the procedure in Exercise 62 by assuming that n data points $(x_1, y_1), (x_2, y_2), \ldots, (x_n, y_n)$ are given. Write the function $E(m, b)$ (summation notation allows for a more compact calculation). Show that the coefficients of the best-fit line are

$$m = \frac{\left(\sum x_k\right)\left(\sum y_k\right) - n\sum x_k y_k}{\left(\sum x_k\right)^2 - n\sum x_k^2},$$

$$b = \frac{1}{n}\left(\sum y_k - m\sum x_k\right),$$

where all sums run from $k = 1$ to $k = n$.

T 64–65. Least squares practice *Use the results of Exercise 63 to find the best-fit line for following data sets. Plot the points and the best-fit line.*

64. $(0, 0), (2, 3), (4, 5)$

65. $(-1, 0), (0, 6), (3, 8)$

Additional Exercises

66. Second Derivative Test Prove that if (a, b) is a critical point of f at which $f_x(a, b) = f_y(a, b) = 0$ and $f_{xx}(a, b) < 0 < f_{yy}(a, b)$ or $f_{yy}(a, b) < 0 < f_{xx}(a, b)$, then f has a saddle point at (a, b).

67. Maximum area triangle Among all triangles with a perimeter of 9 units, find the dimensions of the triangle with the maximum area. It may be easiest to use Heron's formula, which states that the area of a triangle with side length a, b, and c is $A = \sqrt{s(s - a)(s - b)(s - c)}$, where $2s$ is the perimeter of the triangle.

68. Ellipsoid inside a tetrahedron (1946 Putnam Exam) Let P be a plane tangent to the ellipsoid $x^2/a^2 + y^2/b^2 + z^2/c^2 = 1$ at a point in the first octant. Let T be the tetrahedron in the first octant bounded by P and the coordinate planes $x = 0$, $y = 0$, and $z = 0$. Find the minimum volume of T. (The volume of a tetrahedron is one-third the area of the base times the height.)

T 69. Steiner's problem for three points Given three distinct noncollinear points A, B, and C in the plane, find the point P in the plane such that the sum of the distances $|AP| + |BP| + |CP|$ is a minimum. Here is how to proceed with three points, assuming that the triangle formed by the three points has no angle greater than $2\pi/3$ (120°).

a. Assume the coordinates of the three given points are $A(x_1, y_1)$, $B(x_2, y_2)$, and $C(x_3, y_3)$. Let $d_1(x, y)$ be the distance between $A(x_1, y_1)$ and a variable point $P(x, y)$. Compute the gradient of d_1 and show that it is a unit vector pointing along the line between the two points.

b. Define d_2 and d_3 in a similar way and show that ∇d_2 and ∇d_3 are also unit vectors in the direction of the line between the two points.

c. The goal is to minimize $f(x, y) = d_1 + d_2 + d_3$. Show that the condition $f_x = f_y = 0$ implies that $\nabla d_1 + \nabla d_2 + \nabla d_3 = 0$.

d. Explain why part (c) implies that the optimal point P has the property that the three line segments AP, BP, and CP all intersect symmetrically in angles of $2\pi/3$.

e. What is the optimal solution if one of the angles in the triangle is greater than $2\pi/3$ (just draw a picture)?

f. Estimate the Steiner point for the three points $(0, 0)$, $(0, 1)$, $(2, 0)$.

70. Slicing plane Find an equation of the plane passing through the point $(3, 2, 1)$ that slices off the region in the first octant with the least volume.

T 71. Two mountains without a saddle Show that the following two functions have two local maxima but no other extreme points (thus no saddle or basin between the mountains).

a. $f(x, y) = -(x^2 - 1)^2 - (x^2 - e^y)^2$

b. $f(x, y) = 4x^2e^y - 2x^4 - e^{4y}$

Source: Proposed by Ira Rosenholtz, *Mathematics Magazine* (February, 1987).

T 72. Solitary critical points A function of *one* variable has the property that a local maximum (or minimum) occurring at the only critical point is also the absolute maximum (or minimum) (for example, $f(x) = x^2$). Does the same result hold for a function of *two* variables? Show that the following functions have the property that they have a single local maximum (or minimum), occurring at the only critical point, but that the local maximum (or minimum) is not an absolute maximum (or minimum) on $\mathbf{R}^2$.

a. $f(x, y) = 3xe^y - x^3 - e^{3y}$

b. $f(x, y) = (2y^2 - y^4)\left(e^x + \frac{1}{1 + x^2}\right) - \frac{1}{1 + x^2}$

This property has the following interpretation. Suppose that a surface has a single local minimum that is not the absolute minimum. Then water can be poured into the basin around the local minimum and the surface never overflows, even though there are points on the surface below the local minimum.
Source: See three articles in *Mathematics Magazine* (May 1985) and *Calculus and Analytical Geometry*, 2nd ed., Philip Gillett.

QUICK CHECK ANSWERS

1. $f_x(2, -1) = f_y(2, -1) = 0$. **2.** Vertically, in the directions $\langle 0, 0, \pm 1\rangle$ **3.** $D(x, y) = -12x^2y^2$ **4.** It has neither an absolute maximum nor absolute minimum value on this set.

13.9 Lagrange Multipliers

One of many challenges in economics and marketing is predicting the behavior of consumers. Basic models of consumer behavior often involve a *utility function* that expresses consumers' combined preference for several different amenities. For example, a simple utility function might have the form $U = f(\ell, g)$, where ℓ represents the amount of leisure time and g represents the number of consumable goods. The model assumes that consumers try to maximize their utility function, but they do so under certain constraints on the variables of the problem. For example, increasing leisure time may increase utility, but leisure time produces no income for consumable goods. Similarly, consumable goods may also increase utility, but they require income, which reduces leisure time. We first develop a general method for solving such constrained optimization problems and then return to economics problems later in the section.

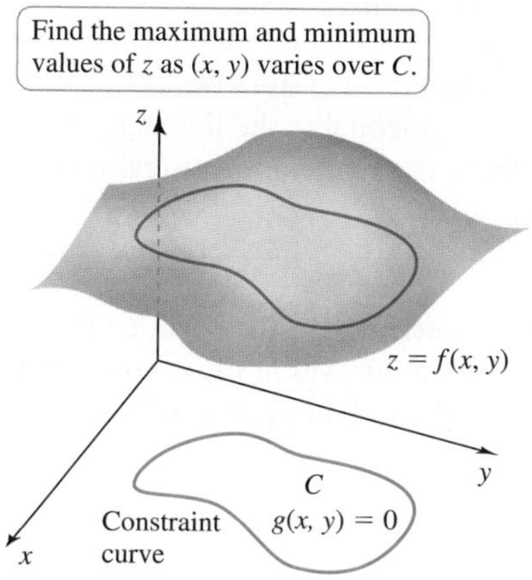

Find the maximum and minimum values of z as (x, y) varies over C.

$z = f(x, y)$

Constraint curve C: $g(x, y) = 0$

FIGURE 13.94

The Basic Idea

We start with a typical constrained optimization problem with two independent variables and give its method of solution; a generalization to more variables then follows. We seek maximum and/or minimum values of a differentiable function f (the **objective function**) with the restriction that x and y must lie on a **constraint** curve C in the xy-plane given by $g(x, y) = 0$ (Figure 13.94).

The problem and a method of solution are easy to visualize if we return to Example 6 of Section 13.8. Part of that problem was to find the maximum value of $f(x, y) = x^2 + y^2 - 2x + 2y + 5$ on the circle $C: \{(x, y): x^2 + y^2 = 4\}$ (Figure 13.95a). In Figure 13.95b we see the level curves of f and the point $P(-\sqrt{2}, \sqrt{2})$ on C at which f has a maximum value. Imagine moving along C toward P; as we approach P, the values of f increase and reach a maximum value at P. Moving past P, the values of f decrease.

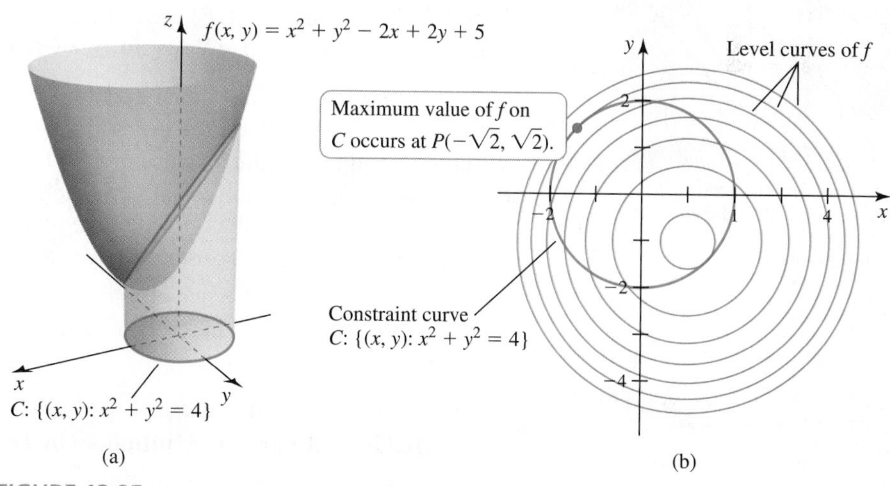

FIGURE 13.95

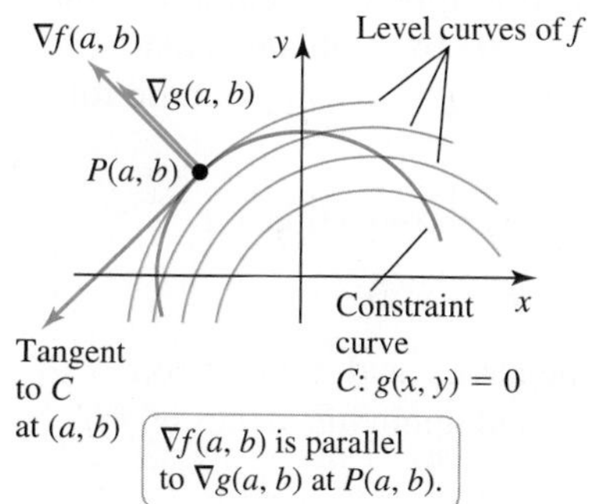

FIGURE 13.96

Figure 13.96 shows what is special about the point P. We already know that at any point $P(a, b)$, the tangent to the level curve of f at P is orthogonal to the gradient $\nabla f(a, b)$ (Theorem 13.12). We also see that the line tangent to the level curve at P is tangent to the constraint curve C at P. We prove this fact shortly.

Furthermore, if we think of the constraint curve C as just one level curve of the function $z = g(x, y)$, then it follows that the gradient $\nabla g(a, b)$ is also orthogonal to C at (a, b), where we assume that $\nabla g(a, b) \neq \mathbf{0}$ (Theorem 13.12). Therefore, the gradients $\nabla f(a, b)$ and $\nabla g(a, b)$ are parallel. These properties characterize the point P at which f has an extreme value on the constraint curve. They are the basis for the method of Lagrange multipliers that we now formalize.

Lagrange Multipliers with Two Independent Variables

The major step in establishing the method of Lagrange multipliers is to prove that Figure 13.96 is drawn correctly; that is, at the point on the constraint curve C where f has an extreme value, the line tangent to C is orthogonal to $\nabla f(a, b)$ and $\nabla g(a, b)$.

> The Greek lowercase ℓ is λ; it is read *lambda*.

THEOREM 13.15 Parallel Gradients (Ball Park Theorem)
Let f be a differentiable function in a region of $\mathbf{R}^2$ that contains the smooth curve C given by $g(x, y) = 0$. Assume that f has a local extreme value (relative to values of f on C) at a point $P(a, b)$ on C. Then, $\nabla f(a, b)$ is orthogonal to the line tangent to C at P. Assuming $\nabla g(a, b) \neq \mathbf{0}$, it follows that there is a real number λ (called a **Lagrange multiplier**) such that $\nabla f(a, b) = \lambda \nabla g(a, b)$.

Proof Because C is smooth it can be expressed parametrically in the form C: $\mathbf{r}(t) = \langle x(t), y(t) \rangle$, where x and y are differentiable functions on an interval in t that contains t_0 with $P(a, b) = (x(t_0), y(t_0))$. As we vary t and follow C, the rate of change of f is given by the Chain Rule:

$$\frac{df}{dt} = \frac{\partial f}{\partial x}\frac{dx}{dt} + \frac{\partial f}{\partial y}\frac{dy}{dt} = \nabla f \cdot \mathbf{r}'(t).$$

At the point $(x(t_0), y(t_0)) = (a, b)$ at which f has a local maximum or minimum value, we have $\left.\frac{df}{dt}\right|_{t=t_0} = 0$, which implies that $\nabla f(a, b) \cdot \mathbf{r}'(t_0) = 0$. Because $\mathbf{r}'(t)$ is tangent to C, the gradient $\nabla f(a, b)$ is orthogonal to the line tangent to C at P.

To prove the second assertion, note that the constraint curve C given by $g(x, y) = 0$ is also a level curve of the surface $z = g(x, y)$. Recall that gradients are orthogonal to level curves. Therefore, at the point $P(a, b)$, $\nabla g(a, b)$ is orthogonal to C at (a, b). Because both $\nabla f(a, b)$ and $\nabla g(a, b)$ are orthogonal to C, the two gradients are parallel, so there is a real number λ such that $\nabla f(a, b) = \lambda \nabla g(a, b)$. ◄

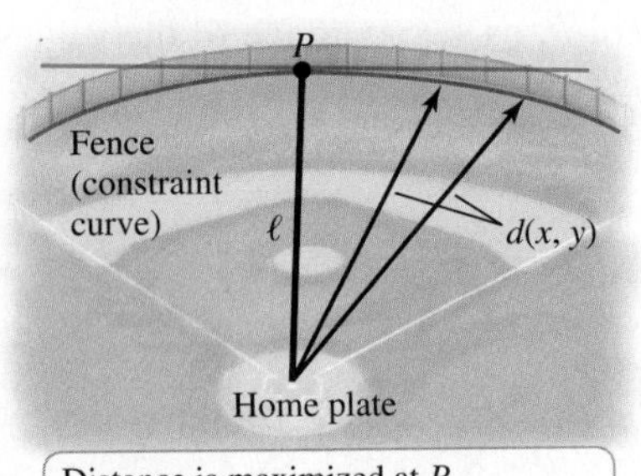

FIGURE 13.97

Theorem 13.15 has a nice geometric interpretation that makes it easy to remember. Suppose you walk along the outfield fence at a ballpark, which represents the constraint curve C, and record the distance $d(x, y)$ between you and home plate (which is the objective function). At some instant you reach a point P that maximizes the distance; it is the point on the fence farthest from home plate. The point P has the property that the line ℓ from P to home plate is orthogonal to the (line tangent to the) fence at P (Figure 13.97).

QUICK CHECK 1 Explain in terms of functions and gradients why the ballpark analogy for Theorem 13.15 is true. ◄

Method of Lagrange Multipliers in Two Variables

Let the objective function f and the constraint function g be differentiable on a region of $\mathbf{R}^2$ with $\nabla g(x, y) \neq \mathbf{0}$ on the curve $g(x, y) = 0$. To locate the maximum and minimum values of f subject to the constraint $g(x, y) = 0$, carry out the following steps.

1. Find the values of x, y, and λ (if they exist) that satisfy the equations
$$\nabla f(x, y) = \lambda \nabla g(x, y) \quad \text{and} \quad g(x, y) = 0.$$
2. Among the values (x, y) found in Step 1, select the largest and smallest corresponding function values, which are the maximum and minimum values of f subject to the constraint.

> *In principle*, it is possible to solve a constrained optimization problem by solving the constraint equation for one of the variables and eliminating that variable in the objective function. In practice, this method is often prohibitive, particularly with three or more variables or two or more constraints.

Notice that $\nabla f = \lambda \nabla g$ is a vector equation: $\langle f_x, f_y \rangle = \lambda \langle g_x, g_y \rangle$. It is satisfied provided $f_x = \lambda g_x$ and $f_y = \lambda g_y$. Therefore, the crux of the method is solving the three equations

$$f_x = \lambda g_x \qquad f_y = \lambda g_y \qquad g(x, y) = 0$$

for the three variables x, y, and λ.

EXAMPLE 1 Lagrange multipliers with two variables Find the maximum and minimum values of the objective function $f(x, y) = 2x^2 + y^2 + 2$, where x and y lie on the ellipse C given by $g(x, y) = x^2 + 4y^2 - 4 = 0$.

SOLUTION Figure 13.98a shows the elliptic paraboloid $z = f(x, y)$ above the ellipse C in the xy-plane. As the ellipse is traversed, the corresponding function values on the surface vary. The goal is to find the minimum and maximum of these function values. An alternative view is given in Figure 13.98b, where we see the level curves of f and the constraint curve C. As the ellipse is traversed, the values of f vary, reaching maximum and minimum values along the way.

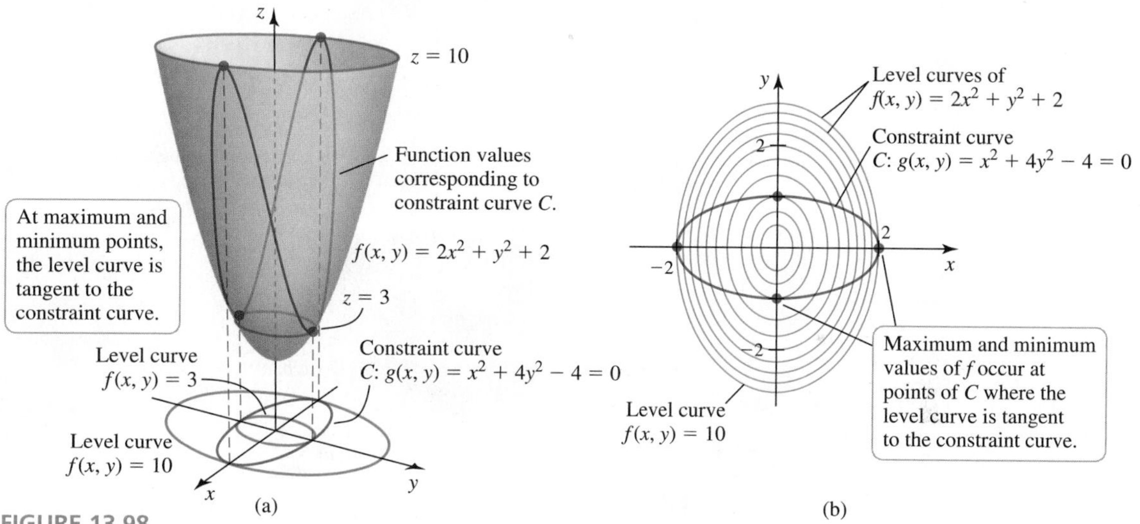

FIGURE 13.98

Noting that $\nabla f(x, y) = \langle 4x, 2y \rangle$ and $\nabla g(x, y) = \langle 2x, 8y \rangle$, the equations that result from $\nabla f = \lambda \nabla g$ and the constraint are

$$\underbrace{4x = \lambda(2x)}_{f_x = \lambda g_x} \qquad \underbrace{2y = \lambda(8y)}_{f_y = \lambda g_y} \qquad \underbrace{x^2 + 4y^2 - 4 = 0}_{g(x,y) = 0}$$

$$x(2 - \lambda) = 0 \ (1) \qquad y(1 - 4\lambda) = 0 \ (2) \qquad x^2 + 4y^2 - 4 = 0 \ (3)$$

The solutions of equation (1) are $x = 0$ or $\lambda = 2$. If $x = 0$, then equation (3) implies that $y = \pm 1$ and (2) implies that $\lambda = \frac{1}{4}$. On the other hand, if $\lambda = 2$, then equation (2) implies that $y = 0$; from (3), we get $x = \pm 2$. Therefore, the candidates for locations of extreme values are $(0, \pm 1)$, with $f(0, \pm 1) = 3$, and $(\pm 2, 0)$, with $f(\pm 2, 0) = 10$. We see that the maximum value of f on C is 10, which occurs at $(2, 0)$ and $(-2, 0)$; the minimum value of f on C is 3, which occurs at $(0, 1)$ and $(0, -1)$. *Related Exercises 5–10*

QUICK CHECK 2 Choose any point on the constraint curve in Figure 13.98b other than a solution point. Draw ∇f and ∇g at that point and show that they are not parallel.

Lagrange Multipliers with Three Independent Variables

The technique just outlined extends to three or more independent variables. With three variables, suppose an objective function $w = f(x, y, z)$ is given; its level surfaces are surfaces in $\mathbf{R}^3$ (Figure 13.99a). The constraint equation takes the form $g(x, y, z) = 0$, which is another surface S in $\mathbf{R}^3$ (Figure 13.99b). To find the maximum and minimum values of f on S (assuming they exist), we must find the points (a, b, c) on S at which $\nabla f(a, b, c)$ is parallel to $\nabla g(a, b, c)$, assuming $\nabla g(a, b, c) \neq \mathbf{0}$ (Figure 13.99c, d). The procedure for finding the maximum and minimum values of $f(x, y, z)$, where (x, y, z) are constrained to lie on S, is similar to the procedure for two variables.

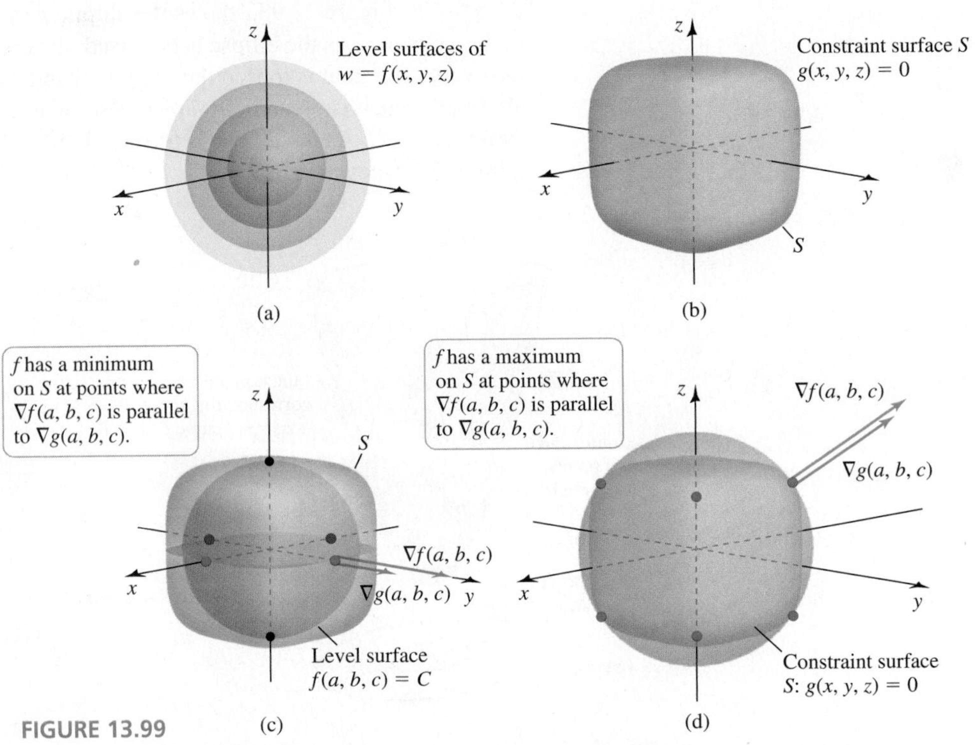

FIGURE 13.99

> Some books formulate the Lagrange multiplier method by defining $L = f - \lambda g$. The conditions of the method then become $\nabla L = \mathbf{0}$, where $\nabla L = \langle L_x, L_y, L_z, L_\lambda \rangle$.

Method of Lagrange Multipliers in Three Variables

Let f and g be differentiable on a region of $\mathbf{R}^3$ with $\nabla g(x, y, z) \neq \mathbf{0}$ on the surface $g(x, y, z) = 0$. To locate the maximum and minimum values of f subject to the constraint $g(x, y, z) = 0$, carry out the following steps.

1. Find the values of x, y, z, and λ that satisfy the equations
$$\nabla f(x, y, z) = \lambda \nabla g(x, y, z) \quad \text{and} \quad g(x, y, z) = 0.$$
2. Among the points (x, y, z) found in Step 1, select the largest and smallest corresponding values of the objective function. These values are the maximum and minimum values of f subject to the constraint.

Now, there are four equations to be solved for x, y, z, and λ:

$$f_x(x, y, z) = \lambda g_x(x, y, z) \qquad f_y(x, y, z) = \lambda g_y(x, y, z)$$
$$f_z(x, y, z) = \lambda g_z(x, y, z) \qquad g(x, y, z) = 0$$

➤ Problems similar to Example 2 were solved in Section 13.8 using ordinary optimization techniques. These methods may or may not be easier to apply than Lagrange multipliers.

EXAMPLE 2 **A geometry problem** Find the least distance between the point $P(3, 4, 0)$ and the surface of the cone $z^2 = x^2 + y^2$.

SOLUTION Figure 13.100 shows both sheets of the cone and the point $P(3, 4, 0)$. Because P is in the xy-plane, we anticipate two solutions, one for each sheet of the cone. The distance between P and any point $Q(x, y, z)$ on the cone is

$$d(x, y, z) = \sqrt{(x - 3)^2 + (y - 4)^2 + z^2}.$$

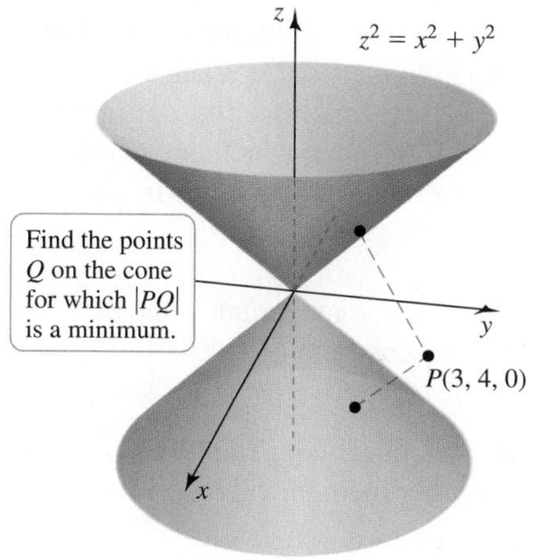

FIGURE 13.100

In many distance problems it is easier to work with the *square* of the distance to avoid dealing with square roots. This maneuver is allowable because if a point minimizes $(d(x, y, z))^2$, it also minimizes $d(x, y, z)$. Therefore, we define

$$f(x, y, z) = (d(x, y, z))^2 = (x - 3)^2 + (y - 4)^2 + z^2.$$

The constraint is the condition that the point (x, y, z) must lie on the cone, which implies $z^2 = x^2 + y^2$, or $g(x, y, z) = z^2 - x^2 - y^2 = 0$.

Now we proceed with Lagrange multipliers; the conditions are

$$f_x(x, y, z) = \lambda g_x(x, y, z), \text{ or } 2(x - 3) = \lambda(-2x), \text{ or } x(1 + \lambda) = 3 \quad (4)$$
$$f_y(x, y, z) = \lambda g_y(x, y, z), \text{ or } 2(y - 4) = \lambda(-2y), \text{ or } y(1 + \lambda) = 4 \quad (5)$$
$$f_z(x, y, z) = \lambda g_z(x, y, z), \text{ or } 2z = \lambda(2z), \text{ or } z = \lambda z \quad (6)$$
$$g(x, y, z) = z^2 - x^2 - y^2 = 0. \quad (7)$$

The solutions of equation (6) (the simplest of the four equations) are either $z = 0$, or $\lambda = 1$ and $z \neq 0$. In the first case, if $z = 0$, then by equation (7), $x = y = 0$; however, $x = 0$ and $y = 0$ do not satisfy (4) and (5). So no solution results from this case.

➤ With three independent variables, it is possible to impose two constraints. These problems are explored in Exercises 53–57.

On the other hand if $\lambda = 1$, then by (4) and (5), we find that $x = \frac{3}{2}$ and $y = 2$. Using (7), the corresponding values of z are $\pm\frac{5}{2}$. Therefore, the two solutions and the values of f are

$$x = \tfrac{3}{2}, \quad y = 2, \quad z = \tfrac{5}{2} \quad \text{with } f\left(\tfrac{3}{2}, 2, \tfrac{5}{2}\right) = \tfrac{25}{2}$$
$$x = \tfrac{3}{2}, \quad y = 2, \quad z = -\tfrac{5}{2} \quad \text{with } f\left(\tfrac{3}{2}, 2, -\tfrac{5}{2}\right) = \tfrac{25}{2}.$$

You can check that moving away from $\left(\frac{3}{2}, 2, \pm\frac{5}{2}\right)$ in any direction on the cone has the effect of increasing the values of f. Therefore, the points correspond to *local* minima of the distance function. Do these points also correspond to *absolute* minima? The domain of this problem is unbounded; however, one can argue geometrically that the distance function increases without bound moving away from $\left(\frac{3}{2}, 2, \pm\frac{5}{2}\right)$. Therefore, these points correspond to absolute minimum values and the points on the cone nearest to $(3, 4, 0)$ are $\left(\frac{3}{2}, 2, \pm\frac{5}{2}\right)$, at a distance of $\sqrt{\frac{25}{2}} = \frac{5}{\sqrt{2}}$.

Related Exercises 11–26 ◀

QUICK CHECK 3 In Example 2, is there a point that *maximizes* the distance between $(3, 4, 0)$ and the cone? If the point $(3, 4, 0)$ were replaced by $(3, 4, 1)$, how many minimizing solutions would there be? ◀

Economic Models

In the opening of this section, we briefly described how utility functions are used to model consumer behavior. We now look in more detail at some specific—admittedly simple—utility functions and the constraints that are imposed upon them.

As described earlier, a prototype model for consumer behavior uses two independent variables: leisure time ℓ and consumable goods g. A utility function $U = f(\ell, g)$ measures consumer preferences for various combinations of leisure time and consumable goods. The following assumptions about utility functions are commonly made:

1. Utility increases if any variable increases (essentially, *more is better*).
2. Various combinations of leisure time and consumable goods have the same utility; that is, giving up some leisure time for additional consumable goods results in the same utility.

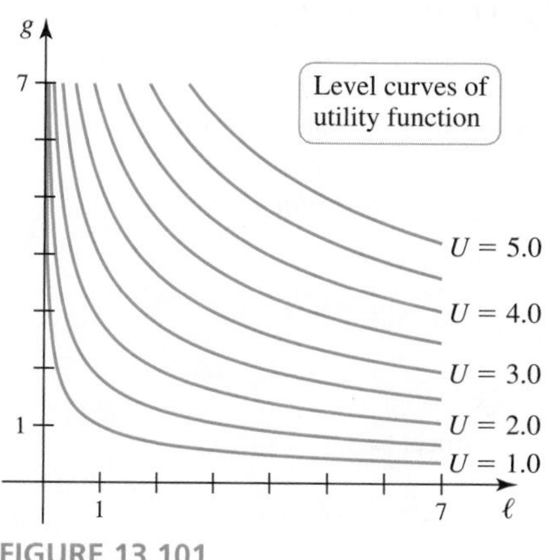

FIGURE 13.101

The level curves of a typical utility function are shown in Figure 13.101. Assumption 1 is reflected by the fact that the utility values on the level curves increase as either ℓ or g

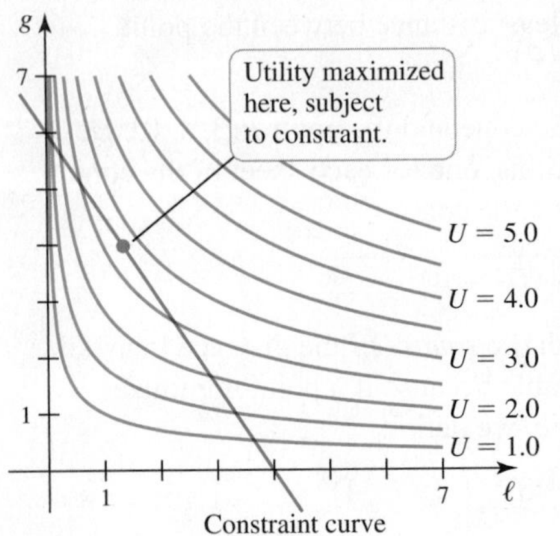

FIGURE 13.102

increases. Consistent with Assumption 2, a single level curve shows the combinations of ℓ and g that have the same utility; for this reason, economists call the level curves *indifference curves*. Notice that if ℓ increases, then g must decrease on a level curve to maintain the same utility, and vice versa.

Economic models assert that consumers maximize utility subject to constraints on leisure time and consumable goods. One assumption that leads to a reasonable constraint is that an increase in leisure time implies a linear decrease in consumable goods. Therefore, the constraint curve is a line with negative slope (Figure 13.102). When such a constraint is superimposed on the level curves of the utility function, the optimization problem becomes evident. Among all points on the constraint line, which one maximizes utility? A solution is marked in the figure; at this point the utility has a maximum value (between 2.5 and 3.0).

EXAMPLE 3 Constrained optimization of utility Find the maximum value of the utility function $U = f(\ell, g) = \ell^{1/3}g^{2/3}$, subject to the constraint $G(\ell, g) = 3\ell + 2g - 12 = 0$, where $\ell \geq 0$ and $g \geq 0$.

SOLUTION The level curves of the utility function and the linear constraint are shown in Figure 13.102. The solution follows the Lagrange multiplier method with two variables. The gradient of the utility function is

$$\nabla f(\ell, g) = \left\langle \frac{\ell^{-2/3}g^{2/3}}{3}, \frac{2\ell^{1/3}g^{-1/3}}{3} \right\rangle = \frac{1}{3}\left\langle \left(\frac{g}{\ell}\right)^{2/3}, 2\left(\frac{\ell}{g}\right)^{1/3} \right\rangle.$$

The gradient of the constraint function is $\nabla G(\ell, g) = \langle 3, 2 \rangle$. Therefore, the equations that must be solved are

$$\frac{1}{3}\left(\frac{g}{\ell}\right)^{2/3} = 3\lambda, \quad \frac{2}{3}\left(\frac{\ell}{g}\right)^{1/3} = 2\lambda, \quad G(\ell, g) = 3\ell + 2g - 12 = 0.$$

Eliminating λ from the first two equations leads to the condition $g = 3\ell$, which, when substituted into the constraint equation, gives the solution $\ell = \frac{4}{3}$ and $g = 4$. The actual value of the utility function at this point is $U = f\left(\frac{4}{3}, 4\right) = 4/\sqrt[3]{3} \approx 2.8$. This solution is consistent with Figure 13.102.

Related Exercises 27–30 ◀

QUICK CHECK 4 In Figure 13.102, explain why, if you move away from the optimal point along the constraint line, the utility decreases. ◀

SECTION 13.9 EXERCISES

Review Questions

1. Explain why, at a point that maximizes or minimizes f subject to a constraint $g(x, y) = 0$, the gradient of f is parallel to the gradient of g. Use a diagram.

2. If $f(x, y) = x^2 + y^2$ and $g(x, y) = 2x + 3y - 4 = 0$, write the Lagrange multiplier conditions that must be satisfied by a point that maximizes or minimizes f subject to $g(x, y) = 0$.

3. If $f(x, y, z) = x^2 + y^2 + z^2$ and $g(x, y, z) = 2x + 3y - 5z + 4 = 0$, write the Lagrange multiplier conditions that must be satisfied by a point that maximizes or minimizes f subject to $g(x, y, z) = 0$.

4. Sketch several level curves of $f(x, y) = x^2 + y^2$ and sketch the constraint line $g(x, y) = 2x + 3y - 4 = 0$. Describe the extrema (if any) that f attains on the constraint line.

Basic Skills

5–10. Lagrange multipliers in two variables *Use Lagrange multipliers to find the maximum and minimum values of f (when they exist) subject to the given constraint.*

5. $f(x, y) = x + 2y$ subject to $x^2 + y^2 = 4$

6. $f(x, y) = xy^2$ subject to $x^2 + y^2 = 1$

7. $f(x, y) = e^{2xy}$ subject to $x^3 + y^3 = 16$

8. $f(x, y) = x^2 + y^2$ subject to $x^6 + y^6 = 1$

9. $f(x, y) = y^2 - 4x^2$ subject to $x^2 + 2y^2 = 4$

10. $f(x, y) = xy + x + y$ subject to $xy = 4$

11–16. Lagrange multipliers in three or more variables *Use Lagrange multipliers to find the maximum and minimum values of f (when they exist) subject to the given constraint.*

11. $f(x, y, z) = x + 3y - z$ subject to $x^2 + y^2 + z^2 = 4$

12. $f(x, y, z) = xyz$ subject to $x^2 + 2y^2 + 4z^2 = 9$

13. $f(x, y, z) = xy^2z^3$ subject to $x^2 + y^2 + 2z^2 = 25$

14. $f(x, y, z) = x^2 + y^2 + z^2$ subject to $z = 1 + 2xy$

15. $f(x, y, z) = x^2 + y^2 + z^2$ subject to $xyz = 4$

16. $f(x, y, z) = (xyz)^{1/2}$ subject to $x + y + z = 1$ with $x \geq 0$, $y \geq 0$, $z \geq 0$

17–26. Applications of Lagrange multipliers *Use Lagrange multipliers in the following problems. When the domain of the objective function is unbounded or open, explain why you have found an absolute maximum or minimum value.*

17. **Shipping regulations** A shipping company requires that the sum of length plus girth of rectangular boxes must not exceed 108 in. Find the dimensions of the box with maximum volume that meets this condition. (The girth is the perimeter of the smallest base of the box.)

18. **Box with minimum surface area** Find the rectangular box with a volume of 16 ft^3 that has minimum surface area.

T 19. **Extreme distances to an ellipse** Find the minimum and maximum distances between the ellipse $x^2 + xy + 2y^2 = 1$ and the origin.

20. **Maximum area rectangle in an ellipse** Find the dimensions of the rectangle of maximum area with sides parallel to the coordinate axes that can be inscribed in the ellipse $4x^2 + 16y^2 = 16$.

21. **Maximum perimeter rectangle in an ellipse** Find the dimensions of the rectangle of maximum perimeter with sides parallel to the coordinate axes that can be inscribed in the ellipse $4x^2 + 9y^2 = 36$.

22. **Minimum distance to a plane** Find the point on the plane $2x + 3y + 6z - 10 = 0$ closest to the point $(-2, 5, 1)$.

T 23. **Minimum distance to a surface** Find the point on the surface $x^2 - 2xy + 2y^2 - x + y = 0$ closest to the point $(1, 2, -3)$.

24. **Minimum distance to a cone** Find the points on the cone $z^2 = x^2 + y^2$ closest to the point $(1, 2, 0)$.

25. **Extreme distances to a sphere** Find the minimum and maximum distances between the sphere $x^2 + y^2 + z^2 = 9$ and the point $(2, 3, 4)$.

26. **Maximum volume cylinder in a sphere** Find the dimensions of a right circular cylinder of maximum volume that can be inscribed in a sphere of radius 16.

27–30. Maximizing utility functions *Find the values of ℓ and g with $\ell \geq 0$ and $g \geq 0$ that maximize the following utility functions subject to the given constraints. Give the value of the utility function at the optimal point.*

27. $U = f(\ell, g) = 10\ell^{1/2}g^{1/2}$ subject to $3\ell + 6g = 18$

28. $U = f(\ell, g) = 32\ell^{2/3}g^{1/3}$ subject to $4\ell + 2g = 12$

29. $U = f(\ell, g) = 8\ell^{4/5}g^{1/5}$ subject to $10\ell + 8g = 40$

30. $U = f(\ell, g) = \ell^{1/6}g^{5/6}$ subject to $4\ell + 5g = 20$

Further Explorations

31. **Explain why or why not** Determine whether the following statements are true and give an explanation or counterexample.

 a. Suppose you are standing at the center of a sphere looking at a point P on the surface of the sphere. Your line of sight to P is orthogonal to the plane tangent to the sphere at P.

 b. At a point that maximizes f on the curve $g(x, y) = 0$, the dot product $\nabla f \cdot \nabla g$ is zero.

32–37. *Solve the following problems from Section 13.8 using Lagrange multipliers.*

32. Exercise 29
33. Exercise 30
34. Exercise 31
35. Exercise 32
36. Exercise 56
37. Exercise 57

T **38–41. Absolute maximum and minimum values** *Find the absolute maximum and minimum values of the following functions over the given regions R. Use Lagrange multipliers to check for extreme points on the boundary.*

38. $f(x, y) = x^2 + 4y^2 + 1$; $R = \{(x, y): x^2 + 4y^2 \leq 1\}$

39. $f(x, y) = x^2 - 4y^2 + xy$; $R = \{(x, y): 4x^2 + 9y^2 \leq 36\}$

40. $f(x, y) = 2x^2 + y^2 + 2x - 3y$; $R = \{(x, y): x^2 + y^2 \leq 1\}$

41. $f(x, y) = (x - 1)^2 + (y + 1)^2$; $R = \{(x, y): x^2 + y^2 \leq 4\}$

42–43. Graphical Lagrange multipliers *The following figures show the level curves of f and the constraint curve $g(x, y) = 0$. Estimate the maximum and minimum values of f subject to the constraint. At each point where an extreme value occurs, indicate the direction of ∇f and a possible direction of ∇g.*

42.

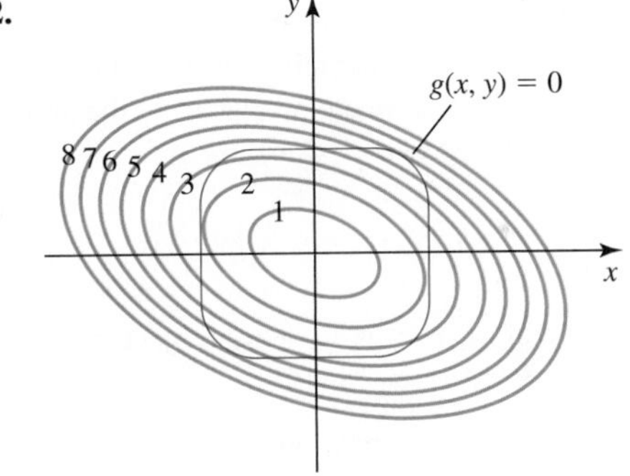

43.

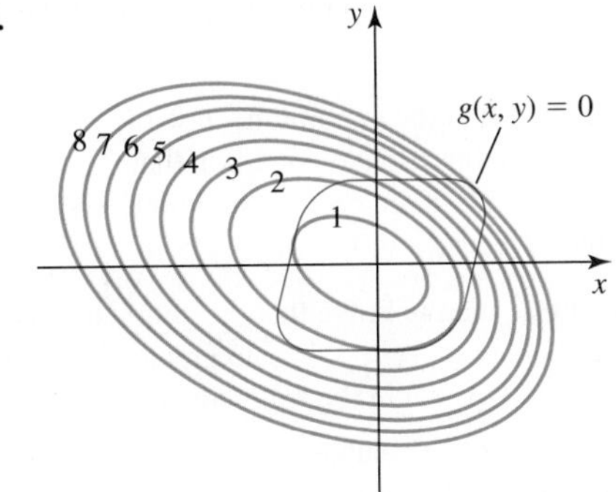

44. **Extreme points on flattened spheres** The equation $x^{2n} + y^{2n} + z^{2n} = 1$, where n is a positive integer, describes a flattened sphere. Define the extreme points to be the points on the flattened sphere with a maximum distance from the origin.

 a. Find all the extreme points on the flattened sphere with $n = 2$. What is the distance between the extreme points and the origin?

b. Find all the extreme points on the flattened sphere for integers $n > 2$. What is the distance between the extreme points and the origin?

c. Give the location of the extreme points in the limit as $n \to \infty$. What is the limiting distance between the extreme points and the origin as $n \to \infty$?

Applications

45–47. Production functions *Economists model the output of manufacturing systems using production functions that have many of the same properties as utility functions. The family of Cobb-Douglas production functions has the form $P = f(K, L) = CK^a L^{1-a}$, where K represents capital, L represents labor, and C and a are positive real numbers with $0 < a < 1$. If the cost of capital is p dollars per unit, the cost of labor is q dollars per unit, and the total available budget is B, then the constraint takes the form $pK + qL = B$. Find the values of K and L that maximize the following production functions subject to the given constraint, assuming $K \geq 0$ and $L \geq 0$.*

45. $P = f(K, L) = K^{1/2}L^{1/2}$ for $20K + 30L = 300$

46. $P = f(K, L) = 10K^{1/3}L^{2/3}$ for $30K + 60L = 360$

47. Given the production function $P = f(K, L) = K^a L^{1-a}$ and the budget constraint $pK + qL = B$, where a, p, q, and B are given, show that P is maximized when $K = aB/p$ and $L = (1 - a)B/q$.

48. Least squares approximation Find the coefficients in the equation of the plane $z = ax + by + c$ that minimize the sum of the squares of the vertical distances between the plane and the points $(1, 2, 3)$, $(-2, 3, 1)$, $(3, 0, -4)$, and $(0, -2, 6)$.

Additional Exercises

49–51. Maximizing a sum

49. Find the maximum value of $x_1 + x_2 + x_3 + x_4$ subject to the condition that $x_1^2 + x_2^2 + x_3^2 + x_4^2 = 16$.

50. Generalize Exercise 49 and find the maximum value of $x_1 + x_2 + \cdots + x_n$ subject to the condition that $x_1^2 + x_2^2 + \cdots + x_n^2 = c^2$ for a real number c and a positive integer n.

51. Generalize Exercise 49 and find the maximum value of $a_1x_1 + a_2x_2 + \cdots + a_nx_n$ subject to the condition that $x_1^2 + x_2^2 + \cdots + x_n^2 = 1$ for given positive real numbers $a_1, \ldots, a_n$ and a positive integer n.

52. Geometric and arithmetic means Prove that the geometric mean of a set of positive numbers $(x_1x_2 \cdots x_n)^{1/n}$ is no greater than the arithmetic mean $(x_1 + \cdots + x_n)/n$ in the following cases.

a. Find the maximum value of xyz, subject to $x + y + z = k$, where k is a real number and $x > 0$, $y > 0$, and $z > 0$. Use the result to prove that

$$(xyz)^{1/3} \leq \frac{x + y + z}{3}.$$

b. Generalize part (a) and show that

$$(x_1x_2 \cdots x_n)^{1/n} \leq \frac{x_1 + \cdots + x_n}{n}.$$

53. Problems with two constraints Given a differentiable function $w = f(x, y, z)$, the goal is to find its maximum and minimum values subject to the constraints $g(x, y, z) = 0$ and $h(x, y, z) = 0$, where g and h are also differentiable.

a. Imagine a level surface of the function f and the constraint surfaces $g(x, y, z) = 0$ and $h(x, y, z) = 0$. Note that g and h intersect (in general) in a curve C on which maximum and minimum values of f must be found. Explain why ∇g and ∇h are orthogonal to their respective surfaces.

b. Explain why ∇f lies in the plane formed by ∇g and ∇h at a point of C where f has a maximum or minimum value.

c. Explain why part (b) implies that $\nabla f = \lambda \nabla g + \mu \nabla h$ at a point of C where f has a maximum or minimum value, where λ and μ (the Lagrange multipliers) are real numbers.

d. Conclude from part (c) that the equations that must be solved for maximum or minimum values of f subject to two constraints are $\nabla f = \lambda \nabla g + \mu \nabla h$, $g(x, y, z) = 0$, and $h(x, y, z) = 0$.

54–57. Two-constraint problems *Use the result of Exercise 53 to solve the following problems.*

54. The planes $x + 2z = 12$ and $x + y = 6$ intersect in a line L. Find the point on L nearest the origin.

55. Find the maximum and minimum values of $f(x, y, z) = xyz$ subject to the conditions that $x^2 + y^2 = 4$ and $x + y + z = 1$.

56. The paraboloid $z = x^2 + 2y^2 + 1$ and the plane $x - y + 2z = 4$ intersect in a curve C. Find the points on C that have minimum and maximum distance from the origin.

57. Find the maximum and minimum values of $f(x, y, z) = x^2 + y^2 + z^2$ on the curve on which the cone $z^2 = 4x^2 + 4y^2$ and the plane $2x + 4z = 5$ intersect.

QUICK CHECK ANSWERS

1. Let $d(x, y)$ be the distance between any point $P(x, y)$ on the fence and home plate O. The key fact is that ∇d always points along the line OP. As P moves along the fence (the constraint curve), $d(x, y)$ increases until a point is reached at which ∇d is orthogonal to the fence. At this point, d has a maximum value. **3.** The distance between $(3, 4, 0)$ and the cone can be arbitrarily large, so there is no maximizing solution. If the point of interest is not in the xy-plane, there is one minimizing solution. **4.** If you move along the constraint line away from the optimal solution in either direction, you cross level curves of the utility function with decreasing values.

CHAPTER 13 REVIEW EXERCISES

1. **Explain why or why not** Determine whether the following statements are true and give an explanation or counterexample.
   a. The equation $4x - 3y = 12$ describes a line in $\mathbf{R}^3$.
   b. The equation $z^2 = 2x^2 - 6y^2$ determines z as a single function of x and y.
   c. If f has continuous partial derivatives of all orders, then $f_{xxy} = f_{yyx}$.
   d. Given the surface $z = f(x, y)$, the gradient $\nabla f(a, b)$ lies in the plane tangent to the surface at $(a, b, f(a, b))$.
   e. There is always a plane orthogonal to both of two distinct intersecting planes.

2. **Equations of planes** Consider the plane that passes through the point $(6, 0, 1)$ with a normal vector $\mathbf{n} = \langle 3, 4, -6 \rangle$.
   a. Find an equation of the plane.
   b. Find the intercepts of the plane with the three coordinate axes.
   c. Make a sketch of the plane.

3. **Equations of planes** Consider the plane passing through the points $(0, 0, 3)$, $(1, 0, -6)$, and $(1, 2, 3)$.
   a. Find an equation of the plane.
   b. Find the intercepts of the plane with the three coordinate axes.
   c. Make a sketch of the plane.

4–5. Intersecting planes *Find an equation of the line that forms the intersection of the following planes Q and R.*

4. $Q: 2x + y - z = 0$, $R: -x + y + z = 1$

5. $Q: -3x + y + 2z = 0$, $R: 3x + 3y + 4z - 12 = 0$

6–7. Equations of planes *Find an equation of the following planes.*

6. The plane passing through $(2, -3, 1)$ normal to the line $\langle x, y, z \rangle = \langle 2 + t, 3t, 2 - 3t \rangle$

7. The plane passing through $(-2, 3, 1)$, $(1, 1, 0)$, and $(-1, 0, 1)$

8–22. Identifying surfaces *Consider the surfaces defined by the following equations.*

   a. *Identify and briefly describe the surface.*
   b. *Find the xy-, xz-, and yz-traces, if they exist.*
   c. *Find the intercepts with the three coordinate axes, if they exist.*
   d. *Make a sketch of the surface.*

8. $z - \sqrt{x} = 0$

9. $3z = \dfrac{x^2}{12} - \dfrac{y^2}{48}$

10. $\dfrac{x^2}{100} + 4y^2 + \dfrac{z^2}{16} = 1$

11. $y^2 = 4x^2 + z^2/25$

12. $\dfrac{4x^2}{9} + \dfrac{9z^2}{4} = y^2$

13. $4z = \dfrac{x^2}{4} + \dfrac{y^2}{9}$

14. $\dfrac{x^2}{16} + \dfrac{z^2}{36} - \dfrac{y^2}{100} = 1$

15. $y^2 + 4z^2 - 2x^2 = 1$

16. $-\dfrac{x^2}{16} + \dfrac{z^2}{36} - \dfrac{y^2}{25} = 4$

17. $\dfrac{x^2}{4} + \dfrac{y^2}{16} - z^2 = 4$

18. $x = \dfrac{y^2}{64} - \dfrac{z^2}{9}$

19. $\dfrac{x^2}{4} + \dfrac{y^2}{16} + z^2 = 4$

20. $y - e^{-x} = 0$

21. $\dfrac{y^2}{49} + \dfrac{x^2}{9} = \dfrac{z^2}{64}$

22. $y = 4x^2 + \dfrac{z^2}{9}$

23–26. Domains *Find the domain of the following functions. Make a rough sketch of the domain in the xy-plane.*

23. $f(x, y) = \dfrac{1}{y^2 + x^2}$

24. $f(x, y) = \ln xy$

25. $f(x, y) = \sqrt{x - y^2}$

26. $f(x, y) = \tan(x + y)$

27. **Matching surfaces** Match functions a–d with surfaces A–D in the figure.
   a. $z = \sqrt{2x^2 + 3y^2 + 1} - 1$
   b. $z = -3y^2$
   c. $z = 2x^2 - 3y^2 + 1$
   d. $z = \sqrt{2x^2 + 3y^2 - 1}$

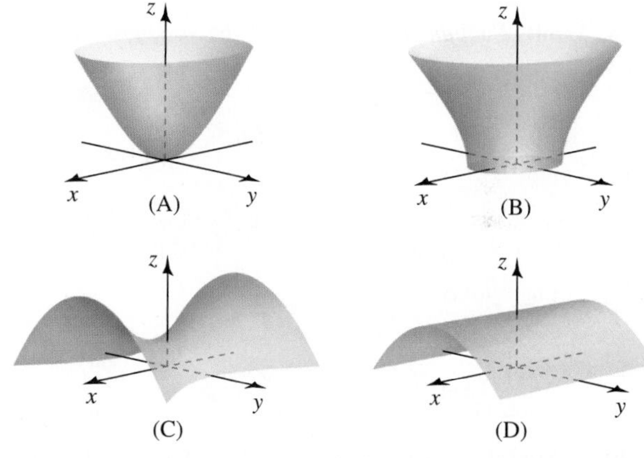

28–29. Level curves *Make a sketch of several level curves of the following functions. Label at least two level curves with their z-values.*

28. $f(x, y) = x^2 - y$

29. $f(x, y) = 2x^2 + 4y^2$

30. **Matching level curves with surfaces** Match level curve plots a–d with surfaces A–D.

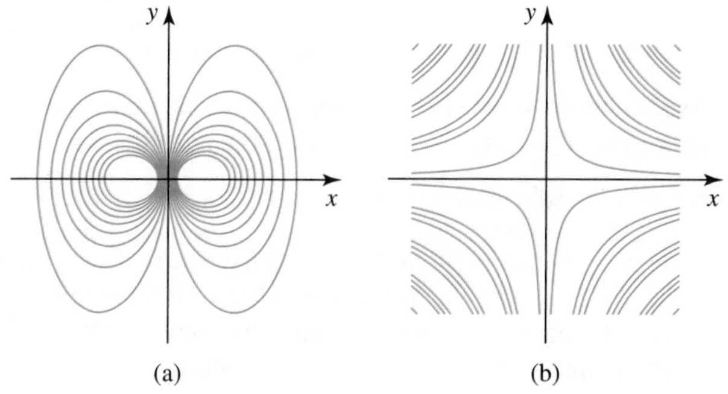

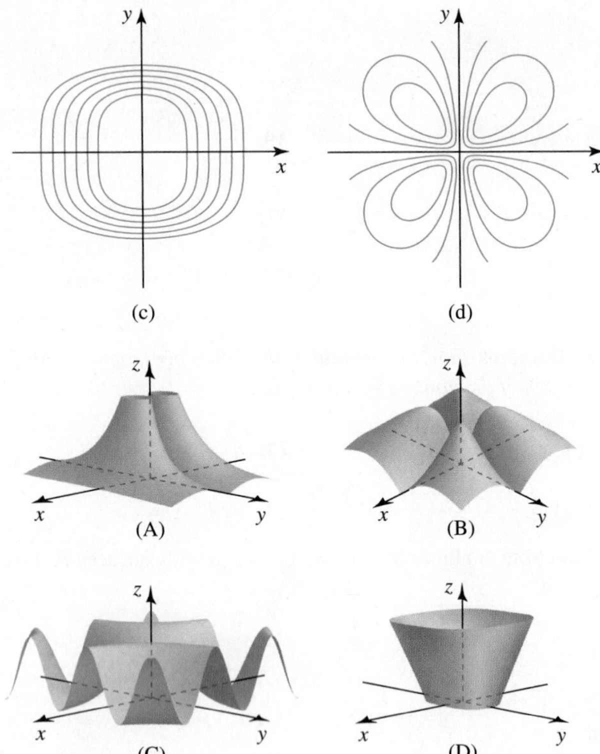

31–36. Limits *Evaluate the following limits or determine that they do not exist.*

31. $\lim_{(x,y)\to(4,-2)} (10x - 5y + 6xy)$ **32.** $\lim_{(x,y)\to(1,1)} \frac{xy}{x + y}$

33. $\lim_{(x,y)\to(-1,1)} \frac{x^2 - y^2}{x^2 - xy - 2y^2}$ **34.** $\lim_{(x,y)\to(1,2)} \frac{x^2y}{x^4 + 2y^2}$

35. $\lim_{(x,y,z)\to(\frac{\pi}{2},0,\frac{\pi}{2})} 4 \cos y \sin\sqrt{xz}$

36. $\lim_{(x,y,z)\to(5,2,-3)} \tan^{-1}\left(\frac{x + y^2}{z^2}\right)$

37–40. Partial derivatives *Find the first partial derivatives of the following functions.*

37. $f(x, y) = xy\,e^{xy}$ **38.** $g(u, v) = u \cos v - v \sin u$

39. $f(x, y, z) = e^{x+2y+3z}$ **40.** $H(p, q, r) = p^2\sqrt{q + r}$

41–42. Laplace's equation *Verify that the following functions satisfy Laplace's equation,* $\frac{\partial^2 u}{\partial x^2} + \frac{\partial^2 u}{\partial y^2} = 0$.

41. $u(x, y) = y(3x^2 - y^2)$ **42.** $u(x, y) = \ln(x^2 + y^2)$

43. Region between spheres Two spheres have the same center with radii r and R, where $0 < r < R$. The volume of the region between the spheres is $V(r, R) = \frac{4\pi}{3}(R^3 - r^3)$.

a. First, use your intuition. If r is held fixed, how does V change as R increases? What is the sign of V_R? If R is held fixed, how does V change as r increases (up to the value of R)? What is the sign of V_r?

b. Compute V_r and V_R. Are the results consistent with part (a)?

c. Consider spheres with $R = 3$ and $r = 1$. Does the volume change more if R is increased by $\Delta R = 0.1$ (with r fixed) or if r is decreased by $\Delta r = 0.1$ (with R fixed)?

44–47. Chain Rule *Use the Chain Rule to evaluate the following derivatives.*

44. $w'(t)$, where $w = xy \sin z$, $x = t^2$, $y = 4t^3$, and $z = t + 1$

45. $w'(t)$, where $w = \sqrt{x^2 + y^2 + z^2}$, $x = \sin t$, $y = \cos t$, and $z = \cos t$

46. w_s and w_t, where $w = xyz$, $x = 2st$, $y = st^2$, and $z = s^2t$

47. w_r, w_s *and* w_t, where $w = \ln(x^2 + y^2 + 1)$, $x = rst$, and $y = r + s + t$

48–49. Implicit differentiation *Find dy/dx for the following implicit relations.*

48. $2x^2 + 3xy - 3y^4 = 2$ **49.** $y \ln(x^2 + y^2) = 4$

50–51. Walking on a surface *Consider the following surfaces and parameterized curves C in the xy-plane.*

a. *In each case find $z'(t)$ on C.*

b. *Imagine that you are walking on the surface directly above C. Find the values of t for which you are walking uphill.*

50. $z = 4x^2 + y^2 - 2$; $C: x = \cos t, y = \sin t$, for $0 \le t \le 2\pi$

51. $z = x^2 - 2y^2 + 4$; $C: x = 2\cos t, y = 2\sin t$, for $0 \le t \le 2\pi$

52. Constant volume cones Suppose the radius of a right circular cone increases as $r(t) = t^a$ and the height decreases as $h(t) = t^{-b}$, for $t \ge 1$, where a and b are positive constants. What is the relationship between a and b such that the volume of the cone remains constant (that is, $V'(t) = 0$, where $V = (\pi/3)r^2h$)?

53. Directional derivatives Consider the function $f(x, y) = 2x^2 - 4y^2 + 10$, whose graph is shown in the figure.

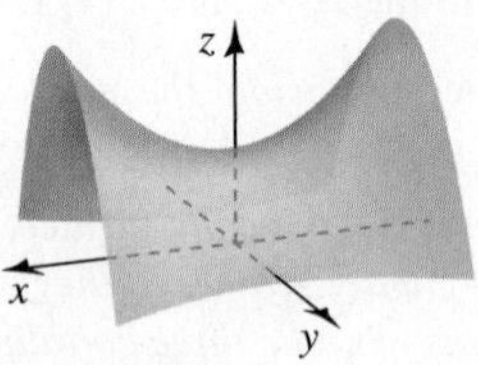

a. Fill in the table showing the value of the directional derivative at points (a, b) in the direction θ.

	$(a, b) = (0, 0)$	$(a, b) = (2, 0)$	$(a, b) = (1, 1)$
$\theta = \pi/4$			
$\theta = 3\pi/4$			
$\theta = 5\pi/4$			

b. Indicate in a sketch of the xy-plane the point and direction for each of the table entries in part (a).

54–57. Computing gradients *Compute the gradient of the following functions, evaluate it at the given point, and evaluate the directional derivative in the given direction.*

54. $f(x, y) = \sin(x - 2y)$; $(-1, -5)$; $\mathbf{u} = \left\langle \frac{1}{\sqrt{2}}, \frac{-1}{\sqrt{2}} \right\rangle$

55. $h(x, y) = \sqrt{2 + x^2 + 2y^2}$; $(2, 1)$; $\mathbf{u} = \left\langle \frac{3}{5}, \frac{4}{5} \right\rangle$

56. $f(x, y, z) = xy + yz + xz + 4$; $(2, -2, 1)$; $\mathbf{u} = \left\langle 0, \frac{-1}{\sqrt{2}}, \frac{-1}{\sqrt{2}} \right\rangle$

57. $f(x, y, z) = 1 + \sin(x + 2y - z)$; $\left(\frac{\pi}{6}, \frac{\pi}{6}, \frac{-\pi}{6}\right)$; $\mathbf{u} = \left\langle \frac{1}{3}, \frac{2}{3}, \frac{2}{3} \right\rangle$

58–59. Direction of steepest ascent and descent

a. *Find the unit vectors that give the direction of steepest ascent and steepest descent at P.*

b. *Find a unit vector that points in a direction of no change.*

58. $f(x, y) = \ln(1 + xy)$; $P(2, 3)$

59. $f(x, y) = \sqrt{4 - x^2 - y^2}$; $P(-1, 1)$

60–61. Level curves *Consider the paraboloid $f(x, y) = 8 - 2x^2 - y^2$. For the following level curves $f(x, y) = C$ and points (a, b), compute the slope of the line tangent to the level curve at (a, b) and verify that the tangent line is orthogonal to the gradient at that point.*

60. $f(x, y) = 5$; $(a, b) = (1, 1)$

61. $f(x, y) = 0$; $(a, b) = (2, 0)$

62. **Directions of zero change** Find the directions in which the function $f(x, y) = 4x^2 - y^2$ has zero change at the point $(1, 1, 3)$. Express the directions in terms of unit vectors.

63. **Electric potential due to a charged cylinder.** An infinitely long charged cylinder of radius R with its axis along the z-axis has an electric potential $V = k \ln(R/r)$, where r is the distance between a variable point $P(x, y)$ and the axis of the cylinder ($r^2 = x^2 + y^2$) and k is a physical constant. The electric field at a point (x, y) in the xy-plane is given by $\mathbf{E} = -\nabla V$, where ∇V is the two-dimensional gradient. Compute the electric field at a point (x, y) with $r > R$.

64–67. Tangent planes *Find an equation of the plane tangent to the following surfaces at the given points.*

64. $xy \sin z - 1 = 0$; $\left(1, 2, \frac{\pi}{6}\right)$ and $\left(-2, -1, \frac{5\pi}{6}\right)$

65. $yze^{xz} - 8 = 0$; $(0, 2, 4)$ and $(0, -8, -1)$

66. $z = x^2 e^{x-y}$; $(2, 2, 4)$ and $(-1, -1, 1)$

67. $z = \ln(1 + xy)$; $(1, 2, \ln 3)$ and $(-2, -1, \ln 3)$

T **68–69. Linear approximation**

a. *Find the linear approximation (the equation of the tangent plane) at the point (a, b).*

b. *Use part (a) to estimate the given function value.*

68. $f(x, y) = 4 \cos(2x - y)$; $(a, b) = \left(\frac{\pi}{4}, \frac{\pi}{4}\right)$; estimate $f(0.8, 0.8)$.

69. $f(x, y) = (x + y)e^{xy}$; $(a, b) = (2, 0)$; estimate $f(1.95, 0.05)$.

70. **Changes in a function** Estimate the change in the function $f(x, y) = -2y^2 + 3x^2 + xy$ when (x, y) changes from $(1, -2)$ to $(1.05, -1.9)$.

71. **Volume of a cylinder** The volume of a cylinder with radius r and height h is $V = \pi r^2 h$. Find the approximate percent change in the volume when the radius decreases by 3% and the height increases by 2%.

72. **Volume of an ellipsoid** The volume of an ellipsoid with axes of length $2a$, $2b$, and $2c$ is $V = \pi abc$. Find the percent change in the volume when a increases by 2%, b increases by 1.5%, and c decreases by 2.5%.

73. **Water level changes** A hemispherical tank with a radius of 1.50 m is filled with water to a depth of 1.00 m. Water is released from the tank and the water level drops by 0.05 m (from 1.00 m to 0.95 m).

a. Approximate the change in the volume of water in the tank. The volume of a spherical cap is $V = \pi h^2 (3r - h)/3$, where r is the radius of the sphere and h is the thickness of the cap (in this case, the depth of the water).

b. Approximate the change in the surface area of the water in the tank.

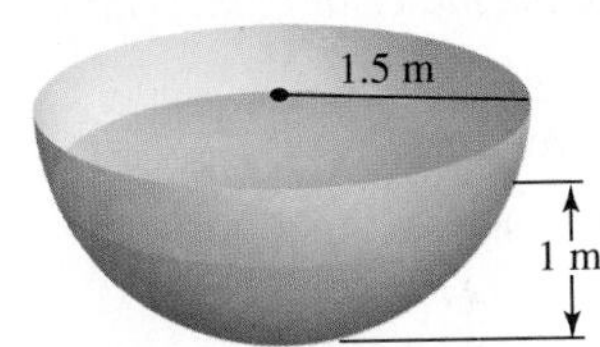

74–77. Analyzing critical points *Identify the critical points of the following functions. Then determine whether each critical point corresponds to a local maximum, local minimum, or saddle point. State when your analysis is inconclusive. Confirm your results using a graphing utility.*

74. $f(x, y) = x^4 + y^4 - 16xy$

75. $f(x, y) = x^3/3 - y^3/3 + 2xy$

76. $f(x, y) = xy(2 + x)(y - 3)$

77. $f(x, y) = 10 - x^3 - y^3 - 3x^2 + 3y^2$

78–79. Absolute maxima and minima *Find the absolute maximum and minimum values of the following functions on the specified set.*

78. $f(x, y) = x^3/3 - y^3/3 + 2xy$ on the rectangle $\{(x, y): 0 \le x \le 3, -1 \le y \le 1\}$

79. $f(x, y) = x^4 + y^4 - 4xy + 1$ on the square $\{(x, y): -2 \le x \le 2, -2 \le y \le 2\}$

80. **Least distance** What point on the plane $x + y + 4z = 8$ is closest to the origin? Give an argument showing you have found an absolute minimum of the distance function.

81–84. Lagrange multipliers *Use Lagrange multipliers to find the minimum and maximum values of f subject to the given constraint.*

81. $f(x, y) = x + 2y$ subject to $x^4 + y^4 = 1$

82. $f(x, y) = x^2y^2$ subject to $2x^2 + y^2 = 1$

83. $f(x, y, z) = x + 2y - z$ subject to $x^2 + y^2 + z^2 = 1$

84. $f(x, y, z) = x^2y^2z$ subject to $2x^2 + y^2 + z^2 = 25$

85. **Maximum perimeter rectangle** Use Lagrange multipliers to find the dimensions of the rectangle with the maximum perimeter that can be inscribed with sides parallel to the coordinate axes in the ellipse $x^2/a^2 + y^2/b^2 = 1$.

86. Minimum surface area cylinder Use Lagrange multipliers to find the dimensions of the right circular cylinder of minimum surface area (including the circular ends) with a volume of 32π in^3.

87. Minimum distance to a cone Find the point(s) on the cone $z^2 - x^2 - y^2 = 0$ that are closest to the point $(1, 3, 1)$. Give an argument showing you have found an absolute minimum of the distance function.

88. Gradient of a distance function Let $P_0(a, b, c)$ be a fixed point in $\mathbf{R}^3$ and let $d(x, y, z)$ be the distance between P_0 and a variable point $P(x, y, z)$.

a. Compute $\nabla d(x, y, z)$.
b. Show that $\nabla d(x, y, z)$ points in the direction from P_0 to P and has magnitude 1 for all (x, y, z).
c. Describe the level surfaces of d and give the direction of $\nabla d(x, y, z)$ relative to the level surfaces of d.
d. Discuss $\lim_{P \to P_0} \nabla d(x, y, z)$.

Chapter 13 Guided Projects

Applications of the material in this chapter and related topics can be found in the following Guided Projects. For additional information, see the Preface.

- Traveling waves
- Economic production functions
- Ecological diversity

14

Multiple Integration

Chapter Preview We have now generalized limits and derivatives to functions of several variables. The next step is to carry out a similar process with respect to integration. As you know, single (one-variable) integrals are developed from Riemann sums and are used to compute areas of regions in $\mathbf{R}^2$. In an analogous way, we use Riemann sums to develop double (two-variable) and triple (three-variable) integrals, which are used to compute volumes of solid regions in $\mathbf{R}^3$. These multiple integrals have many applications in statistics, science, and engineering, including calculating the mass, the center of mass, and moments of inertia of solids with a variable density. Another significant development in this chapter is the appearance of cylindrical and spherical coordinates. These alternative coordinate systems often simplify the evaluation of integrals in three-dimensional space. The chapter closes with the two- and three-dimensional versions of the substitution (change of variables) rule. The overall lesson of the chapter is that we can integrate functions over most geometrical objects, from intervals on the x-axis to regions in the plane bounded by curves to complicated three-dimensional solids.

14.1 Double Integrals over Rectangular Regions

In Chapter 13 the concept of differentiation was extended to functions of several variables. In this chapter we extend integration to multivariable functions. By the close of the chapter, we will have completed Table 14.1, which is a basic road map for calculus.

Table 14.1

	Derivatives	**Integrals**
Single variable: $f(x)$	$f'(x)$	$\int_a^b f(x)\,dx$
Several variables: $f(x, y)$ and $f(x, y, z)$	$\frac{\partial f}{\partial x}, \frac{\partial f}{\partial y}, \frac{\partial f}{\partial z}$	$\iint_R f(x, y)\,dA, \iiint_D f(x, y, z)\,dV$

Volumes of Solids

The problem of finding the net area of a region bounded by a curve led to the definite integral in Chapter 5. Recall that we began that discussion by approximating the region with a collection of rectangles and then formed a Riemann sum of the areas of the rectangles. Under appropriate conditions, as the number of rectangles increases, the sum approaches the value of the definite integral, which is the net area of the region.

We now carry out an analogous procedure with surfaces defined by functions of the form $z = f(x, y)$, where, for the moment, we assume that $f(x, y) \geq 0$ on a region R in the xy-plane (Figure 14.1a). The goal is to determine the volume of the solid bounded by the surface and R. In general terms, the solid is first approximated by *boxes* (Figure 14.1b). The sum of the volumes of these boxes, which is a Riemann sum, approximates the volume of the solid. Under appropriate conditions, as the number of boxes increases, the approximations converge to the value of a *double integral,* which is the volume of the solid.

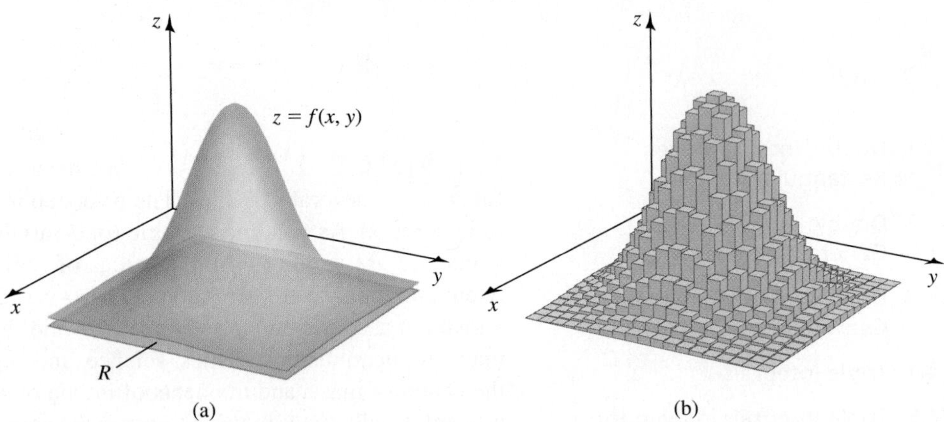
A three-dimensional solid bounded by $z = f(x, y)$ and a region R in the xy-plane is approximated by a collection of boxes.
z
$z = f(x, y)$
x
y
R
(a)
z
x
y
(b)

FIGURE 14.1

➤ We adopt the convention that Δx_k and Δy_k are the side lengths of the kth rectangle, for $k = 1, \ldots, n$, even though there are generally fewer than n different values of Δx_k and Δy_k. An analogous convention is used throughout the chapter.

We assume that $z = f(x, y)$ is a nonnegative continuous function on a *rectangular* region $R = \{(x, y): a \leq x \leq b, c \leq y \leq d\}$. A **partition** of R is formed by dividing R into n rectangular subregions using lines running parallel to the x- and y-axes (not necessarily uniformly spaced). The subregions may be numbered in any systematic way; for example, left to right, and then bottom to top. The side lengths of the kth rectangle are denoted Δx_k and Δy_k, so the area of the kth subregion is $\Delta A_k = \Delta x_k\, \Delta y_k$. We also let $(\overline{x}_k, \overline{y}_k)$ be any point in the kth subregion, for $1 \leq k \leq n$ (Figure 14.2).

To approximate the volume of the solid bounded by the surface $z = f(x, y)$ and the region R, we construct boxes on each of the n subregions; each box has a height of $f(\overline{x}_k, \overline{y}_k)$ and a base with area ΔA_k, for $1 \leq k \leq n$ (Figure 14.3). Therefore, the volume of the kth box is

$$f(\overline{x}_k, \overline{y}_k)\Delta A_k = f(\overline{x}_k, \overline{y}_k)\Delta x_k\, \Delta y_k.$$

The sum of the volumes of the n boxes gives an approximation to the volume of the solid:

$$V \approx \sum_{k=1}^{n} f(\overline{x}_k, \overline{y}_k)\, \Delta A_k$$

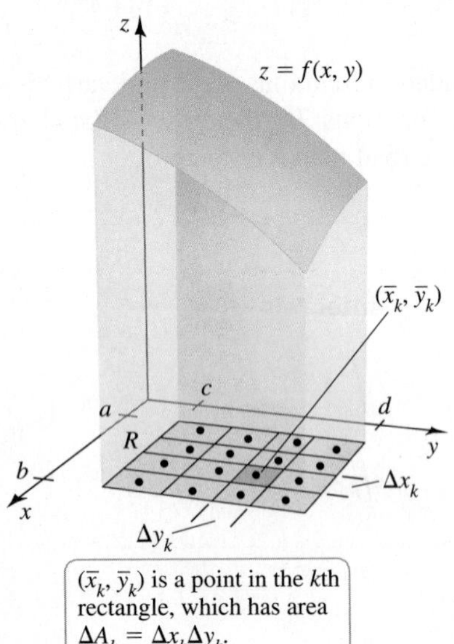
z
$z = f(x, y)$
$(\overline{x}_k, \overline{y}_k)$
a
c
d
R
b
x
y
Δx_k
Δy_k
$(\overline{x}_k, \overline{y}_k)$ is a point in the kth rectangle, which has area $\Delta A_k = \Delta x_k \Delta y_k$.

FIGURE 14.2

QUICK CHECK 1 Explain why the preceding sum for the volume is an approximation. How can the approximation be improved? ◄

We now let Δ be the maximum length of the diagonals of the rectangular subregions in the partition. As $\Delta \to 0$, the areas of *all* the subregions approach zero ($\Delta A_k \to 0$) and the number of subregions increases ($n \to \infty$). Furthermore, as $\Delta \to 0$, the approximations given by these Riemann sums converge to the exact volume of the solid (Figure 14.4). Therefore, we define the volume of the solid to be the limit of the Riemann sum, provided the limit exists.

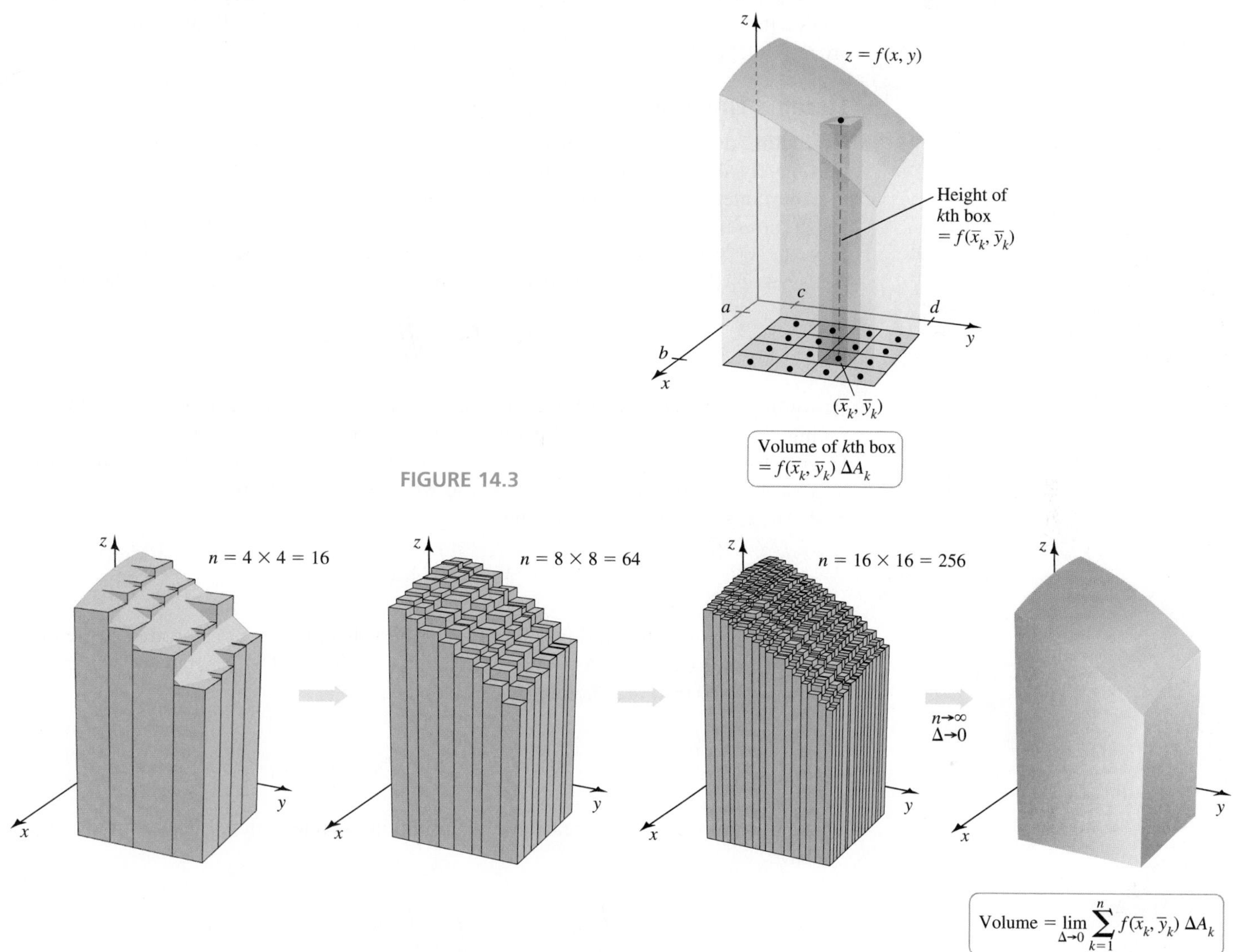

FIGURE 14.3

FIGURE 14.4

> If f is negative on parts of R, the value of the double integral may be zero or negative, and the result is interpreted as a *net volume* (in analogy with *net area* for single variable integrals). See Example 5 of this section.

DEFINITION Volumes and Double Integrals

Let f be defined on a rectangular region R in the xy-plane. If the limit

$$\lim_{\Delta \to 0} \sum_{k=1}^{n} f(\overline{x}_k, \overline{y}_k)\,\Delta A_k$$

exists for all partitions of R and for all choices of $(\overline{x}_k, \overline{y}_k)$ within those partitions, it is called the **double integral of f over R**, denoted $\iint_R f(x, y)\,dA$, and f is said to be **integrable** on R. If f is nonnegative over R, then the double integral equals the **volume** of the solid bounded by $z = f(x, y)$ and the xy-plane over R.

The functions that we encounter in this book are integrable. Advanced methods are needed to prove that continuous functions and many functions with finite discontinuities are also integrable.

Iterated Integrals

Evaluating double integrals using limits of Riemann sums is tedious and rarely done. Fortunately, there is a practical method that reduces a double integral to two single (one-variable) integrals. An example illustrates the technique.

➤ Recall the General Slicing Method. If a solid is sliced parallel to the y-axis and perpendicular to the xy-plane and the cross-sectional area of the slice at the point x is $A(x)$, then the volume of the solid region is

$$V = \int_a^b A(x)\,dx.$$

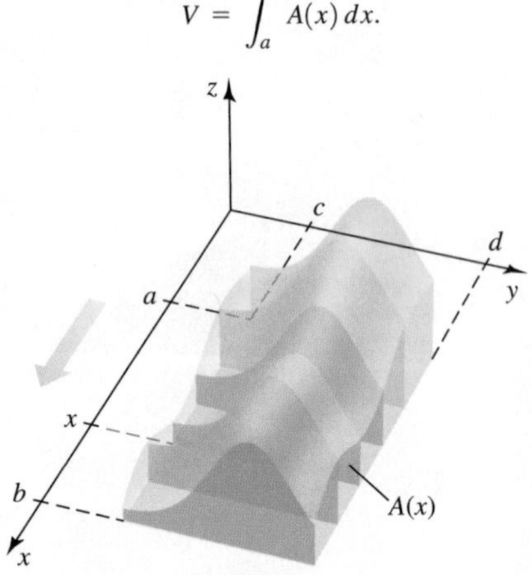

Suppose we wish to compute the volume of the solid region bounded by the plane $z = f(x, y) = 6 - 2x - y$ over the rectangular region $R = \{(x, y): 0 \le x \le 1, 0 \le y \le 2\}$ (Figure 14.5). By definition, the volume is given by the double integral

$$V = \iint_R f(x, y)\,dA = \iint_R (6 - 2x - y)\,dA.$$

According to the General Slicing Method (Section 6.3), we can compute this volume by taking slices through the solid parallel to the y-axis and perpendicular to the xy-plane (Figure 14.5). The slice at the point x has a cross-sectional area denoted $A(x)$. In general, as x varies, the area $A(x)$ also changes, so we integrate these cross-sectional areas from $x = 0$ to $x = 1$ to obtain the volume

$$V = \int_0^1 A(x)\,dx.$$

The important observation is that for a fixed value of x, $A(x)$ is the area of the plane region under the curve $z = 6 - 2x - y$. This area is computed by integrating f with respect to y from $y = 0$ to $y = 2$, holding x fixed; that is,

$$A(x) = \int_0^2 (6 - 2x - y)\,dy,$$

where $0 \le x \le 1$ and x is treated as a constant in the integration. Substituting for $A(x)$, we have

$$V = \int_0^1 A(x)\,dx = \int_0^1 \underbrace{\left[\int_0^2 (6 - 2x - y)\,dy\right]}_{A(x)} dx.$$

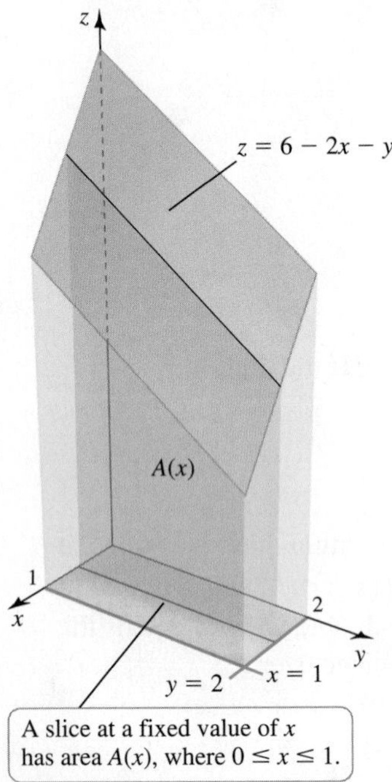

A slice at a fixed value of x has area $A(x)$, where $0 \le x \le 1$.

FIGURE 14.5

The expression that appears on the right side of this equation is called an **iterated integral** (meaning repeated integral). We first evaluate the inner integral with respect to y holding x fixed; the result is a function of x. Then, the outer integral is evaluated with respect to x; the result is a real number, which is the volume of the solid in Figure 14.5. Both these integrals are ordinary one-variable integrals.

EXAMPLE 1 **Evaluating an iterated integral** Evaluate $V = \int_0^1 A(x)\,dx$, where $A(x) = \int_0^2 (6 - 2x - y)\,dy$.

SOLUTION Using the Fundamental Theorem of Calculus, holding x constant, we have

$$\begin{aligned} A(x) &= \int_0^2 (6 - 2x - y)\,dy \\ &= \left(6y - 2xy - \frac{y^2}{2}\right)\Big|_0^2 && \text{Fundamental Theorem of Calculus} \\ &= (12 - 4x - 2) - 0 && \text{Simplify; limits are in } y. \\ &= 10 - 4x. && \text{Simplify.} \end{aligned}$$

Substituting $A(x) = 10 - 4x$ into the volume integral, we have

$$V = \int_0^1 A(x)\,dx$$

$$= \int_0^1 (10 - 4x)\,dx \quad \text{Substitute for } A(x).$$

$$= (10x - 2x^2)\Big|_0^1 \quad \text{Fundamental Theorem}$$

$$= 8. \quad \text{Simplify.}$$

Related Exercises 5–19 ◀

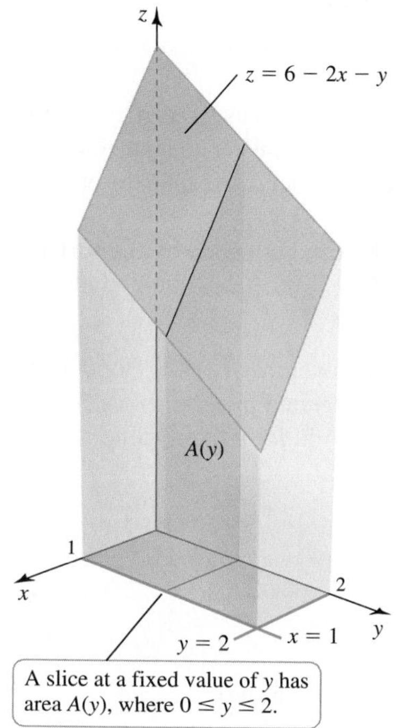

z
z = 6 − 2x − y
A(y)
1
x
2
y
y = 2
x = 1
A slice at a fixed value of y has area A(y), where 0 ≤ y ≤ 2.

FIGURE 14.6

EXAMPLE 2 Same double integral, different order Example 1 used slices through the solid parallel to the y-axis. Compute the volume of the same solid using slices through the solid parallel to the x-axis and perpendicular to the xy-plane, for $0 \le y \le 2$ (Figure 14.6).

SOLUTION In this case, $A(y)$ is the area of a slice through the solid for a fixed value of y in the interval $0 \le y \le 2$. This area is computed by integrating $z = 6 - 2x - y$ from $x = 0$ to $x = 1$, holding y fixed; that is,

$$A(y) = \int_0^1 (6 - 2x - y)\,dx,$$

where $0 \le y \le 2$.

Using the General Slicing Method again, the volume is

$$V = \int_0^2 A(y)\,dy \quad \text{General Slicing Method}$$

$$= \int_0^2 \underbrace{\left[\int_0^1 (6 - 2x - y)\,dx\right]}_{A(y)} dy \quad \text{Substitute for } A(y).$$

$$= \int_0^2 \left[(6x - x^2 - yx)\Big|_0^1\right] dy \quad \text{Fundamental Theorem of Calculus; } y \text{ is constant.}$$

$$= \int_0^2 (5 - y)\,dy \quad \text{Simplify; limits are in } x.$$

$$= \left(5y - \frac{y^2}{2}\right)\Big|_0^2 \quad \text{Evaluate outer integral.}$$

$$= 8. \quad \text{Simplify.}$$

Related Exercises 5–19 ◀

Several important comments are in order. First, the two iterated integrals give the same value for the double integral. Second, the notation of the iterated integral must be used carefully. When we write $\int_c^d \int_a^b f(x, y)\,dx\,dy$, it means $\int_c^d \left[\int_a^b f(x, y)\,dx\right] dy$. The *inner* integral with respect to x is evaluated first, holding y fixed, and the variable runs from $x = a$ to $x = b$. The result of that integration is a constant or a function of y, which is then integrated in the *outer* integral, with the variable running from $y = c$ to $y = d$. The order of integration is signified by the order of dx and dy.

Similarly, $\int_a^b \int_c^d f(x, y)\,dy\,dx$ means $\int_a^b \left[\int_c^d f(x, y)\,dy\right] dx$. The inner integral with respect to y is evaluated first, holding x fixed. The result is then integrated with respect to x.

QUICK CHECK 2 Consider the integral $\int_3^4 \int_1^2 f(x, y)\,dx\,dy$. Give the limits of integration and the variable of integration for the first (inner) integral and the second (outer) integral. Sketch the region of integration. ◀

Examples 1 and 2 illustrate *Fubini's theorem*, a deep result with several versions that relates double integrals to iterated integrals. The first version of the theorem applies to double integrals over rectangular regions.

> The area of the kth rectangular subregion in the partition is $\Delta A_k = \Delta x_k \Delta y_k$, where Δx_k and Δy_k are the lengths of the sides of that rectangle. Accordingly, the *element of area dA* in the double integral becomes $dx\,dy$ or $dy\,dx$ in the iterated integral.

THEOREM 14.1 (Fubini) Double Integrals on Rectangular Regions
Let f be continuous on the rectangular region $R = \{(x, y): a \le x \le b, c \le y \le d\}$. The double integral of f over R may be evaluated by either of two iterated integrals:

$$\iint_R f(x, y)\,dA = \int_c^d \int_a^b f(x, y)\,dx\,dy = \int_a^b \int_c^d f(x, y)\,dy\,dx$$

The importance of Fubini's Theorem is twofold: It says that double integrals may be evaluated by iterated integrals. It *also* says that the order of integration in the iterated integrals does not matter (although in practice, one order of integration is often easier to use than the other).

EXAMPLE 3 A double integral Find the volume of the solid bounded by the surface $z = 4 + 9x^2y^2$ over the region $R = \{(x, y): -1 \le x \le 1, 0 \le y \le 2\}$. Use both possible orders of integration.

SOLUTION The volume of the region is given by the double integral $\iint_R (4 + 9x^2y^2)\,dA$. By Fubini's Theorem, the double integral is evaluated as an iterated integral. If we first integrate with respect to x, the area of a cross section of the solid for a fixed value of y is given by $A(y)$ (Figure 14.7a). The volume of the region is

$$\iint_R (4 + 9x^2y^2)\,dA = \int_0^2 \underbrace{\int_{-1}^1 (4 + 9x^2y^2)\,dx}_{A(y)}\,dy \quad \text{Convert to an iterated integral.}$$

$$= \int_0^2 (4x + 3x^3y^2)\Big|_{-1}^{1}\,dy \quad \text{Evaluate the inner integral with respect to } x$$

$$= \int_0^2 (8 + 6y^2)\,dy \quad \text{Simplify.}$$

$$= (8y + 2y^3)\Big|_0^2 \quad \text{Evaluate the outer integral with respect to } y.$$

$$= 32. \quad \text{Simplify.}$$

Alternatively, if we integrate first with respect to y, the area of a cross section of the solid for a fixed value of x is given by $A(x)$ (Figure 14.7b). The volume of the region is

$$\iint_R (4 + 9x^2y^2)\,dA = \int_{-1}^1 \underbrace{\int_0^2 (4 + 9x^2y^2)\,dy}_{A(x)}\,dx \quad \text{Convert to an iterated integral.}$$

$$= \int_{-1}^1 (4y + 3x^2y^3)\Big|_0^2\,dx \quad \text{Evaluate the inner integral with respect to } y.$$

$$= \int_{-1}^1 (8 + 24x^2)\,dx \quad \text{Simplify}$$

$$= (8x + 8x^3)\Big|_{-1}^1 = 32. \quad \text{Evaluate the outer integral with respect to } x.$$

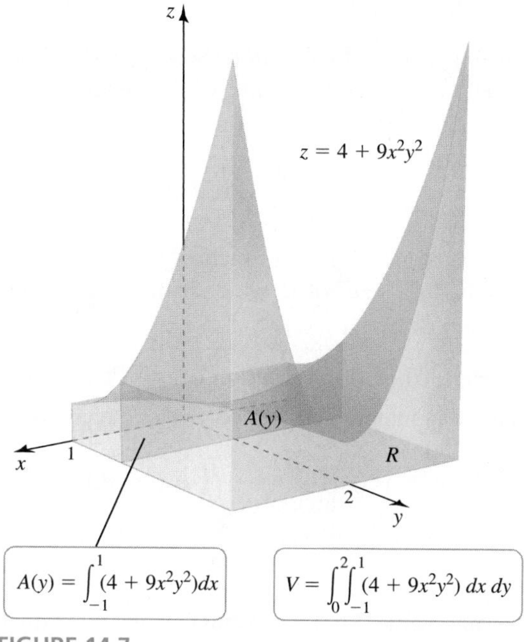

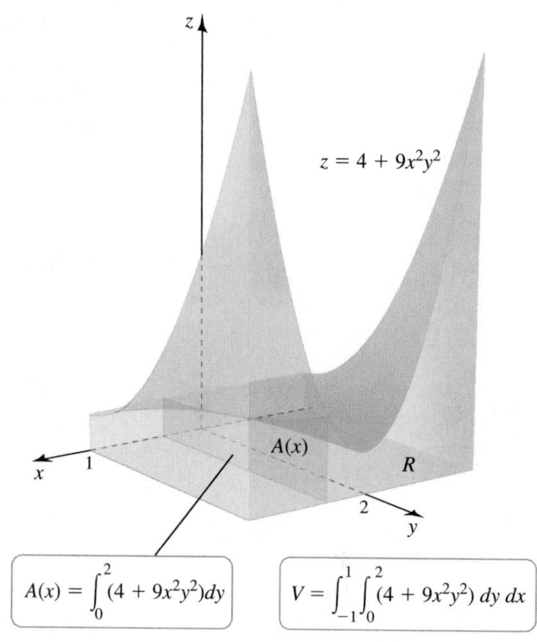

FIGURE 14.7

As guaranteed by Fubini's Theorem, the iterated integrals agree, both giving the value of the double integral and the volume of the solid. *Related Exercises 5–19*

QUICK CHECK 3 Write the iterated integral $\int_{-10}^{10}\int_0^{20}(x^2y + 2xy^3)\,dy\,dx$ with the order of integration reversed.

The following example shows that sometimes the order of integration must be chosen carefully either to save work or to make the integration possible.

EXAMPLE 4 Choosing a convenient order of integration Evaluate $\iint_R ye^{xy}\,dA$, where $R = \{(x, y): 0 \le x \le 1, 0 \le y \le \ln 2\}$.

SOLUTION The iterated integral $\int_0^1\int_0^{\ln 2} ye^{xy}\,dy\,dx$ requires first integrating ye^{xy} with respect to y, which entails integration by parts. An easier approach is to integrate first with respect to x:

$$\int_0^{\ln 2}\int_0^1 ye^{xy}\,dx\,dy = \int_0^{\ln 2}(e^{xy})\Big|_0^1\,dy \qquad \text{Evaluate the inner integral with respect to } x.$$

$$= \int_0^{\ln 2}(e^y - 1)\,dy \qquad \text{Simplify.}$$

$$= (e^y - y)\Big|_0^{\ln 2} \qquad \text{Evaluate the outer integral with respect to } y.$$

$$= 1 - \ln 2 \qquad \text{Simplify.}$$

Related Exercises 20–23

Average Value

The concept of the average value of a function (Section 5.4) extends naturally to functions of two variables. Recall that the average value of the integrable function f over the interval $[a, b]$ is

$$\bar{f} = \frac{1}{b-a}\int_a^b f(x)\,dx.$$

To find the average value of an integrable function f over a region R, we integrate f over R and divide the result by the "size" of R, which is the area of R in the two-variable case.

➤ The same definition of average value applies to more general regions in the plane.

DEFINITION Average Value of a Function over a Plane Region

The **average value** of an integrable function f over a region R is

$$\bar{f} = \frac{1}{\text{area of } R}\iint_R f(x, y)\,dA.$$

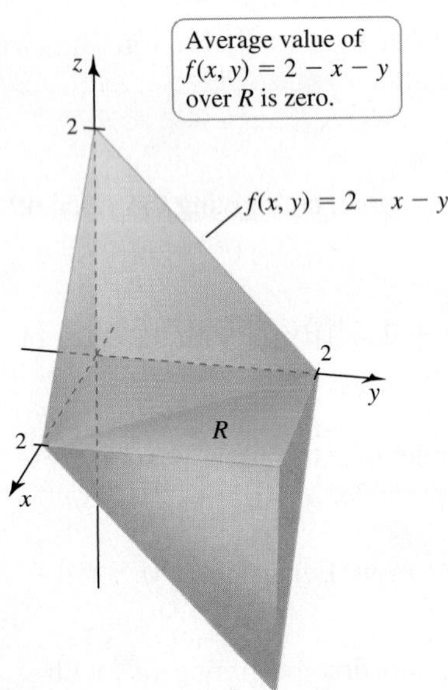

Average value of $f(x, y) = 2 - x - y$ over R is zero.
z
2
$f(x, y) = 2 - x - y$
2
y
R
2
x

FIGURE 14.8

EXAMPLE 5 Average value Find the average value of the quantity $2 - x - y$ over the square $R = \{(x, y): 0 \le x \le 2, 0 \le y \le 2\}$ (Figure 14.8).

SOLUTION The area of the region R is 4. Letting $f(x, y) = 2 - x - y$, the average value of f is

$$\frac{1}{\text{area of } R}\iint_R f(x, y)\,dA = \frac{1}{4}\iint_R (2 - x - y)\,dA$$

$$= \frac{1}{4}\int_0^2\int_0^2 (2 - x - y)\,dx\,dy \qquad \text{Convert to an iterated integral.}$$

$$= \frac{1}{4}\int_0^2 \left(2x - \frac{x^2}{2} - xy\right)\Big|_0^2\,dy \qquad \text{Evaluate the inner integral.}$$

$$= \frac{1}{4}\int_0^2 (2 - 2y)\,dy \qquad \text{Simplify.}$$

$$= 0. \qquad \text{Evaluate the outer integral.}$$

Related Exercises 24–28 ◀

➤ An average value of 0 means that over the region R, the volume of the solid above the xy-plane and below the surface equals the volume of the solid below the xy-plane and above the surface.

SECTION 14.1 EXERCISES

Review Questions

1. Write an iterated integral that gives the volume of the solid bounded by the surface $f(x, y) = xy$ over the square $R = \{(x, y): 0 \le x \le 2, 1 \le y \le 3\}$.

2. Write an iterated integral that gives the volume of a box with height 10 and base $\{(x, y): 0 \le x \le 5, -2 \le y \le 4\}$.

3. Write two iterated integrals that equal $\iint_R f(x, y)\,dA$, where $R = \{(x, y): -2 \le x \le 4, 1 \le y \le 5\}$.

4. Consider the integral $\int_1^3\int_{-1}^1 (2y^2 + xy)\,dy\,dx$. Give the variable of integration in the first (inner) integral and the limits of integration. Give the variable of integration in the second (outer) integral and the limits of integration.

Basic Skills

5–12. Iterated integrals *Evaluate the following iterated integrals.*

5. $\displaystyle\int_1^3\int_0^2 x^2y\,dx\,dy$

6. $\displaystyle\int_0^3\int_{-2}^1 (2x + 3y)\,dx\,dy$

7. $\displaystyle\int_1^3 \int_0^{\pi/2} x \sin y \, dy \, dx$

8. $\displaystyle\int_1^3 \int_1^2 (y^2 + y) \, dx \, dy$

9. $\displaystyle\int_1^4 \int_0^4 \sqrt{uv} \, du \, dv$

10. $\displaystyle\int_0^{\pi/2} \int_0^1 x \cos xy \, dy \, dx$

11. $\displaystyle\int_1^{\ln 5} \int_0^{\ln 3} e^{x+y} \, dx \, dy$

12. $\displaystyle\int_0^{\pi/4} \int_0^3 r \sec \theta \, dr \, d\theta$

13–19. Iterated integrals *Evaluate the following double integrals over the region R.*

13. $\displaystyle\iint_R (x + 2y) \, dA; \ R = \{(x, y): 0 \leq x \leq 3, 1 \leq y \leq 4\}$

14. $\displaystyle\iint_R (x^2 + xy) \, dA; \ R = \{(x, y): 1 \leq x \leq 2, -1 \leq y \leq 1\}$

15. $\displaystyle\iint_R \sqrt{\frac{x}{y}} \, dA; \ R = \{(x, y): 0 \leq x \leq 1, 1 \leq y \leq 4\}$

16. $\displaystyle\iint_R xy \sin x^2 \, dA; \ R = \{(x, y): 0 \leq x \leq \sqrt{\pi/2}, 0 \leq y \leq 1\}$

17. $\displaystyle\iint_R e^{x+2y} \, dA; \ R = \{(x, y): 0 \leq x \leq \ln 2, 1 \leq y \leq \ln 3\}$

18. $\displaystyle\iint_R (x^4 + y^4)^2 \, dA; \ R = \{(x, y): -1 \leq x \leq 1, 0 \leq y \leq 1\}$

19. $\displaystyle\iint_R (x^5 - y^5)^2 \, dA; \ R = \{(x, y): 0 \leq x \leq 1, -1 \leq y \leq 1\}$

20–23. Choose a convenient order *When converted to an iterated integral, the following double integrals are easier to evaluate in one order than the other. Find the best order and evaluate the integral.*

20. $\displaystyle\iint_R x \sec^2 xy \, dA; \ R = \{(x, y): 0 \leq x \leq \pi/3, 0 \leq y \leq 1\}$

21. $\displaystyle\iint_R x^5 e^{x^3 y} \, dA; \ R = \{(x, y): 0 \leq x \leq \ln 2, 0 \leq y \leq 1\}$

22. $\displaystyle\iint_R y^3 \sin xy^2 \, dA; \ R = \{(x, y): 0 \leq x \leq 1, 0 \leq y \leq \sqrt{\pi/2}\}$

23. $\displaystyle\iint_R \frac{x}{(1 + xy)^2} \, dA; \ R = \{(x, y): 0 \leq x \leq 4, 1 \leq y \leq 2\}$

24–26. Average value *Compute the average value of the following functions over the region R.*

24. $f(x, y) = 4 - x - y; \ R = \{(x, y): 0 \leq x \leq 2, 0 \leq y \leq 2\}$

25. $f(x, y) = e^{-y}; \ R = \{(x, y): 0 \leq x \leq 6, 0 \leq y \leq \ln 2\}$

26. $f(x, y) = \sin x \sin y; \ R = \{(x, y): 0 \leq x \leq \pi, 0 \leq y \leq \pi\}$

27–28. Average value

27. Find the average squared distance between the points of $R = \{(x, y): -2 \leq x \leq 2, 0 \leq y \leq 2\}$ and the origin.

28. Find the average squared distance between the points of $R = \{(x, y): 0 \leq x \leq 3, 0 \leq y \leq 3\}$ and the point (3, 3).

Further Explorations

29. **Explain why or why not** Determine whether the following statements are true and give an explanation or counterexample.
    a. The region of integration for $\int_4^6 \int_1^3 4 \, dx \, dy$ is a square.
    b. If f is continuous on $\mathbf{R}^2$, then $\int_4^6 \int_1^3 f(x, y) \, dx \, dy = \int_4^6 \int_1^3 f(x, y) \, dy \, dx$.
    c. If f is continuous on $\mathbf{R}^2$, then $\int_4^6 \int_1^3 f(x, y) \, dx \, dy = \int_1^3 \int_4^6 f(x, y) \, dy \, dx$.

30. **Symmetry** Evaluate the following integrals using symmetry arguments. Let $R = \{(x, y): -a \leq x \leq a, -b \leq y \leq b\}$, where a and b are positive real numbers.
    a. $\displaystyle\iint_R xye^{-(x^2+y^2)} \, dA$
    b. $\displaystyle\iint_R \frac{\sin (x - y)}{x^2 + y^2 + 1} \, dA$

31. **Computing populations** The population densities in nine districts of a rectangular county are shown in the figure.

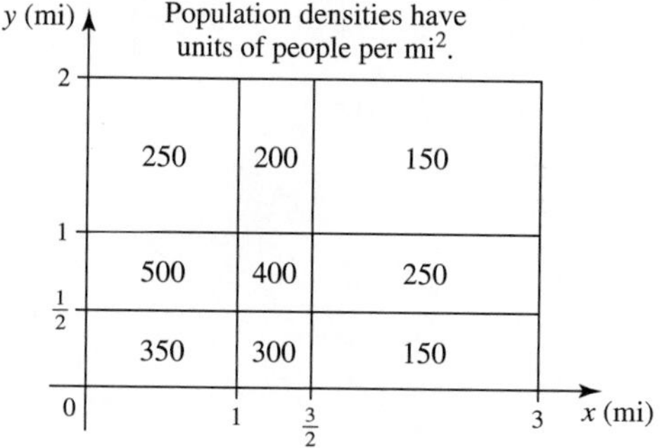

    a. Use the fact that population = (population density) × (area) to estimate the population of the county.
    b. Explain how the calculation of part (a) is related to Riemann sums and double integrals.

T 32. **Approximating water volume** The varying depth of an 18 m × 25 m swimming pool is measured in 15 different rectangles of equal area (see figure). Approximate the volume of water in the pool.

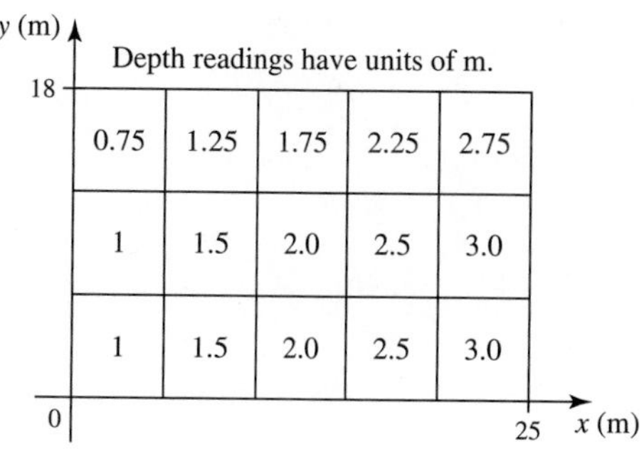

33–34. Pictures of solids *Draw the solid region whose volume is given by the following double integrals. Then find the volume of the solid.*

33. $\int_0^6 \int_1^2 10\, dy\, dx$

34. $\int_0^1 \int_{-1}^1 (4 - x^2 - y^2)\, dx\, dy$

35–38. More integration practice *Evaluate the following iterated integrals.*

35. $\int_1^e \int_0^1 \frac{x}{x + y}\, dy\, dx$

36. $\int_0^2 \int_0^1 x^5 y^2 e^{x^3 y^3}\, dy\, dx$

37. $\int_0^1 \int_1^4 \frac{3y}{\sqrt{x + y^2}}\, dx\, dy$

38. $\int_1^4 \int_0^2 e^{y\sqrt{x}}\, dy\, dx$

39–42. Volumes of solids *Find the volume of the following solids.*

39. The solid between the cylinder $f(x, y) = e^{-x}$ and the region $R = \{(x, y): 0 \le x \le \ln 4, -2 \le y \le 2\}$

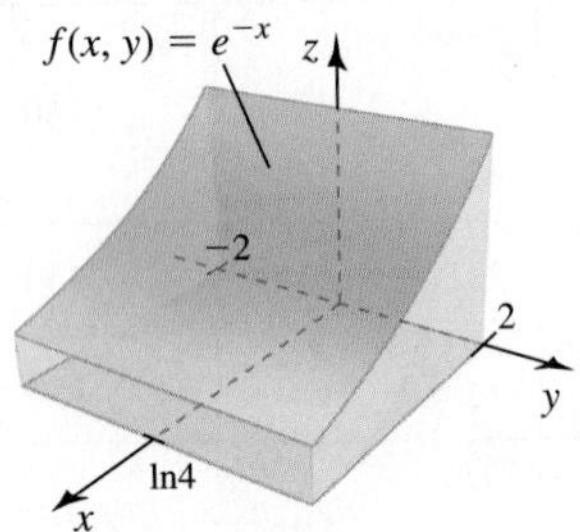

40. The solid beneath the plane $f(x, y) = 6 - x - 2y$ and above the region $R = \{(x, y): 0 \le x \le 2, 0 \le y \le 1\}$

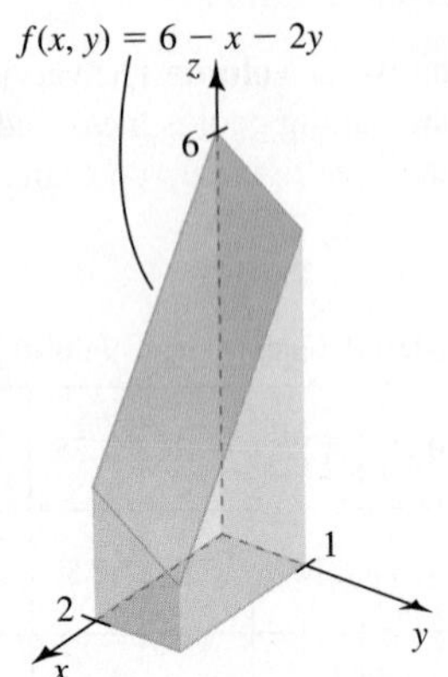

41. The solid beneath the plane $f(x, y) = 24 - 3x - 4y$ and above the region $R = \{(x, y): -1 \le x \le 3, 0 \le y \le 2\}$

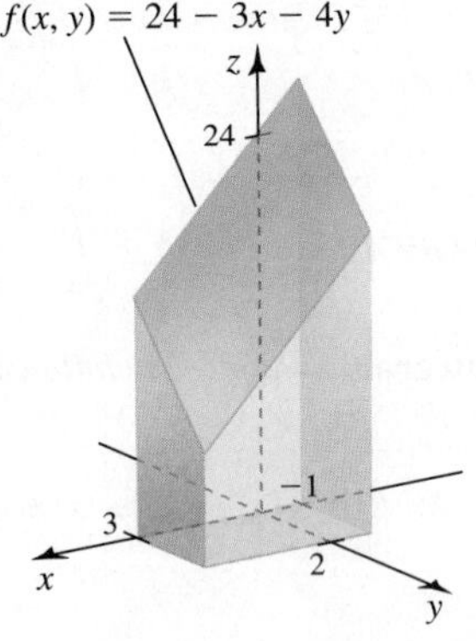

42. The solid beneath the paraboloid $f(x, y) = 12 - x^2 - 2y^2$ and above the region $R = \{(x, y): 1 \le x \le 2, 0 \le y \le 1\}$

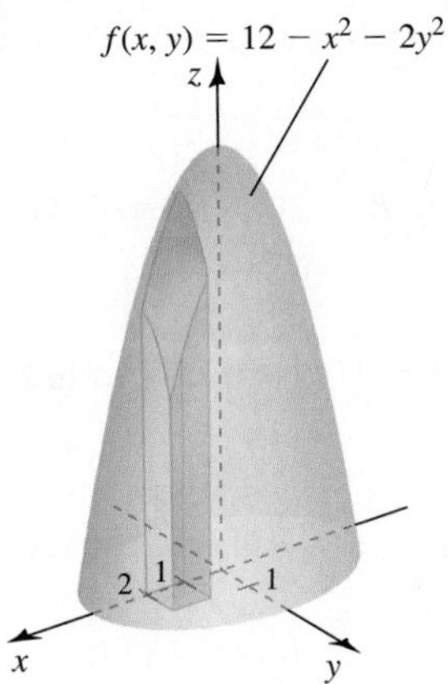

43. **Net volume** Let $R = \{(x, y): 0 \le x \le \pi, 0 \le y \le a\}$. For what values of a, with $0 \le a \le \pi$, is $\iint_R \sin(x + y)\, dA$ equal to 1?

44–45. Zero average value *Let* $R = \{(x, y): 0 \le x \le a, 0 \le y \le a\}$. *Find the value of* $a > 0$ *such that the average value of the following functions over R is zero.*

44. $f(x, y) = x + y - 8$

45. $f(x, y) = 4 - x^2 - y^2$

46. **Maximum integral** Consider the plane $x + 3y + z = 6$ over the rectangle R with vertices at $(0, 0)$, $(a, 0)$, $(0, b)$, and (a, b), where the vertex (a, b) lies on the line where the plane intersects the xy-plane (so $a + 3b = 6$). Find the point (a, b) for which the volume of the solid between the plane and R is a maximum.

Applications

47. **Density and mass** Suppose a thin rectangular plate, represented by a region R in the xy-plane, has a density given by the function $\rho(x, y)$; this function gives the *area density* in units such as g/cm^2. The mass of the plate is $\iint_R \rho(x, y)\, dA$. Assume that $R = \{(x, y): 0 \le x \le \pi/2, 0 \le y \le \pi\}$ and find the mass of the plates with the following density functions.

   a. $\rho(x, y) = 1 + \sin x$
   b. $\rho(x, y) = 1 + \sin y$
   c. $\rho(x, y) = 1 + \sin x \sin y$

48. Approximating volume Propose a method based on Riemann sums to approximate the volume of the shed shown in the figure (the peak of the roof is directly above the rear corner of the shed). Carry out the method and provide an estimate of the volume.

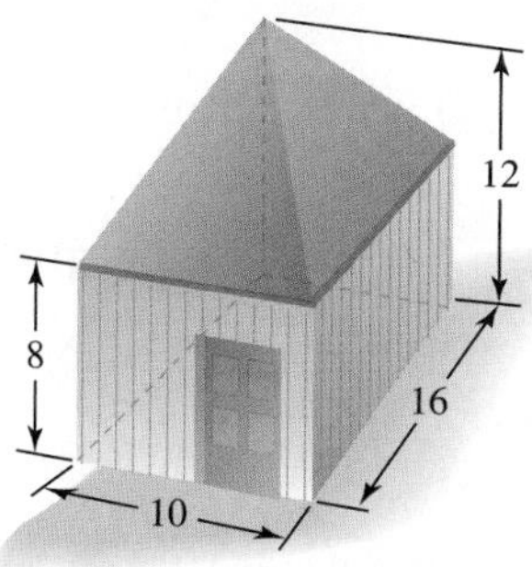

Additional Exercises

49. Cylinders Let S be the solid in $\mathbf{R}^3$ between the cylinder $z = f(x)$ and the region $R = \{(x, y): a \le x \le b, c \le y \le d\}$, where $f(x) \ge 0$ on R. Explain why $\int_c^d \int_a^b f(x)\,dx\,dy$ equals the area of the constant cross section of S multiplied by $(d - c)$, which is the volume of S.

50. Product of integrals Suppose $f(x, y) = g(x)h(y)$, where g and h are continuous functions for all real values.

a. Show that $\int_c^d \int_a^b f(x, y)\,dx\,dy = \left(\int_a^b g(x)\,dx\right)\left(\int_c^d h(y)\,dy\right)$. Interpret this result geometrically.

b. Write $\left(\int_a^b g(x)\,dx\right)^2$ as an iterated integral.

c. Use the result of part (a) to evaluate $\int_0^{2\pi} \int_{10}^{30} (\cos x)\, e^{-4y^2}\,dy\,dx$.

51. An identity Suppose the second partial derivatives of f are continuous on $R = \{(x, y): 0 \le x \le a, 0 \le y \le b\}$. Simplify $\iint_R \frac{\partial^2 f}{\partial x \partial y}\,dA$.

52. Two integrals Let $R = \{(x, y): 0 \le x \le 1, 0 \le y \le 1\}$.

a. Evaluate $\iint_R \cos(x\sqrt{y})\,dA$

b. Evaluate $\iint_R x^3 y \cos(x^2 y^2)\,dA$.

53. A generalization Let R be as in Exercise 52, let F be an antiderivative of f with $F(0) = 0$ and let G be an antiderivative of F. Show that if f and F are integrable, and $r \ge 1$ and $s \ge 1$ are real numbers, then

$$\iint_R x^{2r-1} y^{s-1} f(x^r y^s)\,dA = \frac{G(1) - G(0)}{rs}.$$

QUICK CHECK ANSWERS

1. The sum gives the volume of a collection of rectangular boxes and these boxes do not exactly fill the solid region under the surface. The approximation is improved by using more boxes. **2.** Inner integral: x runs from $x = 1$ to $x = 2$; outer integral: y runs from $y = 3$ to $y = 4$. The region is the rectangle $\{(x, y): 1 \le x \le 2, 3 \le y \le 4\}$.
3. $\int_0^{20} \int_{-10}^{10} (x^2 y + 2xy^3)\,dx\,dy$

14.2 Double Integrals over General Regions

Evaluating double integrals over rectangular regions is a useful place to begin our study of multiple integrals. Problems of practical interest, however, usually involve nonrectangular regions of integration. The goal of this section is to extend the methods presented in Section 14.1 so that they apply to more general regions of integration.

General Regions of Integration

Consider a continuous function f defined over a closed bounded *nonrectangular* region R in the xy-plane. As with rectangular regions, we use a partition consisting of rectangles, but now, such a partition does not cover R exactly. In this case, only the n rectangles that lie entirely within R are considered to be in the partition (Figure 14.9).When f is nonnegative on R, the volume of the solid bounded by the surface $z = f(x, y)$ and the xy-plane over R is approximated by the Riemann sum

$$V \approx \sum_{k=1}^{n} f(\overline{x}_k, \overline{y}_k)\,\Delta A_k,$$

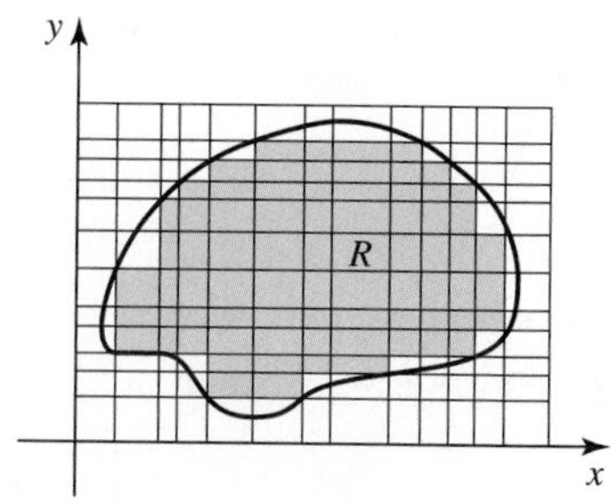

FIGURE 14.9

where $\Delta A_k = \Delta x_k \Delta y_k$ is the area of the kth rectangle and $(\overline{x}_k, \overline{y}_k)$ is any point in the kth rectangle, for $1 \le k \le n$. As before, we define Δ to be the maximum length of the diagonals of the rectangles in the partition.

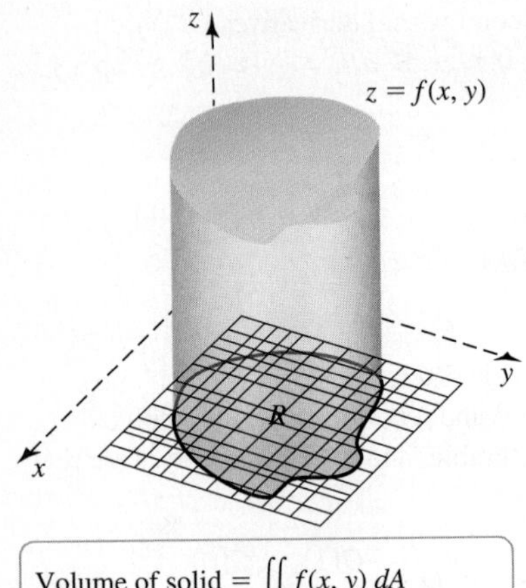

Volume of solid $= \iint_R f(x, y)\, dA$

$= \lim_{\Delta \to 0} \sum_{k=1}^{n} f(\overline{x}_k, \overline{y}_k)\, \Delta A_k$

FIGURE 14.10

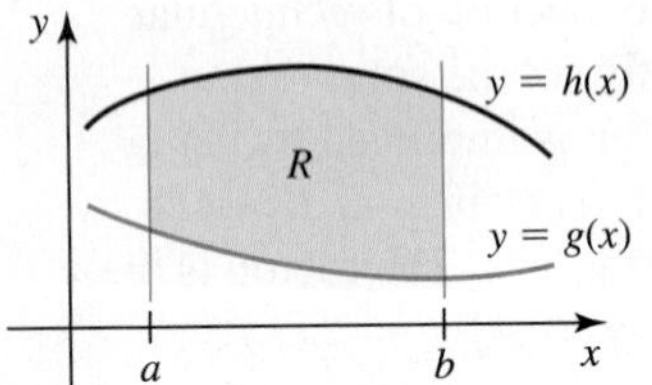

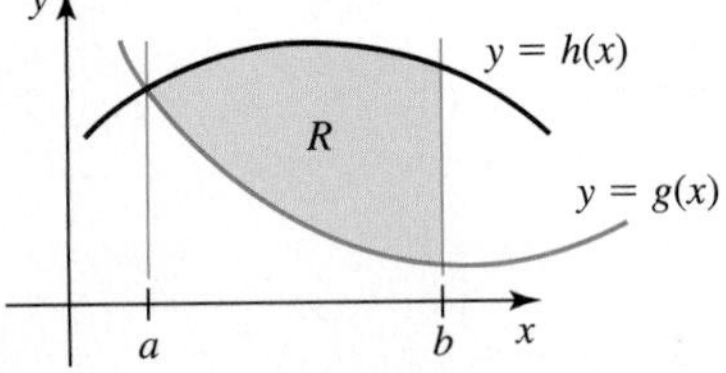

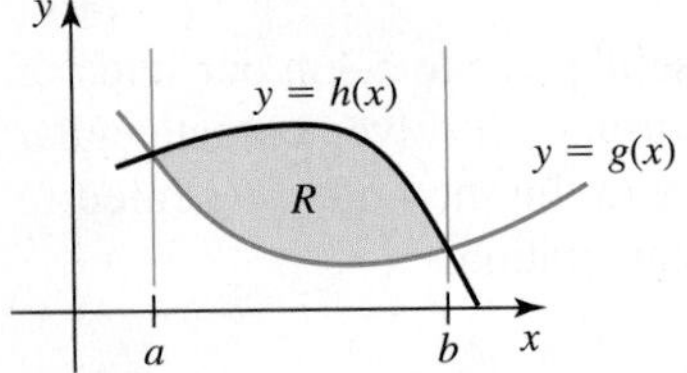

FIGURE 14.11

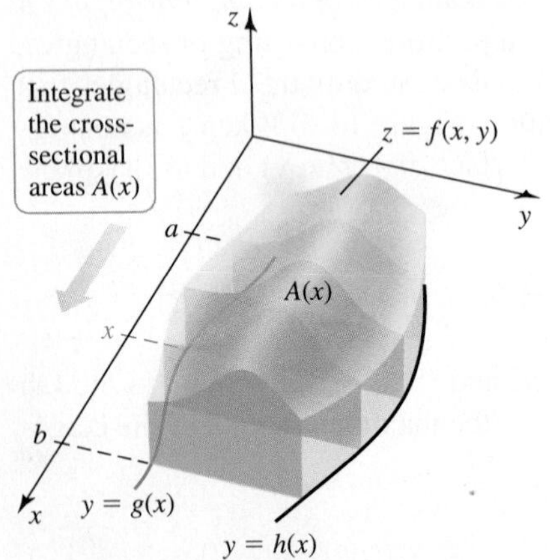

FIGURE 14.12

Under the assumptions that f is continuous on R and that the boundary of R consists of a finite number of smooth curves, two things occur as $\Delta \to 0$ and the number of subregions increases $(n \to \infty)$:

- The rectangles in the partition fill R more and more completely; that is, the union of the rectangles approaches R.
- Over all partitions and all choices of $(\overline{x}_k, \overline{y}_k)$ within a partition, the Riemann sums approach a (unique) limit.

The limit approached by the Riemann sums is the **double integral of f over R**; that is,

$$\lim_{\Delta \to 0} \sum_{k=1}^{n} f(\overline{x}_k, \overline{y}_k)\, \Delta A_k = \iint_R f(x, y)\, dA.$$

When this limit exists, f is **integrable** over R. If f is nonnegative on R, then the double integral equals the volume of the solid bounded by the surface $z = f(x, y)$ and the xy-plane over R (Figure 14.10).

The double integral $\iint_R f(x, y)\, dA$ has another common interpretation. Suppose R represents a thin plate whose density at the point (x, y) is $f(x, y)$. The units of density are mass per unit area, so the product $f(\overline{x}_k, \overline{y}_k)\Delta A_k$ approximates the mass of the kth rectangle in R. Summing the masses of the rectangles gives an approximation to the total mass of R. In the limit as $n \to \infty$ and $\Delta \to 0$, the double integral equals the mass of the plate.

Iterated Integrals

Double integrals over nonrectangular regions are also evaluated using iterated integrals. However, in this more general setting the order of integration is critical. Most of the double integrals we encounter fall into one of two categories determined by the shape of the region R.

The first type of region has the property that its lower and upper boundaries are the graphs of continuous functions $y = g(x)$ and $y = h(x)$, respectively, for $a \le x \le b$. Such regions have any of the forms shown in Figure 14.11.

Once again, we appeal to the general slicing method. Assume for the moment that f is nonnegative on R and consider the solid bounded by the surface $z = f(x, y)$ and R (Figure 14.12). Imagine taking vertical slices through the solid parallel to the y-axis. The cross section through the solid at a fixed value of x extends from the lower curve $y = g(x)$ to the upper curve $y = h(x)$. The area of that cross section is

$$A(x) = \int_{g(x)}^{h(x)} f(x, y)\, dy, \qquad \text{for } a \le x \le b.$$

The volume of the region is given by a double integral; it is evaluated by integrating the cross-sectional areas $A(x)$ from $x = a$ to $x = b$:

$$\iint_R f(x, y)\, dA = \int_a^b \underbrace{\int_{g(x)}^{h(x)} f(x, y)\, dy}_{A(x)}\, dx.$$

EXAMPLE 1 Evaluating a double integral Express the integral $\iint_R 2x^2 y\, dA$ as an iterated integral, where R is the region bounded by the parabolas $y = 3x^2$ and $y = 16 - x^2$. Then, evaluate the integral.

SOLUTION The region R is bounded below and above by the graphs of $g(x) = 3x^2$ and $h(x) = 16 - x^2$, respectively. Solving $3x^2 = 16 - x^2$, we find that these curves intersect at $x = -2$ and $x = 2$, which are the limits of integration in the x-direction (Figure 14.13).

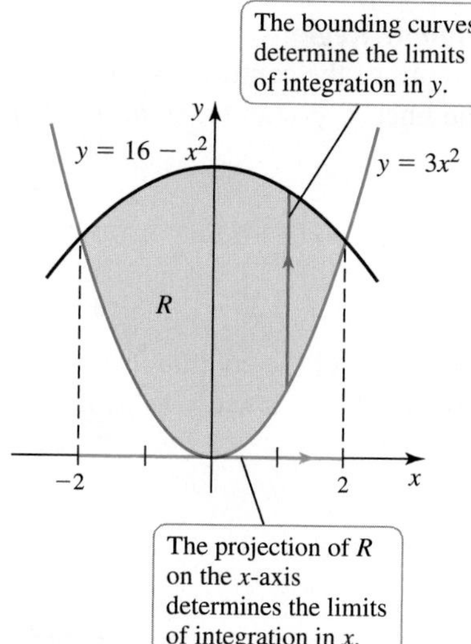

FIGURE 14.13

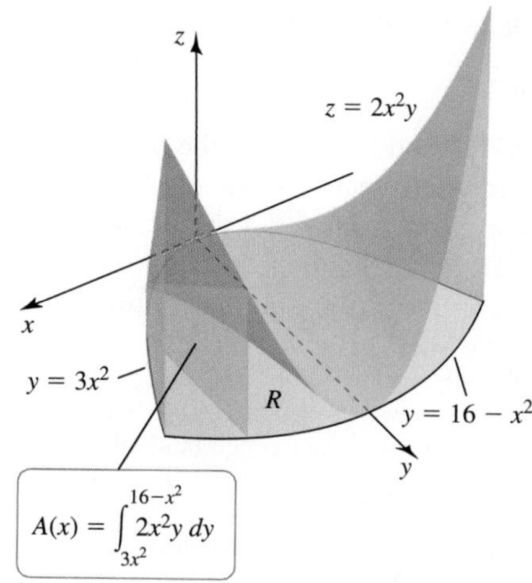

FIGURE 14.14

Figure 14.14 shows the solid bounded by the surface $z = 2x^2 y$ and the region R. A typical vertical cross section through the solid parallel to the y-axis at a fixed value of x has area

$$A(x) = \int_{3x^2}^{16-x^2} 2x^2 y\, dy.$$

Integrating these cross-sectional areas between $x = -2$ and $x = 2$, the iterated integral becomes

$$\iint_R 2x^2 y\, dA = \underbrace{\int_{-2}^{2} \int_{3x^2}^{16-x^2} 2x^2 y\, dy\, dx}_{A(x)} \quad \text{Convert to an iterated integral.}$$

$$= \int_{-2}^{2} (x^2 y^2)\Big|_{3x^2}^{16-x^2} dx \quad \text{Evaluate the inner integral with respect to } y.$$

$$= \int_{-2}^{2} x^2((16 - x^2)^2 - (3x^2)^2)\, dx \quad \text{Simplify.}$$

$$= \int_{-2}^{2} (-8x^6 - 32x^4 + 256x^2)\, dx \quad \text{Simplify.}$$

$$\approx 663.2. \quad \text{Evaluate the outer integral with respect to } x.$$

Related Exercises 7–22 ◀

QUICK CHECK 1 A region R is bounded by the x- and y-axes and the line $x + y = 2$. If we integrate first with respect to y, give the limits of the iterated integral over R. ◀

Change of Perspective Suppose that the region of integration R is bounded on the left and right by the graphs of continuous functions $x = g(y)$ and $x = h(y)$, respectively, on the interval $c \le y \le d$. Such regions may take any of the forms shown in Figure 14.15.

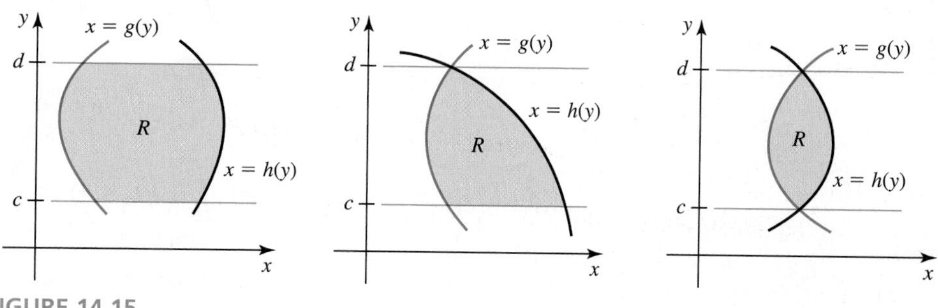

FIGURE 14.15

To find the volume of the solid bounded by the surface $z = f(x, y)$ and R, we now take slices parallel to the x-axis and perpendicular to the xy-plane. In so doing, the double integral $\iint_R f(x, y)\, dA$ is converted to an iterated integral in which the inner integration is with respect to x over the interval $g(y) \le x \le h(y)$ and the outer integration is with respect to y over the interval $c \le y \le d$. The evaluation of double integrals in these two cases is summarized in the following theorem.

Theorem 14.2 is another version of Fubini's Theorem. With integrals over nonrectangular regions, the order of integration cannot be simply switched; that is,

$$\int_a^b \int_{g(x)}^{h(x)} f(x, y)\, dy\, dx \neq \int_{g(x)}^{h(x)} \int_a^b f(x, y)\, dx\, dy.$$

Comparing the double integral to the iterated integral, we see that the element of area is $dA = dy\, dx$ or $dA = dx\, dy$, which is consistent with the area formula for rectangles.

THEOREM 14.2 Double Integrals over Nonrectangular Regions

Let R be a region bounded below and above by the graphs of the continuous functions $y = g(x)$ and $y = h(x)$, respectively, and by the lines $x = a$ and $x = b$. If f is continuous on R, then

$$\iint_R f(x, y)\, dA = \int_a^b \int_{g(x)}^{h(x)} f(x, y)\, dy\, dx.$$

Let R be a region bounded on the left and right by the graphs of the continuous functions $x = g(y)$ and $x = h(y)$, respectively, and the lines $y = c$ and $y = d$. If f is continuous on R, then

$$\iint_R f(x, y)\, dA = \int_c^d \int_{g(y)}^{h(y)} f(x, y)\, dx\, dy.$$

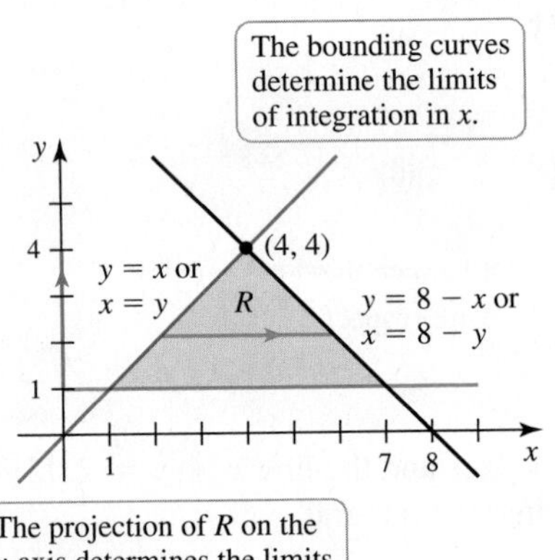

FIGURE 14.16

EXAMPLE 2 Computing a volume Find the volume of the solid below the surface $f(x, y) = 2 + \frac{1}{y}$ and above the region R in the xy-plane bounded by the lines $y = x$, $y = 8 - x$, and $y = 1$. Notice that $f(x, y) > 0$ on R.

SOLUTION The region R is bounded on the left by $x = y$ and bounded on the right by $y = 8 - x$, or $x = 8 - y$ (Figure 14.16). These lines intersect at the point (4, 4). We take vertical slices through the solid parallel to the x-axis from $y = 1$ to $y = 4$. (To visualize these slices, it helps to draw lines through R parallel to the x-axis.)

Integrating the cross-sectional areas of slices from $y = 1$ to $y = 4$, the volume of the solid beneath the graph of f and above R (Figure 14.17) is given by

$$\iint_R \left(2 + \frac{1}{y}\right) dA = \int_1^4 \int_y^{8-y} \left(2 + \frac{1}{y}\right) dx\, dy \quad \text{Convert to an iterated integral.}$$

$$= \int_1^4 \left(2 + \frac{1}{y}\right) x \Big|_y^{8-y} dy \quad \text{Evaluate the inner integral; } 2 + \frac{1}{y} \text{ is constant.}$$

$$= \int_1^4 \left(2 + \frac{1}{y}\right)(8 - 2y)\, dy \quad \text{Simplify.}$$

$$= \int_1^4 \left(14 - 4y + \frac{8}{y}\right) dy \quad \text{Simplify.}$$

$$= (14y - 2y^2 + 8 \ln |y|)\Big|_1^4 \quad \text{Evaluate the outer integral.}$$

$$= 12 + 8 \ln 4 \approx 23.09. \quad \text{Simplify.}$$

Related Exercises 23–38

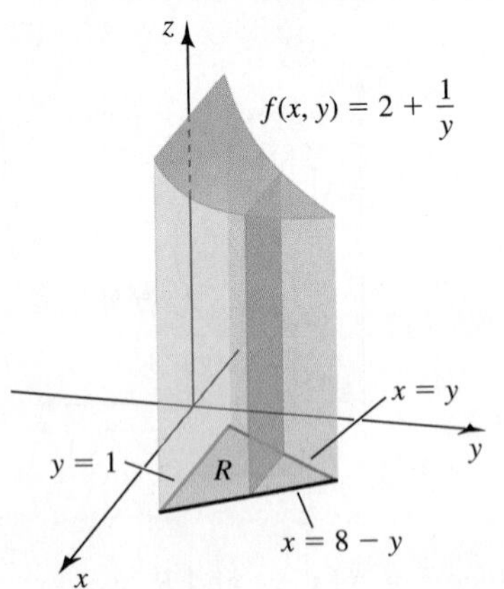

FIGURE 14.17

QUICK CHECK 2 Could the integral in Example 2 be evaluated by integrating first (inner integral) with respect to y?

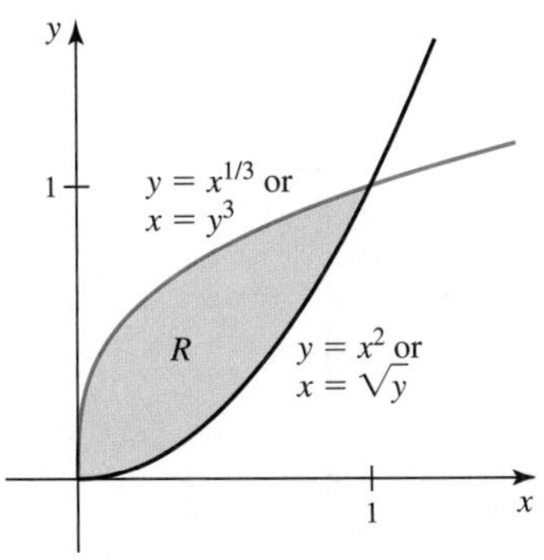

R is bounded above and below, and on the right and left by curves.

FIGURE 14.18

Choosing and Changing the Order of Integration

Occasionally a region of integration is bounded above and below, *and* on the right and the left by curves (Figure 14.18). In these cases, we can choose either of two orders of integration; however, one order of integration may be preferable. The following examples illustrate the valuable techniques of choosing and changing the order of integration.

EXAMPLE 3 **Volume of a tetrahedron** Find the volume of the tetrahedron (pyramid with four triangular faces) in the first octant bounded by the plane $z = c - ax - by$ and the coordinate planes ($x = 0, y = 0, z = 0$). Assume a, b, and c are positive real numbers (Figure 14.19).

SOLUTION Let R be the triangular base of the tetrahedron in the xy-plane; it is formed by the x- and y-axes and the line $ax + by = c$ (found by setting $z = 0$ in the equation of the plane; Figure 14.20). We can view R as being bounded below and above by the lines $y = 0$ and $y = c/b - ax/b$, respectively. The boundaries on the left and right are then $x = 0$ and $x = c/a$, respectively. Therefore, the volume of the solid region between the plane and R is

> In this case, it is just as easy to view R as being bounded on the left and the right by the lines $x = 0$ and $x = c/a - by/a$, respectively, and integrating first with respect to x.

$$\iint_R (c - ax - by)\, dA = \int_0^{c/a} \int_0^{c/b - ax/b} (c - ax - by)\, dy\, dx \quad \text{Convert to an iterated integral.}$$

$$= \int_0^{c/a} \left(cy - axy - \frac{by^2}{2} \right) \Bigg|_0^{c/b - ax/b} dx \quad \text{Evaluate the inner integral.}$$

$$= \int_0^{c/a} \frac{(ax - c)^2}{2b}\, dx \quad \text{Simplify and factor.}$$

$$= \frac{c^3}{6ab}. \quad \text{Evaluate the outer integral.}$$

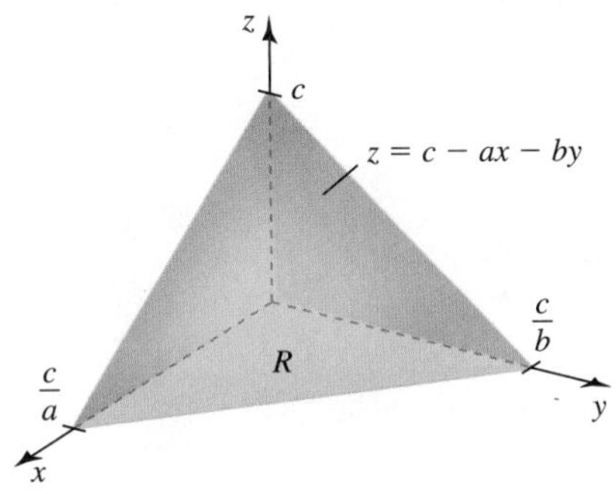

FIGURE 14.19

This result illustrates the volume formula for a tetrahedron. The lengths of the legs of the base are c/a and c/b, which means the area of the base is $c^2/(2ab)$. The height of the tetrahedron is c. The general volume formula is

$$V = \frac{c^3}{6ab} = \frac{1}{3} \underbrace{\frac{c^2}{2ab}}_{\text{area of base}} \underbrace{c}_{\text{height}} = \frac{1}{3}(\text{area of base})(\text{height}).$$

> The volume of *any* tetrahedron is $\frac{1}{3}$(area of base)(height), where any of the faces may be chosen as the base (Exercise 82).

Related Exercises 39–42 ◀

EXAMPLE 4 **Changing the order of integration** Sketch the region of integration and evaluate $\int_0^{\sqrt{\pi}} \int_y^{\sqrt{\pi}} \sin x^2\, dx\, dy$.

SOLUTION The region of integration is $R = \{(x, y): y \le x \le \sqrt{\pi}, 0 \le y \le \sqrt{\pi}\}$, which is a triangle (Figure 14.21a). Evaluating the iterated integral as given (integrating first with respect to x) requires integrating $\sin x^2$, a function whose antiderivative is not expressible in terms of elementary functions. Therefore, this order of integration is not feasible.

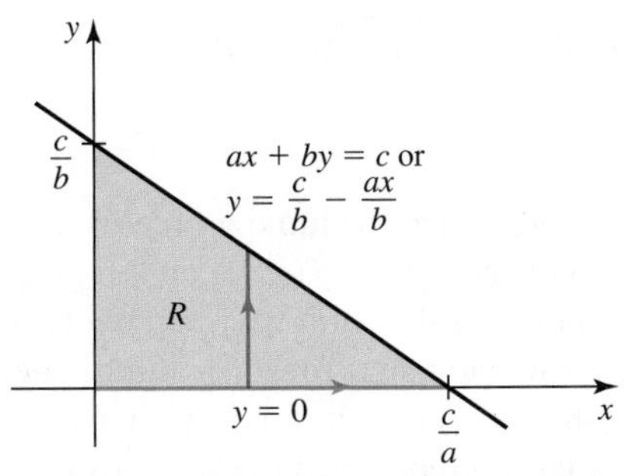

FIGURE 14.20

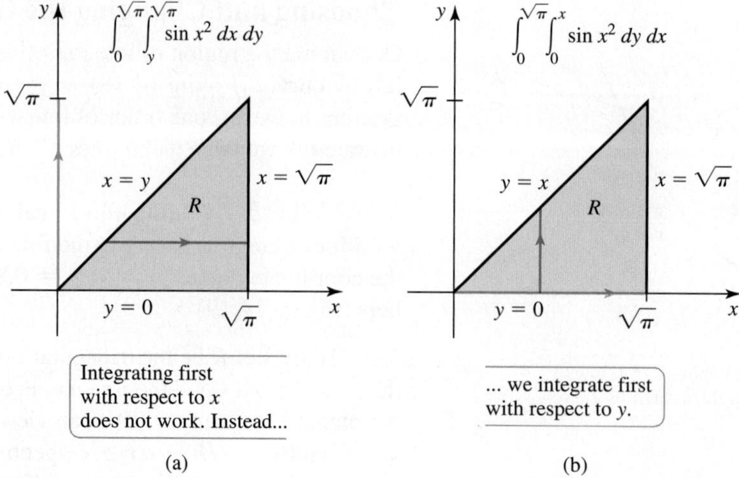

FIGURE 14.21

Instead, we change our perspective on R (Figure 14.21b) and integrate first with respect to y. With this order of integration, y runs from $y = 0$ to $y = x$ in the inner integral and x runs from $x = 0$ to $x = \sqrt{\pi}$ in the outer integral:

$$\iint_R \sin x^2\, dA = \int_0^{\sqrt{\pi}} \int_0^{x} \sin x^2\, dy\, dx$$

$$= \int_0^{\sqrt{\pi}} \left(y \sin x^2\right)\Big|_0^x\, dx \qquad \text{Evaluate the inner integral; } \sin x^2 \text{ is constant.}$$

$$= \int_0^{\sqrt{\pi}} x \sin x^2\, dx \qquad \text{Simplify.}$$

$$= \left(-\frac{1}{2}\cos x^2\right)\Big|_0^{\sqrt{\pi}} \qquad \text{Evaluate the outer integral.}$$

$$= 1 \qquad \text{Simplify.}$$

This example shows that the order of integration can make a practical difference.

Related Exercises 43–54 ◄

QUICK CHECK 3 Change the order of integration of the integral $\int_0^1 \int_0^y f(x, y)\, dx\, dy$. ◄

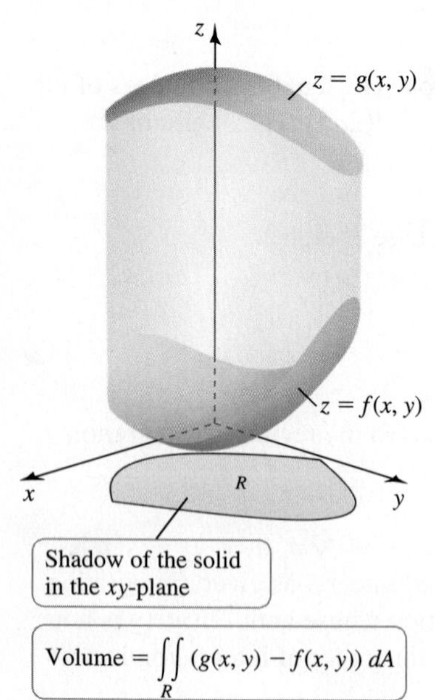

FIGURE 14.22

Regions Between Two Surfaces

An extension of the preceding ideas allows us to solve more general volume problems. Let $z = g(x, y)$ and $z = f(x, y)$ be continuous functions with $g(x, y) \geq f(x, y)$ on a region R in the xy-plane. Suppose we wish to compute the volume of the solid between the two surfaces over the region R (Figure 14.22). Forming a Riemann sum for the volume, the height of a typical box within the solid is the vertical distance $g(x, y) - f(x, y)$ between the upper and lower surfaces. Therefore, the volume of the solid between the surfaces is

$$\text{volume} = \iint_R (g(x,y) - f(x,y))\, dA.$$

EXAMPLE 5 Region bounded by two surfaces Find the volume of the solid region bounded by the paraboloids $z = x^2 + y^2$ and $z = 8 - x^2 - y^2$ (Figure 14.23).

SOLUTION The upper surface bounding the solid is $z = 8 - x^2 - y^2$ and the lower surface is $z = x^2 + y^2$. The two surfaces intersect along a curve C. Solving $8 - x^2 - y^2 = x^2 + y^2$, we find that $x^2 + y^2 = 4$. This circle of radius 2 is the projection of C onto the xy-plane (Figure 14.23); it is also the boundary of the region of integration

$$R = \{(x, y): -\sqrt{4 - x^2} \le y \le \sqrt{4 - x^2}, -2 \le x \le 2\}.$$

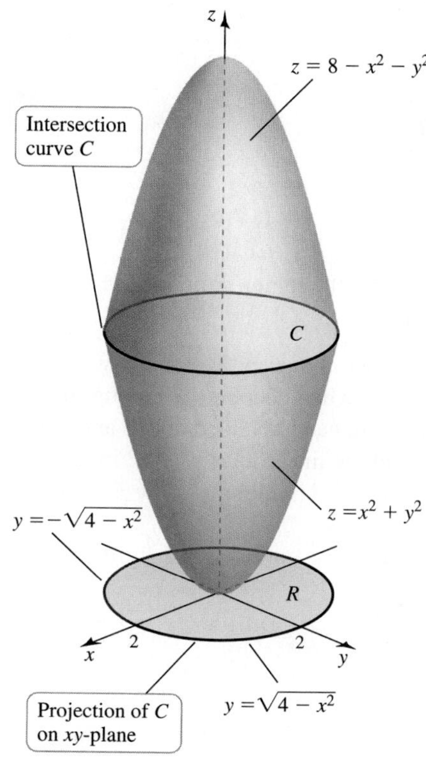

FIGURE 14.23

Notice that R and the solid are symmetric about the x- and y-axes. Therefore, the volume of the entire solid is four times the volume over that part of R in the first quadrant. The volume of the solid is

$$4\int_0^2\int_0^{\sqrt{4-x^2}} ((\underbrace{8 - x^2 - y^2}_{g(x,y)}) - (\underbrace{x^2 + y^2}_{f(x,y)}))\,dy\,dx$$

$$= 8\int_0^2\int_0^{\sqrt{4-x^2}} (4 - x^2 - y^2)\,dy\,dx \quad \text{Simplify the integrand.}$$

$$= 8\int_0^2 \left((4 - x^2)y - \frac{y^3}{3}\right)\Bigg|_0^{\sqrt{4-x^2}} dx \quad \text{Fundamental Theorem of Calculus}$$

$$= \frac{16}{3}\int_0^2 (4 - x^2)^{3/2}\,dx \quad \text{Simplify.}$$

$$= \frac{256}{3}\int_0^{\pi/2} \cos^4\theta\,d\theta \quad \text{Trigonometric substitution: } x = 2\sin\theta$$

$$= 16\pi. \quad \text{Evaluate the outer integral.}$$

Related Exercises 55–58 ◄

➤ To use symmetry to simplify a double integral, you must check that both the region of integration and the integrand have the same symmetry.

Decomposition of Regions

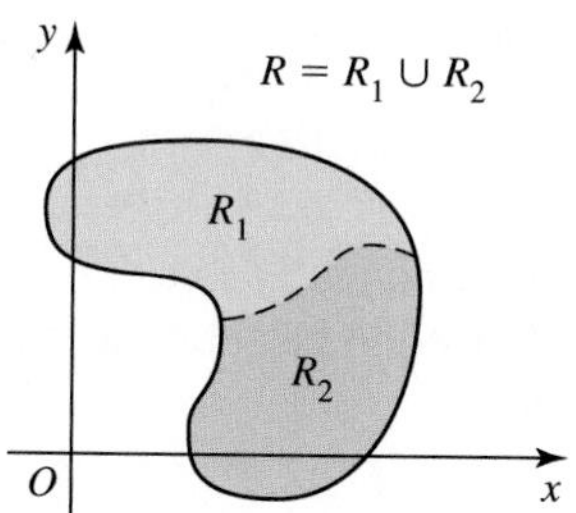

FIGURE 14.24

We occasionally encounter regions that are more complicated than those considered so far. A technique called *decomposition* allows us to subdivide a region of integration into two (or more) subregions. If the integrals over the subregions can be evaluated separately, the results are added to obtain the value of the original integral. For example, the region R in Figure 14.24 is divided into two nonoverlapping subregions R_1 and R_2. By partitioning these regions and using Riemann sums, it can be shown that

$$\iint_R f(x, y)\,dA = \iint_{R_1} f(x, y)\,dA + \iint_{R_2} f(x, y)\,dA.$$

This method is illustrated in Example 6. The analogue of decomposition with single variable integrals is the property $\int_a^b f(x)\,dx = \int_a^c f(x)\,dx + \int_c^b f(x)\,dx$.

Finding Area by Double Integrals

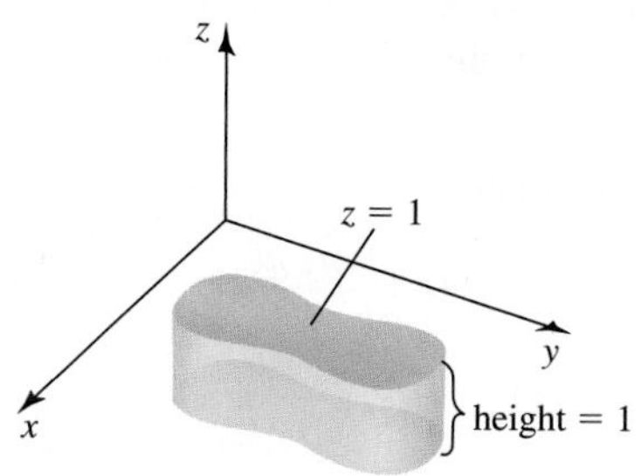

Volume of solid = (Area of R) × (height) = Area of $R = \iint_R 1\,dA$

FIGURE 14.25

An interesting application of double integrals arises when the integrand is $f(x, y) = 1$. The integral $\iint_R 1\,dA$ gives the volume of the solid between the horizontal plane $z = 1$ and the region R. Because the height of this solid is 1, its volume equals (numerically) the area of R (Figure 14.25). Therefore, we have a way to compute areas of regions in the xy-plane using double integrals.

➤ We are solving a familiar area problem first encountered in Section 6.2. Suppose R is bounded above by $y = h(x)$ and below by $y = g(x)$, for $a \le x \le b$. Using a double integral, the area of R is

$$\iint_R dA = \int_a^b \int_{g(x)}^{h(x)} dy\,dx = \int_a^b (h(x) - g(x))\,dx,$$

which is a result obtained in Section 6.2.

Areas of Regions by Double Integrals

Let R be a region in the xy-plane. Then,

$$\text{area of } R = \iint_R dA.$$

EXAMPLE 6 **Area of a plane region** Find the area of the region R bounded by $y = x^2$, $y = -x + 12$, and $y = 4x + 12$ (Figure 14.26).

SOLUTION The region R in its entirety is bounded neither above and below by two curves, nor on the left and right by two curves. However, when decomposed along the y-axis, R may be viewed as two regions R_1 and R_2 that are each bounded above and below by a pair of curves. Notice that the parabola $y = x^2$ and the line $y = -x + 12$ intersect in the first quadrant at the point $(3, 9)$, while the parabola and the line $y = 4x + 12$ intersect in the second quadrant at the point $(-2, 4)$.

To find the area of R, we integrate the function $f(x, y) = 1$ over R_1 and R_2; the area is

$$\iint_{R_1} 1\,dA + \iint_{R_2} 1\,dA \qquad \text{Decompose region.}$$

$$= \int_{-2}^{0} \int_{x^2}^{4x+12} 1\,dy\,dx + \int_{0}^{3} \int_{x^2}^{-x+12} 1\,dy\,dx \qquad \text{Convert to iterated integrals.}$$

$$= \int_{-2}^{0} (4x + 12 - x^2)\,dx + \int_{0}^{3} (-x + 12 - x^2)\,dx \qquad \text{Evaluate the inner integrals.}$$

$$= \left(2x^2 + 12x - \frac{x^3}{3}\right)\Big|_{-2}^{0} + \left(-\frac{x^2}{2} + 12x - \frac{x^3}{3}\right)\Big|_{0}^{3} \qquad \text{Evaluate the outer integrals.}$$

$$= \frac{40}{3} + \frac{45}{2} = \frac{215}{6}. \qquad \text{Simplify.}$$

Related Exercises 59–64 ◀

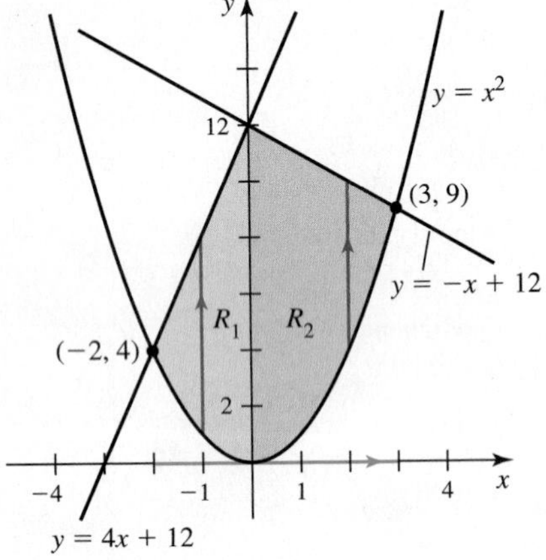

FIGURE 14.26

QUICK CHECK 4 Consider the triangle R with vertices $(-1, 0)$, $(1, 0)$, and $(0, 1)$ as a region of integration. If we integrate first with respect to x, does R need to be subdivided? If we integrate first with respect to y, does R need to be subdivided? ◀

SECTION 14.2 EXERCISES

Review Questions

1. Describe and sketch a region that is bounded above and below by two curves.

2. Describe and a sketch a region that is bounded on the left and on the right by two curves.

3. Which order of integration is preferable to integrate $f(x, y) = xy$ over $R = \{(x, y): y - 1 \le x \le 1 - y, 0 \le y \le 1\}$?

4. Which order of integration would you use to find the area of the region bounded by the x-axis and the lines $y = 2x + 3$ and $y = 3x - 4$ using a double integral?

5. Change the order of integration in the integral $\int_0^1 \int_{y^2}^{\sqrt{y}} f(x, y)\,dx\,dy$.

6. Sketch the region of integration for $\int_{-2}^{2} \int_{x^2}^{4} e^{xy}\,dy\,dx$.

Basic Skills

7–8. Regions of integration *Consider the regions R shown in the figures and write an iterated integral of a continuous function f over R.*

7.

8.

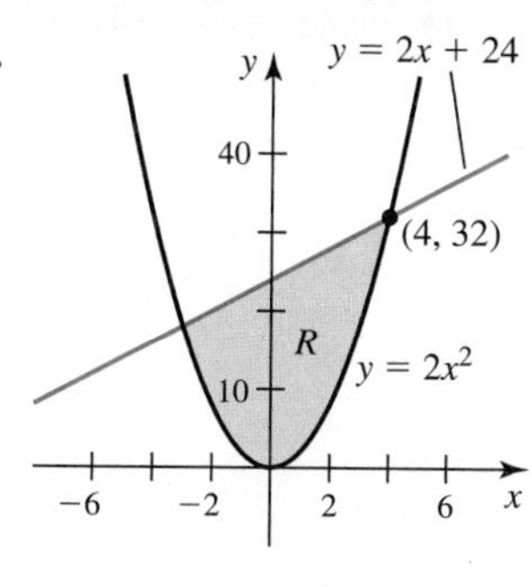

9–12. Regions of integration *Sketch the following regions and write an iterated integral of a continuous function f over the region.*

9. $R = \{(x, y): 0 \le x \le \pi/4, \sin x \le y \le \cos x\}$

10. $R = \{(x, y): 0 \le x \le 2, 3x^2 \le y \le -6x + 24\}$

11. $R = \{(x, y): 1 \le x \le 2, x + 1 \le y \le 2x + 4\}$

12. $R = \{(x, y): 0 \le x \le 4, x^2 \le y \le 8\sqrt{x}\}$

13–18. Evaluating integrals *Evaluate the following integrals as they are written.*

13. $\int_0^2 \int_{x^2}^{2x} xy\, dy\, dx$

14. $\int_0^3 \int_{2x^2}^{2x+12} (x + y)\, dy\, dx$

15. $\int_{-\pi/4}^{\pi/4} \int_{\sin x}^{\cos x} dy\, dx$

16. $\int_0^1 \int_{-\sqrt{1-x^2}}^{\sqrt{1-x^2}} 2x^2 y\, dy\, dx$

17. $\int_{-2}^2 \int_{x^2}^{8-x^2} x\, dy\, dx$

18. $\int_0^{\ln 2} \int_{e^x}^{2} dy\, dx$

19–22. Evaluating integrals *Evaluate the following integrals.*

19. $\iint_R xy\, dA$; R is bounded by $x = 0$, $y = 2x + 1$, and $y = -2x + 5$.

20. $\iint_R (x + y)\, dA$; R is in the region in the first quadrant bounded by $x = 0$, $y = x^2$, and $y = 8 - x^2$.

21. $\iint_R y^2\, dA$; R is bounded by $x = 1$, $y = 2x + 2$, and $y = -x - 1$.

22. $\iint_R x^2 y\, dA$; R is the region in quadrants 1 and 4 bounded by the semicircle of radius 4 centered at (0, 0).

23–24. Regions of integration *Write an iterated integral of a continuous function f over the region R shown in the figure.*

23.

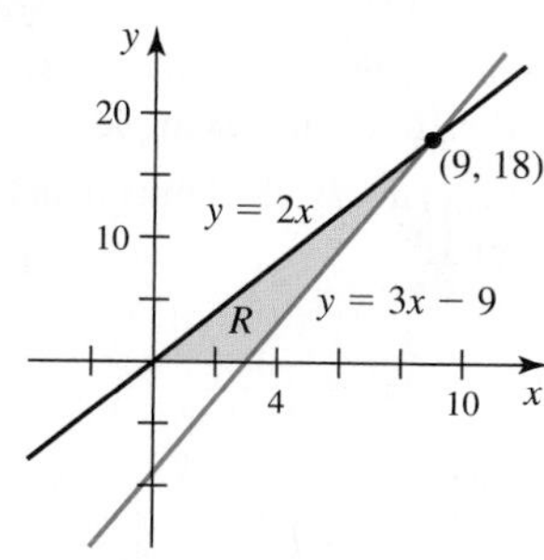

24.

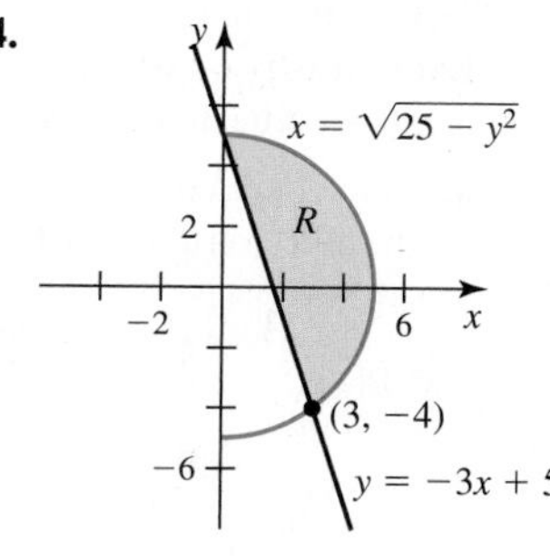

25–28. Regions of integration *Write an iterated integral of a continuous function f over the following regions.*

25. The region bounded by $y = 2x + 3$, $y = 3x - 7$, and $y = 0$

26. $R = \{(x, y): 0 \le x \le y(1 - y)\}$

27. The region bounded by $y = 4 - x$, $y = 1$, and $x = 0$

28. The region in quadrants 2 and 3 bounded by the semicircle with radius 3 centered at (0, 0)

29–34. Evaluating integrals *Sketch the region of integration and evaluate the following integrals as they are written.*

29. $\int_{-1}^2 \int_y^{4-y} dx\, dy$

30. $\int_0^2 \int_0^{4-y^2} (x + y)\, dx\, dy$

31. $\int_0^4 \int_{-\sqrt{16-y^2}}^{\sqrt{16-y^2}} 2xy\, dx\, dy$

32. $\int_0^1 \int_{-2\sqrt{1-y^2}}^{2\sqrt{1-y^2}} 2x\, dx\, dy$

33. $\int_0^{\ln 2} \int_{e^y}^{2} \frac{y}{x}\, dx\, dy$

34. $\int_0^4 \int_y^{2y} xy\, dx\, dy$

35–38. Evaluating integrals *Sketch the regions of integration and evaluate the following integrals.*

35. $\iint_R xy\, dA$; R is bounded by $x = 0$, $y = 0$, and $y = 9 - x^2$.

36. $\iint_R (x + y)\, dA$; R is bounded by $y = |x|$, and $y = 4$.

37. $\iint_R y^2\, dA$; R is bounded by $y = 0$, $y = 2x + 4$, and $y = x^3$.

38. $\iint_R x^2 y\, dA$; R is bounded by $y = 0$, $y = \sqrt{x}$, and $y = x - 2$.

39–42. Volumes *Use double integrals to calculate the volume of the following regions.*

39. The tetrahedron bounded by the coordinate planes ($x = 0, y = 0, z = 0$) and the plane $z = 8 - 2x - 4y$

40. The solid in the first octant bounded by the coordinate planes and the surface $z = 8 - x^2 - 2y^2$

41. The segment of the cylinder $x^2 + y^2 = 1$ bounded above by the plane $z = 12 + x + y$ and below by $z = 0$

42. The solid beneath the cylinder $z = y^2$ and above the region $R = \{(x, y): 0 \le y \le 1, y \le x \le 1\}$

43–48. Changing order of integration *Reverse the order of integration in the following integrals.*

43. $\int_0^2 \int_{x^2}^{2x} f(x, y)\, dy\, dx$

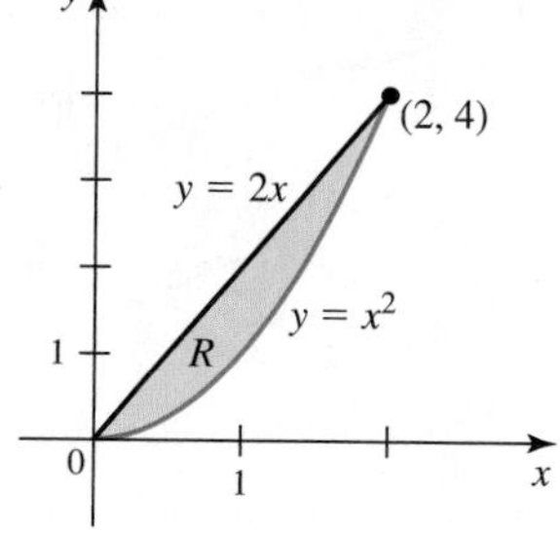

44. $\int_0^3 \int_0^{6-2x} f(x, y)\, dy\, dx$

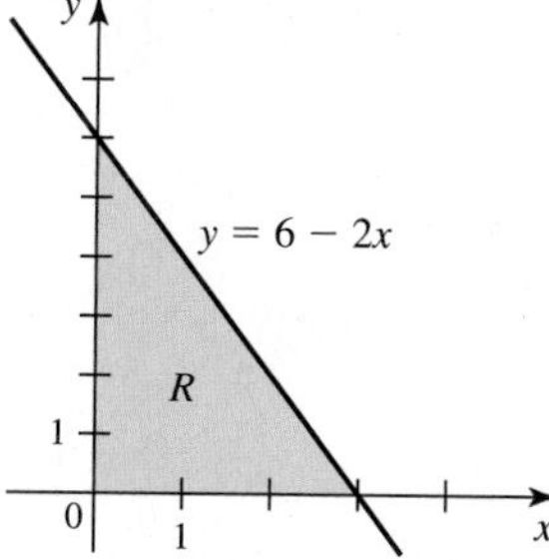

45. $\displaystyle\int_{1/2}^{1}\int_{0}^{-\ln y} f(x, y)\,dx\,dy$ **46.** $\displaystyle\int_{0}^{1}\int_{1}^{e^y} f(x, y)\,dx\,dy$

47. $\displaystyle\int_{0}^{1}\int_{0}^{\cos^{-1} y} f(x, y)\,dx\,dy$ **48.** $\displaystyle\int_{1}^{e}\int_{0}^{\ln x} f(x, y)\,dy\,dx$

49–54. Changing order of integration *The following integrals can be evaluated only by reversing the order of integration. Sketch the region of integration, reverse the order of integration, and evaluate the integral.*

49. $\displaystyle\int_{0}^{1}\int_{y}^{1} e^{x^2}\,dx\,dy$ **50.** $\displaystyle\int_{0}^{\pi}\int_{x}^{\pi} \sin y^2\,dy\,dx$

51. $\displaystyle\int_{0}^{1/2}\int_{y^2}^{1/4} y\cos(16\pi x^2)\,dx\,dy$

52. $\displaystyle\int_{0}^{4}\int_{\sqrt{x}}^{2} \frac{x}{y^5 + 1}\,dy\,dx$

53. $\displaystyle\int_{0}^{\sqrt[3]{\pi}}\int_{y}^{\sqrt[3]{\pi}} x^4\cos(x^2 y)\,dx\,dy$

54. $\displaystyle\int_{0}^{2}\int_{0}^{4-x^2} \frac{xe^{2y}}{4 - y}\,dy\,dx$

55–58. Regions between two surfaces *Find the volume of the following solid regions.*

55. The solid bounded by the paraboloid $z = x^2 + y^2$ and the plane $z = 9$

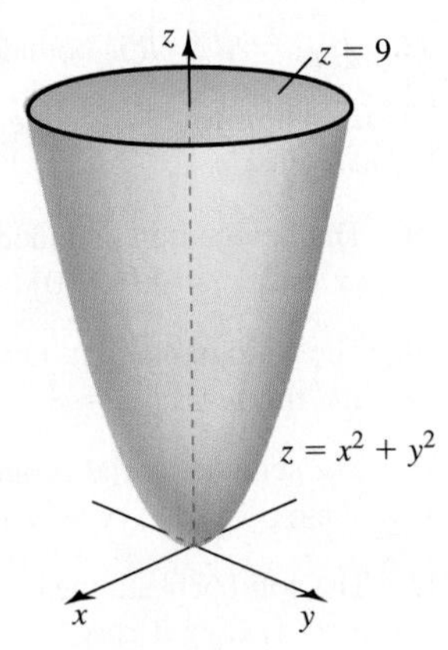

56. The solid bounded by the paraboloids $z = x^2 + y^2$ and $z = 50 - x^2 - y^2$

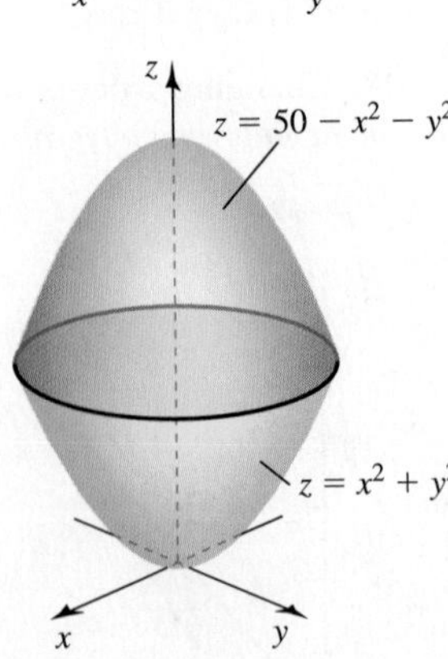

57. The solid above the region $R = \{(x, y): 0 \le x \le 1, 0 \le y \le 2 - x\}$ and between the planes $-4x - 4y + z = 0$ and $-2x - y + z = 8$

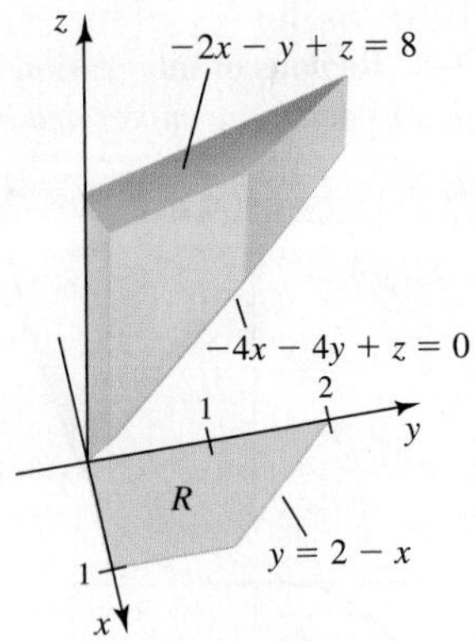

58. The solid S between the surfaces $z = e^{x-y}$ and $z = -e^{x-y}$, where S intersects the xy-plane in the region $R = \{(x, y): 0 \le x \le y, 0 \le y \le 1\}$

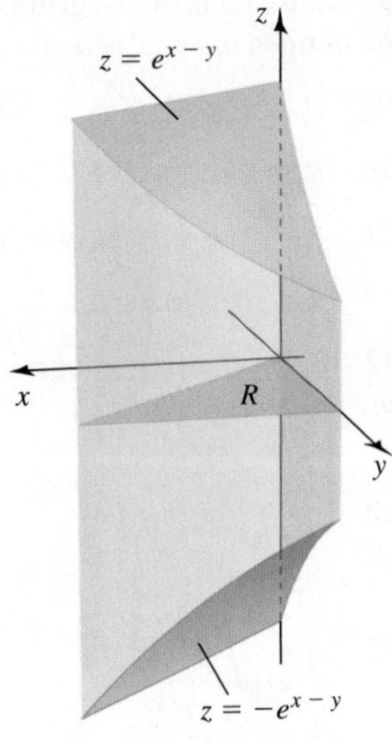

59–64. Area of plane regions *Use a double integral to compute the area of the following regions. Make a sketch of the region.*

59. The region bounded by the parabola $y = x^2$ and the line $y = 4$

60. The region bounded by the parabola $y = x^2$ and the line $y = x + 2$

61. The region in the first quadrant bounded by $y = e^x$ and $x = \ln 2$

62. The region bounded by $y = 1 + \sin x$ and $y = 1 - \sin x$ on the interval $[0, \pi]$

63. The region in the first quadrant bounded by $y = x^2$, $y = 5x + 6$, and $y = 6 - x$

64. The region bounded by the lines $x = 0$, $x = 4$, $y = x$, and $y = 2x + 1$

Further Explorations

65. Explain why or why not Determine whether the following statements are true and give an explanation or counterexample.

a. In the iterated integral $\int_c^d \int_a^b f(x, y)\,dx\,dy$, the limits a and b must be constants or functions of x.

b. In the iterated integral $\int_c^d \int_a^b f(x, y)\, dx\, dy$, the limits c and d must be constants or functions of y.

c. Changing the order of integration gives $\int_0^2 \int_1^y f(x, y)\, dx\, dy = \int_1^y \int_0^2 f(x, y)\, dy\, dx$.

66–69. Miscellaneous integrals *Evaluate the following integrals.*

66. $\displaystyle\iint_R y\, dA;\ R = \{(x, y): 0 \le y \le \sec x, 0 \le x \le \pi/3\}$

67. $\displaystyle\iint_R (x + y)\, dA$; R is the region bounded by $y = 1/x$ and $y = 5/2 - x$.

68. $\displaystyle\iint_R \frac{xy}{1 + x^2 + y^2}\, dA;\ R = \{(x, y): 0 \le y \le x, 0 \le x \le 2\}$

69. $\displaystyle\iint_R x \sec^2 y\, dA;\ R = \{(x, y): 0 \le y \le x^2, 0 \le x \le \sqrt{\pi}/2\}$

70. Paraboloid sliced by plane Find the volume of the solid between the paraboloid $z = x^2 + y^2$ and the plane $z = 1 - 2y$.

71. Two integrals to one Draw the regions of integration and write the following integrals as a single iterated integral:

$$\int_0^1 \int_{e^y}^e f(x, y)\, dx\, dy + \int_{-1}^0 \int_{e^{-y}}^e f(x, y)\, dx\, dy$$

72. Diamond region Consider the region $R = \{(x, y): |x| + |y| \le 1\}$ shown in the figure.

a. Use a double integral to show that the area of R is 2.

b. Find the volume of the square column whose base is R and whose upper surface is $z = 12 - 3x - 4y$.

c. Find the volume of the solid above R and beneath the cylinder $x^2 + z^2 = 1$.

d. Find the volume of the pyramid whose base is R and whose vertex is on the z-axis at $(0, 0, 6)$.

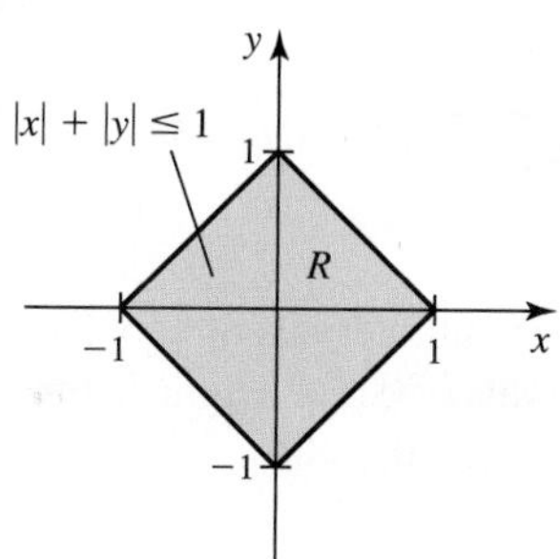

73–74. Average value *Use the definition for the average value of a function over a region R (Section 14.1),* $\bar{f} = \dfrac{1}{\text{area of } R} \displaystyle\iint_R f(x, y)\, dA$.

73. Find the average value of $a - x - y$ over the region $R = \{(x, y): x + y \le a, x \ge 0, y \ge 0\}$, where $a > 0$.

74. Find the average value of $z = a^2 - x^2 - y^2$ over the region $R = \{(x, y): x^2 + y^2 \le a^2\}$, where $a > 0$.

75–76. Area integrals *Consider the following regions R.*

a. Sketch the region R.

b. Evaluate $\iint_R dA$ *to determine the area of the region.*

c. Evaluate $\iint_R xy\, dA$.

75. R is the region between both branches of $y = 1/x$ and the lines $y = x + 3/2$ and $y = x - 3/2$.

76. R is the region bounded by the ellipse $x^2/18 + y^2/36 = 1$ with $y \le 4x/3$.

77–80. Improper integrals *Many improper double integrals may be handled using the techniques for improper integrals in one variable (Section 8.7). For example, under suitable conditions on f,*

$$\int_a^\infty \int_{g(x)}^{h(x)} f(x, y)\, dy\, dx = \lim_{b \to \infty} \int_a^b \int_{g(x)}^{h(x)} f(x, y)\, dy\, dx.$$

Use or extend the one-variable methods for improper integrals to evaluate the following integrals.

77. $\displaystyle\int_1^\infty \int_0^{e^{-x}} xy\, dy\, dx$

78. $\displaystyle\int_1^\infty \int_0^{1/x^2} \frac{2y}{x}\, dy\, dx$

79. $\displaystyle\int_0^\infty \int_0^\infty e^{-x-y}\, dy\, dx$

80. $\displaystyle\int_{-\infty}^\infty \int_{-\infty}^\infty \frac{1}{(x^2 + 1)(y^2 + 1)}\, dy\, dx$

81–85. Volumes *Compute the volume of the following solids.*

81. Sliced block The solid bounded by the planes $x = 0, x = 5, z = y - 1, z = -2y - 1, z = 0, z = 2$

82. Tetrahedron A tetrahedron with vertices at $(0, 0, 0)$, $(a, 0, 0)$, $(b, c, 0)$, and $(0, 0, d)$, where a, b, c, and d are positive real numbers

83. Square column The column with a square base $R = \{(x, y): |x| \le 1, |y| \le 1\}$ cut by the plane $z = 4 - x - y$

84. Wedge The wedge sliced from the cylinder $x^2 + y^2 = 1$ by the planes $z = 1 - x$ and $z = x - 1$

85. Wedge The wedge sliced from the cylinder $x^2 + y^2 = 1$ by the planes $z = a(2 - x)$ and $z = a(x - 2)$, where $a > 0$

Additional Exercises

86. Existence of improper double integral For what values of m and n does the integral $\int_1^\infty \int_0^{1/x} \frac{y^m}{x^n}\, dy\, dx$ have a finite value?

87. Existence of improper double integral Let $R_1 = \{(x, y): x \ge 1, 1 \le y \le 2\}$ and $R_2 = \{(x, y): 1 \le x \le 2, y \ge 1\}$. For $n > 1$, which integral(s) have finite values: $\iint_{R_1} x^{-n}\, dA$ or $\iint_{R_2} x^{-n}\, dA$?

QUICK CHECK ANSWERS

1. Inner integral: $0 \le y \le 2 - x$. Outer integral: $0 \le x \le 2$. **2.** Yes; however, two separate iterated integrals would be required. **3.** $\int_0^1 \int_x^1 f(x, y)\, dy\, dx$ **4.** No; yes

14.3 Double Integrals in Polar Coordinates

In Chapter 11 we explored polar coordinates and saw that in certain situations they simplify problems considerably. The same is true when it comes to integration over plane regions. In this section, we learn how to formulate double integrals in polar coordinates and how to change double integrals from Cartesian coordinates to polar coordinates.

➤ Recall the conversions from Cartesian to polar coordinates (Section 11.2):

$x = r\cos\theta,\ y = r\sin\theta$, or
$r^2 = x^2 + y^2,\ \tan\theta = y/x$.

Polar Rectangular Regions

Suppose we want to find the volume of the solid bounded by the paraboloid $z = 9 - x^2 - y^2$ and the xy-plane (Figure 14.27). The intersection of the paraboloid and the xy-plane ($z = 0$) is the curve $9 - x^2 - y^2 = 0$, or $x^2 + y^2 = 9$. Therefore, the region of integration is the disk of radius 3 centered at the origin in the xy-plane. If we use the relationship $r^2 = x^2 + y^2$ for converting Cartesian to polar coordinates, the region of integration is simply $\{(r, \theta): 0 \le r \le 3\}$. Furthermore, the paraboloid is expressed in polar coordinates as $z = 9 - r^2$. This problem (which is solved in Example 1) illustrates how both the integrand and the region of integration in a double integral can be simplified by working in polar coordinates.

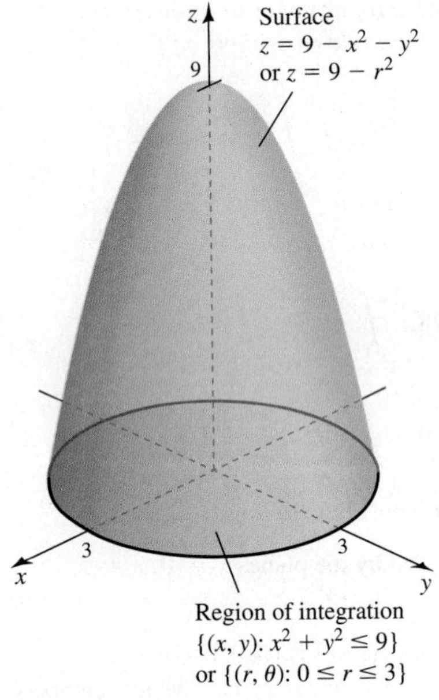

FIGURE 14.27

The region of integration in this problem is an example of a **polar rectangle**. It has the form $R = \{(r, \theta): 0 \le a \le r \le b, \alpha \le \theta \le \beta\}$, where $\beta - \alpha \le 2\pi$ and a, b, α, and β are constants (Figure 14.28). Polar rectangles are the analogs of rectangles in Cartesian coordinates. For this reason, the methods used in Section 14.1 for evaluating double integrals over rectangles can be extended to polar rectangles. The goal is to evaluate integrals of the form $\iint_R f(r, \theta)\, dA$, where f is a continuous function of r and θ, and R is a polar rectangle. If f is nonnegative on R, this integral equals the volume of the solid bounded by the surface $z = f(r, \theta)$ and the region R in the xy-plane.

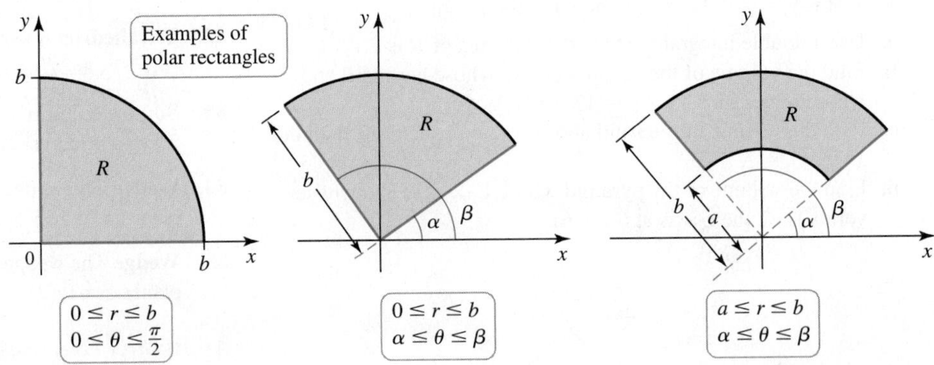

FIGURE 14.28

$R = \{(r, \theta): a \le r \le b, \alpha \le \theta \le \beta\}$

FIGURE 14.29

Our approach is to divide $[a, b]$ into M subintervals of equal length $\Delta r = (b - a)/M$. We similarly divide $[\alpha, \beta]$ into m subintervals of equal length $\Delta\theta = (\beta - \alpha)/m$. Now look at the arcs of the circles centered at the origin with radii

$$r = a, r = a + \Delta r, r = a + 2\Delta r, \ldots, r = b$$

and the rays

$$\theta = \alpha, \theta = \alpha + \Delta\theta, \theta = \alpha + 2\Delta\theta, \ldots, \theta = \beta$$

emanating from the origin (Figure 14.29). These arcs and rays divide the region R into $n = Mm$ polar rectangles that we number in a convenient way from $k = 1$ to $k = n$. The area of the kth rectangle is denoted ΔA_k, and we let $(\bar{r}_k, \bar{\theta}_k)$ be an arbitrary point in that rectangle.

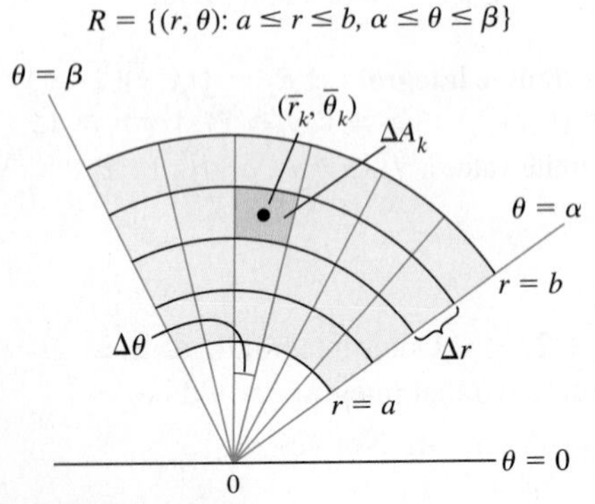

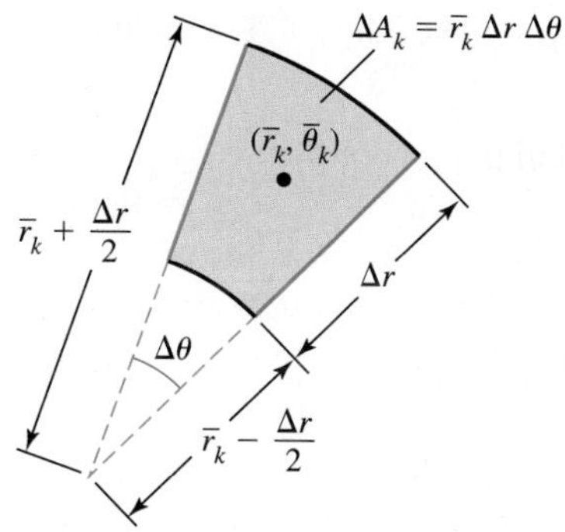

FIGURE 14.30

➤ Recall that the area of a sector of a circle of radius r subtended by an angle θ is $\frac{1}{2}r^2\theta$.

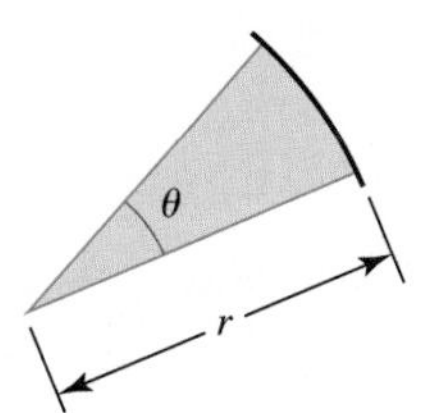

The volume of the "box" whose base is the kth polar rectangle and whose height is $f(\bar{r}_k, \bar{\theta}_k)$ is $f(\bar{r}_k, \bar{\theta}_k)\,\Delta A_k$, for $k = 1, \dots, n$. Therefore, the volume of the solid region beneath the surface $z = f(r, \theta)$ with a base R is approximately

$$V \approx \sum_{k=1}^{n} f(\bar{r}_k, \bar{\theta}_k)\,\Delta A_k.$$

For double integrals in Cartesian coordinates, the next step is to write the double integral as an iterated integral. We take the same step here by expressing ΔA_k in terms of Δr_k and $\Delta\theta_k$.

Figure 14.30 shows the kth polar rectangle, with an area ΔA_k. The point $(\bar{r}_k, \bar{\theta}_k)$ is chosen so that the outer arc of the polar rectangle has radius $\bar{r}_k + \Delta r/2$ and the inner arc has radius $\bar{r}_k - \Delta r/2$. The area of the rectangle is

$$\begin{aligned}\Delta A_k &= (\text{area of outer sector}) - (\text{area of inner sector})\\ &= \frac{1}{2}\left(\bar{r}_k + \frac{\Delta r}{2}\right)^2 \Delta\theta - \frac{1}{2}\left(\bar{r}_k - \frac{\Delta r}{2}\right)^2 \Delta\theta \qquad \text{Area of sector} = \frac{r^2}{2}\Delta\theta\\ &= \bar{r}_k \Delta r \Delta\theta. \qquad \text{Expand and simplify.}\end{aligned}$$

Substituting this expression for ΔA_k into the preceding volume approximation, we have

$$V \approx \sum_{k=1}^{n} f(\bar{r}_k, \bar{\theta}_k)\Delta A_k = \sum_{k=1}^{n} f(\bar{r}_k, \bar{\theta}_k)\,\bar{r}_k\,\Delta r \Delta\theta.$$

This approximation to the volume is another Riemann sum. We let Δ be the maximum value of Δr and $\Delta\theta$. If f is continuous on R, then as $\Delta \to 0$, the sum approaches a double integral:

$$\lim_{\Delta\to 0} \sum_{k=1}^{n} f(\bar{r}_k, \bar{\theta}_k)\bar{r}_k\,\Delta r \Delta\theta = \iint_R f(r, \theta)\, dA$$

A version of Fubini's Theorem is needed to write this double integral as an iterated integral; the proof of this result is found in advanced texts.

➤ The most common error in evaluating integrals in polar coordinates is to omit the factor of r that appears in the integrand. In Cartesian coordinates the element of area is $dx\,dy$; in polar coordinates, the element of area is $r\,dr\,d\theta$, and without the factor of r, area is not measured correctly.

THEOREM 14.3 Double Integrals over Polar Rectangular Regions

Let f be continuous on the region in the xy-plane $R = \{(r, \theta): 0 \le a \le r \le b, \alpha \le \theta \le \beta\}$, where $\beta - \alpha \le 2\pi$. Then

$$\iint_R f(r, \theta)\, dA = \int_\alpha^\beta \int_a^b f(r, \theta)\, r\, dr\, d\theta.$$

QUICK CHECK 1 Describe in polar coordinates the region in the first quadrant between the circles of radius 1 and 2. ◄

Frequently, an integral $\iint_R f(x, y)\, dA$ is given in Cartesian coordinates, but the region of integration is easier to handle in polar coordinates. By using the relations $x = r\cos\theta$, $y = r\sin\theta$, and $x^2 + y^2 = r^2$, the function $f(x, y)$ can be expressed in polar form as $f(r\cos\theta, r\sin\theta)$. This procedure is a change of variables in two variables.

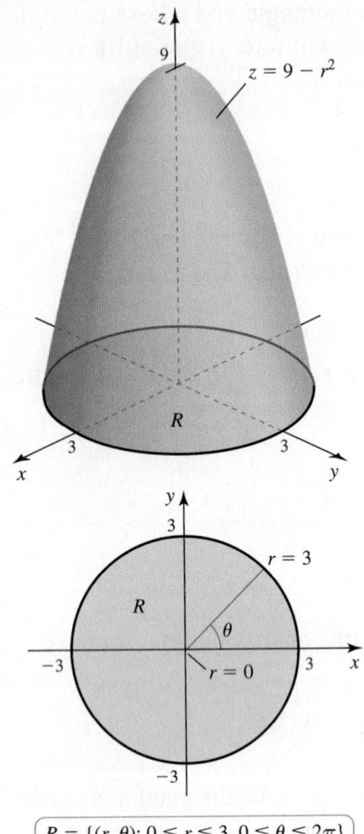

FIGURE 14.31

EXAMPLE 1 **Volume of a paraboloid cap** Find the volume of the solid bounded by the paraboloid $z = 9 - x^2 - y^2$ and the xy-plane.

SOLUTION Using $x^2 + y^2 = r^2$, the surface is described in polar coordinates by $z = 9 - r^2$. The paraboloid intersects the xy-plane ($z = 0$) when $z = 9 - r^2 = 0$, or $r = 3$. Therefore, the intersection curve is the circle of radius 3 centered at the origin. The resulting region of integration is the disk $R = \{(r, \theta): 0 \le r \le 3, 0 \le \theta \le 2\pi\}$ (Figure 14.31). Integrating over R in polar coordinates, the volume is

$$V = \int_0^{2\pi} \int_0^3 \underbrace{(9 - r^2)}_{z} r\,dr\,d\theta \quad \text{Iterated integral for volume}$$

$$= \int_0^{2\pi} \left(\frac{9r^2}{2} - \frac{r^4}{4} \right) \bigg|_0^3 d\theta \quad \text{Evaluate the inner integral.}$$

$$= \int_0^{2\pi} \left(\frac{81}{4} \right) d\theta = \frac{81\pi}{2}. \quad \text{Evaluate the outer integral.}$$

Related Exercises 7–18◀

QUICK CHECK 2 Express the functions $f(x, y) = (x^2 + y^2)^{5/2}$ and $h(x, y) = x^2 - y^2$ in polar coordinates.◀

EXAMPLE 2 **Annular region** Find the volume of the region beneath the surface $z = xy + 10$ and above the annular region $R = \{(r, \theta): 2 \le r \le 4, 0 \le \theta \le 2\pi\}$. (An *annulus* is the region between two concentric circles.)

SOLUTION The region of integration suggests working in polar coordinates (Figure 14.32). Substituting $x = r\cos\theta$ and $y = r\sin\theta$, the integrand becomes

$$xy + 10 = (r\cos\theta)(r\sin\theta) + 10 \quad \text{Substitute for } x \text{ and } y.$$

$$= r^2 \sin\theta\cos\theta + 10 \quad \text{Simplify.}$$

$$= \tfrac{1}{2} r^2 \sin 2\theta + 10. \quad \sin 2\theta = 2\sin\theta\cos\theta$$

Substituting the integrand into the volume integral, we have

$$V = \int_0^{2\pi} \int_2^4 \left(\tfrac{1}{2} r^2 \sin 2\theta + 10 \right) r\,dr\,d\theta \quad \text{Iterated integral for volume}$$

$$= \int_0^{2\pi} \int_2^4 \left(\tfrac{1}{2} r^3 \sin 2\theta + 10r \right) dr\,d\theta \quad \text{Simplify.}$$

$$= \int_0^{2\pi} \left[\frac{r^4}{8} \sin 2\theta + 5r^2 \right] \bigg|_2^4 d\theta \quad \text{Evaluate the inner integral.}$$

$$= \int_0^{2\pi} (30\sin 2\theta + 60)\,d\theta \quad \text{Simplify.}$$

$$= (15(-\cos 2\theta) + 60\theta) \bigg|_0^{2\pi} = 120\pi. \quad \text{Evaluate the outer integral.}$$

Related Exercises 19–28◀

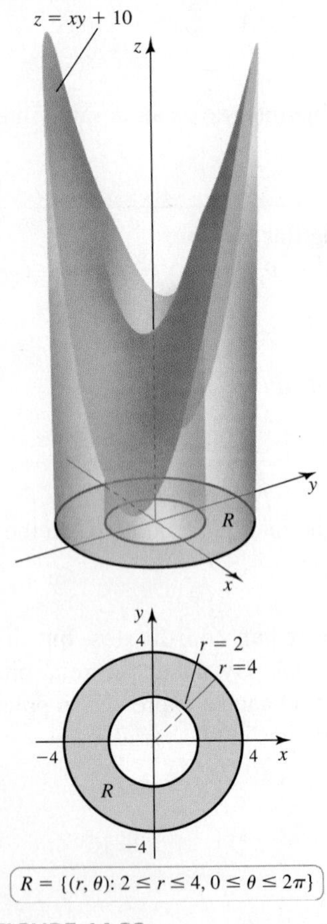

FIGURE 14.32

More General Polar Regions

In Section 14.2 we generalized double integrals over rectangular regions to double integrals over nonrectangular regions. In an analogous way, the method for integrating over a polar rectangle may be extended to more general regions. Consider a region bounded by two rays $\theta = \alpha$ and $\theta = \beta$, where $\beta - \alpha \leq 2\pi$, and two curves $r = g(\theta)$ and $r = h(\theta)$ (Figure 14.33):

$$R = \{(r, \theta): 0 \leq g(\theta) \leq r \leq h(\theta), \alpha \leq \theta \leq \beta\}$$

The double integral $\iint_R f(r, \theta)\, dA$ is expressed as an iterated integral in which the inner integral has limits $r = g(\theta)$ and $r = h(\theta)$, and the outer integral runs from $\theta = \alpha$ to $\theta = \beta$. If f is nonnegative on R, the double integral gives the volume of the solid bounded by the surface $z = f(r, \theta)$ and R.

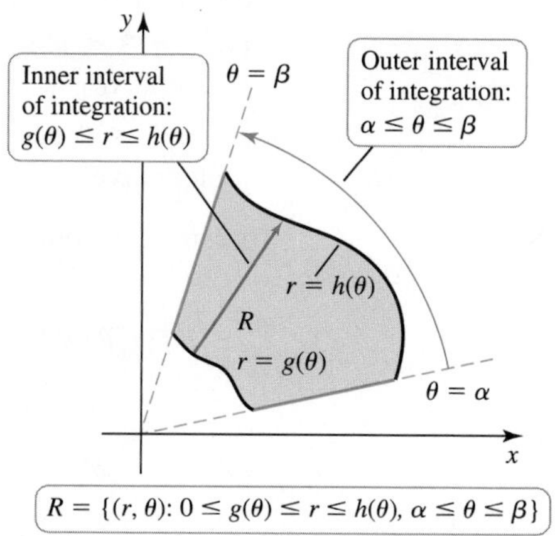

FIGURE 14.33

THEOREM 14.4 Double Integrals over More General Polar Regions
Let f be continuous on the region in the xy-plane

$$R = \{(r, \theta): 0 \leq g(\theta) \leq r \leq h(\theta), \alpha \leq \theta \leq \beta\},$$

where $\beta - \alpha \leq 2\pi$. Then,

$$\iint_R f(r, \theta)\, dA = \int_\alpha^\beta \int_{g(\theta)}^{h(\theta)} f(r, \theta)\, r\, dr\, d\theta.$$

➤ For the type of region described in Theorem 14.4, with the boundaries in the radial direction expressed as functions of θ, the inner integral is always with respect to r.

EXAMPLE 3 Specifying regions Write an iterated integral for $\iint_R f(r, \theta)\, dA$ for the following regions R in the xy-plane.

a. The region outside the circle $r = 2$ (with radius 2 centered at $(0, 0)$) and inside the circle $r = 4 \cos \theta$ (with radius 2 centered at $(2, 0)$)

b. The region inside both circles of part (a)

➤ Recall from Section 11.2 that the polar equation $r = 2a \sin \theta$ describes a circle of radius a with center $(0, a)$. The polar equation $r = 2a \cos \theta$ describes a circle of radius a with center $(a, 0)$.

Radial lines enter the region R at $r = 2$ and exit the region at $r = 4\cos\theta$.

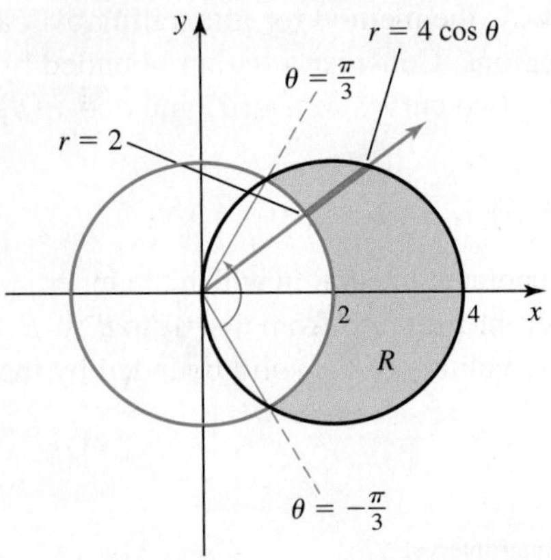

The inner and outer boundaries of R are traversed, for $-\frac{\pi}{3} \le \theta \le \frac{\pi}{3}$

FIGURE 14.34

SOLUTION

a. Equating the two expressions for r, we have $4\cos\theta = 2$ or $\cos\theta = \frac{1}{2}$, so the circles intersect when $\theta = \pm\pi/3$ (Figure 14.34). The inner boundary of R is the circle $r = 2$, and the outer boundary is the circle $r = 4\cos\theta$. Therefore, the region of integration is $R = \{(r,\theta): 2 \le r \le 4\cos\theta, -\pi/3 \le \theta \le \pi/3\}$ and the iterated integral is

$$\iint_R f(r,\theta)\, dA = \int_{-\pi/3}^{\pi/3} \int_2^{4\cos\theta} f(r,\theta)\, r\, dr\, d\theta.$$

b. From part (a) we know that the circles intersect when $\theta = \pm\pi/3$. The region R consists of three subregions (Figure 14.35):

- For $-\pi/2 \le \theta \le -\pi/3$, R is bounded by $r = 0$ (inner curve) and $r = 4\cos\theta$ (outer curve).
- For $-\pi/3 \le \theta \le \pi/3$, R is bounded by $r = 0$ (inner curve) and $r = 2$ (outer curve).
- For $\pi/3 \le \theta \le \pi/2$, R is bounded by $r = 0$ (inner curve) and $r = 4\cos\theta$ (outer curve).

Therefore, the double integral is expressed in three parts:

$$\iint_R f(r,\theta)\, dA = \int_{-\pi/2}^{-\pi/3} \int_0^{4\cos\theta} f(r,\theta)\, r\, dr\, d\theta + \int_{-\pi/3}^{\pi/3} \int_0^{2} f(r,\theta)\, r\, dr\, d\theta$$
$$+ \int_{\pi/3}^{\pi/2} \int_0^{4\cos\theta} f(r,\theta)\, r\, dr\, d\theta$$

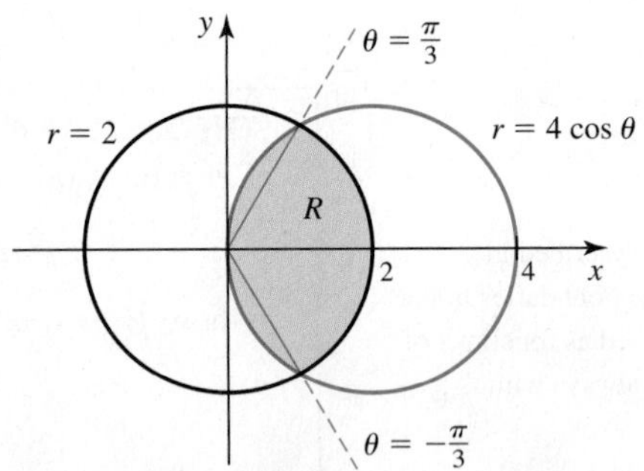

Radial lines begin at the origin and exit at $r = 4\cos\theta$.

Radial lines begin at the origin and exit at $r = 2$.

Radial lines begin at the origin and exit at $r = 4\cos\theta$.

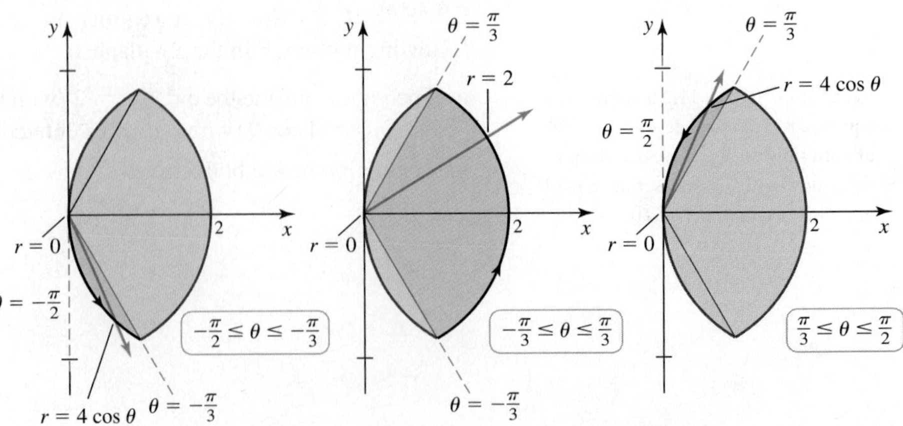

FIGURE 14.35

Related Exercises 29–34◀

Areas of Regions

In Cartesian coordinates, the area of a region R in the xy-plane is computed by integrating the function $f(x, y) = 1$ over R; that is, $A = \iint_R dA$. This fact extends to polar coordinates.

➤ Do not forget the factor of r in the area integral!

> **Area of Polar Regions**
>
> The area of the region $R = \{(r, \theta): 0 \le g(\theta) \le r \le h(\theta), \alpha \le \theta \le \beta\}$, where $\beta - \alpha \le 2\pi$, is
>
> $$A = \iint_R dA = \int_\alpha^\beta \int_{g(\theta)}^{h(\theta)} r\, dr\, d\theta.$$

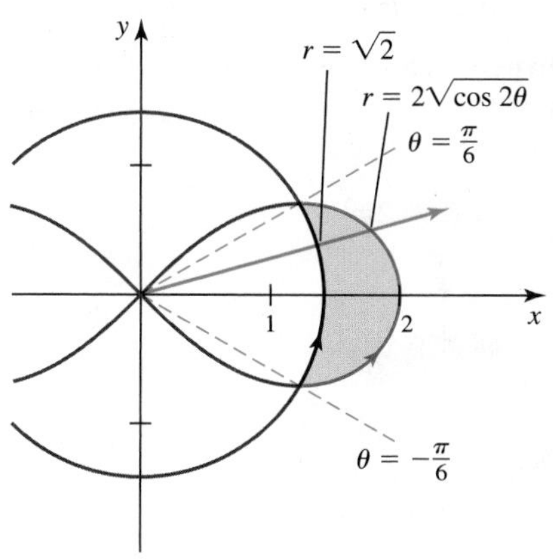

FIGURE 14.36

EXAMPLE 4 **Area within a lemniscate** Compute the area of the region in the first and fourth quadrants outside the circle $r = \sqrt{2}$ and inside the lemniscate $r^2 = 4\cos 2\theta$ (Figure 14.36).

SOLUTION The equation of the circle can be written as $r^2 = 2$. Equating the two expressions for r^2, the circle and the lemniscate intersect when $2 = 4\cos 2\theta$, or $\cos 2\theta = \frac{1}{2}$. The angles in the first and fourth quadrants that satisfy this equation are $\theta = \pm\pi/6$ (Figure 14.36). The region between the two curves is bounded by the inner curve $r = g(\theta) = \sqrt{2}$ and the outer curve $r = h(\theta) = 2\sqrt{\cos 2\theta}$. Therefore, the area of the region is

$$A = \int_{-\pi/6}^{\pi/6} \int_{\sqrt{2}}^{2\sqrt{\cos 2\theta}} r\, dr\, d\theta$$

$$= \int_{-\pi/6}^{\pi/6} \left(\frac{r^2}{2}\right)\Bigg|_{\sqrt{2}}^{2\sqrt{\cos 2\theta}} d\theta \quad \text{Evaluate the inner integral.}$$

$$= \int_{-\pi/6}^{\pi/6} (2\cos 2\theta - 1)\, d\theta \quad \text{Simplify.}$$

$$= (\sin 2\theta - \theta)\Big|_{-\pi/6}^{\pi/6} \quad \text{Evaluate the outer integral.}$$

$$= \sqrt{3} - \frac{\pi}{3}. \quad \text{Simplify.}$$

Related Exercises 35–40 ◀

QUICK CHECK 3 Express the area of the disk $R = \{(r, \theta): 0 \le r \le a, 0 \le \theta \le 2\pi\}$ in terms of a double integral in polar coordinates. ◀

Average Value over a Planar Polar Region

We have encountered the average value of a function in several different settings. To find the average value of a function over a region in polar coordinates, we again integrate the function over the region and divide by the area of the region.

EXAMPLE 5 **Average y-coordinate** Find the average value of the y-coordinates of the points in the semicircular disk of radius a given by $R = \{(r, \theta): 0 \le r \le a, 0 \le \theta \le \pi\}$.

SOLUTION Because the y-coordinates of points in the disk are given by $y = r\sin\theta$, the function whose average value we seek is $f(r, \theta) = r\sin\theta$. We use the fact that the area of R is $\pi a^2/2$. Evaluating the average value integral we find that

$$\bar{y} = \frac{2}{\pi a^2} \int_0^\pi \int_0^a r\sin\theta\, r\, dr\, d\theta$$

$$= \frac{2}{\pi a^2} \int_0^\pi \sin\theta \left(\frac{r^3}{3}\right)\Bigg|_0^a d\theta \quad \text{Evaluate the inner integral.}$$

$$= \frac{2}{\pi a^2} \frac{a^3}{3} \int_0^{\pi} \sin \theta \, d\theta \qquad \text{Simplify.}$$

$$= \frac{2a}{3\pi} (-\cos \theta) \Big|_0^{\pi} \qquad \text{Evaluate the outer integral.}$$

$$= \frac{4a}{3\pi}. \qquad \text{Simplify.}$$

Note that $4/(3\pi) \approx 0.42$, so the average value of the y-coordinates is less than half the radius of the disk.

Related Exercises 41–44 ◀

SECTION 14.3 EXERCISES

Review Questions

1. Draw the region $\{(r, \theta): 1 \le r \le 2, 0 \le \theta \le \pi/2\}$. Why is it called a polar rectangle?
2. Write the double integral $\iint_R f(x, y)\, dA$ as an iterated integral in polar coordinates when $R = \{(r, \theta): a \le r \le b, \alpha \le \theta \le \beta\}$.
3. Sketch the region of integration for the integral $\int_{-\pi/6}^{\pi/6} \int_{1/2}^{\cos 2\theta} f(r, \theta)\, r\, dr\, d\theta$.
4. Explain why the element of area in Cartesian coordinates $dx\, dy$ becomes $r\, dr\, d\theta$ in polar coordinates.
5. How do you find the area of a region $R = \{(r, \theta): g(\theta) \le r \le h(\theta), \alpha \le \theta \le \beta\}$?
6. How do you find the average value of a function over a region that is expressed in polar coordinates?

Basic Skills

7–10. Polar rectangles *Sketch the following polar rectangles.*

7. $R = \{(r, \theta): 0 \le r \le 5, 0 \le \theta \le \pi/2\}$
8. $R = \{(r, \theta): 2 \le r \le 3, \pi/4 \le \theta \le 5\pi/4\}$
9. $R = \{(r, \theta): 1 \le r \le 4, -\pi/4 \le \theta \le 2\pi/3\}$
10. $R = \{(r, \theta): 4 \le r \le 5, -\pi/3 \le \theta \le \pi/2\}$

11–14. Solids bounded by paraboloids *Find the volume of the solid below the paraboloid $z = 4 - x^2 - y^2$ and above the following regions.*

11. $R = \{(r, \theta): 0 \le r \le 1, 0 \le \theta \le 2\pi\}$

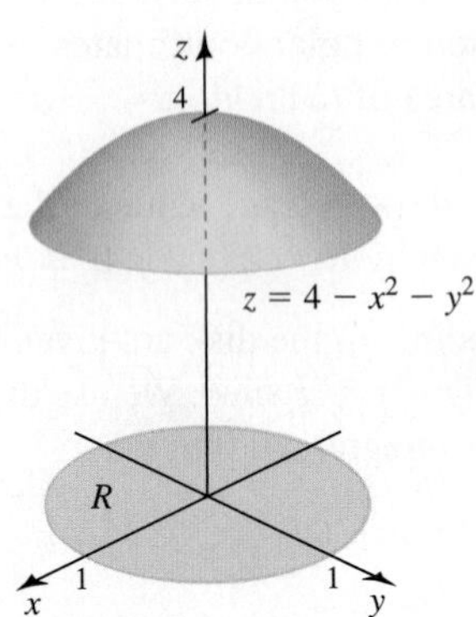

12. $R = \{(r, \theta): 0 \le r \le 2, 0 \le \theta \le 2\pi\}$
13. $R = \{(r, \theta): 1 \le r \le 2, 0 \le \theta \le 2\pi\}$
14. $R = \{(r, \theta): 1 \le r \le 2, -\pi/2 \le \theta \le \pi/2\}$

15–18. Solids bounded by hyperboloids *Find the volume of the solid below the hyperboloid $z = 5 - \sqrt{1 + x^2 + y^2}$ and above the following regions.*

15. $R = \{(r, \theta): 0 \le r \le 2, 0 \le \theta \le 2\pi\}$

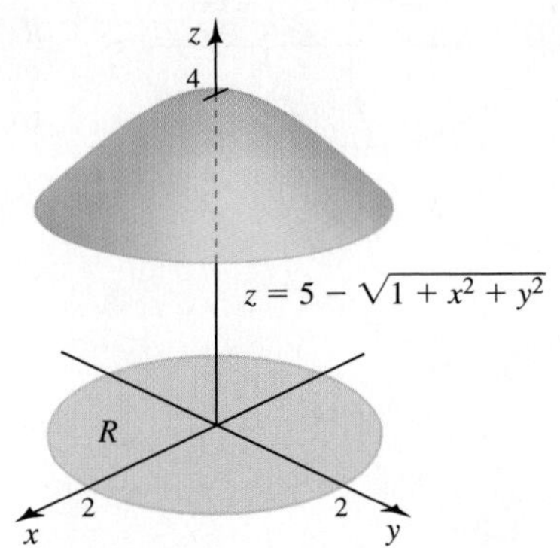

16. $R = \{(r, \theta): 0 \le r \le 1, 0 \le \theta \le \pi\}$
17. $R = \{(r, \theta): 1 \le r \le 2, 0 \le \theta \le 2\pi\}$
18. $R = \{(r, \theta): 1 \le r \le 3, -\pi/2 \le \theta \le \pi/2\}$

19–24. Cartesian to polar coordinates *Sketch the given region of integration R and evaluate the integral over R using polar coordinates.*

19. $\iint_R (x^2 + y^2)\, dA;\ R = \{(r, \theta): 0 \le r \le 4, 0 \le \theta \le 2\pi\}$
20. $\iint_R 2xy\, dA;\ R = \{(r, \theta): 1 \le r \le 3, 0 \le \theta \le \pi/2\}$
21. $\iint_R 2xy\, dA;\ R = \{(x, y): x^2 + y^2 \le 9, y \ge 0\}$
22. $\iint_R \frac{1}{1 + x^2 + y^2}\, dA;\ R = \{(r, \theta): 1 \le r \le 2, 0 \le \theta \le \pi\}$
23. $\iint_R \frac{1}{\sqrt{16 - x^2 - y^2}}\, dA;$ $R = \{(x, y): x^2 + y^2 \le 4, x \ge 0, y \ge 0\}$

24. $\iint_R e^{-x^2-y^2}\,dA;\; R = \{(x, y): x^2 + y^2 \le 9\}$

25–28. Island problems *The surface of an island is defined by the following functions over the region on which the function is nonnegative. Find the volume of the island.*

25. $z = e^{-(x^2+y^2)/8} - e^{-2}$

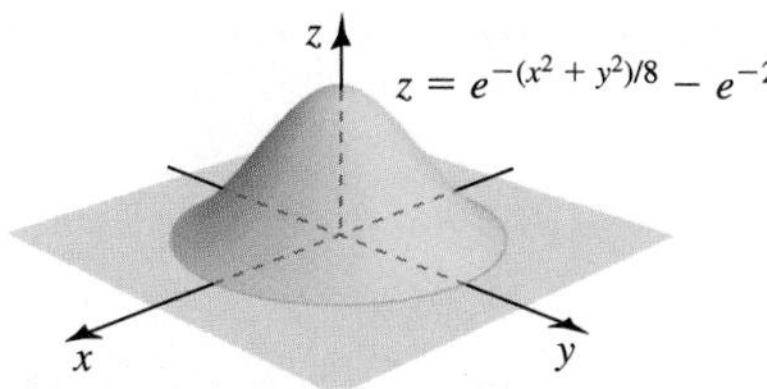

26. $z = 100 - 4(x^2 + y^2)$

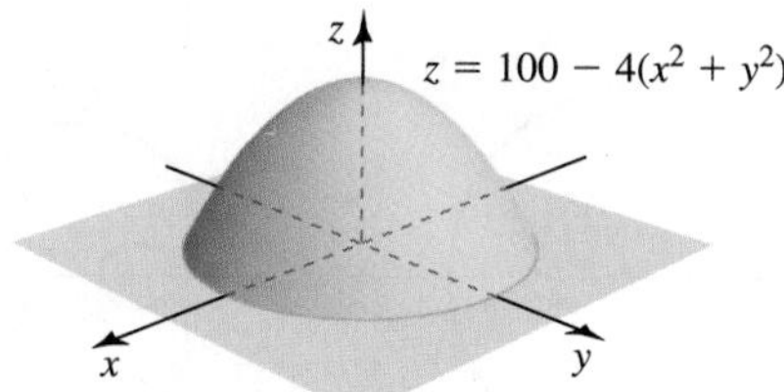

27. $z = 25 - \sqrt{x^2 + y^2}$

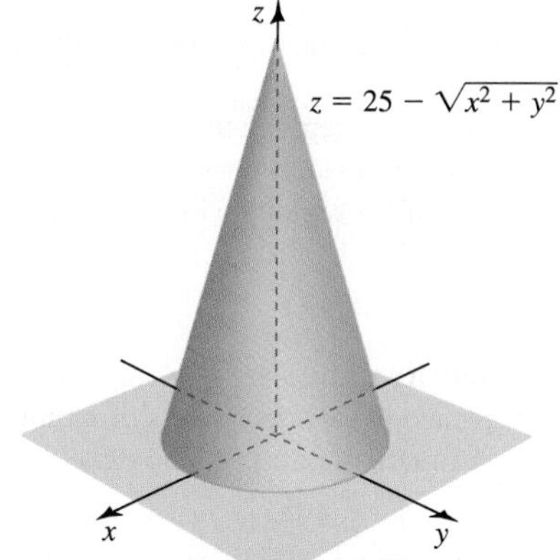

28. $z = \dfrac{20}{1 + x^2 + y^2} - 2$

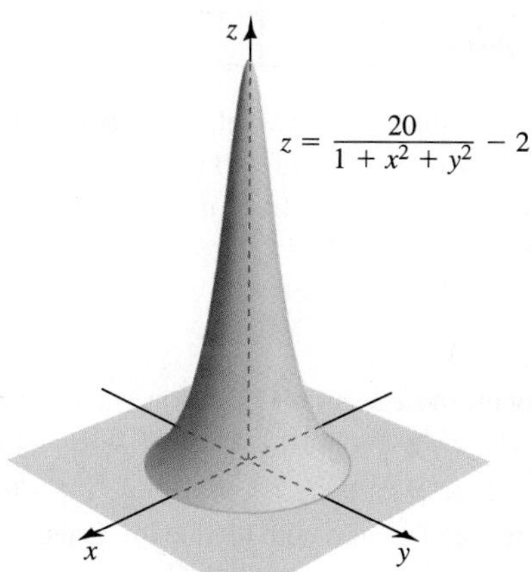

29–34. Describing general regions *Sketch the following regions R. Then express $\iint_R f(r, \theta)\,dA$ as an iterated integral over R.*

29. The region inside the limaçon $r = 1 + \frac{1}{2}\cos\theta$

30. The region inside the leaf of the rose $r = 2\sin 2\theta$ in the first quadrant

31. The region inside the lobe of the lemniscate $r^2 = 2\sin 2\theta$ in the first quadrant

32. The region outside the circle $r = 2$ and inside the circle $r = 4\sin\theta$

33. The region outside the circle $r = 1$ and inside the rose $r = 2\sin 3\theta$ in the first quadrant

34. The region outside the circle $r = \frac{1}{2}$ and inside the cardioid $r = 1 + \cos\theta$

35–40. Computing areas *Sketch each region and use integration to find its area.*

35. The annular region $\{(r, \theta): 1 \le r \le 2, 0 \le \theta \le \pi\}$

36. The region bounded by the cardioid $r = 2(1 - \sin\theta)$

37. The region bounded by all leaves of the rose $r = 2\cos 3\theta$

38. The region inside both the cardioid $r = 1 - \cos\theta$ and the circle $r = 1$

39. The region inside both the cardioid $r = 1 + \sin\theta$ and the cardioid $r = 1 + \cos\theta$

40. The region bounded by the spiral $r = 2\theta$, for $0 \le \theta \le \pi$, and the x-axis.

41–44. Average values *Find the following average values.*

41. The average distance between points of the disk $\{(r, \theta): 0 \le r \le a\}$ and the origin

42. The average distance between points within the cardioid $r = 1 + \cos\theta$ and the origin

43. The average distance squared between points on the unit disk $\{(r, \theta): 0 \le r \le 1\}$ and the point $(1, 1)$

44. The average value of $1/r^2$ over the annulus $\{(r, \theta): 2 \le r \le 4\}$

Further Explorations

45. Explain why or why not Determine whether the following statements are true and give an explanation or counterexample.

a. Let R be the unit disk centered at $(0, 0)$. Then, $\iint_R (x^2 + y^2)\,dA = \int_0^{2\pi}\int_0^1 r^2\,dr\,d\theta$.

b. The average distance between the points of the hemisphere $z = \sqrt{4 - x^2 - y^2}$ and the origin is 2 (no integral needed).

c. The integral $\int_0^1\int_0^{\sqrt{1-y^2}} e^{x^2+y^2}\,dx\,dy$ is easier to evaluate in polar coordinates than in Cartesian coordinates.

46–51. Miscellaneous integrals *Sketch the region of integration and evaluate the following integrals, using the method of your choice.*

46. $\displaystyle\int_0^3\int_0^{\sqrt{9-x^2}} \sqrt{x^2 + y^2}\,dy\,dx$

47. $\displaystyle\int_{-1}^{1}\int_{-\sqrt{1-x^2}}^{\sqrt{1-x^2}} (x^2 + y^2)^{3/2}\, dy\, dx$

48. $\displaystyle\int_{-4}^{4}\int_{0}^{\sqrt{16-y^2}} (16 - x^2 - y^2)\, dx\, dy$

49. $\displaystyle\int_{0}^{\pi/4}\int_{0}^{\sec\theta} r^3\, dr\, d\theta$

50. $\displaystyle\iint_R \frac{x - y}{x^2 + y^2 + 1}\, dA$; R is the region bounded by the unit circle centered at the origin.

51. $\displaystyle\iint_R \frac{1}{4 + \sqrt{x^2 + y^2}}\, dA$; $R = \{(r, \theta): 0 \le r \le 2, \pi/2 \le \theta \le 3\pi/2\}$

52. Areas of circles Use integration to show that the circles $r = 2a\cos\theta$ and $r = 2a\sin\theta$ have the same area, which is πa^2.

53. Filling bowls with water Which bowl holds more water if it is filled to a depth of four units?

- The paraboloid $z = x^2 + y^2$, for $0 \le z \le 4$
- The cone $z = \sqrt{x^2 + y^2}$, for $0 \le z \le 4$
- The hyperboloid $z = \sqrt{1 + x^2 + y^2}$, for $1 \le z \le 5$

54. Equal volumes To what height (above the bottom of the bowl) must the cone and paraboloid bowls of Exercise 53 be filled to hold the same volume of water as the hyperboloid bowl filled to a depth of 4 units ($1 \le z \le 5$)?

55. Volume of a hyperbolic paraboloid Consider the surface $z = x^2 - y^2$.

a. Find the region in the xy-plane in polar coordinates for which $z \ge 0$.

b. Let $R = \{(r, \theta): 0 \le r \le a, -\pi/4 \le \theta \le \pi/4\}$, which is a sector of a circle of radius a. Find the volume of the region below the hyperbolic paraboloid and above the region R.

56. Slicing a hemispherical cake A cake is shaped like a hemisphere of radius 4 with its base on the xy-plane. A wedge of the cake is removed by making two slices from the center of the cake outward, perpendicular to the xy-plane and separated by an angle of φ.

a. Use a double integral to find the volume of the slice for $\varphi = \pi/4$. Use geometry to check your answer.

b. Now suppose the cake is sliced by a plane perpendicular to the xy-plane at $x = a > 0$. Let D be the smaller of the two pieces produced. For what value of a is the volume of D equal to the volume in part (a)?

57–60. Improper integrals *Improper integrals arise in polar coordinates when the radial coordinate r becomes arbitrarily large. Under certain conditions, these integrals are treated in the usual way:*

$$\int_\alpha^\beta \int_a^\infty g(r, \theta)\, r\, dr\, d\theta = \lim_{b\to\infty} \int_\alpha^\beta \int_a^b g(r, \theta)\, r\, dr\, d\theta.$$

Use this technique to evaluate the following integrals.

57. $\displaystyle\int_0^{\pi/2}\int_1^\infty \frac{\cos\theta}{r^3}\, r\, dr\, d\theta$

58. $\displaystyle\iint_R \frac{dA}{(x^2 + y^2)^{5/2}}$; $R = \{(r, \theta): 1 \le r < \infty, 0 \le \theta \le 2\pi\}$

59. $\displaystyle\iint_R e^{-x^2-y^2}\, dA$; $R = \{(r, \theta): 0 \le r < \infty, 0 \le \theta \le \pi/2\}$

60. $\displaystyle\iint_R \frac{1}{(1 + x^2 + y^2)^2}\, dA$; R is the first quadrant.

61. Limaçon loops The limaçon $r = b + a\cos\theta$ has an inner loop if $b < a$ and no inner loop if $b > a$.

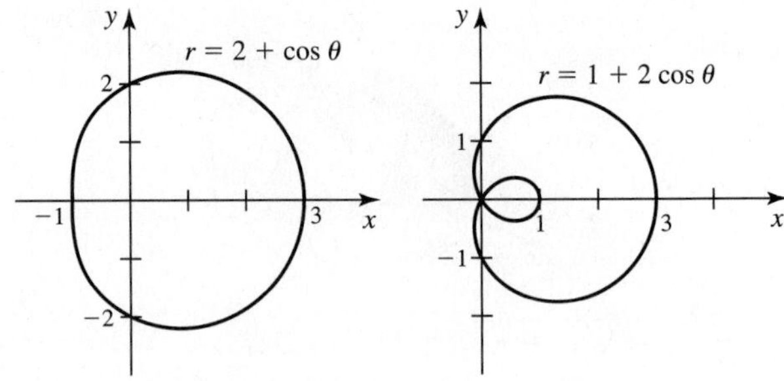

a. Find the area of the region bounded by the limaçon $r = 2 + \cos\theta$.

b. Find the area of the region outside the inner loop and inside the outer loop of the limaçon $r = 1 + 2\cos\theta$.

c. Find the area of the region inside the inner loop of the limaçon $r = 1 + 2\cos\theta$.

Applications

62. Mass from density data The following table gives the density (in units of g/cm^2) at selected points of a thin semicircular plate of radius 3. Estimate the mass of the plate and explain your method.

	$\theta = 0$	$\theta = \pi/4$	$\theta = \pi/2$	$\theta = 3\pi/4$	$\theta = \pi$
$r = 1$	2.0	2.1	2.2	2.3	2.4
$r = 2$	2.5	2.7	2.9	3.1	3.3
$r = 3$	3.2	3.4	3.5	3.6	3.7

63. A mass calculation Suppose the density of a thin plate represented by the region R is $\rho(r, \theta)$ (in units of mass per area). The mass of the plate is $\iint_R \rho(r, \theta)\, dA$. Find the mass of the thin half annulus $R = \{(r, \theta): 1 \le r \le 4, 0 \le \theta \le \pi\}$ with a density $\rho(r, \theta) = 4 + r\sin\theta$.

Additional Exercises

64. Area formula In Section 11.3 it was shown that the area of a region enclosed by the polar curve $r = g(\theta)$ and the rays $\theta = \alpha$ and $\theta = \beta$, where $\beta - \alpha \le 2\pi$, is $A = \frac{1}{2}\int_\alpha^\beta r^2\, d\theta$. Prove this result using the area formula with double integrals.

65. **Normal distribution** An important integral in statistics associated with the normal distribution is $I = \int_{-\infty}^{\infty} e^{-x^2}\,dx$. It is evaluated in the following steps.

a. Assume that $I^2 = \left(\int_{-\infty}^{\infty} e^{-x^2}\,dx\right)\left(\int_{-\infty}^{\infty} e^{-y^2}\,dy\right) = \int_{-\infty}^{\infty}\int_{-\infty}^{\infty} e^{-x^2-y^2}\,dx\,dy$, where we have chosen the variables of integration to be x and y and then written the product as an iterated integral. Evaluate this integral in polar coordinates and show that $I = \sqrt{\pi}$.

b. Evaluate $\int_0^{\infty} e^{-x^2}\,dx$, $\int_0^{\infty} xe^{-x^2}\,dx$, and $\int_0^{\infty} x^2 e^{-x^2}\,dx$ (using part (a) if needed).

66. **Existence of integrals** For what values of p does the integral $\iint_R \frac{k}{(x^2 + y^2)^p}\,dA$ exist in the following cases?

a. $R = \{(r, \theta): 1 \le r < \infty, 0 \le \theta \le 2\pi\}$

b. $R = \{(r, \theta): 0 \le r \le 1, 0 \le \theta \le 2\pi\}$

67. **Integrals in strips** Consider the integral $I = \iint_R \frac{1}{(1 + x^2 + y^2)^2}\,dA$, where $R = \{(x, y): 0 \le x \le 1, 0 \le y \le a\}$.

a. Evaluate I for $a = 1$. (*Hint:* Use polar coordinates.)

b. Evaluate I for arbitrary $a > 0$.

c. Let $a \to \infty$ in part (b) to find I over the infinite strip $R = \{(x, y): 0 \le x \le 1, 0 \le y < \infty\}$.

T 68. **Area of an ellipse** In polar coordinates an equation of an ellipse with eccentricity $0 < e < 1$ and semimajor axis a is

$$r = \frac{a(1 - e^2)}{1 + e\cos\theta}.$$

a. Write the integral that gives the area of the ellipse.

b. Show that the area of an ellipse is πab, where $b^2 = a^2(1 - e^2)$.

QUICK CHECK ANSWERS

1. $R = \{(r, \theta): 1 \le r \le 2, 0 \le \theta \le \pi/2\}$
2. $r^5, r^2(\cos^2\theta - \sin^2\theta) = r^2\cos 2\theta$
3. $\int_0^{2\pi}\int_0^a r\,dr\,d\theta = \pi a^2$ ◀

14.4 Triple Integrals

At this point, you may be able to see the pattern that is developing with respect to integration. In Chapter 5 we introduced integrals of single-variable functions. In the first three sections of this chapter, we moved up one dimension to double integrals of two-variable functions. In this section we take one more step and investigate triple integrals of three-variable functions. There is no end to the progression of multiple integrals. It is possible to define integrals with respect to any number of variables. For example, problems in statistics and statistical mechanics involve integration over regions of many dimensions.

Triple Integrals in Rectangular Coordinates

Consider a function $w = f(x, y, z)$ that is continuous on a closed and bounded region D of $\mathbf{R}^3$. The graph of f is the set of points $(x, y, z, f(x, y, z))$, where (x, y, z) is in D, for which there is no complete three-dimensional representation. Despite the difficulties in representing f in $\mathbf{R}^3$, we may still define the integral of f over D. We first create a partition of D by slicing the region with three sets of planes that run parallel to the xz-, yz-, and xy-planes (Figure 14.37). This partition subdivides D into small boxes that are ordered in a convenient way from $k = 1$ to $k = n$. The partition includes all boxes that are wholly contained in D. The kth box has side lengths Δx_k, Δy_k, and Δz_k, and volume $\Delta V_k = \Delta x_k\,\Delta y_k\,\Delta z_k$. We let $(\bar{x}_k, \bar{y}_k, \bar{z}_k)$ be an arbitrary point in the kth box, for $k = 1, \ldots, n$.

A Riemann sum is now formed, in which the kth term is the function value $f(\bar{x}_k, \bar{y}_k, \bar{z}_k)$ multiplied by the volume of the kth box:

$$\sum_{k=1}^{n} f(\bar{x}_k, \bar{y}_k, \bar{z}_k)\,\Delta V_k$$

We let Δ denote the maximum length of the diagonals of the boxes. As the number of boxes n increases, while Δ approaches zero, two things happen:

- For commonly encountered regions, the region formed by the collection of boxes approaches the region D.
- If f is continuous, the Riemann sum approaches a limit.

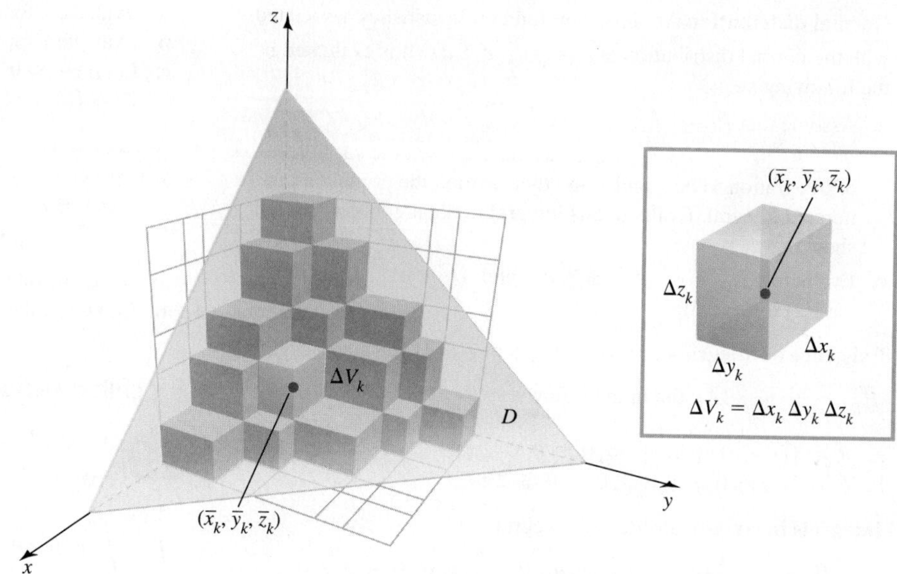

FIGURE 14.37

➤ Notice the analogy between double and triple integrals:

$$\text{area}\,(R) = \iint_R dA \quad \text{and}$$

$$\text{volume}\,(D) = \iiint_D dV$$

The use of triple integrals to compute the mass of an object is discussed in detail in Section 14.6.

The limit of the Riemann sum, called the **triple integral of f over D**, is

$$\lim_{\Delta \to 0} \sum_{k=1}^{n} f(\bar{x}_k, \bar{y}_k, \bar{z}_k)\, \Delta V_k = \iiint_D f(x, y, z)\, dV.$$

We have two immediate interpretations of a triple integral. First, if $f(x, y, z) = 1$, then the Riemann sum simply adds up the volumes of the boxes in the partition. In the limit as $\Delta \to 0$, the triple integral $\iiint_D dV$ gives the volume of the region D.

Second, suppose that D is a solid three-dimensional object and its density varies from point to point according to the function $f(x, y, z)$. The units of density are mass per unit volume, so the product $f(\bar{x}_k, \bar{y}_k, \bar{z}_k)\, \Delta V_k$ approximates the mass of the kth box in D. Summing the masses of the boxes gives an approximation to the total mass of D. In the limit as $\Delta \to 0$, the triple integral gives the mass of the object.

As with double integrals, a version of Fubini's Theorem expresses a triple integral in terms of an iterated integral in x, y, and z. The situation becomes interesting because with three variables, there are *six* possible orders of integration.

The kth box in the partition has volume $\Delta V_k = \Delta x_k \Delta y_k \Delta z_k$, where Δx_k, Δy_k, and Δz_k are the side lengths of the box. Accordingly, the element of volume in the triple integral, which we denote dV, becomes $dx\, dy\, dz$ (or some rearrangement of dx, dy, and dz) in an iterated integral.

QUICK CHECK 1 List the six orders in which the three differentials dx, dy, and dz may be written. ◄

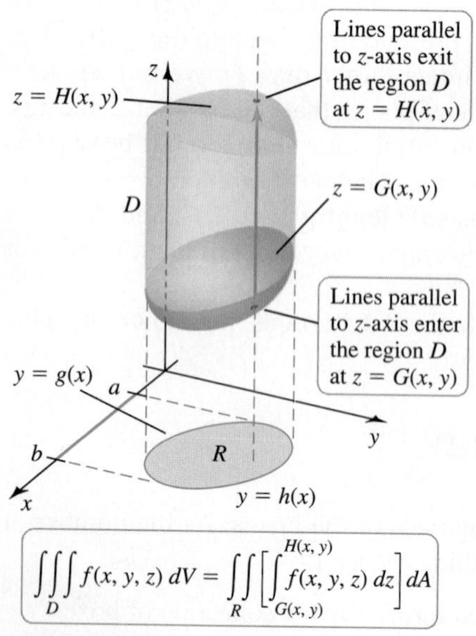

FIGURE 14.38

Finding Limits of Integration We discuss one of the six orders of integration in detail; the others are examined in the examples. Suppose a region D in $\mathbf{R}^3$ is bounded above by a surface $z = H(x, y)$ and below by a surface $z = G(x, y)$ (Figure 14.38). These two surfaces determine the limits of integration in the z-direction.

Once we know the upper and lower boundaries of D, the next step is to project the region D onto the xy-plane to form a region that we call R (Figure 14.39). You can think of R as the shadow of D in the xy-plane. Assume R is bounded above and below by the curves $y = h(x)$ and $y = g(x)$, respectively, and bounded on the right and left by the lines $x = a$ and $x = b$, respectively (Figure 14.39). The remaining integration over R is carried out as a double integral (Section 14.2).

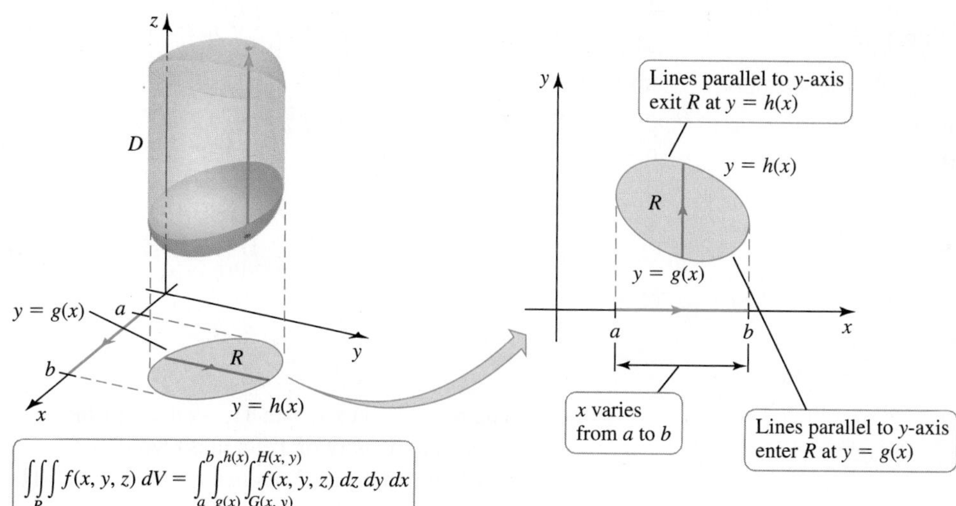

FIGURE 14.39

Table 14.2

Integral	Variable	Interval
Inner	z	$G(x, y) \le z \le H(x, y)$
Middle	y	$g(x) \le y \le h(x)$
Outer	x	$a \le x \le b$

The intervals that describe D are summarized in Table 14.2, which can then be used to formulate the limits of integration. To integrate over all points of D we must

- first integrate with respect to z from $z = G(x, y)$ to $z = H(x, y)$,
- then integrate with respect to y from $y = g(x)$ to $y = h(x)$, and
- finally integrate with respect to x from $x = a$ to $x = b$.

➤ Theorem 14.5 is a version of Fubini's Theorem. Five other versions could be written for the other orders of integration.

THEOREM 14.5 Triple Integrals
Let $D = \{(x, y, z): a \le x \le b, g(x) \le y \le h(x), G(x, y) \le z \le H(x, y)\}$, where g, h, G, H are continuous functions. The triple integral of a continuous function f on D is evaluated as the iterated integral

$$\iiint_D f(x, y, z)\, dV = \int_a^b \int_{g(x)}^{h(x)} \int_{G(x,y)}^{H(x,y)} f(x, y, z)\, dz\, dy\, dx.$$

Notice that the first (inner) integral is with respect to z, and the result is a function of x and y; the second (middle) integral is with respect to y, and the result is a function of x; and the last (outer) integral is with respect to x, and the result is a real number.

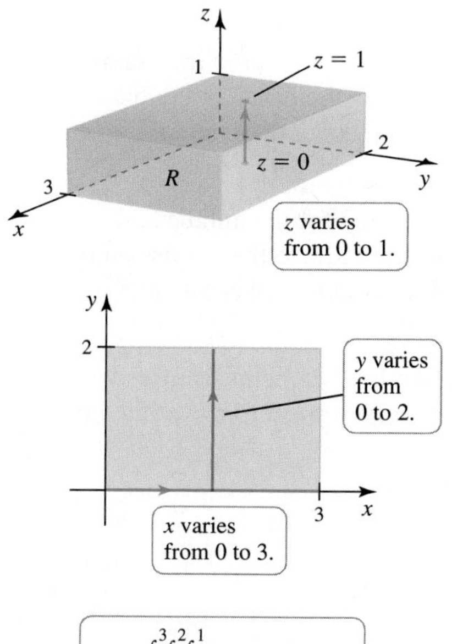

FIGURE 14.40

EXAMPLE 1 Mass of a box A solid box D is bounded by the planes $x = 0$, $x = 3$, $y = 0$, $y = 2$, $z = 0$, and $z = 1$. The density of the box decreases linearly in the z-direction and is given by $f(x, y, z) = 2 - z$. Find the mass of the box.

SOLUTION The mass of the box is found by integrating the density $f(x, y, z) = 2 - z$ over the box. Because the limits of integration for all three variables are constant, the iterated integral may be written in any order (Figure 14.40). Using the order of integration $dz\, dy\, dx$, the limits of integration are shown in Table 14.3.

The mass of the box is

$$M = \iiint_D (2 - z)\, dV$$

$$= \int_0^3 \int_0^2 \int_0^1 (2 - z)\, dz\, dy\, dx \quad \text{Convert to an iterated integral.}$$

Table 14.3

Integral	Variable	Interval
Inner	z	$0 \le z \le 1$
Middle	y	$0 \le y \le 2$
Outer	x	$0 \le x \le 3$

$$= \int_0^3 \int_0^2 \left(2z - \frac{z^2}{2}\right)\Bigg|_0^1 dy\,dx \qquad \text{Evaluate the inner integral with respect to } z.$$

$$= \int_0^3 \int_0^2 \left(\frac{3}{2}\right) dy\,dx \qquad \text{Simplify.}$$

$$= \int_0^3 \left(\frac{3y}{2}\right)\Bigg|_0^2 dx \qquad \text{Evaluate the middle integral with respect to } y.$$

$$= \int_0^3 3\,dx = 9. \qquad \text{Evaluate the outer integral and simplify.}$$

The result makes sense: The density of the box varies linearly from 1 to 2; if the box had a constant density of 1, its mass would be (volume) $\cdot$ (density) $= 6$; if the box had a constant density of 2, its mass would be 12. The actual mass is the average of 6 and 12, as you might expect.

Any other order of integration produces the same result. For example with the order $dy\,dx\,dz$, the iterated integral is

$$M = \iiint_D (2 - z)\,dV = \int_0^1 \int_0^3 \int_0^2 (2 - z)\,dy\,dx\,dz = 9.$$

Related Exercises 7–14 ◀

QUICK CHECK 2 Write the integral in Example 1 in the orders $dx\,dy\,dz$ and $dx\,dz\,dy$. ◀

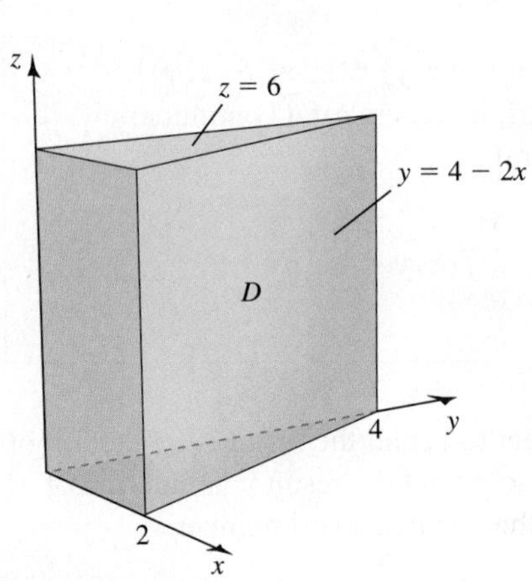

FIGURE 14.41

EXAMPLE 2 **Volume of a prism** Find the volume of the prism D in the first octant bounded by the planes $y = 4 - 2x$ and $z = 6$ (Figure 14.41).

SOLUTION The prism may be viewed in several different ways. If we put the base of the prism in the xz-plane, then the upper surface of the prism is the plane $y = 4 - 2x$, and the lower surface is $y = 0$. The projection of the prism onto the xz-plane is the rectangle $R = \{(x, z): 0 \le x \le 2, 0 \le z \le 6\}$. An order of integration in this case is $dy\,dx\,dz$.

Inner integral with respect to y: A line through the prism parallel to the y-axis enters the prism through the rectangle R at $y = 0$ and exits the prism at the plane $y = 4 - 2x$. Therefore, we first integrate with respect to y over the interval $0 \le y \le 4 - 2x$ (Figure 14.42a).

Middle integral with respect to x: The limits of integration for the middle and outer integrals must cover the region R in the xz-plane. A line parallel to the x-axis enters R at $x = 0$ and exits R at $x = 2$. So we integrate with respect to x over the interval $0 \le x \le 2$ (Figure 14.42b).

Outer integral with respect to z: To cover all of R, the line segments from $x = 0$ to $x = 2$ must run from $z = 0$ to $z = 6$. So, we integrate with respect to z over the interval $0 \le z \le 6$ (Figure 14.42b).

Integrating $f(x, y, z) = 1$, the volume of the prism is

$$V = \iiint_D dV = \int_0^6 \int_0^2 \int_0^{4-2x} dy\,dx\,dz$$

$$= \int_0^6 \int_0^2 (4 - 2x)\,dx\,dz \qquad \text{Evaluate the inner integral with respect to } y.$$

$$= \int_0^6 (4x - x^2)\Big|_0^2 \, dz$$ Evaluate the middle integral with respect to x.

$$= \int_0^6 4\, dz$$ Simplify.

$$= 24.$$ Evaluate the outer integral with respect to z.

➤ The volume of the prism could also be found using geometry: The area of the triangular base in the xy-plane is 4 and the height is 6. Therefore, the volume is $6 \cdot 4 = 24$.

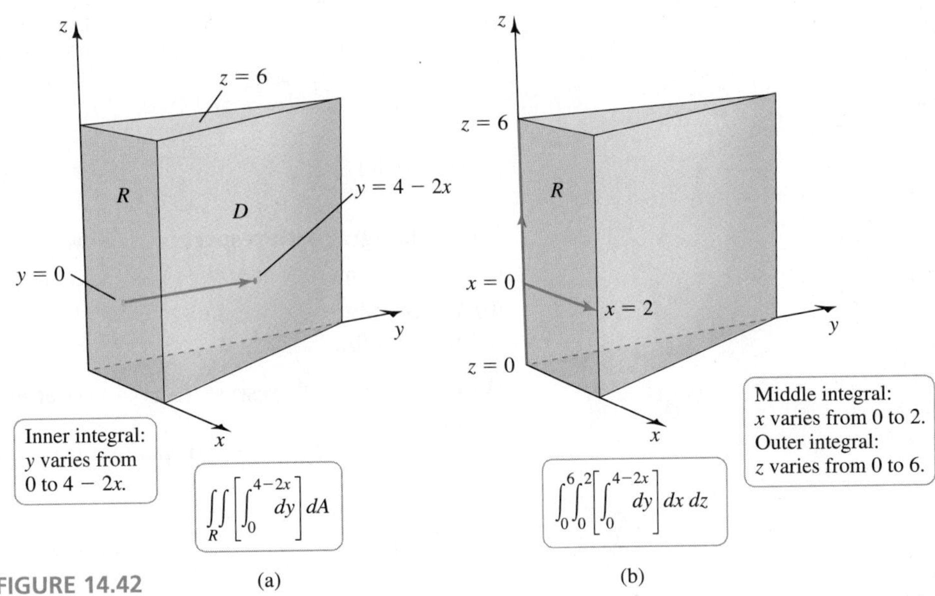

FIGURE 14.42 (a) (b)

Related Exercises 15–24 ◀

QUICK CHECK 3 Write the integral in Example 2 in the orders $dz\,dy\,dx$ and $dx\,dy\,dz$. ◀

EXAMPLE 3 **A volume integral** Find the volume of the region D bounded by the paraboloids $y = x^2 + z^2$ and $y = 16 - 3x^2 - z^2$ (Figure 14.43).

SOLUTION We identify the right boundary of D as the surface $y = 16 - 3x^2 - z^2$; the left boundary is $y = x^2 + z^2$. These surfaces are functions of x and z, so they determine the limits of integration for the inner integral in the y-direction.

A key step in the calculation is finding the curve of intersection between the two surfaces and projecting it onto the xz-plane to form the boundary of the region R. Equating the y-coordinates of the two surfaces, we have $x^2 + z^2 = 16 - 3x^2 - z^2$, which becomes the equation of an ellipse:

$$4x^2 + 2z^2 = 16, \quad \text{or} \quad z = \pm\sqrt{8 - 2x^2}$$

The projection of the solid region D onto the xz-plane is the region R bounded by this ellipse (centered at the origin with axes of length 4 and $4\sqrt{2}$). Here are the observations that lead to the limits of integration with the ordering $dy\,dz\,dx$.

Inner integral with respect to y: A line through the solid parallel to the y-axis enters the solid at $y = x^2 + z^2$ and exits at $y = 16 - 3x^2 - z^2$. Therefore, for fixed values of x and z, we integrate over the interval $x^2 + z^2 \le y \le 16 - 3x^2 - z^2$ (Figure 14.43a).

➤ Note that the problem is symmetric about the x- and z-axes. Therefore, the integral over R could be evaluated over one-quarter of R,

$$\{(x, z): 0 \le z \le \sqrt{8 - 2x^2},\ 0 \le x \le 2\},$$

in which case, the final result must be multiplied by 4.

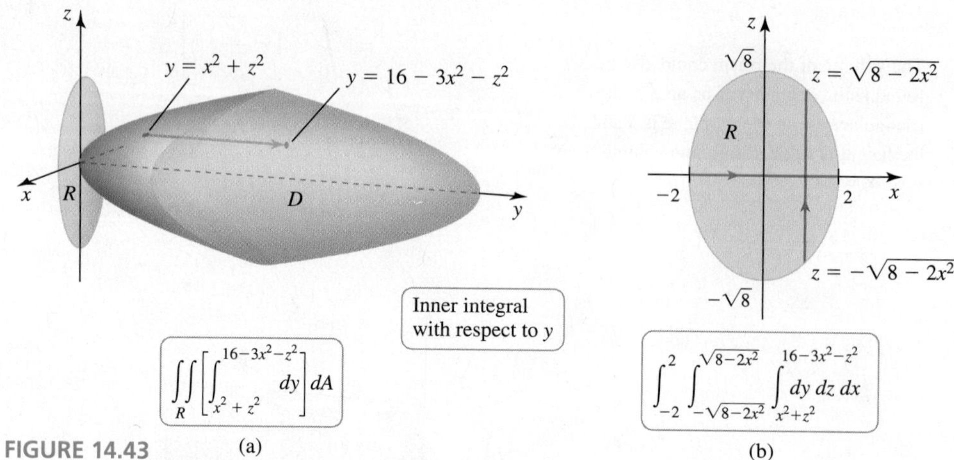

FIGURE 14.43 (a) (b)

Middle integral with respect to z: Now we must cover the region R. A line parallel to the z-axis enters R at $z = -\sqrt{8 - 2x^2}$ and exits R at $z = \sqrt{8 - 2x^2}$. Therefore, for a fixed value of x, we integrate over the interval $-\sqrt{8 - 2x^2} \le z \le \sqrt{8 - 2x^2}$ (Figure 14.43b).

Outer integral with respect to x: To cover all of R, x must run from $x = -2$ to $x = 2$ (Figure 14.43b).

Integrating $f(x, y, z) = 1$, the iterated integral for the volume is

$$V = \int_{-2}^{2}\int_{-\sqrt{8-2x^2}}^{\sqrt{8-2x^2}}\int_{x^2+z^2}^{16-3x^2-z^2} dy\,dz\,dx$$

$$= \int_{-2}^{2}\int_{-\sqrt{8-2x^2}}^{\sqrt{8-2x^2}} (16 - 4x^2 - 2z^2)\,dz\,dx \quad \text{Evaluate the inner integral and simplify.}$$

$$= \int_{-2}^{2}\left(16z - 4x^2 z - \frac{2z^3}{3}\right)\Bigg|_{-\sqrt{8-2x^2}}^{\sqrt{8-2x^2}} dx \quad \text{Evaluate the middle integral.}$$

$$= \frac{16\sqrt{2}}{3}\int_{-2}^{2}(4 - x^2)^{3/2}\,dx = 32\pi\sqrt{2}. \quad \text{Evaluate the outer integral.}$$

The last (outer) integral in this calculation requires the trigonometric substitution $x = 2\sin\theta$.

Related Exercises 25–34 ◀

Changing the Order of Integration

As with double integrals, choosing an appropriate order of integration may simplify the evaluation of a triple integral. Therefore, it is important to become proficient at changing the order of integration.

EXAMPLE 4 **Changing the order of integration** Consider the integral

$$\int_{0}^{\sqrt[4]{\pi}}\int_{0}^{z}\int_{y}^{z} 12y^2 z^3 \sin x^4\,dx\,dy\,dz.$$

a. Sketch the region of integration D.

b. Evaluate the integral by changing the order of integration.

SOLUTION

a. We begin by finding the projection of the region of integration D on the appropriate coordinate plane; call the projection R. Because the inner integration is with respect to x, R lies in the yz-plane, and it is determined by the limits on the middle and outer integrals. We see that

$$R = \{(y, z): 0 \leq y \leq z, 0 \leq z \leq \sqrt[4]{\pi}\},$$

which is a triangular region in the yz-plane bounded by the z-axis and the lines $y = z$ and $z = \sqrt[4]{\pi}$. Using the limits on the inner integral, for each point in R we let x vary from the plane $x = y$ to the plane $x = z$. In so doing, the points fill an inverted tetrahedron in the first octant with its vertex at the origin, which is D (Figure 14.44).

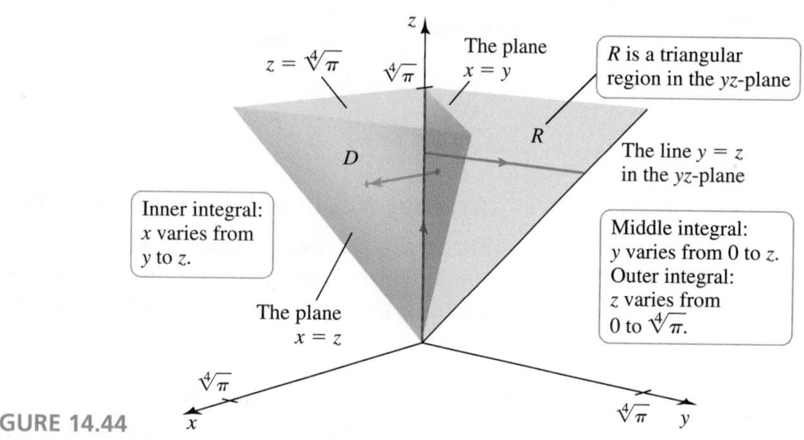

FIGURE 14.44

➤ How do we know to switch the order of integration so the inner integral is with respect to y? Often we do not know in advance whether a new order of integration will work, and some trial and error is needed. In this case, either y^2 or z^3 is easier to integrate than $\sin x^4$, so either y or z is a likely variable for the inner integral. However, we are given that z varies between two constants, so z is the best choice for the variable in the outer integral.

b. It is difficult to evaluate the integral in the given order ($dx\,dy\,dz$) because the antiderivative of $\sin x^4$ is not expressible in terms of elementary functions. If we integrate first with respect to y, we introduce a factor in the integrand that enables us to use a substitution to integrate $\sin x^4$. With the order of integration $dy\,dx\,dz$, the bounds of integration for the inner integral extend from the plane $y = 0$ to the plane $y = x$ (Figure 14.45a). Furthermore, the projection of D onto the xz-plane is the region R, which must be covered by the middle and outer integrals (Figure 14.45b). In this case, we draw a line segment parallel to the x-axis to see that the limits of the middle integral run from $x = 0$ to $x = z$. Then, we include all these segments from $z = 0$ to $z = \sqrt[4]{\pi}$ to obtain the outer limits of integration in z. The integration proceeds as follows:

$$\int_0^{\sqrt[4]{\pi}} \int_0^z \int_0^x 12y^2 z^3 \sin x^4 \,dy\,dx\,dz = \int_0^{\sqrt[4]{\pi}} \int_0^z \left(4y^3 z^3 \sin x^4\right)\Big|_0^x \,dx\,dz \quad \text{Evaluate the inner integral.}$$

$$= \int_0^{\sqrt[4]{\pi}} \int_0^z 4x^3 z^3 \sin x^4 \,dx\,dz \quad \text{Simplify.}$$

$$= \int_0^{\sqrt[4]{\pi}} z^3 \left(-\cos x^4\right)\Big|_0^z \,dz \quad \text{Evaluate the middle integral; } u = x^4.$$

$$= \int_0^{\sqrt[4]{\pi}} z^3 (1 - \cos z^4)\,dz \quad \text{Simplify.}$$

$$= \left(\frac{z^4}{4} - \frac{\sin z^4}{4}\right)\Big|_0^{\sqrt[4]{\pi}} \quad \text{Evaluate the outer integral; } u = z^4.$$

$$= \frac{\pi}{4} \quad \text{Simplify.}$$

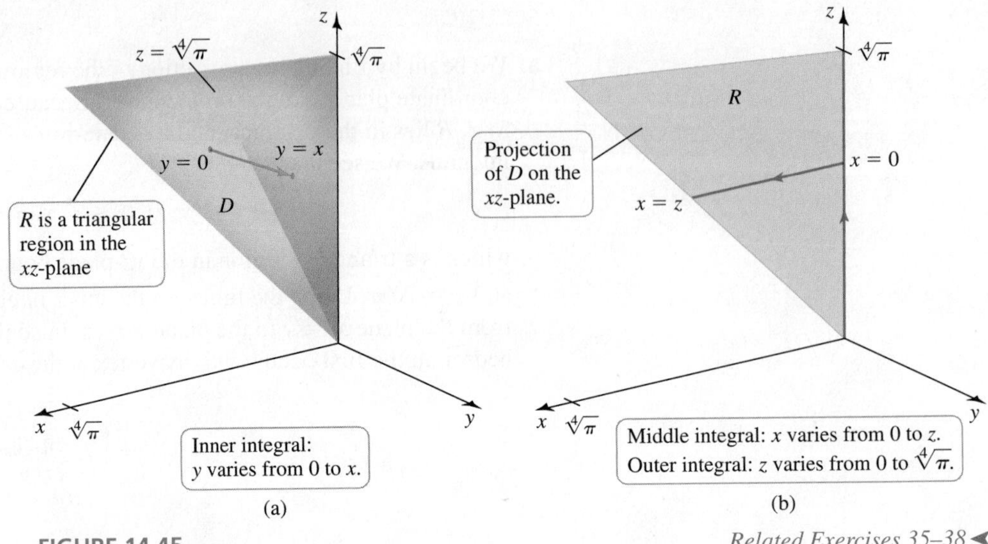

FIGURE 14.45

Related Exercises 35–38 ◀

Average Value of a Function of Three Variables

The idea of the average value of a function extends naturally from the one- and two-variable cases. The average value of a function of three variables is found by integrating the function over the region of interest and dividing by the volume of the region.

> **DEFINITION Average Value of a Function of Three Variables**
>
> If f is continuous on a region D of $\mathbf{R}^3$, then the average value of f over D is
>
> $$\bar{f} = \frac{1}{\text{volume }(D)} \iiint_D f(x, y, z)\, dV.$$

EXAMPLE 5 Average temperature Consider a block of a conducting material occupying the region

$$D = \{(x, y, z): 0 \le x \le 2, 0 \le y \le 2, 0 \le z \le 1\}.$$

Due to heat sources on its boundaries, the temperature in the block is given by $T(x, y, z) = 250xy \sin \pi z$. Find the average temperature over the block.

SOLUTION We must integrate the temperature function over the block and divide by the volume of the block, which is 4. One way to evaluate the temperature integral is as follows:

$$\iiint_D 250xy \sin \pi z\, dV = 250 \int_0^2 \int_0^2 \int_0^1 xy \sin \pi z\, dz\, dy\, dx \qquad \text{Convert to an iterated integral.}$$

$$= 250 \int_0^2 \int_0^2 xy \frac{1}{\pi}(-\cos \pi z)\Big|_0^1 dy\, dx \qquad \text{Evaluate the inner integral.}$$

$$= \frac{500}{\pi} \int_0^2 \int_0^2 xy\, dy\, dx \qquad \text{Simplify.}$$

$$= \frac{500}{\pi} \int_0^2 x \left(\frac{y^2}{2}\right)\Big|_0^2 dx \qquad \text{Evaluate the middle integral.}$$

$$= \frac{1000}{\pi}\int_0^2 x\,dx \qquad \text{Simplify.}$$

$$= \frac{1000}{\pi}\left(\frac{x^2}{2}\right)\bigg|_0^2 = \frac{2000}{\pi} \qquad \text{Evaluate the outer integral.}$$

Dividing by the volume of the region, the average temperature is $(2000/\pi)/4 = 500/\pi \approx 159.2$.

Related Exercises 39–44 ◂

QUICK CHECK 4 Without integrating, what is the average value of $f(x, y, z) = \sin x \sin y \sin z$ on the cube

$$\{(x, y, z): -1 \le x \le 1, -1 \le y \le 1, -1 \le z \le 1\}?$$

Use symmetry arguments. ◂

SECTION 14.4 EXERCISES

Review Questions

1. Sketch the region $D = \{(x, y, z): x^2 + y^2 \le 4, 0 \le z \le 4\}$.

2. Write an iterated integral for $\iiint_D f(x, y, z)\,dV$, where D is the box $\{(x, y, z): 0 \le x \le 3, 0 \le y \le 6, 0 \le z \le 4\}$.

3. Write an iterated integral for $\iiint_D f(x, y, z)\,dV$, where D is a sphere of radius 9 centered at (0, 0, 0). Use the order $dz\,dy\,dx$.

4. Sketch the region of integration for the integral $\int_0^1\int_0^{\sqrt{1-z^2}}\int_0^{\sqrt{1-y^2-z^2}} f(x, y, z)\,dx\,dy\,dz$.

5. Write the integral for the Exercise 4 in the order $dy\,dx\,dz$.

6. Write an integral for the average value of $f(x, y, z) = xyz$ over the region bounded by the paraboloid $z = 9 - x^2 - y^2$ and the xy-plane (assuming the volume of the region is known).

Basic Skills

7–14. Integrals over boxes *Evaluate the following integrals. A sketch of the region of integration may be useful.*

7. $\displaystyle\int_{-2}^{2}\int_{3}^{6}\int_{0}^{2} dx\,dy\,dz$

8. $\displaystyle\int_{-1}^{1}\int_{-1}^{2}\int_{0}^{1} 6xyz\,dy\,dx\,dz$

9. $\displaystyle\int_{-2}^{2}\int_{1}^{2}\int_{1}^{e} \frac{xy^2}{z}\,dz\,dx\,dy$

10. $\displaystyle\int_{1}^{\ln 8}\int_{0}^{\ln 4}\int_{0}^{\ln 2} e^{-x-y-2z}\,dx\,dy\,dz$

11. $\displaystyle\int_{0}^{\pi/2}\int_{0}^{1}\int_{0}^{\pi/2} \sin \pi x \cos y \sin 2z\,dy\,dx\,dz$

12. $\displaystyle\int_{0}^{2}\int_{1}^{2}\int_{0}^{1} yze^x\,dx\,dz\,dy$

13. $\displaystyle\iiint_D (xy + xz + yz)\,dV$; $D = \{(x, y, z): -1 \le x \le 1, -2 \le y \le 2, -3 \le z \le 3\}$

14. $\displaystyle\iiint_D xyze^{-x^2-y^2}\,dV$; $D = \{(x, y, z): 0 \le x \le \sqrt{\ln 2}, 0 \le y \le \sqrt{\ln 4}, 0 \le z \le 1\}$

15–24. Volumes of solids *Find the volume of the following solids using triple integrals.*

15. The region in the first octant bounded by the plane $2x + 3y + 6z = 12$ and the coordinate planes

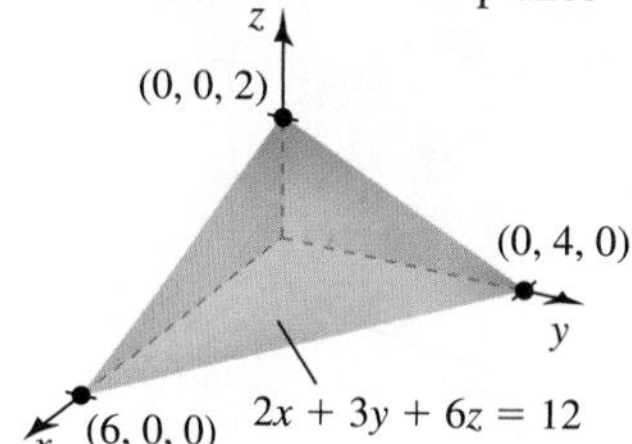

16. The region in the first octant formed when the cylinder $z = \sin y$, for $0 \le y \le \pi$, is sliced by the planes $y = x$ and $x = 0$

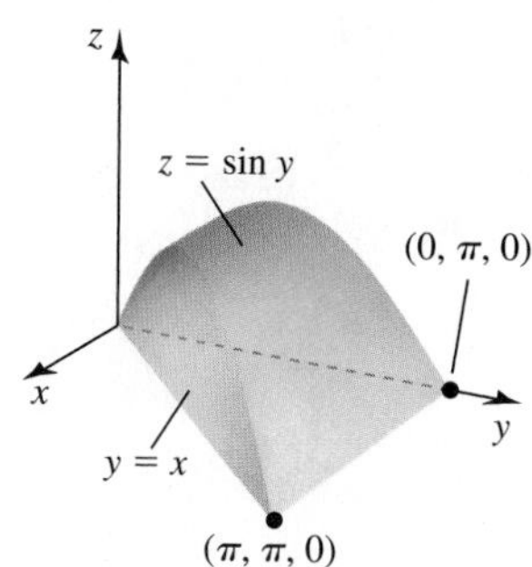

17. The region bounded below by the cone $z = \sqrt{x^2 + y^2}$ and bounded above by the sphere $x^2 + y^2 + z^2 = 8$

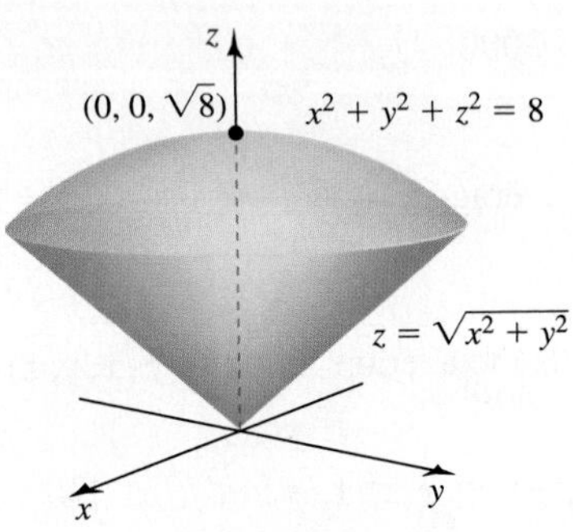

18. The prism in the first octant bounded by $z = 2 - 4x$ and $y = 8$

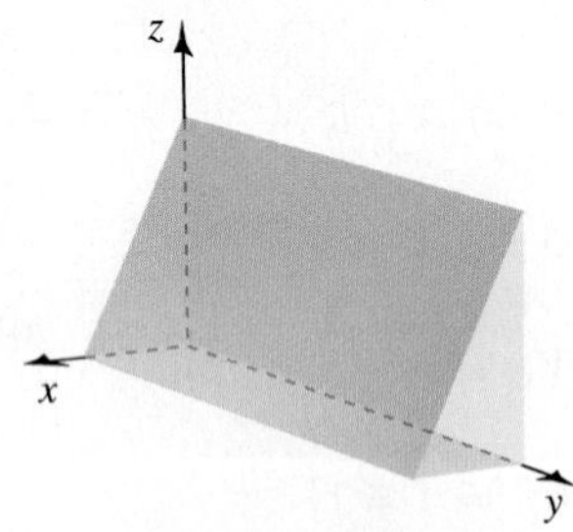

19. The wedge above the xy-plane formed when the cylinder $x^2 + y^2 = 4$ is cut by the planes $z = 0$ and $y = -z$

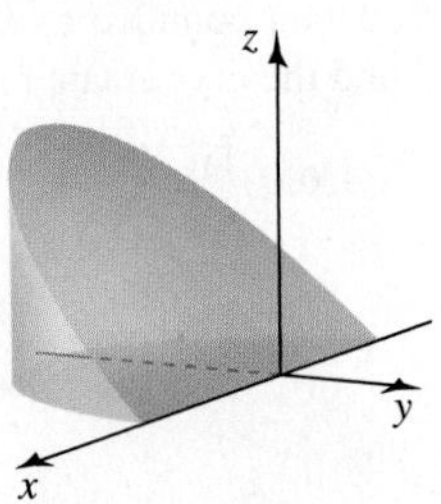

20. The region bounded by the parabolic cylinder $y = x^2$ and the planes $z = 3 - y$ and $z = 0$

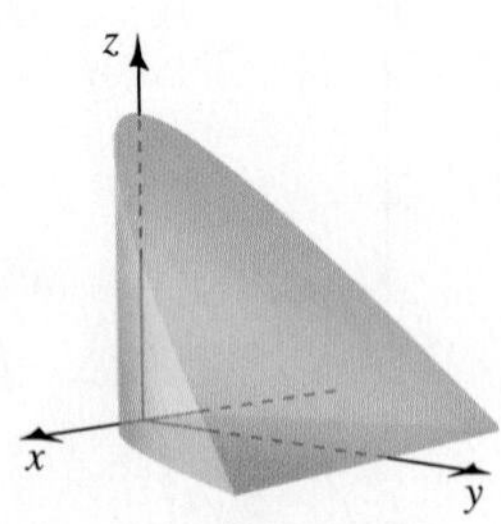

21. The region between the sphere $x^2 + y^2 + z^2 = 19$ and the hyperboloid $z^2 - x^2 - y^2 = 1$, for $z > 0$

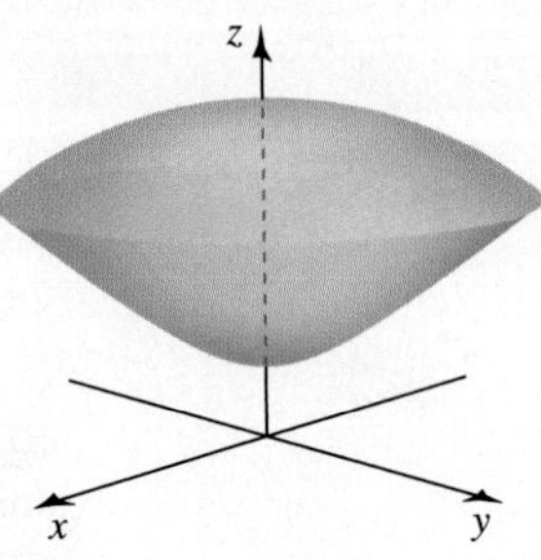

22. The region bounded by the surfaces $z = e^y$ and $z = 1$ over the rectangle $\{(x, y): 0 \leq x \leq 1, 0 \leq y \leq \ln 2\}$

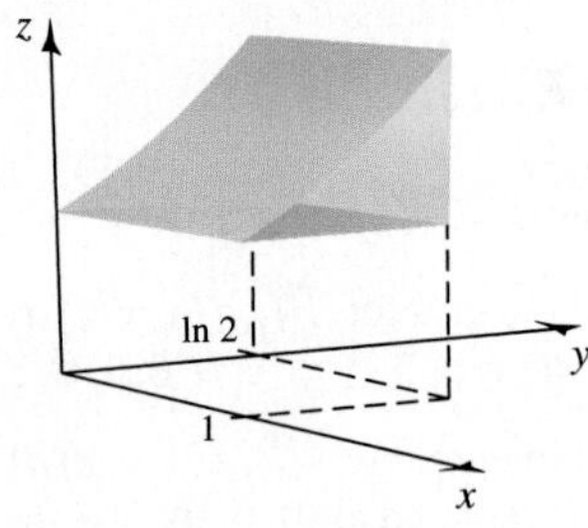

23. The wedge of the cylinder $x^2 + 4y^2 = 4$ created by the planes $z = 3 - x$ and $z = x - 3$

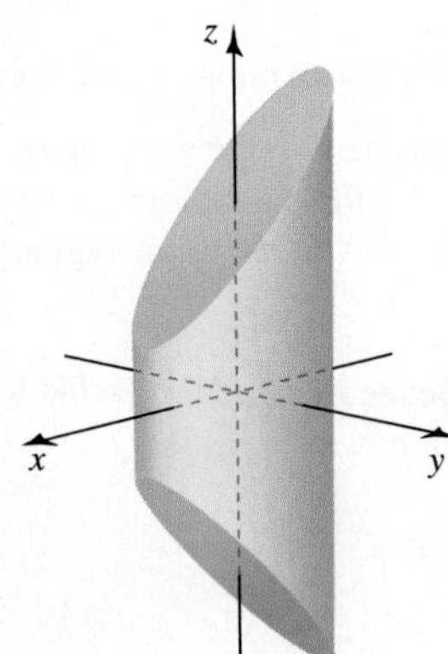

24. The region in the first octant bounded by the cone $z = 1 - \sqrt{x^2 + y^2}$ and the plane $x + y + z = 1$

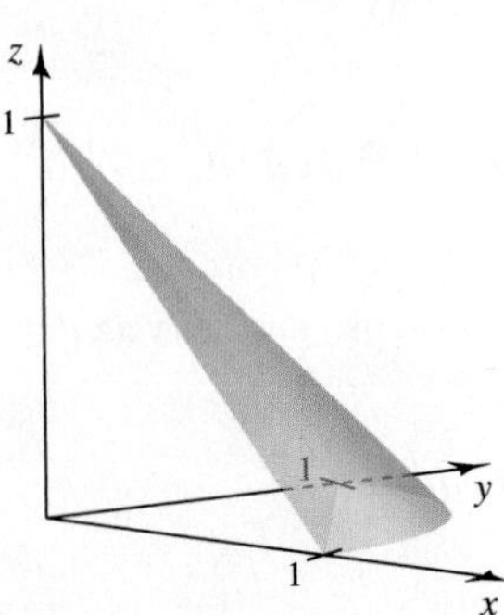

25–34. Triple integrals *Evaluate the following integrals.*

25. $\displaystyle\int_0^1 \int_0^{\sqrt{1-x^2}} \int_0^{\sqrt{1-x^2}} dz\,dy\,dx$

26. $\displaystyle\int_0^1 \int_0^{\sqrt{1-x^2}} \int_0^{\sqrt{1-x^2-y^2}} 2xz\,dz\,dy\,dx$

27. $\displaystyle\int_0^4 \int_{-2\sqrt{16-y^2}}^{2\sqrt{16-y^2}} \int_0^{16-(x^2/4)-y^2} dz\,dx\,dy$

28. $\displaystyle\int_1^6 \int_0^{4-2y/3} \int_0^{12-2y-3z} \frac{1}{y}\,dx\,dz\,dy$

29. $\displaystyle\int_0^3 \int_0^{\sqrt{9-z^2}} \int_0^{\sqrt{1+x^2+z^2}} dy\,dx\,dz$

30. $\displaystyle\int_0^{\pi} \int_0^{\pi} \int_0^{\sin x} \sin y\,dz\,dx\,dy$

31. $\displaystyle\int_1^{\ln 8} \int_1^{\sqrt{z}} \int_{\ln y}^{\ln 2y} e^{x+y^2-z}\,dx\,dy\,dz$

32. $\displaystyle\int_0^1 \int_0^{\sqrt{1-x^2}} \int_0^{2-x} 4yz\,dz\,dy\,dx$

33. $\displaystyle\int_0^2 \int_0^4 \int_{y^2}^4 \sqrt{x}\,dz\,dx\,dy$

34. $\displaystyle\int_0^1 \int_y^{2-y} \int_0^{2-x-y} xy\,dz\,dx\,dy$

35–38. Changing the order of integration *Rewrite the following integrals using the indicated order of integration and then evaluate the resulting integral.*

35. $\displaystyle\int_0^5 \int_{-1}^0 \int_0^{4x+4} dy\,dx\,dz$ in the order $dz\,dx\,dy$

36. $\displaystyle\int_0^1 \int_{-2}^2 \int_0^{\sqrt{4-y^2}} dz\,dy\,dx$ in the order $dy\,dz\,dx$

37. $\displaystyle\int_0^1 \int_0^{\sqrt{1-x^2}} \int_0^{\sqrt{1-x^2}} dy\,dz\,dx$ in the order $dz\,dy\,dx$

38. $\displaystyle\int_0^4 \int_0^{\sqrt{16-x^2}} \int_0^{\sqrt{16-x^2-z^2}} dy\,dz\,dx$ in the order $dx\,dy\,dz$

39–44. Average value *Find the following average values.*

39. The average temperature in the box $D = \{(x, y, z): 0 \le x \le \ln 2, 0 \le y \le \ln 4, 0 \le z \le \ln 8\}$ with a temperature distribution of $T(x, y, z) = 100\,e^{-x-y-z}$

40. The average value of $f(x, y, z) = 6xyz$ over the points inside the hemisphere of radius 4 centered at the origin with its base in the xy-plane

41. The average of the *squared* distance between the origin and points in the solid cylinder $D = \{(x, y, z): x^2 + y^2 \le 4, 0 \le z \le 2\}$

42. The average of the *squared* distance between the origin and points in the solid paraboloid $D = \{(x, y, z): 0 \le z \le 4 - x^2 - y^2\}$

43. The average z-coordinate of points in a hemisphere of radius 4 centered at the origin with its base in the xy-plane

44. The average of the *squared* distance between the z-axis and points in the conical region $D = \{(x, y, z): 2\sqrt{x^2 + y^2} \le z \le 8\}$

Further Explorations

45. Explain why or why not Determine whether the following statements are true and give an explanation or counterexample.

a. An iterated integral of a function over the box $D = \{(x, y, z): 0 \le x \le a, 0 \le y \le b, 0 \le z \le c\}$ can be expressed in eight different ways.

b. One possible iterated integral of f over the prism $D = \{(x, y, z): 0 \le x \le 1, 0 \le y \le 3x - 3, 0 \le z \le 5\}$ is $\int_0^{3x-3} \int_0^1 \int_0^5 f(x, y, z)\,dz\,dx\,dy$.

c. The region $D = \{(x, y, z): 0 \le x \le 1, 0 \le y \le \sqrt{1 - x^2}, 0 \le z \le \sqrt{1 - x^2}\}$ is a sphere.

46. Changing the order of integration Use another order of integration to evaluate $\displaystyle\int_1^4 \int_z^{4z} \int_0^{\pi^2} \frac{\sin\sqrt{yz}}{x^{3/2}}\,dy\,dx\,dz$.

47–51. Miscellaneous volumes *Use a triple integral to compute the volume of the following regions.*

47. The parallelepiped (slanted box) with vertices (0, 0, 0), (1, 0, 0), (0, 1, 0), (1, 1, 0), (0, 1, 1), (1, 1, 1), (0, 2, 1), (1, 2, 1) (Use integration and find the best order of integration.)

48. The larger of two solids formed when the parallelepiped (slanted box) with vertices (0, 0, 0), (2, 0, 0), (0, 2, 0), (2, 2, 0), (0, 1, 1), (2, 1, 1), (0, 3, 1), (2, 3, 1) is sliced by the plane $y = 2$.

49. The pyramid with vertices (0, 0, 0), (2, 0, 0), (2, 2, 0), (0, 2, 0), (0, 0, 4)

50. The region common to the cylinders $z = \sin x$ and $z = \sin y$ over the square $R = \{(x, y): 0 \le x \le \pi, 0 \le y \le \pi\}$ (The figure shows the cylinders, but not the common region.)

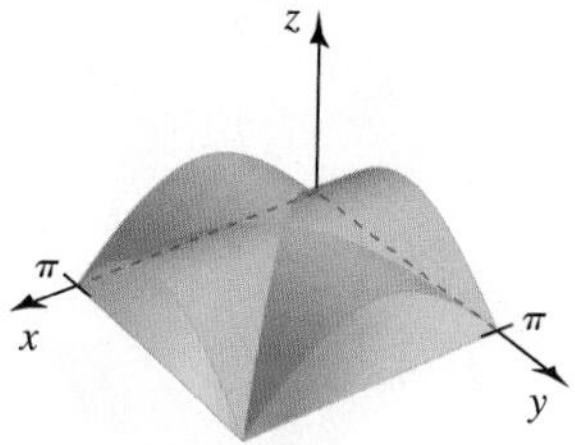

51. The wedge of the square column $|x| + |y| = 1$ created by the planes $z = 0$ and $x + y + z = 1$

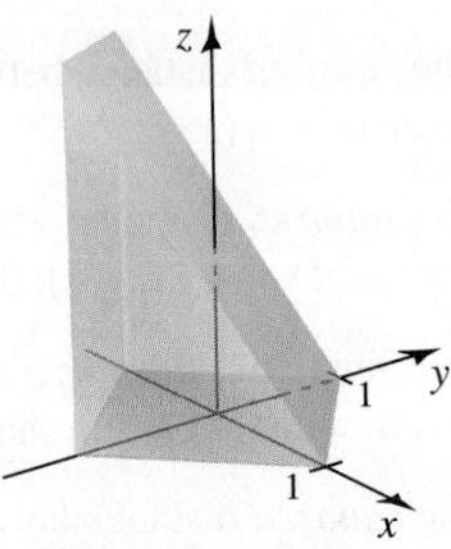

52. Partitioning a cube Consider the region $D_1 = \{(x, y, z): 0 \le x \le y \le z \le 1\}$.

a. Find the volume of D_1.

b. Let $D_2, \ldots, D_6$ be the "cousins" of D_1 formed by rearranging x, y, and z in the inequality $0 \le x \le y \le z \le 1$. Show that the volumes of $D_1, \ldots, D_6$ are equal.

c. Show that the union of $D_1, \ldots, D_6$ is a unit cube.

Applications

53. Comparing two masses Two different tetrahedrons fill the region in the first octant bounded by the coordinate planes and the plane $x + y + z = 4$. Both solids have densities that vary in the z-direction between $\rho = 4$ and $\rho = 8$, according to the functions $\rho_1 = 8 - z$ and $\rho_2 = 4 + z$. Find the mass of each solid.

54. Dividing the cheese Suppose a wedge of cheese fills the region in the first octant bounded by the planes $y = z$, $y = 4$, and $x = 4$. You could divide the wedge into two equal pieces (by volume) if you sliced the wedge with the plane $x = 2$. Instead find a with $0 < a < 4$ such that slicing the wedge with the plane $y = a$ divides the wedge into two equal pieces.

55–59. General volume formulas *Find equations for the bounding surfaces, set up a volume integral, and evaluate the integral to obtain a volume formula for each region. Assume that a, b, c, r, R, and h are positive constants.*

55. Cone Find the volume of a right circular cone with height h and base radius r.

56. Tetrahedron Find the volume of a tetrahedron whose vertices are located at $(0, 0, 0)$, $(a, 0, 0)$, $(0, b, 0)$, and $(0, 0, c)$.

57. Spherical cap Find the volume of the cap of a sphere of radius R with height h.

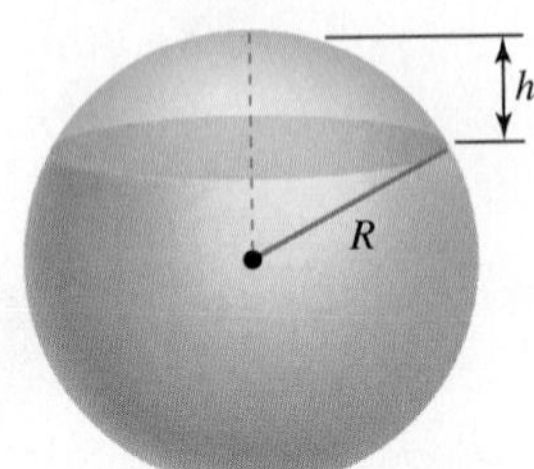

58. Frustum of a cone Find the volume of a truncated cone of height h whose ends have radii r and R.

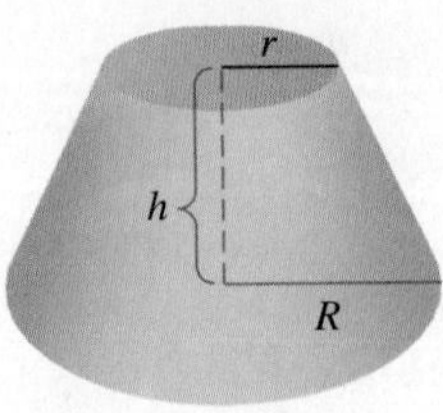

59. Ellipsoid Find the volume of an ellipsoid with axes of length $2a$, $2b$, and $2c$.

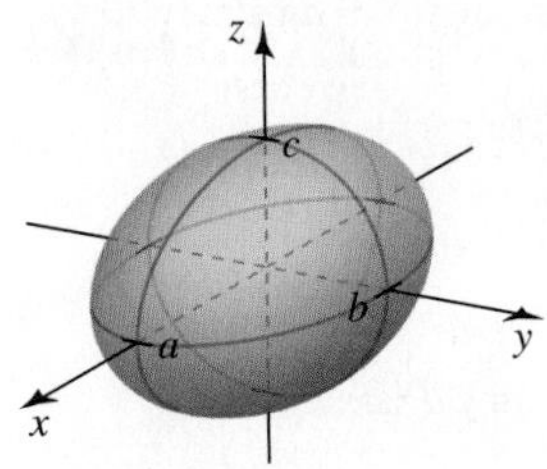

60. Exponential distribution The occurrence of random events (such as phone calls or e-mail messages) is often idealized using an exponential distribution. If λ is the average rate of occurrence of such an event, assumed to be constant over time, then the average time between occurrences is λ^{-1} (for example, if phone calls arrive at a rate of $\lambda = 2/\text{min}$, then the mean time between phone calls is $\lambda^{-1} = \frac{1}{2}$ min). The exponential distribution is given by $f(t) = \lambda e^{-\lambda t}$, for $0 \le t \le \infty$.

a. Suppose you work at a customer service desk and phone calls arrive at an average rate of $\lambda_1 = 0.8/\text{min}$ (meaning the average time between phone calls is $1/0.8 = 1.25$ min). The probability that a phone call arrives during the interval $[0, T]$ is $p(T) = \int_0^T \lambda_1 e^{-\lambda_1 t}\, dt$. Find the probability that a phone call arrives during the first 45 s (0.75 min) that you work at the desk.

b. Now suppose that walk-in customers also arrive at your desk at an average rate of $\lambda_2 = 0.1/\text{min}$. The probability that a phone call *and* a customer arrive during the interval $[0, T]$ is $p(T) = \int_0^T \int_0^T \lambda_1 e^{-\lambda_1 t} \lambda_2 e^{-\lambda_2 s}\, dt\, ds$. Find the probability that a phone call and a customer arrive during the first 45 s that you work at the desk.

c. E-mail messages also arrive at your desk at an average rate of $\lambda_3 = 0.05/\text{min}$. The probability that a phone call *and* a customer *and* an e-mail message arrive during the interval $[0, T]$ is $p(T) = \int_0^T \int_0^T \int_0^T \lambda_1 e^{-\lambda_1 t} \lambda_2 e^{-\lambda_2 s} \lambda_3 e^{-\lambda_3 u}\, dt\, ds\, du$. Find the probability that a phone call and a customer and an e-mail message arrive during the first 45 s that you work at the desk.

Additional Exercises

61. Hypervolume Find the volume of the four-dimensional pyramid bounded by $w + x + y + z + 1 = 0$ and the coordinate planes $w = 0, x = 0, y = 0, z = 0$.

62. An identity (Putnam Exam 1941) Let f be a continuous function on $[0, 1]$. Prove that

$$\int_0^1 \int_x^1 \int_x^y f(x)f(y)f(z)\,dz\,dy\,dx = \frac{1}{6}\left(\int_0^1 f(x)\,dx\right)^3.$$

QUICK CHECK ANSWERS

1. $dx\,dy\,dz, dx\,dz\,dy, dy\,dx\,dz, dy\,dz\,dx, dz\,dx\,dy, dz\,dy\,dx$

2. $\int_0^1 \int_0^2 \int_0^3 (2 - z)\,dx\,dy\,dz, \int_0^2 \int_0^1 \int_0^3 (2 - z)\,dx\,dz\,dy$

3. $\int_0^2 \int_0^{4-2x} \int_0^6 dz\,dy\,dx, \int_0^6 \int_0^4 \int_0^{2-y/2} dx\,dy\,dz$

4. 0 ($\sin x$, $\sin y$ and $\sin z$ are odd functions.)

14.5 Triple Integrals in Cylindrical and Spherical Coordinates

When evaluating triple integrals, you may have noticed that some regions (such as spheres, cones, and cylinders) have awkward descriptions in Cartesian coordinates. In this section we examine two other coordinate systems in $\mathbf{R}^3$ that are easier to use when working with certain types of regions. These coordinate systems are helpful not only for integration, but also for general problem solving.

Cylindrical Coordinates

When we extend polar coordinates from $\mathbf{R}^2$ to $\mathbf{R}^3$, the result is *cylindrical coordinates*. In this coordinate system, a point P in $\mathbf{R}^3$ has coordinates (r, θ, z), where r is the distance between P and the z-axis and θ is the usual polar angle measured counterclockwise from the positive x-axis. As in Cartesian coordinates, the z-coordinate is the signed vertical distance between P and the xy-plane (Figure 14.46). Any point in $\mathbf{R}^3$ can be represented by cylindrical coordinates using the intervals $0 \le r < \infty, 0 \le \theta \le 2\pi$, and $-\infty < z < \infty$.

➤ In cylindrical coordinates, r and θ are the usual polar coordinates, with the additional restriction that $r \ge 0$.

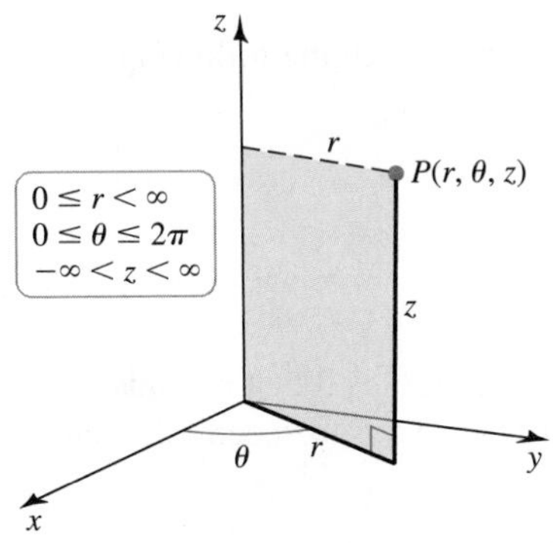

FIGURE 14.46

Many sets of points have simple representations in cylindrical coordinates. For example, the set $\{(r, \theta, z): r = a\}$ is the set of points whose distance from the z-axis is a, which is a right circular cylinder of radius a. The set $\{(r, \theta, z): \theta = \theta_0\}$ is the set of points with a constant θ coordinate; it is a vertical half plane emanating from the z-axis in the direction $\theta = \theta_0$. Table 14.4 summarizes these and other sets that are ideal for integration in cylindrical coordinates.

Table 14.4

Name	Description	Example
Cylinder	$\{(r, \theta, z): r = a\}, a > 0$	
Cylindrical shell	$\{(r, \theta, z): 0 < a \le r \le b\}$	

Table 14.4 (Continued)

Name	Description	Example
Vertical half plane	$\{(r, \theta, z): \theta = \theta_0\}$	
Horizontal plane	$\{(r, \theta, z): z = a\}$	
Cone	$\{(r, \theta, z): z = ar\}, a \neq 0$	

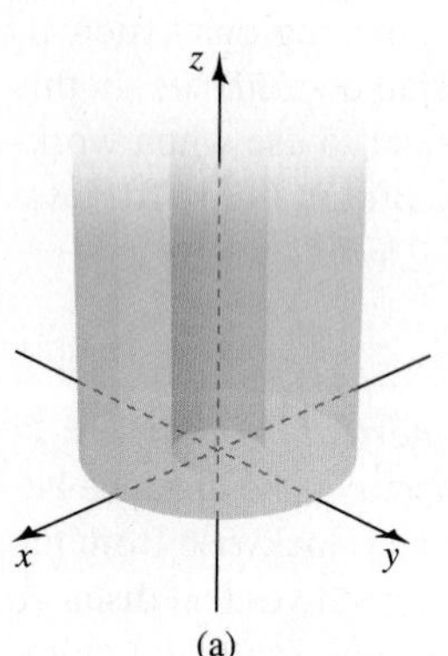

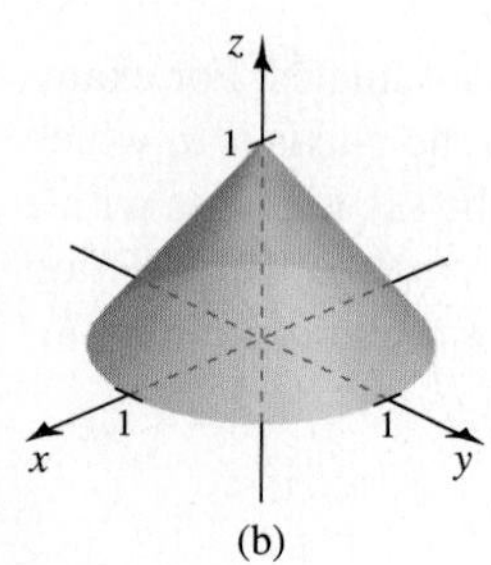

FIGURE 14.47

EXAMPLE 1 Sets in cylindrical coordinates Identify and sketch the following sets in cylindrical coordinates.

a. $Q = \{(r, \theta, z): 1 \leq r \leq 3, z \geq 0\}$

b. $S = \{(r, \theta, z): z = 1 - r, 0 \leq r \leq 1\}$

SOLUTION

a. The set Q is a cylindrical shell with inner radius 1 and outer radius 3 that extends indefinitely along the positive z-axis (Figure 14.47a). Because θ is unspecified, it takes on all values.

b. To identify this solid, it helps to work in steps. The set $S_1 = \{(r, \theta, z): z = r\}$ is a cone that opens *upward* with its vertex at the origin. Similarly, the set $S_2 = \{(r, \theta, z): z = -r\}$ is a cone that opens *downward* with its vertex at the origin. Therefore, S is S_2 shifted vertically upward by one unit; it is a cone that opens downward with its vertex at (0, 0, 1). Because $0 \leq r \leq 1$, the base of the cone is on the xy-plane (Figure 14.47b).

Related Exercises 11–14 ◄

Equations for transforming Cartesian coordinates to cylindrical coordinates, and vice versa, are often needed for integration. We simply use the rules for polar coordinates (Section 11.2) with no change in the z-coordinate (Figure 14.48).

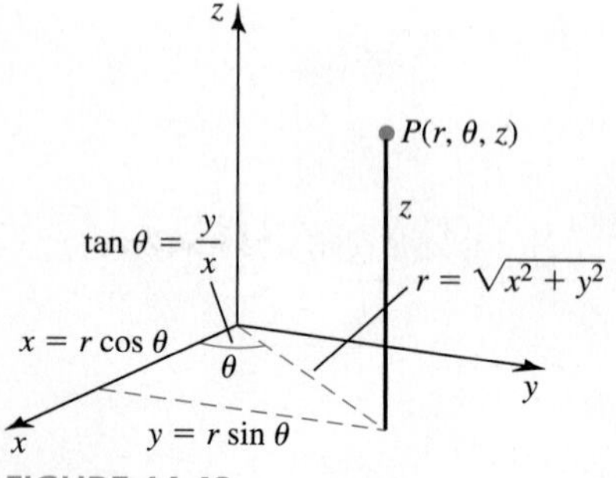

FIGURE 14.48

Transformations Between Cylindrical and Rectangular Coordinates

Rectangular → Cylindrical	**Cylindrical → Rectangular**
$r^2 = x^2 + y^2$	$x = r\cos\theta$
$\tan\theta = y/x$	$y = r\sin\theta$
$z = z$	$z = z$

QUICK CHECK 1 Find the cylindrical coordinates of the point with rectangular coordinates $(1, -1, 5)$. Find the rectangular coordinates of the point with cylindrical coordinates $(2, \pi/3, 5)$. ◀

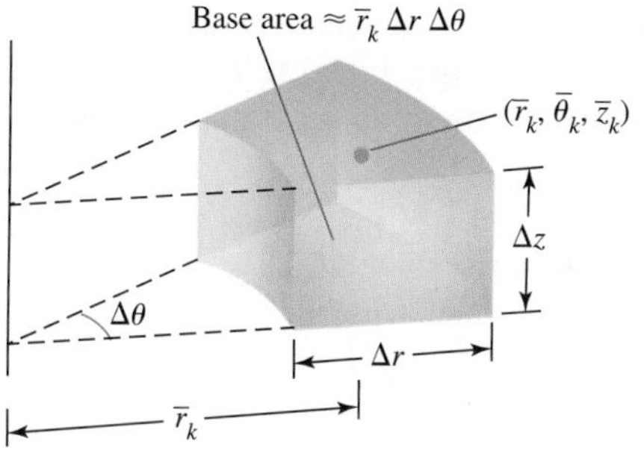

Integration in Cylindrical Coordinates

Base area $\approx \bar{r}_k\,\Delta r\,\Delta\theta$

$(\bar{r}_k, \bar{\theta}_k, \bar{z}_k)$ Δz $\Delta\theta$ Δr $\bar{r}_k$

Approximate volume $\Delta V_k \approx \bar{r}_k\,\Delta r\,\Delta\theta\,\Delta z$

FIGURE 14.49

Among the uses of cylindrical coordinates is the evaluation of triple integrals. We begin with a region D in $\mathbf{R}^3$ and partition it into cylindrical wedges formed by changes of Δr, $\Delta\theta$, and Δz in the coordinate directions (Figure 14.49). Those wedges that lie entirely within D are labeled from $k = 1$ to $k = n$ in some convenient order. We let $(\bar{r}_k, \bar{\theta}_k, \bar{z}_k)$ be an arbitrary point in the kth wedge.

As shown in Figure 14.49, the base of the kth wedge is a polar rectangle with an approximate area of $\bar{r}_k\,\Delta r\,\Delta\theta$ (Section 14.3). The height of the wedge is Δz. Multiplying these dimensions together, the approximate volume of the wedge is $\Delta V_k = \bar{r}_k\,\Delta r\,\Delta\theta\,\Delta z$, for $k = 1, \ldots, n$.

We now assume that f is continuous on D and form a Riemann sum over the region by adding function values multiplied by the corresponding approximate volumes:

$$\sum_{k=1}^{n} f(\bar{r}_k, \bar{\theta}_k, \bar{z}_k)\Delta V_k = \sum_{k=1}^{n} f(\bar{r}_k, \bar{\theta}_k, \bar{z}_k)\,\bar{r}_k\,\Delta r\,\Delta\theta\,\Delta z$$

Let Δ be the maximum value of Δr, $\Delta\theta$, and Δz, for $k = 1, 2, \ldots, n$. As $n \to \infty$ and $\Delta \to 0$, the Riemann sums approach a limit called the **triple integral of f over D in cylindrical coordinates**:

$$\lim_{\Delta\to 0}\sum_{k=1}^{n} f(\bar{r}_k, \bar{\theta}_k, \bar{z}_k)\,\bar{r}_k\,\Delta r\,\Delta\theta\,\Delta z = \iiint_D f(r, \theta, z)\,dV.$$

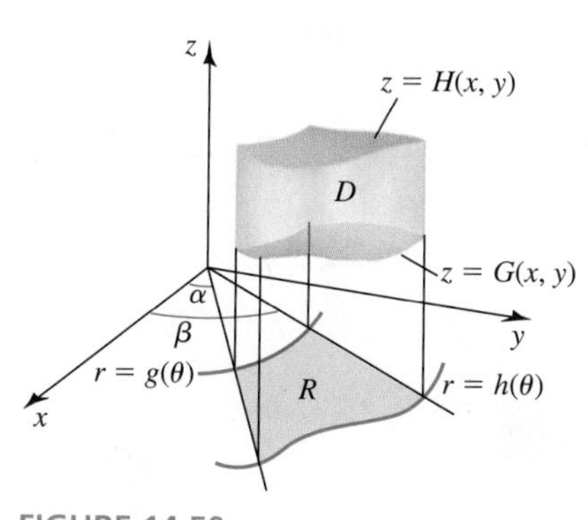

FIGURE 14.50

Finding Limits of Integration We show how to find the limits of integration in one common situation involving cylindrical coordinates. Suppose D is a region in $\mathbf{R}^3$ consisting of points between the surfaces $z = G(x, y)$ and $z = H(x, y)$, where x and y belong to a region R in the xy-plane and $G(x, y) \le H(x, y)$ on R (Figure 14.50). Assuming f is continuous on D, the triple integral of f over D may be expressed as the iterated integral

$$\iiint_D f(x, y, z)\,dV = \iint_R \left[\int_{G(x,y)}^{H(x,y)} f(x, y, z)\,dz\right] dA.$$

The inner integral with respect to z runs from the lower surface $z = G(x, y)$ to the upper surface $z = H(x, y)$, leaving an outer double integral over R.

If the region R is described in polar coordinates by

$$\{(r, \theta): g(\theta) \le r \le h(\theta), \alpha \le \theta \le \beta\},$$

then it makes sense to evaluate the double integral over R in polar coordinates (Section 14.3). The effect is a change of variables from rectangular to cylindrical coordinates. Letting $x = r\cos\theta$ and $y = r\sin\theta$, we have the following result, which is another version of Fubini's Theorem.

THEOREM 14.6 Triple Integrals in Cylindrical Coordinates
Let f be continuous over the region

$$D = \{(r, \theta, z): g(\theta) \le r \le h(\theta), \alpha \le \theta \le \beta, G(x, y) \le z \le H(x, y)\}.$$

Then f is integrable over D and the triple integral of f over D in cylindrical coordinates is

$$\iiint_D f(r, \theta, z)\, dV = \int_\alpha^\beta \int_{g(\theta)}^{h(\theta)} \int_{G(r\cos\theta,\, r\sin\theta)}^{H(r\cos\theta,\, r\sin\theta)} f(r, \theta, z)\, dz\, r\, dr\, d\theta.$$

➤ The order of the differentials specifies the order in which the integrals are evaluated, so we write the volume element as $dz\, r\, dr\, d\theta$. Do not lose sight of the factor of r in the integrand! It plays the same role as it does in the area element $dA = r\, dr\, d\theta$ in polar coordinates.

Notice that the integrand and the limits of integration are converted from Cartesian to cylindrical coordinates. As with triple integrals in Cartesian coordinates, there are two immediate interpretations of this integral. If $f = 1$, then the triple integral $\iiint_D dV$ equals the volume of the region D. Also, if f describes the density of an object occupying the region D, the triple integral equals the mass of the object.

EXAMPLE 2 Switching coordinate systems Evaluate the integral

$$I = \int_0^{2\sqrt{2}} \int_{-\sqrt{8-x^2}}^{\sqrt{8-x^2}} \int_{-1}^{2} \sqrt{1 + x^2 + y^2}\, dz\, dy\, dx.$$

SOLUTION Evaluating this integral as it is given in Cartesian coordinates requires a tricky trigonometric substitution in the middle integral, followed by an even more difficult integral. Notice that z varies between the planes $z = -1$ and $z = 2$, while x and y vary over half of a disk in the xy-plane. Therefore, D is half of a solid cylinder (Figure 14.51a), which suggests a change to cylindrical coordinates.

The limits of integration in cylindrical coordinates are determined as follows:

Inner integral with respect to z A line through the half cylinder parallel to the z-axis enters at $z = -1$ and leaves at $z = 2$, so we integrate over the interval $-1 \le z \le 2$ (Figure 14.51b).

Middle integral with respect to r The projection of the half cylinder onto the xy-plane is the half disk R of radius $2\sqrt{2}$ centered at the origin, so r varies over the interval $0 \le r \le 2\sqrt{2}$.

Outer integral with respect to θ The half disk R is swept out by letting θ vary over the interval $-\pi/2 \le \theta \le \pi/2$ (Figure 14.51c).

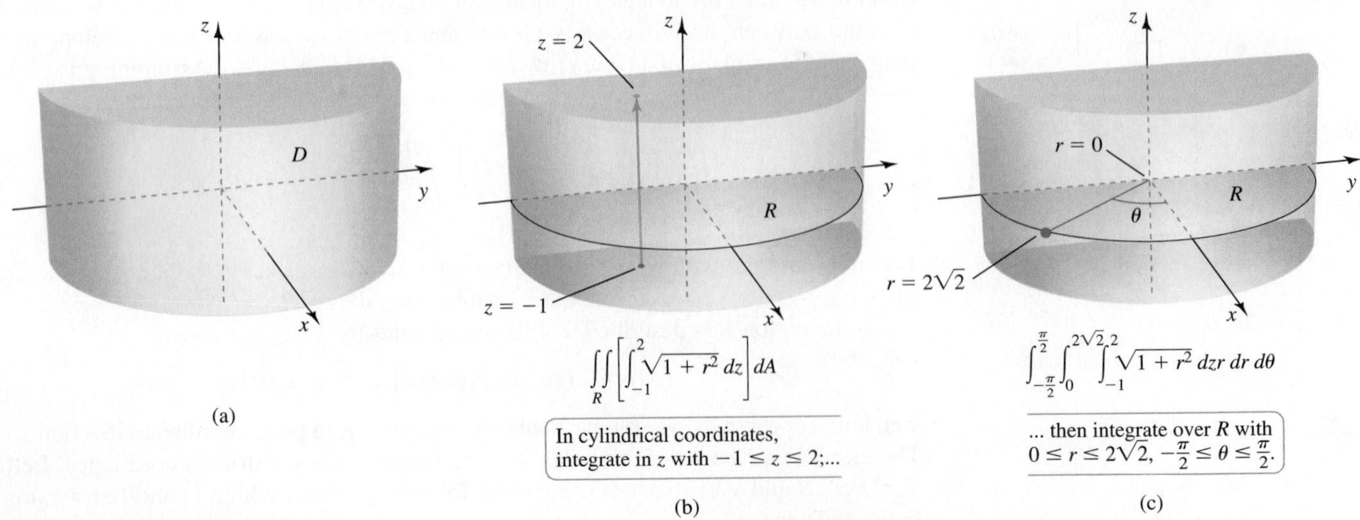

FIGURE 14.51

We also convert the integrand to cylindrical coordinates:

$$f(x, y, z) = \sqrt{1 + \underbrace{x^2 + y^2}_{r^2}} = \sqrt{1 + r^2}.$$

The evaluation of the integral in cylindrical coordinates now follows:

$$I = \int_{-\pi/2}^{\pi/2} \int_0^{2\sqrt{2}} \int_{-1}^{2} \sqrt{1 + r^2}\, dz\, r\, dr\, d\theta \quad \text{Convert to cylindrical coordinates.}$$

$$= 3 \int_{-\pi/2}^{\pi/2} \int_0^{2\sqrt{2}} \sqrt{1 + r^2}\, r\, dr\, d\theta \quad \text{Evaluate the inner integral.}$$

$$= \int_{-\pi/2}^{\pi/2} (1 + r^2)^{3/2} \Big|_0^{2\sqrt{2}}\, d\theta \quad \text{Evaluate the middle integral.}$$

$$= \int_{-\pi/2}^{\pi/2} 26\, d\theta = 26\pi \quad \text{Evaluate the outer integral.}$$

Related Exercises 15–22 ◀

QUICK CHECK 2 Find the limits of integration for a triple integral in cylindrical coordinates that gives the volume of a cylinder with height 20 and a circular base centered at the origin in the xy-plane of radius 10. ◀

As illustrated in Example 2, triple integrals given in rectangular coordinates may be more easily evaluated after converting to cylindrical coordinates. The following questions may help you choose the best coordinate system for a particular integral.

- In which coordinate system is the region of integration most easily described?
- In which coordinate system is the integrand most easily expressed?
- In which coordinate system is the triple integral most easily evaluated?

In general, if an integral in one coordinate system looks difficult, consider using a different coordinate system.

EXAMPLE 3 **Mass of a solid paraboloid** Find the mass of the solid D bounded by the paraboloid $z = 4 - r^2$ and the plane $z = 0$ (Figure 14.52a) when the density of the region is $f(r, \theta, z) = 5 - z$ (heavy near the base and light near the vertex).

SOLUTION The z-coordinate runs from the base ($z = 0$) to the surface $z = 4 - r^2$ (Figure 14.52b). The projection R of the region D onto the xy-plane is found by setting

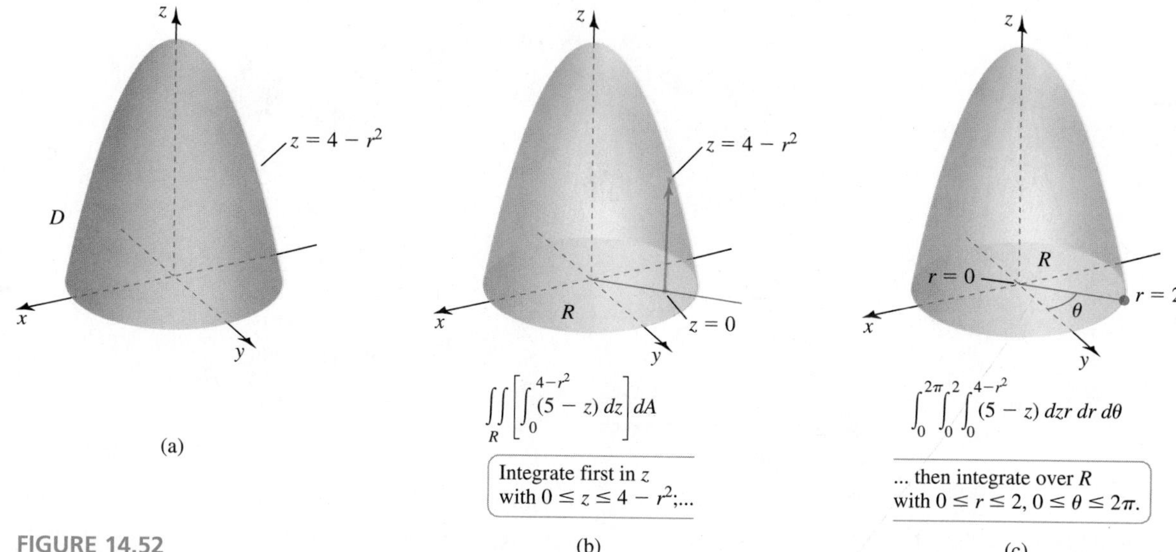

FIGURE 14.52

$z = 0$ in the equation of the surface, $z = 4 - r^2$. Solving $4 - r^2 = 0$ (and discarding the negative root), we have $r = 2$, so $R = \{(r, \theta): 0 \le r \le 2, 0 \le \theta \le 2\pi\}$ is a disk of radius 2 (Figure 14.52c).

The mass is computed by integrating the density function over D:

> In Example 3, the integrand is independent of θ, so the integral with respect to θ could have been done first, producing a factor of 2π.

$$\iiint_D f(r, \theta, z)\, dV = \int_0^{2\pi} \int_0^2 \int_0^{4-r^2} (5 - z)\, dz\, r\, dr\, d\theta \quad \text{Integrate the density.}$$

$$= \int_0^{2\pi} \int_0^2 \left(5z - \frac{z^2}{2}\right)\Bigg|_0^{4-r^2} r\, dr\, d\theta \quad \text{Evaluate the inner integral.}$$

$$= \frac{1}{2}\int_0^{2\pi} \int_0^2 (24r - 2r^3 - r^5)\, dr\, d\theta \quad \text{Simplify.}$$

$$= \int_0^{2\pi} \frac{44}{3}\, d\theta \quad \text{Evaluate the middle integral.}$$

$$= \frac{88\pi}{3} \quad \text{Evaluate the outer integral.}$$

Related Exercises 23–28 ◄

> Recall that to find the volume of a region D using a triple integral, we set $f = 1$ and evaluate
> $$V = \iiint_D dV.$$

EXAMPLE 4 Volume between two surfaces Find the volume of the solid D between the cone $z = \sqrt{x^2 + y^2}$ and the inverted paraboloid $z = 12 - x^2 - y^2$ (Figure 14.53a).

SOLUTION Because $x^2 + y^2 = r^2$, the equation of the cone becomes $z = r$, and the equation of the paraboloid becomes $z = 12 - r^2$. The inner integral in z runs from the cone $z = r$ (the lower surface) to the paraboloid $z = 12 - r^2$ (the upper surface) (Figure 14.53b). We project D onto the xy-plane to produce the region R, whose boundary is determined by the intersection of the two surfaces. Equating the z-coordinates in the equations of the two surfaces, we have $12 - r^2 = r$, or $(r - 3)(r + 4) = 0$. Because $r \ge 0$, the relevant root is $r = 3$. Therefore, the projection of D on the xy-plane is $R = \{(r, \theta): 0 \le r \le 3, 0 \le \theta \le 2\pi\}$, which is a disk of radius 3 centered at $(0, 0)$ (Figure 14.53c).

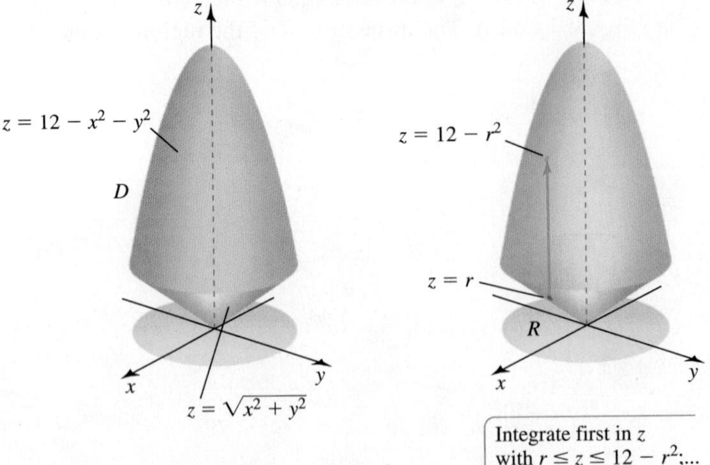

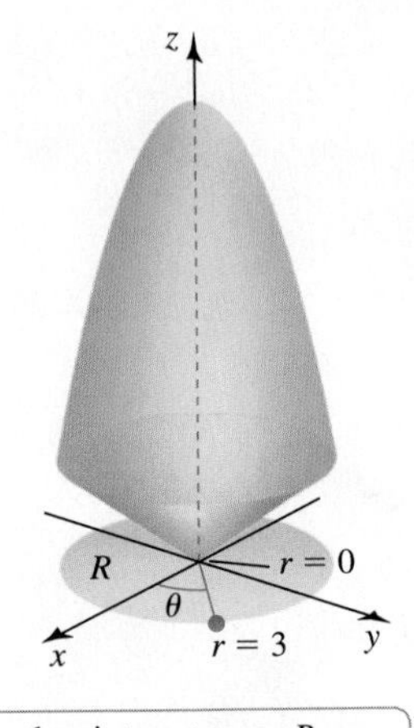

FIGURE 14.53

The volume of the region is

$$\iiint_D dV = \int_0^{2\pi}\int_0^3\int_r^{12-r^2} dz\, r\, dr\, d\theta$$

$$= \int_0^{2\pi}\int_0^3 (12 - r^2 - r)\, r\, dr\, d\theta \quad \text{Evaluate the inner integral.}$$

$$= \int_0^{2\pi} \frac{99}{4}\, d\theta \quad \text{Evaluate the middle integral.}$$

$$= \frac{99\pi}{2}. \quad \text{Evaluate the outer integral.}$$

Related Exercises 29–34

Spherical Coordinates

In spherical coordinates, a point P in $\mathbf{R}^3$ is represented by three coordinates (ρ, φ, θ) (Figure 14.54):

- ρ is the distance from the origin to P.
- φ is the angle between the positive z-axis and the line OP.
- θ is the same angle as in cylindrical coordinates; it measures rotation about the z-axis relative to the positive x-axis.

➤ The coordinate ρ (pronounced "rho") in spherical coordinates should not be confused with r in cylindrical coordinates, which is the distance from P to the z-axis.

➤ The coordinate φ is called the *colatitude* because it is $\pi/2$ minus the latitude of points in the northern hemisphere. Physicists may reverse the roles of θ and φ; that is, θ is the colatitude and φ is the polar angle. Use caution!

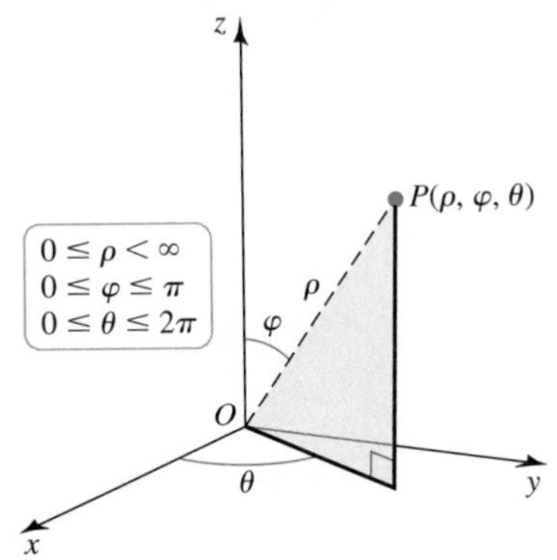

FIGURE 14.54

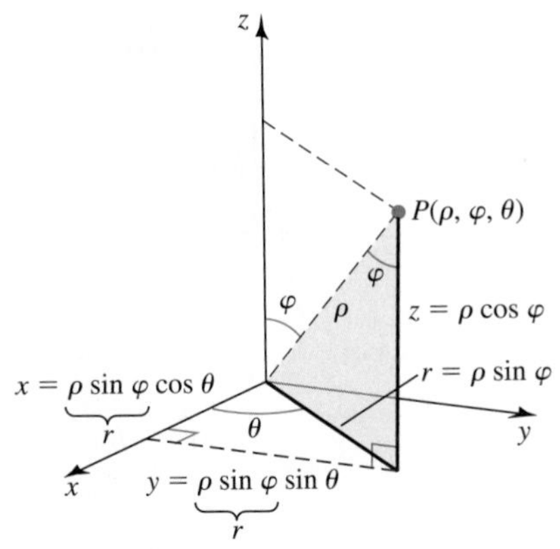

FIGURE 14.55

All points in $\mathbf{R}^3$ can be represented by spherical coordinates using the intervals $0 \le \rho < \infty$, $0 \le \varphi \le \pi$, and $0 \le \theta \le 2\pi$.

Figure 14.55 allows us to find the relationships among rectangular and spherical coordinates. Given the spherical coordinates (ρ, φ, θ) of a point P, the distance from P to the z-axis is $r = \rho \sin \varphi$. We also see from Figure 14.55 that $x = r\cos\theta = \rho \sin\varphi\cos\theta$, $y = r\sin\theta = \rho\sin\varphi\sin\theta$, and $z = \rho\cos\varphi$.

Transformations Between Spherical and Rectangular Coordinates

Rectangular → Spherical	**Spherical → Rectangular**
$\rho^2 = x^2 + y^2 + z^2$	$x = \rho \sin\varphi \cos\theta$
Use trigonometry to find	$y = \rho \sin\varphi \sin\theta$
φ and θ	$z = \rho\cos\varphi$

QUICK CHECK 3 Find the spherical coordinates of the point with rectangular coordinates $(1, \sqrt{3}, 2)$. Find the rectangular coordinates of the point with spherical coordinates $(2, \pi/4, \pi/4)$.

In spherical coordinates, some sets of points have simple representations. For instance, the set $\{(\rho, \varphi, \theta): \rho = a\}$ is the set of points whose ρ coordinate is constant, which is a sphere of radius a centered at the origin. The set $\{(\rho, \varphi, \theta): \varphi = \varphi_0\}$ is the set of points with a constant φ-coordinate; it is a cone with its vertex at the origin and whose sides make an angle φ_0 with the positive z-axis.

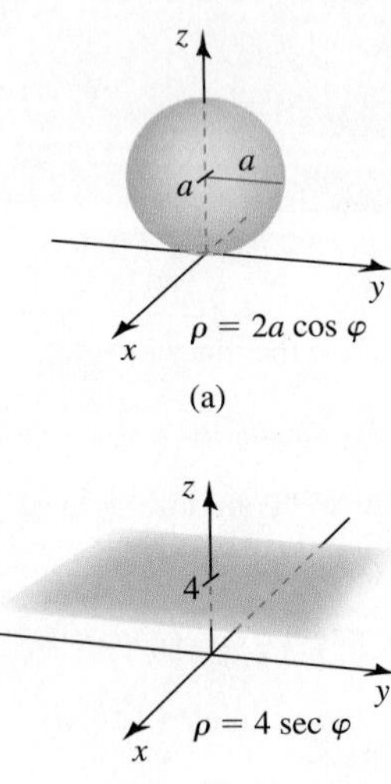

FIGURE 14.56

EXAMPLE 5 Sets in spherical coordinates Express the following sets in rectangular coordinates and identify the set. Assume that a is a positive real number.

a. $\{(\rho, \varphi, \theta): \rho = 2a \cos \varphi, 0 \leq \varphi \leq \pi/2, 0 \leq \theta \leq 2\pi\}$

b. $\{(\rho, \varphi, \theta): \rho = 4 \sec \varphi, 0 \leq \varphi < \pi/2, 0 \leq \theta \leq 2\pi\}$

SOLUTION

a. To avoid working with square roots, we multiply both sides of $\rho = 2a \cos \varphi$ by ρ to obtain $\rho^2 = 2a\,\rho \cos \varphi$. Substituting rectangular coordinates we have $x^2 + y^2 + z^2 = 2az$. Completing the square results in the equation

$$x^2 + y^2 + (z - a)^2 = a^2.$$

This is the equation of a sphere centered at $(0, 0, a)$ with radius a (Figure 14.56a). With the limits $0 \leq \varphi \leq \pi/2$ and $0 \leq \theta \leq 2\pi$, the set describes a full sphere.

b. The equation $\rho = 4 \sec \varphi$ is first written $\rho \cos \varphi = 4$. Noting that $z = \rho \cos \varphi$, the set consists of all points with $z = 4$, which is a horizontal plane (Figure 14.56b).

Related Exercises 35–38 ◀

Table 14.5 summarizes some sets that have simple descriptions in spherical coordinates.

Table 14.5

Name	Description	Example
Sphere, radius a, center $(0, 0, 0)$	$\{(\rho, \varphi, \theta): \rho = a\}, a > 0$	
Cone	$\{(\rho, \varphi, \theta): \varphi = \varphi_0\}, \varphi_0 \neq 0, \pi/2, \pi$	
Vertical half plane	$\{(\rho, \varphi, \theta): \theta = \theta_0\}$	

➤ Notice that the set (ρ, φ, θ) with $\varphi = \pi/2$ is the xy-plane and if $\pi/2 < \varphi_0 < \pi$, the set $\varphi = \varphi_0$ is a cone that opens downward.

(Continued)

Table 14.5 (Continued)

Name	Description	Example
Horizontal plane, $z = a$	$\{(\rho, \varphi, \theta): \rho = a \sec \varphi, 0 \le \varphi < \pi/2\}$	
Cylinder, radius	$\{(\rho, \varphi, \theta): \rho = a \csc \varphi, 0 < \varphi < \pi\}$, $a > 0$	
Sphere, radius a, center $(0, 0, a)$	$\{(\rho, \varphi, \theta): \rho = 2a \cos \varphi, 0 \le \varphi \le \pi/2\}$, $a > 0$	

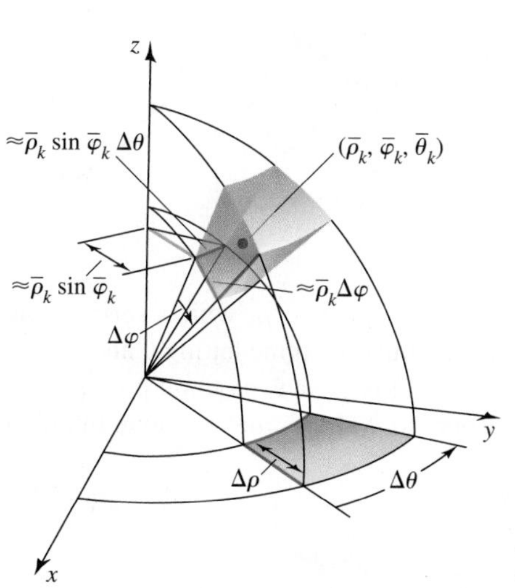

Approximate volume = $\Delta V_k \approx \bar{\rho}_k^2 \sin \bar{\varphi}_k \,\Delta\rho\, \Delta\varphi\, \Delta\theta$

FIGURE 14.57

➤ Recall that the length s of a circular arc of radius r subtended by an angle θ is $s = r\theta$.

Integration in Spherical Coordinates

We now investigate triple integrals in spherical coordinates over a region D in $\mathbf{R}^3$. The region D is partitioned into "spherical boxes" that are formed by changes of $\Delta\rho$, $\Delta\varphi$, and $\Delta\theta$ in the coordinate directions (Figure 14.57). Those boxes that lie entirely within D are labeled from $k = 1$ to $k = n$. We let $(\bar{\rho}_k, \bar{\varphi}_k, \bar{\theta}_k)$ be an arbitrary point in the kth box.

To approximate the volume of a typical box, note that the length of the box in the ρ-direction is $\Delta\rho$ (Figure 14.57). The approximate length of the kth box in the θ-direction is the length of an arc of a circle of radius $\bar{\rho}_k \sin \bar{\varphi}_k$ subtended by an angle $\Delta\theta$; this length is $\bar{\rho}_k \sin \bar{\varphi}_k \Delta\theta$. The approximate length of the box in the φ-direction is the length of an arc of radius $\bar{\rho}_k$ subtended by an angle $\Delta\varphi$; this length is $\bar{\rho}_k \Delta\varphi$. Multiplying these dimensions together, the approximate volume of the kth spherical box is $\Delta V_k = \bar{\rho}_k^{\,2} \sin \bar{\varphi}_k \Delta\rho\, \Delta\varphi\, \Delta\theta$, for $k = 1, \ldots, n$.

We now assume that f is continuous on D and form a Riemann sum over the region by adding function values multiplied by the corresponding approximate volumes:

$$\sum_{k=1}^{n} f(\bar{\rho}_k, \bar{\varphi}_k, \bar{\theta}_k)\, \Delta V_k = \sum_{k=1}^{n} f(\bar{\rho}_k, \bar{\varphi}_k, \bar{\theta}_k) \bar{\rho}_k^{\,2} \sin \bar{\varphi}_k \Delta\rho\, \Delta\varphi\, \Delta\theta.$$

We let Δ denote the maximum value of $\Delta\rho$, $\Delta\varphi$, and $\Delta\theta$. As $n \to \infty$ and $\Delta \to 0$, the Riemann sums approach a limit called the **triple integral of f over D in spherical coordinates**:

$$\lim_{\Delta \to 0} \sum_{k=1}^{n} f(\bar{\rho}_k, \bar{\varphi}_k, \bar{\theta}_k)\, \bar{\rho}_k^{\,2} \sin \bar{\varphi}_k \Delta\rho\, \Delta\varphi\, \Delta\theta = \iiint_D f(\rho, \varphi, \theta)\, dV$$

Finding Limits of Integration We consider a common situation in which the region of integration has the form

$$D = \{(\rho, \varphi, \theta): g(\varphi, \theta) \le \rho \le h(\varphi, \theta), a \le \varphi \le b, \alpha \le \theta \le \beta\}.$$

In other words, D is bounded in the ρ-direction by two surfaces given by g and h. In the angular directions, the region lies between two cones ($a \le \varphi \le b$) and two half planes ($\alpha \le \theta \le \beta$) (Figure 14.58).

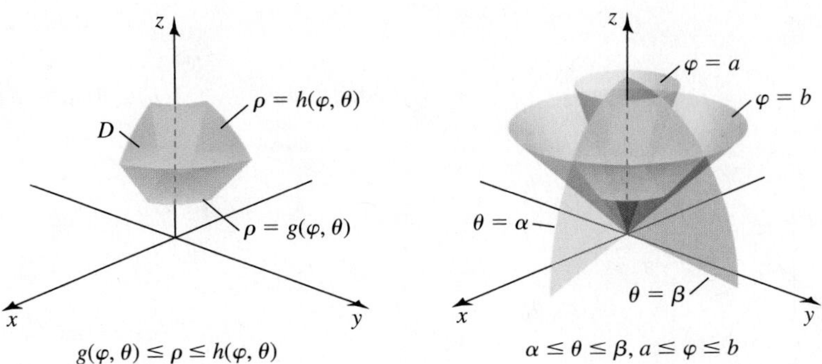

FIGURE 14.58

For this type of region, the inner integral is with respect to ρ, which varies from $\rho = g(\varphi, \theta)$ to $\rho = h(\varphi, \theta)$. As ρ varies between these limits, imagine letting θ and φ vary over the intervals $a \le \varphi \le b$ and $\alpha \le \theta \le \beta$. The effect is to sweep out all points of D. Notice that the middle and outer integrals, with respect to θ and φ, may be done in either order (Figure 14.59).

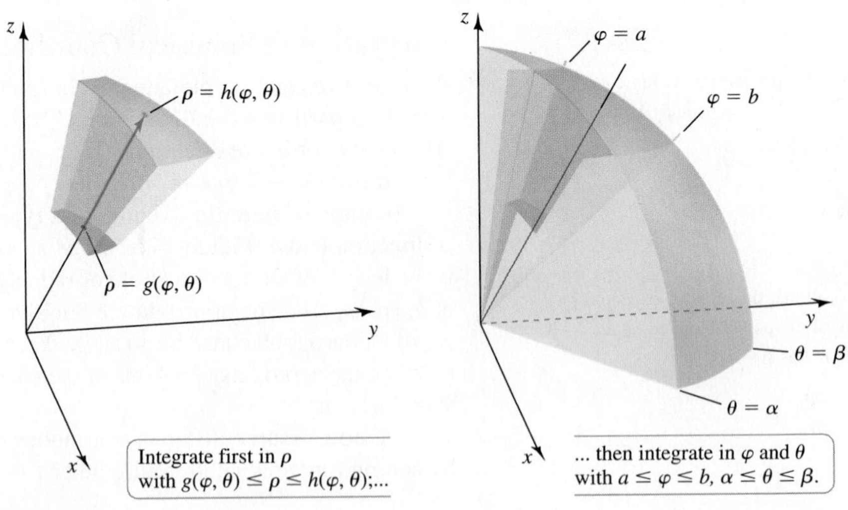

FIGURE 14.59

In summary, to integrate over D we

- first integrate with respect to ρ from $\rho = g(\varphi, \theta)$ to $\rho = h(\varphi, \theta)$,
- then integrate with respect to φ from $\varphi = a$ to $\varphi = b$, and
- finally integrate with respect to θ from $\theta = \alpha$ to $\theta = \beta$.

Another version of Fubini's Theorem expresses the triple integral as an iterated integral.

The element of volume in spherical coordinates is $dV = \rho^2 \sin\varphi \, d\rho \, d\varphi \, d\theta$.

THEOREM 14.7 Triple Integrals in Spherical Coordinates
Let f be continuous over the region

$$D = \{(\rho, \varphi, \theta): g(\varphi, \theta) \leq \rho \leq h(\varphi, \theta), a \leq \varphi \leq b, \alpha \leq \theta \leq \beta\}.$$

Then f is integrable over D and the triple integral of f over D in spherical coordinates is

$$\iiint_D f(\rho, \varphi, \theta) \, dV = \int_\alpha^\beta \int_a^b \int_{g(\varphi,\theta)}^{h(\varphi,\theta)} f(\rho, \varphi, \theta) \, \rho^2 \sin\varphi \, d\rho \, d\varphi \, d\theta.$$

If the integrand is given in terms of Cartesian coordinates x, y, and z, it must be expressed in spherical coordinates before integrating. As with other triple integrals, if $f = 1$, then the triple integral equals the volume of D. If f is a density function for an object occupying the region D, then the triple integral equals the mass of the object.

EXAMPLE 6 A triple integral Evaluate $\iiint_D (x^2 + y^2 + z^2)^{-3/2} \, dV$, where D is the region in the first octant between two spheres of radius 1 and 2 centered at the origin.

SOLUTION Both the integrand f and region D are greatly simplified when expressed in spherical coordinates. The integrand becomes

$$(x^2 + y^2 + z^2)^{-3/2} = (\rho^2)^{-3/2} = \rho^{-3},$$

while the region of integration is (Figure 14.60)

$$D = \{(\rho, \varphi, \theta): 1 \leq \rho \leq 2, 0 \leq \varphi \leq \pi/2, 0 \leq \theta \leq \pi/2\}.$$

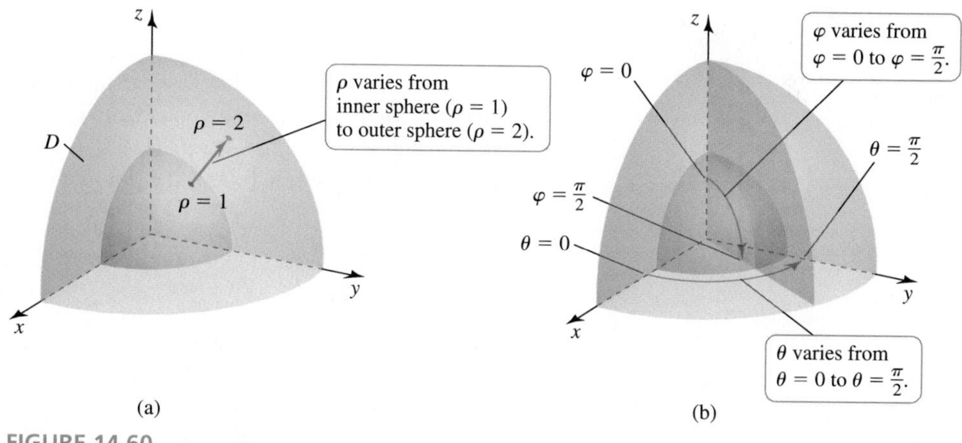

FIGURE 14.60

The integral is evaluated as follows:

$$\begin{aligned}
\iiint_D f(x, y, z) \, dV &= \int_0^{\pi/2} \int_0^{\pi/2} \int_1^2 \rho^{-3} \rho^2 \sin\varphi \, d\rho \, d\varphi \, d\theta && \text{Convert to spherical coordinates.} \\
&= \int_0^{\pi/2} \int_0^{\pi/2} \int_1^2 \rho^{-1} \sin\varphi \, d\rho \, d\varphi \, d\theta && \text{Simplify.} \\
&= \int_0^{\pi/2} \int_0^{\pi/2} (\ln \rho)\Big|_1^2 \sin\varphi \, d\varphi \, d\theta && \text{Evaluate the inner integral.}
\end{aligned}$$

$$= \ln 2 \int_0^{\pi/2} \int_0^{\pi/2} \sin \varphi \, d\varphi \, d\theta \qquad \text{Simplify.}$$

$$= \ln 2 \int_0^{\pi/2} (-\cos \varphi)\Big|_0^{\pi/2} d\theta \qquad \text{Evaluate the middle integral.}$$

$$= \ln 2 \int_0^{\pi/2} d\theta = \frac{\pi \ln 2}{2} \qquad \text{Evaluate the outer integral.}$$

Related Exercises 39–45 ◀

EXAMPLE 7 **Ice cream cone** Find the volume of the solid region D that lies inside the cone $\varphi = \pi/6$ and inside the sphere $\rho = 4$ (Figure 14.61a).

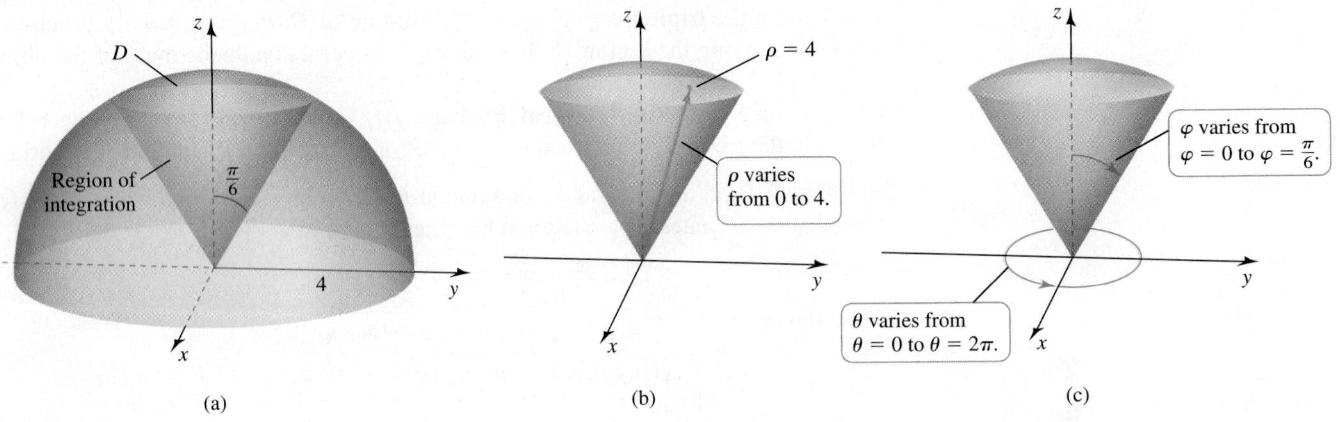

FIGURE 14.61

SOLUTION To find the volume, we evaluate a triple integral with $f(\rho, \varphi, \theta) = 1$. In the radial direction, the region extends from the origin $\rho = 0$ to the sphere $\rho = 4$. To sweep out all points of D, φ varies from 0 to $\pi/6$ and θ varies from 0 to 2π (Figure 14.61b,c). Integrating the function $f = 1$, the volume of the region is

$$\iiint_D dV = \int_0^{2\pi} \int_0^{\pi/6} \int_0^4 \rho^2 \sin \varphi \, d\rho \, d\varphi \, d\theta \qquad \text{Convert to an iterated integral.}$$

$$= \int_0^{2\pi} \int_0^{\pi/6} \left(\frac{\rho^3}{3}\right)\Big|_0^4 \sin \varphi \, d\varphi \, d\theta \qquad \text{Evaluate the inner integral.}$$

$$= \frac{64}{3} \int_0^{2\pi} \int_0^{\pi/6} \sin \varphi \, d\varphi \, d\theta \qquad \text{Simplify.}$$

$$= \frac{64}{3} \int_0^{2\pi} \underbrace{(-\cos \varphi)\Big|_0^{\pi/6}}_{1 - \sqrt{3}/2} d\theta \qquad \text{Evaluate the middle integral.}$$

$$= \frac{32}{3}(2 - \sqrt{3}) \int_0^{2\pi} d\theta \qquad \text{Simplify.}$$

$$= \frac{64\pi}{3}(2 - \sqrt{3}). \qquad \text{Evaluate the outer integral.}$$

Related Exercises 46–52 ◀

SECTION 14.5 EXERCISES

Review Questions

1. Explain how cylindrical coordinates are used to describe a point in $\mathbf{R}^3$.
2. Explain how spherical coordinates are used to describe a point in $\mathbf{R}^3$.
3. Describe the set $\{(r, \theta, z): r = 4z\}$ in cylindrical coordinates.
4. Describe the set $\{(\rho, \varphi, \theta): \varphi = \pi/4\}$ in spherical coordinates.
5. Explain why $dz\, r\, dr\, d\theta$ is the volume of a small "box" in cylindrical coordinates.
6. Explain why $\rho^2 \sin \varphi \, d\rho\, d\varphi\, d\theta$ is the volume of a small "box" in spherical coordinates.
7. Write the integral $\iiint_D f(r, \theta, z)\, dV$ as an iterated integral where $D = \{(r, \theta, z): G(r, \theta) \le z \le H(r, \theta), g(\theta) \le r \le h(\theta), \alpha \le \theta \le \beta\}$.
8. Write the integral $\iiint_D f(\rho, \varphi, \theta)\, dV$ as an iterated integral, where $D = \{(\rho, \varphi, \theta): g(\varphi, \theta) \le \rho \le h(\varphi, \theta), a \le \varphi \le b, \alpha \le \theta \le \beta\}$.
9. What coordinate system is *suggested* if the integrand of a triple integral involves $x^2 + y^2$?
10. What coordinate system is *suggested* if the integrand of a triple integral involves $x^2 + y^2 + z^2$?

Basic Skills

11–14. Sets in cylindrical coordinates *Identify and sketch the following sets in cylindrical coordinates.*

11. $\{(r, \theta, z): 0 \le r \le 3, 0 \le \theta \le \pi/3, 1 \le z \le 4\}$
12. $\{(r, \theta, z): 0 \le \theta \le \pi/2, z = 1\}$
13. $\{(r, \theta, z): 2r \le z \le 4\}$
14. $\{(r, \theta, z): 0 \le z \le 8 - 2r\}$

15–18. Integrals in cylindrical coordinates *Evaluate the following integrals in cylindrical coordinates.*

15. $\displaystyle\int_0^{2\pi}\int_0^1\int_{-1}^1 dz\, r\, dr\, d\theta$

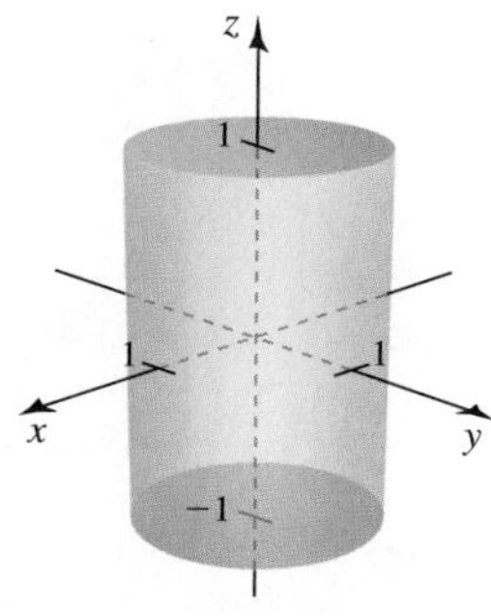

16. $\displaystyle\int_0^3\int_{-\sqrt{9-y^2}}^{\sqrt{9-y^2}}\int_0^{9-3\sqrt{x^2+y^2}} dz\, dx\, dy$

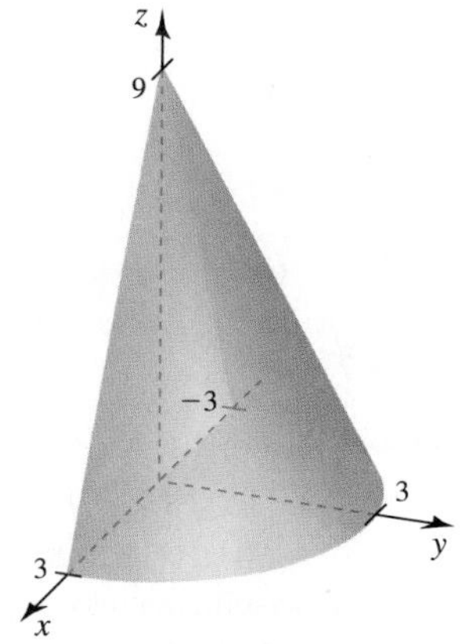

17. $\displaystyle\int_{-1}^1\int_{-\sqrt{1-y^2}}^{\sqrt{1-y^2}}\int_{-1}^1 (x^2 + y^2)^{3/2}\, dz\, dx\, dy$

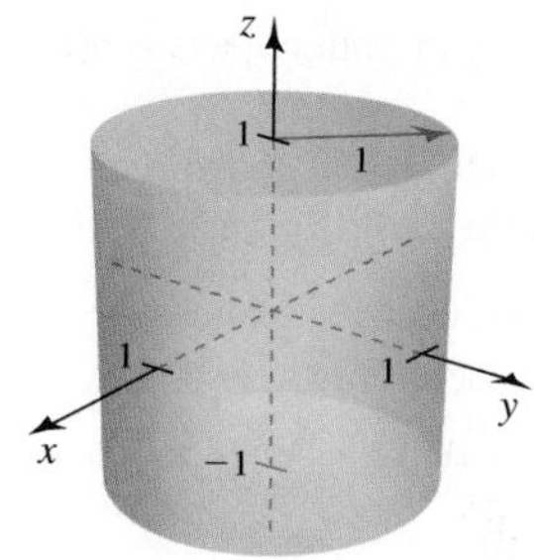

18. $\displaystyle\int_{-3}^3\int_0^{\sqrt{9-x^2}}\int_0^2 \frac{1}{1 + x^2 + y^2}\, dz\, dy\, dx$

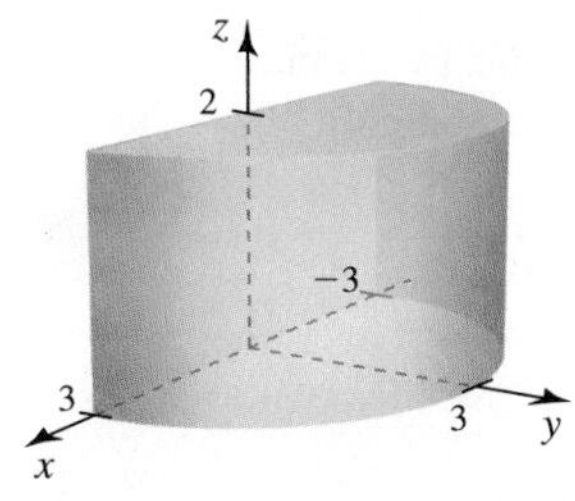

19–22. Integrals in cylindrical coordinates *Evaluate the following integrals in cylindrical coordinates.*

19. $\displaystyle\int_0^4\int_0^{\sqrt{2}/2}\int_x^{\sqrt{1-x^2}} e^{-x^2-y^2}\, dy\, dx\, dz$

20. $\displaystyle\int_{-4}^4\int_{-\sqrt{16-x^2}}^{\sqrt{16-x^2}}\int_{\sqrt{x^2+y^2}}^4 dz\, dy\, dx$

21. $\displaystyle\int_0^3\int_0^{\sqrt{9-x^2}}\int_0^{\sqrt{x^2+y^2}} (x^2 + y^2)^{-1/2}\, dz\, dy\, dx$

22. $\displaystyle\int_{-1}^{1}\int_{0}^{1/2}\int_{\sqrt{3}y}^{\sqrt{1-y^2}} (x^2 + y^2)^{1/2}\,dx\,dy\,dz$

23–26. Mass from density *Find the mass of the following objects with the given density functions.*

23. The solid cylinder $D = \{(r, \theta, z): 0 \le r \le 4, 0 \le z \le 10\}$ with density $\rho(r, \theta, z) = 1 + z/2$

24. The solid cylinder $D = \{(r, \theta, z): 0 \le r \le 3, 0 \le z \le 2\}$, with density $\rho(r, \theta, z) = 5e^{-r^2}$

25. The solid cone $D = \{(r, \theta, z): 0 \le z \le 6 - r, 0 \le r \le 6\}$ with density $\rho(r, \theta, z) = 7 - z$

26. The solid paraboloid $D = \{(r, \theta, z): 0 \le z \le 9 - r^2, 0 \le r \le 3\}$ with density $\rho(r, \theta, z) = 1 + z/9$

27. Which weighs more? For $0 \le r \le 1$, the solid bounded by the cone $z = 4 - 4r$ and the solid bounded by the paraboloid $z = 4 - 4r^2$ have the same base in the xy-plane and the same height. Which object has the greater mass if the density of both objects is $\rho(r, \theta, z) = 10 - 2z$?

28. Which weighs more? Which of the objects in Exercise 27 weighs more if the density of both objects is $\rho(r, \theta, z) = \dfrac{8}{\pi} e^{-z}$?

29–34. Volumes in cylindrical coordinates *Use cylindrical coordinates to find the volume of the following solid regions.*

29. The region bounded by the plane $z = 0$ and the hyperboloid $z = \sqrt{17} - \sqrt{1 + x^2 + y^2}$

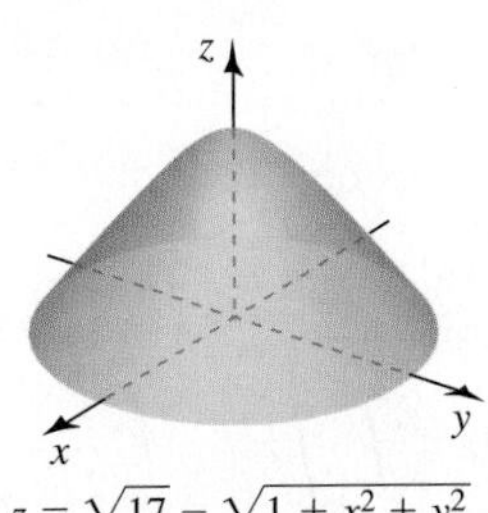

30. The region bounded by the plane $z = 25$ and the paraboloid $z = x^2 + y^2$

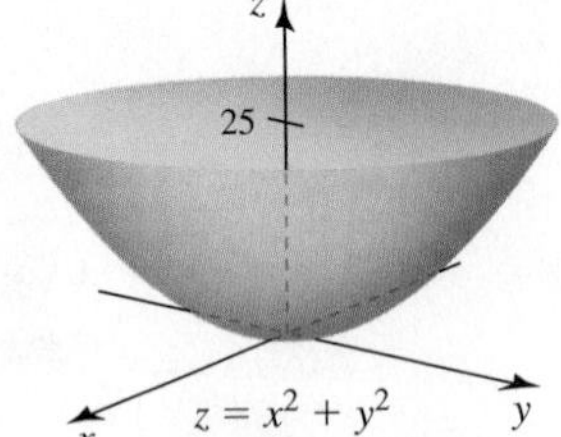

31. The region bounded by the plane $z = \sqrt{29}$ and the hyperboloid $z = \sqrt{4 + x^2 + y^2}$

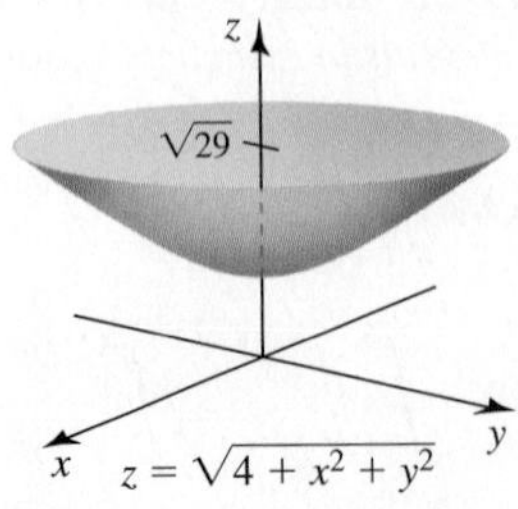

32. The solid cylinder whose height is 4 and whose base is the disk $\{(r, \theta): 0 \le r \le 2\cos\theta\}$

33. The region in the first octant bounded by the cylinder $r = 1$ and the plane $z = x$

34. The region bounded by the cylinders $r = 1$ and $r = 2$ and the planes $z = 4 - x - y$ and $z = 0$

35–38. Sets in spherical coordinates *Identify and sketch the following sets in spherical coordinates.*

35. $\{(\rho, \varphi, \theta): 1 \le \rho \le 3\}$

36. $\{(\rho, \varphi, \theta): \rho = 2\csc\varphi, 0 < \varphi < \pi\}$

37. $\{(\rho, \varphi, \theta): \rho = 4\cos\varphi, 0 \le \varphi \le \pi/2\}$

38. $\{(\rho, \varphi, \theta): \rho = 2\sec\varphi, 0 \le \varphi < \pi/2\}$

39–45. Integrals in spherical coordinates *Evaluate the following integrals in spherical coordinates.*

39. $\displaystyle\iiint_D (x^2 + y^2 + z^2)^{5/2}\,dV$; D is the unit ball.

40. $\displaystyle\iiint_D e^{-(x^2+y^2+z^2)^{3/2}}\,dV$; D is the unit ball.

41. $\displaystyle\iiint_D \frac{1}{(x^2 + y^2 + z^2)^{3/2}}\,dV$; D is the region between the spheres of radius 1 and 2 centered at the origin.

42. $\displaystyle\int_0^{2\pi}\int_0^{\pi/3}\int_0^{4\sec\varphi} \rho^2 \sin\varphi\,d\rho\,d\varphi\,d\theta$

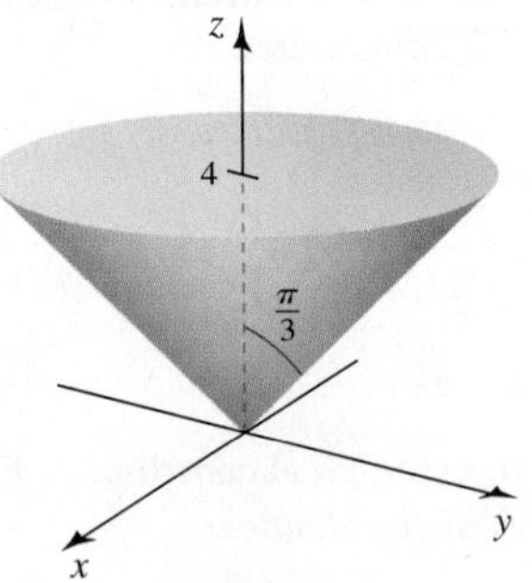

43. $\displaystyle\int_0^{\pi}\int_0^{\pi/6}\int_{2\sec\varphi}^{4} \rho^2 \sin\varphi\,d\rho\,d\varphi\,d\theta$

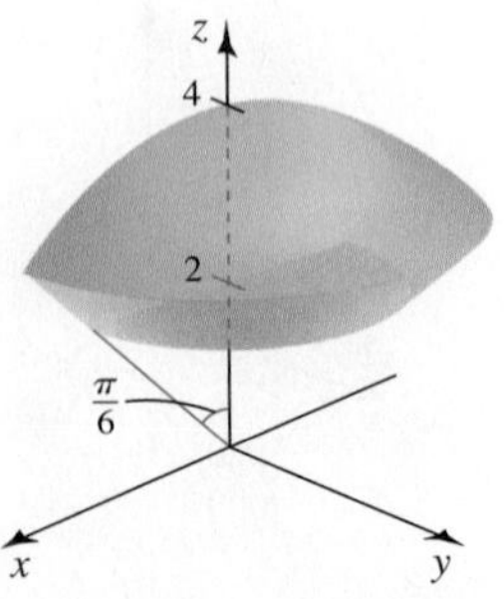

44. $\displaystyle\int_0^{2\pi}\int_0^{\pi/4}\int_1^{2\sec\varphi}(\rho^{-3})\,\rho^2\sin\varphi\,d\rho\,d\varphi\,d\theta$

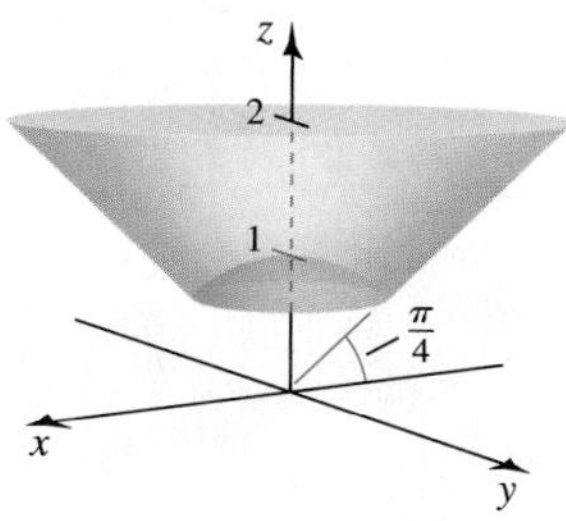

45. $\displaystyle\int_0^{2\pi}\int_{\pi/6}^{\pi/3}\int_0^{2\csc\varphi}\rho^2\sin\varphi\,d\rho\,d\varphi\,d\theta$

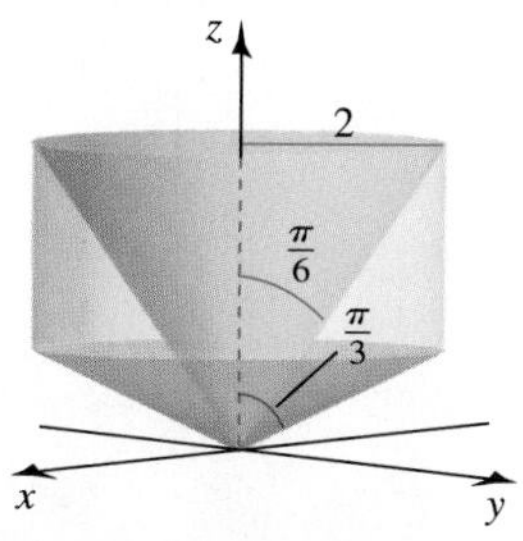

46–52. Volumes in spherical coordinates *Use spherical coordinates to find the volume of the following regions.*

46. A ball of radius $a > 0$.

47. The region bounded by the sphere $\rho = 2\cos\varphi$ and the hemisphere $\rho = 1, z \geq 0$

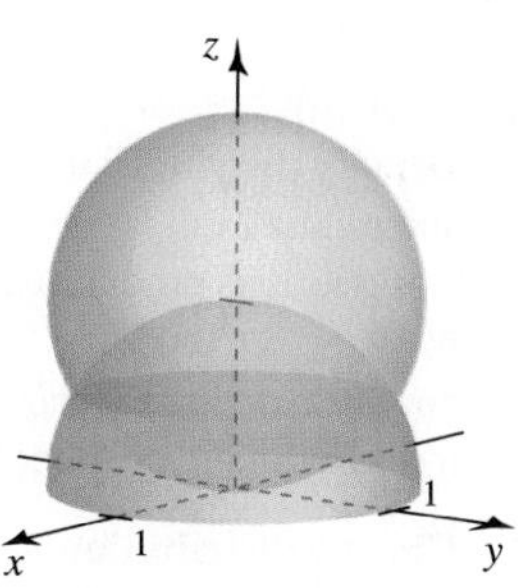

48. The cardioid of revolution $D = \{(\rho, \varphi, \theta): 0 \leq \rho \leq 1 + \cos\varphi, 0 \leq \varphi \leq \pi, 0 \leq \theta \leq 2\pi\}$

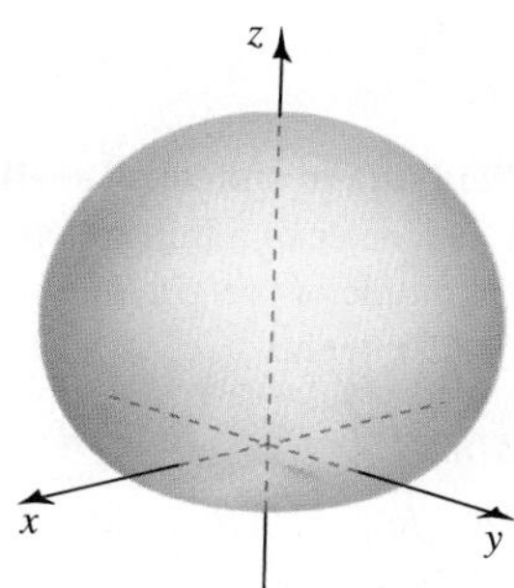

49. The region outside the cone $\varphi = \pi/4$ and inside the sphere $\rho = 4\cos\varphi$

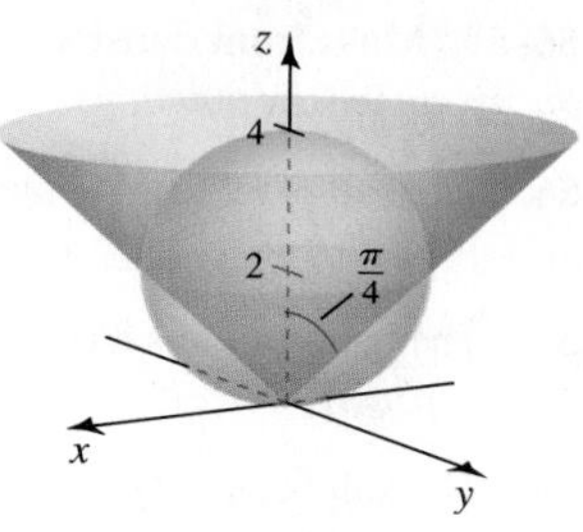

50. The region bounded by the cylinders $r = 1$ and $r = 2$, and the cones $\varphi = \pi/6$ and $\varphi = \pi/3$

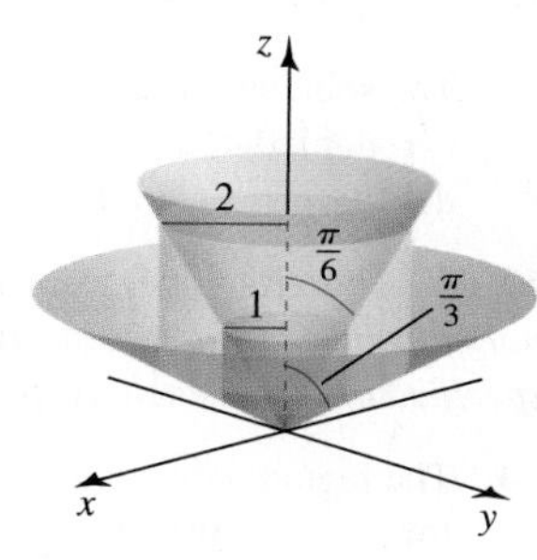

51. That part of the ball $\rho \leq 4$ that lies between the planes $z = 2$ and $z = 2\sqrt{3}$

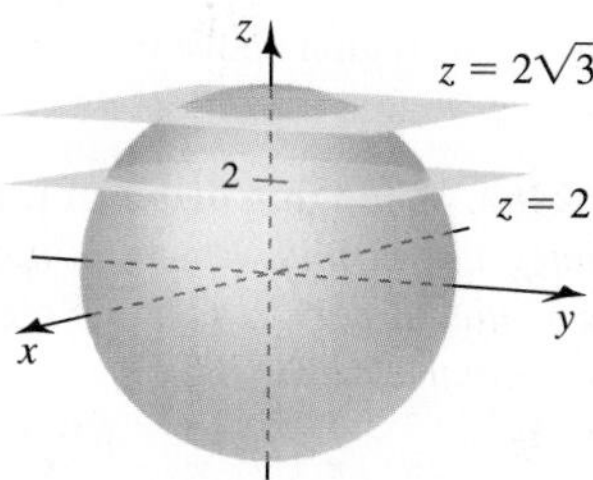

52. The region inside the solid cone $z = (x^2 + y^2)^{1/2}$ that lies between the planes $z = 1$ and $z = 2$

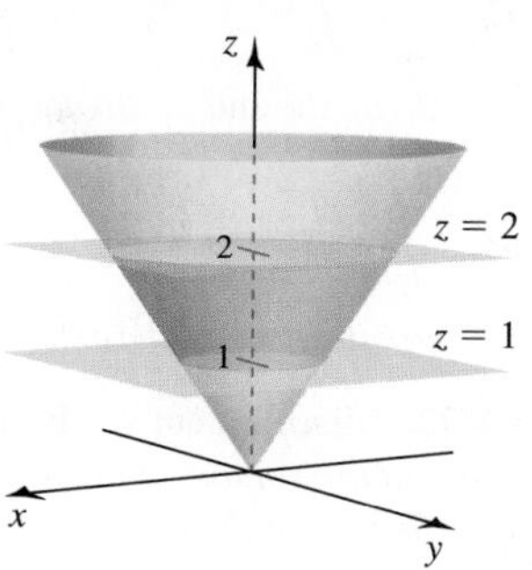

Further Explorations

53. **Explain why or why not** Determine whether the following statements are true and give an explanation or counterexample.
    a. Any point on the z-axis has more than one representation in both cylindrical and spherical coordinates.
    b. The sets $\{(r, \theta, z): r = z\}$ and $\{(\rho, \varphi, \theta): \varphi = \pi/4\}$ are the same.

54. **Spherical to rectangular** Convert the equation $\rho^2 = \sec 2\varphi$, where $0 \leq \varphi < \pi/4$, to rectangular coordinates and identify the surface.

55. **Spherical to rectangular** Convert the equation $\rho^2 = -\sec 2\varphi$, where $\pi/4 < \varphi \leq \pi/2$, to rectangular coordinates and identify the surface.

56–59. Mass from density *Find the mass of the following objects with the given density functions.*

56. The ball of radius 4 centered at the origin with a density $f(\rho, \varphi, \theta) = 1 + \rho$

57. The ball of radius 8 centered at the origin with a density $f(\rho, \varphi, \theta) = 2e^{-\rho^3}$

58. The solid cone $\{(\rho, \varphi, \theta): \varphi \le \pi/3, 0 \le z \le 4\}$ with a density $f(\rho, \varphi, \theta) = 5 - z$

59. The solid cylinder $\{(r, \theta, z): 0 \le r \le 2, 0 \le \theta \le 2\pi, -1 \le z \le 1\}$ with a density $\rho(r, z) = (2 - |z|)(4 - r)$.

60–61. Changing order of integration *If possible, write iterated integrals in cylindrical coordinates for the following regions in the specified orders. Sketch the region of integration.*

60. The region outside the cylinder $r = 1$ and inside the sphere $\rho = 5$ for $z \ge 0$ in the orders $dz\,dr\,d\theta$, $dr\,dz\,d\theta$, and $d\theta\,dz\,dr$

61. The region above the cone $z = r$ and below the sphere $\rho = 2$ for $z \ge 0$ in the orders $dz\,dr\,d\theta$, $dr\,dz\,d\theta$, and $d\theta\,dz\,dr$

62–63. Changing order of integration *If possible, write iterated integrals in spherical coordinates for the following regions in the specified orders. Sketch the region of integration. Assume that f is continuous on the region.*

62. $\displaystyle\int_0^{2\pi}\int_0^{\pi/4}\int_0^{4\sec\varphi} f(\rho, \varphi, \theta)\,\rho^2 \sin\varphi\,d\rho\,d\varphi\,d\theta$ in the orders $d\rho\,d\theta\,d\varphi$ and $d\theta\,d\rho\,d\varphi$

63. $\displaystyle\int_0^{2\pi}\int_{\pi/6}^{\pi/2}\int_{\csc\varphi}^{2} f(\rho, \varphi, \theta)\,\rho^2 \sin\varphi\,d\rho\,d\varphi\,d\theta$ in the orders $d\rho\,d\theta\,d\varphi$ and $d\theta\,d\rho\,d\varphi$

64–72. Miscellaneous volumes *Choose the best coordinate system and find the volume of the following solid regions. Surfaces are specified using the coordinates that give the simplest description, but the simplest integration may be with respect to different variables.*

64. The region inside the sphere $\rho = 1$ and below the cone $\varphi = \pi/4$, for $z \ge 0$

65. That part of the solid cylinder $r \le 2$ that lies between the cones $\varphi = \pi/3$ and $\varphi = 2\pi/3$

66. That part of the ball $\rho \le 2$ that lies between the cones $\varphi = \pi/3$ and $\varphi = 2\pi/3$

67. The region bounded by the cylinder $r = 1$, for $0 \le z \le x + y$

68. The region inside the cylinder $r = 2\cos\theta$, for $0 \le z \le 4 - x$

69. The wedge cut from the cardioid cylinder $r = 1 + \cos\theta$ by the planes $z = 2 - x$ and $z = x - 2$

70. Volume of a drilled hemisphere Find the volume of material remaining in a hemisphere of radius 2 after a cylindrical hole of radius 1 is drilled through the center of the hemisphere perpendicular to its base.

71. Two cylinders The x- and y-axes form the axes of two right circular cylinders with radius 1 (see figure). Find the volume of the region that is common to the two cylinders.

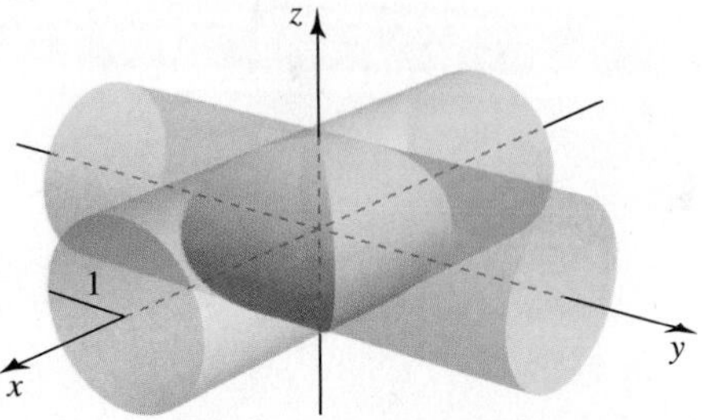

72. Three cylinders The coordinate axes form the axes of three right circular cylinders with radius 1 (see figure). Find the volume of the region that is common to the three cylinders.

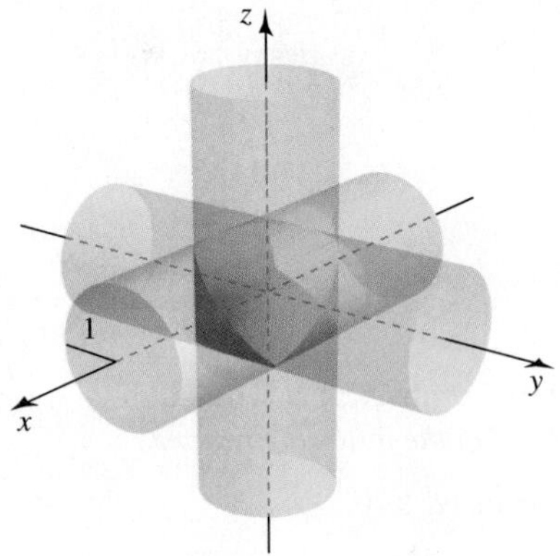

Applications

73. Density distribution A right circular cylinder with height 8 cm and radius 2 cm is filled with water. A heated filament running along its axis produces a variable density in the water given by $\rho(r) = 1 - 0.05e^{-0.01r^2}$ g/cm^3 (ρ stands for density here, not the radial spherical coordinate). Find the mass of the water in the cylinder. Neglect the volume of the filament.

74. Charge distribution A spherical cloud of electric charge has a known charge density $Q(\rho)$, where $0 \le \rho < \infty$ is the spherical coordinate. Find the total charge in the interior of the cloud in the following cases.

a. $Q(\rho) = \dfrac{2 \times 10^{-4}}{1 + \rho^3}$ **b.** $Q(\rho) = (2 \times 10^{-4})e^{-0.01\rho^3}$

75. Gravitational field due to spherical shell A point mass m is a distance d from the center of a thin spherical shell of mass M and radius R. The magnitude of the gravitational force on the point mass is given by the integral

$$F(d) = \frac{GMm}{4\pi}\int_0^{2\pi}\int_0^{\pi}\frac{(d - R\cos\varphi)\sin\varphi}{(R^2 + d^2 - 2Rd\cos\varphi)^{3/2}}\,d\varphi\,d\theta,$$

where G is the gravitational constant.

a. Use the change of variable $x = \cos\varphi$ to evaluate the integral and show that if $d > R$, then $F(d) = \dfrac{GMm}{d^2}$, which means the force is the same as if the mass of the shell were concentrated at its center.

b. Show that if $d < R$ (the point mass is inside the shell), then $F = 0$.

76. Water in a gas tank Before a gasoline-powered engine is started, water must be drained from the bottom of the fuel tank. Suppose the tank is a right circular cylinder on its side with a length of 2 ft and a radius of 1 ft. If the water level is 6 in above the lowest part of the tank, determine how much water must be drained from the tank.

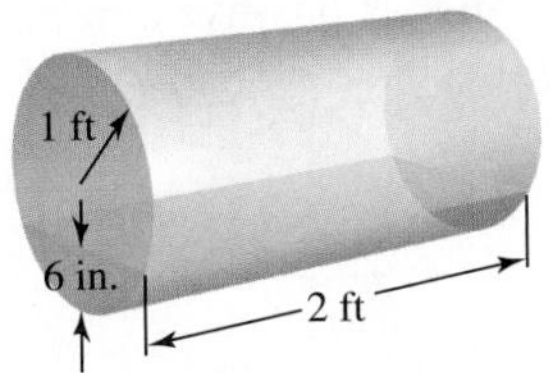

Additional Exercises

77–80. General volume formulas *Use integration to find the volume of the following solids. In each case, choose a convenient coordinate system, find equations for the bounding surfaces, set up a triple integral, and evaluate the integral. Assume that a, b, c, r, R, and h are positive constants.*

77. Cone Find the volume of a solid right circular cone with height h and base radius r.

78. Spherical cap Find the volume of the cap of a sphere of radius R with thickness h.

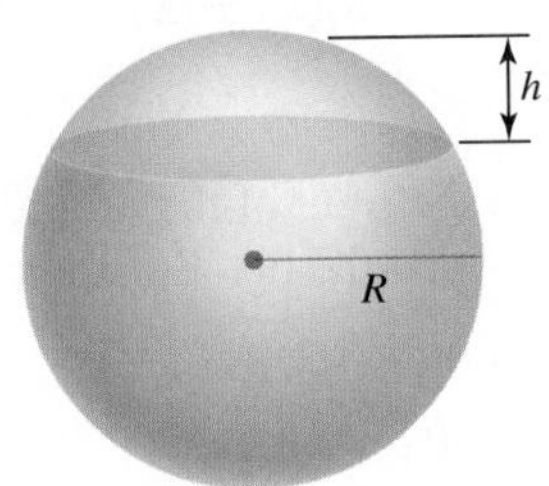

79. Frustum of a cone Find the volume of a truncated solid cone of height h whose ends have radii r and R.

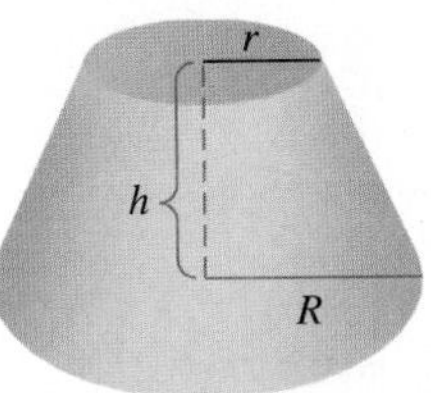

80. Ellipsoid Find the volume of a solid ellipsoid with axes of length $2a$, $2b$, and $2c$.

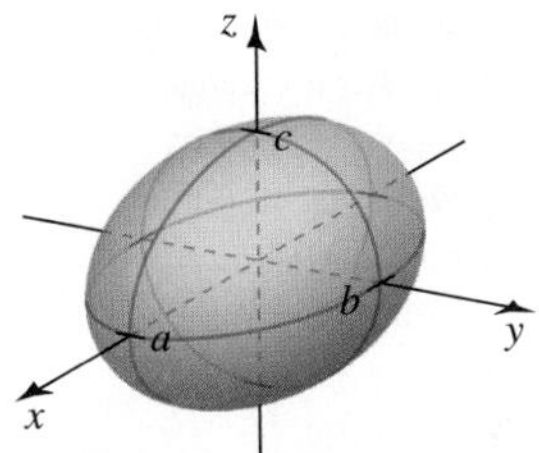

81. Intersecting spheres One sphere is centered at the origin and has a radius of R. Another sphere is centered at $(0, 0, r)$ and has a radius of r, where $r > R/2$. What is the volume of the region common to the two spheres?

QUICK CHECK ANSWERS

1. $(\sqrt{2}, 7\pi/4, 5), (1, \sqrt{3}, 5)$
2. $0 \le r \le 10, 0 \le \theta \le 2\pi, 0 \le z \le 20$
3. $(2\sqrt{2}, \pi/4, \pi/3), (1, 1, \sqrt{2})$

14.6 Integrals for Mass Calculations

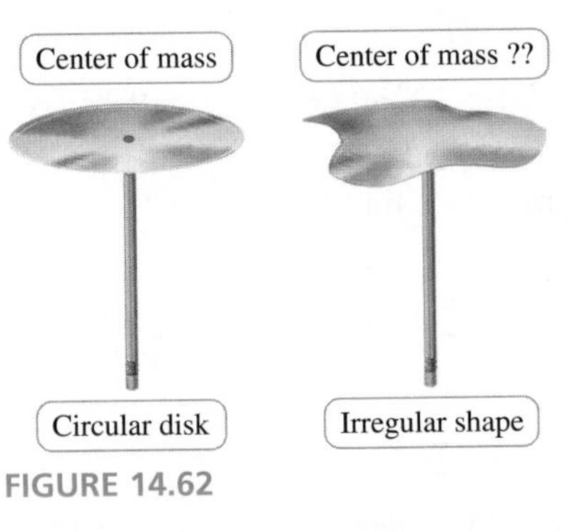

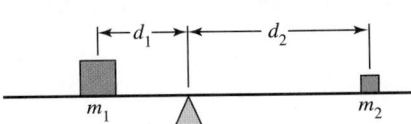

FIGURE 14.62

Intuition says that a thin circular disk (like a DVD without a hole) should balance on a pencil placed at the center of the disk (Figure 14.62). If, however, you were given a thin plate with an irregular shape, then at what point does it balance? This question asks about the *center of mass* of a thin object (thin enough that it can be treated as a two-dimensional plane region). Similarly, given a solid object with an irregular shape and variable density, where is the point at which all of the mass of the object would be located if it were treated as a point mass? In this section we use integration to compute the center of mass of one-, two- and three-dimensional objects.

Sets of Individual Objects

Methods for finding the center of mass of an object are ultimately based on a well-known playground principle: If two people with masses m_1 and m_2 sit at distances d_1 and d_2 from the pivot point of a seesaw (with no mass), then the seesaw balances provided $m_1d_1 = m_2d_2$ (Figure 14.63).

d_1 d_2 m_1 m_2

FIGURE 14.63

QUICK CHECK 1 A 90-kg person sits 2 m from the balance point of a seesaw. How far from that point must a 60-kg person sit to balance the seesaw? Assume the seesaw has no mass.

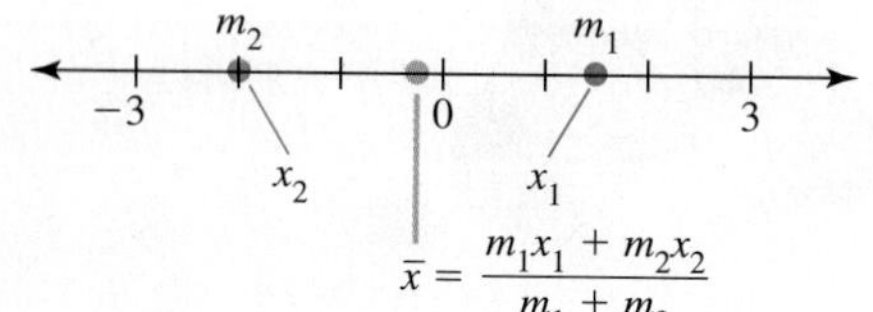

FIGURE 14.64

To generalize the problem we introduce a coordinate system with the origin at $x = 0$ (Figure 14.64). Suppose the location of the balance point $\bar{x}$ is unknown. The coordinates of the two masses m_1 and m_2 are denoted x_1 and x_2, respectively. The mass m_1 is a distance $x_1 - \bar{x}$ from the balance point (because distance is positive and $x_1 > \bar{x}$). The mass m_2 is a distance $\bar{x} - x_2$ from the balance point (because $\bar{x} > x_2$). The playground principle becomes

$$\underbrace{m_1(x_1 - \bar{x})}_{\text{distance from balance point to } m_1} = \underbrace{m_2(\bar{x} - x_2)}_{\text{distance from balance point to } m_2},$$

or $m_1(x_1 - \bar{x}) + m_2(x_2 - \bar{x}) = 0$.

Solving this equation for $\bar{x}$, the balance point or *center of mass* of the two-mass system is located at

$$\bar{x} = \frac{m_1x_1 + m_2x_2}{m_1 + m_2}.$$

The quantities m_1x_1 and m_2x_2 are called **moments about the origin** (or just **moments**). The location of the center of mass is the *sum of the moments divided by the sum of the masses.*

➤ The center of mass may be viewed as the weighted average of the x-coordinates with the masses serving as the weights. Notice how the units work out: If x_1 and x_2 have units of meters and m_1 and m_2 have units of kg, then $\bar{x}$ has units of m.

QUICK CHECK 2 Solve the equation $m_1(x_1 - \bar{x}) + m_2(x_2 - \bar{x}) = 0$ for $\bar{x}$ to verify the preceding expression for the center of mass.

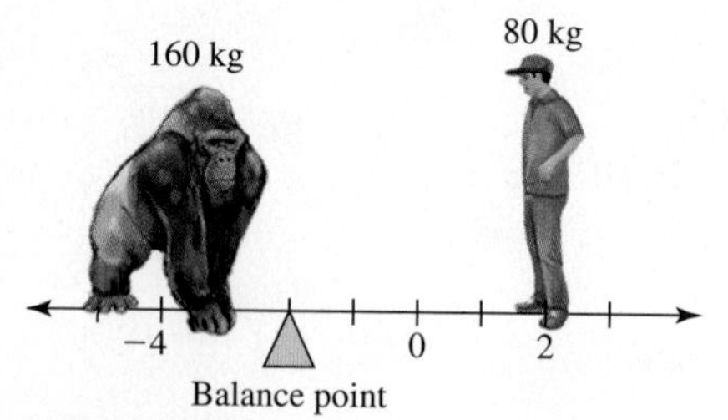

FIGURE 14.65

For example, an 80-kg man sitting 2 m to the right of the origin will balance a 160-kg gorilla sitting 4 m to the left of the origin provided the pivot on their seesaw is placed at

$$\bar{x} = \frac{80 \cdot 2 + 160(-4)}{80 + 160} = -2$$

or 2 m to the left of the origin (Figure 14.65).

Several Objects on a Line Generalizing the preceding argument to n objects having masses $m_1, m_2, \ldots, m_n$ with coordinates $x_1, x_2, \ldots, x_n$, respectively, the balance condition becomes

$$m_1(x_1 - \bar{x}) + m_2(x_2 - \bar{x}) + \cdots + m_n(x_n - \bar{x}) = \sum_{k=1}^{n} m_k(x_k - \bar{x}) = 0.$$

Solving this equation for the location of the center of mass, we find that

$$\bar{x} = \frac{m_1x_1 + m_2x_2 + \cdots + m_nx_n}{m_1 + m_2 + \cdots + m_n} = \frac{\sum_{k=1}^{n} m_kx_k}{\sum_{k=1}^{n} m_k}.$$

Again, the location of the center of mass is the sum of the moments $m_1x_1, m_2x_2, \ldots, m_nx_n$ divided by the sum of the masses.

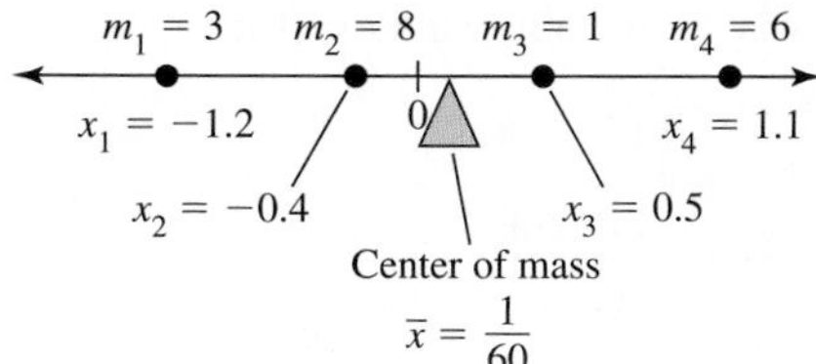

FIGURE 14.66

EXAMPLE 1 **Center of mass for four objects** Find the point at which the system shown in Figure 14.66 balances.

SOLUTION The center of mass is

$$\bar{x} = \frac{m_1x_1 + m_2x_2 + m_3x_3 + m_4x_4}{m_1 + m_2 + m_3 + m_4}$$

$$= \frac{3(-1.2) + 8(-0.4) + 1(0.5) + 6(1.1)}{3 + 8 + 1 + 6}$$

$$= \frac{1}{60} \approx 0.017.$$

The balancing point is slightly to the right of the origin. *Related Exercises 7–8*

Continuous Objects in One Dimension

Now consider a thin rod or wire with density ρ that varies along the length of the rod (Figure 14.67). The density in this case has units of mass per length (for example, g/cm). As before, we want to determine the location $\bar{x}$ at which the rod balances on a pivot.

➤ Density is usually measured in units of *mass per volume*. However, for thin, narrow objects such as rods or wires, linear density with units of *mass per length* is used. For thin, flat objects, such as plates and sheets, area density with units of *mass per area* is used.

QUICK CHECK 3 In Figure 14.67, suppose $a = 0$, $b = 3$, and the density of the rod in g/cm is $\rho(x) = 4 - x$. Where is the rod lightest? Heaviest?

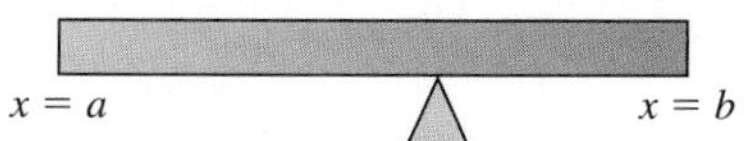

FIGURE 14.67

Using the slice-and-sum strategy, we divide the rod, which corresponds to the interval $a \le x \le b$, into n subintervals, each with a width of $\Delta x = \frac{b - a}{n}$ (Figure 14.68). The corresponding grid points are

$$x_0 = a, x_1 = a + \Delta x, \dots, x_k = a + k\,\Delta x, \dots, x_n = b.$$

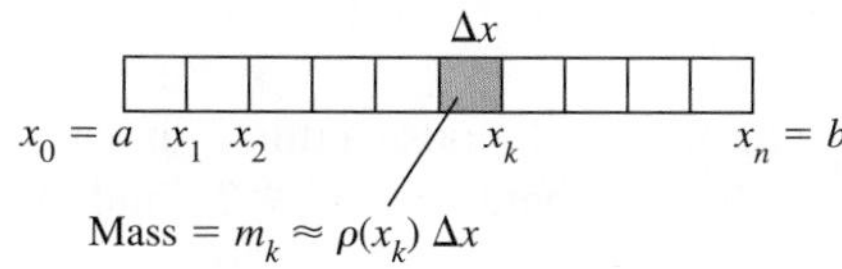

FIGURE 14.68

The mass of the kth segment of the rod is approximately the density at x_k multiplied by the length of the interval, or $m_k \approx \rho(x_k)\,\Delta x$.

The center of mass of the rod is determined by first applying the balance condition for n masses on a line to the n segments of the rod:

$$\sum_{k=1}^{n} m_k(x_k - \bar{x}) \approx \sum_{k=1}^{n} \underbrace{\rho(x_k)\Delta x}_{m_k}(x_k - \bar{x}) = 0$$

To model a rod with a continuous density, we let $\Delta x \to 0$ and $n \to \infty$, which leads to the integral

$$\lim_{\Delta x \to 0} \sum_{k=1}^{n} \rho(x_k)(x_k - \bar{x})\,\Delta x = \int_a^b \rho(x)(x - \bar{x})\,dx.$$

➤ An object consisting of two different materials that meet at an interface has a discontinuous density function. Physical density functions are either continuous or have a finite number of discontinuities.

Therefore, the balance condition becomes

$$\int_a^b \rho(x)(x - \bar{x})\,dx = 0.$$

Splitting the integral into two parts and noting that $\bar{x}$ is a constant, we solve for $\bar{x}$:

$$\bar{x} = \frac{\int_a^b x\rho(x)\,dx}{\int_a^b \rho(x)\,dx} = \frac{M}{m} = \frac{\text{total moment}}{\text{total mass}}$$

As discussed in Section 6.6, we identify the denominator of this fraction, $\int_a^b \rho(x)\,dx$, as the mass of the rod. The numerator is the "sum" of the moments of each piece of the rod, which is called the **total moment**.

> The units of a moment are mass × length. The center of mass is a moment divided by a mass, which has units of length. Notice that if the density is constant, then ρ effectively does not enter the calculation of $\bar{x}$.

DEFINITION Center of Mass in One Dimension

Let ρ be an integrable density function on the interval $[a, b]$ (which represents a thin rod or wire). The **center of mass** is located at the point $\bar{x} = \frac{M}{m}$, where the total moment M and mass m are

$$M = \int_a^b x\rho(x)\,dx \quad \text{and} \quad m = \int_a^b \rho(x)\,dx.$$

Observe the parallels between the discrete and continuous cases:

$$n \text{ individual masses: } \bar{x} = \frac{\sum_{k=1}^{n} x_k m_k}{\sum_{k=1}^{n} m_k} \qquad \text{Continuous mass: } \bar{x} = \frac{\int_a^b x\rho(x)\,dx}{\int_a^b \rho(x)\,dx}$$

EXAMPLE 2 Center of mass of a one-dimensional object Suppose a thin 2-m bar is made of an alloy whose density in kg/m is $\rho(x) = 1 + x^2$, where $0 \leq x \leq 2$. Find the center of mass of the bar.

SOLUTION The total mass of the bar in kilograms is

$$m = \int_a^b \rho(x)\,dx = \int_0^2 (1 + x^2)\,dx = \left(x + \frac{x^3}{3}\right)\Big|_0^2 = \frac{14}{3}.$$

The total moment of the bar, with units kg-m, is

> Notice that the density of the bar increases with x. As a consistency check, our calculation must result in a center of mass to the right of the midpoint of the bar.

$$M = \int_a^b x\rho(x)\,dx = \int_0^2 x(1 + x^2)\,dx = \left(\frac{x^2}{2} + \frac{x^4}{4}\right)\Big|_0^2 = 6.$$

Therefore, the center of mass is located at $\bar{x} = \frac{M}{m} = \frac{9}{7} \approx 1.29$ m.

Related Exercises 9–14 ◄

Two-Dimensional Objects

In two dimensions, we start with an integrable density function $\rho(x, y)$ defined over a closed bounded region R in the xy-plane. The density is now an *area density* with units of mass per area (for example, kg/m^2). The region represents a thin plate (or *lamina*). The center

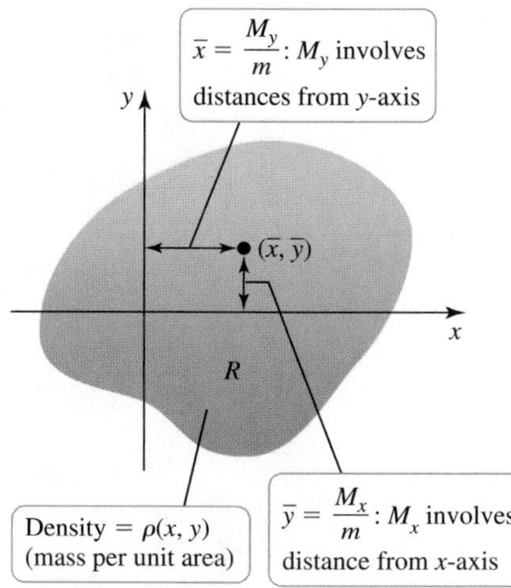

FIGURE 14.69

➤ The moment with respect to the y-axis M_y is a weighted average of distances from the y-axis, so it has x in the integrand (the distance between a point and the y-axis). Similarly, the moment with respect to the x-axis M_x is a weighted average of distances from the x-axis, so it has y in the integrand.

of mass is the point at which a pivot must be located to balance the plate. If the density is constant, the location of the center of mass depends only on the shape of the plate, in which case the center of mass is called the *centroid.*

For a two- or three-dimensional object, the coordinates for the center of mass are computed independently by applying the one-dimensional argument in each coordinate direction (Figure 14.69). The mass of the plate is the integral of the density function over R:

$$m = \iint_R \rho(x, y)\, dA$$

In analogy with the moment calculation in the one-dimensional case, we now define two moments.

DEFINITION Center of Mass in Two Dimensions

Let ρ be an integrable area density function defined over a closed bounded region R in $\mathbf{R}^2$. The coordinates of the **center of mass** of the object represented by R are

$$\bar{x} = \frac{M_y}{m} = \frac{1}{m}\iint_R x\rho(x, y)\, dA \quad \text{and} \quad \bar{y} = \frac{M_x}{m} = \frac{1}{m}\iint_R y\rho(x, y)\, dA,$$

where $m = \iint_R \rho(x, y)\, dA$ is the mass, and M_y and M_x are the moments with respect to the y-axis and x-axis, respectively. If ρ is constant, the center of mass is called the **centroid**.

As before, the center of mass coordinates are weighted averages of the distances from the coordinate axes. For two- and three-dimensional objects, the center of mass need not lie within the object (Exercises 51, 61, and 62).

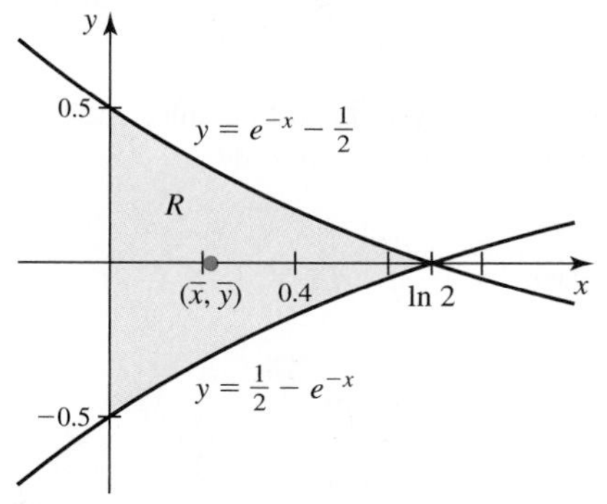

FIGURE 14.70

➤ The density does not enter the center of mass calculation when the density is constant. So, it is easiest to set $\rho = 1$.

➤ If possible, try to arrange the coordinate system so that at least one of the integrations in the center of mass calculation can be avoided by using symmetry. Often the mass (or area) can be found using geometry if the density is constant.

QUICK CHECK 4 Explain why the integral for M_y has x in the integrand. Explain why the density drops out of the center of mass calculation if it is constant. ◄

EXAMPLE 3 Centroid calculation Find the centroid (center of mass) of the constant-density, dart-shaped region bounded by the y-axis and the curves $y = e^{-x} - \frac{1}{2}$ and $y = \frac{1}{2} - e^{-x}$ (Figure 14.70).

SOLUTION Because the region is symmetric about the x-axis and the density is constant, the y-coordinate of the center of mass is $\bar{y} = 0$. This leaves the integrals for m and M_y to evaluate.

The first task is to find the point at which the curves intersect. Solving $e^{-x} - \frac{1}{2} = \frac{1}{2} - e^{-x}$, we find that $x = \ln 2$, from which it follows that $y = 0$. Therefore, the intersection point is $(\ln 2, 0)$. The moment M_y is given by

$$\begin{aligned} M_y &= \int_0^{\ln 2}\int_{1/2-e^{-x}}^{e^{-x}-1/2} x\, dy\, dx \\ &= \int_0^{\ln 2} x\left[\left(e^{-x} - \frac{1}{2}\right) - \left(\frac{1}{2} - e^{-x}\right)\right] dx \\ &= \int_0^{\ln 2} x(2e^{-x} - 1)\, dx. \end{aligned}$$

Using integration by parts for this integral, we find that

$$M_y = \int_0^{\ln 2} \underbrace{x}_{u} \underbrace{(2e^{-x} - 1)\,dx}_{dv}$$

$$= -x(2e^{-x} + x)\Big|_0^{\ln 2} + \int_0^{\ln 2} (2e^{-x} + x)\,dx \quad \text{Integration by parts}$$

$$= 1 - \ln 2 - \frac{1}{2}\ln^2 2 \approx 0.067. \quad \text{Evaluate and simplify.}$$

The mass of the region is given by

$$m = \int_0^{\ln 2} \int_{1/2-e^{-x}}^{e^{-x}-1/2} dy\,dx$$

$$= \int_0^{\ln 2} (2e^{-x} - 1)\,dx$$

$$= (-2e^{-x} - x)\Big|_0^{\ln 2} \quad \text{Fundamental Theorem}$$

$$= 1 - \ln 2 \approx 0.307. \quad \text{Evaluate and simplify.}$$

Therefore, the x-coordinate of the center of mass is $\bar{x} = \dfrac{M_y}{m} \approx 0.217$. The center of mass is located approximately at $(0.217, 0)$.

Related Exercises 15–20 ◀

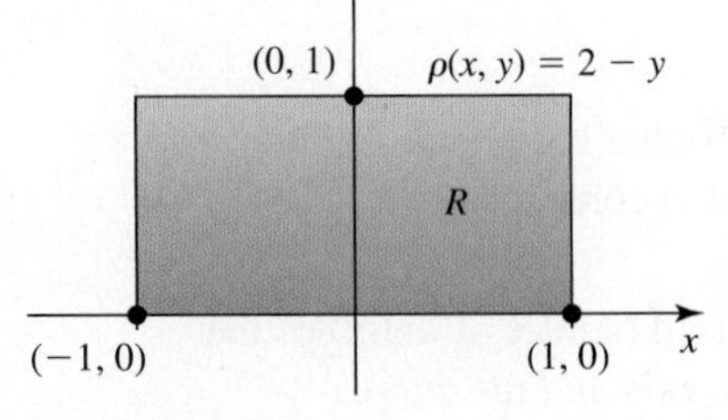

FIGURE 14.71

➤ To verify that $\bar{x} = 0$, notice that to find M_y, we integrate an odd function in x over $-1 \le x \le 1$; the result is zero.

EXAMPLE 4 Variable-density plate Find the center of mass of the rectangular plate $R = \{(x, y): -1 \le x \le 1, 0 \le y \le 1\}$ with a density of $\rho(x, y) = 2 - y$ (heavy at the lower edge and light at the top edge; Figure 14.71).

SOLUTION Because the plate is symmetric with respect to the y-axis and because the density is independent of x, we have $\bar{x} = 0$. We must still compute m and M_x:

$$m = \iint_R \rho(x, y)\,dA = \int_{-1}^{1}\int_0^1 (2 - y)\,dy\,dx = \frac{3}{2}\int_{-1}^{1} dx = 3$$

$$M_x = \iint_R y\rho(x, y)\,dA = \int_{-1}^{1}\int_0^1 y(2 - y)\,dy\,dx = \frac{2}{3}\int_{-1}^{1} dx = \frac{4}{3}$$

Therefore, the center of mass coordinates are

$$\bar{x} = \frac{M_y}{m} = 0 \quad \text{and} \quad \bar{y} = \frac{M_x}{m} = \frac{4/3}{3} = \frac{4}{9}.$$

Related Exercises 21–26 ◀

Three-Dimensional Objects

We now extend the preceding arguments to compute the center of mass of three-dimensional solids. Assume that D is a closed bounded region in $\mathbf{R}^3$, on which an integrable density function ρ is defined. The units of the density are now mass per volume (for example, g/cm^3). The coordinates of the center of mass depend on the mass of the region, which by Section 14.4 is the integral of the density function over D. Three moments now enter the picture: M_{yz} involves distances from the yz-plane; therefore, it has an x in the integrand. Similarly, M_{xz}

involves distances from the xz-plane, so it has a y in the integrand, and M_{xy} involves distances from the xy-plane, so it has a z in the integrand. As before, the coordinates of the center of mass are the total moments divided by the total mass (Figure 14.72).

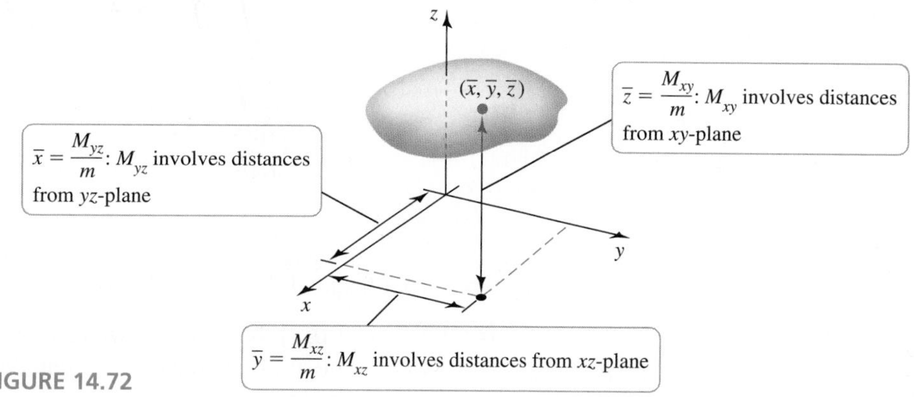

FIGURE 14.72

QUICK CHECK 5 Explain why the integral for the moment M_{xy} has z in the integrand.

DEFINITION Center of Mass in Three Dimensions

Let ρ be an integrable density function on a closed bounded region D in $\mathbf{R}^3$. The coordinates of the **center of mass** of the region are

$$\bar{x} = \frac{M_{yz}}{m} = \frac{1}{m}\iiint_D x\rho(x, y, z)\, dV, \quad \bar{y} = \frac{M_{xz}}{m} = \frac{1}{m}\iiint_D y\rho(x, y, z)\, dV,$$

$$\bar{z} = \frac{M_{xy}}{m} = \frac{1}{m}\iiint_D z\rho(x, y, z)\, dV,$$

where $m = \iiint_D \rho(x, y, z)\, dV$ is the mass, and M_{yz}, M_{xz}, and M_{xy} are the moments with respect to the coordinate planes.

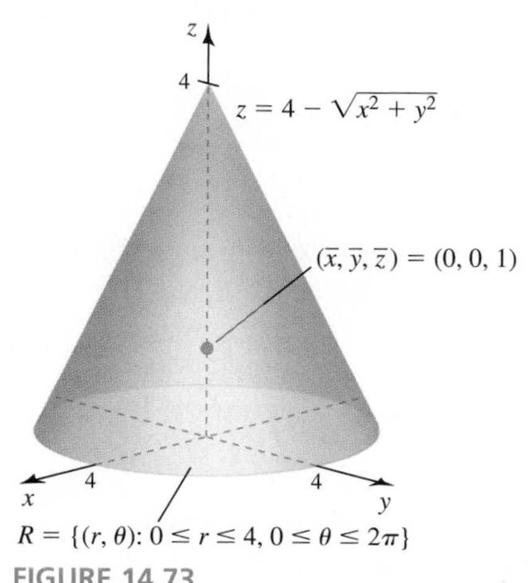

FIGURE 14.73

EXAMPLE 5 Center of mass with constant density Find the center of mass of the constant-density solid cone D bounded by the surface $z = 4 - \sqrt{x^2 + y^2}$ and $z = 0$ (Figure 14.73).

SOLUTION Because the cone is symmetric about the z-axis and has uniform density, the center of mass lies on the z-axis; that is, $\bar{x} = 0$ and $\bar{y} = 0$. Setting $z = 0$, the base of the cone in the xy-plane is the disk of radius 4 centered at the origin. Therefore, the cone has height 4 and radius 4; by the volume formula, its volume is $\pi r^2 h/3 = 64\pi/3$. The cone has a constant density, so we assume that $\rho = 1$ and its mass is $m = 64\pi/3$.

To obtain the value of $\bar{z}$, only M_{xy} needs to be calculated, which is most easily done in cylindrical coordinates. The cone is described by the equation $z = 4 - \sqrt{x^2 + y^2} = 4 - r$. The projection of the cone on the xy-plane, which is the region of integration in the xy-plane, is $R = \{(r, \theta): 0 \le r \le 4, 0 \le \theta \le 2\pi\}$. The integration for M_{xy} now follows:

$$M_{xy} = \iiint_D z\, dV \qquad \text{Definition of } M_{xy} \text{ with } \rho = 1$$

$$= \int_0^{2\pi}\int_0^4\int_0^{4-r} z\, dz\, r\, dr\, d\theta \qquad \text{Convert to an iterated integral.}$$

$$= \int_0^{2\pi} \int_0^4 \left(\frac{z^2}{2}\right)\Big|_0^{4-r} r\,dr\,d\theta \quad \text{Evaluate the inner integral.}$$

$$= \frac{1}{2}\int_0^{2\pi} \int_0^4 r(4-r)^2\,dr\,d\theta \quad \text{Simplify.}$$

$$= \frac{1}{2}\int_0^{2\pi} \frac{64}{3}\,d\theta \quad \text{Evaluate the middle integral.}$$

$$= \frac{64\pi}{3} \quad \text{Evaluate the outer integral.}$$

The z-coordinate of the center of mass is $\bar{z} = \frac{M_{xy}}{m} = \frac{64\pi/3}{64\pi/3} = 1$, and the center of mass is located at $(0, 0, 1)$. It can be shown (Exercise 55) that the center of mass of a constant-density cone height of h is located $h/4$ units from the base on the axis of the cone, independent of the radius.

Related Exercises 27–32 ◀

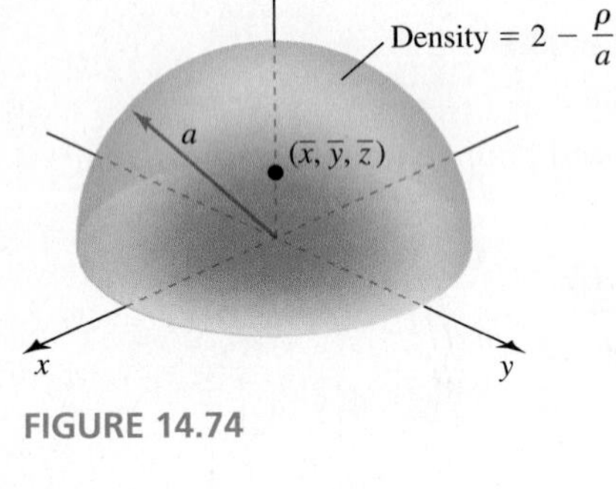

FIGURE 14.74

EXAMPLE 6 Center of mass with variable density Find the center of mass of the interior of the hemisphere D of radius a with its base on the xy-plane. The density of the object is $f(\rho, \varphi, \theta) = 2 - \rho/a$ (heavy near the center and light near the outer surface; Figure 14.74).

SOLUTION The center of mass lies on the z-axis because of the symmetry of the solid and the density function; therefore, $\bar{x} = \bar{y} = 0$. Only the integrals for m and M_{xy} need to be evaluated, and they should be done in spherical coordinates.

The integral for the mass is

$$m = \iiint_D f(\rho, \varphi, \theta)\,dV \quad \text{Definition of } m$$

$$= \int_0^{2\pi} \int_0^{\pi/2} \int_0^a \left(2 - \frac{\rho}{a}\right)\rho^2 \sin\varphi\,d\rho\,d\varphi\,d\theta \quad \text{Convert to an iterated integral.}$$

$$= \int_0^{2\pi} \int_0^{\pi/2} \left(\frac{2\rho^3}{3} - \frac{\rho^4}{4a}\right)\Big|_0^a \sin\varphi\,d\varphi\,d\theta \quad \text{Evaluate the inner integral.}$$

$$= \int_0^{2\pi} \int_0^{\pi/2} \frac{5a^3}{12} \sin\varphi\,d\varphi\,d\theta \quad \text{Simplify.}$$

$$= \frac{5a^3}{12}\int_0^{2\pi} \underbrace{(-\cos\varphi)\Big|_0^{\pi/2}}_{1}\,d\theta \quad \text{Evaluate the middle integral.}$$

$$= \frac{5a^3}{12}\int_0^{2\pi} d\theta \quad \text{Simplify.}$$

$$= \frac{5\pi a^3}{6}. \quad \text{Evaluate the outer integral.}$$

In spherical coordinates, $z = \rho\cos\varphi$, so the integral for the moment M_{xy} is

$$M_{xy} = \iiint_D z\, f(\rho, \varphi, \theta)\, dV \qquad \text{Definition of } M_{xy}$$

$$= \int_0^{2\pi}\int_0^{\pi/2}\int_0^a \underbrace{\rho\cos\varphi}_{z}\left(2 - \frac{\rho}{a}\right)\rho^2 \sin\varphi\, d\rho\, d\varphi\, d\theta \qquad \text{Convert to an iterated integral.}$$

$$= \int_0^{2\pi}\int_0^{\pi/2}\left(\frac{\rho^4}{2} - \frac{\rho^5}{5a}\right)\Bigg|_0^a \sin\varphi\cos\varphi\, d\varphi\, d\theta \qquad \text{Evaluate the inner integral.}$$

$$= \int_0^{2\pi}\int_0^{\pi/2} \frac{3a^4}{10}\underbrace{\sin\varphi\cos\varphi}_{(\sin 2\varphi)/2}\, d\varphi\, d\theta \qquad \text{Simplify.}$$

$$= \frac{3a^4}{10}\int_0^{2\pi}\underbrace{\left(-\frac{\cos 2\varphi}{4}\right)\Bigg|_0^{\pi/2}}_{1/2} d\theta \qquad \text{Evaluate the middle integral.}$$

$$= \frac{3a^4}{20}\int_0^{2\pi} d\theta \qquad \text{Simplify.}$$

$$= \frac{3\pi a^4}{10}. \qquad \text{Evaluate the outer integral.}$$

The z-coordinate of the center of mass is $\bar{z} = \dfrac{M_{xy}}{m} = \dfrac{3\pi a^4/10}{5\pi a^3/6} = \dfrac{9a}{25} = 0.36a$. It can be shown (Exercise 56) that the center of mass of a uniform-density hemispherical solid of radius a is $3a/8 = 0.375a$ units above the base. In this particular case, the variable density shifts the center of mass. *Related Exercises 33–38* ◄

SECTION 14.6 EXERCISES

Review Questions

1. Explain how to find the balance point for two people on opposite ends of a (massless) plank that rests on a pivot.

2. If a thin 1-m cylindrical rod has a density of $\rho = 1\ \text{g/cm}$ for its left half and a density of $\rho = 2\ \text{g/cm}$ for its right half, what is its mass and where is its center of mass?

3. Explain how to find the center of mass of a thin plate with a variable density.

4. In the integral for the moment M_x of a thin plate, why does y appear in the integrand?

5. Explain how to find the center of mass of a three-dimensional object with a variable density.

6. In the integral for the moment M_{xz} of a solid with respect to the xz-plane, why does y appear in the integrand?

Basic Skills

7–8. Individual masses on a line *Sketch the following systems on a number line and find the location of the center of mass.*

7. $m_1 = 10\ \text{kg}$ located at $x = 3\ \text{m}$; $m_2 = 3\ \text{kg}$ located at $x = -1\ \text{m}$

8. $m_1 = 8\ \text{kg}$ located at $x = 2\ \text{m}$; $m_2 = 4\ \text{kg}$ located at $x = -4\ \text{m}$; $m_3 = 1\ \text{kg}$ located at $x = 0\ \text{m}$

9–14. One-dimensional objects *Find the mass and center of mass of the thin rods with the following density functions.*

9. $\rho(x) = 1 + \sin x$, for $0 \le x \le \pi$

10. $\rho(x) = 1 + x^3$, for $0 \le x \le 1$

11. $\rho(x) = 2 - x^2/16$, for $0 \le x \le 4$

12. $\rho(x) = 2 + \cos x$, for $0 \le x \le \pi$

13. $\rho(x) = \begin{cases} 1 & \text{if } 0 \le x \le 2 \\ 1 + x & \text{if } 2 < x \le 4 \end{cases}$

14. $\rho(x) = \begin{cases} x^2 & \text{if } 0 \le x \le 1 \\ x(2 - x) & \text{if } 1 < x \le 2 \end{cases}$

15–20. Centroid calculations *Find the mass and centroid (center of mass) of the following thin plates, assuming a constant density. Sketch the region corresponding to the plate and indicate the location of the center of mass. Use symmetry when possible to simplify your work.*

15. The region bounded by $y = \sin x$ and $y = 1 - \sin x$ between $x = \pi/4$ and $x = 3\pi/4$

16. The region in the first quadrant bounded by $x^2 + y^2 = 16$

17. The region bounded by $y = 1 - |x|$ and the x-axis

18. The region bounded by $y = e^x$, $y = e^{-x}$, and $x = \ln 2$

19. The region bounded by $y = \ln x$, the x-axis, and $x = e$

20. The region bounded by $x^2 + y^2 = 1$ and $x^2 + y^2 = 9$, for $y \geq 0$

21–26. Variable-density plates *Find the coordinates of the center of mass of the following plane regions with variable density. Describe the distribution of mass in the region.*

21. $R = \{(x, y): 0 \leq x \leq 4, 0 \leq y \leq 2\}; \rho(x, y) = 1 + x/2$

22. $R = \{(x, y): 0 \leq x \leq 1, 0 \leq y \leq 5\}; \rho(x, y) = 2e^{-y/2}$

23. The triangular plate in the first quadrant bounded by $x + y = 4$ with $\rho(x, y) = 1 + x + y$

24. The upper half ($y \geq 0$) of the disk bounded by the circle $x^2 + y^2 = 4$ with $\rho(x, y) = 1 + y/2$

25. The upper half ($y \geq 0$) of the region bounded by the ellipse $x^2 + 9y^2 = 9$ with $\rho(x, y) = 1 + y$

26. The quarter disk in the first quadrant bounded by $x^2 + y^2 = 4$ with $\rho(x, y) = 1 + x^2 + y^2$

27–32. Center of mass of constant-density solids *Find the center of mass of the following solids, assuming a constant density. Sketch the region and indicate the location of the centroid. Use symmetry when possible and choose a convenient coordinate system.*

27. The upper half of the ball $x^2 + y^2 + z^2 \leq 16$ (for $z \geq 0$)

28. The region bounded by the paraboloid $z = x^2 + y^2$ and the plane $z = 25$

29. The tetrahedron in the first octant bounded by $z = 1 - x - y$ and the coordinate planes

30. The region bounded by the cone $z = 16 - r$ and the plane $z = 0$

31. The sliced solid cylinder bounded by $x^2 + y^2 = 1$, $z = 0$, and $y + z = 1$

32. The region bounded by the upper half ($z \geq 0$) of the ellipsoid $4x^2 + 4y^2 + z^2 = 16$

33–38. Variable-density solids *Find the coordinates of the center of mass of the following solids with variable density.*

33. $R = \{(x, y, z): 0 \leq x \leq 4, 0 \leq y \leq 1, 0 \leq z \leq 1\}$; $\rho(x, y, z) = 1 + x/2$

34. The region bounded by the paraboloid $z = 4 - x^2 - y^2$ and $z = 0$ with $\rho(x, y, z) = 5 - z$

35. The region bounded by the upper half of the sphere $\rho = 16$ and $z = 0$ with density $f(\rho, \varphi, \theta) = 1 + \rho/4$

36. The interior of the cube in the first octant formed by the planes $x = 1$, $y = 1$, and $z = 1$, with $\rho(x, y, z) = 2 + x + y + z$

37. The interior of the prism formed by $z = x$, $x = 1$, $y = 4$, and the coordinate planes with $\rho(x, y, z) = 2 + y$

38. The region bounded by the cone by $z = 9 - r$ and $z = 0$ with $\rho(r, \theta, z) = 1 + z$

Further Explorations

39. **Explain why or why not** Determine whether the following statements are true and give an explanation or counterexample.

 a. A thin plate of constant density that is symmetric about the x-axis has a center of mass with an x-coordinate of zero.
 b. A thin plate of constant density that is symmetric about both the x-axis and the y-axis has its center of mass at the origin.
 c. The center of mass of a thin plate must lie on the plate.
 d. The center of mass of a connected solid region (all in one piece) must lie within the region.

40. **Limiting center of mass** A thin rod of length L has a linear density given by $\rho(x) = 2e^{-x/3}$ on the interval $0 \leq x \leq L$. Find the mass and center of mass of the rod. How does the center of mass change as $L \to \infty$?

41. **Limiting center of mass** A thin rod of length L has a linear density given by $\rho(x) = \dfrac{10}{1 + x^2}$ on the interval $0 \leq x \leq L$. Find the mass and center of mass of the rod. How does the center of mass change as $L \to \infty$?

42. **Limiting center of mass** A thin plate is bounded by the graphs of $y = e^{-x}$, $y = -e^{-x}$, $x = 0$, and $x = L$. Find its center of mass. How does the center of mass change as $L \to \infty$?

43–44. Two-dimensional plates *Find the mass and center of mass of the thin constant-density plates shown in the figure.*

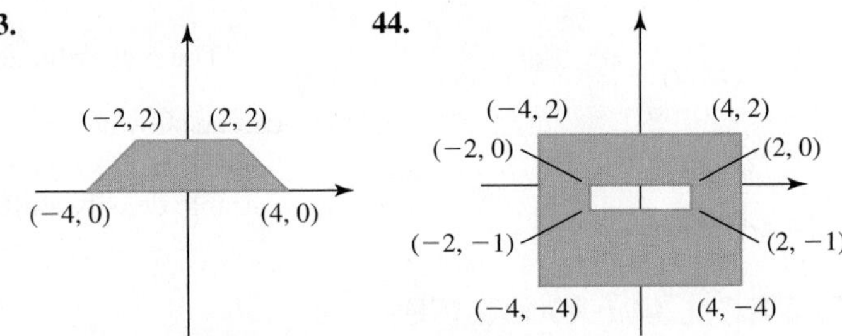

45–50. Centroids *Use polar coordinates to find the centroid of the following constant-density plane regions.*

45. The semicircular disk $R = \{(r, \theta): 0 \leq r \leq 2, 0 \leq \theta \leq \pi\}$

46. The quarter-circular disk $R = \{(r, \theta): 0 \leq r \leq 2, 0 \leq \theta \leq \pi/2\}$

47. The region bounded by the cardioid $r = 1 + \cos\theta$

48. The region bounded by the cardioid $r = 3 - 3\cos\theta$

49. The region bounded by one leaf of the rose $r = \sin 2\theta$ for $0 \leq \theta \leq \pi/2$.

50. The region bounded by the limaçon $r = 2 + \cos\theta$

51. **Semicircular wire** A thin (one-dimensional) wire of constant density is bent into the shape of a semicircle of radius r. Find the location of its center of mass.

52. **Parabolic region** A thin plate of constant density occupies the region between the parabola $y = ax^2$ and the horizontal line $y = b$, where $a > 0$ and $b > 0$. Show that the center of mass is $\left(0, \dfrac{3b}{5}\right)$, independent of a.

53. Circular crescent Find the center of mass of the region in the first quadrant bounded by the circle $x^2 + y^2 = a^2$ and the lines $x = a$ and $y = a$, where $a > 0$.

54–59. Centers of mass for general objects *Consider the following two- and three-dimensional regions with variable dimensions. Specify the surfaces and curves that bound the region, choose a convenient coordinate system, and compute the center of mass assuming constant density. All parameters are positive real numbers.*

54. A solid rectangular box has sides of length a, b, and c. Where is the center of mass relative to the faces of the box?

55. A solid cone has a base with a radius of r and a height of h. How far from the base is the center of mass?

56. A solid is enclosed by a hemisphere of radius a. How far from the base is the center of mass?

57. A region is enclosed by an isosceles triangle with two sides of length s and a base of length b. How far from the base is the center of mass?

58. A tetrahedron is bounded by the coordinate planes and the plane $x/a + y/a + z/a = 1$. What are the coordinates of the center of mass?

59. A solid is enclosed by the upper half of an ellipsoid with a circular base of radius r and a height of a. How far from the base is the center of mass?

Applications

60. Geographic vs. population center Geographers measure the *geographical center* of a country (which is the centroid) and the *population center* of a country (which is the center of mass computed with the population density). A hypothetical country is shown in the figure with the location and population of five towns. Assuming no one lives outside the towns, find the geographical center of the country and the population center of the country.

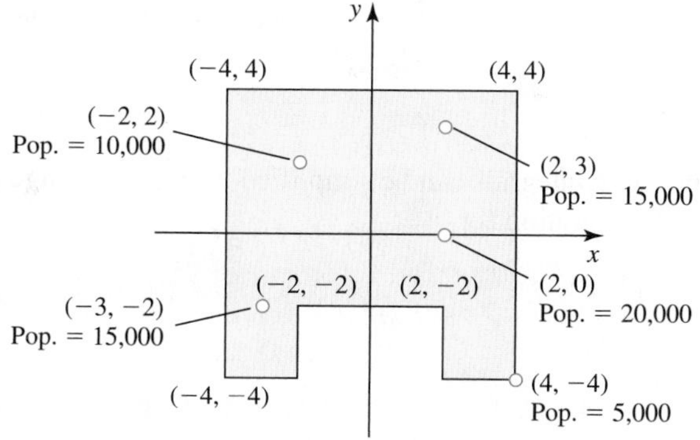

61. Center of mass on the edge Consider the thin constant-density plate $\{(r, \theta): a \le r \le 1, 0 \le \theta \le \pi\}$ bounded by two semicircles and the x-axis.

a. Find and graph the y-coordinate of the center of mass of the plate as a function of a.
b. For what value of a is the center of mass on the edge of the plate?

62. Center of mass on the edge Consider the constant-density solid $\{(\rho, \varphi, \theta): 0 < a \le \rho \le 1, 0 \le \varphi \le \pi/2, 0 \le \theta \le 2\pi\}$ bounded by two hemispheres and the xy-plane.

a. Find and graph the z-coordinate of the center of mass of the plate as a function of a.
b. For what value of a is the center of mass on the edge of the solid?

63. Draining a soda can A cylindrical soda can has a radius of 4 cm and a height of 12 cm. When the can is full of soda, the center of mass of the contents of the can is 6 cm above the base on the axis of the can (halfway along the axis of the can). As the can is drained, the center of mass descends for a while. However, when the can is empty (filled only with air), the center of mass is once again 6 cm above the base on the axis of the can. Find the depth of soda in the can for which the center of mass is at its lowest point. Neglect the mass of the can, and assume the density of the soda is 1 g/cm^3 and the density of air is 0.001 g/cm^3.

Additional Exercises

64. Triangle medians A triangular region has a base that connects the vertices $(0, 0)$ and $(b, 0)$, and a third vertex at (a, h), where $a > 0$, $b > 0$, and $h > 0$.

a. Show that the centroid of the triangle is $\left(\frac{a+b}{3}, \frac{h}{3}\right)$.
b. Recall that the three medians of a triangle extend from each vertex to the midpoint of the opposite side. Knowing that the medians of a triangle intersect in a point M and that each median bisects the triangle, conclude that the centroid of the triangle is M.

65. The golden earring A disk of radius r is removed from a larger disk of radius R to form an earring (see figure). Assume the earring is a thin plate of uniform density.

a. Find the center of mass of the earring in terms of r and R. (*Hint:* Place the origin of a coordinate system either at the center of the large disk or at Q; either way, the earring is symmetric about the x-axis.)
b. Show that the ratio R/r such that the center of mass lies at the point P (on the edge of the inner disk) is the golden mean $(1 + \sqrt{5})/2 \approx 1.618$.

(*Source:* P. Glaister, "Golden Earrings," *Mathematical Gazette* 80 (1996): 224–225.)

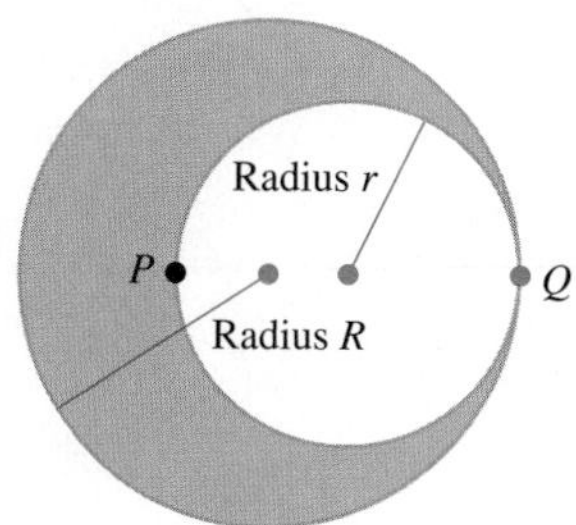

QUICK CHECK ANSWERS

1. 3 m **3.** It is heaviest at $x = 0$ and lightest at $x = 3$. **4.** The distance from the point (x, y) to the y-axis is x. The constant density appears in the integral for the moment, and it appears in the integral for the mass. Therefore, the density cancels when we divide the two integrals. **5.** The distance from the xy-plane to a point (x, y, z) is z.

14.7 Change of Variables in Multiple Integrals

Converting double integrals from rectangular coordinates to polar coordinates (Section 14.3) and converting triple integrals from rectangular coordinates to cylindrical or spherical coordinates (Section 14.5) are examples of a general procedure known as a *change of variables*. The idea is not new: The Substitution Rule introduced in Chapter 5 with single-variable integrals is also an example of a change of variables. The aim of this section is to show how to change variables with double and triple integrals.

Recap of Change of Variables

Recall how a change of variables is used to simplify a single-variable integral. For example, to simplify the integral $\int_0^1 2\sqrt{2x+1}\,dx$, we choose a new variable $u = 2x + 1$, which means that $du = 2dx$. Therefore,

$$\int_0^1 2\sqrt{2x+1}\,dx = \int_1^3 \sqrt{u}\,du.$$

This equality means that the area under the curve $y = 2\sqrt{2x+1}$ from $x = 0$ to $x = 1$ equals the area under the curve $y = \sqrt{u}$ from $u = 1$ to $u = 3$ (Figure 14.75). The relation $du = 2\,dx$ relates the length of a small interval on the u-axis to the length of the corresponding interval on the x-axis.

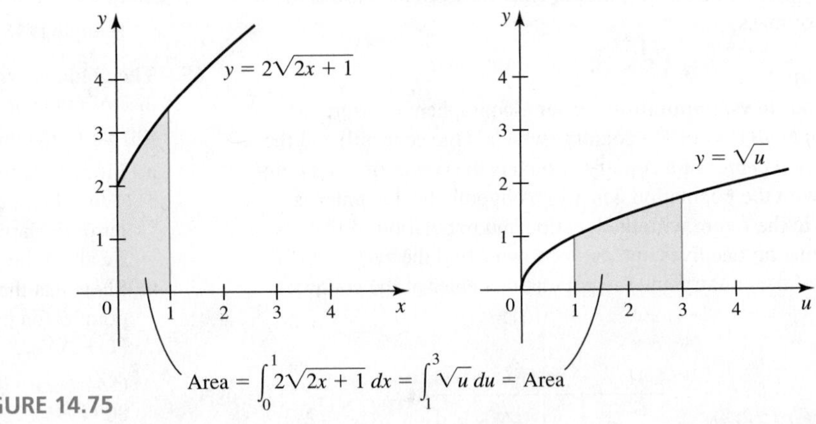

FIGURE 14.75

Similarly, some double and triple integrals can be simplified through a change of variables. For example, the region of integration for

$$\int_0^1 \int_0^{\sqrt{1-x^2}} e^{1-x^2-y^2}\,dy\,dx$$

is the quarter disk $R = \{(x, y): x \ge 0, y \ge 0, x^2 + y^2 \le 1\}$. Changing variables to polar coordinates with $x = r\cos\theta$, $y = r\sin\theta$, and $dy\,dx = r\,dr\,d\theta$, we have

$$\int_0^1 \int_0^{\sqrt{1-x^2}} e^{1-x^2-y^2}\,dy\,dx \overset{\substack{x = r\cos\theta \\ y = r\sin\theta}}{=} \int_0^{\pi/2} \int_0^1 e^{1-r^2}\,r\,dr\,d\theta.$$

In this case, the original region of integration R is transformed into a new region $S = \{(r, \theta): 0 \le r \le 1, 0 \le \theta \le \pi/2\}$, which is a rectangle in the $r\theta$-plane.

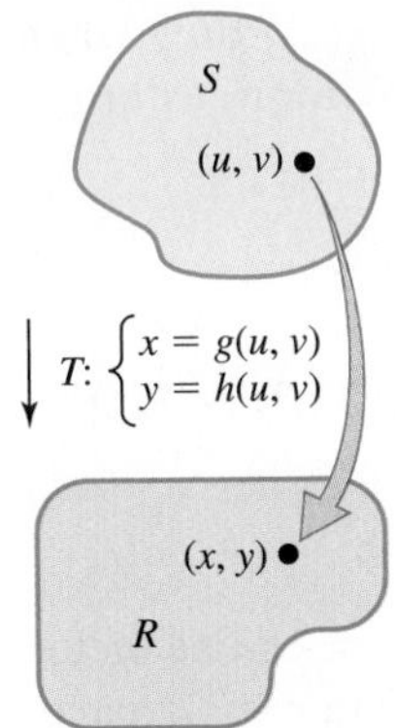

FIGURE 14.76

Transformations in the Plane

A change of variables in a double integral is a *transformation* that relates two sets of variables, (u, v) and (x, y). It is written compactly as $(x, y) = T(u, v)$. Because it relates pairs of variables, T has two components,

$$T: x = g(u, v) \quad \text{and} \quad y = h(u, v).$$

Geometrically, T takes a region S in the uv-plane and "maps" it point by point to a region R in the xy-plane (Figure 14.76). We write the outcome of this process as $R = T(S)$ and call R the **image** of S under T.

> In this example, we have replaced the coordinates u and v by the familiar polar coordinates r and θ.

EXAMPLE 1 **Image of a transformation** Consider the transformation from polar to rectangular coordinates given by

$$T: \quad x = g(r, \theta) = r\cos\theta \quad \text{and} \quad y = h(r, \theta) = r\sin\theta.$$

Find the image under this transformation of the rectangle

$$S = \{(r, \theta): 0 \le r \le 1, 0 \le \theta \le \pi/2\}.$$

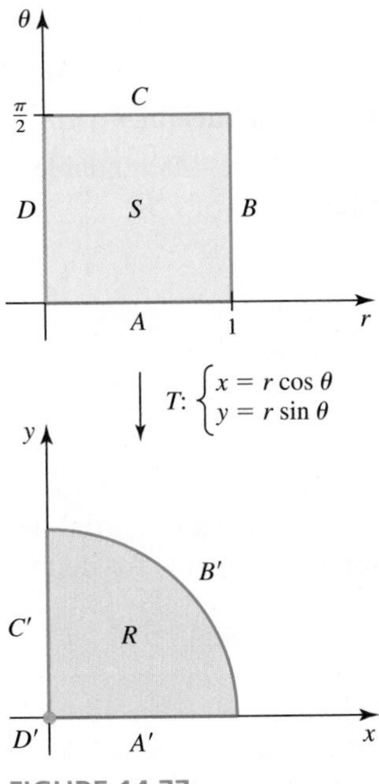

FIGURE 14.77

SOLUTION If we apply T to every point of S (Figure 14.77), what is the resulting set R in the xy-plane? One way to answer this question is to walk around the boundary of S, let's say counterclockwise, and determine the corresponding path in the xy-plane. In the $r\theta$-plane, we let the horizontal axis be the r-axis and the vertical axis be the θ-axis. Starting at the origin, we denote the edges of the rectangle S as follows.

$$A = \{(r, \theta): 0 \le r \le 1, \theta = 0\} \quad \text{Lower boundary}$$

$$B = \left\{(r, \theta): r = 1, 0 \le \theta \le \frac{\pi}{2}\right\} \quad \text{Right boundary}$$

$$C = \left\{(r, \theta): 0 \le r \le 1, \theta = \frac{\pi}{2}\right\} \quad \text{Upper boundary}$$

$$D = \left\{(r, \theta): r = 0, 0 \le \theta \le \frac{\pi}{2}\right\} \quad \text{Left boundary}$$

Table 14.6 shows the effect of the transformation on the four boundaries of S; the corresponding boundaries of R in the xy-plane are denoted A', B', C', and D' (Figure 14.77).

Table 14.6

Boundary of S in $r\theta$-plane	Transformation equations	Boundary of R in xy-plane
A: $0 \le r \le 1, \theta = 0$	$x = r\cos\theta = r$, $y = r\sin\theta = 0$	A': $0 \le x \le 1, y = 0$
B: $r = 1, 0 \le \theta \le \pi/2$	$x = r\cos\theta = \cos\theta$, $y = r\sin\theta = \sin\theta$	B': quarter unit circle
C: $0 \le r \le 1, \theta = \pi/2$	$x = r\cos\theta = 0$, $y = r\sin\theta = r$	C': $x = 0, 0 \le y \le 1$
D: $r = 0, 0 \le \theta \le \pi/2$	$x = r\cos\theta = 0$, $y = r\sin\theta = 0$	D': single point $(0, 0)$

The image of the rectangular boundary of S is the boundary of R. Furthermore, it can be shown that every point in the interior of R is the image of one point in the interior of S. Therefore, the image of S is the quarter disk R in the xy-plane.

Related Exercises 5–16

QUICK CHECK 1 How would the image of S change in Example 1 if $S = \{(r, \theta): 0 \le r \le 1, 0 \le \theta \le \pi\}$?

Recall that a function f is *one-to-one* on an interval I if $f(x_1) = f(x_2)$ only when $x_1 = x_2$, where x_1 and x_2 are points of I. We need an analogous property for transformations when changing variables.

DEFINITION One-to-One Transformation

A transformation T from a region S to a region R is one-to-one on S if $T(P) = T(Q)$ only when $P = Q$, where P and Q are points in S.

Notice that the polar coordinate transformation in Example 1 is *not* one-to-one the rectangle $S = \{(r, \theta): 0 \le r \le 1, 0 \le \theta \le \pi/2\}$ (because all points with $r = 0$ map to the point $(0, 0)$). However, this transformation *is* one-to-one on the interior of S.

We can now anticipate how a transformation (change of variables) is used to simplify a double integral. Suppose we have the integral $\iint_R f(x, y)\, dA$. The goal is to find a transformation to a new set of coordinates (u, v) such that the new equivalent integral $\iint_S f(x(u, v), y(u, v))\, dA$ involves a simple region S (such as a rectangle), a simple integrand, or both. The next theorem allows us to do exactly that, but it first requires a new concept.

➤ The Jacobian is named after the German mathematician Carl Gustav Jacob Jacobi (1804–1851). In some books, the Jacobian is the matrix of partial derivatives. In others, as here, the Jacobian is the determinant of the matrix of partial derivatives. Both $J(u, v)$ and $\dfrac{\partial(x, y)}{\partial(u, v)}$ are used to refer to the Jacobian.

DEFINITION Jacobian Determinant of a Transformation of Two Variables

Given a transformation T: $x = g(u, v)$, $y = h(u, v)$, where g and h are differentiable on a region of the uv-plane, the **Jacobian determinant** (or **Jacobian**) of T is

$$J(u, v) = \frac{\partial(x, y)}{\partial(u, v)} = \begin{vmatrix} \dfrac{\partial x}{\partial u} & \dfrac{\partial x}{\partial v} \\ \dfrac{\partial y}{\partial u} & \dfrac{\partial y}{\partial v} \end{vmatrix} = \frac{\partial x}{\partial u}\frac{\partial y}{\partial v} - \frac{\partial x}{\partial v}\frac{\partial y}{\partial u}.$$

QUICK CHECK 2 Find $J(u, v)$ if $x = u + v$, $y = 2v$. ◄

The Jacobian is easiest to remember as the determinant of a 2×2 matrix of partial derivatives. With the Jacobian in hand, we can state the change-of-variables rule for double integrals.

➤ The condition that g and h have continuous first partial derivatives ensures that the new integrand is integrable.

THEOREM 14.8 Change of Variables for Double Integrals

Let T: $x = g(u, v)$, $y = h(u, v)$ be a transformation that maps a closed bounded region S in the uv-plane onto a region R in the xy-plane. Assume that T is one-to-one on the interior of S and that g and h have continuous first partial derivatives there. If f is continuous on R, then

$$\iint_R f(x, y)\, dA = \iint_S f(g(u, v), h(u, v))\, |J(u, v)|\, dA.$$

➤ In the integral over R, dA corresponds to $dx\, dy$. In the integral over S, dA corresponds to $du\, dv$. The relation $dx\, dy = |J|\, du\, dv$ is the analog of $du = g'(x)\, dx$ in a change of variables with one variable.

The proof of this result is technical and is found in advanced texts. The factor $|J(u, v)|$ that appears in the second integral is the absolute value of the Jacobian. Matching the area elements in the two integrals of Theorem 14.8, we see that $dx\, dy = |J(u, v)|\, du\, dv$. This expression shows that the Jacobian is a magnification (or reduction) factor: It relates the area of a small region $dx\, dy$ in the xy-plane to the area of the corresponding region $du\, dv$ in the uv-plane. If the transformation equations are linear, then this relationship is exact in the sense that area$(T(S)) = |J(u, v)|$ area(S) (see Exercise 60). The way in which the Jacobian arises is explored in Exercise 61.

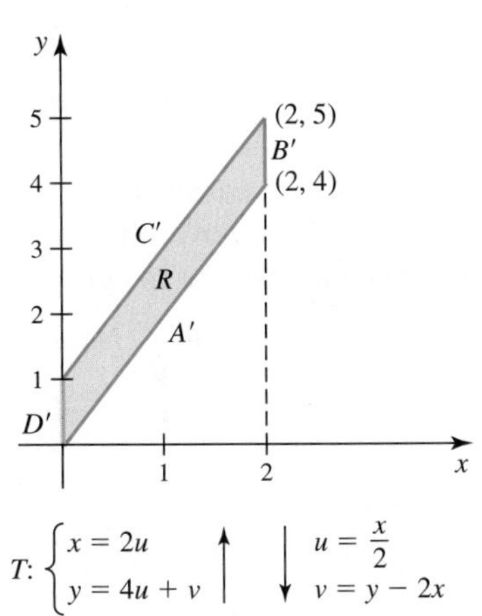

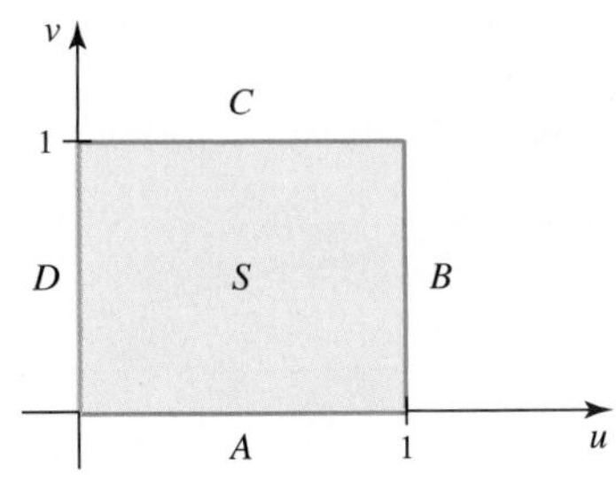

FIGURE 14.78

EXAMPLE 2 Jacobian of the polar to rectangular transformation Compute the Jacobian of the transformation

$$T: \quad x = g(r,\theta) = r\cos\theta, \qquad y = h(r,\theta) = r\sin\theta.$$

SOLUTION The necessary partial derivatives are

$$\frac{\partial x}{\partial r} = \cos\theta, \qquad \frac{\partial x}{\partial \theta} = -r\sin\theta, \qquad \frac{\partial y}{\partial r} = \sin\theta, \qquad \frac{\partial y}{\partial \theta} = r\cos\theta.$$

Therefore,

$$J(r,\theta) = \frac{\partial(x,y)}{\partial(r,\theta)} = \begin{vmatrix} \dfrac{\partial x}{\partial r} & \dfrac{\partial x}{\partial \theta} \\ \dfrac{\partial y}{\partial r} & \dfrac{\partial y}{\partial \theta} \end{vmatrix} = \begin{vmatrix} \cos\theta & -r\sin\theta \\ \sin\theta & r\cos\theta \end{vmatrix} = r(\cos^2\theta + \sin^2\theta) = r.$$

This determinant calculation confirms the change-of-variables formula for polar coordinates: $dx\,dy$ becomes $r\,dr\,d\theta$. *Related Exercises 17–26* ◀

We are now ready for a change of variables. To transform the integral $\iint_R f(x,y)\,dA$ into $\iint_S f(x(u,v), y(u,v))|J(u,v)|\,dA$, we must find the transformation $x = g(u,v)$ and $y = h(u,v)$, and then use it to find the new region of integration S. The next example illustrates how the region S is found, assuming the transformation is given.

EXAMPLE 3 Double integral with a change of variables given Evaluate the integral $\iint_R \sqrt{2x(y-2x)}\,dA$, where R is the parallelogram in the xy-plane with vertices $(0,0)$, $(0,1)$, $(2,4)$, and $(2,5)$ (Figure 14.78). Use the transformation

$$T: x = 2u, y = 4u + v.$$

SOLUTION To what region S in the uv-plane is R mapped? Because T takes points in the uv-plane and assigns them to points in the xy-plane, we must reverse the process by solving $x = 2u$, $y = 4u + v$ for u and v:

➤ The relations that "go the other direction" comprise the inverse transformation, usually denoted T^{-1}.

$$\text{First equation: } x = 2u \Rightarrow u = \frac{x}{2}$$

$$\text{Second equation: } y = 4u + v \Rightarrow v = y - 4u = y - 2x$$

Rather than walk around the boundary of R in the xy-plane to determine the resulting region S in the uv-plane, it suffices to find the images of the vertices of R. You should confirm that the vertices map as shown in Table 14.7.

Table 14.7

(x, y)	(u, v)
(0, 0)	(0, 0)
(0, 1)	(0, 1)
(2, 5)	(1, 1)
(2, 4)	(1, 0)

Connecting the points in the uv-plane in order, we see that S is the unit square $\{(u,v): 0 \le u \le 1, 0 \le v \le 1\}$ (Figure 14.78). These inequalities determine the limits of integration in the uv-plane.

Replacing $2x$ by $4u$ and $y - 2x$ by v, the original integrand becomes $\sqrt{2x(y-2x)} = \sqrt{4uv}$. The Jacobian is

$$J(u,v) = \begin{vmatrix} \dfrac{\partial x}{\partial u} & \dfrac{\partial x}{\partial v} \\ \dfrac{\partial y}{\partial u} & \dfrac{\partial y}{\partial v} \end{vmatrix} = \begin{vmatrix} 2 & 0 \\ 4 & 1 \end{vmatrix} = 2.$$

➤ T is an example of a *shearing transformation*. The greater the u-coordinate of a point, the more that point is displaced in the v-direction. It also involves a uniform stretch in the u-direction.

The integration now follows:

$$\iint_R \sqrt{2x(y-2x)}\,dA = \iint_S \sqrt{4uv}\,\underbrace{|J(u,v)|}_{2}\,dA \qquad \text{Change variables.}$$

$$= \int_0^1\int_0^1 \sqrt{4uv}\,2\,du\,dv \qquad \text{Convert to an iterated integral.}$$

$$= 4\int_0^1 \frac{2}{3}\sqrt{v}\,(u^{3/2})\Big|_0^1\,dv \quad \text{Evaluate the inner integral.}$$

$$= \frac{8}{3}\cdot\frac{2}{3}(v^{3/2})\Big|_0^1 = \frac{16}{9} \quad \text{Evaluate the outer integral.}$$

The effect of the change of variables is illustrated in Figure 14.79, where we see the surface $z = \sqrt{2x(y - 2x)}$ over the region R and the surface $w = 2\sqrt{4uv}$ over the region S. The volumes of the solids beneath the two surfaces are equal, but the integral over S is easier to evaluate.

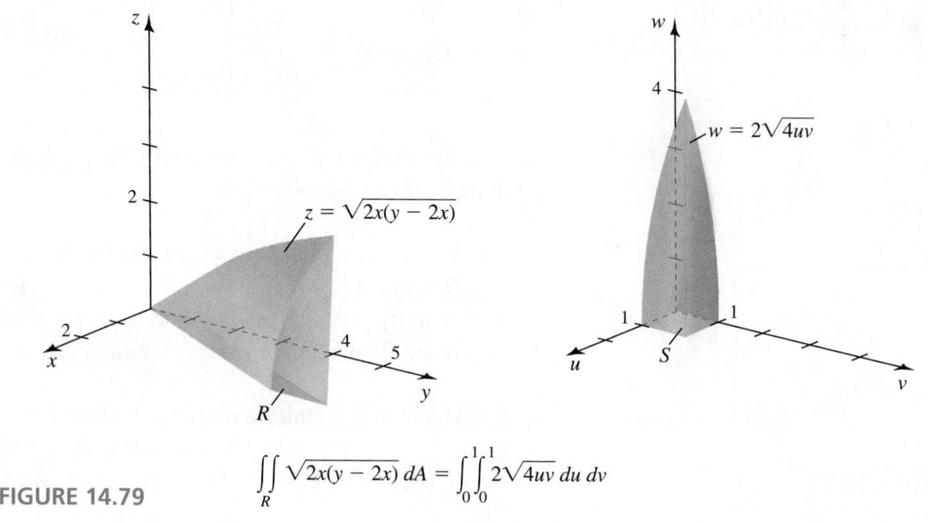

$\iint_R \sqrt{2x(y-2x)}\,dA = \int_0^1\int_0^1 2\sqrt{4uv}\,du\,dv$

FIGURE 14.79

Related Exercises 27–30 ◀

QUICK CHECK 3 Solve the equations $u = x + y, v = -x + 2y$ for x and y. ◀

In Example 3, the required transformation was given. More practically, we must deduce an appropriate transformation from either the integrand or the region of integration.

EXAMPLE 4 Change of variables determined by the integrand Evaluate $\iint_R \sqrt{\frac{x - y}{x + y + 1}}\,dA$, where R is the square with vertices $(0, 0)$, $(1, -1)$, $(2, 0)$, and $(1, 1)$ (Figure 14.80).

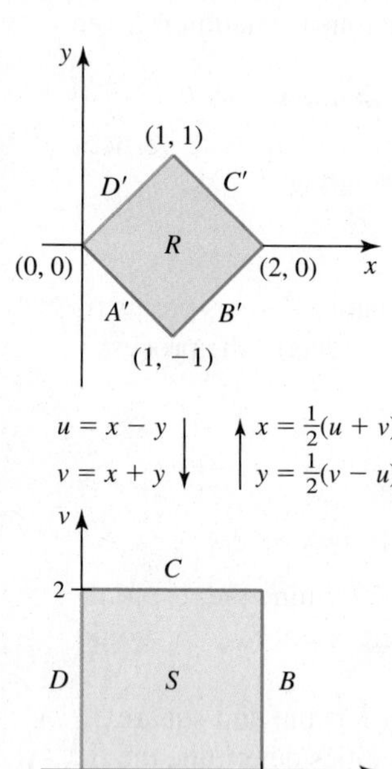

FIGURE 14.80

SOLUTION Evaluating the integral as it stands requires splitting the region R into two subregions; furthermore, the integrand presents difficulties. The terms $x + y$ and $x - y$ in the integrand suggest the new variables

$$u = x - y \quad \text{and} \quad v = x + y.$$

To determine the region S in the uv-plane that corresponds to R under this transformation, we find the images of the vertices of R in the uv-plane and connect them in order. The result is the square $S = \{(u, v): 0 \le u \le 2, 0 \le v \le 2\}$. Before computing the Jacobian, we express x and y in terms of u and v. Adding the two equations and solving for x, we have $x = (u + v)/2$. Subtracting the two equations and solving for y gives $y = (v - u)/2$. The Jacobian now follows:

➤ This transformation is a *rotation*. It rotates the points of R about the origin 45° in the counterclockwise direction (it also increases lengths by a factor of $\sqrt{2}$). In this example, the change of variables $u = x + y$ and $v = x - y$ would work just as well.

$$J(u, v) = \begin{vmatrix} \frac{\partial x}{\partial u} & \frac{\partial x}{\partial v} \\ \frac{\partial y}{\partial u} & \frac{\partial y}{\partial v} \end{vmatrix} = \begin{vmatrix} \frac{1}{2} & \frac{1}{2} \\ -\frac{1}{2} & \frac{1}{2} \end{vmatrix} = \frac{1}{2}$$

With the choice of new variables, the original integrand $\sqrt{\dfrac{x-y}{x+y+1}}$ becomes $\sqrt{\dfrac{u}{v+1}}$. The integration in the uv-plane may now be done:

> An appropriate change of variables for a double integral is not always obvious. Some trial and error is often needed to come up with a transformation that simplifies the integrand and/or the region of integration. Strategies are discussed at the end of this section.

$$\iint_R \sqrt{\frac{x-y}{x+y+1}}\,dA = \iint_S \sqrt{\frac{u}{v+1}}\,|J(u,v)|\,dA \quad \text{Change of variables}$$

$$= \int_0^2\int_0^2 \sqrt{\frac{u}{v+1}}\,\frac{1}{2}\,du\,dv \quad \text{Convert to an iterated integral.}$$

$$= \frac{1}{2}\int_0^2 (v+1)^{-1/2}\,\frac{2}{3}\left(u^{3/2}\right)\Big|_0^2\,dv \quad \text{Evaluate the inner integral.}$$

$$= \frac{2^{3/2}}{3}\,2(v+1)^{1/2}\Big|_0^2 \quad \text{Evaluate the outer integral.}$$

$$= \frac{4\sqrt{2}}{3}\left(\sqrt{3}-1\right) \quad \text{Simplify.}$$

Related Exercises 31–36 ◀

QUICK CHECK 4 In Example 4, what is the ratio of the area of S to the area of R? How is this ratio related to J? ◀

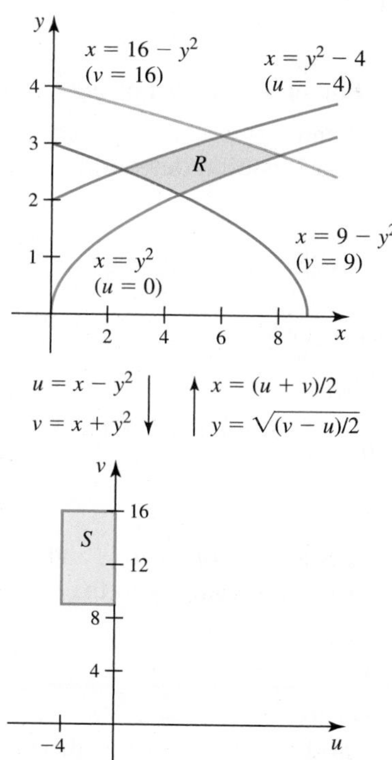

FIGURE 14.81

EXAMPLE 5 Change of variables determined by the region Let R be the region in the first quadrant bounded by the parabolas $x = y^2$, $x = y^2 - 4$, $x = 9 - y^2$, and $x = 16 - y^2$ (Figure 14.81). Evaluate $\iint_R y^2\,dA$.

SOLUTION Notice that the bounding curves may be written as $x - y^2 = 0$, $x - y^2 = -4$, $x + y^2 = 9$, and $x + y^2 = 16$. The first two parabolas have the form $x - y^2 = C$, where C is a constant, which suggests the new variable $u = x - y^2$. The last two parabolas have the form $x + y^2 = C$, which suggests the new variable $v = x + y^2$. Therefore, the new variables are

$$u = x - y^2, \quad v = x + y^2.$$

The boundary curves of S are $u = -4$, $u = 0$, $v = 9$, and $v = 16$. Therefore, the new region is $S = \{(u, v): -4 \le u \le 0, 9 \le v \le 16\}$ (Figure 14.81). To compute the Jacobian, we must find the transformation T by writing x and y in terms of u and v. Solving for x and y, and observing that $y \ge 0$ for all points in R, we find that

$$T:\quad x = \frac{u+v}{2}, \quad y = \sqrt{\frac{v-u}{2}}.$$

The points of S satisfy $v > u$, so $\sqrt{v-u}$ is defined. Now the Jacobian may be computed:

$$J(u,v) = \begin{vmatrix} \dfrac{\partial x}{\partial u} & \dfrac{\partial x}{\partial v} \\[2ex] \dfrac{\partial y}{\partial u} & \dfrac{\partial y}{\partial v} \end{vmatrix} = \begin{vmatrix} \dfrac{1}{2} & \dfrac{1}{2} \\[2ex] -\dfrac{1}{2\sqrt{2(v-u)}} & \dfrac{1}{2\sqrt{2(v-u)}} \end{vmatrix} = \frac{1}{2\sqrt{2(v-u)}}.$$

The change of variables proceeds as follows:

$$\iint_R y^2\,dA = \int_9^{16}\int_{-4}^0 \underbrace{\frac{v-u}{2}}_{y^2}\,\underbrace{\frac{1}{2\sqrt{2(v-u)}}}_{|J(u,v)|}\,du\,dv \quad \text{Convert to an iterated integral.}$$

$$= \frac{1}{4\sqrt{2}}\int_9^{16}\int_{-4}^0 \sqrt{v-u}\,du\,dv \quad \text{Simplify.}$$

$$= \frac{1}{4\sqrt{2}}\frac{2}{3}\int_9^{16} \left(-(v-u)^{3/2}\right)\Big|_{-4}^{0}\, dv \qquad \text{Evaluate the inner integral.}$$

$$= \frac{1}{6\sqrt{2}}\int_9^{16} \left((v+4)^{3/2} - v^{3/2}\right) dv \qquad \text{Simplify.}$$

$$= \frac{1}{6\sqrt{2}}\frac{2}{5}\left((v+4)^{5/2} - v^{5/2}\right)\Big|_9^{16} \qquad \text{Evaluate the outer integral.}$$

$$= \frac{\sqrt{2}}{30}\left(32 \cdot 5^{5/2} - 13^{5/2} - 781\right) \qquad \text{Simplify.}$$

$$\approx 18.79$$

Related Exercises 31–36 ◀

Change of Variables in Triple Integrals

With triple integrals, we work with a transformation T of the form

$$T: \quad x = g(u, v, w), \quad y = h(u, v, w), \quad z = p(u, v, w).$$

In this case, T maps a region S in uvw-space to a region D in xyz-space. As before, the goal is to transform the integral $\iiint_D f(x, y, z)\, dV$ into a new integral over the region S so that the integral is easier to evaluate. First, we need a Jacobian.

➤ Recall that by expanding about the first row,

$$\begin{vmatrix} a_{11} & a_{12} & a_{13} \\ a_{21} & a_{22} & a_{23} \\ a_{31} & a_{32} & a_{33} \end{vmatrix} = a_{11}(a_{22}a_{33} - a_{23}a_{32}) - a_{12}(a_{21}a_{33} - a_{23}a_{31}) + a_{13}(a_{21}a_{32} - a_{22}a_{31}).$$

DEFINITION Jacobian Determinant of a Transformation of Three Variables

Given a transformation T: $x = g(u, v, w)$, $y = h(u, v, w)$, and $z = p(u, v, w)$, where g, h, and p are differentiable on a region of uvw-space, the **Jacobian determinant** (or **Jacobian**) of T is

$$J(u, v, w) = \frac{\partial(x, y, z)}{\partial(u, v, w)} = \begin{vmatrix} \dfrac{\partial x}{\partial u} & \dfrac{\partial x}{\partial v} & \dfrac{\partial x}{\partial w} \\ \dfrac{\partial y}{\partial u} & \dfrac{\partial y}{\partial v} & \dfrac{\partial y}{\partial w} \\ \dfrac{\partial z}{\partial u} & \dfrac{\partial z}{\partial v} & \dfrac{\partial z}{\partial w} \end{vmatrix}.$$

The Jacobian is evaluated as a 3×3 determinant and is a function of u, v, and w. A change of variables with respect to three variables proceeds in analogy to the two-variable case.

➤ If we match the volume elements in both integrals, then $dx\,dy\,dz = |J(u, v, w)|\,du\,dv\,dw$. As before, the Jacobian is a magnification (or reduction) factor, now relating the volume of a small region in xyz-space to the volume of the corresponding region in uvw-space.

THEOREM 14.9 Change of Variables for Triple Integrals

Let T: $x = g(u, v, w)$, $y = h(u, v, w)$, and $z = p(u, v, w)$ be a transformation that maps a closed bounded region S in uvw-space to a region $D = T(S)$ in xyz-space. Assume that T is one-to-one on the interior of S and that g, h, and p have continuous first partial derivatives there. If f is continuous on D, then

$$\iiint_D f(x, y, z)\, dV = \iiint_S f(g(u, v, w), h(u, v, w), p(u, v, w))\, |J(u, v, w)|\, dV.$$

➤ To see that triple integrals in cylindrical and spherical coordinates as derived in Section 14.5 are consistent with this change of variable formulation, see Exercises 46 and 47.

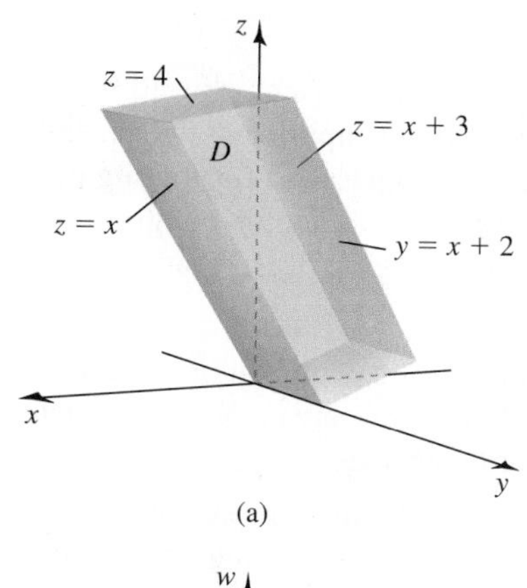

(a)

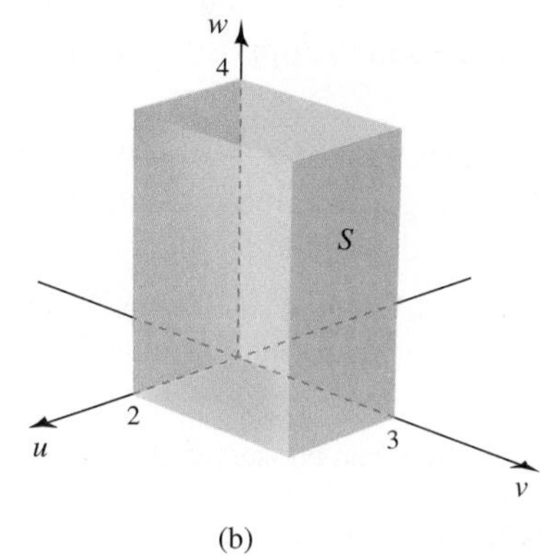

(b)

FIGURE 14.82

➤ It is easiest to expand this determinant about the third row.

EXAMPLE 6 A triple integral Use a change of variables to evaluate $\iiint_D xz\, dV$, where D is a parallelepiped bounded by the planes

$$y = x, \quad y = x + 2, \quad z = x, \quad z = x + 3, \quad z = 0, \quad \text{and} \quad z = 4$$

(Figure 14.82a).

SOLUTION The key is to note that D is bounded by three pairs of parallel planes:

- $y - x = 0$ and $y - x = 2$
- $z - x = 0$ and $z - x = 3$
- $z = 0$ and $z = 4$

These combinations of variables suggest the new variables

$$u = y - x, \quad v = z - x, \quad \text{and} \quad w = z.$$

With this choice, the new region of integration (Figure 14.82b) is the rectangular box

$$S = \{(u, v, w): 0 \le u \le 2, 0 \le v \le 3, 0 \le w \le 4\}.$$

To compute the Jacobian, we must express x, y, and z in terms of u, v, and w. A few steps of algebra lead to the transformation

$$T: \quad x = w - v, \quad y = u - v + w, \quad \text{and} \quad z = w.$$

The resulting Jacobian is

$$J(u, v, w) = \begin{vmatrix} \dfrac{\partial x}{\partial u} & \dfrac{\partial x}{\partial v} & \dfrac{\partial x}{\partial w} \\ \dfrac{\partial y}{\partial u} & \dfrac{\partial y}{\partial v} & \dfrac{\partial y}{\partial w} \\ \dfrac{\partial z}{\partial u} & \dfrac{\partial z}{\partial v} & \dfrac{\partial z}{\partial w} \end{vmatrix} = \begin{vmatrix} 0 & -1 & 1 \\ 1 & -1 & 1 \\ 0 & 0 & 1 \end{vmatrix} = 1.$$

Noting that the integrand is $xz = (w - v)w = w^2 - vw$, the integral may now be evaluated:

$$\begin{aligned} \iiint_D xz\, dV &= \iiint_S (w^2 - vw)\,|J(u, v, w)|\, dV && \text{Change variables.} \\ &= \int_0^4 \int_0^3 \int_0^2 (w^2 - vw) \underbrace{1}_{|J(u,v,w)|} du\, dv\, dw && \text{Convert to an iterated integral.} \\ &= \int_0^4 \int_0^3 2(w^2 - vw)\, dv\, dw && \text{Evaluate the inner integral.} \\ &= 2\int_0^4 \left(vw^2 - \frac{v^2 w}{2} \right)\Big|_0^3 dw && \text{Evaluate the middle integral.} \\ &= 2\int_0^4 \left(3w^2 - \frac{9w}{2} \right) dw && \text{Simplify.} \\ &= 2\left(w^3 - \frac{9w^2}{4} \right)\Big|_0^4 = 56 && \text{Evaluate the outer integral.} \end{aligned}$$

Related Exercises 37–44 ◄

QUICK CHECK 5 Interpret a Jacobian with a value of 1 (as in Example 6). ◄

Strategies for Choosing New Variables

Sometimes a change of variables simplifies the integrand but leads to an awkward region of integration. Conversely, the new region of integration may be simplified at the expense of additional complications in the integrand. Here are a few suggestions for finding new variables of integration. The observations are made with respect to double integrals, but they also apply to triple integrals. As before, R is the original region of integration in the xy-plane and S is the new region in the uv-plane.

1. **Aim for simple regions of integration in the uv-plane** The new region of integration in the uv-plane should be as simple as possible. Double integrals are easiest to evaluate over rectangular regions with sides parallel to the coordinate axes.

> Inverting the transformation means solving for x and y in terms of u and v, or vice versa.

2. **Is $(x, y) \to (u, v)$ or $(u, v) \to (x, y)$ better?** For some problems it is easiest to write (x, y) as functions of (u, v); in other cases the opposite is true. Depending on the problem, inverting the transformation (finding relations that go in the opposite direction) may be easy, difficult, or impossible.
   - If you know (x, y) in terms of (u, v) (that is, $x = g(u, v)$ and $y = h(u, v)$), then computing the Jacobian is straightforward, as is sketching the region R given the region S. However, the transformation must be inverted to determine the shape of S.
   - If you know (u, v) in terms of (x, y) (that is, $u = G(x, y)$ and $v = H(x, y)$), then sketching the region S is straightforward. However, the transformation must be inverted to compute the Jacobian.

3. **Let the integrand suggest new variables** New variables are often chosen to simplify the integrand. For example, the integrand $\sqrt{\frac{x - y}{x + y}}$ calls for new variables $u = x - y$ and $v = x + y$ ($u = x + y, v = x - y$ also works). There is, however, no guarantee that this change of variables will simplify the region of integration. In cases in which only one combination of variables appears, let one new variable be that combination and let the other new variable be unchanged. For example, if the integrand is $(x + 4y)^{3/2}$, try letting $u = x + 4y$ and $v = y$.

4. **Let the region suggest new variables** Example 5 illustrates an ideal situation. It occurs when the region R is bounded by two pairs of "parallel" curves in the families $g(x, y) = C_1$ and $h(x, y) = C_2$ (Figure 14.83). In this case the new region of integration is a rectangle $S = \{(u, v): a_1 \le u \le a_2, b_1 \le v \le b_2\}$, where $u = g(x, y)$ and $v = h(x, y)$.

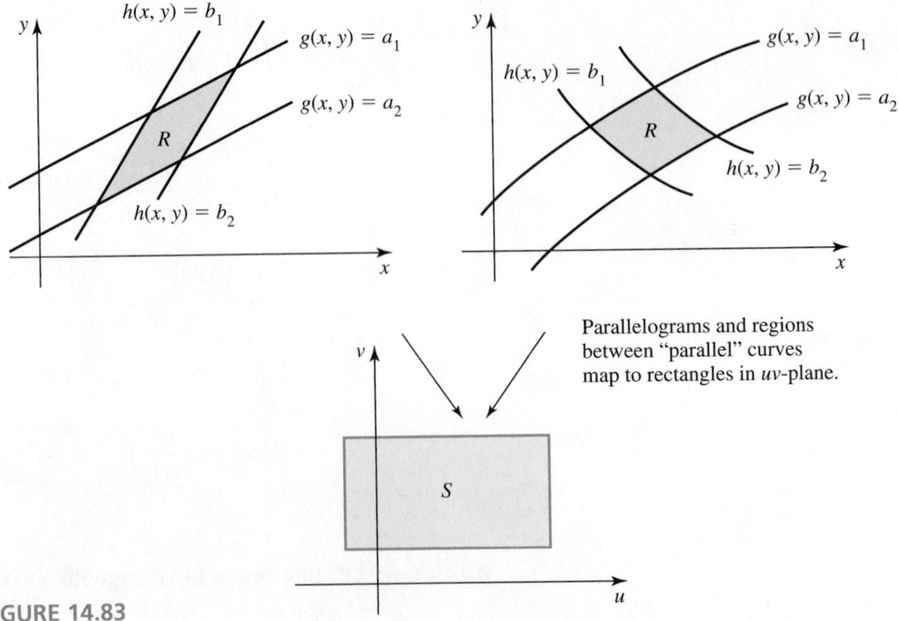

FIGURE 14.83

As another example, suppose the region is bounded by the lines $y = x$ (or $y/x = 1$) and $y = 2x$ (or $y/x = 2$) and by the hyperbolas $xy = 1$ and $xy = 3$. Then the new variables should be $u = xy$ and $v = y/x$ (or vice versa). The new region of integration is the rectangle $S = \{(u, v): 1 \le u \le 3, 1 \le v \le 2\}$.

SECTION 14.7 EXERCISES

Review Questions

1. If S is the unit square in the first quadrant of the uv-plane, describe the image of the transformation $T: x = 2u, y = 2v$.

2. Explain how to compute the Jacobian of the transformation $T: x = g(u, v), y = h(u, v)$.

3. Using the transformation $T: x = u + v, y = u - v$, the image of the unit square $S = \{(u, v): 0 \le u \le 1, 0 \le v \le 1\}$ is a region R in the xy-plane. Explain how to change variables in the integral $\iint_R f(x, y)\, dA$ to find a new integral over S.

4. If S is the unit cube in the first octant of uvw-space with one vertex at the origin, describe the image of the transformation $T: x = u/2, y = v/2, z = w/2$.

Basic Skills

5–12. Transforming a square *Let $S = \{(u, v): 0 \le u \le 1, 0 \le v \le 1\}$ be a unit square in the uv-plane. Find the image of S in the xy-plane under the following transformations.*

5. $T: x = 2u, y = v/2$

6. $T: x = -u, y = -v$

7. $T: x = (u + v)/2, y = (u - v)/2$

8. $T: x = 2u + v, y = 2u$

9. $T: x = u^2 - v^2, y = 2uv$

10. $T: x = 2uv, y = u^2 - v^2$

11. $T: x = u \cos(\pi v), y = u \sin(\pi v)$

12. $T: x = v \sin(\pi u), y = v \cos(\pi u)$

13–16. Images of regions *Find the image R in the xy-plane of the region S using the given transformation T. Sketch both R and S.*

13. $S = \{(u, v): v \le 1 - u, u \ge 0, v \ge 0\}$; $T: x = u, y = v^2$

14. $S = \{(u, v): u^2 + v^2 \le 1\}$; $T: x = 2u, y = 4v$

15. $S = \{(u, v): 1 \le u \le 3, 2 \le v \le 4\}$; $T: x = u/v, y = v$

16. $S = \{(u, v): 2 \le u \le 3, 3 \le v \le 6\}$; $T: x = u, y = v/u$

17–22. Computing Jacobians *Compute the Jacobian $J(u, v)$ for the following transformations.*

17. $T: x = 3u, y = -3v$

18. $T: x = 4v, y = -2u$

19. $T: x = 2uv, y = u^2 - v^2$

20. $T: x = u \cos(\pi v), y = u \sin(\pi v)$

21. $T: x = (u + v)/\sqrt{2}, y = (u - v)/\sqrt{2}$

22. $T: x = u/v, y = v$

23–26. Solve and compute Jacobians *Solve the following relations for x and y, and compute the Jacobian $J(u, v)$.*

23. $u = x + y, v = 2x - y$

24. $u = xy, v = x$

25. $u = 2x - 3y, v = y - x$

26. $u = x + 4y, v = 3x + 2y$

27–30. Double integrals—transformation given *To evaluate the following integrals carry out these steps.*

a. *Sketch the original region of integration R in the xy-plane and the new region S in the uv-plane using the given change of variables.*

b. *Find the limits of integration for the new integral with respect to u and v.*

c. *Compute the Jacobian.*

d. *Change variables and evaluate the new integral.*

27. $\iint_R xy\, dA$, where R is the square with vertices $(0, 0)$, $(1, 1)$, $(2, 0)$, and $(1, -1)$; use $x = u + v, y = u - v$.

28. $\iint_R x^2 y\, dA$, where $R = \{(x, y): 0 \le x \le 2, x \le y \le x + 4\}$; use $x = 2u, y = 4v + 2u$.

29. $\iint_R x^2\sqrt{x + 2y}\, dA$, where $R = \{(x, y): 0 \le x \le 2, -x/2 \le y \le 1 - x\}$; use $x = 2u, y = v - u$.

30. $\iint_R xy\, dA$, where R is bounded by the ellipse $9x^2 + 4y^2 = 36$; use $x = 2u, y = 3v$.

31–36. Double integrals—your choice of transformation *Evaluate the following integrals using a change of variables of your choice. Sketch the original and new regions of integration, R and S.*

31. $\int_0^1 \int_y^{y+2} \sqrt{x - y}\, dx\, dy$

32. $\iint_R \sqrt{y^2 - x^2}\, dA$, where R is the diamond bounded by $y - x = 0, y - x = 2, y + x = 0$, and $y + x = 2$

33. $\iint_R \left(\frac{y - x}{y + 2x + 1}\right)^4 dA$, where R is the parallelogram bounded by $y - x = 1, y - x = 2, y + 2x = 0$, and $y + 2x = 4$

34. $\displaystyle\iint_R e^{xy}\,dA$, where R is the region bounded by the hyperbolas $xy = 1$ and $xy = 4$, and the lines $y/x = 1$ and $y/x = 3$

35. $\displaystyle\iint_R xy\,dA$, where R is the region bounded by the hyperbolas $xy = 1$ and $xy = 4$, and the lines $y = 1$ and $y = 3$

36. $\displaystyle\iint_R (x - y)\sqrt{x - 2y}\,dA$, where R is the triangular region bounded by $y = 0$, $x - 2y = 0$, and $x - y = 1$

37–40. Jacobians in three variables *Evaluate the Jacobians $J(u, v, w)$ for the following transformations.*

37. $x = v + w, y = u + w, z = u + v$

38. $x = u + v - w, y = u - v + w, z = -u + v + w$

39. $x = vw, y = uw, z = u^2 - v^2$

40. $u = x - y, v = x - z, w = y + z$ (Solve for x, y, and z first.)

41–44. Triple integrals *Use a change of variables to evaluate the following integrals.*

41. $\displaystyle\iiint_D xy\,dV$; D is bounded by the planes $y - x = 0$, $y - x = 2, z - y = 0, z - y = 1, z = 0, z = 3$.

42. $\displaystyle\iiint_D dV$; D is bounded by the planes $y - 2x = 0, y - 2x = 1$, $z - 3y = 0, z - 3y = 1, z - 4x = 0, z - 4x = 3$.

43. $\displaystyle\iiint_D z\,dV$; D is bounded by the paraboloid $z = 16 - x^2 - 4y^2$ and the xy-plane. Use $x = 4u\cos v, y = 2u\sin v, z = w$.

44. $\displaystyle\iiint_D dV$; D is bounded by the upper half of the ellipsoid $x^2/9 + y^2/4 + z^2 = 1$ and the xy-plane. Use $x = 3u$, $y = 2v, z = w$.

Further Explorations

45. **Explain why or why not** Determine whether the following statements are true and give an explanation or counterexample.
   a. If the transformation $T: x = g(u, v), y = h(u, v)$ is linear in u and v, then the Jacobian is a constant.
   b. The transformation $x = au + bv, y = cu + dv$ generally maps triangular regions to triangular regions.
   c. The transformation $x = 2v, y = -2u$ maps circles to circles.

46. **Cylindrical coordinates** Evaluate the Jacobian for the transformation from cylindrical coordinates (r, θ, Z) to rectangular coordinates (x, y, z): $x = r\cos\theta, y = r\sin\theta, z = Z$. Show that $J(r, \theta, Z) = r$.

47. **Spherical coordinates** Evaluate the Jacobian for the transformation from spherical to rectangular coordinates: $x = \rho\sin\varphi\cos\theta, y = \rho\sin\varphi\sin\theta, z = \rho\cos\varphi$. Show that $J(\rho, \varphi, \theta) = \rho^2\sin\varphi$.

48–52. Ellipse problems *Let R be the region bounded by the ellipse $x^2/a^2 + y^2/b^2 = 1$, where $a > 0$ and $b > 0$ are real numbers. Let T be the transformation $x = au, y = bv$.*

48. Find the area of R.

49. Evaluate $\displaystyle\iint_R |xy|\,dA$.

50. Find the center of mass of the upper half of R ($y \geq 0$) assuming it has a constant density.

51. Find the average square of the distance between points of R and the origin.

52. Find the average distance between points in the upper half of R and the x-axis.

53–56. Ellipsoid problems *Let D be the region bounded by the ellipsoid $x^2/a^2 + y^2/b^2 + z^2/c^2 = 1$, where $a > 0, b > 0$, and $c > 0$ are real numbers. Let T be the transformation $x = au, y = bv, z = cw$.*

53. Find the volume of D.

54. Evaluate $\displaystyle\iiint_D |xyz|\,dA$.

55. Find the center of mass of the upper half of D ($z \geq 0$) assuming it has a constant density.

56. Find the average square of the distance between points of D and the origin.

57. **Parabolic coordinates** Let T be the transformation $x = u^2 - v^2$, $y = 2uv$.
   a. Show that the lines $u = a$ in the uv-plane map to parabolas in the xy-plane that open in the negative x-direction with vertices on the positive x-axis.
   b. Show that the lines $v = b$ in the uv-plane map to parabolas in the xy-plane that open in the positive x-direction with vertices on the negative x-axis.
   c. Evaluate $J(u, v)$.
   d. Use a change of variables to find the area of the region bounded by $x = 4 - y^2/16$ and $x = y^2/4 - 1$.
   e. Use a change of variables to find the area of the curved rectangle above the x-axis bounded by $x = 4 - y^2/16$, $x = 9 - y^2/36, x = y^2/4 - 1$, and $x = y^2/64 - 16$.
   f. Describe the effect of the transformation $x = 2uv$, $y = u^2 - v^2$ on horizontal and vertical lines in the uv-plane.

Applications

58. **Shear transformations in $\mathbf{R}^2$** The transformation T in $\mathbf{R}^2$ given by $x = au + bv, y = cv$, where a, b, and c are positive real numbers, is a *shear transformation*. Let S be the unit square $\{(u, v): 0 \leq u \leq 1, 0 \leq v \leq 1\}$. Let $R = T(S)$ be the image of S.
   a. Explain with pictures the effect of T on S.
   b. Compute the Jacobian of T.
   c. Find the area of R and compare it to the area of S (which is 1).
   d. Assuming a constant density, find the center of mass of R (in terms of a, b, and c) and compare it to the center of mass of S (which is $(\frac{1}{2}, \frac{1}{2})$).
   e. Find an analogous transformation that gives a shear in the y-direction.

59. Shear transformations in $\mathbf{R}^3$ The transformation T in $\mathbf{R}^3$ given by

$$x = au + bv + cw, \qquad y = dv + ew, \qquad z = w,$$

where a, b, c, d, and e are positive real numbers, is one of many possible shear transformations in $\mathbf{R}^3$. Let S be the unit cube $\{(u, v, w): 0 \le u \le 1, 0 \le v \le 1, 0 \le w \le 1\}$. Let $D = T(S)$ be the image of S.

a. Explain with pictures and words the effect of T on S.
b. Compute the Jacobian of T.
c. Find the volume of D and compare it to the volume of S (which is 1).
d. Assuming a constant density, find the center of mass of D and compare it to the center of mass of S (which is $\left(\frac{1}{2}, \frac{1}{2}, \frac{1}{2}\right)$).

Additional Exercises

60. Linear transformations Consider the linear transformation T in $\mathbf{R}^2$ given by $x = au + bv$, $y = cu + dv$, where a, b, c, and d are real numbers, with $ad \ne bc$.

a. Find the Jacobian of T.
b. Let S be the square in the uv-plane with vertices $(0, 0)$, $(1, 0)$, $(0, 1)$, and $(1, 1)$, and let $R = T(S)$. Show that $\text{area}(R) = |J(u, v)|$.
c. Let ℓ be the line segment joining the points P and Q in the uv-plane. Show that $T(\ell)$ (the image of ℓ under T) is the line segment joining $T(P)$ and $T(Q)$ in the xy-plane. (*Hint:* Use vectors.)
d. Show that if S is a parallelogram in the uv-plane and $R = T(S)$, then $\text{area}(R) = |J(u, v)|\,\text{area}(S)$. (*Hint:* Without loss of generality, assume the vertices of S are $(0, 0)$, $(A, 0)$, (B, C), and $(A + B, C)$, where A, B, and C are positive, and use vectors.)

61. Meaning of the Jacobian The Jacobian is a magnification (or reduction) factor that relates the area of a small region near the point (u, v) to the area of the image of that region near the point (x, y).

a. Suppose S is a rectangle in the uv-plane with vertices $O(0, 0)$, $P(\Delta u, 0)$, $(\Delta u, \Delta v)$, and $Q(0, \Delta v)$ (see figure). The image of S under the transformation $x = g(u, v)$, $y = h(u, v)$ is a region R in the xy-plane. Let O', P' and Q' be the images of O, P, and Q, respectively, in the xy-plane where O', P', and Q' do not all lie on a line. Explain why the coordinates of O', P', and Q' are $(g(0, 0), h(0, 0))$, $(g(\Delta u, 0), h(\Delta u, 0))$ and $(g(0, \Delta v), h(0, \Delta v))$, respectively.
b. Use a Taylor series in both variables to show that

$$\begin{aligned} g(\Delta u, 0) &\approx g(0, 0) + g_u(0, 0)\Delta u \\ g(0, \Delta v) &\approx g(0, 0) + g_v(0, 0)\Delta v \\ h(\Delta u, 0) &\approx h(0, 0) + h_u(0, 0)\Delta u \\ h(0, \Delta v) &\approx h(0, 0) + h_v(0, 0)\Delta v \end{aligned}$$

where $g_u(0, 0)$ is $\dfrac{\partial g}{\partial u} = \dfrac{\partial x}{\partial u}$ evaluated at $(0, 0)$, with similar meanings for g_v, h_u, and h_v.
c. Consider the vectors $\overrightarrow{O'P'}$ and $\overrightarrow{O'Q'}$ and the parallelogram, two of whose sides are $\overrightarrow{O'P'}$ and $\overrightarrow{O'Q'}$. Use the cross product to show that the area of the parallelogram is $|J(u, v)|\,\Delta u\,\Delta v$.
d. Explain why the ratio of the area of R to the area of S is approximately $|J(u, v)|$.

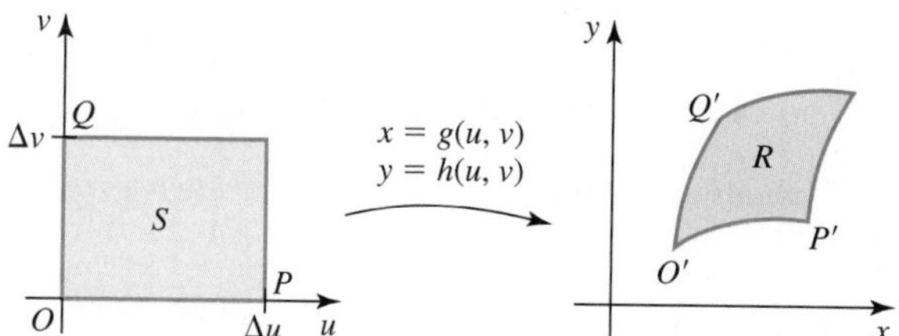

62. Open and closed boxes Consider the region R bounded by three pairs of parallel planes: $ax + by = 0$, $ax + by = 1$, $cx + dz = 0$, $cx + dz = 1$, $ey + fz = 0$, $ey + fz = 1$, where a, b, c, d, e, and f are real numbers. For the purposes of evaluating triple integrals, when do these six planes bound a finite region? Carry out the following steps.

a. Find three vectors $\mathbf{n}_1$, $\mathbf{n}_2$, and $\mathbf{n}_3$ each of which is normal to one of the three pairs of planes.
b. Show that the three normal vectors lie in a plane if their triple scalar product $\mathbf{n}_1 \cdot (\mathbf{n}_2 \times \mathbf{n}_3)$ is zero.
c. Show that the three normal vectors lie in a plane if $ade + bcf = 0$.
d. Assuming $\mathbf{n}_1$, $\mathbf{n}_2$, and $\mathbf{n}_3$ lie in a plane P, find a vector $\mathbf{N}$ that is normal to P. Explain why a line in the direction of $\mathbf{N}$ does not intersect any of the six planes, and thus the six planes do not form a bounded region.
e. Consider the change of variables $u = ax + by$, $v = cx + dz$, $w = ey + fz$. Show that

$$J(x, y, z) = \frac{\partial(u, v, w)}{\partial(x, y, z)} = -ade - bcf.$$

What is the value of the Jacobian if R is unbounded?

QUICK CHECK ANSWERS

1. The image is a semicircular disk of radius 1. **2.** $J(u, v) = 2$ **3.** $x = 2u/3 - v/3$, $y = u/3 + v/3$ **4.** The ratio is 2, which is $1/J(u, v)$. **5.** It means that the volume of a small region in xyz-space is unchanged when it is transformed by T to a small region in uvw-space.

CHAPTER 14 REVIEW EXERCISES

1. **Explain why or why not** Determine whether the following statements are true and give an explanation or counterexample.
   a. Assuming g is integrable and a, b, c, and d are constants, $\int_c^d \int_a^b g(x,y)\,dx\,dy = \left(\int_a^b g(x,y)\,dx\right)\left(\int_c^d g(x,y)\,dy\right)$.
   b. $\{(\rho,\varphi,\theta): \varphi = \pi/2\} = \{(r,\theta,z): z = 0\} = \{(x,y,z): z = 0\}$
   c. The transformation $T: x = v, y = -u$ maps a square in the uv-plane into a triangle in the xy-plane.

2–4. Evaluating integrals *Evaluate the following integrals as they are written.*

2. $\displaystyle\int_1^2 \int_1^4 \frac{xy}{(x^2+y^2)^2}\,dx\,dy$

3. $\displaystyle\int_1^3 \int_1^{e^x} \frac{x}{y}\,dy\,dx$

4. $\displaystyle\int_1^2 \int_0^{\ln x} x^3 e^y\,dy\,dx$

5–7. Changing the order of integration *Assuming f is integrable, change the order of integration in the following integrals.*

5. $\displaystyle\int_{-1}^1 \int_{x^2}^1 f(x,y)\,dy\,dx$

6. $\displaystyle\int_0^2 \int_{y-1}^1 f(x,y)\,dx\,dy$

7. $\displaystyle\int_0^1 \int_0^{\sqrt{1-y^2}} f(x,y)\,dx\,dy$

8–10. Area of plane regions *Use a double integral to compute the area of the following regions. Make a sketch of the region.*

8. The region bounded by the lines $y = -x - 4$, $y = x$, and $y = 2x - 4$

9. The region bounded by $y = |x|$ and $y = 20 - x^2$

10. The region between the curves $y = x^2$ and $y = 1 + x - x^2$

11–16. Miscellaneous double integrals *Choose a convenient method for evaluating the following integrals.*

11. $\displaystyle\iint_R \frac{2y}{\sqrt{x^4+1}}\,dA$; R is the region bounded by $x = 1$, $x = 2$, $y = x^{3/2}$, and $y = 0$.

12. $\displaystyle\iint_R x^{-1/2} e^y\,dA$; R is the region bounded by $x = 1$, $x = 4$, $y = \sqrt{x}$, and $y = 0$.

13. $\displaystyle\iint_R (x+y)\,dA$; R is the disk bounded by the circle $r = 4\sin\theta$.

14. $\displaystyle\iint_R (x^2+y^2)\,dA$; R is the region $\{(x,y): 0 \le x \le 2, 0 \le y \le x\}$.

15. $\displaystyle\int_0^1 \int_{y^{1/3}}^1 x^{10}\cos(\pi x^4 y)\,dx\,dy$

16. $\displaystyle\int_0^2 \int_{y^2}^4 x^8 y\sqrt{1 + x^4y^2}\,dx\,dy$

17–18. Cartesian to polar coordinates *Evaluate the following integrals over the specified region.*

17. $\displaystyle\iint_R 3x^2y\,dA$; $R = \{(r,\theta): 0 \le r \le 1, 0 \le \theta \le \pi/2\}$

18. $\displaystyle\iint_R \frac{1}{(1+x^2+y^2)^2}\,dA$; $R = \{(r,\theta): 1 \le r \le 4, 0 \le \theta \le \pi\}$

19–21. Computing areas *Sketch the following regions and use integration to find their areas.*

19. The region bounded by all leaves of the rose $r = 3\cos 2\theta$

20. The region inside both of the circles $r = 2$ and $r = 4\cos\theta$

21. The region that lies inside both of the cardioids $r = 2 - 2\cos\theta$ and $r = 2 + 2\cos\theta$

22–23. Average values

22. Find the average value of $z = \sqrt{16 - x^2 - y^2}$ over the disk in the xy-plane centered at the origin with radius 4.

23. Find the average distance from the points in the solid cone bounded by $z = 2\sqrt{x^2+y^2}$ to the z-axis, for $0 \le z \le 8$.

24–26. Changing order of integration *Rewrite the following integrals using the indicated order of integration.*

24. $\displaystyle\int_0^1 \int_0^{\sqrt{1-x^2}} \int_0^{\sqrt{1-x^2}} f(x,y,z)\,dy\,dz\,dx$ in the order $dz\,dy\,dx$

25. $\displaystyle\int_0^4 \int_0^{\sqrt{16-x^2}} \int_0^{\sqrt{16-x^2-z^2}} f(x,y,z)\,dy\,dz\,dx$ in the order $dx\,dy\,dz$

26. $\displaystyle\int_0^2 \int_0^{9-x^2} \int_0^x f(x,y,z)\,dy\,dz\,dx$ in the order $dz\,dx\,dy$

27–31. Triple integrals *Evaluate the following integrals, changing the order of integration if needed.*

27. $\displaystyle\int_0^1 \int_{-z}^z \int_{-\sqrt{1-x^2}}^{\sqrt{1-x^2}} dy\,dx\,dz$

28. $\displaystyle\int_0^\pi \int_0^y \int_0^{\sin x} dz\,dx\,dy$

29. $\displaystyle\int_0^9 \int_0^1 \int_{2y}^2 \frac{4\sin x^2}{\sqrt{z}}\,dx\,dy\,dz$

30. $\int_0^2 \int_{-\sqrt{2-x^2/2}}^{\sqrt{2-x^2/2}} \int_{x^2+3y^2}^{8-x^2-y^2} dz\,dy\,dx$

31. $\int_0^2 \int_0^{y^{1/3}} \int_0^{y^2} yz^5(1 + x + y^2 + z^6)^2\,dx\,dz\,dy$

32–36. Volumes of solids *Find the volume of the following solids.*

32. The prism in the first octant bounded by the planes $y = 3 - 3x$ and $z = 2$

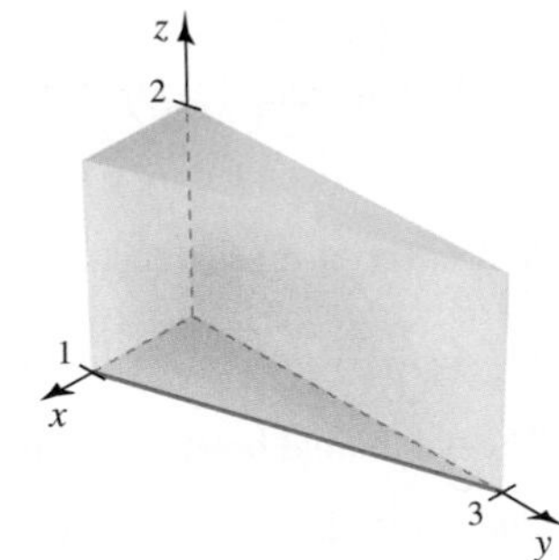

33. One of the wedges formed when the cylinder $x^2 + y^2 = 4$ is cut by the planes $z = 0$ and $y = z$

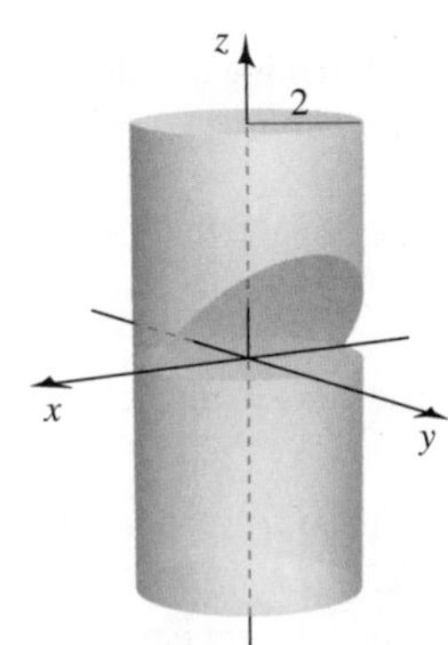

34. The region inside the parabolic cylinder $y = x^2$ between the planes $z = 3 - y$ and $z = 0$

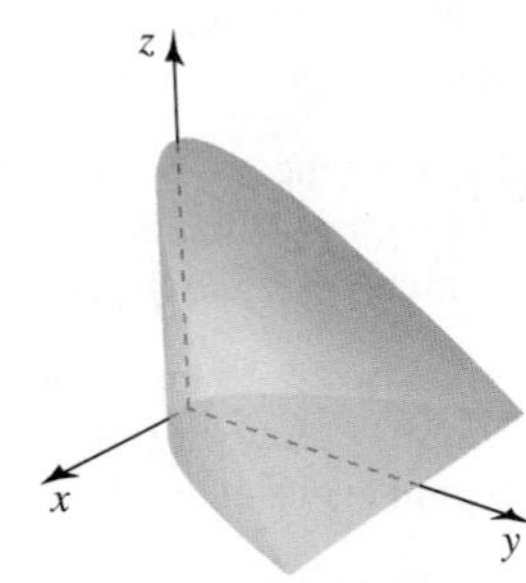

35. The region common to the two cylinders $x^2 + y^2 = 4$ and $x^2 + z^2 = 4$

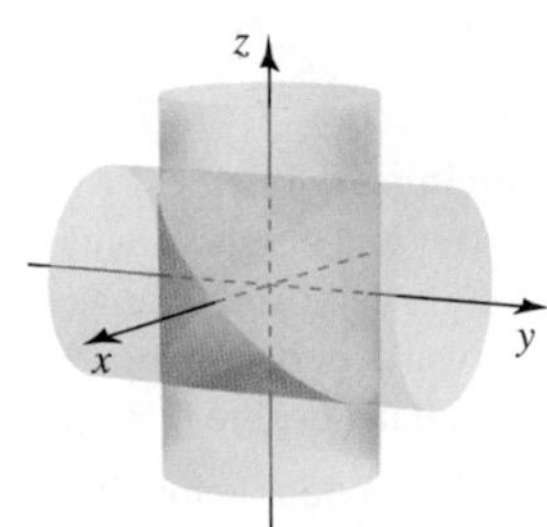

36. The tetrahedron with vertices $(0, 0, 0)$, $(1, 0, 0)$, $(1, 1, 0)$, and $(1, 1, 1)$

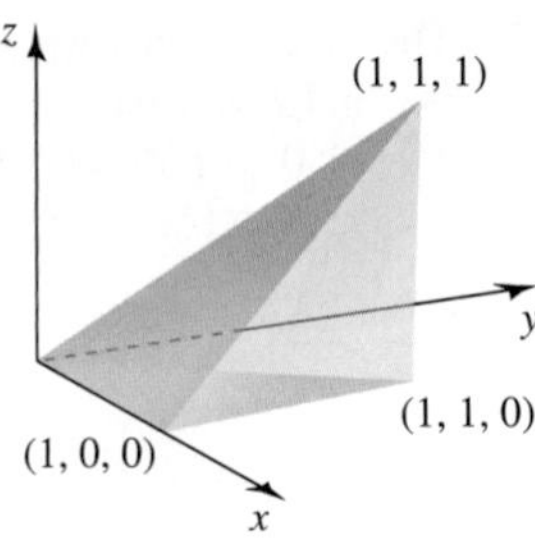

37. **Single to double integral** Evaluate $\int_0^{1/2} (\sin^{-1}(2x) - \sin^{-1} x)\,dx$ by converting it to a double integral.

38. **Tetrahedron limits** Let D be the tetrahedron with vertices at $(0, 0, 0)$, $(1, 0, 0)$, $(0, 2, 0)$, and $(0, 0, 3)$. Suppose the volume of D is to be found using a triple integral. Give the limits of integration for the six possible orderings of the variables.

39. **A "polynomial cube"** Let $D = \{(x, y, z): 0 \le x \le y^2, 0 \le y \le z^3, 0 \le z \le 2\}$.

   a. Use a triple integral to find the volume of D.
   b. In theory, how many other possible orderings of the variables (besides the one used in part (a)) can be used to find the volume of D? Verify the result of part (a) using one of these other orderings.
   c. What is the volume of the region $D = \{(x, y, z): 0 \le x \le y^p, 0 \le y \le z^q, 0 \le z \le 2\}$, where p and q are positive real numbers?

40–41. Average value

40. Find the average of the *square* of the distance between the origin and the points in the solid paraboloid $D = \{(x, y, z): 0 \le z \le 4 - x^2 - y^2\}$.

41. Find the average x-coordinate of the points in the prism $D = \{(x, y, z): 0 \le x \le 1, 0 \le y \le 3 - 3x, 0 \le z \le 2\}$.

42–43. Integrals in cylindrical coordinates *Evaluate the following integrals in cylindrical coordinates.*

42. $\int_0^3 \int_0^{\sqrt{9-x^2}} \int_0^3 (x^2 + y^2)^{3/2}\,dz\,dy\,dx$

43. $\int_{-2}^2 \int_{-1}^1 \int_0^{\sqrt{1-z^2}} \frac{1}{(1 + x^2 + z^2)^2}\,dx\,dz\,dy$

44–45. Volumes in cylindrical coordinates *Use integration in cylindrical coordinates to find the volume of the following regions.*

44. The region bounded by the plane $z = \sqrt{29}$ and the hyperboloid $z = \sqrt{4 + x^2 + y^2}$

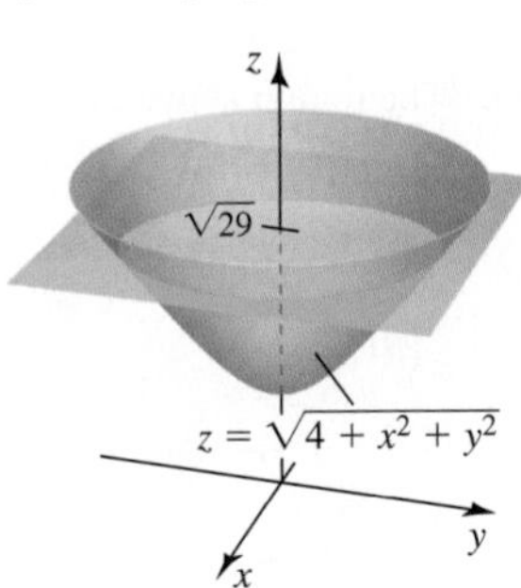

45. The solid cylinder whose height is 4 and whose base is the disk $\{(r, \theta): 0 \le r \le 2\cos\theta, 0 \le \theta \le \pi\}$

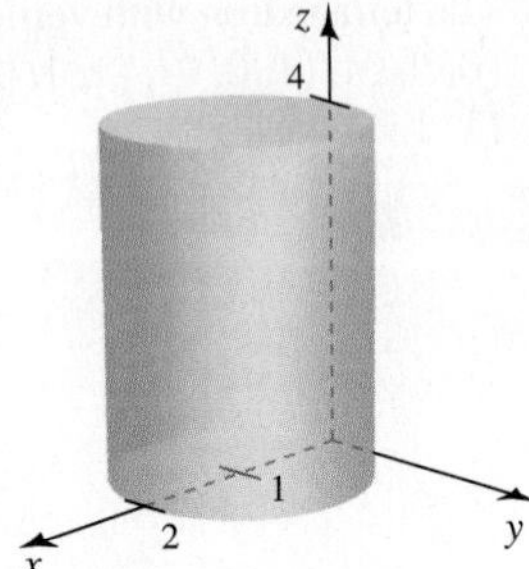

46–47. Integrals in spherical coordinates *Evaluate the following integrals in spherical coordinates.*

46. $\displaystyle\int_0^{2\pi}\int_0^{\pi/2}\int_0^{2\cos\varphi} \rho^2 \sin\varphi \, d\rho \, d\varphi \, d\theta$

47. $\displaystyle\int_0^{\pi}\int_0^{\pi/4}\int_{2\sec\varphi}^{4\sec\varphi} \rho^2 \sin\varphi \, d\rho \, d\varphi \, d\theta$

48–50. Volumes in spherical coordinates *Use integration in spherical coordinates to find the volume of the following regions.*

48. The cardioid of revolution $D = \{(\rho, \varphi, \theta): 0 \le \rho \le (1 - \cos\varphi)/2, 0 \le \varphi \le \pi, 0 \le \theta \le 2\pi\}$

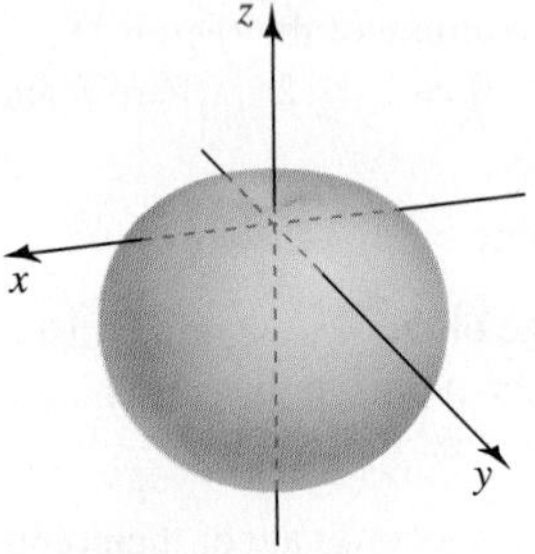

49. The rose petal of revolution $D = \{(\rho, \varphi, \theta): 0 \le \rho \le 4\sin 2\varphi, 0 \le \varphi \le \pi/2, 0 \le \theta \le 2\pi\}$

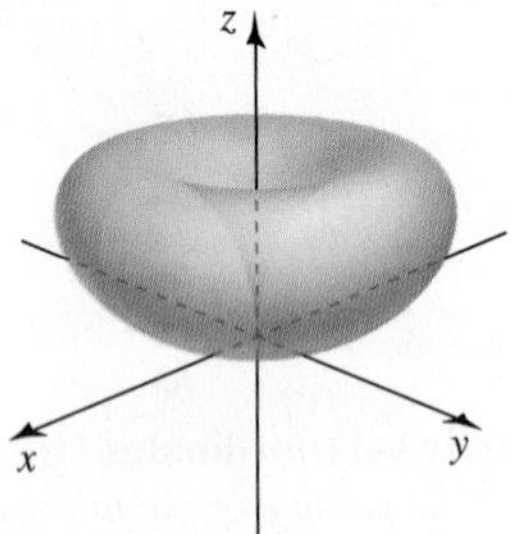

50. The region above the cone $\varphi = \pi/4$ and inside the sphere $\rho = 4\cos\varphi$

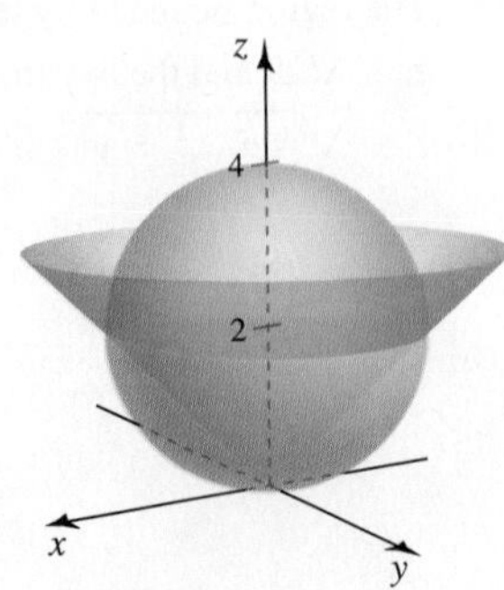

51–54. Constant density plates *Find the center of mass (centroid) of the following thin constant-density plates. Sketch the region corresponding to the plate and indicate the location of the center of mass. Use symmetry whenever possible to simplify your work.*

51. The region bounded by $y = \sin x$ and $y = 0$ between $x = 0$ and $x = \pi$

52. The region bounded by $y = x^3$ and $y = x^2$ between $x = 0$ and $x = 1$

53. The half annulus $\{(r, \theta): 2 \le r \le 4, 0 \le \theta \le \pi\}$

54. The region bounded by $y = x^2$ and $y = a^2 - x^2$

55–56. Center of mass of constant density solids *Find the center of mass of the following solids, assuming a constant density. Use symmetry whenever possible and choose a convenient coordinate system.*

55. The paraboloid bowl bounded by $z = x^2 + y^2$ and $z = 36$

56. The tetrahedron bounded by $z = 4 - x - 2y$ and the coordinate planes

57–58. Variable density solids *Find the coordinates of the center of mass of the following solids with the given density.*

57. The upper half of a ball $\{(\rho, \varphi, \theta): 0 \le \rho \le 16, 0 \le \varphi \le \frac{\pi}{2}, 0 \le \theta \le 2\pi\}$ with density $f(\rho, \varphi, \theta) = 1 + \rho/4$

58. The cube in the first octant bounded by the planes $x = 2, y = 2, z = 2$, with $\rho(x, y, z) = 1 + x + y + z$

59–62. Centers of mass for general objects *Consider the following two- and three-dimensional regions. Compute the center of mass assuming constant density. All parameters are positive real numbers.*

59. A region is bounded by a paraboloid with a circular base of radius R and height h. How far from the base is the center of mass?

60. Let R be the region enclosed by an equilateral triangle with sides of length s. What is the perpendicular distance between the center of mass of R and the edges of R?

61. An isosceles triangle has two sides of length s and a base of length b. How far from the base is the center of mass of the region enclosed by the triangle?

62. A tetrahedron is bounded by the coordinate planes and the plane $x + y/2 + z/3 = 1$. What are the coordinates of the center of mass?

63. Slicing a conical cake A cake is shaped like a solid cone with radius 4 and height 2, with its base on the xy-plane. A wedge of the cake is removed by making two slices from the axis of the cone outward, perpendicular to the xy-plane separated by an angle of Q radians, where $0 < Q < 2\pi$.

a. Use a double integral to find the volume of the slice for $Q = \pi/4$. Use geometry to check your answer.

b. Use a double integral to find the volume of the slice for any $0 < Q < 2\pi$. Use geometry to check your answer.

64. Volume and weight of a fish tank A spherical fish tank with a radius of 1 ft is filled with water to a level 6 in below the top of the tank.

a. Determine the volume and weight of the water in the fish tank. (The weight density of water is about $62.5\,\text{lb/ft}^3$.)

b. How much additional water must be added to completely fill the tank?

65–68. Transforming a square *Let* $S = \{(u, v): 0 \le u \le 1, 0 \le v \le 1\}$ *be a unit square in the uv-plane. Find the image of S in the xy-plane under the following transformations.*

65. $T: x = v, y = u$

66. $T: x = -v, y = u$

67. $T: x = (u + v)/2, y = (u - v)/2$

68. $T: x = u, y = 2v + 2$

69–72. Computing Jacobians *Compute the Jacobian* $J(u, v)$ *of the following transformations.*

69. $T: x = 4u - v, y = -2u + 3v$

70. $T: x = u + v, y = u - v$

71. $T: x = 3u, y = 2v + 2$

72. $T: x = u^2 - v^2, y = 2uv$

73–76. Double integrals—transformation given *To evaluate the following integrals carry out the following steps.*

a. *Sketch the original region of integration R and the new region S using the given change of variables.*

b. *Find the limits of integration for the new integral with respect to u and v.*

c. *Compute the Jacobian.*

d. *Change variables and evaluate the new integral.*

73. $\iint_R xy^2\,dA$; $R = \{(x, y): y/3 \le x \le (y + 6)/3, 0 \le y \le 3\}$; use $x = u + v/3, y = v$.

74. $\iint_R 3xy^2\,dA$; $R = \{(x, y): 0 \le x \le 2, x \le y \le x + 4\}$; use $x = 2u, y = 4v + 2u$.

75. $\iint_R x^2\sqrt{x + 2y}\,dA$; $R = \{(x, y): 0 \le x \le 2, -x/2 \le y \le 1 - x\}$; use $x = 2u, y = v - u$.

76. $\iint_R xy^2\,dA$; R is the region between the hyperbolas $xy = 1$ and $xy = 4$ and the lines $y = 1$ and $y = 4$; use $x = u/v, y = v$.

77–78. Double integrals *Evaluate the following integrals using a change of variables of your choice. Sketch the original and new regions of integration, R and S.*

77. $\iint_R y^4\,dA$; R is the region bounded by the hyperbolas $xy = 1$ and $xy = 4$ and the lines $y/x = 1$ and $y/x = 3$.

78. $\iint_R (y^2 + xy - 2x^2)\,dA$; R is the region bounded by the lines $y = x, y = x - 3, y = -2x + 3, y = -2x - 3$.

79–80. Triple integrals *Use a change of variables to evaluate the following integrals.*

79. $\iiint_D yz\,dV$; D is bounded by the planes $x + 2y = 1, x + 2y = 2, x - z = 0, x - z = 2, 2y - z = 0$, and $2y - z = 3$.

80. $\iiint_D x\,dV$; D is bounded by the planes $y - 2x = 0, y - 2x = 1, z - 3y = 0, z - 3y = 1, z - 4x = 0$, and $z - 4x = 3$.

Chapter 14 Guided Projects

Applications of the material in this chapter and related topics can be found in the following Guided Projects. For additional information, see the Preface.

- The exponential Eiffel Tower
- The tilted cylinder problem
- How big are n-balls?
- Electric field integrals
- Gravitational fields
- Moments of inertia

15

Vector Calculus

Chapter Preview This culminating chapter of the book provides a beautiful, unifying conclusion to our study of calculus. Many ideas and themes that have appeared throughout the book come together in these final pages. First, we combine vector-valued functions (Chapter 12) and functions of several variables (Chapter 13) to form *vector fields*. Once vector fields have been introduced and illustrated through their many applications, we begin exploring the calculus of vector fields. Concepts such as limits and continuity carry over directly. The extension of derivatives to vector fields leads to two new operations that underlie this chapter: the *curl* and the *divergence*. When integration is extended to vector fields, we discover new versions of the Fundamental Theorem of Calculus. The chapter ends with a final look at the Fundamental Theorem of Calculus and the several related forms in which it has appeared throughout the book.

15.1 Vector Fields

A velocity vector field models the motion of air particles in a breeze at a single moment in time. Individual vectors indicate direction of motion, and their lengths indicate speed.

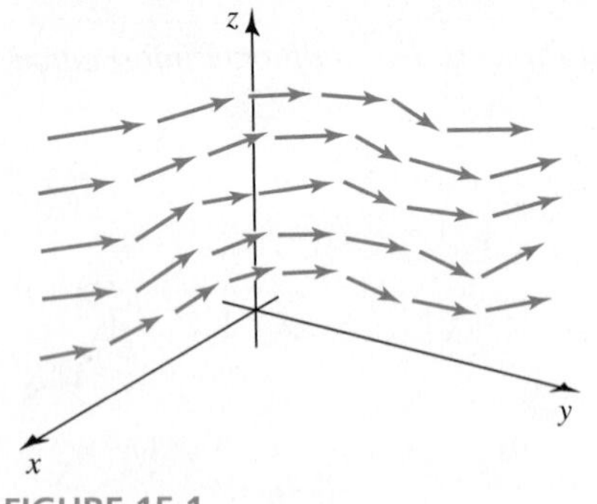

FIGURE 15.1

It is not difficult to find everyday examples of vector fields. Imagine sitting on a beach in a breeze: Focus on a point in space and consider the motion of the air at that point at a single instant of time. The motion is described by a velocity vector with three components (east-west, north-south, up-down). At another point in space at the same time, the air is moving with a different direction and speed, and a different velocity vector is associated with that point. In general, at one instant in time, every point in space has a velocity vector associated with it (Figure 15.1). This collection of velocity vectors is a vector field.

Other examples of vector fields include the wind patterns in a hurricane (Figure 15.2a), the flow of air around an airplane wing, and the circulation of water in a heat exchanger (Figure 15.2b). Gravitational, magnetic, and electric force fields are represented by vector fields (Figure 15.2c), as are the stresses and strains in buildings and bridges. Beyond physics and engineering, the transport of a chemical pollutant in a lake or human migration patterns can be modeled by vector fields.

Vector Fields in Two Dimensions

To solidify the idea of a vector field, we begin by exploring vector fields in $\mathbf{R}^2$. From there, it is a short step to vector fields in $\mathbf{R}^3$.

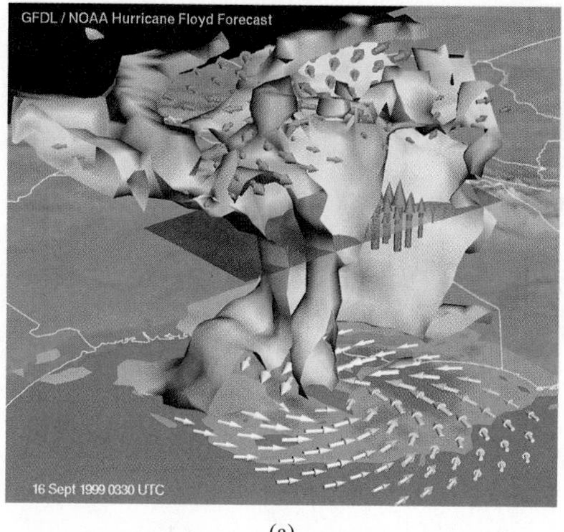
GFDL / NOAA Hurricane Floyd Forecast
16 Sept 1999 0330 UTC
(a)

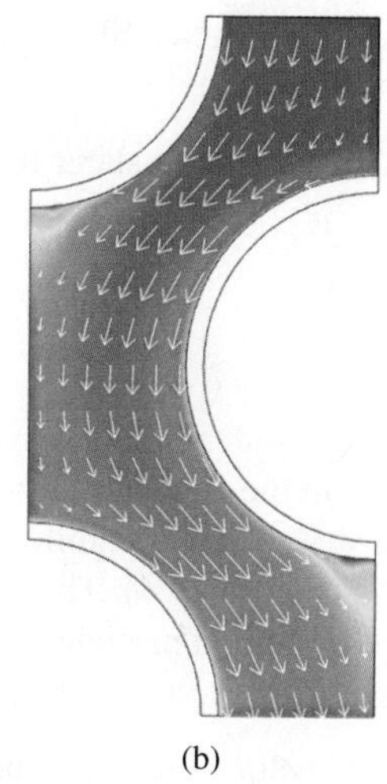
(b)

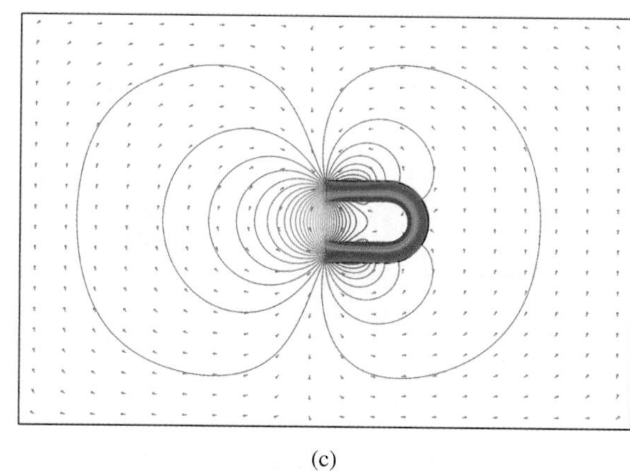
(c)

FIGURE 15.2

DEFINITION Vector Fields in Two Dimensions

Let f and g be defined on a region R of $\mathbf{R}^2$. A **vector field** in $\mathbf{R}^2$ is a function $\mathbf{F}$ that assigns to each point in R a vector $\langle f(x, y), g(x, y)\rangle$. The vector field is written as

$$\mathbf{F}(x, y) = \langle f(x, y), g(x, y)\rangle \quad \text{or}$$
$$\mathbf{F}(x, y) = f(x, y)\mathbf{i} + g(x, y)\mathbf{j}.$$

A vector field $\mathbf{F} = \langle f, g\rangle$ is continuous or differentiable on a region R of $\mathbf{R}^2$ if f and g are continuous or differentiable on R, respectively.

A vector field cannot be represented by a single curve or surface. Instead, we plot a representative sample of vectors that illustrate the general appearance of the vector field. Consider the vector field defined by

$$\mathbf{F}(x, y) = \langle x, y\rangle = x\mathbf{i} + y\mathbf{j}.$$

At selected points $P(x, y)$, we plot a vector with its tail at P equal to the value of $\mathbf{F}(x, y)$. For example, $\mathbf{F}(1, 1) = \langle 1, 1\rangle$, so we draw a vector equal to $\langle 1, 1\rangle$ with its tail at the point $(1, 1)$. Similarly, $\mathbf{F}(-2, -3) = \langle -2, -3\rangle$, so at the point $(-2, -3)$, we draw a vector equal to $\langle -2, -3\rangle$. We can make the following general observations about the vector field $\mathbf{F}(x, y) = \langle x, y\rangle$.

- For every (x, y) except $(0, 0)$, the vector $\mathbf{F}(x, y)$ points in the direction of $\langle x, y\rangle$, which is directly outward from the origin.
- The length of $\mathbf{F}(x, y)$ is $|\mathbf{F}| = |\langle x, y\rangle| = \sqrt{x^2 + y^2}$, which increases with distance from the origin.

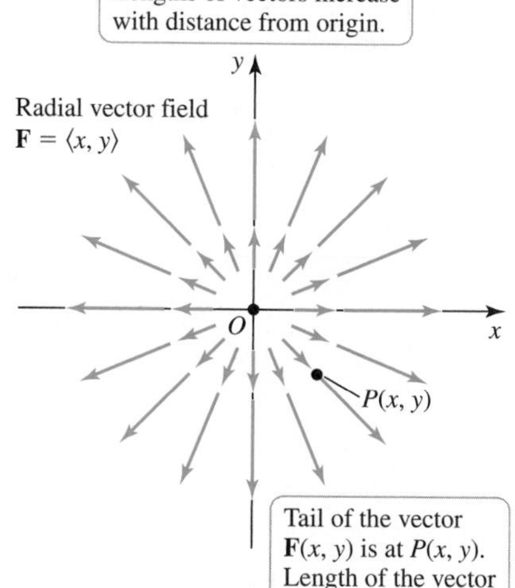
Lengths of vectors increase with distance from origin.
Radial vector field
F = ⟨x, y⟩
y
x
O
P(x, y)
Tail of the vector F(x, y) is at P(x, y). Length of the vector is |OP|.
FIGURE 15.3

The vector field $\mathbf{F} = \langle x, y\rangle$ is an example of a *radial vector field* (because its vectors point radially away from the origin; Figure 15.3). If $\mathbf{F}$ represents the velocity of a fluid moving in two dimensions, the graph of the vector field gives a vivid image of how a small object, such as a cork, moves through the fluid. In this case, at every point of the field, a particle moves in the direction of the arrow at that point with a speed equal to the length of the arrow. For this reason, vector fields are sometimes called *flows*. When sketching vector fields, it is often useful to draw continuous curves that are aligned with the vector field. Such curves are called *flow curves* or *streamlines*.

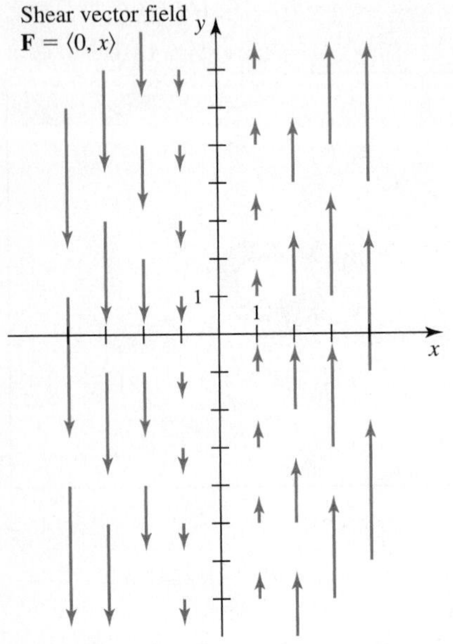

FIGURE 15.4

➤ Drawing vectors with their actual length often leads to cluttered pictures of vector fields. For this reason, most of the vector fields in this chapter are illustrated with proportional scaling: All vectors are multiplied by a scalar chosen to make the vector field as understandable as possible.

➤ A useful observation for two-dimensional vector fields $\mathbf{F} = \langle f, g\rangle$ is that the slope of the vector at (x, y) is $g(x, y)/f(x, y)$. In Example 1a, the slopes are everywhere undefined; in part (b), the slopes are everywhere 0, and in part (c), the slopes are $-x/y$.

EXAMPLE 1 **Vector fields** Sketch representative vectors of the following vector fields.

a. $\mathbf{F}(x, y) = \langle 0, x\rangle = x\mathbf{j}$ (a shear field)

b. $\mathbf{F}(x, y) = \langle 1 - y^2, 0\rangle = (1 - y^2)\mathbf{i}$, for $|y| \leq 1$ (channel flow)

c. $\mathbf{F}(x, y) = \langle -y, x\rangle = -y\mathbf{i} + x\mathbf{j}$ (a rotation field)

SOLUTION

a. This vector field is independent of y. Furthermore, because the x-component of $\mathbf{F}$ is zero, all vectors in the field (for $x \neq 0$) point in the y-direction: upward for $x > 0$ and downward for $x < 0$. The magnitudes of the vectors in the field increase with distance from the y-axis (Figure 15.4). The flow curves for this field are vertical lines. If $\mathbf{F}$ represents a velocity field, a particle right of the y-axis moves upward, a particle left of the y-axis moves downward, and a particle on the y-axis is stationary.

b. In this case, the vector field is independent of x and the y-component of $\mathbf{F}$ is zero. Because $1 - y^2 > 0$ for $|y| < 1$, vectors in this region point in the positive x-direction. The x-component of the vector field is zero at the boundaries $y = \pm 1$ and increases to 1 along the center of the strip, $y = 0$. The vector field might model the flow of water in a straight shallow channel (Figure 15.5); its flow curves are horizontal lines, indicating motion in the direction of the positive x-axis.

c. It often helps to determine the vector field along the coordinate axes.

- When $y = 0$ (along the x-axis), we have $\mathbf{F}(x, 0) = \langle 0, x\rangle$. With $x > 0$, this vector field consists of vectors pointing upward, increasing in length as x increases. With $x < 0$, the vectors point downward, increasing in length as $|x|$ increases.
- When $x = 0$ (along the y-axis), we have $\mathbf{F}(0, y) = \langle -y, 0\rangle$. If $y > 0$, the vectors point in the negative x-direction, increasing in length as y increases. If $y < 0$, the vectors point in the positive x-direction, increasing in length as $|y|$ increases.

A few more representative vectors show that the vector field has a counterclockwise rotation about the origin; the magnitudes of the vectors increase with distance from the origin (Figure 15.6).

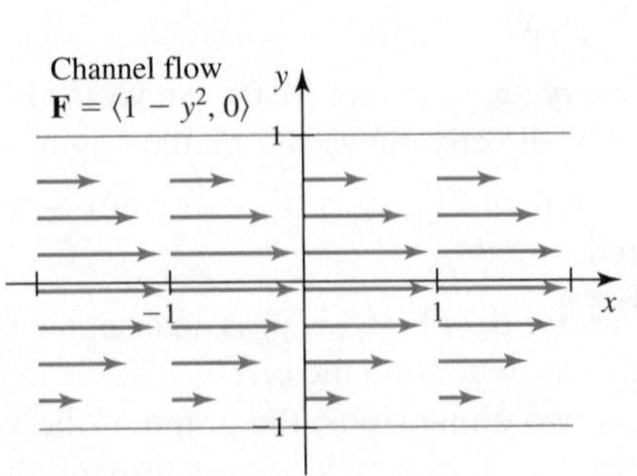

FIGURE 15.5

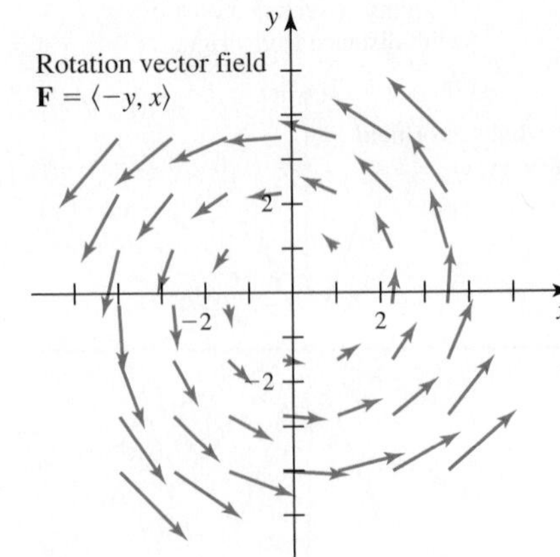

FIGURE 15.6

Related Exercises 6–16 ◀

QUICK CHECK 1 If the vector field in Example 1c describes the velocity of a fluid and you place a small cork in the plane at $(2, 0)$, what path do you think it will follow? ◀

Radial Vector Fields in $\mathbf{R}^2$ Radial vector fields in $\mathbf{R}^2$ have the property that their vectors point directly toward or away from the origin at all points (except the origin), parallel to the position vectors $\mathbf{r} = \langle x, y \rangle$. We will work with radial vector fields of the form

$$\mathbf{F}(x, y) = \frac{\mathbf{r}}{|\mathbf{r}|^p} = \frac{\langle x, y \rangle}{|\mathbf{r}|^p} = \underbrace{\frac{\mathbf{r}}{|\mathbf{r}|}}_{\text{unit vector}} \underbrace{\frac{1}{|\mathbf{r}|^{p-1}}}_{\text{magnitude}},$$

where p is a real number. Figure 15.7 illustrates radial fields with $p = 1$ and $p = 3$. These vector fields (and their three-dimensional counterparts) play an important role in many applications. For example, central forces, such as gravitational or electrostatic forces between point masses or charges, are described by radial vector fields with $p = 3$. These forces obey an inverse square law in which the magnitude of the force is proportional to $1/|\mathbf{r}|^2$.

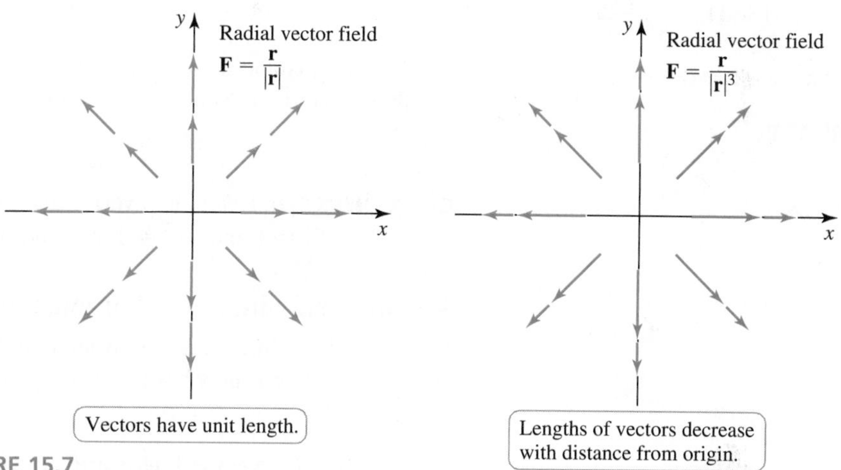

FIGURE 15.7

> **DEFINITION Radial Vector Fields in $\mathbf{R}^2$**
>
> Let $\mathbf{r} = \langle x, y \rangle$. A vector field of the form $\mathbf{F} = f(x, y)\,\mathbf{r}$, where f is a scalar-valued function, is a **radial vector field**. Of specific interest are the radial vector fields
>
> $$\mathbf{F}(x, y) = \frac{\mathbf{r}}{|\mathbf{r}|^p} = \frac{\langle x, y \rangle}{|\mathbf{r}|^p},$$
>
> where p is a real number. At every point (except the origin), the vectors of this field are directed outward from the origin with a magnitude of $|\mathbf{F}| = \dfrac{1}{|\mathbf{r}|^{p-1}}$.

EXAMPLE 2 Normal and tangential vectors Let C be the circle $x^2 + y^2 = a^2$, where $a > 0$.

a. Show that at each point of C, the radial vector field $\mathbf{F}(x, y) = \dfrac{\mathbf{r}}{|\mathbf{r}|} = \dfrac{\langle x, y \rangle}{\sqrt{x^2 + y^2}}$ is orthogonal to the line tangent to C at that point.

b. Show that at each point of C, the rotation vector field $\mathbf{G}(x, y) = \dfrac{\langle -y, x \rangle}{\sqrt{x^2 + y^2}}$ is parallel to the line tangent to C at that point.

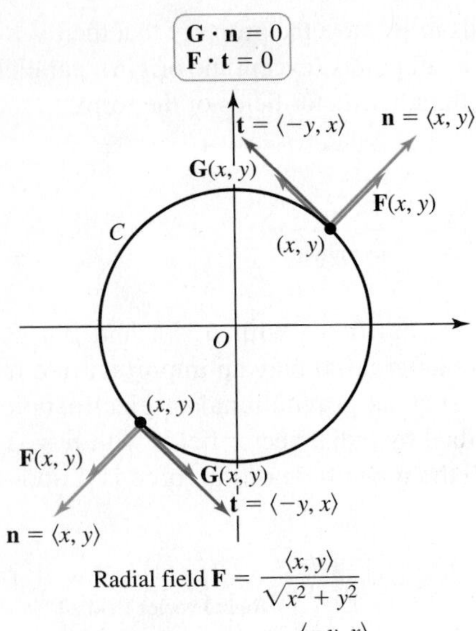

FIGURE 15.8

SOLUTION In Chapter 12 we showed that a vector tangent to the circle C at (x, y) is $\mathbf{t} = \langle -y, x \rangle$. The vector $\mathbf{n} = \langle x, y \rangle$ is orthogonal to $\mathbf{t}$ (check that $\mathbf{t} \cdot \mathbf{n} = 0$); therefore, $\mathbf{n}$ is orthogonal to C at the point (x, y) (Figure 15.8).

a. At all points of C, we see that $\mathbf{F}$ is a scalar multiple of $\mathbf{n}$, which is orthogonal to $\mathbf{t}$. Therefore, $\mathbf{F}$ and $\mathbf{t}$ are orthogonal to each other on C. Alternatively, note that

$$\mathbf{F}(x, y) \cdot \mathbf{t}(x, y) = \frac{\langle x, y \rangle}{\sqrt{x^2 + y^2}} \cdot \langle -y, x \rangle = 0,$$

which also implies that $\mathbf{F}$ and $\mathbf{t}$ are orthogonal at all points of C. Because $\mathbf{t}$ is tangent to C, $\mathbf{F}$ is orthogonal to C (Figure 15.8).

b. This vector field is the rotation field of Example 1c normalized to have unit length (check that $|\mathbf{G}| = 1$ everywhere except the origin). In this case,

$$\mathbf{G}(x, y) \cdot \mathbf{n}(x, y) = \frac{\langle -y, x \rangle}{\sqrt{x^2 + y^2}} \cdot \langle x, y \rangle = 0.$$

Therefore, $\mathbf{G}$ and $\mathbf{n}$ are orthogonal at all points of C. Because $\mathbf{n}$ is orthogonal to C at all points of C, $\mathbf{G}$ is parallel to the line tangent to C at any point of C (Figure 15.8).

Related Exercises 17–20 ◄

QUICK CHECK 2 In Example 2 verify that $\mathbf{t} \cdot \mathbf{n} = 0$. In parts (a) and (b) of Example 2, verify that $|\mathbf{F}| = 1$ and $|\mathbf{G}| = 1$ at all points excluding the origin. ◄

Vector Fields in Three Dimensions

Vector fields in three dimensions are conceptually the same as vector fields in two dimensions. The vector $\mathbf{F}$ now has three components, each of which depends on three variables.

DEFINITION Vector Fields and Radial Vector Fields in $\mathbf{R}^3$

Let f, g, and h be defined on a region D of $\mathbf{R}^3$. A **vector field** in $\mathbf{R}^3$ is a function $\mathbf{F}$ that assigns to each point in D a vector $\langle f(x, y, z), g(x, y, z), h(x, y, z) \rangle$. The vector field is written as

$$\mathbf{F}(x, y, z) = \langle f(x, y, z), g(x, y, z), h(x, y, z) \rangle \quad \text{or}$$
$$\mathbf{F}(x, y, z) = f(x, y, z)\mathbf{i} + g(x, y, z)\mathbf{j} + h(x, y, z)\mathbf{k}.$$

A vector field $\mathbf{F} = \langle f, g, h \rangle$ is continuous or differentiable on a region D of $\mathbf{R}^3$ if f, g, and h are continuous or differentiable on D, respectively. Of particular importance are the **radial vector fields**

$$\mathbf{F}(x, y, z) = \frac{\mathbf{r}}{|\mathbf{r}|^p} = \frac{\langle x, y, z \rangle}{|\mathbf{r}|^p},$$

where p is a real number.

EXAMPLE 3 Vector fields in $\mathbf{R}^3$ Sketch and discuss the following vector fields.

a. $\mathbf{F}(x, y, z) = \langle x, y, e^{-z} \rangle$, for $z \geq 0$

b. $\mathbf{F}(x, y, z) = \langle 0, 0, 1 - x^2 - y^2 \rangle$, for $x^2 + y^2 \leq 1$

SOLUTION

a. First consider the x- and y-components of $\mathbf{F}$ in the xy-plane ($z = 0$), where $\mathbf{F} = \langle x, y, 1 \rangle$. This vector field looks like a radial field in the first two components, increasing in magnitude with distance from the z-axis. However, each vector also has a constant vertical component of 1. In horizontal planes $z = z_0 > 0$, the radial pattern remains the same, but the vertical component decreases as z increases. As $z \to \infty$, $e^{-z} \to 0$ and the vector field becomes a horizontal radial field (Figure 15.9).

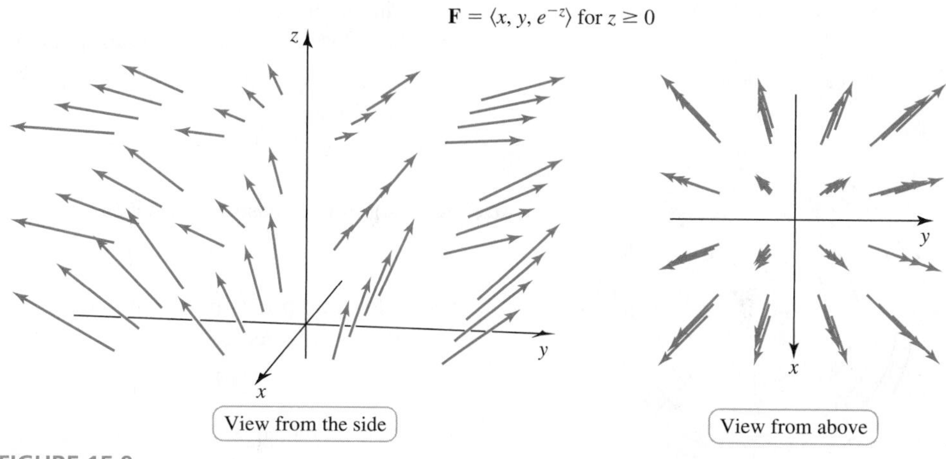

FIGURE 15.9

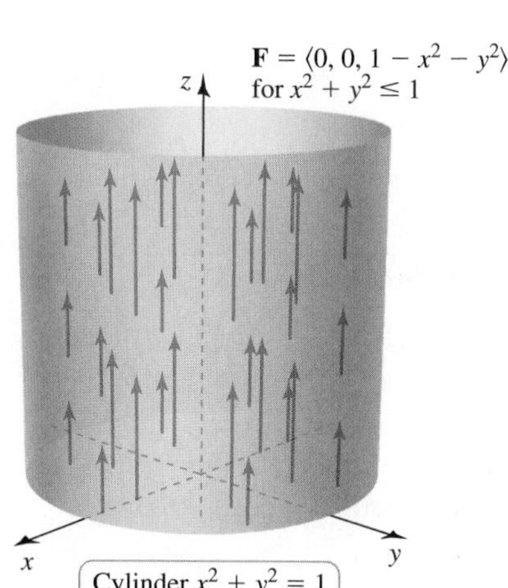

FIGURE 15.10

b. Regarding $\mathbf{F}$ as a velocity field, for points in and on the cylinder $x^2 + y^2 = 1$, there is no motion in the x- or y-directions. The z-component of the vector field may be written $1 - r^2$, where $r^2 = x^2 + y^2$ is the square of the distance from the z-axis. We see that the z-component increases from 0 on the boundary of the cylinder ($r = 1$) to a maximum value of 1 along the centerline of the cylinder ($r = 0$) (Figure 15.10). This vector field models the flow of a fluid inside a tube (such as a blood vessel).

Related Exercises 21–24 ◀

Gradient Fields and Potential Functions One way to generate a vector field is to start with a differentiable scalar-valued function φ, take its gradient, and let $\mathbf{F} = \nabla\varphi$. A vector field defined as the gradient of a scalar-valued function φ is called a **gradient field** and the function φ is called a **potential function**.

➤ Physicists often use the convention that a gradient field and its potential are related by $\mathbf{F} = -\nabla\varphi$.

Suppose φ is a differentiable function on a region R of $\mathbf{R}^2$ and consider the surface $z = \varphi(x, y)$. Recall from Chapter 13 that this function may also be represented by level curves in the xy-plane. At each point (a, b) on a level curve, the gradient $\nabla\varphi(a, b) = \langle \varphi_x(a, b), \varphi_y(a, b) \rangle$ is orthogonal to the level curve at (a, b) (Figure 15.11). Therefore, the vectors of $\mathbf{F} = \nabla\varphi$ point in a direction orthogonal to the level curves of φ.

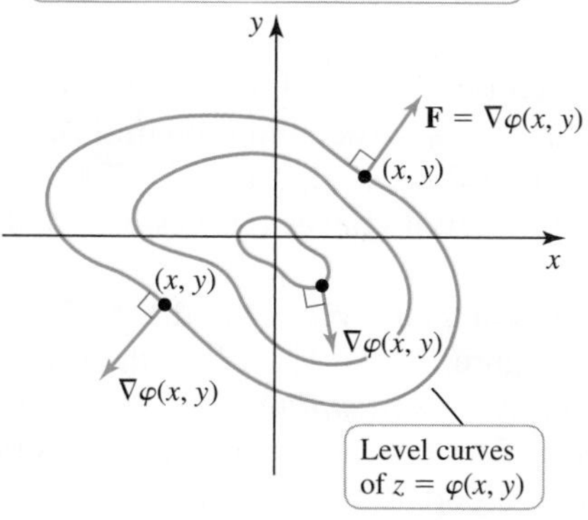

FIGURE 15.11

The idea extends to gradients of functions of three variables. If φ is differentiable on a region D of $\mathbf{R}^3$, then $\mathbf{F} = \nabla\varphi = \langle \varphi_x, \varphi_y, \varphi_z \rangle$ is a vector field that points in a direction orthogonal to the level *surfaces* of φ.

Gradient fields are useful because of the physical meaning of the gradient. For example, if φ represents the temperature in a conducting material, then the gradient $\nabla\varphi$ at a point indicates the direction in which the temperature increases most rapidly. According to a basic physical law, heat diffuses in the direction of the vector field $-\nabla\varphi$, the direction in which the temperature *decreases* most rapidly; that is, heat flows "down the gradient" from relatively hot regions to cooler regions.

QUICK CHECK 3 Find the gradient field associated with the function $\varphi(x, y, z) = xyz$. ◀

➤ A potential function plays the role of an antiderivative of a vector field: Derivatives of the potential function produce the vector field. If φ is a potential function for a gradient field, then $\varphi + C$ is also a potential function for that gradient field, for any constant C.

DEFINITION Gradient Fields and Potential Functions

Let $z = \varphi(x, y)$ and $w = \varphi(x, y, z)$ be differentiable functions on regions of $\mathbf{R}^2$ and $\mathbf{R}^3$, respectively. The vector field $\mathbf{F} = \nabla\varphi$ is a **gradient field**, and the function φ is a **potential function** for $\mathbf{F}$.

EXAMPLE 4 Gradient fields

a. Sketch and interpret the gradient field associated with the temperature function $T = 200 - x^2 - y^2$ on the circular plate $R = \{(x, y): x^2 + y^2 \le 25\}$.

b. Sketch and interpret the gradient field associated with the velocity potential $\varphi = \tan^{-1}(y/x)$.

SOLUTION

a. The gradient field associated with T is

$$\mathbf{F} = \nabla T = \langle -2x, -2y \rangle = -2\langle x, y \rangle.$$

This vector field points inward toward the origin at all points of R except $(0, 0)$. The magnitudes of the vectors,

$$|\mathbf{F}| = \sqrt{(-2x)^2 + (-2y)^2} = 2\sqrt{x^2 + y^2},$$

are greatest on the edge of the disk, where $x^2 + y^2 = 25$ and $|\mathbf{F}| = 10$. The magnitudes of the vectors in the field decrease toward the center of the plate with $|\mathbf{F}(0, 0)| = 0$. Figure 15.12 shows the level curves of the temperature function with several gradient vectors, all orthogonal to the level curves. Note that the plate is hottest at the center and coolest on the edge, so heat diffuses *outward*, in the direction opposite to that of the gradient.

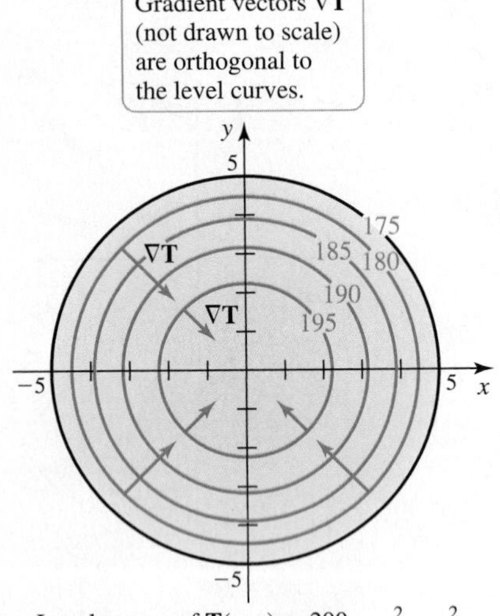
Gradient vectors ∇T (not drawn to scale) are orthogonal to the level curves.
y
5
175
180
185
190
195
∇T
∇T
−5
5
x
−5
Level curves of $\mathbf{T}(x, y) = 200 - x^2 - y^2$

FIGURE 15.12

b. The gradient of a velocity potential gives the velocity components of a two-dimensional flow; that is, $\mathbf{F} = \langle u, v \rangle = \nabla\varphi$, where u and v are the velocities in the x- and y-directions, respectively. Computing the gradient, we find that

$$\mathbf{F} = \langle \varphi_x, \varphi_y \rangle = \left\langle \frac{1}{1 + (y/x)^2} \cdot \frac{-y}{x^2}, \frac{1}{1 + (y/x)^2} \cdot \frac{1}{x} \right\rangle = \left\langle -\frac{y}{x^2 + y^2}, \frac{x}{x^2 + y^2} \right\rangle.$$

This vector field is a rotation field. Notice that the level curves of φ are the lines $\frac{y}{x} = C$ or $y = Cx$. At all points off the y-axis, the vector field is orthogonal to the level curves, which gives a rotation field (Figure 15.13).

Related Exercises 25–32 ◀

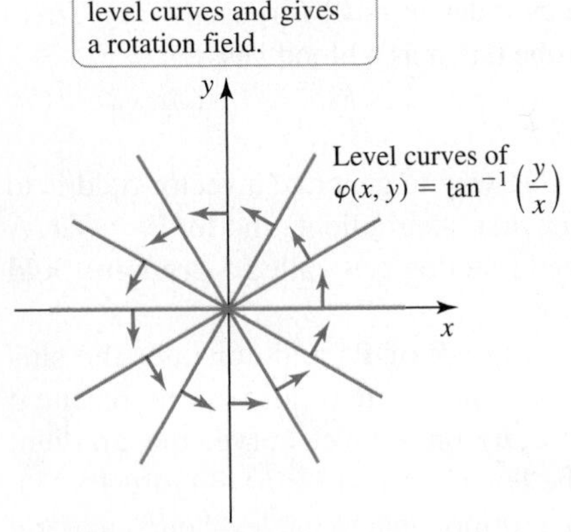
F = ∇φ is orthogonal to level curves and gives a rotation field.
y
Level curves of φ(x, y) = tan⁻¹(y/x)
x
FIGURE 15.13

Equipotential Curves and Surfaces The preceding example illustrates a beautiful geometric connection between a gradient field and its associated potential function. Let φ be a potential function for the vector field $\mathbf{F}$ in $\mathbf{R}^2$; that is, $\mathbf{F} = \nabla\varphi$. The level curves of a potential function are called **equipotential curves** (curves on which the potential function is constant).

Because the equipotential curves are level curves of φ, the vector field $\mathbf{F} = \nabla\varphi$ is everywhere orthogonal to the equipotential curves (Figure 15.14). Therefore, the vector field is visualized by drawing continuous *flow curves* or *streamlines* that are everywhere orthogonal to the equipotential curves. These ideas also apply to vector fields in $\mathbf{R}^3$ in which case the vector field is orthogonal to the **equipotential surfaces**.

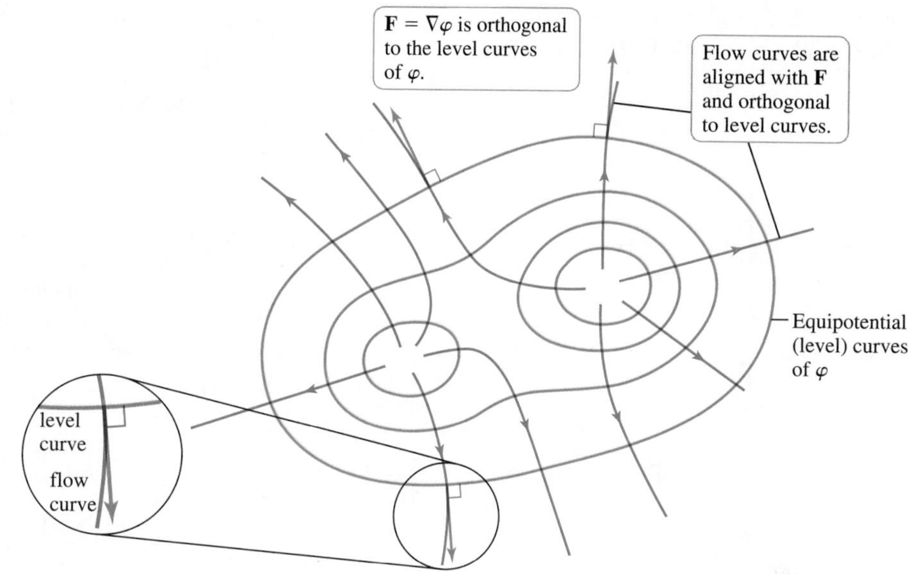

FIGURE 15.14

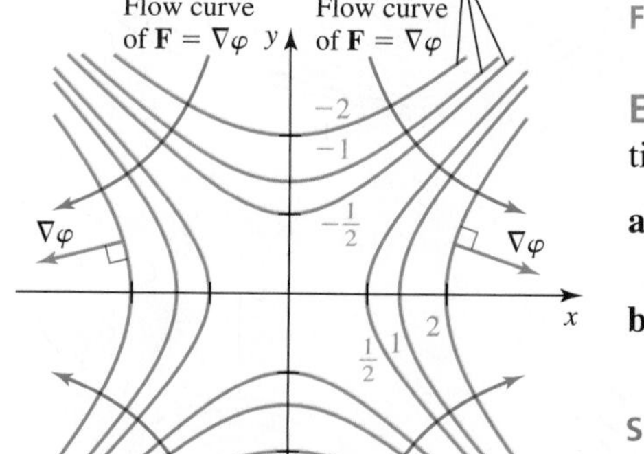

FIGURE 15.15

EXAMPLE 5 Equipotential curves The equipotential curves for the potential function $\varphi(x, y) = (x^2 - y^2)/2$ are shown in Figure 15.15.

a. Find the gradient field associated with φ and verify that the gradient field is orthogonal to the equipotential curve at $(2, 1)$.

b. Verify that the vector field $\mathbf{F} = \nabla\varphi$ is orthogonal to the equipotential curves at all points (x, y).

SOLUTION

a. The level (or equipotential) curves are the hyperbolas $(x^2 - y^2)/2 = C$, where C is a constant. The slope at any point on a level curve $\varphi(x, y) = C$ (Section 13.5) is

$$\frac{dy}{dx} = -\frac{\varphi_x}{\varphi_y} = \frac{x}{y}.$$

At the point $(2, 1)$, the slope of the level curve is $dy/dx = 2$, so the vector tangent to the curve points in the direction $\langle 1, 2\rangle$. The gradient field is given by $\mathbf{F} = \nabla\varphi = \langle x, -y\rangle$, so $\mathbf{F}(2, 1) = \nabla\varphi(2, 1) = \langle 2, -1\rangle$. The dot product of the tangent vector $\langle 1, 2\rangle$ and the gradient is $\langle 1, 2\rangle \cdot \langle 2, -1\rangle = 0$; therefore, the two vectors are orthogonal.

➤ We use the fact that a line with slope a/b points in the direction of the vectors $\langle 1, a/b\rangle$ or $\langle b, a\rangle$.

b. In general, the line tangent to the equipotential curve at (x, y) is parallel to the vector $\langle y, x\rangle$, while the vector field at that point is $\mathbf{F} = \langle x, -y\rangle$. The vector field and the tangent vectors are orthogonal because $\langle y, x\rangle \cdot \langle x, -y\rangle = 0$. *Related Exercises 33–36* ◄

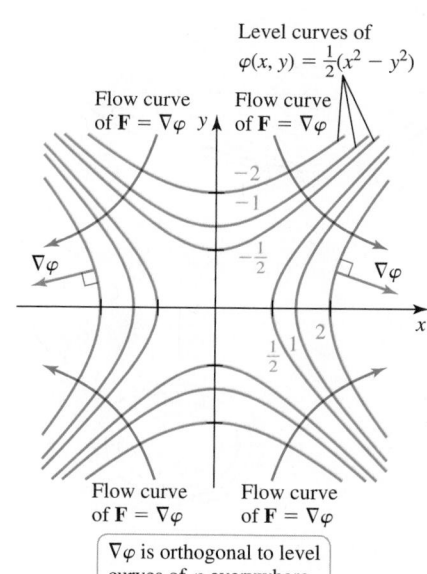

SECTION 15.1 EXERCISES

Review Questions

1. Explain how a vector field $\mathbf{F} = \langle f, g, h\rangle$ is used to describe the motion of the air in a room at one instant in time.
2. Sketch the vector field $\mathbf{F} = \langle x, y\rangle$.
3. How do you graph the vector field $\mathbf{F} = \langle f(x, y), g(x, y)\rangle$?
4. Given a function φ, how does the gradient of φ produce a vector field?
5. Interpret the gradient field of the temperature function $T = f(x, y)$.

Basic Skills

6–15. Two-dimensional vector fields *Make a sketch of the following vector fields.*

6. $\mathbf{F} = \langle 1, y\rangle$
7. $\mathbf{F} = \langle x, 0\rangle$
8. $\mathbf{F} = \langle -x, -y\rangle$
9. $\mathbf{F} = \langle x, -y\rangle$
10. $\mathbf{F} = \langle 2x, 3y\rangle$
11. $\mathbf{F} = \langle y, -x\rangle$
12. $\mathbf{F} = \langle x + y, y\rangle$
13. $\mathbf{F} = \langle x, y - x\rangle$
14. $\mathbf{F} = \langle \sin x, \sin y\rangle$
15. $\mathbf{F} = \langle e^{-x}, 0\rangle$

16. **Matching vector field with graphs** Match vector fields a–d with graphs A–D.

a. $\mathbf{F} = \langle 0, x^2 \rangle$ **b.** $\mathbf{F} = \langle x - y, x \rangle$
c. $\mathbf{F} = \langle 2x, -y \rangle$ **d.** $\mathbf{F} = \langle y, x \rangle$

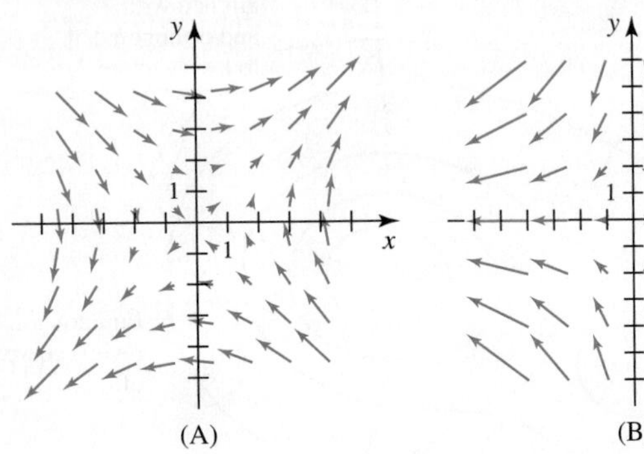

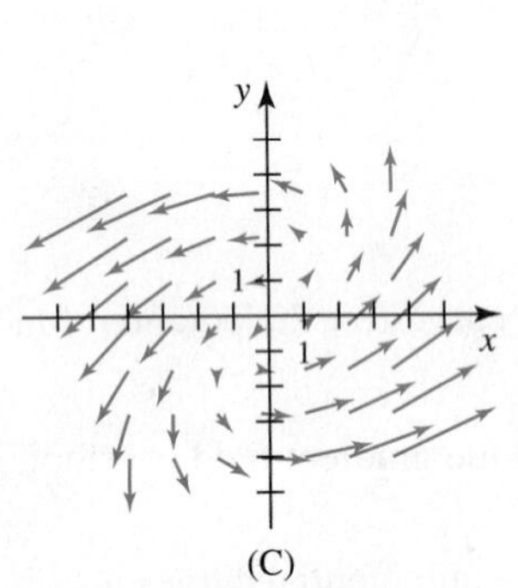

(C)

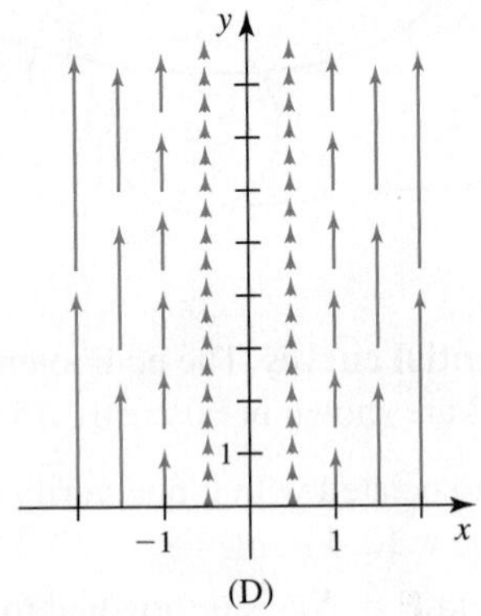

(D)

17–20. Normal and tangential components *Determine whether the vector field* **F** *is tangent to or normal to the curve C at points on C. A vector* **n** *normal to C is also given. Sketch C and a few representative vectors of* **F**.

17. $\mathbf{F} = \langle x, y \rangle$, where $C = \{(x, y): x^2 + y^2 = 4\}$ and $\mathbf{n} = \langle x, y \rangle$

18. $\mathbf{F} = \langle y, -x \rangle$, where $C = \{(x, y): x^2 + y^2 = 1\}$ and $\mathbf{n} = \langle x, y \rangle$

19. $\mathbf{F} = \langle x, y \rangle$, where $C = \{(x, y): x = 1\}$ and $\mathbf{n} = \langle 1, 0 \rangle$

20. $\mathbf{F} = \langle y, x \rangle$, where $C = \{(x, y): x^2 + y^2 = 1\}$ and $\mathbf{n} = \langle x, y \rangle$

T **21–24. Three-dimensional vector fields** *Sketch a few representative vectors of the following vector fields.*

21. $\mathbf{F} = \langle 1, 0, z \rangle$

22. $\mathbf{F} = \langle x, y, z \rangle$

23. $\mathbf{F} = \langle y, -x, 0 \rangle$

24. $\mathbf{F} = \dfrac{\langle x, y, z \rangle}{\sqrt{x^2 + y^2 + z^2}}$

T **25–28. Gradient fields** *Find the gradient field* $\mathbf{F} = \nabla\varphi$ *for the potential function* φ. *Sketch a few level curves of* φ *and a few vectors of* **F**.

25. $\varphi(x, y) = x^2 + y^2$, for $x^2 + y^2 \le 16$

26. $\varphi(x, y) = \sqrt{x^2 + y^2}$, for $x^2 + y^2 \le 9$, $(x, y) \ne (0, 0)$

27. $\varphi(x, y) = \sin x \sin y$, for $|x| \le \pi$, $|y| \le \pi$

28. $\varphi(x, y) = 2xy$, for $|x| \le 2$, $|y| \le 2$

29–32. Gradient fields *Find the gradient field* $\mathbf{F} = \nabla\varphi$ *for the following potential functions* φ.

29. $\varphi(x, y, z) = (x^2 + y^2 + z^2)/2$

30. $\varphi(x, y, z) = \ln(1 + x^2 + y^2 + z^2)$

31. $\varphi(x, y, z) = (x^2 + y^2 + z^2)^{-1/2}$

32. $\varphi(x, y, z) = e^{-z} \sin(x + y)$

33–36. Equipotential curves *Consider the following potential functions and graphs of their equipotential curves.*

a. Find the associated gradient field $\mathbf{F} = \nabla\varphi$.
b. Show that the vector field is orthogonal to the equipotential curve at the point (1, 1). Illustrate this result on the figure.
c. Show that the vector field is orthogonal to the equipotential curve at all points (x, y).
d. Sketch two flow curves representing **F** *that are everywhere orthogonal to the equipotential curves.*

33. $\varphi(x, y) = 2x + 3y$

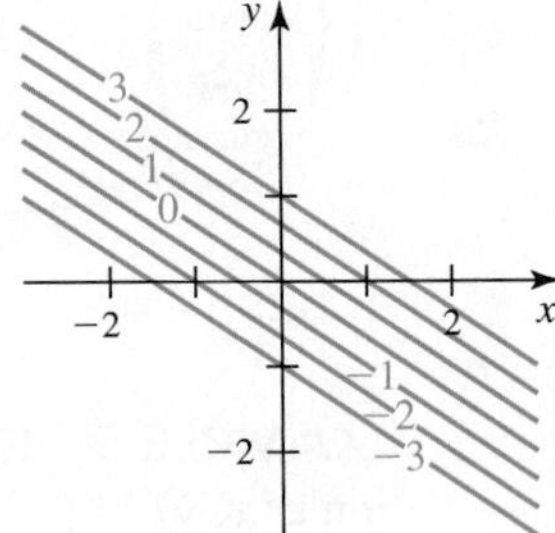

34. $\varphi(x, y) = x + y^2$

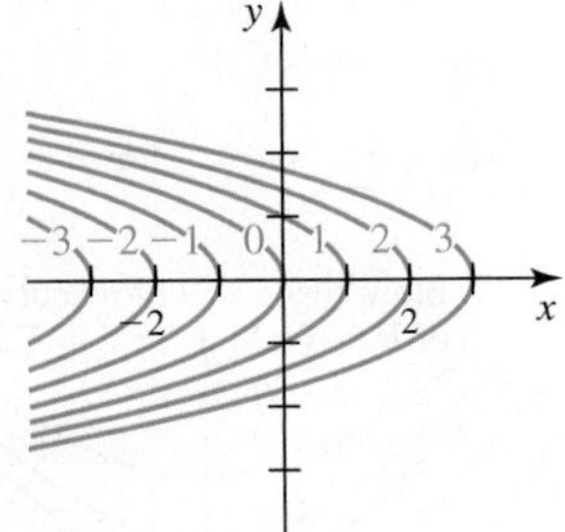

35. $\varphi(x, y) = e^{x-y}$

36. $\varphi(x, y) = x^2 + 2y^2$

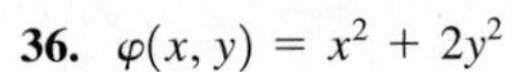

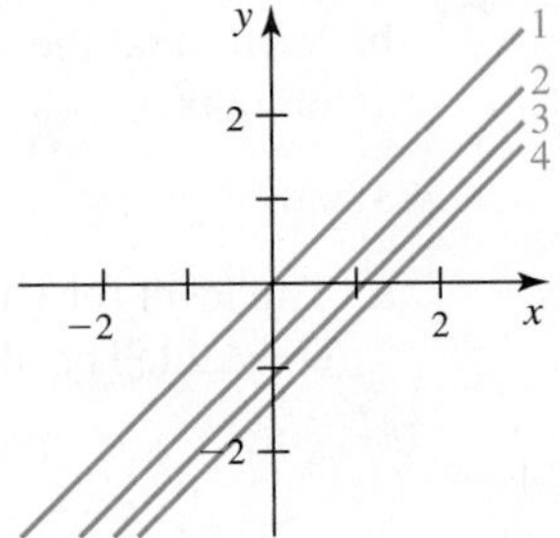

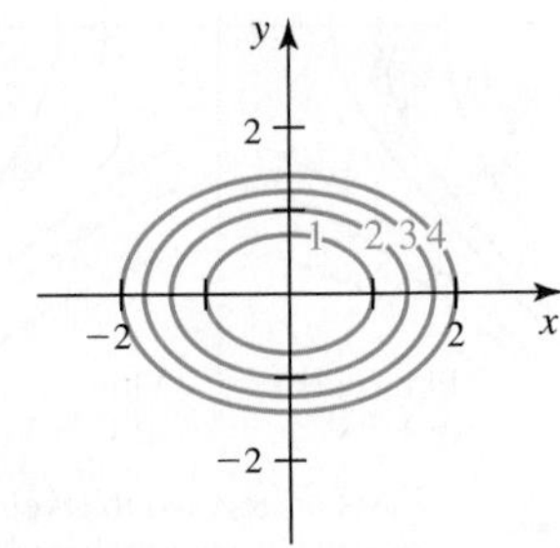

Further Explorations

37. Explain why or why not Determine whether the following statements are true and give an explanation or counterexample.

a. The vector field $\mathbf{F} = \langle 3x^2, 1 \rangle$ is a gradient field for both $\varphi_1(x, y) = x^3 + y$ and $\varphi_2(x, y) = y + x^3 + 100$.

b. The vector field $\mathbf{F} = \dfrac{\langle y, x \rangle}{\sqrt{x^2 + y^2}}$ is constant in direction and magnitude on the unit circle.

c. The vector field $\mathbf{F} = \dfrac{\langle y, x \rangle}{\sqrt{x^2 + y^2}}$ is neither a radial field nor a rotation field.

38–39. Vector fields on regions *Let* $S = \{(x, y): |x| \le 1 \text{ and } |y| \le 1\}$ *(a square centered at the origin),* $D = \{(x, y): |x| + |y| \le 1\}$ *(a diamond centered at the origin), and* $C = \{(x, y): x^2 + y^2 \le 1\}$ *(a disk centered at the origin). For each vector field* **F**, *draw pictures and analyze the vector field to answer the following questions.*

a. At what points of S, D, and C does the vector field have its maximum magnitude?
b. At what points on the boundary of each region is the vector field directed out of the region?

38. $\mathbf{F} = \langle x, y \rangle$

39. $\mathbf{F} = \langle -y, x \rangle$

40–43. Design your vector field *Specify the component functions of a vector field* $\mathbf{F}$ *in* $\mathbf{R}^2$ *with the following properties. Solutions are not unique.*

40. $\mathbf{F}$ is everywhere normal to the line $x = 2$.

41. $\mathbf{F}$ is everywhere normal to the line $x = y$.

42. The flow of $\mathbf{F}$ is counterclockwise around the origin, increasing in magnitude with distance from the origin.

43. At all points except $(0, 0)$, $\mathbf{F}$ has unit magnitude and points away from the origin along radial lines.

Applications

44. Electric field due to a point charge The electric field in the xy-plane due to a point charge at $(0, 0)$ is a gradient field with a potential function $V(x, y) = \dfrac{k}{\sqrt{x^2 + y^2}}$, where $k > 0$ is a physical constant.

a. Find the components of the electric field in the x- and y-directions, where $\mathbf{E}(x, y) = -\nabla V(x, y)$.

b. Show that the vectors of the electric field point in the radial direction (outward from the origin) and the radial component of $\mathbf{E}$ can be expressed as $E_r = k/r^2$, where $r = \sqrt{x^2 + y^2}$.

c. Show that the vector field is orthogonal to the equipotential curves at all points in the domain of V.

45. Electric field due to a line of charge The electric field in the xy-plane due to an infinite line of charge along the z-axis is a gradient field with a potential function $V(x, y) = c \ln \left(\dfrac{r_0}{\sqrt{x^2 + y^2}} \right)$, where $c > 0$ is a constant and r_0 is a reference distance at which the potential is assumed to be 0 (see figure).

a. Find the components of the electric field in the x- and y-directions, where $\mathbf{E}(x, y) = -\nabla V(x, y)$.

b. Show that the electric field at a point in the xy-plane is directed outward from the origin and has magnitude $|\mathbf{E}| = c/r$, where $r = \sqrt{x^2 + y^2}$.

c. Show that the vector field is orthogonal to the equipotential curves at all points in the domain of V.

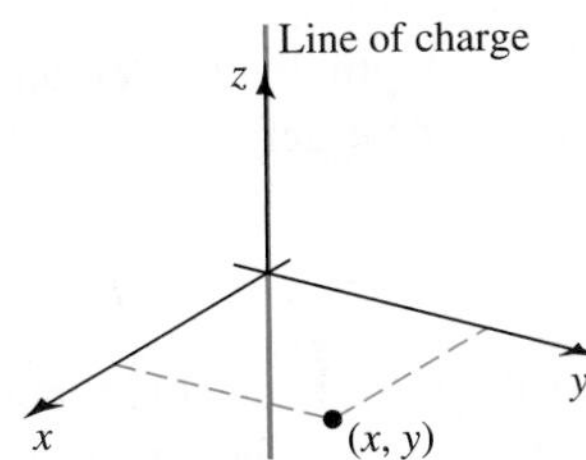

46. Gravitational force due to a mass The gravitational force on a point mass m due to a point mass M is a gradient field with potential $U(r) = \dfrac{GMm}{r}$, where G is the gravitational constant and $r = \sqrt{x^2 + y^2 + z^2}$ is the distance between the masses.

a. Find the components of the gravitational force in the x-, y-, and z-directions, where $\mathbf{F}(x, y, z) = -\nabla U(x, y, z)$.

b. Show that the gravitational force points in the radial direction (outward from point mass M) and the radial component is
$$F(r) = \frac{GMm}{r^2}.$$

c. Show that the vector field is orthogonal to the equipotential surfaces at all points in the domain of U.

Additional Exercises

47–51. Streamlines in the plane *Let* $\mathbf{F}(x, y) = \langle f(x, y), g(x, y) \rangle$ *be defined on* $\mathbf{R}^2$.

47. Explain why the flow curves or streamlines of $\mathbf{F}$ satisfy $y' = g(x, y)/f(x, y)$ and are everywhere tangent to the vector field.

T **48.** Find and graph the streamlines for the vector field $\mathbf{F} = \langle 1, x \rangle$.

T **49.** Find and graph the streamlines for the vector field $\mathbf{F} = \langle x, x \rangle$.

T **50.** Find and graph the streamlines for the vector field $\mathbf{F} = \langle y, x \rangle$. Note that $d/dx(y^2) = 2yy'(x)$.

T **51.** Find and graph the streamlines for the vector field $\mathbf{F} = \langle -y, x \rangle$.

52–53. Unit vectors in polar coordinates

52. Vectors in $\mathbf{R}^2$ may also be expressed in terms of polar coordinates. The standard coordinate unit vectors in polar coordinates are denoted $\mathbf{u}_r$ and $\mathbf{u}_\theta$ (see figure). Unlike the coordinate unit vectors in Cartesian coordinates, $\mathbf{u}_r$ and $\mathbf{u}_\theta$ change their direction depending on the point (r, θ). Use the figure to show that for $r > 0$, the following relationships between the unit vectors in Cartesian and polar coordinates hold:

$$\mathbf{u}_r = \cos\theta\,\mathbf{i} + \sin\theta\,\mathbf{j} \qquad \mathbf{i} = \mathbf{u}_r \cos\theta - \mathbf{u}_\theta \sin\theta$$
$$\mathbf{u}_\theta = -\sin\theta\,\mathbf{i} + \cos\theta\,\mathbf{j} \qquad \mathbf{j} = \mathbf{u}_r \sin\theta + \mathbf{u}_\theta \cos\theta$$

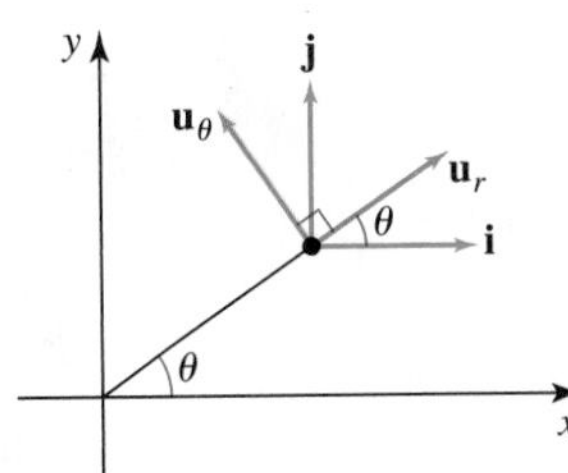

53. Verify that the relationships in Exercise 52 are consistent when $\theta = 0, \pi/2, \pi, 3\pi/2$.

54–56. Vector fields in polar coordinates *A vector field in polar coordinates has the form* $\mathbf{F}(r, \theta) = f(r, \theta)\,\mathbf{u}_r + g(r, \theta)\,\mathbf{u}_\theta$, *where the unit vectors are defined in Exercise 52. Sketch the following vector fields and express them in Cartesian coordinates.*

54. $\mathbf{F} = \mathbf{u}_r$

55. $\mathbf{F} = \mathbf{u}_\theta$

56. $\mathbf{F} = r\mathbf{u}_\theta$

57. Write the vector field $\mathbf{F} = \langle -y, x \rangle$ in polar coordinates and sketch the field.

QUICK CHECK ANSWERS

1. The particle follows a circular path. **3.** $\nabla\varphi = \langle yz, xz, xy \rangle$

15.2 Line Integrals

With integrals of a single variable, we integrate over intervals in $\mathbf{R}^1$ (the real line). With double and triple integrals, we integrate over regions in $\mathbf{R}^2$ or $\mathbf{R}^3$. *Line integrals* (which really should be called *curve integrals*) are another class of integrals that play an important role in vector calculus. They are used to integrate either scalar-valued functions or vector fields along curves.

Suppose a thin, circular plate has a known temperature distribution and you must compute the average temperature along the edge of the plate. The required calculation involves integrating the temperature function over the *curved* boundary of the plate. Similarly, to calculate the amount of work needed to put a satellite into orbit, we integrate the gravitational force (a vector field) along the curved path of the satellite. Both these calculations require line integrals. As you will see, line integrals take several different forms. It is the goal of this section to distinguish these various forms and show how and when each form should be used.

Scalar Line Integrals in the Plane

We first consider line integrals of scalar-valued functions over curves in the plane. Figure 15.16 shows a surface $z = f(x, y)$ and a parameterized curve C in the xy-plane; for the moment we assume that $f(x, y) \geq 0$ for (x, y) on C. Now visualize the curtain-like surface formed by the vertical line segments joining the surface $z = f(x, y)$ and C. The goal is to find the area of one side of this curtain in terms of a line integral. As with other integrals we have studied, we begin with Riemann sums.

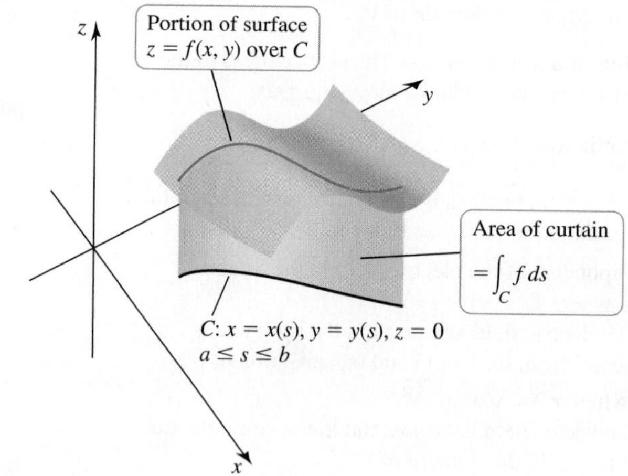

FIGURE 15.16

Assume that C is a smooth curve of finite length, parameterized in terms of arc length as $\mathbf{r}(s) = \langle x(s), y(s)\rangle$, for $a \leq s \leq b$, and let f be defined on C. We subdivide C into n small arcs by forming a partition of $[a, b]$:

$$a = s_0 < s_1 < \cdots < s_{n-1} < s_n = b.$$

Let $\bar{s}_k$ be a point in the kth subinterval $[s_{k-1}, s_k]$, which corresponds to a point $(x(\bar{s}_k), y(\bar{s}_k))$ on the kth arc of C, for $k = 1, 2, \ldots, n$. The length of the kth arc is denoted Δs_k. This partition also divides the curtain into n panels. The kth panel has an approximate height of $f(x(\bar{s}_k), y(\bar{s}_k))$ and a base of length Δs_k; therefore, the approximate area of the kth panel is $f(x(\bar{s}_k), y(\bar{s}_k))\Delta s_k$ (Figure 15.17). Summing the areas of the panels, the approximate area of the curtain is given by the Riemann sum

$$\text{area} \approx \sum_{k=1}^{n} f(x(\bar{s}_k), y(\bar{s}_k))\,\Delta s_k.$$

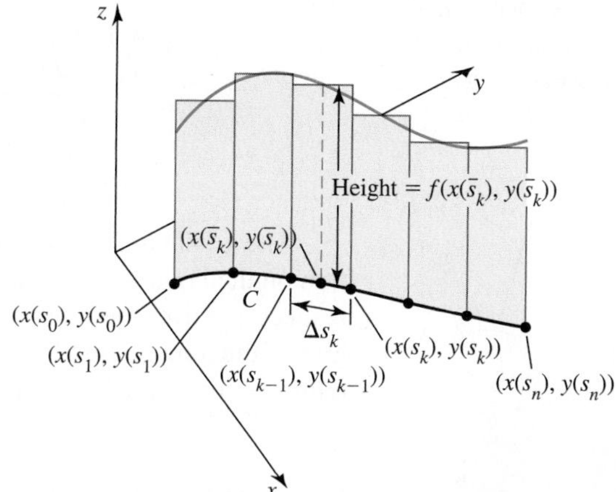

FIGURE 15.17

We now let Δ be the maximum value of $\Delta s_1, \ldots, \Delta s_n$. If the limit of the Riemann sums as $n \to \infty$ and $\Delta \to 0$ exists over all partitions, the limit is called a *line integral*, and it gives the area of the curtain.

DEFINITION Scalar Line Integral in the Plane, Arc Length Parameter

Suppose the scalar-valued function f is defined on the smooth curve C: $\mathbf{r}(s) = \langle x(s), y(s) \rangle$, parameterized by the arc length s. The **line integral of f over C** is

$$\int_C f(x(s), y(s))\, ds = \lim_{\Delta \to 0} \sum_{k=1}^{n} f(x(\bar{s}_k), y(\bar{s}_k))\Delta s_k,$$

provided this limit exists over all partitions of C. When the limit exists, f is said to be **integrable** on C.

The more compact notation $\int_C f(\mathbf{r}(s))\, ds$, $\int_C f(x, y)\, ds$, or $\int_C f\, ds$ is often used for the line integral of f over C. It can be shown that if f is continuous on a region containing C, then the line integral of f over C exists. If $f(x, y) = 1$, the line integral $\int_C ds$ gives the length of the curve, just as the ordinary integral $\int_a^b dx$ gives the length of the interval $[a, b]$, which is $b - a$.

➤ When we compute the average value by an ordinary integral, we divide by the length of the interval of integration. Analogously, when we compute the average value by a line integral, we divide by the length of the curve.

EXAMPLE 1 Average temperature on a circle The temperature of the circular plate $R = \{(x, y): x^2 + y^2 \le 1\}$ is $T(x, y) = 100(x^2 + 2y^2)$. Find the average temperature along the edge of the plate.

SOLUTION Calculating the average value requires integrating the temperature function over the boundary circle $C = \{(x, y): x^2 + y^2 = 1\}$ and dividing by the length (circumference) of C. The first step is to find a parametric description for C. Recall from Section 12.9 that a parametric description of a unit circle using arc length as the parameter is $\mathbf{r} = \langle x, y \rangle = \langle \cos s, \sin s \rangle$, for $0 \le s \le 2\pi$. We substitute $x = \cos s$ and $y = \sin s$ into the temperature function and express the line integral as an ordinary integral:

$$\int_C T(x, y)\, ds = \int_0^{2\pi} \underbrace{100[x(s)^2 + 2y(s)^2]}_{T(s)}\, ds \qquad \text{Write the line integral with respect to } s.$$

$$= 100 \int_0^{2\pi} (\cos^2 s + 2 \sin^2 s)\, ds \qquad \text{Substitute for } x \text{ and } y.$$

➤ The line integral in Example 1 also gives the area of the cylindrical curtain that hangs between the surface and C in Figure 15.18.

$$= 100 \underbrace{\int_0^{2\pi} (1 + \sin^2 s)\, ds}_{3\pi} \qquad \cos^2 s + \sin^2 s = 1$$

$$= 300\pi \qquad \text{Use } \sin^2 s = \frac{1 - \cos 2s}{2} \text{ and integrate.}$$

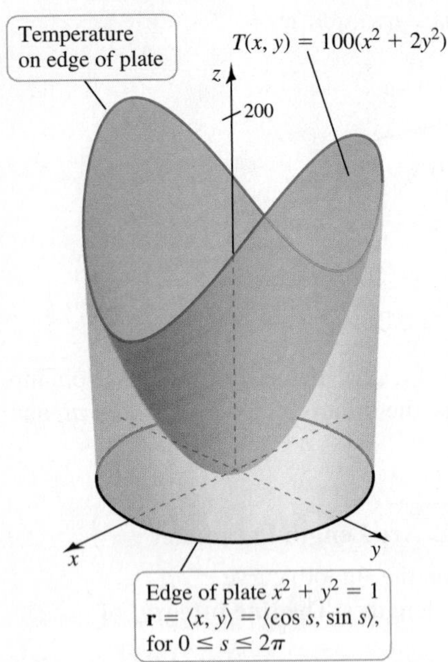

FIGURE 15.18

The geometry of this line integral is shown in Figure 15.18. The temperature function on the boundary of C is a function of s. The line integral is an ordinary integral with respect to s over the interval $[0, 2\pi]$. To find the average value we divide the line integral of the temperature by the length of the curve, which is 2π. Therefore, the average temperature on the boundary of the plate is $300\pi/(2\pi) = 150$.

Related Exercises 11–14 ◀

Parameters Other than Arc Length The line integral in Example 1 is straightforward because a circle is easily parameterized in terms of the arc length. Suppose we have a parameterized curve with a parameter t that is *not* the arc length. The key is a change of variables. Assume the curve C is described by $\mathbf{r}(t) = \langle x(t), y(t) \rangle$, for $a \leq t \leq b$. Recall from Section 12.9 that the length of C over the interval $[a, t]$ is

$$s(t) = \int_a^t |\mathbf{r}'(u)|\, du.$$

Differentiating both sides of this equation and using the Fundamental Theorem of Calculus yields $s'(t) = |\mathbf{r}'(t)|$. We now make a standard change of variables using the relationship

$$ds = s'(t)\, dt = |\mathbf{r}'(t)|\, dt.$$

➤ If t represents time, then the relationship $ds = |\mathbf{r}'(t)|\, dt$ is a generalization of the familiar formula *distance* = (*speed*)(*time*).

The original line integral with respect to s is now converted into an ordinary integral with respect to t:

$$\int_C f\, ds = \int_a^b f(x(t), y(t)) \underbrace{|\mathbf{r}'(t)|\, dt}_{ds}$$

QUICK CHECK 1 Explain mathematically why differentiating the arc length integral leads to $s'(t) = |\mathbf{r}'(t)|$. ◀

➤ The value of a line integral of a scalar-valued function is independent of the parameterization of C and independent of the direction in which C is traversed (Exercises 54–55).

THEOREM 15.1 Evaluating Scalar Line Integrals in $\mathbf{R}^2$

Let f be continuous on a region containing a smooth curve C: $\mathbf{r}(t) = \langle x(t), y(t) \rangle$, for $a \leq t \leq b$. Then

$$\int_C f\, ds = \int_a^b f(x(t), y(t))|\mathbf{r}'(t)|\, dt$$

$$= \int_a^b f(x(t), y(t))\sqrt{x'(t)^2 + y'(t)^2}\, dt.$$

If t represents time and C is the path of a moving object, then $|\mathbf{r}'(t)|$ is the speed of the object. The *speed factor* $|\mathbf{r}'(t)|$ that appears in the integral relates distance traveled along the curve as measured by s to the elapsed time as measured by the parameter t.

Notice that if t is the arc length s, then $|\mathbf{r}'(t)| = 1$ and we recover the line integral with respect to the arc length s:

$$\int_C f\,ds = \int_a^b f(x(s), y(s))\,ds$$

If $f(x, y) = 1$, then the line integral is $\int_a^b \sqrt{x'(t)^2 + y'(t)^2}\,dt$, which is the arc length formula for C. Theorem 15.1 leads to the following procedure for evaluating line integrals.

PROCEDURE Evaluating the Line Integral $\int_C f\,ds$

1. Find a parametric description of C in the form $\mathbf{r}(t) = \langle x(t), y(t)\rangle$, for $a \le t \le b$.
2. Compute $|\mathbf{r}'(t)| = \sqrt{x'(t)^2 + y'(t)^2}$.
3. Make substitutions for x and y in the integrand and evaluate an ordinary integral:

$$\int_C f\,ds = \int_a^b f(x(t), y(t))|\mathbf{r}'(t)|\,dt$$

EXAMPLE 2 Average temperature on a circle The temperature of the circular plate $R = \{(x, y): x^2 + y^2 \le 1\}$ is $T(x, y) = 100(x^2 + 2y^2)$ as in Example 1. Confirm the average temperature computed in Example 1 when the circle has the parametric description

$$C = \{(x, y): x = \cos t^2, y = \sin t^2, 0 \le t \le \sqrt{2\pi}\}.$$

SOLUTION The speed factor on C (using $\sin^2 t^2 + \cos^2 t^2 = 1$) is

$$|\mathbf{r}'(t)| = \sqrt{x'(t)^2 + y'(t)^2} = \sqrt{(-2t\sin t^2)^2 + (2t\cos t^2)^2} = 2t.$$

Making the appropriate substitutions, the value of the line integral is

$$\int_C T\,ds = \int_0^{\sqrt{2\pi}} 100(x(t)^2 + 2y(t)^2)|\mathbf{r}'(t)|\,dt$$ Write the line integral with respect to t.

$$= \int_0^{\sqrt{2\pi}} 100(\cos^2 t^2 + 2\sin^2 t^2)\underbrace{2t}_{|\mathbf{r}'(t)|}\,dt$$ Substitute for x and y.

$$= 100\underbrace{\int_0^{2\pi} (\cos^2 u + 2\sin^2 u)\,du}_{\pi + 2\pi}$$ Simplify and let $u = t^2$, $du = 2t\,dt$.

$$= 300\pi.$$ Evaluate the integral.

Dividing by the length of C, the average temperature on the boundary of the plate is $300\pi/(2\pi) = 150$, as found in Example 1. *Related Exercises 15–24* ◂

Line Integrals in $\mathbf{R}^3$

The argument that leads to line integrals on plane curves extends immediately to three or more dimensions. Here is the corresponding evaluation theorem for line integrals in $\mathbf{R}^3$.

THEOREM 15.2 Evaluating Scalar Line Integrals in $\mathbf{R}^3$
Let f be continuous on a smooth curve C: $\mathbf{r}(t) = \langle x(t), y(t), z(t)\rangle$, for $a \le t \le b$. Then

$$\int_C f\,ds = \int_a^b f(x(t), y(t), z(t))|\mathbf{r}'(t)|\,dt$$
$$= \int_a^b f(x(t), y(t), z(t))\sqrt{x'(t)^2 + y'(t)^2 + z'(t)^2}\,dt.$$

As before, if t is the arc length s, then $|\mathbf{r}'(t)| = 1$ and

$$\int_C f\,ds = \int_a^b f(x(s), y(s), z(s))\,ds.$$

If $f(x, y, z) = 1$, then the line integral gives the length of C.

➤ A parametric equation of a line is

$$\mathbf{r}(t) = \langle x_0, y_0, z_0\rangle + t\langle a, b, c\rangle,$$

where $\langle x_0, y_0, z_0\rangle$ is a position vector associated with a fixed point on the line and $\langle a, b, c\rangle$ is a vector parallel to the line.

EXAMPLE 3 Line integrals in $\mathbf{R}^3$ Evaluate $\int_C (xy + 2z)\,ds$ on the following lines.

a. The line from $P(1, 0, 0)$ to $Q(0, 1, 1)$

b. The line from $Q(0, 1, 1)$ to $P(1, 0, 0)$

SOLUTION

a. A parametric description of the line from $P(1, 0, 0)$ to $Q(0, 1, 1)$ is

$$\mathbf{r}(t) = \langle 1, 0, 0\rangle + t\langle -1, 1, 1\rangle = \langle 1 - t, t, t\rangle, \quad \text{for } 0 \le t \le 1.$$

The speed factor is

$$|r'(t)| = \sqrt{x'(t)^2 + y'(t)^2 + z'(t)^2} = \sqrt{(-1)^2 + 1^2 + 1^2} = \sqrt{3}.$$

Substituting $x = 1 - t$, $y = t$, and $z = t$, the value of the line integral is

$$\int_C (xy + 2z)\,ds = \int_0^1 ((\underbrace{1 - t}_{x})\,(\underbrace{t}_{y}) + 2(\underbrace{t}_{z}))\sqrt{3}\,dt \quad \text{Substitute for } x, y, z.$$

$$= \sqrt{3}\int_0^1 (3t - t^2)\,dt \quad \text{Simplify.}$$

$$= \sqrt{3}\left(\frac{3t^2}{2} - \frac{t^3}{3}\right)\Big|_0^1 \quad \text{Integrate.}$$

$$= \frac{7\sqrt{3}}{6}. \quad \text{Evaluate.}$$

b. The line from $Q(0, 1, 1)$ to $P(1, 0, 0)$ may be described parametrically by

$$\mathbf{r}(t) = \langle 0, 1, 1\rangle + t\langle 1, -1, -1\rangle = \langle t, 1 - t, 1 - t\rangle, \quad \text{for } 0 \le t \le 1.$$

The speed factor is

$$|\mathbf{r}'(t)| = \sqrt{x'(t)^2 + y'(t)^2 + z'(t)^2} = \sqrt{1^2 + (-1)^2 + (-1)^2} = \sqrt{3}.$$

We substitute $x = t$, $y = 1 - t$, and $z = 1 - t$ and do a calculation similar to that in part (a). The value of the line integral is again $\frac{7\sqrt{3}}{6}$, emphasizing the fact that a scalar line integral is independent of the orientation and parameterization of the curve.

Related Exercises 25–30 ◀

EXAMPLE 4 **Flight of an eagle** An eagle soars on the ascending spiral path

$$C\colon \mathbf{r}(t) = \langle x(t), y(t), z(t)\rangle = \left\langle 2400 \cos \frac{t}{2}, 2400 \sin \frac{t}{2}, 500t \right\rangle,$$

where x, y, and z are measured in feet and t is measured in minutes. How far does the eagle fly over the time interval $0 \le t \le 10$?

➤ Because we are finding the length of a curve, the integrand in this line integral is $f(x, y, z) = 1$.

SOLUTION The distance traveled is found by integrating the element of arc length ds along C, that is, $L = \int_C ds$. We now make a change of variables to the parameter t using

$$\begin{aligned} |\mathbf{r}'(t)| &= \sqrt{x'(t)^2 + y'(t)^2 + z'(t)^2} \\ &= \sqrt{\left(-1200 \sin \frac{t}{2}\right)^2 + \left(1200 \cos \frac{t}{2}\right)^2 + 500^2} && \text{Substitute derivatives.} \\ &= \sqrt{1200^2 + 500^2} = 1300 && \sin^2 \frac{t}{2} + \cos^2 \frac{t}{2} = 1 \end{aligned}$$

QUICK CHECK 2 What is the speed of the eagle in Example 4? ◀

It follows that the distance traveled is

$$L = \int_C ds = \int_0^{10} |\mathbf{r}'(t)|\, dt = \int_0^{10} 1300\, dt = 13{,}000 \text{ ft.}$$

Related Exercises 31–32 ◀

Line Integrals of Vector Fields

Line integrals along curves in $\mathbf{R}^2$ or $\mathbf{R}^3$ may also have integrands that involve vector fields. Such line integrals are different from scalar line integrals in two respects:

- Recall that an *oriented curve* is a parameterized curve for which a direction is specified. The *positive*, or *forward*, orientation is the direction in which the curve is generated as the parameter increases. For example, the positive direction of the circle $\mathbf{r}(t) = \langle \cos t, \sin t\rangle$, for $0 \le t \le 2\pi$, is counterclockwise. As we will see, vector line integrals must be evaluated on oriented curves, and the value of a line integral depends on the orientation.
- The line integral of a vector field $\mathbf{F}$ along an oriented curve involves a specific component of $\mathbf{F}$ relative to the curve. We begin by defining vector line integrals for the *tangential* component of $\mathbf{F}$, a situation that has many physical applications.

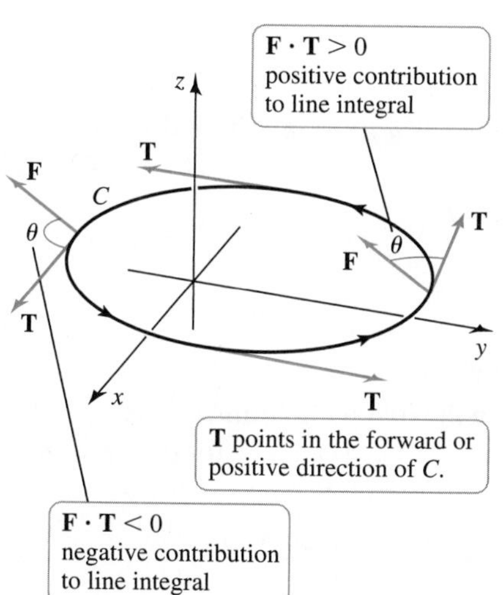

FIGURE 15.19

Let $C\colon \mathbf{r}(s) = \langle x(s), y(s), z(s)\rangle$ be a smooth oriented curve in $\mathbf{R}^3$ parameterized by arc length and let $\mathbf{F}$ be a vector field that is continuous on a region containing C. At each point of C, the unit tangent vector $\mathbf{T}$ points in the positive direction on C (Figure 15.19). The component of $\mathbf{F}$ in the direction of $\mathbf{T}$ at a point of C is $|\mathbf{F}| \cos \theta$, where θ is the angle between $\mathbf{F}$ and $\mathbf{T}$. Because $\mathbf{T}$ is a unit vector,

➤ The component of $\mathbf{F}$ in the direction of $\mathbf{T}$ is the scalar component of $\mathbf{F}$ in the direction of $\mathbf{T}$, $\text{scal}_{\mathbf{T}}\, \mathbf{F}$, as defined in Section 12.3. Note that $|\mathbf{T}| = 1$.

$$|\mathbf{F}| \cos \theta = |\mathbf{F}||\mathbf{T}| \cos \theta = \mathbf{F} \cdot \mathbf{T}.$$

The first line integral of a vector field $\mathbf{F}$ that we introduce is the line integral of the scalar $\mathbf{F} \cdot \mathbf{T}$ along the curve C. When we integrate $\mathbf{F} \cdot \mathbf{T}$ along C, the effect is to add up the components of $\mathbf{F}$ in the direction of C at each point of C.

➤ Some books let $d\mathbf{s}$ stand for $\mathbf{T}\, ds$. Then the line integral $\int_C \mathbf{F} \cdot \mathbf{T}\, ds$ is written $\int_C \mathbf{F} \cdot d\mathbf{s}$.

DEFINITION **Line Integral of a Vector Field**

Let $\mathbf{F}$ be a vector field that is continuous on a region containing a smooth oriented curve C parameterized by arc length. Let $\mathbf{T}$ be the unit tangent vector at each point of C consistent with the orientation. The line integral of $\mathbf{F}$ over C is $\int_C \mathbf{F} \cdot \mathbf{T}\, ds$.

We need a method for evaluating vector line integrals, particularly when the parameter is *not* the arc length. Suppose that C has a parameterization $\mathbf{r}(t) = \langle x(t), y(t), z(t)\rangle$, for $a \le t \le b$. Recall from Section 12.6 that the unit tangent vector at a point on the curve is $\mathbf{T} = \dfrac{\mathbf{r}'(t)}{|\mathbf{r}'(t)|}$. Using the fact that $ds = |\mathbf{r}'(t)|\,dt$, the line integral becomes

$$\int_C \mathbf{F}\cdot\mathbf{T}\,ds = \int_a^b \mathbf{F}\cdot\underbrace{\frac{\mathbf{r}'(t)}{|\mathbf{r}'(t)|}}_{\mathbf{T}}\underbrace{|\mathbf{r}'(t)|\,dt}_{ds} = \int_a^b \mathbf{F}\cdot\mathbf{r}'(t)\,dt.$$

This integral may be written in several different forms. If $\mathbf{F} = \langle f, g, h\rangle$, then the line integral may be evaluated in component form as

$$\int_C \mathbf{F}\cdot\mathbf{T}\,ds = \int_a^b \mathbf{F}\cdot\mathbf{r}'(t)\,dt = \int_a^b (f\,x'(t) + g\,y'(t) + h\,z'(t))\,dt,$$

where f stands for $f(x(t), y(t), z(t))$, with analogous expressions for g and h.

Another useful form is obtained by noting that

$$dx = x'(t)\,dt, \qquad dy = y'(t)\,dt, \qquad dz = z'(t)\,dt.$$

Making these replacements in the previous integral results in the form

$$\int_C \mathbf{F}\cdot\mathbf{T}\,ds = \int_C f\,dx + g\,dy + h\,dz.$$

Finally, if we let $d\mathbf{r} = \langle dx, dy, dz\rangle$, then $f\,dx + g\,dy + h\,dz = \mathbf{F}\cdot d\mathbf{r}$, and we have

$$\int_C \mathbf{F}\cdot\mathbf{T}\,ds = \int_C \mathbf{F}\cdot d\mathbf{r}.$$

Different Forms of Line Integrals of Vector Fields

The line integral $\int_C \mathbf{F}\cdot\mathbf{T}\,ds$ may be expressed in the following forms, where $\mathbf{F} = \langle f, g, h\rangle$ and C has a parameterization $\mathbf{r}(t) = \langle x(t), y(t), z(t)\rangle$, for $a \le t \le b$:

$$\begin{aligned}\int_a^b \mathbf{F}\cdot\mathbf{r}'(t)\,dt &= \int_a^b (f\,x'(t) + g\,y'(t) + h\,z'(t))\,dt\\ &= \int_C f\,dx + g\,dy + h\,dz\\ &= \int_C \mathbf{F}\cdot d\mathbf{r}\end{aligned}$$

For line integrals in the plane, we let $\mathbf{F} = \langle f, g\rangle$ and assume C is parameterized in the form $\mathbf{r}(t) = \langle x(t), y(t)\rangle$, for $a \le t \le b$. Then

$$\int_C \mathbf{F}\cdot\mathbf{T}\,ds = \int_a^b (f\,x'(t) + g\,y'(t))\,dt = \int_C f\,dx + g\,dy = \int_C \mathbf{F}\cdot d\mathbf{r}.$$

We use the convention that $-C$ is the curve C with the opposite orientation.

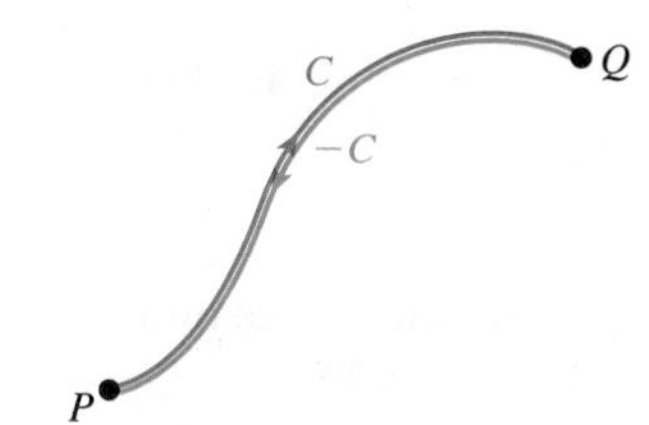

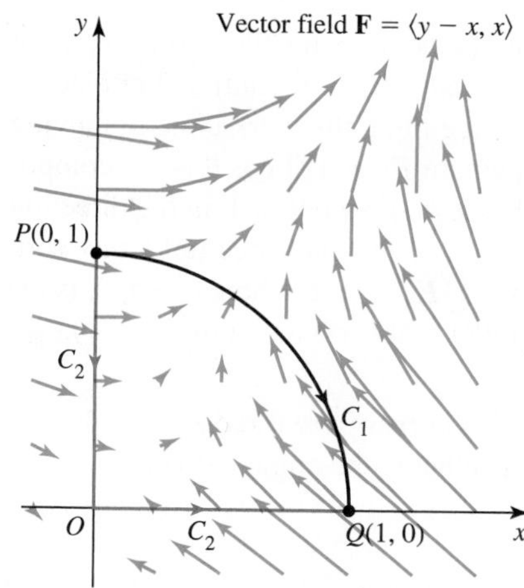

FIGURE 15.20

$$\int_{-C} \mathbf{F} \cdot \mathbf{T}\, ds = -\int_C \mathbf{F} \cdot \mathbf{T}\, ds$$

EXAMPLE 5 Different paths Evaluate the line integral of $\mathbf{F} = \langle y - x, x \rangle$ on the following oriented paths in $\mathbf{R}^2$ (Figure 15.20).

a. The quarter circle C_1 from $P(0, 1)$ to $Q(1, 0)$

b. The quarter circle $-C_1$ from $Q(1, 0)$ to $P(0, 1)$

c. The path C_2 from P to Q via two line segments through $O(0, 0)$

SOLUTION

a. Working in $\mathbf{R}^2$, a parametric description of the curve C_1 with the required (clockwise) orientation is $\mathbf{r}(t) = \langle \sin t, \cos t \rangle$, for $0 \le t \le \pi/2$. Along C_1 the vector field is

$$\mathbf{F} = \langle y - x, x \rangle = \langle \cos t - \sin t, \sin t \rangle.$$

The velocity vector is $\mathbf{r}'(t) = \langle \cos t, -\sin t \rangle$, so the integrand of the line integral is

$$\mathbf{F} \cdot \mathbf{r}'(t) = \langle \cos t - \sin t, \sin t \rangle \cdot \langle \cos t, -\sin t \rangle = \underbrace{\cos^2 t - \sin^2 t}_{\cos 2t} - \underbrace{\sin t \cos t}_{\frac{1}{2}\sin 2t}.$$

The value of the line integral of $\mathbf{F}$ over C_1 is

$$\begin{aligned} \int_0^{\pi/2} \mathbf{F} \cdot \mathbf{r}'(t)\, dt &= \int_0^{\pi/2} \left(\cos 2t - \frac{1}{2} \sin 2t \right) dt && \text{Substitute for } \mathbf{F} \cdot \mathbf{r}'(t). \\ &= \left(\frac{1}{2} \sin 2t + \frac{1}{4} \cos 2t \right) \Big|_0^{\pi/2} && \text{Evaluate the integral.} \\ &= -\frac{1}{2}. && \text{Simplify.} \end{aligned}$$

b. A parameterization of the curve $-C_1$ from Q to P is $\mathbf{r}(t) = \langle \cos t, \sin t \rangle$ for $0 \le t \le \pi/2$. The vector field along the curve is

$$\mathbf{F} = \langle y - x, x \rangle = \langle \sin t - \cos t, \cos t \rangle$$

and the velocity vector is $\mathbf{r}'(t) = \langle -\sin t, \cos t \rangle$. A calculation very similar to that in part (a) results in

$$\int_{-C_1} \mathbf{F} \cdot \mathbf{T}\, ds = \int_0^{\pi/2} \mathbf{F} \cdot \mathbf{r}'(t)\, dt = \frac{1}{2}.$$

The results of parts (a) and (b) illustrate the important fact that reversing the orientation of a curve reverses the sign of the line integral of a vector field.

c. The path C_2 consists of two line segments:

- The segment from P to O is parameterized by $\mathbf{r}(t) = \langle 0, 1 - t \rangle$, for $0 \le t \le 1$. Therefore, $\mathbf{r}'(t) = \langle 0, -1 \rangle$ and $\mathbf{F} = \langle y - x, x \rangle = \langle 1 - t, 0 \rangle$.
- The line segment from O to Q is parameterized by $\mathbf{r}(t) = \langle t, 0 \rangle$, for $0 \le t \le 1$. Therefore, $\mathbf{r}'(t) = \langle 1, 0 \rangle$ and $\mathbf{F} = \langle y - x, x \rangle = \langle -t, t \rangle$.

The line integral is split into two parts and evaluated as follows:

$$\begin{aligned} \int_{C_2} \mathbf{F} \cdot \mathbf{T}\, ds &= \int_{PO} \mathbf{F} \cdot \mathbf{T}\, ds + \int_{OQ} \mathbf{F} \cdot \mathbf{T}\, ds \\ &= \int_0^1 \langle 1 - t, 0 \rangle \cdot \langle 0, -1 \rangle\, dt + \int_0^1 \langle -t, t \rangle \cdot \langle 1, 0 \rangle\, dt && \text{Substitute for } x, y, \mathbf{r}'. \end{aligned}$$

$$= \int_0^1 0\,dt + \int_0^1 (-t)\,dt \qquad \text{Simplify.}$$

$$= -\frac{1}{2} \qquad \text{Evaluate the integrals.}$$

The line integrals in parts (a) and (c) have the same value and run from P to Q, but along different paths. We might ask: For what vector fields are the values of a line integral independent of path? We return to this question in Section 15.3.

Related Exercises 33–38 ◀

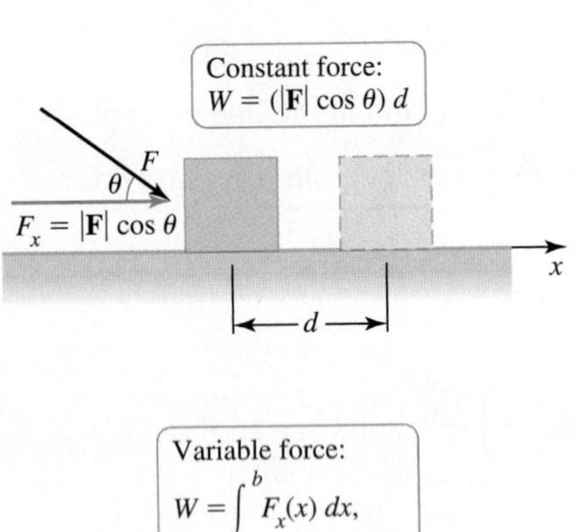

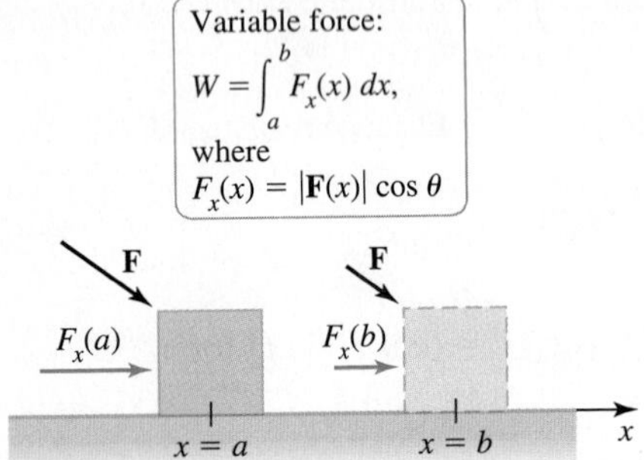

FIGURE 15.21

Work Integrals A common application of line integrals of vector fields is computing the work done in moving an object in a force field (for example, a gravitational or electric field). First recall (Section 6.6) that if $\mathbf{F}$ is a *constant* force field, the work done in moving an object a distance d along the x-axis is $W = F_x d$, where $F_x = |\mathbf{F}| \cos \theta$ is the component of the force along the x-axis (Figure 15.21). Only the component of $\mathbf{F}$ in the direction of motion contributes to the work. More generally, if $\mathbf{F}$ is a *variable* force field, the work done in moving an object from $x = a$ to $x = b$ is $W = \int_a^b F_x(x)\, dx$, where again F_x is the component of the force in the direction of motion (parallel to the x-axis, Figure 15.21).

QUICK CHECK 3 Suppose a two-dimensional force field is everywhere directed outward from the origin and C is a circle centered at the origin. What is the angle between the field and the unit vectors tangent to C? ◀

We now take this progression one step further. Let $\mathbf{F}$ be a variable force field defined in a region D of $\mathbf{R}^3$, and suppose C is a smooth, oriented curve in D, along which an object moves. The direction of motion at each point of C is given by the unit tangent vector $\mathbf{T}$. Therefore, the component of $\mathbf{F}$ in the direction of motion is $\mathbf{F} \cdot \mathbf{T}$, which is the tangential component of $\mathbf{F}$ along C. Summing the contributions to the work at each point of C, the work done in moving an object along C in the presence of the force is the line integral of $\mathbf{F} \cdot \mathbf{T}$ (Figure 15.22).

➤ Just to be clear, a work integral is nothing more than a line integral of the tangential component of a force field.

DEFINITION Work Done in a Force Field

Let $\mathbf{F}$ be a continuous force field in a region D of $\mathbf{R}^3$ and let C: $\mathbf{r}(t) = \langle x(t), y(t), z(t) \rangle$, for $a \le t \le b$, be a smooth curve in D with a unit tangent vector $\mathbf{T}$ consistent with the orientation. The work done in moving an object along C in the positive direction is

$$W = \int_C \mathbf{F} \cdot \mathbf{T}\, ds = \int_a^b \mathbf{F} \cdot \mathbf{r}'(t)\, dt.$$

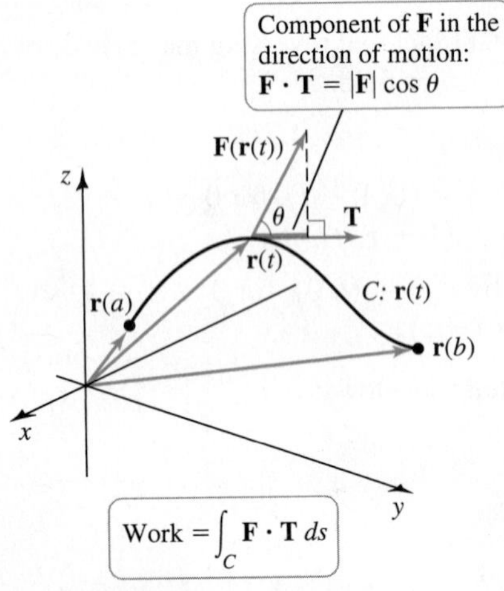

FIGURE 15.22

EXAMPLE 6 An inverse square force Gravitational and electrical forces between point masses and point charges obey inverse square laws: They act along the line joining the centers and they vary as $1/r^2$, where r is the distance between the centers. The force of attraction (or repulsion) of an inverse square force field is given by the vector field $\mathbf{F} = \dfrac{k\langle x, y, z \rangle}{(x^2 + y^2 + z^2)^{3/2}}$, where k is a physical constant. Because $\mathbf{r} = \langle x, y, z \rangle$, this force may also be written $\mathbf{F} = \dfrac{k\mathbf{r}}{|\mathbf{r}|^3}$. Find the work done in moving an object along the following paths:

a. C_1 is the line segment from $(1, 1, 1)$ to (a, a, a), where $a > 1$.

b. C_2 is the extension of C_1 produced by letting $a \to \infty$.

SOLUTION

a. A parametric description of C_1 consistent with the orientation is $\mathbf{r}(t) = \langle t, t, t \rangle$, for $1 \le t \le a$, with $\mathbf{r}'(t) = \langle 1, 1, 1 \rangle$. In terms of the parameter t, the force field is

$$\mathbf{F} = \frac{k\langle x, y, z \rangle}{(x^2 + y^2 + z^2)^{3/2}} = \frac{k\langle t, t, t \rangle}{(3t^2)^{3/2}}.$$

The dot product that appears in the work integral is

$$\mathbf{F} \cdot \mathbf{r}'(t) = \frac{k\langle t, t, t \rangle}{(3t^2)^{3/2}} \cdot \langle 1, 1, 1 \rangle = \frac{3kt}{3\sqrt{3}\, t^3} = \frac{k}{\sqrt{3}\, t^2}.$$

Therefore, the work done is

$$W = \int_1^a \mathbf{F} \cdot \mathbf{r}'(t)\, dt = \frac{k}{\sqrt{3}} \int_1^a t^{-2}\, dt = \frac{k}{\sqrt{3}}\left(1 - \frac{1}{a}\right).$$

b. The path C_2 is obtained by letting $a \to \infty$ in part (a). The required work is

$$W = \lim_{a \to \infty} \frac{k}{\sqrt{3}}\left(1 - \frac{1}{a}\right) = \frac{k}{\sqrt{3}}.$$

If $\mathbf{F}$ is a gravitational field, this result implies that the work required to escape Earth's gravitational field is finite (which makes space flight possible).

Related Exercises 39–46 ◀

Circulation and Flux of a Vector Field

Line integrals are useful for investigating two important properties of vector fields: *circulation* and *flux*. These properties apply to any vector field, but they are particularly relevant and easy to visualize if you think of $\mathbf{F}$ as the velocity field for a moving fluid.

➤ In the definition of circulation, a *closed curve* is a curve whose initial and terminal points are the same, as defined formally in Section 15.3.

Circulation We assume that $\mathbf{F} = \langle f, g, h \rangle$ is a continuous vector field on a region D of $\mathbf{R}^3$, and we take C to be a *closed* smooth oriented curve in D. The *circulation* of $\mathbf{F}$ along C is a measure of how much of the vector field points in the direction of C. More simply, as you travel along C in the forward direction, how often is the vector field at your back and how often is it in your face? To determine the circulation, we simply "add up" the components of $\mathbf{F}$ in the direction of the unit tangent vector $\mathbf{T}$ at each point. Therefore, circulation integrals are another example of line integrals of vector fields.

> **DEFINITION Circulation**
>
> Let $\mathbf{F}$ be a continuous vector field on a region D of $\mathbf{R}^3$ and let C be a closed smooth oriented curve in D. The **circulation** of $\mathbf{F}$ on C is $\int_C \mathbf{F} \cdot \mathbf{T}\, ds$, where $\mathbf{T}$ is the unit vector tangent to C consistent with the orientation.

EXAMPLE 7 Circulation of two-dimensional flows Let C be the unit circle with counterclockwise orientation. Find the circulation on C for the following vector fields.

a. The radial flow field $\mathbf{F} = \langle x, y \rangle$

b. The rotation flow field $\mathbf{F} = \langle -y, x \rangle$

SOLUTION

a. The unit circle with the specified orientation is described parametrically by $\mathbf{r}(t) = \langle \cos t, \sin t \rangle$, for $0 \le t \le 2\pi$. Therefore, $\mathbf{r}'(t) = \langle -\sin t, \cos t \rangle$ and the circulation of the radial field $\mathbf{F} = \langle x, y \rangle$ is

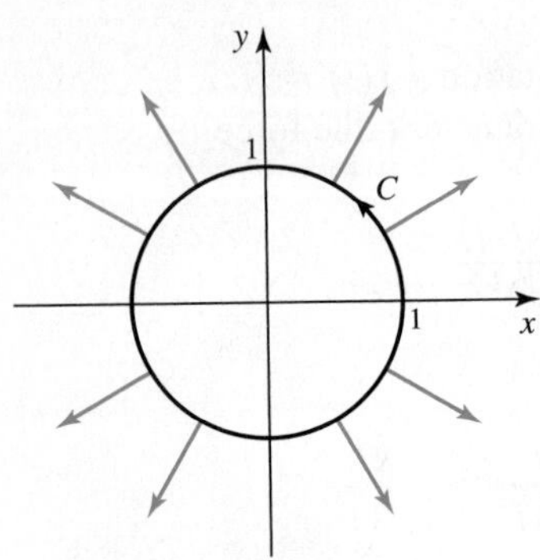

On the unit circle, $\mathbf{F} = \langle x, y \rangle$ is orthogonal to C and has zero circulation on C.

(a)

$$\int_C \mathbf{F} \cdot \mathbf{T}\, ds = \int_0^{2\pi} \mathbf{F} \cdot \mathbf{r}'(t)\, dt \qquad \text{Evaluation of a line integral}$$

$$= \int_0^{2\pi} \underbrace{\langle \cos t, \sin t \rangle}_{\mathbf{F} = \langle x, y \rangle} \cdot \underbrace{\langle -\sin t, \cos t \rangle}_{\mathbf{r}'(t)}\, dt \qquad \text{Substitute for } \mathbf{F} \text{ and } \mathbf{r}'.$$

$$= \int_0^{2\pi} 0\, dt = 0. \qquad \text{Simplify.}$$

The tangential component of the radial vector field is zero everywhere on C, so the circulation is zero (Figure 15.23a).

b. The circulation for the rotation field $\mathbf{F} = \langle -y, x \rangle$ is

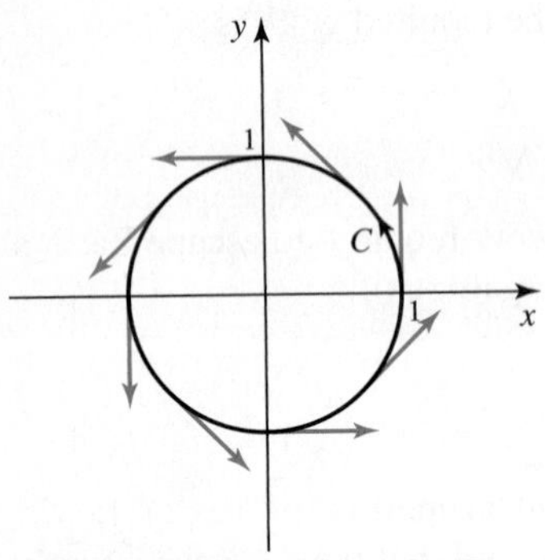

On the unit circle, $\mathbf{F} = \langle -y, x \rangle$ is tangent to C and has positive circulation on C.

(b)

FIGURE 15.23

$$\int_C \mathbf{F} \cdot \mathbf{T}\, ds = \int_0^{2\pi} \mathbf{F} \cdot \mathbf{r}'(t)\, dt \qquad \text{Evaluation of a line integral}$$

$$= \int_0^{2\pi} \underbrace{\langle -\sin t, \cos t \rangle}_{\mathbf{F} = \langle -y, x \rangle} \cdot \underbrace{\langle -\sin t, \cos t \rangle}_{\mathbf{r}'(t)}\, dt \qquad \text{Substitute for } \mathbf{F} \text{ and } \mathbf{r}'.$$

$$= \int_0^{2\pi} \underbrace{(\sin^2 t + \cos^2 t)}_{1}\, dt \qquad \text{Simplify.}$$

$$= 2\pi.$$

In this case, at every point of C, the vector field is in the direction of the tangent vector; the result is a positive circulation (Figure 15.23b). *Related Exercises 47–48* ◄

EXAMPLE 8 **Circulation of a three-dimensional flow** Find the circulation of the vector field $\mathbf{F} = \langle z, x, -y \rangle$ on the tilted ellipse C: $\mathbf{r}(t) = \langle \cos t, \sin t, \cos t \rangle$, for $0 \le t \le 2\pi$ (Figure 15.24a).

SOLUTION We first determine that

$$\mathbf{r}'(t) = \langle x'(t), y'(t), z'(t) \rangle = \langle -\sin t, \cos t, -\sin t \rangle.$$

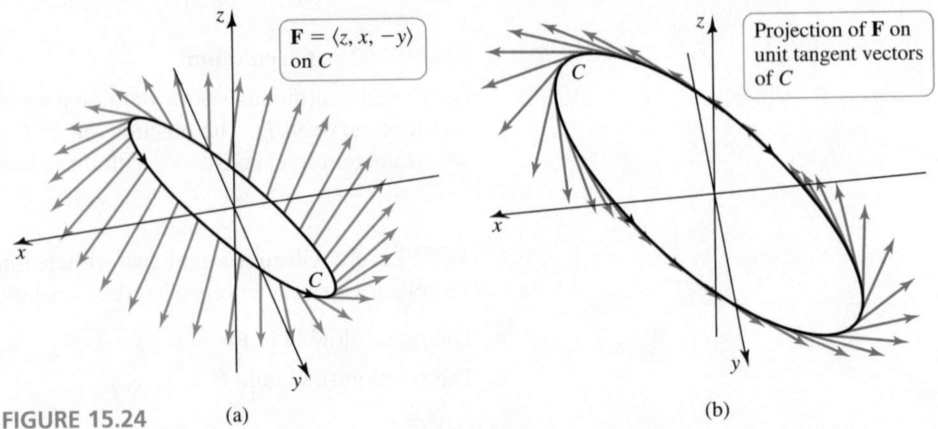

FIGURE 15.24 (a) (b)

Substituting $x = \cos t$, $y = \sin t$, and $z = \cos t$ into $\mathbf{F} = \langle z, x, -y \rangle$, the circulation is

$$\int_C \mathbf{F} \cdot \mathbf{T}\, ds = \int_0^{2\pi} \mathbf{F} \cdot \mathbf{r}'(t)\, dt$$ Evaluation of a line integral

$$= \int_0^{2\pi} \langle \cos t, \cos t, -\sin t \rangle \cdot \langle -\sin t, \cos t, -\sin t \rangle\, dt$$ Substitute for $\mathbf{F}$ and $\mathbf{r}'$.

$$= \int_0^{2\pi} (-\sin t \cos t + 1)\, dt$$ Simplify; $\sin^2 t + \cos^2 t = 1$.

$$= 2\pi.$$ Evaluate the integral.

Figure 15.24b shows the projection of the vector field on the unit tangent vectors at various points on C. The circulation is the "sum" of the magnitudes of these projections, which, in this case, is positive. *Related Exercises 47–48* ◀

➤ In the definition of flux, the non-self-intersecting property of C means that C is a *simple* curve, as defined formally in Section 15.3.

➤ Recall that $\mathbf{a} \times \mathbf{b}$ is orthogonal to $\mathbf{a}$ and $\mathbf{b}$.

Flux of Two-Dimensional Vector Fields Assume that $\mathbf{F} = \langle f, g \rangle$ is a continuous vector field on a region R of $\mathbf{R}^2$. We let C be a smooth oriented curve in R that does not intersect itself; C may or may not be closed. To compute the *flux* of the vector field across C, we "add up" the components of $\mathbf{F}$ *orthogonal* or *normal* to C at each point of C. Notice that every point on C has *two* unit vectors normal to C. Therefore, we let $\mathbf{n}$ denote the unit vector in the xy-plane normal to C in a direction to be defined momentarily. Once the direction of $\mathbf{n}$ is defined, the component of $\mathbf{F}$ normal to C is $\mathbf{F} \cdot \mathbf{n}$, and the flux is the line integral of $\mathbf{F} \cdot \mathbf{n}$ along C, which we denote $\int_C \mathbf{F} \cdot \mathbf{n}\, ds$.

The first step is to define the unit normal vector at a point P of C. Because C lies in the xy-plane, the unit vector $\mathbf{T}$ tangent to C at P also lies in the xy-plane. Therefore, its z-component is 0, and we let $\mathbf{T} = \langle T_x, T_y, 0 \rangle$. As always, $\mathbf{k} = \langle 0, 0, 1 \rangle$ is the unit vector in the z-direction. Because a unit vector $\mathbf{n}$ in the xy-plane normal to C is orthogonal to both $\mathbf{T}$ and $\mathbf{k}$, we determine the direction of $\mathbf{n}$ by letting $\mathbf{n} = \mathbf{T} \times \mathbf{k}$. This choice has two implications (Figure 15.25a):

- If C is a closed curve oriented counterclockwise (when viewed from above), the unit normal vector points *outward* along the curve (Figure 15.25b).
- If C is not a closed curve, the unit normal vector points to the right (when viewed from above) as the curve is traversed in the forward direction.

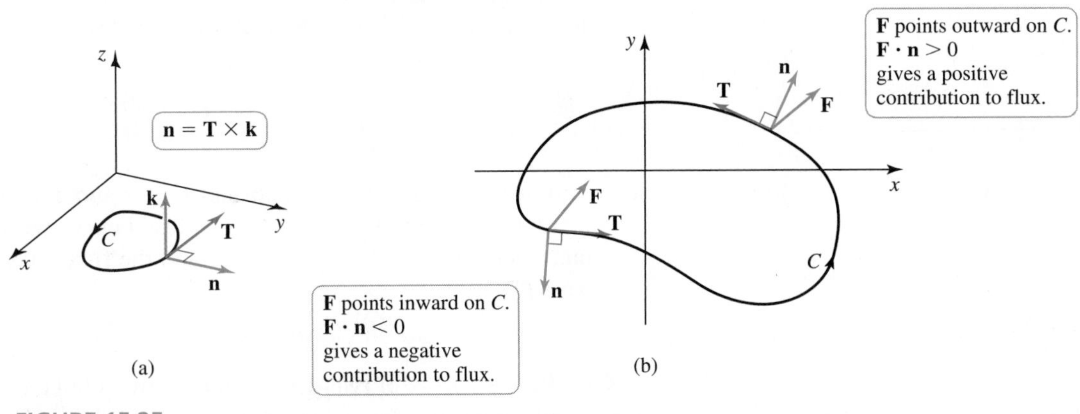
z
n = T × k
k
C
T
y
x
n
(a)
y
T
n
F
F points outward on C.
F · n > 0
gives a positive
contribution to flux.
x
F
T
n
C
F points inward on C.
F · n < 0
gives a negative
contribution to flux.
(b)

FIGURE 15.25

QUICK CHECK 4 Draw a closed curve on a sheet of paper and draw a unit tangent vector $\mathbf{T}$ on the curve pointing in the counterclockwise direction. Explain why $\mathbf{n} = \mathbf{T} \times \mathbf{k}$ is an *outward* unit normal vector.

Calculating the cross product for the unit normal vector, we find that

$$\mathbf{n} = \mathbf{T} \times \mathbf{k} = \begin{vmatrix} \mathbf{i} & \mathbf{j} & \mathbf{k} \\ T_x & T_y & 0 \\ 0 & 0 & 1 \end{vmatrix} = T_y\mathbf{i} - T_x\mathbf{j}.$$

Because $\mathbf{T} = \dfrac{\mathbf{r}'(t)}{|\mathbf{r}'(t)|}$, the components of $\mathbf{T}$ are

$$\mathbf{T} = \langle T_x, T_y, 0 \rangle = \frac{\langle x'(t), y'(t), 0 \rangle}{|\mathbf{r}'(t)|}.$$

We now have an expression for the unit normal vector:

$$\mathbf{n} = T_y\mathbf{i} - T_x\mathbf{j} = \frac{y'(t)}{|\mathbf{r}'(t)|}\mathbf{i} - \frac{x'(t)}{|\mathbf{r}'(t)|}\mathbf{j} = \frac{\langle y'(t), -x'(t) \rangle}{|\mathbf{r}'(t)|}$$

To evaluate the flux integral $\int_C \mathbf{F} \cdot \mathbf{n}\, ds$, we make a familiar change of variables by letting $ds = |\mathbf{r}'(t)|\, dt$. The flux of $\mathbf{F} = \langle f, g \rangle$ across C is then

$$\int_C \mathbf{F} \cdot \mathbf{n}\, ds = \int_a^b \mathbf{F} \cdot \underbrace{\frac{\langle y'(t), -x'(t) \rangle}{|\mathbf{r}'(t)|}}_{n} \underbrace{|\mathbf{r}'(t)|\, dt}_{ds} = \int_a^b (f\, y'(t) - g\, x'(t))\, dt.$$

This is one useful form of the flux integral. Alternatively, we can note that $dx = x'(t)\, dt$ and $dy = y'(t)\, dt$ and write

$$\int_C \mathbf{F} \cdot \mathbf{n}\, ds = \int_C f\, dy - g\, dx.$$

DEFINITION Flux

Let $\mathbf{F} = \langle f, g \rangle$ be a continuous vector field on a region R of $\mathbf{R}^2$. Let C: $\mathbf{r}(t) = \langle x(t), y(t) \rangle$, for $a \le t \le b$, be a smooth oriented curve in R that does not intersect itself. The **flux** of the vector field across C is

$$\int_C \mathbf{F} \cdot \mathbf{n}\, ds = \int_a^b (f\, y'(t) - g\, x'(t))\, dt,$$

where $\mathbf{n} = \mathbf{T} \times \mathbf{k}$ is the unit normal vector and $\mathbf{T}$ is the unit tangent vector consistent with the orientation. If C is a closed curve with counterclockwise orientation, $\mathbf{n}$ is the outward normal vector and the flux integral gives the **outward flux** across C.

EXAMPLE 9 **Flux of two-dimensional flows** Find the outward flux across the unit circle with counterclockwise orientation for the following vector fields.

a. The radial vector field $\mathbf{F} = \langle x, y \rangle$

b. The rotation flow field $\mathbf{F} = \langle -y, x \rangle$

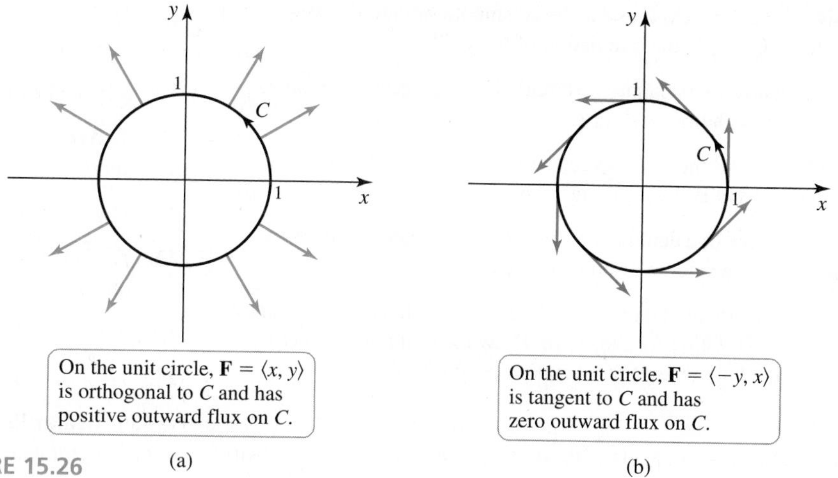

On the unit circle, $\mathbf{F} = \langle x, y \rangle$ is orthogonal to C and has positive outward flux on C.

On the unit circle, $\mathbf{F} = \langle -y, x \rangle$ is tangent to C and has zero outward flux on C.

FIGURE 15.26 (a) (b)

SOLUTION

a. The unit circle with counterclockwise orientation has a description $\mathbf{r}(t) = \langle x(t), y(t) \rangle = \langle \cos t, \sin t \rangle$, for $0 \le t \le 2\pi$. Therefore, $x'(t) = -\sin t$ and $y'(t) = \cos t$. The components of $\mathbf{F}$ are $f = x(t) = \cos t$ and $g = y(t) = \sin t$. It follows that the outward flux is

$$\int_a^b (f\, y'(t) - g\, x'(t))\, dt = \int_0^{2\pi} (\underbrace{\cos t}_{f}\, \underbrace{\cos t}_{y'(t)} - \underbrace{\sin t}_{g}\, \underbrace{(-\sin t)}_{x'(t)})\, dt$$

$$= \int_0^{2\pi} 1\, dt = 2\pi. \qquad \cos^2 t + \sin^2 t = 1$$

Because the radial vector field points outward and is aligned with the unit normal vectors on C, the outward flux is positive (Figure 15.26a).

b. For the rotation field, $f = -y(t) = -\sin t$ and $g = x(t) = \cos t$. The outward flux is

$$\int_a^b (f\, y'(t) - g\, x'(t))\, dt = \int_0^{2\pi} (\underbrace{-\sin t}_{f}\, \underbrace{\cos t}_{y'(t)} - \underbrace{\cos t}_{g}\, \underbrace{(-\sin t)}_{x'(t)})\, dt$$

$$= \int_0^{2\pi} 0\, dt = 0.$$

Because the rotation field is orthogonal to $\mathbf{n}$ at all points of C, the outward flux across C is zero (Figure 15.26b). The results of Examples 7 and 9 are worth remembering: On a unit circle centered at the origin, the *radial* vector field $\langle x, y \rangle$ has outward flux 2π and zero circulation. The *rotation* vector field $\langle -y, x \rangle$ has zero outward flux and circulation 2π.

Related Exercises 49–50 ◀

SECTION 15.2 EXERCISES

Review Questions

1. Explain how a line integral differs from a single-variable integral $\int_a^b f(x)\, dx$.

2. Explain how to evaluate the line integral $\int_C f\, ds$, where C is parameterized by a parameter other than arc length.

3. If a curve C is given by $\mathbf{r}(t) = \langle t, t^2 \rangle$, what is $|\mathbf{r}'(t)|$?

4. Given a vector field $\mathbf{F}$ and a parameterized curve C, explain how to evaluate the line integral $\int_C \mathbf{F} \cdot \mathbf{T}\, ds$.

5. Explain how $\int_C \mathbf{F} \cdot \mathbf{T}\, ds$ can be written in the alternate form $\int_a^b (f\, x'(t) + g\, y'(t) + h\, z'(t))\, dt$.

6. Given a vector field $\mathbf{F}$ and a closed smooth oriented curve C, what is the meaning of the circulation of $\mathbf{F}$ on C?

7. Explain how to calculate the circulation of a vector field on a closed smooth oriented curve.

8. Given a two-dimensional vector field $\mathbf{F}$ and a smooth oriented curve C, what is the meaning of the flux of $\mathbf{F}$ across C?

9. Explain how to calculate the flux of a two-dimensional vector field across a smooth oriented curve C.

10. Sketch the oriented quarter circle from $(1, 0)$ to $(0, 1)$ and supply a parameterization for the curve. Draw the unit normal vector (as defined in the text) at several points on the curve.

Basic Skills

11–14. Scalar line integrals with arc length as parameter *Evaluate the following line integrals.*

11. $\int_C xy\,ds$; C is the unit circle $\mathbf{r}(s) = \langle \cos s, \sin s \rangle$, for $0 \le s \le 2\pi$.

12. $\int_C (x + y)\,ds$; C is the circle of radius 1 centered at $(0, 0)$.

13. $\int_C (x^2 - 2y^2)\,ds$; C is the line $\mathbf{r}(s) = \langle s/\sqrt{2}, s/\sqrt{2} \rangle$, for $0 \le s \le 4$.

14. $\int_C x^2 y\,ds$; C is the line $\mathbf{r}(s) = \langle s/\sqrt{2}, 1 - s/\sqrt{2} \rangle$, for $0 \le s \le 4$.

15–20. Scalar line integrals in the plane

a. *Find a parametric description for C in the form* $\mathbf{r}(t) = \langle x(t), y(t) \rangle$, *if it is not given.*

b. *Evaluate* $|\mathbf{r}'(t)|$.

c. *Convert the line integral to an ordinary integral with respect to the parameter and evaluate it.*

15. $\int_C (x^2 + y^2)\,ds$; C is the circle of radius 4 centered at $(0, 0)$.

16. $\int_C (x^2 + y^2)\,ds$; C is the line segment from $(0, 0)$ to $(5, 5)$.

17. $\int_C \frac{x}{x^2 + y^2}\,ds$; C is the line segment from $(1, 1)$ to $(10, 10)$.

18. $\int_C (xy)^{1/3}\,ds$; C is the curve $y = x^2$, for $0 \le x \le 1$.

19. $\int_C (x - y)\,ds$; C is the upper half of an ellipse, $x = 2\cos t$, $y = 4 \sin t$, for $0 \le t \le \pi$.

20. $\int_C (2x - 3y)\,ds$; C is the line segment from $(-1, 0)$ to $(0, 1)$ followed by the line segment from $(0, 1)$ to $(1, 0)$.

21–24. Average values *Find the average value of the following functions on the given curves.*

21. $f(x, y) = x + 2y$ on the line segment from $(1, 1)$ to $(2, 5)$

22. $f(x, y) = x^2 + 4y^2$ on the circle of radius 9 centered at the origin

23. $f(x, y) = 4x^3 - 3y$ on the curve $x = y^3$, for $-1 \le y \le 1$

24. $f(x, y) = xe^y$ on the circle of radius 1 centered at the origin

25–30. Scalar line integrals in $\mathbf{R}^3$ *Convert the line integral to an ordinary integral with respect to the parameter and evaluate it.*

25. $\int_C (x + y + z)\,ds$; C is the circle $\mathbf{r}(t) = \langle 2\cos t, 0, 2\sin t \rangle$, for $0 \le t \le 2\pi$.

26. $\int_C (x - y + 2z)\,ds$; C is the circle $\mathbf{r}(t) = \langle 1, 3\cos t, 3\sin t \rangle$, for $0 \le t \le 2\pi$.

27. $\int_C xyz\,ds$; C is the line segment from $(0, 0, 0)$ to $(1, 2, 3)$.

28. $\int_C \frac{xy}{z}\,ds$; C is the line segment from $(1, 4, 1)$ to $(3, 6, 3)$.

29. $\int_C (y - z)\,ds$; C is the helix $\mathbf{r}(t) = \langle 3\cos t, 3\sin t, t \rangle$, for $0 \le t \le 2\pi$.

30. $\int_C xe^{yz}\,ds$; C is $\mathbf{r}(t) = \langle t, 2t, -4t \rangle$, for $1 \le t \le 2$.

31–32. Length of curves *Use a scalar line integral to find the length of the following curves.*

31. $\mathbf{r}(t) = \langle 20\sin t/4, 20\cos t/4, t/2 \rangle$, for $0 \le t \le 2$

32. $\mathbf{r}(t) = \langle 30\sin t, 40\sin t, 50\cos t \rangle$, for $0 \le t \le 2\pi$

33–38. Line integrals of vector fields in the plane *Given the following vector fields and oriented curves C, evaluate* $\int_C \mathbf{F} \cdot \mathbf{T}\,ds$.

33. $\mathbf{F} = \langle x, y \rangle$ on the parabola $\mathbf{r}(t) = \langle 4t, t^2 \rangle$, for $0 \le t \le 1$

34. $\mathbf{F} = \langle -y, x \rangle$ on the semicircle $\mathbf{r}(t) = \langle 4\cos t, 4\sin t \rangle$, for $0 \le t \le \pi$

35. $\mathbf{F} = \langle y, x \rangle$ on the line segment from $(1, 1)$ to $(5, 10)$

36. $\mathbf{F} = \frac{\langle x, y \rangle}{(x^2 + y^2)^{3/2}}$ on the line segment from $(2, 2)$ to $(10, 10)$

37. $\mathbf{F} = \dfrac{\langle x, y \rangle}{(x^2 + y^2)^{3/2}}$ on the curve $\mathbf{r}(t) = \langle t^2, 3t^2 \rangle$, for $1 \leq t \leq 2$

38. $\mathbf{F} = \dfrac{\langle x, y \rangle}{x^2 + y^2}$ on the line $\mathbf{r}(t) = \langle t, 4t \rangle$, for $1 \leq t \leq 10$

39–42. Work integrals *Given the force field* $\mathbf{F}$, *find the work required to move an object on the given oriented curve.*

39. $\mathbf{F} = \langle y, -x \rangle$ on the path consisting of the line segment from $(1, 2)$ to $(0, 0)$ followed by the line segment from $(0, 0)$ to $(0, 4)$

40. $\mathbf{F} = \langle x, y \rangle$ on the path consisting of the line segment from $(-1, 0)$ to $(0, 8)$ followed by the line segment from $(0, 8)$ to $(2, 8)$

41. $\mathbf{F} = \langle y, x \rangle$ on the parabola $y = 2x^2$ from $(0, 0)$ to $(2, 8)$

42. $\mathbf{F} = \langle y, -x \rangle$ on the line $y = 10 - 2x$ from $(1, 8)$ to $(3, 4)$

43–46. Work integrals in $\mathbf{R}^3$ *Given the force field* $\mathbf{F}$, *find the work required to move an object on the given oriented curve.*

43. $\mathbf{F} = \langle x, y, z \rangle$ on the tilted ellipse $\mathbf{r}(t) = \langle 4 \cos t, 4 \sin t, 4 \cos t \rangle$, for $0 \leq t \leq 2\pi$

44. $\mathbf{F} = \langle -y, x, z \rangle$ on the helix $\mathbf{r}(t) = \langle 2 \cos t, 2 \sin t, t/2\pi \rangle$, for $0 \leq t \leq 2\pi$

45. $\mathbf{F} = \dfrac{\langle x, y, z \rangle}{(x^2 + y^2 + z^2)^{3/2}}$ on the line segment from $(1, 1, 1)$ to $(10, 10, 10)$

46. $\mathbf{F} = \dfrac{\langle x, y, z \rangle}{x^2 + y^2 + z^2}$ on the line segment from $(1, 1, 1)$ to $(8, 4, 2)$

47–48. Circulation *Consider the following vector fields* $\mathbf{F}$ *and closed oriented curves C in the plane (see figures).*

a. *Based on the picture, make a conjecture about whether the circulation of* $\mathbf{F}$ *on C is positive, negative, or zero.*

b. *Compute the circulation and interpret the result.*

47. $\mathbf{F} = \langle y - x, x \rangle$; C: $\mathbf{r}(t) = \langle 2 \cos t, 2 \sin t \rangle$, for $0 \leq t \leq 2\pi$

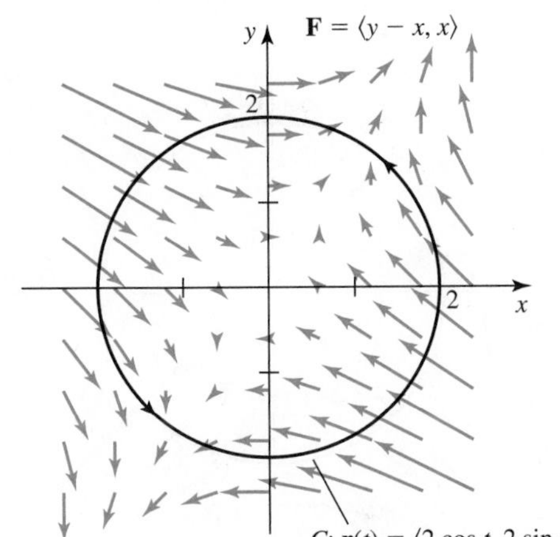

48. $\mathbf{F} = \dfrac{\langle x, y \rangle}{(x^2 + y^2)^{1/2}}$; C is the boundary of the square with vertices $(\pm 2, \pm 2)$, traversed counterclockwise.

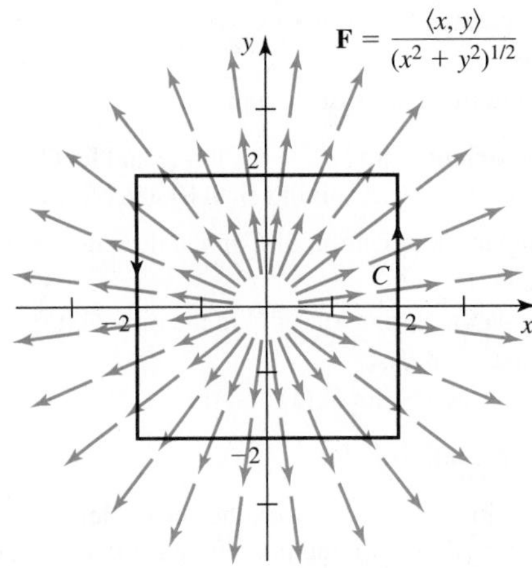

49–50. Flux *Consider the vector fields and curves in Exercises 47–48.*

a. *Based on the picture make a conjecture about whether the outward flux of* $\mathbf{F}$ *across C is positive, negative, or zero.*

b. *Compute the flux for the vector fields and curves.*

49. $\mathbf{F}$ and C given in Exercise 47

50. $\mathbf{F}$ and C given in Exercise 48

Further Explorations

51. Explain why or why not Determine whether the following statements are true and give an explanation or counterexample.

a. If a curve has a parametric description $\mathbf{r}(t) = \langle x(t), y(t), z(t) \rangle$, where t is the arc length, then $|\mathbf{r}'(t)| = 1$.

b. The vector field $\mathbf{F} = \langle y, x \rangle$ has both zero circulation along and zero flux across the unit circle centered at the origin.

c. If at points of a path a force acts in a direction orthogonal to the path, then no work is done in moving an object along the path.

d. The flux of a vector field across a curve in $\mathbf{R}^2$ can be computed using a line integral.

52. Flying into a headwind An airplane flies in the xz-plane, where x increases in the eastward direction and $z \geq 0$ represents vertical distance above the ground. A wind blows horizontally out of the west, producing a force $\mathbf{F} = \langle 150, 0 \rangle$. On which path between the points $(100, 0)$ and $(-100, 0)$ is the most work done overcoming the wind:

a. The straight line $\mathbf{r}(t) = \langle x(t), z(t) \rangle = \langle -t, 50 \rangle$, for $-100 \leq t \leq 100$ or

b. The arc of a circle $\mathbf{r}(t) = \langle 100 \cos t, 100 \sin t \rangle$, for $0 \leq t \leq \pi$?

53. Flying into a headwind

a. How does the result of Exercise 52 change if the force due to the wind is $\mathbf{F} = \langle 141, 50 \rangle$ (approximately the same magnitude, but different direction)?

b. How does the result of Exercise 52 change if the force due to the wind is $\mathbf{F} = \langle 141, -50 \rangle$ (approximately the same magnitude, but different direction)?

54. Changing orientation Let $f(x, y) = x + 2y$ and let C be the unit circle.

a. Find a parameterization of C with a counterclockwise orientation and evaluate $\int_C f\, ds$.
b. Find a parameterization of C with a clockwise orientation and evaluate $\int_C f\, ds$.
c. Compare the results of (a) and (b).

55. Changing orientation Let $f(x, y) = x$ and let C be the segment of the parabola $y = x^2$ joining $O(0, 0)$ and $P(1, 1)$.

a. Find a parameterization of C in the direction from O to P. Evaluate $\int_C f\, ds$.
b. Find a parameterization of C in the direction from P to O. Evaluate $\int_C f\, ds$.
c. Compare the results of (a) and (b).

56–57. Zero circulation fields

56. For what values of b and c does the vector field $\mathbf{F} = \langle by, cx \rangle$ have zero circulation on the unit circle centered at the origin and oriented counterclockwise?

57. Consider the vector field $\mathbf{F} = \langle ax + by, cx + dy \rangle$. Show that $\mathbf{F}$ has zero circulation on any oriented circle centered at the origin, for any a, b, c, and d, provided $b = c$.

58–59. Zero flux fields

58. For what values of a and d does the vector field $\mathbf{F} = \langle ax, dy \rangle$ have zero flux across the unit circle centered at the origin and oriented counterclockwise?

59. Consider the vector field $\mathbf{F} = \langle ax + by, cx + dy \rangle$. Show that $\mathbf{F}$ has zero flux across any oriented circle centered at the origin, for any a, b, c, and d, provided $a = -d$.

60. Work in a rotation field Consider the rotation field $\mathbf{F} = \langle -y, x \rangle$ and the three paths shown in the figure. Compute the work done on each of the three paths. Does it appear that the line integral $\int_C \mathbf{F} \cdot \mathbf{T}\, ds$ is independent of the path, where C is a path from $(1, 0)$ to $(0, 1)$?

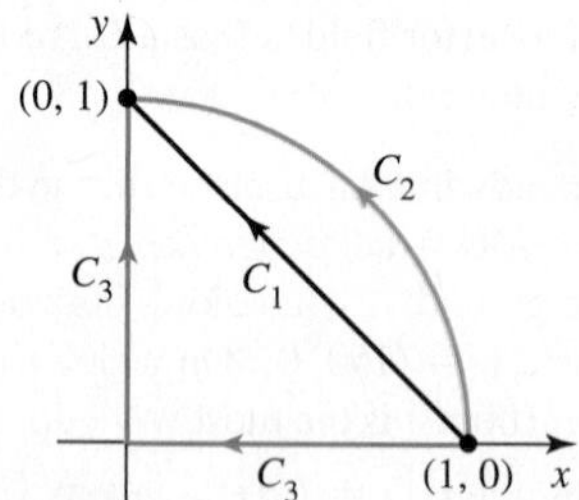

61. Work in a hyperbolic field Consider the hyperbolic force field $\mathbf{F} = \langle y, x \rangle$ (the streamlines are hyperbolas) and the three paths shown in the figure for Exercise 60. Compute the work done on each of the three paths. Does it appear that the line integral $\int_C \mathbf{F} \cdot \mathbf{T}\, ds$ is independent of the path, where C is a path from $(1, 0)$ to $(0, 1)$?

Applications

62–63. Mass and density *A thin wire represented by the smooth curve C with a density ρ (units of mass per length) has a mass $M = \int_C \rho\, ds$. Find the mass of the following wires with the given density.*

62. C: $\mathbf{r}(\theta) = \langle \cos \theta, \sin \theta \rangle$, for $0 \le \theta \le \pi$; $\rho(\theta) = 2\theta/\pi + 1$

T **63.** C: $\{(x, y): y = 2x^2, 0 \le x \le 3\}$; $\rho(x, y) = 1 + xy$

64. Heat flux in a plate A square plate $R = \{(x, y): 0 \le x \le 1, 0 \le y \le 1\}$ has a temperature distribution $T(x, y) = 100 - 50x - 25y$.

a. Sketch two level curves of the temperature in the plate.
b. Find the gradient of the temperature $\nabla T(x, y)$.
c. Assume that the flow of heat is determined by the vector field $\mathbf{F} = -\nabla T(x, y)$. Compute $\mathbf{F}$.
d. Find the outward heat flux across the boundary $\{(x, y): x = 1, 0 \le y \le 1\}$.
e. Find the outward heat flux across the boundary $\{(x, y): 0 \le x \le 1, y = 1\}$.

65. Inverse force fields Consider the radial field $\mathbf{F} = \dfrac{\mathbf{r}}{|\mathbf{r}|^p} = \dfrac{\langle x, y, z \rangle}{|\mathbf{r}|^p}$, where $p > 1$ (the inverse square law corresponds to $p = 3$). Let C be the line from $(1, 1, 1)$ to (a, a, a), where $a > 1$, given by $\mathbf{r}(t) = \langle t, t, t \rangle$, for $1 \le t \le a$.

a. Find the work done in moving an object along C with $p = 2$.
b. If $a \to \infty$ in part (a), is the work finite?
c. Find the work done in moving an object moving along C with $p = 4$.
d. If $a \to \infty$ in part (c), is the work finite?
e. Find the work done in moving an object moving along C for any $p > 1$.
f. If $a \to \infty$ in part (e), for what values of p is the work finite?

66. Flux across curves in a flow field Consider the flow field $\mathbf{F} = \langle y, x \rangle$ shown in the figure.

a. Compute the outward flux across the quarter circle C: $\mathbf{r}(t) = \langle 2 \cos t, 2 \sin t \rangle$, for $0 \le t \le \pi/2$.
b. Compute the outward flux across the quarter circle C: $\mathbf{r}(t) = \langle 2 \cos t, 2 \sin t \rangle$, for $\pi/2 \le t \le \pi$.
c. Explain why the flux across the quarter circle in the third quadrant equals the flux computed in part (a).
d. Explain why the flux across the quarter circle in the fourth quadrant equals the flux computed in part (b).
e. What is the outward flux across the full circle?

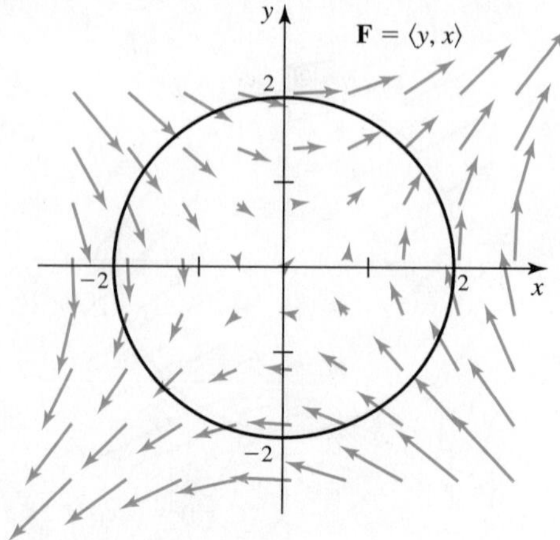

Additional Exercises

67–68. Looking ahead: area from line integrals *The area of a region R in the plane, whose boundary is the curve C, may be computed using line integrals with the formula*

$$\text{area of } R = \int_C x\,dy = -\int_C y\,dx.$$

These ideas reappear later in the chapter.

67. Let R be the rectangle with vertices $(0, 0)$, $(a, 0)$, $(0, b)$, (a, b) and let C be the boundary of R oriented counterclockwise. Compute the area of R using the formula $A = \int_C x\,dy$.

68. Let $R = \{(r, \theta): 0 \le r \le a, 0 \le \theta \le 2\pi\}$ be the disk of radius a centered at the origin and let C be the boundary of R oriented counterclockwise. Compute the area of R using the formula $A = -\int_C y\,dx$.

QUICK CHECK ANSWERS

1. The Fundamental Theorem of Calculus says that $\dfrac{d}{dt}\displaystyle\int_a^t f(u)\,du = f(t)$, which applies to differentiating the arc length integral. **2.** 1300 ft/min **3.** $\pi/2$ **4.** **T** and **k** are unit vectors, so **n** is a unit vector. By the right-hand rule for cross products, **n** points outward from the curve.

15.3 Conservative Vector Fields

This is an action-packed section in which several fundamental ideas come together. At the heart of the matter are two questions:

- When can a vector field be expressed as the gradient of a potential function? A vector field with this property will be defined as a *conservative* vector field.
- What special properties do conservative vector fields have?

After some preliminary definitions, we present a test to determine whether a vector field in $\mathbf{R}^2$ or $\mathbf{R}^3$ is conservative. This test is followed by a procedure to find a potential function for a conservative field. We then develop several equivalent properties shared by all conservative vector fields.

Types of Curves and Regions

Many of the results in the remainder of the book rely on special properties of regions and curves. It's best to collect these definitions in one place before they are used.

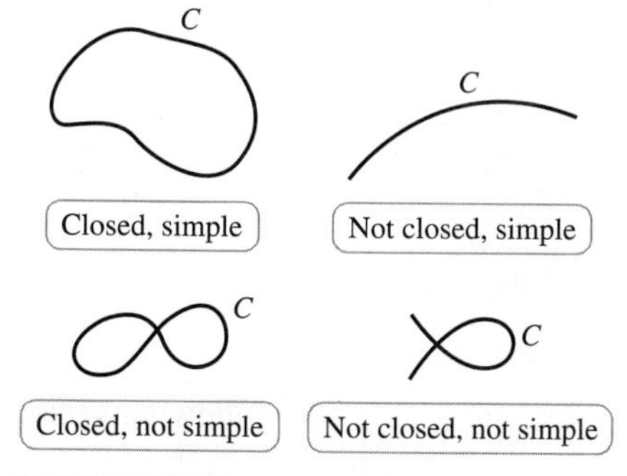

FIGURE 15.27

DEFINITION Simple and Closed Curves

Suppose a curve C (in $\mathbf{R}^2$ or $\mathbf{R}^3$) is described parametrically by $\mathbf{r}(t)$, where $a \le t \le b$. Then C is a **simple curve** if $\mathbf{r}(t_1) \ne \mathbf{r}(t_2)$ for all t_1 and t_2, with $a < t_1 < t_2 < b$; that is, C never intersects itself between its endpoints. The curve C is **closed** if $\mathbf{r}(a) = \mathbf{r}(b)$; that is, the initial and terminal points of C are the same (Figure 15.27).

Recall that all points of an open set are interior points. An open set does not contain its boundary points.

In all that follows, we generally assume that R in $\mathbf{R}^2$ (or D in $\mathbf{R}^3$) is an open region. Open regions are further classified according to whether they are *connected* and whether they are *simply connected*.

Roughly speaking, connected means that R is all in one piece and simply connected in $\mathbf{R}^2$ means that R has no holes. $\mathbf{R}^2$ and $\mathbf{R}^3$ are themselves connected and simply connected.

DEFINITION Connected and Simply Connected Regions

An open region R in $\mathbf{R}^2$ (or D in $\mathbf{R}^3$) is **connected** if it is possible to connect any two points of R by a continuous curve lying in R. An open region R is **simply connected** if every closed simple curve in R can be deformed and contracted to a point in R (Figure 15.28).

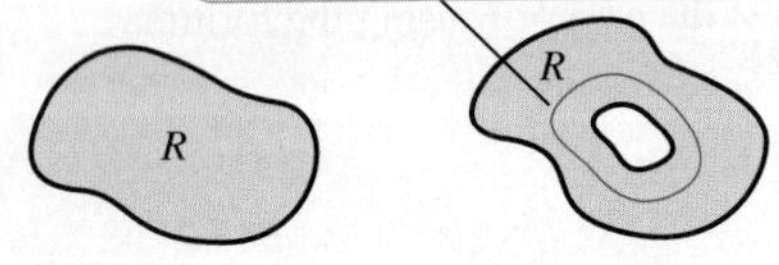

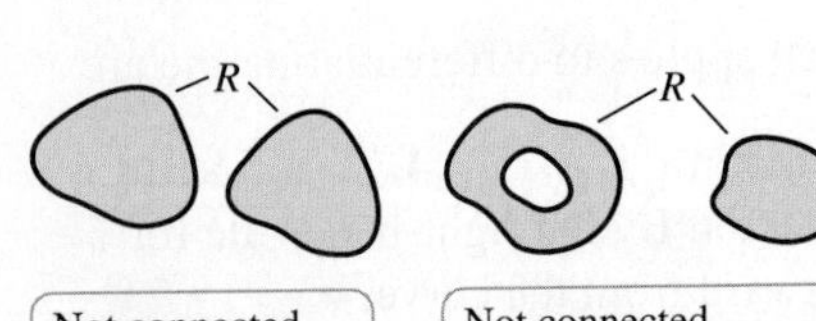

FIGURE 15.28

➤ The term *conservative* refers to conservation of energy. See Exercise 52 for an example of conservation of energy in a conservative force field.

➤ Depending on the context and the interpretation of the vector field, the potential may be defined such that $\mathbf{F} = -\nabla\varphi$ (with a negative sign).

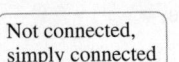

QUICK CHECK 1 Is a figure–8 curve simple? Closed? Is a torus connected? Simply connected?

Test for Conservative Vector Fields

We begin with the central definition of this section.

> **DEFINITION Conservative Vector Field**
> A vector field $\mathbf{F}$ is said to be **conservative** on a region (in $\mathbf{R}^2$ or $\mathbf{R}^3$) if there exists a scalar function φ such that $\mathbf{F} = \nabla\varphi$ on that region.

Suppose that the components of $\mathbf{F} = \langle f, g, h\rangle$ have continuous first partial derivatives on a region D in $\mathbf{R}^3$. Also assume that $\mathbf{F}$ is conservative, which means by definition that there is a potential function φ such that $\mathbf{F} = \nabla\varphi$. Matching the components of $\mathbf{F}$ and $\nabla\varphi$, we see that $f = \varphi_x$, $g = \varphi_y$, and $h = \varphi_z$. Recall from Theorem 13.4 that if a function has continuous second partial derivatives, the order of differentiation in the second partial derivatives does not matter. Under these conditions on φ, we conclude the following:

- $\varphi_{xy} = \varphi_{yx}$, which implies that $f_y = g_x$
- $\varphi_{xz} = \varphi_{zx}$, which implies that $f_z = h_x$
- $\varphi_{yz} = \varphi_{zy}$, which implies that $g_z = h_y$

These observations comprise half of the proof of the following theorem. The remainder of the proof is given in Section 15.4.

> **THEOREM 15.3 Test for Conservative Vector Fields**
> Let $\mathbf{F} = \langle f, g, h\rangle$ be a vector field defined on a connected and simply connected region D of $\mathbf{R}^3$, where f, g, and h have continuous first partial derivatives on D. Then, $\mathbf{F}$ is a conservative vector field on D (there is a potential function φ such that $\mathbf{F} = \nabla\varphi$) if and only if
> $$\frac{\partial f}{\partial y} = \frac{\partial g}{\partial x}, \quad \frac{\partial f}{\partial z} = \frac{\partial h}{\partial x}, \quad \text{and} \quad \frac{\partial g}{\partial z} = \frac{\partial h}{\partial y}.$$
> For vector fields in $\mathbf{R}^2$, we have the single condition $\dfrac{\partial f}{\partial y} = \dfrac{\partial g}{\partial x}$.

EXAMPLE 1 Testing for conservative fields Determine whether the following vector fields are conservative on $\mathbf{R}^2$ and $\mathbf{R}^3$, respectively.

a. $\mathbf{F} = \langle e^x \cos y, -e^x \sin y\rangle$

b. $\mathbf{F} = \langle 2xy - z^2, x^2 + 2z, 2y - 2xz\rangle$

SOLUTION

a. Letting $f = e^x \cos y$ and $g = -e^x \sin y$, we see that

$$\frac{\partial f}{\partial y} = -e^x \sin y = \frac{\partial g}{\partial x}.$$

The conditions of Theorem 15.3 are met and $\mathbf{F}$ is conservative.

b. Letting $f = 2xy - z^2$, $g = x^2 + 2z$, and $h = 2y - 2xz$, we have

$$\frac{\partial f}{\partial y} = 2x = \frac{\partial g}{\partial x}, \quad \frac{\partial f}{\partial z} = -2z = \frac{\partial h}{\partial x}, \quad \frac{\partial g}{\partial z} = 2 = \frac{\partial h}{\partial y}.$$

By Theorem 15.3, **F** is conservative. *Related Exercises 9–14* ◀

Finding Potential Functions

Like antiderivatives, potential functions, for most practical purposes, are determined up to an arbitrary additive constant. Unless an additive constant in a potential function has some physical meaning, it is usually omitted. Given a conservative vector field, there are several methods for finding a potential function. One method is shown in the following example. Another approach is illustrated in Exercise 57.

QUICK CHECK 2 Explain why a potential function for a conservative vector field is determined up to an additive constant. ◀

EXAMPLE 2 **Finding potential functions** Find a potential function for the conservative vector fields in Example 1.

a. $\mathbf{F} = \langle e^x \cos y, -e^x \sin y \rangle$

b. $\mathbf{F} = \langle 2xy - z^2, x^2 + 2z, 2y - 2xz \rangle$

SOLUTION

a. A potential function φ for $\mathbf{F} = \langle f, g \rangle$ has the property that $\mathbf{F} = \nabla\varphi$ and satisfies the conditions

$$\varphi_x = f(x, y) = e^x \cos y \quad \text{and} \quad \varphi_y = g(x, y) = -e^x \sin y.$$

The first equation is integrated with respect to x (holding y fixed) to obtain

$$\int \varphi_x \, dx = \int e^x \cos y \, dx,$$

which implies that

$$\varphi(x, y) = e^x \cos y + c(y).$$

▶ This procedure may begin with either of the two conditions, $\varphi_x = f$ or $\varphi_y = g$.

In this case, the "constant of integration" $c(y)$ is an arbitrary function of y. You can check the preceding calculation by noting that

$$\frac{\partial \varphi}{\partial x} = \frac{\partial}{\partial x}[e^x \cos y + c(y)] = e^x \cos y = f(x, y).$$

To find the arbitrary function $c(y)$, we differentiate $\varphi(x, y) = e^x \cos y + c(y)$ with respect to y and equate the result to g (recall that $\varphi_y = g$):

$$\varphi_y = -e^x \sin y + c'(y) \quad \text{and} \quad g = -e^x \sin y$$

We conclude that $c'(y) = 0$, which implies that $c(y)$ is any real number, which we typically take to be zero. So a potential function is $\varphi(x, y) = e^x \cos y$, a result that may be checked by differentiation.

b. The method of part (a) is more elaborate with three variables. A potential function φ must now satisfy these conditions:

▶ This procedure may begin with any of the three conditions.

$$\varphi_x = f = 2xy - z^2 \qquad \varphi_y = g = x^2 + 2z \qquad \varphi_z = h = 2y - 2xz$$

Integrating the first condition with respect to x (holding y and z fixed), we have

$$\varphi = \int (2xy - z^2)\,dx = x^2y - xz^2 + c(y, z).$$

Because the integration is with respect to x, the arbitrary "constant" is a function of y and z. To find $c(y, z)$, we differentiate φ with respect to y, which results in

$$\varphi_y = x^2 + c_y(y, z).$$

Equating φ_y and $g = x^2 + 2z$, we see that $c_y(y, z) = 2z$. To obtain $c(y, z)$, we integrate $c_y(y, z) = 2z$ with respect to y (holding z fixed), which results in $c(y, z) = 2yz + d(z)$. The "constant" of integration is now a function of z, which we call $d(z)$. At this point, a potential function looks like

$$\varphi(x, y, z) = x^2y - xz^2 + 2yz + d(z).$$

To determine $d(z)$, we differentiate φ with respect to z:

$$\varphi_z = -2xz + 2y + d'(z)$$

Equating φ_z and $h = 2y - 2xz$, we see that $d'(z) = 0$, or $d(z)$ is a real number, which we generally take to be zero. Putting it all together, a potential function is

$$\varphi = x^2y - xz^2 + 2yz.$$

Related Exercises 15–26 ◀

QUICK CHECK 3 Verify by differentiation that the potential functions found in Example 2 produce the corresponding vector fields. ◀

PROCEDURE Finding Potential Functions in $\mathbf{R}^3$

Suppose $\mathbf{F} = \langle f, g, h \rangle$ is a conservative vector field. To find φ such that $\mathbf{F} = \nabla\varphi$, take the following steps:

1. Integrate $\varphi_x = f$ with respect to x to obtain φ, which includes an arbitrary function $c(y, z)$.
2. Compute φ_y and equate it to g to obtain an expression for $c_y(y, z)$.
3. Integrate $c_y(y, z)$ with respect to y to obtain $c(y, z)$, including an arbitrary function $d(z)$.
4. Compute φ_z and equate it to h to get $d(z)$.

Beginning the procedure with $\varphi_y = g$ or $\varphi_z = h$ may be easier in some cases.

Fundamental Theorem for Line Integrals and Path Independence

Knowing how to find potential functions, we now investigate their properties. The first property is one of several beautiful parallels to the Fundamental Theorem of Calculus.

THEOREM 15.4 Fundamental Theorem for Line Integrals

Let $\mathbf{F}$ be a continuous vector field on an open connected region R in $\mathbf{R}^2$ (or D in $\mathbf{R}^3$). There exists a potential function φ with $\mathbf{F} = \nabla\varphi$ (which means that $\mathbf{F}$ is conservative) if and only if

$$\int_C \mathbf{F}\cdot\mathbf{T}\,ds = \int_C \mathbf{F}\cdot d\mathbf{r} = \varphi(B) - \varphi(A),$$

for all points A and B in R and all smooth oriented curves C from A to B.

➤ Compare the two versions of the Fundamental Theorem.

$$\int_a^b F'(x)\,dx = F(b) - F(a)$$

$$\int_C \nabla\varphi\cdot d\mathbf{r} = \varphi(B) - \varphi(A)$$

Here is the meaning of this theorem: If **F** is a conservative vector field, then the value of a line integral of **F** depends only on the endpoints of the path. More simply, *the line integral is independent of path*, which means a parameterization of the path is not needed to evaluate line integrals of conservative fields.

If we think of φ as an antiderivative of the vector field **F**, then the parallel to the Fundamental Theorem of Calculus is clear. The line integral of **F** is the difference of the values of φ evaluated at the endpoints.

Proof We prove the theorem in one direction: If **F** is conservative, then the line integral is path-independent. The technical proof in the other direction is omitted.

Let the curve C in $\mathbf{R}^3$ be given by $\mathbf{r}(t) = \langle x(t), y(t), z(t)\rangle$, for $a \le t \le b$, where $\mathbf{r}(a)$ and $\mathbf{r}(b)$ are the position vectors for the points A and B, respectively. By the Chain Rule, the rate of change of φ with respect to t along C is

$$\begin{aligned}\frac{d\varphi}{dt} &= \frac{\partial\varphi}{\partial x}\frac{dx}{dt} + \frac{\partial\varphi}{\partial y}\frac{dy}{dt} + \frac{\partial\varphi}{\partial z}\frac{dz}{dt} && \text{Chain Rule}\\ &= \left\langle \frac{\partial\varphi}{\partial x}, \frac{\partial\varphi}{\partial y}, \frac{\partial\varphi}{\partial z}\right\rangle \cdot \left\langle \frac{dx}{dt}, \frac{dy}{dt}, \frac{dz}{dt}\right\rangle && \text{Identify the dot product.}\\ &= \nabla\varphi \cdot \mathbf{r}'(t) && \mathbf{r} = \langle x, y, z\rangle\\ &= \mathbf{F}\cdot\mathbf{r}'(t). && \mathbf{F} = \nabla\varphi\end{aligned}$$

Evaluating the line integral and using the Fundamental Theorem of Calculus, it follows that

$$\begin{aligned}\int_C \mathbf{F}\cdot d\mathbf{r} &= \int_a^b \mathbf{F}\cdot\mathbf{r}'(t)\,dt\\ &= \int_a^b \frac{d\varphi}{dt}\,dt && \mathbf{F}\cdot\mathbf{r}'(t) = \frac{d\varphi}{dt}\\ &= \varphi(B) - \varphi(A). && \text{Fundamental Theorem of Calculus; } t = b \text{ corresponds to } B \text{ and } t = a \text{ corresponds to } A.\end{aligned}$$

◀

EXAMPLE 3 **Verifying path independence** Consider the potential function $\varphi(x, y) = (x^2 - y^2)/2$ and its gradient field $\mathbf{F} = \langle x, -y\rangle$. Let C_1 be the quarter circle $\mathbf{r}(t) = \langle \cos t, \sin t\rangle$, for $0 \le t \le \pi/2$, from $A(1, 0)$ to $B(0, 1)$. Let C_2 be the line $\mathbf{r}(t) = \langle 1 - t, t\rangle$, for $0 \le t \le 1$, also from A to B. Evaluate the line integrals of **F** on C_1 and C_2, and show that both are equal to $\varphi(B) - \varphi(A)$.

SOLUTION On C_1 we have $\mathbf{r}'(t) = \langle -\sin t, \cos t\rangle$ and $\mathbf{F} = \langle x, -y\rangle = \langle \cos t, -\sin t\rangle$. The line integral on C_1 is

$$\begin{aligned}\int_{C_1} \mathbf{F}\cdot d\mathbf{r} &= \int_{C_1} \mathbf{F}\cdot\mathbf{r}'(t)\,dt\\ &= \int_0^{\pi/2} \underbrace{\langle \cos t, -\sin t\rangle}_{\mathbf{F}} \cdot \underbrace{\langle -\sin t, \cos t\rangle\,dt}_{\mathbf{r}'(t)\,dt} && \text{Substitute for } \mathbf{F} \text{ and } \mathbf{r}'.\\ &= \int_0^{\pi/2} (-\sin 2t)\,dt && 2\sin t\cos t = \sin 2t\\ &= \left(\frac{1}{2}\cos 2t\right)\Big|_0^{\pi/2} = -1. && \text{Evaluate the integral.}\end{aligned}$$

On C_2 we have $\mathbf{r}'(t) = \langle -1, 1 \rangle$ and $\mathbf{F} = \langle x, -y \rangle = \langle 1 - t, -t \rangle$; therefore,

$$\int_{C_2} \mathbf{F} \cdot d\mathbf{r} = \int_0^1 \underbrace{\langle 1 - t, -t \rangle}_{\mathbf{F}} \cdot \underbrace{\langle -1, 1 \rangle\, dt}_{d\mathbf{r}} \quad \text{Substitute for } \mathbf{F} \text{ and } d\mathbf{r}.$$

$$= \int_0^1 (-1)\, dt = -1. \quad \text{Simplify.}$$

The two line integrals have the same value, which is

$$\varphi(B) - \varphi(A) = \varphi(0, 1) - \varphi(1, 0) = -\frac{1}{2} - \frac{1}{2} = -1.$$

Related Exercises 27–32 ◄

EXAMPLE 4 **Line integral of a conservative vector field** Evaluate

$$\int_C ((2xy - z^2)\mathbf{i} + (x^2 + 2z)\mathbf{j} + (2y - 2xz)\mathbf{k}) \cdot d\mathbf{r},$$

where C is a simple curve from $A(-3, -2, -1)$ to $B(1, 2, 3)$.

SOLUTION This vector field is conservative and has a potential function $\varphi = x^2y - xz^2 + 2yz$ (Example 2). By the Fundamental Theorem for line integrals,

$$\int_C ((2xy - z^2)\mathbf{i} + (x^2 + 2z)\mathbf{j} + (2y - 2xz)\mathbf{k}) \cdot d\mathbf{r}$$

$$= \int_C \nabla \underbrace{(x^2y - xz^2 + 2yz)}_{\varphi} \cdot d\mathbf{r}$$

$$= \varphi(1, 2, 3) - \varphi(-3, -2, -1) = 16.$$

Related Exercises 27–32 ◄

QUICK CHECK 4 Explain why the vector field $\nabla(xy + xz - yz)$ is a conservative field. ◄

Line Integrals on Closed Curves

It is a short step to another characterization of conservative vector fields. Suppose C is a simple *closed* smooth oriented curve in $\mathbf{R}^2$ or $\mathbf{R}^3$. To distinguish line integrals on closed curves, we adopt the notation $\oint_C \mathbf{F} \cdot d\mathbf{r}$, where the small circle on the integral sign indicates that C is a closed curve. Let A be any point on C and think of A as both the initial point and the final point of C. Assuming that $\mathbf{F}$ is a conservative vector field on an open connected region R containing C, it follows by Theorem 15.4 that

$$\oint_C \mathbf{F} \cdot d\mathbf{r} = \varphi(A) - \varphi(A) = 0.$$

➤ Notice the analogy with $\int_a^a f(x)\, dx = 0$, which is true of all integrable functions.

Because A is an arbitrary point on C, we see that the line integral of a conservative vector field on a closed curve is zero.

An argument can be made in the opposite direction as well: Suppose $\oint_C \mathbf{F} \cdot d\mathbf{r} = 0$ on all simple closed smooth oriented curves in a region R and let A and B be distinct points in R. Let C_1 denote any curve from A to B, let C_2 be any curve from B to A (distinct from and not intersecting C_1), and let C be the closed curve consisting of C_1 followed by C_2 (Figure 15.29). Then

$$\oint_C \mathbf{F} \cdot d\mathbf{r} = \int_{C_1} \mathbf{F} \cdot d\mathbf{r} + \int_{C_2} \mathbf{F} \cdot d\mathbf{r} = 0.$$

➤ Line integrals of vector fields satisfy properties similar to ordinary integrals. If C is a smooth curve from A to B and P is a point on C between A and B then

$$\int_{AB} \mathbf{F} \cdot d\mathbf{r} = -\int_{BA} \mathbf{F} \cdot d\mathbf{r}$$

and

$$\int_{AB} \mathbf{F} \cdot d\mathbf{r} = \int_{AP} \mathbf{F} \cdot d\mathbf{r} + \int_{PB} \mathbf{F} \cdot d\mathbf{r}$$

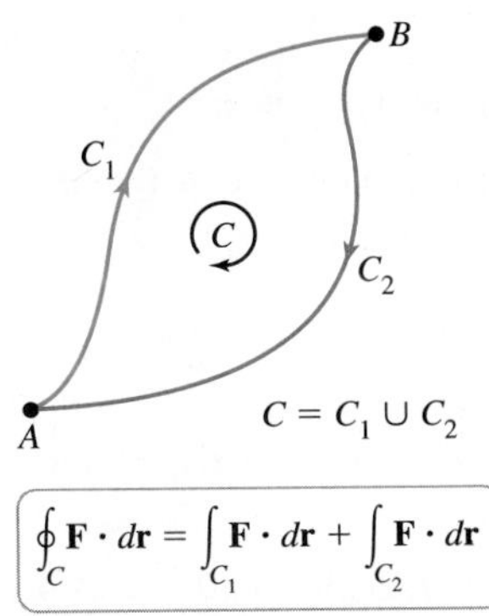

FIGURE 15.29

Therefore, $\int_{C_1} \mathbf{F} \cdot d\mathbf{r} = -\int_{C_2} \mathbf{F} \cdot d\mathbf{r} = \int_{-C_2} \mathbf{F} \cdot d\mathbf{r}$, where $-C_2$ is the curve C_2 traversed in the opposite direction (from A to B). We see that the line integral has the same value on two arbitrary paths between A and B. It follows that the value of the line integral is independent of path, and by Theorem 15.4, **F** is conservative. This argument is a proof of the following theorem.

> THEOREM 15.5 **Line Integrals on Closed Curves**
> Let R in $\mathbf{R}^2$ (or D in $\mathbf{R}^3$) be an open region. Then **F** is a conservative vector field on R if and only if $\oint_C \mathbf{F} \cdot d\mathbf{r} = 0$ on all simple closed smooth oriented curves C in R.

EXAMPLE 5 **A closed curve line integral in $\mathbf{R}^3$** Evaluate $\int_C \nabla(-xy + xz + yz) \cdot d\mathbf{r}$ on the curve C: $\mathbf{r}(t) = \langle \sin t, \cos t, \sin t \rangle$, for $0 \leq t \leq 2\pi$, without using Theorems 15.4 or 15.5.

SOLUTION The components of the vector field are

$$\mathbf{F} = \nabla(-xy + xz + yz) = \langle -y + z, -x + z, x + y \rangle.$$

Note that $\mathbf{r}'(t) = \langle \cos t, -\sin t, \cos t \rangle$ and $d\mathbf{r} = \mathbf{r}'(t)\, dt$. Substituting values of x, y, and z, the value of the line integral is

$$\oint_C \mathbf{F} \cdot d\mathbf{r} = \oint_C \langle -y + z, -x + z, x + y \rangle \cdot d\mathbf{r} \quad \text{Substitute for } \mathbf{F}.$$

$$= \int_0^{2\pi} \sin 2t \, dt \quad \text{Substitute for } x, y, z, d\mathbf{r}.$$

$$= -\frac{1}{2} \cos 2t \Big|_0^{2\pi} = 0. \quad \text{Evaluate the integral.}$$

The line integral of this conservative vector field on the closed curve C is zero. In fact, by Theorem 15.5, the line integral vanishes on any simple closed curve.

Related Exercises 33–38 ◀

Summary of the Properties of Conservative Vector Fields

We have established three equivalent properties of conservative vector fields **F** defined on an open connected region R in $\mathbf{R}^2$ (or D in $\mathbf{R}^3$):

- There exists a potential function φ such that $\mathbf{F} = \nabla\varphi$.
- $\int_C \mathbf{F} \cdot d\mathbf{r} = \varphi(B) - \varphi(A)$ for all points A and B in R and all smooth oriented curves C from A to B (path independence).
- $\oint_C \mathbf{F} \cdot d\mathbf{r} = 0$ on all simple smooth closed oriented curves C in R.

The connections between these properties were established by Theorems 15.4 and 15.5 in the following way:

$$\text{Path-independence} \overset{\text{Theorem 15.4}}{\Leftrightarrow} \mathbf{F} \text{ is conservative } (\nabla\varphi = \mathbf{F}) \overset{\text{Theorem 15.5}}{\Leftrightarrow} \oint_C \mathbf{F} \cdot d\mathbf{r} = 0$$

SECTION 15.3 EXERCISES

Review Questions

1. Explain with pictures what is meant by a simple curve and a closed curve.

2. Explain with pictures what is meant by a connected region and a simply connected region.

3. How do you determine whether a vector field in $\mathbf{R}^2$ is conservative (has a potential function φ such that $\mathbf{F} = \nabla\varphi$)?

4. How do you determine whether a vector field in $\mathbf{R}^3$ is conservative?

5. Briefly describe how to find a potential function φ for a conservative vector field $\mathbf{F} = \langle f, g \rangle$.

6. If $\mathbf{F}$ is a conservative vector field on a region R, how do you evaluate $\int_C \mathbf{F} \cdot d\mathbf{r}$, where C is a path between two points A and B in R?

7. If $\mathbf{F}$ is a conservative vector field on a region R, what is the value of $\oint_C \mathbf{F} \cdot d\mathbf{r}$, where C is a simple closed smooth oriented curve in R?

8. Give three equivalent properties of conservative vector fields.

Basic Skills

9–14. Testing for conservative vector fields *Determine whether the following vector fields are conservative on* $\mathbf{R}^2$.

9. $\mathbf{F} = \langle 1, 1 \rangle$

10. $\mathbf{F} = \langle x, y \rangle$

11. $\mathbf{F} = \langle -y, -x \rangle$

12. $\mathbf{F} = \langle -y, x + y \rangle$

13. $\mathbf{F} = \langle e^{-x} \cos y, e^{-x} \sin y \rangle$

14. $\mathbf{F} = \langle 2x^3 + xy^2, 2y^3 + x^2y \rangle$

15–26. Finding potential functions *Determine whether the following vector fields are conservative on the specified region. If so, determine a potential function. Let* R^* *and* D^* *be open regions of* $\mathbf{R}^2$ *and* $\mathbf{R}^3$*, respectively, that do not include the origin.*

15. $\mathbf{F} = \langle x, y \rangle$ on $\mathbf{R}^2$

16. $\mathbf{F} = \langle -y, -x \rangle$ on $\mathbf{R}^2$

17. $\mathbf{F} = \langle x^3 - xy, x^2/2 + y \rangle$ on $\mathbf{R}^2$

18. $\mathbf{F} = \dfrac{\langle x, y \rangle}{x^2 + y^2}$ on R^*

19. $\mathbf{F} = \dfrac{\langle x, y \rangle}{\sqrt{x^2 + y^2}}$ on R^*

20. $\mathbf{F} = \langle y, x, 1 \rangle$ on $\mathbf{R}^3$

21. $\mathbf{F} = \langle z, 1, x \rangle$ on $\mathbf{R}^3$

22. $\mathbf{F} = \langle yz, xz, xy \rangle$ on $\mathbf{R}^3$

23. $\mathbf{F} = \langle y + z, x + z, x + y \rangle$ on $\mathbf{R}^3$

24. $\mathbf{F} = \dfrac{\langle x, y, z \rangle}{x^2 + y^2 + z^2}$ on D^*

25. $\mathbf{F} = \dfrac{\langle x, y, z \rangle}{\sqrt{x^2 + y^2 + z^2}}$ on D^*

26. $\mathbf{F} = \langle x^3, 2y, -z^3 \rangle$ on $\mathbf{R}^3$

27–32. Evaluating line integrals *Evaluate the line integral* $\int_C \nabla\varphi \cdot d\mathbf{r}$ *for the following functions* φ *and oriented curves C in two ways.*

a. Use a parametric description of C and evaluate the integral directly.

b. Use the Fundamental Theorem for line integrals.

27. $\varphi(x, y) = xy$; C: $\mathbf{r}(t) = \langle \cos t, \sin t \rangle$, for $0 \le t \le \pi$

28. $\varphi(x, y) = (x^2 + y^2)/2$; C: $\mathbf{r}(t) = \langle \sin t, \cos t \rangle$, for $0 \le t \le \pi$

29. $\varphi(x, y) = x + 3y$; C: $\mathbf{r}(t) = \langle 2 - t, t \rangle$, for $0 \le t \le 2$

30. $\varphi(x, y, z) = x + y + z$; C: $\mathbf{r}(t) = \langle \sin t, \cos t, t/\pi \rangle$, for $0 \le t \le \pi$

31. $\varphi(x, y, z) = (x^2 + y^2 + z^2)/2$; C: $\mathbf{r}(t) = \langle \cos t, \sin t, t/\pi \rangle$, for $0 \le t \le 2\pi$

32. $\varphi(x, y, z) = xy + xz + yz$; C: $\mathbf{r}(t) = \langle t, 2t, 3t \rangle$, for $0 \le t \le 4$

33–38. Line integrals of vector fields on closed curves *Evaluate* $\oint_C \mathbf{F} \cdot d\mathbf{r}$ *for the following vector fields and closed oriented curves C by parameterizing C. If the integral is not zero, give an explanation.*

33. $\mathbf{F} = \langle x, y \rangle$; C is the circle of radius 4 centered at the origin oriented counterclockwise.

34. $\mathbf{F} = \langle y, x \rangle$; C is the circle of radius 8 centered at the origin oriented counterclockwise.

35. $\mathbf{F} = \langle x, y \rangle$; C is the triangle with vertices $(0, \pm 1)$ and $(1, 0)$ oriented counterclockwise.

36. $\mathbf{F} = \langle y, -x \rangle$; C is the circle of radius 3 centered at the origin oriented counterclockwise.

37. $\mathbf{F} = \langle x, y, z \rangle$; C: $\mathbf{r}(t) = \langle \cos t, \sin t, 2 \rangle$, for $0 \le t \le 2\pi$

38. $\mathbf{F} = \langle y - z, z - x, x - y \rangle$; C: $\mathbf{r}(t) = \langle \cos t, \sin t, \cos t \rangle$, for $0 \le t \le 2\pi$

Further Explorations

39. **Explain why or why not** Determine whether the following statements are true and give an explanation or counterexample.
    a. If $\mathbf{F} = \langle -y, x \rangle$ and C is the circle of radius 4 centered at $(1, 0)$ oriented counterclockwise, then $\oint_C \mathbf{F} \cdot d\mathbf{r} = 0$.
    b. If $\mathbf{F} = \langle x, -y \rangle$ and C is the circle of radius 4 centered at $(1, 0)$ oriented counterclockwise, then $\oint_C \mathbf{F} \cdot d\mathbf{r} = 0$.
    c. A constant vector field is conservative on $\mathbf{R}^2$.
    d. The vector field $\mathbf{F} = \langle f(x), g(y) \rangle$ is conservative on $\mathbf{R}^2$.

40–43. Line integrals *Evaluate the following line integrals using a method of your choice.*

40. $\displaystyle\int_C \nabla(1 + x^2yz) \cdot d\mathbf{r}$, where C is the helix $\mathbf{r}(t) = \langle \cos 2t, \sin 2t, t \rangle$, for $0 \le t \le 4\pi$

41. $\displaystyle\int_C \nabla(e^{-x} \cos y) \cdot d\mathbf{r}$, where C is the line from $(0, 0)$ to $(\ln 2, 2\pi)$

42. $\displaystyle\oint_C e^{-x}(\cos y\, dx + \sin y\, dy)$, where C is the square with vertices $(\pm 1, \pm 1)$ oriented counterclockwise

43. $\oint_C \mathbf{F} \cdot d\mathbf{r}$, where $\mathbf{F} = \langle 2xy + z^2, x^2, 2xz \rangle$ and C is the circle $\mathbf{r}(t) = \langle 3\cos t, 4\cos t, 5\sin t \rangle$, for $0 \le t \le 2\pi$.

44. Closed curve integrals Evaluate $\oint_C ds$, $\oint_C dx$, and $\oint_C dy$, where C is the unit circle oriented counterclockwise.

45–48. Work in force fields *Find the work required to move an object in the following force fields along a straight line between the given points. Check to see if the force is conservative.*

45. $\mathbf{F} = \langle x, 2 \rangle$ from $A(0, 0)$ to $B(2, 4)$

46. $\mathbf{F} = \langle x, y \rangle$ from $A(1, 1)$ to $B(3, -6)$

47. $\mathbf{F} = \langle x, y, z \rangle$ from $A(1, 2, 1)$ to $B(2, 4, 6)$

48. $\mathbf{F} = e^{x+y}\langle 1, 1, z \rangle$ from $A(0, 0, 0)$ to $B(-1, 2, -4)$

49–50. Work from graphs *Determine whether* $\int_C \mathbf{F} \cdot d\mathbf{r}$ *along the paths* C_1 *and* C_2 *shown in the following vector fields is positive or negative. Explain your reasoning.*

49.

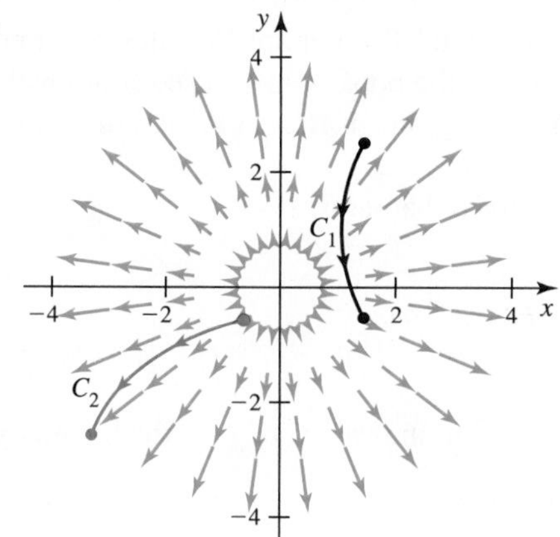

50.

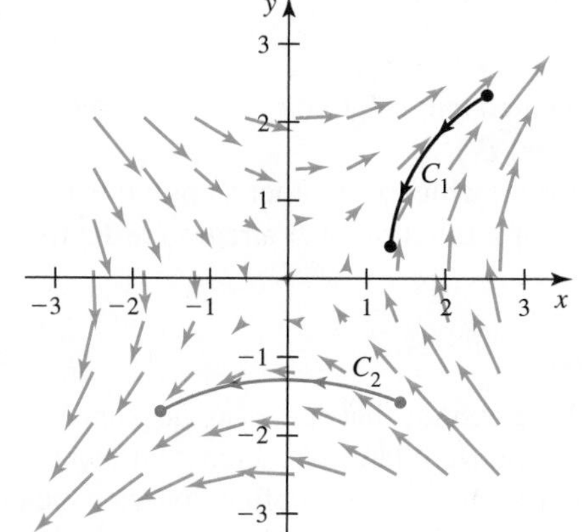

Applications

51. Work by a constant force Evaluate a line integral to show that the work done in moving an object from point A to point B in the presence of a constant force $\mathbf{F} = \langle a, b, c \rangle$ is $\mathbf{F} \cdot \overrightarrow{AB}$.

52. Conservation of energy Suppose an object with mass m moves in a conservative force field given by $\mathbf{F} = -\nabla\varphi$, where φ is a potential function in a region R. The motion of the object is governed by Newton's Second Law of Motion, $\mathbf{F} = m\mathbf{a}$, where $\mathbf{a}$ is the acceleration. Suppose the object moves (either in the plane or in space) from point A to point B in R.

a. Show that the equation of motion is $m\dfrac{d\mathbf{v}}{dt} = -\nabla\varphi$.

b. Show that $\dfrac{d\mathbf{v}}{dt} \cdot \mathbf{v} = \dfrac{1}{2}\dfrac{d}{dt}(\mathbf{v} \cdot \mathbf{v})$.

c. Take the dot product of both sides of the equation in part (a) with $\mathbf{v}(t) = \mathbf{r}'(t)$ and integrate along a curve between A and B. Use part (b) and the fact that $\mathbf{F}$ is conservative to show that the total energy (kinetic plus potential) $\frac{1}{2}m|\mathbf{v}|^2 + \varphi$ is the same at A and B. Conclude that because A and B are arbitrary, energy is conserved in R.

53. Gravitational potential The gravitational force between two point masses M and m is

$$\mathbf{F} = GMm\frac{\mathbf{r}}{|\mathbf{r}|^3} = GMm\frac{\langle x, y, z \rangle}{(x^2 + y^2 + z^2)^{3/2}},$$

where G is the gravitational constant.

a. Verify that this force field is conservative on any region excluding the origin.

b. Find a potential function φ for this force field such that $\mathbf{F} = -\nabla\varphi$.

c. Suppose the object with mass m is moved from a point A to a point B, where A is a distance r_1 from M and B is a distance r_2 from M. Show that the work done in moving the object is $GMm\left(\dfrac{1}{r_2} - \dfrac{1}{r_1}\right)$.

d. Does the work depend on the path between A and B? Explain.

Additional Exercises

54. Radial fields in $\mathbf{R}^3$ are conservative Prove that the radial field $\mathbf{F} = \dfrac{\mathbf{r}}{|\mathbf{r}|^p}$, where $\mathbf{r} = \langle x, y, z \rangle$ and p is a real number, is conservative on any region not containing the origin. For what values of p is $\mathbf{F}$ conservative on a region that contains the origin?

55. Rotation fields are usually not conservative

a. Prove that the rotation field $\mathbf{F} = \dfrac{\langle -y, x \rangle}{|\mathbf{r}|^p}$, where $\mathbf{r} = \langle x, y \rangle$ is not conservative for $p \ne 2$.

b. For $p = 2$, show that $\mathbf{F}$ is conservative on any region not containing the origin.

c. Find a potential function for $\mathbf{F}$ when $p = 2$.

56. Linear and quadratic vector fields

a. For what values of a, b, c, and d is the field $\mathbf{F} = \langle ax + by, cx + dy \rangle$ conservative?

b. For what values of a, b, and c is the field $\mathbf{F} = \langle ax^2 - by^2, cxy \rangle$ conservative?

57. Alternative construction of potential functions in $\mathbf{R}^2$ Assume that the vector field $\mathbf{F}$ is conservative on $\mathbf{R}^2$, so that the line integral $\int_C \mathbf{F} \cdot d\mathbf{r}$ is independent of path. Use the following procedure to construct a potential function φ for the vector field $\mathbf{F} = \langle f, g \rangle = \langle 2x - y, -x + 2y \rangle$.

a. Let A be $(0, 0)$ and let B be an arbitrary point (x, y). Define $\varphi(x, y)$ to be the work required to move an object from A to B, where $\varphi(A) = 0$. Let C_1 be the path from A to $(x, 0)$ to B and let C_2 be the path from A to $(0, y)$ to B. Draw a picture.

b. Evaluate $\int_{C_1} \mathbf{F} \cdot d\mathbf{r} = \int_{C_1} f\,dx + g\,dy$ and conclude that $\varphi(x, y) = x^2 - xy + y^2$.

c. Verify that the same potential function is obtained by evaluating the line integral over C_2.

58–61. Alternative construction of potential functions *Use the procedure in Exercise 57 to construct potential functions for the following fields*

58. $\mathbf{F} = \langle -y, -x \rangle$

59. $\mathbf{F} = \langle x, y \rangle$

60. $\mathbf{F} = \mathbf{r}/|\mathbf{r}|$, where $\mathbf{r} = \langle x, y \rangle$

61. $\mathbf{F} = \langle 2x^3 + xy^2, 2y^3 + x^2y \rangle$

QUICK CHECK ANSWERS

1. A figure–8 is closed but not simple; a torus is connected, but not simply connected. **2.** The vector field is obtained by differentiating the potential function. So additive constants in the potential give the same vector field: $\nabla(\varphi + C) = \nabla\varphi$, when C is a constant. **3.** Show that $\nabla(e^x \cos y) = \langle e^x \cos y, -e^x \sin y \rangle$, which is the original vector field. A similar calculation may be done for part (b). **4.** The vector field $\nabla(xy + xz - yz)$ is the gradient of $xy + xz - yz$, so the vector field is conservative.

15.4 Green's Theorem

The preceding section gave a version of the Fundamental Theorem of Calculus that applies to line integrals. In this and the remaining sections of the book, you will see additional extensions of the Fundamental Theorem that apply to regions in $\mathbf{R}^2$ and $\mathbf{R}^3$. All these fundamental theorems share a common feature.

Part 2 of the Fundamental Theorem of Calculus (Chapter 5) says

$$\int_a^b \frac{df}{dx}\,dx = f(b) - f(a),$$

which relates the integral of $\frac{df}{dx}$ on an interval $[a, b]$ to the values of f on the boundary of $[a, b]$. The Fundamental Theorem for line integrals says

$$\int_C \nabla\varphi \cdot d\mathbf{r} = \varphi(B) - \varphi(A),$$

which relates the integral of $\nabla\varphi$ on a smooth oriented curve C to the boundary values of φ. (The boundary consists of the two endpoints A and B.)

The subject of this section is Green's Theorem, which is another step in this progression. It relates the double integral of derivatives of a function over a region in $\mathbf{R}^2$ to function values on the boundary of that region.

Circulation Form of Green's Theorem

Throughout this section, unless otherwise stated, we assume that curves in the plane are simple, closed, oriented curves that have a continuous nonzero tangent vector at all points. By a result called the *Jordan Curve Theorem*, such curves have a well-defined interior such that when the curve is traversed in the counterclockwise direction (viewed from above), the interior is on the left. With this orientation, there is a unique outward unit normal vector that points to the right. We also assume that curves in the plane lie in regions that are both connected and simply connected.

Suppose the vector field $\mathbf{F}$ is defined on a region R enclosed by a closed curve C. As we have seen, the circulation $\oint_C \mathbf{F} \cdot d\mathbf{r}$ (Section 15.2) measures the net component of $\mathbf{F}$ in the direction tangential to C. It is easiest to visualize the circulation if $\mathbf{F}$ represents the velocity of a fluid moving in two dimensions. For example, let C be the unit circle with a counterclockwise orientation. The vector field $\mathbf{F} = \langle -y, x \rangle$ has a positive circulation of 2π on C

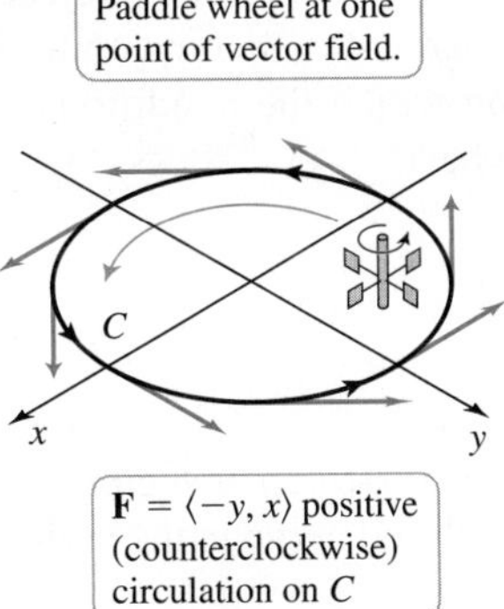
Paddle wheel at one point of vector field.
C
x
y
F = ⟨−y, x⟩ positive (counterclockwise) circulation on C

FIGURE 15.30

(Section 15.2) because the vector field is everywhere tangent to C (Figure 15.30). A nonzero circulation on a closed curve says that the vector field must have some property *inside* the curve that produces the circulation. You can think of this property as a *net rotation.*

To visualize the rotation of a vector field, imagine a small paddle wheel, fixed at a point in the vector field, with its axis perpendicular to the xy-plane (Figure 15.30). The strength of the rotation at that point is seen in the speed at which the paddle wheel spins, while the direction of the rotation is the direction in which the paddle wheel spins. At a different point in the vector field, the paddle wheel will, in general, have a different speed and direction of rotation.

The first form of Green's Theorem relates the circulation on C to the double integral, over the region R, of a factor that measures rotation.

THEOREM 15.6 Green's Theorem—Circulation Form
Let C be a simple closed smooth curve, oriented counterclockwise, that encloses a connected and simply connected region R in the plane. Assume $\mathbf{F} = \langle f, g \rangle$, where f and g have continuous first partial derivatives in R. Then

$$\underbrace{\oint_C \mathbf{F} \cdot d\mathbf{r}}_{\text{circulation}} = \underbrace{\oint_C f\,dx + g\,dy}_{\text{circulation}} = \iint_R \left(\frac{\partial g}{\partial x} - \frac{\partial f}{\partial y} \right) dA.$$

The circulation form of Green's Theorem is also called the *tangential*, or *curl*, form.

The proof of a special case of the theorem is given at the end of this section. Notice that the two line integrals on the left side of Green's Theorem give the circulation of the vector field on C. The double integral on the right side involves the factor $\frac{\partial g}{\partial x} - \frac{\partial f}{\partial y}$, which describes the rotation of the vector field *within* C that produces the circulation *on* C. This factor is called the **two-dimensional curl** of the vector field.

Figure 15.31 illustrates how the curl measures the rotation of one particular vector field at a point P. If the horizontal component of the field decreases in the y-direction at P ($f_y < 0$) and the vertical component increases in the x-direction at P ($g_x > 0$), then $\frac{\partial g}{\partial x} - \frac{\partial f}{\partial y} > 0$, and the field has a counterclockwise rotation at P. The double integral in Green's Theorem computes the net rotation of the field throughout R. The theorem says that the net rotation throughout R equals the circulation on the boundary of R.

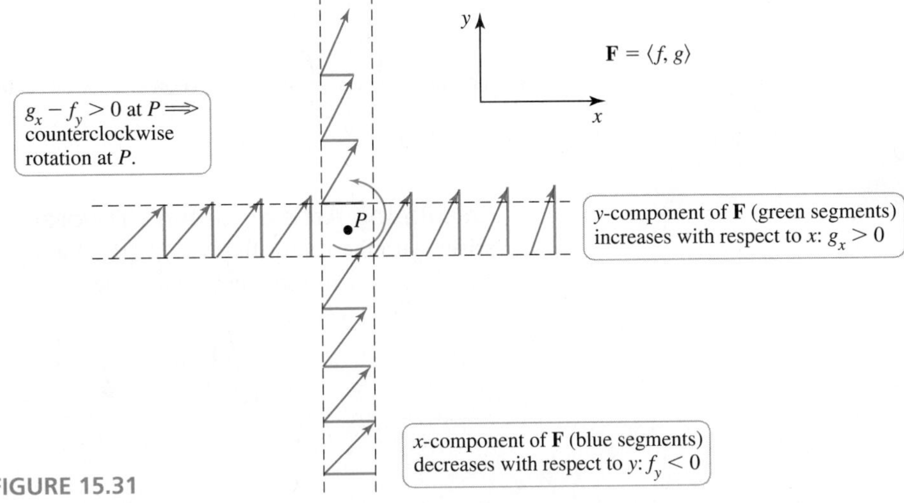
y
x
F = ⟨f, g⟩
$g_x - f_y > 0$ at $P \Longrightarrow$ counterclockwise rotation at P.
P
y-component of F (green segments) increases with respect to x: $g_x > 0$
x-component of F (blue segments) decreases with respect to y: $f_y < 0$

FIGURE 15.31

QUICK CHECK 1 Compute $\frac{\partial g}{\partial x} - \frac{\partial f}{\partial y}$ for the radial vector field $\mathbf{F} = \langle x, y \rangle$. What does this tell you about the circulation on a simple closed curve?

Green's Theorem has an important consequence when applied to a conservative vector field. Recall from Theorem 15.3 that if $\mathbf{F} = \langle f, g \rangle$ is conservative, then its components satisfy the condition $f_y = g_x$. If R is a region of $\mathbf{R}^2$ on which the conditions of Green's Theorem are satisfied, then for a conservative field we have

$$\oint_C \mathbf{F} \cdot d\mathbf{r} = \iint_R \underbrace{\left(\frac{\partial g}{\partial x} - \frac{\partial f}{\partial y} \right)}_{0} dA = 0.$$

Green's Theorem confirms the fact (Theorem 15.5) that if $\mathbf{F}$ is a conservative vector field in a region, then the circulation $\oint_C \mathbf{F} \cdot d\mathbf{r}$ is zero on any simple closed curve in the region. A two-dimensional vector field $\mathbf{F} = \langle f, g \rangle$ for which $\frac{\partial g}{\partial x} - \frac{\partial f}{\partial y} = 0$ at all points of a region is said to be *irrotational*, because it produces zero circulation on closed curves in the region. Irrotational vector fields in $\mathbf{R}^2$ are conservative.

➤ In some cases, the rotation of a vector field may not be obvious. For example, the parallel flow in a channel $\mathbf{F} = \langle 0, 1 - x^2 \rangle$ for $|x| \le 1$ has a nonzero curl for $x \neq 0$. See Exercise 66.

DEFINITION Two-Dimensional Curl

The **two-dimensional curl** of the vector field $\mathbf{F} = \langle f, g \rangle$ is $\frac{\partial g}{\partial x} - \frac{\partial f}{\partial y}$. If the curl is zero throughout a region, the vector field is said to be **irrotational** on that region.

Evaluating line integrals of conservative vector fields on closed curves is easy. The integral is always zero. Green's Theorem provides a way to evaluate such integrals for nonconservative vector fields.

EXAMPLE 1 Circulation of a rotation field Consider the rotation vector field $\mathbf{F} = \langle -y, x \rangle$ on the unit disk $R = \{(x, y): x^2 + y^2 \le 1\}$ (Figure 15.30). In Example 7 of Section 15.2, we showed that $\oint_C \mathbf{F} \cdot d\mathbf{r} = 2\pi$, where C is the boundary of R oriented counterclockwise. Confirm this result using Green's Theorem.

SOLUTION Note that $f(x, y) = -y$ and $g(x, y) = x$; therefore, the curl of $\mathbf{F}$ is $\frac{\partial g}{\partial x} - \frac{\partial f}{\partial y} = 2$. By Green's Theorem,

$$\oint_C \mathbf{F} \cdot d\mathbf{r} = \iint_R \underbrace{\left(\frac{\partial g}{\partial x} - \frac{\partial f}{\partial y} \right)}_{2} dA = \iint_R 2\, dA = 2 \times (\text{area of } R) = 2\pi.$$

The curl $\frac{\partial g}{\partial x} - \frac{\partial f}{\partial y}$ is nonzero on R, which indicates a nonzero circulation on the boundary of R.

Related Exercises 11–16 ◀

Calculating Area by Green's Theorem A useful consequence of Green's Theorem arises with the vector fields $\mathbf{F} = \langle 0, x \rangle$ and $\mathbf{F} = \langle y, 0 \rangle$. In the first case, we have $g_x = 1$ and $f_y = 0$; therefore, by Green's Theorem,

$$\oint_C \mathbf{F} \cdot d\mathbf{r} = \underbrace{\oint_C x\, dy}_{\mathbf{F} \cdot d\mathbf{r}} = \underbrace{\iint_R dA}_{\frac{\partial g}{\partial x} - \frac{\partial f}{\partial y} = 1} = \text{area of } R.$$

In the second case, $g_x = 0$ and $f_y = 1$, and Green's Theorem says

$$\oint_C \mathbf{F} \cdot d\mathbf{r} = \oint_C y\,dx = -\iint_R dA = -\text{area of } R.$$

These two results may be combined in one statement.

Area of a Plane Region by Line Integrals

Under the conditions of Green's Theorem, the area of a region R enclosed by a curve C is

$$\oint_C x\,dy = -\oint_C y\,dx = \frac{1}{2}\oint_C (x\,dy - y\,dx).$$

A remarkably simple calculation of the area of an ellipse follows from this result.

EXAMPLE 2 **Area of an ellipse** Find the area of the ellipse $\dfrac{x^2}{a^2} + \dfrac{y^2}{b^2} = 1$.

SOLUTION The ellipse is described parametrically by $\mathbf{r}(t) = \langle x, y \rangle = \langle a \cos t, b \sin t \rangle$, for $0 \le t \le 2\pi$. Noting that $dx = -a \sin t\,dt$ and $dy = b \cos t\,dt$, we have

$$\begin{aligned} x\,dy - y\,dx &= (a \cos t)(b \cos t)\,dt - (b \sin t)(-a \sin t)\,dt \\ &= ab\,(\cos^2 t + \sin^2 t)\,dt \\ &= ab\,dt. \end{aligned}$$

Expressing the line integral as an ordinary integral with respect to t, the area of the ellipse is

$$\frac{1}{2}\oint_C \underbrace{(x\,dy - y\,dx)}_{ab\,dt} = \frac{ab}{2}\int_0^{2\pi} dt = \pi ab.$$

Related Exercises 17–22

Flux Form of Green's Theorem

> The flux form of Green's Theorem is also called the *normal*, or *divergence*, form.

Let C be a closed curve enclosing a region R in $\mathbf{R}^2$ and let $\mathbf{F}$ be a vector field defined on R. We assume that C and R have the previously stated properties; specifically, C is oriented counterclockwise with an outward normal vector $\mathbf{n}$. Recall that the outward flux of $\mathbf{F}$ across C is $\oint_C \mathbf{F} \cdot \mathbf{n}\,ds$ (Section 15.2). The second form of Green's Theorem relates the flux across C to a property of the vector field within R that produces the flux.

THEOREM 15.7' **Green's Theorem, Flux Form**

Let C be a simple closed smooth curve, oriented counterclockwise, that encloses a connected and simply connected region R in the plane. Assume $\mathbf{F} = \langle f, g \rangle$, where f and g have continuous first partial derivatives in R. Then

$$\underbrace{\oint_C \mathbf{F} \cdot \mathbf{n}\,ds}_{\text{outward flux}} = \underbrace{\oint_C f\,dy - g\,dx}_{\text{outward flux}} = \iint_R \left(\frac{\partial f}{\partial x} + \frac{\partial g}{\partial y} \right) dA,$$

where $\mathbf{n}$ is the outward unit normal vector on the curve.

> The two forms of Green's Theorem are related in the following way: Applying the circulation form of the theorem to $\mathbf{F} = \langle -g, f \rangle$ results in the flux form, and applying the flux form of the theorem to $\mathbf{F} = \langle g, -f \rangle$ results in the circulation form.

The two line integrals on the left side of Theorem 15.7 give the outward flux of the vector field across C. The double integral on the right side involves the factor $\frac{\partial f}{\partial x} + \frac{\partial g}{\partial y}$, which is the property of the vector field that produces the flux across C. This factor is called the **two-dimensional divergence**.

Figure 15.32 illustrates how the divergence measures the flux of one particular vector field at a point P. If $f_x > 0$ at P, it indicates an expansion of the vector field in the x-direction (if f_x is negative, it indicates a contraction). Similarly, if $g_y > 0$ at P, it indicates an expansion of the vector field in the y-direction. The combined effect of $f_x + g_y > 0$ at a point is a net outward flux across a small circle enclosing P.

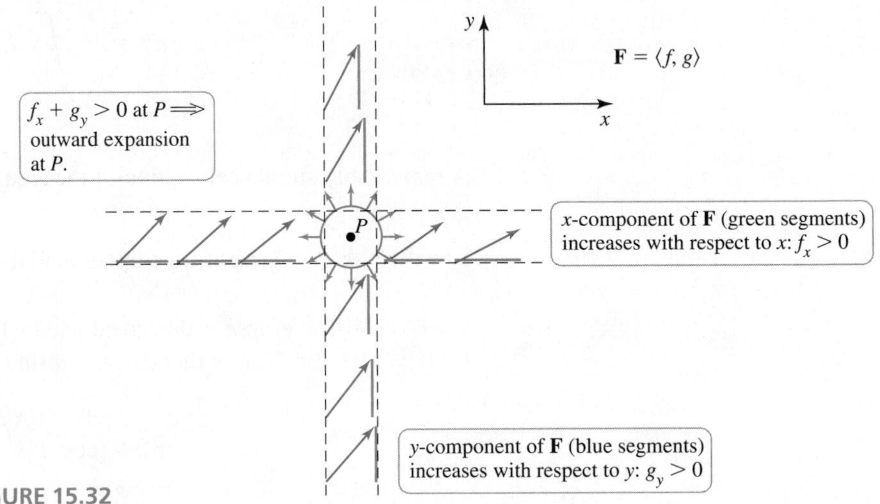

FIGURE 15.32

If the divergence of **F** is zero throughout a region on which **F** satisfies the conditions of Theorem 15.7, then the outward flux across the boundary is zero. Vector fields with a zero divergence are said to be *source-free*. If the divergence is positive throughout R, the outward flux across C is positive, meaning that the vector field acts as a *source* in R. If the divergence is negative throughout R, the outward flux across C is negative, meaning that the vector field acts as a *sink* in R.

DEFINITION Two-Dimensional Divergence

The **two-dimensional divergence** of the vector field $\mathbf{F} = \langle f, g \rangle$ is $\frac{\partial f}{\partial x} + \frac{\partial g}{\partial y}$. If the divergence is zero throughout a region, the vector field is said to be **source-free** on that region.

QUICK CHECK 2 Compute $\frac{\partial f}{\partial x} + \frac{\partial g}{\partial y}$ for the rotation field $\mathbf{F} = \langle -y, x \rangle$. What does this tell you about the outward flux of **F** across a simple closed curve?

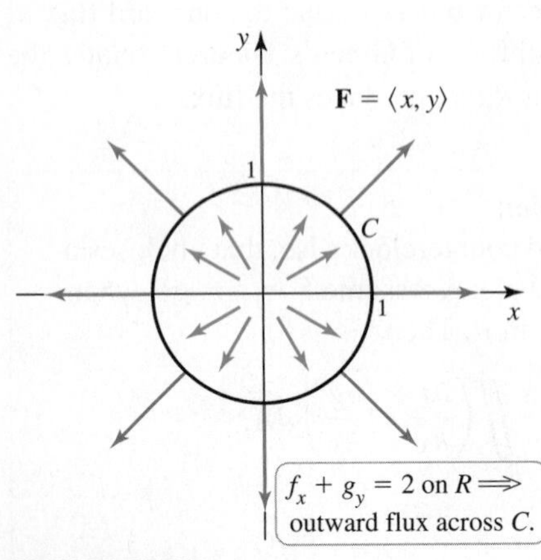

FIGURE 15.33

EXAMPLE 3 Outward flux of a radial field Use Green's Theorem to compute the outward flux of the radial field $\mathbf{F} = \langle x, y \rangle$ across the unit circle $C = \{(x, y): x^2 + y^2 = 1\}$ (Figure 15.33). Interpret the result.

SOLUTION We have already calculated the outward flux of the radial field across C as a line integral and found it to be 2π (Section 15.2). Computing the outward flux using

Green's Theorem, note that $f(x, y) = x$ and $g(x, y) = y$; therefore, the divergence of **F** is $\dfrac{\partial f}{\partial x} + \dfrac{\partial g}{\partial y} = 2$. By Green's Theorem, we have

$$\oint_C \mathbf{F}\cdot\mathbf{n}\,ds = \iint_R \underbrace{\left(\frac{\partial f}{\partial x} + \frac{\partial g}{\partial y}\right)}_{2} dA = \iint_R 2\,dA = 2 \times (\text{area of } R) = 2\pi.$$

The positive divergence on R results in an outward flux of the vector field across the boundary of R. *Related Exercises 23–28* ◀

As with the circulation form, the flux form of Green's Theorem can be used in either direction: to simplify line integrals or to simplify double integrals.

EXAMPLE 4 **Line integral as a double integral** Evaluate $\oint_C (4x^3 + \sin y^2)\,dy - (4y^3 + \cos x^2)\,dx$, where C is the boundary of the disk $R = \{(x, y): x^2 + y^2 \le 4\}$ oriented counterclockwise.

SOLUTION Letting $f(x, y) = 4x^3 + \sin y^2$ and $g(x, y) = 4y^3 + \cos x^2$, Green's Theorem takes the form

$$\oint_C \underbrace{(4x^3 + \sin y^2)}_{f}\,dy - \underbrace{(4y^3 + \cos x^2)}_{g}\,dx$$

$$= \iint_R (\underbrace{12x^2}_{f_x} + \underbrace{12y^2}_{g_y})\,dA \qquad \text{Green's Theorem, flux form}$$

$$= 12\int_0^{2\pi}\int_0^2 r^2\, r\,dr\,d\theta \qquad \text{Polar coordinates: } x^2 + y^2 = r^2$$

$$= 12\int_0^{2\pi} \frac{r^4}{4}\Big|_0^2\,d\theta \qquad \text{Evaluate the inner integral.}$$

$$= 48\int_0^{2\pi} d\theta = 96\pi. \qquad \text{Evaluate the outer integral.}$$

Related Exercises 29–34 ◀

Circulation and Flux on More General Regions

Some ingenuity is required to extend both forms of Green's Theorem to more complicated regions. The next two examples illustrate Green's Theorem on two such regions: a half annulus and a full annulus.

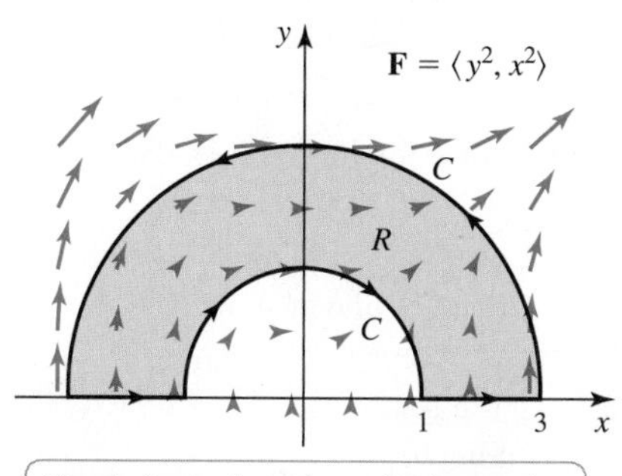

Circulation on boundary of R is negative.

FIGURE 15.34

EXAMPLE 5 **Circulation on a half annulus** Consider the vector field $\mathbf{F} = \langle y^2, x^2\rangle$ on the half annulus $R = \{(x, y): 1 \le x^2 + y^2 \le 9, y \ge 0\}$, whose boundary is C. Find the circulation on C, assuming it has the orientation shown in Figure 15.34.

SOLUTION The circulation on C is

$$\oint_C f\,dx + g\,dy = \oint_C y^2\,dx + x^2\,dy.$$

With the given orientation, the curve runs counterclockwise on the outer semicircle and clockwise on the inner semicircle. Identifying $f(x, y) = y^2$ and $g(x, y) = x^2$, the circulation form of Green's Theorem converts the line integral into a double integral. The double integral is most easily evaluated in polar coordinates using $x = r\cos\theta$ and $y = r\sin\theta$:

$$\oint_C y^2\,dx + x^2\,dy = \iint_R (\underbrace{2x}_{g_x} - \underbrace{2y}_{f_y})\,dA \qquad \text{Green's Theorem}$$

$$= 2\int_0^{\pi}\int_1^3 (r\cos\theta - r\sin\theta)\,r\,dr\,d\theta \qquad \text{Convert to polar coordinates.}$$

$$= 2\int_0^{\pi} (\cos\theta - \sin\theta)\left(\frac{r^3}{3}\right)\bigg|_1^3\,d\theta \qquad \text{Evaluate the inner integral.}$$

$$= \frac{52}{3}\int_0^{\pi} (\cos\theta - \sin\theta)\,d\theta \qquad \text{Simplify.}$$

$$= -\frac{104}{3} \qquad \text{Evaluate the outer integral.}$$

The vector field (Figure 15.34) suggests why the circulation is negative. The field is roughly *opposed* to the direction of C on the outer semicircle but roughly aligned with the direction of C on the inner semicircle. Because the outer semicircle is longer and the field has greater magnitudes on the outer curve than the inner curve, the greater contribution to the circulation is negative. *Related Exercises 35–38* ◀

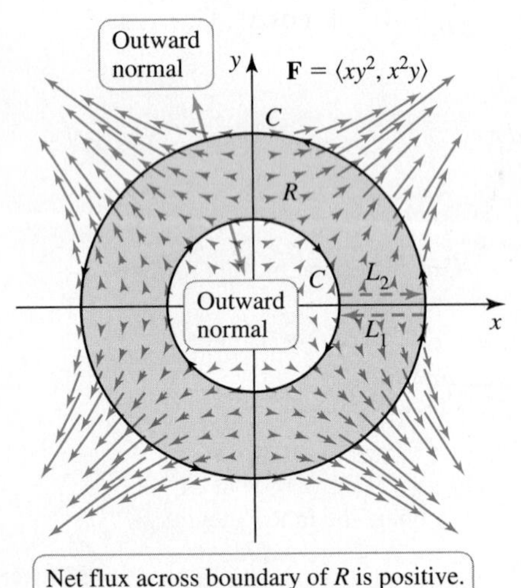

FIGURE 15.35

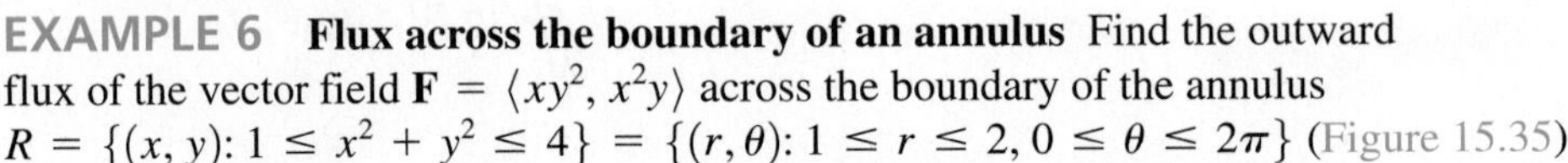

EXAMPLE 6 Flux across the boundary of an annulus Find the outward flux of the vector field $\mathbf{F} = \langle xy^2, x^2y\rangle$ across the boundary of the annulus $R = \{(x, y): 1 \le x^2 + y^2 \le 4\} = \{(r,\theta): 1 \le r \le 2, 0 \le \theta \le 2\pi\}$ (Figure 15.35).

SOLUTION Because the annulus R is not simply connected, Green's Theorem does not apply as stated in Theorem 15.7. This difficulty is overcome by defining the curve C shown in Figure 15.35, which is simple, closed, and *piecewise* smooth. The connecting links L_1 and L_2 along the x-axis are parallel and are traversed in opposite directions. Therefore, the contributions to the line integral cancel on L_1 and L_2. Because of this cancellation, we take C to be the curve that runs counterclockwise on the outer boundary and clockwise on the inner boundary.

Using the flux form of Green's Theorem and converting to polar coordinates, we have

$$\oint_C \mathbf{F}\cdot\mathbf{n}\,ds = \oint_C f\,dy - g\,dx = \oint_C xy^2\,dy - x^2y\,dx \qquad \text{Substitute for } f \text{ and } g.$$

$$= \iint_R (\underbrace{y^2}_{f_x} + \underbrace{x^2}_{g_y})\,dA \qquad \text{Green's Theorem}$$

$$= \int_0^{2\pi}\int_1^2 (r^2)\,r\,dr\,d\theta \qquad \text{Polar coordinates; } x^2 + y^2 = r^2$$

$$= \int_0^{2\pi} \frac{r^4}{4}\bigg|_1^2\,d\theta \qquad \text{Evaluate the inner integral.}$$

$$= \frac{15}{4}\int_0^{2\pi} d\theta \qquad \text{Simplify.}$$

$$= \frac{15\pi}{2}. \qquad \text{Evaluate the outer integral.}$$

➤ Another way to deal with the flux across the annulus is to apply Green's Theorem to the entire disk $|r| \le 2$ and compute the flux across the outer circle. Then apply Green's Theorem to the disk $|r| \le 1$ and compute the flux across the inner circle. Note that the flux *out* of the inner disk is a flux *into* the annulus. Therefore, the difference of the two fluxes gives the net flux for the annulus.

> Notice that the divergence of the vector field in Example 6 is $x^2 + y^2$, which is positive on R, also explaining the outward flux across C.

Figure 15.35 shows the vector field and explains why the flux across C is positive. Because the field increases in magnitude at greater distances from the origin, the outward flux across the outer boundary is greater than the inward flux across the inner boundary. Hence, the net outward flux across C is positive. *Related Exercises 35–38* ◀

Stream Functions

We can now see a wonderful parallel between circulation properties (and conservative vector fields) and flux properties (and source-free fields). We need one more piece to complete the picture; it is the *stream function*, which plays the same role for source-free fields that the potential function plays for conservative fields.

> Potential function:
> $\varphi_x = f$ and $\varphi_y = g$
> Stream function:
> $\psi_x = -g$ and $\psi_y = f$

Consider a two-dimensional vector field $\mathbf{F} = \langle f, g \rangle$ that is differentiable on a region R. A **stream function** for the vector field—if it exists—is a function ψ (pronounced *psigh* or *psee*) that satisfies

$$\frac{\partial \psi}{\partial y} = f, \qquad \frac{\partial \psi}{\partial x} = -g.$$

If we compute the divergence of a vector field $\mathbf{F} = \langle f, g \rangle$ that has a stream function and use the fact that $\psi_{xy} = \psi_{yx}$, then

$$\frac{\partial f}{\partial x} + \frac{\partial g}{\partial y} = \underbrace{\frac{\partial}{\partial x}\left(\frac{\partial \psi}{\partial y}\right) + \frac{\partial}{\partial y}\left(-\frac{\partial \psi}{\partial x}\right)}_{\psi_{yx} = \psi_{xy}} = 0.$$

We see that the existence of a stream function guarantees that the vector field has zero divergence or, equivalently, is source-free. The converse is also true on simply connected regions of $\mathbf{R}^2$.

The level curves of a stream function are called **streamlines**—and for good reason. It can be shown (Exercise 64) that the vector field $\mathbf{F}$ is everywhere tangent to the streamlines, which means that a graph of the streamlines shows the flow of the vector field. Finally, just as circulation integrals of a conservative vector field are path-independent, flux integrals of a source-free field are also path-independent (Exercise 63).

QUICK CHECK 3 Show that $\psi = \frac{1}{2}(y^2 - x^2)$ is a stream function for the vector field $\mathbf{F} = \langle y, x \rangle$. Show that $\mathbf{F}$ has zero divergence. ◀

Table 15.1 shows the parallel properties of conservative and source-free vector fields in two dimensions. We assume that C is a simple smooth oriented curve and is either closed or has endpoints A and B.

Table 15.1

Conservative Fields $\mathbf{F} = \langle f, g \rangle$	Source-Free Fields $\mathbf{F} = \langle f, g \rangle$
curl $= \dfrac{\partial g}{\partial x} - \dfrac{\partial f}{\partial y} = 0$	divergence $= \dfrac{\partial f}{\partial x} + \dfrac{\partial g}{\partial y} = 0$
Potential function φ with	Stream function ψ with
$\mathbf{F} = \nabla \varphi$ or $\dfrac{\partial \varphi}{\partial x} = f, \quad \dfrac{\partial \varphi}{\partial y} = g$	$\dfrac{\partial \psi}{\partial y} = f, \quad \dfrac{\partial \psi}{\partial x} = -g$
Circulation $= \oint_C \mathbf{F} \cdot d\mathbf{r} = 0$ on all closed curves C.	Flux $= \oint_C \mathbf{F} \cdot \mathbf{n}\, ds = 0$ on all closed curves C.
Path independence	Path independence
$\int_C \mathbf{F} \cdot d\mathbf{r} = \varphi(B) - \varphi(A)$	$\int_C \mathbf{F} \cdot \mathbf{n}\, ds = \psi(B) - \psi(A)$

> In fluid dynamics, velocity fields that are both conservative and source-free are called *ideal flows*. They model fluids that are irrotational and incompressible.

Vector fields that are both conservative and source-free are quite interesting mathematically. They have both a potential function and a stream function whose level curves form orthogonal families. Such vector fields have zero curl ($g_x - f_y = 0$) and zero divergence ($f_x + g_y = 0$). If we write the zero divergence condition in terms of the potential function φ, we find that

$$0 = f_x + g_y = \varphi_{xx} + \varphi_{yy}.$$

Writing the zero curl condition in terms of the stream function ψ, we find that

$$0 = g_x - f_y = -\psi_{xx} - \psi_{yy}.$$

> Methods for finding solutions of Laplace's equation are discussed in advanced mathematics courses.

We see that the potential function and the stream function both satisfy an important equation known as **Laplace's equation**:

$$\varphi_{xx} + \varphi_{yy} = \psi_{xx} + \psi_{yy} = 0.$$

Any function satisfying Laplace's equation can be used as a potential function or stream function for a conservative, source-free vector field. These vector fields are used in fluid dynamics, electrostatics, and other modeling applications.

Proof of Green's Theorem on Special Regions

The proof of Green's Theorem is straightforward when restricted to special regions. We consider regions R enclosed by a simple closed piecewise smooth curve C oriented in the counterclockwise direction. Furthermore, we require that there are functions G_1, G_2, H_1, and H_2 such that the region can be expressed in two ways (Figure 15.36):

> This restriction on R means that lines parallel to the coordinate axes intersect the boundary of R at most twice.

- $R = \{(x, y): a \le x \le b, G_1(x) \le y \le G_2(x)\}$ or
- $R = \{(x, y): H_1(y) \le x \le H_2(y), c \le y \le d\}$

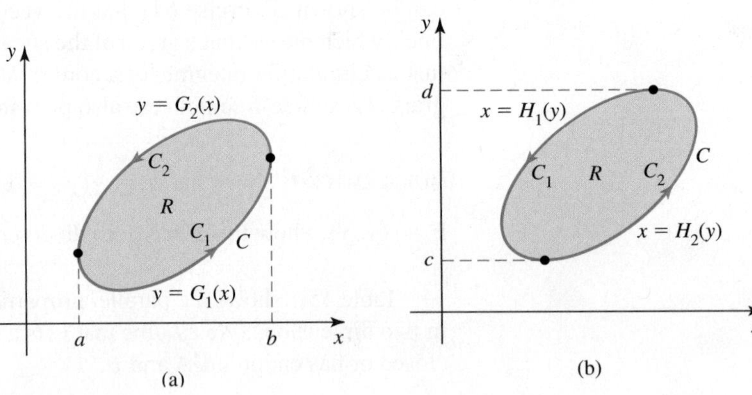

FIGURE 15.36

Under these conditions, we prove the circulation form of Green's Theorem:

$$\oint_C f\,dx + g\,dy = \iint_R \left(\frac{\partial g}{\partial x} - \frac{\partial f}{\partial y}\right) dA$$

Beginning with the term $\iint_R \frac{\partial f}{\partial y}\,dA$, we write this double integral as an iterated integral, where $G_1(x) \le y \le G_2(x)$ in the inner integral and $a \le x \le b$ in the outer integral (Figure 15.36a). The upper curve is labeled C_2, and the lower curve is labeled C_1. Notice that the inner integral of $\dfrac{\partial f}{\partial y}$ with respect to y gives $f(x, y)$. Therefore, the first step of the double integration is

$$\iint\limits_R \frac{\partial f}{\partial y}\, dA = \int_a^b \int_{G_1(x)}^{G_2(x)} \frac{\partial f}{\partial y}\, dy\, dx \qquad \text{Convert to an iterated integral.}$$

$$= \int_a^b [\underbrace{f(x, G_2(x))}_{\text{on } C_2} - \underbrace{f(x, G_1(x))}_{\text{on } C_1}]\, dx.$$

Over the interval $a \le x \le b$, the points $(x, G_2(x))$ trace out the upper part of C (labeled C_2) in the *negative* (clockwise) direction. Similarly, over the interval $a \le x \le b$, the points $(x, G_1(x))$ trace out the lower part of C (labeled C_1) in the *positive* (counterclockwise) direction.

Therefore,

$$\iint\limits_R \frac{\partial f}{\partial y}\, dA = \int_a^b (f(x, G_2(x)) - f(x, G_1(x)))\, dx$$

$$= \int_{-C_2} f\, dx - \int_{C_1} f\, dx$$

$$= -\int_{C_2} f\, dx - \int_{C_1} f\, dx \qquad \int_{-C_2} = -\int_{C_2}$$

$$= -\oint_C f\, dx. \qquad \int_C = \int_{C_1} + \int_{C_2}$$

A similar argument applies to the double integral of $\dfrac{\partial g}{\partial x}$, except we use the bounding curves $x = H_1(y)$ and $x = H_2(y)$, where C_1 is the left curve and C_2 is the right curve (Figure 15.36b). We have

$$\iint\limits_R \frac{\partial g}{\partial x}\, dA = \int_c^d \int_{H_1(y)}^{H_2(y)} \frac{\partial g}{\partial x}\, dx\, dy \qquad \text{Convert to an iterated integral.}$$

$$= \int_c^d [\underbrace{g(H_2(y), y)}_{C_2} - \underbrace{g(H_1(y), y)}_{-C_1}]\, dy \qquad \int \frac{\partial g}{\partial x}\, dx = g$$

$$= \int_{C_2} g\, dy - \int_{-C_1} g\, dy$$

$$= \int_{C_2} g\, dy + \int_{C_1} g\, dy \qquad \int_{-C_1} = -\int_{C_1}$$

$$= \oint_C g\, dy. \qquad \int_C = \int_{C_1} + \int_{C_2}$$

Combining these two calculations results in

$$\iint_R \left(\frac{\partial g}{\partial x} - \frac{\partial f}{\partial y}\right) dA = \oint_C f\,dx + g\,dy.$$

As mentioned earlier, with a change of notation (replace g by f and f by $-g$), the flux form of Green's Theorem is obtained. This proof also completes the list of equivalent properties of conservative fields given in Section 15.3: From Green's Theorem it follows that if $\frac{\partial g}{\partial x} = \frac{\partial f}{\partial y}$ on a simply connected region R, then the vector field $\mathbf{F} = \langle f, g\rangle$ is conservative on R.

QUICK CHECK 4 Explain why Green's Theorem proves that if $g_x = f_y$, then the vector field $\mathbf{F} = \langle f, g\rangle$ is conservative.

SECTION 15.4 EXERCISES

Review Questions

1. Explain why the two forms of Green's Theorem are analogs of the Fundamental Theorem of Calculus.

2. Referring to both forms of Green's Theorem, match each idea in Column 1 to an idea in Column 2:

Line integral for flux	Double integral of the curl
Line integral for circulation	Double integral of the divergence

3. Compute the two-dimensional curl of $\mathbf{F} = \langle 4x^3y, xy^2 + x^4\rangle$.

4. Compute the two-dimensional divergence of $\mathbf{F} = \langle 4x^3y, xy^2 + x^4\rangle$.

5. How do you use a line integral to compute the area of a plane region?

6. Why does a two-dimensional vector field with zero curl on a region have zero circulation on a closed curve that bounds the region?

7. Why does a two-dimensional vector field with zero divergence on a region have zero outward flux across a closed curve that bounds the region?

8. Sketch a two-dimensional vector field that has zero curl everywhere in the plane.

9. Sketch a two-dimensional vector field that has zero divergence everywhere in the plane.

10. Discuss one of the parallels between a conservative vector field and a source-free vector field.

Basic Skills

11–16. Green's Theorem, circulation form *Consider the following regions R and vector fields* **F**.

a. *Compute the two-dimensional curl of the vector field.*
b. *Evaluate both integrals in Green's Theorem and check for consistency.*
c. *State whether the vector field is conservative.*

11. $\mathbf{F} = \langle x, y\rangle$; $R = \{(x, y): x^2 + y^2 \le 2\}$

12. $\mathbf{F} = \langle y, x\rangle$; R is the square with vertices $(0, 0), (1, 0), (1, 1), (0, 1)$.

13. $\mathbf{F} = \langle 2y, -2x\rangle$; R is the region bounded by $y = \sin x$ and $y = 0$, for $0 \le x \le \pi$.

14. $\mathbf{F} = \langle -3y, 3x\rangle$; R is the triangle with vertices $(0, 0), (1, 0), (0, 2)$.

15. $\mathbf{F} = \langle 2xy, x^2 - y^2\rangle$; R is the region bounded by $y = x(2 - x)$ and $y = 0$.

16. $\mathbf{F} = \langle 0, x^2 + y^2\rangle$; $R = \{(x, y): x^2 + y^2 \le 1\}$.

17–22. Area of regions *Use a line integral on the boundary to find the area of the following regions.*

17. A disk of radius 5

18. A region bounded by an ellipse with semimajor and semiminor axes of length 6 and 4, respectively

19. $\{(x, y): x^2 + y^2 \le 16\}$

20. $\{(x, y): x^2/25 + y^2/9 \le 1\}$

21. The region bounded by the parabolas $\mathbf{r}(t) = \langle t, 2t^2\rangle$ and $\mathbf{r}(t) = \langle t, 12 - t^2\rangle$, for $-2 \le t \le 2$

22. The region bounded by the curve $\mathbf{r}(t) = \langle t(1 - t^2), 1 - t^2\rangle$, for $-1 \le t \le 1$ (*Hint:* Plot the curve.)

23–28. Green's Theorem, flux form *Consider the following regions R and vector fields* **F**.

a. *Compute the two-dimensional divergence of the vector field.*
b. *Evaluate both integrals in Green's Theorem and check for consistency.*
c. *State whether the vector field is source-free.*

23. $\mathbf{F} = \langle x, y\rangle$; $R = \{(x, y): x^2 + y^2 \le 4\}$

24. $\mathbf{F} = \langle y, -x\rangle$; R is the square with vertices $(0, 0), (1, 0), (1, 1), (0, 1)$.

25. $\mathbf{F} = \langle y, -3x\rangle$; R is the region bounded by $y = 4 - x^2$ and $y = 0$.

26. $\mathbf{F} = \langle -3y, 3x\rangle$; R is the triangle with vertices $(0, 0), (3, 0), (0, 1)$.

27. $\mathbf{F} = \langle 2xy, x^2 - y^2\rangle$; R is the region bounded by $y = x(2 - x)$ and $y = 0$.

28. $\mathbf{F} = \langle x^2 + y^2, 0\rangle$; $R = \{(x, y): x^2 + y^2 \le 1\}$.

29–34. Line integrals *Use Green's Theorem to evaluate the following line integrals. Unless stated otherwise, assume all curves are oriented counterclockwise.*

29. $\oint_C (2x + e^{y^2})\,dy - (4y^2 + e^{x^2})\,dx$, where C is the boundary of the square with vertices $(0, 0), (1, 0), (1, 1), (0, 1)$

30. $\int_C (2x - 3y)\,dy - (3x + 4y)\,dx$, where C is the unit circle

31. $\int_C f\,dy - g\,dx$, where $\langle f, g\rangle = \langle 0, xy\rangle$ and C is the triangle with vertices $(0, 0), (2, 0), (0, 4)$

32. $\oint_C f\,dy - g\,dx$, where $\langle f, g\rangle = \langle x^2, 2y^2\rangle$ and C is the upper half of the unit circle and the line segment $-1 \le x \le 1$ oriented *clockwise*

33. The circulation line integral of $\mathbf{F} = \langle 2xy^2 + x, 4x^3 + y\rangle$, where C is the boundary of $\{(x, y): 0 \le y \le \sin x, 0 \le x \le \pi\}$

34. The flux line integral of $\mathbf{F} = \langle e^{x-y}, e^{y-x}\rangle$, where C is the boundary of $\{(x, y): 0 \le y \le x, 0 \le x \le 1\}$

35–38. General regions *For the following vector fields, compute (a) the circulation on and (b) the outward flux across the boundary of the given region. Assume boundary curves are oriented counterclockwise.*

35. $\mathbf{F} = \langle x, y\rangle$; R is the half annulus $\{(r, \theta): 1 \le r \le 2, 0 \le \theta \le \pi\}$.

36. $\mathbf{F} = \langle -y, x\rangle$; R is the annulus $\{(r, \theta): 1 \le r \le 3, 0 \le \theta \le 2\pi\}$.

37. $\mathbf{F} = \langle 2x + y, x - 4y\rangle$; R is the quarter annulus $\{(r, \theta): 1 \le r \le 4, 0 \le \theta \le \pi/2\}$.

38. $\mathbf{F} = \langle x - y, -x + 2y\rangle$; R is the parallelogram $\{(x, y): 1 - x \le y \le 3 - x, 0 \le x \le 1\}$.

Further Explorations

39. **Explain why or why not** Determine whether the following statements are true and give an explanation or counterexample.
    a. The work required to move an object around a closed curve C in the presence of a vector force field is the circulation of the vector field on the curve.
    b. If a vector field has zero divergence throughout a region (on which the conditions of Green's Theorem are met), then the circulation on the boundary of that region is zero.
    c. If the two-dimensional curl of a vector field is positive throughout a region (on which the conditions of Green's Theorem are met), then the circulation on the boundary of that region is positive (assuming counterclockwise orientation).

40–43. Circulation and flux *For the following vector fields, compute (a) the circulation on and (b) the outward flux across the boundary of the given region. Assume boundary curves have counterclockwise orientation.*

40. $\mathbf{F} = \left\langle \ln(x^2 + y^2), \tan^{-1}\left(\frac{y}{x}\right)\right\rangle$, where R is the annulus $\{(r, \theta): 1 \le r \le 2, 0 \le \theta \le 2\pi\}$

41. $\mathbf{F} = \nabla\left(\sqrt{x^2 + y^2}\right)$, where R is the half annulus $\{(r, \theta): 1 \le r \le 3, 0 \le \theta \le \pi\}$

42. $\mathbf{F} = \langle y\cos x, -\sin x\rangle$, where R is the square $\{(x, y): 0 \le x \le \pi/2, 0 \le y \le \pi/2\}$

43. $\mathbf{F} = \langle x + y^2, x^2 - y\rangle$, where $R = \{(x, y): 3y^2 \le x \le 36 - y^2\}$

44–45. Special line integrals *Prove the following identities, where C is a simple closed smooth oriented curve.*

44. $\oint_C dx = \oint_C dy = 0$

45. $\oint_C f(x)\,dx + g(y)\,dy = 0$, where f and g have continuous derivatives on the region enclosed by C

46. **Double integral to line integral** Use the flux form of Green's Theorem to evaluate $\iint_R (2xy + 4y^3)\,dA$, where R is the triangle with vertices $(0, 0), (1, 0)$, and $(0, 1)$.

47. **Area line integral** Show that the value of

$$\oint_C xy^2\,dx + (x^2y + 2x)\,dy$$

depends only on the area of the region enclosed by C.

48. **Area line integral** In terms of the parameters a and b, how is the value of $\oint_C ay\,dx + bx\,dy$ related to the area of the region enclosed by C, assuming counterclockwise orientation of C?

49–52. Stream function *Recall that if the vector field $\mathbf{F} = \langle f, g\rangle$ is source-free (zero divergence), then a stream function ψ exists such that $f = \psi_y$ and $g = -\psi_x$.*

a. *Verify that the given vector field has zero divergence.*
b. *Integrate the relations $f = \psi_y$ and $g = -\psi_x$ to find a stream function for the field.*

49. $\mathbf{F} = \langle 4, 2\rangle$

50. $\mathbf{F} = \langle y^2, x^2\rangle$

51. $\mathbf{F} = \langle -e^{-x}\sin y, e^{-x}\cos y\rangle$

52. $\mathbf{F} = \langle x^2, -2xy\rangle$

Applications

53–56. Ideal flow *A two-dimensional vector field describes* ideal flow *if it has both zero curl and zero divergence on a simply connected region.*

a. *Verify that the curl and divergence of the given field is zero.*
b. *Find a potential function φ and a stream function ψ for the field.*
c. *Verify that φ and ψ satisfy Laplace's equation $\varphi_{xx} + \varphi_{yy} = \psi_{xx} + \psi_{yy} = 0$.*

53. $\mathbf{F} = \langle e^x\cos y, -e^x\sin y\rangle$

54. $\mathbf{F} = \langle x^3 - 3xy^2, y^3 - 3x^2y\rangle$

55. $\mathbf{F} = \left\langle \tan^{-1}(y/x), \frac{1}{2}\ln(x^2 + y^2)\right\rangle$

56. $\mathbf{F} = \dfrac{\langle x, y\rangle}{x^2 + y^2}$

57. Flow in an ocean basin An idealized two-dimensional ocean is modeled by the square region $R = [-\pi/2, \pi/2] \times [-\pi/2, \pi/2]$ with boundary C. Consider the stream function $\psi(x, y) = 4 \cos x \cos y$ defined on R (see figure).

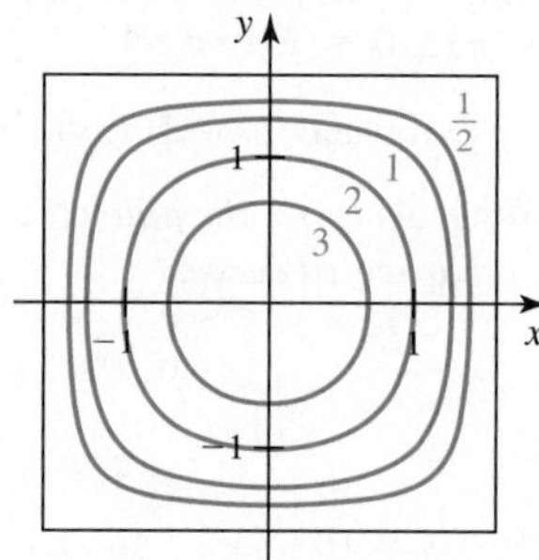

a. The horizontal (east-west) component of the velocity is $u = \psi_y$ and the vertical (north-south) component of the velocity is $v = -\psi_x$. Sketch a few representative velocity vectors and show that the flow is counterclockwise around the region.

b. Is the velocity field source-free? Explain.

c. Is the velocity field irrotational? Explain.

d. Let C be the boundary of R. Find the total outward flux across C.

e. Find the circulation around C assuming counterclockwise orientation.

Additional Exercises

58. Green's Theorem as a Fundamental Theorem of Calculus Show that if the circulation form of Green's theorem is applied to the vector field $\langle 0, f(x)/c\rangle$ and $R = \{(x, y): a \le x \le b, 0 \le y \le c\}$, then the result is the Fundamental Theorem of Calculus,

$$\int_a^b \frac{df}{dx}\,dx = f(b) - f(a).$$

59. Green's Theorem as a Fundamental Theorem of Calculus Show that if the flux form of Green's theorem is applied to the vector field $\langle f(x)/c, 0\rangle$ and $R = \{(x, y): a \le x \le b, 0 \le y \le c\}$, then the result is the Fundamental Theorem of Calculus,

$$\int_a^b \frac{df}{dx}\,dx = f(b) - f(a).$$

60. What's wrong? Consider the rotation field $\mathbf{F} = \dfrac{\langle -y, x\rangle}{x^2 + y^2}$.

a. Verify that the two-dimensional curl of $\mathbf{F}$ is zero, which suggests that the double integral in the circulation form of Green's Theorem is zero.

b. Use a line integral to verify that the circulation on the unit circle of the vector field is 2π.

c. Explain why the results of parts (a) and (b) do not agree.

61. What's wrong? Consider the radial field $\mathbf{F} = \dfrac{\langle x, y\rangle}{x^2 + y^2}$.

a. Verify that the divergence of $\mathbf{F}$ is zero, which suggests that the double integral in the flux form of Green's Theorem is zero.

b. Use a line integral to verify that the outward flux across the unit circle of the vector field is 2π.

c. Explain why the results of parts (a) and (b) do not agree.

62. Conditions for Green's Theorem Consider the radial field $\mathbf{F} = \langle f, g\rangle = \dfrac{\langle x, y\rangle}{\sqrt{x^2 + y^2}} = \dfrac{\mathbf{r}}{|\mathbf{r}|}$.

a. Explain why the conditions of Green's Theorem do not apply to $\mathbf{F}$ on a region that includes the origin.

b. Let R be the unit disk centered at the origin and compute

$$\iint_R \left(\frac{\partial f}{\partial x} + \frac{\partial g}{\partial y}\right) dA.$$

c. Evaluate the line integral in the flux form of Green's Theorem on the boundary of R.

d. Do the results of parts (b) and (c) agree? Explain.

63. Flux integrals Assume the vector field $\mathbf{F} = \langle f, g\rangle$ is source-free (zero divergence) with stream function ψ. Let C be any smooth simple curve from A to the distinct point B. Show that the flux integral $\int_C \mathbf{F} \cdot \mathbf{n}\, ds$ is independent of path; that is, $\int_C \mathbf{F} \cdot \mathbf{n}\, ds = \psi(B) - \psi(A)$.

64. Streamlines are tangent to the vector field Assume that the vector field $\mathbf{F} = \langle f, g\rangle$ is related to the stream function ψ by $\psi_y = f$ and $\psi_x = -g$ on a region R. Prove that at all points of R, the vector field is tangent to the streamlines (the level curves of the stream function).

65. Streamlines and equipotential lines Assume that on $\mathbf{R}^2$ the vector field $\mathbf{F} = \langle f, g\rangle$ has a potential function φ such that $f = \varphi_x$ and $g = \varphi_y$, and it has a stream function ψ such that $f = \psi_y$ and $g = -\psi_x$. Show that the equipotential curves (level curves of φ) and the streamlines (level curves of ψ) are everywhere orthogonal.

66. Channel flow The flow in a long shallow channel is modeled by the velocity field $\mathbf{F} = \langle 0, 1 - x^2\rangle$, where $R = \{(x, y): |x| \le 1 \text{ and } |y| < \infty\}$.

a. Sketch R and several streamlines of $\mathbf{F}$.

b. Evaluate the curl of $\mathbf{F}$ on the lines $x = 0$, $x = \frac{1}{4}$, $x = \frac{1}{2}$, and $x = 1$.

c. Compute the circulation on the boundary of the region $R = \{(x, y): |x| \le 1, 0 \le y \le 1\}$.

d. How do you explain the fact that the curl of $\mathbf{F}$ is nonzero at points of R, but the circulation is zero?

QUICK CHECK ANSWERS

1. $g_x - f_y = 0$, which implies zero circulation on a closed curve. **2.** $f_x + g_y = 0$, which implies zero flux across a closed curve. **3.** $\psi_y = y$ is the x-component of $\mathbf{F} = \langle y, x\rangle$ and $-\psi_x = x$ is the y-component of $\mathbf{F}$. Also the divergence of $\mathbf{F}$ is $y_x + x_y = 0$. **4.** If the curl is zero on a region, then all closed-path integrals are zero, which is a condition (Section 15.3) for a conservative field.

15.5 Divergence and Curl

Green's Theorem sets the stage for the final act in our exploration of calculus. The last four sections of the book have the following goal: to lift both forms of Green's Theorem out of the plane ($\mathbf{R}^2$) and into space ($\mathbf{R}^3$). It is done as follows.

- The circulation form of Green's Theorem relates a line integral over a simple closed oriented curve in the plane to a double integral over the enclosed region. In an analogous manner, we will see that *Stokes' Theorem* (Section 15.7) relates a line integral over a simple closed oriented curve in $\mathbf{R}^3$ to a double integral over a surface bounded by that curve.
- The flux form of Green's Theorem relates a line integral over a simple closed oriented curve in the plane to a double integral over the enclosed region. Similarly, the *Divergence Theorem* (Section 15.8) relates an integral over a closed oriented surface in $\mathbf{R}^3$ to a triple integral over the region enclosed by that surface.

In order to make these extensions, we need a few more tools.

- The two-dimensional divergence and two-dimensional curl must be extended to three dimensions (this section).
- The idea of a *surface integral* must be introduced (Section 15.6).

The Divergence

➤ Review: The flux form of Green's Theorem implies that if the two-dimensional divergence of a vector field is zero throughout a simply connected plane region, the outward flux across the boundary of the region is zero. If the divergence is nonzero, Green's Theorem gives the outward flux across the boundary. The divergence measures the expansion or contraction of the field at each point.

Recall that in two dimensions the divergence of the vector field $\mathbf{F} = \langle f, g \rangle$ is $\dfrac{\partial f}{\partial x} + \dfrac{\partial g}{\partial y}$. The extension to three dimensions is straightforward. If $\mathbf{F} = \langle f, g, h \rangle$ is a differentiable vector field defined on a region of $\mathbf{R}^3$, the divergence is $\dfrac{\partial f}{\partial x} + \dfrac{\partial g}{\partial y} + \dfrac{\partial h}{\partial z}$. The interpretation of the three-dimensional divergence is much the same as it is in two dimensions. It measures the expansion or contraction of the vector field at each point. If the divergence is zero at all points of a region, the vector field is **source-free** on that region.

Recall the *del operator* ∇ that was introduced in Section 13.6 to define the gradient:

$$\nabla = \mathbf{i}\frac{\partial}{\partial x} + \mathbf{j}\frac{\partial}{\partial y} + \mathbf{k}\frac{\partial}{\partial z} = \left\langle \frac{\partial}{\partial x}, \frac{\partial}{\partial y}, \frac{\partial}{\partial z} \right\rangle$$

This object is not really a vector; it is an operation that is applied to a function or a vector field. Applying it directly to a scalar function f results in the gradient of f:

$$\nabla f = \frac{\partial f}{\partial x}\mathbf{i} + \frac{\partial f}{\partial y}\mathbf{j} + \frac{\partial f}{\partial z}\mathbf{k} = \langle f_x, f_y, f_z \rangle$$

➤ In evaluating $\nabla \cdot \mathbf{F}$ as a dot product, each component of ∇ is applied to the corresponding component of $\mathbf{F}$, producing $f_x + g_y + h_z$.

However, if we form the *dot product* of ∇ and a vector field $\mathbf{F} = \langle f, g, h \rangle$, the result is

$$\nabla \cdot \mathbf{F} = \left\langle \frac{\partial}{\partial x}, \frac{\partial}{\partial y}, \frac{\partial}{\partial z} \right\rangle \cdot \langle f, g, h \rangle = \frac{\partial f}{\partial x} + \frac{\partial g}{\partial y} + \frac{\partial h}{\partial z},$$

which is the divergence of $\mathbf{F}$, also denoted div $\mathbf{F}$. Like all dot products, the divergence is a scalar; in this case, it is a scalar-valued function.

DEFINITION Divergence of a Vector Field

The **divergence** of a vector field $\mathbf{F} = \langle f, g, h \rangle$ that is differentiable on a region of $\mathbf{R}^3$ is

$$\text{div}\,\mathbf{F} = \nabla \cdot \mathbf{F} = \frac{\partial f}{\partial x} + \frac{\partial g}{\partial y} + \frac{\partial h}{\partial z}.$$

If $\nabla \cdot \mathbf{F} = 0$, the vector field is **source-free**.

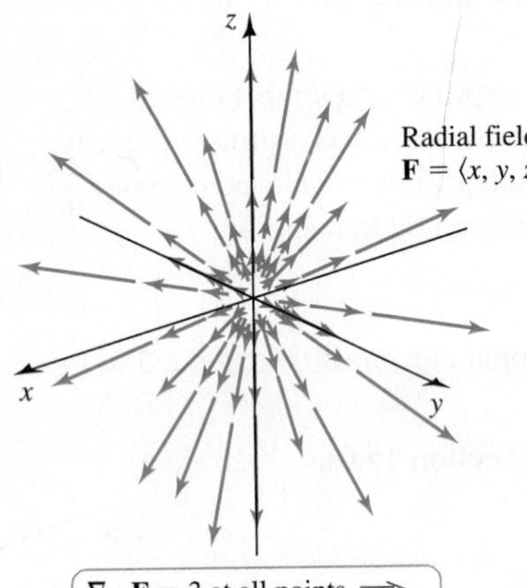

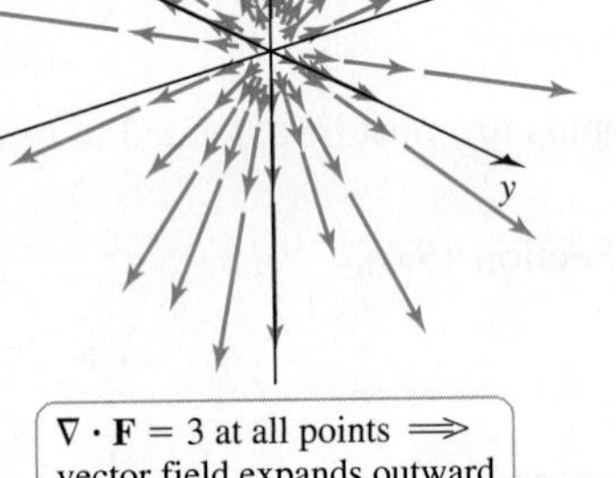

(a)

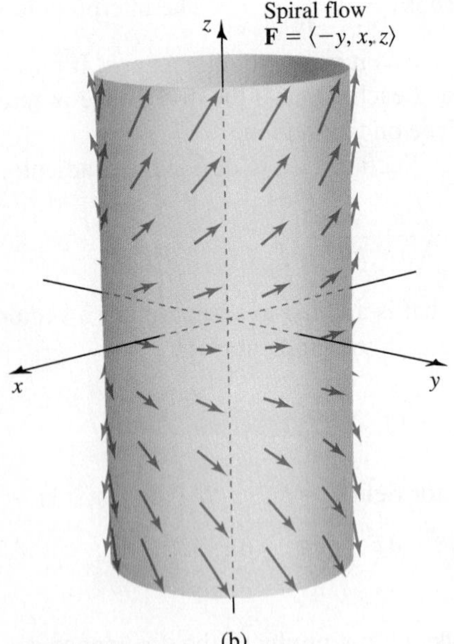

(b)

FIGURE 15.37

EXAMPLE 1 Computing the divergence Compute the divergence of the following vector fields.

a. $\mathbf{F} = \langle x, y, z \rangle$ (a radial field)

b. $\mathbf{F} = \langle -y, z, x \rangle$ (a rotation field)

c. $\mathbf{F} = \langle -y, x, z \rangle$ (a spiral flow)

SOLUTION

a. The divergence is $\nabla \cdot \mathbf{F} = \nabla \cdot \langle x, y, z \rangle = \dfrac{\partial x}{\partial x} + \dfrac{\partial y}{\partial y} + \dfrac{\partial z}{\partial z} = 1 + 1 + 1 = 3.$

Because the divergence is positive, the flow expands outward at all points (Figure 15.37a).

b. The divergence is

$$\nabla \cdot \mathbf{F} = \nabla \cdot \langle -y, z, x \rangle = \frac{\partial(-y)}{\partial x} + \frac{\partial z}{\partial y} + \frac{\partial x}{\partial z} = 0 + 0 + 0 = 0,$$

so the field is source-free.

c. This field is a combination of the two-dimensional rotation field $\mathbf{F} = \langle -y, x \rangle$ and a vertical flow in the z-direction; the net effect is a field that spirals upward for $z > 0$ and spirals downward for $z < 0$. The divergence is

$$\nabla \cdot \mathbf{F} = \nabla \cdot \langle -y, x, z \rangle = \frac{\partial(-y)}{\partial x} + \frac{\partial x}{\partial y} + \frac{\partial z}{\partial z} = 0 + 0 + 1 = 1.$$

The rotational part of the field in x and y does not contribute to the divergence. However, the z-component of the field produces a nonzero divergence (Figure 15.37b).

Related Exercises 9–16 ◀

Divergence of a Radial Vector Field The vector field considered in Example 1a is just one of many radial fields that have important applications (for example, the inverse square laws of gravitation and electrostatics). The following example leads to a general result for the divergence of radial vector fields.

QUICK CHECK 1 Show that if a vector field has the form $\mathbf{F} = \langle f(y, z), g(x, z), h(x, y) \rangle$, then $\text{div}\,\mathbf{F} = 0$. ◀

EXAMPLE 2 Divergence of a radial field Compute the divergence of the radial vector field

$$\mathbf{F} = \frac{\mathbf{r}}{|\mathbf{r}|} = \frac{\langle x, y, z \rangle}{\sqrt{x^2 + y^2 + z^2}}.$$

SOLUTION This radial field has the property that is it directed outward from the origin and all vectors have unit length ($|\mathbf{F}| = 1$). Let's compute one piece of the divergence;

the others follow the same pattern. Using the Quotient Rule, the derivative with respect to x of the first component of $\mathbf{F}$ is

$$\frac{\partial}{\partial x}\left(\frac{x}{(x^2+y^2+z^2)^{1/2}}\right) = \frac{\sqrt{x^2+y^2+z^2} - x^2(x^2+y^2+z^2)^{-1/2}}{x^2+y^2+z^2} \quad \text{Quotient Rule}$$

$$= \frac{|\mathbf{r}| - x^2|\mathbf{r}|^{-1}}{|\mathbf{r}|^2} \quad \sqrt{x^2+y^2+z^2} = |\mathbf{r}|$$

$$= \frac{|\mathbf{r}|^2 - x^2}{|\mathbf{r}|^3}. \quad \text{Simplify.}$$

A similar calculation of the y- and z-derivatives yields $\dfrac{|\mathbf{r}|^2 - y^2}{|\mathbf{r}|^3}$ and $\dfrac{|\mathbf{r}|^2 - z^2}{|\mathbf{r}|^3}$, respectively. Adding the three terms, we find that

$$\nabla \cdot \mathbf{F} = \frac{|\mathbf{r}|^2 - x^2}{|\mathbf{r}|^3} + \frac{|\mathbf{r}|^2 - y^2}{|\mathbf{r}|^3} + \frac{|\mathbf{r}|^2 - z^2}{|\mathbf{r}|^3}$$

$$= 3\frac{|\mathbf{r}|^2}{|\mathbf{r}|^3} - \frac{x^2+y^2+z^2}{|\mathbf{r}|^3} \quad \text{Collect terms.}$$

$$= \frac{2}{|\mathbf{r}|}. \quad x^2+y^2+z^2 = |\mathbf{r}|^2$$

Related Exercises 17–20 ◀

Examples 1a and 2 give two special cases of the following theorem about the divergence of radial vector fields (Exercise 71).

> **THEOREM 15.8 Divergence of Radial Vector Fields**
> For a real number p, the divergence of the radial vector field
>
> $$\mathbf{F} = \frac{\mathbf{r}}{|\mathbf{r}|^p} = \frac{\langle x, y, z\rangle}{(x^2+y^2+z^2)^{p/2}} \quad \text{is} \quad \nabla \cdot \mathbf{F} = \frac{3-p}{|\mathbf{r}|^p}.$$

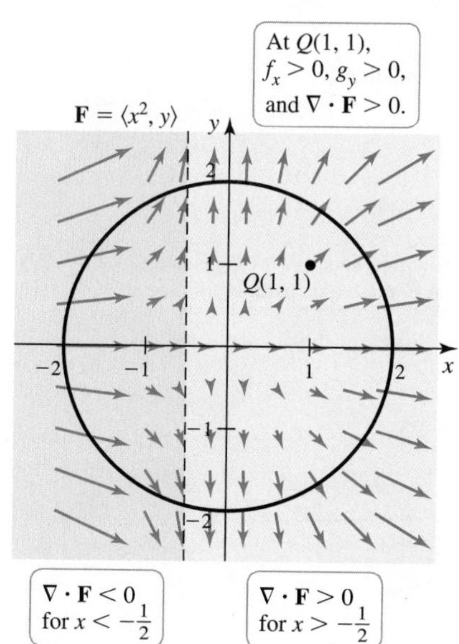

FIGURE 15.38

EXAMPLE 3 Divergence from a graph To gain some intuition about the divergence, consider the two-dimensional vector field $\mathbf{F} = \langle f, g\rangle = \langle x^2, y\rangle$ and a circle C of radius 2 centered at the origin (Figure 15.38).

a. Without computing it, determine whether the two-dimensional divergence is positive or negative at the point $Q(1, 1)$. Why?

b. Confirm your conjecture in part (a) by computing the two-dimensional divergence at Q.

c. Based on part (b), over what regions within the circle is the divergence positive and over what regions within the circle is the divergence negative?

d. By inspection of the figure, on what part of the circle is the flux across the boundary outward? Is the net flux out of the circle positive or negative?

SOLUTION

a. At $Q(1, 1)$ the x-component and the y-component of the field are increasing ($f_x > 0$ and $g_y > 0$), so the field is expanding at that point and the two-dimensional divergence is positive.

➤ To be more specific, as you move through the point Q from left to right, the horizontal components of the vectors increase in length ($f_x > 0$). As you move through the point Q in the upward direction, the vertical components of the vectors also increase in length ($g_y > 0$).

b. Calculating the two-dimensional divergence, we find that

$$\nabla \cdot \mathbf{F} = \frac{\partial}{\partial x}(x^2) + \frac{\partial}{\partial y}(y) = 2x + 1.$$

At $Q(1, 1)$ the divergence is 3, confirming part (a).

c. From part (b) we see that $\nabla \cdot \mathbf{F} = 2x + 1 > 0$ for $x > -\frac{1}{2}$ and $\nabla \cdot \mathbf{F} < 0$ for $x < -\frac{1}{2}$. To the left of the line $x = -\frac{1}{2}$ the field is contracting and to the right of the line the field is expanding.

QUICK CHECK 2 Verify the claim made in part (d) of Example 3 by showing the outward flux of **F** across *C* is positive. (*Hint:* If you use Green's Theorem to evaluate the integral $\int_C f\,dy - g\,dx$, convert to polar coordinates.) ◀

d. Using Figure 15.38, it appears that the field is tangent to the circle at two points with $x \approx -1$. For points on the circle with $x < -1$, the flow is into the circle; for points on the circle with $x > -1$, the flow is out of the circle. It appears that the net outward flux across *C* is positive. The points where the field changes from inward to outward may be determined exactly (Exercise 44). *Related Exercises 21–22* ◀

The Curl

➤ Review: The *two-dimensional curl* $g_x - f_y$ measures the rotation of a vector field at a point. In two dimensions, if the curl of a field is zero throughout a simply connected region, then the circulation on the boundary of the region is also zero. If the curl is nonzero, Green's Theorem gives the circulation along the curve.

Just as the divergence $\nabla \cdot \mathbf{F}$ is the dot product of the *del operator* and **F**, the three-dimensional curl is the cross product $\nabla \times \mathbf{F}$. If we formally use the notation for the cross product in terms of a 3×3 determinant, we obtain the definition of the curl:

$$\nabla \times \mathbf{F} = \begin{vmatrix} \mathbf{i} & \mathbf{j} & \mathbf{k} \\ \dfrac{\partial}{\partial x} & \dfrac{\partial}{\partial y} & \dfrac{\partial}{\partial z} \\ f & g & h \end{vmatrix} \begin{matrix} \leftarrow \text{Unit vectors} \\ \leftarrow \text{Components of } \nabla \\ \leftarrow \text{Components of } \mathbf{F} \end{matrix}$$

$$= \left(\frac{\partial h}{\partial y} - \frac{\partial g}{\partial z}\right)\mathbf{i} + \left(\frac{\partial f}{\partial z} - \frac{\partial h}{\partial x}\right)\mathbf{j} + \left(\frac{\partial g}{\partial x} - \frac{\partial f}{\partial y}\right)\mathbf{k}$$

The curl of a vector field, also denoted curl **F**, is a vector with three components. Notice that the **k**-component of the curl $(g_x - f_y)$ is the two-dimensional curl that gives the rotation in the *xy*-plane at a point. The **i**- and **j**-components of the curl correspond to the rotation of the vector field in planes parallel to the *yz*-plane (orthogonal to **i**) and in planes parallel to the *xz*-plane (orthogonal to **j**) (Figure 15.39).

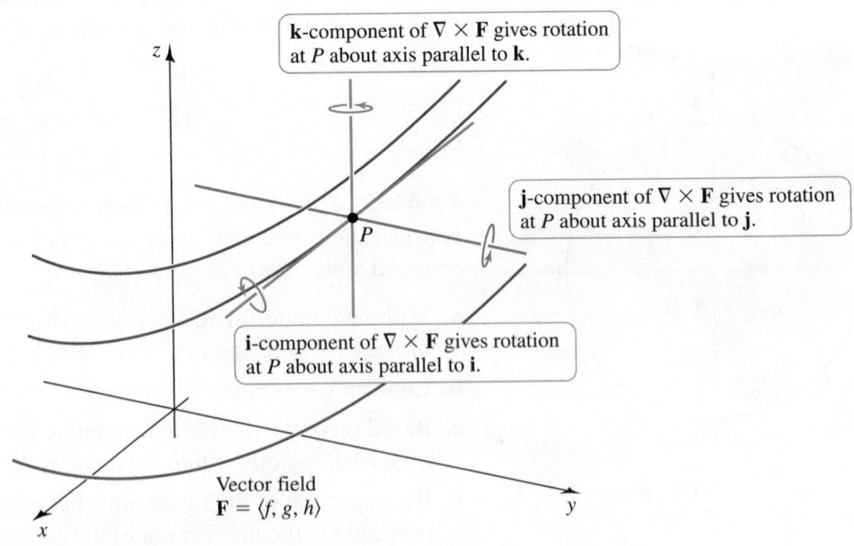
k-component of ∇ × F gives rotation at P about axis parallel to k.
j-component of ∇ × F gives rotation at P about axis parallel to j.
i-component of ∇ × F gives rotation at P about axis parallel to i.
P
z
x
y
Vector field
F = ⟨f, g, h⟩

FIGURE 15.39

DEFINITION Curl of a Vector Field

The curl of a vector field $\mathbf{F} = \langle f, g, h \rangle$ that is differentiable on a region of $\mathbf{R}^3$ is

$$\nabla \times \mathbf{F} = \text{curl } \mathbf{F}$$

$$= \left(\frac{\partial h}{\partial y} - \frac{\partial g}{\partial z}\right)\mathbf{i} + \left(\frac{\partial f}{\partial z} - \frac{\partial h}{\partial x}\right)\mathbf{j} + \left(\frac{\partial g}{\partial x} - \frac{\partial f}{\partial y}\right)\mathbf{k}.$$

If $\nabla \times \mathbf{F} = \mathbf{0}$, the vector field is **irrotational**.

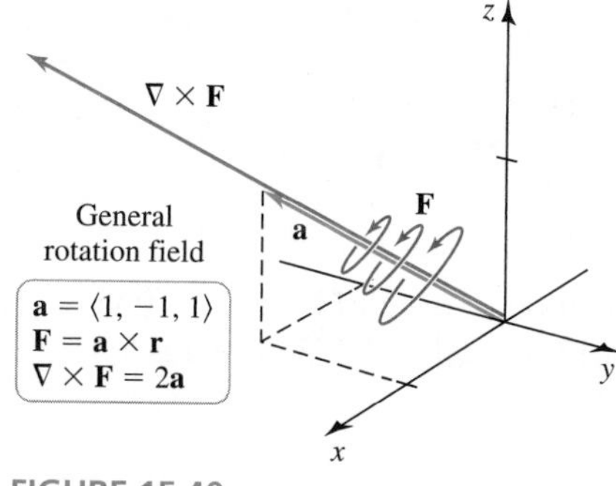

FIGURE 15.40

Curl of a General Rotation Vector Field We can clarify the physical meaning of the curl by considering the vector field $\mathbf{F} = \mathbf{a} \times \mathbf{r}$, where $\mathbf{a} = \langle a_1, a_2, a_3 \rangle$ is a nonzero constant vector and $\mathbf{r} = \langle x, y, z \rangle$. Writing out its components, we see that

$$\mathbf{F} = \mathbf{a} \times \mathbf{r} = \begin{vmatrix} \mathbf{i} & \mathbf{j} & \mathbf{k} \\ a_1 & a_2 & a_3 \\ x & y & z \end{vmatrix} = (a_2 z - a_3 y)\mathbf{i} + (a_3 x - a_1 z)\mathbf{j} + (a_1 y - a_2 x)\mathbf{k}.$$

This vector field is a *general rotation field* in three dimensions. With $a_1 = a_2 = 0$, and $a_3 = 1$, we have the familiar two-dimensional rotation field $\langle -y, x \rangle$ with its axis in the **k**-direction. More generally, **F** is the superposition of three rotation fields with axes in the **i**-, **j**-, and **k**-directions. The result is a single rotation field with an axis in the direction of **a** (Figure 15.40).

Two calculations tell us a lot about the general rotation field. The first calculation confirms that $\nabla \cdot \mathbf{F} = 0$ (Exercise 42). Just as with rotation fields in two dimensions, the divergence of a general rotation field is zero.

The second calculation (Exercise 43) says that $\nabla \times \mathbf{F} = 2\mathbf{a}$. Therefore, the curl of the general rotation field is in the direction of the axis of rotation **a** (Figure 15.40). The magnitude of the curl is $|\nabla \times \mathbf{F}| = 2|\mathbf{a}|$. It can be shown (Exercise 50) that $|\mathbf{a}|$ is the constant angular speed of rotation of the vector field, denoted ω. The angular speed is the rate (radians per unit time) at which a small particle in the vector field rotates about the axis of the field. Therefore, the angular speed is half the magnitude of the curl, or

$$\omega = |\mathbf{a}| = \frac{1}{2}|\nabla \times \mathbf{F}|.$$

The rotation field $\mathbf{F} = \mathbf{a} \times \mathbf{r}$ suggests a related question. Suppose a paddle wheel is placed in the vector field **F** at a point P with the axis of the wheel in the direction of a unit vector **n** (Figure 15.41). How should **n** be chosen so the paddle wheel spins fastest? The scalar component of **curl F** in the direction of **n** is

$$(\nabla \times \mathbf{F}) \cdot \mathbf{n} = |\nabla \times \mathbf{F}| \cos \theta \qquad (|\mathbf{n}| = 1),$$

➤ Just as $\nabla f \cdot \mathbf{n}$ is the directional derivative in the direction **n**, $(\nabla \times \mathbf{F}) \cdot \mathbf{n}$ is the directional spin in the direction **n**.

where θ is the angle between $\nabla \times \mathbf{F}$ and **n**. The scalar component is greatest in magnitude and the paddle wheel spins fastest when $\theta = 0$ or $\theta = \pi$; that is, when **n** and $\nabla \times \mathbf{F}$ are parallel. If the axis of the paddle wheel is orthogonal to $\nabla \times \mathbf{F}$ ($\theta = \pm\pi/2$), the wheel doesn't spin.

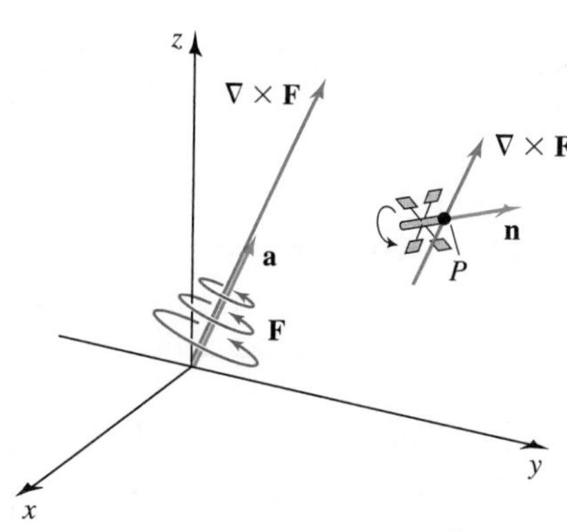

FIGURE 15.41

> **General Rotation Vector Field**
>
> The general rotation vector field is $\mathbf{F} = \mathbf{a} \times \mathbf{r}$, where the nonzero constant vector $\mathbf{a} = \langle a_1, a_2, a_3 \rangle$ is the axis of rotation and $\mathbf{r} = \langle x, y, z \rangle$. For all choices of **a**, $|\nabla \times \mathbf{F}| = 2|\mathbf{a}|$ and $\nabla \cdot \mathbf{F} = 0$. The constant angular speed of the vector field is
>
> $$\omega = |\mathbf{a}| = \frac{1}{2}|\nabla \times \mathbf{F}|.$$

QUICK CHECK 3 Show that if a vector field has the form $\mathbf{F} = \langle f(x), g(y), h(z) \rangle$, then $\nabla \times \mathbf{F} = \mathbf{0}$. ◄

EXAMPLE 4 **Curl of a rotation field** Compute the curl of the rotational field $\mathbf{F} = \mathbf{a} \times \mathbf{r}$, where $\mathbf{a} = \langle 1, -1, 1 \rangle$ and $\mathbf{r} = \langle x, y, z \rangle$. What is the direction and the magnitude of the curl?

SOLUTION A quick calculation shows that

$$\mathbf{F} = \mathbf{a} \times \mathbf{r} = (-y - z)\mathbf{i} + (x - z)\mathbf{j} + (x + y)\mathbf{k}.$$

The curl of the field is

$$\nabla \times \mathbf{F} = \begin{vmatrix} \mathbf{i} & \mathbf{j} & \mathbf{k} \\ \dfrac{\partial}{\partial x} & \dfrac{\partial}{\partial y} & \dfrac{\partial}{\partial z} \\ -y - z & x - z & x + y \end{vmatrix} = 2\mathbf{i} - 2\mathbf{j} + 2\mathbf{k}.$$

We have confirmed that curl $\mathbf{F} = 2\mathbf{a}$ and that the direction of the curl is the direction of $\mathbf{a}$, which is the axis of rotation. The magnitude of curl $\mathbf{F}$ is $|2\mathbf{a}| = 2\sqrt{3}$, which is twice the angular speed of rotation.

Related Exercises 23–34 ◀

Working with Divergence and Curl

The divergence and curl satisfy many of the same properties that ordinary derivatives satisfy. For example, given a real number c and differentiable vector fields $\mathbf{F}$ and $\mathbf{G}$, we have the following properties.

Divergence Properties	**Curl Properties**
$\nabla \cdot (\mathbf{F} + \mathbf{G}) = \nabla \cdot \mathbf{F} + \nabla \cdot \mathbf{G}$	$\nabla \times (\mathbf{F} + \mathbf{G}) = (\nabla \times \mathbf{F}) + (\nabla \times \mathbf{G})$
$\nabla \cdot (c\mathbf{F}) = c(\nabla \cdot \mathbf{F})$	$\nabla \times (c\mathbf{F}) = c(\nabla \times \mathbf{F})$

These and other properties are explored in Exercises 63–70.

Additional properties that have importance in theory and applications are presented in the following theorems and examples.

THEOREM 15.9 Curl of a Conservative Vector Field
Suppose that $\mathbf{F}$ is a conservative vector field on an open region D of $\mathbf{R}^3$. Let $\mathbf{F} = \nabla\varphi$, where φ is a potential function with continuous second partial derivatives on D. Then $\nabla \times \mathbf{F} = \nabla \times \nabla\varphi = \mathbf{0}$; that is, the curl of the gradient is the zero vector and $\mathbf{F}$ is irrotational.

Proof We must calculate $\nabla \times \nabla\varphi$:

$$\nabla \times \nabla\varphi = \begin{vmatrix} \mathbf{i} & \mathbf{j} & \mathbf{k} \\ \dfrac{\partial}{\partial x} & \dfrac{\partial}{\partial y} & \dfrac{\partial}{\partial z} \\ \varphi_x & \varphi_y & \varphi_z \end{vmatrix} = \underbrace{(\varphi_{zy} - \varphi_{yz})}_{0}\mathbf{i} + \underbrace{(\varphi_{xz} - \varphi_{zx})}_{0}\mathbf{j} + \underbrace{(\varphi_{yx} - \varphi_{xy})}_{0}\mathbf{k} = \mathbf{0}.$$

The mixed partial derivatives are equal by Clairaut's Theorem (Theorem 13.4).

The converse of this theorem (if $\nabla \times \mathbf{F} = \mathbf{0}$, then $\mathbf{F}$ is a conservative field) is handled in Section 15.7 by means of Stokes' Theorem. ◀

➤ First note that $\nabla \times \mathbf{F}$ is a vector, so it makes sense to take the divergence of the curl.

THEOREM 15.10 Divergence of the Curl
Suppose that $\mathbf{F} = \langle f, g, h \rangle$, where f, g, and h have continuous second partial derivatives. Then $\nabla \cdot (\nabla \times \mathbf{F}) = 0$: The divergence of the curl is zero.

Proof Again, a calculation is needed:

$$\begin{aligned} &\nabla \cdot (\nabla \times \mathbf{F}) \\ &\quad = \frac{\partial}{\partial x}\left(\frac{\partial h}{\partial y} - \frac{\partial g}{\partial z}\right) + \frac{\partial}{\partial y}\left(\frac{\partial f}{\partial z} - \frac{\partial h}{\partial x}\right) + \frac{\partial}{\partial z}\left(\frac{\partial g}{\partial x} - \frac{\partial f}{\partial y}\right) \\ &\quad = \underbrace{(h_{yx} - h_{xy})}_{0} + \underbrace{(g_{xz} - g_{zx})}_{0} + \underbrace{(f_{zy} - f_{yz})}_{0} = 0 \end{aligned}$$

Clairaut's Theorem assures that the mixed partial derivatives are equal. ◀

The gradient, the divergence, and the curl may be combined in many ways—some of which are undefined. For example, the gradient of the curl $(\nabla(\nabla \times \mathbf{F}))$ and the curl of the divergence $(\nabla \times (\nabla \cdot \mathbf{F}))$ are undefined. However, a combination that *is* defined and is important is the divergence of the gradient $\nabla \cdot \nabla u$, where u is a scalar-valued function. This combination is denoted $\nabla^2 u$ and is called the **Laplacian** of u; it arises in many physical situations (Exercises 54–56, 60). Carrying out the calculation, we find that

$$\nabla \cdot \nabla u = \frac{\partial}{\partial x}\frac{\partial u}{\partial x} + \frac{\partial}{\partial y}\frac{\partial u}{\partial y} + \frac{\partial}{\partial z}\frac{\partial u}{\partial z} = \frac{\partial^2 u}{\partial x^2} + \frac{\partial^2 u}{\partial y^2} + \frac{\partial^2 u}{\partial z^2}.$$

We close with a result that is useful in its own right but also intriguing because it parallels the Product Rule from single-variable calculus.

THEOREM 15.11 Product Rule for the Divergence
Let u be a scalar-valued function that is differentiable on a region D and let $\mathbf{F}$ be a vector field that is differentiable on D. Then

$$\nabla \cdot (u\mathbf{F}) = \nabla u \cdot \mathbf{F} + u(\nabla \cdot \mathbf{F}).$$

The rule says that the "derivative" of the product is the "derivative" of the first function multiplied by the second function plus the first function multiplied by the "derivative" of the second function. However, in each instance "derivative" must be interpreted correctly for the operations to make sense. The proof of the theorem requires a direct calculation (Exercise 65). Other similar vector calculus identities are presented in Exercises 66–70.

QUICK CHECK 4 Is $\nabla \cdot (u\mathbf{F})$ a vector function or a scalar function?

EXAMPLE 5 More properties of radial fields Let $\mathbf{r} = \langle x, y, z \rangle$ and let $\varphi = \dfrac{1}{|\mathbf{r}|} = (x^2 + y^2 + z^2)^{-1/2}$ be a potential function.

a. Find the associated gradient field $\mathbf{F} = \nabla\left(\dfrac{1}{|\mathbf{r}|}\right)$.

b. Compute $\nabla \cdot \mathbf{F}$.

SOLUTION

a. The gradient has three components. Computing the first component reveals a pattern:

$$\frac{\partial \varphi}{\partial x} = \frac{\partial}{\partial x}(x^2 + y^2 + z^2)^{-1/2} = -\frac{1}{2}(x^2 + y^2 + z^2)^{-3/2}\, 2x = -\frac{x}{|\mathbf{r}|^3}.$$

Making a similar calculation for the y- and z-derivatives, the gradient is

$$\mathbf{F} = \nabla\left(\frac{1}{|\mathbf{r}|}\right) = -\frac{\langle x, y, z \rangle}{|\mathbf{r}|^3} = -\frac{\mathbf{r}}{|\mathbf{r}|^3}.$$

This result reveals that $\mathbf{F}$ is an inverse square vector field (for example, a gravitational or electric field), and its potential function is $\varphi = \dfrac{1}{|\mathbf{r}|}$.

b. The divergence $\nabla \cdot \mathbf{F} = \nabla \cdot \left(-\dfrac{\mathbf{r}}{|\mathbf{r}|^3}\right)$ involves a product of the vector function $\mathbf{r} = \langle x, y, z \rangle$ and the scalar function $|\mathbf{r}|^{-3}$. Applying Theorem 15.11, we find that

$$\nabla \cdot \mathbf{F} = \nabla \cdot \left(-\frac{\mathbf{r}}{|\mathbf{r}|^3}\right) = -\nabla \cdot \mathbf{r}\frac{1}{|\mathbf{r}|^3} - \mathbf{r} \cdot \nabla\frac{1}{|\mathbf{r}|^3}.$$

A calculation similar to part (a) shows that $\nabla \frac{1}{|\mathbf{r}|^3} = \frac{-3\mathbf{r}}{|\mathbf{r}|^5}$ (Exercise 35). Therefore,

$$\nabla \cdot \mathbf{F} = \nabla \cdot \left(-\frac{\mathbf{r}}{|\mathbf{r}|^3}\right) = -\underbrace{\nabla \cdot \mathbf{r}}_{3} \frac{1}{|\mathbf{r}|^3} - \mathbf{r} \cdot \underbrace{\nabla \frac{1}{|\mathbf{r}|^3}}_{-3\mathbf{r}/|\mathbf{r}|^5}$$

$$= -\frac{3}{|\mathbf{r}|^3} - \mathbf{r} \cdot \frac{-3\mathbf{r}}{|\mathbf{r}|^5} \quad \text{Substitute for } \nabla \frac{1}{|\mathbf{r}|^3}.$$

$$= -\frac{3}{|\mathbf{r}|^3} + \frac{3|\mathbf{r}|^2}{|\mathbf{r}|^5} \quad \mathbf{r} \cdot \mathbf{r} = |\mathbf{r}|^2$$

$$= 0.$$

The result is consistent with Theorem 15.8 (with $p = 3$): The divergence of an inverse square vector field in $\mathbf{R}^3$ is zero. It does not happen for any other radial fields of this form.

Related Exercises 35–38 ◀

Summary of Properties of Conservative Vector Fields

We can now extend the list of equivalent properties of conservative vector fields $\mathbf{F}$ defined on an open connected region. Theorem 15.9 is added to the list given at the end of Section 15.3.

Properties of a Conservative Vector Field

Let $\mathbf{F}$ be a conservative vector field whose components have continuous second partial derivatives on an open connected region D in $\mathbf{R}^3$. Then $\mathbf{F}$ has the following equivalent properties.

1. There exists a potential function φ such that $\mathbf{F} = \nabla\varphi$ (definition).
2. $\int_C \mathbf{F} \cdot d\mathbf{r} = \varphi(B) - \varphi(A)$ for all points A and B in D and all smooth oriented curves C from A to B.
3. $\oint_C \mathbf{F} \cdot d\mathbf{r} = 0$ on all simple smooth closed oriented curves C in D.
4. $\nabla \times \mathbf{F} = \mathbf{0}$ at all points of D.

SECTION 15.5 EXERCISES

Review Questions

1. Explain how to compute the divergence of the vector field $\mathbf{F} = \langle f, g, h \rangle$.
2. Interpret the divergence of a vector field.
3. What does it mean if the divergence of a vector field is zero throughout a region?
4. Explain how to compute the curl of the vector field $\mathbf{F} = \langle f, g, h \rangle$.
5. Interpret the curl of a general rotation vector field.
6. What does it mean if the curl of a vector field is zero throughout a region?
7. What is the value of $\nabla \cdot (\nabla \times \mathbf{F})$?
8. What is the value of $\nabla \times \nabla u$?

Basic Skills

9–16. Divergence of vector fields *Find the divergence of the following vector fields.*

9. $\mathbf{F} = \langle 2x, 4y, -3z \rangle$
10. $\mathbf{F} = \langle -2y, 3x, z \rangle$
11. $\mathbf{F} = \langle 12x, -6y, -6z \rangle$
12. $\mathbf{F} = \langle x^2yz, -xy^2z, -xyz^2 \rangle$
13. $\mathbf{F} = \langle x^2 - y^2, y^2 - z^2, z^2 - x^2 \rangle$
14. $\mathbf{F} = \langle e^{-x+y}, e^{-y+z}, e^{-z+x} \rangle$
15. $\mathbf{F} = \frac{\langle x, y, z \rangle}{1 + x^2 + y^2}$
16. $\mathbf{F} = \langle yz \sin x, xz \cos y, xy \cos z \rangle$

17–20. Divergence of radial fields *Calculate the divergence of the following radial fields. Express the result in terms of the position vector* $\mathbf{r}$ *and its length* $|\mathbf{r}|$. *Check for agreement with Theorem 15.8.*

17. $\mathbf{F} = \dfrac{\langle x, y, z\rangle}{x^2 + y^2 + z^2} = \dfrac{\mathbf{r}}{|\mathbf{r}|^2}$

18. $\mathbf{F} = \dfrac{\langle x, y, z\rangle}{(x^2 + y^2 + z^2)^{3/2}} = \dfrac{\mathbf{r}}{|\mathbf{r}|^3}$

19. $\mathbf{F} = \dfrac{\langle x, y, z\rangle}{(x^2 + y^2 + z^2)^2} = \dfrac{\mathbf{r}}{|\mathbf{r}|^4}$

20. $\mathbf{F} = \langle x, y, z\rangle(x^2 + y^2 + z^2) = \mathbf{r}|\mathbf{r}|^2$

21–22. Divergence and flux from graphs *Consider the following vector fields, the circle C, and two points P and Q.*

a. *Without computing the divergence, does the graph suggest that the divergence is positive or negative at P and Q? Justify your answer.*

b. *Compute the divergence and confirm your conjecture in part (a).*

c. *On what part of C is the flux outward? Inward?*

d. *Is the net outward flux across C positive or negative?*

21. $\mathbf{F} = \langle x, x + y\rangle$

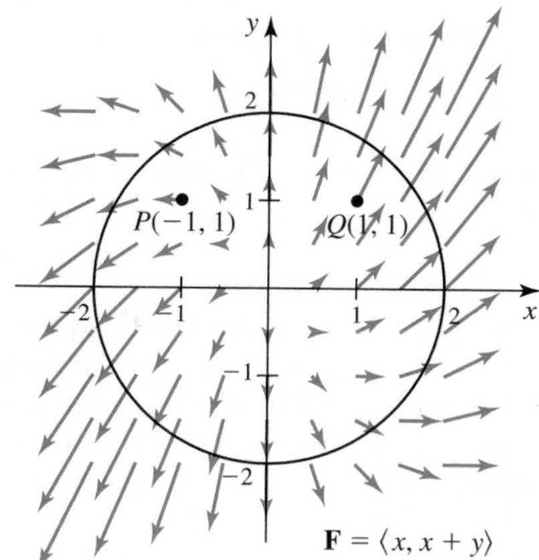

22. $\mathbf{F} = \langle x, y^2\rangle$

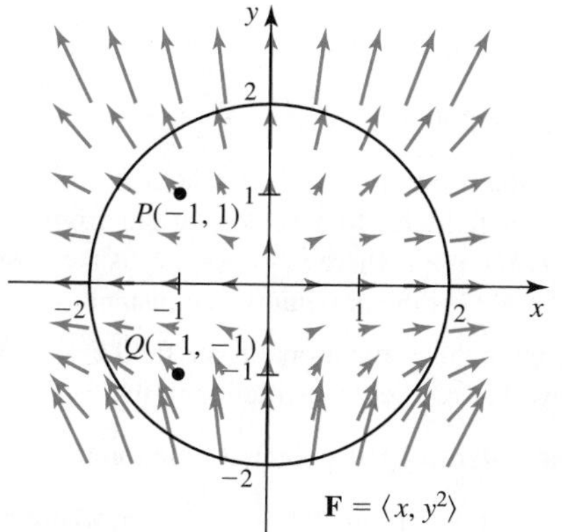

23–26. Curl of a rotational field *Consider the following vector fields, where* $\mathbf{r} = \langle x, y, z\rangle$.

a. *Compute the curl of the field and verify that it has the same direction as the axis of rotation.*

b. *Compute the magnitude of the curl of the field.*

23. $\mathbf{F} = \langle 1, 0, 0\rangle \times \mathbf{r}$

24. $\mathbf{F} = \langle 1, -1, 0\rangle \times \mathbf{r}$

25. $\mathbf{F} = \langle 1, -1, 1\rangle \times \mathbf{r}$

26. $\mathbf{F} = \langle 1, -2, -3\rangle \times \mathbf{r}$

27–34. Curl of a vector field *Compute the curl of the following vector fields.*

27. $\mathbf{F} = \langle x^2 - y^2, xy, z\rangle$

28. $\mathbf{F} = \langle 0, z^2 - y^2, -yz\rangle$

29. $\mathbf{F} = \langle x^2 - z^2, 1, 2xz\rangle$

30. $\mathbf{F} = \mathbf{r} = \langle x, y, z\rangle$

31. $\mathbf{F} = \dfrac{\langle x, y, z\rangle}{(x^2 + y^2 + z^2)^{3/2}} = \dfrac{\mathbf{r}}{|\mathbf{r}|^3}$

32. $\mathbf{F} = \dfrac{\langle x, y, z\rangle}{(x^2 + y^2 + z^2)^{1/2}} = \dfrac{\mathbf{r}}{|\mathbf{r}|}$

33. $\mathbf{F} = \langle z^2 \sin y, xz^2 \cos y, 2xz \sin y\rangle$

34. $\mathbf{F} = \langle 3xz^3 e^{y^2}, 2xz^3 e^{y^2}, 3xz^2 e^{y^2}\rangle$

35–38. Derivative rules *Prove the following identities. Use Theorem 15.11 (Product Rule) whenever possible.*

35. $\nabla\left(\dfrac{1}{|\mathbf{r}|^3}\right) = \dfrac{-3\mathbf{r}}{|\mathbf{r}|^5}$ (used in Example 5)

36. $\nabla\left(\dfrac{1}{|\mathbf{r}|^2}\right) = \dfrac{-2\mathbf{r}}{|\mathbf{r}|^4}$

37. $\nabla \cdot \nabla\left(\dfrac{1}{|\mathbf{r}|^2}\right) = \dfrac{2}{|\mathbf{r}|^4}$ (use Exercise 36)

38. $\nabla(\ln |\mathbf{r}|) = \dfrac{\mathbf{r}}{|\mathbf{r}|^2}$

Further Explorations

39. **Explain why or why not** Determine whether the following statements are true and give an explanation or counterexample.

a. For a function f of a single variable, if $f'(x) = 0$ for all x in the domain, then f is a constant function. If $\nabla \cdot \mathbf{F} = 0$ for all points in the domain, then $\mathbf{F}$ is constant.

b. If $\nabla \times \mathbf{F} = \mathbf{0}$, then $\mathbf{F}$ is constant.

c. A vector field consisting of parallel vectors has zero curl.

d. A vector field consisting of parallel vectors has zero divergence.

e. curl $\mathbf{F}$ is orthogonal to $\mathbf{F}$.

40. **Another derivative combination** Let $\mathbf{F} = \langle f, g, h\rangle$ and let u be a differentiable scalar-valued function.

a. Take the dot product of $\mathbf{F}$ and the del operator; then apply the result to u to show that

$$(\mathbf{F} \cdot \nabla)\, u = \left(f\frac{\partial}{\partial x} + g\frac{\partial}{\partial y} + h\frac{\partial}{\partial z}\right)u = f\frac{\partial u}{\partial x} + g\frac{\partial u}{\partial y} + h\frac{\partial u}{\partial z}$$

b. Evaluate $(\mathbf{F} \cdot \nabla)(xy^2z^3)$ at $(1, 1, 1)$, where $\mathbf{F} = \langle 1, 1, 1\rangle$.

41. Does it make sense? Are the following expressions defined? If so, state whether the result is a scalar or a vector. Assume **F** is a sufficiently differentiable vector field and φ is a sufficiently differentiable scalar-valued function.

a. $\nabla \cdot \varphi$ **b.** $\nabla \mathbf{F}$ **c.** $\nabla \cdot \nabla \varphi$
d. $\nabla(\nabla \cdot \varphi)$ **e.** $\nabla(\nabla \times \varphi)$ **f.** $\nabla \cdot (\nabla \cdot \mathbf{F})$
g. $\nabla \times \nabla \varphi$ **h.** $\nabla \times (\nabla \cdot \mathbf{F})$ **i.** $\nabla \times (\nabla \times \mathbf{F})$

42. Zero divergence of the rotation field Show that the general rotation field $\mathbf{F} = \mathbf{a} \times \mathbf{r}$, where **a** is a nonzero constant vector and $\mathbf{r} = \langle x, y, z \rangle$, has zero divergence.

43. Curl of the rotation field For the general rotation field $\mathbf{F} = \mathbf{a} \times \mathbf{r}$, where **a** is a nonzero constant vector and $\mathbf{r} = \langle x, y, z \rangle$, show that curl $\mathbf{F} = 2\mathbf{a}$.

44. Inward to outward Find the exact points on the circle $x^2 + y^2 = 4$ at which the field $\mathbf{F} = \langle f, g \rangle = \langle x^2, y \rangle$ switches from pointing inward to outward on the circle, or vice versa.

45. Maximum divergence Within the cube $\{(x, y, z): |x| \le 1, |y| \le 1, |z| \le 1\}$, where does div **F** have the greatest magnitude when $\mathbf{F} = \langle x^2 - z^2, xy^2z, 2xz \rangle$?

46. Maximum curl Let $\mathbf{F} = \langle z, 0, -y \rangle$.

a. What is the component of curl **F** in the direction $\mathbf{n} = \langle 1, 0, 0 \rangle$?
b. What is the component of curl **F** in the direction $\mathbf{n} = \langle 1, -1, 1 \rangle$?
c. In what direction **n** is (curl **F**) $\cdot$ **n** a maximum?

47. Zero component of the curl For what vectors **n** is (curl **F**) $\cdot$ **n** = 0 when $\mathbf{F} = \langle y, -2z, -x \rangle$?

48–49. Find a vector field *Find a vector field* **F** *with the given curl. In each case, is the vector field you found unique?*

48. curl $\mathbf{F} = \langle 0, 1, 0 \rangle$.　**49.** curl $\mathbf{F} = \langle 0, z, -y \rangle$

50. Curl and angular speed Consider the rotational velocity field $\mathbf{v} = \mathbf{a} \times \mathbf{r}$, where **a** is a nonzero constant vector and $\mathbf{r} = \langle x, y, z \rangle$. Use the fact that an object moving in a circular path of radius R with speed $|\mathbf{v}|$ has an angular speed of $\omega = |\mathbf{v}|/R$.

a. Sketch a position vector **a**, which is the axis of rotation for the vector field, and a position vector **r** of a point P in $\mathbf{R}^3$. Let θ be the angle between the two vectors. Show that the perpendicular distance from P to the axis of rotation is $R = |\mathbf{r}| \sin \theta$.
b. Show that the speed of a particle in the velocity field is $|\mathbf{a} \times \mathbf{r}|$ and that the angular speed of the object is $|\mathbf{a}|$.
c. Conclude that $\omega = \frac{1}{2}|\nabla \times \mathbf{v}|$.

51. Paddle wheel in a vector field Let $\mathbf{F} = \langle z, 0, 0 \rangle$ and let **n** be a unit vector aligned with the axis of a paddle wheel located on the x-axis (see figure).

a. If the paddle wheel is oriented with $\mathbf{n} = \langle 1, 0, 0 \rangle$, in what direction (if any) does the wheel spin?
b. If the paddle wheel is oriented with $\mathbf{n} = \langle 0, 1, 0 \rangle$, in what direction (if any) does the wheel spin?
c. If the paddle wheel is oriented with $\mathbf{n} = \langle 0, 0, 1 \rangle$, in what direction (if any) does the wheel spin?

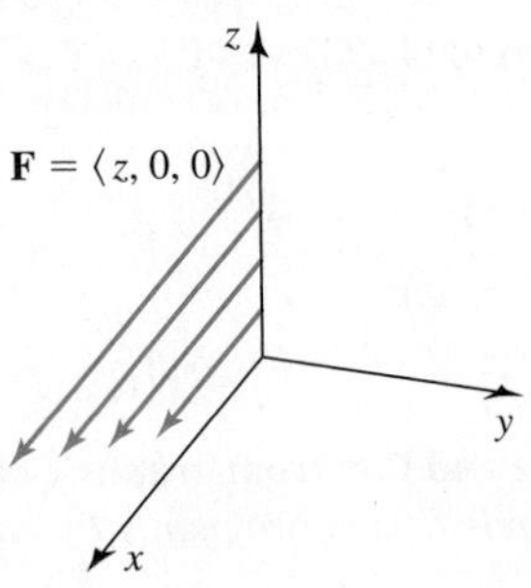

52. Angular speed Consider the rotational velocity field $\mathbf{v} = \langle -2y, 2z, 0 \rangle$.

a. If a paddle wheel is placed in the xy-plane with its axis normal to this plane, what is its angular speed?
b. If a paddle wheel is placed in the xz-plane with its axis normal to this plane, what is its angular speed?
c. If a paddle wheel is placed in the yz-plane with its axis normal to this plane, what is its angular speed?

53. Angular speed Consider the rotational velocity field $\mathbf{v} = \langle 0, 10z, -10y \rangle$. If a paddle wheel is placed in the plane $x + y + z = 1$ with its axis normal to this plane, how fast does the paddle wheel spin (revolutions per unit time)?

Applications

54–56. Heat flux *Suppose a solid object in* $\mathbf{R}^3$ *has a temperature distribution given by* $T(x, y, z)$. *The heat flow vector field in the object is* $\mathbf{F} = -k\nabla T$, *where the conductivity* $k > 0$ *is a property of the material. Note that the heat flow vector points in the direction opposite to that of the gradient, which is the direction of greatest temperature* decrease. *The divergence of the heat flow vector is* $\nabla \cdot \mathbf{F} = -k\nabla \cdot \nabla T = -k\nabla^2 T$ *(the Laplacian of* T*). Compute the heat flow vector field and its divergence for the following temperature distributions.*

54. $T(x, y, z) = 100e^{-\sqrt{x^2+y^2+z^2}}$

55. $T(x, y, z) = 100e^{-x^2+y^2+z^2}$

56. $T(x, y, z) = 100(1 + \sqrt{x^2 + y^2 + z^2})$

57. Gravitational potential The potential function for the gravitational force field due to a mass M at the origin acting on a mass m is $\varphi = GMm/|\mathbf{r}|$, where $\mathbf{r} = \langle x, y, z \rangle$ is the position vector of the mass m and G is the gravitational constant.

a. Compute the gravitational force field $\mathbf{F} = -\nabla\varphi$.
b. Show that the field is irrotational; that is $\nabla \times \mathbf{F} = \mathbf{0}$.

58. Electric potential The potential function for the force field due to a charge q at the origin is $\varphi = \dfrac{1}{4\pi\varepsilon_0} \dfrac{q}{|\mathbf{r}|}$, where $\mathbf{r} = \langle x, y, z \rangle$ is the position vector of a point in the field and ε_0 is the permittivity of free space.

a. Compute the force field $\mathbf{F} = -\nabla\varphi$.
b. Show that the field is irrotational; that is $\nabla \times \mathbf{F} = \mathbf{0}$.

59. Navier-Stokes equation The Navier-Stokes equation is the fundamental equation of fluid dynamics that models the motion of water in everything from bathtubs to oceans. In one of its many forms (incompressible, viscous flow), the equation is

$$\rho\left(\frac{\partial \mathbf{V}}{\partial t} + (\mathbf{V}\cdot\nabla)\mathbf{V}\right) = -\nabla p + \mu(\nabla\cdot\nabla)\mathbf{V}.$$

In this notation $\mathbf{V} = \langle u, v, w\rangle$ is the three-dimensional velocity field, p is the (scalar) pressure, ρ is the constant density of the fluid, and μ is the constant viscosity. Write out the three component equations of this vector equation. (See Exercise 40 for an interpretation of the operations.)

60. Stream function and vorticity The rotation of a three-dimensional velocity field $\mathbf{V} = \langle u, v, w\rangle$ is measured by the **vorticity** $\boldsymbol{\omega} = \nabla\times\mathbf{V}$. If $\boldsymbol{\omega} = \mathbf{0}$ at all points in the domain, the flow is irrotational.

a. Which of the following velocity fields is irrotational: $\mathbf{V} = \langle 2, -3y, 5z\rangle$ or $\mathbf{V} = \langle y, x - z, -y\rangle$?

b. Recall that for a two-dimensional source-free flow $\mathbf{V} = \langle u, v, 0\rangle$, a stream function $\psi(x, y)$ may be defined such that $u = \psi_y$ and $v = -\psi_x$. For such a two-dimensional flow, let $\zeta = \mathbf{k}\cdot\nabla\times\mathbf{V}$ be the $\mathbf{k}$-component of the vorticity. Show that $\nabla^2\psi = \nabla\cdot\nabla\psi = -\zeta$.

c. Consider the stream function $\psi(x, y) = \sin x \sin y$ on the square region $R = \{(x, y): 0 \le x \le \pi, 0 \le y \le \pi\}$. Find the velocity components u and v; then sketch the velocity field.

d. For the stream function in part (c) find the vorticity function ζ as defined in part (b). Plot several level curves of the vorticity function. Where on R is it a maximum? A minimum?

61. Maxwell's equation One of Maxwell's equations for electromagnetic waves (also called Ampere's Law) is $\nabla\times\mathbf{B} = C\dfrac{\partial\mathbf{E}}{\partial t}$, where $\mathbf{E}$ is the electric field, $\mathbf{B}$ is the magnetic field, and C is a constant.

a. Show that the fields

$$\mathbf{E}(z, t) = A\sin(kz - \omega t)\mathbf{i} \qquad \mathbf{B}(z, t) = A\sin(kz - \omega t)\mathbf{j}$$

satisfy the equation for constants A, k, and ω, provided $\omega = k/C$.

b. Make a rough sketch showing the directions of $\mathbf{E}$ and $\mathbf{B}$.

Additional Exercises

62. Splitting a vector field Express the vector field $\mathbf{F} = \langle xy, 0, 0\rangle$ in the form $\mathbf{V} + \mathbf{W}$, where $\nabla\cdot\mathbf{V} = 0$ and $\nabla\times\mathbf{W} = \mathbf{0}$.

63. Properties of div and curl Prove the following properties of the divergence and curl. Assume $\mathbf{F}$ and $\mathbf{G}$ are differentiable vector fields and c is a real number.

a. $\nabla\cdot(\mathbf{F} + \mathbf{G}) = \nabla\cdot\mathbf{F} + \nabla\cdot\mathbf{G}$

b. $\nabla\times(\mathbf{F} + \mathbf{G}) = \nabla\times\mathbf{F} + \nabla\times\mathbf{G}$

c. $\nabla\cdot(c\mathbf{F}) = c(\nabla\cdot\mathbf{F})$

d. $\nabla\times(c\mathbf{F}) = c(\nabla\times\mathbf{F})$

64. Equal curls and divergence If two functions of one variable, f and g, have the property that $f' = g'$, then f and g differ by a constant. Prove or disprove: If $\mathbf{F}$ and $\mathbf{G}$ are nonconstant vector fields in $\mathbf{R}^2$ with curl $\mathbf{F}$ = curl $\mathbf{G}$ and div $\mathbf{F}$ = div $\mathbf{G}$ at all points of $\mathbf{R}^2$, then $\mathbf{F}$ and $\mathbf{G}$ differ by a constant vector.

65–70. Identities *Prove the following identities. Assume that φ is a differentiable scalar-valued function and* $\mathbf{F}$ *and* $\mathbf{G}$ *are differentiable vector fields, all defined on a region of* $\mathbf{R}^3$.

65. $\nabla\cdot(\varphi\mathbf{F}) = \nabla\varphi\cdot\mathbf{F} + \varphi\nabla\cdot\mathbf{F}$ (Product Rule)

66. $\nabla\times(\varphi\mathbf{F}) = \nabla\varphi\times\mathbf{F} + \varphi\nabla\times\mathbf{F}$ (Product Rule)

67. $\nabla\cdot(\mathbf{F}\times\mathbf{G}) = \mathbf{G}\cdot(\nabla\times\mathbf{F}) - \mathbf{F}\cdot(\nabla\times\mathbf{G})$

68. $\nabla\times(\mathbf{F}\times\mathbf{G}) = (\mathbf{G}\cdot\nabla)\mathbf{F} - \mathbf{G}(\nabla\cdot\mathbf{F}) - (\mathbf{F}\cdot\nabla)\mathbf{G} + \mathbf{F}(\nabla\cdot\mathbf{G})$

69. $\nabla(\mathbf{F}\cdot\mathbf{G}) = (\mathbf{G}\cdot\nabla)\mathbf{F} + (\mathbf{F}\cdot\nabla)\mathbf{G} + \mathbf{G}\times(\nabla\times\mathbf{F}) + \mathbf{F}\times(\nabla\times\mathbf{G})$

70. $\nabla\times(\nabla\times\mathbf{F}) = \nabla(\nabla\cdot\mathbf{F}) - (\nabla\cdot\nabla)\mathbf{F}$

71. Divergence of radial fields Prove that for a real number p, with $\mathbf{r} = \langle x, y, z\rangle$, $\nabla\cdot\dfrac{\langle x, y, z\rangle}{|\mathbf{r}|^p} = \dfrac{3 - p}{|\mathbf{r}|^p}$.

72. Gradients and radial fields Prove that for a real number p, with $\mathbf{r} = \langle x, y, z\rangle$, $\nabla\left(\dfrac{1}{|\mathbf{r}|^p}\right) = \dfrac{-p\mathbf{r}}{|\mathbf{r}|^{p+2}}$.

73. Divergence of gradient fields Prove that for a real number p, with $\mathbf{r} = \langle x, y, z\rangle$, $\nabla\cdot\nabla\left(\dfrac{1}{|\mathbf{r}|^p}\right) = \dfrac{p(p - 1)}{|\mathbf{r}|^{p+2}}$.

QUICK CHECK ANSWERS

1. The x-derivative of the divergence is applied to $f(y, z)$, which gives zero. Similarly, the y- and z-derivatives are zero. **2.** 4π **3.** In the curl, the first component of $\mathbf{F}$ is differentiated only with respect to y and z, so the contribution from the first component is zero. Similarly, the second and third components of $\mathbf{F}$ make no contribution to the curl. **4.** The divergence is a scalar-valued function. ◄

15.6 Surface Integrals

We have studied integrals on intervals, on regions in the plane, on solid regions in space, and along curves in space. One situation is still unexplored. Suppose a sphere has a known temperature distribution; perhaps it is cold near the poles and warm near the equator. How do you find the average temperature over the entire sphere? In analogy with other average value calculations, we should expect to "add up" the temperature values over the sphere and divide by the surface area of the sphere. Because the temperature varies continuously over the sphere, adding up means integrating. How do you integrate a function over a surface? This question leads to *surface integrals*.

It helps to keep curves, arc length, and line integrals in mind as we discuss surfaces, surface area, and surface integrals. What we discover about surfaces parallels what we already know about curves—all "lifted" up one dimension.

Parallel Concepts

Curves	Surfaces
Arc length	Surface area
Line integrals	Surface integrals
One-parameter description	Two-parameter description

Parameterized Surfaces

A curve in $\mathbf{R}^2$ is defined parametrically by $\mathbf{r}(t) = \langle x(t), y(t) \rangle$, for $a \le t \le b$; it requires one parameter and two dependent variables. Stepping up one dimension, to define a surface in $\mathbf{R}^3$ we need *two* parameters and *three* dependent variables. Letting u and v be parameters, the general parametric description of a surface has the form

$$\mathbf{r}(u, v) = \langle x(u, v), y(u, v), z(u, v) \rangle;$$

we make the assumption that the parameters vary over a rectangle $R = \{(u, v): a \le u \le b, c \le v \le d\}$ (Figure 15.42). As the parameters (u, v) vary over R, the vector $\mathbf{r}(u, v) = \langle x(u, v), y(u, v), z(u, v) \rangle$ sweeps out a surface S in $\mathbf{R}^3$.

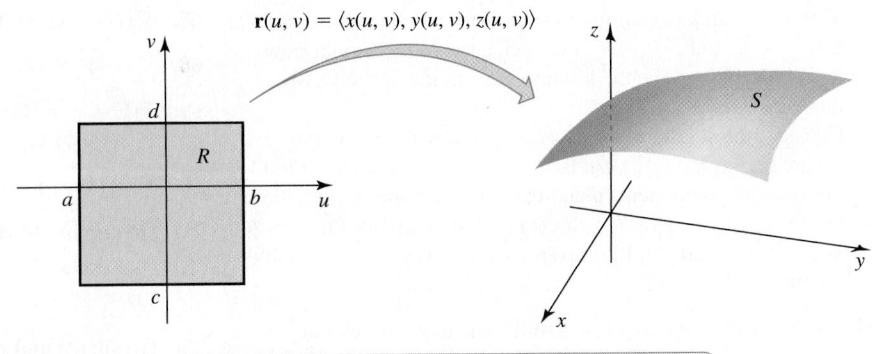

FIGURE 15.42

We work extensively with three surfaces that are easily described in parametric form. As with parameterized curves, a parametric description of a surface is not unique.

Cylinders In Cartesian coordinates, the set

$$\{(x, y, z): x = a \cos \theta, y = a \sin \theta, 0 \le \theta \le 2\pi, 0 \le z \le h\}$$

is a cylindrical surface of radius a and height h with its axis along the z-axis. Using the parameters $u = \theta$ and $v = z$, a parametric description of the cylinder is

$$\mathbf{r}(u, v) = \langle x(u, v), y(u, v), z(u, v) \rangle = \langle a \cos u, a \sin u, v \rangle,$$

where $0 \le u \le 2\pi$ and $0 \le v \le h$ (Figure 15.43).

QUICK CHECK 1 Describe the surface $\mathbf{r}(u, v) = \langle 2 \cos u, 2 \sin u, v \rangle$, for $0 \le u \le \pi$ and $0 \le v \le 1$. ◀

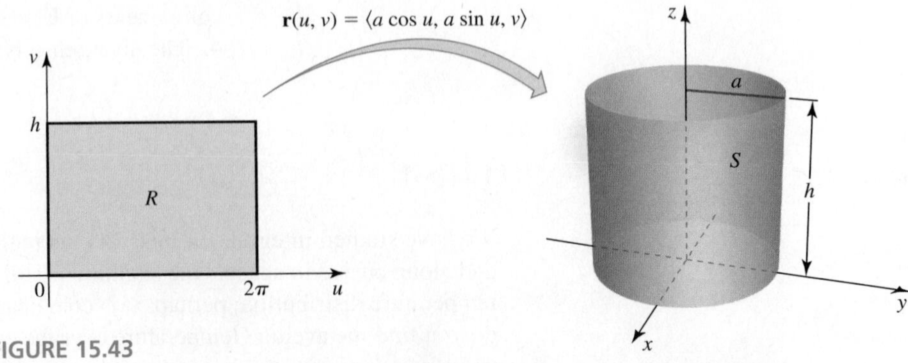

FIGURE 15.43

Cones The surface of a cone of height h and radius a with its vertex at the origin is described in cylindrical coordinates by

> Note that when $r = 0$, $z = 0$ and when $r = a$, $z = h$.

$$\{(r, \theta, z): 0 \le r \le a, 0 \le \theta \le 2\pi, z = rh/a\}.$$

For a fixed value of z, we have $r = az/h$; therefore, on the surface of the cone

> Recall the relationships among polar and rectangular coordinates:
>
> $x = r\cos\theta$, $y = r\sin\theta$, and $x^2 + y^2 = r^2$.

$$x = r\cos\theta = \frac{az}{h}\cos\theta \quad\text{and}\quad y = r\sin\theta = \frac{az}{h}\sin\theta.$$

Using the parameters $u = \theta$ and $v = z$, the parametric description of the conical surface is

$$\mathbf{r}(u, v) = \langle x(u, v), y(u, v), z(u, v)\rangle = \left\langle \frac{av}{h}\cos u, \frac{av}{h}\sin u, v \right\rangle,$$

where $0 \le u \le 2\pi$ and $0 \le v \le h$ (Figure 15.44).

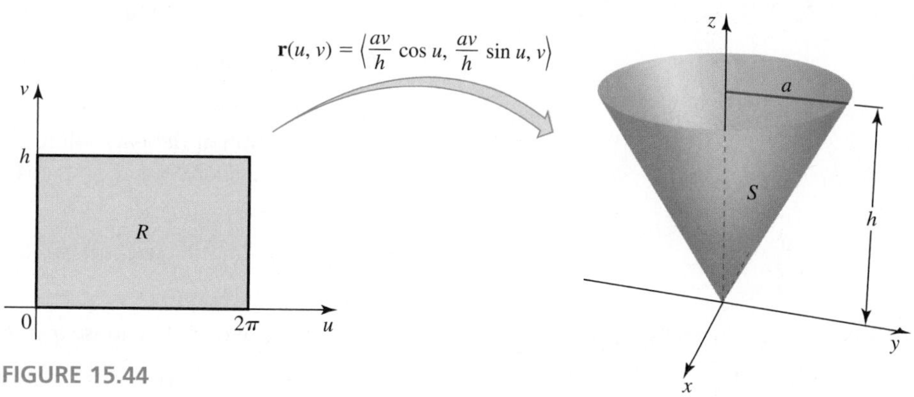

FIGURE 15.44

QUICK CHECK 2 Describe the surface $\mathbf{r}(u, v) = \langle v\cos u, v\sin u, v\rangle$, for $0 \le u \le \pi$ and $0 \le v \le 10$.

> The complete cylinder, cone, and sphere are generated as the angle variable θ varies over the half-open interval $[0, 2\pi)$. As in previous chapters, we will use the closed interval $[0, 2\pi]$.

Spheres The parametric description of a sphere of radius a centered at the origin comes directly from spherical coordinates:

$$\{(\rho, \varphi, \theta): \rho = a, 0 \le \varphi \le \pi, 0 \le \theta \le 2\pi\}.$$

Recall the following relationships among spherical and rectangular coordinates (Section 14.5):

$$x = a\sin\varphi\cos\theta, \qquad y = a\sin\varphi\sin\theta, \qquad z = a\cos\varphi.$$

When we define the parameters $u = \varphi$ and $v = \theta$, a parametric description of the sphere is

$$\mathbf{r}(u, v) = \langle a\sin u\cos v, a\sin u\sin v, a\cos u\rangle,$$

where $0 \le u \le \pi$ and $0 \le v \le 2\pi$ (Figure 15.45).

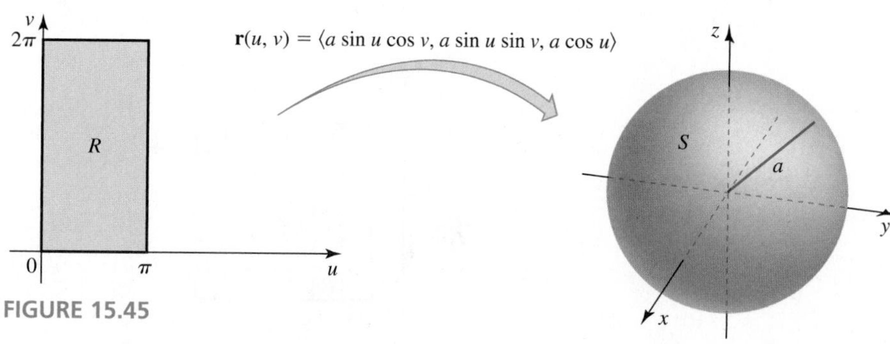

FIGURE 15.45

QUICK CHECK 3 Describe the surface $\mathbf{r}(u, v) = \langle 4 \sin u \cos v, 4 \sin u \sin v, 4 \cos u \rangle$, for $0 \le u \le \pi/2$ and $0 \le v \le \pi$.

EXAMPLE 1 **Parametric surfaces** Find parametric descriptions for the following surfaces.

a. The plane $3x - 2y + z = 2$

b. The paraboloid $z = x^2 + y^2$, for $0 \le z \le 9$

SOLUTION

a. Defining the parameters $u = x$ and $v = y$, we find that

$$z = 2 - 3x + 2y = 2 - 3u + 2v.$$

Therefore, a parametric description of the plane is

$$\mathbf{r}(u, v) = \langle u, v, 2 - 3u + 2v \rangle,$$

for $-\infty < u < \infty$ and $-\infty < v < \infty$.

b. Thinking in terms of polar coordinates, we let $u = \theta$ and $v = \sqrt{z}$, which means that $z = v^2$. The equation of the paraboloid is $x^2 + y^2 = z = v^2$, so v plays the role of the polar coordinate r. Therefore, $x = v \cos \theta$ and $y = v \sin \theta$. A parametric description for the paraboloid is

$$\mathbf{r}(u, v) = \langle v \cos u, v \sin u, v^2 \rangle,$$

where $0 \le u \le 2\pi$ and $0 \le v \le 3$.

Alternatively, we could choose $u = \theta$ and $v = z$. The resulting description is

$$\mathbf{r}(u, v) = \langle \sqrt{v} \cos u, \sqrt{v} \sin u, v \rangle,$$

where $0 \le u \le 2\pi$ and $0 \le v \le 9$.

Related Exercises 11–20

Surface Integrals of Scalar-Valued Functions

We now develop the surface integral of a scalar-valued function f on a smooth parameterized surface S described by the equation

$$\mathbf{r}(u, v) = \langle x(u, v), y(u, v), z(u, v) \rangle,$$

where the parameters vary over a rectangle $R = \{(u, v): a \le u \le b, c \le v \le d\}$. The functions x, y, and z are assumed to have continuous partial derivatives with respect to u and v. The rectangular region R in the uv-plane is partitioned into rectangles, with sides of length Δu and Δv, that are ordered in some convenient way, for $k = 1, \ldots, n$. The kth rectangle R_k corresponds to a curved patch S_k on the surface S (Figure 15.46), which has

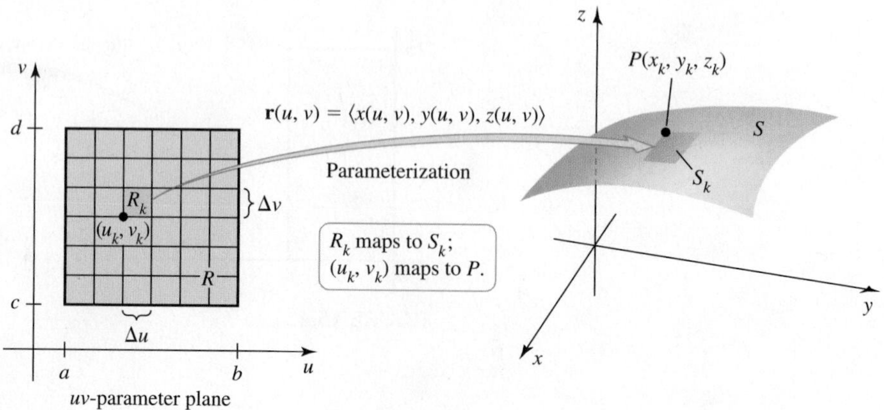

FIGURE 15.46

➤ A more general approach allows (u_k, v_k) to be an arbitrary point in the kth rectangle. The outcome of the two approaches is the same.

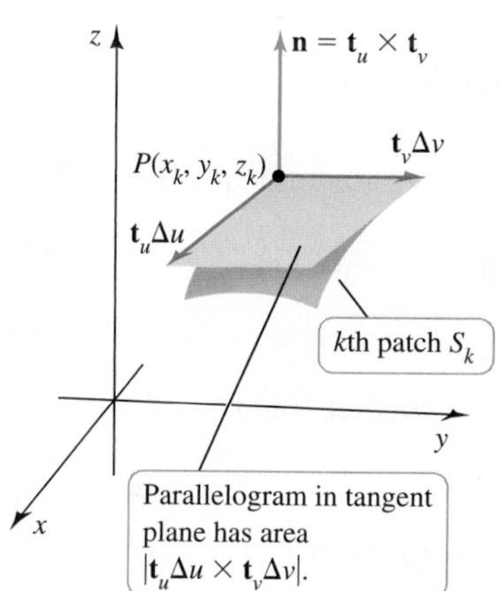

FIGURE 15.47

➤ In general, the vectors $\mathbf{t}_u$ and $\mathbf{t}_v$ are different for each patch, so they should carry a subscript k. To keep the notation as simple as possible, we have suppressed the subscripts on these vectors with the understanding that they change with k. These tangent vectors are given by partial derivatives because in each case, either u or v is held constant, while the other variable changes.

➤ The factor $|\mathbf{t}_u \times \mathbf{t}_v|\, dA$ plays an analogous role in surface integrals as the factor $|\mathbf{r}'(t)|\, dt$ in line integrals.

area ΔS_k. We let (u_k, v_k) be the lower-left corner point of R_k. The parameterization then assigns (u_k, v_k) to a point $P(x(u_k, v_k), y(u_k, v_k), z(u_k, v_k))$, or more simply, $P(x_k, y_k, z_k)$, on S_k. To construct the surface integral we define a Riemann sum, which adds up function values multiplied by areas of the respective patches:

$$\sum_{k=1}^{n} f(x(u_k, v_k), y(u_k, v_k), z(u_k, v_k))\Delta S_k.$$

The crucial step is computing ΔS_k, the area of the kth patch S_k.

Figure 15.47 shows the patch S_k and the point $P(x_k, y_k, z_k)$. Two special vectors are tangent to the surface at P:

- $\mathbf{t}_u$ is a vector tangent to the surface corresponding to a change in u with v constant in the uv-plane.
- $\mathbf{t}_v$ is a vector tangent to the surface corresponding to a change in v with u constant in the uv-plane.

Because the surface S may be written $\mathbf{r}(u, v) = \langle x(u, v), y(u, v), z(u, v)\rangle$, a tangent vector corresponding to a change in u with v fixed is

$$\mathbf{t}_u = \frac{\partial \mathbf{r}}{\partial u} = \left\langle \frac{\partial x}{\partial u}, \frac{\partial y}{\partial u}, \frac{\partial z}{\partial u} \right\rangle.$$

Similarly, a tangent vector corresponding to a change in v with u fixed is

$$\mathbf{t}_v = \frac{\partial \mathbf{r}}{\partial v} = \left\langle \frac{\partial x}{\partial v}, \frac{\partial y}{\partial v}, \frac{\partial z}{\partial v} \right\rangle.$$

Now consider an increment Δu in u with v fixed. The tangent vector $\mathbf{t}_u\,\Delta u$ forms one side of a parallelogram (Figure 15.47). Similarly, with an increment Δv in v with u fixed, the tangent vector $\mathbf{t}_v\,\Delta v$ forms the other side of that parallelogram. The area of this parallelogram is an approximation to the area of the patch S_k, which is ΔS_k.

Appealing to the cross product (Section 12.4), the area of the parallelogram is

$$|\mathbf{t}_u\,\Delta u \times \mathbf{t}_v\,\Delta v| = |\mathbf{t}_u \times \mathbf{t}_v|\,\Delta u\,\Delta v \approx \Delta S_k.$$

Note that $\mathbf{t}_u \times \mathbf{t}_v$ is evaluated at (u_k, v_k) and is a vector normal to the surface at P, which we assume to be nonzero at all points of S.

We write the Riemann sum with the observation that the areas of the parallelograms approximate the areas of the patches S_k:

$$\sum_{k=1}^{n} f(x(u_k, v_k), y(u_k, v_k), z(u_k, v_k))\Delta S_k$$
$$\approx \sum_{k=1}^{n} f(x(u_k, v_k), y(u_k, v_k), z(u_k, v_k))\underbrace{|\mathbf{t}_u \times \mathbf{t}_v|\,\Delta u\,\Delta v}_{\approx \Delta S_k}.$$

We now assume that f is continuous on S. As Δu and Δv approach zero, the areas of the parallelograms approach the areas of the corresponding patches on S. In this limit, the Riemann sum approaches the surface integral of f over the surface S, which we write $\iint_S f(x, y, z)\, dS$:

$$\lim_{\Delta u, \Delta v \to 0} \sum_{k=1}^{n} f(x(u_k, v_k), y(u_k,v_k), z(u_k, v_k))|\mathbf{t}_u \times \mathbf{t}_v|\,\Delta u\,\Delta v$$
$$= \iint_R f(x(u, v), y(u, v), z(u, v))|\mathbf{t}_u \times \mathbf{t}_v|\, dA$$
$$= \iint_S f(x, y, z)\, dS.$$

The integral over S is evaluated as an ordinary double integral over the region R in the uv-plane. If R is a rectangular region, as we have assumed, the double integral becomes an iterated integral with respect to u and v with constant limits. In the special case that $f(x, y, z) = 1$, the integral gives the surface area of S.

> The condition that $\mathbf{t}_u \times \mathbf{t}_v$ be nonzero means $\mathbf{t}_u$ and $\mathbf{t}_v$ are non-zero and not parallel. If $\mathbf{t}_u \times \mathbf{t}_v \neq \mathbf{0}$ at all points, then the surface is *smooth*. The value of the integral is independent of the parameterization of S.

DEFINITION Surface Integral of Scalar-Valued Functions on Parameterized Surfaces

Let f be a continuous function on a smooth surface S given parametrically by $\mathbf{r}(u, v) = \langle x(u, v), y(u, v), z(u, v)\rangle$, where $R = \{(u, v): a \le u \le b, c \le v \le d\}$. Assume also that the tangent vectors $\mathbf{t}_u = \frac{\partial \mathbf{r}}{\partial u} = \left\langle \frac{\partial x}{\partial u}, \frac{\partial y}{\partial u}, \frac{\partial z}{\partial u}\right\rangle$ and $\mathbf{t}_v = \frac{\partial \mathbf{r}}{\partial v} = \left\langle \frac{\partial x}{\partial v}, \frac{\partial y}{\partial v}, \frac{\partial z}{\partial v}\right\rangle$ are continuous on R and the normal vector $\mathbf{n} = \mathbf{t}_u \times \mathbf{t}_v$ is nonzero on R. Then the **surface integral** of the scalar-valued function f over S is

$$\iint_S f(x, y, z)\, dS = \iint_R f(x(u, v), y(u, v), z(u, v))|\mathbf{t}_u \times \mathbf{t}_v|\, dA.$$

If $f(x, y, z) = 1$, the integral equals the surface area of S.

EXAMPLE 2 Surface area of a cylinder and sphere Find the surface area of the following surfaces.

a. A cylinder with radius $a > 0$ and height h (excluding the circular ends)

b. A sphere of radius a

SOLUTION The critical step is evaluating the normal vector $\mathbf{t}_u \times \mathbf{t}_v$. It needs to be done only once for any given surface.

a. As shown before, a parametric description of the cylinder is

$$\mathbf{r}(u, v) = \langle x(u, v), y(u, v), z(u, v)\rangle = \langle a\cos u, a\sin u, v\rangle,$$

where $0 \le u \le 2\pi$ and $0 \le v \le h$. A normal vector is

$$\mathbf{n} = \mathbf{t}_u \times \mathbf{t}_v = \begin{vmatrix} \mathbf{i} & \mathbf{j} & \mathbf{k} \\ \frac{\partial x}{\partial u} & \frac{\partial y}{\partial u} & \frac{\partial z}{\partial u} \\ \frac{\partial x}{\partial v} & \frac{\partial y}{\partial v} & \frac{\partial z}{\partial v} \end{vmatrix} \quad \text{Definition of cross product}$$

$$= \begin{vmatrix} \mathbf{i} & \mathbf{j} & \mathbf{k} \\ -a\sin u & a\cos u & 0 \\ 0 & 0 & 1 \end{vmatrix} \quad \text{Evaluate the derivatives.}$$

$$= \langle a\cos u, a\sin u, 0\rangle. \quad \text{Compute the cross product.}$$

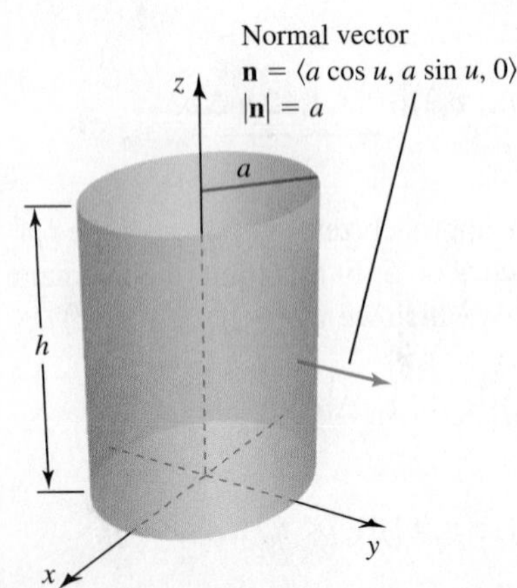

Cylinder: $\mathbf{r}(u, v) = \langle a\cos u, a\sin u, v\rangle$, $0 \le u \le 2\pi$ and $0 \le v \le h$

FIGURE 15.48

Notice that the normal vector points outward from the cylinder, away from the z-axis (Figure 15.48). It now follows that

$$|\mathbf{t}_u \times \mathbf{t}_v| = \sqrt{a^2\cos^2 u + a^2\sin^2 u} = a.$$

Setting $f(x, y, z) = 1$, the surface area of the cylinder is

$$\iint_S 1\, dS = \iint_R \underbrace{|\mathbf{t}_u \times \mathbf{t}_v|}_{a}\, dA = \int_0^{2\pi}\int_0^h a\, dv\, du = 2\pi a h,$$

confirming the formula for the surface area of a cylinder (excluding the ends).

> Recall that for the sphere, $u = \varphi$ and $v = \theta$, where φ and θ are spherical coordinates. The element of surface area in spherical coordinates is $dS = a^2 \sin\varphi \, d\varphi \, d\theta$.

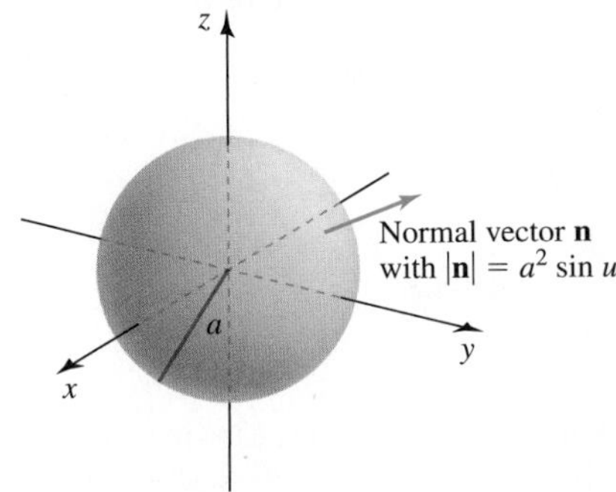

FIGURE 15.49

b. A parametric description of the sphere is

$$\mathbf{r}(u, v) = \langle a \sin u \cos v, a \sin u \sin v, a \cos u \rangle,$$

where $0 \le u \le \pi$ and $0 \le v \le 2\pi$. A normal vector is

$$\mathbf{n} = \mathbf{t}_u \times \mathbf{t}_v = \begin{vmatrix} \mathbf{i} & \mathbf{j} & \mathbf{k} \\ a \cos u \cos v & a \cos u \sin v & -a \sin u \\ -a \sin u \sin v & a \sin u \cos v & 0 \end{vmatrix}$$

$$= \langle a^2 \sin^2 u \cos v, a^2 \sin^2 u \sin v, a^2 \sin u \cos u \rangle.$$

Computing $|\mathbf{t}_u \times \mathbf{t}_v|$ requires several steps (Exercise 70). However, the needed result is quite simple: $|\mathbf{t}_u \times \mathbf{t}_v| = a^2 \sin u$ and the normal vector $\mathbf{n} = \mathbf{t}_u \times \mathbf{t}_v$ points outward from the surface of the sphere (Figure 15.49). With $f(x, y, z) = 1$, the surface area of the sphere is

$$\iint_S 1 \, dS = \iint_R \underbrace{|\mathbf{t}_u \times \mathbf{t}_v|}_{a^2 \sin u} \, dA = \int_0^{2\pi} \int_0^{\pi} a^2 \sin u \, du \, dv = 4\pi a^2,$$

confirming the formula for the surface area of a sphere. *Related Exercises 21–26* ◄

EXAMPLE 3 **Surface area of a partial cylinder** Find the surface area of the cylinder $\{(r, \theta): r = 4, 0 \le \theta \le 2\pi\}$ between the planes $z = 0$ and $z = 16 - 2x$.

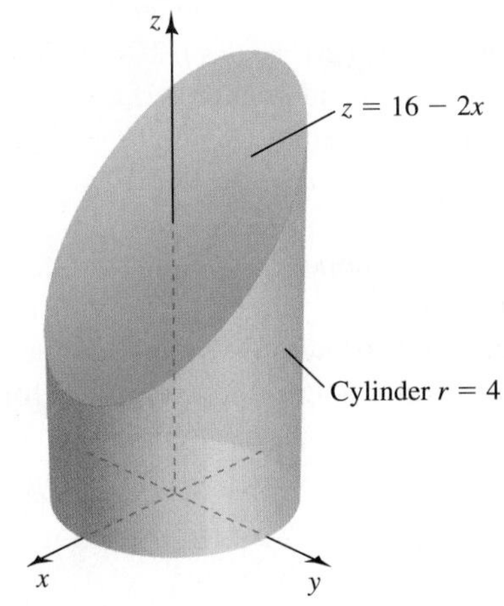

FIGURE 15.50

SOLUTION Figure 15.50 shows the cylinder bounded by the two planes. With $u = \theta$ and $v = z$, a parametric description of the cylinder is

$$\mathbf{r}(u, v) = \langle x(u, v), y(u, v), z(u, v) \rangle = \langle 4 \cos u, 4 \sin u, v \rangle.$$

The challenge is finding the limits on v, which is the z-coordinate. The plane $z = 16 - 2x$ intersects the cylinder in an ellipse; along this ellipse, as u varies between 0 and 2π, the parameter v also changes. To find the relationship between u and v along this intersection curve, notice that at any point on the cylinder, we have $x = 4 \cos u$ (remember that $u = \theta$). Making this substitution in the equation of the plane, we have

$$z = 16 - 2x = 16 - 2(4 \cos u) = 16 - 8 \cos u.$$

Substituting $v = z$, the relationship between u and v is $v = 16 - 8 \cos u$ (Figure 15.51). Therefore, the region of integration in the uv-plane is

$$R = \{(u, v): 0 \le u \le 2\pi, \ 0 \le v \le 16 - 8 \cos u\}.$$

Recall from Example 2a that for the cylinder, $|\mathbf{t}_u \times \mathbf{t}_v| = a = 4$. Setting $f(x, y, z) = 1$, the surface integral for the area is

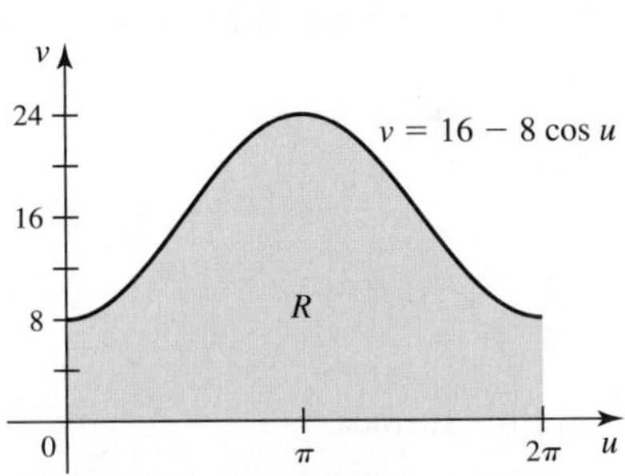

FIGURE 15.51

$$\iint_S 1 \, dS = \iint_R \underbrace{|\mathbf{t}_u \times \mathbf{t}_v|}_{4} \, dA$$

$$= \int_0^{2\pi} \int_0^{16 - 8\cos u} 4 \, dv \, du$$

$$= 4 \int_0^{2\pi} (16 - 8 \cos u) \, du \quad \text{Evaluate the inner integral.}$$

$$= 4(16u - 8 \sin u) \Big|_0^{2\pi} \quad \text{Evaluate the outer integral.}$$

$$= 128\pi. \quad \text{Simplify.}$$

Related Exercises 21–26 ◄

EXAMPLE 4 **Average temperature on a sphere** The temperature on the surface of a sphere of radius a varies with latitude according to the function $T(\varphi, \theta) = 10 + 50 \sin \varphi$, for $0 \le \varphi \le \pi$ and $0 \le \theta \le 2\pi$ (φ and θ are spherical coordinates, so the temperature is 10° at the poles, increasing to 60° at the equator). Find the average temperature over the sphere.

SOLUTION We use the parametric description of a sphere. With $u = \varphi$ and $v = \theta$, the temperature function becomes $f(u, v) = 10 + 50 \sin u$. Integrating the temperature over the sphere using the fact that $|\mathbf{t}_u \times \mathbf{t}_v| = a^2 \sin u$ (Example 2b), we have

$$\iint_S (10 + 50 \sin u)\, dS = \iint_R (10 + 50 \sin u)\underbrace{|\mathbf{t}_u \times \mathbf{t}_v|}_{a^2 \sin u}\, dA$$

$$= \int_0^{\pi}\int_0^{2\pi} (10 + 50 \sin u) a^2 \sin u \, dv\, du$$

$$= 2\pi a^2 \int_0^{\pi} (10 + 50 \sin u) \sin u \, du \qquad \text{Evaluate the inner integral.}$$

$$= 10\pi a^2 (4 + 5\pi). \qquad \text{Evaluate the outer integral.}$$

The average temperature is the integrated temperature $10\pi a^2(4 + 5\pi)$ divided by the surface area of the sphere $4\pi a^2$; so the average temperature is $(20 + 25\pi)/2 \approx 49.3°$. Notice that the equatorial region has both higher temperatures and greater surface area, so the average temperature is weighted toward the maximum temperature.

Related Exercises 27–30 ◄

Surface Integrals on Explicitly Defined Surfaces Suppose a smooth surface S is defined not parametrically, but explicitly, in the form $z = g(x, y)$ over a region R in the xy-plane. Such a surface may be treated as a parameterized surface. We simply define the parameters to be $u = x$ and $v = y$. Making these substitutions into the expression for $\mathbf{t}_u$ and $\mathbf{t}_v$, a short calculation (Exercise 71) reveals that $\mathbf{t}_u = \langle 1, 0, z_x \rangle$, $\mathbf{t}_v = \langle 0, 1, z_y \rangle$, and a normal vector is a scalar multiple of

$$\mathbf{n} = \mathbf{t}_u \times \mathbf{t}_v = \langle -z_x, -z_y, 1 \rangle.$$

➤ This is a familiar result: A normal to the surface $z = g(x, y)$ at a point is a constant multiple of the gradient of $z - g(x, y)$, which is $\langle -g_x, -g_y, 1 \rangle = \langle -z_x, -z_y, 1 \rangle$. The factor $\sqrt{z_x^2 + z_y^2 + 1}$ is analogous to the factor $\sqrt{(f'(x))^2 + 1}$ that appears in arc length integrals.

It follows that

$$|\mathbf{t}_x \times \mathbf{t}_y| = |\langle -z_x, -z_y, 1 \rangle| = \sqrt{z_x^2 + z_y^2 + 1}.$$

With these observations, the surface integral over S can be expressed as a double integral over a region R in the xy-plane.

THEOREM 15.12 **Evaluation of Surface Integrals of Scalar-Valued Functions on Explicitly Defined Surfaces**
Let f be a continuous function on a smooth surface S given by $z = g(x, y)$, for (x, y) in a region R. The surface integral of f over S is

$$\iint_S f(x, y, z)\, dS = \iint_R f(x, y, g(x, y))\sqrt{z_x^2 + z_y^2 + 1}\, dA.$$

If $f(x, y, z) = 1$, the surface integral equals the area of the surface.

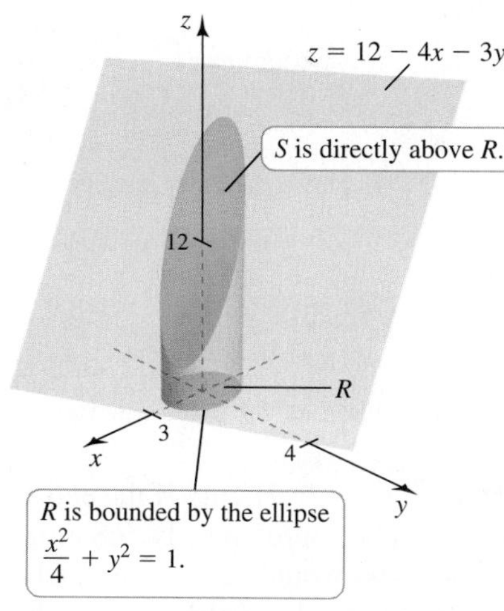

$z = 12 - 4x - 3y$
S is directly above R.
12
R
3
4
x
y
R is bounded by the ellipse $\frac{x^2}{4} + y^2 = 1$.
Area of $S = \sqrt{26}$ (Area of R).

FIGURE 15.52

EXAMPLE 5 **Area of a roof over an ellipse** Find the area of the surface S that lies in the plane $z = 12 - 4x - 3y$ directly above the region R bounded by the ellipse $x^2/4 + y^2 = 1$ (Figure 15.52).

SOLUTION Because we are computing the area of the surface, we take $f(x, y, z) = 1$. Note that $z_x = -4$ and $z_y = -3$, so the factor $\sqrt{z_x^2 + z_y^2 + 1}$ has the value $\sqrt{(-4)^2 + (-3)^2 + 1} = \sqrt{26}$ (a constant because the surface is a plane). The relevant surface integral is

$$\iint_S 1\, dS = \iint_R \underbrace{\sqrt{z_x^2 + z_y^2 + 1}}_{\sqrt{26}}\, dA = \sqrt{26} \iint_R dA.$$

The double integral that remains is simply the area of the region R bounded by the ellipse. Because the ellipse has semiaxes of length $a = 2$ and $b = 1$, its area is $\pi ab = 2\pi$. Therefore, the area of S is $2\pi\sqrt{26}$.

This result has a useful interpretation. The plane surface S is not horizontal, so it has a greater area than the horizontal region R beneath it. The factor that converts the area of R to the area of S is $\sqrt{26}$. Notice that if the roof *were* horizontal, then the surface would be $z = c$, the area conversion factor would be 1, and the area of the roof would equal the area of the floor beneath it. *Related Exercises 31–34* ◀

QUICK CHECK 4 The plane $z = y$ forms a 45° angle with the xy-plane. Suppose the plane is the roof of a room and the xy-plane is the floor of the room. Then 1 ft^2 on the floor becomes how many square feet when projected on the roof? ◀

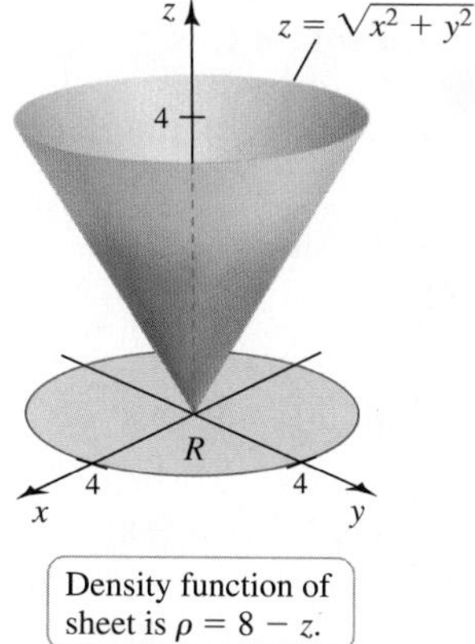

$z = \sqrt{x^2 + y^2}$
4
R
4
4
x
y
Density function of sheet is $\rho = 8 - z$.

FIGURE 15.53

EXAMPLE 6 **Mass of a conical sheet** A thin conical sheet is described by the surface $z = (x^2 + y^2)^{1/2}$, for $0 \le z \le 4$. The density of the sheet is $\rho = f(x, y, z) = (8 - z)$ g/cm^2 (decreasing from 8 g/cm^2 at the tip to 4 g/cm^2 at the top; Figure 15.53). What is the mass of the cone?

SOLUTION We find the mass by integrating the density function over the surface of the cone. The projection of the cone in the xy-plane is found by setting $z = 4$ (the top of the cone) in the equation of the cone. We find that $(x^2 + y^2)^{1/2} = 4$; therefore, the region of integration is the disk $R = \{(x, y): x^2 + y^2 \le 16\}$. We first find z_x and z_y in order to compute $\sqrt{z_x^2 + z_y^2 + 1}$. Differentiating $z^2 = x^2 + y^2$ implicitly gives $2zz_x = 2x$, or $z_x = x/z$. Similarly, $z_y = y/z$. Using the fact that $z^2 = x^2 + y^2$, we have

$$\sqrt{z_x^2 + z_y^2 + 1} = \sqrt{(x/z)^2 + (y/z)^2 + 1} = \sqrt{\underbrace{\frac{x^2 + y^2}{z^2}}_{1} + 1} = \sqrt{2}.$$

To integrate the density over the conical surface, we set $f(x, y, z) = 8 - z$. Replacing z in the integrand by $r = (x^2 + y^2)^{1/2}$ and using polar coordinates, the mass in grams is given by

$$\iint_S f(x, y, z)\, dS = \iint_R f(x, y, z) \underbrace{\sqrt{z_x^2 + z_y^2 + 1}}_{\sqrt{2}}\, dA$$

$$= \sqrt{2} \iint_R (8 - z)\, dA \qquad \text{Substitute.}$$

$$= \sqrt{2} \iint_R \left(8 - \sqrt{x^2 + y^2}\right) dA \qquad z = \sqrt{x^2 + y^2}$$

$$= \sqrt{2}\int_0^{2\pi}\int_0^4 (8 - r)\, r\, dr\, d\theta \qquad \text{Polar coordinates}$$

$$= \sqrt{2}\int_0^{2\pi}\left(4r^2 - \frac{r^3}{3}\right)\Big|_0^4 d\theta \qquad \text{Evaluate the inner integral.}$$

$$= \frac{128\sqrt{2}}{3}\int_0^{2\pi} d\theta \qquad \text{Simplify.}$$

$$= \frac{256\pi\sqrt{2}}{3} \approx 379. \qquad \text{Evaluate the outer integral.}$$

As a check, note that the surface area of the cone is $\pi r\sqrt{r^2 + h^2} \approx 71\text{ cm}^2$. If the entire cone had the maximum density $\rho = 8\text{ g/cm}^2$, its mass would be approximately 568 g. If the entire cone had the minimum density $\rho = 4\text{ g/cm}^2$, its mass would be approximately 284 g. The actual mass is between these extremes and closer to the low value because the cone is lighter at the top, where the surface area is greater. *Related Exercises 35–42* ◂

Table 15.2 summarizes the essential relationships for the explicit and parametric descriptions of cylinders, cones, spheres, and paraboloids. The listed normal vectors are chosen to point away from the z-axis.

Table 15.2

	Explicit Description $z = g(x, y)$		Parametric Description	
Surface	**Equation**	**Normal** $\mathbf{n} = \pm\langle -z_x, -z_y, 1\rangle$	**Equation**	**Normal** $\mathbf{n} = \mathbf{t}_u \times \mathbf{t}_v$
Cylinder	$x^2 + y^2 = a^2$, $0 \le z \le h$	$\mathbf{n} = \langle x, y, 0\rangle$, $\lvert\mathbf{n}\rvert = a$	$\mathbf{r} = \langle a\cos u, a\sin u, v\rangle$, $0 \le u \le 2\pi, 0 \le v \le h$	$\mathbf{n} = \langle a\cos u, a\sin u, 0\rangle$, $\lvert\mathbf{n}\rvert = a$.
Cone	$z^2 = x^2 + y^2$, $0 \le z \le h$	$\mathbf{n} = \langle x/z, y/z, -1\rangle$, $\lvert\mathbf{n}\rvert = \sqrt{2}$	$\mathbf{r} = \langle v\cos u, v\sin u, v\rangle$, $0 \le u \le 2\pi, 0 \le v \le h$	$\mathbf{n} = \langle v\cos u, v\sin u, -v\rangle$, $\lvert\mathbf{n}\rvert = \sqrt{2}v$
Sphere	$x^2 + y^2 + z^2 = a^2$	$\mathbf{n} = \langle x/z, y/z, 1\rangle$, $\lvert\mathbf{n}\rvert = a/z$	$\mathbf{r} = \langle a\sin u\cos v$, $a\sin u\sin v, a\cos u\rangle$, $0 \le u \le \pi, 0 \le v \le 2\pi$	$\mathbf{n} = \langle a^2\sin^2 u\cos v, a^2\sin^2 u\sin v$, $a^2\sin u\cos u\rangle$, $\lvert\mathbf{n}\rvert = a^2\sin u$
Paraboloid	$z = x^2 + y^2$, $0 \le z \le h$	$\mathbf{n} = \langle 2x, 2y, -1\rangle$, $\lvert\mathbf{n}\rvert = \sqrt{1 + 4(x^2 + y^2)}$	$\mathbf{r} = \langle v\cos u, v\sin u, v^2\rangle$, $0 \le u \le 2\pi, 0 \le v \le \sqrt{h}$	$\mathbf{n} = \langle 2v^2\cos u, 2v^2\sin u, -v\rangle$, $\lvert\mathbf{n}\rvert = v\sqrt{1 + 4v^2}$

QUICK CHECK 5 Explain why the explicit description for a cylinder $x^2 + y^2 = a^2$ cannot be used for a surface integral over a cylinder and a parametric description must be used. ◂

Surface Integrals of Vector Fields

Before beginning a discussion of surface integrals of vector fields, two technical issues about surfaces and normal vectors must be addressed.

The surfaces we consider in this book are called **two-sided**, or **orientable**, surfaces. To be orientable, a surface must have the property that the normal vectors vary continuously over the surface. In other words, when you walk on any closed path on an orientable surface and return to your starting point, your head must point in the same direction it did when you started. The most famous example of a *non-orientable* surface is the Möbius strip (Figure 15.54). Suppose you start walking along the surface of the Möbius strip at a point P with your head pointing upward. When you return to P, your head points in the opposite direction, or downward. Therefore, the Möbius strip is not orientable.

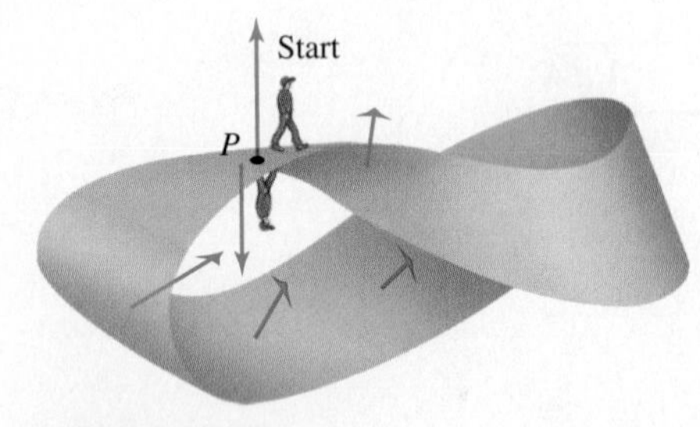

FIGURE 15.54

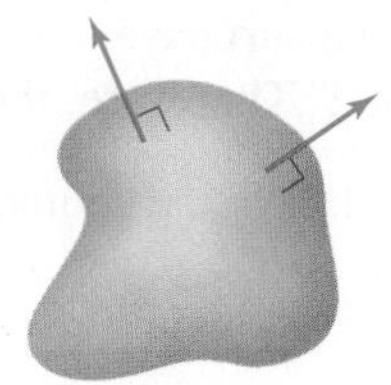

Closed surfaces are oriented so normal vectors point in the outward direction.

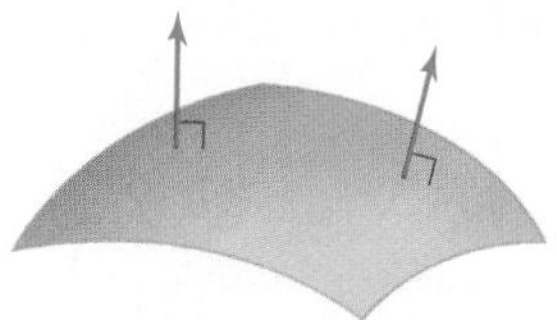

For other surfaces, the orientation of the surface must be specified.

FIGURE 15.55

At any point of a parameterized orientable surface, there are two unit normal vectors. Therefore, the second point concerns the orientation of the surface or, equivalently, the choice of the direction of the normal vectors. Once the orientation is determined, the surface becomes **oriented**.

We make the common assumption that—unless specified otherwise—a closed orientable surface that fully encloses a region (such as a sphere) is oriented so that the normal vectors point in the *outward direction*. For a surface that is not closed, we assume that the orientation is specified in some way. For example, we might specify that the normal vectors for a particular surface point in the positive z-direction (Figure 15.55).

Now recall that the parameterization of a surface defines a normal vector $\mathbf{t}_u \times \mathbf{t}_v$ at each point. In many cases, the normal vectors are consistent with the specified orientation, in which case no adjustments need to be made. If the direction of $\mathbf{t}_u \times \mathbf{t}_v$ is not consistent with the specified orientation, then the sign of $\mathbf{t}_u \times \mathbf{t}_v$ must be reversed before doing calculations. This process is demonstrated in the following examples.

Flux Integrals It turns out that the most common surface integral of a vector field is a *flux integral*. Consider a vector field $\mathbf{F} = \langle f, g, h \rangle$, continuous on a region in $\mathbf{R}^3$, that represents the flow of a fluid or the transport of a substance. Given a smooth oriented surface S, we aim to compute the net flux of the vector field across the surface. In a small region containing a point P, the flux across the surface is proportional to the component of $\mathbf{F}$ in the direction of the unit normal vector $\mathbf{n}$ at P. If θ is the angle between $\mathbf{F}$ and $\mathbf{n}$, then this component is $\mathbf{F} \cdot \mathbf{n} = |\mathbf{F}|\,|\mathbf{n}| \cos \theta = |\mathbf{F}| \cos \theta$ (because $|\mathbf{n}| = 1$; Figure 15.56a). We have the following special cases.

- If $\mathbf{F}$ and the unit normal vector are aligned at P ($\theta = 0$), then the component of $\mathbf{F}$ in the direction $\mathbf{n}$ is $\mathbf{F} \cdot \mathbf{n} = |\mathbf{F}|$; that is, all of $\mathbf{F}$ flows across the surface in the direction of $\mathbf{n}$ (Figure 15.56b).
- If $\mathbf{F}$ and the unit normal vector point in opposite directions at P ($\theta = \pi$), then the component of $\mathbf{F}$ in the direction $\mathbf{n}$ is $\mathbf{F} \cdot \mathbf{n} = -|\mathbf{F}|$; that is, all of $\mathbf{F}$ flows across the surface in the direction opposite to that of $\mathbf{n}$ (Figure 15.56c).
- If $\mathbf{F}$ and the unit normal vector are orthogonal at P ($\theta = \pi/2$), then the component of $\mathbf{F}$ in the direction $\mathbf{n}$ is $\mathbf{F} \cdot \mathbf{n} = 0$; that is, none of $\mathbf{F}$ flows across the surface at that point (Figure 15.56d).

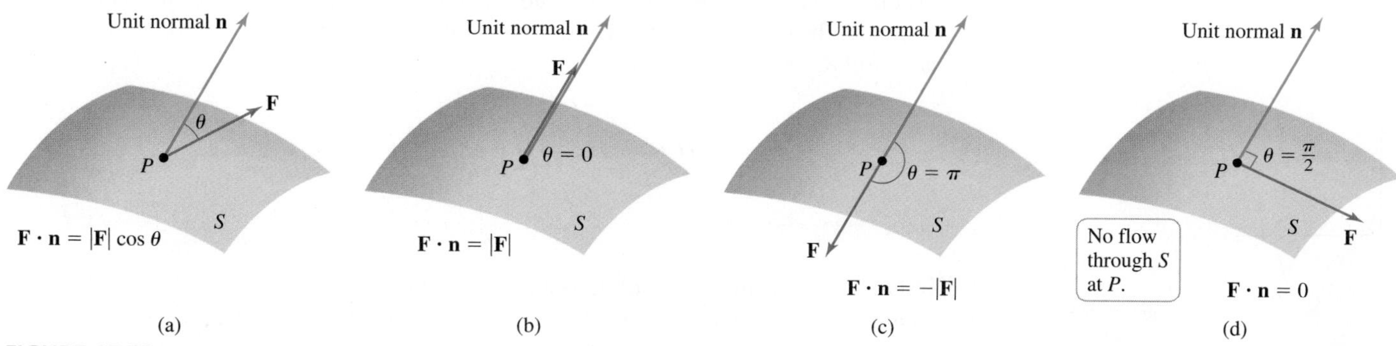

FIGURE 15.56

The flux integral, denoted $\iint_S \mathbf{F} \cdot \mathbf{n}\, dS$ or $\iint_S \mathbf{F} \cdot d\mathbf{S}$, simply adds up the components of $\mathbf{F}$ normal to the surface at all points of the surface. Notice that $\mathbf{F} \cdot \mathbf{n}$ is a scalar-valued function. Here is how the flux integral is computed.

Suppose the smooth oriented surface S is parameterized in the form

$$\mathbf{r}(u, v) = \langle x(u, v), y(u, v), z(u, v) \rangle,$$

➤ If $\mathbf{t}_u \times \mathbf{t}_v$ is not consistent with the specified orientation, its sign must be reversed.

where u and v vary over a region R in the uv-plane. A normal to the surface at a point is $\mathbf{t}_u \times \mathbf{t}_v$, which we assume to be consistent with the orientation of S. Therefore, the *unit* normal vector consistent with the orientation is $\mathbf{n} = \dfrac{\mathbf{t}_u \times \mathbf{t}_v}{|\mathbf{t}_u \times \mathbf{t}_v|}$. Appealing to the definition of the surface integral for parameterized surfaces, the flux integral is

$$\iint_S \mathbf{F}\cdot\mathbf{n}\,dS = \iint_R \mathbf{F}\cdot\mathbf{n}|\mathbf{t}_u \times \mathbf{t}_v|\,dA \qquad \text{Definition of surface integral}$$

$$= \iint_R \mathbf{F}\cdot\underbrace{\frac{\mathbf{t}_u \times \mathbf{t}_v}{|\mathbf{t}_u \times \mathbf{t}_v|}}_{\mathbf{n}}|\mathbf{t}_u \times \mathbf{t}_v|\,dA \qquad \text{Substitute for } \mathbf{n}.$$

$$= \iint_R \mathbf{F}\cdot(\mathbf{t}_u \times \mathbf{t}_v)\,dA. \qquad \text{Convenient cancellation}$$

The remarkable occurrence in the flux integral is the cancellation of the factor $|\mathbf{t}_u \times \mathbf{t}_v|$. The flux integral turns out to be a double integral with respect to u and v.

The special case in which the surface S is specified in the form $z = g(x, y)$ follows directly by recalling that a vector normal to the surface is $\mathbf{t}_u \times \mathbf{t}_v = \langle -z_x, -z_y, 1\rangle$. In this case, with $\mathbf{F} = \langle f, g, h\rangle$, the integrand of the surface integral is $\mathbf{F}\cdot(\mathbf{t}_u \times \mathbf{t}_v) = -fz_x - gz_y + h$.

➤ The value of the surface integral is independent of the parameterization. However, in contrast to a surface integral of a scalar-valued function, the value of a surface integral of a vector field depends on the orientation of the surface. Changing the orientation changes the sign of the result.

DEFINITION Surface Integral of a Vector Field

Suppose $\mathbf{F} = \langle f, g, h\rangle$ is a continuous vector field on a region of $\mathbf{R}^3$ containing a smooth oriented surface S. If S is defined parametrically as $\mathbf{r}(u, v) = \langle x(u, v), y(u, v), z(u, v)\rangle$, for (u, v) in a region R, then

$$\iint_S \mathbf{F}\cdot\mathbf{n}\,dS = \iint_R \mathbf{F}\cdot(\mathbf{t}_u \times \mathbf{t}_v)\,dA,$$

where $\mathbf{t}_u = \dfrac{\partial \mathbf{r}}{\partial u} = \left\langle \dfrac{\partial x}{\partial u}, \dfrac{\partial y}{\partial u}, \dfrac{\partial z}{\partial u}\right\rangle$ and $\mathbf{t}_v = \dfrac{\partial \mathbf{r}}{\partial v} = \left\langle \dfrac{\partial x}{\partial v}, \dfrac{\partial y}{\partial v}, \dfrac{\partial z}{\partial v}\right\rangle$ are continuous on R, the normal vector $\mathbf{n} = \mathbf{t}_u \times \mathbf{t}_v$ is nonzero on R, and the direction of $\mathbf{n}$ is consistent with the orientation of S. If S is defined in the form $z = g(x, y)$, for (x, y) in a region R, then

$$\iint_S \mathbf{F}\cdot\mathbf{n}\,dS = \iint_R (-fz_x - gz_y + h)\,dA.$$

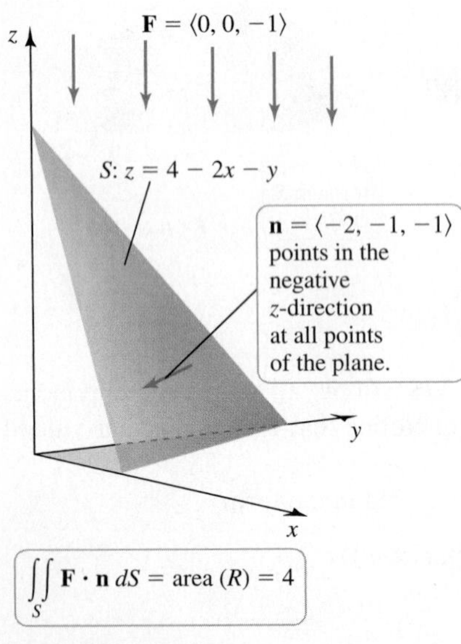
F = ⟨0, 0, −1⟩
z
S: z = 4 − 2x − y
n = ⟨−2, −1, −1⟩ points in the negative z-direction at all points of the plane.
y
x
∬_S F · n dS = area (R) = 4

FIGURE 15.57

EXAMPLE 7 Rain on a roof Consider the vertical vector field $\mathbf{F} = \langle 0, 0, -1\rangle$, corresponding to a constant downward flow. Find the flux in the downward (negative z) direction across the surface S, which is the plane $z = 4 - 2x - y$ in the first octant.

SOLUTION In this case, the surface is given explicitly. With $z = 4 - 2x - y$, we have $z_x = -2$ and $z_y = -1$. Therefore, a vector normal to the plane is $\langle -z_x, -z_y, 1\rangle = \langle 2, 1, 1\rangle$, which points *upward* (Figure 15.57). Because we are interested in the *downward* flux of $\mathbf{F}$ across S, the surface must be oriented so the normal vectors point in the negative z-direction. So, we take the normal vector to be $\mathbf{n} = \langle -2, -1, -1\rangle$. Noting that $\mathbf{F} = \langle f, g, h\rangle = \langle 0, 0, -1\rangle$, the flux integral is

$$\iint_S \mathbf{F}\cdot\mathbf{n}\,dS = \iint_R \langle 0, 0, -1\rangle\cdot\langle -2, -1, -1\rangle\,dA = \iint_R dA = \text{area}(R).$$

The base R is a triangle in the xy-plane with vertices $(0, 0)$, $(2, 0)$, and $(0, 4)$, so its area is 4. Therefore, the *downward* flux across S is 4.

This flux integral has an interesting interpretation. If the vector field $\mathbf{F}$ represents the rate of rainfall with units of, say, g/m^2 per unit time, then the flux integral gives the mass of rain (in grams) that falls on the surface in a unit of time. This result says that (because the vector field is vertical) the mass of rain that falls on the roof equals the mass that would fall on the floor beneath the roof if the roof were not there. This property is explored further in Exercise 73. *Related Exercises 43–48* ◀

EXAMPLE 8 **Flux of the radial field** Consider the radial vector field $\mathbf{F} = \langle f, g, h \rangle = \langle x, y, z \rangle$. Is the *upward* flux of the field greater across the hemisphere $x^2 + y^2 + z^2 = 1$, for $z \geq 0$, or across the paraboloid $z = 1 - x^2 - y^2$, for $z \geq 0$? Note that the two surfaces have the same base in the xy-plane and the same high point $(0, 0, 1)$. Use the explicit description for the hemisphere and a parametric description for the paraboloid.

SOLUTION The base of both surfaces in the xy-plane is the unit disk $R = \{(x, y): x^2 + y^2 \leq 1\} = \{(r, \theta): 0 \leq r \leq 1, 0 \leq \theta \leq 2\pi\}$. To use the explicit description for the hemisphere, we must compute z_x and z_y. Differentiating $x^2 + y^2 + z^2 = 1$ implicitly, we find that $z_x = -x/z$ and $z_y = -y/z$. Therefore, a normal vector is $\langle x/z, y/z, 1 \rangle$, which points *upward* on the surface. The flux integral is evaluated by substituting for f, g, h, z_x, and z_y; eliminating z from the integrand; and converting the integral in x and y to an integral in polar coordinates:

▶ Recall that a normal vector for an explicitly defined surface $z = g(x, y)$ is $\langle -z_x, -z_y, 1 \rangle$.

$$\iint_S \mathbf{F} \cdot \mathbf{n}\, dS = \iint_R (-f z_x - g z_y + h)\, dA$$

$$= \iint_R \left(x\frac{x}{z} + y\frac{y}{z} + z \right) dA \qquad \text{Substitute.}$$

$$= \iint_R \left(\frac{x^2 + y^2 + z^2}{z} \right) dA \qquad \text{Simplify.}$$

$$= \iint_R \left(\frac{1}{z} \right) dA \qquad x^2 + y^2 + z^2 = 1$$

$$= \iint_R \left(\frac{1}{\sqrt{1 - x^2 - y^2}} \right) dA \qquad z = \sqrt{1 - x^2 - y^2}$$

$$= \int_0^{2\pi} \int_0^1 \left(\frac{1}{\sqrt{1 - r^2}} \right) r\, dr\, d\theta \qquad \text{Polar coordinates}$$

$$= \int_0^{2\pi} \left(-\sqrt{1 - r^2} \right) \Big|_0^1 d\theta \qquad \text{Evaluate the inner integral as an improper integral.}$$

$$= \int_0^{2\pi} d\theta = 2\pi \qquad \text{Evaluate the outer integral.}$$

For the paraboloid $z = 1 - x^2 - y^2$, we use the parametric description (Example 4b or Table 15.2)

$$\mathbf{r}(u, v) = \langle x, y, z \rangle = \langle v \cos u, v \sin u, 1 - v^2 \rangle,$$

for $0 \leq u \leq 2\pi$ and $0 \leq v \leq 1$. A vector normal to the surface is

$$\mathbf{t}_u \times \mathbf{t}_v = \begin{vmatrix} \mathbf{i} & \mathbf{j} & \mathbf{k} \\ -v \sin u & v \cos u & 0 \\ \cos u & \sin u & -2v \end{vmatrix}$$
$$= \langle -2v^2 \cos u, -2v^2 \sin u, -v \rangle.$$

Notice that the normal vectors point *downward* on the surface (because the z-component is negative for $0 \le v \le 1$). In order to find the *upward* flux, we negate the normal vector and use the *upward* normal vector

$$\mathbf{n} = -(\mathbf{t}_u \times \mathbf{t}_v) = \langle 2v^2 \cos u, 2v^2 \sin u, v \rangle.$$

The flux integral is evaluated by substituting for $\mathbf{F} = \langle x, y, z \rangle$ and $\mathbf{n}$, and then evaluating an iterated integral in u and v:

$$\iint_S \mathbf{F} \cdot \mathbf{n}\, dS = \int_0^1 \int_0^{2\pi} \langle v \cos u, v \sin u, 1 - v^2 \rangle \cdot \langle 2v^2 \cos u, 2v^2 \sin u, v \rangle\, du\, dv$$

Substitute for **F** and **n**.

$$= \int_0^1 \int_0^{2\pi} (v^3 + v)\, du\, dv$$

Simplify.

$$= 2\pi \left(\frac{v^4}{4} + \frac{v^2}{2} \right) \Bigg|_0^1 = \frac{3\pi}{2}$$

Evaluate integrals.

QUICK CHECK 6 Explain why the upward flux for the radial field in Example 8 is greater for the hemisphere than for the paraboloid. ◂

We see that the upward flux is greater for the hemisphere than for the paraboloid.

Related Exercises 43–48 ◂

SECTION 15.6 EXERCISES

Review Questions

1. Give a parametric description for a cylinder with radius a and height h, including the intervals for the parameters.
2. Give a parametric description for a cone with radius a and height h, including the intervals for the parameters.
3. Give a parametric description for a sphere with radius a, including the intervals for the parameters.
4. Explain how to compute the surface integral of a scalar-valued function f over a cone using an explicit description of the cone.
5. Explain how to compute the surface integral of a scalar-valued function f over a sphere using a parametric description of the sphere.
6. Explain how to compute a flux integral $\iint_S \mathbf{F} \cdot \mathbf{n}\, dS$ over a cone using an explicit description and a given orientation of the cone.
7. Explain how to compute a surface integral $\iint_S \mathbf{F} \cdot \mathbf{n}\, dS$ over a sphere using a parametric description of the sphere and a given orientation.
8. Explain what it means for a surface to be orientable.
9. Describe the usual orientation of a closed surface such as a sphere.
10. Why is the upward flux of a vertical vector field $\mathbf{F} = \langle 0, 0, 1 \rangle$ across a surface equal to the area of the projection of the surface in the xy-plane?

Basic Skills

11–16. Parametric descriptions *Give a parametric description of the form $\mathbf{r}(u, v) = \langle x(u, v), y(u, v), z(u, v) \rangle$ for the following surfaces. The descriptions are not unique.*

11. The plane $2x - 4y + 3z = 16$
12. The cap of the sphere $x^2 + y^2 + z^2 = 16$, for $4/\sqrt{2} \le z \le 4$
13. The frustum of the cone $z^2 = x^2 + y^2$, for $2 \le z \le 8$
14. The hyperboloid $z^2 = 1 + x^2 + y^2$, for $1 \le z \le 10$
15. The portion of the cylinder $x^2 + y^2 = 9$ in the first octant, for $0 \le z \le 3$
16. The cylinder $y^2 + z^2 = 36$, for $0 \le x \le 9$

17–20. Identify the surface *Describe the surface with the given parametric representation.*

17. $\mathbf{r}(u, v) = \langle u, v, 2u + 3v - 1 \rangle$, for $1 \le u \le 3, 2 \le v \le 4$
18. $\mathbf{r}(u, v) = \langle u, u + v, 2 - u - v \rangle$, for $0 \le u \le 2, 0 \le v \le 2$
19. $\mathbf{r}(u, v) = \langle v \cos u, v \sin u, 4v \rangle$, for $0 \le u \le \pi, 0 \le v \le 3$
20. $\mathbf{r}(u, v) = \langle v, 6 \cos u, 6 \sin u \rangle$, for $0 \le u \le 2\pi, 0 \le v \le 2$

21–26. Surface area using a parametric description *Find the area of the following surfaces using a parametric description of the surface.*

21. The half cylinder $\{(r, \theta, z): r = 4, 0 \le \theta \le \pi, 0 \le z \le 7\}$

22. The plane $z = 3 - x - 3y$ in the first octant

23. The plane $z = 10 - x - y$ above the square $|x| \leq 2, |y| \leq 2$

24. The hemisphere $x^2 + y^2 + z^2 = 100$, for $z \geq 0$

25. A cone with base radius r and height h, where r and h are positive constants

26. The cap of the sphere $x^2 + y^2 + z^2 = 4$, for $1 \leq z \leq 2$

27–30. Surface integrals using a parametric description *Evaluate the surface integral $\iint_S f(x, y, z)\,dS$ using a parametric description of the surface.*

27. $f(x, y, z) = x^2 + y^2$, where S is the hemisphere $x^2 + y^2 + z^2 = 36$, for $z \geq 0$

28. $f(x, y, z) = y$, where S is the cylinder $x^2 + y^2 = 9, 0 \leq z \leq 3$

29. $f(x, y, z) = x$, where S is the cylinder $x^2 + z^2 = 1, 0 \leq y \leq 3$

30. $f(\rho, \varphi, \theta) = \cos \varphi$, where S is the part of the unit sphere in the first octant

31–34. Surface area using an explicit description *Find the area of the following surfaces using an explicit description of the surface.*

31. The cone $z^2 = 4(x^2 + y^2)$, for $0 \leq z \leq 4$

32. The paraboloid $z = 2(x^2 + y^2)$, for $0 \leq z \leq 8$

33. The trough $z = x^2$, for $-2 \leq x \leq 2, 0 \leq y \leq 4$

34. The part of the hyperbolic paraboloid $z = x^2 - y^2$ above the sector $R = \{(r, \theta): 0 \leq r \leq 4, -\pi/4 \leq \theta \leq \pi/4\}$

35–38. Surface integrals using an explicit description *Evaluate the surface integral $\iint_S f(x, y, z)\,dS$ using an explicit representation of the surface.*

35. $f(x, y, z) = xy$; S is the plane $z = 2 - x - y$ in the first octant.

36. $f(x, y, z) = x^2 + y^2$; S is the paraboloid $z = x^2 + y^2$ for $0 \leq z \leq 4$.

37. $f(x, y, z) = 25 - x^2 - y^2$; S is the hemisphere centered at the origin with radius 5, for $z \geq 0$.

38. $f(x, y, z) = e^z$; S is the plane $z = 8 - x - 2y$ in the first octant.

39–42. Average values

39. Find the average temperature on that part of the plane $3x + 4y + z = 6$ over the square $|x| \leq 1, |y| \leq 1$, where the temperature is given by $T(x, y, z) = e^{-z}$.

40. Find the average squared distance between the origin and the points on the paraboloid $z = 4 - x^2 - y^2$, for $z \geq 0$.

41. Find the average value of the function $f(x, y, z) = xyz$ on the unit sphere in the first octant.

42. Find the average value of the temperature function $T(x, y, z) = 100 - 25z$ on the cone $z^2 = x^2 + y^2$, for $0 \leq z \leq 2$.

43–48. Surface integrals of vector fields *Find the flux of the following vector fields across the given surface with the specified orientation. You may use either an explicit or parametric description of the surface.*

43. $\mathbf{F} = \langle 0, 0, -1 \rangle$ across the slanted face of the tetrahedron $z = 4 - x - y$ in the first octant; normal vectors point in the positive z-direction.

44. $\mathbf{F} = \langle x, y, z \rangle$ across the slanted face of the tetrahedron $z = 10 - 2x - 5y$ in the first octant; normal vectors point in the positive z-direction.

45. $\mathbf{F} = \langle x, y, z \rangle$ across the slanted surface of the cone $z^2 = x^2 + y^2$ for $0 \leq z \leq 1$; normal vectors point in the positive z-direction.

46. $\mathbf{F} = \langle e^{-y}, 2z, xy \rangle$ across the curved sides of the surface $S = \{(x, y, z): z = \cos y, |y| \leq \pi, 0 \leq x \leq 4\}$; normal vectors point upward.

47. $\mathbf{F} = \mathbf{r}/|\mathbf{r}|^3$ across the sphere of radius a centered at the origin, where $\mathbf{r} = \langle x, y, z \rangle$; normal vectors point outward.

48. $\mathbf{F} = \langle -y, x, 1 \rangle$ across the cylinder $y = x^2$ for $0 \leq x \leq 1$, $0 \leq z \leq 4$; normal vectors point in the positive y-direction.

Further Explorations

49. Explain why or why not Determine whether the following statements are true and give an explanation or counterexample.

a. If the surface S is given by $\{(x, y, z): 0 \leq x \leq 1, 0 \leq y \leq 1, z = 10\}$, then $\iint_S f(x, y, z)\,dS = \int_0^1 \int_0^1 f(x, y, 10)\,dx\,dy$.

b. If the surface S is given by $\{(x, y, z): 0 \leq x \leq 1, 0 \leq y \leq 1, z = x\}$, then $\iint_S f(x, y, z)\,dS = \int_0^1 \int_0^1 f(x, y, x)\,dx\,dy$.

c. The surface $\mathbf{r} = \langle v \cos u, v \sin u, v^2 \rangle$, for $0 \leq u \leq \pi$, $0 \leq v \leq 2$ is the same as the surface $\mathbf{r} = \langle \sqrt{v} \cos 2u, \sqrt{v} \sin 2u, v \rangle$, for $0 \leq u \leq \pi/2, 0 \leq v \leq 4$.

d. Given the standard parameterization of a sphere, the normal vectors $\mathbf{t}_u \times \mathbf{t}_v$ are outward normal vectors.

50–53. Miscellaneous surface integrals *Evaluate the following integrals using the method of your choice. Assume normal vectors point either outward or in the positive z-direction.*

50. $\iint_S \nabla \ln r \cdot \mathbf{n}\,dS$, where S is the hemisphere $x^2 + y^2 + z^2 = a^2$, for $z \geq 0$, where $r = |\langle x, y, z \rangle|$

51. $\iint_S |\mathbf{r}|\,dS$, where S is the cylinder $x^2 + y^2 = 4$, for $0 \leq z \leq 8$, where $\mathbf{r} = \langle x, y, z \rangle$

52. $\iint_S xyz\,dS$, where S is that part of the plane $z = 6 - y$ that lies in the cylinder $x^2 + y^2 = 4$

53. $\displaystyle\iint_S \frac{\langle x, 0, z \rangle}{\sqrt{x^2 + z^2}} \cdot \mathbf{n}\,dS$, where S is the cylinder $x^2 + z^2 = a^2$, $|y| \leq 2$

54. Cone and sphere The cone $z^2 = x^2 + y^2$, for $z \geq 0$, cuts the sphere $x^2 + y^2 + z^2 = 16$ along a curve C.

a. Find the surface area of the sphere below C, for $z \geq 0$.
b. Find the surface area of the sphere above C.
c. Find the surface area of the cone below C, for $z \geq 0$.

55. Cylinder and sphere Consider the sphere $x^2 + y^2 + z^2 = 4$ and the cylinder $(x - 1)^2 + y^2 = 1$, for $z \geq 0$.

a. Find the surface area of the cylinder inside the sphere.
b. Find the surface area of the sphere inside the cylinder.

56. Flux on a tetrahedron Find the upward flux of the field $\mathbf{F} = \langle x, y, z \rangle$ across the plane $x/a + y/b + z/c = 1$ in the first octant. Show that the flux equals c times the area of the base of the region. Interpret the result physically.

57. Flux across a cone Consider the field $\mathbf{F} = \langle x, y, z \rangle$ and the cone $z^2 = (x^2 + y^2)/a^2$, for $0 \leq z \leq 1$.

a. Show that when $a = 1$, the outward flux across the cone is zero. Interpret the result.

b. Find the outward flux (away from the z-axis), for any $a > 0$. Interpret the result.

58. Surface area formula for cones Find the general formula for the surface area of a cone with height h and base radius a (excluding the base).

59. Surface area formula for spherical cap A sphere of radius a is sliced parallel to the equatorial plane at a distance $a - h$ from the equatorial plane (see figure). Find the general formula for the surface area of the resulting spherical cap (excluding the base) with thickness h.

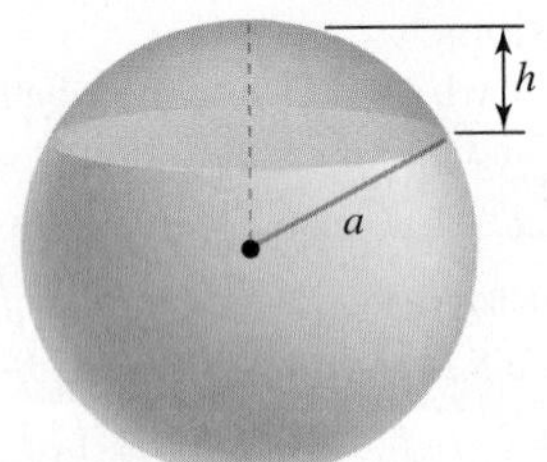

60. Radial fields and spheres Consider the radial field $\mathbf{F} = \mathbf{r}/|\mathbf{r}|^p$, where $\mathbf{r} = \langle x, y, z \rangle$ and p is a real number. Let S be the sphere of radius a centered at the origin. Show that the outward flux of $\mathbf{F}$ across the sphere is $4\pi/a^{p-3}$. It is instructive to do the calculation using both an explicit and parametric description of the sphere.

Applications

61–63. Heat flux *The heat flow vector field for conducting objects is $\mathbf{F} = -k\nabla T$, where $T(x, y, z)$ is the temperature in the object and $k > 0$ is a constant that depends on the material. Compute the outward flux of $\mathbf{F}$ across the following surfaces S for the given temperature distributions. Assume $k = 1$.*

61. $T(x, y, z) = 100e^{-x-y}$; S consists of the faces of the cube $|x| \leq 1, |y| \leq 1, |z| \leq 1$.

62. $T(x, y, z) = 100e^{-x^2-y^2-z^2}$; S is the sphere $x^2 + y^2 + z^2 = a^2$.

63. $T(x, y, z) = -\ln(x^2 + y^2 + z^2)$; S is the sphere $x^2 + y^2 + z^2 = a^2$.

64. Flux across a cylinder Let S be the cylinder $x^2 + y^2 = a^2$, for $-L \leq z \leq L$.

a. Find the outward flux of the field $\mathbf{F} = \langle x, y, 0 \rangle$ across S.

b. Find the outward flux of the field $\mathbf{F} = \dfrac{\langle x, y, 0 \rangle}{(x^2 + y^2)^{p/2}} = \dfrac{\mathbf{r}}{|\mathbf{r}|^p}$ across S, where $|\mathbf{r}|$ is the distance from the z-axis and p is a real number.

c. In part (b), for what values of p is the flux finite as $a \to \infty$ (with L fixed)?

d. In part (b), for what values of p is the flux finite as $L \to \infty$ (with a fixed)?

65. Flux across concentric spheres Consider the radial fields $\mathbf{F} = \dfrac{\langle x, y, z \rangle}{(x^2 + y^2 + z^2)^{p/2}} = \dfrac{\mathbf{r}}{|\mathbf{r}|^p}$, where p is a real number. Let S consist of the spheres A and B centered at the origin with radii $0 < a < b$, respectively. The total outward flux across S consists of the *outward* flux across the outer sphere B minus the flux into S across the inner sphere A.

a. Find the total flux across S with $p = 0$. Interpret the result.

b. Show that for $p = 3$ (an inverse square law), the flux across S is independent of a and b.

66–69. Mass and center of mass *Let S be a surface that represents a thin shell with density ρ. The moments about the coordinate planes (see Section 14.6) are $M_{yz} = \iint_S x\rho(x, y, z)\, dS$, $M_{xz} = \iint_S y\rho(x, y, z)\, dS$, $M_{xy} = \iint_S z\rho(x, y, z)\, dS$. The coordinates of the center of mass of the shell are $\bar{x} = \dfrac{M_{yz}}{m}$, $\bar{y} = \dfrac{M_{xz}}{m}$, $\bar{z} = \dfrac{M_{xy}}{m}$, where m is the mass of the shell. Find the mass and center of mass of the following shells. Use symmetry whenever possible.*

66. The constant-density hemispherical shell $x^2 + y^2 + z^2 = a^2, z \geq 0$

67. The constant-density cone with radius a, height h, and base in the xy-plane

68. The constant-density half cylinder $x^2 + z^2 = a^2, -h/2 \leq y \leq h/2, z \geq 0$

69. The cylinder $x^2 + y^2 = a^2, 0 \leq z \leq 2$, with density $\rho(x, y, z) = 1 + z$

Additional Exercises

70. Outward normal to a sphere Show that $|\mathbf{t}_u \times \mathbf{t}_v| = a^2 \sin u$ for a sphere of radius a defined parametrically by $\mathbf{r}(u, v) = \langle a \sin u \cos v, a \sin u \sin v, a \cos u \rangle$, where $0 \leq u \leq \pi$ and $0 \leq v \leq 2\pi$.

71. Special case of surface integrals of scalar-valued functions Suppose that a surface S is defined as $z = g(x, y)$ on a region R. Show that $\mathbf{t}_x \times \mathbf{t}_y = \langle -z_x, -z_y, 1 \rangle$ and that $\iint_S f(x, y, z)\, dS = \iint_R f(x, y, z) \sqrt{z_x^{\,2} + z_y^{\,2} + 1}\, dA$.

72. Surfaces of revolution Let $y = f(x)$ be a curve in the xy-plane with $f(x) \neq 0$, for $a \leq x \leq b$. Let S be the surface generated when the graph of f on $[a, b]$ is revolved about the x-axis.

a. Show that S is described parametrically by $\mathbf{r}(u, v) = \langle u, f(u) \cos v, f(u) \sin v \rangle$, for $a \leq u \leq b, 0 \leq v \leq 2\pi$.

b. Find an integral that gives the surface area of S.

c. Apply the result of part (b) to the surface generated with $f(x) = x^3$, for $1 \leq x \leq 2$.

d. Apply the result of part (b) to the surface generated with $f(x) = (25 - x^2)^{1/2}$, for $3 \leq x \leq 4$.

73. Rain on roofs Let $z = s(x, y)$ define a surface over a region R in the xy-plane, where $z \geq 0$ on R. Show that the downward flux of the vertical vector field $\mathbf{F} = \langle 0, 0, -1 \rangle$ across S equals the area of R. Interpret the result physically.

74. Surface area of a torus

a. Show that a torus with radii $R > r$ (see figure) may be described parametrically by

$$r(u, v) = \langle (R + r\cos u)\cos v, (R + r\cos u)\sin v, r\sin u\rangle,$$

for $0 \le u \le 2\pi$, $0 \le v \le 2\pi$.

b. Show that the surface area of the torus is $4\pi^2 Rr$.

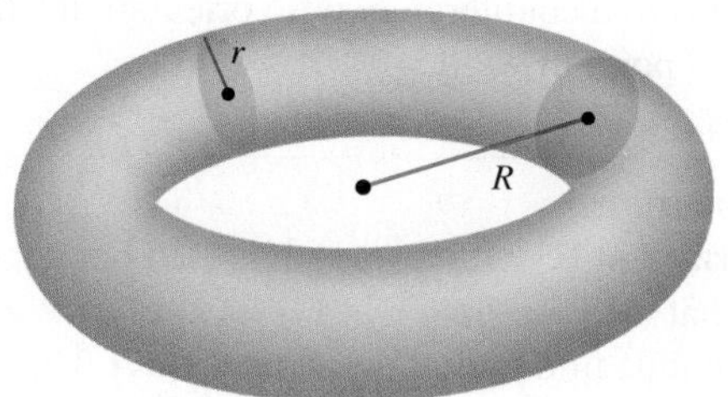

QUICK CHECK ANSWERS

1. A half cylinder with height 1 and radius 2 with its axis along the z-axis **2.** A half-cone with height 10 and radius 10 with its axis along the z-axis **3.** A quarter sphere with radius 4 **4.** $\sqrt{2}$ **5.** The cylinder $x^2 + y^2 = a^2$ does not represent a function, so z_x and z_y cannot be computed. **6.** The vector field is everywhere orthogonal to the hemisphere, so the hemisphere has maximum flux at every point. ◄

15.7 Stokes' Theorem

➤ Born in Ireland, George Gabriel Stokes (1819–1903) led a long and distinguished life as one of the prominent mathematicians and physicists of his day. He entered Cambridge University as a student and remained there as a professor for most of his life, taking the Lucasian chair of mathematics, once held by Sir Isaac Newton. The first statement of Stokes' Theorem was given by William Thomson (Lord Kelvin).

With the divergence, the curl, and surface integrals in hand, we are ready to present two of the crowning results of calculus. Fortunately, all of the heavy lifting has been done. In this section, you will see Stokes' Theorem, and in the next section we present the Divergence Theorem.

Stokes' Theorem

Stokes' Theorem is the three-dimensional version of the circulation form of Green's Theorem. Recall that if C is a closed simple smooth oriented curve in the xy-plane enclosing a region R and $\mathbf{F} = \langle f, g\rangle$ is a differentiable vector field on R, Green's Theorem says that

$$\underbrace{\oint_C \mathbf{F}\cdot d\mathbf{r}}_{\text{circulation}} = \iint_R \underbrace{(g_x - f_y)}_{\text{curl or rotation}}\, dA.$$

The line integral on the left gives the circulation along the boundary of R. The double integral on the right sums the curl of the vector field over all points of R. If $\mathbf{F}$ represents a fluid flow, the theorem says the cumulative rotation of the flow within R equals the circulation along the boundary.

In Stokes' Theorem, the plane region R in Green's Theorem becomes an oriented surface S in $\mathbf{R}^3$. The circulation integral in Green's Theorem remains a circulation integral, but now over the closed simple smooth oriented curve C that forms the boundary of S. The double integral of the curl in Green's Theorem becomes a surface integral of the three-dimensional curl (Figure 15.58).

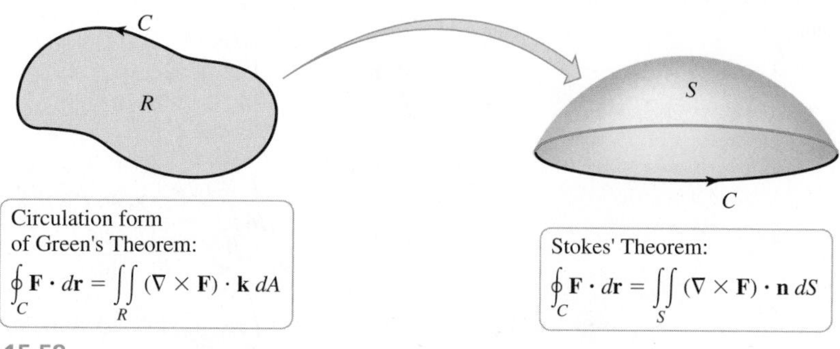

FIGURE 15.58

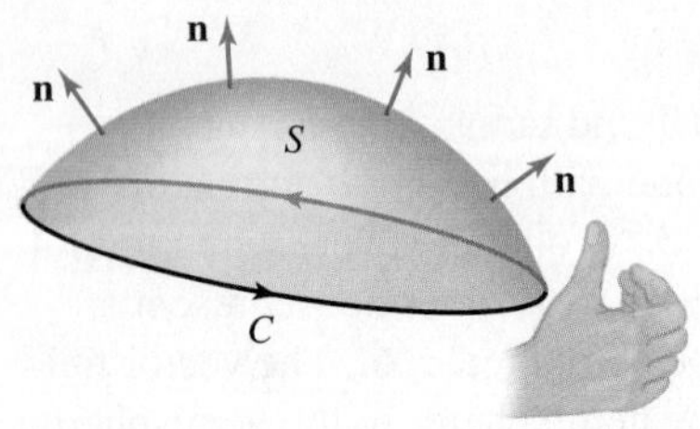

FIGURE 15.59

➤ The right-hand rule tells you which of two normal vectors at a point of S to use; for example, the general direction may be upward rather than downward. Remember that the direction of normal vectors changes continuously on an oriented surface.

Stokes' Theorem involves an oriented curve C and an oriented surface S on which there are two unit normal vectors at every point. These orientations must be consistent and the normal vectors must be chosen correctly. Here is the right-hand rule that relates the orientations of S and C, and determines the choice of the normal vectors:

> If the fingers of your right hand curl in the positive direction around C, then your right thumb points in the (general) direction of the vectors normal to S (Figure 15.59).

A common situation occurs when C has a counterclockwise orientation when viewed from above; then, the vectors normal to S point upward.

THEOREM 15.13 Stokes' Theorem
Let S be a smooth oriented surface in $\mathbf{R}^3$ with a smooth closed boundary C whose orientation is consistent with that of S. Assume that $\mathbf{F} = \langle f, g, h \rangle$ is a vector field whose components have continuous first partial derivatives on S. Then

$$\oint_C \mathbf{F} \cdot d\mathbf{r} = \iint_S (\nabla \times \mathbf{F}) \cdot \mathbf{n}\, dS,$$

where $\mathbf{n}$ is the unit vector normal to S determined by the orientation of S.

QUICK CHECK 1 Suppose that S is a region in the xy-plane with a boundary oriented counterclockwise. What is the normal to S? Explain why Stokes' Theorem becomes the circulation form of Green's Theorem. ◄

The meaning of Stokes' Theorem is much the same as for the circulation form of Green's Theorem: Under the proper conditions, the accumulated rotation of the vector field over the surface S (as given by the normal component of the curl) equals the net circulation on the boundary of S. An outline of the proof of Stokes' Theorem is given at the end of this section. First, we look at some special cases and give further insight into the theorem with examples.

If $\mathbf{F}$ is a conservative vector field on a domain D, then it has a potential function φ such that $\mathbf{F} = \nabla\varphi$. Because $\nabla \times \nabla\varphi = \mathbf{0}$, it follows that $\nabla \times \mathbf{F} = \mathbf{0}$ (Theorem 15.9); therefore, the circulation integral is zero on all closed curves in D. Recall that the circulation integral is also a work integral for the force field $\mathbf{F}$, which emphasizes the fact that no work is done in moving an object on a closed path in a conservative force field. Among the important conservative vector fields are the radial fields $\mathbf{F} = \mathbf{r}/|\mathbf{r}|^p$, which generally have zero curl and zero circulation on closed curves.

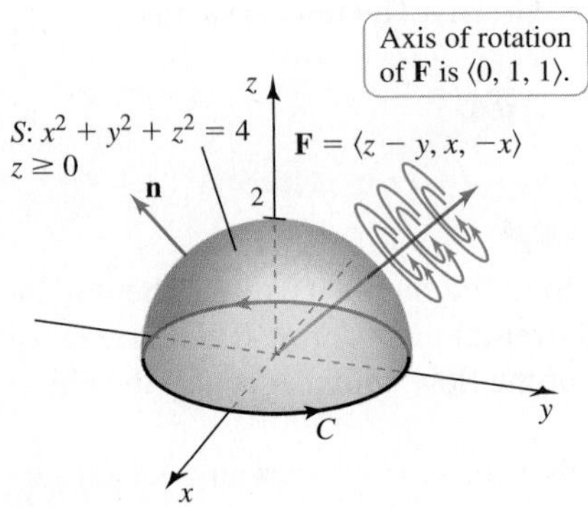

FIGURE 15.60

➤ Recall that for a constant nonzero vector $\mathbf{a}$ and the position vector $\mathbf{r} = \langle x, y, z \rangle$, the field $\mathbf{F} = \mathbf{a} \times \mathbf{r}$ is a rotational field. In Example 1,

$$\mathbf{F} = \langle 0, 1, 1 \rangle \times \langle x, y, z \rangle.$$

EXAMPLE 1 Verifying Stokes' Theorem Confirm that Stokes' Theorem holds for the vector field $\mathbf{F} = \langle z - y, x, -x \rangle$, where S is the hemisphere $x^2 + y^2 + z^2 = 4$, for $z \geq 0$, and C is the circle $x^2 + y^2 = 4$ oriented counterclockwise.

SOLUTION The orientation of C says that the vectors normal to S point in the outward direction. The vector field is a rotation field $\mathbf{a} \times \mathbf{r}$, where $\mathbf{a} = \langle 0, 1, 1 \rangle$ and $\mathbf{r} = \langle x, y, z \rangle$; so the axis of rotation points in the direction of the vector $\langle 0, 1, 1 \rangle$ (Figure 15.60). We first compute the circulation integral in Stokes' Theorem. The curve C with the given orientation is parameterized as $\mathbf{r}(t) = \langle 2\cos t, 2\sin t, 0 \rangle$, for $0 \leq t \leq 2\pi$; therefore, $\mathbf{r}'(t) = \langle -2\sin t, 2\cos t, 0 \rangle$. The circulation integral is

$$\oint_C \mathbf{F} \cdot d\mathbf{r} = \int_0^{2\pi} \mathbf{F} \cdot \mathbf{r}'(t)\, dt \qquad \text{Definition of line integral}$$

$$= \int_0^{2\pi} \langle \underbrace{z - y}_{0 - 2\sin t}, \underbrace{x}_{2\cos t}, -x \rangle \cdot \langle -2\sin t, 2\cos t, 0 \rangle\, dt \qquad \text{Substitute.}$$

$$= \int_0^{2\pi} 4(\sin^2 t + \cos^2 t)\, dt \qquad \text{Simplify.}$$

$$= 4\int_0^{2\pi} dt \qquad \sin^2 t + \cos^2 t = 1$$

$$= 8\pi. \qquad \text{Evaluate the integral.}$$

The surface integral requires computing the curl of the vector field:

$$\nabla \times \mathbf{F} = \nabla \times \langle z - y, x, -x \rangle = \begin{vmatrix} \mathbf{i} & \mathbf{j} & \mathbf{k} \\ \dfrac{\partial}{\partial x} & \dfrac{\partial}{\partial y} & \dfrac{\partial}{\partial z} \\ z - y & x & -x \end{vmatrix} = \langle 0, 2, 2 \rangle.$$

Recall from Section 15.6 (Table 15.2) that an outward normal to the hemisphere is $\langle x/z, y/z, 1 \rangle$. The region of integration is the base of the hemisphere in the xy-plane, which is

$$\mathbf{R} = \{(x, y): x^2 + y^2 \le 4\} = \{(r, \theta): 0 \le r \le 2, 0 \le \theta \le 2\pi\}.$$

Combining these results, the surface integral in Stokes' Theorem is

$$\iint_S \underbrace{(\nabla \times \mathbf{F})}_{\langle 0,2,2\rangle} \cdot \mathbf{n}\, dS = \iint_R \langle 0, 2, 2 \rangle \cdot \left\langle \frac{x}{z}, \frac{y}{z}, 1 \right\rangle dA \qquad \text{Substitute and convert to a double integral over } R.$$

$$= \iint_R \left(\frac{2y}{\sqrt{4 - x^2 - y^2}} + 2 \right) dA \qquad \text{Simplify and use } z = \sqrt{4 - x^2 - y^2}.$$

$$= \int_0^{2\pi} \int_0^2 \left(\frac{2r \sin \theta}{\sqrt{4 - r^2}} + 2 \right) r\, dr\, d\theta. \qquad \text{Convert to polar coordinates.}$$

➤ In eliminating the first term of this double integral, we note that the improper integral $\displaystyle\int_0^2 \frac{r^2}{\sqrt{4 - r^2}}\, dr$ has a finite value.

We integrate first with respect to θ because the integral of $\sin \theta$ from 0 to 2π is zero and the first term in the integral is eliminated. Therefore, the surface integral reduces to

$$\iint_S (\nabla \times \mathbf{F}) \cdot \mathbf{n}\, dS = \int_0^2 \int_0^{2\pi} \left(\frac{2r^2 \sin \theta}{\sqrt{4 - r^2}} + 2r \right) d\theta\, dr$$

$$= \int_0^2 \int_0^{2\pi} 2r\, d\theta\, dr \qquad \int_0^{2\pi} \sin \theta\, d\theta = 0$$

$$= 4\pi \int_0^2 r\, dr \qquad \text{Evaluate the inner integral.}$$

$$= 8\pi. \qquad \text{Evaluate the outer integral.}$$

Computed either as a line integral or a surface integral, the vector field has a positive circulation along the boundary of S, which is produced by the net rotation of the field over the surface S.

Related Exercises 5–10 ◀

In Example 1, it was possible to evaluate both sides of Stokes' Theorem. Often the theorem provides an easier way to evaluate difficult line integrals.

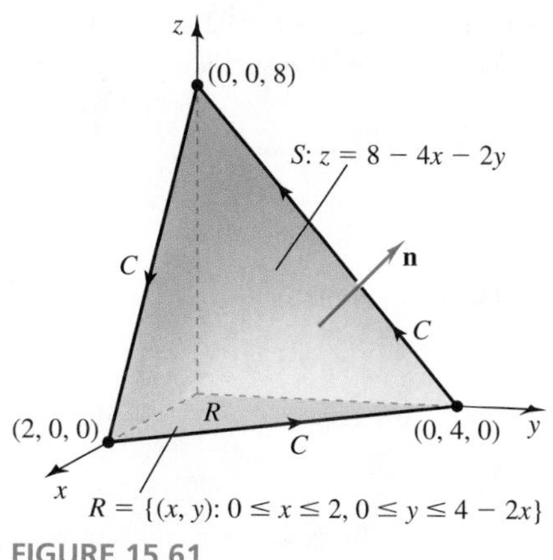

FIGURE 15.61

EXAMPLE 2 Using Stokes' Theorem to evaluate a line integral Evaluate the line integral $\oint_C \mathbf{F} \cdot d\mathbf{r}$, where $\mathbf{F} = z\mathbf{i} - z\mathbf{j} + (x^2 - y^2)\mathbf{k}$ and C consists of the three line segments that bound the plane $z = 8 - 4x - 2y$ in the first octant, oriented as shown in Figure 15.61.

SOLUTION Evaluating the line integral directly involves parameterizing the three line segments. Instead, we use Stokes' Theorem to convert the line integral to a surface integral, where S is that portion of the plane $z = 8 - 4x - 2y$ that lies in the first octant. The curl of the vector field is

$$\nabla \times \mathbf{F} = \nabla \times \langle z, -z, x^2 - y^2 \rangle = \begin{vmatrix} \mathbf{i} & \mathbf{j} & \mathbf{k} \\ \dfrac{\partial}{\partial x} & \dfrac{\partial}{\partial y} & \dfrac{\partial}{\partial z} \\ z & -z & x^2 - y^2 \end{vmatrix} = \langle 1 - 2y, 1 - 2x, 0 \rangle.$$

➤ Recall that for an explicitly defined surface S given by $z = g(x, y)$ over a region R with $\mathbf{F} = \langle f, g, h \rangle$

$$\iint_S \mathbf{F} \cdot \mathbf{n}\, dS = \iint_R (-f z_x - g z_y + h)\, dA.$$

In Example 2, $\mathbf{F}$ is replaced by $\nabla \times \mathbf{F}$.

The appropriate vector normal to the plane $z = 8 - 4x - 2y$ is $\langle -z_x, -z_y, 1 \rangle = \langle 4, 2, 1 \rangle$, which points upward, consistent with the orientation of C. The triangular region R in the xy-plane beneath the plane is found by setting $z = 0$ in the equation of the plane; we find that $R = \{(x, y): 0 \le x \le 2, 0 \le y \le 4 - 2x\}$. The surface integral in Stokes' Theorem may now be evaluated:

$$\iint_S \underbrace{(\nabla \times \mathbf{F})}_{\langle 1-2y,\, 1-2x,\, 0 \rangle} \cdot \mathbf{n}\, dS = \iint_R \langle 1 - 2y, 1 - 2x, 0 \rangle \cdot \langle 4, 2, 1 \rangle\, dA \quad \text{Substitute and convert to a double integral over } R.$$

$$= \int_0^2 \int_0^{4-2x} (6 - 4x - 8y)\, dy\, dx \quad \text{Simplify.}$$

$$= -\frac{88}{3} \quad \text{Evaluate the integrals.}$$

The circulation around the boundary of R is negative, indicating a net circulation in the clockwise direction (looking from above) on C. *Related Exercises 11–16* ◀

In other situations, Stokes' Theorem may be used to convert a difficult surface integral into a relatively easy line integral, as illustrated in the next example.

EXAMPLE 3 Using Stokes' Theorem to evaluate a surface integral Evaluate the integral $\iint_S (\nabla \times \mathbf{F}) \cdot \mathbf{n}\, dS$, where $\mathbf{F} = -xz\mathbf{i} + yz\mathbf{j} + xye^z\mathbf{k}$ and S is the cap of the paraboloid $z = 5 - x^2 - y^2$ above the plane $z = 3$ (Figure 15.62). Assume $\mathbf{n}$ points in the positive z-direction on S.

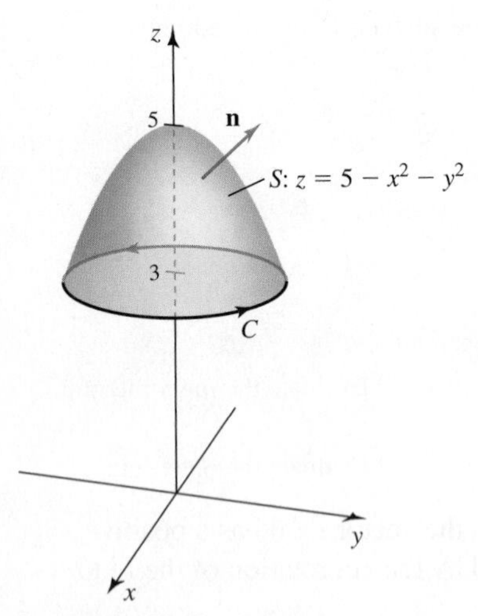

FIGURE 15.62

SOLUTION We use Stokes' Theorem to convert the surface integral to a line integral along the curve C that bounds S. That curve is the intersection between the paraboloid $z = 5 - x^2 - y^2$ and the plane $z = 3$. Eliminating z from these equations, we find that C is the circle $x^2 + y^2 = 2$, with $z = 3$. By the orientation of S, we see that C is oriented counterclockwise, so a parametric description of C is $\mathbf{r}(t) = \langle \sqrt{2} \cos t, \sqrt{2} \sin t, 3 \rangle$, which implies that $\mathbf{r}'(t) = \langle -\sqrt{2} \sin t, \sqrt{2} \cos t, 0 \rangle$. The value of the surface integral is

$$\iint_S (\nabla \times \mathbf{F}) \cdot \mathbf{n}\, dS = \oint_C \mathbf{F} \cdot d\mathbf{r} \quad \text{Stokes' Theorem}$$

$$= \int_0^{2\pi} \mathbf{F} \cdot \mathbf{r}'(t)\, dt \quad \text{Definition of line integral}$$

$$= \int_0^{2\pi} \langle -xz, yz, xye^z \rangle \cdot \langle -\sqrt{2} \sin t, \sqrt{2} \cos t, 0 \rangle\, dt \quad \text{Substitute.}$$

$$= \int_0^{2\pi} 12 \sin t \cos t\, dt \quad \text{Substitute for } x, y, \text{ and } z, \text{ and simplify.}$$

$$= 6 \int_0^{2\pi} \sin 2t\, dt = 0. \quad \sin 2t = 2 \sin t \cos t$$

Related Exercises 17–20 ◀

QUICK CHECK 2 In Example 3, the z-component of the vector field did not enter the calculation; it could have been anything. Explain why. ◀

Interpreting the Curl

Stokes' Theorem leads to another interpretation of the curl at a point in a vector field. We need the idea of the **average circulation**. If C is the boundary of an oriented surface S, we define the average circulation of $\mathbf{F}$ over S as

$$\frac{1}{\text{area }(S)}\oint_C \mathbf{F}\cdot d\mathbf{r} = \frac{1}{\text{area }(S)}\iint_S (\nabla \times \mathbf{F})\cdot \mathbf{n}\, dS,$$

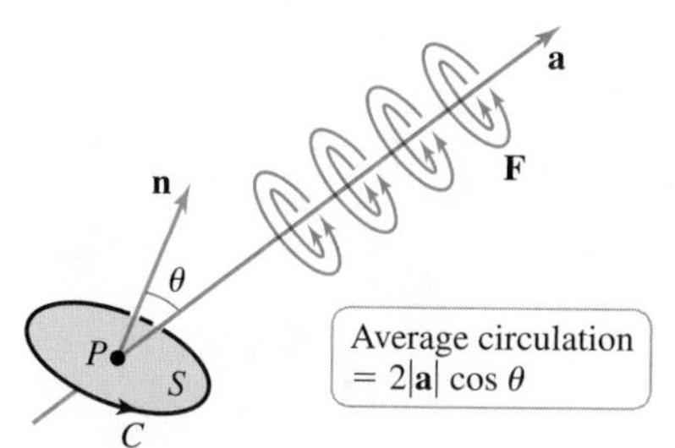

FIGURE 15.63

where Stokes' theorem is used to convert the circulation integral to a surface integral.

First consider a general rotation field $\mathbf{F} = \mathbf{a} \times \mathbf{r}$, where $\mathbf{a} = \langle a_1, a_2, a_3\rangle$ is a constant nonzero vector and $\mathbf{r} = \langle x, y, z\rangle$. Recall that $\mathbf{F}$ describes the rotation about an axis in the direction of $\mathbf{a}$ with angular speed $\omega = |\mathbf{a}|$. We also showed that $\mathbf{F}$ has a constant curl, $\nabla \times \mathbf{F} = \nabla \times (\mathbf{a} \times \mathbf{r}) = 2\mathbf{a}$. We now take S to be a small circular disk centered at a point P, whose normal vector $\mathbf{n}$ makes an angle θ with the axis $\mathbf{a}$ (Figure 15.63). Let C be the boundary of S with a counterclockwise orientation.

The average circulation of this vector field on S is

➤ Recall that $\mathbf{n}$ is a unit normal vector with $|\mathbf{n}| = 1$. By definition, the dot product gives $\mathbf{a}\cdot\mathbf{n} = |\mathbf{a}|\cos\theta$.

$$\frac{1}{\text{area }(S)}\iint_S \underbrace{(\nabla \times \mathbf{F})\cdot \mathbf{n}}_{\text{constant}}\, dS \qquad \text{Definition}$$

$$= \frac{1}{\text{area }(S)}(\nabla \times \mathbf{F})\cdot \mathbf{n}\cdot \text{area }(S) \qquad \iint_S dS = \text{area }(S)$$

$$= \underbrace{(\nabla \times \mathbf{F})}_{2\mathbf{a}}\cdot \mathbf{n} \qquad \text{Simplify.}$$

$$= 2|\mathbf{a}|\cos\theta. \qquad |\mathbf{n}| = 1, |\nabla \times \mathbf{F}| = 2|\mathbf{a}|$$

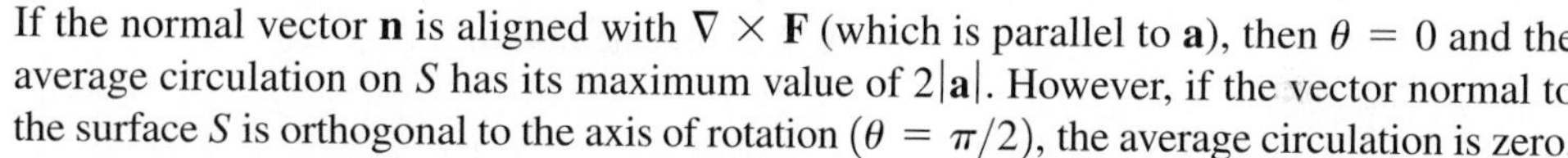

If the normal vector $\mathbf{n}$ is aligned with $\nabla \times \mathbf{F}$ (which is parallel to $\mathbf{a}$), then $\theta = 0$ and the average circulation on S has its maximum value of $2|\mathbf{a}|$. However, if the vector normal to the surface S is orthogonal to the axis of rotation ($\theta = \pi/2$), the average circulation is zero.

We see that for a general rotation field $\mathbf{F} = \mathbf{a} \times \mathbf{r}$, the curl of $\mathbf{F}$ has the following interpretations, where S is a small disk centered at a point P with a normal vector $\mathbf{n}$:

- The scalar component of $\nabla \times \mathbf{F}$ at P in the direction of $\mathbf{n}$ is the average circulation of $\mathbf{F}$ on S.
- The direction of $\nabla \times \mathbf{F}$ at P is the direction that maximizes the average circulation of $\mathbf{F}$ on S. Equivalently, it is the direction in which you should orient the axis of a paddle wheel to obtain the maximum angular speed.

A similar argument may be applied to a general vector field (with a variable curl) to give an analogous interpretation of the curl at a point (Exercise 44).

EXAMPLE 4 **Horizontal channel flow** Consider the velocity field $\mathbf{v} = \langle 0, 1 - x^2, 0\rangle$, for $|x| \le 1$ and $|z| \le 1$, which represents a horizontal flow in the y-direction (Figure 15.64a).

a. Suppose you place a paddle wheel at the point $P\left(\frac{1}{2}, 0, 0\right)$. Using physical arguments, in which of the coordinate directions should the axis of the wheel point in order for the wheel to spin? In which direction does it spin?

b. Compute and graph the curl of $\mathbf{v}$ and provide an interpretation.

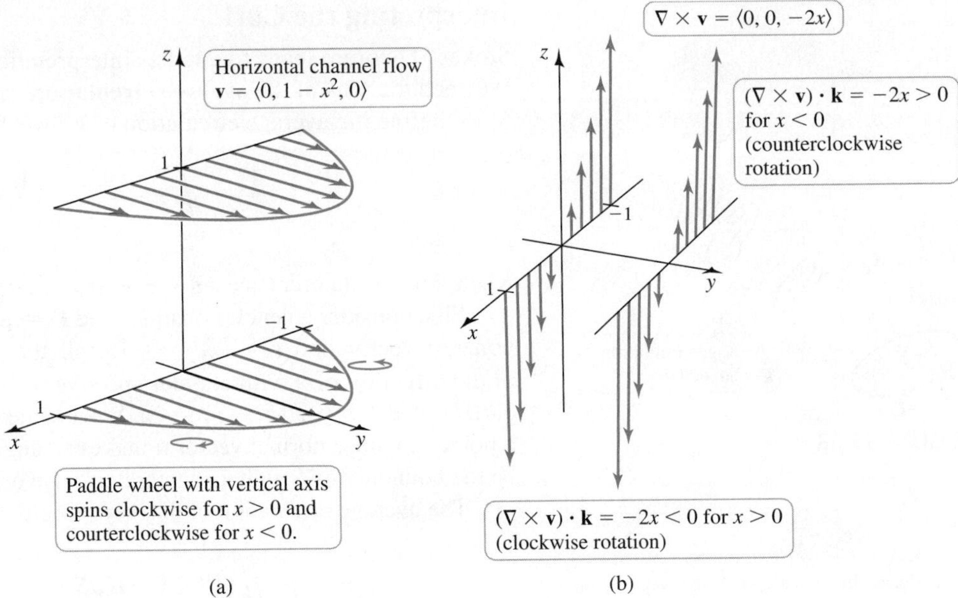

FIGURE 15.64

SOLUTION

a. If the axis of the wheel is aligned with the x-axis at P, the flow strikes the upper and lower halves of the wheel symmetrically and the wheel does not spin. If the axis of the wheel is aligned with the y-axis, the flow strikes the face of the wheel and it does not spin. If the axis of the wheel is aligned with the z-axis at P, the flow in the y-direction is greater for $x < \frac{1}{2}$ than it is for $x > \frac{1}{2}$. Therefore, a wheel located at $\left(\frac{1}{2}, 0, 0\right)$ spins in the clockwise direction, looking from above.

b. A short calculation shows that

$$\nabla \times \mathbf{v} = \begin{vmatrix} \mathbf{i} & \mathbf{j} & \mathbf{k} \\ \dfrac{\partial}{\partial x} & \dfrac{\partial}{\partial y} & \dfrac{\partial}{\partial z} \\ 0 & 1 - x^2 & 0 \end{vmatrix} = -2x\,\mathbf{k}.$$

As shown in Figure 15.64b, the curl points in the z-direction, which is the direction of the paddle wheel axis that gives the maximum angular speed of the wheel. Consider the z-component of the curl, which is $(\nabla \times \mathbf{v}) \cdot \mathbf{k} = -2x$. At $x = 0$, this component is zero, meaning the wheel does not spin at any point along the y-axis when its axis of the wheel is aligned with the z-axis. For $x > 0$, we see that $(\nabla \times \mathbf{v}) \cdot \mathbf{k} < 0$, which corresponds to clockwise rotation of the vector field. For $x < 0$, we have $(\nabla \times \mathbf{v}) \cdot \mathbf{k} > 0$, corresponding to counterclockwise rotation. *Related Exercises 21–24*

QUICK CHECK 3 In Example 4, explain why a paddle wheel with its axis aligned with the z-axis does not spin when placed on the y-axis.

Proof of Stokes' Theorem

The proof of the most general case of Stokes' Theorem is intricate. However, a proof of a special case is instructive and it relies on several previous results.

Consider the case in which the surface S is the graph of the function $z = s(x, y)$, defined on a region in the xy-plane. Let C be the curve that bounds S with a counterclockwise orientation, and let R be the projection of S and C' the projection of C in the xy-plane (Figure 15.65).

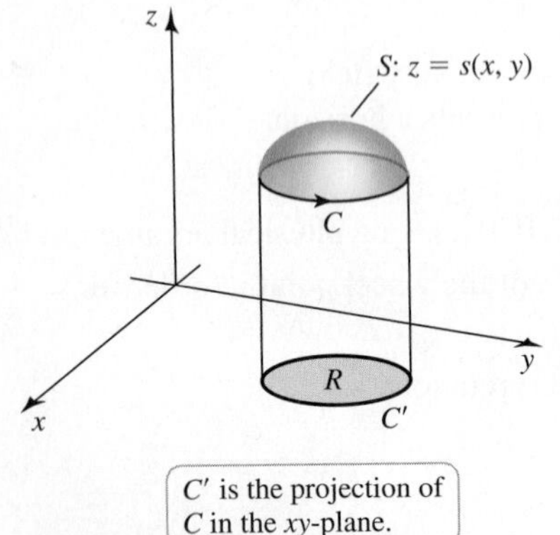

C′ is the projection of C in the xy-plane.

FIGURE 15.65

Letting $\mathbf{F} = \langle f, g, h \rangle$, the line integral in Stokes' Theorem is

$$\oint_C \mathbf{F} \cdot d\mathbf{r} = \oint_C f\,dx + g\,dy + h\,dz.$$

The key observation for this integral is that along C, $dz = z_x\,dx + z_y\,dy$. Making this substitution, we convert the line integral on C to a line integral on C' in the xy-plane:

$$\oint_C \mathbf{F}\cdot d\mathbf{r} = \oint_{C'} f\,dx + g\,dy + h(\underbrace{z_x\,dx + z_y\,dy}_{dz})$$

$$= \oint_{C'} \underbrace{(f + hz_x)}_{M(x,y)}\,dx + \underbrace{(g + hz_y)}_{N(x,y)}\,dy$$

We now apply the circulation form of Green's Theorem to this line integral with $M(x, y) = f + hz_x$ and $N(x, y) = g + hz_y$; the result is

$$\oint_{C'} M\,dx + N\,dy = \iint_R (N_x - M_y)\,dA.$$

A careful application of the Chain Rule (remembering that z is a function of x and y, Exercise 45) reveals that

$$M_y = f_y + f_z\,z_y + hz_{xy} + z_x(h_y + h_z z_y) \quad \text{and}$$
$$N_x = g_x + g_z\,z_x + hz_{yx} + z_y(h_x + h_z z_x)$$

Making these substitutions in the line integral and simplifying (note that $z_{xy} = z_{yx}$ is needed), we have

$$\oint_C \mathbf{F}\cdot d\mathbf{r} = \iint_R (z_x(g_z - h_y) + z_y(h_x - f_z) + (g_x - f_y))\,dA. \quad (1)$$

Now let's look at the surface integral in Stokes' Theorem. The upward vector normal to the surface is $\langle -z_x, -z_y, 1\rangle$. Substituting the components of $\nabla \times \mathbf{F}$ the surface integral takes the form

$$\iint_S (\nabla \times \mathbf{F})\cdot\mathbf{n}\,dS = \iint_R ((h_y - g_z)(-z_x) + (f_z - h_x)(-z_y) + (g_x - f_y))\,dA,$$

which upon rearrangement becomes the integral in (1). ◄

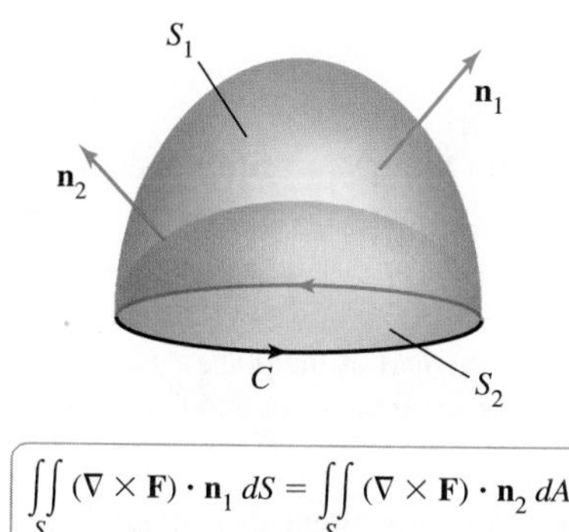

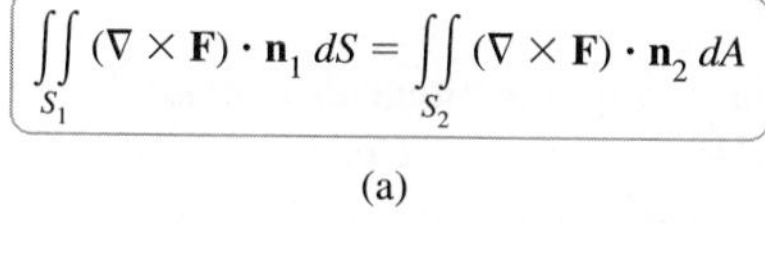

$$\iint_{S_1} (\nabla \times \mathbf{F})\cdot\mathbf{n}_1\,dS = \iint_{S_2} (\nabla \times \mathbf{F})\cdot\mathbf{n}_2\,dA$$

(a)

$S = S_1 \cup S_2$

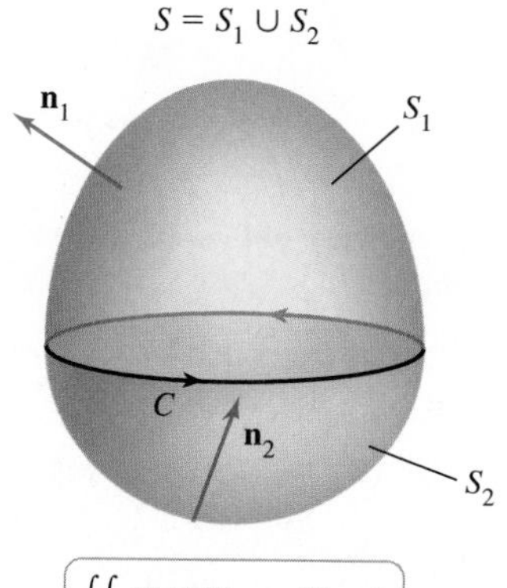

$$\iint_S (\nabla \times \mathbf{F})\cdot\mathbf{n}\,dS = 0$$

(b)

FIGURE 15.66

Two Final Notes on Stokes' Theorem

1. Stokes' Theorem allows a surface integral $\iint_S (\nabla \times \mathbf{F})\cdot\mathbf{n}\,dS$ to be evaluated using only the values of the vector field on the boundary C. This means that if a closed curve C is the boundary of two different smooth oriented surfaces S_1 and S_2, which both have an orientation consistent with that of C, then the integrals of $(\nabla \times \mathbf{F})\cdot\mathbf{n}$ on the two surfaces are equal; that is,

$$\iint_{S_1} (\nabla \times \mathbf{F})\cdot\mathbf{n}_1\,dS = \iint_{S_2} (\nabla \times \mathbf{F})\cdot\mathbf{n}_2\,dS,$$

where $\mathbf{n}_1$ and $\mathbf{n}_2$ are the respective unit normal vectors consistent with the orientation of the surfaces (Figure 15.66a).

Now let's take a different perspective. Suppose S is a *closed* surface consisting of S_1 and S_2 with a common boundary curve C (Figure 15.66b). Let $\mathbf{n}$ be the outward normal vectors for the entire surface S. Either the vectors normal to S_1 point out of the enclosed region (in the direction of $\mathbf{n}$) and the vectors normal to S_2 point into that region (opposite $\mathbf{n}$), or vice versa. In either case, $\iint_{S_1} (\nabla \times \mathbf{F}) \cdot \mathbf{n}_1 \, dS$ and $\iint_{S_2} (\nabla \times \mathbf{F}) \cdot \mathbf{n}_2 \, dS$ are equal in magnitude and of opposite sign; therefore,

$$\iint_S (\nabla \times \mathbf{F}) \cdot \mathbf{n} \, dS = \iint_{S_1} (\nabla \times \mathbf{F}) \cdot \mathbf{n}_1 \, dS + \iint_{S_2} (\nabla \times \mathbf{F}) \cdot \mathbf{n}_2 \, dS = 0.$$

This argument can be adapted to show that $\iint_S (\nabla \times \mathbf{F}) \cdot \mathbf{n} \, dS = 0$ over any closed oriented surface S (Exercise 46).

2. We can now resolve an assertion made in Section 15.5. There we proved (Theorem 15.9) that if $\mathbf{F}$ is a conservative vector field, then $\nabla \times \mathbf{F} = \mathbf{0}$; we claimed, but did not prove, that the converse is true. The converse follows directly from Stokes' Theorem.

THEOREM 15.14 Curl F = 0 Implies F Is Conservative
Suppose that $\nabla \times \mathbf{F} = \mathbf{0}$ throughout an open simply connected region D of $\mathbf{R}^3$. Then $\oint_C \mathbf{F} \cdot d\mathbf{r} = 0$ on all closed simple smooth curves C in D and $\mathbf{F}$ is a conservative vector field.

Proof Given a closed simple smooth curve C, an advanced result states that C is the boundary of at least one smooth oriented surface S in D. By Stokes' Theorem

$$\oint_C \mathbf{F} \cdot d\mathbf{r} = \iint_S \underbrace{(\nabla \times \mathbf{F})}_{0} \cdot \mathbf{n} \, dS = 0.$$

Because the line integral equals zero over all such curves in D, the vector field is conservative on D by Theorem 15.5. ◄

SECTION 15.7 EXERCISES

Review Questions

1. Explain the meaning of the integral $\oint_C \mathbf{F} \cdot d\mathbf{r}$ in Stokes' Theorem.
2. Explain the meaning of the integral $\iint_S (\nabla \times \mathbf{F}) \cdot \mathbf{n} \, dS$ in Stokes' Theorem.
3. Explain the meaning of Stokes' Theorem.
4. Why does a conservative vector field produce zero circulation around a closed curve?

Basic Skills

5–10. Verifying Stokes' Theorem *Verify that the line integral and the surface integral of Stokes' Theorem are equal for the following vector fields, surfaces S, and closed curves C. Assume that C has counterclockwise orientation and S has a consistent orientation.*

5. $\mathbf{F} = \langle y, -x, 10 \rangle$; S is the upper half of the sphere $x^2 + y^2 + z^2 = 1$ and C is the circle $x^2 + y^2 = 1$ in the xy-plane.
6. $\mathbf{F} = \langle 0, -x, y \rangle$; S is the upper half of the sphere $x^2 + y^2 + z^2 = 4$ and C is the circle $x^2 + y^2 = 4$ in the xy-plane.
7. $\mathbf{F} = \langle x, y, z \rangle$; S is the paraboloid $z = 8 - x^2 - y^2$, for $0 \le z \le 8$, and C is the circle $x^2 + y^2 = 8$ in the xy-plane.
8. $\mathbf{F} = \langle 2z, -4x, 3y \rangle$; S is the cap of the sphere $x^2 + y^2 + z^2 = 169$ above the plane $z = 12$ and C is the boundary of S.
9. $\mathbf{F} = \langle y - z, z - x, x - y \rangle$; S is the cap of the sphere $x^2 + y^2 + z^2 = 16$ above the plane $z = \sqrt{7}$ and C is the boundary of S.
10. $\mathbf{F} = \langle -y, -x - z, y - x \rangle$; S is the part of the plane $z = 6 - y$ that lies in the cylinder $x^2 + y^2 = 16$ and C is the boundary of S.

11–16. Stokes' Theorem for evaluating line integrals *Evaluate the line integral $\oint_C \mathbf{F} \cdot d\mathbf{r}$ by evaluating the surface integral in Stokes' Theorem with an appropriate choice of S. Assume that C has a counterclockwise orientation.*

11. $\mathbf{F} = \langle 2y, -z, x \rangle$; C is the circle $x^2 + y^2 = 12$ in the plane $z = 0$.
12. $\mathbf{F} = \langle y, xz, -y \rangle$; C is the ellipse $x^2 + y^2/4 = 1$ in the plane $z = 1$.
13. $\mathbf{F} = \langle x^2 - z^2, y, 2xz \rangle$; C is the boundary of the plane $z = 4 - x - y$ in the first octant.
14. $\mathbf{F} = \langle x^2 - y^2, z^2 - x^2, y^2 - z^2 \rangle$; C is the boundary of the square $|x| \le 1$, $|y| \le 1$ in the plane $z = 0$.
15. $\mathbf{F} = \langle y^2, -z^2, x \rangle$; C is the circle $\mathbf{r}(t) = \langle 3 \cos t, 4 \cos t, 5 \sin t \rangle$, for $0 \le t \le 2\pi$.
16. $\mathbf{F} = \langle 2xy \sin z, x^2 \sin z, x^2 y \cos z \rangle$; C is the boundary of the plane $z = 8 - 2x - 4y$ in the first octant.

17–20. Stokes' Theorem for evaluating surface integrals *Evaluate the line integral in Stokes' Theorem to evaluate the surface integral $\iint_S (\nabla \times \mathbf{F}) \cdot \mathbf{n} \, dS$. Assume that $\mathbf{n}$ points in the positive z-direction.*

17. $\mathbf{F} = \langle x, y, z \rangle$; S is the upper half of the ellipsoid $x^2/4 + y^2/9 + z^2 = 1$.

18. $\mathbf{F} = \mathbf{r}/|\mathbf{r}|$; S is the paraboloid $x = 9 - y^2 - z^2$, for $0 \le x \le 9$ (excluding its base), and $\mathbf{r} = \langle x, y, z \rangle$.

19. $\mathbf{F} = \langle 2y, -z, x - y - z \rangle$; S is the cap of the sphere (excluding its base) $x^2 + y^2 + z^2 = 25$, for $3 \le x \le 5$.

20. $\mathbf{F} = \langle x + y, y + z, z + x \rangle$; S is the tilted disk enclosed by $\mathbf{r}(t) = \langle \cos t, 2 \sin t, \sqrt{3} \cos t \rangle$.

21–24. Interpreting and graphing the curl *For the following velocity fields, compute the curl, make a sketch of the curl, and interpret the curl.*

21. $\mathbf{v} = \langle 0, 0, y \rangle$

22. $\mathbf{v} = \langle 1 - z^2, 0, 0 \rangle$

23. $\mathbf{v} = \langle -2z, 0, 1 \rangle$

24. $\mathbf{v} = \langle 0, -z, y \rangle$

Further Explorations

25. Explain why or why not Determine whether the following statements are true and give an explanation or counterexample.

a. A paddle wheel with its axis in the direction $\langle 0, 1, -1 \rangle$ would not spin when put in the vector field $\mathbf{F} = \langle 1, 1, 2 \rangle \times \langle x, y, z \rangle$.

b. Stokes' Theorem relates the flux of a vector field $\mathbf{F}$ across a surface to the values of $\mathbf{F}$ on the boundary of the surface.

c. A vector field of the form $\mathbf{F} = \langle a + f(x), b + g(y), c + h(z) \rangle$, where a, b, and c are constants, has zero circulation on a closed curve.

d. If a vector field has zero circulation on all simple closed smooth curves C in a region D, then $\mathbf{F}$ is conservative on R.

26–29. Conservative fields *Use Stokes' Theorem to find the circulation of the following vector fields around any simple closed smooth curve C.*

26. $\mathbf{F} = \langle 2x, -2y, 2z \rangle$

27. $\mathbf{F} = \nabla(x \sin ye^z)$

28. $\mathbf{F} = \langle 3x^2y, x^3 + 2yz^2, 2y^2z \rangle$

29. $\mathbf{F} = \langle y^2z^3, 2xyz^3, 3xy^2z^2 \rangle$

30–34. Tilted disks *Let S be the disk enclosed by the curve* C: $\mathbf{r}(t) = \langle \cos \varphi \cos t, \sin t, \sin \varphi \cos t \rangle$, *for* $0 \le t \le 2\pi$, *where* $0 \le \varphi \le \pi/2$ *is a fixed angle.*

30. What is the area of S (in terms of φ)? Find a vector normal to S.

31. What is the length of C (in terms of φ)?

32. Use Stokes' Theorem and a surface integral to find the circulation on C of the vector field $\mathbf{F} = \langle -y, x, 0 \rangle$ as a function of φ. For what value of φ is the circulation a maximum?

33. What is the circulation on C of the vector field $\mathbf{F} = \langle -y, -z, x \rangle$ as a function of φ? For what value of φ is the circulation a maximum?

34. Consider the vector field $\mathbf{F} = \mathbf{a} \times \mathbf{r}$, where $\mathbf{a} = \langle a_1, a_2, a_3 \rangle$ is a constant nonzero vector and $\mathbf{r} = \langle x, y, z \rangle$. Show that the circulation is a maximum when $\mathbf{a}$ points in the direction of the normal to S.

35. Circulation in a plane A circle C in the plane $x + y + z = 8$ has a radius of 4 and center $(2, 3, 3)$. Evaluate $\oint_C \mathbf{F} \cdot d\mathbf{r}$ for $\mathbf{F} = \langle 0, -z, 2y \rangle$ where C has a counterclockwise orientation when viewed from above. Does the circulation depend on the radius of the circle? Does it depend on the location of the center of the circle?

36. No integrals Let $\mathbf{F} = \langle 2z, z, 2y + x \rangle$ and let S be the hemisphere of radius a with its base in the xy-plane and center at the origin.

a. Evaluate $\iint_S (\nabla \times \mathbf{F}) \cdot \mathbf{n}\, dS$ by computing $\nabla \times \mathbf{F}$ and appealing to symmetry.

b. Evaluate the line integral using Stokes' Theorem to check part (a).

37. Compound surface and boundary Begin with the paraboloid $z = x^2 + y^2$, for $0 \le z \le 4$, and slice it with the plane $y = 0$. Let S be the surface that remains for $y \ge 0$ (including the planar surface in the xz-plane) (see figure). Let C be the semicircle and line segment that bound the cap of S in the plane $z = 4$ with counterclockwise orientation. Let $\mathbf{F} = \langle 2z + y, 2x + z, 2y + x \rangle$.

a. Describe the direction of the vectors normal to the surface.

b. Evaluate $\iint_S (\nabla \times \mathbf{F}) \cdot \mathbf{n}\, dS$.

c. Evaluate $\oint_C \mathbf{F} \cdot d\mathbf{r}$ and check for agreement with part (b).

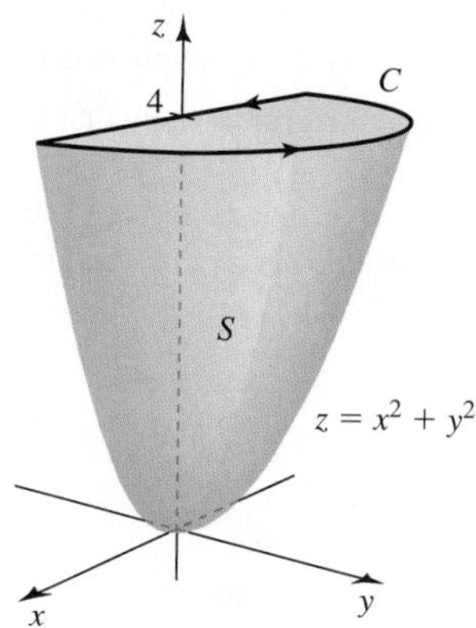

Applications

38. Ampère's Law The French physicist André-Marie Ampère (1775–1836) discovered that an electrical current I in a wire produces a magnetic field $\mathbf{B}$. A special case of Ampère's Law relates the current to the magnetic field through the equation $\oint_C \mathbf{B} \cdot d\mathbf{r} = \mu I$, where C is any closed curve through which the wire passes and μ is a physical constant. Assume that the current I is given in terms of the current density $\mathbf{J}$ as $I = \iint_S \mathbf{J} \cdot \mathbf{n}\, dS$, where S is an oriented surface with C as a boundary. Use Stokes' Theorem to show that an equivalent form of Ampère's Law is $\nabla \times \mathbf{B} = \mu \mathbf{J}$.

39. Maximum surface integral Let S be the paraboloid $z = a(1 - x^2 - y^2)$, for $z \ge 0$, where $a > 0$ is a real number. Let $\mathbf{F} = \langle x - y, y + z, z - x \rangle$. For what value(s) of a (if any) does $\iint_S (\nabla \times \mathbf{F}) \cdot \mathbf{n}\, dS$ have its maximum value?

40. Area of a region in a plane Let R be a region in a plane that has a unit normal vector $\mathbf{n} = \langle a, b, c \rangle$ and boundary C. Let $\mathbf{F} = \langle bz, cx, ay \rangle$.

a. Show that $\nabla \times \mathbf{F} = \mathbf{n}$.

b. Use Stokes' Theorem to show that

$$\text{area of } R = \oint_C \mathbf{F} \cdot d\mathbf{r}.$$

c. Consider the curve C given by $\mathbf{r} = \langle 5 \sin t, 13 \cos t, 12 \sin t \rangle$, for $0 \le t \le 2\pi$. Prove that C lies in a plane by showing that $\mathbf{r} \times \mathbf{r}'$ is constant for all t.

d. Use part (b) to find the area of the region enclosed by C in part (c). (*Hint:* Find the unit normal vector that is consistent with the orientation of C.)

41. Choosing a more convenient surface The goal is to evaluate $A = \iint_S (\nabla \times \mathbf{F}) \cdot \mathbf{n}\, dS$, where $\mathbf{F} = \langle yz, -xz, xy \rangle$ and S is the surface of the upper half of the ellipsoid $x^2 + y^2 + 8z^2 = 1$ $(z \geq 0)$.

a. Evaluate a surface integral over a more convenient surface to find the value of A.

b. Evaluate A using a line integral.

Additional Exercises

42. Radial fields and zero circulation Consider the radial vector fields $\mathbf{F} = \mathbf{r}/|\mathbf{r}|^p$, where p is a real number and $\mathbf{r} = \langle x, y, z \rangle$. Let C be any circle in the xy-plane centered at the origin.

a. Evaluate a line integral to show that the field has zero circulation on C.

b. For what values of p does Stokes' Theorem apply? For those values of p, use the surface integral in Stokes' Theorem to show that the field has zero circulation on C.

43. Zero curl Consider the vector field

$$\mathbf{F} = \frac{-y}{x^2 + y^2}\mathbf{i} + \frac{x}{x^2 + y^2}\mathbf{j} + z\mathbf{k}.$$

a. Show that $\nabla \times \mathbf{F} = \mathbf{0}$.

b. Show that $\oint_C \mathbf{F} \cdot d\mathbf{r}$ is not zero on a circle C in the xy-plane enclosing the origin.

c. Explain why Theorem 15.13 does not apply in this case.

44. Average circulation Let S be a small circular disk of radius R centered at the point P with a unit normal vector $\mathbf{n}$. Let C be the boundary of S.

a. Express the average circulation of the vector field $\mathbf{F}$ on S as a surface integral of $\nabla \times \mathbf{F}$.

b. Argue that for small R, the average circulation approaches $(\nabla \times \mathbf{F})_P \cdot \mathbf{n}$ (the component of $\nabla \times \mathbf{F}$ in the direction of $\mathbf{n}$ evaluated at P) with the approximation improving as $R \to 0$.

45. Proof of Stokes' Theorem Confirm the following step in the proof of Stokes' Theorem. If $z = s(x, y)$ and f, g, and h are functions of x, y, and z, with $M = f + hz_x$ and $N = g + hz_y$, then

$$M_y = f_y + f_z z_y + h z_{xy} + z_x (h_y + h_z z_y) \quad \text{and}$$
$$N_x = g_x + g_z z_x + h z_{yx} + z_y (h_x + h_z z_x).$$

46. Stokes' Theorem on closed surfaces Prove that if $\mathbf{F}$ satisfies the conditions of Stokes' Theorem, then $\iint_S (\nabla \times \mathbf{F}) \cdot \mathbf{n}\, dS = 0$, where S is a smooth surface that encloses a region.

47. Rotated Green's Theorem Use Stokes' Theorem to write the circulation form of Green's Theorem in the yz-plane.

QUICK CHECK ANSWERS

1. If S is a region in the xy-plane, $\mathbf{n} = \mathbf{k}$, and $(\nabla \times \mathbf{F}) \cdot \mathbf{n}$ becomes $g_x - f_y$. 2. The tangent vector $\mathbf{r}'$ lies in the xy-plane and is orthogonal to the z-component of $\mathbf{F}$. This component does not contribute to the circulation along C. 3. The vector field is symmetric about the y-axis. ◄

15.8 Divergence Theorem

Vector fields can represent electric or magnetic fields, air velocities in hurricanes, or blood flow in an artery. These and other vector phenomena suggest movement of a "substance." A frequent question concerns the amount of a substance that flows across a surface—for example, the amount of water that passes across the membrane of a cell per unit time. Such flux calculations may be done using flux integrals as in Section 15.6. The Divergence Theorem offers an alternative method. In effect, it says that instead of integrating the flow in and out of a region across its boundary, you may also add up all the sources (or sinks) of the flow throughout the region.

Divergence Theorem

➤ Circulation form of Green's Theorem → Stokes' Theorem

Flux form of Green's Theorem → Divergence Theorem

The Divergence Theorem is the three-dimensional version of the flux form of Green's Theorem. Recall that if R is a region in the xy-plane, C is the simple closed oriented boundary of R, and $\mathbf{F} = \langle f, g \rangle$ is a vector field, Green's Theorem says that

$$\underbrace{\oint_C \mathbf{F} \cdot \mathbf{n}\, ds}_{\text{flux across C}} = \iint_R \underbrace{(f_x + g_y)}_{\text{divergence}}\, dA.$$

The line integral on the left gives the flux across the boundary of R. The double integral on the right measures the net expansion or contraction of the vector field within R. If $\mathbf{F}$ represents a fluid flow or the transport of a material, the theorem says that the cumulative effect of the sources (or sinks) of the flow within R equals the net flow across its boundary.

The Divergence Theorem is a direct extension of Green's Theorem. The plane region in Green's Theorem becomes a solid region D in $\mathbf{R}^3$, and the closed curve in Green's Theorem becomes the oriented surface S that encloses D. The flux integral in Green's Theorem becomes a surface integral over S, and the double integral in Green's Theorem becomes a triple integral over D of the three-dimensional divergence (Figure 15.67).

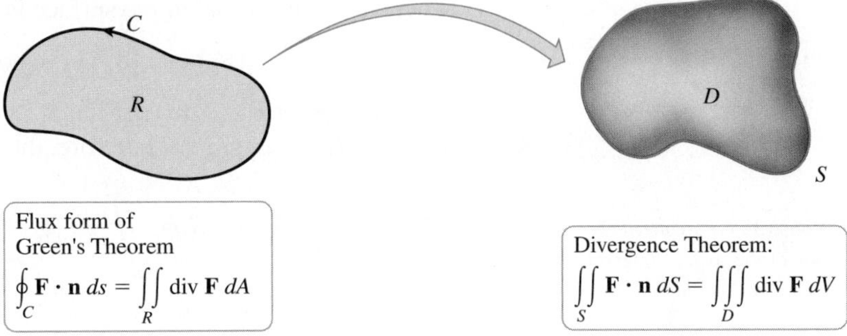

Flux form of Green's Theorem

$$\oint_C \mathbf{F}\cdot\mathbf{n}\,ds = \iint_R \operatorname{div}\mathbf{F}\,dA$$

Divergence Theorem:

$$\iint_S \mathbf{F}\cdot\mathbf{n}\,dS = \iiint_D \operatorname{div}\mathbf{F}\,dV$$

FIGURE 15.67

THEOREM 15.15 Divergence Theorem

Let $\mathbf{F}$ be a vector field whose components have continuous first partial derivatives in a connected and simply connected region D enclosed by a smooth oriented surface S. Then

$$\iint_S \mathbf{F}\cdot\mathbf{n}\,dS = \iiint_D \nabla\cdot\mathbf{F}\,dV,$$

where $\mathbf{n}$ is the unit outward normal vector on S.

The surface integral on the left gives the flux of the vector field across the boundary; a positive flux integral means there is a net flow of the field out of the region. The triple integral on the right is the cumulative expansion or contraction of the field over the region D. The proof of a special case of the theorem is given later in this section.

QUICK CHECK 1 Interpret the Divergence Theorem in the case that $\mathbf{F} = \langle a, b, c\rangle$ is a constant vector field and D is a ball. ◀

EXAMPLE 1 Verifying the Divergence Theorem Consider the radial field $\mathbf{F} = \langle x, y, z\rangle$ and let S be the sphere $x^2 + y^2 + z^2 = a^2$ that encloses the region D. Assume $\mathbf{n}$ is the outward normal vector on the sphere. Evaluate both integrals of the Divergence Theorem.

SOLUTION The divergence of $\mathbf{F}$ is

$$\nabla\cdot\mathbf{F} = \frac{\partial}{\partial x}(x) + \frac{\partial}{\partial y}(y) + \frac{\partial}{\partial z}(z) = 3.$$

Integrating over D, we have

$$\iiint_D \nabla\cdot\mathbf{F}\,dV = \iiint_D 3\,dV = 3 \times \text{volume}(D) = 4\pi a^3.$$

To evaluate the surface integral, we parameterize the sphere (Section 15.6, Table 15.2) in the form

$$\mathbf{r} = \langle x, y, z\rangle = \langle a\sin u\cos v, a\sin u\sin v, a\cos u\rangle,$$

where $R = \{(u, v): 0 \le u \le \pi, 0 \le v \le 2\pi\}$ (u and v are the spherical coordinates φ and θ, respectively). The surface integral is

$$\iint_S \mathbf{F} \cdot \mathbf{n}\, dS = \iint_R \mathbf{F} \cdot (\mathbf{t}_u \times \mathbf{t}_v)\, dA,$$

where a vector normal to the surface is

$$\mathbf{t}_u \times \mathbf{t}_v = \langle a^2 \sin^2 u \cos v, a^2 \sin^2 u \sin v, a^2 \sin u \cos u \rangle.$$

Substituting for $\mathbf{F} = \langle x, y, z \rangle$ and $\mathbf{t}_u \times \mathbf{t}_v$, we find after simplifying that $\mathbf{F} \cdot (\mathbf{t}_u \times \mathbf{t}_v) = a^3 \sin u$. Therefore, the surface integral becomes

➤ See Exercise 32 for an alternative evaluation of the surface integral.

$$\begin{aligned}
\iint_S \mathbf{F} \cdot \mathbf{n}\, dS &= \iint_R \underbrace{\mathbf{F} \cdot (\mathbf{t}_u \times \mathbf{t}_v)}_{a^3 \sin u}\, dA \\
&= \int_0^{2\pi} \int_0^{\pi} a^3 \sin u\, du\, dv && \text{Substitute for } \mathbf{F} \text{ and } \mathbf{t}_u \times \mathbf{t}_v. \\
&= 4\pi a^3. && \text{Evaluate integrals.}
\end{aligned}$$

The two integrals of the Divergence Theorem are equal. *Related Exercises 9–12* ◀

EXAMPLE 2 Divergence Theorem with a rotation field Consider the rotation field

$$\mathbf{F} = \mathbf{a} \times \mathbf{r} = \langle 1, 0, 1 \rangle \times \langle x, y, z \rangle = \langle -y, x - z, y \rangle.$$

Let S be the hemisphere $x^2 + y^2 + z^2 = a^2$, for $z \ge 0$, together with its base in the xy-plane. Find the net outward flux across S.

SOLUTION To find the flux using surface integrals, two surfaces must be considered (the hemisphere and its base). The Divergence Theorem gives a simpler solution. Note that

$$\nabla \cdot \mathbf{F} = \frac{\partial}{\partial x}(-y) + \frac{\partial}{\partial y}(x - z) + \frac{\partial}{\partial z}(y) = 0.$$

We see that the flux across the hemisphere is zero. *Related Exercises 13–16* ◀

With Stokes' Theorem, rotation fields are noteworthy because they have a nonzero curl. With the Divergence Theorem, the situation is reversed. As suggested by Example 2, pure rotation fields of the form $\mathbf{F} = \mathbf{a} \times \mathbf{r}$ have zero divergence (Exercise 16). However, with the Divergence Theorem, radial fields are interesting and have many physical applications.

EXAMPLE 3 Computing flux with the Divergence Theorem Find the net outward flux of the field $\mathbf{F} = xyz\langle 1, 1, 1 \rangle$ across the boundaries of the cube $D = \{(x, y, z): 0 \le x \le 1, 0 \le y \le 1, 0 \le z \le 1\}$.

SOLUTION Computing a surface integral involves the six faces of the cube. The Divergence Theorem gives the outward flux with a single integral over D. The divergence of the field is

$$\nabla \cdot \mathbf{F} = \frac{\partial}{\partial x}(xyz) + \frac{\partial}{\partial y}(xyz) + \frac{\partial}{\partial z}(xyz) = yz + xz + xy.$$

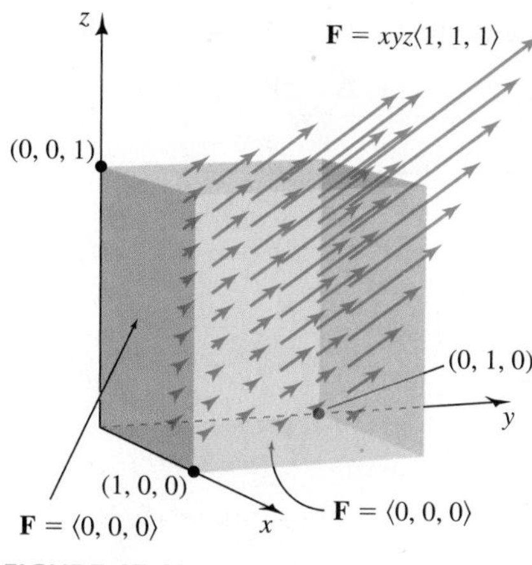

FIGURE 15.68

The integral over D is a standard triple integral:

$$\iiint_D \nabla \cdot \mathbf{F}\, dV = \iiint_D (yz + xz + xy)\, dV$$

$$= \int_0^1 \int_0^1 \int_0^1 (yz + xz + xy)\, dx\, dy\, dz \quad \text{Convert to a triple integral.}$$

$$= \frac{3}{4} \quad \text{Evaluate integrals.}$$

On three faces of the cube (those that lie in the coordinate planes), we see that $\mathbf{F}(0, y, z) = \mathbf{F}(x, 0, z) = \mathbf{F}(x, y, 0) = \mathbf{0}$, so there is no contribution to the flux on these faces (Figure 15.68). On the other three faces, the vector field has components out of the cube. Therefore, the net outward flux is positive, as calculated. *Related Exercises 17–24* ◀

QUICK CHECK 2 In Example 3, does the vector field have negative components anywhere in the cube D? Is the divergence negative anywhere in D? ◀

Interpretation of the Divergence Using Mass Transport Suppose that $\mathbf{v}$ is the velocity field of a material, such as water or molasses, and ρ is its constant density. The vector field $\mathbf{F} = \rho\mathbf{v} = \langle f, g, h \rangle$ describes the **mass transport** of the material, with units of (mass/vol.) × (length/time) = mass/(area-time); typical units of mass transport are g/m^2/s. This means that $\mathbf{F}$ gives the mass of material flowing past a point (in each of the three coordinate directions) per unit of surface area per unit of time. When $\mathbf{F}$ is multiplied by an area, the result is the *flux*, with units of mass/unit time.

➤ The mass transport is also called the *flux density*; when multiplied by an area, it gives the flux. We use the convention that flux has units of mass per unit time.

Now consider a small cube located in the vector field with its faces parallel to the coordinate planes. One vertex is located at $(0, 0, 0)$, the opposite vertex is at $(\Delta x, \Delta y, \Delta z)$, and (x, y, z) is an arbitrary point in the cube (Figure 15.69). The goal is to compute the approximate flux of material across the faces of the cube. A positive flux means there is a net flow of material *out of the cube.* We begin with the flux across the two parallel faces $x = 0$ and $x = \Delta x$.

➤ Check the units: if $\mathbf{F}$ has units of mass/(area-time), then the flux has units of mass/time ($\mathbf{n}$ has no units).

The outward unit vectors normal to the faces $x = 0$ and $x = \Delta x$ are $\langle -1, 0, 0 \rangle$ and $\langle 1, 0, 0 \rangle$, respectively. Each face has area $\Delta y\, \Delta z$, so the approximate net flux across these faces is

$$\underbrace{\mathbf{F}(\Delta x, y, z)}_{x = \Delta x \text{ face}} \cdot \underbrace{\mathbf{n}}_{\langle 1,0,0\rangle} \Delta y\, \Delta z + \underbrace{\mathbf{F}(0, y, z)}_{x = 0 \text{ face}} \cdot \underbrace{\mathbf{n}}_{\langle -1,0,0\rangle} \Delta y\, \Delta z$$

$$= (f(\Delta x, y, z) - f(0, y, z))\, \Delta y\, \Delta z.$$

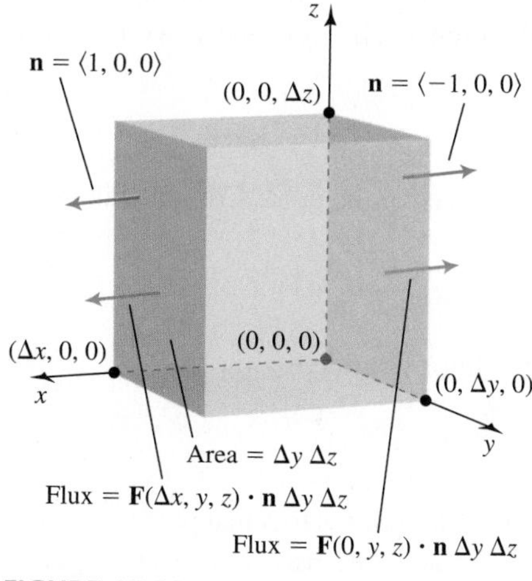

FIGURE 15.69

Note that if $f(\Delta x, y, z) > f(0, y, z)$, the net flux across these two faces of the cube is positive, which means the net flow is *out* of the cube. Letting $\Delta V = \Delta x\, \Delta y\, \Delta z$ be the volume of the cube, we rewrite the net flux as

$$(f(\Delta x, y, z) - f(0, y, z))\, \Delta y\, \Delta z$$

$$= \frac{f(\Delta x, y, z) - f(0, y, z)}{\Delta x} \Delta x\, \Delta y\, \Delta z \quad \text{Multiply by } \frac{\Delta x}{\Delta x}$$

$$= \frac{f(\Delta x, y, z) - f(0, y, z)}{\Delta x} \Delta V \quad \Delta V = \Delta x\, \Delta y\, \Delta z$$

A similar argument can be applied to the other two pairs of faces. The approximate net flux across the faces $y = 0$ and $y = \Delta y$ is

$$\frac{g(x, \Delta y, z) - g(x, 0, z)}{\Delta y} \Delta V$$

and the approximate net flux across the faces $z = 0$ and $z = \Delta z$ is

$$\frac{h(x, y, \Delta z) - h(x, y, 0)}{\Delta z} \Delta V.$$

Adding these three individual fluxes gives the approximate net flux out of the cube:

$$\text{net flux out of cube} \approx \Bigg(\underbrace{\frac{f(\Delta x, y, z) - f(0, y, z)}{\Delta x}}_{\approx \frac{\partial f}{\partial x}(0,0,0)} + \underbrace{\frac{g(x, \Delta y, z) - g(x, 0, z)}{\Delta y}}_{\approx \frac{\partial g}{\partial y}(0,0,0)}$$

$$+ \underbrace{\frac{h(x, y, \Delta z) - h(x, y, 0)}{\Delta z}}_{\approx \frac{\partial h}{\partial z}(0,0,0)}\Bigg) \Delta V$$

$$\approx \left(\frac{\partial f}{\partial x} + \frac{\partial g}{\partial y} + \frac{\partial h}{\partial z}\right)\bigg|_{(0,0,0)} \Delta V$$

$$= (\nabla \cdot \mathbf{F})(0, 0, 0)\, \Delta V$$

Notice how the three quotients approximate partial derivatives when Δx, Δy, and Δz are small. A similar argument may be made at any point in the region.

Taking one more step, we show informally how the Divergence Theorem arises. Suppose the small cube we just analyzed is one of many small cubes of volume ΔV that fill a region D. We label the cubes $k = 1, \ldots, n$ and apply the preceding argument to each cube, letting $(\nabla \cdot \mathbf{F})_k$ be the divergence evaluated at a point in the kth cube. Adding the individual contributions to the net flux from each cube, we obtain the approximate net flux across the boundary of D:

➤ In making this argument, notice that for two adjacent cubes the flux into one cube equals the flux out of the other cube across the common face. Thus, there is a cancellation of fluxes throughout the interior of D.

$$\text{net flux out of } D \approx \sum_{k=1}^{n} (\nabla \cdot \mathbf{F})_k\, \Delta V$$

Letting the volume of the cubes ΔV approach 0 and letting the number of cubes n increase, we obtain an integral over D:

$$\text{net flux out of } D = \lim_{n \to \infty} \sum_{k=1}^{n} (\nabla \cdot \mathbf{F})_k\, \Delta V = \iiint_D \nabla \cdot \mathbf{F}\, dV$$

The net flux across the boundary of D is also given by $\iint_S \mathbf{F} \cdot \mathbf{n}\, dS$. Equating the surface integral and the volume integral gives the Divergence Theorem. Now we look at a formal proof.

QUICK CHECK 3 Draw the unit cube $D = \{(x, y, z): 0 \le x \le 1, 0 \le y \le 1, 0 \le z \le 1\}$ and sketch the vector field $\mathbf{F} = \langle x, -y, 2z \rangle$ on the six faces of the cube. Compute and interpret div $\mathbf{F}$. ◄

Proof of the Divergence Theorem

We prove the Divergence Theorem under special conditions on the region D. Let R be the projection of D in the xy-plane (Figure 15.70); that is,

$$R = \{(x, y): (x, y, z) \text{ is in } D\}.$$

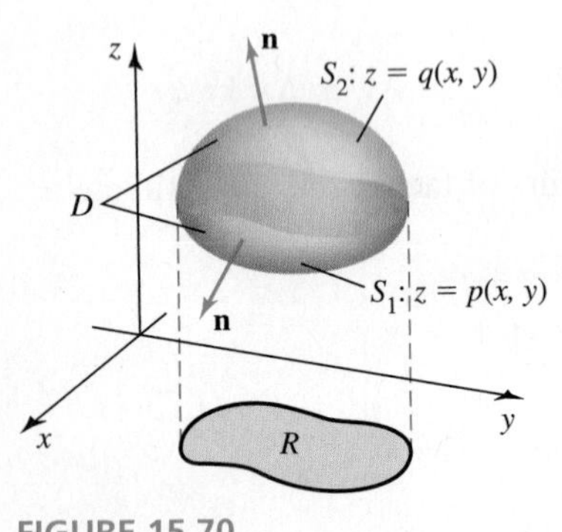

FIGURE 15.70

Assume that the boundary of D is S and let $\mathbf{n}$ be the unit vector normal to S that points outward.

Letting $\mathbf{F} = \langle f, g, h \rangle = f\mathbf{i} + g\mathbf{j} + h\mathbf{k}$, the surface integral in the Divergence Theorem is

$$\iint_S \mathbf{F} \cdot \mathbf{n}\, dS = \iint_S (f\mathbf{i} + g\mathbf{j} + h\mathbf{k}) \cdot \mathbf{n}\, dS$$

$$= \iint_S f\,\mathbf{i} \cdot \mathbf{n}\, dS + \iint_S g\mathbf{j} \cdot \mathbf{n}\, dS + \iint_S h\mathbf{k} \cdot \mathbf{n}\, dS.$$

The volume integral in the Divergence Theorem is

$$\iiint_D \nabla \cdot \mathbf{F}\, dV = \iiint_D \left(\frac{\partial f}{\partial x} + \frac{\partial g}{\partial y} + \frac{\partial h}{\partial z} \right) dV.$$

Matching terms of the surface and volume integrals, the theorem is proved by showing that

$$\iint_S f\mathbf{i} \cdot \mathbf{n}\, dS = \iiint_D \frac{\partial f}{\partial x}\, dV \tag{1}$$

$$\iint_S g\mathbf{j} \cdot \mathbf{n}\, dS = \iiint_D \frac{\partial g}{\partial y}\, dV \tag{2}$$

$$\iint_S h\mathbf{k} \cdot \mathbf{n}\, dS = \iiint_D \frac{\partial h}{\partial z}\, dV. \tag{3}$$

We work on equation (3) assuming special properties for D. Suppose D is bounded by two surfaces S_1: $z = p(x, y)$ and S_2: $z = q(x, y)$, where $p(x, y) \leq q(x, y)$ on R (Figure 15.70). The Fundamental Theorem of Calculus is used in the triple integral to show that

$$\iiint_D \frac{\partial h}{\partial z}\, dV = \iint_R \int_{p(x,y)}^{q(x,y)} \frac{\partial h}{\partial z}\, dz\, dx\, dy$$

$$= \iint_R \big(h(x, y, q(x, y)) - h(x, y, p(x, y))\big)\, dx\, dy \quad \text{Evaluate the inner integral.}$$

Now let's turn to the surface integral in equation (3), $\iint_S h\mathbf{k} \cdot \mathbf{n}\, dS$, and note that S consists of three pieces: the lower surface S_1, the upper surface S_2, and the vertical sides S_3 of the surface (if they exist). The normal to S_3 is everywhere orthogonal to $\mathbf{k}$, so $\mathbf{k} \cdot \mathbf{n} = 0$ and the S_3 integral makes no contribution. What remains is to compute the surface integrals over S_1 and S_2.

An outward normal to S_2 (which is the graph of $z = q(x, y)$) is $\langle -q_x, -q_y, 1\rangle$. An outward normal to S_1 (which is the graph of $z = p(x, y)$) points *downward*, so it is given by $\langle p_x, p_y, -1\rangle$. The surface integral of (3) becomes

$$\iint_S h\mathbf{k} \cdot \mathbf{n}\, dS = \iint_{S_2} h(x, y, z)\mathbf{k} \cdot \mathbf{n}\, dS + \iint_{S_1} h(x, y, z)\mathbf{k} \cdot \mathbf{n}\, dS$$

$$= \iint_R h(x, y, q(x, y)) \underbrace{\mathbf{k} \cdot \langle -q_x, -q_y, 1\rangle}_{1}\, dx\, dy$$

$$+ \iint_R h(x, y, p(x, y)) \underbrace{\mathbf{k} \cdot \langle p_x, p_y, -1\rangle}_{-1}\, dx\, dy \quad \text{Convert to an area integral.}$$

$$= \iint_R h(x, y, q(x, y))\, dx\, dy - \iint_R h(x, y, p(x, y))\, dx\, dy. \quad \text{Simplify.}$$

Observe that both the volume integral and the surface integral of (3) reduce to the same integral over R. Therefore, $\iint_S h\mathbf{k}\cdot\mathbf{n}\,dS = \iiint_D \frac{\partial h}{\partial z}\,dV$.

Equations (1) and (2) are handled in a similar way.

- To prove (1), we make the special assumption that D is also bounded by two surfaces, S_1: $x = s(y, z)$ and S_2: $x = t(y, z)$, where $s(x, y) \le t(x, y)$.
- To prove (2), we assume that D is bounded by two surfaces, S_1: $y = u(x, z)$ and S_2: $y = v(x, z)$, where $u(x, y) \le v(x, y)$.

When combined, the three equations—(1), (2), and (3)—yield the Divergence Theorem. ◄

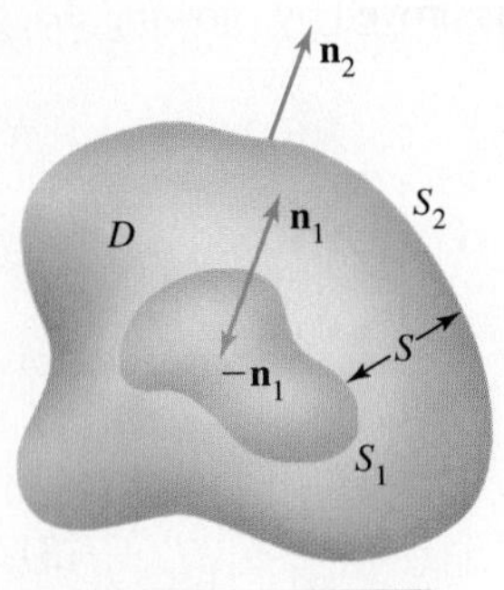

$\mathbf{n}_1$ is outward normal to S_1 and points into D.
Outward normal to S on S_1 is $-\mathbf{n}_1$.

FIGURE 15.71

Divergence Theorem for Hollow Regions

The Divergence Theorem may be extended to more general (non–simply connected) solid regions. Here we consider the important case of hollow regions. Suppose that D is a region consisting of all points inside a closed oriented surface S_2 and outside a closed oriented surface S_1, where S_1 lies within S_2 (Figure 15.71). Therefore, the boundary of D consists of S_1 and S_2.

We let $\mathbf{n}_1$ and $\mathbf{n}_2$ be the outward unit normal vectors for S_1 and S_2, respectively. Note that $\mathbf{n}_1$ points into D, so the outward normal to S on S_1 is $-\mathbf{n}_1$. With that observation, the Divergence Theorem takes the following form.

➤ It's important to point out again that $\mathbf{n}_1$ is the normal that we would use for S_1 alone, independent of S. It is the outward normal to S_1, but it points into D.

THEOREM 15.16 Divergence Theorem for Hollow Regions
Suppose the vector field $\mathbf{F}$ satisfies the conditions of the Divergence Theorem on a region D bounded by two smooth oriented surfaces S_1 and S_2, where S_1 lies within S_2. Let S be the entire boundary of D ($S = S_1 \cup S_2$) and let $\mathbf{n}_1$ and $\mathbf{n}_2$ be the outward unit normal vectors for S_1 and S_2, respectively. Then

$$\iiint_D \nabla\cdot\mathbf{F}\,dV = \iint_S \mathbf{F}\cdot\mathbf{n}\,dS = \iint_{S_2} \mathbf{F}\cdot\mathbf{n}_2\,dS - \iint_{S_1} \mathbf{F}\cdot\mathbf{n}_1\,dS.$$

This form of the Divergence Theorem is applicable to vector fields that are not differentiable at the origin, as is the case with some important radial vector fields.

EXAMPLE 4 Flux for an inverse square field Consider the inverse square vector field

$$\mathbf{F} = \frac{\mathbf{r}}{|\mathbf{r}|^3} = \frac{\langle x, y, z\rangle}{(x^2 + y^2 + z^2)^{3/2}}.$$

➤ Recall that an inverse square force is proportional to $1/|\mathbf{r}|^2$ multiplied by a unit vector in the radial direction, which is $\mathbf{r}/|\mathbf{r}|$. Combining these two factors gives $\mathbf{F} = \mathbf{r}/|\mathbf{r}|^3$.

a. Find the net outward flux of $\mathbf{F}$ across the surface of the region $D = \{(x, y, z): a^2 \le x^2 + y^2 + z^2 \le b^2\}$ that lies between concentric spheres with radii a and b.

b. Find the outward flux of $\mathbf{F}$ across any sphere that encloses the origin.

SOLUTION

a. Although the vector field is undefined at the origin, it is defined and differentiable in D, which excludes the origin. In Section 15.5 (Exercise 71) it was shown that the divergence of the radial field $\mathbf{F} = \frac{\mathbf{r}}{|\mathbf{r}|^p}$ with $p = 3$ is 0. We let S be the union of S_2, the larger sphere of radius b, and S_1, the smaller sphere of radius a. Because $\iiint_D \nabla \cdot \mathbf{F}\, dV = 0$, the Divergence Theorem implies that

$$\iint_S \mathbf{F} \cdot \mathbf{n}\, dS = \iint_{S_2} \mathbf{F} \cdot \mathbf{n}_2\, dS - \iint_{S_1} \mathbf{F} \cdot \mathbf{n}_1\, dS = 0.$$

Therefore, the next flux across S is zero.

b. Part (a) implies that

$$\underbrace{\iint_{S_2} \mathbf{F} \cdot \mathbf{n}_2\, dS}_{\text{out of } D} = \underbrace{\iint_{S_1} \mathbf{F} \cdot \mathbf{n}_1\, dS.}_{\text{into } D}$$

We see that the flux out of D across S_2 equals the flux into D across S_1. To find that flux, we evaluate the surface integral over S_1 on which $|\mathbf{r}| = a$. (Because the fluxes are equal, S_2 could also be used.)

The easiest way to evaluate the surface integral is to note that on the sphere S_1, the unit outward normal vector is $\mathbf{n}_1 = \mathbf{r}/|\mathbf{r}|$. Therefore, the surface integral is

$$\begin{aligned} \iint_{S_1} \mathbf{F} \cdot \mathbf{n}_1\, dS &= \iint_{S_1} \frac{\mathbf{r}}{|\mathbf{r}|^3} \cdot \frac{\mathbf{r}}{|\mathbf{r}|}\, dS && \text{Substitute for } \mathbf{F} \text{ and } \mathbf{n}_1. \\ &= \iint_{S_1} \frac{|\mathbf{r}|^2}{|\mathbf{r}|^4}\, dS && \mathbf{r} \cdot \mathbf{r} = |\mathbf{r}|^2 \\ &= \iint_{S_1} \frac{1}{a^2}\, dS && |\mathbf{r}| = a \\ &= \frac{4\pi a^2}{a^2} && \text{Surface area} = 4\pi a^2 \\ &= 4\pi. \end{aligned}$$

The same result is obtained using S_2 or any smooth surface enclosing the origin. The flux of the inverse square field across any surface enclosing the origin is 4π. As shown in Exercise 46, among radial fields, this property is held only by the inverse square field ($p = 3$). *Related Exercises 25–30* ◀

Gauss' Law

Applying the Divergence Theorem to electric fields leads to one of the fundamental laws of physics. The electric field due to a point charge Q located at the origin is given by the inverse square law,

$$\mathbf{E}(x, y, z) = \frac{Q}{4\pi\varepsilon_0} \frac{\mathbf{r}}{|\mathbf{r}|^3},$$

where $\mathbf{r} = \langle x, y, z \rangle$ and ε_0 is a physical constant called the *permittivity of free space*.

According to the calculation of Example 4, the flux of the field $\dfrac{\mathbf{r}}{|\mathbf{r}|^3}$ across any surface that encloses the origin is 4π. Therefore, the flux of the electric field across any surface enclosing the origin is $\dfrac{Q}{4\pi\varepsilon_0} \cdot 4\pi = \dfrac{Q}{\varepsilon_0}$ (Figure 15.72). This is one statement of

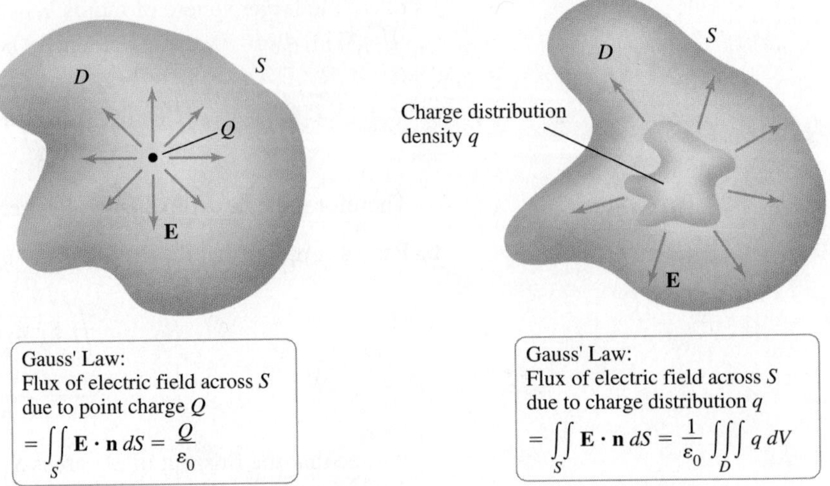

FIGURE 15.72

Gauss' Law: If S is a surface that encloses a point charge Q, then the flux of the electric field across S is

$$\iint_S \mathbf{E} \cdot \mathbf{n}\, dS = \frac{Q}{\varepsilon_0}.$$

In fact, Gauss' Law applies to more general charge distributions (Exercise 39). If $q(x, y, z)$ is a charge density (charge per unit volume) defined on a region D enclosed by S, then the total charge within D is $Q = \iiint_D q(x, y, z)\, dV$. Replacing Q by this triple integral, Gauss' Law takes the form

$$\iint_S \mathbf{E} \cdot \mathbf{n}\, dS = \frac{1}{\varepsilon_0} \underbrace{\iiint_D q(x, y, z)\, dV}_{Q}.$$

Gauss' Law applies to other inverse square fields. In a slightly different form, it also governs heat transfer. If T is the temperature distribution in a solid body D, then the heat flow vector field is $\mathbf{F} = -k\nabla T$. (Heat flows down the temperature gradient.) If $q(x, y, z)$ represents the sources of heat within D, Gauss' Law says

$$\iint_S \mathbf{F} \cdot \mathbf{n}\, dS = -k \iint_S \nabla T \cdot \mathbf{n}\, dS = \iiint_D q(x, y, z)\, dV.$$

We see that, in general, the flux of material (fluid, heat, electric field lines) across the boundary of a region is the cumulative effect of the sources within the region.

A Final Perspective

We now stand back and look at the progression of fundamental theorems of calculus that have appeared throughout this book. Each theorem builds on its predecessors, extending the same basic idea to a different situation or to higher dimensions.

In all cases, the statement is effectively the same: The cumulative (integrated) effect of the *derivatives* of a function throughout a region is determined by the values of the function on the boundary of that region. This principle underlies much of our understanding of the world around us.

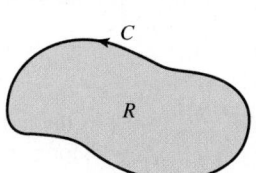

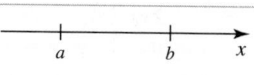

Fundamental Theorem of Calculus	$\int_a^b f'(x)\,dx = f(b) - f(a)$	
Fundamental Theorem of Line Integrals	$\int_C \nabla f \cdot d\mathbf{r} = f(B) - f(A)$	
Green's Theorem (Circulation form)	$\iint_R (g_x - f_y)\,dA = \oint_C f\,dx + g\,dy$	
Stokes' Theorem	$\iint_S (\nabla \times \mathbf{F}) \cdot \mathbf{n}\,dS = \oint_C \mathbf{F} \cdot d\mathbf{r}$	
Divergence Theorem	$\iiint_D \nabla \cdot \mathbf{F}\,dV = \iint_S \mathbf{F} \cdot \mathbf{n}\,dS$	

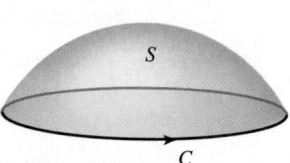

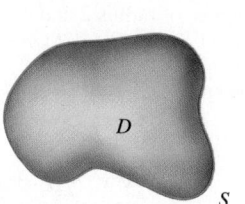

SECTION 15.8 EXERCISES

Review Questions

1. Explain the meaning of the surface integral in the Divergence Theorem.
2. Explain the meaning of the volume integral in the Divergence Theorem.
3. Explain the meaning of the Divergence Theorem.
4. What is the net outward flux of the rotation field $\mathbf{F} = \langle 2z + y, -x, -2x \rangle$ across the surface that encloses any region?
5. What is the net outward flux of the radial field $\mathbf{F} = \langle x, y, z \rangle$ across the sphere of radius 2 centered at the origin?
6. What is the divergence of an inverse square vector field?
7. Suppose div $\mathbf{F} = 0$ in a region enclosed by two concentric spheres. What is the relationship between the outward fluxes across the two spheres?
8. If div $\mathbf{F} > 0$ in a region enclosed by a small cube, is the net flux of the field into or out of the cube?

Basic Skills

9–12. Verifying the Divergence Theorem *Evaluate both integrals of the Divergence Theorem for the following vector fields and regions. Check for agreement.*

9. $\mathbf{F} = \langle 2x, 3y, 4z \rangle$; $D = \{(x, y, z): x^2 + y^2 + z^2 \le 4\}$
10. $\mathbf{F} = \langle -x, -y, -z \rangle$; $D = \{(x, y, z): |x| \le 1, |y| \le 1, |z| \le 1\}$
11. $\mathbf{F} = \langle z - y, x, -x \rangle$;
$D = \{(x, y, z): x^2/4 + y^2/8 + z^2/12 \le 1\}$
12. $\mathbf{F} = \langle x^2, y^2, z^2 \rangle$; $D = \{(x, y, z): |x| \le 1, |y| \le 2, |z| \le 3\}$

13–16. Rotation fields

13. Find the net outward flux of the field $\mathbf{F} = \langle 2z - y, x, -2x \rangle$ across the sphere of radius 1 centered at the origin.
14. Find the net outward flux of the field $\mathbf{F} = \langle z - y, x - z, y - x \rangle$ across the boundary of the cube $\{(x, y, z): |x| \le 1, |y| \le 1, |z| \le 1\}$.
15. Find the net outward flux of the field $\mathbf{F} = \langle bz - cy, cx - az, ay - bx \rangle$ across any smooth closed surface in $\mathbf{R}^3$, where a, b, and c are constants.
16. Find the net outward flux of $\mathbf{F} = \mathbf{a} \times \mathbf{r}$ across any smooth closed surface in $\mathbf{R}^3$, where $\mathbf{a}$ is a constant nonzero vector and $\mathbf{r} = \langle x, y, z \rangle$.

17–24. Computing flux *Use the Divergence Theorem to compute the net outward flux of the following fields across the given surfaces S.*

17. $\mathbf{F} = \langle x, -2y, 3z \rangle$; S is the sphere $\{(x, y, z): x^2 + y^2 + z^2 = 6\}$.

18. $\mathbf{F} = \langle x^2, 2xz, y^2 \rangle$; S is the surface of the cube cut from the first octant by the planes $x = 1$, $y = 1$, and $z = 1$.

19. $\mathbf{F} = \langle x, 2y, z \rangle$; S is the boundary of the tetrahedron in the first octant formed by the plane $x + y + z = 1$.

20. $\mathbf{F} = \langle x^2, y^2, z^2 \rangle$; S is the sphere $\{(x, y, z): x^2 + y^2 + z^2 = 25\}$.

21. $\mathbf{F} = \langle y - 2x, x^3 - y, y^2 - z \rangle$; S is the sphere $\{(x, y, z): x^2 + y^2 + z^2 = 4\}$.

22. $\mathbf{F} = \langle y + z, x + z, x + y \rangle$; S consists of the faces of the cube $\{(x, y, z): |x| \le 1, |y| \le 1, |z| \le 1\}$.

23. $\mathbf{F} = \langle x, y, z \rangle$; S is the surface of the paraboloid $z = 4 - x^2 - y^2$, for $z \ge 0$, plus its base in the xy-plane.

24. $\mathbf{F} = \langle x, y, z \rangle$; S is the surface of the cone $z^2 = x^2 + y^2$, for $0 \le z \le 4$, plus its top surface in the plane $z = 4$.

25–30. Divergence Theorem for more general regions *Use the Divergence Theorem to compute the net outward flux of the following vector fields across the boundary of the given regions D.*

25. $\mathbf{F} = \langle z - x, x - y, 2y - z \rangle$; D is the region between the spheres of radius 2 and 4 centered at the origin.

26. $\mathbf{F} = \mathbf{r}|\mathbf{r}| = \langle x, y, z \rangle \sqrt{x^2 + y^2 + z^2}$; D is the region between the spheres of radius 1 and 2 centered at the origin.

27. $\mathbf{F} = \dfrac{\mathbf{r}}{|\mathbf{r}|} = \dfrac{\langle x, y, z \rangle}{\sqrt{x^2 + y^2 + z^2}}$; D is the region between the spheres of radius 1 and 2 centered at the origin.

28. $\mathbf{F} = \langle z - y, x - z, 2y - x \rangle$; D is the region between two cubes: $\{(x, y, z): 1 \le |x| \le 3, 1 \le |y| \le 3, 1 \le |z| \le 3\}$.

29. $\mathbf{F} = \langle x^2, -y^2, z^2 \rangle$; D is the region in the first octant between the planes $z = 4 - x - y$ and $z = 2 - x - y$.

30. $\mathbf{F} = \langle x, 2y, 3z \rangle$; D is the region between the cylinders $x^2 + y^2 = 1$ and $x^2 + y^2 = 4$, for $0 \le z \le 8$.

Further Explorations

31. Explain why or why not Determine whether the following statements are true and give an explanation or counterexample.

a. If $\nabla \cdot \mathbf{F} = 0$ at all points of a region D, then $\mathbf{F} \cdot \mathbf{n} = 0$ at all points of the boundary of D.
b. If $\iint_S \mathbf{F} \cdot \mathbf{n}\, dS = 0$ on all closed surfaces in $\mathbf{R}^3$, then $\mathbf{F}$ is constant.
c. If $|\mathbf{F}| < 1$, then $|\iiint_D \nabla \cdot \mathbf{F}\, dV|$ is less than the area of the surface of D.

32. Flux across a sphere Consider the radial field $\mathbf{F} = \langle x, y, z \rangle$ and let S be the sphere of radius a centered at the origin. Compute the outward flux of $\mathbf{F}$ across S using the representation $z = \pm\sqrt{a^2 - x^2 - y^2}$ for the sphere (either symmetry or two surfaces must be used).

33–35. Flux integrals *Compute the outward flux of the following vector fields across the given surfaces S. You should decide which integral of the Divergence Theorem to use.*

33. $\mathbf{F} = \langle x^2 e^y \cos z, -4xe^y \cos z, 2xe^y \sin z \rangle$; S is the boundary of the ellipsoid $x^2/4 + y^2 + z^2 = 1$.

34. $\mathbf{F} = \langle -yz, xz, 1 \rangle$; S is the boundary of the ellipsoid $x^2/4 + y^2/4 + z^2 = 1$.

35. $\mathbf{F} = \langle x \sin y, -\cos y, z \sin y \rangle$; S is the boundary of the region bounded by the planes $x = 1$, $y = 0$, $y = \pi/2$, $z = 0$, and $z = x$.

36. Radial fields Consider the radial vector field $\mathbf{F} = \dfrac{\mathbf{r}}{|\mathbf{r}|^p} = \dfrac{\langle x, y, z \rangle}{(x^2 + y^2 + z^2)^{p/2}}$. Let S be the sphere of radius a centered at the origin.

a. Use a surface integral to show that the outward flux of $\mathbf{F}$ across S is $4\pi a^{3-p}$. Recall that the unit normal to the sphere is $\mathbf{r}/|\mathbf{r}|$.
b. For what values of p does $\mathbf{F}$ satisfy the conditions of the Divergence Theorem? For these values of p, use the fact (Theorem 15.8) that $\nabla \cdot \mathbf{F} = \dfrac{3 - p}{|\mathbf{r}|^p}$ to compute the flux across S using the Divergence Theorem.

37. Singular radial field Consider the radial field

$$\mathbf{F} = \frac{\mathbf{r}}{|\mathbf{r}|} = \frac{\langle x, y, z \rangle}{(x^2 + y^2 + z^2)^{1/2}}.$$

a. Evaluate a surface integral to show that $\iint_S \mathbf{F} \cdot \mathbf{n}\, dS = 4\pi a^2$, where S is the surface of a sphere of radius a centered at the origin.
b. Note that the first partial derivatives of the components of $\mathbf{F}$ are undefined at the origin, so the Divergence Theorem does not apply directly. Nevertheless the flux across the sphere as computed in part (a) is finite. Evaluate the triple integral of the Divergence Theorem as an improper integral as follows. Integrate div $\mathbf{F}$ over the region between two spheres of radius a and $0 < \varepsilon < a$. Then let $\varepsilon \to 0^+$ to obtain the flux computed in part (a).

38. Logarithmic potential Consider the potential function

$$\varphi(x, y, z) = \tfrac{1}{2} \ln (x^2 + y^2 + z^2) = \ln |\mathbf{r}|,$$

where $\mathbf{r} = \langle x, y, z \rangle$.

a. Show that the gradient field associated with φ is

$$\mathbf{F} = \frac{\mathbf{r}}{|\mathbf{r}|^2} = \frac{\langle x, y, z \rangle}{x^2 + y^2 + z^2}.$$

b. Show that $\iint_S \mathbf{F} \cdot \mathbf{n}\, dS = 4\pi a$, where S is the surface of a sphere of radius a centered at the origin.
c. Compute div $\mathbf{F}$.
d. Note that $\mathbf{F}$ is undefined at the origin, so the Divergence Theorem does not apply directly. Evaluate the volume integral as described in Exercise 37.

Applications

39. Gauss' Law for electric fields The electric field due to a point charge Q is $\mathbf{E} = \dfrac{Q}{4\pi\varepsilon_0} \dfrac{\mathbf{r}}{|\mathbf{r}|^3}$, where $\mathbf{r} = \langle x, y, z \rangle$, and ε_0 is a constant.

a. Show that the flux of the field across a sphere of radius a centered at the origin is $\iint_S \mathbf{E} \cdot \mathbf{n}\, dS = \dfrac{Q}{\varepsilon_0}$.
b. Let S be the boundary of the region between two spheres centered at the origin of radius a and b with $a < b$.

Use the Divergence Theorem to show that the net outward flux across S is zero.

c. Suppose there is a distribution of charge within a region D. Let $q(x, y, z)$ be the charge density (charge per unit volume). Interpret the statement that

$$\iint_S \mathbf{E}\cdot\mathbf{n}\,dS = \frac{1}{\varepsilon_0}\iiint_D q(x, y, z)\,dV.$$

d. Assuming $\mathbf{E}$ satisfies the conditions of the Divergence Theorem, conclude from part (c) that $\nabla\cdot\mathbf{E} = \dfrac{q}{\varepsilon_0}$.

e. Because the electric force is conservative, it has a potential function φ. From part (d) conclude that $\nabla^2\varphi = \nabla\cdot\nabla\varphi = \dfrac{q}{\varepsilon_0}$.

40. Gauss' Law for gravitation The gravitational force due to a point mass M is proportional to $\mathbf{F} = GM\mathbf{r}/|\mathbf{r}|^3$, where $\mathbf{r} = \langle x, y, z\rangle$ and G is the gravitational constant.

a. Show that the flux of the force field across a sphere of radius a centered at the origin is $\iint_S \mathbf{F}\cdot\mathbf{n}\,dS = 4\pi GM$.

b. Let S be the boundary of the region between two spheres centered at the origin of radius a and b with $a < b$. Use the Divergence Theorem to show that the net outward flux across S is zero.

c. Suppose there is a distribution of mass within a region D containing the origin. Let $\rho(x, y, z)$ be the mass density (mass per unit volume). Interpret the statement that

$$\iint_S \mathbf{F}\cdot\mathbf{n}\,dS = 4\pi G\iiint_D \rho(x, y, z)\,dV$$

d. Assuming $\mathbf{F}$ satisfies the conditions of the Divergence Theorem, conclude from part (c) that $\nabla\cdot\mathbf{F} = 4\pi G\rho$.

e. Because the gravitational force is conservative, it has a potential function φ. From part (d) conclude that $\nabla^2\varphi = 4\pi G\rho$.

41–45. Heat transfer *Fourier's Law of heat transfer (or heat conduction) states that the heat flow vector* $\mathbf{F}$ *at a point is proportional to the negative gradient of the temperature; that is,* $\mathbf{F} = -k\nabla T$, *which means that heat energy flows from hot regions to cold regions. The constant* $k > 0$ *is called the conductivity, which has metric units of* J/m-s-K *or* W/m-K. *A temperature function for a region D is given. Find the net outward heat flux* $\iint_S \mathbf{F}\cdot\mathbf{n}\,dS = -k\iint_S \nabla T\cdot\mathbf{n}\,dS$ *across the boundary S of D. In some cases it may be easier to use the Divergence Theorem and evaluate a triple integral. Assume that* $k = 1$.

41. $T(x, y, z) = 100 + x + 2y + z$;
$D = \{(x, y, z): 0 \le x \le 1, 0 \le y \le 1, 0 \le z \le 1\}$

42. $T(x, y, z) = 100 + x^2 + y^2 + z^2$;
$D = \{(x, y, z): 0 \le x \le 1, 0 \le y \le 1, 0 \le z \le 1\}$

43. $T(x, y, z) = 100 + e^{-z}$;
$D = \{(x, y, z): 0 \le x \le 1, 0 \le y \le 1, 0 \le z \le 1\}$

44. $T(x, y, z) = 100 + x^2 + y^2 + z^2$; D is the unit sphere centered at the origin.

45. $T(x, y, z) = 100e^{-x^2-y^2-z^2}$; D is the sphere of radius a centered at the origin.

Additional Exercises

46. Inverse square fields are special Let $\mathbf{F}$ be a radial field $\mathbf{F} = \mathbf{r}/|\mathbf{r}|^p$, where p is a real number and $\mathbf{r} = \langle x, y, z\rangle$. With $p = 3$, $\mathbf{F}$ is an inverse square field.

a. Show that the net flux across a sphere centered at the origin is independent of the radius of the sphere only for $p = 3$.

b. Explain the observation in part (a) by finding the flux of $\mathbf{F} = \mathbf{r}/|\mathbf{r}|^p$ across the boundaries of a spherical box $\{(\rho, \varphi, \theta): a \le \rho \le b, \varphi_0 \le \varphi \le \varphi_1, \theta_1 \le \theta \le \theta_2\}$ for various values of p.

47. A beautiful flux integral Consider the potential function $\varphi(x, y, z,) = G(\rho)$, where G is any twice differentiable function and $\rho = \sqrt{x^2 + y^2 + z^2}$; therefore, G depends only on the distance from the origin.

a. Show that the gradient vector field associated with φ is $\mathbf{F} = \nabla\varphi = G'(\rho)\dfrac{\mathbf{r}}{\rho}$, where $\mathbf{r} = \langle x, y, z\rangle$ and $\rho = |\mathbf{r}|$.

b. Let S be the sphere of radius a centered at the origin and let D be the region enclosed by S. Show that the flux of $\mathbf{F}$ across S is $\iint_S \mathbf{F}\cdot\mathbf{n}\,dA = 4\pi a^2 G'(a)$.

c. Show that $\nabla\cdot\mathbf{F} = \nabla\cdot\nabla\varphi = \dfrac{2G'(\rho)}{\rho} + G''(\rho)$.

d. Use part (c) to show that the flux across S (as given in part (b)) is also obtained by the volume integral $\iiint_D \nabla\cdot\mathbf{F}\,dV$. (*Hint:* use spherical coordinates and integrate by parts.)

48. Integration by parts (Gauss' formula) Recall the Product Rule of Theorem 15.11: $\nabla\cdot(u\mathbf{F}) = u\nabla\cdot\mathbf{F} + \mathbf{F}\cdot\nabla u$.

a. Integrate both sides of this identity over a solid region D with a closed boundary S and use the Divergence Theorem to prove an integration by parts rule:

$$\iiint_D u\nabla\cdot\mathbf{F}\,dV = \iint_S u\mathbf{F}\cdot\mathbf{n}\,dS - \iiint_D \mathbf{F}\cdot\nabla u\,dV.$$

b. Explain the correspondence between this rule and the integration by parts rule for single-variable functions.

c. Use integration by parts to evaluate $\iiint_D (x^2y + y^2z + z^2x)\,dV$, where D is the cube in the first octant cut by the planes $x = 1$, $y = 1$, and $z = 1$.

49. Green's Formula Write Gauss' Formula of Exercise 48 in two dimensions—that is, where $\mathbf{F} = \langle f, g\rangle$, D is a plane region R and C is the boundary of R. Show that the result is Green's Formula:

$$\iint_R u(f_x + g_y)\,dA = \oint_C u(\mathbf{F}\cdot\mathbf{n})\,ds - \iint_R (fu_x + gu_y)\,dA.$$

Show that with $u = 1$, one form of Green's *Theorem* appears. Which form of Green's Theorem is it?

50. Green's First Identity Prove Green's First Identity for twice differentiable scalar-valued functions u and v defined on a region D:

$$\iiint_D (u\nabla^2 v + \nabla u\cdot\nabla v)\,dV = \iint_S u\nabla v\cdot\mathbf{n}\,dS,$$

where $\nabla^2 v = \nabla\cdot\nabla v$. You may apply Gauss' Formula in Exercise 48 to $\mathbf{F} = \nabla v$ or apply the Divergence Theorem to $\mathbf{F} = u\nabla v$.

51. Green's Second Identity Prove Green's Second Identity for scalar-valued functions u and v defined on a region D:

$$\iiint_D (u\nabla^2 v - v\nabla^2 u)\, dV = \iint_S (u\nabla v - v\nabla u)\cdot \mathbf{n}\, dS.$$

(*Hint:* Reverse the roles of u and v in Green's First Identity.)

52–54. Harmonic functions *A scalar-valued function φ is* ***harmonic*** *on a region D if $\nabla^2\varphi = \nabla\cdot\nabla\varphi = 0$ at all points of D.*

52. Show that the potential function $\varphi(x, y, z) = |\mathbf{r}|^{-p}$ is harmonic provided $p = 0$ or $p = 1$, where $\mathbf{r} = \langle x, y, z\rangle$. To what vector fields do these potentials correspond?

53. Show that if φ is harmonic on a region D enclosed by a surface S, then $\iint_S \nabla\varphi\cdot\mathbf{n}\, dS = 0$.

54. Show that if u is harmonic on a region D enclosed by a surface S, then $\iint_S u\,\nabla u\cdot\mathbf{n}\, dS = \iiint_D |\nabla u|^2\, dV$.

55. Miscellaneous integral identities Prove the following identities.

a. $\iiint_D \nabla\times\mathbf{F}\, dV = \iint_S (\mathbf{n}\times\mathbf{F})\, dS$ (*Hint:* Apply the Divergence Theorem to each component of the identity.)

b. $\iint_S (\mathbf{n}\times\nabla\varphi)\, dS = \oint_C \varphi\, d\mathbf{r}$ (*Hint:* Apply Stokes' Theorem to each component of the identity.)

QUICK CHECK ANSWERS

1. If $\mathbf{F}$ is constant, then $\text{div}(\mathbf{F}) = 0$, so $\iiint_D \nabla\cdot\mathbf{F}\, dV = \iint_S \mathbf{F}\cdot\mathbf{n}\, dS = 0$. This means that all the "material" that flows into one side of D flows out of the other side of D. **2.** The vector field and the divergence are positive throughout D. **3.** The vector field has no flow into or out of the cube on the faces $x = 0$, $y = 0$, and $z = 0$ because the vectors of $\mathbf{F}$ on these faces are parallel to the faces. The vector field points out of the cube on the $x = 1$ and $z = 1$ faces and into the cube on the $y = 1$ face. $\text{div}(\mathbf{F}) = 2$, so there is a net flow out of the cube.

CHAPTER 15 REVIEW EXERCISES

1. Explain why or why not Determine whether the following statements are true and give an explanation or counterexample.

a. The rotational field $\mathbf{F} = \langle -y, x\rangle$ has zero curl and zero divergence.

b. $\nabla\times\nabla\varphi = \mathbf{0}$

c. Two vector fields with the same curl differ by a constant vector field.

d. Two vector fields with the same divergence differ by a constant vector field.

e. If $\mathbf{F} = \langle x, y, z\rangle$ and S encloses a region D, then $\iint_S \mathbf{F}\cdot\mathbf{n}\, dS$ is three times the volume of D.

2. Matching vector fields Match vector fields a–f with the graphs A–F. Let $\mathbf{r} = \langle x, y\rangle$.

a. $\mathbf{F} = \langle x, y\rangle$ **b.** $\mathbf{F} = \langle -2y, 2x\rangle$

c. $\mathbf{F} = \mathbf{r}/|\mathbf{r}|$ **d.** $\mathbf{F} = \langle y - x, x\rangle$

e. $\mathbf{F} = \langle e^{-y}, e^{-x}\rangle$ **f.** $\mathbf{F} = \langle \sin \pi x, \sin \pi y\rangle$

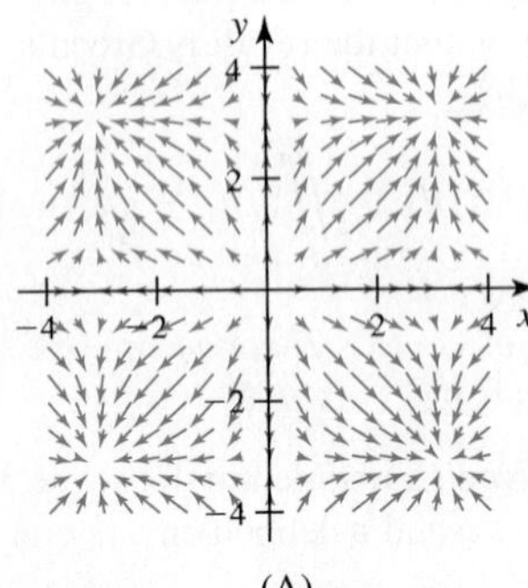
(A)

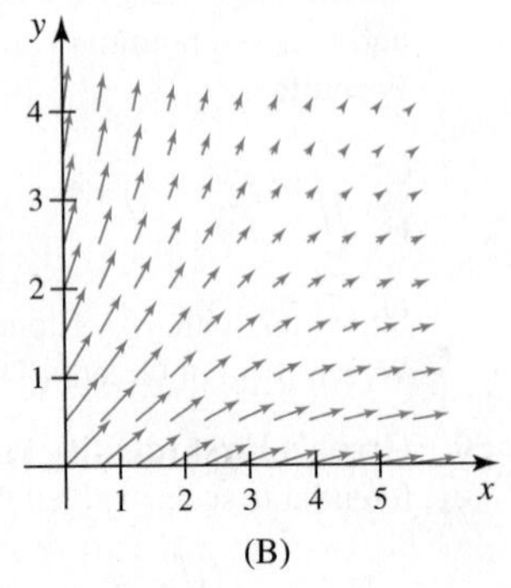
(B)

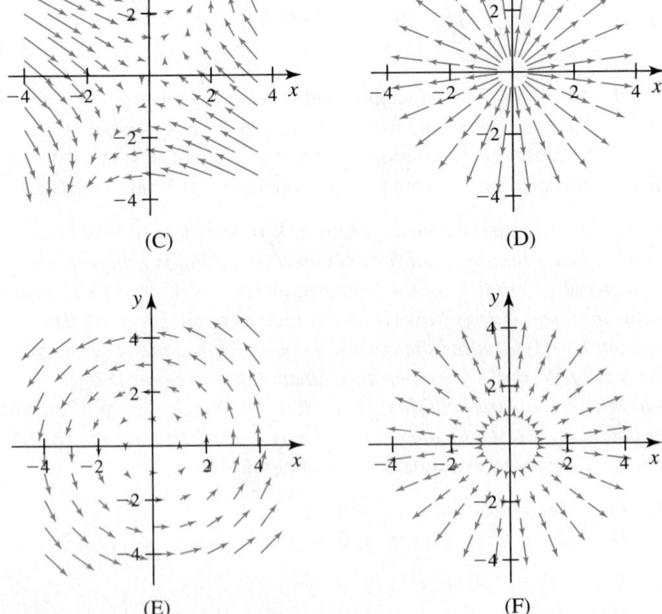
(C) (D) (E) (F)

3–4. Gradient fields in $\mathbf{R}^2$ *Find the vector field $\mathbf{F} = \nabla\varphi$ for the following potential functions. Sketch a few level curves of φ and sketch the general appearance of $\mathbf{F}$ in relation to the level curves.*

3. $\varphi(x, y) = x^2 + 4y^2$, for $|x| \le 5$, $|y| \le 5$

4. $\varphi(x, y) = (x^2 - y^2)/2$, for $|x| \le 2$, $|y| \le 2$

5–6. Gradient fields in $\mathbf{R}^3$ *Find the vector field $\mathbf{F} = \nabla\varphi$ for the following potential functions.*

5. $\varphi(x, y, z) = 1/|\mathbf{r}|$, where $\mathbf{r} = \langle x, y, z\rangle$

6. $\varphi(x, y, z) = \frac{1}{2}e^{-x^2-y^2-z^2}$

7. **Normal component** Let C be the circle of radius 2 centered at the origin with counterclockwise orientation.
   - **a.** Give the unit outward normal vector at any point (x, y) on C.
   - **b.** Find the normal component of the vector field $\mathbf{F} = 2\langle y, -x\rangle$ at any point on C.
   - **c.** Find the normal component of the vector field $\mathbf{F} = \dfrac{\langle x, y\rangle}{x^2 + y^2}$ at any point on C.

8–10. Line integrals *Evaluate the following line integrals.*

8. $\int_C (x^2 - 2xy + y^2)\, ds$; C is the upper half of a circle $\mathbf{r}(t) = \langle 5\cos t, 5\sin t\rangle$, for $0 \le t \le \pi$, with counterclockwise orientation.

9. $\int_C ye^{-xz}\, ds$; C is the path $\mathbf{r}(t) = \langle t, 3t, -6t\rangle$, for $0 \le t \le \ln 8$.

10. $\int_C xz - y^2\, ds$; C is the line segment from $(0, 1, 2)$ to $(-3, 7, -1)$.

11. **Two parameterizations** Verify that $\oint_C (x - 2y + 3z)\, ds$ has the same value when C is given by $\mathbf{r}(t) = \langle 2\cos t, 2\sin t, 0\rangle$, for $0 \le t \le 2\pi$ and by $\mathbf{r}(t) = \langle 2\cos t^2, 2\sin t^2, 0\rangle$, for $0 \le t \le \sqrt{2\pi}$.

12. **Work integral** Find the work done in moving an object from $P(1, 0, 0)$ to $Q(0, 1, 0)$ in the presence of the force $\mathbf{F} = \langle 1, 2y, -4z\rangle$ along the following paths.
    - **a.** The line segment from P to Q
    - **b.** The line segments from P to $O(0, 0, 0)$ followed by the line segment from O to Q
    - **c.** The arc of the quarter circle from P to Q
    - **d.** Is the work independent of the path?

13–14. Work integrals in $\mathbf{R}^3$ *Given the following force fields, find the work required to move an object on the given curve.*

13. $\mathbf{F} = \langle -y, z, x\rangle$ on the path consisting of the line segments from $(0, 0, 0)$ to $(0, 1, 0)$ followed by the line segment from $(0, 1, 0)$ to $(0, 1, 4)$

14. $\mathbf{F} = \dfrac{\langle x, y, z\rangle}{(x^2 + y^2 + z^2)^{3/2}}$ on the path $\mathbf{r}(t) = \langle t^2, 3t^2, -t^2\rangle$, for $1 \le t \le 2$

15–18. Circulation and flux *Find the circulation and the outward flux of the following vector fields for the curve $\mathbf{r}(t) = \langle 2\cos t, 2\sin t\rangle$, for $0 \le t \le 2\pi$.*

15. $\mathbf{F} = \langle y - x, y\rangle$

16. $\mathbf{F} = \langle x, y\rangle$

17. $\mathbf{F} = \mathbf{r}/|\mathbf{r}|^2$, where $\mathbf{r} = \langle x, y\rangle$

18. $\mathbf{F} = \langle x - y, x\rangle$

19. **Flux in channel flow** Consider the flow of water in a channel whose boundaries are the planes $y = \pm L$ and $z = \pm\frac{1}{2}$. The velocity field in the channel is $\mathbf{v} = \langle v_0(L^2 - y^2), 0, 0\rangle$. Find the flux across the cross section of the channel at $x = 0$ in terms of v_0 and L.

20–23. Conservative vector fields and potentials *Determine whether the following vector fields are conservative on their domains. If so, find a potential function.*

20. $\mathbf{F} = \langle y^2, 2xy\rangle$

21. $\mathbf{F} = \langle y, x + z^2, 2yz\rangle$

22. $\mathbf{F} = \langle e^x\cos y, -e^x\sin y\rangle$

23. $\mathbf{F} = e^z\langle y, x, xy\rangle$

24–27. Evaluating line integrals *Evaluate the line integral $\int_C \mathbf{F}\cdot d\mathbf{r}$ for the following vector fields $\mathbf{F}$ and curves C in two ways.*

a. By parameterizing C

b. By using the Fundamental Theorem for line integrals, if possible

24. $\mathbf{F} = \nabla(x^2y)$; C: $\mathbf{r}(t) = \langle 9 - t^2, t\rangle$, for $0 \le t \le 3$

25. $\mathbf{F} = \nabla(xyz)$; C: $\mathbf{r}(t) = \langle \cos t, \sin t, t/\pi\rangle$, for $0 \le t \le \pi$

26. $\mathbf{F} = \langle x, -y\rangle$; C is the square with vertices $(\pm1, \pm1)$ with counterclockwise orientation.

27. $\mathbf{F} = \langle y, z, -x\rangle$; C: $\mathbf{r}(t) = \langle \cos t, \sin t, 4\rangle$, for $0 \le t \le 2\pi$

28. **Radial fields in $\mathbf{R}^2$ are conservative** Prove that the radial field $\mathbf{F} = \dfrac{\mathbf{r}}{|\mathbf{r}|^p}$, where $\mathbf{r} = \langle x, y\rangle$ and p is a real number, is conservative on $\mathbf{R}^2$ with the origin removed. For what value of p is $\mathbf{F}$ conservative on $\mathbf{R}^2$ (including the origin)?

29–32. Green's Theorem for line integrals *Use either form of Green's Theorem to evaluate the following line integrals.*

29. $\oint_C xy^2\, dx + x^2y\, dy$; C is the triangle with vertices $(0, 0)$, $(2, 0)$, $(0, 2)$ with counterclockwise orientation.

30. $\oint_C (-3y + x^{3/2})\, dx + (x - y^{2/3})\, dy$; C is the boundary of the half disk $\{(x, y): x^2 + y^2 \le 2, y \ge 0\}$ with counterclockwise orientation.

31. $\oint_C (x^3 + xy)\, dy + (2y^2 - 2x^2y)\, dx$; C is the square with vertices $(\pm1, \pm1)$ with counterclockwise orientation.

32. $\oint_C 3x^3\, dy - 3y^3\, dx$; C is the circle of radius 4 centered at the origin with *clockwise* orientation.

33–34. Areas of plane regions *Find the area of the following regions using a line integral.*

33. The region enclosed by the ellipse $x^2 + 4y^2 = 16$

34. The region bounded by the hypocycloid $\mathbf{r}(t) = \langle \cos^3 t, \sin^3 t\rangle$, for $0 \le t \le 2\pi$

35–36. Circulation and flux *Consider the following vector fields.*

a. *Compute the circulation on the boundary of the region R (with counterclockwise orientation).*

b. *Compute the outward flux across the boundary of R.*

35. $\mathbf{F} = \mathbf{r}/|\mathbf{r}|$, where $\mathbf{r} = \langle x, y\rangle$ and R is the half annulus $\{(r, \theta): 1 \le r \le 3, 0 \le \theta \le \pi\}$

36. $\mathbf{F} = \langle -\sin y, x\cos y\rangle$, where R is the square $\{(x, y): 0 \le x \le \pi/2, 0 \le y \le \pi/2\}$

37. Parameters Let $\mathbf{F} = \langle ax + by, cx + dy\rangle$, where a, b, c, and d are constants.

a. For what values of a, b, c, and d is $\mathbf{F}$ conservative?

b. For what values of a, b, c, and d is $\mathbf{F}$ source-free?

c. For what values of a, b, c, and d is $\mathbf{F}$ conservative and source-free?

38–41. Divergence and curl *Compute the divergence and curl of the following vector fields. State whether the field is source-free or irrotational.*

38. $\mathbf{F} = \langle yz, xz, xy\rangle$

39. $\mathbf{F} = \mathbf{r}|\mathbf{r}| = \langle x, y, z\rangle\sqrt{x^2 + y^2 + z^2}$

40. $\mathbf{F} = \langle \sin xy, \cos yz, \sin xz\rangle$

41. $\mathbf{F} = \langle 2xy + z^4, x^2, 4xz^3\rangle$

42. Identities Prove that $\nabla\left(\frac{1}{|\mathbf{r}|^4}\right) = -\frac{4\mathbf{r}}{|\mathbf{r}|^6}$, and use the result to prove that $\nabla \cdot \nabla\left(\frac{1}{|\mathbf{r}|^4}\right) = \frac{12}{|\mathbf{r}|^6}$.

43. Maximum curl Let $\mathbf{F} = \langle z, x, -y\rangle$.

a. What are the components of curl $\mathbf{F}$ in the directions $\mathbf{n} = \langle 1, 0, 0\rangle$ and $\mathbf{n} = \langle 0, -1/\sqrt{2}, 1/\sqrt{2}\rangle$?

b. In what direction is the scalar component of curl $\mathbf{F}$ a maximum?

44. Paddle wheel in a vector field Let $\mathbf{F} = \langle 0, 2x, 0\rangle$ and let $\mathbf{n}$ be a unit vector aligned with the axis of a paddle wheel located on the y-axis.

a. If the axis of the paddle wheel is aligned with $\mathbf{n} = \langle 1, 0, 0\rangle$, how fast does it spin?

b. If the axis of the paddle wheel is aligned with $\mathbf{n} = \langle 0, 0, 1\rangle$, how fast does it spin?

c. For what direction $\mathbf{n}$ does the paddle wheel spin fastest?

45–48. Surface areas *Use a surface integral to find the area of the following surfaces.*

45. The hemisphere $x^2 + y^2 + z^2 = 9$, for $z \ge 0$ (excluding the base)

46. The frustum of the cone $z^2 = x^2 + y^2$, for $2 \le z \le 4$ (excluding the bases)

47. The plane $z = 6 - x - y$ above the square $|x| \le 1$, $|y| \le 1$

48. The surface $f(x, y) = \sqrt{2}\,xy$ above the region $\{(r, \theta): 0 \le r \le 2, 0 \le \theta \le 2\pi\}$

49–51. Surface integrals *Evaluate the following surface integrals.*

49. $\iint_S (1 + yz)\,dS$; S is the plane $x + y + z = 2$ in the first octant.

50. $\iint_S \langle 0, y, z\rangle \cdot \mathbf{n}\,dS$; S is the curved surface of the cylinder $y^2 + z^2 = a^2$, $|x| \le 8$ with outward normal vectors.

51. $\iint_S (x - y + z)\,dS$; S is the entire surface including the base of the hemisphere $x^2 + y^2 + z^2 = 4$, for $z \ge 0$.

52–53. Flux integrals *Find the flux of the following vector fields across the given surface. Assume the normal vectors to the surface point outward.*

52. $\mathbf{F} = \langle x, y, z\rangle$ across the curved surface of the cylinder $x^2 + y^2 = 1$, for $|z| \le 8$

53. $\mathbf{F} = \mathbf{r}/|\mathbf{r}|$ across the sphere of radius a centered at the origin, where $\mathbf{r} = \langle x, y, z\rangle$

54. Three methods Find the surface area of the paraboloid $z = x^2 + y^2$, for $0 \le z \le 4$, in three ways.

a. Use an explicit description of the surface.

b. Use the parametric description $\mathbf{r} = \langle v\cos u, v\sin u, v^2\rangle$.

c. Use the parametric description $\mathbf{r} = \langle \sqrt{v}\cos u, \sqrt{v}\sin u, v\rangle$.

55. Flux across hemispheres and paraboloids Let S be the hemisphere $x^2 + y^2 + z^2 = a^2$, for $z \ge 0$, and let T be the paraboloid $z = a - (x^2 + y^2)/a$, for $z \ge 0$, where $a > 0$. Assume the surfaces have outward normal vectors.

a. Verify that S and T have the same base ($x^2 + y^2 \le a^2$) and the same high point $(0, 0, a)$.

b. Which surface has the greater area?

c. Show that the flux of the radial field $\mathbf{F} = \langle x, y, z\rangle$ across S is $2\pi a^3$.

d. Show that the flux of the radial field $\mathbf{F} = \langle x, y, z\rangle$ across T is $3\pi a^3/2$.

56. Surface area of an ellipsoid Consider the ellipsoid $x^2/a^2 + y^2/b^2 + z^2/c^2 = 1$, where a, b, and c are positive real numbers.

a. Show that the surface is described by the parametric equations

$$\mathbf{r}(u, v) = \langle a\cos u\sin v, b\sin u\sin v, c\cos v\rangle$$

for $0 \le u \le 2\pi$, $0 \le v \le \pi$.

b. Write an integral for the surface area of the ellipsoid.

57–58. Stokes' Theorem for line integrals *Evaluate the line integral* $\oint_C \mathbf{F} \cdot d\mathbf{r}$ *using Stokes' Theorem. Assume C has counterclockwise orientation.*

57. $\mathbf{F} = \langle xz, yz, xy\rangle$; C is the circle $x^2 + y^2 = 4$ in the xy-plane.

58. $\mathbf{F} = \langle x^2 - y^2, x, 2yz\rangle$; C is the boundary of the plane $z = 6 - 2x - y$ in the first octant.

59–60. Stokes' Theorem for surface integrals *Use Stokes' Theorem to evaluate the surface integral* $\iint_S (\nabla \times \mathbf{F}) \cdot \mathbf{n}\,dS$. *Assume that* $\mathbf{n}$ *is the outward normal.*

59. $\mathbf{F} = \langle -z, x, y\rangle$, where S is the hyperboloid $z = 10 - \sqrt{1 + x^2 + y^2}$, for $z \ge 0$

60. $\mathbf{F} = \langle x^2 - z^2, y^2, xz \rangle$, where S is the hemisphere $x^2 + y^2 + z^2 = 4$, for $y \geq 0$

61. Conservative fields Use Stokes' Theorem to find the circulation of the vector field $\mathbf{F} = \nabla(10 - x^2 + y^2 + z^2)$ around any smooth closed curve C with counterclockwise orientation.

62–64. Computing fluxes *Use the Divergence Theorem to compute the outward flux of the following vector fields across the given surfaces S.*

62. $\mathbf{F} = \langle -x, x - y, x - z \rangle$; S is the surface of the cube cut from the first octant by the planes $x = 1$, $y = 1$, and $z = 1$.

63. $\mathbf{F} = \langle x^3, y^3, z^3 \rangle / 3$; S is the sphere $\{(x, y, z): x^2 + y^2 + z^2 = 9\}$.

64. $\mathbf{F} = \langle x^2, y^2, z^2 \rangle$; S is the cylinder $\{(x, y, z): x^2 + y^2 = 4, 0 \leq z \leq 8\}$.

65–66. General regions *Use the Divergence Theorem to compute the outward flux of the following vector fields across the boundary of the given regions D.*

65. $\mathbf{F} = \langle x^3, y^3, 10 \rangle$; D is the region between the hemispheres of radius 1 and 2 centered at the origin with bases in the xy-plane.

66. $\mathbf{F} = \dfrac{\mathbf{r}}{|\mathbf{r}|^3} = \dfrac{\langle x, y, z \rangle}{(x^2 + y^2 + z^2)^{3/2}}$; D is the region between two spheres of radius 1 and 2 centered at $(5, 5, 5)$.

67. Flux integrals Compute the outward flux of the field $\mathbf{F} = \langle x^2 + x \sin y, y^2 + 2 \cos y, z^2 + z \sin y \rangle$ across the surface S that is the boundary of the prism bounded by the planes $y = 1 - x$, $x = 0$, $y = 0$, $z = 0$, $z = 4$.

68. Stokes' Theorem on a compound surface Consider the surface S consisting of the quarter-sphere $x^2 + y^2 + z^2 = a^2$, for $z \geq 0$ and $x \geq 0$, and the half disk in the yz-plane $y^2 + z^2 \leq a^2$, for $z \geq 0$. The boundary of S in the xy-plane is C, which consists of the semicircle $x^2 + y^2 = a^2$, for $x \geq 0$, and the line segment $[-a, a]$ on the y-axis, with a counterclockwise orientation. Let $\mathbf{F} = \langle 2z - y, x - z, y - 2x \rangle$.

a. Describe the direction in which the normal vectors point on S.

b. Evaluate $\oint_C \mathbf{F} \cdot d\mathbf{r}$

c. Evaluate $\iint_S (\nabla \times \mathbf{F}) \cdot \mathbf{n}\, dS$ and check for agreement with part (b).

Chapter 15 Guided Projects

Applications of the material in this chapter and related topics can be found in the following Guided Projects. For additional information, see the Preface.

- Ideal fluid flow
- Planimeters and vector fields
- Maxwell's equations
- Vector calculus in other coordinate systems

16

First-Order Differential Equations

OVERVIEW We introduced differential equations of the form $dy/dx = f(x)$, where f is given and y is an unknown function of x. When f is continuous over some interval, we found the general solution $y(x)$ by integration, $y = \int f(x)\,dx$. Such equations arise when investigating exponential growth or decay, for example. In this chapter we study some other types of first-order differential equations. They involve only first derivatives of the unknown function.

16.1 Solutions, Slope Fields, and Euler's Method

We begin this section by defining general differential equations involving first derivatives. We then look at slope fields, which give a geometric picture of the solutions to such equations. Many differential equations cannot be solved by obtaining an explicit formula for the solution. However, we can often find numerical approximations to solutions. We present one such method here, called Euler's method, upon which many other numerical methods are based.

General First-Order Differential Equations and Solutions

A **first-order differential equation** is an equation

$$\frac{dy}{dx} = f(x, y) \tag{1}$$

in which $f(x, y)$ is a function of two variables defined on a region in the xy-plane. The equation is of *first order* because it involves only the first derivative dy/dx (and not higher-order derivatives). We point out that the equations

$$y' = f(x, y) \qquad \text{and} \qquad \frac{d}{dx}y = f(x, y)$$

are equivalent to Equation (1) and all three forms will be used interchangeably in the text.

A **solution** of Equation (1) is a differentiable function $y = y(x)$ defined on an interval I of x-values (perhaps infinite) such that

$$\frac{d}{dx}y(x) = f(x, y(x))$$

on that interval. That is, when $y(x)$ and its derivative $y'(x)$ are substituted into Equation (1), the resulting equation is true for all x over the interval I. The **general solution** to a first-order differential equation is a solution that contains all possible solutions. The general solution always contains an arbitrary constant, but having this property doesn't mean a solution is the general solution. That is, a solution may contain an arbitrary constant without being the general solution. Establishing that a solution *is* the general solution may require deeper results from the theory of differential equations and is best studied in a more advanced course.

EXAMPLE 1 Show that every member of the family of functions

$$y = \frac{C}{x} + 2$$

is a solution of the first-order differential equation

$$\frac{dy}{dx} = \frac{1}{x}(2 - y)$$

on the interval $(0, \infty)$, where C is any constant.

SOLUTION Differentiating $y = C/x + 2$ gives

$$\frac{dy}{dx} = C\frac{d}{dx}\left(\frac{1}{x}\right) + 0 = -\frac{C}{x^2}.$$

We need to show that the differential equation is satisfied when we substitute into it the expressions $(C/x) + 2$ for y, and $-C/x^2$ for dy/dx. That is, we need to verify that for all $x \in (0, \infty)$,

$$-\frac{C}{x^2} = \frac{1}{x}\left[2 - \left(\frac{C}{x} + 2\right)\right].$$

This last equation follows immediately by expanding the expression on the right-hand side:

$$\frac{1}{x}\left[2 - \left(\frac{C}{x} + 2\right)\right] = \frac{1}{x}\left(-\frac{C}{x}\right) = -\frac{C}{x^2}.$$

Therefore, for every value of C, the function $y = C/x + 2$ is a solution of the differential equation.

As was the case in finding antiderivatives, we often need a *particular* rather than the general solution to a first-order differential equation $y' = f(x, y)$. The **particular solution** satisfying the initial condition $y(x_0) = y_0$ is the solution $y = y(x)$ whose value is y_0 when $x = x_0$. Thus the graph of the particular solution passes through the point (x_0, y_0) in the xy-plane. A **first-order initial value problem** is a differential equation $y' = f(x, y)$ whose solution must satisfy an initial condition $y(x_0) = y_0$.

EXAMPLE 2 Show that the function

$$y = (x + 1) - \frac{1}{3}e^x$$

is a solution to the first-order initial value problem

$$\frac{dy}{dx} = y - x, \qquad y(0) = \frac{2}{3}.$$

SOLUTION The equation

$$\frac{dy}{dx} = y - x$$

is a first-order differential equation with $f(x, y) = y - x$.

On the left side of the equation:

$$\frac{dy}{dx} = \frac{d}{dx}\left(x + 1 - \frac{1}{3}e^x\right) = 1 - \frac{1}{3}e^x.$$

On the right side of the equation:

$$y - x = (x + 1) - \frac{1}{3}e^x - x = 1 - \frac{1}{3}e^x.$$

The function satisfies the initial condition because

$$y(0) = \left[(x + 1) - \frac{1}{3}e^x\right]_{x=0} = 1 - \frac{1}{3} = \frac{2}{3}.$$

The graph of the function is shown in Figure 16.1.

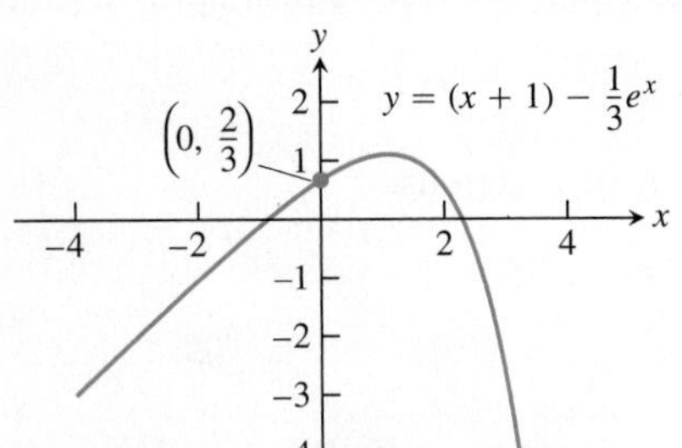

FIGURE 16.1 Graph of the solution to the initial value problem in Example 2.

Slope Fields: Viewing Solution Curves

Each time we specify an initial condition $y(x_0) = y_0$ for the solution of a differential equation $y' = f(x, y)$, the **solution curve** (graph of the solution) is required to pass through the point (x_0, y_0) and to have slope $f(x_0, y_0)$ there. We can picture these slopes graphically by drawing short line segments of slope $f(x, y)$ at selected points (x, y) in the region of the xy-plane that constitutes the domain of f. Each segment has the same slope as the solution curve through (x, y) and so is tangent to the curve there. The resulting picture is called a **slope field** (or **direction field**) and gives a visualization of the general shape of the solution curves. Figure 16.2a shows a slope field, with a particular solution sketched into it in Figure 16.2b. We see how these line segments indicate the direction the solution curve takes at each point it passes through.

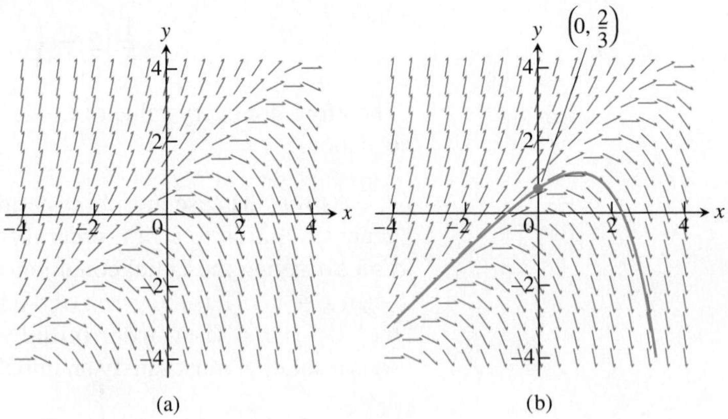

FIGURE 16.2 (a) Slope field for $\frac{dy}{dx} = y - x$. (b) The particular solution curve through the point $\left(0, \frac{2}{3}\right)$ (Example 2).

Figure 16.3 shows three slope fields and we see how the solution curves behave by following the tangent line segments in these fields. Slope fields are useful because they display the overall behavior of the family of solution curves for a given differential equation. For instance, the slope field in Figure 16.3b reveals that every solution $y(x)$ to the differential equation specified in the figure satisfies $\lim_{x\to\pm\infty} y(x) = 0$. We will see that knowing the overall behavior of the solution curves is often critical to understanding and predicting outcomes in a real-world system modeled by a differential equation.

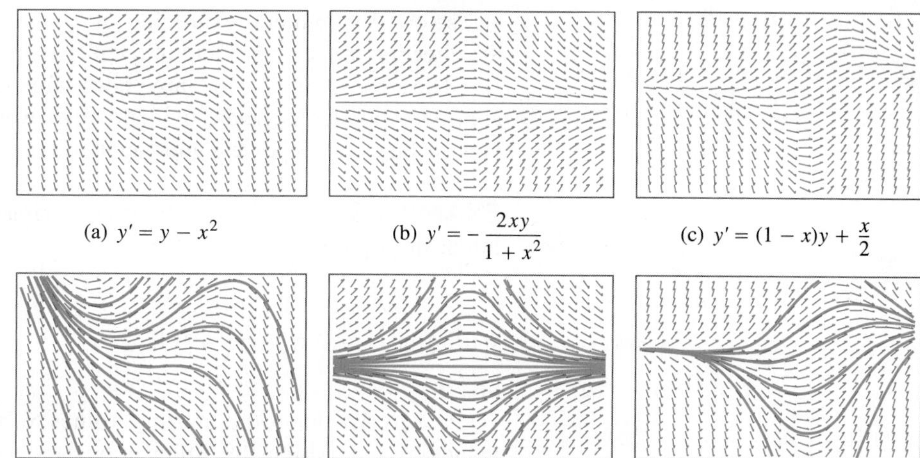

FIGURE 16.3 Slope fields (top row) and selected solution curves (bottom row). In computer renditions, slope segments are sometimes portrayed with arrows, as they are here. This is not to be taken as an indication that slopes have directions, however, for they do not.

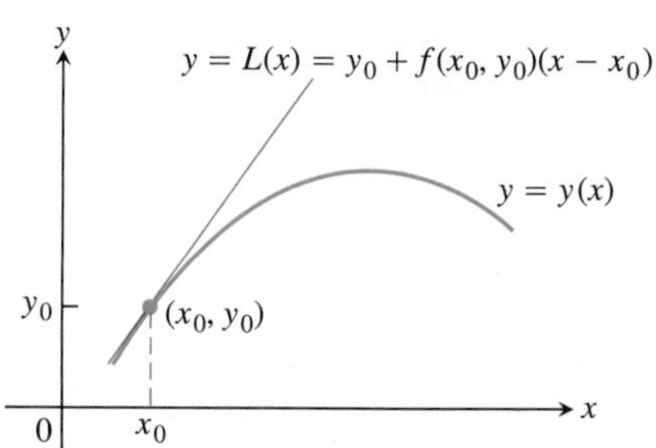

FIGURE 16.4 The linearization $L(x)$ of $y = y(x)$ at $x = x_0$.

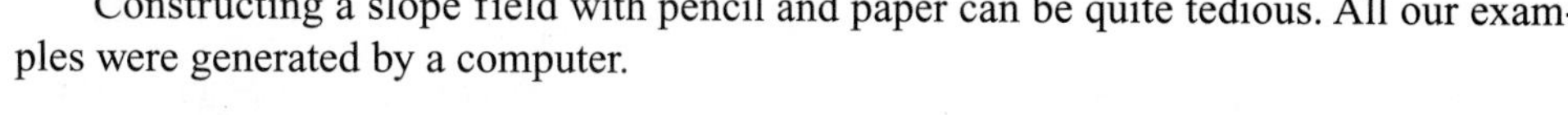

Constructing a slope field with pencil and paper can be quite tedious. All our examples were generated by a computer.

Euler's Method

If we do not require or cannot immediately find an *exact* solution giving an explicit formula for an initial value problem $y' = f(x, y), y(x_0) = y_0$, we can often use a computer to generate a table of approximate numerical values of y for values of x in an appropriate interval. Such a table is called a **numerical solution** of the problem, and the method by which we generate the table is called a **numerical method**.

Given a differential equation $dy/dx = f(x, y)$ and an initial condition $y(x_0) = y_0$, we can approximate the solution $y = y(x)$ by its linearization

$$L(x) = y(x_0) + y'(x_0)(x - x_0) \quad \text{or} \quad L(x) = y_0 + f(x_0, y_0)(x - x_0).$$

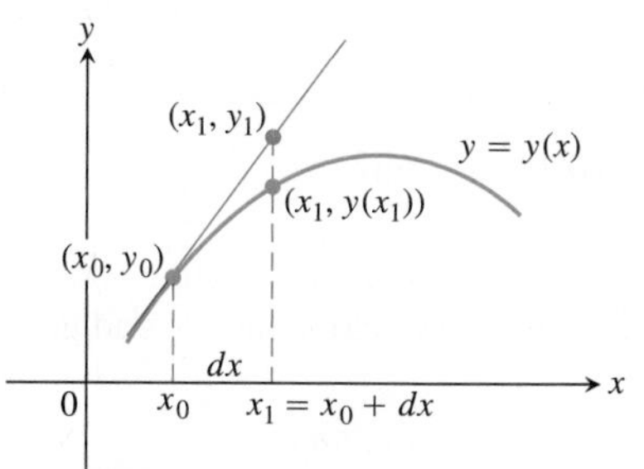

FIGURE 16.5 The first Euler step approximates $y(x_1)$ with $y_1 = L(x_1)$.

The function $L(x)$ gives a good approximation to the solution $y(x)$ in a short interval about x_0 (Figure 16.4). The basis of Euler's method is to patch together a string of linearizations to approximate the curve over a longer stretch. Here is how the method works.

We know the point (x_0, y_0) lies on the solution curve. Suppose that we specify a new value for the independent variable to be $x_1 = x_0 + dx$. (Recall that $dx = \Delta x$ in the definition of differentials.) If the increment dx is small, then

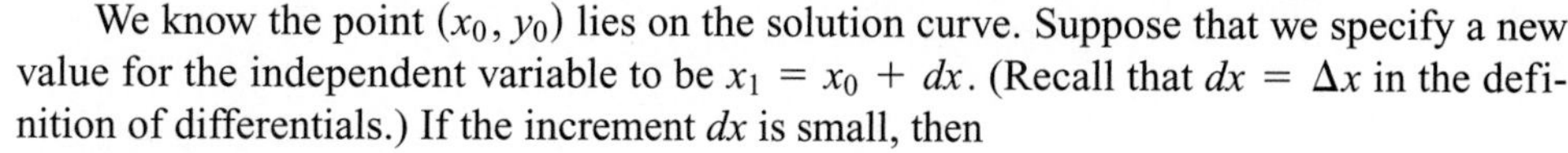

$$y_1 = L(x_1) = y_0 + f(x_0, y_0)\, dx$$

is a good approximation to the exact solution value $y = y(x_1)$. So from the point (x_0, y_0), which lies *exactly* on the solution curve, we have obtained the point (x_1, y_1), which lies very close to the point $(x_1, y(x_1))$ on the solution curve (Figure 16.5).

Using the point (x_1, y_1) and the slope $f(x_1, y_1)$ of the solution curve through (x_1, y_1), we take a second step. Setting $x_2 = x_1 + dx$, we use the linearization of the solution curve through (x_1, y_1) to calculate

$$y_2 = y_1 + f(x_1, y_1)\, dx.$$

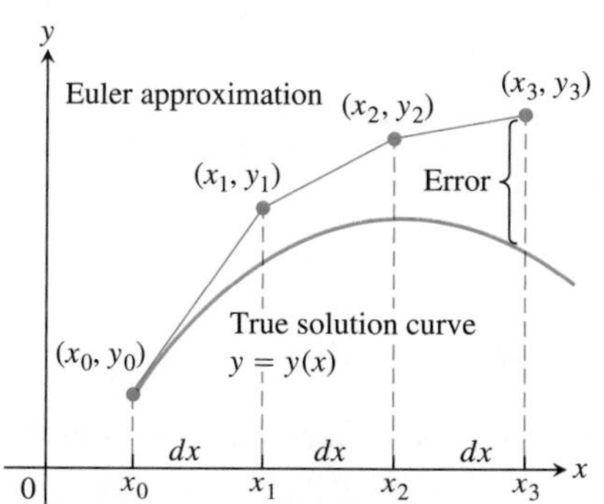

FIGURE 16.6 Three steps in the Euler approximation to the solution of the initial value problem $y' = f(x, y), y(x_0) = y_0$. As we take more steps, the errors involved usually accumulate, but not in the exaggerated way shown here.

This gives the next approximation (x_2, y_2) to values along the solution curve $y = y(x)$ (Figure 16.6). Continuing in this fashion, we take a third step from the point (x_2, y_2) with slope $f(x_2, y_2)$ to obtain the third approximation

$$y_3 = y_2 + f(x_2, y_2)\, dx,$$

and so on. We are literally building an approximation to one of the solutions by following the direction of the slope field of the differential equation.

The steps in Figure 16.6 are drawn large to illustrate the construction process, so the approximation looks crude. In practice, dx would be small enough to make the red curve hug the blue one and give a good approximation throughout.

EXAMPLE 3 Find the first three approximations y_1, y_2, y_3 using Euler's method for the initial value problem

$$y' = 1 + y, \qquad y(0) = 1,$$

starting at $x_0 = 0$ with $dx = 0.1$.

SOLUTION We have the starting values $x_0 = 0$ and $y_0 = 1$. Next we determine the values of x at which the Euler approximations will take place: $x_1 = x_0 + dx = 0.1$, $x_2 = x_0 + 2\,dx = 0.2$, and $x_3 = x_0 + 3\,dx = 0.3$. Then we find

$$\begin{aligned}
\textit{First:} \quad y_1 &= y_0 + f(x_0, y_0)\,dx \\
&= y_0 + (1 + y_0)\,dx \\
&= 1 + (1 + 1)(0.1) = 1.2 \\
\textit{Second:} \quad y_2 &= y_1 + f(x_1, y_1)\,dx \\
&= y_1 + (1 + y_1)\,dx \\
&= 1.2 + (1 + 1.2)(0.1) = 1.42 \\
\textit{Third:} \quad y_3 &= y_2 + f(x_2, y_2)\,dx \\
&= y_2 + (1 + y_2)\,dx \\
&= 1.42 + (1 + 1.42)(0.1) = 1.662
\end{aligned}$$

The step-by-step process used in Example 3 can be continued easily. Using equally spaced values for the independent variable in the table for the numerical solution, and generating n of them, set

$$\begin{aligned}
x_1 &= x_0 + dx \\
x_2 &= x_1 + dx \\
&\vdots \\
x_n &= x_{n-1} + dx.
\end{aligned}$$

Then calculate the approximations to the solution,

$$\begin{aligned}
y_1 &= y_0 + f(x_0, y_0)\,dx \\
y_2 &= y_1 + f(x_1, y_1)\,dx \\
&\vdots \\
y_n &= y_{n-1} + f(x_{n-1}, y_{n-1})\,dx.
\end{aligned}$$

The number of steps n can be as large as we like, but errors can accumulate if n is too large.

HISTORICAL BIOGRAPHY

Leonhard Euler (1703–1783)

Euler's method is easy to implement on a computer or calculator. A computer program generates a table of numerical solutions to an initial value problem, allowing us to input x_0 and y_0, the number of steps n, and the step size dx. It then calculates the approximate solution values $y_1, y_2, \ldots, y_n$ in iterative fashion, as just described.

Solving the separable equation in Example 3, we find that the exact solution to the initial value problem is $y = 2e^x - 1$. We use this information in Example 4.

EXAMPLE 4 Use Euler's method to solve

$$y' = 1 + y, \qquad y(0) = 1,$$

on the interval $0 \leq x \leq 1$, starting at $x_0 = 0$ and taking **(a)** $dx = 0.1$ and **(b)** $dx = 0.05$. Compare the approximations with the values of the exact solution $y = 2e^x - 1$.

SOLUTION

(a) We used a computer to generate the approximate values in Table 16.1. The "error" column is obtained by subtracting the unrounded Euler values from the unrounded values found using the exact solution. All entries are then rounded to four decimal places.

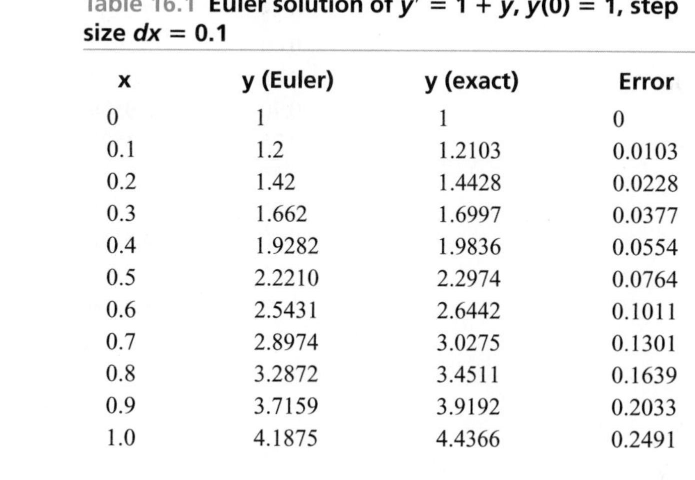

Table 16.1 **Euler solution of $y' = 1 + y$, $y(0) = 1$, step size $dx = 0.1$**

x	y (Euler)	y (exact)	Error
0	1	1	0
0.1	1.2	1.2103	0.0103
0.2	1.42	1.4428	0.0228
0.3	1.662	1.6997	0.0377
0.4	1.9282	1.9836	0.0554
0.5	2.2210	2.2974	0.0764
0.6	2.5431	2.6442	0.1011
0.7	2.8974	3.0275	0.1301
0.8	3.2872	3.4511	0.1639
0.9	3.7159	3.9192	0.2033
1.0	4.1875	4.4366	0.2491

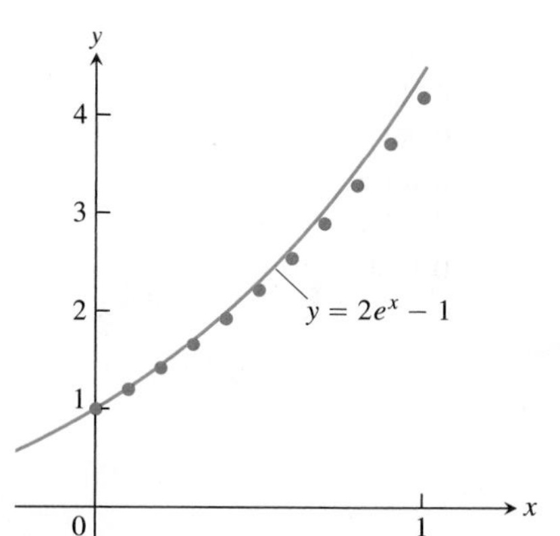

FIGURE 16.7 The graph of $y = 2e^x - 1$ superimposed on a scatterplot of the Euler approximations shown in Table 16.1 (Example 4).

By the time we reach $x = 1$ (after 10 steps), the error is about 5.6% of the exact solution. A plot of the exact solution curve with the scatterplot of Euler solution points from Table 16.1 is shown in Figure 16.7.

(b) One way to try to reduce the error is to decrease the step size. Table 16.2 shows the results and their comparisons with the exact solutions when we decrease the step size to 0.05, doubling the number of steps to 20. As in Table 16.1, all computations are performed before rounding. This time when we reach $x = 1$, the relative error is only about 2.9%.

It might be tempting to reduce the step size even further in Example 4 to obtain greater accuracy. Each additional calculation, however, not only requires additional computer time but more importantly adds to the buildup of round-off errors due to the approximate representations of numbers inside the computer.

The analysis of error and the investigation of methods to reduce it when making numerical calculations are important but are appropriate for a more advanced course. There are numerical methods more accurate than Euler's method, usually presented in a further study of differential equations.

Table 16.2 Euler solution of $y' = 1 + y$, $y(0) = 1$, step size $dx = 0.05$

x	y (Euler)	y (exact)	Error
0	1	1	0
0.05	1.1	1.1025	0.0025
0.10	1.205	1.2103	0.0053
0.15	1.3153	1.3237	0.0084
0.20	1.4310	1.4428	0.0118
0.25	1.5526	1.5681	0.0155
0.30	1.6802	1.6997	0.0195
0.35	1.8142	1.8381	0.0239
0.40	1.9549	1.9836	0.0287
0.45	2.1027	2.1366	0.0340
0.50	2.2578	2.2974	0.0397
0.55	2.4207	2.4665	0.0458
0.60	2.5917	2.6442	0.0525
0.65	2.7713	2.8311	0.0598
0.70	2.9599	3.0275	0.0676
0.75	3.1579	3.2340	0.0761
0.80	3.3657	3.4511	0.0853
0.85	3.5840	3.6793	0.0953
0.90	3.8132	3.9192	0.1060
0.95	4.0539	4.1714	0.1175
1.00	4.3066	4.4366	0.1300

SECTION 16.1 EXERCISES

Slope Fields

In Exercises 1–4, match the differential equations with their slope fields, graphed here.

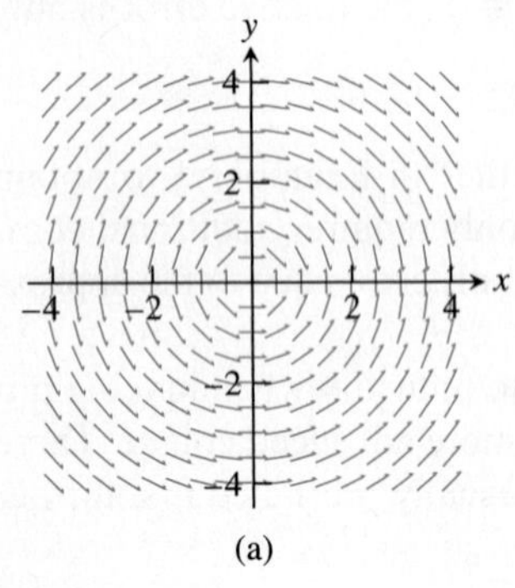

(a)

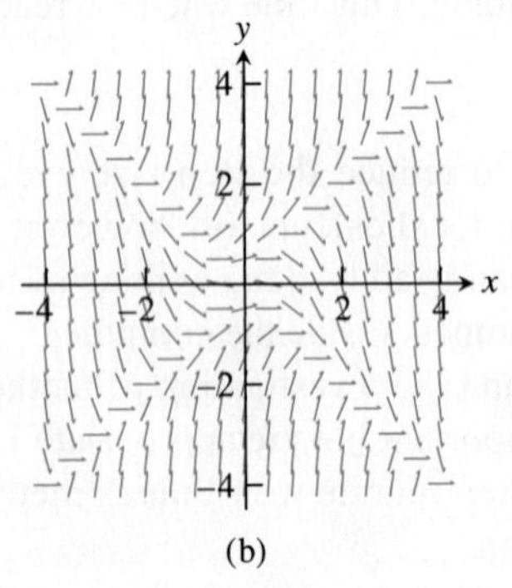

(b)

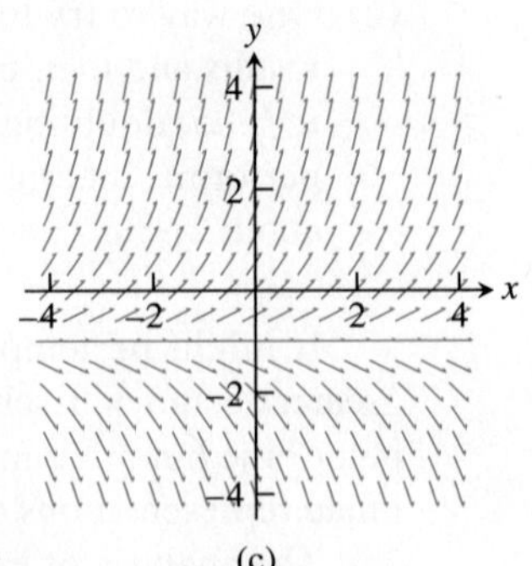

(c)

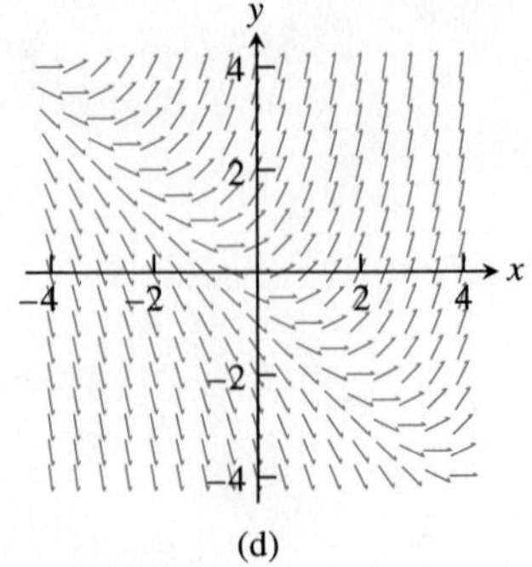

(d)

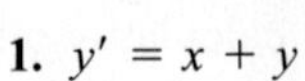

1. $y' = x + y$

2. $y' = y + 1$

3. $y' = -\dfrac{x}{y}$

4. $y' = y^2 - x^2$

In Exercises 5 and 6, copy the slope fields and sketch in some of the solution curves.

5. $y' = (y + 2)(y - 2)$

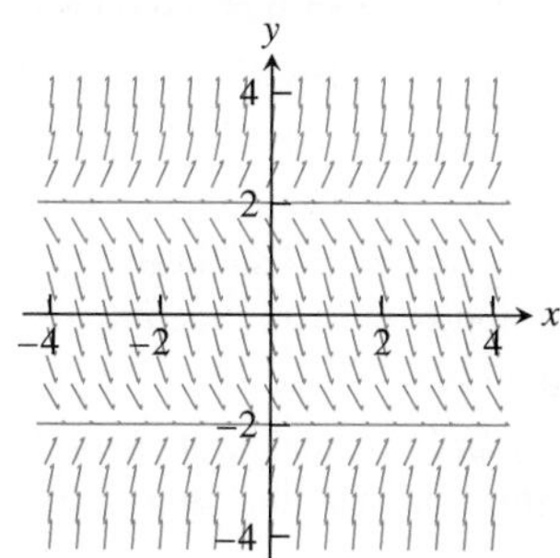

6. $y' = y(y + 1)(y - 1)$

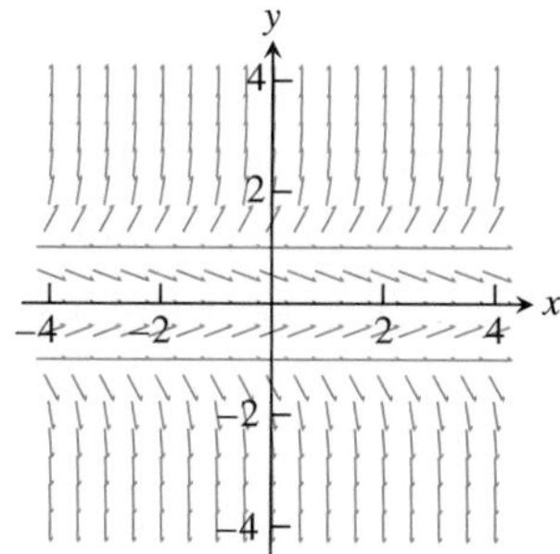

Integral Equations

In Exercises 7–10, write an equivalent first-order differential equation and initial condition for y.

7. $y = -1 + \int_1^x (t - y(t))\, dt$

8. $y = \int_1^x \frac{1}{t}\, dt$

9. $y = 2 - \int_0^x (1 + y(t)) \sin t\, dt$

10. $y = 1 + \int_0^x y(t)\, dt$

Using Euler's Method

In Exercises 11–16, use Euler's method to calculate the first three approximations to the given initial value problem for the specified increment size. Calculate the exact solution and investigate the accuracy of your approximations. Round your results to four decimal places.

11. $y' = 1 - \frac{y}{x}, \quad y(2) = -1, \quad dx = 0.5$

12. $y' = x(1 - y), \quad y(1) = 0, \quad dx = 0.2$

13. $y' = 2xy + 2y, \quad y(0) = 3, \quad dx = 0.2$

14. $y' = y^2(1 + 2x), \quad y(-1) = 1, \quad dx = 0.5$

T 15. $y' = 2xe^{x^2}, \quad y(0) = 2, \quad dx = 0.1$

T 16. $y' = ye^x, \quad y(0) = 2, \quad dx = 0.5$

17. Use the Euler method with $dx = 0.2$ to estimate $y(1)$ if $y' = y$ and $y(0) = 1$. What is the exact value of $y(1)$?

18. Use the Euler method with $dx = 0.2$ to estimate $y(2)$ if $y' = y/x$ and $y(1) = 2$. What is the exact value of $y(2)$?

19. Use the Euler method with $dx = 0.5$ to estimate $y(5)$ if $y' = y^2/\sqrt{x}$ and $y(1) = -1$. What is the exact value of $y(5)$?

20. Use the Euler method with $dx = 1/3$ to estimate $y(2)$ if $y' = x \sin y$ and $y(0) = 1$. What is the exact value of $y(2)$?

21. Show that the solution of the initial value problem

$$y' = x + y, \quad y(x_0) = y_0$$

is

$$y = -1 - x + (1 + x_0 + y_0)\, e^{x - x_0}.$$

22. What integral equation is equivalent to the initial value problem $y' = f(x),\ y(x_0) = y_0$?

Computer Explorations

In Exercises 23–28, obtain a slope field and add to it graphs of the solution curves passing through the given points.

23. $y' = y$ with

a. $(0, 1)$ **b.** $(0, 2)$ **c.** $(0, -1)$

24. $y' = 2(y - 4)$ with

a. $(0, 1)$ **b.** $(0, 4)$ **c.** $(0, 5)$

25. $y' = y(x + y)$ with

a. $(0, 1)$ **b.** $(0, -2)$ **c.** $(0, 1/4)$ **d.** $(-1, -1)$

26. $y' = y^2$ with

a. $(0, 1)$ **b.** $(0, 2)$ **c.** $(0, -1)$ **d.** $(0, 0)$

27. $y' = (y - 1)(x + 2)$ with

a. $(0, -1)$ **b.** $(0, 1)$ **c.** $(0, 3)$ **d.** $(1, -1)$

28. $y' = \dfrac{xy}{x^2 + 4}$ with

a. $(0, 2)$ **b.** $(0, -6)$ **c.** $\left(-2\sqrt{3}, -4\right)$

In Exercises 29 and 30, obtain a slope field and graph the particular solution over the specified interval. Use your CAS DE solver to find the general solution of the differential equation.

29. **A logistic equation** $y' = y(2 - y), \quad y(0) = 1/2;$ $0 \le x \le 4, \quad 0 \le y \le 3$

30. $y' = (\sin x)(\sin y), \quad y(0) = 2; \quad -6 \le x \le 6, \quad -6 \le y \le 6$

Exercises 31 and 32 have no explicit solution in terms of elementary functions. Use a CAS to explore graphically each of the differential equations.

31. $y' = \cos(2x - y), \quad y(0) = 2; \quad 0 \le x \le 5, \quad 0 \le y \le 5$

32. **A Gompertz equation** $y' = y(1/2 - \ln y), \quad y(0) = 1/3;$ $0 \le x \le 4, \quad 0 \le y \le 3$

33. Use a CAS to find the solutions of $y' + y = f(x)$ subject to the initial condition $y(0) = 0$, if $f(x)$ is

a. $2x$ **b.** $\sin 2x$ **c.** $3e^{x/2}$ **d.** $2e^{-x/2} \cos 2x$.

Graph all four solutions over the interval $-2 \le x \le 6$ to compare the results.

34. **a.** Use a CAS to plot the slope field of the differential equation

$$y' = \frac{3x^2 + 4x + 2}{2(y - 1)}$$

over the region $-3 \le x \le 3$ and $-3 \le y \le 3$.

b. Separate the variables and use a CAS integrator to find the general solution in implicit form.

c. Using a CAS implicit function grapher, plot solution curves for the arbitrary constant values $C = -6, -4, -2, 0, 2, 4, 6$.

d. Find and graph the solution that satisfies the initial condition $y(0) = -1$.

In Exercises 35–38, use Euler's method with the specified step size to estimate the value of the solution at the given point x^*. Find the value of the exact solution at x^*.

35. $y' = 2xe^{x^2}$, $y(0) = 2$, $dx = 0.1$, $x^* = 1$

36. $y' = 2y^2(x - 1)$, $y(2) = -1/2$, $dx = 0.1$, $x^* = 3$

37. $y' = \sqrt{x}/y$, $y > 0$, $y(0) = 1$, $dx = 0.1$, $x^* = 1$

38. $y' = 1 + y^2$, $y(0) = 0$, $dx = 0.1$, $x^* = 1$

Use a CAS to explore graphically each of the differential equations in Exercises 39–42. Perform the following steps to help with your explorations.

a. Plot a slope field for the differential equation in the given xy-window.

b. Find the general solution of the differential equation using your CAS DE solver.

c. Graph the solutions for the values of the arbitrary constant $C = -2, -1, 0, 1, 2$ superimposed on your slope field plot.

d. Find and graph the solution that satisfies the specified initial condition over the interval $[0, b]$.

e. Find the Euler numerical approximation to the solution of the initial value problem with 4 subintervals of the x-interval and plot the Euler approximation superimposed on the graph produced in part (d).

f. Repeat part (e) for 8, 16, and 32 subintervals. Plot these three Euler approximations superimposed on the graph from part (e).

g. Find the error $(y(\text{exact}) - y(\text{Euler}))$ at the specified point $x = b$ for each of your four Euler approximations. Discuss the improvement in the percentage error.

39. $y' = x + y$, $y(0) = -7/10$; $-4 \le x \le 4$, $-4 \le y \le 4$; $b = 1$

40. $y' = -x/y$, $y(0) = 2$; $-3 \le x \le 3$, $-3 \le y \le 3$; $b = 2$

41. $y' = y(2 - y)$, $y(0) = 1/2$; $0 \le x \le 4$, $0 \le y \le 3$; $b = 3$

42. $y' = (\sin x)(\sin y)$, $y(0) = 2$; $-6 \le x \le 6$, $-6 \le y \le 6$; $b = 3\pi/2$

16.2 First-Order Linear Equations

A first-order **linear** differential equation is one that can be written in the form

$$\frac{dy}{dx} + P(x)y = Q(x), \tag{1}$$

where P and Q are continuous functions of x. Equation (1) is the linear equation's **standard form**. Since the exponential growth/decay equation $dy/dx = ky$ can be put in the standard form

$$\frac{dy}{dx} - ky = 0,$$

we see it is a linear equation with $P(x) = -k$ and $Q(x) = 0$. Equation (1) is *linear* (in y) because y and its derivative dy/dx occur only to the first power, they are not multiplied together, nor do they appear as the argument of a function $\left(\text{such as } \sin y,\ e^y, \text{ or } \sqrt{dy/dx}\right)$.

EXAMPLE 1 Put the following equation in standard form:

$$x\frac{dy}{dx} = x^2 + 3y, \qquad x > 0.$$

SOLUTION

$$x\frac{dy}{dx} = x^2 + 3y$$

$$\frac{dy}{dx} = x + \frac{3}{x}y \qquad \text{Divide by } x.$$

$$\frac{dy}{dx} - \frac{3}{x}y = x \qquad \text{Standard form with } P(x) = -3/x \text{ and } Q(x) = x$$

Notice that $P(x)$ is $-3/x$, not $+3/x$. The standard form is $y' + P(x)y = Q(x)$, so the minus sign is part of the formula for $P(x)$.

Solving Linear Equations

We solve the equation

$$\frac{dy}{dx} + P(x)y = Q(x)$$

by multiplying both sides by a *positive* function $v(x)$ that transforms the left-hand side into the derivative of the product $v(x) \cdot y$. We will show how to find v in a moment, but first we want to show how, once found, it provides the solution we seek.

Here is why multiplying by $v(x)$ works:

$$\frac{dy}{dx} + P(x)y = Q(x) \qquad \text{Original equation is in standard form.}$$

$$v(x)\frac{dy}{dx} + P(x)v(x)y = v(x)Q(x) \qquad \text{Multiply by positive } v(x).$$

$$\frac{d}{dx}(v(x) \cdot y) = v(x)Q(x) \qquad v(x) \text{ is chosen to make } v\frac{dy}{dx} + Pvy = \frac{d}{dx}(v \cdot y).$$

$$v(x) \cdot y = \int v(x)Q(x)\,dx \qquad \text{Integrate with respect to } x.$$

$$y = \frac{1}{v(x)}\int v(x)Q(x)\,dx \tag{2}$$

Equation (2) expresses the solution of Equation (1) in terms of the functions $v(x)$ and $Q(x)$. We call $v(x)$ an **integrating factor** for Equation (1) because its presence makes the equation integrable.

Why doesn't the formula for $P(x)$ appear in the solution as well? It does, but indirectly, in the construction of the positive function $v(x)$. We have

$$\frac{d}{dx}(vy) = v\frac{dy}{dx} + Pvy \qquad \text{Condition imposed on } v$$

$$v\frac{dy}{dx} + y\frac{dv}{dx} = v\frac{dy}{dx} + Pvy \qquad \text{Derivative Product Rule}$$

$$y\frac{dv}{dx} = Pvy \qquad \text{The terms } v\frac{dy}{dx} \text{ cancel.}$$

This last equation will hold if

$$\frac{dv}{dx} = Pv$$

$$\frac{dv}{v} = P\,dx \qquad \text{Variables separated, } v > 0$$

$$\int \frac{dv}{v} = \int P\,dx \qquad \text{Integrate both sides.}$$

$$\ln v = \int P\,dx$$ Since $v > 0$, we do not need absolute value signs in $\ln v$.

$$e^{\ln v} = e^{\int P\,dx}$$ Exponentiate both sides to solve for v.

$$v = e^{\int P\,dx} \tag{3}$$

Thus a formula for the general solution to Equation (1) is given by Equation (2), where $v(x)$ is given by Equation (3). However, rather than memorizing the formula, just remember how to find the integrating factor once you have the standard form so $P(x)$ is correctly identified. Any antiderivative of P works for Equation (3).

> To solve the linear equation $y' + P(x)y = Q(x)$, multiply both sides by the integrating factor $v(x) = e^{\int P(x)\,dx}$ and integrate both sides.

When you integrate the product on the left-hand side in this procedure, you always obtain the product $v(x)y$ of the integrating factor and solution function y because of the way v is defined.

EXAMPLE 2 Solve the equation

$$x\frac{dy}{dx} = x^2 + 3y, \qquad x > 0.$$

HISTORICAL BIOGRAPHY

Adrien Marie Legendre (1752–1833)

SOLUTION First we put the equation in standard form (Example 1):

$$\frac{dy}{dx} - \frac{3}{x}y = x,$$

so $P(x) = -3/x$ is identified.

The integrating factor is

$$\begin{aligned} v(x) = e^{\int P(x)\,dx} &= e^{\int(-3/x)\,dx} \\ &= e^{-3\ln|x|} && \text{Constant of integration is 0, so } v \text{ is as simple as possible.} \\ &= e^{-3\ln x} && x > 0 \\ &= e^{\ln x^{-3}} = \frac{1}{x^3}. \end{aligned}$$

Next we multiply both sides of the standard form by $v(x)$ and integrate:

$$\begin{aligned} \frac{1}{x^3}\cdot\left(\frac{dy}{dx} - \frac{3}{x}y\right) &= \frac{1}{x^3}\cdot x \\ \frac{1}{x^3}\frac{dy}{dx} - \frac{3}{x^4}y &= \frac{1}{x^2} \\ \frac{d}{dx}\left(\frac{1}{x^3}y\right) &= \frac{1}{x^2} && \text{Left-hand side is } \frac{d}{dx}(v\cdot y). \\ \frac{1}{x^3}y &= \int\frac{1}{x^2}\,dx && \text{Integrate both sides.} \\ \frac{1}{x^3}y &= -\frac{1}{x} + C. \end{aligned}$$

Solving this last equation for y gives the general solution:

$$y = x^3\left(-\frac{1}{x} + C\right) = -x^2 + Cx^3, \qquad x > 0.$$

EXAMPLE 3 Find the particular solution of

$$3xy' - y = \ln x + 1, \qquad x > 0,$$

satisfying $y(1) = -2$.

SOLUTION With $x > 0$, we write the equation in standard form:

$$y' - \frac{1}{3x}y = \frac{\ln x + 1}{3x}.$$

Then the integrating factor is given by

$$v = e^{\int -dx/3x} = e^{(-1/3)\ln x} = x^{-1/3}. \qquad x > 0$$

Thus

$$x^{-1/3}y = \frac{1}{3}\int (\ln x + 1)x^{-4/3}\,dx. \qquad \text{Left-hand side is } vy.$$

Integration by parts of the right-hand side gives

$$x^{-1/3}y = -x^{-1/3}(\ln x + 1) + \int x^{-4/3}\,dx + C.$$

Therefore

$$x^{-1/3}y = -x^{-1/3}(\ln x + 1) - 3x^{-1/3} + C$$

or, solving for y,

$$y = -(\ln x + 4) + Cx^{1/3}.$$

When $x = 1$ and $y = -2$ this last equation becomes

$$-2 = -(0 + 4) + C,$$

so

$$C = 2.$$

Substitution into the equation for y gives the particular solution

$$y = 2x^{1/3} - \ln x - 4.$$

In solving the linear equation in Example 2, we integrated both sides of the equation after multiplying each side by the integrating factor. However, we can shorten the amount of work, as in Example 3, by remembering that the left-hand side *always* integrates into the product $v(x) \cdot y$ of the integrating factor times the solution function. From Equation (2) this means that

$$v(x)y = \int v(x)Q(x)\,dx. \tag{4}$$

We need only integrate the product of the integrating factor $v(x)$ with $Q(x)$ on the right-hand side of Equation (1) and then equate the result with $v(x)y$ to obtain the general solution. Nevertheless, to emphasize the role of $v(x)$ in the solution process, we sometimes follow the complete procedure as illustrated in Example 2.

Observe that if the function $Q(x)$ is identically zero in the standard form given by Equation (1), the linear equation is separable and can be solved by the method:

$$\frac{dy}{dx} + P(x)y = Q(x)$$

$$\frac{dy}{dx} + P(x)y = 0 \qquad Q(x) \equiv 0$$

$$\frac{dy}{y} = -P(x)\,dx \qquad \text{Separating the variables}$$

RL Circuits

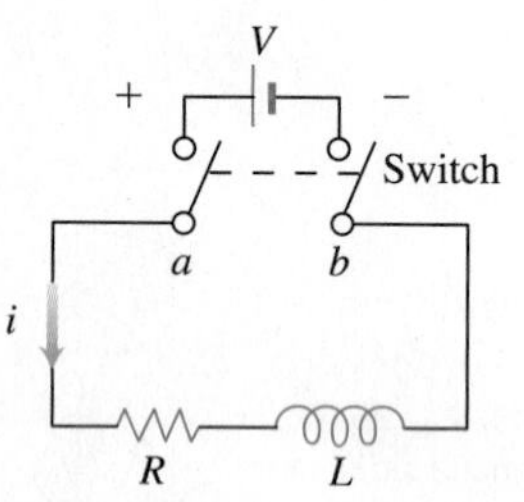

FIGURE 16.8 The RL circuit in Example 4.

The diagram in Figure 16.8 represents an electrical circuit whose total resistance is a constant R ohms and whose self-inductance, shown as a coil, is L henries, also a constant. There is a switch whose terminals at a and b can be closed to connect a constant electrical source of V volts.

Ohm's Law, $V = RI$, has to be augmented for such a circuit. The correct equation accounting for both resistance and inductance is

$$L\frac{di}{dt} + Ri = V, \tag{5}$$

where i is the current in amperes and t is the time in seconds. By solving this equation, we can predict how the current will flow after the switch is closed.

EXAMPLE 4 The switch in the *RL* circuit in Figure 16.8 is closed at time $t = 0$. How will the current flow as a function of time?

SOLUTION Equation (5) is a first-order linear differential equation for i as a function of t. Its standard form is

$$\frac{di}{dt} + \frac{R}{L}i = \frac{V}{L}, \tag{6}$$

and the corresponding solution, given that $i = 0$ when $t = 0$, is

$$i = \frac{V}{R} - \frac{V}{R}e^{-(R/L)t}. \tag{7}$$

(We leave the calculation of the solution for you to do in Exercise 28.) Since R and L are positive, $-(R/L)$ is negative and $e^{-(R/L)t} \to 0$ as $t \to \infty$. Thus,

$$\lim_{t\to\infty} i = \lim_{t\to\infty}\left(\frac{V}{R} - \frac{V}{R}e^{-(R/L)t}\right) = \frac{V}{R} - \frac{V}{R}\cdot 0 = \frac{V}{R}.$$

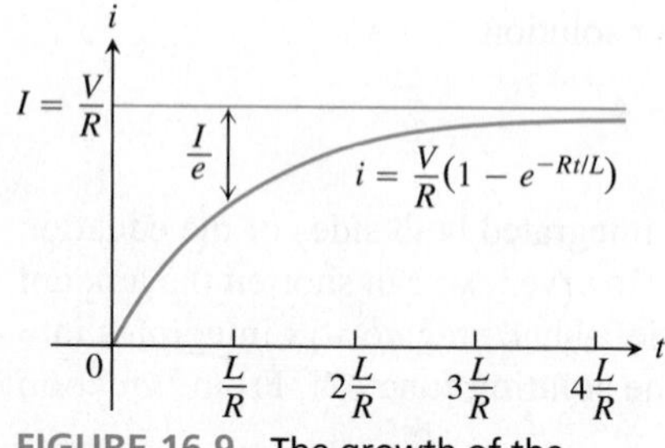

FIGURE 16.9 The growth of the current in the *RL* circuit in Example 4. I is the current's steady-state value. The number $t = L/R$ is the time constant of the circuit. The current gets to within 5% of its steady-state value in 3 time constants (Exercise 27).

At any given time, the current is theoretically less than V/R, but as time passes, the current approaches the **steady-state value** V/R. According to the equation

$$L\frac{di}{dt} + Ri = V,$$

$I = V/R$ is the current that will flow in the circuit if either $L = 0$ (no inductance) or $di/dt = 0$ (steady current, $i =$ constant) (Figure 16.9).

Equation (7) expresses the solution of Equation (6) as the sum of two terms: a steady-state solution V/R and a transient solution $-(V/R)e^{-(R/L)t}$ that tends to zero as $t \to \infty$.

SECTION 16.2 EXERCISES

First-Order Linear Equations

Solve the differential equations in Exercises 1–14.

1. $x\frac{dy}{dx} + y = e^x, \quad x > 0$

2. $e^x\frac{dy}{dx} + 2e^x y = 1$

3. $xy' + 3y = \frac{\sin x}{x^2}, \quad x > 0$

4. $y' + (\tan x)y = \cos^2 x, \quad -\pi/2 < x < \pi/2$

5. $x\frac{dy}{dx} + 2y = 1 - \frac{1}{x}, \quad x > 0$

6. $(1 + x)y' + y = \sqrt{x}$

7. $2y' = e^{x/2} + y$

8. $e^{2x}y' + 2e^{2x}y = 2x$

9. $xy' - y = 2x\ln x$

10. $x\frac{dy}{dx} = \frac{\cos x}{x} - 2y, \quad x > 0$

11. $(t - 1)^3\frac{ds}{dt} + 4(t - 1)^2 s = t + 1, \quad t > 1$

12. $(t + 1)\frac{ds}{dt} + 2s = 3(t + 1) + \frac{1}{(t + 1)^2}, \quad t > -1$

13. $\sin\theta\frac{dr}{d\theta} + (\cos\theta)r = \tan\theta, \quad 0 < \theta < \pi/2$

14. $\tan\theta\frac{dr}{d\theta} + r = \sin^2\theta, \quad 0 < \theta < \pi/2$

Solving Initial Value Problems

Solve the initial value problems in Exercises 15–20.

15. $\frac{dy}{dt} + 2y = 3, \quad y(0) = 1$

16. $t\frac{dy}{dt} + 2y = t^3, \quad t > 0, \quad y(2) = 1$

17. $\theta\frac{dy}{d\theta} + y = \sin\theta, \quad \theta > 0, \quad y(\pi/2) = 1$

18. $\theta\frac{dy}{d\theta} - 2y = \theta^3\sec\theta\tan\theta, \quad \theta > 0, \quad y(\pi/3) = 2$

19. $(x + 1)\frac{dy}{dx} - 2(x^2 + x)y = \frac{e^{x^2}}{x + 1}, \quad x > -1, \quad y(0) = 5$

20. $\frac{dy}{dx} + xy = x, \quad y(0) = -6$

21. Solve the exponential growth/decay initial value problem for y as a function of t by thinking of the differential equation as a first-order linear equation with $P(x) = -k$ and $Q(x) = 0$:

$$\frac{dy}{dt} = ky \quad (k \text{ constant}), \quad y(0) = y_0$$

22. Solve the following initial value problem for u as a function of t:

$$\frac{du}{dt} + \frac{k}{m}u = 0 \quad (k \text{ and } m \text{ positive constants}), \quad u(0) = u_0$$

   a. as a first-order linear equation.

   b. as a separable equation.

Theory and Examples

23. Is either of the following equations correct? Give reasons for your answers.

   a. $x\int\frac{1}{x}\,dx = x\ln|x| + C$ **b.** $x\int\frac{1}{x}\,dx = x\ln|x| + Cx$

24. Is either of the following equations correct? Give reasons for your answers.

   a. $\frac{1}{\cos x}\int\cos x\,dx = \tan x + C$

   b. $\frac{1}{\cos x}\int\cos x\,dx = \tan x + \frac{C}{\cos x}$

25. **Current in a closed *RL* circuit** How many seconds after the switch in an RL circuit is closed will it take the current i to reach half of its steady-state value? Notice that the time depends on R and L and not on how much voltage is applied.

26. **Current in an open *RL* circuit** If the switch is thrown open after the current in an RL circuit has built up to its steady-state value $I = V/R$, the decaying current (see accompanying figure) obeys the equation

$$L\frac{di}{dt} + Ri = 0,$$

which is Equation (5) with $V = 0$.

   a. Solve the equation to express i as a function of t.

   b. How long after the switch is thrown will it take the current to fall to half its original value?

   c. Show that the value of the current when $t = L/R$ is I/e. (The significance of this time is explained in the next exercise.)

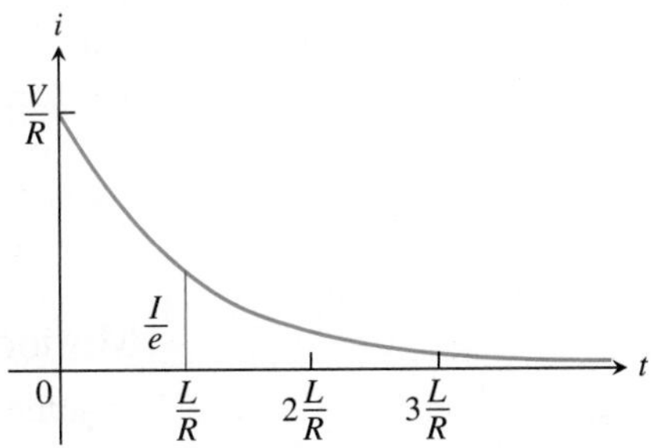

27. **Time constants** Engineers call the number L/R the *time constant* of the RL circuit in Figure 16.9. The significance of the time constant is that the current will reach 95% of its final value within 3 time constants of the time the switch is closed (Figure 16.9). Thus, the time constant gives a built-in measure of how rapidly an individual circuit will reach equilibrium.

   a. Find the value of i in Equation (7) that corresponds to $t = 3L/R$ and show that it is about 95% of the steady-state value $I = V/R$.

   b. Approximately what percentage of the steady-state current will be flowing in the circuit 2 time constants after the switch is closed (i.e., when $t = 2L/R$)?

28. Derivation of Equation (7) in Example 4

a. Show that the solution of the equation

$$\frac{di}{dt} + \frac{R}{L}i = \frac{V}{L}$$

is

$$i = \frac{V}{R} + Ce^{-(R/L)t}.$$

b. Then use the initial condition $i(0) = 0$ to determine the value of C. This will complete the derivation of Equation (7).

c. Show that $i = V/R$ is a solution of Equation (6) and that $i = Ce^{-(R/L)t}$ satisfies the equation

$$\frac{di}{dt} + \frac{R}{L}i = 0.$$

HISTORICAL BIOGRAPHY

James Bernoulli
(1654–1705)

A **Bernoulli differential equation** is of the form

$$\frac{dy}{dx} + P(x)y = Q(x)y^n.$$

Observe that, if $n = 0$ or 1, the Bernoulli equation is linear. For other values of n, the substitution $u = y^{1-n}$ transforms the Bernoulli equation into the linear equation

$$\frac{du}{dx} + (1 - n)P(x)u = (1 - n)Q(x).$$

For example, in the equation

$$\frac{dy}{dx} - y = e^{-x}y^2$$

we have $n = 2$, so that $u = y^{1-2} = y^{-1}$ and $du/dx = -y^{-2}\,dy/dx$. Then $dy/dx = -y^2\,du/dx = -u^{-2}\,du/dx$. Substitution into the original equation gives

$$-u^{-2}\frac{du}{dx} - u^{-1} = e^{-x}u^{-2}$$

or, equivalently,

$$\frac{du}{dx} + u = -e^{-x}.$$

This last equation is linear in the (unknown) dependent variable u.

Solve the Bernoulli equations in Exercises 29–32.

29. $y' - y = -y^2$

30. $y' - y = xy^2$

31. $xy' + y = y^{-2}$

32. $x^2y' + 2xy = y^3$

16.3 Applications

We now look at four applications of first-order differential equations. The first application analyzes an object moving along a straight line while subject to a force opposing its motion. The second is a model of population growth. The third application considers a curve or curves intersecting each curve in a second family of curves *orthogonally* (that is, at right angles). The final application analyzes chemical concentrations entering and leaving a container. The various models involve separable or linear first-order equations.

Motion with Resistance Proportional to Velocity

In some cases it is reasonable to assume that the resistance encountered by a moving object, such as a car coasting to a stop, is proportional to the object's velocity. The faster the object moves, the more its forward progress is resisted by the air through which it passes. Picture the object as a mass m moving along a coordinate line with position function s and velocity v at time t. From Newton's second law of motion, the resisting force opposing the motion is

$$\text{Force} = \text{mass} \times \text{acceleration} = m\frac{dv}{dt}.$$

If the resisting force is proportional to velocity, we have

$$m\frac{dv}{dt} = -kv \quad \text{or} \quad \frac{dv}{dt} = -\frac{k}{m}v \quad (k > 0).$$

This is a separable differential equation representing exponential change. The solution to the equation with initial condition $v = v_0$ at $t = 0$ is

$$v = v_0 e^{-(k/m)t}. \tag{1}$$

What can we learn from Equation (1)? For one thing, we can see that if m is something large, like the mass of a 20,000-ton ore boat in Lake Erie, it will take a long time for the velocity to approach zero (because t must be large in the exponent of the equation in order to make kt/m large enough for v to be small). We can learn even more if we integrate Equation (1) to find the position s as a function of time t.

Suppose that a body is coasting to a stop and the only force acting on it is a resistance proportional to its speed. How far will it coast? To find out, we start with Equation (1) and solve the initial value problem

$$\frac{ds}{dt} = v_0 e^{-(k/m)t}, \qquad s(0) = 0.$$

Integrating with respect to t gives

$$s = -\frac{v_0 m}{k} e^{-(k/m)t} + C.$$

Substituting $s = 0$ when $t = 0$ gives

$$0 = -\frac{v_0 m}{k} + C \qquad \text{and} \qquad C = \frac{v_0 m}{k}.$$

The body's position at time t is therefore

$$s(t) = -\frac{v_0 m}{k} e^{-(k/m)t} + \frac{v_0 m}{k} = \frac{v_0 m}{k}\left(1 - e^{-(k/m)t}\right). \tag{2}$$

To find how far the body will coast, we find the limit of $s(t)$ as $t \to \infty$. Since $-(k/m) < 0$, we know that $e^{-(k/m)t} \to 0$ as $t \to \infty$, so that

$$\begin{aligned}\lim_{t\to\infty} s(t) &= \lim_{t\to\infty} \frac{v_0 m}{k}\left(1 - e^{-(k/m)t}\right)\\ &= \frac{v_0 m}{k}(1 - 0) = \frac{v_0 m}{k}.\end{aligned}$$

Thus,

$$\text{Distance coasted} = \frac{v_0 m}{k}. \tag{3}$$

The number $v_0 m/k$ is only an upper bound (albeit a useful one). It is true to life in one respect, at least: if m is large, the body will coast a long way.

In the English system, where weight is measured in pounds, mass is measured in **slugs**. Thus,

$$\text{Pounds} = \text{slugs} \times 32,$$

assuming the gravitational constant is 32 ft/sec^2.

EXAMPLE 1 For a 192-lb ice skater, the k in Equation (1) is about 1/3 slug/sec and $m = 192/32 = 6$ slugs. How long will it take the skater to coast from 11 ft/sec (7.5 mph) to 1 ft/sec? How far will the skater coast before coming to a complete stop?

SOLUTION We answer the first question by solving Equation (1) for t:

$$\begin{aligned}11e^{-t/18} &= 1 && \text{Eq. (1) with } k = 1/3,\ m = 6,\ v_0 = 11,\ v = 1\\ e^{-t/18} &= 1/11\\ -t/18 &= \ln(1/11) = -\ln 11\\ t &= 18 \ln 11 \approx 43 \text{ sec}.\end{aligned}$$

We answer the second question with Equation (3):

$$\text{Distance coasted} = \frac{v_0 m}{k} = \frac{11 \cdot 6}{1/3}$$

$$= 198 \text{ ft}.$$

Inaccuracy of the Exponential Population Growth Model

Previously, we modeled population growth with the Law of Exponential Change:

$$\frac{dP}{dt} = kP, \qquad P(0) = P_0$$

where P is the population at time t, $k > 0$ is a constant growth rate, and P_0 is the size of the population at time $t = 0$. We found the solution $P = P_0 e^{kt}$ to this model.

To assess the model, notice that the exponential growth differential equation says that

$$\frac{dP/dt}{P} = k \tag{4}$$

Table 16.3 **World population (midyear)**

Year	Population (millions)	$\Delta P/P$
1980	4454	$76/4454 \approx 0.0171$
1981	4530	$80/4530 \approx 0.0177$
1982	4610	$80/4610 \approx 0.0174$
1983	4690	$80/4690 \approx 0.0171$
1984	4770	$81/4770 \approx 0.0170$
1985	4851	$82/4851 \approx 0.0169$
1986	4933	$85/4933 \approx 0.0172$
1987	5018	$87/5018 \approx 0.0173$
1988	5105	$85/5105 \approx 0.0167$
1989	5190	

Source: U.S. Bureau of the Census (Sept., 2007): www.census.gov/ipc/www/idb.

is constant. This rate is called the **relative growth rate**. Now, Table 16.3 gives the world population at midyear for the years 1980 to 1989. Taking $dt = 1$ and $dP \approx \Delta P$, we see from the table that the relative growth rate in Equation (4) is approximately the constant 0.017. Thus, based on the tabled data with $t = 0$ representing 1980, $t = 1$ representing 1981, and so forth, the world population could be modeled by the initial value problem,

$$\frac{dP}{dt} = 0.017P, \qquad P(0) = 4454.$$

The solution to this initial value problem gives the population function $P = 4454e^{0.017t}$. In year 2008 (so $t = 28$), the solution predicts the world population in midyear to be about 7169 million, or 7.2 billion (Figure 16.10), which is more than the actual population of 6707 million from the U.S. Bureau of the Census. A more realistic model would consider environmental and other factors affecting the growth rate, which has been steadily declining to about 0.012 since 1987. We consider one such model in Section 16.4.

Orthogonal Trajectories

An **orthogonal trajectory** of a family of curves is a curve that intersects each curve of the family at right angles, or *orthogonally* (Figure 16.11). For instance, each straight line

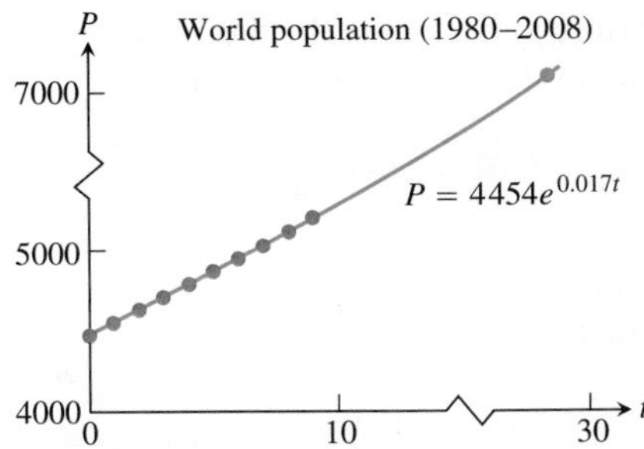

FIGURE 16.10 Notice that the value of the solution $P = 4454e^{0.017t}$ is 7169 when $t = 28$, which is nearly 7% more than the actual population in 2008.

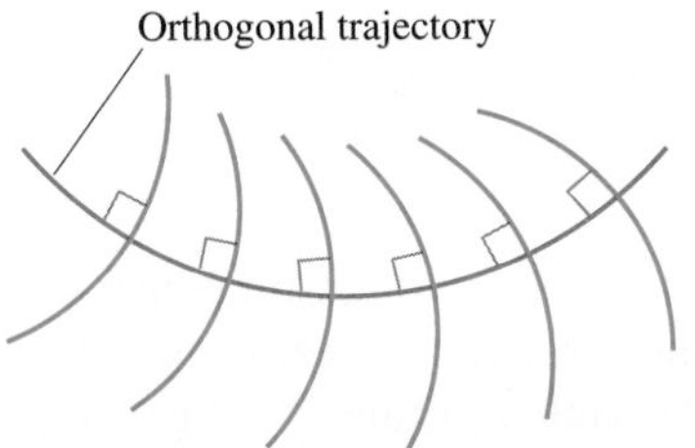

FIGURE 16.11 An orthogonal trajectory intersects the family of curves at right angles, or orthogonally.

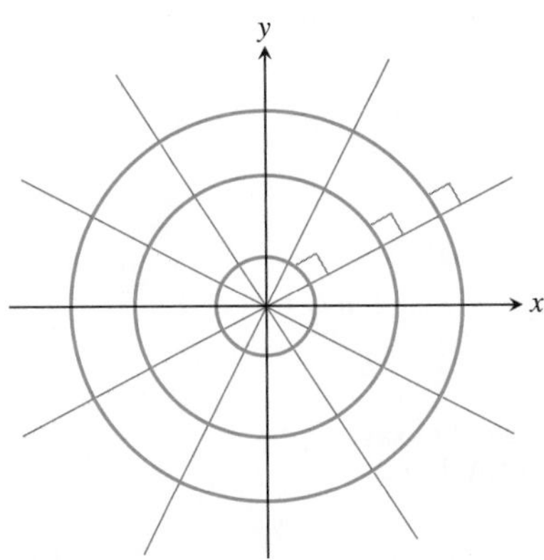

FIGURE 16.12 Every straight line through the origin is orthogonal to the family of circles centered at the origin.

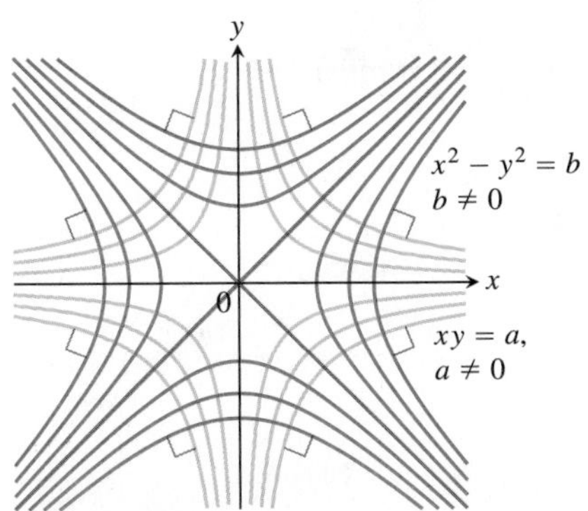

FIGURE 16.13 Each curve is orthogonal to every curve it meets in the other family (Example 2).

through the origin is an orthogonal trajectory of the family of circles $x^2 + y^2 = a^2$, centered at the origin (Figure 16.12). Such mutually orthogonal systems of curves are of particular importance in physical problems related to electrical potential, where the curves in one family correspond to strength of an electric field and those in the other family correspond to constant electric potential. They also occur in hydrodynamics and heat-flow problems.

EXAMPLE 2 Find the orthogonal trajectories of the family of curves $xy = a$, where $a \neq 0$ is an arbitrary constant.

SOLUTION The curves $xy = a$ form a family of hyperbolas having the coordinate axes as asymptotes. First we find the slopes of each curve in this family, or their dy/dx values. Differentiating $xy = a$ implicitly gives

$$x\frac{dy}{dx} + y = 0 \qquad \text{or} \qquad \frac{dy}{dx} = -\frac{y}{x}.$$

Thus the slope of the tangent line at any point (x, y) on one of the hyperbolas $xy = a$ is $y' = -y/x$. On an orthogonal trajectory the slope of the tangent line at this same point must be the negative reciprocal, or x/y. Therefore, the orthogonal trajectories must satisfy the differential equation

$$\frac{dy}{dx} = \frac{x}{y}.$$

This differential equation is separable and we solve it as:

$$y\,dy = x\,dx \qquad \text{Separate variables.}$$

$$\int y\,dy = \int x\,dx \qquad \text{Integrate both sides.}$$

$$\frac{1}{2}y^2 = \frac{1}{2}x^2 + C$$

$$y^2 - x^2 = b, \tag{5}$$

where $b = 2C$ is an arbitrary constant. The orthogonal trajectories are the family of hyperbolas given by Equation (5) and sketched in Figure 16.13.

Mixture Problems

Suppose a chemical in a liquid solution (or dispersed in a gas) runs into a container holding the liquid (or the gas) with, possibly, a specified amount of the chemical dissolved as well. The mixture is kept uniform by stirring and flows out of the container at a known rate. In this process, it is often important to know the concentration of the chemical in the container at any given time. The differential equation describing the process is based on the formula

$$\begin{matrix}\text{Rate of change} \\ \text{of amount} \\ \text{in container}\end{matrix} = \begin{pmatrix}\text{rate at which} \\ \text{chemical} \\ \text{arrives}\end{pmatrix} - \begin{pmatrix}\text{rate at which} \\ \text{chemical} \\ \text{departs.}\end{pmatrix} \tag{6}$$

If $y(t)$ is the amount of chemical in the container at time t and $V(t)$ is the total volume of liquid in the container at time t, then the departure rate of the chemical at time t is

$$\begin{aligned}\text{Departure rate} &= \frac{y(t)}{V(t)} \cdot (\text{outflow rate}) \\ &= \left(\begin{matrix}\text{concentration in} \\ \text{container at time } t\end{matrix}\right) \cdot (\text{outflow rate}).\end{aligned} \tag{7}$$

Accordingly, Equation (6) becomes

$$\frac{dy}{dt} = (\text{chemical's arrival rate}) - \frac{y(t)}{V(t)} \cdot (\text{outflow rate}). \tag{8}$$

If, say, y is measured in pounds, V in gallons, and t in minutes, the units in Equation (8) are

$$\frac{\text{pounds}}{\text{minutes}} = \frac{\text{pounds}}{\text{minutes}} - \frac{\text{pounds}}{\text{gallons}} \cdot \frac{\text{gallons}}{\text{minutes}}.$$

EXAMPLE 3 In an oil refinery, a storage tank contains 2000 gal of gasoline that initially has 100 lb of an additive dissolved in it. In preparation for winter weather, gasoline containing 2 lb of additive per gallon is pumped into the tank at a rate of 40 gal/min. The well-mixed solution is pumped out at a rate of 45 gal/min. How much of the additive is in the tank 20 min after the pumping process begins (Figure 16.14)?

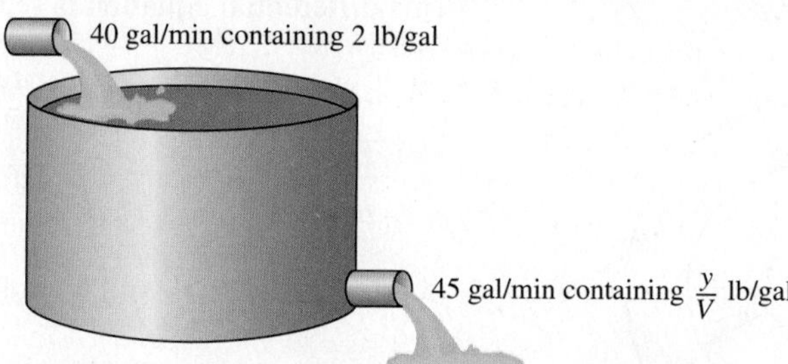

FIGURE 16.14 The storage tank in Example 3 mixes input liquid with stored liquid to produce an output liquid.

SOLUTION Let y be the amount (in pounds) of additive in the tank at time t. We know that $y = 100$ when $t = 0$. The number of gallons of gasoline and additive in solution in the tank at any time t is

$$\begin{aligned}V(t) &= 2000 \text{ gal} + \left(40\frac{\text{gal}}{\text{min}} - 45\frac{\text{gal}}{\text{min}}\right)(t \text{ min}) \\ &= (2000 - 5t) \text{ gal}.\end{aligned}$$

Therefore,

$$\begin{aligned}\text{Rate out} &= \frac{y(t)}{V(t)} \cdot \text{outflow rate} && \text{Eq. (7)} \\ &= \left(\frac{y}{2000 - 5t}\right) 45 && \text{Outflow rate is 45 gal/min and } v = 2000 - 5t. \\ &= \frac{45y}{2000 - 5t} \frac{\text{lb}}{\text{min}}.\end{aligned}$$

Also,

$$\text{Rate in} = \left(2\,\frac{\text{lb}}{\text{gal}}\right)\left(40\,\frac{\text{gal}}{\text{min}}\right)$$
$$= 80\,\frac{\text{lb}}{\text{min}}.$$

The differential equation modeling the mixture process is

$$\frac{dy}{dt} = 80 - \frac{45y}{2000 - 5t} \qquad \text{Eq. (8)}$$

in pounds per minute.

To solve this differential equation, we first write it in standard linear form:

$$\frac{dy}{dt} + \frac{45}{2000 - 5t}\,y = 80.$$

Thus, $P(t) = 45/(2000 - 5t)$ and $Q(t) = 80$. The integrating factor is

$$\begin{aligned} v(t) &= e^{\int P\,dt} = e^{\int \frac{45}{2000-5t}\,dt} \\ &= e^{-9\ln(2000-5t)} \qquad 2000 - 5t > 0 \\ &= (2000 - 5t)^{-9}. \end{aligned}$$

Multiplying both sides of the standard equation by $v(t)$ and integrating both sides gives

$$(2000 - 5t)^{-9}\cdot\left(\frac{dy}{dt} + \frac{45}{2000 - 5t}\,y\right) = 80(2000 - 5t)^{-9}$$

$$(2000 - 5t)^{-9}\,\frac{dy}{dt} + 45(2000 - 5t)^{-10}\,y = 80(2000 - 5t)^{-9}$$

$$\frac{d}{dt}\left[(2000 - 5t)^{-9}y\right] = 80(2000 - 5t)^{-9}$$

$$(2000 - 5t)^{-9}y = \int 80(2000 - 5t)^{-9}\,dt$$

$$(2000 - 5t)^{-9}y = 80\cdot\frac{(2000 - 5t)^{-8}}{(-8)(-5)} + C.$$

The general solution is

$$y = 2(2000 - 5t) + C(2000 - 5t)^{9}.$$

Because $y = 100$ when $t = 0$, we can determine the value of C:

$$100 = 2(2000 - 0) + C(2000 - 0)^{9}$$

$$C = -\frac{3900}{(2000)^{9}}.$$

The particular solution of the initial value problem is

$$y = 2(2000 - 5t) - \frac{3900}{(2000)^9}(2000 - 5t)^9.$$

The amount of additive 20 min after the pumping begins is

$$y(20) = 2[2000 - 5(20)] - \frac{3900}{(2000)^9}[2000 - 5(20)]^9 \approx 1342 \text{ lb}.$$

SECTION 16.3 EXERCISES

Motion Along a Line

1. **Coasting bicycle** A 66-kg cyclist on a 7-kg bicycle starts coasting on level ground at 9 m/sec. The k in Equation (1) is about 3.9 kg/sec.
   a. About how far will the cyclist coast before reaching a complete stop?
   b. How long will it take the cyclist's speed to drop to 1 m/sec?
2. **Coasting battleship** Suppose that an Iowa class battleship has mass around 51,000 metric tons (51,000,000 kg) and a k value in Equation (1) of about 59,000 kg/sec. Assume that the ship loses power when it is moving at a speed of 9 m/sec.
   a. About how far will the ship coast before it is dead in the water?
   b. About how long will it take the ship's speed to drop to 1 m/sec?
3. The data in Table 16.4 were collected with a motion detector and a CBL™ by Valerie Sharritts, a mathematics teacher at St. Francis DeSales High School in Columbus, Ohio. The table shows the distance s (meters) coasted on in-line skates in t sec by her daughter Ashley when she was 10 years old. Find a model for Ashley's position given by the data in Table 16.4 in the form of Equation (2). Her initial velocity was $v_0 = 2.75$ m/sec, her mass $m = 39.92$ kg (she weighed 88 lb), and her total coasting distance was 4.91 m.

Table 16.4 Ashley Sharritts skating data

t (sec)	s (m)	t (sec)	s (m)	t (sec)	s (m)
0	0	2.24	3.05	4.48	4.77
0.16	0.31	2.40	3.22	4.64	4.82
0.32	0.57	2.56	3.38	4.80	4.84
0.48	0.80	2.72	3.52	4.96	4.86
0.64	1.05	2.88	3.67	5.12	4.88
0.80	1.28	3.04	3.82	5.28	4.89
0.96	1.50	3.20	3.96	5.44	4.90
1.12	1.72	3.36	4.08	5.60	4.90
1.28	1.93	3.52	4.18	5.76	4.91
1.44	2.09	3.68	4.31	5.92	4.90
1.60	2.30	3.84	4.41	6.08	4.91
1.76	2.53	4.00	4.52	6.24	4.90
1.92	2.73	4.16	4.63	6.40	4.91
2.08	2.89	4.32	4.69	6.56	4.91

4. **Coasting to a stop** Table 16.5 shows the distance s (meters) coasted on in-line skates in terms of time t (seconds) by Kelly Schmitzer. Find a model for her position in the form of Equation (2). Her initial velocity was $v_0 = 0.80$ m/sec, her mass $m = 49.90$ kg (110 lb), and her total coasting distance was 1.32 m.

Table 16.5 Kelly Schmitzer skating data

t (sec)	s (m)	t (sec)	s (m)	t (sec)	s (m)
0	0	1.5	0.89	3.1	1.30
0.1	0.07	1.7	0.97	3.3	1.31
0.3	0.22	1.9	1.05	3.5	1.32
0.5	0.36	2.1	1.11	3.7	1.32
0.7	0.49	2.3	1.17	3.9	1.32
0.9	0.60	2.5	1.22	4.1	1.32
1.1	0.71	2.7	1.25	4.3	1.32
1.3	0.81	2.9	1.28	4.5	1.32

Orthogonal Trajectories

In Exercises 5–10, find the orthogonal trajectories of the family of curves. Sketch several members of each family.

5. $y = mx$
6. $y = cx^2$
7. $kx^2 + y^2 = 1$
8. $2x^2 + y^2 = c^2$
9. $y = ce^{-x}$
10. $y = e^{kx}$
11. Show that the curves $2x^2 + 3y^2 = 5$ and $y^2 = x^3$ are orthogonal.
12. Find the family of solutions of the given differential equation and the family of orthogonal trajectories. Sketch both families.
    a. $x\,dx + y\,dy = 0$
    b. $x\,dy - 2y\,dx = 0$

Mixture Problems

13. **Salt mixture** A tank initially contains 100 gal of brine in which 50 lb of salt are dissolved. A brine containing 2 lb/gal of salt runs into the tank at the rate of 5 gal/min. The mixture is kept uniform by stirring and flows out of the tank at the rate of 4 gal/min.
    a. At what rate (pounds per minute) does salt enter the tank at time t?
    b. What is the volume of brine in the tank at time t?
    c. At what rate (pounds per minute) does salt leave the tank at time t?

d. Write down and solve the initial value problem describing the mixing process.

e. Find the concentration of salt in the tank 25 min after the process starts.

14. Mixture problem A 200-gal tank is half full of distilled water. At time $t = 0$, a solution containing 0.5 lb/gal of concentrate enters the tank at the rate of 5 gal/min, and the well-stirred mixture is withdrawn at the rate of 3 gal/min.

a. At what time will the tank be full?

b. At the time the tank is full, how many pounds of concentrate will it contain?

15. Fertilizer mixture A tank contains 100 gal of fresh water. A solution containing 1 lb/gal of soluble lawn fertilizer runs into the tank at the rate of 1 gal/min, and the mixture is pumped out of the tank at the rate of 3 gal/min. Find the maximum amount of fertilizer in the tank and the time required to reach the maximum.

16. Carbon monoxide pollution An executive conference room of a corporation contains 4500 ft^3 of air initially free of carbon monoxide. Starting at time $t = 0$, cigarette smoke containing 4% carbon monoxide is blown into the room at the rate of 0.3 ft^3/min. A ceiling fan keeps the air in the room well circulated and the air leaves the room at the same rate of 0.3 ft^3/min. Find the time when the concentration of carbon monoxide in the room reaches 0.01%.

16.4 Graphical Solutions of Autonomous Equations

The sign of the first derivative tells where the graph of a function is increasing and where it is decreasing. The sign of the second derivative tells the concavity of the graph. We can build on our knowledge of how derivatives determine the shape of a graph to solve differential equations graphically. We will see that the ability to discern physical behavior from graphs is a powerful tool in understanding real-world systems. The starting ideas for a graphical solution are the notions of *phase line* and *equilibrium value*. We arrive at these notions by investigating what happens when the derivative of a differentiable function is zero.

Equilibrium Values and Phase Lines

When we differentiate implicitly the equation

$$\frac{1}{5}\ln(5y - 15) = x + 1,$$

we obtain

$$\frac{1}{5}\left(\frac{5}{5y - 15}\right)\frac{dy}{dx} = 1.$$

Solving for $y' = dy/dx$ we find $y' = 5y - 15 = 5(y - 3)$. In this case the derivative y' is a function of y only (the dependent variable) and is zero when $y = 3$.

A differential equation for which dy/dx is a function of y only is called an **autonomous** differential equation. Let's investigate what happens when the derivative in an autonomous equation equals zero. We assume any derivatives are continuous.

DEFINITION If $dy/dx = g(y)$ is an autonomous differential equation, then the values of y for which $dy/dx = 0$ are called **equilibrium values** or **rest points.**

Thus, equilibrium values are those at which no change occurs in the dependent variable, so y is at *rest*. The emphasis is on the value of y where $dy/dx = 0$, not the value of x. For example, the equilibrium values for the autonomous differential equation

$$\frac{dy}{dx} = (y + 1)(y - 2)$$

are $y = -1$ and $y = 2$.

To construct a graphical solution to an autonomous differential equation, we first make a **phase line** for the equation, a plot on the y-axis that shows the equation's equilibrium values along with the intervals where dy/dx and d^2y/dx^2 are positive and negative. Then we know where the solutions are increasing and decreasing, and the concavity of the solution curves. We can determine the shapes of the solution curves without having to find formulas for them.

EXAMPLE 1 Draw a phase line for the equation

$$\frac{dy}{dx} = (y + 1)(y - 2)$$

and use it to sketch solutions to the equation.

SOLUTION

1. *Draw a number line for y and mark the equilibrium values $y = -1$ and $y = 2$, where $dy/dx = 0$.*

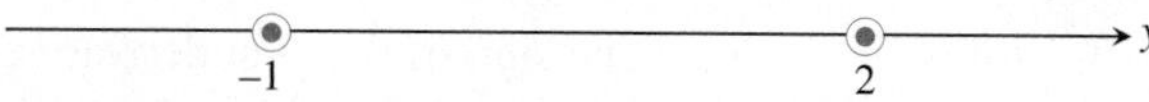

2. *Identify and label the intervals where $y' > 0$ and $y' < 0$.* We are marking the y-axis instead of the x-axis.

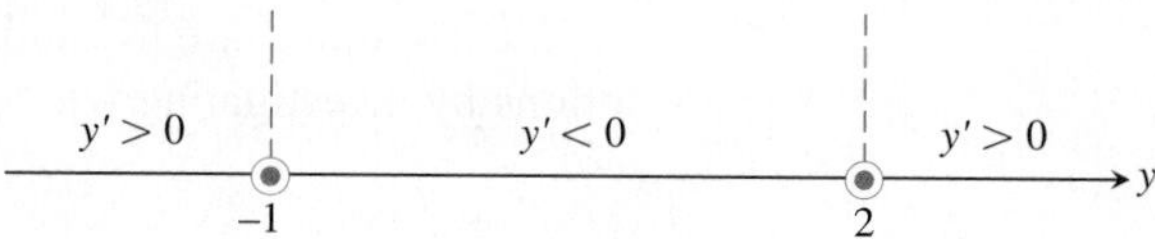

We can encapsulate the information about the sign of y' on the phase line itself. Since $y' > 0$ on the interval to the left of $y = -1$, a solution of the differential equation with a y-value less than -1 will increase from there toward $y = -1$. We display this information by drawing an arrow on the interval pointing to -1.

Similarly, $y' < 0$ between $y = -1$ and $y = 2$, so any solution with a value in this interval will decrease toward $y = -1$.

For $y > 2$, we have $y' > 0$, so a solution with a y-value greater than 2 will increase from there without bound.

In short, solution curves below the horizontal line $y = -1$ in the xy-plane rise toward $y = -1$. Solution curves between the lines $y = -1$ and $y = 2$ fall away from $y = 2$ toward $y = -1$. Solution curves above $y = 2$ rise away from $y = 2$ and keep going up.

3. *Calculate y'' and mark the intervals where $y'' > 0$ and $y'' < 0$.* To find y'', we differentiate y' *with respect to x*, using implicit differentiation.

$$y' = (y + 1)(y - 2) = y^2 - y - 2 \qquad \text{Formula for } y' \ldots$$

$$\begin{aligned} y'' &= \frac{d}{dx}(y') = \frac{d}{dx}(y^2 - y - 2) \\ &= 2yy' - y' \qquad \text{differentiated implicitly with respect to } x \\ &= (2y - 1)y' \\ &= (2y - 1)(y + 1)(y - 2). \end{aligned}$$

From this formula, we see that y'' changes sign at $y = -1, y = 1/2$, and $y = 2$. We add the sign information to the phase line.

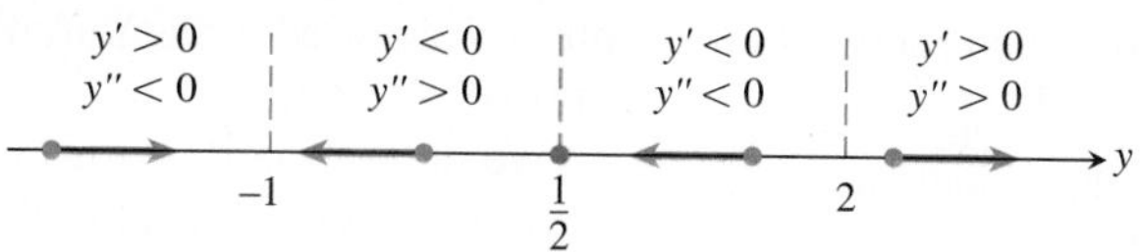

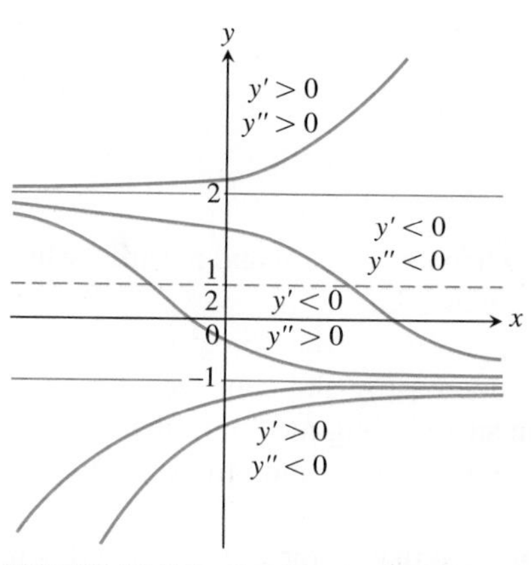

FIGURE 16.15 Graphical solutions from Example 1 include the horizontal lines $y = -1$ and $y = 2$ through the equilibrium values. No two solution curves can ever cross or touch each other.

4. *Sketch an assortment of solution curves in the xy-plane.* The horizontal lines $y = -1, y = 1/2$, and $y = 2$ partition the plane into horizontal bands in which we know the signs of y' and y''. In each band, this information tells us whether the solution curves rise or fall and how they bend as x increases (Figure 16.15).

The "equilibrium lines" $y = -1$ and $y = 2$ are also solution curves. (The constant functions $y = -1$ and $y = 2$ satisfy the differential equation.) Solution curves that cross the line $y = 1/2$ have an inflection point there. The concavity changes from concave down (above the line) to concave up (below the line).

As predicted in Step 2, solutions in the middle and lower bands approach the equilibrium value $y = -1$ as x increases. Solutions in the upper band rise steadily away from the value $y = 2$.

Stable and Unstable Equilibria

Look at Figure 16.15 once more, in particular at the behavior of the solution curves near the equilibrium values. Once a solution curve has a value near $y = -1$, it tends steadily toward that value; $y = -1$ is a **stable equilibrium**. The behavior near $y = 2$ is just the opposite: all solutions except the equilibrium solution $y = 2$ itself move *away* from it as x increases. We call $y = 2$ an **unstable equilibrium**. If the solution is *at* that value, it stays, but if it is off by any amount, no matter how small, it moves away. (Sometimes an equilibrium value is unstable because a solution moves away from it only on one side of the point.)

Now that we know what to look for, we can already see this behavior on the initial phase line (the second diagram in Step 2 of Example 1). The arrows lead away from $y = 2$ and, once to the left of $y = 2$, toward $y = -1$.

We now present several applied examples for which we can sketch a family of solution curves to the differential equation models using the method in Example 1.

Newton's Law of Cooling

We solved analytically the differential equation

$$\frac{dH}{dt} = -k(H - H_S), \qquad k > 0$$

modeling Newton's law of cooling. Here H is the temperature of an object at time t and H_S is the constant temperature of the surrounding medium.

Suppose that the surrounding medium (say a room in a house) has a constant Celsius temperature of 15°C. We can then express the difference in temperature as $H(t) - 15$. Assuming H is a differentiable function of time t, by Newton's law of cooling, there is a constant of proportionality $k > 0$ such that

$$\frac{dH}{dt} = -k(H - 15) \tag{1}$$

(*minus* k to give a negative derivative when $H > 15$).

Since $dH/dt = 0$ at $H = 15$, the temperature 15°C is an equilibrium value. If $H > 15$, Equation (1) tells us that $(H - 15) > 0$ and $dH/dt < 0$. If the object is hotter

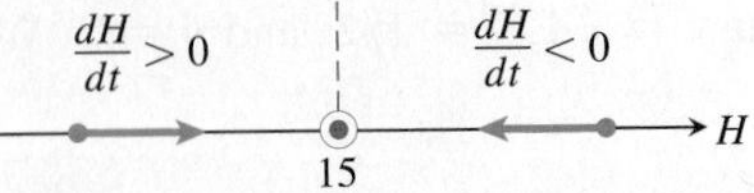

FIGURE 16.16 First step in constructing the phase line for Newton's law of cooling. The temperature tends towards the equilibrium (surrounding-medium) value in the long run.

than the room, it will get cooler. Similarly, if $H < 15$, then $(H - 15) < 0$ and $dH/dt > 0$. An object cooler than the room will warm up. Thus, the behavior described by Equation (1) agrees with our intuition of how temperature should behave. These observations are captured in the initial phase line diagram in Figure 16.16. The value $H = 15$ is a stable equilibrium.

We determine the concavity of the solution curves by differentiating both sides of Equation (1) with respect to t:

$$\frac{d}{dt}\left(\frac{dH}{dt}\right) = \frac{d}{dt}(-k(H - 15))$$

$$\frac{d^2H}{dt^2} = -k\frac{dH}{dt}.$$

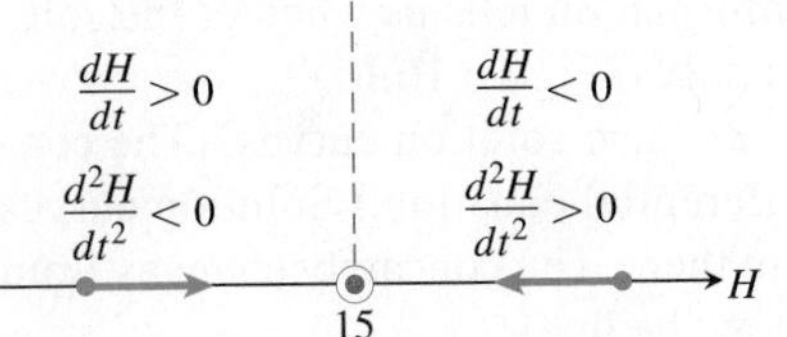

FIGURE 16.17 The complete phase line for Newton's law of cooling.

Since $-k$ is negative, we see that d^2H/dt^2 is positive when $dH/dt < 0$ and negative when $dH/dt > 0$. Figure 16.17 adds this information to the phase line.

The completed phase line shows that if the temperature of the object is above the equilibrium value of 15°C, the graph of $H(t)$ will be decreasing and concave upward. If the temperature is below 15°C (the temperature of the surrounding medium), the graph of $H(t)$ will be increasing and concave downward. We use this information to sketch typical solution curves (Figure 16.18).

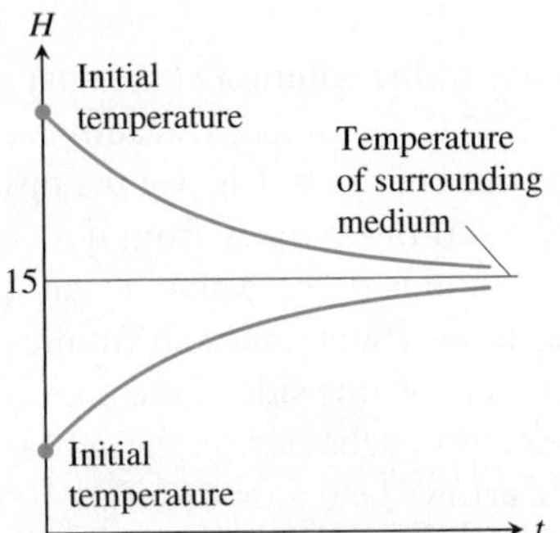

FIGURE 16.18 Temperature versus time. Regardless of initial temperature, the object's temperature $H(t)$ tends toward 15°C, the temperature of the surrounding medium.

From the upper solution curve in Figure 16.18, we see that as the object cools down, the rate at which it cools slows down because dH/dt approaches zero. This observation is implicit in Newton's law of cooling and contained in the differential equation, but the flattening of the graph as time advances gives an immediate visual representation of the phenomenon.

A Falling Body Encountering Resistance

Newton observed that the rate of change in momentum encountered by a moving object is equal to the net force applied to it. In mathematical terms,

$$F = \frac{d}{dt}(mv), \tag{2}$$

where F is the net force acting on the object, and m and v are the object's mass and velocity. If m varies with time, as it will if the object is a rocket burning fuel, the right-hand side of Equation (2) expands to

$$m\frac{dv}{dt} + v\frac{dm}{dt}$$

using the Derivative Product Rule. In many situations, however, m is constant, $dm/dt = 0$, and Equation (2) takes the simpler form

$$F = m\frac{dv}{dt} \quad \text{or} \quad F = ma, \tag{3}$$

known as *Newton's second law of motion* (see Section 16.3).

In free fall, the constant acceleration due to gravity is denoted by g and the one force acting downward on the falling body is

$$F_p = mg,$$

the force due to gravity. If, however, we think of a real body falling through the air—say, a penny from a great height or a parachutist from an even greater height—we know that at

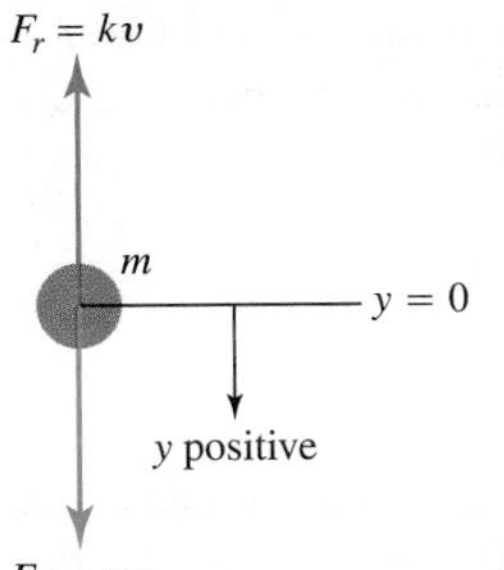

FIGURE 16.19 An object falling under the influence of gravity with a resistive force assumed to be proportional to the velocity.

some point air resistance is a factor in the speed of the fall. A more realistic model of free fall would include air resistance, shown as a force F_r in the schematic diagram in Figure 16.19.

For low speeds well below the speed of sound, physical experiments have shown that F_r is approximately proportional to the body's velocity. The net force on the falling body is therefore

$$F = F_p - F_r,$$

giving

$$m\frac{dv}{dt} = mg - kv$$

$$\frac{dv}{dt} = g - \frac{k}{m}v. \tag{4}$$

We can use a phase line to analyze the velocity functions that solve this differential equation.

The equilibrium point, obtained by setting the right-hand side of Equation (4) equal to zero, is

$$v = \frac{mg}{k}.$$

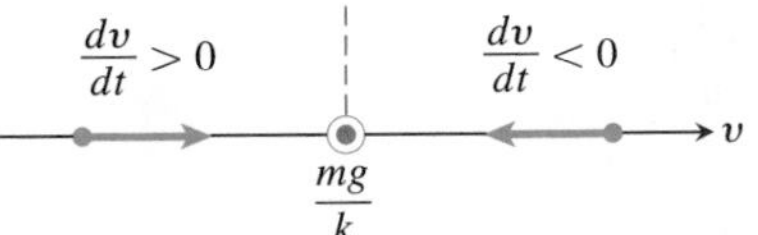

FIGURE 16.20 Initial phase line for the falling body encountering resistance.

If the body is initially moving faster than this, dv/dt is negative and the body slows down. If the body is moving at a velocity below mg/k, then $dv/dt > 0$ and the body speeds up. These observations are captured in the initial phase line diagram in Figure 16.20.

We determine the concavity of the solution curves by differentiating both sides of Equation (4) with respect to t:

$$\frac{d^2v}{dt^2} = \frac{d}{dt}\left(g - \frac{k}{m}v\right) = -\frac{k}{m}\frac{dv}{dt}.$$

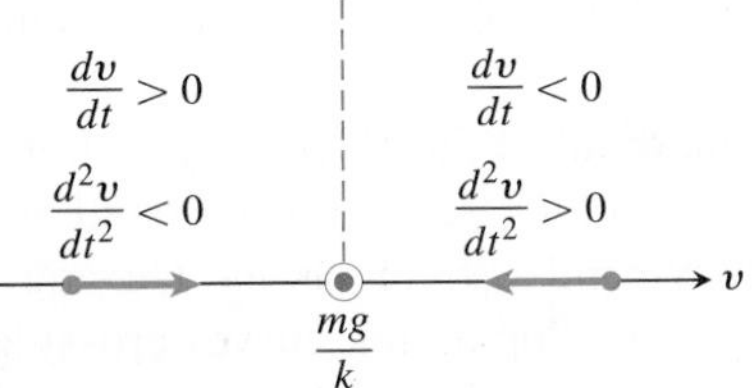

FIGURE 16.21 The completed phase line for the falling body.

We see that $d^2v/dt^2 < 0$ when $v < mg/k$ and $d^2v/dt^2 > 0$ when $v > mg/k$. Figure 16.21 adds this information to the phase line. Notice the similarity to the phase line for Newton's law of cooling (Figure 16.17). The solution curves are similar as well (Figure 16.22).

Figure 16.22 shows two typical solution curves. Regardless of the initial velocity, we see the body's velocity tending toward the limiting value $v = mg/k$. This value, a stable equilibrium point, is called the body's **terminal velocity**. Skydivers can vary their terminal velocity from 95 mph to 180 mph by changing the amount of body area opposing the fall, which affects the value of k.

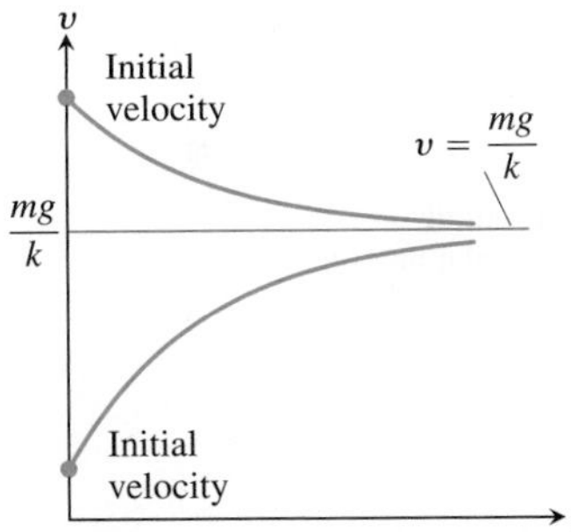

FIGURE 16.22 Typical velocity curves for a falling body encountering resistance. The value $v = mg/k$ is the terminal velocity.

Logistic Population Growth

In Section 16.3 we examined population growth using the model of exponential change. That is, if P represents the number of individuals and we neglect departures and arrivals, then

$$\frac{dP}{dt} = kP, \tag{5}$$

where $k > 0$ is the birth rate minus the death rate per individual per unit time.

Because the natural environment has only a limited number of resources to sustain life, it is reasonable to assume that only a maximum population M can be accommodated. As the population approaches this **limiting population** or **carrying capacity**, resources become less abundant and the growth rate k decreases. A simple relationship exhibiting this behavior is

$$k = r(M - P),$$

where $r > 0$ is a constant. Notice that k decreases as P increases toward M and that k is negative if P is greater than M. Substituting $r(M - P)$ for k in Equation (5) gives the differential equation

$$\frac{dP}{dt} = r(M - P)P = rMP - rP^2. \tag{6}$$

The model given by Equation (6) is referred to as **logistic growth**.

We can forecast the behavior of the population over time by analyzing the phase line for Equation (6). The equilibrium values are $P = M$ and $P = 0$, and we can see that $dP/dt > 0$ if $0 < P < M$ and $dP/dt < 0$ if $P > M$. These observations are recorded on the phase line in Figure 16.23.

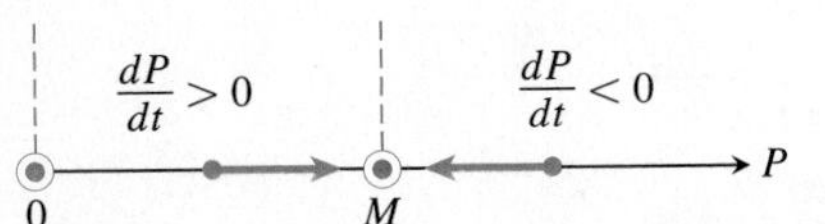

FIGURE 16.23 The initial phase line for logistic growth (Equation 6).

We determine the concavity of the population curves by differentiating both sides of Equation (6) with respect to t:

$$\begin{aligned}\frac{d^2P}{dt^2} &= \frac{d}{dt}(rMP - rP^2)\\ &= rM\frac{dP}{dt} - 2rP\frac{dP}{dt}\\ &= r(M - 2P)\frac{dP}{dt}.\end{aligned} \tag{7}$$

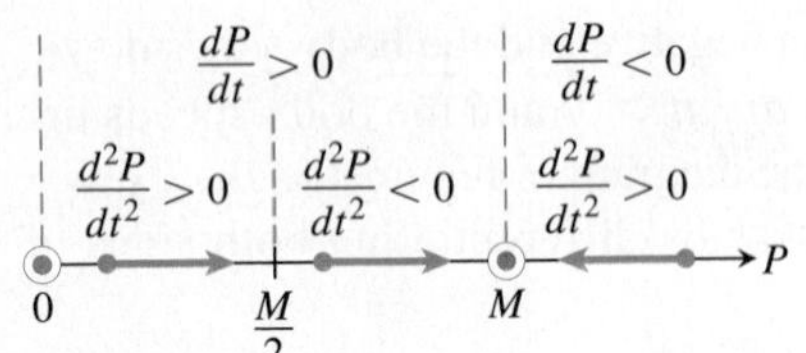

FIGURE 16.24 The completed phase line for logistic growth (Equation 6).

If $P = M/2$, then $d^2P/dt^2 = 0$. If $P < M/2$, then $(M - 2P)$ and dP/dt are positive and $d^2P/dt^2 > 0$. If $M/2 < P < M$, then $(M - 2P) < 0$, $dP/dt > 0$, and $d^2P/dt^2 < 0$. If $P > M$, then $(M - 2P)$ and dP/dt are both negative and $d^2P/dt^2 > 0$. We add this information to the phase line (Figure 16.24).

The lines $P = M/2$ and $P = M$ divide the first quadrant of the tP-plane into horizontal bands in which we know the signs of both dP/dt and d^2P/dt^2. In each band, we know how the solution curves rise and fall, and how they bend as time passes. The equilibrium lines $P = 0$ and $P = M$ are both population curves. Population curves crossing the line $P = M/2$ have an inflection point there, giving them a **sigmoid** shape (curved in two directions like a letter S). Figure 16.25 displays typical population curves. Notice that each population curve approaches the limiting population M as $t \to \infty$.

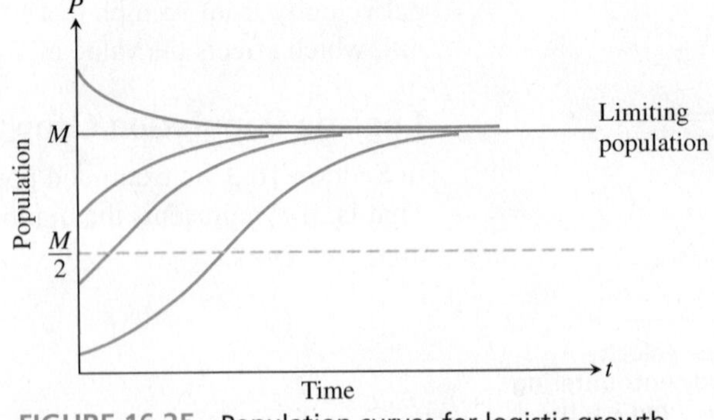

FIGURE 16.25 Population curves for logistic growth.

SECTION 16.4 EXERCISES

Phase Lines and Solution Curves

In Exercises 1–8,

a. Identify the equilibrium values. Which are stable and which are unstable?

b. Construct a phase line. Identify the signs of y' and y''.

c. Sketch several solution curves.

1. $\dfrac{dy}{dx} = (y + 2)(y - 3)$

2. $\dfrac{dy}{dx} = y^2 - 4$

3. $\dfrac{dy}{dx} = y^3 - y$

4. $\dfrac{dy}{dx} = y^2 - 2y$

5. $y' = \sqrt{y}, \quad y > 0$

6. $y' = y - \sqrt{y}, \quad y > 0$

7. $y' = (y - 1)(y - 2)(y - 3)$

8. $y' = y^3 - y^2$

Models of Population Growth

The autonomous differential equations in Exercises 9–12 represent models for population growth. For each exercise, use a phase line analysis to sketch solution curves for $P(t)$, selecting different starting values $P(0)$. Which equilibria are stable, and which are unstable?

9. $\dfrac{dP}{dt} = 1 - 2P$

10. $\dfrac{dP}{dt} = P(1 - 2P)$

11. $\dfrac{dP}{dt} = 2P(P - 3)$

12. $\dfrac{dP}{dt} = 3P(1 - P)\left(P - \dfrac{1}{2}\right)$

13. **Catastrophic change in logistic growth** Suppose that a healthy population of some species is growing in a limited environment and that the current population P_0 is fairly close to the carrying capacity M_0. You might imagine a population of fish living in a freshwater lake in a wilderness area. Suddenly a catastrophe such as the Mount St. Helens volcanic eruption contaminates the lake and destroys a significant part of the food and oxygen on which the fish depend. The result is a new environment with a carrying capacity M_1 considerably less than M_0 and, in fact, less than the current population P_0. Starting at some time before the catastrophe, sketch a "before-and-after" curve that shows how the fish population responds to the change in environment.

14. **Controlling a population** The fish and game department in a certain state is planning to issue hunting permits to control the deer population (one deer per permit). It is known that if the deer population falls below a certain level m, the deer will become extinct. It is also known that if the deer population rises above the carrying capacity M, the population will decrease back to M through disease and malnutrition.

    a. Discuss the reasonableness of the following model for the growth rate of the deer population as a function of time:

    $$\frac{dP}{dt} = rP(M - P)(P - m),$$

    where P is the population of the deer and r is a positive constant of proportionality. Include a phase line.

    b. Explain how this model differs from the logistic model $dP/dt = rP(M - P)$. Is it better or worse than the logistic model?

    c. Show that if $P > M$ for all t, then $\lim_{t\to\infty} P(t) = M$.

    d. What happens if $P < m$ for all t?

    e. Discuss the solutions to the differential equation. What are the equilibrium points of the model? Explain the dependence of the steady-state value of P on the initial values of P. About how many permits should be issued?

Applications and Examples

15. **Skydiving** If a body of mass m falling from rest under the action of gravity encounters an air resistance proportional to the square of velocity, then the body's velocity t seconds into the fall satisfies the equation

    $$m\frac{dv}{dt} = mg - kv^2, \qquad k > 0$$

    where k is a constant that depends on the body's aerodynamic properties and the density of the air. (We assume that the fall is too short to be affected by changes in the air's density.)

    a. Draw a phase line for the equation.

    b. Sketch a typical velocity curve.

    c. For a 110-lb skydiver ($mg = 110$) and with time in seconds and distance in feet, a typical value of k is 0.005. What is the diver's terminal velocity? Repeat for a 200-lb skydiver.

16. **Resistance proportional to $\sqrt{v}$** A body of mass m is projected vertically downward with initial velocity v_0. Assume that the resisting force is proportional to the square root of the velocity and find the terminal velocity from a graphical analysis.

17. **Sailing** A sailboat is running along a straight course with the wind providing a constant forward force of 50 lb. The only other force acting on the boat is resistance as the boat moves through the water. The resisting force is numerically equal to five times the boat's speed, and the initial velocity is 1 ft/sec. What is the maximum velocity in feet per second of the boat under this wind?

18. **The spread of information** Sociologists recognize a phenomenon called *social diffusion*, which is the spreading of a piece of information, technological innovation, or cultural fad among a population. The members of the population can be divided into two classes: those who have the information and those who do not. In a fixed population whose size is known, it is reasonable to assume that the rate of diffusion is proportional to the number who have the information times the number yet to receive it. If X denotes the number of individuals who have the information in a population of N people, then a mathematical model for social diffusion is given by

    $$\frac{dX}{dt} = kX(N - X),$$

    where t represents time in days and k is a positive constant.

    a. Discuss the reasonableness of the model.

    b. Construct a phase line identifying the signs of X' and X''.

    c. Sketch representative solution curves.

    d. Predict the value of X for which the information is spreading most rapidly. How many people eventually receive the information?

19. **Current in an RL-circuit** The accompanying diagram represents an electrical circuit whose total resistance is a constant R ohms and whose self-inductance, shown as a coil, is L henries, also a constant. There is a switch whose terminals at a and b can be closed to connect a constant electrical source of V volts. From Section 16.2, we have

    $$L\frac{di}{dt} + Ri = V,$$

    where i is the current in amperes and t is the time in seconds.

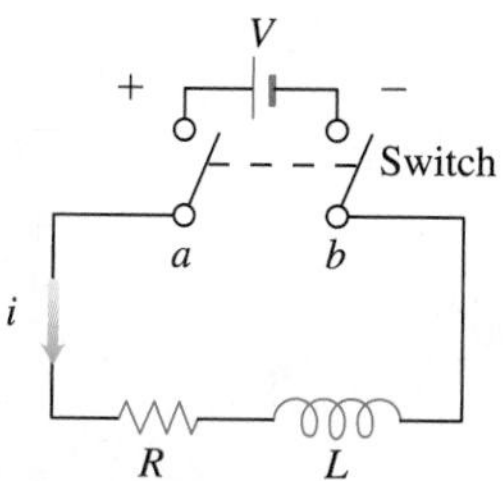

Use a phase line analysis to sketch the solution curve assuming that the switch in the RL-circuit is closed at time $t = 0$. What happens to the current as $t \to \infty$? This value is called the *steady-state solution*.

20. A pearl in shampoo Suppose that a pearl is sinking in a thick fluid, like shampoo, subject to a frictional force opposing its fall and proportional to its velocity. Suppose that there is also a resistive buoyant force exerted by the shampoo. According to *Archimedes' principle*, the buoyant force equals the weight of the fluid displaced by the pearl. Using m for the mass of the pearl and P for the mass of the shampoo displaced by the pearl as it descends, complete the following steps.

a. Draw a schematic diagram showing the forces acting on the pearl as it sinks, as in Figure 16.19.

b. Using $v(t)$ for the pearl's velocity as a function of time t, write a differential equation modeling the velocity of the pearl as a falling body.

c. Construct a phase line displaying the signs of v' and v''.

d. Sketch typical solution curves.

e. What is the terminal velocity of the pearl?

16.5 Systems of Equations and Phase Planes

In some situations we are led to consider not one, but several first-order differential equations. Such a collection is called a **system** of differential equations. In this section we present an approach to understanding systems through a graphical procedure known as a *phase-plane analysis*. We present this analysis in the context of modeling the populations of trout and bass living in a common pond.

Phase Planes

A general system of two first-order differential equations may take the form

$$\frac{dx}{dt} = F(x, y),$$

$$\frac{dy}{dt} = G(x, y).$$

Such a system of equations is called **autonomous** because dx/dt and dy/dt do not depend on the independent variable time t, but only on the dependent variables x and y. A **solution** of such a system consists of a pair of functions $x(t)$ and $y(t)$ that satisfies both of the differential equations simultaneously for every t over some time interval (finite or infinite).

We cannot look at just one of these equations in isolation to find solutions $x(t)$ or $y(t)$ since each derivative depends on both x and y. To gain insight into the solutions, we look at both dependent variables together by plotting the points $(x(t), y(t))$ in the xy-plane starting at some specified point. Therefore the solution functions define a solution curve through the specified point, called a **trajectory** of the system. The xy-plane itself, in which these trajectories reside, is referred to as the **phase plane**. Thus we consider both solutions together and study the behavior of all the solution trajectories in the phase plane. It can be proved that two trajectories can never cross or touch each other.

A Competitive-Hunter Model

Imagine two species of fish, say trout and bass, competing for the same limited resources (such as food and oxygen) in a certain pond. We let $x(t)$ represent the number of trout and $y(t)$ the number of bass living in the pond at time t. In reality $x(t)$ and $y(t)$ are always integer valued, but we will approximate them with real-valued differentiable functions. This allows us to apply the methods of differential equations.

Several factors affect the rates of change of these populations. As time passes, each species breeds, so we assume its population increases proportionally to its size. Taken by itself, this would lead to exponential growth in each of the two populations. However, there is a countervailing effect from the fact that the two species are in competition. A large number of bass tends to cause a decrease in the number of trout, and vice-versa. Our model takes the size of this effect to be proportional to the frequency with which the two species interact, which in turn is proportional to xy, the product of the two populations. These considerations lead to the following model for the growth of the trout and bass in the pond:

$$\frac{dx}{dt} = (a - by)x, \tag{1a}$$

$$\frac{dy}{dt} = (m - nx)y. \tag{1b}$$

Here $x(t)$ represents the trout population, $y(t)$ the bass population, and a, b, m, n are positive constants. A solution of this system then consists of a pair of functions $x(t)$ and $y(t)$ that gives the population of each fish species at time t. Each equation in (1) contains both of the unknown functions x and y, so we are unable to solve them individually. Instead, we will use a graphical analysis to study the solution trajectories of this **competitive-hunter model**.

We now examine the nature of the phase plane in the trout-bass population model. We will be interested in the 1st quadrant of the xy-plane, where $x \geq 0$ and $y \geq 0$, since populations cannot be negative. First, we determine where the bass and trout populations are both constant. Noting that the $(x(t), y(t))$ values remain unchanged when $dx/dt = 0$ and $dy/dt = 0$, Equations (1a and 1b) then become

$$(a - by)x = 0,$$
$$(m - nx)y = 0.$$

This pair of simultaneous equations has two solutions: $(x, y) = (0, 0)$ and $(x, y) = (m/n, a/b)$. At these (x, y) values, called **equilibrium** or **rest points**, the two populations remain at constant values over all time. The point $(0, 0)$ represents a pond containing no members of either fish species; the point $(m/n, a/b)$ corresponds to a pond with an unchanging number of each fish species.

Next, we note that if $y = a/b$, then Equation (1a) implies $dx/dt = 0$, so the trout population $x(t)$ is constant. Similarly, if $x = m/n$, then Equation (1b) implies $dy/dt = 0$, and the bass population $y(t)$ is constant. This information is recorded in Figure 16.26.

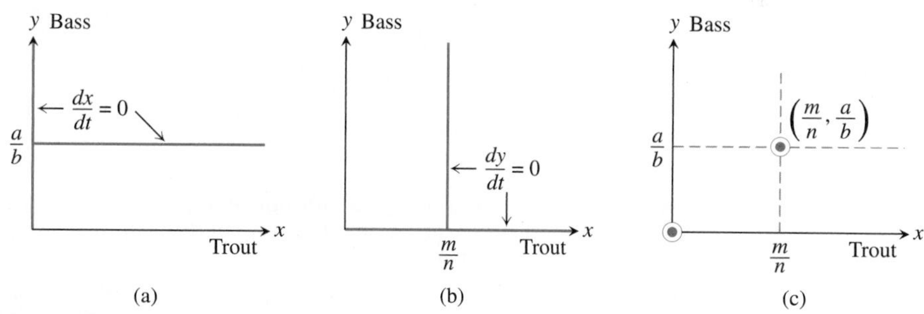

FIGURE 16.26 Rest points in the competitive-hunter model given by Equations (1a) and (1b).

In setting up our competitive-hunter model, precise values of the constants a, b, m, n will not generally be known. Nonetheless, we can analyze the system of Equations (1) to learn the nature of its solution trajectories. We begin by determining the signs of dx/dt and dy/dt throughout the phase plane. Although $x(t)$ represents the number of trout and $y(t)$ the number of bass at time t, we are thinking of the pair of values $(x(t), y(t))$ as a point tracing out a trajectory curve in the phase plane. When dx/dt is positive, $x(t)$ is increasing and the point is moving to the right in the phase plane. If dx/dt is negative, the point is moving to the left. Likewise, the point is moving upward where dy/dt is positive and downward where dy/dt is negative.

We saw that $dy/dt = 0$ along the vertical line $x = m/n$. To the left of this line, dy/dt is positive since $dy/dt = (m - nx)y$ and $x < m/n$. So the trajectories on this side of the line are directed upward. To the right of this line, dy/dt is negative and the trajectories point downward. The directions of the associated trajectories are indicated in Figure 16.27.

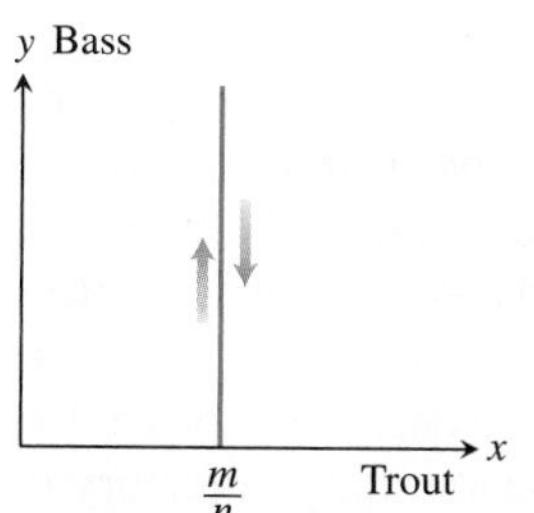

FIGURE 16.27 To the left of the line $x = m/n$ the trajectories move upward, and to the right they move downward.

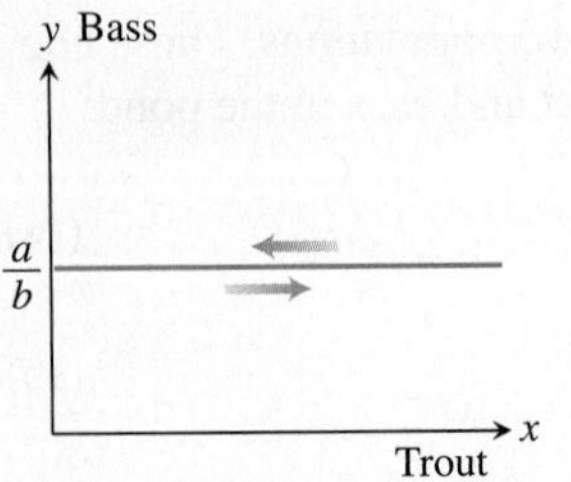

FIGURE 16.28 Above the line $y = a/b$ the trajectories move to the left, and below it they move to the right.

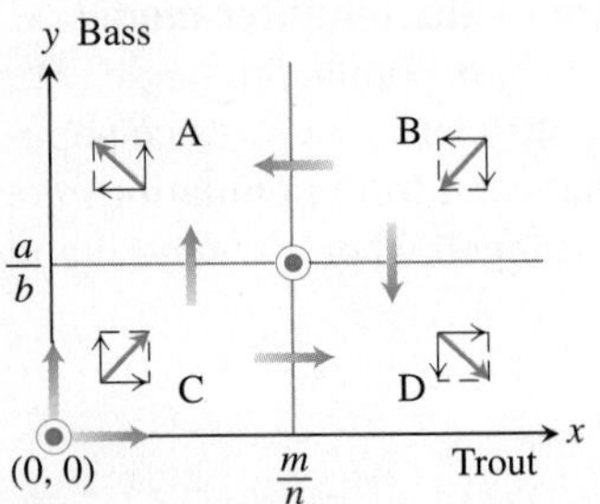

FIGURE 16.29 Composite graphical analysis of the trajectory directions in the four regions determined by $x = m/n$ and $y = a/b$.

Similarly, above the horizontal line $y = a/b$, we have $dx/dt < 0$ and the trajectories head leftward; below this line they head rightward, as shown in Figure 16.28. Combining this information gives four distinct regions in the plane A, B, C, D, with their respective trajectory directions shown in Figure 16.29.

Next, we examine what happens near the two equilibrium points. The trajectories near (0, 0) point away from it, upward and to the right. The behavior near the equilibrium point $(m/n, a/b)$ depends on the region in which a trajectory begins. If it starts in region B, for instance, then it will move downward and leftward towards the equilibrium point. Depending on where the trajectory begins, it may move downward into region D, leftward into region A, or perhaps straight into the equilibrium point. If it enters into regions A or D, then it will continue to move away from the rest point. We say that both rest points are **unstable**, meaning (in this setting) there are trajectories near each point that head away from them. These features are indicated in Figure 16.30.

It turns out that in each of the half-planes above and below the line $y = a/b$, there is exactly one trajectory approaching the equilibrium point $(m/n, a/b)$ (see Exercise 7). Above these two trajectories the bass population increases and below them it decreases. The two trajectories approaching the equilibrium point are suggested in Figure 16.31.

Our graphical analysis leads us to conclude that, under the assumptions of the competitive-hunter model, it is unlikely that both species will reach equilibrium levels. This is because it would be almost impossible for the fish populations to move exactly along one of the two approaching trajectories for all time. Furthermore, the initial populations point (x_0, y_0) determines which of the two species is likely to survive over time, and mutual coexistence of the species is highly improbable.

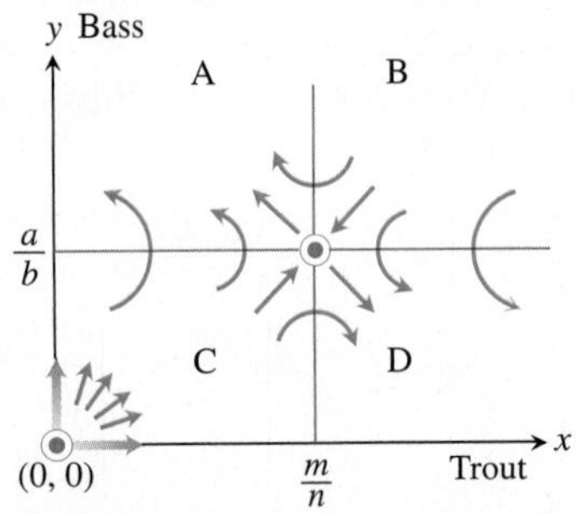

FIGURE 16.30 Motion along the trajectories near the rest points (0, 0) and $(m/n, a/b)$.

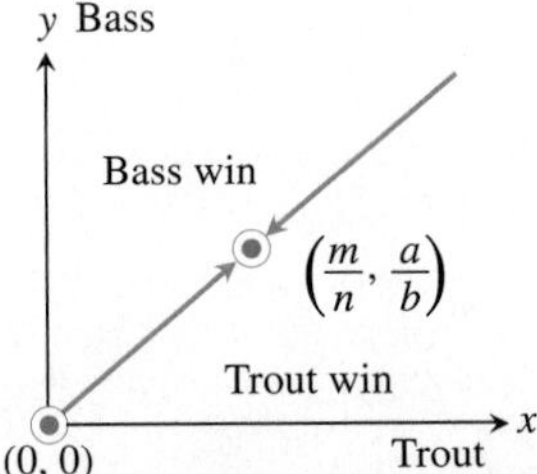

FIGURE 16.31 Qualitative results of analyzing the competitive-hunter model. There are exactly two trajectories approaching the point $(m/n, a/b)$.

Limitations of the Phase-Plane Analysis Method

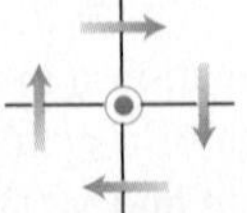
FIGURE 16.32 Trajectory direction near the rest point (0, 0).

Unlike the situation for the competitive-hunter model, it is not always possible to determine the behavior of trajectories near a rest point. For example, suppose we know that the trajectories near a rest point, chosen here to be the origin (0, 0), behave as in Figure 16.32. The information provided by Figure 16.32 is not sufficient to distinguish between the three possible trajectories shown in Figure 16.33. Even if we could determine that a trajectory near an equilibrium point resembles that of Figure 16.33c, we would still not know how the other trajectories behave. It could happen that a trajectory closer to the origin behaves like the motions displayed in Figure 16.33a or 16.33b. The spiraling trajectory in Figure 16.33b can never actually reach the rest point in a finite time period.

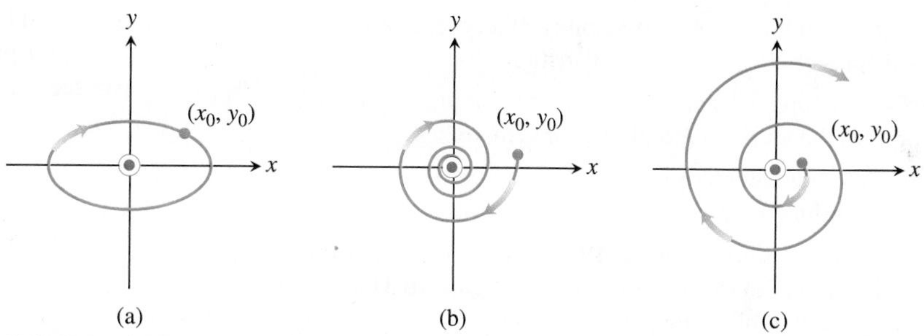

FIGURE 16.33 Three possible trajectory motions: (a) periodic motion, (b) motion toward an asymptotically stable rest point, and (c) motion near an unstable rest point.

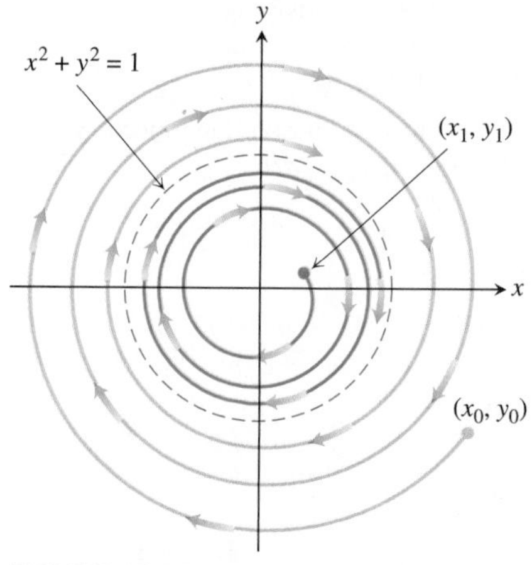

FIGURE 16.34 The solution $x^2 + y^2 = 1$ is a limit cycle.

Another Type of Behavior

The system

$$\frac{dx}{dt} = y + x - x(x^2 + y^2), \tag{2a}$$

$$\frac{dy}{dt} = -x + y - y(x^2 + y^2) \tag{2b}$$

can be shown to have only one equilibrium point at (0, 0). Yet any trajectory starting on the unit circle traverses it clockwise because, when $x^2 + y^2 = 1$, we have $dy/dx = -x/y$ (see Exercise 2). If a trajectory starts inside the unit circle, it spirals outward, asymptotically approaching the circle as $t \to \infty$. If a trajectory starts outside the unit circle, it spirals inward, again asymptotically approaching the circle as $t \to \infty$. The circle $x^2 + y^2 = 1$ is called a **limit cycle** of the system (Figure 16.34). In this system, the values of x and y eventually become periodic.

SECTION 16.5 EXERCISES

1. List three important considerations that are ignored in the competitive-hunter model as presented in the text.

2. For the system (2a) and (2b), show that any trajectory starting on the unit circle $x^2 + y^2 = 1$ will traverse the unit circle in a periodic solution. First introduce polar coordinates and rewrite the system as $dr/dt = r(1 - r^2)$ and $-d\theta/dt = -1$.

3. Develop a model for the growth of trout and bass, assuming that in isolation trout demonstrate exponential decay [so that $a < 0$ in Equations (1a) and (1b)] and that the bass population grows logistically with a population limit M. Analyze graphically the motion in the vicinity of the rest points in your model. Is coexistence possible?

4. How might the competitive-hunter model be validated? Include a discussion of how the various constants a, b, m, and n might be estimated. How could state conservation authorities use the model to ensure the survival of both species?

5. Consider another competitive-hunter model defined by

$$\frac{dx}{dt} = a\left(1 - \frac{x}{k_1}\right)x - bxy,$$

$$\frac{dy}{dt} = m\left(1 - \frac{y}{k_2}\right)y - nxy,$$

where x and y represent trout and bass populations, respectively.

a. What assumptions are implicitly being made about the growth of trout and bass in the absence of competition?

b. Interpret the constants a, b, m, n, k_1, and k_2 in terms of the physical problem.

c. Perform a graphical analysis:

i) Find the possible equilibrium levels.

ii) Determine whether coexistence is possible.

iii) Pick several typical starting points and sketch typical trajectories in the phase plane.

iv) Interpret the outcomes predicted by your graphical analysis in terms of the constants a, b, m, n, k_1, and k_2.

Note: When you get to part (iii), you should realize that five cases exist. You will need to analyze all five cases.

6. An economic model Consider the following economic model. Let P be the price of a single item on the market. Let Q be the quantity of the item available on the market. Both P and Q are functions of time. If one considers price and quantity as two interacting species, the following model might be proposed:

$$\frac{dP}{dt} = aP\left(\frac{b}{Q} - P\right),$$

$$\frac{dQ}{dt} = cQ(fP - Q),$$

where a, b, c, and f are positive constants. Justify and discuss the adequacy of the model.

a. If $a = 1$, $b = 20{,}000$, $c = 1$, and $f = 30$, find the equilibrium points of this system. If possible, classify each equilibrium point with respect to its stability. If a point cannot be readily classified, give some explanation.

b. Perform a graphical stability analysis to determine what will happen to the levels of P and Q as time increases.

c. Give an economic interpretation of the curves that determine the equilibrium points.

7. **Two trajectories approach equilibrium** Show that the two trajectories leading to $(m/n, a/b)$ shown in Figure 16.31 are unique by carrying out the following steps.

a. From system (1a) and (1b) apply the Chain Rule to derive the following equation:

$$\frac{dy}{dx} = \frac{(m - nx)y}{(a - by)x}.$$

b. Separate the variables, integrate, and exponentiate to obtain

$$y^a e^{-by} = Kx^m e^{-nx},$$

where K is a constant of integration.

c. Let $f(y) = y^a/e^{by}$ and $g(x) = x^m/e^{nx}$. Show that $f(y)$ has a unique maximum of $M_y = (a/eb)^a$ when $y = a/b$ as shown in Figure 16.35. Similarly, show that $g(x)$ has a unique maximum $M_x = (m/en)^m$ when $x = m/n$, also shown in Figure 16.35.

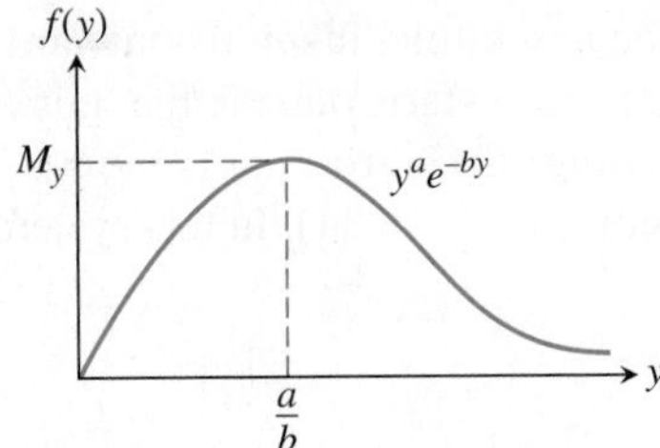

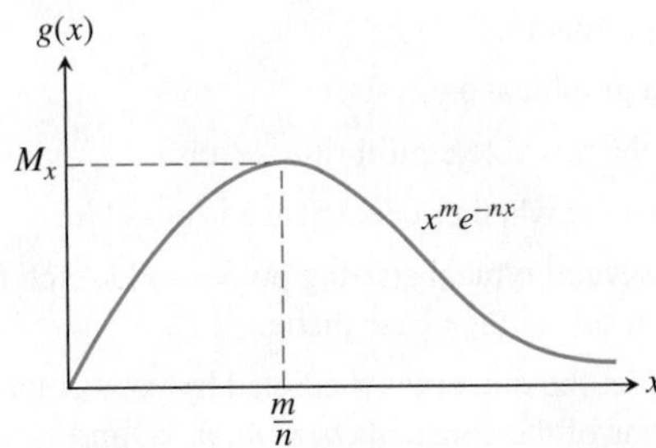

FIGURE 16.35 Graphs of the functions $f(y) = y^a/e^{by}$ and $g(x) = x^m/e^{nx}$.

d. Consider what happens as (x, y) approaches $(m/n, a/b)$. Take limits in part (b) as $x \to m/n$ and $y \to a/b$ to show that either

$$\lim_{\substack{x \to m/n \\ y \to a/b}} \left[\left(\frac{y^a}{e^{by}}\right)\left(\frac{e^{nx}}{x^m}\right)\right] = K$$

or $M_y/M_x = K$. Thus any solution trajectory that approaches $(m/n, a/b)$ must satisfy

$$\frac{y^a}{e^{by}} = \left(\frac{M_y}{M_x}\right)\left(\frac{x^m}{e^{nx}}\right).$$

e. Show that only one trajectory can approach $(m/n, a/b)$ from below the line $y = a/b$. Pick $y_0 < a/b$. From Figure 16.35 you can see that $f(y_0) < M_y$, which implies that

$$\frac{M_y}{M_x}\left(\frac{x^m}{e^{nx}}\right) = {y_0}^a/e^{by_0} < M_y.$$

This in turn implies that

$$\frac{x^m}{e^{nx}} < M_x.$$

Figure 16.35 tells you that for $g(x)$ there is a unique value $x_0 < m/n$ satisfying this last inequality. That is, for each $y < a/b$ there is a unique value of x satisfying the equation in part (d). Thus there can exist only one trajectory solution approaching $(m/n, a/b)$ from below, as shown in Figure 16.36.

f. Use a similar argument to show that the solution trajectory leading to $(m/n, a/b)$ is unique if $y_0 > a/b$.

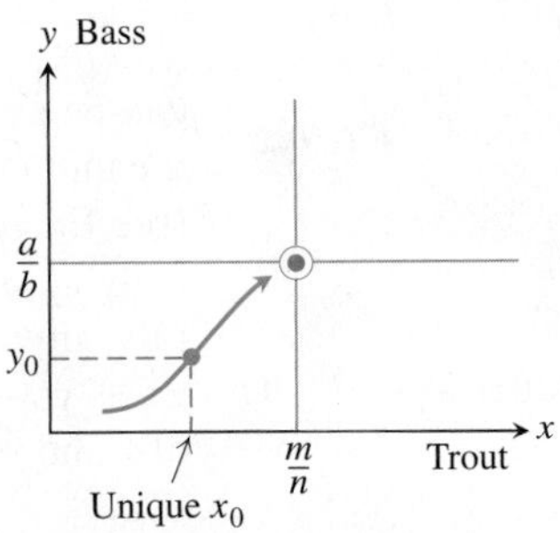

FIGURE 16.36 For any $y < a/b$ only one solution trajectory leads to the rest point $(m/n, a/b)$.

8. Show that the second-order differential equation $y'' = F(x, y, y')$ can be reduced to a system of two first-order differential equations

$$\frac{dy}{dx} = z,$$

$$\frac{dz}{dx} = F(x, y, z).$$

Can something similar be done to the nth-order differential equation $y^{(n)} = F\left(x, y, y', y'', \ldots, y^{(n-1)}\right)$?

Lotka-Volterra Equations for a Predator-Prey Model

In 1925 Lotka and Volterra introduced the *predator-prey* equations, a system of equations that models the populations of two species, one of which preys on the other. Let $x(t)$ represent the number of rabbits living in a region at time t, and $y(t)$ the number of foxes in the same region. As time passes, the number of rabbits increases at a rate proportional to their population, and decreases at a rate proportional to the number of encounters between rabbits and foxes. The foxes, which compete for food, increase in number at a rate proportional to the number of encounters with rabbits but decrease at a rate proportional to the number of foxes. The number of encounters between rabbits and foxes is assumed to be proportional to the product of the two populations. These assumptions lead to the autonomous system

$$\frac{dx}{dt} = (a - by)x$$
$$\frac{dy}{dt} = (-c + dx)y$$

where a, b, c, d are positive constants. The values of these constants vary according to the specific situation being modeled. We can study the nature of the population changes without setting these constants to specific values.

9. What happens to the rabbit population if there are no foxes present?

10. What happens to the fox population if there are no rabbits present?

11. Show that $(0, 0)$ and $(c/d, a/b)$ are equilibrium points. Explain the meaning of each of these points.

12. Show, by differentiating, that the function

$$C(t) = a \ln y(t) - by(t) - dx(t) + c \ln x(t)$$

is constant when $x(t)$ and $y(t)$ are positive and satisfy the predator-prey equations.

While x and y may change over time, $C(t)$ does not. Thus, C is a *conserved quantity* and its existence gives a *conservation law*. A trajectory that begins at a point (x, y) at time $t = 0$ gives a value of C that remains unchanged at future times. Each value of the constant C gives a trajectory for the autonomous system, and these trajectories close up, rather than spiraling inwards or outwards. The rabbit and fox populations oscillate through repeated cycles along a fixed trajectory. Figure 16.37 shows several trajectories for the predator-prey system.

13. Using a procedure similar to that in the text for the competitive-hunter model, show that each trajectory is traversed in a counterclockwise direction as time t increases.

Along each trajectory, both the rabbit and fox populations fluctuate between their maximum and minimum levels. The maximum and minimum levels for the rabbit population occur where the trajectory intersects the horizontal line $y = a/b$. For the fox population, they occur where the trajectory intersects the vertical line $x = c/d$. When the rabbit population is at its maximum, the fox population is below its maximum value. As the rabbit population declines from this point in time, we move counterclockwise around the trajectory, and the fox population grows until it reaches its maximum value. At this point the rabbit population has declined to $x = c/d$ and is no longer at its peak value. We see that the fox population reaches its maximum value at a later time than the rabbits. The predator population *lags behind* that of the prey in achieving its maximum values. This lag effect is shown in Figure 16.38, which graphs both $x(t)$ and $y(t)$.

14. At some time during a trajectory cycle, a wolf invades the rabbit-fox territory, eats some rabbits, and then leaves. Does this mean that the fox population will from then on have a lower maximum value? Explain your answer.

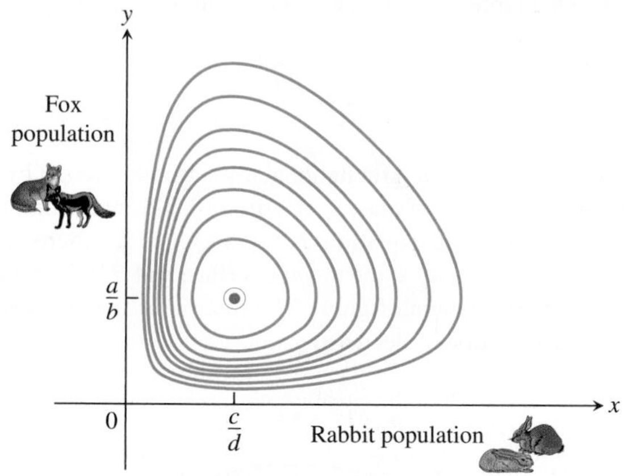

FIGURE 16.37 Some trajectories along which C is conserved.

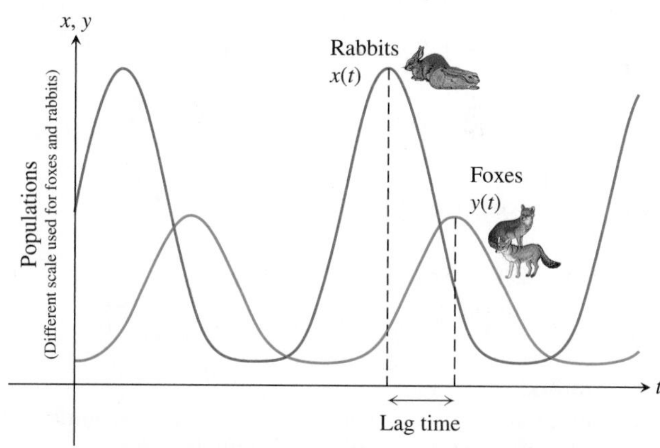

FIGURE 16.38 The fox and rabbit populations oscillate periodically, with the maximum fox population lagging the maximum rabbit population.

CHAPTER 16 Questions to Guide Your Review

1. What is a first-order differential equation? When is a function a solution of such an equation?
2. What is a general solution? A particular solution?
3. What is the slope field of a differential equation $y' = f(x, y)$? What can we learn from such fields?
4. Describe Euler's method for solving the initial value problem $y' = f(x, y), y(x_0) = y_0$ numerically. Give an example. Comment on the method's accuracy. Why might you want to solve an initial value problem numerically?
5. How do you solve linear first-order differential equations?
6. What is an orthogonal trajectory of a family of curves? Describe how one is found for a given family of curves.
7. What is an autonomous differential equation? What are its equilibrium values? How do they differ from critical points? What is a stable equilibrium value? Unstable?

8. How do you construct the phase line for an autonomous differential equation? How does the phase line help you produce a graph which qualitatively depicts a solution to the differential equation?

9. Why is the exponential model unrealistic for predicting long-term population growth? How does the logistic model correct for the deficiency in the exponential model for population growth? What is the logistic differential equation? What is the form of its solution? Describe the graph of the logistic solution.

10. What is an autonomous system of differential equations? What is a solution to such a system? What is a trajectory of the system?

CHAPTER 16 Practice Exercises

In Exercises 1–16 solve the differential equation.

1. $y' = xe^y\sqrt{x-2}$ **2.** $y' = xye^{x^2}$

3. $\sec x\, dy + x\cos^2 y\, dx = 0$ **4.** $2x^2\, dx - 3\sqrt{y}\csc x\, dy = 0$

5. $y' = \dfrac{e^y}{xy}$ **6.** $y' = xe^{x-y}\csc y$

7. $x(x-1)\, dy - y\, dx = 0$ **8.** $y' = (y^2 - 1)x^{-1}$

9. $2y' - y = xe^{x/2}$ **10.** $\dfrac{y'}{2} + y = e^{-x}\sin x$

11. $xy' + 2y = 1 - x^{-1}$ **12.** $xy' - y = 2x\ln x$

13. $(1 + e^x)\, dy + (ye^x + e^{-x})\, dx = 0$

14. $e^{-x}\, dy + (e^{-x}y - 4x)\, dx = 0$

15. $(x + 3y^2)\, dy + y\, dx = 0$ (*Hint:* $d(xy) = y\, dx + x\, dy$)

16. $x\, dy + (3y - x^{-2}\cos x)\, dx = 0,\quad x > 0$

Initial Value Problems

In Exercises 17–22 solve the initial value problem.

17. $(x+1)\dfrac{dy}{dx} + 2y = x,\quad x > -1,\quad y(0) = 1$

18. $x\dfrac{dy}{dx} + 2y = x^2 + 1,\quad x > 0,\quad y(1) = 1$

19. $\dfrac{dy}{dx} + 3x^2y = x^2,\quad y(0) = -1$

20. $x\, dy + (y - \cos x)\, dx = 0,\quad y\left(\dfrac{\pi}{2}\right) = 0$

21. $xy' + (x - 2)y = 3x^3e^{-x},\quad y(1) = 0$

22. $y\, dx + (3x - xy + 2)\, dy = 0,\quad y(2) = -1,\quad y < 0$

Euler's Method

In Exercises 23 and 24, use Euler's method to solve the initial value problem on the given interval starting at x_0 with $dx = 0.1$.

T **23.** $y' = y + \cos x,\quad y(0) = 0;\quad 0 \le x \le 2;\quad x_0 = 0$

T **24.** $y' = (2 - y)(2x + 3),\quad y(-3) = 1;\ -3 \le x \le -1;\quad x_0 = -3$

In Exercises 25 and 26, use Euler's method with $dx = 0.05$ to estimate $y(c)$ where y is the solution to the given initial value problem.

T **25.** $c = 3;\quad \dfrac{dy}{dx} = \dfrac{x - 2y}{x + 1},\quad y(0) = 1$

T **26.** $c = 4;\quad \dfrac{dy}{dx} = \dfrac{x^2 - 2y + 1}{x},\quad y(1) = 1$

In Exercises 27 and 28, use Euler's method to solve the initial value problem graphically, starting at $x_0 = 0$ with

a. $dx = 0.1$. **b.** $dx = -0.1$.

27. $\dfrac{dy}{dx} = \dfrac{1}{e^{x+y+2}},\quad y(0) = -2$

28. $\dfrac{dy}{dx} = -\dfrac{x^2 + y}{e^y + x},\quad y(0) = 0$

Slope Fields

In Exercises 29–32, sketch part of the equation's slope field. Then add to your sketch the solution curve that passes through the point $P(1, -1)$. Use Euler's method with $x_0 = 1$ and $dx = 0.2$ to estimate $y(2)$. Round your answers to four decimal places. Find the exact value of $y(2)$ for comparison.

29. $y' = x$ **30.** $y' = 1/x$

31. $y' = xy$ **32.** $y' = 1/y$

Autonomous Differential Equations and Phase Lines

In Exercises 33 and 34:

a. Identify the equilibrium values. Which are stable and which are unstable?

b. Construct a phase line. Identify the signs of y' and y''.

c. Sketch a representative selection of solution curves.

33. $\dfrac{dy}{dx} = y^2 - 1$ **34.** $\dfrac{dy}{dx} = y - y^2$

Applications

35. Escape velocity The gravitational attraction F exerted by an airless moon on a body of mass m at a distance s from the moon's center is given by the equation $F = -mg\,R^2s^{-2}$, where g is the acceleration of gravity at the moon's surface and R is the moon's radius (see accompanying figure). The force F is negative because it acts in the direction of decreasing s.

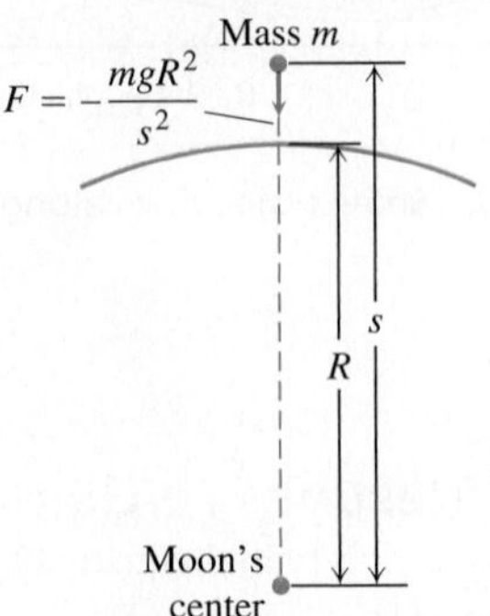

a. If the body is projected vertically upward from the moon's surface with an initial velocity v_0 at time $t = 0$, use Newton's second law, $F = ma$, to show that the body's velocity at position s is given by the equation

$$v^2 = \frac{2gR^2}{s} + v_0^2 - 2gR.$$

Thus, the velocity remains positive as long as $v_0 \geq \sqrt{2gR}$. The velocity $v_0 = \sqrt{2gR}$ is the moon's **escape velocity**. A body projected upward with this velocity or a greater one will escape from the moon's gravitational pull.

b. Show that if $v_0 = \sqrt{2gR}$, then

$$s = R\left(1 + \frac{3v_0}{2R}t\right)^{2/3}.$$

36. Coasting to a stop Table 16.6 shows the distance s (meters) coasted on in-line skates in t sec by Johnathon Krueger. Find a model for his position in the form of Equation (2) of Section 16.3. His initial velocity was $v_0 = 0.86$ m/sec, his mass $m = 30.84$ kg (he weighed 68 lb), and his total coasting distance 0.97 m.

Table 16.6 **Johnathon Krueger skating data**

t (sec)	s (m)	t (sec)	s (m)	t (sec)	s (m)
0	0	0.93	0.61	1.86	0.93
0.13	0.08	1.06	0.68	2.00	0.94
0.27	0.19	1.20	0.74	2.13	0.95
0.40	0.28	1.33	0.79	2.26	0.96
0.53	0.36	1.46	0.83	2.39	0.96
0.67	0.45	1.60	0.87	2.53	0.97
0.80	0.53	1.73	0.90	2.66	0.97

CHAPTER 16 Additional and Advanced Exercises

Theory and Applications

1. Transport through a cell membrane Under some conditions, the result of the movement of a dissolved substance across a cell's membrane is described by the equation

$$\frac{dy}{dt} = k\frac{A}{V}(c - y).$$

In this equation, y is the concentration of the substance inside the cell and dy/dt is the rate at which y changes over time. The letters k, A, V, and c stand for constants, k being the *permeability coefficient* (a property of the membrane), A the surface area of the membrane, V the cell's volume, and c the concentration of the substance outside the cell. The equation says that the rate at which the concentration changes within the cell is proportional to the difference between it and the outside concentration.

a. Solve the equation for $y(t)$, using y_0 to denote $y(0)$.

b. Find the steady-state concentration, $\lim_{t\to\infty} y(t)$.

2. Height of a rocket If an external force F acts upon a system whose mass varies with time, Newton's law of motion is

$$\frac{d(mv)}{dt} = F + (v + u)\frac{dm}{dt}.$$

In this equation, m is the mass of the system at time t, v is its velocity, and $v + u$ is the velocity of the mass that is entering (or leaving) the system at the rate dm/dt. Suppose that a rocket of initial mass m_0 starts from rest, but is driven upward by firing some of its mass directly backward at the constant rate of $dm/dt = -b$ units per second and at constant speed relative to the rocket $u = -c$. The only external force acting on the rocket is $F = -mg$ due to gravity. Under these assumptions, show that the height of the rocket above the ground at the end of t seconds (t small compared to m_0/b) is

$$y = c\left[t + \frac{m_0 - bt}{b}\ln\frac{m_0 - bt}{m_0}\right] - \frac{1}{2}gt^2.$$

3. a. Assume that $P(x)$ and $Q(x)$ are continuous over the interval $[a, b]$. Use the Fundamental Theorem of Calculus, Part 1 to show that any function y satisfying the equation

$$v(x)y = \int v(x)Q(x)\,dx + C$$

for $v(x) = e^{\int P(x)\,dx}$ is a solution to the first-order linear equation

$$\frac{dy}{dx} + P(x)y = Q(x).$$

b. If $C = y_0 v(x_0) - \int_{x_0}^{x} v(t)Q(t)\,dt$, then show that any solution y in part (a) satisfies the initial condition $y(x_0) = y_0$.

4. (*Continuation of Exercise 3.*) Assume the hypotheses of Exercise 3, and assume that $y_1(x)$ and $y_2(x)$ are both solutions to the first-order linear equation satisfying the initial condition $y(x_0) = y_0$.

a. Verify that $y(x) = y_1(x) - y_2(x)$ satisfies the initial value problem

$$y' + P(x)y = 0, \quad y(x_0) = 0.$$

b. For the integrating factor $v(x) = e^{\int P(x)\,dx}$, show that

$$\frac{d}{dx}(v(x)[y_1(x) - y_2(x)]) = 0.$$

Conclude that $v(x)[y_1(x) - y_2(x)] \equiv$ constant.

c. From part (a), we have $y_1(x_0) - y_2(x_0) = 0$. Since $v(x) > 0$ for $a < x < b$, use part (b) to establish that $y_1(x) - y_2(x) \equiv 0$ on the interval (a, b). Thus $y_1(x) = y_2(x)$ for all $a < x < b$.

Homogeneous Equations

A first-order differential equation of the form

$$\frac{dy}{dx} = F\left(\frac{y}{x}\right)$$

is called *homogeneous*. It can be transformed into an equation whose variables are separable by defining the new variable $v = y/x$. Then, $y = vx$ and

$$\frac{dy}{dx} = v + x\frac{dv}{dx}.$$

Substitution into the original differential equation and collecting terms with like variables then gives the separable equation

$$\frac{dx}{x} + \frac{dv}{v - F(v)} = 0.$$

After solving this separable equation, the solution of the original equation is obtained when we replace v by y/x.

Solve the homogeneous equations in Exercises 5–10. First put the equation in the form of a homogeneous equation.

5. $(x^2 + y^2)\,dx + xy\,dy = 0$

6. $x^2\,dy + (y^2 - xy)\,dx = 0$

7. $(xe^{y/x} + y)\,dx - x\,dy = 0$

8. $(x + y)\,dy + (x - y)\,dx = 0$

9. $y' = \frac{y}{x} + \cos\frac{y - x}{x}$

10. $\left(x\sin\frac{y}{x} - y\cos\frac{y}{x}\right)dx + x\cos\frac{y}{x}\,dy = 0$

CHAPTER 16 Technology Application Projects

Mathematica/Maple Modules:

Drug Dosages: Are They Effective? Are They Safe?

Formulate and solve an initial value model for the absorption of a drug in the bloodstream.

First-Order Differential Equations and Slope Fields

Plot slope fields and solution curves for various initial conditions to selected first-order differential equations.

17

Second-Order Differential Equations

OVERVIEW In this chapter we extend our study of differential equations to those of *second order*. Second-order differential equations arise in many applications in the sciences and engineering. For instance, they can be applied to the study of vibrating springs and electric circuits. You will learn how to solve such differential equations by several methods in this chapter.

17.1 Second-Order Linear Equations

An equation of the form

$$P(x)y''(x) + Q(x)y'(x) + R(x)y(x) = G(x), \tag{1}$$

which is linear in y and its derivatives, is called a **second-order linear differential equation**. We assume that the functions P, Q, R, and G are continuous throughout some open interval I. If $G(x)$ is identically zero on I, the equation is said to be **homogeneous**; otherwise it is called **nonhomogeneous**. Therefore, the form of a second-order linear homogeneous differential equation is

$$P(x)y'' + Q(x)y' + R(x)y = 0. \tag{2}$$

We also assume that $P(x)$ is never zero for any $x \in I$.

Two fundamental results are important to solving Equation (2). The first of these says that if we know two solutions y_1 and y_2 of the linear homogeneous equation, then any **linear combination** $y = c_1y_1 + c_2y_2$ is also a solution for any constants c_1 and c_2.

THEOREM 1 The Superposition Principle

If $y_1(x)$ and $y_2(x)$ are two solutions to the linear homogeneous equation (2), then for any constants c_1 and c_2, the function

$$y(x) = c_1y_1(x) + c_2y_2(x)$$

is also a solution to Equation (2).

PROOF Substituting y into Equation (2), we have

$$\begin{aligned}
&P(x)y'' + Q(x)y' + R(x)y \\
&\quad = P(x)(c_1y_1 + c_2y_2)'' + Q(x)(c_1y_1 + c_2y_2)' + R(x)(c_1y_1 + c_2y_2) \\
&\quad = P(x)(c_1y_1'' + c_2y_2'') + Q(x)(c_1y_1' + c_2y_2') + R(x)(c_1y_1 + c_2y_2) \\
&\quad = c_1\underbrace{(P(x)y_1'' + Q(x)y_1' + R(x)y_1)}_{=0,\ y_1 \text{ is a solution}} + c_2\underbrace{(P(x)y_2'' + Q(x)y_2' + R(x)y_2)}_{=0,\ y_2 \text{ is a solution}} \\
&\quad = c_1(0) + c_2(0) = 0.
\end{aligned}$$

Therefore, $y = c_1y_1 + c_2y_2$ is a solution of Equation (2).

Theorem 1 immediately establishes the following facts concerning solutions to the linear homogeneous equation.

1. A sum of two solutions $y_1 + y_2$ to Equation (2) is also a solution. (Choose $c_1 = c_2 = 1$.)
2. A constant multiple ky_1 of any solution y_1 to Equation (2) is also a solution. (Choose $c_1 = k$ and $c_2 = 0$.)
3. The **trivial solution** $y(x) \equiv 0$ is always a solution to the linear homogeneous equation. (Choose $c_1 = c_2 = 0$.)

The second fundamental result about solutions to the linear homogeneous equation concerns its **general solution** or solution containing all solutions. This result says that there are two solutions y_1 and y_2 such that any solution is some linear combination of them for suitable values of the constants c_1 and c_2. However, not just any pair of solutions will do. The solutions must be **linearly independent**, which means that neither y_1 nor y_2 is a constant multiple of the other. For example, the functions $f(x) = e^x$ and $g(x) = xe^x$ are linearly independent, whereas $f(x) = x^2$ and $g(x) = 7x^2$ are not (so they are linearly dependent). These results on linear independence and the following theorem are proved in more advanced courses.

THEOREM 2 If P, Q, and R are continuous over the open interval I and $P(x)$ is never zero on I, then the linear homogeneous equation (2) has two linearly independent solutions y_1 and y_2 on I. Moreover, if y_1 and y_2 are *any* two linearly independent solutions of Equation (2), then the general solution is given by

$$y(x) = c_1y_1(x) + c_2y_2(x),$$

where c_1 and c_2 are arbitrary constants.

We now turn our attention to finding two linearly independent solutions to the special case of Equation (2), where P, Q, and R are constant functions.

Constant-Coefficient Homogeneous Equations

Suppose we wish to solve the second-order homogeneous differential equation

$$ay'' + by' + cy = 0, \tag{3}$$

where a, b, and c are constants. To solve Equation (3), we seek a function which when multiplied by a constant and added to a constant times its first derivative plus a constant times its second derivative sums identically to zero. One function that behaves this way is the exponential function $y = e^{rx}$, when r is a constant. Two differentiations of this exponential function give $y' = re^{rx}$ and $y'' = r^2e^{rx}$, which are just constant multiples of the original exponential. If we substitute $y = e^{rx}$ into Equation (3), we obtain

$$ar^2e^{rx} + bre^{rx} + ce^{rx} = 0.$$

Since the exponential function is never zero, we can divide this last equation through by e^{rx}. Thus, $y = e^{rx}$ is a solution to Equation (3) if and only if r is a solution to the algebraic equation

$$ar^2 + br + c = 0. \tag{4}$$

Equation (4) is called the **auxiliary equation** (or **characteristic equation**) of the differential equation $ay'' + by' + cy = 0$. The auxiliary equation is a quadratic equation with roots

$$r_1 = \frac{-b + \sqrt{b^2 - 4ac}}{2a} \quad \text{and} \quad r_2 = \frac{-b - \sqrt{b^2 - 4ac}}{2a}.$$

There are three cases to consider which depend on the value of the discriminant $b^2 - 4ac$.

Case 1: $b^2 - 4ac > 0$. In this case the auxiliary equation has two real and unequal roots r_1 and r_2. Then $y_1 = e^{r_1x}$ and $y_2 = e^{r_2x}$ are two linearly independent solutions to Equation (3) because e^{r_2x} is not a constant multiple of e^{r_1x} (see Exercise 61). From Theorem 2 we conclude the following result.

THEOREM 3 If r_1 and r_2 are two real and unequal roots to the auxiliary equation $ar^2 + br + c = 0$, then

$$y = c_1e^{r_1x} + c_2e^{r_2x}$$

is the general solution to $ay'' + by' + cy = 0$.

EXAMPLE 1 Find the general solution of the differential equation

$$y'' - y' - 6y = 0.$$

SOLUTION Substitution of $y = e^{rx}$ into the differential equation yields the auxiliary equation

$$r^2 - r - 6 = 0,$$

which factors as

$$(r - 3)(r + 2) = 0.$$

The roots are $r_1 = 3$ and $r_2 = -2$. Thus, the general solution is

$$y = c_1e^{3x} + c_2e^{-2x}.$$

Case 2: $b^2 - 4ac = 0$. In this case $r_1 = r_2 = -b/2a$. To simplify the notation, let $r = -b/2a$. Then we have one solution $y_1 = e^{rx}$ with $2ar + b = 0$. Since multiplication of e^{rx} by a constant fails to produce a second linearly independent solution, suppose we try multiplying by a *function* instead. The simplest such function would be $u(x) = x$, so let's see if $y_2 = xe^{rx}$ is also a solution. Substituting y_2 into the differential equation gives

$$\begin{aligned} ay_2'' + by_2' + cy_2 &= a(2re^{rx} + r^2xe^{rx}) + b(e^{rx} + rxe^{rx}) + cxe^{rx} \\ &= (2ar + b)e^{rx} + (ar^2 + br + c)xe^{rx} \\ &= 0(e^{rx}) + (0)xe^{rx} = 0. \end{aligned}$$

The first term is zero because $r = -b/2a$; the second term is zero because r solves the auxiliary equation. The functions $y_1 = e^{rx}$ and $y_2 = xe^{rx}$ are linearly independent (see Exercise 62). From Theorem 2 we conclude the following result.

THEOREM 4 If r is the only (repeated) real root to the auxiliary equation $ar^2 + br + c = 0$, then

$$y = c_1e^{rx} + c_2xe^{rx}$$

is the general solution to $ay'' + by' + cy = 0$.

EXAMPLE 2 Find the general solution to

$$y'' + 4y' + 4y = 0.$$

SOLUTION The auxiliary equation is

$$r^2 + 4r + 4 = 0,$$

which factors into

$$(r + 2)^2 = 0.$$

Thus, $r = -2$ is a double root. Therefore, the general solution is

$$y = c_1e^{-2x} + c_2xe^{-2x}.$$

Case 3: $b^2 - 4ac < 0$. In this case the auxiliary equation has two complex roots $r_1 = \alpha + i\beta$ and $r_2 = \alpha - i\beta$, where α and β are real numbers and $i^2 = -1$. (These real numbers are $\alpha = -b/2a$ and $\beta = \sqrt{4ac - b^2}/2a$.) These two complex roots then give rise to two linearly independent solutions

$$y_1 = e^{(\alpha+i\beta)x} = e^{\alpha x}(\cos \beta x + i \sin \beta x) \quad \text{and} \quad y_2 = e^{(\alpha-i\beta)x} = e^{\alpha x}(\cos \beta x - i \sin \beta x).$$

(The expressions involving the sine and cosine terms follow from Euler's identity in Section 9.9.) However, the solutions y_1 and y_2 are *complex valued* rather than real valued. Nevertheless, because of the superposition principle (Theorem 1), we can obtain from them the two real-valued solutions

$$y_3 = \frac{1}{2}y_1 + \frac{1}{2}y_2 = e^{\alpha x}\cos \beta x \quad \text{and} \quad y_4 = \frac{1}{2i}y_1 - \frac{1}{2i}y_2 = e^{\alpha x}\sin \beta x.$$

The functions y_3 and y_4 are linearly independent (see Exercise 63). From Theorem 2 we conclude the following result.

THEOREM 5 If $r_1 = \alpha + i\beta$ and $r_2 = \alpha - i\beta$ are two complex roots to the auxiliary equation $ar^2 + br + c = 0$, then

$$y = e^{\alpha x}(c_1 \cos \beta x + c_2 \sin \beta x)$$

is the general solution to $ay'' + by' + cy = 0$.

EXAMPLE 3 Find the general solution to the differential equation

$$y'' - 4y' + 5y = 0.$$

SOLUTION The auxiliary equation is

$$r^2 - 4r + 5 = 0.$$

The roots are the complex pair $r = (4 \pm \sqrt{16 - 20})/2$ or $r_1 = 2 + i$ and $r_2 = 2 - i$. Thus, $\alpha = 2$ and $\beta = 1$ give the general solution

$$y = e^{2x}(c_1 \cos x + c_2 \sin x).$$

Initial Value and Boundary Value Problems

To determine a unique solution to a first-order linear differential equation, it was sufficient to specify the value of the solution at a single point. Since the general solution to a second-order equation contains two arbitrary constants, it is necessary to specify two conditions. One way of doing this is to specify the value of the solution function and the value of its derivative at a single point: $y(x_0) = y_0$ and $y'(x_0) = y_1$. These conditions are called **initial conditions**. The following result is proved in more advanced texts and guarantees the existence of a unique solution for both homogeneous and nonhomogeneous second-order linear initial value problems.

THEOREM 6 If P, Q, R, and G are continuous throughout an open interval I, then there exists one and only one function $y(x)$ satisfying both the differential equation

$$P(x)y''(x) + Q(x)y'(x) + R(x)y(x) = G(x)$$

on the interval I, and the initial conditions

$$y(x_0) = y_0 \quad \text{and} \quad y'(x_0) = y_1$$

at the specified point $x_0 \in I$.

It is important to realize that any real values can be assigned to y_0 and y_1 and Theorem 6 applies. Here is an example of an initial value problem for a homogeneous equation.

EXAMPLE 4 Find the particular solution to the initial value problem

$$y'' - 2y' + y = 0, \qquad y(0) = 1, \quad y'(0) = -1.$$

SOLUTION The auxiliary equation is

$$r^2 - 2r + 1 = (r - 1)^2 = 0.$$

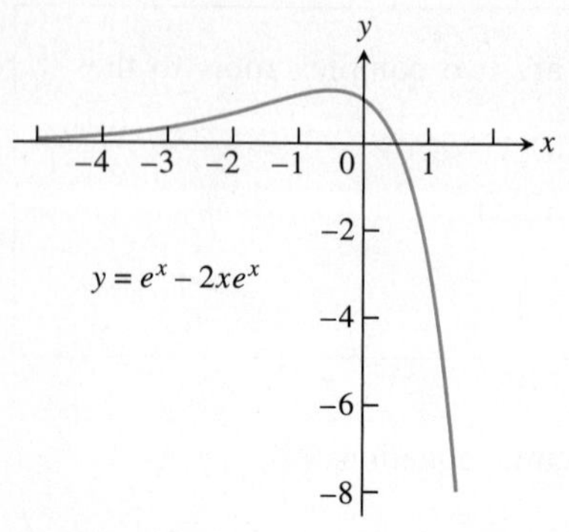

FIGURE 17.1 Particular solution curve for Example 4.

The repeated real root is $r = 1$, giving the general solution

$$y = c_1 e^x + c_2 x e^x.$$

Then,

$$y' = c_1 e^x + c_2(x + 1)e^x.$$

From the initial conditions we have

$$1 = c_1 + c_2 \cdot 0 \qquad \text{and} \qquad -1 = c_1 + c_2 \cdot 1.$$

Thus, $c_1 = 1$ and $c_2 = -2$. The unique solution satisfying the initial conditions is

$$y = e^x - 2xe^x.$$

The solution curve is shown in Figure 17.1.

Another approach to determine the values of the two arbitrary constants in the general solution to a second-order differential equation is to specify the values of the solution function at *two different points* in the interval I. That is, we solve the differential equation subject to the **boundary values**

$$y(x_1) = y_1 \qquad \text{and} \qquad y(x_2) = y_2,$$

where x_1 and x_2 both belong to I. Here again the values for y_1 and y_2 can be any real numbers. The differential equation together with specified boundary values is called a **boundary value problem.** Unlike the result stated in Theorem 6, boundary value problems do not always possess a solution or more than one solution may exist (see Exercise 65). These problems are studied in more advanced texts, but here is an example for which there is a unique solution.

EXAMPLE 5 Solve the boundary value problem

$$y'' + 4y = 0, \qquad y(0) = 0, \quad y\left(\frac{\pi}{12}\right) = 1.$$

SOLUTION The auxiliary equation is $r^2 + 4 = 0$, which has the complex roots $r = \pm 2i$. The general solution to the differential equation is

$$y = c_1 \cos 2x + c_2 \sin 2x.$$

The boundary conditions are satisfied if

$$y(0) = c_1 \cdot 1 + c_2 \cdot 0 = 0$$

$$y\left(\frac{\pi}{12}\right) = c_1 \cos\left(\frac{\pi}{6}\right) + c_2 \sin\left(\frac{\pi}{6}\right) = 1.$$

It follows that $c_1 = 0$ and $c_2 = 2$. The solution to the boundary value problem is

$$y = 2 \sin 2x.$$

SECTION 17.1 EXERCISES

In Exercises 1–30, find the general solution of the given equation.

1. $y'' - y' - 12y = 0$
2. $3y'' - y' = 0$
3. $y'' + 3y' - 4y = 0$
4. $y'' - 9y = 0$
5. $y'' - 4y = 0$
6. $y'' - 64y = 0$
7. $2y'' - y' - 3y = 0$
8. $9y'' - y = 0$
9. $8y'' - 10y' - 3y = 0$
10. $3y'' - 20y' + 12y = 0$
11. $y'' + 9y = 0$
12. $y'' + 4y' + 5y = 0$
13. $y'' + 25y = 0$
14. $y'' + y = 0$
15. $y'' - 2y' + 5y = 0$
16. $y'' + 16y = 0$
17. $y'' + 2y' + 4y = 0$
18. $y'' - 2y' + 3y = 0$
19. $y'' + 4y' + 9y = 0$
20. $4y'' - 4y' + 13y = 0$
21. $y'' = 0$
22. $y'' + 8y' + 16y = 0$
23. $\dfrac{d^2y}{dx^2} + 4\dfrac{dy}{dx} + 4y = 0$
24. $\dfrac{d^2y}{dx^2} - 6\dfrac{dy}{dx} + 9y = 0$
25. $\dfrac{d^2y}{dx^2} + 6\dfrac{dy}{dx} + 9y = 0$
26. $4\dfrac{d^2y}{dx^2} - 12\dfrac{dy}{dx} + 9y = 0$
27. $4\dfrac{d^2y}{dx^2} + 4\dfrac{dy}{dx} + y = 0$
28. $4\dfrac{d^2y}{dx^2} - 4\dfrac{dy}{dx} + y = 0$
29. $9\dfrac{d^2y}{dx^2} + 6\dfrac{dy}{dx} + y = 0$
30. $9\dfrac{d^2y}{dx^2} - 12\dfrac{dy}{dx} + 4y = 0$

In Exercises 31–40, find the unique solution of the second-order initial value problem.

31. $y'' + 6y' + 5y = 0, \quad y(0) = 0, \ y'(0) = 3$
32. $y'' + 16y = 0, \quad y(0) = 2, \ y'(0) = -2$
33. $y'' + 12y = 0, \quad y(0) = 0, \ y'(0) = 1$
34. $12y'' + 5y' - 2y = 0, \quad y(0) = 1, \ y'(0) = -1$
35. $y'' + 8y = 0, \quad y(0) = -1, \ y'(0) = 2$
36. $y'' + 4y' + 4y = 0, \quad y(0) = 0, \ y'(0) = 1$
37. $y'' - 4y' + 4y = 0, \quad y(0) = 1, \ y'(0) = 0$
38. $4y'' - 4y' + y = 0, \quad y(0) = 4, \ y'(0) = 4$
39. $4\dfrac{d^2y}{dx^2} + 12\dfrac{dy}{dx} + 9y = 0, \quad y(0) = 2, \ \dfrac{dy}{dx}(0) = 1$
40. $9\dfrac{d^2y}{dx^2} - 12\dfrac{dy}{dx} + 4y = 0, \quad y(0) = -1, \ \dfrac{dy}{dx}(0) = 1$

In Exercises 41–55, find the general solution.

41. $y'' - 2y' - 3y = 0$
42. $6y'' - y' - y = 0$
43. $4y'' + 4y' + y = 0$
44. $9y'' + 12y' + 4y = 0$
45. $4y'' + 20y = 0$
46. $y'' + 2y' + 2y = 0$
47. $25y'' + 10y' + y = 0$
48. $6y'' + 13y' - 5y = 0$
49. $4y'' + 4y' + 5y = 0$
50. $y'' + 4y' + 6y = 0$
51. $16y'' - 24y' + 9y = 0$
52. $6y'' - 5y' - 6y = 0$
53. $9y'' + 24y' + 16y = 0$
54. $4y'' + 16y' + 52y = 0$
55. $6y'' - 5y' - 4y = 0$

In Exercises 56–60, solve the initial value problem.

56. $y'' - 2y' + 2y = 0, \quad y(0) = 0, \ y'(0) = 2$
57. $y'' + 2y' + y = 0, \quad y(0) = 1, \ y'(0) = 1$
58. $4y'' - 4y' + y = 0, \quad y(0) = -1, \ y'(0) = 2$
59. $3y'' + y' - 14y = 0, \quad y(0) = 2, \ y'(0) = -1$
60. $4y'' + 4y' + 5y = 0, \quad y(\pi) = 1, \ y'(\pi) = 0$
61. Prove that the two solution functions in Theorem 3 are linearly independent.
62. Prove that the two solution functions in Theorem 4 are linearly independent.
63. Prove that the two solution functions in Theorem 5 are linearly independent.
64. Prove that if y_1 and y_2 are linearly independent solutions to the homogeneous equation (2), then the functions $y_3 = y_1 + y_2$ and $y_4 = y_1 - y_2$ are also linearly independent solutions.
65. **a.** Show that there is no solution to the boundary value problem
$$y'' + 4y = 0, \quad y(0) = 0, \ y(\pi) = 1.$$
b. Show that there are infinitely many solutions to the boundary value problem
$$y'' + 4y = 0, \quad y(0) = 0, \ y(\pi) = 0.$$
66. Show that if a, b, and c are positive constants, then all solutions of the homogeneous differential equation
$$ay'' + by' + cy = 0$$
approach zero as $x \to \infty$.

17.2 Nonhomogeneous Linear Equations

In this section we study two methods for solving second-order linear nonhomogeneous differential equations with constant coefficients. These are the methods of *undetermined coefficients* and *variation of parameters*. We begin by considering the form of the general solution.

Form of the General Solution

Suppose we wish to solve the nonhomogeneous equation

$$ay'' + by' + cy = G(x), \tag{1}$$

where a, b, and c are constants and G is continuous over some open interval I. Let $y_c = c_1y_1 + c_2y_2$ be the general solution to the associated **complementary equation**

$$ay'' + by' + cy = 0. \tag{2}$$

(We learned how to find y_c in Section 17.1.) Now suppose we could somehow come up with a particular function y_p that solves the nonhomogeneous equation (1). Then the sum

$$y = y_c + y_p \tag{3}$$

also solves the nonhomogeneous equation (1) because

$$\begin{aligned} a(y_c + y_p)'' + b(y_c + y_p)' + c(y_c + y_p) \\ &= (ay_c'' + by_c' + cy_c) + (ay_p'' + by_p' + cy_p) \\ &= 0 + G(x) \qquad y_c \text{ solves Eq. (2) and } y_p \text{ solves Eq. (1)} \\ &= G(x). \end{aligned}$$

Moreover, if $y = y(x)$ is the general solution to the nonhomogeneous equation (1), it must have the form of Equation (3). The reason for this last statement follows from the observation that for any function y_p satisfying Equation (1), we have

$$\begin{aligned} a(y - y_p)'' + b(y - y_p)' + c(y - y_p) \\ &= (ay'' + by' + cy) - (ay_p'' + by_p' + cy_p) \\ &= G(x) - G(x) = 0. \end{aligned}$$

Thus, $y_c = y - y_p$ is the general solution to the homogeneous equation (2). We have established the following result.

THEOREM 7 The general solution $y = y(x)$ to the nonhomogeneous differential equation (1) has the form

$$y = y_c + y_p,$$

where the **complementary solution** y_c is the general solution to the associated homogeneous equation (2) and y_p is any **particular solution** to the nonhomogeneous equation (1).

The Method of Undetermined Coefficients

This method for finding a particular solution y_p to the nonhomogeneous equation (1) applies to special cases for which $G(x)$ is a sum of terms of various polynomials $p(x)$ multiplying an exponential with possibly sine or cosine factors. That is, $G(x)$ is a sum of terms of the following forms:

$$p_1(x)e^{rx}, \qquad p_2(x)e^{\alpha x}\cos\beta x, \qquad p_3(x)e^{\alpha x}\sin\beta x.$$

For instance, $1 - x$, e^{2x}, xe^x, $\cos x$, and $5e^x - \sin 2x$ represent functions in this category. (Essentially these are functions solving homogeneous linear differential equations with constant coefficients, but the equations may be of order higher than two.) We now present several examples illustrating the method.

EXAMPLE 1 Solve the nonhomogeneous equation $y'' - 2y' - 3y = 1 - x^2$.

SOLUTION The auxiliary equation for the complementary equation $y'' - 2y' - 3y = 0$ is

$$r^2 - 2r - 3 = (r + 1)(r - 3) = 0.$$

It has the roots $r = -1$ and $r = 3$ giving the complementary solution

$$y_c = c_1e^{-x} + c_2e^{3x}.$$

Now $G(x) = 1 - x^2$ is a polynomial of degree 2. It would be reasonable to assume that a particular solution to the given nonhomogeneous equation is also a polynomial of degree 2 because if y is a polynomial of degree 2, then $y'' - 2y' - 3y$ is also a polynomial of degree 2. So we seek a particular solution of the form

$$y_p = Ax^2 + Bx + C.$$

We need to determine the unknown coefficients A, B, and C. When we substitute the polynomial y_p and its derivatives into the given nonhomogeneous equation, we obtain

$$2A - 2(2Ax + B) - 3(Ax^2 + Bx + C) = 1 - x^2$$

or, collecting terms with like powers of x,

$$-3Ax^2 + (-4A - 3B)x + (2A - 2B - 3C) = 1 - x^2.$$

This last equation holds for all values of x if its two sides are identical polynomials of degree 2. Thus, we equate corresponding powers of x to get

$$-3A = -1, \qquad -4A - 3B = 0, \qquad \text{and} \qquad 2A - 2B - 3C = 1.$$

These equations imply in turn that $A = 1/3$, $B = -4/9$, and $C = 5/27$. Substituting these values into the quadratic expression for our particular solution gives

$$y_p = \frac{1}{3}x^2 - \frac{4}{9}x + \frac{5}{27}.$$

By Theorem 7, the general solution to the nonhomogeneous equation is

$$y = y_c + y_p = c_1e^{-x} + c_2e^{3x} + \frac{1}{3}x^2 - \frac{4}{9}x + \frac{5}{27}.$$

EXAMPLE 2 Find a particular solution of $y'' - y' = 2\sin x$.

SOLUTION If we try to find a particular solution of the form

$$y_p = A\sin x$$

and substitute the derivatives of y_p in the given equation, we find that A must satisfy the equation

$$-A \sin x + A \cos x = 2 \sin x$$

for all values of x. Since this requires A to equal both -2 and 0 at the same time, we conclude that the nonhomogeneous differential equation has no solution of the form $A \sin x$.

It turns out that the required form is the sum

$$y_p = A \sin x + B \cos x.$$

The result of substituting the derivatives of this new trial solution into the differential equation is

$$-A \sin x - B \cos x - (A \cos x - B \sin x) = 2 \sin x$$

or

$$(B - A) \sin x - (A + B) \cos x = 2 \sin x.$$

This last equation must be an identity. Equating the coefficients for like terms on each side then gives

$$B - A = 2 \qquad \text{and} \qquad A + B = 0.$$

Simultaneous solution of these two equations gives $A = -1$ and $B = 1$. Our particular solution is

$$y_p = \cos x - \sin x.$$

EXAMPLE 3 Find a particular solution of $y'' - 3y' + 2y = 5e^x$.

SOLUTION If we substitute

$$y_p = Ae^x$$

and its derivatives in the differential equation, we find that

$$Ae^x - 3Ae^x + 2Ae^x = 5e^x$$

or

$$0 = 5e^x.$$

However, the exponential function is never zero. The trouble can be traced to the fact that $y = e^x$ is already a solution of the related homogeneous equation

$$y'' - 3y' + 2y = 0.$$

The auxiliary equation is

$$r^2 - 3r + 2 = (r - 1)(r - 2) = 0,$$

which has $r = 1$ as a root. So we would expect Ae^x to become zero when substituted into the left-hand side of the differential equation.

The appropriate way to modify the trial solution in this case is to multiply Ae^x by x. Thus, our new trial solution is

$$y_p = Axe^x.$$

The result of substituting the derivatives of this new candidate into the differential equation is

$$(Axe^x + 2Ae^x) - 3(Axe^x + Ae^x) + 2Axe^x = 5e^x$$

or

$$-Ae^x = 5e^x.$$

Thus, $A = -5$ gives our sought-after particular solution

$$y_p = -5xe^x.$$

EXAMPLE 4 Find a particular solution of $y'' - 6y' + 9y = e^{3x}$.

SOLUTION The auxiliary equation for the complementary equation

$$r^2 - 6r + 9 = (r - 3)^2 = 0$$

has $r = 3$ as a repeated root. The appropriate choice for y_p in this case is neither Ae^{3x} nor Axe^{3x} because the complementary solution contains both of those terms already. Thus, we choose a term containing the next higher power of x as a factor. When we substitute

$$y_p = Ax^2e^{3x}$$

and its derivatives in the given differential equation, we get

$$(9Ax^2e^{3x} + 12Axe^{3x} + 2Ae^{3x}) - 6(3Ax^2e^{3x} + 2Axe^{3x}) + 9Ax^2e^{3x} = e^{3x}$$

or

$$2Ae^{3x} = e^{3x}.$$

Thus, $A = 1/2$, and the particular solution is

$$y_p = \frac{1}{2}x^2e^{3x}.$$

When we wish to find a particular solution of Equation (1) and the function $G(x)$ is the sum of two or more terms, we choose a trial function for each term in $G(x)$ and add them.

EXAMPLE 5 Find the general solution to $y'' - y' = 5e^x - \sin 2x$.

SOLUTION We first check the auxiliary equation

$$r^2 - r = 0.$$

Its roots are $r = 1$ and $r = 0$. Therefore, the complementary solution to the associated homogeneous equation is

$$y_c = c_1e^x + c_2.$$

We now seek a particular solution y_p. That is, we seek a function that will produce $5e^x - \sin 2x$ when substituted into the left-hand side of the given differential equation. One part of y_p is to produce $5e^x$, the other $-\sin 2x$.

Since any function of the form c_1e^x is a solution of the associated homogeneous equation, we choose our trial solution y_p to be the sum

$$y_p = Axe^x + B\cos 2x + C\sin 2x,$$

including xe^x where we might otherwise have included only e^x. When the derivatives of y_p are substituted into the differential equation, the resulting equation is

$$\begin{aligned}&(Axe^x + 2Ae^x - 4B\cos 2x - 4C\sin 2x)\\ &\qquad - (Axe^x + Ae^x - 2B\sin 2x + 2C\cos 2x) = 5e^x - \sin 2x\end{aligned}$$

or

$$Ae^x - (4B + 2C)\cos 2x + (2B - 4C)\sin 2x = 5e^x - \sin 2x.$$

This equation will hold if

$$A = 5, \qquad 4B + 2C = 0, \qquad 2B - 4C = -1,$$

or $A = 5$, $B = -1/10$, and $C = 1/5$. Our particular solution is

$$y_p = 5xe^x - \frac{1}{10}\cos 2x + \frac{1}{5}\sin 2x.$$

The general solution to the differential equation is

$$y = y_c + y_p = c_1 e^x + c_2 + 5xe^x - \frac{1}{10}\cos 2x + \frac{1}{5}\sin 2x.$$

You may find the following table helpful in solving the problems at the end of this section.

Table 17.1 The method of undetermined coefficients for selected equations of the form

$$ay'' + by' + cy = G(x).$$

If $G(x)$ has a term that is a constant multiple of . . .	And if	Then include this expression in the trial function for y_p.
e^{rx}	r is not a root of the auxiliary equation	Ae^{rx}
	r is a single root of the auxiliary equation	Axe^{rx}
	r is a double root of the auxiliary equation	Ax^2e^{rx}
$\sin kx$, $\cos kx$	ki is not a root of the auxiliary equation	$B\cos kx + C\sin kx$
$px^2 + qx + m$	0 is not a root of the auxiliary equation	$Dx^2 + Ex + F$
	0 is a single root of the auxiliary equation	$Dx^3 + Ex^2 + Fx$
	0 is a double root of the auxiliary equation	$Dx^4 + Ex^3 + Fx^2$

The Method of Variation of Parameters

This is a general method for finding a particular solution of the nonhomogeneous equation (1) once the general solution of the associated homogeneous equation is known. The method consists of replacing the constants c_1 and c_2 in the complementary solution by functions $v_1 = v_1(x)$ and $v_2 = v_2(x)$ and requiring (in a way to be explained) that the resulting expression satisfy the nonhomogeneous equation (1). There are two functions to be determined, and requiring that Equation (1) be satisfied is only one condition. As a second condition, we also require that

$$v_1'y_1 + v_2'y_2 = 0. \tag{4}$$

Then we have

$$\begin{aligned} y &= v_1y_1 + v_2y_2, \\ y' &= v_1y_1' + v_2y_2', \\ y'' &= v_1y_1'' + v_2y_2'' + v_1'y_1' + v_2'y_2'. \end{aligned}$$

If we substitute these expressions into the left-hand side of Equation (1), we obtain

$$v_1(ay_1'' + by_1' + cy_1) + v_2(ay_2'' + by_2' + cy_2) + a(v_1'y_1' + v_2'y_2') = G(x).$$

The first two parenthetical terms are zero since y_1 and y_2 are solutions of the associated homogeneous equation (2). So the nonhomogeneous equation (1) is satisfied if, in addition to Equation (4), we require that

$$a(v_1'y_1' + v_2'y_2') = G(x). \tag{5}$$

Equations (4) and (5) can be solved together as a pair

$$v_1'y_1 + v_2'y_2 = 0,$$

$$v_1'y_1' + v_2'y_2' = \frac{G(x)}{a}$$

for the unknown functions v_1' and v_2'. The usual procedure for solving this simple system is to use the *method of determinants* (also known as *Cramer's Rule*), which will be demonstrated in the examples to follow. Once the derivative functions v_1' and v_2' are known, the two functions $v_1 = v_1(x)$ and $v_2 = v_2(x)$ can be found by integration. Here is a summary of the method.

VARIATION OF PARAMETERS PROCEDURE

To use the method of variation of parameters to find a particular solution to the nonhomogeneous equation

$$ay'' + by' + cy = G(x),$$

we can work directly with Equations (4) and (5). It is not necessary to rederive them. The steps are as follows.

1. Solve the associated homogeneous equation

$$ay'' + by' + cy = 0$$

to find the functions y_1 and y_2.

2. Solve the equations

$$v_1'y_1 + v_2'y_2 = 0,$$

$$v_1'y_1' + v_2'y_2' = \frac{G(x)}{a}$$

simultaneously for the derivative functions v_1' and v_2'.

3. Integrate v_1' and v_2' to find the functions $v_1 = v_1(x)$ and $v_2 = v_2(x)$.

4. Write down the particular solution to nonhomogeneous equation (1) as

$$y_p = v_1y_1 + v_2y_2.$$

EXAMPLE 6 Find the general solution to the equation

$$y'' + y = \tan x.$$

SOLUTION The solution of the homogeneous equation

$$y'' + y = 0$$

is given by

$$y_c = c_1 \cos x + c_2 \sin x.$$

Since $y_1(x) = \cos x$ and $y_2(x) = \sin x$, the conditions to be satisfied in Equations (4) and (5) are

$$v_1' \cos x + v_2' \sin x = 0,$$

$$-v_1' \sin x + v_2' \cos x = \tan x. \qquad a = 1$$

Solution of this system gives

$$v_1' = \frac{\begin{vmatrix} 0 & \sin x \\ \tan x & \cos x \end{vmatrix}}{\begin{vmatrix} \cos x & \sin x \\ -\sin x & \cos x \end{vmatrix}} = \frac{-\tan x \sin x}{\cos^2 x + \sin^2 x} = \frac{-\sin^2 x}{\cos x}.$$

Likewise,

$$v_2' = \frac{\begin{vmatrix} \cos x & 0 \\ -\sin x & \tan x \end{vmatrix}}{\begin{vmatrix} \cos x & \sin x \\ -\sin x & \cos x \end{vmatrix}} = \sin x.$$

After integrating v_1' and v_2', we have

$$\begin{aligned} v_1(x) &= \int \frac{-\sin^2 x}{\cos x}\, dx \\ &= -\int (\sec x - \cos x)\, dx \\ &= -\ln|\sec x + \tan x| + \sin x, \end{aligned}$$

and

$$v_2(x) = \int \sin x\, dx = -\cos x.$$

Note that we have omitted the constants of integration in determining v_1 and v_2. They would merely be absorbed into the arbitrary constants in the complementary solution.

Substituting v_1 and v_2 into the expression for y_p in Step 4 gives

$$\begin{aligned} y_p &= [-\ln|\sec x + \tan x| + \sin x]\cos x + (-\cos x)\sin x \\ &= (-\cos x)\ln|\sec x + \tan x|. \end{aligned}$$

The general solution is

$$y = c_1 \cos x + c_2 \sin x - (\cos x)\ln|\sec x + \tan x|.$$

EXAMPLE 7 Solve the nonhomogeneous equation

$$y'' + y' - 2y = xe^x.$$

SOLUTION The auxiliary equation is

$$r^2 + r - 2 = (r + 2)(r - 1) = 0$$

giving the complementary solution

$$y_c = c_1 e^{-2x} + c_2 e^x.$$

The conditions to be satisfied in Equations (4) and (5) are

$$\begin{aligned} v_1' e^{-2x} + v_2' e^x &= 0, \\ -2v_1' e^{-2x} + v_2' e^x &= xe^x. \qquad a = 1 \end{aligned}$$

Solving the above system for $v_1{}'$ and $v_2{}'$ gives

$$v_1{}' = \frac{\begin{vmatrix} 0 & e^x \\ xe^x & e^x \end{vmatrix}}{\begin{vmatrix} e^{-2x} & e^x \\ -2e^{-2x} & e^x \end{vmatrix}} = \frac{-xe^{2x}}{3e^{-x}} = -\frac{1}{3}xe^{3x}.$$

Likewise,

$$v_2{}' = \frac{\begin{vmatrix} e^{-2x} & 0 \\ -2e^{-2x} & xe^x \end{vmatrix}}{3e^{-x}} = \frac{xe^{-x}}{3e^{-x}} = \frac{x}{3}.$$

Integrating to obtain the parameter functions, we have

$$\begin{aligned} v_1(x) &= \int -\frac{1}{3}xe^{3x}\,dx \\ &= -\frac{1}{3}\left(\frac{xe^{3x}}{3} - \int \frac{e^{3x}}{3}\,dx\right) \\ &= \frac{1}{27}(1 - 3x)e^{3x}, \end{aligned}$$

and

$$v_2(x) = \int \frac{x}{3}\,dx = \frac{x^2}{6}.$$

Therefore,

$$\begin{aligned} y_p &= \left[\frac{(1 - 3x)e^{3x}}{27}\right]e^{-2x} + \left(\frac{x^2}{6}\right)e^x \\ &= \frac{1}{27}e^x - \frac{1}{9}xe^x + \frac{1}{6}x^2e^x. \end{aligned}$$

The general solution to the differential equation is

$$y = c_1e^{-2x} + c_2e^x - \frac{1}{9}xe^x + \frac{1}{6}x^2e^x,$$

where the term $(1/27)e^x$ in y_p has been absorbed into the term c_2e^x in the complementary solution.

SECTION 17.2 EXERCISES

Solve the equations in Exercises 1–16 by the method of undetermined coefficients.

1. $y'' - 3y' - 10y = -3$
2. $y'' - 3y' - 10y = 2x - 3$
3. $y'' - y' = \sin x$
4. $y'' + 2y' + y = x^2$
5. $y'' + y = \cos 3x$
6. $y'' + y = e^{2x}$
7. $y'' - y' - 2y = 20 \cos x$
8. $y'' + y = 2x + 3e^x$
9. $y'' - y = e^x + x^2$
10. $y'' + 2y' + y = 6 \sin 2x$
11. $y'' - y' - 6y = e^{-x} - 7 \cos x$
12. $y'' + 3y' + 2y = e^{-x} + e^{-2x} - x$
13. $\dfrac{d^2y}{dx^2} + 5\dfrac{dy}{dx} = 15x^2$
14. $\dfrac{d^2y}{dx^2} - \dfrac{dy}{dx} = -8x + 3$
15. $\dfrac{d^2y}{dx^2} - 3\dfrac{dy}{dx} = e^{3x} - 12x$
16. $\dfrac{d^2y}{dx^2} + 7\dfrac{dy}{dx} = 42x^2 + 5x + 1$

Solve the equations in Exercises 17–28 by variation of parameters.

17. $y'' + y' = x$
18. $y'' + y = \tan x, \quad -\frac{\pi}{2} < x < \frac{\pi}{2}$
19. $y'' + y = \sin x$
20. $y'' + 2y' + y = e^x$
21. $y'' + 2y' + y = e^{-x}$
22. $y'' - y = x$
23. $y'' - y = e^x$
24. $y'' - y = \sin x$
25. $y'' + 4y' + 5y = 10$
26. $y'' - y' = 2^x$
27. $\dfrac{d^2y}{dx^2} + y = \sec x, \quad -\frac{\pi}{2} < x < \frac{\pi}{2}$
28. $\dfrac{d^2y}{dx^2} - \dfrac{dy}{dx} = e^x \cos x, \quad x > 0$

In each of Exercises 29–32, the given differential equation has a particular solution y_p of the form given. Determine the coefficients in y_p. Then solve the differential equation.

29. $y'' - 5y' = xe^{5x}, \quad y_p = Ax^2e^{5x} + Bxe^{5x}$
30. $y'' - y' = \cos x + \sin x, \quad y_p = A\cos x + B\sin x$
31. $y'' + y = 2\cos x + \sin x, \quad y_p = Ax\cos x + Bx\sin x$
32. $y'' + y' - 2y = xe^x, \quad y_p = Ax^2e^x + Bxe^x$

In Exercises 33–36, solve the given differential equations **(a)** by variation of parameters and **(b)** by the method of undetermined coefficients.

33. $\dfrac{d^2y}{dx^2} - \dfrac{dy}{dx} = e^x + e^{-x}$
34. $\dfrac{d^2y}{dx^2} - 4\dfrac{dy}{dx} + 4y = 2e^{2x}$
35. $\dfrac{d^2y}{dx^2} - 4\dfrac{dy}{dx} - 5y = e^x + 4$
36. $\dfrac{d^2y}{dx^2} - 9\dfrac{dy}{dx} = 9e^{9x}$

Solve the differential equations in Exercises 37–46. Some of the equations can be solved by the method of undetermined coefficients, but others cannot.

37. $y'' + y = \cot x, \quad 0 < x < \pi$
38. $y'' + y = \csc x, \quad 0 < x < \pi$
39. $y'' - 8y' = e^{8x}$
40. $y'' + 4y = \sin x$
41. $y'' - y' = x^3$
42. $y'' + 4y' + 5y = x + 2$
43. $y'' + 2y' = x^2 - e^x$
44. $y'' + 9y = 9x - \cos x$
45. $y'' + y = \sec x \tan x, \quad -\frac{\pi}{2} < x < \frac{\pi}{2}$
46. $y'' - 3y' + 2y = e^x - e^{2x}$

The method of undetermined coefficients can sometimes be used to solve first-order ordinary differential equations. Use the method to solve the equations in Exercises 47–50.

47. $y' - 3y = e^x$
48. $y' + 4y = x$
49. $y' - 3y = 5e^{3x}$
50. $y' + y = \sin x$

Solve the differential equations in Exercises 51 and 52 subject to the given initial conditions.

51. $\dfrac{d^2y}{dx^2} + y = \sec^2 x, \quad -\frac{\pi}{2} < x < \frac{\pi}{2}; \quad y(0) = y'(0) = 1$
52. $\dfrac{d^2y}{dx^2} + y = e^{2x}; \quad y(0) = 0,\ y'(0) = \frac{2}{5}$

In Exercises 53–58, verify that the given function is a particular solution to the specified nonhomogeneous equation. Find the general solution and evaluate its arbitrary constants to find the unique solution satisfying the equation and the given initial conditions.

53. $y'' + y' = x, \quad y_p = \dfrac{x^2}{2} - x, \quad y(0) = 0,\ y'(0) = 0$
54. $y'' + y = x, \quad y_p = 2\sin x + x, \quad y(0) = 0,\ y'(0) = 0$
55. $\frac{1}{2}y'' + y' + y = 4e^x(\cos x - \sin x),$
    $y_p = 2e^x \cos x, \quad y(0) = 0,\ y'(0) = 1$
56. $y'' - y' - 2y = 1 - 2x, \quad y_p = x - 1, \quad y(0) = 0,\ y'(0) = 1$
57. $y'' - 2y' + y = 2e^x, \quad y_p = x^2e^x, \quad y(0) = 1,\ y'(0) = 0$
58. $y'' - 2y' + y = x^{-1}e^x,\ x > 0,$
    $y_p = xe^x \ln x, \quad y(1) = e,\ y'(1) = 0$

In Exercises 59 and 60, two linearly independent solutions y_1 and y_2 are given to the associated homogeneous equation of the variable-coefficient nonhomogeneous equation. Use the method of variation of parameters to find a particular solution to the nonhomogeneous equation. Assume $x > 0$ in each exercise.

59. $x^2y'' + 2xy' - 2y = x^2, \quad y_1 = x^{-2},\ y_2 = x$
60. $x^2y'' + xy' - y = x, \quad y_1 = x^{-1},\ y_2 = x$

17.3 Applications

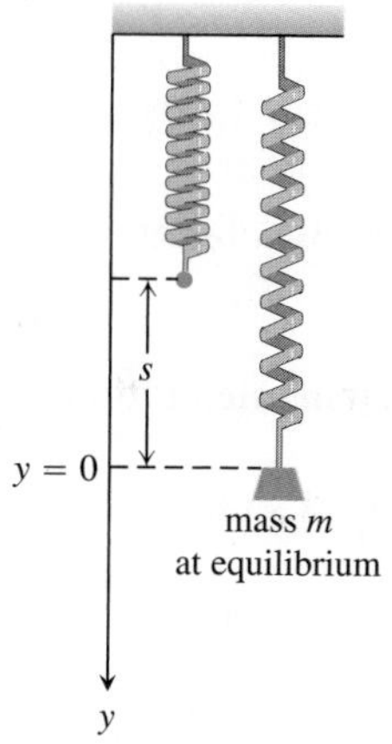

FIGURE 17.2 Mass m stretches a spring by length s to the equilibrium position at $y = 0$.

In this section we apply second-order differential equations to the study of vibrating springs and electric circuits.

Vibrations

A spring has its upper end fastened to a rigid support, as shown in Figure 17.2. An object of mass m is suspended from the spring and stretches it a length s when the spring comes to rest in an equilibrium position. According to Hooke's Law (Section 6.5), the tension force in the spring is ks, where k is the spring constant. The force due to gravity pulling down on the spring is mg, and equilibrium requires that

$$ks = mg. \tag{1}$$

Suppose that the object is pulled down an additional amount y_0 beyond the equilibrium position and then released. We want to study the object's motion, that is, the vertical position of its center of mass at any future time.

Let y, with positive direction downward, denote the displacement position of the object away from the equilibrium position $y = 0$ at any time t after the motion has started. Then the forces acting on the object are (see Figure 17.3)

$F_p = mg$, the propulsion force due to gravity,

$F_s = k(s + y)$, the restoring force of the spring's tension,

$F_r = \delta \dfrac{dy}{dt}$, a frictional force assumed proportional to velocity.

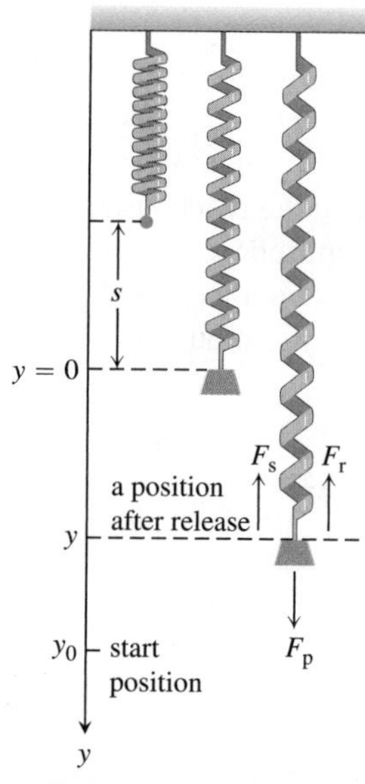

FIGURE 17.3 The propulsion force (weight) F_p pulls the mass downward, but the spring restoring force F_s and frictional force F_r pull the mass upward. The motion starts at $y = y_0$ with the mass vibrating up and down.

The frictional force tends to retard the motion of the object. The resultant of these forces is $F = F_p - F_s - F_r$, and by Newton's second law $F = ma$, we must then have

$$m\frac{d^2y}{dt^2} = mg - ks - ky - \delta\frac{dy}{dt}.$$

By Equation (1), $mg - ks = 0$, so this last equation becomes

$$m\frac{d^2y}{dt^2} + \delta\frac{dy}{dt} + ky = 0, \tag{2}$$

subject to the initial conditions $y(0) = y_0$ and $y'(0) = 0$. (Here we use the prime notation to denote differentiation with respect to time t.)

You might expect that the motion predicted by Equation (2) will be oscillatory about the equilibrium position $y = 0$ and eventually damp to zero because of the retarding frictional force. This is indeed the case, and we will show how the constants m, δ, and k determine the nature of the damping. You will also see that if there is no friction (so $\delta = 0$), then the object will simply oscillate indefinitely.

Simple Harmonic Motion

Suppose first that there is no retarding frictional force. Then $\delta = 0$ and there is no damping. If we substitute $\omega = \sqrt{k/m}$ to simplify our calculations, then the second-order equation (2) becomes

$$y'' + \omega^2 y = 0, \quad \text{with} \quad y(0) = y_0 \quad \text{and} \quad y'(0) = 0.$$

The auxiliary equation is

$$r^2 + \omega^2 = 0,$$

having the imaginary roots $r = \pm\omega i$. The general solution to the differential equation in (2) is

$$y = c_1 \cos \omega t + c_2 \sin \omega t. \tag{3}$$

To fit the initial conditions, we compute

$$y' = -c_1\omega \sin \omega t + c_2\omega \cos \omega t$$

and then substitute the conditions. This yields $c_1 = y_0$ and $c_2 = 0$. The particular solution

$$y = y_0 \cos \omega t \tag{4}$$

describes the motion of the object. Equation (4) represents **simple harmonic motion** of amplitude y_0 and period $T = 2\pi/\omega$.

The general solution given by Equation (3) can be combined into a single term by using the trigonometric identity

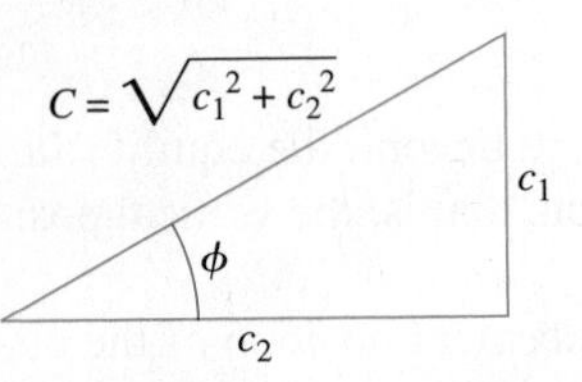

FIGURE 17.4 $c_1 = C \sin \phi$ and $c_2 = C \cos \phi$.

$$\sin(\omega t + \phi) = \cos \omega t \sin \phi + \sin \omega t \cos \phi.$$

To apply the identity, we take (see Figure 17.4)

$$c_1 = C \sin \phi \qquad \text{and} \qquad c_2 = C \cos \phi,$$

where

$$C = \sqrt{c_1^2 + c_2^2} \qquad \text{and} \qquad \phi = \tan^{-1} \frac{c_1}{c_2}.$$

Then the general solution in Equation (3) can be written in the alternative form

$$y = C \sin(\omega t + \phi). \tag{5}$$

Here C and ϕ may be taken as two new arbitrary constants, replacing the two constants c_1 and c_2. Equation (5) represents simple harmonic motion of amplitude C and period $T = 2\pi/\omega$. The angle $\omega t + \phi$ is called the **phase angle**, and ϕ may be interpreted as its initial value. A graph of the simple harmonic motion represented by Equation (5) is given in Figure 17.5.

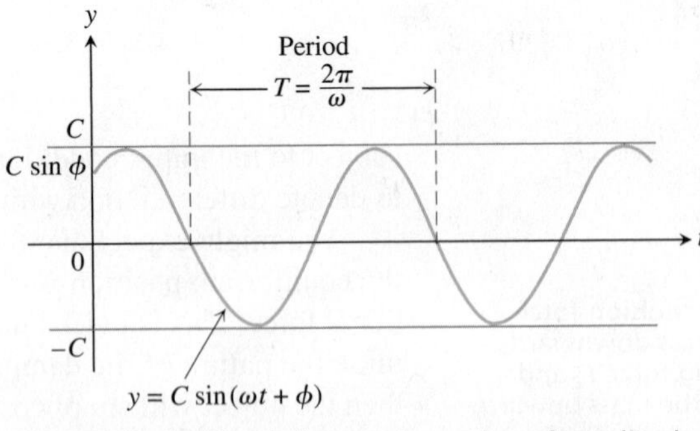

FIGURE 17.5 Simple harmonic motion of amplitude C and period T with initial phase angle ϕ (Equation 5).

Damped Motion

Assume now that there is friction in the spring system, so $\delta \neq 0$. If we substitute $\omega = \sqrt{k/m}$ and $2b = \delta/m$, then the differential equation (2) is

$$y'' + 2by' + \omega^2 y = 0. \tag{6}$$

The auxiliary equation is

$$r^2 + 2br + \omega^2 = 0,$$

with roots $r = -b \pm \sqrt{b^2 - \omega^2}$. Three cases now present themselves, depending upon the relative sizes of b and ω.

Case 1: $b = \omega$. The double root of the auxiliary equation is real and equals $r = \omega$. The general solution to Equation (6) is

$$y = (c_1 + c_2 t)e^{-\omega t}.$$

This situation of motion is called **critical damping** and is not oscillatory. Figure 17.6a shows an example of this kind of damped motion.

Case 2: $b > \omega$. The roots of the auxiliary equation are real and unequal, given by $r_1 = -b + \sqrt{b^2 - \omega^2}$ and $r_2 = -b - \sqrt{b^2 - \omega^2}$. The general solution to Equation (6) is given by

$$y = c_1 e^{\left(-b+\sqrt{b^2-\omega^2}\right)t} + c_2 e^{\left(-b-\sqrt{b^2-\omega^2}\right)t}.$$

Here again the motion is not oscillatory and both r_1 and r_2 are negative. Thus y approaches zero as time goes on. This motion is referred to as **overdamping** (see Figure 17.6b).

Case 3: $b < \omega$. The roots to the auxiliary equation are complex and given by $r = -b \pm i\sqrt{\omega^2 - b^2}$. The general solution to Equation (6) is given by

$$y = e^{-bt}\left(c_1 \cos\sqrt{\omega^2 - b^2}\, t + c_2 \sin\sqrt{\omega^2 - b^2}\, t\right).$$

This situation, called **underdamping**, represents damped oscillatory motion. It is analogous to simple harmonic motion of period $T = 2\pi/\sqrt{\omega^2 - b^2}$ except that the amplitude is not constant but damped by the factor e^{-bt}. Therefore, the motion tends to zero as t increases, so the vibrations tend to die out as time goes on. Notice that the period $T = 2\pi/\sqrt{\omega^2 - b^2}$ is larger than the period $T_0 = 2\pi/\omega$ in the friction-free system. Moreover, the larger the value of $b = \delta/2m$ in the exponential damping factor, the more quickly the vibrations tend to become unnoticeable. A curve illustrating underdamped motion is shown in Figure 17.6c.

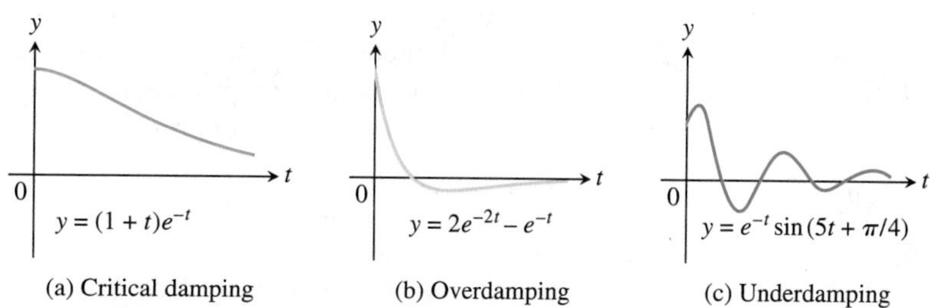

FIGURE 17.6 Three examples of damped vibratory motion for a spring system with friction, so $\delta \neq 0$.

An external force $F(t)$ can also be added to the spring system modeled by Equation (2). The forcing function may represent an external disturbance on the system. For instance, if the equation models an automobile suspension system, the forcing function might represent periodic bumps or potholes in the road affecting the performance of the suspension system; or it might represent the effects of winds when modeling the vertical motion of a suspension bridge. Inclusion of a forcing function results in the second-order nonhomogeneous equation

$$m\frac{d^2y}{dt^2} + \delta\frac{dy}{dt} + ky = F(t). \tag{7}$$

We leave the study of such spring systems to a more advanced course.

Electric Circuits

The basic quantity in electricity is the **charge** q (analogous to the idea of mass). In an electric field we use the flow of charge, or **current** $I = dq/dt$, as we might use velocity in a gravitational field. There are many similarities between motion in a gravitational field and the flow of electrons (the carriers of charge) in an electric field.

Consider the electric circuit shown in Figure 17.7. It consists of four components: voltage source, resistor, inductor, and capacitor. Think of electrical flow as being like a fluid flow, where the voltage source is the pump and the resistor, inductor, and capacitor tend to block the flow. A battery or generator is an example of a source, producing a voltage that causes the current to flow through the circuit when the switch is closed. An electric light bulb or appliance would provide resistance. The inductance is due to a magnetic field that opposes any change in the current as it flows through a coil. The capacitance is normally created by two metal plates that alternate charges and thus reverse the current flow. The following symbols specify the quantities relevant to the circuit:

q: charge at a cross section of a conductor measured in **coulombs** (abbreviated c);
I: current or rate of change of charge dq/dt (flow of electrons) at a cross section of a conductor measured in **amperes** (abbreviated A);
E: electric (potential) source measured in **volts** (abbreviated V);
V: difference in potential between two points along the conductor measured in **volts** (V).

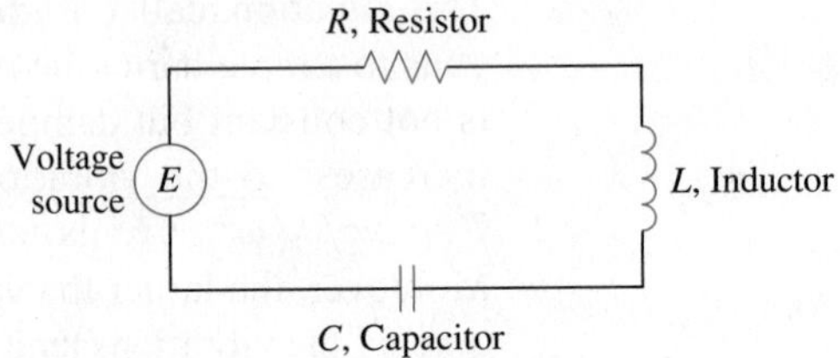

FIGURE 17.7 An electric circuit.

Ohm observed that the current I flowing through a resistor, caused by a potential difference across it, is (approximately) proportional to the potential difference (voltage drop). He named his constant of proportionality $1/R$ and called R the **resistance**. So *Ohm's law* is

$$I = \frac{1}{R}V.$$

Similarly, it is known from physics that the voltage drops across an inductor and a capacitor are

$$L\frac{dI}{dt} \quad \text{and} \quad \frac{q}{C},$$

where L is the **inductance** and C is the **capacitance** (with q the charge on the capacitor).

The German physicist Gustav R. Kirchhoff (1824–1887) formulated the law that the sum of the voltage drops in a closed circuit is equal to the supplied voltage $E(t)$. Symbolically, this says that

$$RI + L\frac{dI}{dt} + \frac{q}{C} = E(t).$$

Since $I = dq/dt$, Kirchhoff's law becomes

$$L\frac{d^2q}{dt^2} + R\frac{dq}{dt} + \frac{1}{C}q = E(t). \tag{8}$$

The second-order differential equation (8), which models an electric circuit, has exactly the same form as Equation (7) modeling vibratory motion. Both models can be solved using the methods developed in Section 17.2.

Summary

The following chart summarizes our analogies for the physics of motion of an object in a spring system versus the flow of charged particles in an electrical circuit.

LINEAR SECOND-ORDER CONSTANT-COEFFICIENT MODELS

Mechanical System		**Electrical System**	
$my'' + \delta y' + ky = F(t)$		$Lq'' + Rq' + \frac{1}{C}q = E(t)$	
y:	displacement	q:	charge
y':	velocity	q':	current
y'':	acceleration	q'':	change in current
m:	mass	L:	inductance
δ:	damping constant	R:	resistance
k:	spring constant	$1/C$:	where C is the capacitance
$F(t)$:	forcing function	$E(t)$:	voltage source

SECTION 17.3 EXERCISES

1. A 16-lb weight is attached to the lower end of a coil spring suspended from the ceiling and having a spring constant of 1 lb/ft. The resistance in the spring–mass system is numerically equal to the instantaneous velocity. At $t = 0$ the weight is set in motion from a position 2 ft below its equilibrium position by giving it a downward velocity of 2 ft/sec. Write an initial value problem that models the given situation.

2. An 8-lb weight stretches a spring 4 ft. The spring–mass system resides in a medium offering a resistance to the motion that is numerically equal to 1.5 times the instantaneous velocity. If the weight is released at a position 2 ft above its equilibrium position with a downward velocity of 3 ft/sec, write an initial value problem modeling the given situation.

3. A 20-lb weight is hung on an 18-in. spring and stretches it 6 in. The weight is pulled down 5 in. and 5 lb are added to the weight. If the weight is now released with a downward velocity of v_0 in./sec, write an initial value problem modeling the vertical displacement.

4. A 10-lb weight is suspended by a spring that is stretched 2 in. by the weight. Assume a resistance whose magnitude is $20/\sqrt{g}$ lb times the instantaneous velocity v in feet per second. If the weight is pulled down 3 in. below its equilibrium position and released, formulate an initial value problem modeling the behavior of the spring–mass system.

5. An (open) electrical circuit consists of an inductor, a resistor, and a capacitor. There is an initial charge of 2 coulombs on the capacitor. At the instant the circuit is closed, a current of 3 amperes is present and a voltage of $E(t) = 20 \cos t$ is applied. In this circuit the voltage drop across the resistor is 4 times the instantaneous change in the charge, the voltage drop across the capacitor is 10 times the charge, and the voltage drop across the inductor is 2 times the instantaneous change in the current. Write an initial value problem to model the circuit.

6. An inductor of 2 henrys is connected in series with a resistor of 12 ohms, a capacitor of 1/16 farad, and a 300 volt battery. Initially, the charge on the capacitor is zero and the current is zero. Formulate an initial value problem modeling this electrical circuit.

Mechanical units in the British and metric systems may be helpful in doing the following problems.

Unit	**British System**	**MKS System**
Distance	Feet (ft)	Meters (m)
Mass	Slugs	Kilograms (kg)
Time	Seconds (sec)	Seconds (sec)
Force	Pounds (lb)	Newtons (N)
g(earth)	32 ft/sec^2	9.81 m/sec^2

7. A 16-lb weight is attached to the lower end of a coil spring suspended from the ceiling and having a spring constant of 1 lb/ft. The resistance in the spring–mass system is numerically equal to the instantaneous velocity. At $t = 0$ the weight is set in motion from a position 2 ft below its equilibrium position by giving it a downward velocity of 2 ft/sec. At the end of π sec, determine whether the mass is above or below the equilibrium position and by what distance.

8. An 8-lb weight stretches a spring 4 ft. The spring–mass system resides in a medium offering a resistance to the motion equal to 1.5 times the instantaneous velocity. If the weight is released at a position 2 ft above its equilibrium position with a downward velocity of 3 ft/sec, find its position relative to the equilibrium position 2 sec later.

9. A 20-lb weight is hung on an 18-in. spring stretching it 6 in. The weight is pulled down 5 in. and 5 lb are added to the weight. If the weight is now released with a downward velocity of v_0 in./sec, find the position of mass relative to the equilibrium in terms of v_0 and valid for any time $t \geq 0$.

10. A mass of 1 slug is attached to a spring whose constant is 25/4 lb/ft. Initially the mass is released 1 ft above the equilibrium position with a downward velocity of 3 ft/sec, and the subsequent motion takes place in a medium that offers a damping force numerically equal to 3 times the instantaneous velocity. An external force $f(t)$ is driving the system, but assume that initially $f(t) \equiv 0$. Formulate and solve an initial value problem that models the given system. Interpret your results.

11. A 10-lb weight is suspended by a spring that is stretched 2 in. by the weight. Assume a resistance whose magnitude is $40/\sqrt{g}$ lb times the instantaneous velocity in feet per second. If the weight is pulled down 3 in. below its equilibrium position and released, find the time required to reach the equilibrium position for the first time.

12. A weight stretches a spring 6 in. It is set in motion at a point 2 in. below its equilibrium position with a downward velocity of 2 in./sec.

a. When does the weight return to its starting position?

b. When does it reach its highest point?

c. Show that the maximum velocity is $2\sqrt{2g+1}$ in./sec.

13. A weight of 10 lb stretches a spring 10 in. The weight is drawn down 2 in. below its equilibrium position and given an initial velocity of 4 in./sec. An identical spring has a different weight attached to it. This second weight is drawn down from its equilibrium position a distance equal to the amplitude of the first motion and then given an initial velocity of 2 ft/sec. If the amplitude of the second motion is twice that of the first, what weight is attached to the second spring?

14. A weight stretches one spring 3 in. and a second weight stretches another spring 9 in. If both weights are simultaneously pulled down 1 in. below their respective equilibrium positions and then released, find the first time after $t = 0$ when their velocities are equal.

15. A weight of 16 lb stretches a spring 4 ft. The weight is pulled down 5 ft below the equilibrium position and then released. What initial velocity v_0 given to the weight would have the effect of doubling the amplitude of the vibration?

16. A mass weighing 8 lb stretches a spring 3 in. The spring–mass system resides in a medium with a damping constant of 2 lb-sec/ft. If the mass is released from its equilibrium position with a velocity of 4 in./sec in the downward direction, find the time required for the mass to return to its equilibrium position for the first time.

17. A weight suspended from a spring executes damped vibrations with a period of 2 sec. If the damping factor decreases by 90% in 10 sec, find the acceleration of the weight when it is 3 in. below its equilibrium position and is moving upward with a speed of 2 ft/sec.

18. A 10-lb weight stretches a spring 2 ft. If the weight is pulled down 6 in. below its equilibrium position and released, find the highest point reached by the weight. Assume the spring–mass system resides in a medium offering a resistance of $10/\sqrt{g}$ lb times the instantaneous velocity in feet per second.

19. An *LRC* circuit is set up with an inductance of 1/5 henry, a resistance of 1 ohm, and a capacitance of 5/6 farad. Assuming the initial charge is 2 coulombs and the initial current is 4 amperes, find the solution function describing the charge on the capacitor at any time. What is the charge on the capacitor after a long period of time?

20. An (open) electrical circuit consists of an inductor, a resistor, and a capacitor. There is an initial charge of 2 coulombs on the capacitor. At the instant the circuit is closed, a current of 3 amperes is present but no external voltage is being applied. In this circuit the voltage drops at three points are numerically related as follows: across the capacitor, 10 times the charge; across the resistor, 4 times the instantaneous change in the charge; and across the inductor, 2 times the instantaneous change in the current. Find the charge on the capacitor as a function of time.

21. A 16-lb weight stretches a spring 4 ft. This spring–mass system is in a medium with a damping constant of 4.5 lb-sec/ft, and an external force given by $f(t) = 4 + e^{-2t}$ (in pounds) is being applied. What is the solution function describing the position of the mass at any time if the mass is released from 2 ft below the equilibrium position with an initial velocity of 4 ft/sec downward?

22. A 10-kg mass is attached to a spring having a spring constant of 140 N/m. The mass is started in motion from the equilibrium position with an initial velocity of 1 m/sec in the upward direction and with an applied external force given by $f(t) = 5 \sin t$ (in newtons). The mass is in a viscous medium with a coefficient of resistance equal to 90 N-sec/m. Formulate an initial value problem that models the given system; solve the model and interpret the results.

23. A 2-kg mass is attached to the lower end of a coil spring suspended from the ceiling. The mass comes to rest in its equilibrium position thereby stretching the spring 1.96 m. The mass is in a viscous medium that offers a resistance in newtons numerically equal to 4 times the instantaneous velocity measured in meters per second. The mass is then pulled down 2 m below its equilibrium position and released with a downward velocity of 3 m/sec. At this same instant an external force given by $f(t) = 20 \cos t$ (in newtons) is applied to the system. At the end of π sec determine if the mass is above or below its equilibrium position and by how much.

24. An 8-lb weight stretches a spring 4 ft. The spring–mass system resides in a medium offering a resistance to the motion equal to 1.5 times the instantaneous velocity, and an external force given by $f(t) = 6 + e^{-t}$ (in pounds) is being applied. If the weight is released at a position 2 ft above its equilibrium position with downward velocity of 3 ft/sec, find its position relative to the equilibrium after 2 sec have elapsed.

25. Suppose $L = 10$ henrys, $R = 10$ ohms, $C = 1/500$ farads, $E = 100$ volts, $q(0) = 10$ coulombs, and $q'(0) = i(0) = 0$. Formulate and solve an initial value problem that models the given *LRC* circuit. Interpret your results.

26. A series circuit consisting of an inductor, a resistor, and a capacitor is open. There is an initial charge of 2 coulombs on the capacitor, and 3 amperes of current is present in the circuit at the instant the circuit is closed. A voltage given by $E(t) = 20 \cos t$ is applied. In this circuit the voltage drops are numerically equal to the following: across the resistor to 4 times the instantaneous change in the charge, across the capacitor to 10 times the charge, and across the inductor to 2 times the instantaneous change in the current. Find the charge on the capacitor as a function of time. Determine the charge on the capacitor and the current at time $t = 10$.

17.4 Euler Equations

In Section 17.1 we introduced the second-order linear homogeneous differential equation

$$P(x)y''(x) + Q(x)y'(x) + R(x)y(x) = 0$$

and showed how to solve this equation when the coefficients P, Q, and R are constants. If the coefficients are not constant, we cannot generally solve this differential equation in terms of elementary functions we have studied in calculus. In this section you will learn how to solve the equation when the coefficients have the special forms

$$P(x) = ax^2, \qquad Q(x) = bx, \qquad \text{and} \qquad R(x) = c,$$

where a, b, and c are constants. These special types of equations are called **Euler equations**, in honor of Leonhard Euler who studied them and showed how to solve them. Such equations arise in the study of mechanical vibrations.

The General Solution of Euler Equations

Consider the Euler equation

$$ax^2y'' + bxy' + cy = 0, \quad x > 0. \tag{1}$$

To solve Equation (1), we first make the change of variables

$$z = \ln x \qquad \text{and} \qquad y(x) = Y(z).$$

We next use the chain rule to find the derivatives $y'(x)$ and $y''(x)$:

$$y'(x) = \frac{d}{dx}Y(z) = \frac{d}{dz}Y(z)\frac{dz}{dx} = Y'(z)\frac{1}{x}$$

and

$$y''(x) = \frac{d}{dx}y'(x) = \frac{d}{dx}Y'(z)\frac{1}{x} = -\frac{1}{x^2}Y'(z) + \frac{1}{x}Y''(z)\frac{dz}{dx} = -\frac{1}{x^2}Y'(z) + \frac{1}{x^2}Y''(z).$$

Substituting these two derivatives into the left-hand side of Equation (1), we find

$$\begin{aligned} ax^2y'' + bxy' + cy &= ax^2\left(-\frac{1}{x^2}Y'(z) + \frac{1}{x^2}Y''(z)\right) + bx\left(\frac{1}{x}Y'(z)\right) + cY(z) \\ &= aY''(z) + (b - a)Y'(z) + cY(z). \end{aligned}$$

Therefore, the substitutions give us the second-order linear differential equation with constant coefficients

$$aY''(z) + (b - a)Y'(z) + cY(z) = 0. \tag{2}$$

We can solve Equation (2) using the method of Section 17.1. That is, we find the roots to the associated auxiliary equation

$$ar^2 + (b - a)r + c = 0 \tag{3}$$

to find the general solution for $Y(z)$. After finding $Y(z)$, we can determine $y(x)$ from the substitution $z = \ln x$.

EXAMPLE 1 Find the general solution of the equation $x^2y'' + 2xy' - 2y = 0$.

SOLUTION This is an Euler equation with $a = 1$, $b = 2$, and $c = -2$. The auxiliary equation (3) for $Y(z)$ is

$$r^2 + (2 - 1)r - 2 = (r - 1)(r + 2) = 0,$$

with roots $r = -2$ and $r = 1$. The solution for $Y(z)$ is given by

$$Y(z) = c_1 e^{-2z} + c_2 e^{z}.$$

Substituting $z = \ln x$ gives the general solution for $y(x)$:

$$y(x) = c_1 e^{-2 \ln x} + c_2 e^{\ln x} = c_1 x^{-2} + c_2 x$$

EXAMPLE 2 Solve the Euler equation $x^2 y'' - 5xy' + 9y = 0$.

SOLUTION Since $a = 1$, $b = -5$, and $c = 9$, the auxiliary equation (3) for $Y(z)$ is

$$r^2 + (-5 - 1)r + 9 = (r - 3)^2 = 0.$$

The auxiliary equation has the double root $r = 3$ giving

$$Y(z) = c_1 e^{3z} + c_2 z e^{3z}.$$

Substituting $z = \ln x$ into this expression gives the general solution

$$y(x) = c_1 e^{3 \ln x} + c_2 \ln x \, e^{3 \ln x} = c_1 x^3 + c_2 x^3 \ln x$$

EXAMPLE 3 Find the particular solution to $x^2 y'' - 3xy' + 68y = 0$ that satisfies the initial conditions $y(1) = 0$ and $y'(1) = 1$.

SOLUTION Here $a = 1$, $b = -3$, and $c = 68$ substituted into the auxiliary equation (3) gives

$$r^2 - 4r + 68 = 0.$$

The roots are $r = 2 + 8i$ and $r = 2 - 8i$ giving the solution

$$Y(z) = e^{2z}(c_1 \cos 8z + c_2 \sin 8z).$$

Substituting $z = \ln x$ into this expression gives

$$y(x) = e^{2 \ln x}\big(c_1 \cos(8 \ln x) + c_2 \sin(8 \ln x)\big).$$

From the initial condition $y(1) = 0$, we see that $c_1 = 0$ and

$$y(x) = c_2 x^2 \sin(8 \ln x).$$

To fit the second initial condition, we need the derivative

$$y'(x) = c_2\big(8x \cos(8 \ln x) + 2x \sin(8 \ln x)\big).$$

Since $y'(1) = 1$, we immediately obtain $c_2 = 1/8$. Therefore, the particular solution satisfying both initial conditions is

$$y(x) = \frac{1}{8} x^2 \sin(8 \ln x).$$

Since $-1 \le \sin(8 \ln x) \le 1$, the solution satisfies

$$-\frac{x^2}{8} \le y(x) \le \frac{x^2}{8}.$$

A graph of the solution is shown in Figure 17.8.

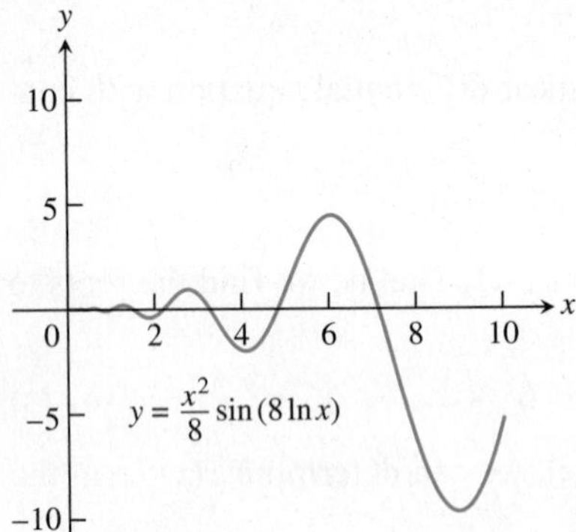

FIGURE 17.8 Graph of the solution to Example 3.

SECTION 17.4 EXERCISES

In Exercises 1–24, find the general solution to the given Euler equation. Assume $x > 0$ throughout.

1. $x^2y'' + 2xy' - 2y = 0$

2. $x^2y'' + xy' - 4y = 0$

3. $x^2y'' - 6y = 0$

4. $x^2y'' + xy' - y = 0$

5. $x^2y'' - 5xy' + 8y = 0$

6. $2x^2y'' + 7xy' + 2y = 0$

7. $3x^2y'' + 4xy' = 0$

8. $x^2y'' + 6xy' + 4y = 0$

9. $x^2y'' - xy' + y = 0$

10. $x^2y'' - xy' + 2y = 0$

11. $x^2y'' - xy' + 5y = 0$

12. $x^2y'' + 7xy' + 13y = 0$

13. $x^2y'' + 3xy' + 10y = 0$

14. $x^2y'' - 5xy' + 10y = 0$

15. $4x^2y'' + 8xy' + 5y = 0$

16. $4x^2y'' - 4xy' + 5y = 0$

17. $x^2y'' + 3xy' + y = 0$

18. $x^2y'' - 3xy' + 9y = 0$

19. $x^2y'' + xy' = 0$

20. $4x^2y'' + y = 0$

21. $9x^2y'' + 15xy' + y = 0$

22. $16x^2y'' - 8xy' + 9y = 0$

23. $16x^2y'' + 56xy' + 25y = 0$

24. $4x^2y'' - 16xy' + 25y = 0$

In Exercises 25–30, solve the given initial value problem.

25. $x^2y'' + 3xy' - 3y = 0, \quad y(1) = 1, \; y'(1) = -1$

26. $6x^2y'' + 7xy' - 2y = 0, \quad y(1) = 0, \; y'(1) = 1$

27. $x^2y'' - xy' + y = 0, \quad y(1) = 1, \; y'(1) = 1$

28. $x^2y'' + 7xy' + 9y = 0, \quad y(1) = 1, \; y'(1) = 0$

29. $x^2y'' - xy' + 2y = 0, \quad y(1) = -1, \; y'(1) = 1$

30. $x^2y'' + 3xy' + 5y = 0, \quad y(1) = 1, \; y'(1) = 0$

17.5 Power-Series Solutions

In this section we extend our study of second-order linear homogeneous equations with variable coefficients. With the Euler equations in Section 17.4, the power of the variable x in the nonconstant coefficient had to match the order of the derivative with which it was paired: x^2 with y'', x^1 with y', and $x^0\,(=1)$ with y. Here we drop that requirement so we can solve more general equations.

Method of Solution

The **power-series method** for solving a second-order homogeneous differential equation consists of finding the coefficients of a power series

$$y(x) = \sum_{n=0}^{\infty} c_n x^n = c_0 + c_1x + c_2x^2 + \cdots \tag{1}$$

which solves the equation. To apply the method we substitute the series and its derivatives into the differential equation to determine the coefficients $c_0, c_1, c_2, \ldots$. The technique for finding the coefficients is similar to that used in the method of undetermined coefficients presented in Section 17.2.

In our first example we demonstrate the method in the setting of a simple equation whose general solution we already know. This is to help you become more comfortable with solutions expressed in series form.

EXAMPLE 1 Solve the equation $y'' + y = 0$ by the power-series method.

SOLUTION We assume the series solution takes the form of

$$y = \sum_{n=0}^{\infty} c_n x^n$$

and calculate the derivatives

$$y' = \sum_{n=1}^{\infty} nc_n x^{n-1} \qquad \text{and} \qquad y'' = \sum_{n=2}^{\infty} n(n-1)c_n x^{n-2}.$$

Substitution of these forms into the second-order equation gives us

$$\sum_{n=2}^{\infty} n(n-1)c_n x^{n-2} + \sum_{n=0}^{\infty} c_n x^n = 0.$$

Next, we equate the coefficients of each power of x to zero as summarized in the following table.

Power of x	Coefficient Equation		
x^0	$2(1)c_2 + c_0 = 0$	or	$c_2 = -\frac{1}{2}c_0$
x^1	$3(2)c_3 + c_1 = 0$	or	$c_3 = -\frac{1}{3\cdot 2}c_1$
x^2	$4(3)c_4 + c_2 = 0$	or	$c_4 = -\frac{1}{4\cdot 3}c_2$
x^3	$5(4)c_5 + c_3 = 0$	or	$c_5 = -\frac{1}{5\cdot 4}c_3$
x^4	$6(5)c_6 + c_4 = 0$	or	$c_6 = -\frac{1}{6\cdot 5}c_4$
$\vdots$	$\vdots$		$\vdots$
x^{n-2}	$n(n-1)c_n + c_{n-2} = 0$	or	$c_n = -\frac{1}{n(n-1)}c_{n-2}$

From the table we notice that the coefficients with even indices ($n = 2k, k = 1, 2, 3, \ldots$) are related to each other and the coefficients with odd indices ($n = 2k + 1$) are also interrelated. We treat each group in turn.

Even indices: Here $n = 2k$, so the power is x^{2k-2}. From the last line of the table, we have

$$2k(2k-1)c_{2k} + c_{2k-2} = 0$$

or

$$c_{2k} = -\frac{1}{2k(2k-1)}c_{2k-2}.$$

From this recursive relation we find

$$\begin{aligned} c_{2k} &= \left[-\frac{1}{2k(2k-1)}\right]\left[-\frac{1}{(2k-2)(2k-3)}\right]\cdots\left[-\frac{1}{4(3)}\right]\left[-\frac{1}{2}\right]c_0 \\ &= \frac{(-1)^k}{(2k)!}c_0. \end{aligned}$$

Odd indices: Here $n = 2k + 1$, so the power is x^{2k-1}. Substituting this into the last line of the table yields

$$(2k+1)(2k)c_{2k+1} + c_{2k-1} = 0$$

or

$$c_{2k+1} = -\frac{1}{(2k+1)(2k)}c_{2k-1}.$$

Thus,

$$\begin{aligned} c_{2k+1} &= \left[-\frac{1}{(2k+1)(2k)}\right]\left[-\frac{1}{(2k-1)(2k-2)}\right]\cdots\left[-\frac{1}{5(4)}\right]\left[-\frac{1}{3(2)}\right]c_1 \\ &= \frac{(-1)^k}{(2k+1)!}c_1. \end{aligned}$$

Writing the power series by grouping its even and odd powers together and substituting for the coefficients yields

$$\begin{aligned} y &= \sum_{n=0}^{\infty} c_n x^n \\ &= \sum_{k=0}^{\infty} c_{2k} x^{2k} + \sum_{k=0}^{\infty} c_{2k+1} x^{2k+1} \\ &= c_0 \sum_{k=0}^{\infty} \frac{(-1)^k}{(2k)!} x^{2k} + c_1 \sum_{k=0}^{\infty} \frac{(-1)^k}{(2k+1)!} x^{2k+1}. \end{aligned}$$

From Table 9.1 in Section 9.10, we see that the first series on the right-hand side of the last equation represents the cosine function and the second series represents the sine. Thus, the general solution to $y'' + y = 0$ is

$$y = c_0 \cos x + c_1 \sin x.$$

EXAMPLE 2 Find the general solution to $y'' + xy' + y = 0$.

SOLUTION We assume the series solution form

$$y = \sum_{n=0}^{\infty} c_n x^n$$

and calculate the derivatives

$$y' = \sum_{n=1}^{\infty} n c_n x^{n-1} \quad \text{and} \quad y'' = \sum_{n=2}^{\infty} n(n-1) c_n x^{n-2}.$$

Substitution of these forms into the second-order equation yields

$$\sum_{n=2}^{\infty} n(n-1) c_n x^{n-2} + \sum_{n=1}^{\infty} n c_n x^n + \sum_{n=0}^{\infty} c_n x^n = 0.$$

We equate the coefficients of each power of x to zero as summarized in the following table.

Power of x	**Coefficient Equation**		
x^0	$2(1)c_2 + c_0 = 0$	or	$c_2 = -\frac{1}{2}c_0$
x^1	$3(2)c_3 + c_1 + c_1 = 0$	or	$c_3 = -\frac{1}{3}c_1$
x^2	$4(3)c_4 + 2c_2 + c_2 = 0$	or	$c_4 = -\frac{1}{4}c_2$
x^3	$5(4)c_5 + 3c_3 + c_3 = 0$	or	$c_5 = -\frac{1}{5}c_3$
x^4	$6(5)c_6 + 4c_4 + c_4 = 0$	or	$c_6 = -\frac{1}{6}c_4$
$\vdots$	$\vdots$		$\vdots$
x^n	$(n+2)(n+1)c_{n+2} + (n+1)c_n = 0$	or	$c_{n+2} = -\frac{1}{n+2}c_n$

From the table notice that the coefficients with even indices are interrelated and the coefficients with odd indices are also interrelated.

Even indices: Here $n = 2k - 2$, so the power is x^{2k-2}. From the last line in the table, we have

$$c_{2k} = -\frac{1}{2k} c_{2k-2}.$$

From this recurrence relation we obtain

$$c_{2k} = \left(-\frac{1}{2k}\right)\left(-\frac{1}{2k-2}\right)\cdots\left(-\frac{1}{6}\right)\left(-\frac{1}{4}\right)\left(-\frac{1}{2}\right)c_0$$

$$= \frac{(-1)^k}{(2)(4)(6)\cdots(2k)}c_0.$$

Odd indices: Here $n = 2k - 1$, so the power is x^{2k-1}. From the last line in the table, we have

$$c_{2k+1} = -\frac{1}{2k+1}c_{2k-1}.$$

From this recurrence relation we obtain

$$c_{2k+1} = \left(-\frac{1}{2k+1}\right)\left(-\frac{1}{2k-1}\right)\cdots\left(-\frac{1}{5}\right)\left(-\frac{1}{3}\right)c_1$$

$$= \frac{(-1)^k}{(3)(5)\cdots(2k+1)}c_1.$$

Writing the power series by grouping its even and odd powers and substituting for the coefficients yields

$$y = \sum_{k=0}^{\infty} c_{2k}x^{2k} + \sum_{k=0}^{\infty} c_{2k+1}x^{2k+1}$$

$$= c_0\sum_{k=0}^{\infty}\frac{(-1)^k}{(2)(4)\cdots(2k)}x^{2k} + c_1\sum_{k=0}^{\infty}\frac{(-1)^k}{(3)(5)\cdots(2k+1)}x^{2k+1}.$$

EXAMPLE 3 Find the general solution to

$$(1 - x^2)y'' - 6xy' - 4y = 0, \qquad |x| < 1.$$

SOLUTION Notice that the leading coefficient is zero when $x = \pm 1$. Thus, we assume the solution interval I: $-1 < x < 1$. Substitution of the series form

$$y = \sum_{n=0}^{\infty} c_n x^n$$

and its derivatives gives us

$$(1 - x^2)\sum_{n=2}^{\infty} n(n-1)c_n x^{n-2} - 6\sum_{n=1}^{\infty} nc_n x^n - 4\sum_{n=0}^{\infty} c_n x^n = 0,$$

$$\sum_{n=2}^{\infty} n(n-1)c_n x^{n-2} - \sum_{n=2}^{\infty} n(n-1)c_n x^n - 6\sum_{n=1}^{\infty} nc_n x^n - 4\sum_{n=0}^{\infty} c_n x^n = 0.$$

Next, we equate the coefficients of each power of x to zero as summarized in the following table.

Power of x	Coefficient Equation		
x^0	$2(1)c_2 - 4c_0 = 0$	or	$c_2 = \frac{4}{2}c_0$
x^1	$3(2)c_3 - 6(1)c_1 - 4c_1 = 0$	or	$c_3 = \frac{5}{3}c_1$
x^2	$4(3)c_4 - 2(1)c_2 - 6(2)c_2 - 4c_2 = 0$	or	$c_4 = \frac{6}{4}c_2$
x^3	$5(4)c_5 - 3(2)c_3 - 6(3)c_3 - 4c_3 = 0$	or	$c_5 = \frac{7}{5}c_3$
$\vdots$	$\vdots$		$\vdots$
x^n	$(n+2)(n+1)c_{n+2} - [n(n-1) + 6n + 4]c_n = 0$		
	$(n+2)(n+1)c_{n+2} - (n+4)(n+1)c_n = 0$	or	$c_{n+2} = \dfrac{n+4}{n+2}c_n$

Again we notice that the coefficients with even indices are interrelated and those with odd indices are interrelated.

Even indices: Here $n = 2k - 2$, so the power is x^{2k}. From the right-hand column and last line of the table, we get

$$\begin{aligned} c_{2k} &= \frac{2k+2}{2k}c_{2k-2} \\ &= \left(\frac{2k+2}{2k}\right)\left(\frac{2k}{2k-2}\right)\left(\frac{2k-2}{2k-4}\right)\cdots\frac{6}{4}\left(\frac{4}{2}\right)c_0 \\ &= (k+1)c_0. \end{aligned}$$

Odd indices: Here $n = 2k - 1$, so the power is x^{2k+1}. The right-hand column and last line of the table gives us

$$\begin{aligned} c_{2k+1} &= \frac{2k+3}{2k+1}c_{2k-1} \\ &= \left(\frac{2k+3}{2k+1}\right)\left(\frac{2k+1}{2k-1}\right)\left(\frac{2k-1}{2k-3}\right)\cdots\frac{7}{5}\left(\frac{5}{3}\right)c_1 \\ &= \frac{2k+3}{3}c_1. \end{aligned}$$

The general solution is

$$\begin{aligned} y &= \sum_{n=0}^{\infty} c_n x^n \\ &= \sum_{k=0}^{\infty} c_{2k}x^{2k} + \sum_{k=0}^{\infty} c_{2k+1}x^{2k+1} \\ &= c_0\sum_{k=0}^{\infty}(k+1)x^{2k} + c_1\sum_{k=0}^{\infty}\frac{2k+3}{3}x^{2k+1}. \end{aligned}$$

EXAMPLE 4 Find the general solution to $y'' - 2xy' + y = 0$.

SOLUTION Assuming that

$$y = \sum_{n=0}^{\infty} c_n x^n,$$

substitution into the differential equation gives us

$$\sum_{n=2}^{\infty} n(n-1)c_n x^{n-2} - 2\sum_{n=1}^{\infty} nc_n x^n + \sum_{n=0}^{\infty} c_n x^n = 0.$$

We next determine the coefficients, listing them in the following table.

Power of x	Coefficient Equation		
x^0	$2(1)c_2 \quad\quad + c_0 = 0$	or	$c_2 = -\frac{1}{2}c_0$
x^1	$3(2)c_3 - 2c_1 + c_1 = 0$	or	$c_3 = \frac{1}{3 \cdot 2}c_1$
x^2	$4(3)c_4 - 4c_2 + c_2 = 0$	or	$c_4 = \frac{3}{4 \cdot 3}c_2$
x^3	$5(4)c_5 - 6c_3 + c_3 = 0$	or	$c_5 = \frac{5}{5 \cdot 4}c_3$
x^4	$6(5)c_6 - 8c_4 + c_4 = 0$	or	$c_6 = \frac{7}{6 \cdot 5}c_4$
$\vdots$	$\vdots$		$\vdots$
x^n	$(n+2)(n+1)c_{n+2} - (2n-1)c_n = 0$	or	$c_{n+2} = \frac{2n-1}{(n+2)(n+1)}c_n$

From the recursive relation

$$c_{n+2} = \frac{2n-1}{(n+2)(n+1)}c_n,$$

we write out the first few terms of each series for the general solution:

$$y = c_0\left(1 - \frac{1}{2}x^2 - \frac{3}{4!}x^4 - \frac{21}{6!}x^6 - \cdots\right)$$

$$+ c_1\left(x + \frac{1}{3!}x^3 + \frac{5}{5!}x^5 + \frac{45}{7!}x^7 + \cdots\right).$$

SECTION 17.5 EXERCISES

In Exercises 1–18, use power series to find the general solution of the differential equation.

1. $y'' + 2y' = 0$
2. $y'' + 2y' + y = 0$
3. $y'' + 4y = 0$
4. $y'' - 3y' + 2y = 0$
5. $x^2y'' - 2xy' + 2y = 0$
6. $y'' - xy' + y = 0$
7. $(1 + x)y'' - y = 0$
8. $(1 - x^2)y'' - 4xy' + 6y = 0$
9. $(x^2 - 1)y'' + 2xy' - 2y = 0$
10. $y'' + y' - x^2y = 0$
11. $(x^2 - 1)y'' - 6y = 0$
12. $xy'' - (x + 2)y' + 2y = 0$
13. $(x^2 - 1)y'' + 4xy' + 2y = 0$
14. $y'' - 2xy' + 4y = 0$
15. $y'' - 2xy' + 3y = 0$
16. $(1 - x^2)y'' - xy' + 4y = 0$
17. $y'' - xy' + 3y = 0$
18. $x^2y'' - 4xy' + 6y = 0$

18 Infinite Sequences and Series

18.1 Fourier Series

HISTORICAL BIOGRAPHY

Jean-Baptiste Joseph Fourier (1768–1830)

We have seen how Taylor series can be used to approximate a function f by polynomials. The Taylor polynomials give a close fit to f near a particular point $x = a$, but the error in the approximation can be large at points that are far away. There is another method that often gives good approximations on wide intervals, and often works with discontinuous functions for which Taylor polynomials fail. Introduced by Joseph Fourier, this method approximates functions with sums of sine and cosine functions. It is well suited for analyzing periodic functions, such as radio signals and alternating currents, for solving heat transfer problems, and for many other problems in science and engineering.

Suppose we wish to approximate a function f on the interval $[0, 2\pi]$ by a sum of sine and cosine functions,

$$\begin{aligned} f_n(x) &= a_0 + (a_1 \cos x + b_1 \sin x) + (a_2 \cos 2x + b_2 \sin 2x) + \cdots \\ &\quad + (a_n \cos nx + b_n \sin nx) \end{aligned}$$

or, in sigma notation,

$$f_n(x) = a_0 + \sum_{k=1}^{n} (a_k \cos kx + b_k \sin kx). \tag{1}$$

We would like to choose values for the constants $a_0, a_1, a_2, \ldots a_n$ and $b_1, b_2, \ldots, b_n$ that make $f_n(x)$ a "best possible" approximation to $f(x)$. The notion of "best possible" is defined as follows:

1. $f_n(x)$ and $f(x)$ give the same value when integrated from 0 to 2π.
2. $f_n(x) \cos kx$ and $f(x) \cos kx$ give the same value when integrated from 0 to 2π $(k = 1, \ldots, n)$.
3. $f_n(x) \sin kx$ and $f(x) \sin kx$ give the same value when integrated from 0 to 2π $(k = 1, \ldots, n)$.

Altogether we impose $2n + 1$ conditions on f_n:

$$\int_0^{2\pi} f_n(x)\, dx = \int_0^{2\pi} f(x)\, dx,$$

$$\int_0^{2\pi} f_n(x) \cos kx\, dx = \int_0^{2\pi} f(x) \cos kx\, dx, \qquad k = 1, \ldots, n,$$

$$\int_0^{2\pi} f_n(x) \sin kx\, dx = \int_0^{2\pi} f(x) \sin kx\, dx, \qquad k = 1, \ldots, n.$$

It is possible to choose $a_0, a_1, a_2, \ldots a_n$ and $b_1, b_2, \ldots, b_n$ so that all these conditions are satisfied, by proceeding as follows. Integrating both sides of Equation (1) from 0 to 2π gives

$$\int_0^{2\pi} f_n(x)\,dx = 2\pi a_0$$

since the integral over $[0, 2\pi]$ of $\cos kx$ equals zero when $k \geq 1$, as does the integral of $\sin kx$. Only the constant term a_0 contributes to the integral of f_n over $[0, 2\pi]$. A similar calculation applies with each of the other terms. If we multiply both sides of Equation (1) by $\cos x$ and integrate from 0 to 2π then we obtain

$$\int_0^{2\pi} f_n(x)\cos x\,dx = \pi a_1.$$

This follows from the fact that

$$\int_0^{2\pi} \cos px \cos px\,dx = \pi$$

and

$$\int_0^{2\pi} \cos px \cos qx\,dx = \int_0^{2\pi} \cos px \sin mx\,dx = \int_0^{2\pi} \sin px \sin qx\,dx = 0$$

whenever p, q and m are integers and p is not equal to q (Exercises 9–13). If we multiply Equation (1) by $\sin x$ and integrate from 0 to 2π we obtain

$$\int_0^{2\pi} f_n(x)\sin x\,dx = \pi b_1.$$

Proceeding in a similar fashion with

$$\cos 2x, \sin 2x, \ldots, \cos nx, \sin nx$$

we obtain only one nonzero term each time, the term with a sine-squared or cosine-squared term. To summarize,

$$\int_0^{2\pi} f_n(x)\,dx = 2\pi a_0$$

$$\int_0^{2\pi} f_n(x)\cos kx\,dx = \pi a_k, \qquad k = 1, \ldots, n$$

$$\int_0^{2\pi} f_n(x)\sin kx\,dx = \pi b_k, \qquad k = 1, \ldots, n$$

We chose f_n so that the integrals on the left remain the same when f_n is replaced by f, so we can use these equations to find $a_0, a_1, a_2, \ldots a_n$ and $b_1, b_2, \ldots, b_n$ from f:

$$a_0 = \frac{1}{2\pi}\int_0^{2\pi} f(x)\,dx \tag{2}$$

$$a_k = \frac{1}{\pi}\int_0^{2\pi} f(x)\cos kx\,dx, \qquad k = 1, \ldots, n \tag{3}$$

$$b_k = \frac{1}{\pi}\int_0^{2\pi} f(x)\sin kx\,dx, \qquad k = 1, \ldots, n \tag{4}$$

The only condition needed to find these coefficients is that the integrals above must exist. If we let $n \to \infty$ and use these rules to get the coefficients of an infinite series, then the resulting sum is called the **Fourier series for $f(x)$**,

$$a_0 + \sum_{k=1}^{\infty}(a_k \cos kx + b_k \sin kx). \tag{5}$$

EXAMPLE 1 Finding a Fourier Series Expansion

Fourier series can be used to represent some functions that cannot be represented by Taylor series; for example, the step function f shown in Figure 18.1a.

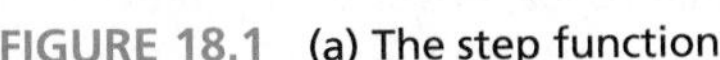

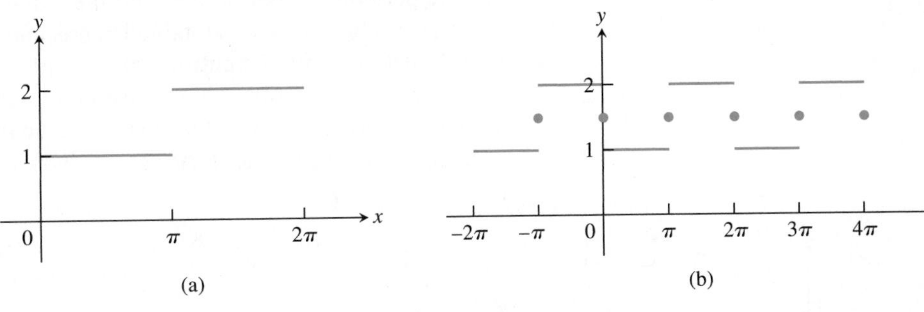

FIGURE 18.1 (a) The step function

$$f(x) = \begin{cases} 1, & 0 \le x \le \pi \\ 2, & \pi < x \le 2\pi \end{cases}$$

(b) The graph of the Fourier series for f is periodic and has the value $3/2$ at each point of discontinuity (Example 1).

The coefficients of the Fourier series of f are computed using Equations (2), (3), and (4).

$$\begin{aligned} a_0 &= \frac{1}{2\pi}\int_0^{2\pi} f(x)\,dx \\ &= \frac{1}{2\pi}\left(\int_0^{\pi} 1\,dx + \int_{\pi}^{2\pi} 2\,dx\right) = \frac{3}{2} \end{aligned}$$

$$\begin{aligned} a_k &= \frac{1}{\pi}\int_0^{2\pi} f(x)\cos kx\,dx \\ &= \frac{1}{\pi}\left(\int_0^{\pi} \cos kx\,dx + \int_{\pi}^{2\pi} 2\cos kx\,dx\right) \\ &= \frac{1}{\pi}\left(\left[\frac{\sin kx}{k}\right]_0^{\pi} + \left[\frac{2\sin kx}{k}\right]_{\pi}^{2\pi}\right) = 0, \qquad k \ge 1 \end{aligned}$$

$$\begin{aligned} b_k &= \frac{1}{\pi}\int_0^{2\pi} f(x)\sin kx\,dx \\ &= \frac{1}{\pi}\left(\int_0^{\pi} \sin kx\,dx + \int_{\pi}^{2\pi} 2\sin kx\,dx\right) \\ &= \frac{1}{\pi}\left(\left[-\frac{\cos kx}{k}\right]_0^{\pi} + \left[-\frac{2\cos kx}{k}\right]_{\pi}^{2\pi}\right) \\ &= \frac{\cos k\pi - 1}{k\pi} = \frac{(-1)^k - 1}{k\pi}. \end{aligned}$$

So

$$a_0 = \frac{3}{2}, \quad a_1 = a_2 = \cdots = 0,$$

and

$$b_1 = -\frac{2}{\pi}, \quad b_2 = 0, \quad b_3 = -\frac{2}{3\pi}, \quad b_4 = 0, \quad b_5 = -\frac{2}{5\pi}, \quad b_6 = 0, \ldots$$

The Fourier series is

$$\frac{3}{2} - \frac{2}{\pi}\left(\sin x + \frac{\sin 3x}{3} + \frac{\sin 5x}{5} + \cdots\right).$$

Notice that at $x = \pi$, where the function $f(x)$ jumps from 1 to 2, all the sine terms vanish, leaving $3/2$ as the value of the series. This is not the value of f at π, since $f(\pi) = 1$. The Fourier series also sums to $3/2$ at $x = 0$ and $x = 2\pi$. In fact, all terms in the Fourier series are periodic, of period 2π, and the value of the series at $x + 2\pi$ is the same as its value at x. The series we obtained represents the periodic function graphed in Figure 11.16b, with domain the entire real line and a pattern that repeats over every interval of width 2π. The function jumps discontinuously at $x = n\pi, n = 0, \pm 1, \pm 2, \ldots$ and at these points has value $3/2$, the average value of the one-sided limits from each side. The convergence of the Fourier series of f is indicated in Figure 18.2.

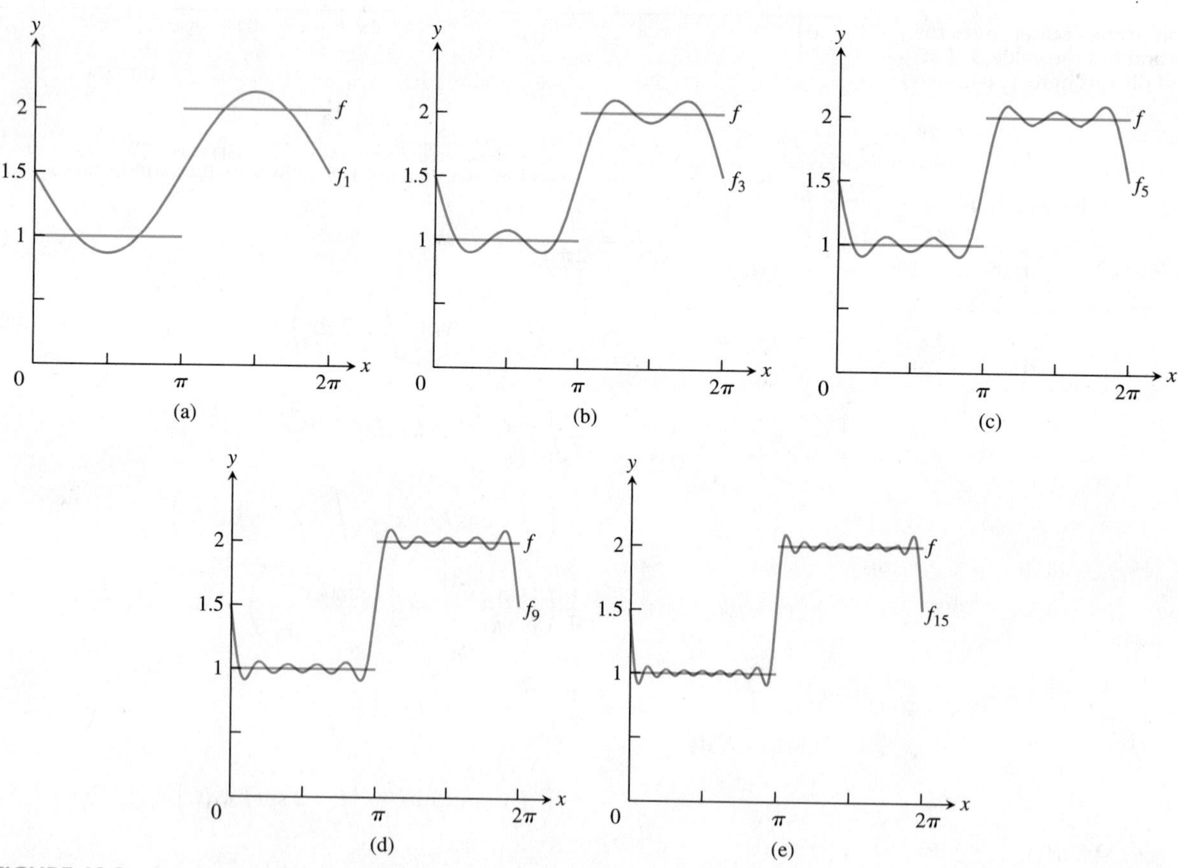

FIGURE 18.2 The Fourier approximation functions f_1, f_3, f_5, f_9, and f_{15} of the function $f(x) = \begin{cases} 1, & 0 \le x \le \pi \\ 2, & \pi < x \le 2\pi \end{cases}$ in Example 1

Convergence of Fourier Series

Taylor series are computed from the value of a function and its derivatives at a single point $x = a$, and cannot reflect the behavior of a discontinuous function such as f in Example 1 past a discontinuity. The reason that a Fourier series can be used to represent such functions is that the Fourier series of a function depends on the existence of certain *integrals*, whereas the Taylor series depends on derivatives of a function near a single point. A function can be fairly "rough," even discontinuous, and still be integrable.

The coefficients used to construct Fourier series are precisely those one should choose to minimize the integral of the square of the error in approximating f by f_n. That is,

$$\int_0^{2\pi} [f(x) - f_n(x)]^2\, dx$$

is minimized by choosing $a_0, a_1, a_2, \ldots a_n$ and $b_1, b_2, \ldots, b_n$ as we did. While Taylor series are useful to approximate a function and its derivatives near a point, Fourier series minimize an error which is distributed over an interval.

We state without proof a result concerning the convergence of Fourier series. A function is **piecewise continuous** over an interval I if it has finitely many discontinuities on the interval, and at these discontinuities one-sided limits exist from each side.

THEOREM 24 Let $f(x)$ be a function such that f and f' are piecewise continuous on the interval $[0, 2\pi]$. Then f is equal to its Fourier series at all points where f is continuous. At a point c where f has a discontinuity, the Fourier series converges to

$$\frac{f(c^+) + f(c^-)}{2}$$

where $f(c^+)$ and $f(c^-)$ are the right- and left-hand limits of f at c.

SECTION 18.1 EXERCISES

Finding Fourier Series

In Exercises 1–8, find the Fourier series associated with the given functions. Sketch each function.

1. $f(x) = 1 \quad 0 \le x \le 2\pi$.

2. $f(x) = \begin{cases} 1, & 0 \le x \le \pi \\ -1, & \pi < x \le 2\pi \end{cases}$

3. $f(x) = \begin{cases} x, & 0 \le x \le \pi \\ x - 2\pi, & \pi < x \le 2\pi \end{cases}$

4. $f(x) = \begin{cases} x^2, & 0 \le x \le \pi \\ 0, & \pi < x \le 2\pi \end{cases}$

5. $f(x) = e^x \quad 0 \le x \le 2\pi$.

6. $f(x) = \begin{cases} e^x, & 0 \le x \le \pi \\ 0, & \pi < x \le 2\pi \end{cases}$

7. $f(x) = \begin{cases} \cos x, & 0 \le x \le \pi \\ 0, & \pi < x \le 2\pi \end{cases}$

8. $f(x) = \begin{cases} 2, & 0 \le x \le \pi \\ -x, & \pi < x \le 2\pi \end{cases}$

Theory and Examples

Establish the results in Exercises 9–13, where p and q are positive integers.

9. $\displaystyle\int_0^{2\pi} \cos px\, dx = 0$ for all p.

10. $\displaystyle\int_0^{2\pi} \sin px\, dx = 0$ for all p.

11. $\displaystyle\int_0^{2\pi} \cos px \cos qx\, dx = \begin{cases} 0, & \text{if } p \ne q \\ \pi, & \text{if } p = q \end{cases}.$

(*Hint:* $\cos A \cos B = (1/2)[\cos(A + B) + \cos(A - B)]$.)

12. $\displaystyle\int_0^{2\pi} \sin px \sin qx\, dx = \begin{cases} 0, & \text{if } p \ne q \\ \pi, & \text{if } p = q \end{cases}.$

(*Hint:* $\sin A \sin B = (1/2)[\cos(A - B) - \cos(A + B)]$.)

13. $\displaystyle\int_0^{2\pi} \sin px \cos qx\, dx = 0$ for all p and q.

(*Hint*: $\sin A \cos B = (1/2)[\sin(A + B) + \sin(A - B)]$.)

14. **Fourier series of sums of functions** If f and g both satisfy the conditions of Theorem 24, is the Fourier series of $f + g$ on $[0, 2\pi]$ the sum of the Fourier series of f and the Fourier series of g? Give reasons for your answer.

15. **Term-by-term differentiation**
   a. Use Theorem 24 to verify that the Fourier series for $f(x)$ in Exercise 3 converges to $f(x)$ for $0 < x < 2\pi$.
   b. Although $f'(x) = 1$, show that the series obtained by term-by-term differentiation of the Fourier series in part (a) diverges.

16. Use Theorem 24 to find the Value of the Fourier series determined in Exercise 4 and show that $\dfrac{\pi^2}{6} = \displaystyle\sum_{n=1}^{\infty} \frac{1}{n^2}$.

19 Applications of Integration

INTRODUCTION

Kurt's basement was flooded with 3.5 ft of water after a heavy rainfall. The amount of *work* required to pump the water out of the basement can be calculated using integrals. In this chapter we study some of the technical applications of integrals.

Objectives

- Find an area bounded by two or more curves.
- Find a volume of revolution.
- Find the center of mass of a linear system.
- Find the centroid of a region bounded by given curves.
- Find moments of inertia.
- Use integration to solve work, fluid pressure, and average value problems.

19.1 AREA BETWEEN CURVES

In Chapter 5 we studied the process of computing the area between a given curve and the x-axis. Now consider the problem of finding the area *between* two given curves. First, observe that the area between one given curve $y = f(x)$ and the x-axis between $x = a$ and $x = b$ is a definite integral:

$$A = \int_a^b f(x)\,dx = F(b) - F(a)$$

where $F'(x) = f(x)$.

Further recall that definite integration as applied to area is a summation process. That is, the definite integral is the limit of sums of approximating rectangles where the area of a typical rectangle is $f(t)\,\Delta x$ as shown in Fig. 19.1. The typical rectangle, which is shaded, is called an *element* of the area. Note the correspondence between the form of the expression for the area of the element, $f(t)\,\Delta x$, and that for the differential, $f(x)\,dx$, which is to be integrated:

$$f(t)\,\Delta x \leftrightarrow f(x)\,dx$$

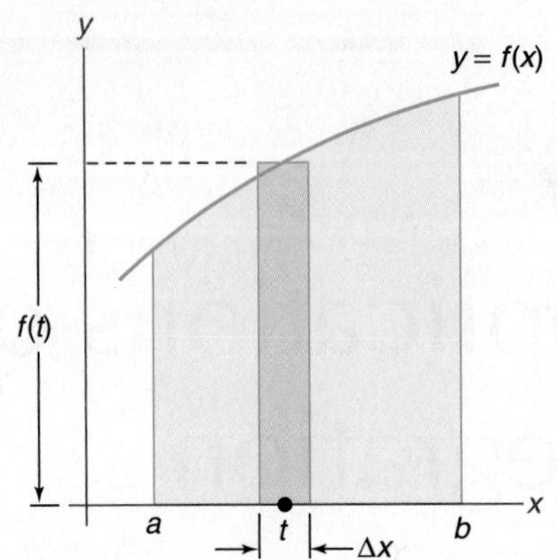

Figure 19.1 Area under the curve $y = f(x)$.

Noting this correspondence will be a visual aid in setting up the appropriate integrals for computing areas between curves. The correct form for $f(x)\,dx$ can be found by finding the appropriate expression $f(t)\,\Delta x$ from viewing a sketch of the area.

Now let's determine the area bounded by the curves $y = f(x)$, $y = g(x)$, $x = a$, and $x = b$ as shown in Fig. 19.2.

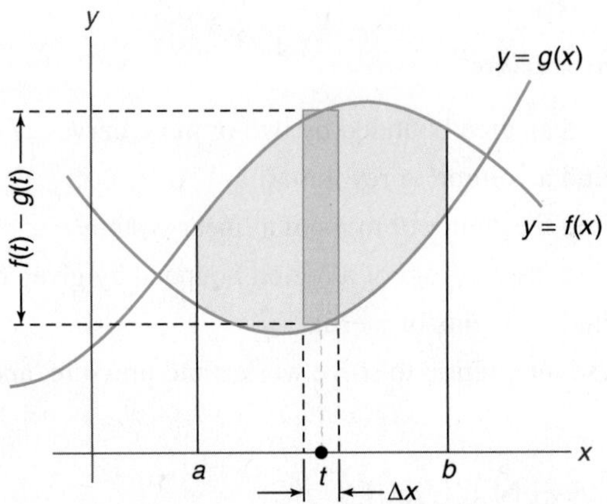

Figure 19.2 Area between two curves.

Between a and b, $g(x) \le f(x)$, that is, the curve $y = g(x)$ lies below the curve $y = f(x)$. The area of the element shown, used in approximating the area between the two curves, is

$$[f(t) - g(t)]\,\Delta x$$

This corresponds to the differential

$$[f(x) - g(x)]\,dx$$

We therefore use the definite integral

$$\int_a^b [f(x) - g(x)]\,dx$$

to find the desired area.

EXAMPLE 1

Find the area between the curves $y = 8 - x^2$ and $y = x + 2$.

The area is bounded by a parabola and a straight line. First, find the points where the two curves intersect by solving the two equations simultaneously.

$$\begin{aligned} 8 - x^2 &= x + 2 \\ 0 &= x^2 + x - 6 \\ 0 &= (x - 2)(x + 3) \\ x = 2 \quad &\text{or} \quad x = -3 \end{aligned}$$

The curves intersect at the points $(-3, -1)$ and $(2, 4)$. Note that between $x = -3$ and $x = 2$, the line $y = x + 2$ is below the parabola $y = 8 - x^2$. The length of the element shown in Fig. 19.3 is the difference between the upper curve $y = 8 - x^2$ and the lower curve $y = x + 2$ at a given value of x.

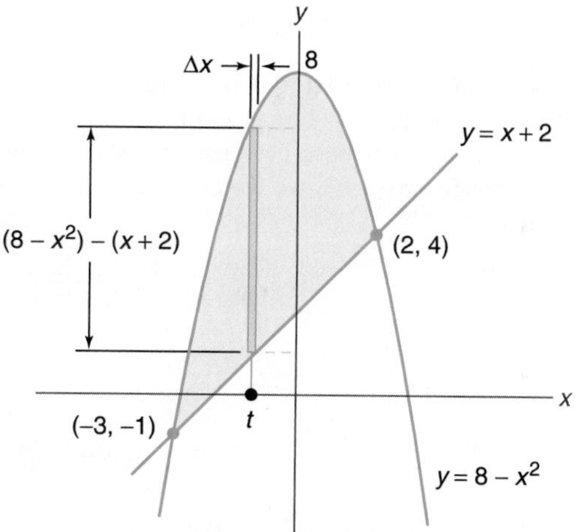

Figure 19.3

The area A between the curves is the value of the definite integral.

$$\begin{aligned} A &= \int_{-3}^{2} [(8 - x^2) - (x + 2)]\, dx \\ &= \int_{-3}^{2} (6 - x - x^2)\, dx \\ &= \left(6x - \frac{x^2}{2} - \frac{x^3}{3}\right)\Bigg|_{-3}^{2} \\ &= \left(12 - 2 - \frac{8}{3}\right) - \left(-18 - \frac{9}{2} + 9\right) = 20\frac{5}{6} \end{aligned}$$

The limits of integration are determined by the points where the curves intersect. The lower limit is the smallest value of x where the curves intersect, and the upper limit is the largest value of x where the curves intersect.

EXAMPLE 2

Find the area between the line $y = -x + 2$ and the parabola $x = 4 - y^2$.

The points of intersection of these two curves are $(0, 2)$ and $(3, -1)$. In this example, we run into a problem. If we use vertical elements to approximate the area as in Fig. 19.4, then

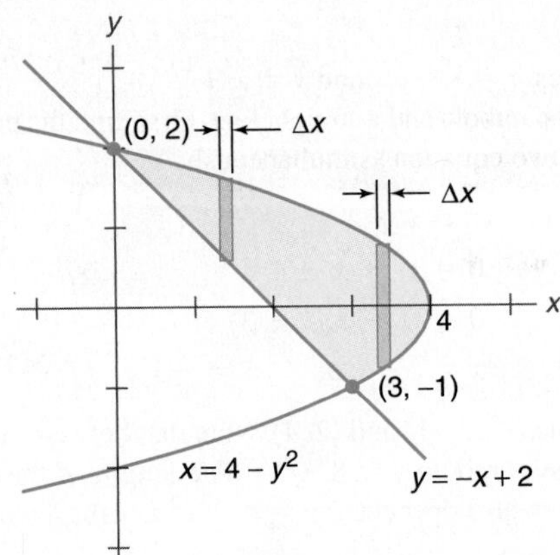

Figure 19.4

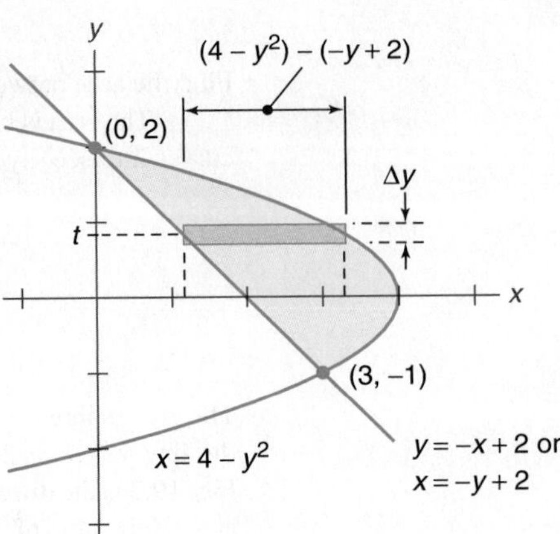

Figure 19.5

between $x = 0$ and $x = 3$ the height of the element is the difference between the curves $x = 4 - y^2$ $(y = \sqrt{4 - x})$ and $y = -x + 2$; between $x = 3$ and $x = 4$ the height of the element is the difference between $y = \sqrt{4 - x}$ and $y = -\sqrt{4 - x}$. Because of the change in boundaries at $x = 3$, we would have to find the desired area A by separately computing the areas

$$A_1 = \int_0^3 [(\sqrt{4 - x}) - (-x + 2)]\, dx$$

and

$$A_2 = \int_3^4 [(\sqrt{4 - x}) - (-\sqrt{4 - x})]\, dx$$

Then $A = A_1 + A_2$. By integrating, we find $A_1 = \frac{19}{6}$ and $A_2 = \frac{4}{3}$. So

$$A = \frac{19}{6} + \frac{4}{3} = \frac{9}{2}$$

Sometimes, as in this example, it is easier to set up the problem using horizontal elements as in Fig. 19.5. Then express the given curves as functions of y instead of x: $x = 4 - y^2$ and $x = -y + 2$; and integrate with respect to the y variable and use limits of integration based on the y-coordinates of the points of intersection: $y = -1$ and $y = 2$. With respect to *the y-axis*, the curve $x = 4 - y^2$ lies above $x = -y + 2$ from $y = -1$ to $y = 2$. The length of a typical horizontal element is then $(4 - y^2) - (-y + 2)$.

$$\begin{aligned}
A &= \int_{-1}^{2} [(4 - y^2) - (-y + 2)]\, dy \\
&= \int_{-1}^{2} (2 + y - y^2)\, dy \\
&= \left(2y + \frac{y^2}{2} - \frac{y^3}{3}\right)\Big|_{-1}^{2} \\
&= \left(4 + 2 - \frac{8}{3}\right) - \left(-2 + \frac{1}{2} + \frac{1}{3}\right) = \frac{9}{2}
\end{aligned}$$

Note: Using horizontal elements and working in terms of dy is usually simpler than using vertical elements and working in terms of dx when one of the curves does not represent a function (contains a y^2-term, for instance).

In summary, to find the area between two given curves between $x = a$ and $x = b$:

1. Find the points of intersection of the two curves, if necessary.
2. Sketch the two curves:
   (a) Determine whether to use vertical elements with the curves expressed as functions of x or horizontal elements with curves expressed as functions of y.
   (b) Determine which curve lies above the other.
3. Find the height of a typical element based on Step 2(b).
4. Write the definite integral:

$$\int_a^b [f(x) - g(x)]\, dx$$

where $f(x) - g(x)$ is the length of vertical elements between $x = a$ and $x = b$ with $a < b$, or

$$\int_c^d [f(y) - g(y)]\, dy$$

where $f(y) - g(y)$ is the length of horizontal elements between $y = c$ and $y = d$ with $c < d$.

Note that the choice of using vertical or horizontal elements depends on the difficulty of the resulting definite integral. Also, the curves do not need to lie above the x- or y-axis in order to find the area between them.

EXAMPLE 3

Find the area between the curves $x = y^3$ and $x = -y^2$.

The points of intersection are $(0, 0)$ and $(-1, -1)$. We could use either vertical or horizontal elements. We will use horizontal elements as in Fig. 19.6. Since the curve $x = y^3$ lies *above* $x = -y^2$ (*in the positive direction along the x-axis*) from $y = -1$ to $y = 0$, we have

$$\begin{aligned} A &= \int_{-1}^{0} [y^3 - (-y^2)]\, dy \\ &= \left(\frac{y^4}{4} + \frac{y^3}{3}\right)\Bigg|_{-1}^{0} \\ &= 0 - \left(\frac{1}{4} - \frac{1}{3}\right) = \frac{1}{12} \end{aligned}$$

Using a calculator, we have

2nd 7 y^3-(-y^2),y,-1,0) **ENTER**

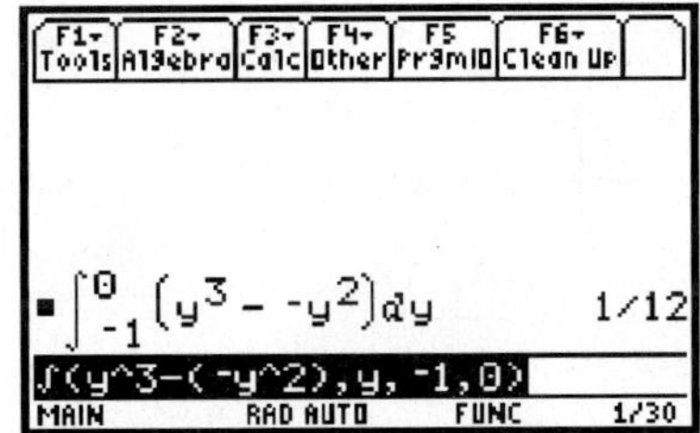

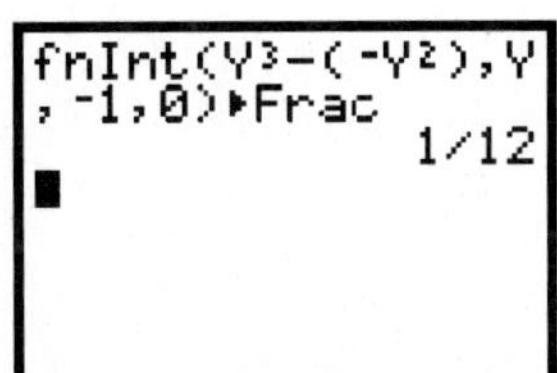

MATH 9 ALPHA Y MATH 3 -(-**ALPHA Y** $\mathbf{x^2}$), **ALPHA Y** ,-1,0) **MATH 1 ENTER**

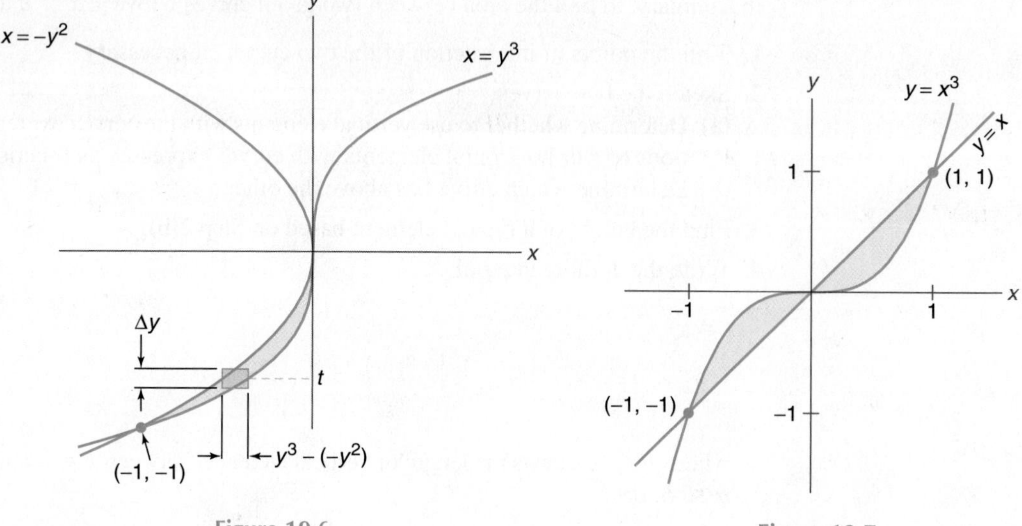

Figure 19.6

Figure 19.7

EXAMPLE 4

Find the area between the curves $y = x$ and $y = x^3$.

There are three points of intersection: $(-1, -1)$, $(0, 0)$, and $(1, 1)$. Between $x = -1$ and $x = 0$, $y = x^3$ lies above $y = x$. Between $x = 0$ and $x = 1$, $y = x$ lies above $y = x^3$. We need to compute the two areas as in Fig. 19.7.

$$A_1 = \int_{-1}^{0} (x^3 - x)\,dx \qquad \text{and} \quad A_2 = \int_{0}^{1} (x - x^3)\,dx$$

$$A_1 = \left(\frac{x^4}{4} - \frac{x^2}{2}\right)\Big|_{-1}^{0} = \frac{1}{4} \quad \text{and} \quad A_2 = \left(\frac{x^2}{2} - \frac{x^4}{4}\right)\Big|_{0}^{1} = \frac{1}{4}$$

The desired area $A = A_1 + A_2 = \frac{1}{4} + \frac{1}{4} = \frac{1}{2}$.

Using the symmetry of the two areas, note that $A_1 = A_2$. We could also compute

$$A = 2\int_{0}^{1} (x - x^3)\,dx$$

EXAMPLE 5

Find the area between the x-axis and $y = x^2 - 4$.

The desired region lies between $x = -2$ and $x = 2$. Note that in this region the curve $y = x^2 - 4$ lies below the x-axis in Fig. 19.8. Since the x-axis is the curve $y = 0$, we have

$$\begin{aligned} A &= \int_{-2}^{2} [0 - (x^2 - 4)]\,dx \\ &= \int_{-2}^{2} (4 - x^2)\,dx \\ &= \left(4x - \frac{x^3}{3}\right)\Big|_{-2}^{2} \\ &= \left(8 - \frac{8}{3}\right) - \left(-8 + \frac{8}{3}\right) = \frac{32}{3} \end{aligned}$$

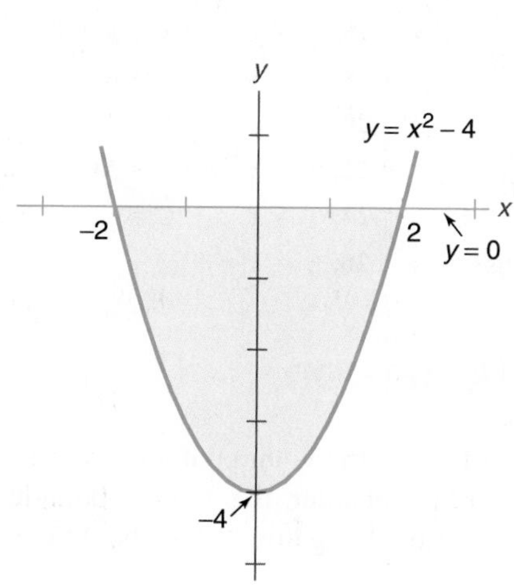

Figure 19.8

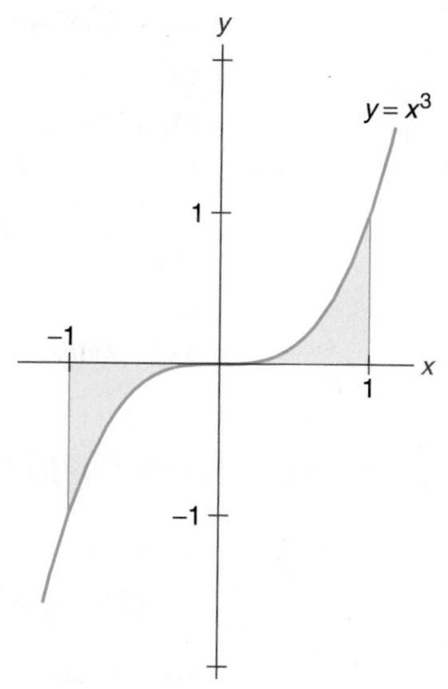

Figure 19.9

EXAMPLE 6

Find the area between the x-axis and $y = x^3$ from $x = -1$ to $x = 1$.

You may be tempted to simply form the integral $\int_{-1}^{1} x^3\,dx$. But

$$\int_{-1}^{1} x^3\,dx = \left.\frac{x^4}{4}\right|_{-1}^{1} = \frac{1}{4} - \frac{1}{4} = 0$$

We have incorrectly obtained the value zero since we failed to observe that at $x = 0$ the curve $y = x^3$ crosses the x-axis as in Fig. 19.9. To the left of $x = 0$ the curve is below the x-axis, but to the right of $x = 0$ the curve is above the x-axis. We must therefore separate the computation into two integrals as in Example 4:

$$\begin{aligned} A &= \int_{-1}^{0} [0 - (x^3)]\,dx + \int_{0}^{1} [(x^3) - 0]\,dx \\ &= -\int_{-1}^{0} x^3\,dx + \int_{0}^{1} x^3\,dx \\ &= -\left(\frac{x^4}{4}\right)\Bigg|_{-1}^{0} + \left.\frac{x^4}{4}\right|_{0}^{1} \\ &= -\left(-\frac{1}{4}\right) + \frac{1}{4} = \frac{1}{2} \end{aligned}$$

Exercises 19.1

Find each area bounded by the curves.

1. $y = x^2$, $y = 0$, and $x = 1$
2. $y = x^2$, $y = 0$, $x = 1$, and $x = 2$
3. $y = 1 - x$, $x = 0$, and $y = 0$
4. $y = 2x$, $y = 0$, $x = 1$, and $x = 2$
5. $y = 2 - x^2$ and $y + x = 0$
6. $y = x^2 - 2x$ and $y = 3$
7. $y^2 = x$ and $x = 4$
8. $y^2 = 4x$, $x = 0$, $y = -1$, and $y = 4$
9. $y = x^2$ and $y = x$
10. $y = 2x^2$ and $y^2 = 4x$

11. $x = y^2 - 2y$ and $y = x$
12. $y = x^3, y = 2 - x^2, x = 0$, and $x = 1$
13. $y = x^3 - x, y = 0, x = -1$, and $x = 1$
14. $y^3 = x, y = 1$, and $x = -1$
15. $x = y + 1$ and $x = 3 - y^2$
16. $x = y^2$ and $x = y + 2$
17. $y = 4 - 4x^2$ and $y = 1 - x^2$
18. $y = x^2$ and $y = 8 - x^2$
19. $x = y^4$ and $x = 2 - y^2$
20. $x = y^2$ and $x = 4 + 2y - y^2$
21. $y = x^2 - 3x - 4$ and $y = 6$
22. $y = x^2$ and $y = \sqrt{x}$
23. $x^2y = 8, y = x, x = 5$, and $y = 0$
24. $y = x, x + y = 6$, and $2y = x$
25. $y = x(x - 1)(x - 3)$ and the x-axis
26. $y = x(x + 3)(x - 2)$ and the x-axis

19.2 VOLUMES OF REVOLUTION: DISK METHOD

Another application of integration is finding the volume of a solid resulting from rotating an area about an axis. For example, consider the region bounded by the curves $y = f(x), x = a, x = b$, and the x-axis. Revolving this region about the x-axis determines a solid figure as in Fig. 19.10(a).

The area ΔA of a typical rectangle used in Chapter 5 to approximate the area under the curve $y = f(x)$ is $\Delta A = f(t)\,\Delta x$, where t is a point at the base of the rectangle, Δx is the width, and $f(t)$ is the height. If we now rotate this area about the x-axis as in Fig. 19.10(b), we obtain a cylindrical disk with volume

$$\Delta V = \pi r^2 h$$

where the radius r is $f(t)$ and the thickness h is the width Δx. So

$$\Delta V = \pi[f(t)]^2\,\Delta x$$

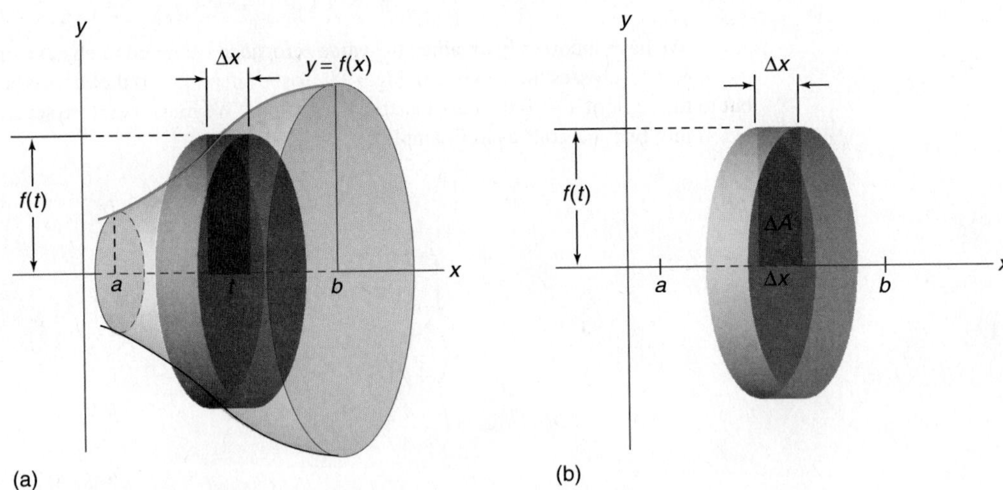

Figure 19.10 Disk of a solid of revolution about the x-axis.

By a method similar to approximating the area under a curve by rectangles, we approximate the volume of revolution by using the sum of the volumes of differential disks (see Fig. 19.11).

For areas, the integral

$$A = \int_a^b f(x)\,dx$$

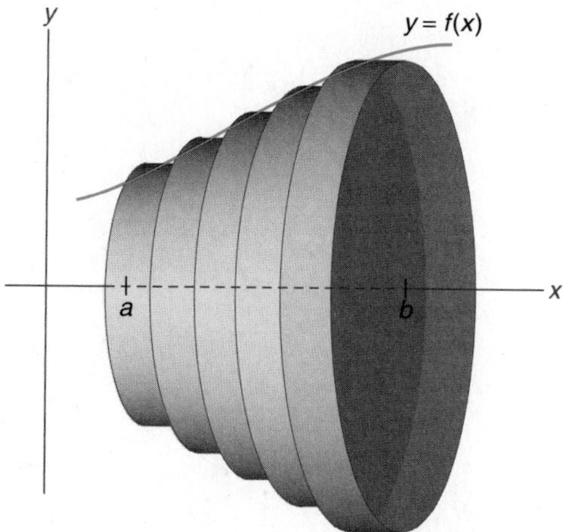

Figure 19.11 Approximating the volume of revolution about the x-axis by using the sum of the volumes of differential disks.

gives the exact area for a region that is approximated by summing the areas of rectangles:

$$\Delta A = f(t)\,\Delta x$$

In a similar manner, the integral

$$V = \pi \int_a^b [f(x)]^2\,dx = \pi \int_a^b y^2\,dx$$

gives the exact volume for the solid of revolution about the x-axis which is approximated by summing the volumes of disks: $\Delta V = \pi[f(t)]^2\,\Delta x$. This method of computing the volume of a solid is called the *disk method*.

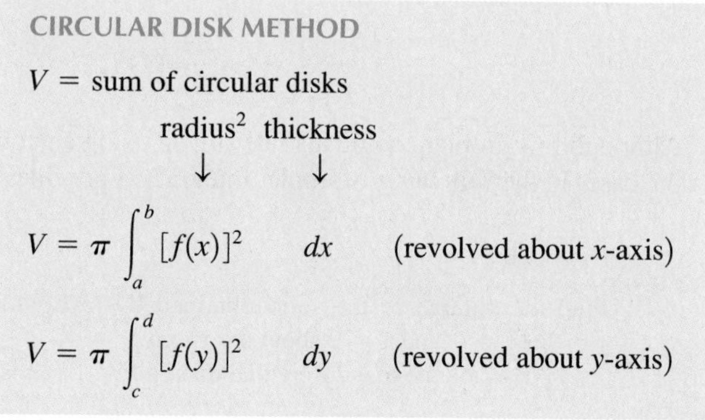

CIRCULAR DISK METHOD

$V =$ sum of circular disks

radius^2 thickness

↓ ↓

$$V = \pi \int_a^b [f(x)]^2 \quad dx \qquad \text{(revolved about } x\text{-axis)}$$

$$V = \pi \int_c^d [f(y)]^2 \quad dy \qquad \text{(revolved about } y\text{-axis)}$$

EXAMPLE 1

Find the volume of the solid formed by revolving the curve $y = x$ from $x = 0$ to $x = 2$ about the x-axis.

The area rotated about the x-axis is a triangle as in Fig. 19.12(a). The resulting solid is a cone. The volume of a typical differential disk in Fig. 19.12(b) is

$$\Delta V = \pi[f(t)]^2\,\Delta x = \pi(t)^2\,\Delta x$$

So, the integral giving the exact volume is

$$V = \pi \int_a^b [f(x)]^2\,dx$$

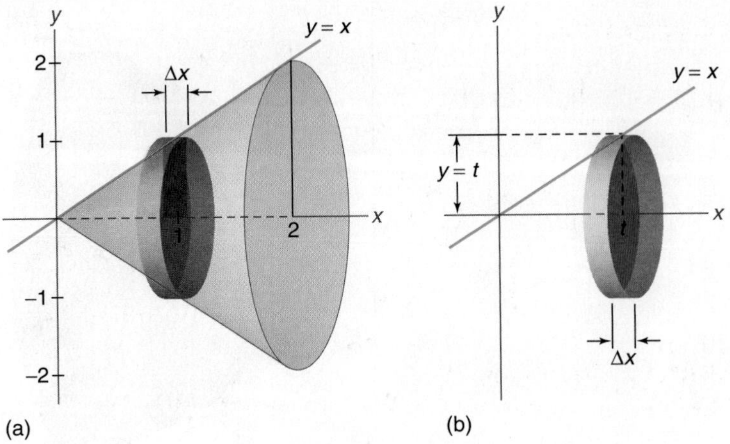

Figure 19.12

$$= \pi \int_0^2 x^2\, dx \qquad (y = x)$$

$$= \pi \frac{x^3}{3}\Big|_0^2$$

$$= \pi\left[\frac{8}{3} - \frac{0}{3}\right]$$

$$= \frac{8\pi}{3}$$

This same volume could also be found using the formula for the volume of a cone from geometry, $V = \frac{1}{3}\pi r^2 h$. In this example, $r = 2$ (radius of the base of the cone) and $h = 2$ (the altitude). So,

$$V = \frac{1}{3}\pi(2)^2(2) = \frac{8\pi}{3}$$

Although this problem could also be solved using a geometrical formula, this is not always the case. In the following example, integration provides the only solution.

EXAMPLE 2

Find the volume of the solid obtained by revolving the region bounded by the curves $y = x^2$, $y = 0$, and $x = 2$ about the x-axis.

The volume of a differential disk in Fig. 19.13 is

$$\Delta V = \pi[f(t)]^2\, \Delta x = \pi[t^2]^2\, \Delta x$$

The exact volume is then

$$V = \pi \int_a^b [f(x)]^2\, dx = \pi \int_0^2 (x^2)^2\, dx \qquad (y = x^2)$$

$$= \pi \int_0^2 x^4\, dx$$

$$= \pi \frac{x^5}{5}\Big|_0^2$$

$$= \frac{32\pi}{5}$$

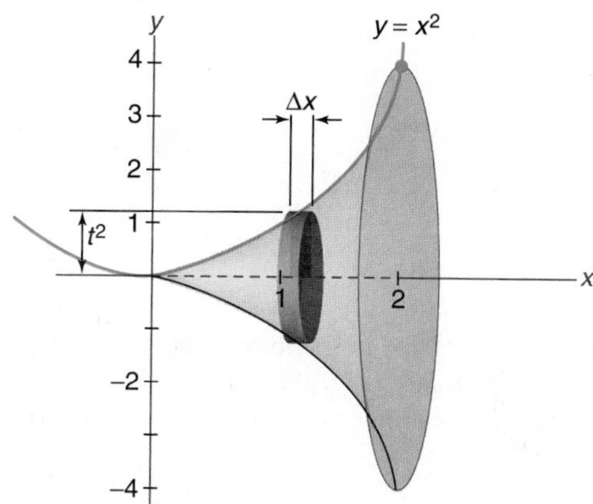

Figure 19.13

When a solid is formed by revolving an area about the y-axis, the integral giving the volume is

$$V = \pi \int_c^d [f(y)]^2\,dy = \pi \int_c^d x^2\,dy$$

Here, express the radius of a differential disk as a distance x from the y-axis and the width of the disk as an increment of y, Δy (see Fig. 19.14).

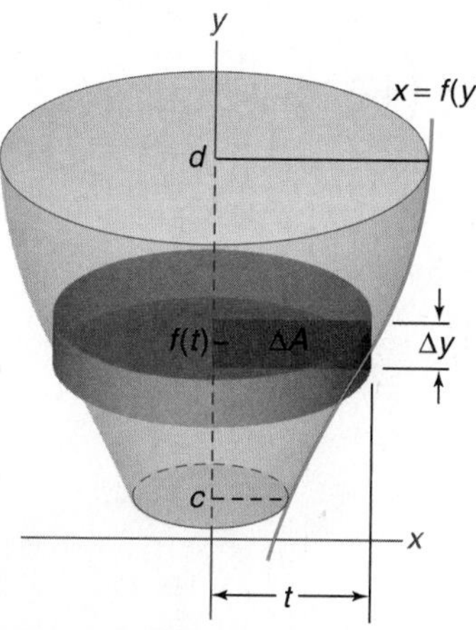

Figure 19.14 Disk of a solid of revolution about the y-axis.

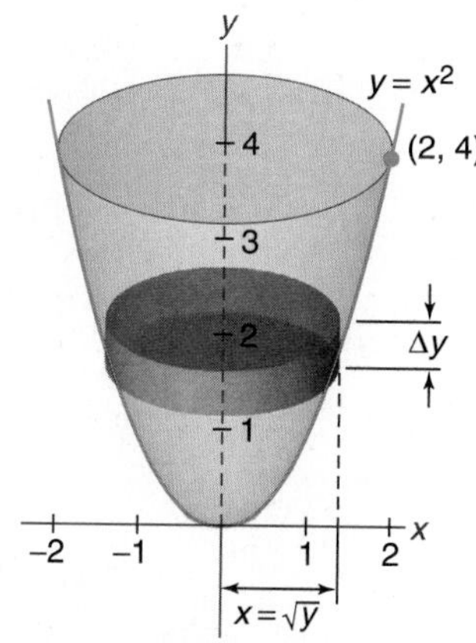

Figure 19.15

EXAMPLE 3

Find the volume of the solid obtained by revolving the region bounded by the curves $y = x^2, x = 0$, and $y = 4$ about the y-axis.

When revolving the area about the y-axis as in Fig. 19.15, the boundary curve $(y = x^2)$ must be determined in a manner that expresses x as a function of y. That is,

$$x = \sqrt{y} \qquad (\text{for } 0 \leq y \leq 4)$$

Note that the boundary curve determines the radius of the differential disks.

The volume of the solid is then given by

$$V = \pi \int_c^d [f(y)]^2\,dy = \pi \int_0^4 (\sqrt{y})^2\,dy \qquad (x = \sqrt{y})$$

$$= \pi \int_0^4 y\, dy$$

$$= \pi \frac{y^2}{2}\Big|_0^4 = \pi\left(\frac{16}{2} - 0\right)$$

$$= 8\pi$$

EXAMPLE 4

Find the volume of the solid formed by revolving the region bounded by the curves $y = 4 - x^2$, $x = 0$, and $y = 0$ about the y-axis.

Expressing the radius of a differential disk in terms of x, we have

$$y = 4 - x^2$$
$$x^2 = 4 - y$$
$$x = \sqrt{4 - y}$$

The desired volume in Fig. 19.16 is then

$$V = \pi \int_c^d [f(y)]^2\, dy$$

$$= \pi \int_0^4 (\sqrt{4 - y})^2\, dy \qquad (x = \sqrt{4 - y})$$

$$= \pi \int_0^4 (4 - y)\, dy$$

$$= \pi\left(4y - \frac{y^2}{2}\right)\Big|_0^4$$

$$= \pi\left[\left(16 - \frac{16}{2}\right) - (0)\right]$$

$$= 8\pi$$

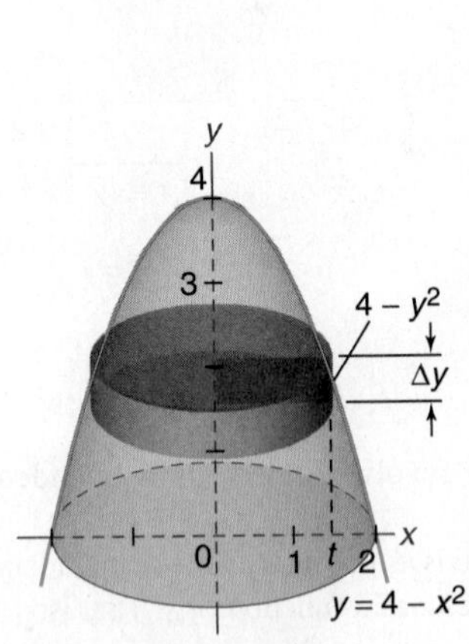

Figure 19.16

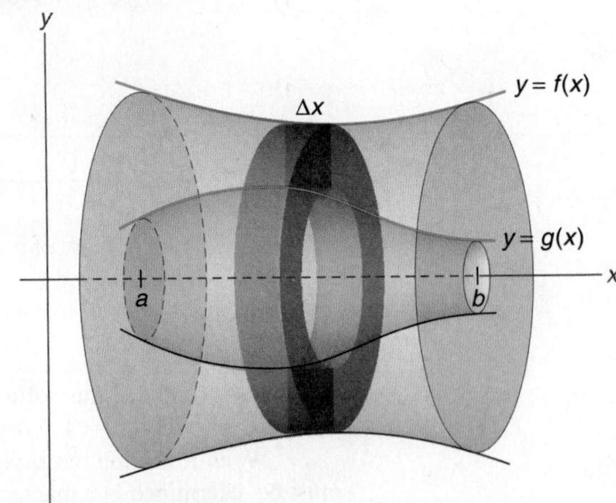

Figure 19.17 Washer-type solid of revolution about the x-axis.

Washer Method

When the region between two curves is rotated as shown in Fig. 19.17 about the x-axis, the rotation results in a *washer*-type solid. If $y = f(x)$ is the outer radius and $y = g(x)$

is the inner radius of the region being revolved, the volume of the resulting solid is

$$V = \pi \int_a^b \{[f(x)]^2 - [g(x)]^2\}\, dx$$

EXAMPLE 5

Find the volume of the solid formed by revolving the region bounded by $y = x^2$ and $y = x$ about the x-axis.

From Fig. 19.18, we have

$$\begin{aligned} V &= \pi \int_0^1 [(x)^2 - (x^2)^2]\, dx \\ &= \pi \int_0^1 (x^2 - x^4)\, dx \\ &= \pi\left(\frac{x^3}{3} - \frac{x^5}{5}\right)\Bigg|_0^1 \\ &= \pi\left[\left(\frac{1}{3} - \frac{1}{5}\right) - (0)\right] \\ &= \frac{2\pi}{15} \end{aligned}$$

EXAMPLE 6

Drill a hole of radius 3 in. through the center of a metal sphere of radius 5 in. Find the volume of the resulting ring.

First, rotate the shaded portion of the circle $x^2 + y^2 = 25$ about the x-axis as shown in Fig. 19.19. Its outer radius is $y = \sqrt{25 - x^2}$ and its inner radius (radius of hole) is $y = 3$. Thus,

$$\begin{aligned} V &= \pi \int_{-4}^{4} [(\sqrt{25 - x^2})^2 - (3)^2]\, dx \\ &= \pi \int_{-4}^{4} (16 - x^2)\, dx \end{aligned}$$

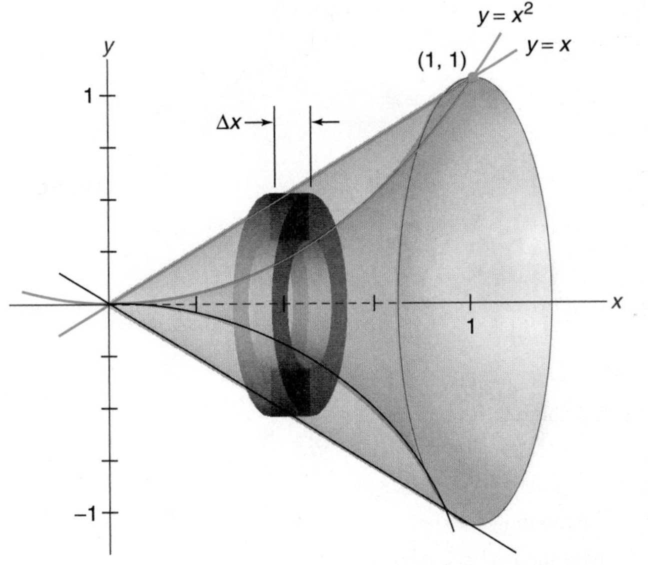

Figure 19.18

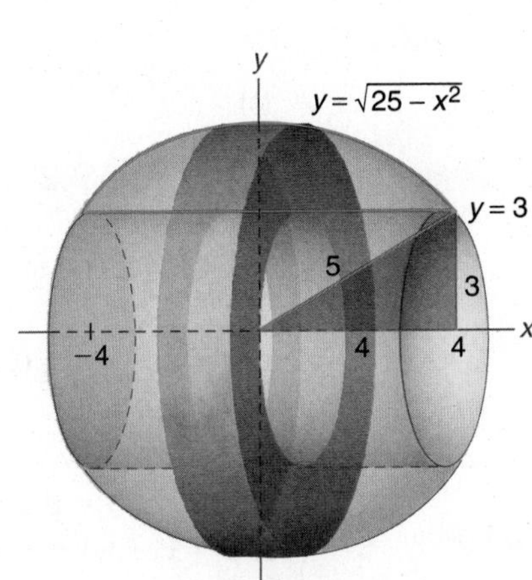

Figure 19.19

$$= \pi\left(16x - \frac{x^3}{3}\right)\Big|_{-4}^{4}$$

$$= \pi\left[\left(64 - \frac{64}{3}\right) - \left(-64 + \frac{64}{3}\right)\right]$$

$$= \frac{256\pi}{3}\text{ in}^3$$

EXAMPLE 7

Find the volume of the solid obtained by revolving the region bounded by the curves $y = x^2$, $x = 2$, and the x-axis about the line $x = 2$.

Note that the radius of the differential disk in Fig. 19.20(b) is $2 - x$ and its thickness is Δy with $0 \le y \le 4$.

$$V = \pi \int_0^4 (2 - x)^2\, dy$$

$$= \pi \int_0^4 (4 - 4x + x^2)\, dy$$

$$= \pi \int_0^4 (4 - 4\sqrt{y} + y)\, dy \qquad (x^2 = y \text{ and } x = \sqrt{y})$$

$$= \pi\left(4y - \frac{8}{3}y^{3/2} + \frac{y^2}{2}\right)\Big|_0^4$$

$$= \pi\left[\left(16 - \frac{8}{3}\cdot 8 + 8\right) - (0)\right]$$

$$= \frac{8\pi}{3}$$

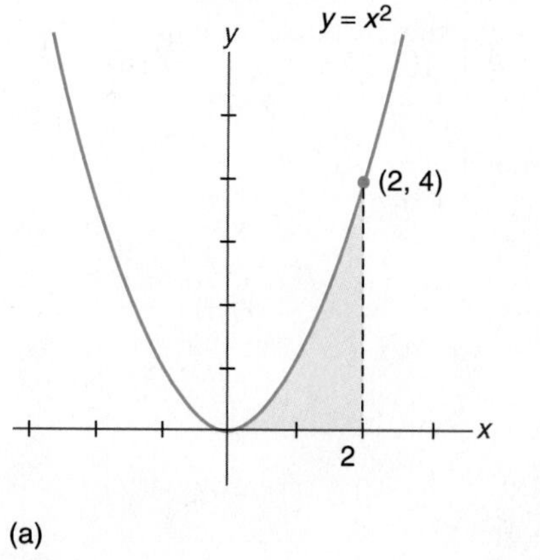

(a)

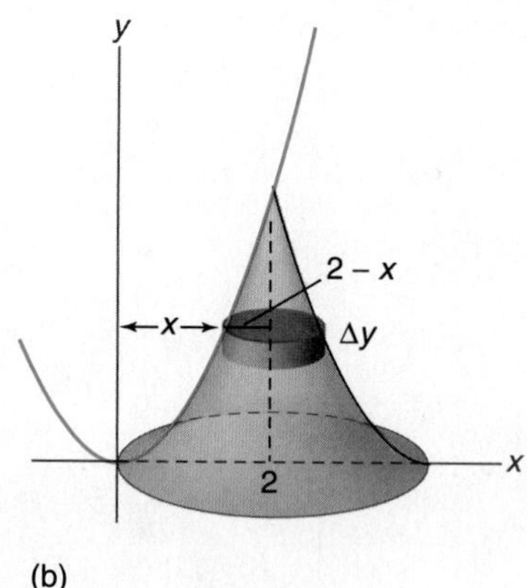

(b)

Figure 19.20

Exercises 19.2

Find the volume of each solid formed by revolving the region bounded by the given curves about the given line.

1. $y = x + 1, y = 0, x = 0$, and $x = 2$ about the x-axis
2. $y = x, y = 0, x = 2$, and $x = 4$ about the x-axis
3. $y = x^2 + 1, y = 0, x = 1$, and $x = 2$ about the x-axis
4. $y = \sqrt{x}, y = 0, x = 1$, and $x = 4$ about the x-axis
5. $y = x - 1, x = 0$, and $y = 1$ about the y-axis
6. $y^2 = 2x, x = 0$, and $y = 2$ about the y-axis
7. $y = 4x^2, x = 0$, and $y = 4$ about the y-axis

8. $y = 4 - x^2, x = 0, y = 1$, and $y = 2$ about the y-axis
9. $y = x, x = 1$, and $y = 0$ about $x = 1$
10. $y = x^2, x = 2$, and $y = 0$ about $x = 2$
11. $y = x, x = 1, x = 2$, and $y = 1$ about $y = 1$
12. $y = x^2, x = 1, x = 2$, and $y = 1$ about $y = 1$
13. $4y = x^2, y = 0$, and $x = 2$ about the y-axis
14. $y^2 = x, y = 0$, and $x = 4$ about the y-axis
15. $y^2 = x, y = 0$, and $x = 4$ about the x-axis
16. $y = x^3$ and $y = x$ from $x = 0$ to $x = 1$ about the x-axis
17. $y = x^3$ and $y = x$ from $x = 0$ to $x = 1$ about the y-axis
18. $y = 2 - x^2, y = x$, and $x = 0$ about the x-axis
19. $y = 2 - x^2, y = x$, and $x = 0$ about the y-axis
20. $2y = x$ and $y^2 = x$ about the y-axis
21. $2y = x$ and $y^2 = x$ about the x-axis
22. $x = y^2$ and $x = 2 - y^2$ about the y-axis
23. $y = 3 - x^2$ and $y = x^2 + 1$ about the x-axis
24. $x = 2y^2 + 1$ and $x = 4 - y^2$ about the y-axis
25. The area bounded by the first and second quadrants of the ellipse $9x^2 + 25y^2 = 225$ is revolved about the x-axis. Find the volume.
26. The area bounded by the first and fourth quadrants of the ellipse $9x^2 + 25y^2 = 225$ is revolved about the y-axis. Find the volume.
27. Drill a hole of radius 2 in. through the center of the solid (along the x-axis) described in Exercise 25. Find the volume of the resulting solid.
28. Drill a hole of radius 2 in. through the center of the solid (along the y-axis) described in Exercise 26. Find the volume of the resulting solid.
29. Use the disk method to verify that the volume of a sphere of radius r is $V = \frac{4}{3}\pi r^3$.
30. Use the disk method to verify that the volume of a right circular cone is $V = \frac{1}{3}\pi r^2 h$, where r is the radius of the base and h is the height.

19.3 VOLUMES OF REVOLUTION: SHELL METHOD

A second method of obtaining the volume of a solid uses cylindrical shells instead of disks. Let's use this method to find the volume of the solid described in Example 4 of Section 19.2.

The volume ΔV of a typical shell in Fig. 19.21(a) is

$$\Delta V = \pi r_2^2 h - \pi r_1^2 h$$

where

$$r_1 = t \qquad \text{(radius of inside wall of the shell)}$$
$$r_2 = t + \Delta x \qquad \text{(radius of outside wall of the shell)}$$

Now

$$\begin{aligned} \Delta V &= \pi r_2^2 h - \pi r_1^2 h \\ &= \pi h(r_2^2 - r_1^2) \\ &= \pi h(r_2 + r_1)(r_2 - r_1) \\ &= 2\pi h\left(\frac{r_2 + r_1}{2}\right)(r_2 - r_1) \qquad \text{(Multiply numerator and denominator by 2.)} \end{aligned}$$

↑ average radius

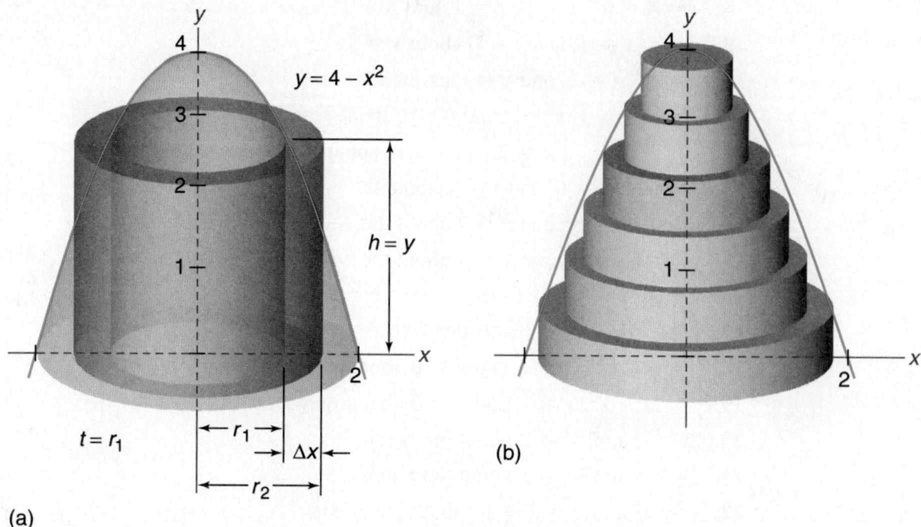

Figure 19.21 Shell method about the *y*-axis.

or

$$\Delta V = 2\pi y\left(\frac{2t + \Delta x}{2}\right)(\Delta x) \qquad [r_2 + r_1 = (t + \Delta x) + t = 2t + \Delta x]$$

$$= 2\pi y\left(t + \frac{\Delta x}{2}\right)\Delta x$$

$$= 2\pi f(x)\, x\, \Delta x \qquad \left(\text{where we let } x = t + \frac{\Delta x}{2}\right)$$

This expression for ΔV is the product of the circumference of the shell of radius *x*, its height $f(x)$, and its thickness Δx. By taking the sum of the volumes of all such approximating shells as in Fig. 19.21(b), we obtain another approximation for the desired volume.

Again using the methods of Chapter 5, we find that this approximation leads to the integral

$$V = 2\pi \int_a^b x f(x)\, dx$$

which gives the exact volume of the solid.

Expressing *y* as a function of *x*, we have $y = f(x) = 4 - x^2$ and

$$V = 2\pi \int_0^2 x(4 - x^2)\, dx$$

$$= 2\pi \int_0^2 (4x - x^3)\, dx$$

$$= 2\pi\left(2x^2 - \frac{x^4}{4}\right)\Bigg|_0^2 = 2\pi[(8 - 4) - (0)] = 8\pi$$

This method of computing the volume of a solid is called the *shell method*.

CYLINDRICAL SHELL METHOD

$V =$ sum of concentric cylindrical shells

$$V = 2\pi \int_a^b \underset{\text{radius}}{x} \; \underset{\text{height}}{f(x)} \; \underset{\text{thickness}}{dx} \quad \text{(shells parallel to } y\text{-axis)}$$

$$V = 2\pi \int_c^d y \; f(y) \; dy \quad \text{(shells parallel to } x\text{-axis)}$$

EXAMPLE 1

Find the volume of the solid formed by the region under $y = x^2 + 1$ from $x = 0$ to $x = 2$ revolved about the y-axis. Note that the disk method would not readily solve this problem (some pieces would be disks and others would be washers, so there is no typical unit of volume for that approach). Instead, revolve vertical rectangles about the y-axis to form cylindrical shells (see Fig. 19.22).

$$\Delta V = 2\pi(x)(y)\Delta x$$

where x is the radius of the shell, y is the height, and Δx is the thickness. The integral for the volume is

$$\begin{aligned} V &= 2\pi \int_0^2 x\,y\,dx \\ &= 2\pi \int_0^2 x(x^2 + 1)\,dx \\ &= 2\pi \int_0^2 (x^3 + x)\,dx \\ &= 2\pi\left(\frac{x^4}{4} + \frac{x^2}{2}\right)\Bigg|_0^2 \\ &= 2\pi\left(\frac{2^4}{4} + \frac{2^2}{2} - 0\right) = 12\pi \end{aligned}$$

The volume is 12π cubic units.

EXAMPLE 2

Find the volume of the solid formed by revolving the region bounded by $y = x^2$, $y = 0$, and $x = 1$ about the line $x = 1$.

In this example the shell method is more convenient than the disk method. The volume of a typical shell in Fig. 19.23 is

$$\Delta V = 2\pi(1 - x)y\,\Delta x$$

where $1 - x$ is the radius of the shell, y is the height, and Δx is its thickness. The integral for V then becomes

$$V = 2\pi \int_0^1 (1 - x)y\,dx$$

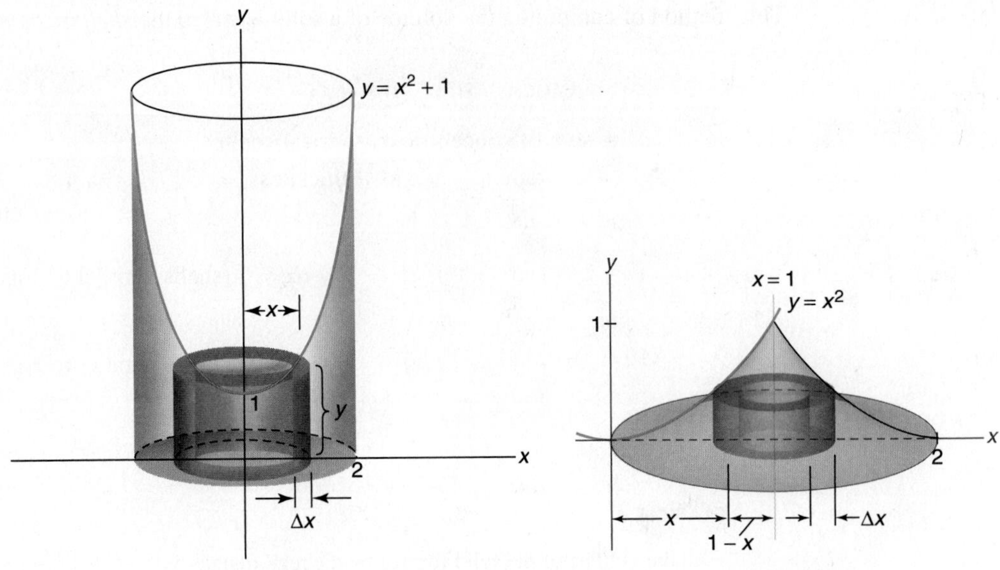

Figure 19.22

Figure 19.23

$$V = 2\pi \int_0^1 (1 - x)(x^2)\,dx \qquad (y = x^2)$$

$$= 2\pi \int_0^1 (x^2 - x^3)\,dx$$

$$= 2\pi\left(\frac{x^3}{3} - \frac{x^4}{4}\right)\Bigg|_0^1$$

$$= 2\pi\left[\left(\frac{1}{3} - \frac{1}{4}\right) - (0)\right]$$

$$= \frac{\pi}{6}$$

EXAMPLE 3

Find the volume of the solid formed by revolving the region bounded by $y = x^2$ and $y = x$ about the x-axis.

The volume of a typical shell in Fig. 19.24 is

$$\Delta V = 2\pi y(x_2 - x_1)\,\Delta y$$

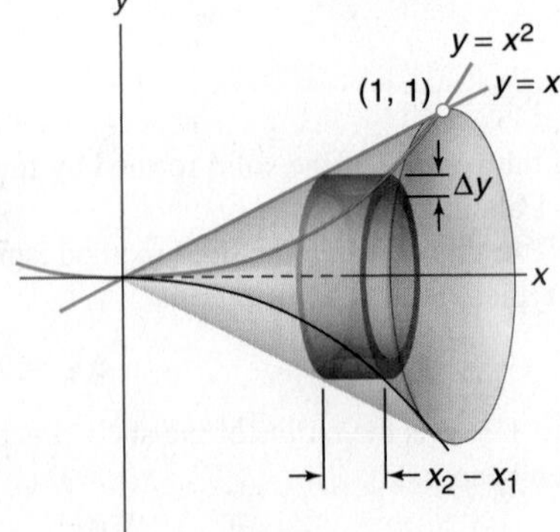

Figure 19.24

where y is the radius of the shell, $x_2 - x_1$ is the height of the shell, and Δy is its thickness. The height of the shell, $x_2 - x_1$, is found by subtracting the curve $x_1 = f(y) = y$ from the curve $x_2 = g(y) = \sqrt{y}$.

The integral for V then becomes

$$\begin{aligned} V &= 2\pi \int_c^d y[g(y) - f(y)]\,dy \\ &= 2\pi \int_0^1 y(x_2 - x_1)\,dy \\ &= 2\pi \int_0^1 y(\sqrt{y} - y)\,dy \\ &= 2\pi \int_0^1 (y^{3/2} - y^2)\,dy \\ &= 2\pi\left(\frac{2}{5}y^{5/2} - \frac{y^3}{3}\right)\Bigg|_0^1 \\ &= 2\pi\left[\left(\frac{2}{5} - \frac{1}{3}\right) - (0)\right] \\ &= \frac{2\pi}{15} \end{aligned}$$

Exercises 19.3

Find the volume of each solid formed by revolving the region bounded by the given curves about the given line using the shell method.

1. $y = 4x^2$, $x = 0$, and $y = 4$ about the y-axis
2. $y = 4x^2$, $x = 0$, and $y = 4$ about the x-axis
3. $4y = x^2$, $y = 0$, and $x = 2$ about the y-axis
4. $y^2 = x$, $y = 0$, and $x = 4$ about the y-axis
5. $y^2 = 2x$, $x = 0$, and $y = 2$ about the x-axis
6. $y = x^3$, $y = 0$, and $x = 2$ about the y-axis
7. $y = x^3$, $y = 0$, and $x = 2$ about the x-axis
8. $y = \sqrt{x}$, $x = 0$, and $y = 2$ about the x-axis
9. $y = 2x - x^2$ and the x-axis about the y-axis
10. $x = 3y - y^2$ and the y-axis about the x-axis
11. $y = x$, $x = 1$, and $y = 0$ about $x = 1$
12. $y = x^2$, $x = 2$, and $y = 0$ about $x = 2$
13. $x = y^2$, $y = 1$, and $x = 0$ about $y = 2$
14. $y = x^2$ and $y = 4$ about $y = -2$
15. $y = x^3$ and $y = x$ from $x = 0$ to $x = 1$ about the x-axis
16. $y = x^3$ and $y = x$ from $x = 0$ to $x = 1$ about the y-axis
17. $y = x^2 - 3x + 2$ and $y = 0$ about the y-axis
18. $x = y^2 - 6y + 8$ and $x = 0$ about the x-axis
19. $y = x(x - 2)^2$ and $y = 0$ about $x = 2$
20. $y = x(x - 2)^2$ and $y = 0$ about the y-axis

19.4 CENTER OF MASS OF A SYSTEM OF PARTICLES

The next application of integration involves finding the center of mass, which is discussed in the next two sections. We find the center of mass of a system of particles in this section and the center of mass of a thin plate and of a solid of revolution in the next section. Finding the center of mass is of fundamental importance in the study of mechanics. The *center of mass or center of gravity* of an object or system of objects is the point at which the object or system balances or at which the entire mass can be considered to be concentrated.

Before finding the center of mass of a system of particles, we must first introduce the concept of a moment. The *moment* about a point P produced by some mass m is given by

$$\text{moment} = md$$

where d is the length of the *moment arm,* which is the distance between the mass and point P (see Fig. 19.25).

Suppose we have a 15-kg sign hanging from a support 0.8 m from a building as shown in Fig. 19.26. The length of the moment arm is 0.8 m, the distance from the mass to P. The mass is 15 kg. Therefore,

$$\text{moment} = md = (15 \text{ kg})(0.8 \text{ m}) = 12 \text{ kg m}$$

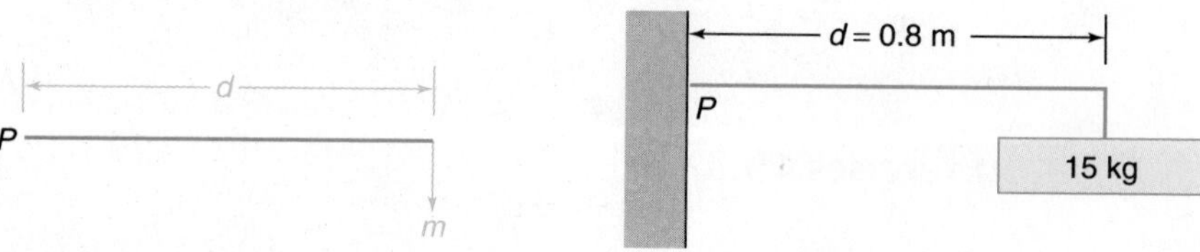

Figure 19.25 Length of moment arm.

Figure 19.26

Consider the mobile that is balanced by the five weights as shown in Fig. 19.27. Let the masses m_1, m_2, m_3, m_4, and m_5 be at distances d_1, d_2, d_3, d_4, and d_5, respectively, from a point P. The moment of the system about P is

$$\text{moment} = m_1d_1 + m_2d_2 + m_3d_3 + m_4d_4 + m_5d_5$$

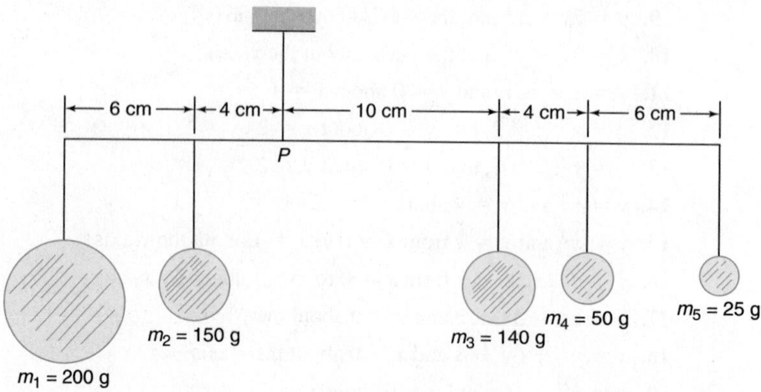

Figure 19.27

If we let P be the origin of the x-axis, $d_1 = -10$, $d_2 = -4$, $d_3 = 10$, $d_4 = 14$, and $d_5 = 20$. Then the moment about P is

$$\begin{aligned}\text{moment} &= (200)(-10) + (150)(-4) + (140)(10) + (50)(14) + (25)(20)\\ &= -2000 - 600 + 1400 + 700 + 500\\ &= 0\end{aligned}$$

If the moment is zero, the system is in equilibrium, that is, the mobile balances.

Note: Point P may be any point from which the lengths of the moment arms are measured. We usually choose point P to be the center of mass or the pivot point.

MOMENT IN A LINEAR SYSTEM ALONG THE X-AXIS

Let $\bar{x}$ be the center of mass or balancing point of a linear system along the x-axis with n masses. That is, $\bar{x}$ is the point where all the mass seems to be concentrated. So

$$(m_1 + m_2 + m_3 + \cdots + m_n)\bar{x} = m_1x_1 + m_2x_2 + m_3x_3 + \cdots + m_nx_n$$

Then

$$\bar{x} = \frac{m_1x_1 + m_2x_2 + m_3x_3 + \cdots + m_nx_n}{m_1 + m_2 + m_3 + \cdots + m_n}$$

If we let M_0 be the moment about the origin, $\bar{x}$ be the center of mass, and m be the total mass of the system, then

$$\bar{x} = \frac{M_0}{m}$$

EXAMPLE 1

Find the center of mass of the linear system $m_1 = 10, x_1 = -4$; $m_2 = 25, x_2 = 2$; $m_3 = 40$, $x_3 = 5$; $m_4 = 15, x_4 = 10$.

The moment about the origin is

$$\begin{aligned}M_0 &= m_1x_1 + m_2x_2 + m_3x_3 + m_4x_4\\ &= (10)(-4) + (25)(2) + (40)(5) + (15)(10)\\ &= -40 + 50 + 200 + 150 = 360\end{aligned}$$

The total mass of the system is

$$m = 10 + 25 + 40 + 15 = 90$$

The center of mass is

$$\bar{x} = \frac{M_0}{m} = \frac{360}{90} = 4$$

We extend these concepts to two dimensions as in Fig. 19.28:

MOMENTS OF A TWO-DIMENSIONAL SYSTEM

Consider n masses $m_1, m_2, \ldots, m_n$ located in the xy-plane at points $(x_1, y_1)(x_2, y_2), \ldots,$ (x_n, y_n), respectively. Their moments with respect to the x-axis and the y-axis are defined as follows: The moment about the y-axis M_y is

$$M_y = m_1x_1 + m_2x_2 + \cdots + m_nx_n$$

and the moment about the x-axis M_x is

$$M_x = m_1y_1 + m_2y_2 + \cdots + m_ny_n$$

If we let m be the total mass of the system, the center of mass $(\bar{x}, \bar{y})$ is given by

$$\bar{x} = \frac{M_y}{m} \quad \text{and} \quad \bar{y} = \frac{M_x}{m}$$

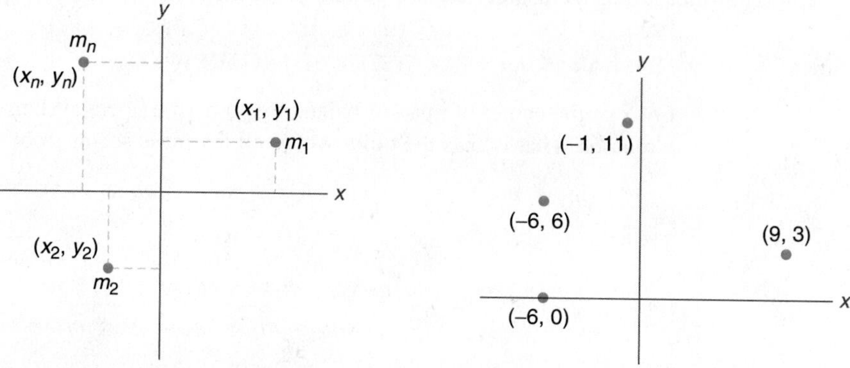

Figure 19.28 Moments of a two-dimensional system.

Figure 19.29

The quantities $m\bar{x}$ and $m\bar{y}$ are regarded as the moments about the y-axis and the x-axis, respectively, of a mass m located at $(\bar{x}, \bar{y})$. That is, $(\bar{x}, \bar{y})$ is the point where the total mass that would give the same moments M_y and M_x seems to be concentrated.

EXAMPLE 2

Find the center of mass of the system $m_1 = 10$ at $(9, 3)$, $m_2 = 6$ at $(-1, 11)$, $m_3 = 8$ at $(-6, 6)$, and $m_4 = 12$ at $(-6, 0)$.

From Fig. 19.29,

$$m = 10 + 6 + 8 + 12 = 36$$
$$M_y = (10)(9) + (6)(-1) + (8)(-6) + (12)(-6) = -36$$
$$M_x = (10)(3) + (6)(11) + (8)(6) + (12)(0) = 144$$

Then,

$$\bar{x} = \frac{M_y}{m} = \frac{-36}{36} = -1$$
$$\bar{y} = \frac{M_x}{m} = \frac{144}{36} = 4$$

So, the center of mass of this system is $(-1, 4)$.

Exercises 19.4

Find the center of mass of each linear system.

1. $m_1 = 3, x_1 = -5; m_2 = 7, x_2 = 3; m_3 = 4, x_3 = 6$

2. $m_1 = 6, x_1 = -12; m_2 = 3, x_2 = -3; m_3 = 10, x_3 = 0; m_4 = 5, x_4 = 9$

3. $m_1 = 24, x_1 = -15; m_2 = 15, x_2 = -9; m_3 = 12, x_3 = 3; m_4 = 9, x_4 = 6$

4. $m_1 = 8, x_1 = -15; m_2 = 15, x_2 = -9; m_3 = 7, x_3 = -1; m_4 = 20, x_4 = 8; m_5 = 24, x_5 = 12$

5. There is a mass of 6 at $(9, 0)$ and a mass of 18 at $(-2, 0)$. Find where a mass of 3 should be placed on the x-axis so that the origin is the center of mass.

6. There is a mass of 30 at $(-4, 0)$, a mass of 9 at $(2, 0)$, and a mass of 15 at $(8, 0)$. Find where a mass of 3 should be placed on the x-axis so that the origin is the center of mass.

7. There is a mass of 24 at $(-8, 0)$ and a mass of 36 at $(12, 0)$. Find where a mass of 9 should be placed on the x-axis so that $(3, 0)$ is the center of mass.

8. There is a mass of 15 at $(-8, 0)$, a mass of 5 at $(-4, 0)$, and a mass of 12 at $(3, 0)$. Find where a mass of 8 should be placed on the x-axis so that $(-3, 0)$ is the center of mass.

9. There is a mass of 6 at $(-3, 0)$ and a mass of 9 at $(12, 0)$. Find what mass should be placed at $(-6, 0)$ so that the origin is the center of mass.

10. There is a mass of 4 at $(-5, 0)$, a mass of 16 at $(3, 0)$, and a mass of 24 at $(8, 0)$. Find what mass should be placed at $(-4, 0)$ so that the origin is the center of mass.

11. There is a mass of 25 at $(-6, 0)$, a mass of 45 at $(8, 0)$, and a mass of 40 at $(10, 0)$. Find what mass should be placed at $(-4, 0)$ so that $(3, 0)$ is the center of mass.

12. There is a mass of 18 at $(3, 0)$, a mass of 54 at $(9, 0)$, a mass of 24 at $(12, 0)$, and a mass of 36 at $(15, 0)$. Find what mass should be placed at $(4, 0)$ so that $(6, 0)$ is the center of mass.

13. A straight road connects Flatville (population 75,000), Pleasant Hill (population 50,000), and Harristown (population 25,000). Pleasant Hill is 18 mi north of Flatville and Harristown is 30 mi north of Flatville. Where is the best place to locate an airport to serve these three communities?

14. A straight road connects Leadville (population 1750), Branburg (population 2800), Princeton (population 970), and Four Oaks (population 480). The distance from Leadville to Branburg is 4 mi, to Princeton is 10 mi, and to Four Oaks is 13 mi. Where is the best place to locate a hospital to serve these four communities?

Find the center of mass of each two-dimensional system.

15. $m_1 = 6$ at $(1, 4)$, $m_2 = 3$ at $(6, 2)$, $m_3 = 12$ at $(3, 3)$

16. $m_1 = 20$ at $(-5, 10)$, $m_2 = 15$ at $(-10, -15)$, $m_3 = 40$ at $(0, -5)$

17. $m_1 = 8$ at $(8, 12)$, $m_2 = 16$ at $(-12, 8)$, $m_3 = 20$ at $(-16, -4)$, $m_4 = 36$ at $(4, -20)$

18. $m_1 = 9$ at $(3, 6)$, $m_2 = 12$ at $(-6, 12)$, $m_3 = 18$ at $(0, -9)$, $m_4 = 30$ at $(15, 0)$, $m_5 = 15$ at $(-12, -9)$

19. There is a mass of 6 at $(4, 2)$ and a mass of 9 at $(-5, 8)$. Find where a mass of 10 should be placed so that the origin is the center of mass.

20. There is a mass of 18 at $(-4, 6)$, a mass of 12 at $(1, -2)$, and a mass of 9 at $(8, 0)$. Find where a mass of 6 should be placed so that $(2, -3)$ is the center of mass.

21. There is a mass of 15 at $(10, 3)$, a mass of 25 at $(-6, -1)$, and a mass of 40 at $(8, -2)$. Find what mass should be placed at $(-5, -3)$ so that $(-1, -2)$ is the center of mass.

22. There is a mass of 4 at $(-5, -3)$, a mass of 16 at $(-4, 3)$, and a mass of 12 at $(6, -4)$. Find what mass should be placed at $(2, 2)$ so that the origin is the center of mass.

23. Three towns plan to build a new health clinic to serve all three communities. Town B (population 8200) is 6 mi east and 3 mi south of Town A (population 12,500). Town C (population 5200) is 2 mi west and 8 mi south of Town A. Find the best location for the new health clinic. Do not consider new roads in determining the best location.

24. Four cities plan to build a new airport to serve all four communities. City B (population 180,000) is 4 mi north and 3 mi west of City A (population 75,000). City C (population 240,000) is 6 mi east and 12 mi south of City A. City D (population 105,000) is 15 mi due south of City A. Find the best location for the airport. Do not consider new roads in determining the best location.

19.5 CENTER OF MASS OF CONTINUOUS MASS DISTRIBUTIONS

As we saw in Section 19.4, the center of mass of any system of finite particles may be found arithmetically by summing the moments and the masses and dividing. Recall that the center of mass of a linear system along the x-axis with n masses is given by

$$\bar{x} = \frac{M_0}{m} = \frac{m_1x_1 + m_2x_2 + m_3x_3 + \cdots + m_nx_n}{m_1 + m_2 + m_3 + \cdots + m_n}$$

For a continuous mass distribution, the center of mass is found by integration. For example, to find the center of mass of a straight thin wire of constant density ρ, place the wire on the x-axis as shown in Fig. 19.30. Then, subdivide the wire into n equal lengths, each of length Δx and mass Δm. The mass of the ith length is

$$\begin{aligned} \text{mass} &= (\text{density})(\text{length}) \\ m &= \quad \rho \qquad\quad \Delta x \end{aligned}$$

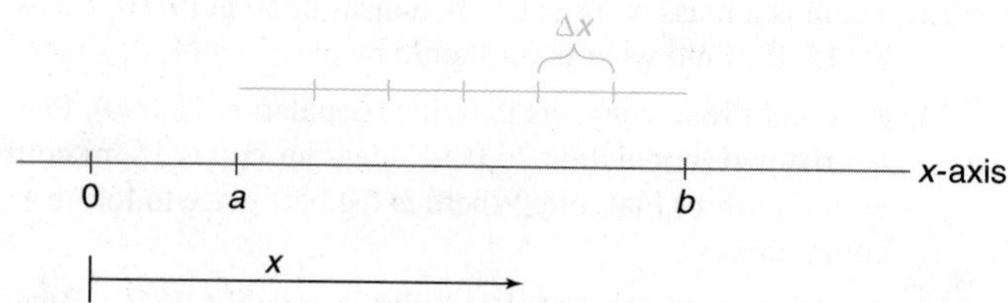

Figure 19.30 Center of mass of a straight thin wire of constant density.

The total mass of the wire is the integral

$$m = \rho\int_a^b dx$$

Next, find the moment of the ith length:

$$\begin{aligned} \text{moment} &= (\text{mass})(\text{length of moment arm}) \\ &= (\rho\ \Delta x)(x) \end{aligned}$$

So, the moment of the entire wire about the origin is the integral

$$M_0 = \rho\int_a^b x\,dx$$

Then, the center of mass is given as follows:

CENTER OF MASS OF A CONTINUOUS THIN UNIFORM MASS

$$\bar{x} = \frac{M_0}{m} = \frac{\displaystyle\int_a^b x\,dx}{\displaystyle\int_a^b dx}$$

Note: The density ρ cancels in all such cases when it is constant or uniform. For any homogeneous mass distribution having constant density (constant mass per unit length, per unit area, or per unit volume), the *centroid* is the same as the center of mass. The centroid often refers to the geometric center.

EXAMPLE 1

Find the center of mass of a straight wire 12 cm long and of uniform density.

$$\bar{x} = \frac{\int_a^b x\,dx}{\int_a^b dx} = \frac{\int_0^{12} x\,dx}{\int_0^{12} dx} = \frac{\left.\frac{x^2}{2}\right|_0^{12}}{\left.x\right|_0^{12}} = \frac{72}{12} = 6$$

This result should be no surprise. For a uniform linear object, the center of mass is at its center, the point at which the object can be supported. For example, a metre stick is supported on one's finger at the 50-cm mark as in Fig. 19.31.

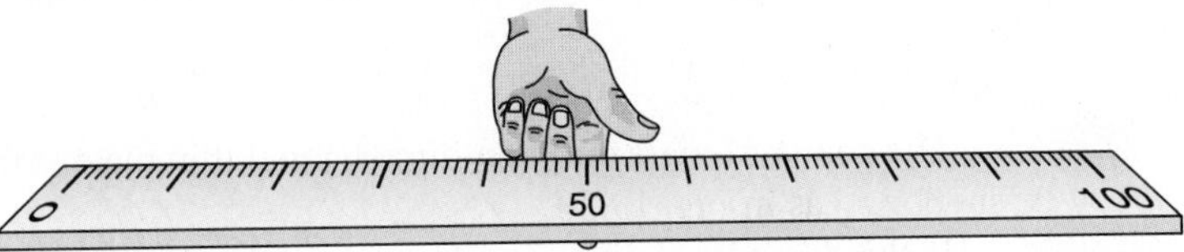

Figure 19.31 The center of mass, or centroid, of a metre stick is the 50-cm mark, the point at which it can be balanced on one's finger.

For a nonuniform object, the center of mass is usually not at its geometric center, but at the point at which it can be supported in equilibrium by a single force or the point about which it spins if allowed to spin freely in space as in Fig. 19.32.

When the density of a continuous thin mass is not uniform, the center of mass is found as follows:

CENTER OF MASS OF A CONTINUOUS THIN MASS OF VARIABLE DENSITY

$$\bar{x} = \frac{M_0}{m} = \frac{\int_a^b \rho(x)\,x\,dx}{\int_a^b \rho(x)\,dx}$$

where $\rho(x)$ is the density expressed as a function of x. Density is mass per unit length.

EXAMPLE 2

Find the center of mass of a straight wire 16 cm long and whose density is given by $\rho(x) = 4\sqrt{x}$, where x is the distance from one end of the wire.

$$\bar{x} = \frac{M_0}{m} = \frac{\int_a^b \rho(x)\,x\,dx}{\int_a^b \rho(x)\,dx} = \frac{\int_0^{16} 4\sqrt{x}\,x\,dx}{\int_0^{16} 4\sqrt{x}\,dx} = \frac{\int_0^{16} x^{3/2}\,dx}{\int_0^{16} x^{1/2}\,dx} = \frac{\left.\frac{2}{5}x^{5/2}\right|_0^{16}}{\left.\frac{2}{3}x^{3/2}\right|_0^{16}}$$

$$= \frac{\frac{2}{5}[16^{5/2} - 0]}{\frac{2}{3}[16^{3/2} - 0]} = \frac{\frac{2}{5}(1024)}{\frac{2}{3}(64)} = \frac{48}{5} = 9.6 \text{ cm from the lighter end}$$

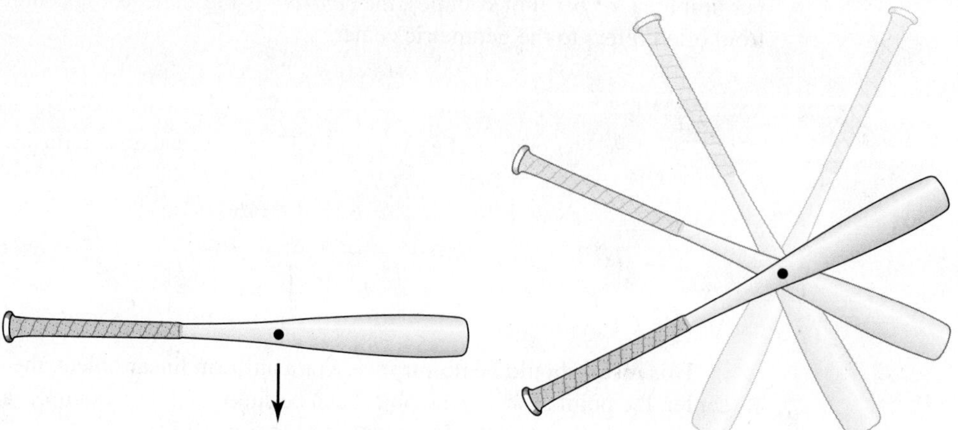

Figure 19.32 The center of mass of any object is the point about which it spins freely in space.

The center of mass of a two-dimensional thin plate is the point at which the plate can be supported as in Fig. 19.33.

If the thin plate is in a regular geometric shape, its center of mass is its geometric center because of its symmetry. Examples of four common geometric figures with each corresponding center of mass are shown in Fig. 19.34.

The center of mass of a more complex but uniformly thin object can be found by subdividing the object into combinations of simpler figures. Find the center of each simpler figure. Consider the mass of each simpler figure to be concentrated at its center and proceed using the method for moments of a two-dimensional system used in Example 2 of Section 19.4.

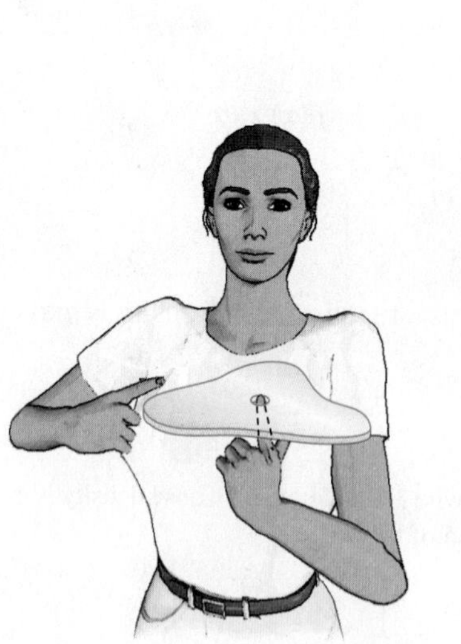

Figure 19.33 The center of mass, or centroid, of a thin plate is the point at which the plate can be supported.

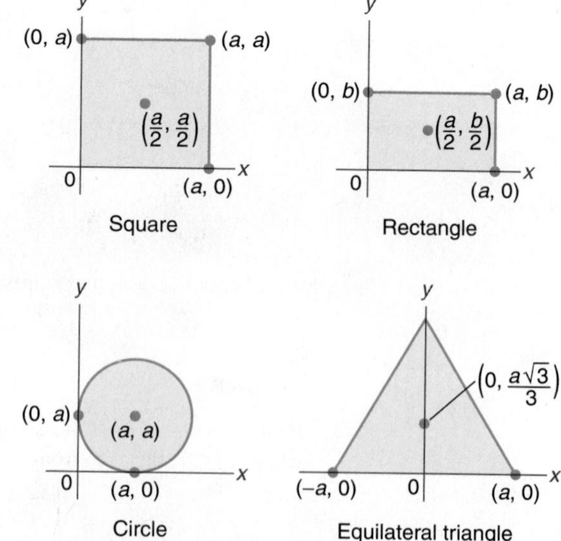

Figure 19.34 Centers of mass, or centroids, of some common geometric shapes placed in the xy-plane.

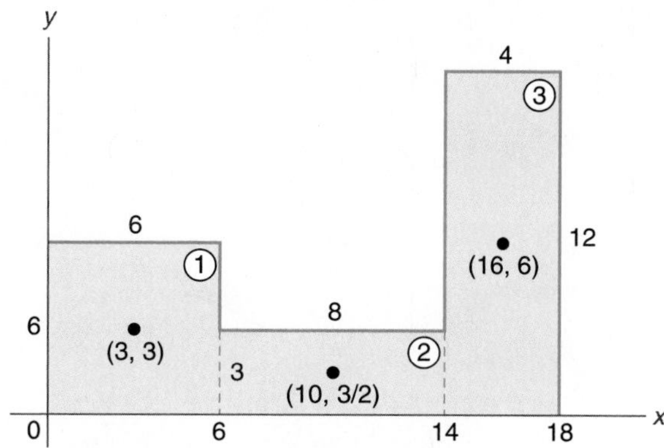

Figure 19.35

EXAMPLE 3

Find the center of mass of the uniform thin plate in Fig. 19.35.

The center of region 1 (square) is $(3, 3)$, of region 2 (rectangle) is $(10, \frac{3}{2})$, and of region 3 (rectangle) is $(16, 6)$. Since the plate is uniform, the mass in each region is proportional to its area. The area of region 1 is 36 units, of region 2 is 24 units, and of region 3 is 48 units. So

$$\begin{aligned} m &= 36 + 24 + 48 = 108 \\ M_y &= m_1x_1 + m_2x_2 + m_3x_3 \\ &= (36)(3) + (24)(10) + (48)(16) \\ &= 1116 \\ M_x &= m_1y_1 + m_2y_2 + m_3y_3 \\ &= (36)(3) + (24)(\tfrac{3}{2}) + (48)(6) \\ &= 432 \end{aligned}$$

Then

$$\bar{x} = \frac{M_y}{m} = \frac{1116}{108} = 10\tfrac{1}{3}$$

$$\bar{y} = \frac{M_x}{m} = \frac{432}{108} = 4$$

The center of mass of the plate is $(10\frac{1}{3}, 4)$.

Note that in Example 3 the center of mass is not on the surface of the plate.

Next, let's find the centroid of an irregular-shaped area (or thin plate) of constant density ρ between the curves shown in Fig. 19.36. First divide the area into n rectangles, each of width Δx. Let (x_i, y_i) be the center of mass of the ith rectangle. The y-value of the geometric center of the ith rectangle is

$$y_i = \frac{f(x_i) + g(x_i)}{2}$$

The area of the ith rectangle is $[f(x_i) - g(x_i)]\,\Delta x$. The mass of the ith rectangle is

$$\begin{aligned} \text{mass} &= (\text{density})(\text{area}) \\ &= \rho[f(x_i) - g(x_i)]\,\Delta x \end{aligned}$$

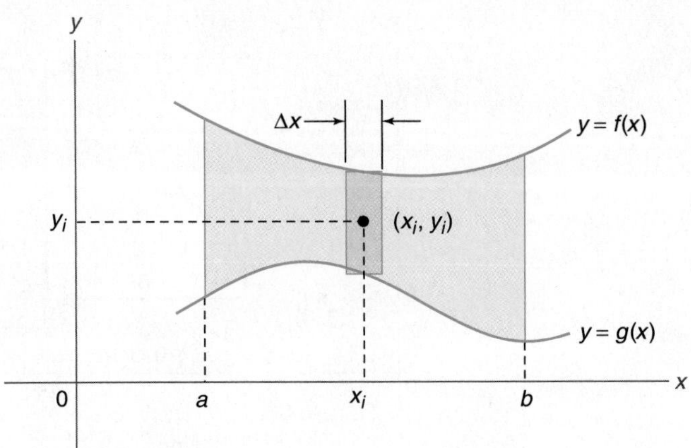

Figure 19.36 Finding the centroid of an irregular-shaped area or thin plate of constant density.

The total mass is the integral

$$m = \rho \int_a^b [f(x) - g(x)]\, dx = \rho A$$

where A is the area of the region.

Next, find the moment of the ith rectangle about the x-axis:

$$\begin{aligned} \text{moment} &= (\text{mass})(\text{moment arm}) \\ &= \rho[f(x_i) - g(x_i)]\, \Delta x \cdot y_i \\ &= \rho[f(x_i) - g(x_i)]\, \Delta x \cdot \frac{f(x_i) + g(x_i)}{2} \\ &= \frac{\rho}{2}\{[f(x_i)]^2 - [g(x_i)]^2\}\, \Delta x \end{aligned}$$

The moment about the x-axis is the integral

$$M_x = \frac{\rho}{2}\int_a^b \{[f(x)]^2 - [g(x)]^2\}\, dx$$

Similarly, the moment about the y-axis is the integral

$$M_y = \rho \int_a^b x[f(x) - g(x)]\, dx$$

MOMENTS AND CENTER OF MASS OF A PLANE AREA OR THIN PLATE

Let $g(x) \le f(x)$ be continuous functions on $a \le x \le b$ for the area of uniform density ρ bounded by $y = f(x)$, $y = g(x)$, $x = a$, and $x = b$. The moments about the x-axis and the y-axis are, respectively,

$$M_x = \frac{\rho}{2}\int_a^b \{[f(x)]^2 - [g(x)]^2\}\, dx \quad \text{and} \quad M_y = \rho \int_a^b x[f(x) - g(x)]\, dx$$

Its mass is given by

$$m = \rho \int_a^b [f(x) - g(x)]\, dx$$

and its center of mass is $(\bar{x}, \bar{y})$, where

$$\bar{x} = \frac{M_y}{m} \quad \text{and} \quad \bar{y} = \frac{M_x}{m}$$

EXAMPLE 4

Find the center of mass of the uniformly thin plate of density ρ bounded by $y = x^2$ and $y = x + 2$.

First, graph the equations and find the points of intersection as in Fig. 19.37.

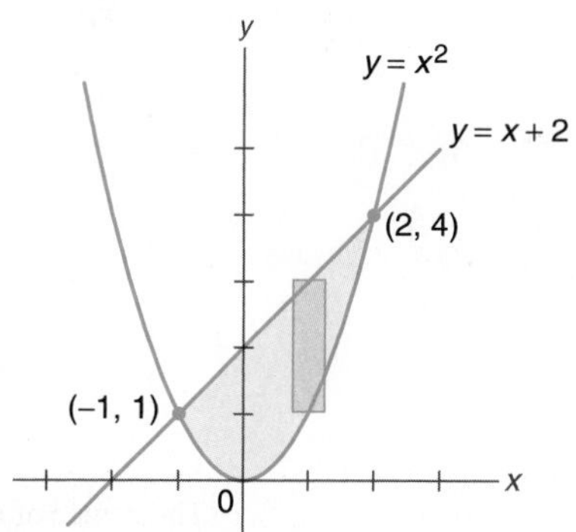

Figure 19.37

$$\begin{aligned} x^2 &= x + 2 \\ x^2 - x - 2 &= 0 \\ (x - 2)(x + 1) &= 0 \\ x &= 2, -1 \end{aligned}$$

$$\begin{aligned} M_x &= \frac{\rho}{2}\int_a^b \{[f(x)]^2 - [g(x)]^2\}\, dx \\ &= \frac{\rho}{2}\int_{-1}^2 [(x + 2)^2 - (x^2)^2]\, dx \\ &= \frac{\rho}{2}\int_{-1}^2 [x^2 + 4x + 4 - x^4]\, dx \\ &= \frac{\rho}{2}\left(\frac{x^3}{3} + 2x^2 + 4x - \frac{x^5}{5}\right)\bigg|_{-1}^2 \\ &= \frac{\rho}{2}\left[\left(\frac{8}{3} + 8 + 8 - \frac{32}{5}\right) - \left(-\frac{1}{3} + 2 - 4 + \frac{1}{5}\right)\right] \\ &= \frac{\rho}{2}\left(\frac{72}{5}\right) \\ &= \frac{36\rho}{5} \end{aligned}$$

$$\begin{aligned} M_y &= \rho\int_a^b x[f(x) - g(x)]\, dx \\ &= \rho\int_{-1}^2 x(x + 2 - x^2)\, dx \\ &= \rho\int_{-1}^2 (x^2 + 2x - x^3)\, dx \\ &= \rho\left(\frac{x^3}{3} + x^2 - \frac{x^4}{4}\right)\bigg|_{-1}^2 \end{aligned}$$

$$= \rho\left[\left(\frac{8}{3} + 4 - 4\right) - \left(-\frac{1}{3} + 1 - \frac{1}{4}\right)\right]$$

$$= \frac{9\rho}{4}$$

$$m = \rho \int_a^b [f(x) - g(x)]\, dx$$

$$= \rho \int_{-1}^{2} (x + 2 - x^2)\, dx$$

$$= \rho\left(\frac{x^2}{2} + 2x - \frac{x^3}{3}\right)\Bigg|_{-1}^{2}$$

$$= \rho\left[\left(2 + 4 - \frac{8}{3}\right) - \left(\frac{1}{2} - 2 + \frac{1}{3}\right)\right]$$

$$= \frac{9\rho}{2}$$

Then

$$\bar{x} = \frac{M_y}{m} = \frac{9\rho/4}{9\rho/2} = \frac{1}{2}$$

$$\bar{y} = \frac{M_x}{m} = \frac{36\rho/5}{9\rho/2} = \frac{8}{5}$$

The center of mass is $\left(\frac{1}{2}, \frac{8}{5}\right)$.

Note that the density ρ cancels in both $\bar{x}$ and $\bar{y}$. That is, the center of mass of a thin plate or area of uniform density depends only on its shape and not its density. Thus we may find the centroid as follows:

CENTROID OF A PLANE REGION OR THIN PLATE

Let $g(x) \le f(x)$ be continuous functions on $a \le x \le b$. The centroid $(\bar{x}, \bar{y})$ of the region bounded by $y = f(x)$, $y = g(x)$, $x = a$, and $y = b$ is

$$\bar{x} = \frac{\displaystyle\int_a^b x[f(x) - g(x)]\, dx}{A}$$

and

$$\bar{y} = \frac{\displaystyle\frac{1}{2}\int_a^b \{[f(x)]^2 - [g(x)]^2\}\, dx}{A}$$

where A is the area of the region.

EXAMPLE 5

Find the centroid of the region bounded by $y = x^4$ and $y = x$.

First, graph the equations and find the points of intersection (see Fig. 19.38).

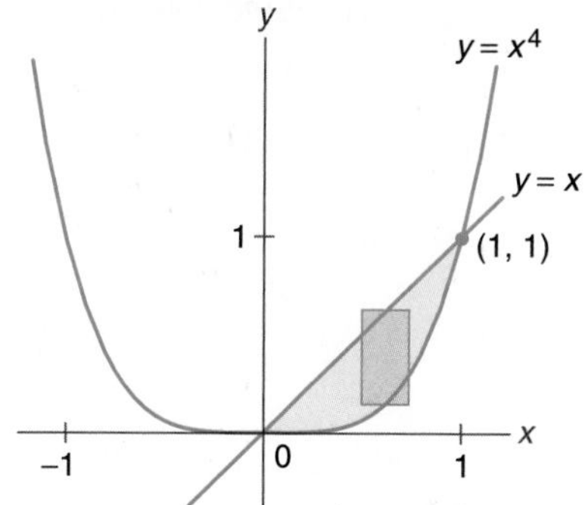

Figure 19.38

$$A = \int_0^1 (x - x^4)\,dx$$
$$= \left(\frac{x^2}{2} - \frac{x^5}{5}\right)\Bigg|_0^1$$
$$= \left(\frac{1}{2} - \frac{1}{5}\right) - (0) = \frac{3}{10}$$
$$\bar{x} = \frac{\int_a^b x[f(x) - g(x)]\,dx}{A}$$
$$= \frac{\int_0^1 x(x - x^4)\,dx}{3/10}$$
$$= \frac{10}{3}\int_0^1 (x^2 - x^5)\,dx$$
$$= \frac{10}{3}\left(\frac{x^3}{3} - \frac{x^6}{6}\right)\Bigg|_0^1$$
$$= \frac{10}{3}\left[\left(\frac{1}{3} - \frac{1}{6}\right) - (0)\right]$$
$$= \frac{10}{3}\left(\frac{1}{6}\right) = \frac{5}{9}$$
$$\bar{y} = \frac{\frac{1}{2}\int_a^b \{[f(x)]^2 - [g(x)]^2\}\,dx}{A}$$
$$= \frac{\frac{1}{2}\int_0^1 [(x)^2 - (x^4)^2]\,dx}{3/10}$$
$$= \frac{5}{3}\int_0^1 (x^2 - x^8)\,dx$$
$$= \frac{5}{3}\left(\frac{x^3}{3} - \frac{x^9}{9}\right)\Bigg|_0^1$$
$$= \frac{5}{3}\left[\left(\frac{1}{3} - \frac{1}{9}\right) - (0)\right]$$
$$= \frac{5}{3}\left(\frac{2}{9}\right)$$
$$= \frac{10}{27}$$

The centroid is $\left(\frac{5}{9}, \frac{10}{27}\right)$.

The most general case of finding the center of mass of a two-dimensional mass distribution requires double integration and is not treated in this text.

A solid of revolution of constant density has its centroid on its axis of revolution. Let the area bounded by $y = f(x)$, $x = a$, and $x = b$ be revolved about the x-axis. We have drawn a typical disk in Fig. 19.39. Its center of mass is x units from the y-axis; therefore, the length of its moment arm is x. Its volume is $\pi y^2\,dx$. Since the solid is of constant density ρ, its mass is proportional to its volume, that is, $m = \rho\pi y^2\,dx$. Thus the moment about the y-axis is

$$md = (\rho\pi y^2\,dx)x = \rho\pi x y^2\,dx$$

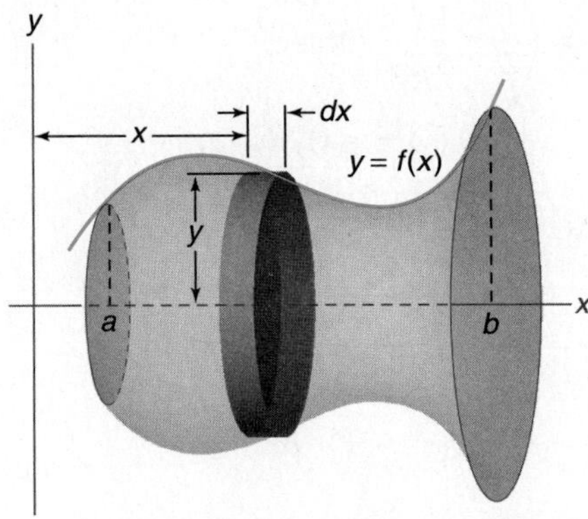

Figure 19.39 Finding the center of mass, or centroid, of a solid of revolution about the x-axis.

The sum of the moments of all such disks may be expressed by the integral

$$M_y = \rho\pi \int_a^b xy^2\,dx$$

The mass of the solid may be expressed by the integral

$$m = \rho\pi \int_a^b y^2\,dx$$

CENTROID OF A SOLID OF REVOLUTION ABOUT THE X-AXIS

$$\bar{x} = \frac{M_y}{m} = \frac{\int_a^b xy^2\,dx}{\int_a^b y^2\,dx} \quad \text{and} \quad \bar{y} = 0$$

Note: The ρ and π factors cancel.
In a similar manner, we can show:

CENTROID OF A SOLID OF REVOLUTION ABOUT THE Y-AXIS

$$\bar{y} = \frac{M_x}{m} = \frac{\int_c^d yx^2\,dy}{\int_c^d x^2\,dy} \quad \text{and} \quad \bar{x} = 0$$

EXAMPLE 6

Find the centroid of the solid formed by revolving the region bounded by $y = x^2$, $x = 1$, and $y = 0$ about the x-axis (see Fig. 19.40).

$$\bar{x} = \frac{\int_a^b xy^2\,dx}{\int_a^b y^2\,dx}$$

$$= \frac{\int_0^1 x(x^2)^2\,dx}{\int_0^1 (x^2)^2\,dx}$$

$$= \frac{\int_0^1 x^5\,dx}{\int_0^1 x^4\,dx}$$

$$= \frac{\left.\frac{x^6}{6}\right|_0^1}{\left.\frac{x^5}{5}\right|_0^1} = \frac{\frac{1}{6}}{\frac{1}{5}} = \frac{5}{6}$$

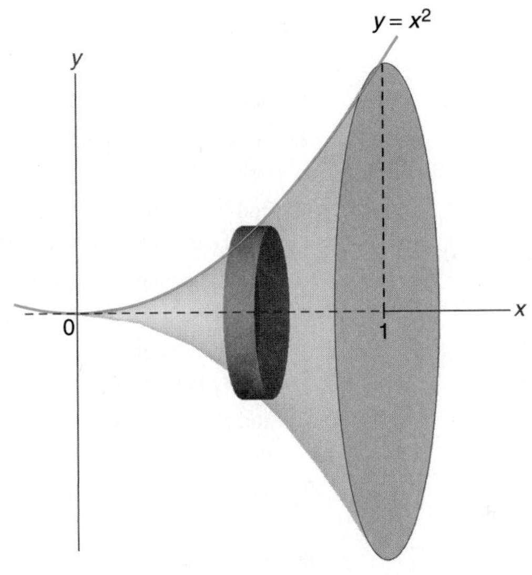

Figure 19.40

The centroid is $\left(\frac{5}{6}, 0\right)$.

EXAMPLE 7

Find the centroid of the solid formed by revolving the region bounded by $y = 4 - x^2$, $x = 0$, and $y = 0$ about the y-axis (see Fig. 19.41).

$$\bar{y} = \frac{\int_c^d yx^2\,dy}{\int_c^d x^2\,dy}$$

$$= \frac{\int_0^4 y(4 - y)\,dy}{\int_0^4 (4 - y)\,dy} \qquad (Note\text{: } x^2 = 4 - y.)$$

$$= \frac{\int_0^4 (4y - y^2)\,dy}{\int_0^4 (4 - y)\,dy}$$

$$= \frac{\left.\left(2y^2 - \frac{y^3}{3}\right)\right|_0^4}{\left.\left(4y - \frac{y^2}{2}\right)\right|_0^4} = \frac{\left(32 - \frac{64}{3}\right) - (0)}{(16 - 8) - (0)} = \frac{32/3}{8} = \frac{4}{3}$$

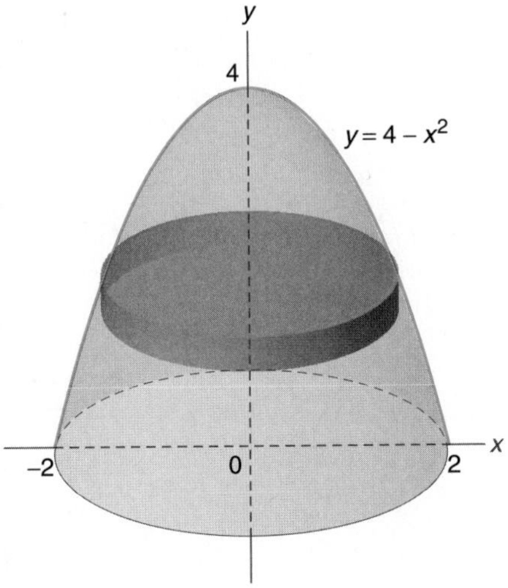

Figure 19.41

The centroid is $\left(0, \frac{4}{3}\right)$.

The most general case of finding the center of mass of a three-dimensional mass distribution requires triple integration and is not treated in this text.

Exercises 19.5

1. Find the center of mass of a straight wire 20 cm long and of uniform density.
2. Show that the center of mass of a straight wire of length L and of uniform density is at its midpoint.
3. Find the center of mass measured from the lighter end of a straight wire 10 cm long whose density is given by $\rho(x) = 0.1x$, where x is the distance from one end.
4. Find the center of mass measured from the lighter end of a straight wire 8 cm long whose density is given by $\rho(x) = 0.1x^2$, where x is the distance from one end.
5. Find the center of mass measured from the lighter end of a straight wire 12 cm long whose density is given by $\rho(x) = 4 + x^2$, where x is the distance from one end.
6. Find the center of mass measured from the lighter end of a straight wire 9 cm long whose density is given by $\rho(x) = 3 - \sqrt{x}$, where x is the distance from one end.
7. The density of a straight wire 6 cm long is directly proportional to the distance from one end. Find its center of mass.
8. The density of a straight wire 9 cm long varies inversely as the square root of the distance from one end. Find its center of mass.

Find the center of mass of each uniform thin plate.

9.

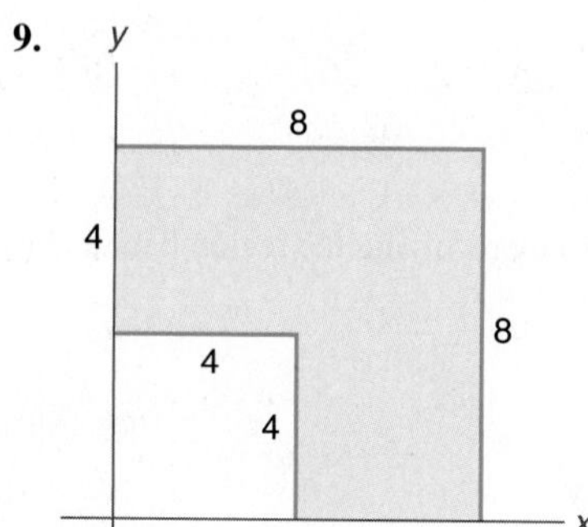

10.

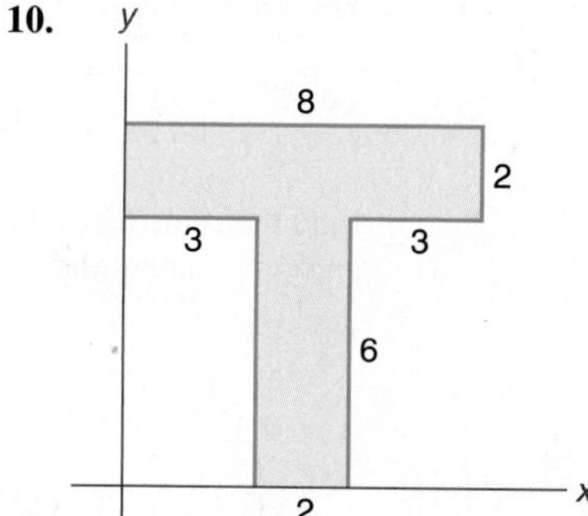

11.

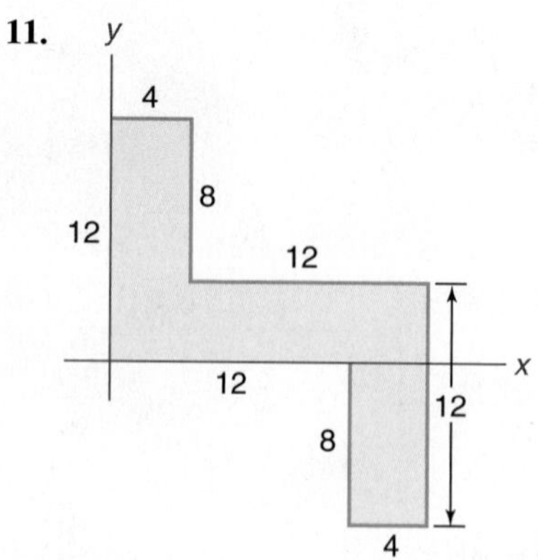

12.

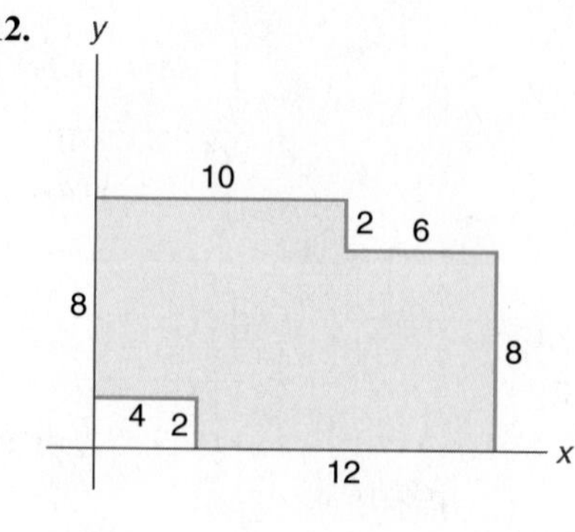

13.

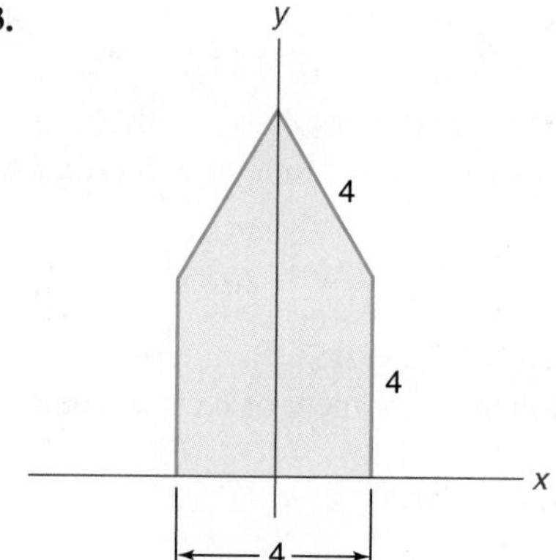

14.

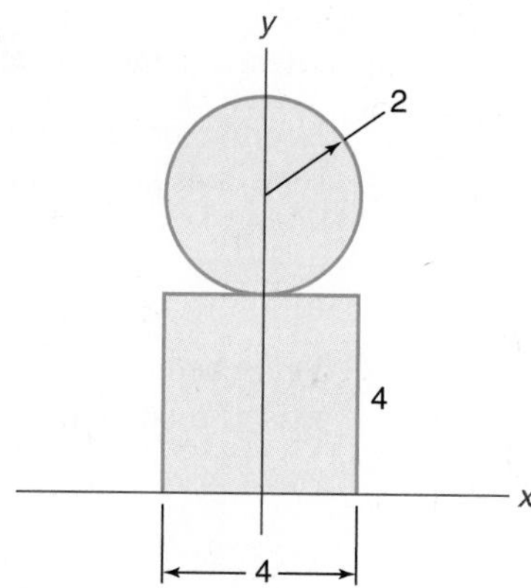

Find the centroid of each region bounded by the given curves.

15. $y = \sqrt{x}, y = 0$, and $x = 9$

16. $y = x^2$ and $y = 4$

17. $y = x^2 - 2x$ and $y = 0$

18. $y = 4 - x^2$ and $y = x^2 - 4$

19. $y = 4 - x^2$ and $y = 0$

20. $y = 4 - x^2$ and $y = x + 2$

21. $y = x^3$ and $y = x$ (first quadrant)

22. $y = x^3, x = 0$, and $y = 1$

23. Find the centroid of the semicircle of radius 1 with center at the origin lying in the first and second quadrants.

24. Find the centroid of the quarter circle of radius 1 with center at the origin lying in the first quadrant.

Find the centroid of the solid formed by revolving each region bounded by the given curves about the given axis.

25. $y = x^3, y = 0$, and $x = 1$ about the x-axis

26. $y = x^3, y = 0$, and $x = 1$ about the y-axis

27. $y = 3 - x, x = 0$, and $y = 0$ about the x-axis

28. $y = 3 - 2x, x = 0$, and $y = 0$ about the y-axis

29. $y = x^2, x = 1$, and $y = 0$ about the y-axis

30. $x^2 + y^2 = 1, x = 0$, and $y = 0$ about the x-axis

19.6 MOMENTS OF INERTIA

In Sections 19.4 and 19.5 we used moments to find centers of mass and centroids. Each moment was the product of the mass and its distance from some line. This case is called the first moment.

The second moment, called the *moment of inertia* about a line, is defined as the product of a mass m and the square of its distance d from a given line, that is,

$$I = md^2$$

Inertia is a property of an object that resists a change in its motion. That is, inertia is a property of an object that causes it to remain at rest if it is at rest or to continue moving with constant velocity.

MOMENT OF INERTIA OF A SYSTEM

Let masses $m_1, m_2, m_3, \ldots, m_n$ be at distances $d_1, d_2, d_3, \ldots, d_n$, respectively, from some axis about which they are rotating. The moment of inertia I of the system is

$$I = m_1d_1^2 + m_2d_2^2 + m_3d_3^2 + \cdots + m_nd_n^2$$

Let m be the sum of all the masses in the systems and let R be the distance from the axis of rotation that gives the same total moment of inertia. Then

$$I = mR^2 = m_1d_1^2 + m_2d_2^2 + m_3d_3^2 + \cdots + m_nd_n^2$$

R is called the *radius* of *gyration*. It tells how far from the axis of rotation the entire mass would be concentrated to have the same moment of inertia. This is a convenient way to express the moment of inertia of the mass of a body in terms of its mass and a length.

EXAMPLE 1

Find the moment of inertia and the radius of gyration about the y-axis of the system $m_1 = 8$ at $(2, -4)$, $m_2 = 3$ at $(-9, 8)$, and $m_3 = 6$ at $(-5, 2)$.

$$I_y = m_1x_1^2 + m_2x_2^2 + m_3x_3^2$$
$$I_y = 8(2)^2 + 3(-9)^2 + 6(-5)^2 = 425$$
$$m = m_1 + m_2 + m_3 = 8 + 3 + 6 = 17$$
$$I_y = mR^2$$
$$R = \sqrt{\frac{I_y}{m}} = \sqrt{\frac{425}{17}} = 5$$

Now, let's find the moment of inertia of an area of constant density ρ about the y-axis as shown in Fig. 19.42. First, divide the area into n rectangles, each of width Δx. Let (x_i, y_i) be the center of mass of the ith rectangle. As we saw in the preceding sections, the y-value

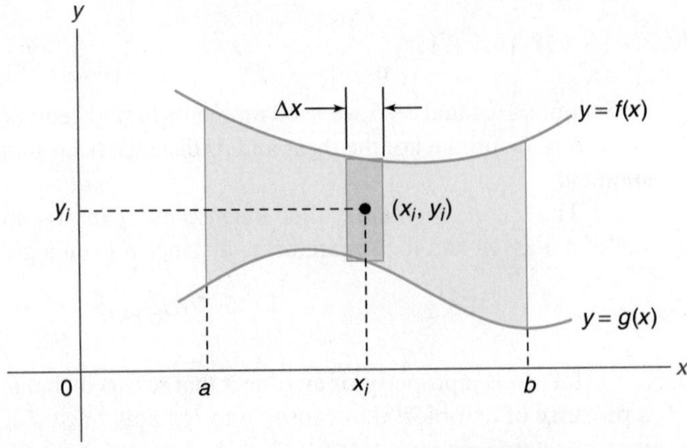

Figure 19.42 Finding the moment of inertia of an area of constant density about the y-axis.

of the geometric center of the ith rectangle is

$$y_i = \frac{f(x_i) + g(x_i)}{2}$$

Its area is $[f(x_i) - g(x_i)]\,\Delta x$ and its mass is $\rho[f(x_i) - g(x_i)]\,\Delta x$. The total mass is the integral

$$m = \rho \int_a^b [f(x) - g(x)]dx = \rho A$$

where A is the area of the region.

The distance of the center of the ith rectangle from the y-axis is x_i. Its moment of inertia, its second moment, is then

$$(\text{mass})(\text{moment arm})^2 = \rho[f(x_i) - g(x_i)]\,\Delta x \cdot (x_i)^2$$

Summing the moments of all such rectangles, we obtain the moment of inertia of the region about the y-axis as the integral

$$I_y = \rho \int_a^b x^2[f(x) - g(x)]\,dx$$

Similarly, the moment of inertia of an area about the x-axis is

$$I_x = \rho \int_c^d y^2[f(y) - g(y)]\,dy$$

The radius of gyration for each moment is as follows:

About y-axis	About x-axis
$I_y = mR^2$	$I_x = mR^2$
$R = \sqrt{\dfrac{I_y}{m}}$	$R = \sqrt{\dfrac{I_x}{m}}$

MOMENTS OF INERTIA OF AN AREA OF CONSTANT DENSITY ABOUT THE x- AND y-AXES

Let $g(x) \le f(x)$ be continuous functions on $a \le x \le b$ for the area of constant density ρ bounded by $y = f(x)$, $y = g(x)$, $x = a$, and $x = b$. The moment of inertia about the y-axis is

$$I_y = \rho \int_a^b x^2[f(x) - g(x)]\,dx \qquad \left(R = \sqrt{\frac{I_y}{m}}\right)$$

Similarly, the moment of inertia about the x-axis is

$$I_x = \rho \int_c^d y^2[f(y) - g(y)]\,dy \qquad \left(R = \sqrt{\frac{I_x}{m}}\right)$$

EXAMPLE 2

Find the moment of inertia and the radius of gyration about the y-axis of the region bounded by $y = x^2$, $y = 0$, and $x = 3$, where the region has a constant density of 5 (see Fig. 19.43).

$$\begin{aligned}
I_y &= \rho \int_a^b x^2[f(x) - g(x)]\,dx \\
&= 5 \int_0^3 x^2[x^2 - 0]\,dx \\
&= 5 \int_0^3 x^4\,dx \\
&= 5 \cdot \frac{x^5}{5}\bigg|_0^3 \\
&= 243 \\
m &= \rho \int_a^b [f(x) - g(x)]\,dx \\
&= 5 \int_0^3 (x^2 - 0)\,dx \\
&= 5 \cdot \frac{x^3}{3}\bigg|_0^3 \\
&= 45 \\
R &= \sqrt{\frac{I_y}{m}} = \sqrt{\frac{243}{45}} = 2.32
\end{aligned}$$

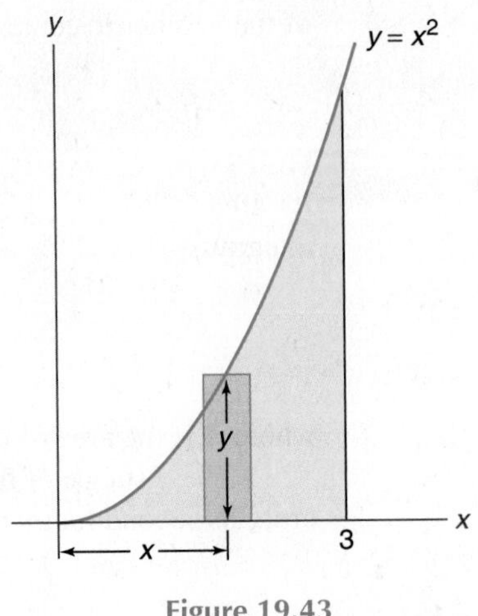

Figure 19.43

EXAMPLE 3

Find the moment of inertia and the radius of gyration about the x-axis of the region described in Example 2 (see Fig. 19.44).

$$\begin{aligned}
I_x &= \rho \int_c^d y^2[f(y) - g(y)]\,dy \\
&= 5 \int_0^9 y^2[3 - \sqrt{y}]\,dy \qquad (3 - x = 3 - \sqrt{y}) \\
&= 5 \int_0^9 [3y^2 - y^{5/2}]\,dy
\end{aligned}$$

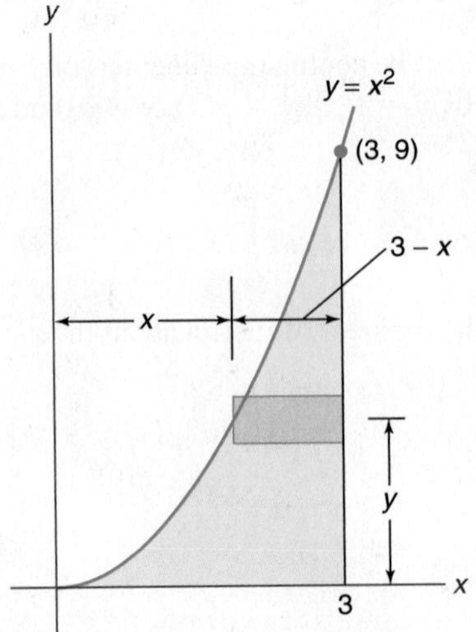

Figure 19.44

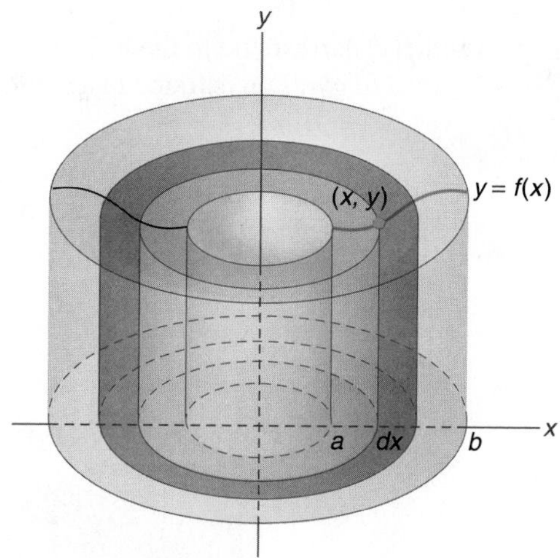

Figure 19.45 Finding the moment of inertia of a solid of revolution with respect to its y-axis of revolution.

$$= 5\left[y^3 - \frac{y^{7/2}}{7/2}\right]\Bigg|_0^9$$

$$= 5\left[9^3 - \frac{9^{7/2}}{7/2}\right] - 5[0] = 521 \qquad \text{(three significant digits)}$$

$$R = \sqrt{\frac{I_x}{m}} = \sqrt{\frac{521}{45}} = 3.40$$

To find the moment of inertia of a solid of revolution with respect to its axis of revolution, it is most convenient to use the shell method. Let the area bounded by $y = f(x)$, $y = 0$, $x = a$, and $x = b$ be revolved about the y-axis. We have drawn a typical shell in Fig. 19.45. The mass of the solid is proportional to its volume, $m = \rho V$:

$$m = 2\pi\rho \int_a^b x f(x)\, dx$$

and x^2 is the square of its distance from the y-axis. Summing all such shells gives the following results:

MOMENTS OF INERTIA OF A SOLID OF REVOLUTION

The moment of inertia of a solid of revolution about the y-axis is given by the integral

$$I_y = 2\pi\rho \int_a^b x^3 f(x)\, dx$$

Similarly, let the area bounded by $x = f(y)$, $x = 0$, $y = c$, and $y = d$ be revolved about the x-axis as in Fig. 19.46. Its moment of inertia about the x-axis is given by the integral

$$I_x = 2\pi\rho \int_c^d y^3 f(y)\, dy$$

Note: $f(x)$ and $f(y)$ correspond to the height of the shell.

Each radius of gyration is found in a similar way as that for a plane region, that is,

$$R = \sqrt{\frac{I_y}{m}} \quad \text{or} \quad R = \sqrt{\frac{I_x}{m}}$$

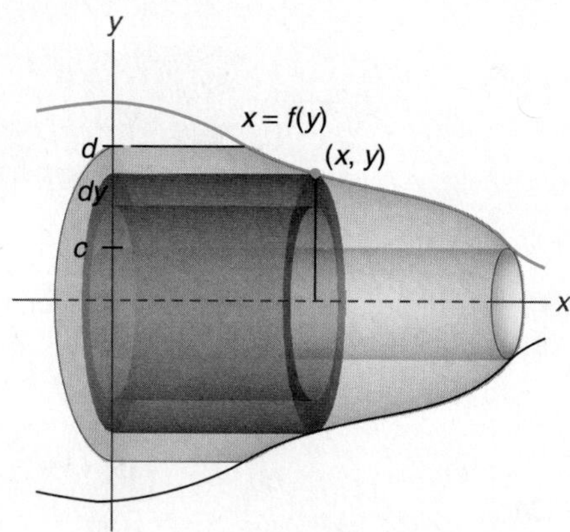

Figure 19.46 Finding the moment of inertia of a solid of revolution with respect to its x-axis of revolution.

EXAMPLE 4

Find the moment of inertia and the radius of gyration of the solid formed by revolving the region bounded by $y = 2x$, $y = 0$, and $x = 3$ about the y-axis. Assume that $\rho = 5$ (see Fig. 19.47).

$$\begin{aligned}
I_y &= 2\pi\rho \int_a^b x^3 f(x)\,dx \\
&= 2\pi(5) \int_0^3 x^3(2x)\,dx \\
&= 20\pi \int_0^3 x^4\,dx \\
&= 20\pi \cdot \frac{x^5}{5}\Big|_0^3 = 972\pi \\
m &= 2\pi\rho \int_a^b x f(x)\,dx \\
&= 2\pi(5) \int_0^3 x(2x)\,dx \\
&= 20\pi \int_0^3 x^2\,dx \\
&= 20\pi \cdot \frac{x^3}{3}\Big|_0^3 = 180\pi \\
R &= \sqrt{\frac{I_y}{m}} = \sqrt{\frac{927\pi}{180\pi}} = 2.32
\end{aligned}$$

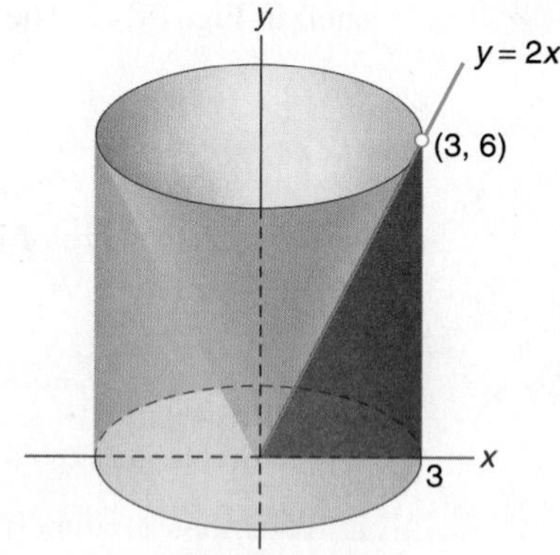

Figure 19.47

EXAMPLE 5

Find the moment of inertia and the radius of gyration of the solid formed by revolving the region bounded by $y = x^2$, $y = 0$, and $x = 2$ about the x-axis. Assume that $\rho = 1$ (see Fig. 19.48).

$$I_x = 2\pi\rho \int_c^d y^3 f(y)\,dy$$

$$= 2\pi(1) \int_0^4 y^3(2 - \sqrt{y})\,dy \qquad (2 - x = 2 - \sqrt{y})$$

$$= 2\pi \int_0^4 (2y^3 - y^{7/2})\,dy$$

$$= 2\pi\left(\frac{y^4}{2} - \frac{y^{9/2}}{9/2}\right)\Bigg|_0^4$$

$$= 2\pi\left(128 - \frac{1024}{9}\right) = \frac{256\pi}{9}$$

$$m = 2\pi\rho \int_c^d y f(y)\,dy$$

$$= 2\pi(1) \int_0^4 y(2 - \sqrt{y})\,dy$$

$$= 2\pi \int_0^4 (2y - y^{3/2})\,dy$$

$$= 2\pi\left(y^2 - \frac{y^{5/2}}{5/2}\right)\Bigg|_0^4$$

$$= 2\pi\left(16 - \frac{64}{5}\right) = \frac{32\pi}{5}$$

$$R = \sqrt{\frac{I_x}{m}} = \sqrt{\frac{256\pi/9}{32\pi/5}} = 2.11$$

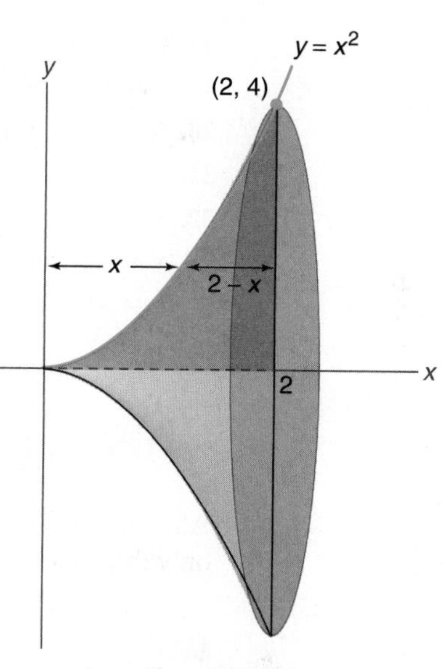

Figure 19.48

Exercises 19.6

Find the moment of inertia and the radius of gyration about the y-axis of each system.

1. $m_1 = 9$ at $(3, -2)$, $m_2 = 12$ at $(5, 4)$, $m_3 = 15$ at $(3, 7)$
2. $m_1 = 3$ at $(-6, 2)$, $m_2 = 9$ at $(-5, 8)$, $m_3 = 8$ at $(7, -2)$
3. $m_1 = 15$ at $(3, -9)$, $m_2 = 10$ at $(6, -4)$, $m_3 = 18$ at $(9, 2)$, $m_4 = 12$ at $(1, 3)$
4. $m_1 = 24$ at $(-6, 3)$, $m_2 = 36$ at $(7, -9)$, $m_3 = 15$ at $(4, 4)$, $m_4 = 12$ at $(-2, -5)$, $m_5 = 18$ at $(8, 6)$

Find the moment of inertia and the radius of gyration about the x-axis of each system.

5. The system in Exercise 1
6. $m_1 = 8$ at $(-3, 9)$, $m_2 = 16$ at $(8, -6)$, $m_3 = 14$ at $(4, 2)$
7. $m_1 = 9$ at $(-5, -9)$, $m_2 = 5$ at $(8, -2)$, $m_3 = 8$ at $(5, 0)$, $m_4 = 10$ at $(-3, 1)$
8. The system in Exercise 4

Find the moment of inertia and the radius of gyration of each region bounded by the given curves about the given axis.

9. $y = x^2$, $x = 0$, and $y = 4$ about the y-axis ($\rho = 5$)
10. Region of Exercise 9 about the x-axis

11. $y = x^2$, $y = x$, and $x > 0$ about the x-axis ($\rho = 4$)

12. Region of Exercise 11 about the y-axis

13. $y = 5 - x^2$, $y = 1$, and $x = 0$ about the y-axis ($\rho = 3$)

14. $x = 1 + y^2$, $x = 10$, and $y = 0$ about the x-axis ($\rho = 5$)

15. $y = 1/x^2$, $y = 0$, $x = 1$, and $x = 2$ about the y-axis ($\rho = 2$)

16. $y = 4x - x^2$ and $y = 0$ about the y-axis ($\rho = 15$)

Find the moment of inertia and the radius of gyration of the solid formed by revolving the region bounded by the given curves about the given axis.

17. $y = 3x$, $y = 0$, and $x = 2$ about the y-axis ($\rho = 15$)

18. Region of Exercise 17 about the x-axis

19. $y = 4x^2$, $y = 0$, and $x = 2$ about the x-axis ($\rho = 1$)

20. Region of Exercise 19 about the y-axis

21. $y = 9 - x^2$, $y = 0$, and $x = 0$ about the y-axis ($\rho = 12$)

22. $x = 4 - y^2$, $y = 0$, and $x = 0$ about the x-axis ($\rho = 6$)

23. $y = 4x - x^2$ and $y = 0$ about the y-axis ($\rho = 15$)

24. $y = 1/x^3$, $x = 0$, $y = 1$, and $y = 8$ about the x-axis ($\rho = 2$)

19.7 WORK, FLUID PRESSURE, AND AVERAGE VALUE

Although there are still many more technical applications of the integral, we will consider only three more in this section: work, fluid pressure, and average value.

Work

When a constant force F is applied to an object, moving it through a distance s, the technical term *work* is defined to be the product $F \cdot s$. That is, work W is the product of the force and the distance through which the force acts.

EXAMPLE 1

A 70-lb container is lifted 8 ft above the floor. Find the work done.

$$\begin{aligned} W &= F \cdot s \\ &= (70 \text{ lb})(8 \text{ ft}) \\ &= 560 \text{ ft-lb} \end{aligned}$$

This formula for work is appropriate when the force remains constant. However, if an object is moved from a to b by a variable force F, then we can approximate the work done as follows: Divide the interval from a to b into intervals, each of width Δx. Let F_k represent the value of the force acting on the object somewhere in the kth interval (see Fig. 19.49).

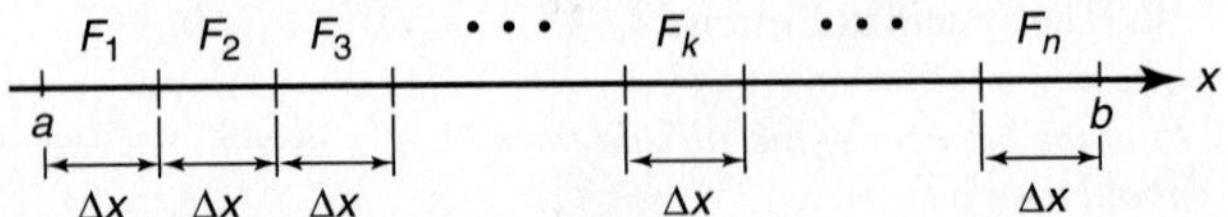

Figure 19.49 The work done by a variable force in moving an object from a to b is the sum of the work done in each interval of width Δx.

Then $\Delta W_k = F_k \cdot \Delta x$ is an approximation for the work done in the kth interval. If there are n intervals, each of width Δx, from a to b, then

$$W_{\text{approx}} = F_1 \cdot \Delta x + F_2 \cdot \Delta x + F_3 \cdot \Delta x + \cdots + F_n \cdot \Delta x$$

is an approximation for the work done moving the object from a to b. If the variable force can be expressed as a function of the distance traveled by the object, then it is possible to use integration techniques to find the actual work done. Suppose that $F = f(x)$ expresses the force as a function of the distance traveled by the object. Then

$$W_{\text{approx}} = f(x_1) \cdot \Delta x + f(x_2) \cdot \Delta x + f(x_3) \cdot \Delta x + \cdots + f(x_k) \cdot \Delta x + \cdots + f(x_n) \cdot \Delta x$$

is an approximation for W, the actual work done, where x_k is a number in the kth interval.

The smaller we choose Δx, the better approximation we obtain for W_{approx}. In fact, if we let Δx approach 0, then W_{approx} approaches the actual work done W. Then

WORK

$$W = \int_a^b f(x)\, dx$$

since this is how the definite integral of $f(x)$ from a to b was described in Chapter 5.

Note that work is the integral of force with respect to the displacement x. Thus, in setting up a work calculation, the force must be modeled as a function of the displacement. The reason for this comment is that work is not the only application that involves the integral of a force function. In physics, for example, *impulse* is defined as the integral of force with respect to the time variable t.

EXAMPLE 2

Find the work done by a force F moving an object from $x = 1$ to $x = 2$ according to $F = f(x) = x^2$.

$$\begin{aligned} W &= \int_1^2 x^2\, dx \\ &= \frac{x^3}{3}\bigg|_1^2 = \frac{8}{3} - \frac{1}{3} = \frac{7}{3} \end{aligned}$$

EXAMPLE 3

Hooke's law states that the force required to stretch a spring is directly proportional to the amount that it is stretched. Find the work done in stretching a spring 3 in. if it requires 12 lb of force to stretch it 10 in.

Let x represent the distance stretched by the force $F = f(x)$. Then, by Hooke's law

$$f(x) = kx$$

At $x = 10$ we know that $f(10) = 12$, so

$$\begin{aligned} 12 &= k(10) \\ k &= \frac{6}{5} \end{aligned}$$

Then,

$$f(x) = \frac{6}{5}x$$

and

$$W = \int_a^b f(x)\, dx$$

$$= \int_0^3 \frac{6}{5}x\,dx$$

$$= \frac{6}{5}\left(\frac{x^2}{2}\right)\Big|_0^3 = \frac{6}{5}\left(\frac{9}{2} - 0\right)$$

$$= \frac{27}{5} \text{ in.-lb}$$

EXAMPLE 4

Two charged particles separated by a distance x (in metres) attract each other with a force $F = 4.65 \times 10^{-20} x^{-2}$ newton (N). Find the work done (in joules) in separating them over an interval from $x = 0.01$ m to $x = 0.1$ m.

$$W = \int_{0.01}^{0.1} 4.65 \times 10^{-20} x^{-2}\,dx$$

$$= 4.65 \times 10^{-20} \int_{0.01}^{0.1} x^{-2}\,dx$$

$$= 4.65 \times 10^{-20}\left(\frac{x^{-1}}{-1}\Big|_{0.01}^{0.1}\right)$$

$$= 4.65 \times 10^{-20}\left(\frac{-1}{x}\Big|_{0.01}^{0.1}\right)$$

$$= 4.65 \times 10^{-20}\left(\frac{-1}{0.1} - \frac{-1}{0.01}\right)$$

$$= 4.65 \times 10^{-20}(-10 + 100)$$

$$= 4.19 \times 10^{-18} \text{ N m}$$

$$= 4.19 \times 10^{-18} \text{ J}$$

Note: The metric system unit of work is the joule (J). 1 J = 1 N m.

EXAMPLE 5

A chain 50 ft long and weighing 4 lb/ft is hanging from a pulley. (a) How much work is needed to pull 30 ft of the chain to the top? (b) How much work is needed to pull all of the chain to the top?

The force needed to lift the chain at any one time equals the weight of the chain hanging down at that time. If x feet of chain are hanging down and the chain weighs 4 lb/ft, the force is

$$f(x) = F = 4x$$

(a) $W = \int_{20}^{50} 4x\,dx$

$= 2x^2\Big|_{20}^{50} = 4200$ ft-lb

(b) $W = \int_{0}^{50} 4x\,dx$

$= 2x^2\Big|_{0}^{50} = 5000$ ft-lb

EXAMPLE 6

A cylindrical tank 10 ft in diameter and 12 ft high is full of water. How much work is needed to pump all the water out over the top? The density of water $\rho = 62.4$ lb/ft^3.

First, divide the tank into n layers, each of thickness Δx as in Fig. 19.50. Let x be the distance that each layer travels as it is pumped to the top. The force is the weight of each layer of water. $F = \rho V$.

Each layer is in the shape of a cylinder, whose volume is given by

$$V = \pi r^2 h$$

So,

$$F = \rho V = 62.4\pi(5^2)\,\Delta x$$

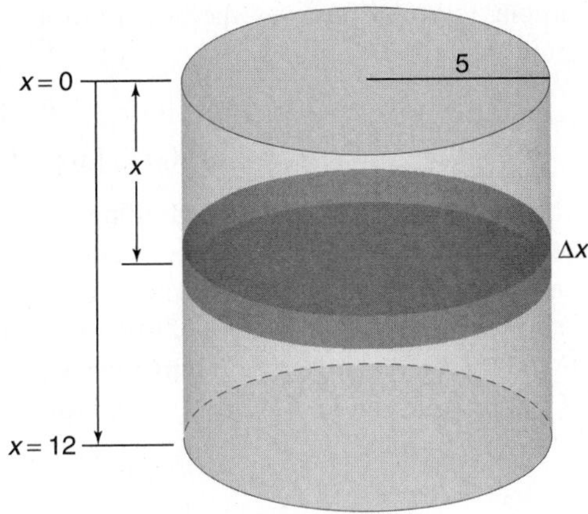

Figure 19.50

is the force of each layer. Since each layer travels a distance of x feet, the work needed to move one layer to the top is

$$\begin{aligned} W &= F \cdot s = 62.4\pi(5^2)\Delta x \cdot x \\ &= 1560\pi x \, \Delta x \end{aligned}$$

Summing the work of such layers gives

$$\begin{aligned} W &= \int_0^{12} 1560\pi x \, dx \\ &= 780\pi \, x^2 \Big|_0^{12} \\ &= 112{,}320\pi \text{ ft-lb} \end{aligned}$$

Fluid Pressure

As a body goes deeper under water, the pressure on it increases because the water's weight increases with depth. Fluids are different in this respect from solids in that, where solids exert only a downward force due to gravity, the force exerted by fluids is the same in all directions. *Hydrostatic pressure* is the pressure at any given depth in a fluid due to its weight and may be expressed by

$$p = \rho g h$$

where p is the pressure, ρ is the mass density of the fluid, g is the force of gravity, and h is the height or depth of the fluid. For example, if you are in a swimming pool 12 ft below the surface, the pressure you feel is

$$\begin{aligned} p &= \rho g h \\ p &= (62.4 \text{ lb/ft}^3)(12 \text{ ft}) \qquad (\rho g = 62.4 \text{ lb/ft}^3) \\ &= 748.8 \text{ lb/ft}^2 \end{aligned}$$

The total force is given by

$$F = pA$$

One main interest in fluid pressure is determining the total force exerted by a fluid on the walls of its container. If the container has vertical sides, it is simple to calculate the total force on the *bottom* of the container, that is,

$$F = \rho g h A$$

For example, the total force on the bottom of a rectangular swimming pool 12 ft × 30 ft when the water is 8 ft deep is

$$F = (62.4 \text{ lb/ft}^3)(8 \text{ ft})(12 \text{ ft} \times 30 \text{ ft})$$
$$F = 180{,}000 \text{ lb (approx.)}$$

The more difficult problem is finding the total force against the *vertical sides* of a container because the pressure is not constant. The pressure increases as the depth increases.

Let a vertical plane region be submerged into a fluid of constant density ρ as shown in Fig. 19.51. We need to find the total force against this region from depth $h - a$ to $h - b$. First, divide the interval $a \leq y \leq b$ into n rectangles each of width Δy. The ith rectangle has length L_i, area $L_i\,\Delta y$, and depth $h - y_i$. The force on the ith rectangle is

$$\Delta F_i = \rho g(h - y_i)L_i\,\Delta y$$

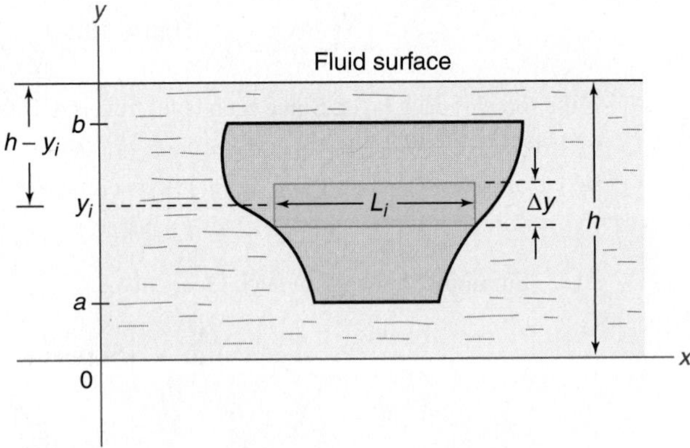

Figure 19.51 Finding the force exerted by a fluid against a submerged vertical plane.

Summing the forces on all such rectangles gives the following integral:

FORCE EXERTED BY A FLUID

The force F exerted by a fluid of constant mass density ρ against a submerged vertical plane region from $y = a$ to $y = b$ is given by

$$F = \rho g \int_a^b (h - y)L\,dy$$

where h is the total depth of the fluid and L is the horizontal length of the region at y.

Note: In the metric system, the mass density ρ must be known and $g = 9.80 \text{ m/s}^2$. In the English system, the weight density ρg must be known.

EXAMPLE 7

A vertical gate in a dam is in the shape of an isosceles trapezoid 12 ft across the top and 8 ft across the bottom, with a height of 10 ft. Find the total force against the gate if the water surface is at the top of the gate.

The solution can be simplified if we position the trapezoid in the plane as shown in Fig. 19.52. The equation of the line through (4, 0) and (6, 10) is

$$y - 0 = 5(x - 4)$$
$$x = \frac{y + 20}{5}$$

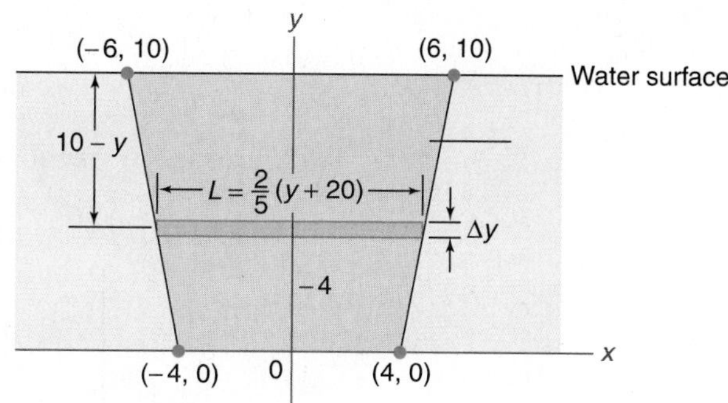

Figure 19.52

The width of the ith rectangle is Δy; its length L may be written as

$$L = 2x = 2\left(\frac{y + 20}{5}\right) = \frac{2}{5}(y + 20)$$

and its depth is $10 - y$. So

$$F = \rho g \int_a^b (h - y)L\, dy$$

$$F = 62.4 \int_0^{10} (10 - y)\frac{2}{5}(y + 20)\, dy$$

$$= 24.96 \int_0^{10} (10 - y)(y + 20)\, dy$$

$$= 24.96 \int_0^{10} (200 - 10y - y^2)\, dy$$

$$= 24.96\left(200y - 5y^2 - \frac{y^3}{3}\right)\Bigg|_0^{10}$$

$$= 24.96\left(2000 - 500 - \frac{1000}{3}\right)$$

$$= 29{,}120 \text{ lb}$$

EXAMPLE 8

A vertical gate in a dam is semicircular and has a diameter of 8 m. Find the total force against the gate if the water level is 1 m from the top of the gate.

Here place the semicircle with center at the origin as in Fig. 19.53. Its equation is $x^2 + y^2 = 16$. Other positions make the integration more difficult.

$$L = 2x = 2\sqrt{16 - y^2}$$

The depth of the rectangle is $0 - y$, or $-y$; $\rho = 1000$ kg/m^3; and $g = 9.80$ m/s^2.

$$F = \rho g \int_a^b (h - y)\, L\, dy$$

$$F = 9800 \int_{-4}^{-1} (-y)\, 2\sqrt{16 - y^2}\, dy$$

$$= -19{,}600 \int_{-4}^{-1} y(16 - y^2)^{1/2}\, dy$$

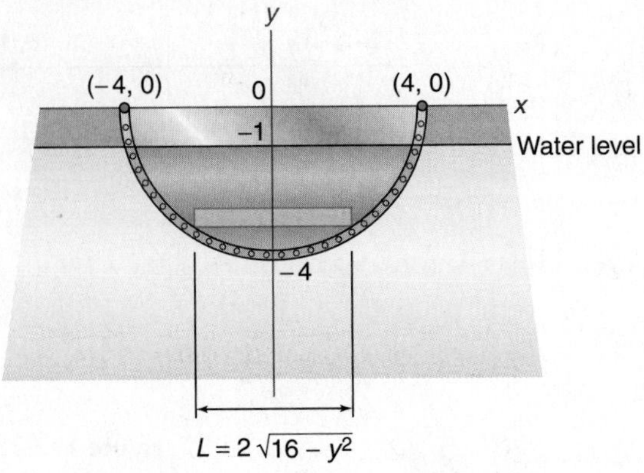

Figure 19.53

$$= -19{,}600 \int y u^{1/2} \frac{du}{-2y}$$

$u = 16 - y^2$
$du = -2y\, dy$

$$= 9800 \int u^{1/2}\, du$$

$$= 9800 \cdot \frac{u^{3/2}}{3/2} + C$$

$$= \frac{19{,}600}{3}(16 - y^2)^{3/2}\Big|_{-4}^{-1}$$

$$= \frac{19{,}600}{3}(15^{3/2} - 0)$$

$$= 379{,}600 \text{ N} \qquad \text{(4 significant digits)}$$

EXAMPLE 9

A swimming pool is 15 ft wide and 20 ft long. The bottom is flat but sloped so that the water is 4 ft deep at one end and 12 ft deep at the other end. Find the force of the water on one 20-ft side.

First, let's position the vertical side in the plane as shown in Fig. 19.54. Notice that the right ends of the horizontal strips sometimes are on the vertical line $x = 20$ and sometimes on the line through (0, 0) and (20, 8), whose equation is $y = 2x/5$. Thus we need two integrals. For each integral $L = x$.

$$F = 62.4 \int_0^8 (12 - y)x\, dy + 62.4 \int_8^{12} (12 - y)x\, dy$$

$$= 62.4 \int_0^8 (12 - y)\left(\frac{5}{2}y\right) dy + 62.4 \int_8^{12} (12 - y)(20)\, dy$$

$$= 156 \int_0^8 (12y - y^2)\, dy + 1248 \int_8^{12} (12 - y)\, dy$$

$$= 156\left(6y^2 - \frac{y^3}{3}\right)\Big|_0^8 + 1248\left(12y - \frac{y^2}{2}\right)\Big|_8^{12}$$

$$= 33{,}280 + 9984$$

$$= 43{,}264 \text{ lb}$$

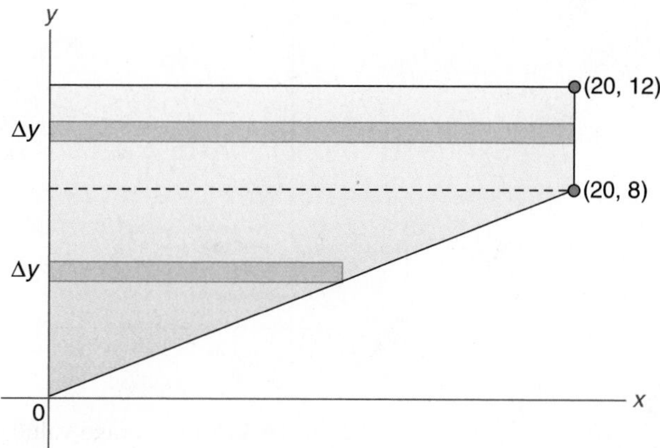

Figure 19.54

Note: The position of the vertical side in the xy-plane has no effect on the final result. You should repeat this problem using other positions.

Average Value

Finding the average value of a function y_{av} is another application of integration. The sum

$$y_{av} = \frac{f(x_1) + f(x_2) + f(x_3) + \cdots + f(x_n)}{n}$$

is the average value of a function for the given values of x: $x_1, x_2, x_3, \ldots, x_n$.

For example, if $f(x_1) = 3, f(x_2) = 5$, and $f(x_3) = 4$, then

$$y_{av} = \frac{3 + 5 + 4}{3} = 4$$

is the average of the three given values.

Now,

$$\begin{aligned} y_{av} &= \frac{f(x_1) + f(x_2) + f(x_3) + \cdots + f(x_n)}{n} \\ &= \frac{[f(x_1) + f(x_2) + f(x_3) + \cdots + f(x_n)]\,\Delta x}{n\,\Delta x} \quad \text{(Multiply numerator and denominator by } \Delta x.) \\ &= \frac{1}{n\,\Delta x}[f(x_1)\,\Delta x + f(x_2)\,\Delta x + f(x_3)\,\Delta x + \cdots + f(x_n)\,\Delta x] \end{aligned}$$

In Fig. 19.55, $n\,\Delta x = b - a$, so that

$$y_{av} = \frac{1}{b - a}[f(x_1)\,\Delta x + f(x_2)\,\Delta x + f(x_3)\,\Delta x + \cdots + f(x_n)\,\Delta x]$$

As we let Δx approach 0, the right-hand factor approaches the integral

$$\int_a^b f(x)\,dx$$

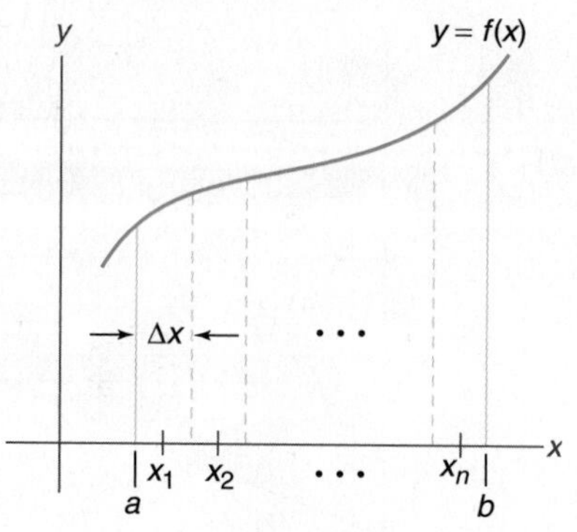

Figure 19.55 The average value of $y = f(x)$.

We then have the following result:

AVERAGE VALUE

The *average value* of the function $y = f(x)$ over the interval $x = a$ to $x = b$ is

$$y_{av} = \frac{1}{b - a}\int_a^b f(x)\,dx$$

A geometrical interpretation can be given to y_{av} as the height of a rectangle with base $b - a$ having the same area as the area bounded by the curve $y = f(x)$, $x = a$, $x = b$, and the x-axis as shown in Fig. 19.56.

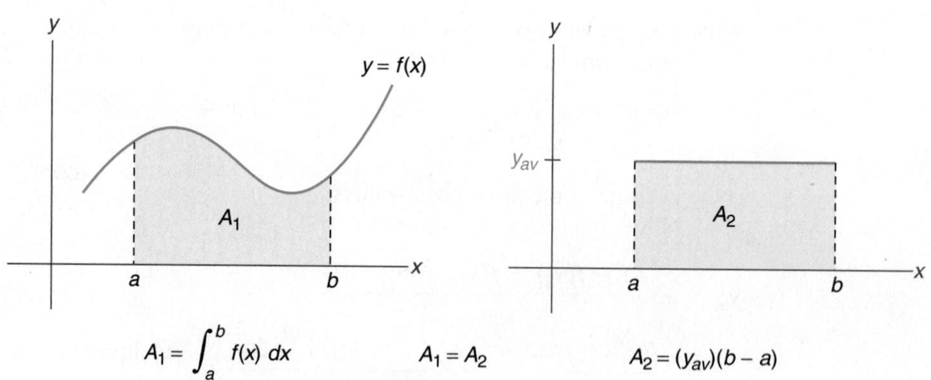

Figure 19.56 Geometrically, y_{av} is the height of a rectangle with base $b - a$ having the same area as the area under the curve $y = f(x)$ from $x = a$ to $x = b$.

EXAMPLE 10

Find the average value of the function $y = 4 - x^2$ from $x = 0$ to $x = 2$.

$$y_{av} = \frac{1}{b - a}\int_a^b f(x)\,dx = \frac{1}{2 - 0}\int_0^2 (4 - x^2)\,dx$$

$$= \frac{1}{2}\left(4x - \frac{x^3}{3}\right)\Big|_0^2 = \frac{1}{2}\left[\left(8 - \frac{8}{3}\right) - (0)\right] = \frac{8}{3}$$

A rectangle with height $\frac{8}{3}$ and width 2 has area also equal to A: $\left(\frac{8}{3}\right)(2) = \frac{16}{3}$ (see Fig. 19.57).

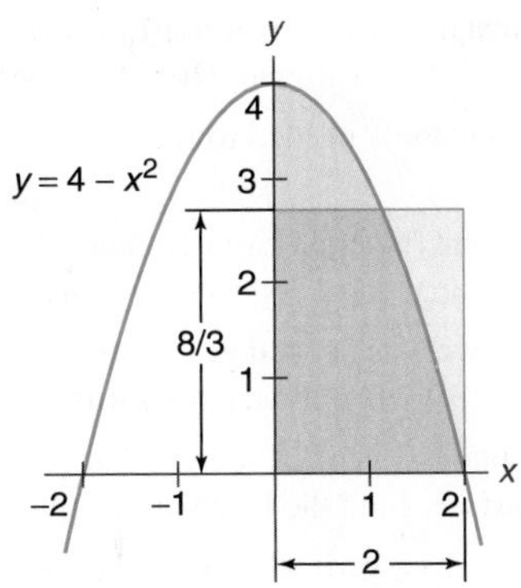

Figure 19.57

EXAMPLE 11

The power developed in a resistor is given by $p = 0.5i^3$. Find the average power (in watts) as the current changes from 1 A to 3 A.

$$\begin{aligned} p_{av} &= \frac{1}{3-1}\int_1^3 0.5i^3\, di \\ &= \frac{0.5}{2} \cdot \frac{i^4}{4}\bigg|_1^3 \\ &= \frac{0.5}{2}\left(\frac{81}{4} - \frac{1}{4}\right) \\ &= 5.0 \text{ W} \end{aligned}$$

Exercises 19.7

1. A force moves an object from $x = 0$ to $x = 3$ according to $F = x^3 - x$. Find the work done.
2. A force moves an object from $x = 1$ to $x = 100$ according to $F = \sqrt{x}$. Find the work done.
3. Find the work done in stretching a spring 5 in. if it requires a 20-lb force to stretch it 10 in.
4. Find the work done in stretching a spring 12 in. if it requires a 10-lb force to stretch it 8 in.
5. A spring with a natural length of 8 cm measures 12 cm after a 150-N weight is attached. Find the work required to stretch the spring 6 cm from its natural length.
6. A spring with a natural length of 10 cm measures 14 cm after a 60-N weight is attached. Find the work done in stretching the spring 10 cm from its natural length.
7. Two charged particles separated by a distance x attract each other with a force $F = 3.62 \times 10^{-16}x^{-2}$ N. Find the work done (in joules) in separating them over an interval from $x = 0.01$ m to $x = 0.05$ m.
8. Two charged particles separated by a distance x attract each other with a force $F = 4.52 \times 10^{-18}x^{-2}$ N. Find the work done (in joules) in separating them over an interval from $x = 0.02$ m to $x = 0.08$ m.
9. A chain 50 ft long and weighing 2 lb/ft is hanging over a pulley. How much work is needed to pull (a) 10 ft of the chain to the top? (b) half of the chain to the top? (c) all of the chain to the top?
10. Find the amount of work done in winding all of a 300-ft hanging cable that weighs 120 lb.
11. A cylindrical tank 8 ft in diameter and 12 ft high is full of water. How much work is needed to pump all the water out over the top?
12. How much work is needed in Exercise 11 to pump half the water out over the top of the tank?

13. Suppose that the tank in Exercise 11 is placed on a 10-ft platform. How much work is needed to fill the tank from the ground when the water is pumped in through a hole in the bottom of the tank?

14. How much work is needed to fill the tank in Exercise 13 if the water is pumped into the top of the tank?

15. A conical tank (inverted right circular cone) filled with water is 10 ft across the top and 12 ft high. How much work is needed to pump all the water out over the top?

16. How much work is needed in Exercise 15 to pump 4 ft of water out over the top (a) when the tank is full? (b) when the tank has 4 ft of water in it?

17. A dam contains a vertical rectangular gate 10 ft high and 8 ft wide. The top of the gate is at the water's surface. Find the force on the gate.

18. A dam contains a vertical rectangular gate 6 ft high and 8 ft wide. The top of the gate is 4 ft below the water's surface. Find the force on the gate.

19. A rectangular tank is 8 m wide and 4 m deep. If the tank is $\frac{3}{4}$ full of water, find the force against the side.

20. A cylindrical tank is lying on its side and is half-filled with water. If its diameter is 6 m, find the force against an end.

21. A cylindrical tank of oil is half full of oil ($\rho = 870$ kg/m^3) and lying on its side. If the diameter of the tank is 10 m, find the force on an end of the tank.

22. A rectangular porthole on a vertical side of a ship is 1 ft square. Find the total force on the porthole if its top is 20 ft below the water's surface.

23. A trough is 12 ft long and 2 ft high. Vertical cross sections are isosceles right triangles with the hypotenuse horizontal. Find the force on one end if the trough is filled with water.

24. A trough is 12 m long and 1 m high. Vertical cross sections are equilateral triangles with the top side horizontal. Find the force on one end if the trough is filled with alcohol ($\rho = 790$ kg/m^3).

25. A dam has a vertical gate in the shape of an isosceles trapezoid with upper base 10 ft, lower base 16 ft, and height 6 ft. Find the force on the gate if the upper base is 8 ft below the water's surface.

26. Find the force on the gate in Exercise 25 if the gate is inverted.

27. A swimming pool is 12 ft wide and 18 ft long. The bottom is flat but sloped so that the water is 3 ft deep at one end and 9 ft deep at the other end. Find the force on one 18-ft side.

28. A dam is in the shape of a parabola 12 ft high and 8 ft across its top. Find the force on it when the water's surface is at the top.

Find the average value of each function.

29. $y = x^2$ from $x = 1$ to $x = 3$

30. $y = \sqrt{x}$ from $x = 1$ to $x = 4$

31. $y = \dfrac{1}{\sqrt{x-1}}$ from $x = 5$ to $x = 10$

32. $y = x^2 - 1/x^2$ from $x = 1$ to $x = 3$

33. The electric current for a certain circuit is given by $i = 6t - t^2$. Find the average value of the current (in amperes) over the interval from $t = 0.1$ s to $t = 0.5$ s.

34. The power developed in a resistor is given by $P = 0.28i^3$. Find the average power (in watts) as the current changes from 1 A to 4 A.

CHAPTER 19 SUMMARY

1. The *area between two curves* $y = f(x)$ and $y = g(x)$ between $x = a$ and $x = b$ is

$$\int_a^b [f(x) - g(x)]\,dx$$

for $f(x) \geq g(x)$ and $a \leq x \leq b$. The *area between two curves* $x = f(y)$ and $x = g(y)$ between $y = c$ and $y = d$ is

$$\int_c^d [f(y) - g(y)]\, dy$$

for $f(y) \geq g(y)$ and $c \leq y \leq d$.

2. *Volume of revolution, disk method:*

$$\begin{array}{llll} & \text{radius}^2 & \text{thickness} & \\ & \downarrow & \downarrow & \\ V = \pi \int_a^b & [f(x)]^2 & dx & \text{(revolved about } x\text{-axis)} \\ V = \pi \int_c^d & [f(y)]^2 & dy & \text{(revolved about } y\text{-axis)} \\ V = \pi \int_a^b & \{[f(x)]^2 - [g(x)]^2\} & dx & \text{(washer revolved about } x\text{-axis)} \end{array}$$

3. *Volume of revolution, shell method:*

$$\begin{array}{lllll} & \text{radius} & \text{height} & \text{thickness} & \\ & \downarrow & \downarrow & \downarrow & \\ V = 2\pi \int_a^b & x & f(x) & dx & \text{(shells parallel to } y\text{-axis)} \\ V = 2\pi \int_c^d & y & f(y) & dy & \text{(shells parallel to } x\text{-axis)} \end{array}$$

4. *Moment in a linear system along the x-axis:* Let $\overline{x}$ be the center of mass of a linear system along the x-axis with n masses; then,

$$\overline{x} = \frac{m_1x_1 + m_2x_2 + m_3x_3 + \cdots + m_nx_n}{m_1 + m_2 + m_3 + \cdots + m_n}$$

If we let M_0 be the moment about the origin and m be the total mass of the system, then

$$\overline{x} = \frac{M_0}{m}$$

5. *Moments of a two-dimensional system:* Consider n masses $m_1, m_2, \ldots, m_n$ located at points $(x_1, y_1), (x_2, y_2), \ldots, (x_n, y_n)$, respectively. The moment about the y-axis M_y is

$$M_y = m_1x_1 + m_2x_2 + \cdots + m_nx_n$$

and the moment about the x-axis M_x is

$$M_x = m_1y_1 + m_2y_2 + \cdots + m_ny_n.$$

If we let m be the total mass of the system, the center of mass $(\overline{x}, \overline{y})$ is

$$\overline{x} = \frac{M_y}{m} \quad \text{and} \quad \overline{y} = \frac{M_x}{m}$$

6. *Center of mass of a continuous thin mass of variable density* from $x = a$ to $x = b$ is given by

$$\bar{x} = \frac{M_0}{m} = \frac{\int_a^b \rho(x)\, x\, dx}{\int_a^b \rho(x)\, dx}$$

where $\rho(x)$ is the density expressed as a function of x. If the density is constant, ρ will cancel.

7. *Moments and center of mass of a plane area or thin plate:* Let $g(x) \le f(x)$ be continuous functions on $a \le x \le b$ for the area of uniform density ρ bounded by $y = f(x)$, $y = g(x)$, $x = a$, and $x = b$; the moments about the x-axis and the y-axis are

$$M_x = \frac{\rho}{2} \int_a^b \{[f(x)]^2 - [g(x)]^2\}\, dx \quad \text{and} \quad M_y = \rho \int_a^b x[f(x) - g(x)]\, dx$$

Its mass is given by

$$m = \rho \int_a^b [f(x) - g(x)]\, dx$$

and its center of mass is $(\bar{x}, \bar{y})$, where

$$\bar{x} = \frac{M_y}{m} \quad \text{and} \quad \bar{y} = \frac{M_x}{m}$$

8. *Centroid of a plane region or thin plate:* Let $g(x) \le f(x)$ be continuous functions on $a \le x \le b$. The centroid $(\bar{x}, \bar{y})$ of the region bounded by $y = f(x)$, $y = g(x)$, $x = a$, and $x = b$ is

$$\bar{x} = \frac{\int_a^b x[f(x) - g(x)]\, dx}{A} \quad \text{and} \quad \bar{y} = \frac{\frac{1}{2}\int_a^b \{[f(x)]^2 - [g(x)]^2\}\, dx}{A}$$

where A is the area of the region.

9. *Centroid of a solid of revolution:*

$$\bar{x} = \frac{M_y}{m} = \frac{\int_a^b xy^2\, dx}{\int_a^b y^2\, dx} \quad \text{and} \quad \bar{y} = 0 \qquad \text{(revolved about } x\text{-axis)}$$

$$\bar{y} = \frac{M_x}{m} = \frac{\int_c^d yx^2\, dy}{\int_c^d x^2\, dy} \quad \text{and} \quad \bar{x} = 0 \qquad \text{(revolved about } y\text{-axis)}$$

10. *Moment of inertia of a system:* Let masses $m_1, m_2, m_3, \ldots, m_n$ be at distances $d_1, d_2, d_3, \ldots, d_n$, respectively, rotating about some axis. The moment of inertia I of the system is

$$I = m_1 d_1^2 + m_2 d_2^2 + m_3 d_3^2 + \cdots + m_n d_n^2$$

Let m be the sum of all the masses in the system and let R be the distance from the axis of rotation that gives the same total moment of inertia:

$$I = mR^2$$

R is called the radius of gyration.

11. *Moments of inertia of an area of constant density about the x- and y-axes:* Let $g(x) \le f(x)$ be continuous functions on $a \le x \le b$ for the area of constant density ρ bounded by $y = f(x)$, $y = g(x)$, $x = a$, and $x = b$. The moment of inertia about the y-axis is

$$I_y = \rho \int_a^b x^2[f(x) - g(x)]\,dx \quad \text{and} \quad R = \sqrt{\frac{I_y}{m}}$$

Similarly, the moment of inertia about the x-axis is

$$I_x = \rho \int_c^d y^2[f(y) - g(y)]\,dy \quad \text{and} \quad R = \sqrt{\frac{I_x}{m}}$$

12. *Moment of inertia of a solid of revolution:* Let the area bounded by $y = f(x)$, $y = 0$, $x = a$, and $x = b$ be revolved about the y-axis. The moment of inertia about the y-axis is

$$I_y = 2\pi\rho \int_a^b x^3 f(x)\,dx$$

Its radius of gyration is $R = \sqrt{\dfrac{I_y}{m}}$, where $m = 2\pi\rho \displaystyle\int_a^b x f(x)\,dx$.

Similarly, let the area bounded by $x = f(y)$, $x = 0$, $y = c$, and $y = d$ be revolved about the x-axis. Its moment of inertia about the x-axis is

$$I_x = 2\pi\rho \int_c^d y^3 f(y)\,dy$$

Its radius of gyration is $R = \sqrt{\dfrac{I_x}{m}}$, where $m = 2\pi\rho \displaystyle\int_c^d y f(y)\,dy$.

Note: $f(x)$ and $f(y)$ correspond to the height of the shell.

13. *Work of a variable force* $f(x)$ acting through the distance from $x = a$ to $x = b$:

$$W = \int_a^b f(x)\,dx$$

14. *Force exerted by a fluid:* The force F exerted by a fluid of constant density ρ against a submerged vertical plane region from $y = a$ to $y = b$ is

$$F = \rho g \int_a^b (h - y)\,L\,dy$$

where h is the total depth of the fluid and L is the horizontal length of the region at y.

15. *Average value:* The average value of the function $y = f(x)$ over the interval $x = a$ to $x = b$ is

$$y_{\text{av}} = \frac{1}{b - a} \int_a^b f(x)\,dx$$

CHAPTER 19 REVIEW

Find each area bounded by the curves.

1. $y = x^2 + 3$, $y = 0$, $x = 1$, and $x = 2$
2. $y = 1 - x^2$, $y = 0$, and $x = 0$
3. $x = y^2 - y^3$ and the y-axis
4. $y = 3x^2 - 12x + 9$, $y = 0$, $x = 0$, and $x = 4$
5. $x = y^4 - 2y^2$ and $x = 2y^2$
6. $x = y^2$ and $x = 9$

Find the volume of each solid formed by revolving the region bounded by the given curves about the given line.

7. $y = \sqrt{x}$, $y = 0$, and $x = 4$ about the x-axis (shell method)
8. $y = \sqrt{x}$, $y = 0$, and $x = 4$ about the x-axis (disk method)
9. $y = x - x^2$ and $y = 0$ about the x-axis
10. $y = x$ and $y = 3x - x^2$ about the y-axis
11. $y = 3x^2 - x^3$ and $y = 0$ about the y-axis
12. $y = x^2 + 1$, $y = 0$, $x = 0$, and $x = 3$ about the y-axis
13. $x = y^2$ and $x = 4$ about the y-axis
14. $x = 4y - y^2$, $x = 0$, and $y = 3$ about the x-axis
15. Find the center of mass of the linear system $m_1 = 12$, $x_1 = -4$; $m_2 = 20$, $x_2 = 9$; $m_3 = 24$, $x_3 = 12$.
16. Find the center of mass of the system $m_1 = 24$ at $(11, -3)$; $m_2 = 36$ at $(-4, -15)$; $m_3 = 30$ at $(-7, 0)$.
17. Find the center of mass of the uniform thin plate in Fig. 19.58.

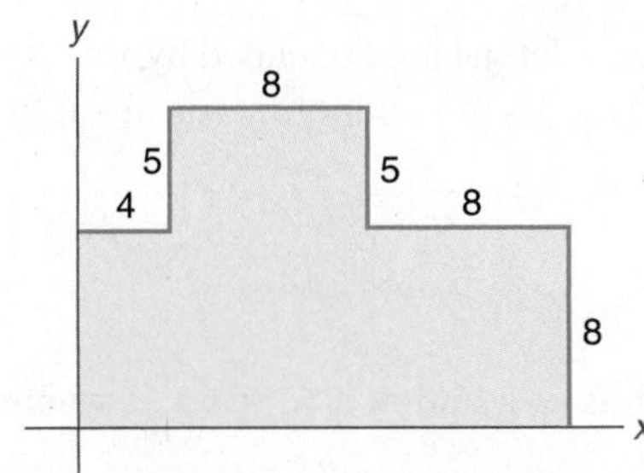

Figure 19.58

Find the centroid of each region bounded by the given curves.

18. $y = 5x$, $x = 4$, and $y = 0$
19. $y = 6x - x^2$ and $y = 3x$
20. $y = x^2 - 6x$ and $y = 0$

Find the centroid of the solid formed by revolving each region bounded by the given curves about the given axis.

21. $y = 2x$, $x = 0$, and $y = 2$ about the y-axis
22. $y = x^2$, $x = 0$, and $y = 1$ about the x-axis
23. $x = y^2 - 4y$ and $x = 0$ about the y-axis
24. Find the moment of inertia and the radius of gyration about the x-axis of the system $m_1 = 10$ at $(3, 2)$, $m_2 = 6$ at $(5, 7)$, and $m_3 = 8$ at $(8, -4)$.

Find the moment of inertia and the radius of gyration of each region bounded by the given curves about the given axis.

25. $y = 3x$, $x = 4$, and $y = 0$ about the y-axis ($\rho = 1$)

26. Region in Exercise 25 about the x-axis

27. $x = 1 - y^2, y = 0$, and $x = 0$ about the x-axis ($\rho = 4$)

Find the moment of inertia and the radius of gyration of the solid formed by revolving the region bounded by the given curves about the given axis.

28. $y = x^3, y = 0$, and $x = 1$ about the x-axis ($\rho = 4$)

29. Region of Exercise 28 about the y-axis

30. $y = 1/x, y = 0, x = 1$, and $x = 4$ about the y-axis ($\rho = 3$)

31. Find the work done in stretching a spring 10 in. if it requires a 16-lb force to stretch it 4 in.

32. Two charged particles separated by a distance x attract each other with a force $F = 5.24 \times 10^{-18}x^{-2}$ N. Find the work done (in joules) in separating them over an interval from $x = 0.01$ m to $x = 0.02$ m.

33. A cable weighs 4 lb/ft and has a 250-lb weight attached in a hole 200 ft below the ground. Find the amount of work needed to pull the cable and weight to ground level.

34. A dam contains a vertical rectangular gate 8 ft high and 10 ft wide. The top of the gate is 6 ft below the water's surface. Find the force on the gate.

35. A cylindrical tank 10 m in diameter is lying on its side and is half full of water. Find the force against an end.

36. Find the average value of the voltage V_{av} in an electric circuit from $t = 0$ s to $t = 3$ s if $V = t^2 + 3t + 2$.

37. Find the average value of the current i_{av} in an electric circuit from $t = 4$ s to $t = 9$ s if $i = 4t^{3/2}$.

38. The power in a circuit varies according to $p = 2t^3$. Find the average power p_{av} (in watts) from $t = 1$ s to $t = 3$ s.

Appendix

The goal of this appendix is to establish the essential notation, terminology, and algebraic skills that are used throughout the book.

Algebra

EXAMPLE 1 Algebra review

a. Evaluate $(-32)^{2/5}$.

b. Simplify $\frac{1}{x - 2} - \frac{1}{x + 2}$.

c. Solve the equation $\frac{x^4 - 5x^2 + 4}{x - 1} = 0$.

SOLUTION

a. Recall that $(-32)^{2/5} = [(-32)^{1/5}]^2$. Because $(-32)^{1/5} = \sqrt[5]{-32} = -2$, we have $(-32)^{2/5} = (-2)^2 = 4$.
Another option is to write $(-32)^{2/5} = [(-32)^2]^{1/5} = 1024^{1/5} = 4$.

b. Finding a common denominator and simplifying leads to

$$\frac{1}{x - 2} - \frac{1}{x + 2} = \frac{(x + 2) - (x - 2)}{(x - 2)(x + 2)} = \frac{4}{x^2 - 4}.$$

c. Notice that $x = 1$ cannot be a solution of the equation because the left side of the equation is undefined at $x = 1$. Because $x \neq 1$, both sides of the equation can be multiplied by $x - 1$ to produce $x^4 - 5x^2 + 4 = 0$. After factoring, this equation becomes $(x^2 - 4)(x^2 - 1) = 0$, which implies $x^2 - 4 = (x - 2)(x + 2) = 0$ or $x^2 - 1 = (x - 1)(x + 1) = 0$. The roots of $x^2 - 4 = 0$ are $x = \pm 2$ and the roots of $x^2 - 1 = 0$ are $x = \pm 1$. Excluding $x = 1$, the roots of the original equation are $x = -1$ and $x = \pm 2$. *Related Exercises 15–26* ◀

Sets of Real Numbers

Figure A.1 shows the notation for **open intervals**, **closed intervals**, and various **bounded** and **unbounded** intervals. Notice that either interval notation or set notation may be used.

	$[a, b] = \{x: a \le x \le b\}$	Closed, bounded interval
	$(a, b] = \{x: a < x \le b\}$	Bounded interval
	$[a, b) = \{x: a \le x < b\}$	Bounded interval
	$(a, b) = \{x: a < x < b\}$	Open, bounded interval
	$[a, \infty) = \{x: x \ge a\}$	Unbounded interval
	$(a, \infty) = \{x: x > a\}$	Unbounded interval
	$(-\infty, b] = \{x: x \le b\}$	Unbounded interval
	$(-\infty, b) = \{x: x < b\}$	Unbounded interval
FIGURE A.1	$(-\infty, \infty)$	Unbounded interval

EXAMPLE 2 **Solving inequalities** Solve the following inequalities.

a. $-x^2 + 5x - 6 < 0$ **b.** $\dfrac{x^2 - x - 2}{x - 3} \le 0$

SOLUTION

a. We multiply by -1, reverse the inequality, and then factor:

$$x^2 - 5x + 6 > 0 \quad \text{Multiply by } -1.$$
$$(x - 2)(x - 3) > 0 \quad \text{Factor.}$$

The roots of the corresponding equation $(x - 2)(x - 3) = 0$ are $x = 2$ and $x = 3$. These roots partition the number line (Figure A.2) into three intervals: $(-\infty, 2)$, $(2, 3)$, and $(3, \infty)$. On each interval, the product $(x - 2)(x - 3)$ does not change sign. To determine the sign of the product on a given interval, a **test value** x is selected and the sign of $(x - 2)(x - 3)$ is determined at x.

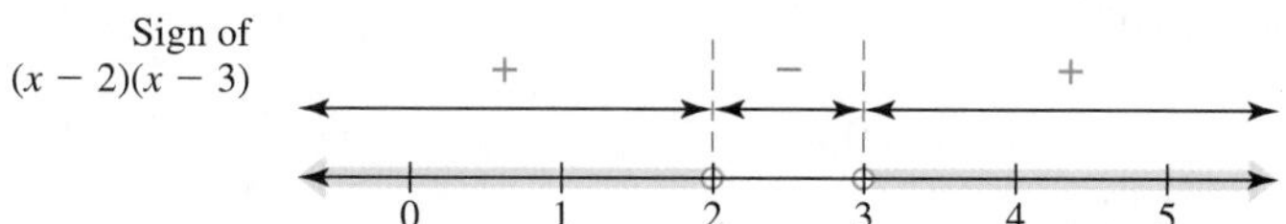

FIGURE A.2

A convenient choice for x in $(-\infty, 2)$ is $x = 0$. At this test value,

$$(x - 2)(x - 3) = (-2)(-3) > 0.$$

Using a test value of $x = 2.5$ in the interval $(2, 3)$, we have

$$(x - 2)(x - 3) = (0.5)(-0.5) < 0.$$

A test value of $x = 4$ in $(3, \infty)$ gives

$$(x - 2)(x - 3) = (2)(1) > 0.$$

Therefore, $(x - 2)(x - 3) > 0$ on $(-\infty, 2)$ and $(3, \infty)$. We conclude that the inequality $-x^2 + 5x - 6 < 0$ is satisfied for all x in either $(-\infty, 2)$ or $(3, \infty)$ (Figure A.2).

➤ The set of numbers $\{x: x \text{ is in } (-\infty, 2) \text{ or } (3, \infty)\}$ may also be expressed using the union symbol:

$$(-\infty, 2) \cup (3, \infty)$$

b. The expression $\frac{x^2 - x - 2}{x - 3}$ changes sign only at points where the numerator or denominator of $\frac{x^2 - x - 2}{x - 3}$ equals 0. Because

$$\frac{x^2 - x - 2}{x - 3} = \frac{(x + 1)(x - 2)}{x - 3},$$

the numerator is 0 when $x = -1$ and $x = 2$, and the denominator is 0 at $x = 3$. Therefore, we examine the sign of $\frac{(x + 1)(x - 2)}{x - 3}$ on the intervals $(-\infty, -1)$, $(-1, 2)$, $(2, 3)$, and $(3, \infty)$.

Test Value	$x + 1$	$x - 2$	$x - 3$	Result
−2	−	−	−	−
0	+	−	−	+
2.5	+	+	−	−
4	+	+	+	+

Using test values on these intervals, we see that $\frac{(x + 1)(x - 2)}{x - 3} < 0$ on $(-\infty, -1)$ and $(2, 3)$. Furthermore, the expression is 0 when $x = -1$ and $x = 2$. Therefore, $\frac{x^2 - x - 2}{x - 3} \leq 0$ for all values of x in either $(-\infty, -1]$ or $[2, 3)$ (Figure A.3).

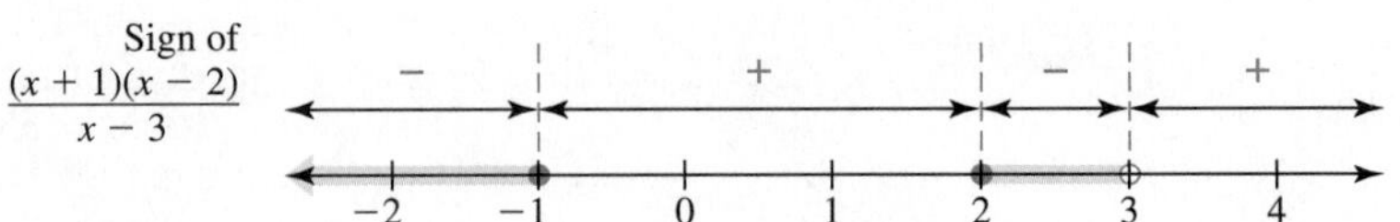

FIGURE A.3

Related Exercises 27–30

Absolute Value

The **absolute value** of a real number x, denoted $|x|$, is the distance between x and the origin on the number line. (Figure A.4) More generally, $|x - y|$ is the distance between the points x and y on the number line. The absolute value has the following definition and properties:

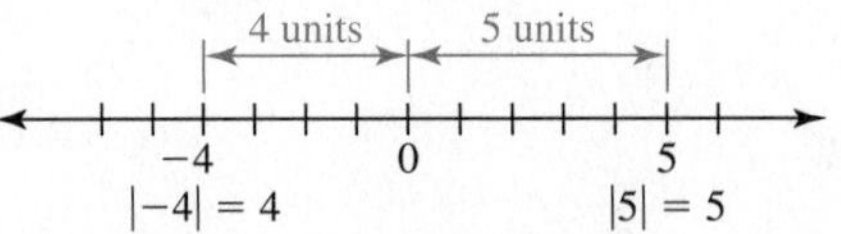

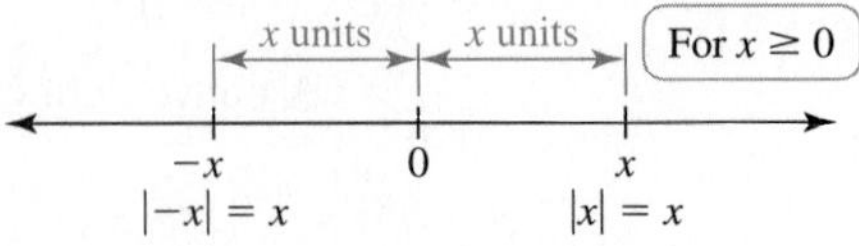

FIGURE A.4

➤ The absolute value is useful in simplifying square roots. Because $\sqrt{a}$ is nonnegative, we have $\sqrt{a^2} = |a|$. For example, $\sqrt{3^2} = 3$ and $\sqrt{(-3)^2} = \sqrt{9} = 3$. Note that the solutions of $x^2 = 9$ are $|x| = 3$ or $x = \pm 3$.

Definition and Properties of the Absolute Value

The absolute value of a real number x is defined as

$$|x| = \begin{cases} x & \text{if } x \geq 0 \\ -x & \text{if } x < 0 \end{cases}$$

Let a be a positive real number.

1. $|x| = a \Leftrightarrow x = \pm a$

2. $|x| < a \Leftrightarrow -a < x < a$

3. $|x| > a \Leftrightarrow x > a$ or $x < -a$

4. $|x| \leq a \Leftrightarrow -a \leq x \leq a$

5. $|x| \geq a \Leftrightarrow x \geq a$ or $x \leq -a$

6. $|x + y| \leq |x| + |y|$

➤ Property 6 is called the **triangle inequality**.

EXAMPLE 3 **Inequalities with absolute values** Solve the following inequalities. Then sketch the solution on the number line and express it in interval notation.

a. $|x - 2| < 3$ **b.** $|2x - 6| \geq 10$

SOLUTION

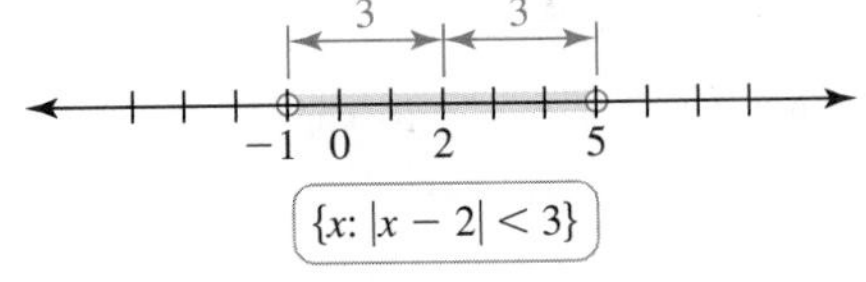

FIGURE A.5

a. Using Property 2 of the absolute value, $|x - 2| < 3$ is written as

$$-3 < x - 2 < 3.$$

Adding 2 to each term of these inequalities results in $-1 < x < 5$ (Figure A.5). This set of numbers is written as $(-1, 5)$ in interval notation.

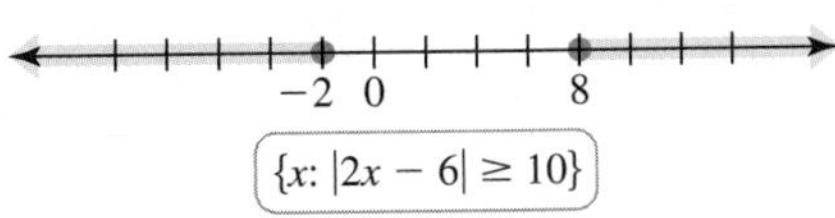

FIGURE A.6

b. Using Property 5, the inequality $|2x - 6| \geq 10$ implies that

$$2x - 6 \geq 10 \quad \text{or} \quad 2x - 6 \leq -10.$$

We add 6 to both sides of the first inequality to obtain $2x \geq 16$, which implies $x \geq 8$. Similarly, the second inequality yields $x \leq -2$ (Figure A.6). In interval notation, the solution is $(-\infty, -2]$ or $[8, \infty)$.

Related Exercises 31–34

Cartesian Coordinate System

The conventions of the **Cartesian coordinate system** or ***xy*-coordinate system** are illustrated in Figure A.7.

➤ The familiar (x, y) coordinate system is named after René Descartes (1596–1650). However, it was introduced independently and simultaneously by Pierre de Fermat (1601–1665).

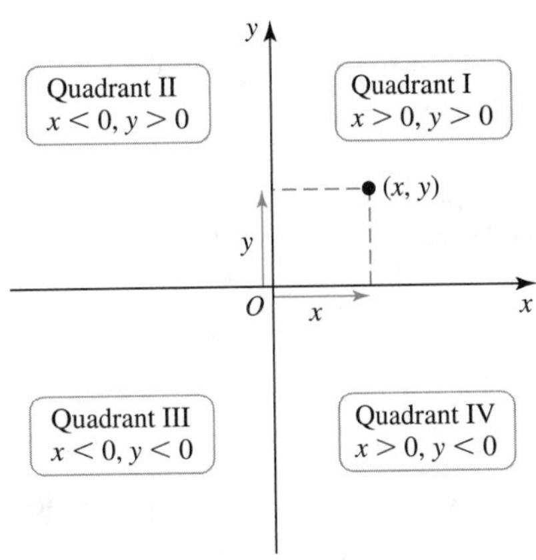

FIGURE A.7

For any right triangle, $a^2 + b^2 = c^2$.

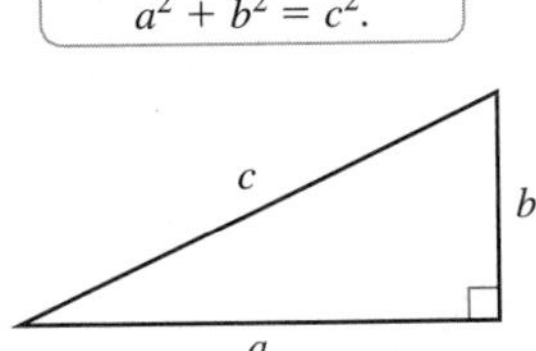

$P_2(x_2, y_2)$

$\sqrt{(x_2 - x_1)^2 + (y_2 - y_1)^2}$ $|y_2 - y_1|$

$P_1(x_1, y_1)$ (x_2, y_1)

$|x_2 - x_1|$

FIGURE A.8

Distance Formula and Circles

By the Pythagorean theorem (Figure A.8), we have the following formula for the distance between two points $P_1(x_1, y_1)$ and $P_2(x_2, y_2)$.

> **Distance Formula**
>
> The distance between the points $P_1(x_1, y_1)$ and $P_2(x_2, y_2)$ is
>
> $$|P_1P_2| = \sqrt{(x_2 - x_1)^2 + (y_2 - y_1)^2}.$$

A **circle** is the set of points in the plane whose distance from a fixed point (the **center**) is a constant (the **radius**). This definition leads to the following equations that describe a circle.

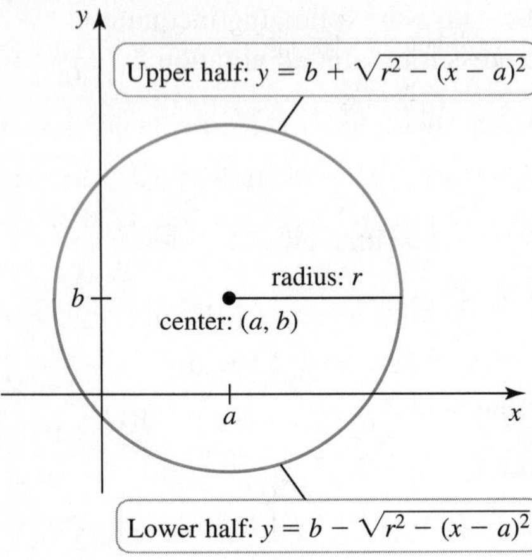

FIGURE A.9

Equation of a Circle

The equation of a circle centered at (a, b) with radius r is

$$(x - a)^2 + (y - b)^2 = r^2.$$

Solving for y, the equations of the upper and lower halves of the circle (Figure A.9) are

$$y = b + \sqrt{r^2 - (x - a)^2} \quad \text{upper half of the circle}$$
$$y = b - \sqrt{r^2 - (x - a)^2} \quad \text{lower half of the circle.}$$

EXAMPLE 4 Sets involving circles

a. Find the equation of the circle with center $(2, 4)$ passing through $(-2, 1)$.

b. Describe the set of points satisfying $x^2 + y^2 - 4x - 6y < 12$.

SOLUTION

a. The radius of the circle is the length of the line segment between the center $(2, 4)$ and the point on the circle $(-2, 1)$, which is

$$\sqrt{(2 - (-2))^2 + (4 - 1)^2} = 5.$$

Therefore, the equation of the circle is

$$(x - 2)^2 + (y - 4)^2 = 25.$$

b. To put this inequality in a recognizable form, we complete the square on the left side of the inequality:

$$\begin{aligned} x^2 + y^2 - 4x - 6y &= x^2 - 4x \underbrace{+ 4 - 4}_{\text{Add and subtract the square of half the coefficient of } x.} + y^2 - 6y \underbrace{+ 9 - 9}_{\text{Add and subtract the square of half the coefficient of } y.} \\ &= \underbrace{x^2 - 4x + 4}_{(x-2)^2} + \underbrace{y^2 - 6y + 9}_{(y-3)^2} - 4 - 9 \\ &= (x - 2)^2 + (y - 3)^2 - 13 \end{aligned}$$

> Recall that the procedure shown here for completing the square works when the coefficient on the quadratic term is 1. When the coefficient is not 1, it must be factored out before completing the square.

Therefore, the original inequality becomes

$$(x - 2)^2 + (y - 3)^2 - 13 < 12, \quad \text{or} \quad (x - 2)^2 + (y - 3)^2 < 25.$$

This inequality describes those points that lie within the circle centered at $(2, 3)$ with radius 5 (Figure A.10). Note that a dashed curve is used to indicate that the circle itself is not part of the solution.

> A **circle** is the set of all points whose distance from a fixed point is a constant. A **disk** is the set of all points within and possibly on a circle.

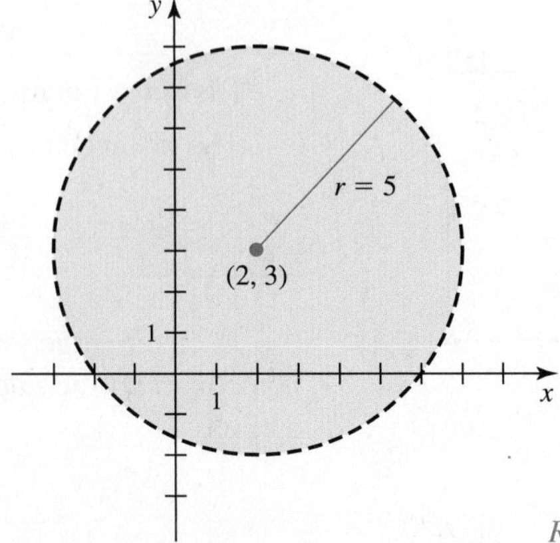

FIGURE A.10

Related Exercises 35–36

Equations of Lines

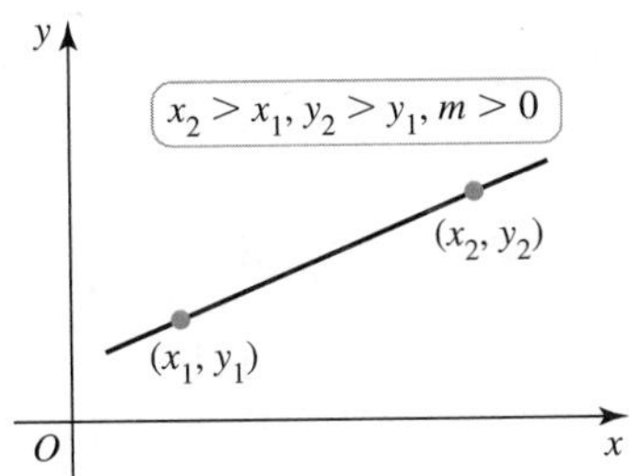

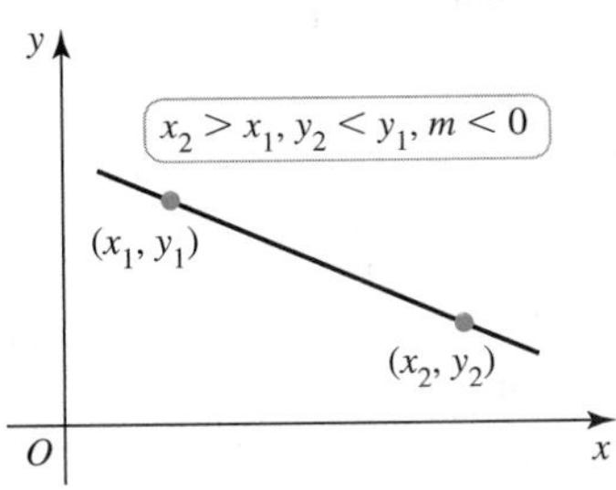

FIGURE A.11

The **slope** m of the line passing through the points $P_1(x_1, y_1)$ and $P_2(x_2, y_2)$ is the *rise over run* (Figure A.11), computed as

$$m = \frac{\text{change in vertical coordinate}}{\text{change in horizontal coordinate}} = \frac{y_2 - y_1}{x_2 - x_1}.$$

Equations of a Line

Point-slope form The equation of the line with slope m passing through the point (x_1, y_1) is $y - y_1 = m(x - x_1)$.

Slope-intercept form The equation of the line with slope m and y-intercept $(0, b)$ is $y = mx + b$ (Figure A.12a).

General linear equation The equation $Ax + By + C = 0$ describes a line in the plane, provided A and B are not both zero.

Vertical and horizontal lines The vertical line that passes through $(a, 0)$ has an equation $x = a$; its slope is undefined. The horizontal line through $(0, b)$ has an equation $y = b$, with slope equal to 0 (Figure A.12b).

➤ Given a particular line, we often talk about *the* equation of a line. But the equation of a specific line is not unique. Having found one equation, we can multiply it by any nonzero constant to produce another equation of the same line.

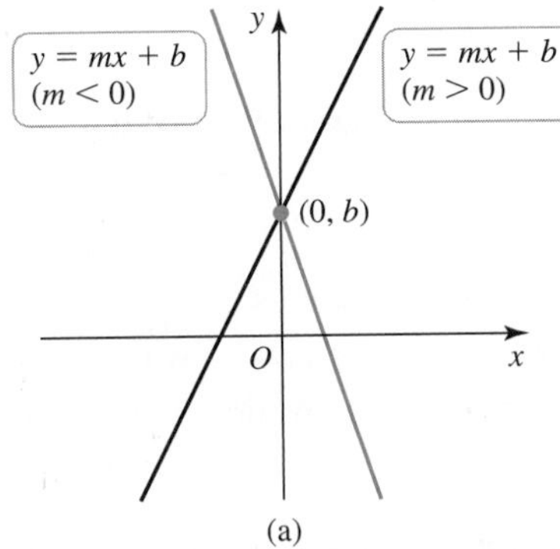

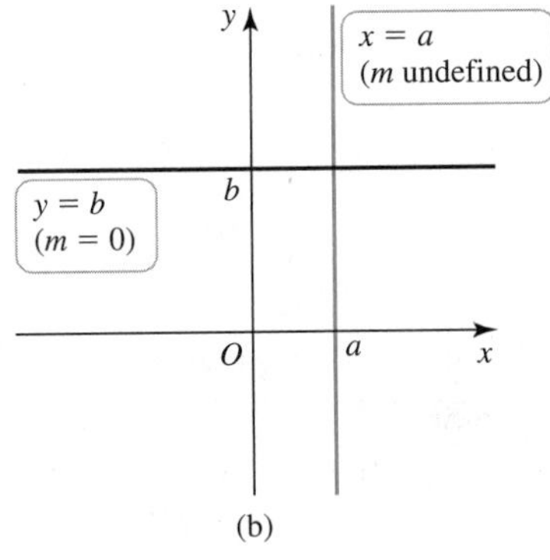

FIGURE A.12

EXAMPLE 5 Working with linear equations Find an equation of the line passing through the points $(1, -2)$ and $(-4, 5)$.

SOLUTION The slope of the line through the points $(1, -2)$ and $(-4, 5)$ is

$$m = \frac{5 - (-2)}{-4 - 1} = \frac{7}{-5} = -\frac{7}{5}.$$

Using the point $(1, -2)$, the point-slope form of the equation is

$$y - (-2) = -\frac{7}{5}(x - 1).$$

Solving for y yields the slope-intercept form of the equation:

$$y = -\frac{7}{5}x - \frac{3}{5}$$

➤ Because both points $(1, -2)$ and $(-4, 5)$ lie on the line and must satisfy the equation of the line, either point can be used to determine an equation of the line.

Related Exercises 37–40 ◀

Parallel and Perpendicular Lines

Two lines in the plane may have either of two special relationships to each other: They may be parallel or perpendicular.

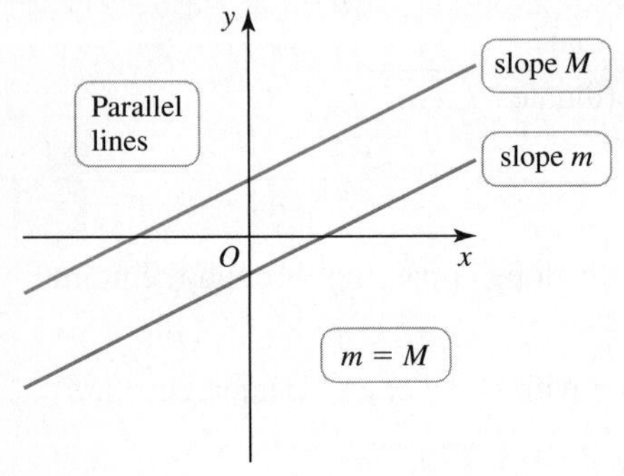

> **Parallel Lines**
>
> Two distinct nonvertical lines are **parallel** if they have the same slope; that is, the lines with equations $y = mx + b$ and $y = Mx + B$ are parallel if and only if $m = M$. Two distinct vertical lines are parallel.

EXAMPLE 6 **Parallel lines** Find an equation of the line parallel to $3x - 6y + 12 = 0$ that intersects the x-axis at $(4, 0)$.

SOLUTION Solving the equation $3x - 6y + 12 = 0$ for y, we have

$$y = \frac{1}{2}x + 2.$$

This line has a slope of $\frac{1}{2}$ and any line parallel to it has a slope of $\frac{1}{2}$. Therefore, the line that passes through $(4, 0)$ with slope $\frac{1}{2}$ has the point-slope equation $y - 0 = \frac{1}{2}(x - 4)$. After simplifying, an equation of the line is

$$y = \frac{1}{2}x - 2.$$

Notice that the slopes of the two lines are the same; only the y-intercepts differ.

Related Exercises 41–42 ◄

➤ The slopes of perpendicular lines are *negative reciprocals* of each other.

> **Perpendicular Lines**
>
> Two lines with slopes $m \neq 0$ and $M \neq 0$ are **perpendicular** if and only if $mM = -1$, or equivalently, $m = -1/M$.

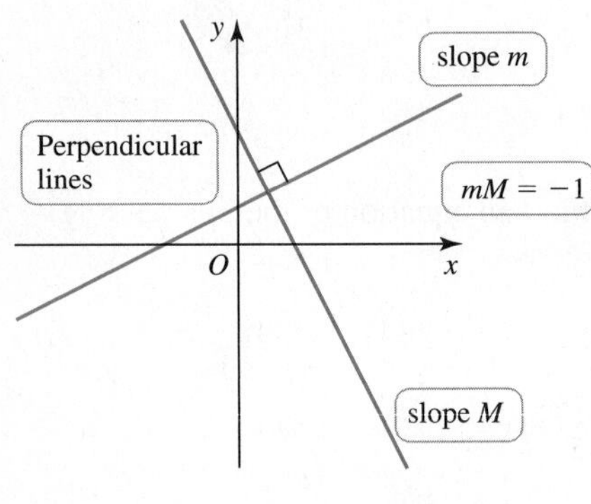

EXAMPLE 7 **Perpendicular lines** Find an equation of the line passing through the point $(-2, 5)$ perpendicular to the line ℓ: $4x - 2y + 7 = 0$.

SOLUTION The equation of ℓ can be written $y = 2x + \frac{7}{2}$, which reveals that its slope is 2. Therefore, the slope of any line perpendicular to ℓ is $-\frac{1}{2}$. The line with slope $-\frac{1}{2}$ passing through the point $(-2, 5)$ is

$$y - 5 = -\frac{1}{2}(x + 2), \quad \text{or} \quad y = -\frac{x}{2} + 4.$$

Related Exercises 43–44 ◄

APPENDIX A EXERCISES

Review Questions

1. State the meaning of $\{x: -4 < x \leq 10\}$ in words. Express the set $\{x: -4 < x \leq 10\}$ using interval notation and draw it on a number line.
2. Write the interval $(-\infty, 2)$ in set notation and draw it on a number line.
3. Give the definition of $|x|$.
4. Write the inequality $|x - 2| \leq 3$ without absolute value symbols.
5. Write the inequality $|2x - 4| \geq 3$ without absolute value symbols.
6. Write an equation of the set of all points that are a distance 5 units from the point (2, 3).

7. Explain how to find the distance between two points whose coordinates are known.

8. Sketch the set of points $\{(x, y): x^2 + (y - 2)^2 > 16\}$.

9. What is the equation of the upper half of the circle centered at the origin with radius 6?

10. What are the possible solution sets of the equation $x^2 + y^2 + Cx + Dy + E = 0$?

11. Give an equation of the line with slope m that passes through the point $(4, -2)$.

12. Give an equation of the line with slope m and y-intercept $(0, 6)$.

13. What is the relationship between the slopes of two parallel lines?

14. What is the relationship between the slopes of two perpendicular lines?

Basic Skills

15–20. Algebra review *Simplify or evaluate the following expressions without a calculator.*

15. $(1/8)^{-2/3}$

16. $\sqrt[3]{-125} + \sqrt{1/25}$

17. $(u + v)^2 - (u - v)^2$

18. $\dfrac{(a + h)^2 - a^2}{h}$

19. $\dfrac{1}{x + h} - \dfrac{1}{x}$

20. $\dfrac{2}{x + 3} - \dfrac{2}{x - 3}$

21–26. Algebra review

21. Factor $y^2 - y^{-2}$.

22. Solve $x^3 - 9x = 0$.

23. Solve $u^4 - 11u^2 + 18 = 0$.

24. Solve $4^x - 6(2^x) = -8$.

25. Simplify $\dfrac{(x + h)^3 - x^3}{h}$ for $h \neq 0$.

26. Rewrite $\dfrac{\sqrt{x + h} - \sqrt{x}}{h}$, where $h \neq 0$, without square roots in the numerator.

27–30. Solving inequalities *Solve the following inequalities and draw the solution on a number line.*

27. $x^2 - 6x + 5 < 0$

28. $\dfrac{x + 1}{x + 2} < 6$

29. $\dfrac{x^2 - 9x + 20}{x - 6} \leq 0$

30. $x\sqrt{x - 1} > 0$

31–34. Inequalities with absolute values *Solve the following inequalities. Then draw the solution on a number line and express it using interval notation.*

31. $|3x - 4| > 8$

32. $1 \leq |x| \leq 10$

33. $3 < |2x - 1| < 5$

34. $2 < \left|\frac{x}{2} - 5\right| < 6$

35–36. Circle calculations *Solve the following problems using the distance formula.*

35. Find the equation of the lower half of the circle with center $(-1, 2)$ and radius 3.

36. Describe the set of points that satisfy $x^2 + y^2 + 6x + 8y \geq 25$.

37–40. Working with linear equations *Find an equation of the line ℓ that satisfies the given condition. Then draw the graph of ℓ.*

37. ℓ has slope $5/3$ and y-intercept $(0, 4)$.

38. ℓ has undefined slope and passes through $(0, 5)$.

39. ℓ has y-intercept $(0, -4)$ and x-intercept $(5, 0)$.

40. ℓ is parallel to the x-axis and passes through the point $(2, 3)$.

41–42. Parallel lines *Find an equation of the following lines and draw their graphs.*

41. the line with y-intercept $(0, 12)$ parallel to the line $x + 2y = 8$

42. the line with x-intercept $(-6, 0)$ parallel to the line $2x - 5 = 0$.

43–44. Perpendicular lines *Find an equation of the following lines.*

43. the line passing through $(3, -6)$ perpendicular to the line $y = -3x + 2$

44. the perpendicular bisector of the line joining the points $(-9, 2)$ and $(3, -5)$

Further Explorations

45. **Explain why or why not** State whether the following statements are true and give an explanation or counterexample.
    a. $\sqrt{16} = \pm 4$
    b. $\sqrt{4^2} = \sqrt{(-4)^2}$
    c. There are two real numbers that satisfy the condition $|x| = -2$.
    d. $|\pi^2 - 9| < 0$.
    e. The point $(1, 1)$ is inside the circle of radius 1 centered at the origin.
    f. $\sqrt{x^4} = x^2$ for all real numbers x.
    g. $\sqrt{a^2} < \sqrt{b^2}$ implies $a < b$ for all real numbers a and b.

46–48. Intervals to sets *Express the following intervals in set notation. Use absolute value notation when possible.*

46. $(-\infty, 12)$

47. $(-\infty, -2]$ or $[4, \infty)$

48. $(2, 3]$ or $[4, 5)$

49–50. Sets in the plane *Graph each set in the xy-plane.*

49. $\{(x, y): |x - y| = 0\}$

50. $\{(x, y): |x| = |y|\}$

B

Appendix

Proofs of Selected Theorems

> **THEOREM 2.3 Limit Laws**
> Assume $\lim_{x \to a} f(x)$ and $\lim_{x \to a} g(x)$ exist. The following properties hold, where c is a real number and $m > 0$ and $n > 0$ are integers.
>
> 1. **Sum** $\lim_{x \to a} [f(x) + g(x)] = \lim_{x \to a} f(x) + \lim_{x \to a} g(x)$
> 2. **Difference** $\lim_{x \to a} [f(x) - g(x)] = \lim_{x \to a} f(x) - \lim_{x \to a} g(x)$
> 3. **Constant multiple** $\lim_{x \to a} [cf(x)] = c \lim_{x \to a} f(x)$
> 4. **Product** $\lim_{x \to a} [f(x)g(x)] = [\lim_{x \to a} f(x)][\lim_{x \to a} g(x)]$
> 5. **Quotient** $\lim_{x \to a} \left[\dfrac{f(x)}{g(x)}\right] = \dfrac{\lim_{x \to a} f(x)}{\lim_{x \to a} g(x)}$ provided $\lim_{x \to a} g(x) \neq 0$
> 6. **Power** $\lim_{x \to a} [f(x)]^n = [\lim_{x \to a} f(x)]^n$
> 7. **Fractional power** $\lim_{x \to a} [f(x)]^{n/m} = [\lim_{x \to a} f(x)]^{n/m}$ provided $f(x) \geq 0$ for x near a if m is even and n/m is reduced to lowest terms

Proof The proof of Law 1 is given in Example 5 of Section 2.7. The proof of Law 2 is analogous to that of Law 1; the triangle inequality in the form $|x - y| \leq |x| + |y|$ is used. The proof of Law 3 is outlined in Exercise 26 of Section 2.7. The proofs of Laws 4 and 5 are given below. The proof of Law 6 involves the repeated use of Law 4. The proof of Law 7 is given in advanced texts. ◄

Proof of Product Law Let $L = \lim_{x \to a} f(x)$ and $M = \lim_{x \to a} g(x)$. Using the definition of a limit, the goal is to show that given any $\varepsilon > 0$, it is possible to specify a $\delta > 0$ such that $|f(x)g(x) - LM| < \varepsilon$ whenever $0 < |x - a| < \delta$. Notice that

$$\begin{aligned}
|f(x)g(x) - LM| &= |f(x)g(x) - Lg(x) + Lg(x) - LM| && \text{Add and subtract } Lg(x). \\
&= |(f(x) - L)g(x) + (g(x) - M)L| && \text{Group terms.} \\
&\leq |(f(x) - L)g(x)| + |(g(x) - M)L| && \text{Triangle inequality} \\
&= |f(x) - L||g(x)| + |g(x) - M||L|. && |xy| = |x||y|
\end{aligned}$$

➤ Real numbers x and y obey the triangle inequality $|x + y| \leq |x| + |y|$.

We now use the definition of the limits of f and g and note that L and M are fixed real numbers. Given $\varepsilon > 0$, there exist $\delta_1 > 0$ and $\delta_2 > 0$ such that

$$|f(x) - L| < \frac{\varepsilon}{2(|M| + 1)} \quad \text{and} \quad |g(x) - M| < \frac{\varepsilon}{2(|L| + 1)}$$

whenever $0 < |x - a| < \delta_1$ and $0 < |x - a| < \delta_2$, respectively. Furthermore, by the definition of the limit of g, there exits a $\delta_3 > 0$ such that $|g(x) - M| < 1$ whenever $0 < |x - a| < \delta_3$. It follows that $|g(x)| < |M| + 1$ whenever $0 < |x - a| < \delta_3$. Now take δ to be the minimum of δ_1, δ_2, and δ_3. Then for $0 < |x - a| < \delta$, we have

➤ $|g(x) - M| < 1$ implies that $g(x)$ is less than 1 unit from M. Therefore, whether $g(x)$ and M are positive or negative, $|g(x)| < |M| + 1$.

$$\begin{aligned} |f(x)g(x) - LM| &\le \underbrace{|f(x) - L|}_{<\frac{\varepsilon}{2(|M|+1)}}\underbrace{|g(x)|}_{<(|M|+1)} + \underbrace{|g(x) - M|}_{<\frac{\varepsilon}{2(|L|+1)}}|L| \\ &< \frac{\varepsilon}{2} + \frac{\varepsilon}{2}\underbrace{\frac{|L|}{|L| + 1}}_{<1} < \frac{\varepsilon}{2} + \frac{\varepsilon}{2} = \varepsilon. \end{aligned}$$

It follows that $\lim_{x\to a} [f(x)g(x)] = LM$. ◄

Proof of Quotient Law We first prove that if $\lim_{x\to a} g(x) = M$ exists, where $M \neq 0$, then $\lim_{x\to a} \frac{1}{g(x)} = \frac{1}{M}$. The Quotient Law then follows by replacing g by $1/g$ in the Product Law. Therefore, the goal is to show that given any $\varepsilon > 0$, it is possible to specify a $\delta > 0$ such that $\left|\frac{1}{g(x)} - \frac{1}{M}\right| < \varepsilon$ whenever $0 < |x - a| < \delta$. First note that $M \neq 0$ and $g(x)$ can be made arbitrarily close to M. For this reason, there exists a $\delta_1 > 0$ such that $|g(x)| > |M|/2$ whenever $0 < |x - a| < \delta_1$. Furthermore, using the definition of the limit of g, given any $\varepsilon > 0$, there exists a $\delta_2 > 0$ such that $|g(x) - M| < \frac{\varepsilon|M|^2}{2}$ whenever $0 < |x - a| < \delta_2$. Now take δ to be the minimum of δ_1 and δ_2. Then for $0 < |x - a| < \delta$, we have

$$\begin{aligned} \left|\frac{1}{g(x)} - \frac{1}{M}\right| &= \left|\frac{M - g(x)}{Mg(x)}\right| && \text{Common denominator} \\ &= \frac{1}{|M|}\underbrace{\frac{1}{|g(x)|}}_{<\frac{2}{|M|}}\underbrace{|g(x) - M|}_{<\frac{\varepsilon|M|^2}{2}} && \text{Rewrite.} \\ &< \frac{1}{|M|}\frac{2}{|M|}\cdot\frac{\varepsilon|M|^2}{2} = \varepsilon. && \text{Simplify.} \end{aligned}$$

➤ Note that if $|g(x)| > |M|/2$, then $1/|g(x)| < 2/|M|$.

By the definition of a limit, we have $\lim_{x\to a} \frac{1}{g(x)} = \frac{1}{M}$. The proof can be completed by applying the Product Rule with g replaced by $1/g$. ◄

THEOREM 10.3 Convergence of Power Series

A power series $\sum_{k=0}^{\infty} c_k(x-a)^k$ centered at a converges in one of three ways:

1. The series converges absolutely for all x, in which case the interval of convergence is $(-\infty, \infty)$ and the radius of convergence is $R = \infty$.
2. There is a real number $R > 0$ such that the series converges absolutely for $|x-a| < R$ and diverges for $|x-a| > R$, in which case the radius of convergence is R.
3. The series converges only at a, in which case the radius of convergence is $R = 0$.

Proof Without loss of generality, we take $a = 0$. (If $a \neq 0$, the following argument may be shifted so it is centered at $x = a$.) The proof hinges on a preliminary result:

If $\sum_{k=0}^{\infty} c_k x^k$ converges for $x = b \neq 0$, then it converges absolutely for $|x| < |b|$. If $\sum_{k=0}^{\infty} c_k x^k$ diverges for $x = d$, then it diverges for $|x| > |d|$.

To prove this fact, assume that $\sum_{k=0}^{\infty} c_k b^k$ converges, which implies that $\lim_{k\to\infty} c_k b^k = 0$. Then there exists a real number $M > 0$ such that $|c_k b^k| < M$, for $k = 0, 1, 2, 3, \ldots$. It follows that

$$\sum_{k=0}^{\infty} |c_k x^k| = \sum_{k=0}^{\infty} \underbrace{|c_k b^k|}_{M} \left|\frac{x}{b}\right|^k < M \sum_{k=0}^{\infty} \left|\frac{x}{b}\right|^k.$$

If $|x| < |b|$, then $|x/b| < 1$ and $\sum_{k=0}^{\infty} \left|\frac{x}{b}\right|^k$ is a convergent geometric series. Therefore, $\sum_{k=0}^{\infty} |c_k x^k|$ converges by the comparison test, which implies that $\sum_{k=0}^{\infty} c_k x^k$ converges absolutely for $|x| < |b|$. The second half of the preliminary result is proved by supposing the series diverges at $x = d$. The series cannot converge at a point x_0 with $|x_0| > |d|$ because by the preceding argument, it would converge for all $|x| < |x_0|$, which includes $x = d$. Therefore, the series diverges for all $|x| > |d|$.

> The Least Upper Bound Property for real numbers states that if a nonempty set S is bounded (that is, there is exists a number M, called an *upper bound*, such that $x \le M$ for all x in S), then S has a *least upper bound L*, which is the smallest of the upper bounds.

Now we may deal with the three cases in the theorem. Let S be the set of real numbers for which the series converges, which always includes 0. If $S = \{0\}$, then we have Case 3. If S consists of all real numbers, then we have Case 1. For Case 2, assume that $d \neq 0$ is a point at which the series diverges. By the preliminary result, the series diverges for $|x| > |d|$. Therefore, if x is in S, then $|x| < |d|$, which implies that S is bounded. By the Least Upper Bound Property for real numbers, S has a least upper bound R, such that $x \le R$ for all x in S. If $|x| > R$, then x is not in S and the series diverges. If $|x| < R$, then x is not the least upper bound of S and there exists a number b in S with $|x| < b \le R$. Because the series converges at $x = b$, by the preliminary result, $\sum_{k=0}^{\infty} |c_k x^k|$ converges for $|x| < |b|$. Therefore, the series $\sum_{k=0}^{\infty} c_k x^k$ converges absolutely for $|x| < R$ and diverges for $|x| > R$. ◀

> **THEOREM 11.3 Eccentricity-Directrix Theorem**
> Let ℓ be a line, F be a point not on ℓ, and $e > 0$ be a real number. Let C be the set of points P in a plane with the property that $\frac{|PF|}{|PL|} = e$, where $|PL|$ is the perpendicular distance from P to ℓ.
>
> 1. If $e = 1$, C is a **parabola**.
> 2. If $0 < e < 1$, C is an **ellipse**.
> 3. If $e > 1$, C is a **hyperbola**.

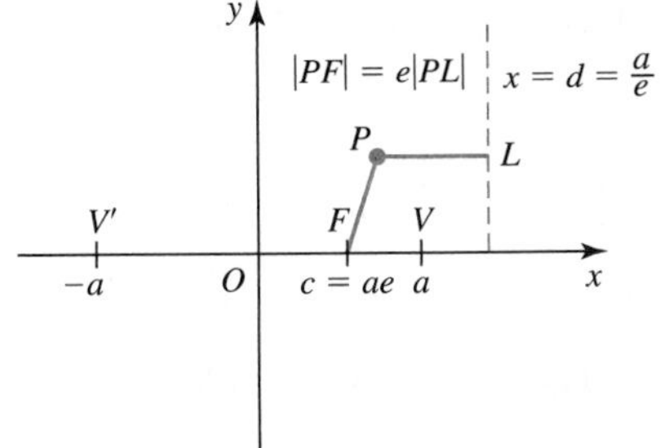

FIGURE B.1

Proof If $e = 1$, then the defining property becomes $|PF| = |PL|$, which is the standard definition of a parabola (Section 11.4). We prove the result for ellipses $(0 < e < 1)$ and a small modification handles the case of hyperbolas $(e > 1)$.

Let E be the curve whose points satisfy $|PF| = e\,|PL|$; the goal is to show that E is an ellipse. We locate the point F (a *focus*) at $(c, 0)$ and label the line ℓ (a *directrix*) $x = d$, where $c > 0$ and $d > 0$. It can be shown that E intersects the x-axis at the symmetric points (the *vertices*) $V(a, 0)$ and $V'(-a, 0)$ (Figure B.1). These choices place the center of E at the origin. Notice that we have four parameters (a, c, d, and e) that must be related.

Because the vertex $V(a, 0)$ is on E, it satisfies the defining property $|PF| = e\,|PL|$, with $P = V$. This condition implies that $a - c = e(d - a)$. Because the vertex $V'(-a, 0)$ is on the ellipse, it also satisfies the defining property $|PF| = e\,|PL|$, with $P = V'$. This condition implies that $a + c = e(d + a)$. Solving these two equations for c and d, we find that $c = ae$ and $d = a/e$. To summarize, the parameters a, c, d, and e are related by the equations

$$c = ae \quad \text{and} \quad a = de.$$

Because $e < 1$, it follows that $c < a < d$.

We now use the property $|PF| = e\,|PL|$ with an arbitrary point on the ellipse $P(x, y)$. Figure B.1 shows the geometry with the focus $(c, 0) = (ae, 0)$ and the directrix $x = d = a/e$. The condition $|PF| = e\,|PL|$ becomes

$$\sqrt{(x - ae)^2 + y^2} = e\left(\frac{a}{e} - x\right).$$

The goal is to find the simplest possible relationship between x and y. Squaring both sides and collecting terms, we have

$$(1 - e^2)x^2 + y^2 = a^2(1 - e^2).$$

Dividing through by $a^2(1 - e^2)$ gives the equation of the standard ellipse:

$$\frac{x^2}{a^2} + \frac{y^2}{a^2(1 - e^2)} = \frac{x^2}{a^2} + \frac{y^2}{b^2} = 1, \quad \text{where} \quad b^2 = a^2(1 - e^2).$$

This is the equation of an ellipse centered at the origin with vertices and foci on the x-axis.

The preceding proof is now applied with $e > 1$. The argument for ellipses with $0 < e < 1$ led to the equation

$$\frac{x^2}{a^2} + \frac{y^2}{a^2(1 - e^2)} = 1.$$

With $e > 1$, we have $1 - e^2 < 0$, so we write $(1 - e^2) = -(e^2 - 1)$. The resulting equation describes a hyperbola centered at the origin with the foci on the x-axis:

$$\frac{x^2}{a^2} - \frac{y^2}{b^2} = 1, \quad \text{where} \quad b^2 = a^2(e^2 - 1).$$

◄

> **THEOREM 13.3 Continuity of Composite Functions**
> If $u = g(x, y)$ is continuous at (a, b) and $z = f(u)$ is continuous at $g(a, b)$, then the composite function $z = f(g(x, y))$ is continuous at (a, b).

Proof Let P and P_0 represent the points (x, y) and (a, b), respectively. Let $u = g(P)$ and $u_0 = g(P_0)$. The continuity of f at u_0 means that $\lim_{u \to u_0} f(u) = f(u_0)$. This limit implies that given any $\varepsilon > 0$, there exists a $\delta^* > 0$ such that

$$|f(u) - f(u_0)| < \varepsilon \quad \text{whenever} \quad 0 < |u - u_0| < \delta^*.$$

The continuity of g at P_0 means that $\lim_{P \to P_0} g(P) = g(P_0)$. Letting $|P - P_0|$ denote the distance between P and P_0, this limit implies that given any $\delta^* > 0$, there exists a $\delta > 0$ such that

$$|g(P) - g(P_0)| = |u - u_0| < \delta^* \quad \text{whenever} \quad 0 < |P - P_0| < \delta.$$

We now combine these two statements. Given any $\varepsilon > 0$, there exists a $\delta > 0$ such that

$$|f(g(P)) - f(g(P_0))| = |f(u) - f(u_0)| < \varepsilon \quad \text{whenever} \quad 0 < |P - P_0| < \delta.$$

Therefore, $\lim_{(x,y) \to (a,b)} f(g(x, y)) = f(g(a, b))$ and $z = f(g(x, y))$ is continuous at (a, b). ◀

> **THEOREM 13.5 Conditions for Differentiability**
> Suppose the function f has partial derivatives f_x and f_y defined in a region containing (a, b) with f_x and f_y continuous at (a, b). Then f is differentiable at (a, b).

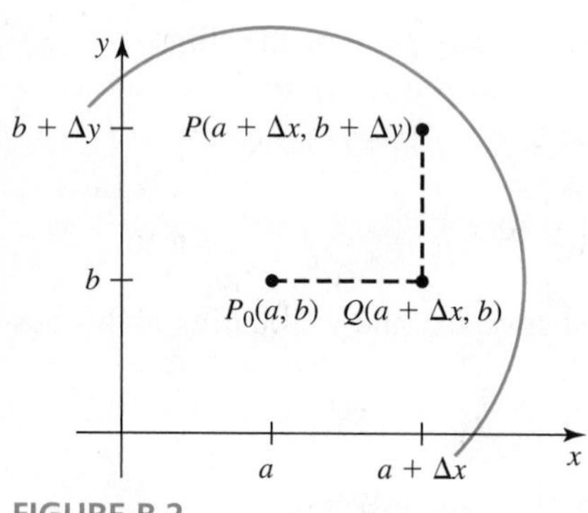

FIGURE B.2

Proof Figure B.2 shows a region on which the conditions of the theorem are satisfied containing the points $P_0(a, b)$, $Q(a + \Delta x, b)$, and $P(a + \Delta x, b + \Delta y)$. By the definition of differentiability of f at P_0, we must show that

$$\Delta z = f(P) - f(P_0) = f_x(a, b)\Delta x + f_y(a, b)\Delta y + \varepsilon_1 \Delta x + \varepsilon_2 \Delta y,$$

where ε_1 and ε_2 depend only on $a, b, \Delta x$, and Δy, with $(\varepsilon_1, \varepsilon_2) \to (0, 0)$ as $(\Delta x, \Delta y) \to (0, 0)$. We can view the change Δz taking place in two stages:

- $\Delta z_1 = f(a + \Delta x, b) - f(a, b)$ is the change in z as (x, y) moves from P_0 to Q.
- $\Delta z_2 = f(a + \Delta x, b + \Delta y) - f(a + \Delta x, b)$ is the change in z as (x, y) moves from Q to P.

Applying the Mean Value Theorem to the first variable and noting that f is differentiable with respect to x, we have

$$\Delta z_1 = f(a + \Delta x, b) - f(a, b) = f_x(c, b)\,\Delta x,$$

where c lies in the interval $(a, a + \Delta x)$. Similarly, applying the Mean Value Theorem to the second variable and noting that f is differentiable with respect to y, we have

$$\Delta z_2 = f(a + \Delta x, b + \Delta y) - f(a + \Delta x, b) = f_y(a + \Delta x, d)\,\Delta y,$$

where d lies in the interval $(b, b + \Delta y)$. We now express Δz as the sum of Δz_1 and Δz_2:

$$\begin{aligned}\Delta z &= \Delta z_1 + \Delta z_2 \\ &= f_x(c, b)\Delta x + f_y(a + \Delta x, d)\Delta y \\ &= (\underbrace{f_x(c, b) - f_x(a, b)}_{\varepsilon_1} + f_x(a, b))\Delta x \qquad \text{Add and subtract } f_x(a, b). \\ &\quad + (\underbrace{f_y(a + \Delta x, d) - f_y(a, b)}_{\varepsilon_2} + f_y(a, b))\Delta y \qquad \text{Add and subtract } f_y(a, b). \\ &= (f_x(a, b) + \varepsilon_1)\Delta x + (f_y(a, b) + \varepsilon_2)\Delta y\end{aligned}$$

Note that as $\Delta x \to 0$ and $\Delta y \to 0$, we have $c \to a$ and $d \to b$. Because f_x and f_y are continuous at (a, b) it follows that

$$\varepsilon_1 = f_x(c, b) - f_x(a, b) \to 0 \quad \text{and} \quad \varepsilon_2 = f_y(a + \Delta x, d) - f_y(a, b) \to 0.$$

Therefore, the condition for differentiability of f at (a, b) has been proved. ◄

THEOREM 13.7 Chain Rule (One Independent Variable)
Let $z = f(x, y)$ be a differentiable function of x and y on its domain, where x and y are differentiable functions of t on an interval I. Then

$$\frac{dz}{dt} = \frac{\partial f}{\partial x}\frac{dx}{dt} + \frac{\partial f}{\partial y}\frac{dy}{dt}.$$

Proof Assume $(a, b) = (x(t_0), y(t_0))$ is in the domain of f, where t is in I. Let $\Delta x = x(t + \Delta t) - x(t)$ and $\Delta y = y(t + \Delta t) - y(t)$. Because f is differentiable at (a, b), we know (Section 13.4) that

$$\Delta z = \frac{\partial f}{\partial x}(a, b)\,\Delta x + \frac{\partial f}{\partial y}(a, b)\,\Delta y + \varepsilon_1\Delta x + \varepsilon_2\Delta y,$$

where $(\varepsilon_1, \varepsilon_2) \to (0, 0)$ as $(\Delta x, \Delta y) \to (0, 0)$. Dividing this equation by Δt gives

$$\frac{\Delta z}{\Delta t} = \frac{\partial f}{\partial x}\frac{\Delta x}{\Delta t} + \frac{\partial f}{\partial y}\frac{\Delta y}{\Delta t} + \varepsilon_1\frac{\Delta x}{\Delta t} + \varepsilon_2\frac{\Delta y}{\Delta t}.$$

As $\Delta t \to 0$, several things occur. First, because $x = g(t)$ and $y = h(t)$ are differentiable on I, $\frac{\Delta x}{\Delta t}$ and $\frac{\Delta y}{\Delta t}$ approach $\frac{dx}{dt}$ and $\frac{dy}{dt}$, respectively. Similarly, $\frac{\Delta z}{\Delta t}$ approaches $\frac{dz}{dt}$ as $\Delta t \to 0$. The fact that x and y are continuous on I (because they are differentiable there), means that $\Delta x \to 0$ and $\Delta y \to 0$ as $\Delta t \to 0$. Therefore, because $(\varepsilon_1, \varepsilon_2) \to (0, 0)$ as $(\Delta x, \Delta y) \to (0, 0)$, it follows that $(\varepsilon_1, \varepsilon_2) \to (0, 0)$ as $\Delta t \to 0$. Letting $\Delta t \to 0$, we have

$$\underbrace{\lim_{\Delta t \to 0}\frac{\Delta z}{\Delta t}}_{\frac{dz}{dt}} = \frac{\partial f}{\partial x}\underbrace{\lim_{\Delta t \to 0}\frac{\Delta x}{\Delta t}}_{\frac{dx}{dt}} + \frac{\partial f}{\partial y}\underbrace{\lim_{\Delta t \to 0}\frac{\Delta y}{\Delta t}}_{\frac{dy}{dt}} + \lim_{\Delta t \to 0}\underbrace{\varepsilon_1}_{\to 0}\underbrace{\frac{\Delta x}{\Delta t}}_{\to \frac{dx}{dt}} + \lim_{\Delta t \to 0}\underbrace{\varepsilon_2}_{\to 0}\underbrace{\frac{\Delta y}{\Delta t}}_{\to \frac{dy}{dt}}$$

or

$$\frac{dz}{dt} = \frac{\partial f}{\partial x}\frac{dx}{dt} + \frac{\partial f}{\partial y}\frac{dy}{dt}.$$ ◄

> **THEOREM 13.14 Second Derivative Test**
> Suppose that the second partial derivatives of f are continuous throughout an open disk centered at the point (a, b) where $f_x(a, b) = f_y(a, b) = 0$. Let $D(x, y) = f_{xx}f_{yy} - f_{xy}^2$.
>
> **1.** If $D(a, b) > 0$ and $f_{xx}(a, b) < 0$, then f has a local maximum value at (a, b).
> **2.** If $D(a, b) > 0$ and $f_{xx}(a, b) > 0$, then f has a local minimum value at (a, b).
> **3.** If $D(a, b) < 0$, then f has a saddle point at (a, b).
> **4.** If $D(a, b) = 0$, then the test is inconclusive.

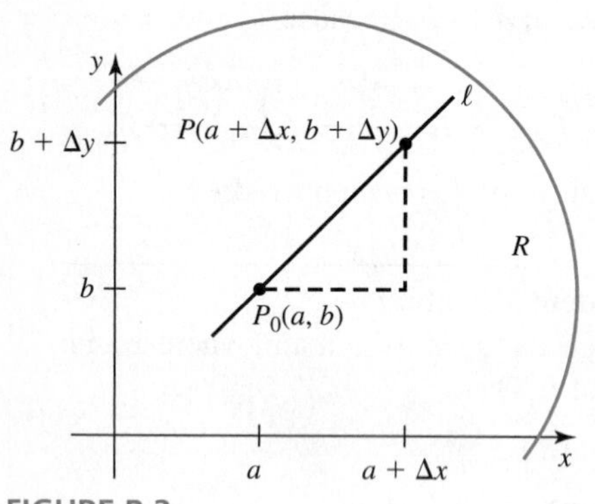

FIGURE B.3

Proof The proof relies on a two-variable version of Taylor's Theorem, which we prove first. Figure B.3 shows the open disk R on which the conditions of the theorem are satisfied; it contains the points $P_0(a, b)$ and $P(a + \Delta x, b + \Delta y)$. The line ℓ through P_0P has a parametric description

$$\langle x(t), y(t)\rangle = \langle a + t\Delta x, b + t\Delta y\rangle,$$

where $t = 0$ corresponds to P_0 and $t = 1$ corresponds to P.

We now let $F(t) = f(a + t\Delta x, b + t\Delta y)$ be the value of f along that part of ℓ that lies in R. By the Chain Rule we have

$$F'(t) = f_x \underbrace{x'(t)}_{\Delta x} + f_y \underbrace{y'(t)}_{\Delta y} = f_x\Delta x + f_y\Delta y.$$

Differentiating again with respect to t (f_x and f_y are differentiable), we use $f_{xy} = f_{yx}$ to obtain

$$\begin{aligned} F''(t) &= \frac{\partial F'}{\partial x}\underbrace{x'(t)}_{\Delta x} + \frac{\partial F'}{\partial y}\underbrace{y'(t)}_{\Delta y} \\ &= \frac{\partial}{\partial x}(f_x\Delta x + f_y\Delta y)\Delta x + \frac{\partial}{\partial y}(f_x\Delta x + f_y\Delta y)\Delta y \\ &= f_{xx}\Delta x^2 + 2f_{xy}\Delta x\Delta y + f_{yy}\Delta y^2. \end{aligned}$$

Noting that F meets the conditions of Taylor's Theorem for one variable with $n = 1$, we write

$$F(t) = F(0) + F'(0)(t - 0) + \frac{1}{2}F''(c)(t - 0)^2,$$

where c is between 0 and t. Setting $t = 1$, it follows that

$$F(1) = F(0) + F'(0) + \frac{1}{2}F''(c), \qquad (1)$$

where $0 < c < 1$. Recalling that $F(t) = f(a + t\Delta x, b + t\Delta y)$ and invoking the condition $f_x(a, b) = f_y(a, b) = 0$,

$$\begin{aligned} F(1) &= f(a + \Delta x, b + \Delta y) \\ &= f(a, b) + \underbrace{f_x(a, b)\Delta x + f_y(a, b)\Delta y}_{F'(0) = 0} \\ &\quad + \frac{1}{2}(f_{xx}\Delta x^2 + 2f_{xy}\Delta x\Delta y + f_{yy}\Delta y^2)\Big|_{(a+c\Delta x, b+c\Delta y)} \\ &= f(a, b) + \frac{1}{2}\underbrace{(f_{xx}\Delta x^2 + 2f_{xy}\Delta x\Delta y + f_{yy}\Delta y^2)\Big|_{(a+c\Delta x, b+c\Delta y)}}_{H(c)} \\ &= f(a, b) + \frac{1}{2}H(c) \end{aligned}$$

The existence and type of extreme point at (a, b) is determined by the sign of $f(a + \Delta x, b + \Delta y) - f(a, b)$ (for example, if $f(a + \Delta x, b + \Delta y) - f(a, b) \geq 0$ for all Δx and Δy near 0, then f has a local minimum at (a, b)). Note that $f(a + \Delta x, b + \Delta y) - f(a, b)$ has the same sign as the quantity we have denoted $H(c)$. Assuming $H(0) \neq 0$, for Δx and Δy sufficiently small and nonzero, the sign of $H(c)$ is the same as the sign of

$$H(0) = \Delta x^2 f_{xx}(a, b) + 2\Delta x \Delta y\, f_{xy}(a, b) + \Delta y^2 f_{yy}(a, b)$$

(because the second partial derivatives are continuous at (a, b) and $(a + c\Delta x, b + c\Delta y)$ can be made arbitrarily close to (a, b)). Multiplying both sides of the previous expression by f_{xx} and rearranging terms leads to

$$\begin{aligned} f_{xx} H(0) &= f_{xx}{}^2 \Delta x^2 + 2 f_{xy} f_{xx} \Delta x \Delta y + f_{yy} f_{xx} \Delta y^2 \\ &= \underbrace{(\Delta x\, f_{xx} + \Delta y\, f_{xy})^2}_{\geq 0} + (f_{xx} f_{yy} - f_{xy}{}^2)\Delta y^2, \end{aligned}$$

where all derivatives are evaluated at (a, b). Recall that the signs of $H(0)$ and $f(a + \Delta x, b + \Delta y) - f(a, b)$ are the same. Letting $D(a, b) = (f_{xx} f_{yy} - f_{xy}{}^2)|_{(a,b)}$, we reach the following conclusions:

- If $D(a, b) > 0$ and $f_{xx}(a, b) < 0$, then $H(0) < 0$ (for Δx and Δy sufficiently close to 0) and $f(a + \Delta x, b + \Delta y) - f(a, b) < 0$. Therefore, f has a local maximum value at (a, b).
- If $D(a, b) > 0$ and $f_{xx}(a, b) > 0$, then $H(0) > 0$ (for Δx and Δy sufficiently close to 0) and $f(a + \Delta x, b + \Delta y) - f(a, b) > 0$. Therefore, f has a local minimum value at (a, b).
- If $D(a, b) < 0$, then $H(0) > 0$ for some small nonzero values of Δx and Δy (implying $f(a + \Delta x, b + \Delta y) > f(a, b)$), *and* $H(0) < 0$ for other small nonzero values of Δx and Δy (implying $f(a + \Delta x, b + \Delta y) < f(a, b)$). (The relative sizes of $(f_{xx} \Delta x + f_{xy} \Delta y)^2$ and $(f_{xx} f_{yy} - f_{xy}{}^2) \Delta y^2$ can be adjusted by varying Δx and Δy.) Therefore, f has a saddle point at (a, b).
- If $D(a, b) = 0$, then $H(0)$ may be zero, in which case the sign of $H(c)$ cannot be determined. Therefore, the test is inconclusive. ◄

C

Appendix

Hyperbolic Functions

When we construct trigonometric-like functions with respect to a hyperbola rather than a circle, the result is a new family of six functions that involve e^x and e^{-x}. They are called the hyperbolic trigonometric functions. We begin with the *hyperbolic sine* and *hyperbolic cosine* functions.

➤ sinh is pronounced *sinch* and cosh is pronounced *cosh*.

DEFINITION Hyperbolic sine and cosine

Hyperbolic sine $\sinh x = \dfrac{e^x - e^{-x}}{2}$

Hyperbolic cosine $\cosh x = \dfrac{e^x + e^{-x}}{2}$

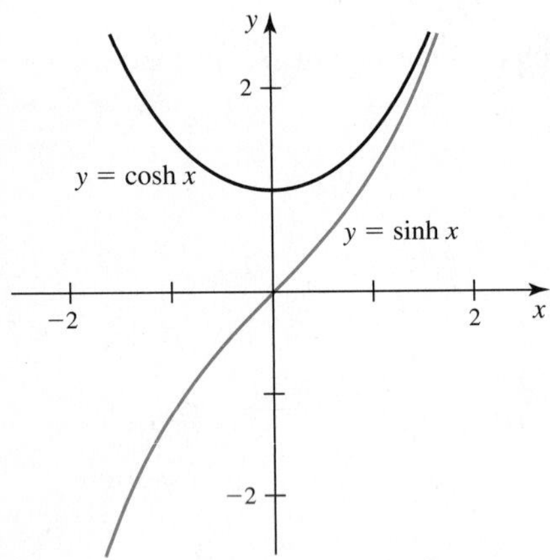

FIGURE C.1

The properties of the exponential function lead immediately to the following properties of the hyperbolic sine and cosine.

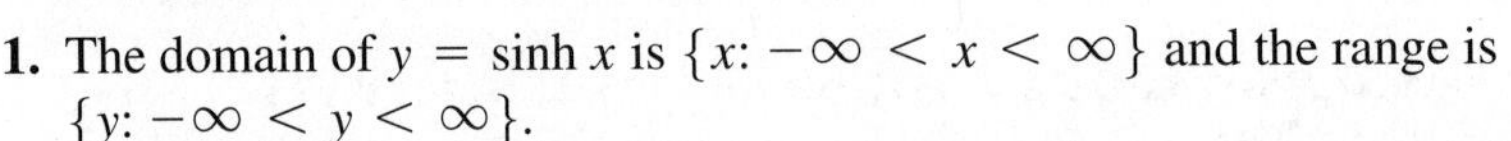

1. The domain of $y = \sinh x$ is $\{x: -\infty < x < \infty\}$ and the range is $\{y: -\infty < y < \infty\}$.
2. The domain of $y = \cosh x$ is $\{x: -\infty < x < \infty\}$ and the range is $\{y: y \geq 1\}$.
3. $\sinh 0 = 0$, $\cosh 0 = 1$.
4. $\lim_{x\to\infty} \sinh x = \lim_{x\to\infty} \cosh x = \infty$, $\lim_{x\to-\infty} \sinh x = -\infty$, $\lim_{x\to-\infty} \cosh x = \infty$.
5. $\sinh x$ is an odd function ($\sinh(-x) = -\sinh x$) and $\cosh x$ is an even function ($\cosh(-x) = \cosh x$).
6. $\cosh^2 x - \sinh^2 x = 1$.
7. The graphs of $\sinh x$ and $\cosh x$ are shown in Figure C.1.

Two quick calculations lead to the derivatives of $\sinh x$ and $\cosh x$:

$$\frac{d}{dx}(\sinh x) = \frac{d}{dx}\left(\frac{e^x - e^{-x}}{2}\right) = \frac{1}{2}(e^x + e^{-x}) = \cosh x$$

$$\frac{d}{dx}(\cosh x) = \frac{d}{dx}\left(\frac{e^x + e^{-x}}{2}\right) = \frac{1}{2}(e^x - e^{-x}) = \sinh x$$

As shown in Figure C.1, $\sinh x$ is increasing for all x (because its derivative $\cosh x$ is positive for all x). Similarly, $\cosh x$ is decreasing for $x < 0$ (because its derivative $\sinh x$ is negative for $x < 0$) and $\cosh x$ is increasing for $x > 0$ (because $\sinh x > 0$ for $x > 0$).

The corresponding indefinite integrals are just as easy to remember:

$$\int \sinh x\, dx = \cosh x + C \quad \text{and} \quad \int \cosh x\, dx = \sinh x + C$$

EXAMPLE 1 Derivatives and integrals of hyperbolic functions

a. Evaluate $\frac{d}{dx}(x \sinh 3x)$. **b.** Evaluate $\int_1^3 x \cosh(x^2 - 1)\, dx$.

SOLUTION

a.

$$\begin{aligned} \frac{d}{dx}(x \sinh 3x) &= \frac{d}{dx}(x) \cdot \sinh 3x + x \frac{d}{dx}(\sinh 3x) && \text{Product Rule} \\ &= \sinh 3x + 3x \cosh 3x && \text{Chain Rule} \end{aligned}$$

b. Using the substitution $u = x^2 - 1$ and noting that $du = 2x\, dx$, we find that

$$\begin{aligned} \int_1^3 x \cosh(x^2 - 1)\, dx &= \frac{1}{2}\int_0^8 \cosh u\, du && u = x^2 - 1,\ u(3) = 8,\ u(1) = 0 \\ &= \frac{1}{2} \sinh u \Big|_0^8 \\ &= \frac{1}{2} \sinh 8 \approx 745.24. \end{aligned}$$

Related Exercises 3–8 ◄

➤ To see all the connections between the hyperbolic trigonometric functions and the regular (or circular) trigonometric functions it is necessary to write all these functions in terms of a complex variable. Then all the properties of one family (for example, identities, derivatives, integrals) have mirror properties in the other family.

The derivative results for $\sinh x$ and $\cosh x$ show the parallels between the hyperbolic trigonometric functions and the ordinary trigonometric functions. In fact, the connections are much deeper. So perhaps it is not surprising that we can define four more hyperbolic trigonometric functions.

DEFINITION Other hyperbolic functions

Hyperbolic tangent $\tanh x = \dfrac{\sinh x}{\cosh x} = \dfrac{e^x - e^{-x}}{e^x + e^{-x}}$

Hyperbolic cotangent $\coth x = \dfrac{\cosh x}{\sinh x} = \dfrac{e^x + e^{-x}}{e^x - e^{-x}}$

Hyperbolic secant $\operatorname{sech} x = \dfrac{1}{\cosh x} = \dfrac{2}{e^x + e^{-x}}$

Hyperbolic cosecant $\operatorname{csch} x = \dfrac{1}{\sinh x} = \dfrac{2}{e^x - e^{-x}}$

The graphs of the other four hyperbolic trigonometric functions are shown in Figure C.2. The derivatives of these functions are given in Example 2 and Exercise 9.

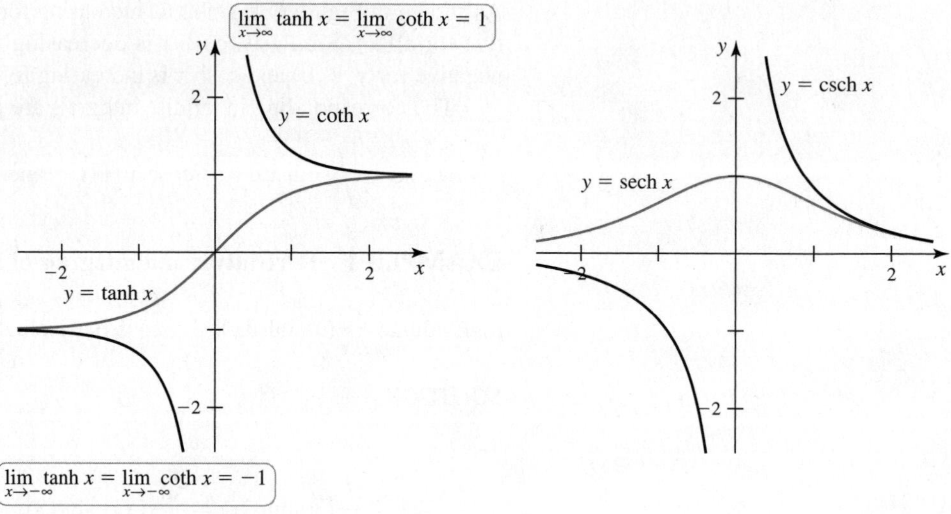

FIGURE C.2

EXAMPLE 2 **Derivatives and integrals of hyperbolic functions**

a. Evaluate $\frac{d}{dx}(\tanh x)$.

b. Evaluate $\int \tanh ax\, dx$ for real numbers a.

SOLUTION

a.

$$
\begin{aligned}
\frac{d}{dx}(\tanh x) &= \frac{d}{dx}\left(\frac{\sinh x}{\cosh x}\right) \\
&= \frac{\cosh x \frac{d}{dx}(\sinh x) - \sinh x \frac{d}{dx}(\cosh x)}{\cosh^2 x} && \text{Quotient Rule} \\
&= \frac{\cosh^2 x - \sinh^2 x}{\cosh^2 x} && \text{Simplify.} \\
&= \frac{1}{\cosh^2 x} && \cosh^2 x - \sinh^2 x = 1 \\
&= \operatorname{sech}^2 x
\end{aligned}
$$

It follows from this result that $\int \operatorname{sech}^2 x\, dx = \tanh x + C$.

b.

$$
\begin{aligned}
\int \tanh ax\, dx &= \int \frac{\sinh ax}{\cosh ax}\, dx \\
&= \frac{1}{a}\int \frac{du}{u} && u = \cosh ax,\ du = a \sinh ax \\
&= \frac{1}{a} \ln |u| + C && \text{Evaluate integral.} \\
&= \frac{1}{a} \ln \cosh x + C && u = \cosh x, \cosh x > 0
\end{aligned}
$$

Related Exercises 10–18 ◀

A well-known application of hyperbolic trigonometric functions arises in the field of statics. A flexible chain or cable, hanging at its ends and acted on only by the gravitational force (its own weight) takes the shape of a **catenary**, described by the function $y = a\cosh(x/a)$ (Figure C.3). (The term comes from the Latin for *chain*; however, Thomas Jefferson is often credited with introducing the English word.) See Exercise 27 for an example.

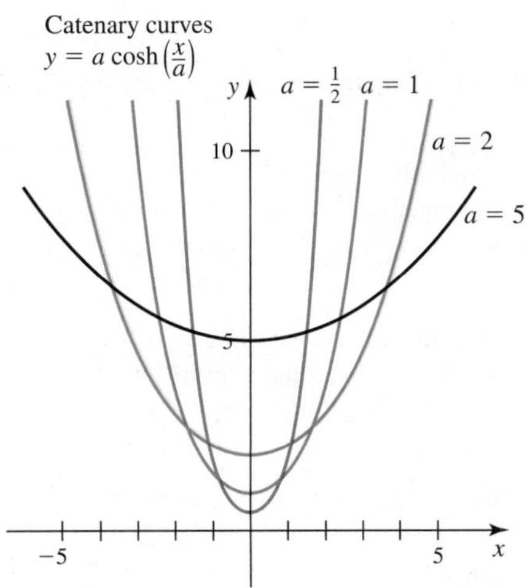

FIGURE C.3

Finally, the hyperbolic trigonometric functions are either one-to-one on $(-\infty, \infty)$ ($\sinh x$ and $\tanh x$), or they can be restricted to be one-to-one on either $(-\infty, 0)$, or $(0, \infty)$ ($\cosh x$, $\coth x$, $\operatorname{sech} x$, and $\operatorname{csch} x$). It follows that inverse hyperbolic trigonometric functions can be defined on the appropriate intervals (Exercises 23–24).

APPENDIX C EXERCISES

1. **Domains** Find the domain of $\tanh x$, $\coth x$, $\operatorname{sech} x$, and $\operatorname{csch} x$.

2. **Identities** Prove each identity. When possible, give the analogous identity for ordinary trigonometric functions.
   a. $\cosh^2 x - \sinh^2 x = 1$
   b. $\operatorname{sech}^2 x + \tanh^2 x = 1$
   c. $\coth^2 x - \operatorname{csch}^2 x = 1$
   d. $\sinh 2x = 2\sinh x\cosh x$
   e. $\sinh(\ln x) = (x - x^{-1})/2 \quad \text{for } x > 0$
   f. $\cosh(\ln x) = (x + x^{-1})/2 \quad \text{for } x > 0$

3–8. Derivatives and integrals with sinh x and cosh x *Evaluate the following derivatives and integrals.*

3. $\dfrac{d}{dx}\left(\dfrac{\cosh 3x}{x^2}\right)$

4. $\dfrac{d}{dx}\left(\sinh\sqrt{x^2+1}\right)$

5. Find $y'(x)$ when $\sinh(xy) = x + 8$

6. $\displaystyle\int x\sinh(x^2+4)\,dx$

7. $\displaystyle\int_0^{\ln 3} \sinh^2 x\cosh x\,dx$

8. $\displaystyle\int x\cosh x\,dx$ (Integrate by parts.)

9. **Derivatives** Prove the following derivative results.

$$\frac{d}{dx}(\coth x) = -\operatorname{csch}^2 x \qquad \frac{d}{dx}(\operatorname{sech} x) = -\operatorname{sech} x\tanh x$$

$$\frac{d}{dx}(\operatorname{csch} x) = -\operatorname{csch} x\coth x$$

10–12. More derivatives *Use Example 2 and Exercise 9 to evaluate the following derivatives.*

10. $\dfrac{d}{dx}(x\tanh x)$

11. $\dfrac{d}{dx}(\sqrt{\tanh 3x})$

12. $\dfrac{d}{dx}(\ln\coth 3x)$

13–18. More integrals *Use Example 2 and Exercise 9 to evaluate the following integrals.*

13. $\displaystyle\int \operatorname{csch}^2 x\,dx$

14. $\displaystyle\int \operatorname{sech} 2x\tanh 2x\,dx$

15. $\displaystyle\int \coth 5x\,dx$

16. $\displaystyle\int \operatorname{sech}^5 x\operatorname{csch} x\,dx$

17. $\displaystyle\int_1^4 \frac{\tanh\sqrt{x}}{\sqrt{x}}\,dx$

18. $\displaystyle\int_{\ln 2}^{\ln 3} \frac{dx}{\coth x}$

19. Area under sech x Is the area of the region bounded by the graph of $y = \operatorname{sech} x$ and the x-axis on $(-\infty, \infty)$ finite? If so, what is its value? Use the fact that $\int \operatorname{sech} x\, dx = 2 \tan^{-1}(e^x) + C$.

20. Area under cosh x Let R be the region bounded by the graph of $y = \cosh x$ and the line $y = 2$.

a. Find the area of R.
b. Find the volume of the solid generated when R is revolved about the x-axis. (Use $\cosh^2 x = (1 + \cosh 2x)/2$.)

21. Arc length Show that the arc length of $y = \cosh x$ on the interval $[0, a]$ is $\sinh a$.

22. Differential equations Hyperbolic trigonometric functions are useful in solving differential equations. Show that the functions $y = A \sinh kx$ and $y = B \cosh kx$, where A, B, and k are constants, satisfy the equation $y''(x) - k^2 y(x) = 0$.

23. Inverse hyperbolic sine Because the hyperbolic sine is one-to-one on $(-\infty, \infty)$, it has an inverse on that interval.

a. Solve the equation $y = \sinh x = \dfrac{e^x - e^{-x}}{2}$ for x in terms of y to show that the inverse hyperbolic sine function is $\sinh^{-1} x = \ln(x + \sqrt{x^2 + 1})$.
b. Give the domain and range of $\sinh^{-1} x$.
c. Graph $\sinh^{-1} x$ (using either a graphing utility or the reflection property of the graphs of a function and its inverse).
d. Show that $\dfrac{d}{dx}(\sinh^{-1} x) = \dfrac{1}{\sqrt{x^2 + 1}}$.

24. Inverse hyperbolic cosine Because the hyperbolic cosine is one-to-one on $[0, \infty)$, it has an inverse on that interval.

a. Solve the equation $y = \cosh x = \dfrac{e^x + e^{-x}}{2}$ for x in terms of y to show that the inverse hyperbolic cosine function is $\cosh^{-1} x = \ln(x + \sqrt{x^2 - 1})$.
b. Give the domain and range of $\cosh^{-1} x$ (as it is defined here).
c. Graph $\cosh^{-1} x$ (using either a graphing utility or the reflection property of the graphs of a function and its inverse).
d. Show that $\dfrac{d}{dx}(\cosh^{-1} x) = \dfrac{1}{\sqrt{x^2 - 1}}$, for $x > 1$.

25–26. "Trigonometric" substitutions *Use the change of variables $x = a \sinh u$ to evaluate the following integrals.*

25. $\displaystyle\int \frac{dx}{\sqrt{x^2 + 9}}$

26. $\displaystyle\int_0^4 \sqrt{x^2 + 9}\, dx$

27. Catenary A flexible chain hangs from the tops of two poles of equal length whose bases are at $x = \pm L$. The height of the chain above the ground $(y = 0)$ is given by $y = a \cosh\left(\dfrac{x}{a}\right)$.

a. The lowest point of the chain is at $x = 0$, where the chain is 2 m above the ground. Find a.
b. If the poles are 4 m high, find L.
c. Graph the resulting catenary.

Answers

CHAPTER 1

Section 1.1 Exercises, pp. 7–9

1. A function is a rule that assigns to each value of the independent variable in the domain a unique value of the dependent variable in the range. **3.** A graph represents a function provided no vertical line intersects the graph more than once. **5.** The first statement is true of a function, by definition. **7.** $f(g(2)) = 2$; $g(f(-2)) = -2$
9. $f(-x) = f(x)$

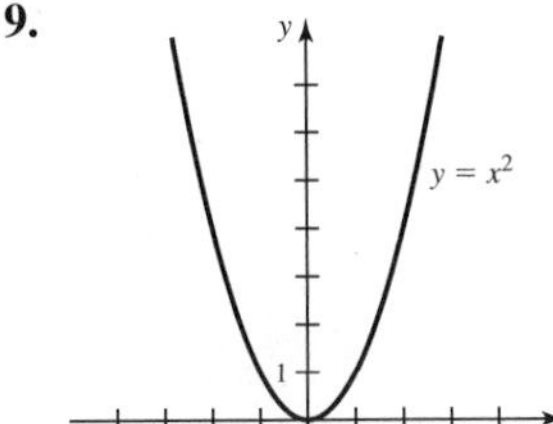

11. B **13.** D = **R**, R = $[-10, \infty)$ **15.** D = $[-2, 2]$, R = $[0, 2]$ **17.** D = **R**, R = **R** **19.** The independent variable is t; the dependent variable is d. D = $[0, 8]$ **21.** 96 **23.** $1/z^3$
25. $1/(y^3 - 3)$ **27.** $(u^2 - 4)^3$ **29.** $\dfrac{x - 3}{10 - 3x}$
31. $g(x) = x^3 - 5$; $f(x) = x^{10}$; D = **R**
33. $g(x) = x^4 + 2$, $f(x) = \sqrt{x}$; D = **R**
35. $(f \circ g)(x) = |x^2 - 4|$; D = **R**
37. $(f \circ G)(x) = \dfrac{1}{|x - 2|}$; D = $\{x: x \neq 2\}$
39. $(G \circ g \circ f)(x) = \dfrac{1}{x^2 - 6}$; D = $\{x: x \neq \sqrt{6}, -\sqrt{6}\}$
41. $f(x) = x^2$ **43.** $f(x) = x^2$ **45. a.** 4 **b.** 1 **c.** 3 **d.** 3 **e.** 7 **f.** 8 **47.** y-axis **49.** no symmetry **51.** x-axis, y-axis, origin **53.** A is even, B is odd, C is even **55. a.** True **b.** False **c.** True **d.** False **e.** False **f.** True **g.** True **h.** False **i.** True.
57.

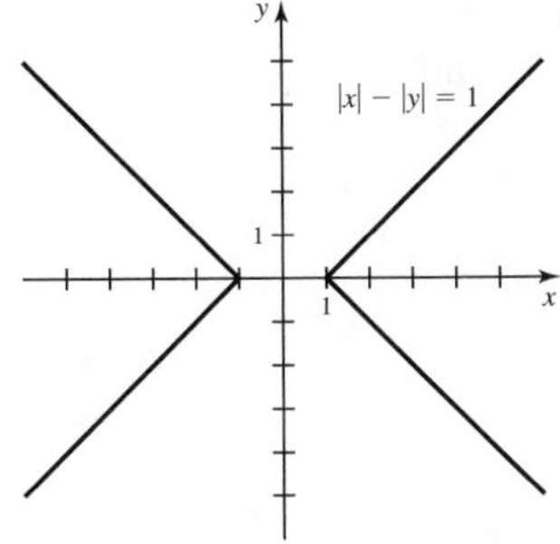

59. $f(x) = 3x - 2$ **61.** $f(x) = x^2 - 6$ **63. a.** $[0, 3 + \sqrt{14}]$

b.

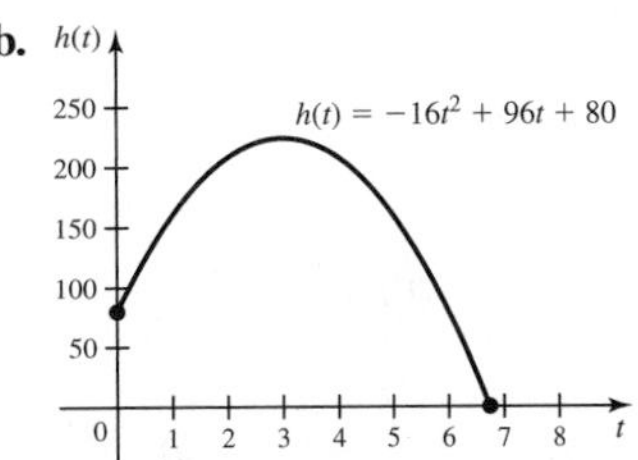

At time $t = 3$, the maximum height is 224 ft.

65. None **67.** Symmetry about the origin **69.** y-axis **71.** y-axis **73.** 4, 4 **75.** $-1/(2ax)$; $-1/(2x(x + h))$

Section 1.2 Exercises, pp. 19–22

1. A formula, a graph, a table, words **3.** Set of all real numbers except points at which the denominator is zero
5.

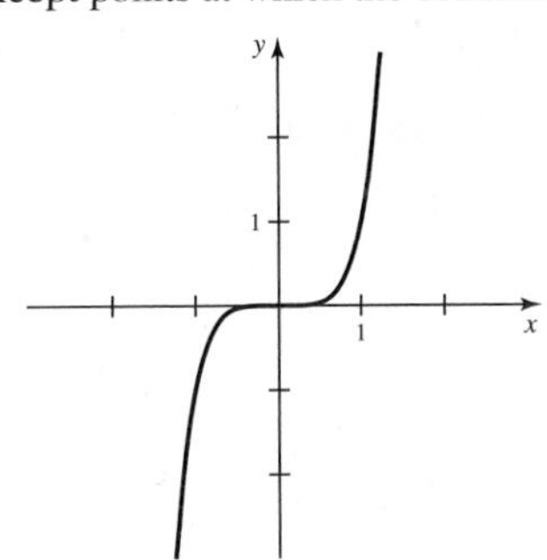

7. Shift the graph to the left 2 units **9.** Compress the graph horizontally by a factor of 3 **11.** $y = -\frac{2}{3}x - 1$
13. $d = -3p/50 + 27$; D = $[0, 450]$

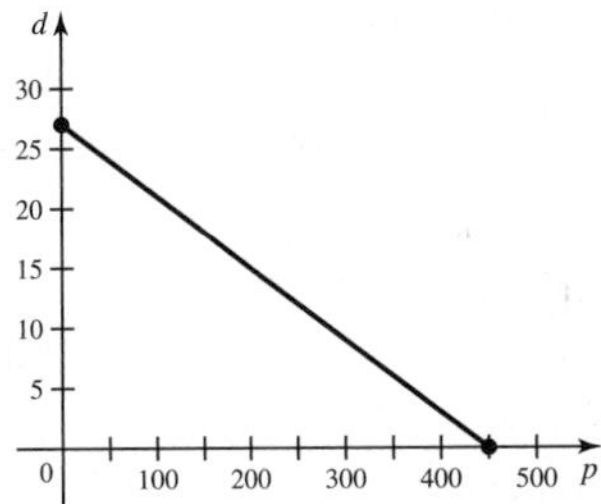

15. $y = \begin{cases} x + 3 & \text{if } x < 0 \\ -\frac{1}{2}x + 3 & \text{if } x \geq 0 \end{cases}$

17.

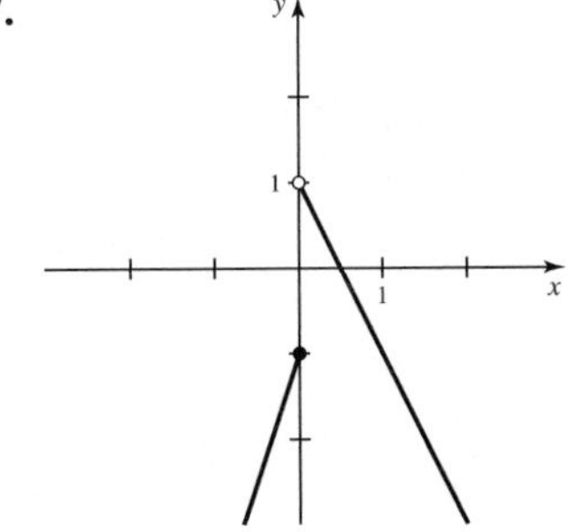

19.

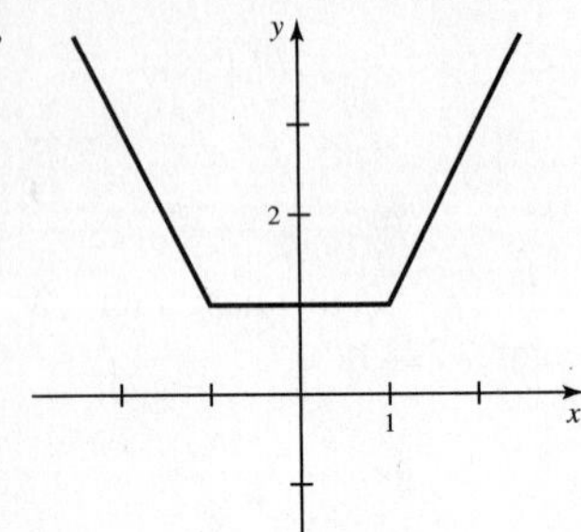

21. a.

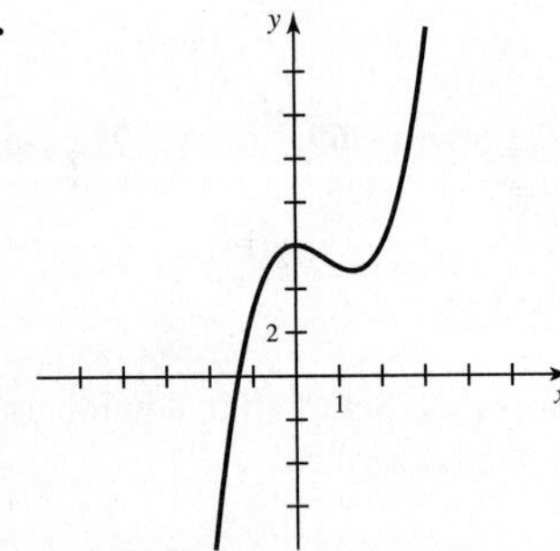

b. Polynomial function; D = **R** **c.** one peak near $x = 0$; one valley near $x = 4/3$; x-intercept near $x = -1.34$, y-intercept at $(0, 6)$

23. a.

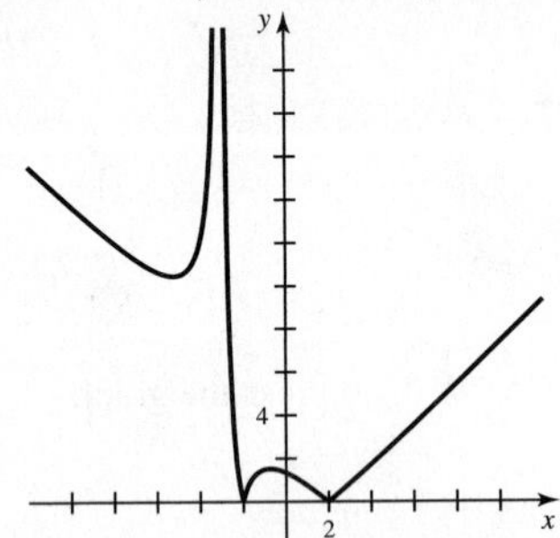

b. Absolute value of a rational function; D = $\{x: x \neq -3\}$
c. Undefined at $x = -3$; a valley near $x = -5.2$; x-intercepts (and valleys) at $x = -2$ and $x = 2$; a peak near $x = -0.8$

25. $g(x) = \begin{cases} 1 & \text{if } x < 0 \\ -\frac{1}{2} & \text{if } x > 0 \end{cases}$ **27. a.** 12 **b.** 36 **c.** $A(x) = 6x$

29. $f(x) = |x - 2| + 3$; $g(x) = -|x + 2| - 1$
31. a. Shift 3 units to the right

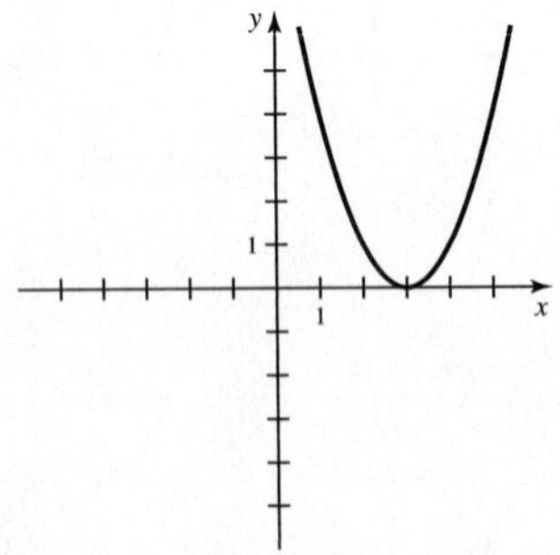

b. Compress horizontally by a factor of 2, then shift 2 units to the right.

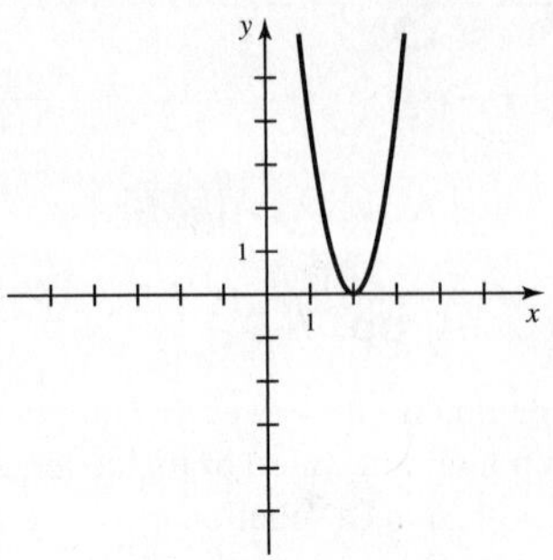

c. Shift to the right 2 units, vertical scaling and flip by a factor of 3, shift up 4 units

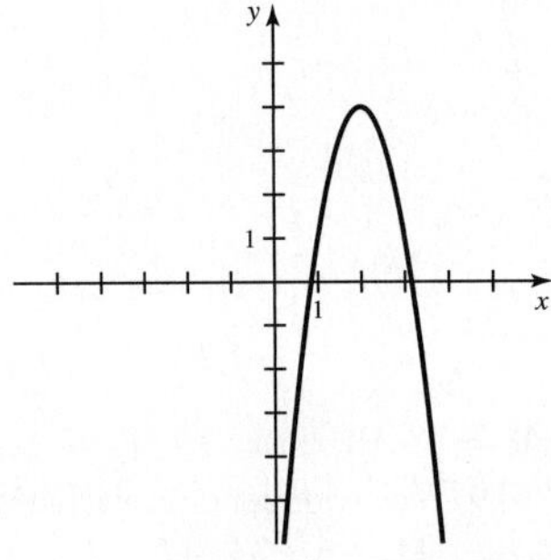

d. Horizontal scaling by a factor of $\frac{1}{3}$, horizontal shift right 2 units, vertical scaling by a factor of 6, vertical shift up 1 unit

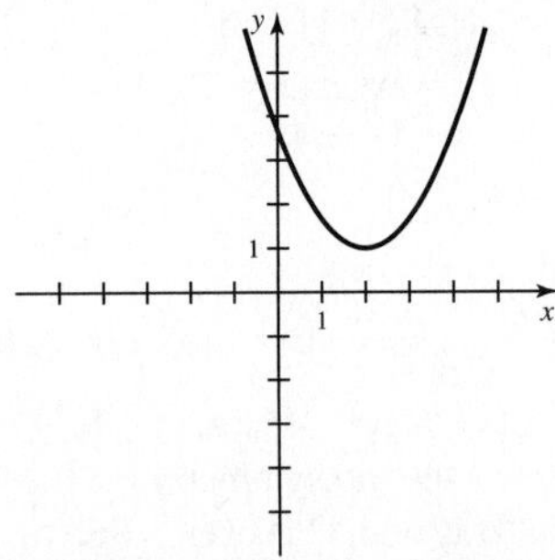

33. Stretch the graph of $y = x^2$ vertically by a factor of 3; then reflect across the x-axis. **35.** Shift the graph of $y = x^2$ left 3 units and stretch vertically by a factor of 2. **37.** Shift the graph of $y = x^2$ to the left $\frac{1}{2}$ unit, stretch vertically by a factor of 4, reflect through the x-axis, and then shift up 13 units to obtain the graph of h. **39. a.** True **b.** False **c.** True **d.** False **41.** $(0, 0)$ and $(4, 16)$
43. $y = \sqrt{x} - 1$
45. $y = 5x$; D = $[0, 4]$ hr

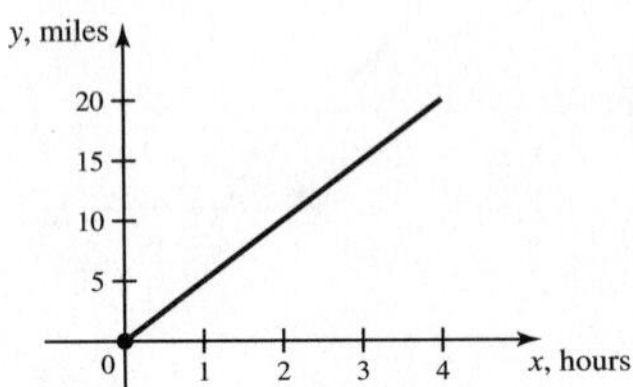

47. $y = 3200/x$; D $= [0, 5)$

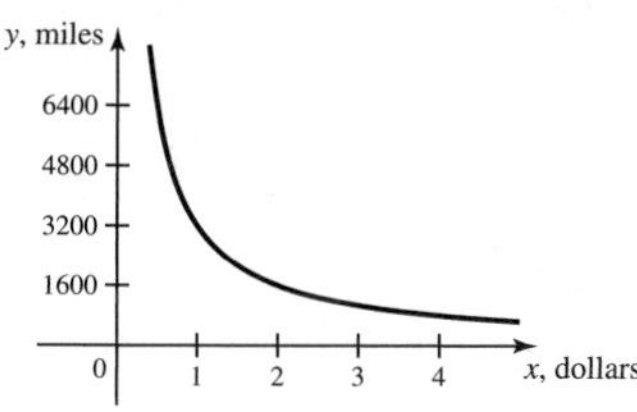

49. $y = \lceil x \rceil$

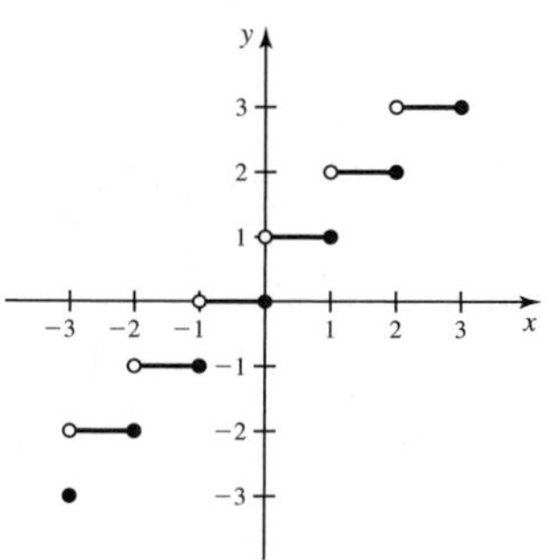

51.

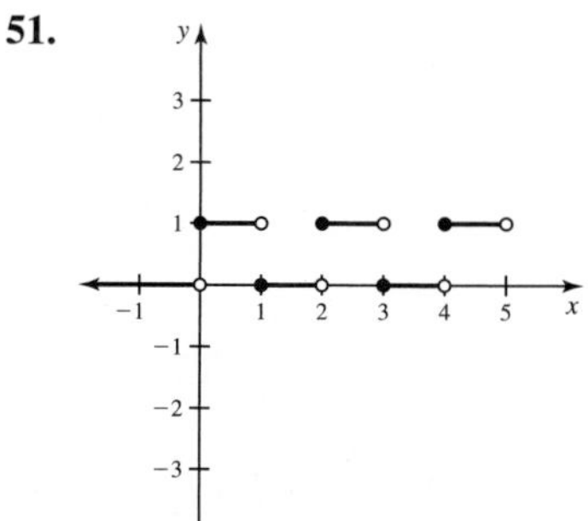

53.

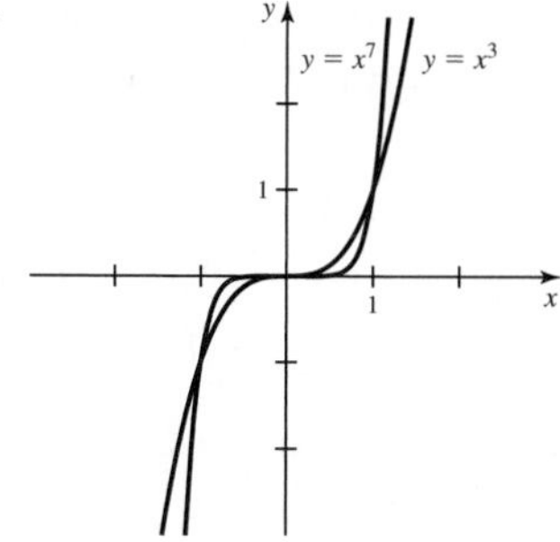

55. a. $p(t) = 328.3t + 1875$ **b.** 4830
57. a. $f(m) = 350m + 1200$ **b.** Buy
59. $0 \le h \le 2$

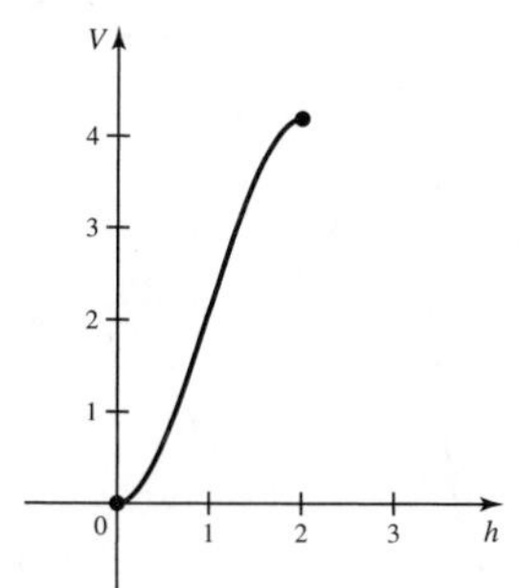

61. a. $S(x) = x^2 + \dfrac{500}{x}$ **b.** ≈ 6.30 ft

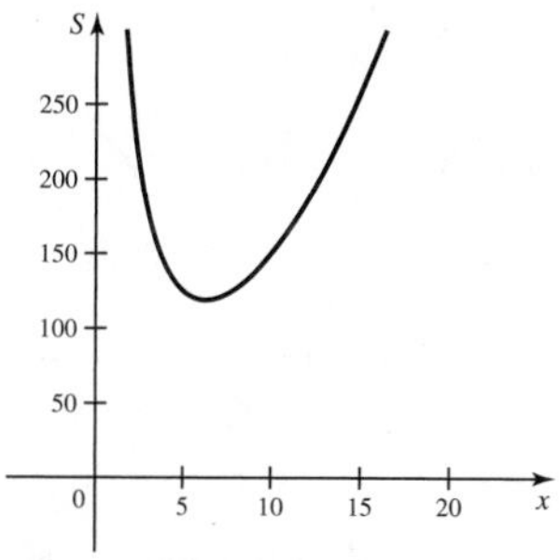

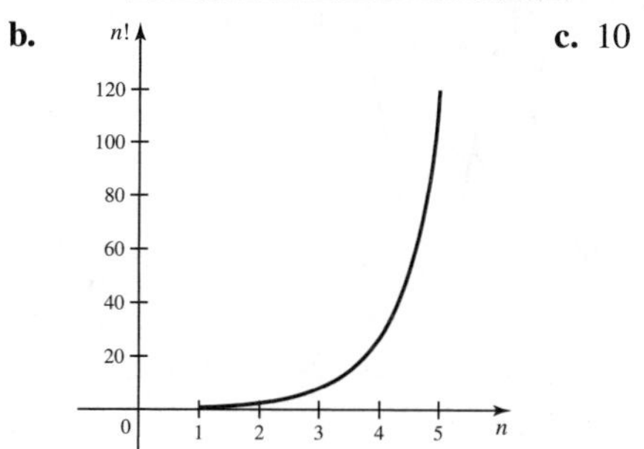

65. a.

n	1	2	3	4	5
$f(n)$	1	2	6	24	120

b. **c.** 10

67. a.

n	1	2	3	4	5	6	7	8	9	10
$T(n)$	1	5	14	30	55	91	140	204	285	385

b. D $= \{n: n$ is a positive integer$\}$ **c.** 14

Section 1.3 Exercises, pp. 27–29

1. $\sin\theta = \text{opp/hyp}$; $\cos\theta = \text{adj/hyp}$; $\tan\theta = \text{opp/adj}$ $\cot\theta = \text{adj/opp}$; $\sec\theta = \text{hyp/adj}$; $\csc\theta = \text{hyp/opp}$ **3.** The radian measure of an angle θ is the length of an arc s on the unit circle associated with θ. **5.** $\sin^2\theta + \cos^2\theta = 1$, $1 + \cot^2\theta = \csc^2\theta$, $\tan^2\theta + 1 = \sec^2\theta$ **7.** $\{x: x$ is an odd multiple of $\pi/2\}$ **9.** $-\frac{1}{2}$ **11.** 1 **13.** $-1/\sqrt{3}$ **15.** $1/\sqrt{3}$ **17.** Dividing both sides of $\cos^2\theta + \sin^2\theta = 1$ by $\cos^2\theta$ gives $1 + \tan^2\theta = \sec^2\theta$. **19.** If α and β are complementary angles, we have seen that $\cos\alpha = \sin\beta$. Thus $1/(\cos\alpha) = 1/(\sin\beta)$. Letting $\alpha = \pi/2 - \theta$ and $\beta = \theta$, $\sec(\pi/2 - \theta) = \csc\theta$. **21.** $\dfrac{\sqrt{2 + \sqrt{3}}}{2}$ or $\dfrac{\sqrt{6} + \sqrt{2}}{4}$ **23.** $\pi/4 + n\pi, n = 0, \pm1, \pm2, \ldots$ **25.** $\pi/4 + 2n\pi, 3\pi/4 + 2n\pi$, $n = 0, \pm1, \pm2, \ldots$ **27.** $\{\pi/12, 5\pi/12, 3\pi/4, 13\pi/12, 17\pi/12, 7\pi/4\}$
29. a. False **b.** False **c.** False **d.** False **e.** True
31. $\sin\theta = \frac{12}{13}$; $\tan\theta = \frac{12}{5}$; $\sec\theta = \frac{13}{5}$; $\csc\theta = \frac{13}{12}$; $\cot\theta = \frac{5}{12}$
33. $\sin\theta = \frac{12}{13}$; $\cos\theta = \frac{5}{13}$; $\tan\theta = \frac{12}{5}$; $\sec\theta = \frac{13}{5}$; $\cot\theta = \frac{5}{12}$
35. amp $= 3$; period $= 6\pi$ **37.** amp $= 3.6$; period $= 48$

39. Stretch the graph of $y = \cos x$ horizontally by a factor of 3; stretch vertically by a factor of 2; and reflect through the x-axis

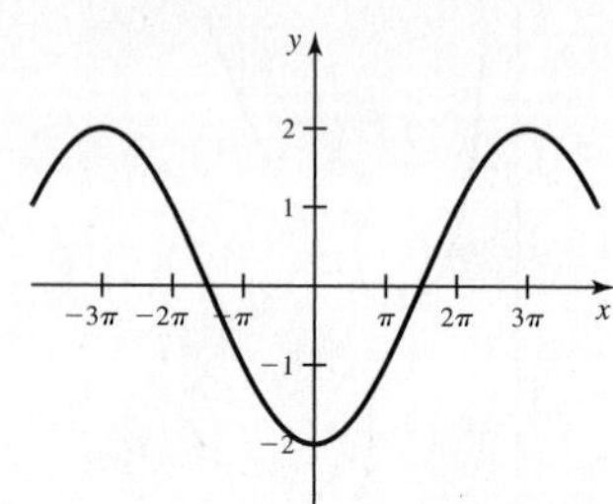

41. Stretch the graph of $y = \cos x$ horizontally by a factor of $24/\pi$; then stretch it vertically by a factor of 3.6 and shift it up 2 units

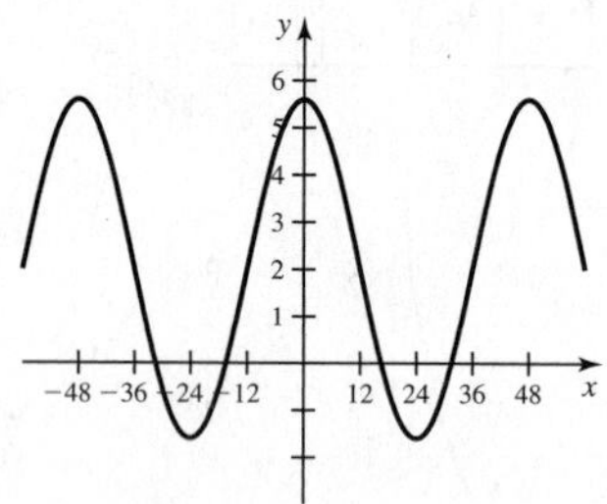

43. $y = 3\sin(\pi x/12 - 3\pi/4) + 13$ **45.** $d(t) = 10\cos(4\pi t/3)$
47. $\sqrt{a^2 - h^2} + k$

49. $s(t) = 117.5 - 87.5\sin\left(\dfrac{\pi}{182.5}(t - 95)\right)$

$S(t) = 843.5 + 87.5\sin\left(\dfrac{\pi}{182.5}(t - 67)\right)$

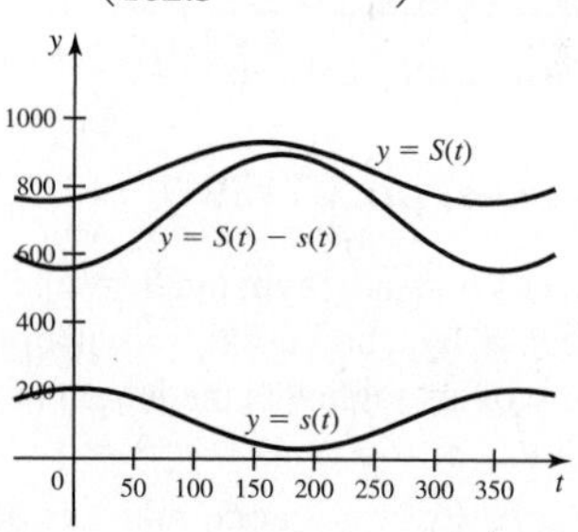

Chapter 1 Review Exercises, pp. 29–31

1. a. True **b.** False **c.** False **d.** True **e.** False

3. a.

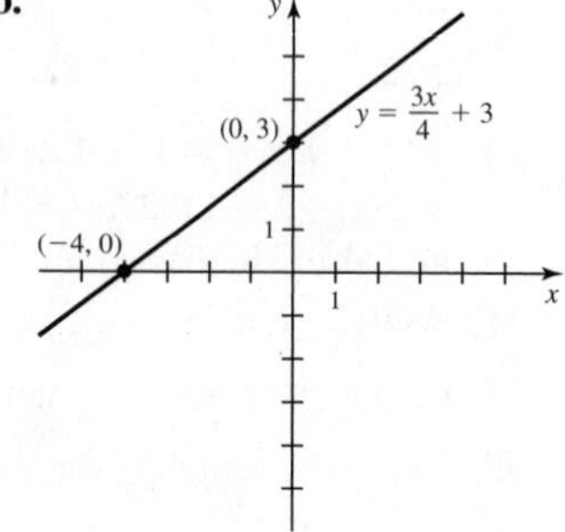

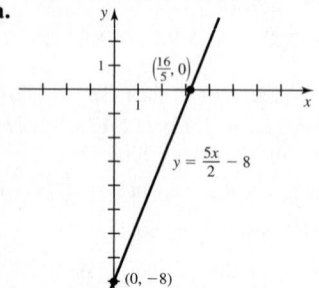

b.

c.

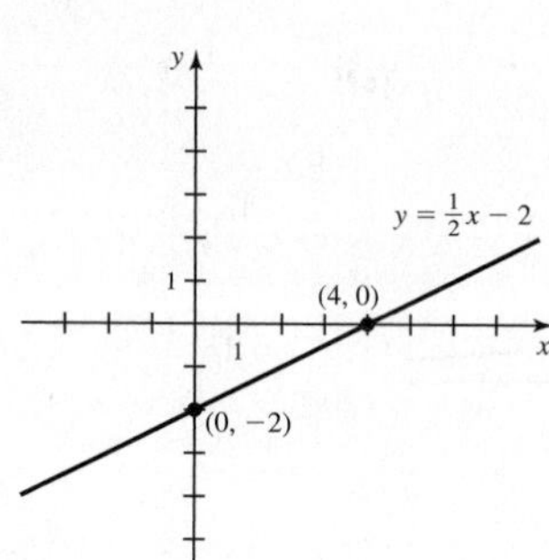

5. $f(x) = \begin{cases} 0 & \text{if } x \geq 0 \\ 4x & \text{if } x < 0 \end{cases}$

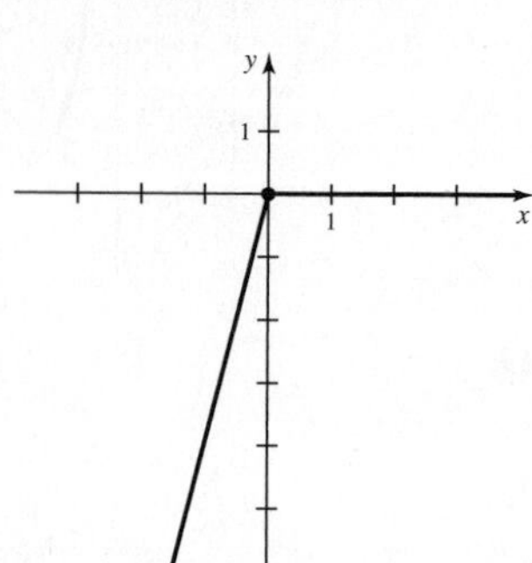

7. a.

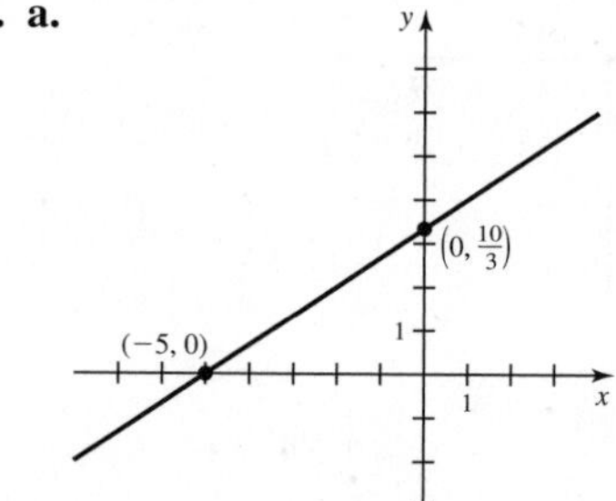

b.

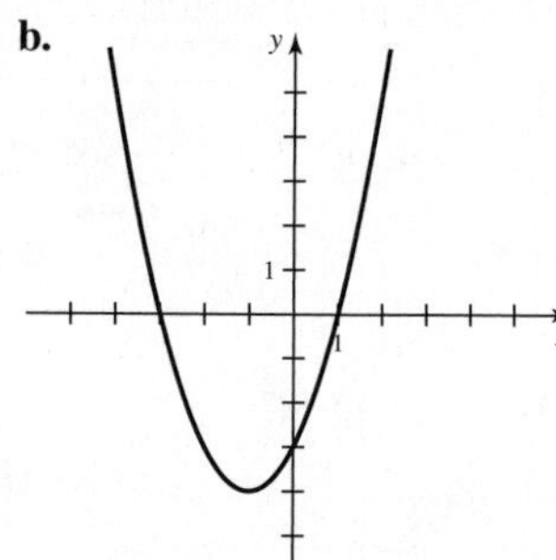

c.

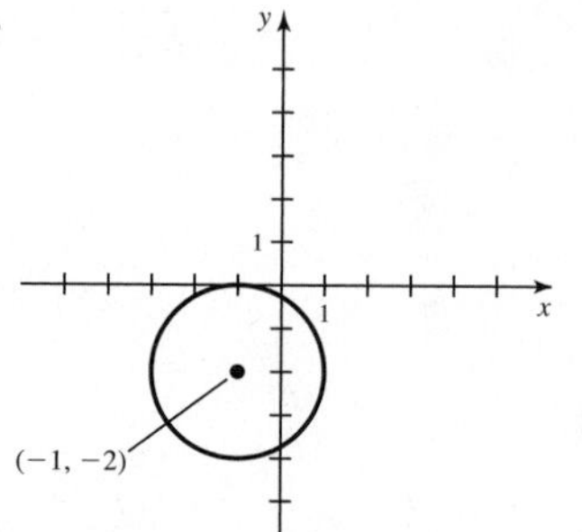

d.

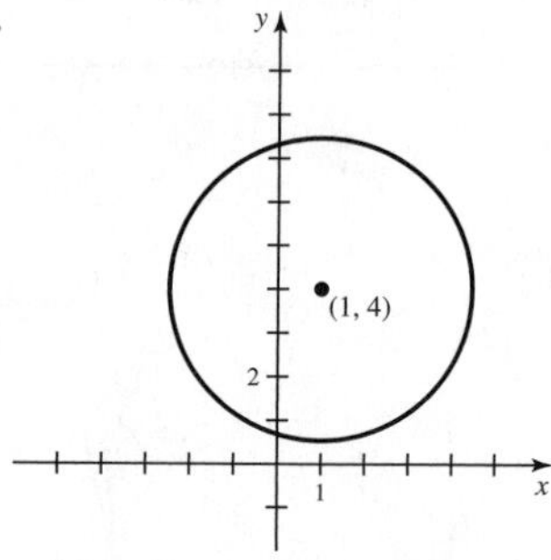

9. $D_f = \mathbf{R}, R_f = \mathbf{R}; D_g = [0, \infty), R_g = [0, \infty)$

11. $B = -\dfrac{a}{500} + 212$

13. a.

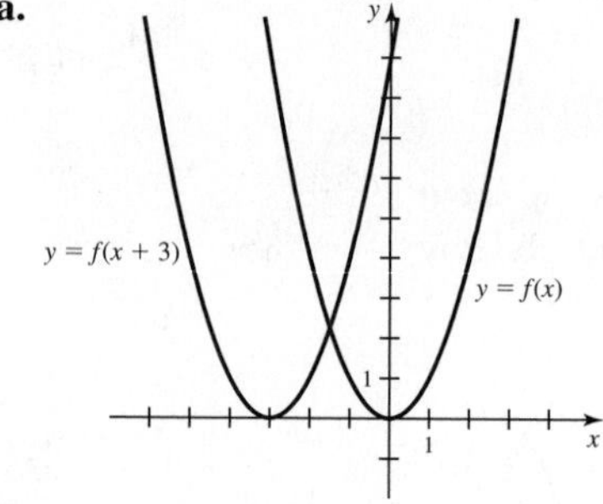

b.

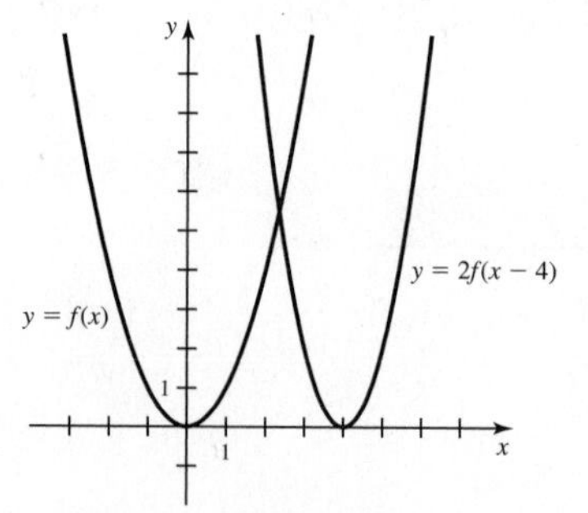

c.

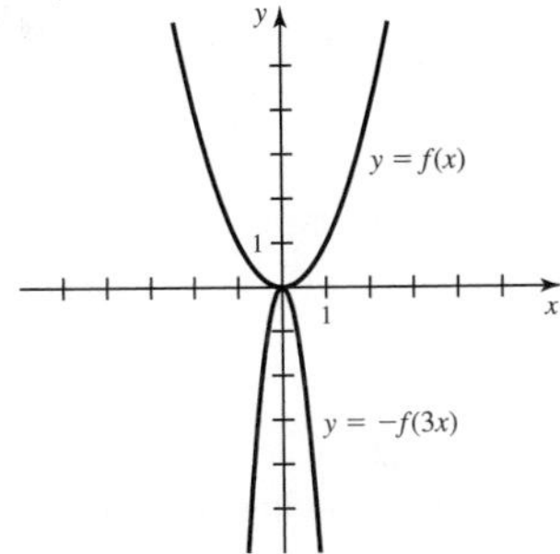

d.

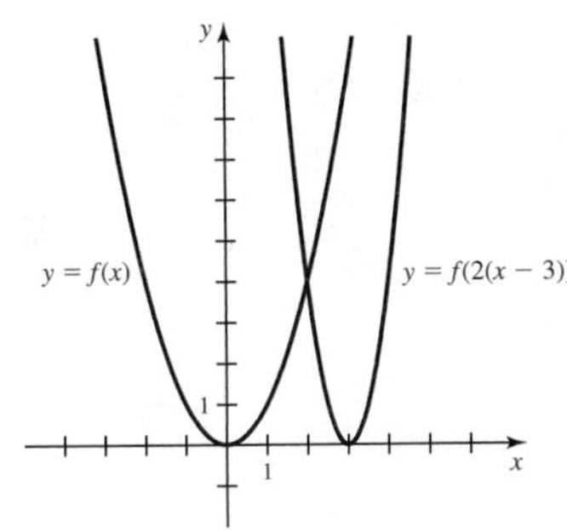

15. a. 1 **b.** $\sqrt{x^3}$ **c.** $\sin^3 \sqrt{x}$ **d.** $[-\infty, \infty)$ **e.** $[-1, 1]$
17. a. y-axis **b.** y-axis **c.** x-axis, y-axis, origin
19. a. $3\pi/4$ **b.** 144° **c.** $40\pi/3$ **21. a.** $f(t) = -2\cos\left(\frac{\pi t}{3}\right)$
b. $f(t) = 5\sin\left(\frac{\pi t}{12}\right) + 15$ **23. a.** F **b.** E **c.** D **d.** B
e. C **f.** A

CHAPTER 2

Section 2.1 Exercises, pp. 37–38

1. $\frac{s(b) - s(a)}{b - a}$ **3.** $\frac{f(b) - f(a)}{b - a}$ **5.** The instantaneous velocity at $t = a$ is the slope of the tangent line to the position curve at $t = a$.
7. a. 48 **b.** 64 **c.** 80 **d.** $16(7 - h)$

9.

Time interval	Average velocity
[1, 2]	80
[1, 1.5]	88
[1, 1.1]	94.4
[1, 1.01]	95.84
[1, 1.001]	95.984
$v_{\text{inst}} = 96$	

11.

Time interval	Average velocity
[2, 3]	20
[2.9, 3]	5.60
[2.99, 3]	4.16
[2.999, 3]	4.016
[2.9999, 3]	4.002
$v_{\text{inst}} = 4$	

13.

Time interval	Average velocity
[3, 3.5]	−24
[3, 3.1]	−17.6
[3, 3.01]	−16.16
[3, 3.001]	−16.016
[3, 3.0001]	−16.002
$v_{\text{inst}} = -16$	

15.

Time interval	Average velocity
[0, 1]	36.372
[0, 0.5]	67.318
[0, 0.1]	79.468
[0, 0.01]	79.995
[0, 0.001]	80.000
$v_{\text{inst}} = 80$	

17.

Interval	Slope of secant line
[1, 2]	6
[1.5, 2]	7
[1.9, 2]	7.8
[1.99, 2]	7.98
[1.999, 2]	7.998
$m_{\tan} = 8$	

19.

Interval	Slope of secant line
[1, 2]	−3
[1, 1.5]	−2.5
[1, 1.1]	−2.1
[1, 1.01]	−2.01
[1, 1.001]	−2.001
$m_{\tan} = 2$	

21. a.

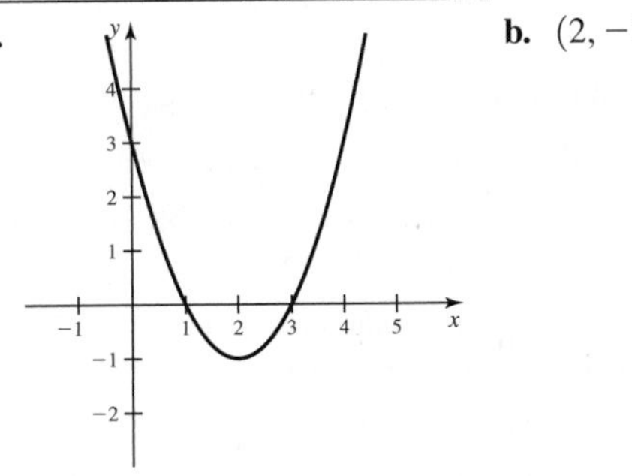

b. $(2, -1)$

c.

Interval	Slope of secant line
[2, 2.5]	0.5
[2, 2.1]	0.1
[2, 2.01]	0.01
[2, 2.001]	0.001
[2, 2.0001]	0.0001
$m_{\tan} = 0$	

23. a. 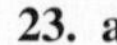
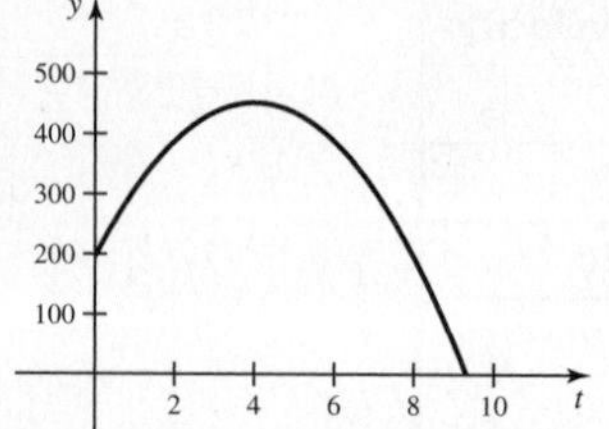

b. $t = 4$

c.

Interval	Slope of secant line
[4, 4.5]	−8
[4, 4.1]	−1.6
[4, 4.01]	−0.16
[4, 4.001]	−0.016
[4, 4.0001]	−0.0012
$v_{\text{inst}} = 0$	

d. $0 \le t < 4$ **e.** $4 < t \le 9$ **25.** 0.6366, 0.9589, 0.9996, 1

Section 2.2 Exercises, pp. 43–46

1. As x approaches a from either side, the values of $f(x)$ approach L. **3.** As x approaches a from the right, the values of $f(x)$ approach L. **5.** L must equal M. **7. a.** 5 **b.** 3 **c.** Does not exist **d.** 1 **e.** 2 **9. a.** −1 **b.** 1 **c.** 2 **d.** 2

11. a.

x	$f(x)$	x	$f(x)$
1.9	3.9	2.1	4.1
1.99	3.99	2.01	4.01
1.999	3.999	2.001	4.001
1.9999	3.9999	2.0001	4.0001

b. 4

13. a.

t	$g(t)$	t	$g(t)$
8.9	5.983287	9.1	6.016621
8.99	5.998333	9.01	6.001666
8.999	5.999833	9.001	6.000167

b. 6

15. $\lim_{x\to 5^+} f(x) = 10$; $\lim_{x\to 5^-} f(x) = 10$; $\lim_{x\to 5} f(x) = 10$
17. a. 0 **b.** 1 **c.** 0 **d.** Does not exist; $\lim_{x\to 1^-} f(x) \ne \lim_{x\to 1^+} f(x)$
19. a. 3 **b.** 2 **c.** 2 **d.** 2 **e.** 2 **f.** 4 **g.** 1 **h.** Does not exist; $\lim_{x\to 3^-} f(x) \ne \lim_{x\to 3^+} f(x)$ **i.** 3 **j.** 3 **k.** 3 **l.** 3

21. a.

x	$\sin\left(\frac{1}{x}\right)$
$2/\pi$	1
$2/(3\pi)$	−1
$2/(5\pi)$	1
$2/(7\pi)$	−1
$2/(9\pi)$	1
$2/(11\pi)$	−1

The values alternate between 1 and −1.

b. The alternation between 1 and −1 happens infinitely many times on the interval $(0, h)$ no matter how small $h > 0$ becomes. **c.** $\lim_{x\to 0} \sin(1/x)$ does not exist. **23. a.** False **b.** False **c.** False

25.

27. 3 **29.** 0 **31. a.** −2, −1, 1, 2 **b.** 2, 2, 2
c. $\lim_{x\to a^-} \lfloor x \rfloor = a - 1$ and $\lim_{x\to a^+} \lfloor x \rfloor = a$, if a is an integer
d. $\lim_{x\to a^-} \lfloor x \rfloor = \lfloor a \rfloor$ and $\lim_{x\to a^+} \lfloor x \rfloor = \lfloor a \rfloor$, if a is not an integer
e. $\lim_{x\to a} \lfloor x \rfloor$ exists only if a is not an integer. **33.** $\frac{16}{9} \approx 1.78$

35. a.

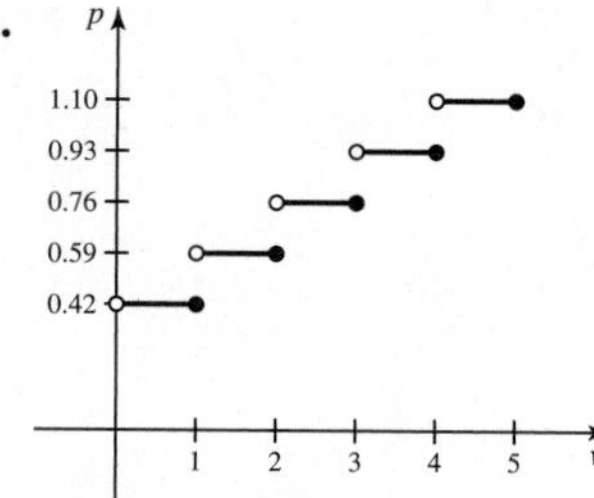

b. \$0.95

c. $\lim_{x\to 1^+} f(w)$ is the cost of a letter that weighs just over 1 oz. $\lim_{x\to 1^-} f(w)$ is the cost of a letter that weighs just under 1 oz.
d. No; $\lim_{x\to 4^+} f(w) \ne \lim_{x\to 4^-} f(w)$ **39. a.** 8 **b.** 5
41. a. 2; 3; 4 **b.** n **43.** $\frac{n}{m}$

Section 2.3 Exercises, pp. 54–56

1. $\lim_{x\to a} f(x) = f(a)$ **3.** Those values of a for which the denominator is not zero **5.** $\frac{x^2 - 7x + 12}{x - 3} = x - 4$ for $x \ne 3$. **7.** 20
9. 4 **11.** 5 **13.** −45 **15.** 4 **17.** 32; Constant Multiple Law **19.** 12; Quotient and Product Laws **21.** 32; Power Law **23.** 8 **25.** 3 **27.** 3 **29.** −5 **31. a.** 2 **b.** 0 **c.** Does not exist **33. a.** 0 **b.** $\sqrt{x - 2}$ is not defined for $x < 2$. **35.** Show that $\lim_{x\to 0^-} |x| = \lim_{x\to 0^-} (x) = 0$ and $\lim_{x\to 0^+} |x| = \lim_{x\to 0^+} x = 0$ **37.** 2
39. −8 **41.** −1 **43.** −12 **45.** $\frac{1}{6}$ **47.** $\frac{1}{8}$
49. a. Because $\left|\sin\left(\frac{1}{x}\right)\right| \le 1$ for all $x \ne 0$, we have that

$$|x|\left|\sin\left(\frac{1}{x}\right)\right| \le |x|.$$

That is, $\left|x \sin\left(\frac{1}{x}\right)\right| \le |x|$, so that $-|x| \le x \sin\left(\frac{1}{x}\right) \le |x|$ for all $x \ne 0$.

b.

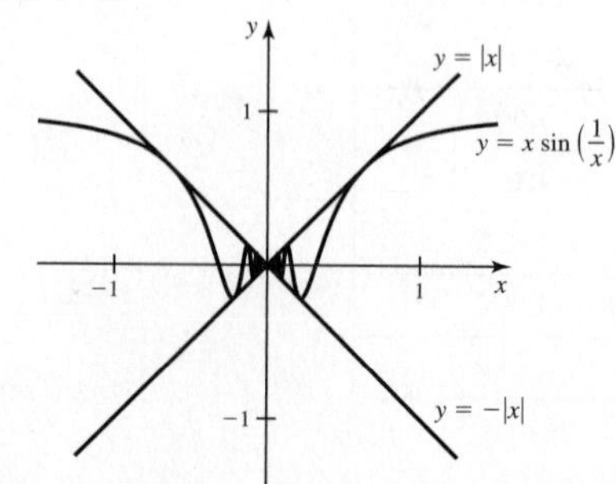

c. $\lim_{x\to 0} -|x| = 0$ and $\lim_{x\to 0} |x| = 0$; by part (a) and the Squeeze Theorem, $\lim_{x\to 0} x \sin\left(\frac{1}{x}\right) = 0$

51. a.

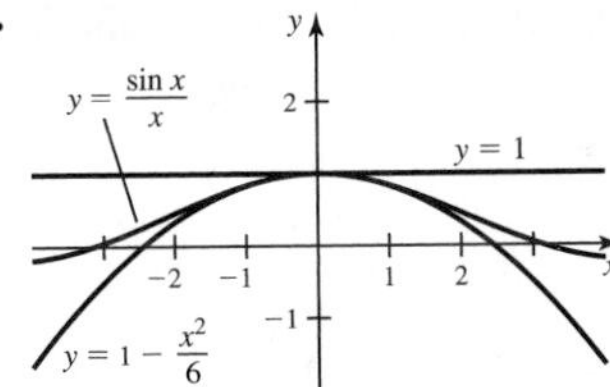

b. $\lim_{x\to 0} \frac{\sin x}{x} = 1$ **53. a.** False **b.** False **c.** False **d.** False **e.** False **55.** 8 **57.** 5 **59.** 10 **61.** −3 **63.** $a = -13$; $\lim_{x\to -1} g(x) = 6$. **65.** 6 **67.** $5a^4$ **69.** $\frac{1}{3}$ **71.** 2 **73.** −54

75. $f(x) = x - 1, g(x) = \frac{5}{x-1}$ **77.** $b = 2$ and $c = -8$; yes

79. $\lim_{S\to 0^+} r(S) = 0$; the radius of the cylinder approaches 0 as the surface area of the cylinder approaches 0. **81.** 0.0435 N/C **83.** 6; 4

Section 2.4 Exercises, pp. 63–65

1. $\lim_{x\to a^+} f(x) = -\infty$ means that as x approaches a from the right, the values of $f(x)$ are negative and become arbitrarily large in magnitude. **3.** A vertical line $x = a$, which the graph of a function approaches as x approaches a **5.** $-\infty$ **7.** ∞ **9. a.** ∞ **b.** ∞ **c.** ∞ **d.** ∞ **e.** $-\infty$ **f.** Does not exist **11. a.** $-\infty$ **b.** $-\infty$ **c.** $-\infty$ **d.** ∞ **e.** $-\infty$ **f.** Does not exist **13. a.** ∞ **b.** $-\infty$ **c.** $-\infty$ **d.** ∞

15.

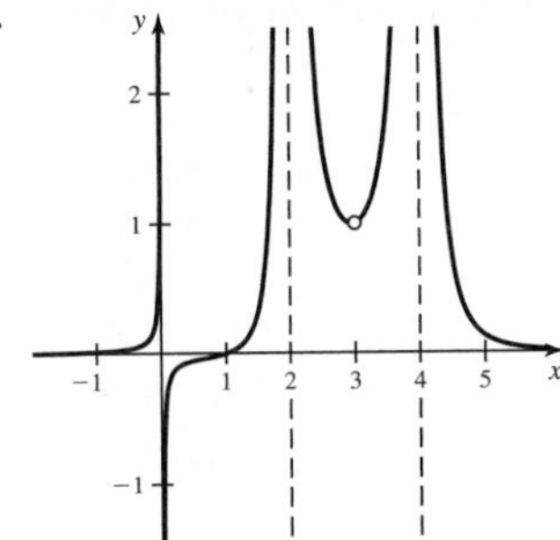

17. a. ∞ **b.** $-\infty$ **c.** Does not exist **19.** −5 **21.** ∞

23. $x = 3$; $\lim_{x\to 3^+} f(x) = -\infty$; $\lim_{x\to 3^-} f(x) = \infty$; $\lim_{x\to 3} f(x)$ does not exist. **25.** $x = 0$ and $x = 2$; $\lim_{x\to 0^+} f(x) = \infty$; $\lim_{x\to 0^-} f(x) = -\infty$; $\lim_{x\to 0} f(x)$ does not exist; $\lim_{x\to 2^+} f(x) = \infty$; $\lim_{x\to 2^-} f(x) = \infty$; $\lim_{x\to 2} f(x) = \infty$ **27.** ∞ **29.** $-\infty$ **31. a.** $-\infty$ **b.** ∞ **c.** $-\infty$ **d.** ∞ **33. a.** False **b.** True **c.** False

35. $f(x) = \frac{1}{x-6}$ **37.** $x = 0$ **39.** $x = -1$ **41.** $\theta = (2k+1)5$ for any integer k **43.** $x = 0$ **45. a.** $a = 4$ or $a = 3$ **b.** Either $a > 4$ or $a < 3$ **c.** $3 < a < 4$

47. a. $\frac{1}{\sqrt[3]{h}}$, regardless of the sign of h **b.** $\lim_{h\to 0^+} \frac{1}{\sqrt[3]{h}} = \infty$; $\lim_{h\to 0^-} \frac{1}{\sqrt[3]{h}} = -\infty$; the tangent line at (0, 0) is vertical.

Section 2.5 Exercises, pp. 72–73

1. The values of $f(x)$ approache 10 as of x increases without bound negatively. **3.** 0 **5.** $\lim_{x\to\infty} f(x) = -\infty$; $\lim_{x\to -\infty} f(x) = \infty$

7. $-\frac{1}{2}, 0, -\infty$ **9.** 3 **11.** 0 **13.** 0 **15.** ∞ **17.** $-\infty$ **19.** 0

21. $\lim_{x\to\infty} f(x) = 2$; $\lim_{x\to -\infty} f(x) = 2$; $y = 2$

23. $\lim_{x\to\infty} f(x) = \lim_{x\to -\infty} f(x) = 0$; $y = 0$

25. $\lim_{x\to\infty} f(x) = \infty$; $\lim_{x\to -\infty} f(x) = -\infty$; none

27. $\lim_{x\to\infty} f(x) = \frac{2}{3}$; $\lim_{x\to -\infty} f(x) = -2$; $y = \frac{2}{3}$; $y = -2$

29. $\lim_{x\to\infty} f(x) = \lim_{x\to -\infty} f(x) = \frac{1}{4+\sqrt{3}}$; $y = \frac{1}{4+\sqrt{3}}$

31. a. False **b.** False **c.** True

33. a. $\lim_{x\to\infty} f(x) = 2$; $\lim_{x\to -\infty} f(x) = 2$; $y = 2$

b. $x = 0$; $\lim_{x\to 0^+} f(x) = \infty$; $\lim_{x\to 0^-} f(x) = -\infty$

35. a. $\lim_{x\to\infty} f(x) = 3$; $\lim_{x\to -\infty} f(x) = 3$; $y = 3$

b. $x = -3$ and $x = 4$; $\lim_{x\to -3^-} f(x) = \infty$; $\lim_{x\to 3^+} f(x) = -\infty$; $\lim_{x\to 4^-} f(x) = -\infty$; $\lim_{x\to 4^+} f(x) = \infty$

37. a. $\lim_{x\to\infty} f(x) = 1$; $\lim_{x\to -\infty} f(x) = 1$; $y = 1$

b. $x = 0$; $\lim_{x\to 0^+} f(x) = \infty$; $\lim_{x\to 0^-} f(x) = -\infty$

39. a. $\lim_{x\to\infty} f(x) = 1$; $\lim_{x\to -\infty} f(x) = -1$; $y = 1$ and $y = -1$

b. No vertical asymptotes **41. a.** $\lim_{x\to\infty} f(x) = 0$; $\lim_{x\to -\infty} f(x) = 0$; $y = 0$ **b.** No vertical asymptotes

43.

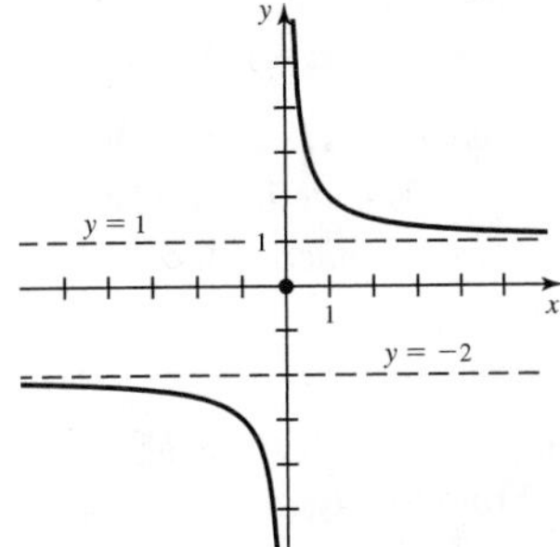

45. $x = 0$ is a vertical asymptote; $y = 2$ is a horizontal asymptote **47.** 3500 **49.** 2 **51.** 1 **53.** 0

55. a. $y = x - 6$ **b.** $x = -6$

c.

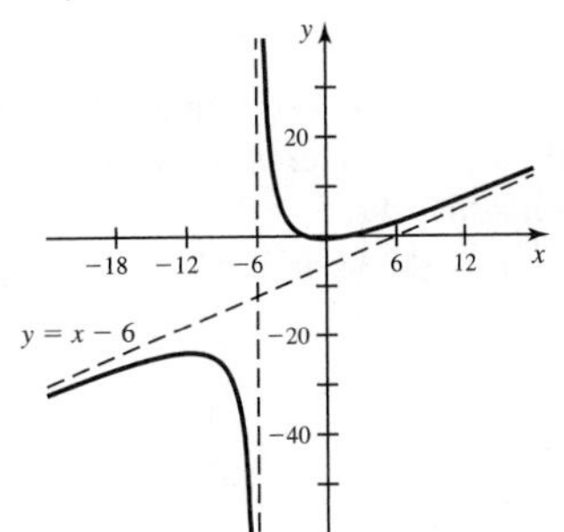

57. a. $y = \frac{1}{3}x - \frac{4}{9}$ **b.** $x = \frac{2}{3}$

c.

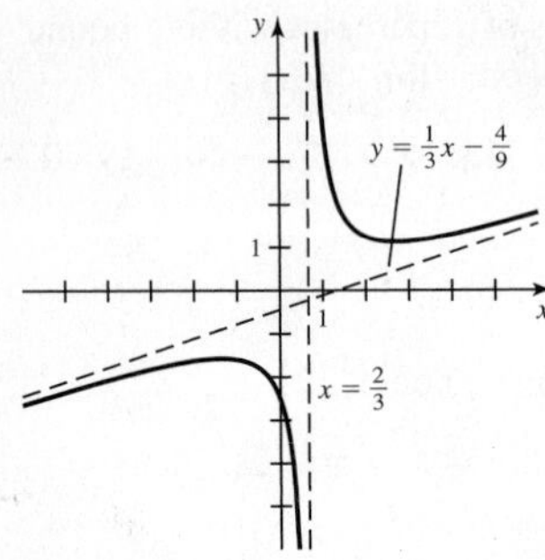

59. a. $y = 4x + 4$ **b.** No vertical asymptotes

c.

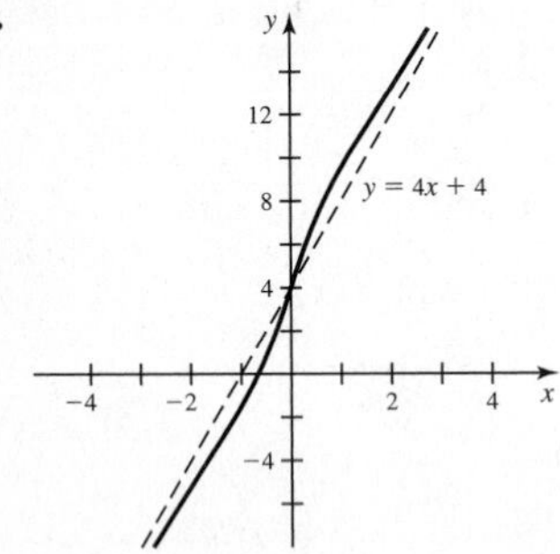

Section 2.6 Exercises, pp. 81–85

1. a, c **3.** A function is continuous on an interval if it is continuous at each point of the interval. **5. a.** $\lim_{x\to a^-} f(x) = f(a)$ **b.** $\lim_{x\to a^+} f(x) = f(a)$ **7.** $\{x: -1 \le x \le 1\}, \{x: -1 \le x \le 1\}$ **9.** $a = 2$, item 3; $a = 3$, item 2; $a = 1$, item 1 **11.** $a = 1$, item 1; $a = 2$, item 2; $a = 3$, item 1 **13.** No; $f(1)$ is undefined. **15.** No; $\lim_{x\to 1} f(x) = 2$ but $f(1) = 3$ **17.** No; $f(4)$ is undefined. **19.** $(-\infty, \infty)$ **21.** $\{x: x \ne 3 \text{ and } x \ne -3\}$ **23.** $\{x: x \ne 2 \text{ and } x \ne -2\}$ **25.** 1 **27.** 16 **29.** $[0, 1), (1, 2), (2, 3], (3, 4]$ **31.** $[0, 1), (1, 2), [2, 3), (3, 5]$ **33. a.** $\lim_{x\to 1} f(x)$ does not exist. **b.** From the right **c.** $(-\infty, 1), [1, \infty)$ **35.** $(-\infty, -2\sqrt{2}]; [2\sqrt{2}, \infty)$ **37.** $(-\infty, \infty)$ **39.** $(-\infty, \infty)$ **41.** 3 **43.** 4 **45.** $\{x: x \ne n\pi$, where n is an integer$\}; \sqrt{2}, -\infty$ **47.** $\{x: x \ne \frac{k\pi}{2}$, where k is an odd integer$\}; \infty, \sqrt{3} - 2$ **49. a.** A is continuous on $[0, 0.08]$ and 7000 is between $A(0) = 5000$ and $A(0.08) = 11{,}098.20$. So, by the Intermediate Value Theorem, there is at least one c in $(0, 0.08)$ such that $A(c) = 7000$.

b. $c \approx 0.034$ or 3.4%

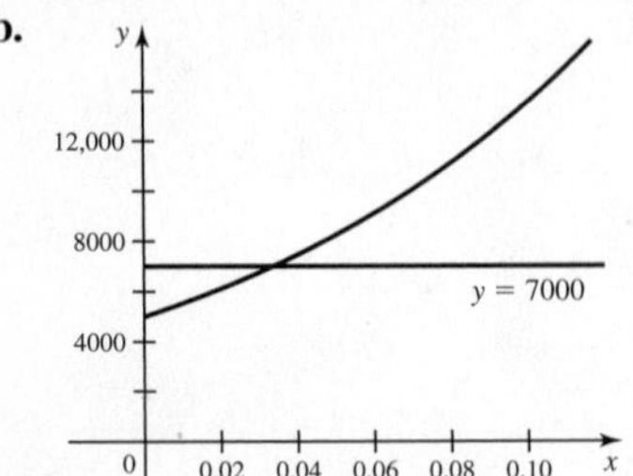

51. a. $2x^3 + x - 2$ is continuous on $[-1, 1]$ and takes on the values -5 and 1 at the endpoints of this interval. Since $-5 < 0 < 1$, there exists c in $(-1, 1)$ such that $2c^3 + c - 2 = 0$. **b.** $x \approx 0.835$

53. a. $x^3 - 5x^2 + 2x$ is continuous on $[-1, 5]$ and takes on the values -8 and 10 at the endpoints. Since $-8 < -1 < 10$, there exists c in $(-1, 5)$ such that $c^3 - 5c^2 + 2c = -1$. **b.** $x \approx -0.285$; $x \approx 0.778$; $x \approx 4.507$ **55. a.** True **b.** True **c.** False **d.** False **57.** $(-\infty, \infty)$ **59.** $[0, 16), (16, \infty)$ **61.** 1 **63.** 2 **65.** $-\frac{1}{2}$ **67.** The vertical line segments should not appear.

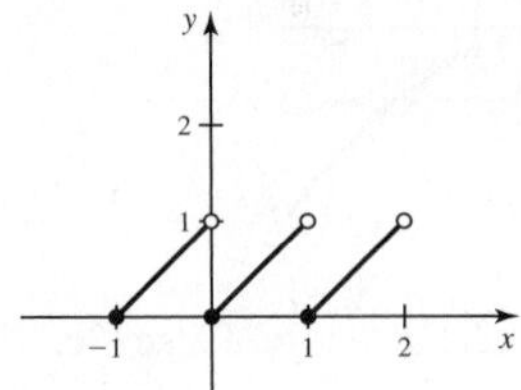

69. a, b.

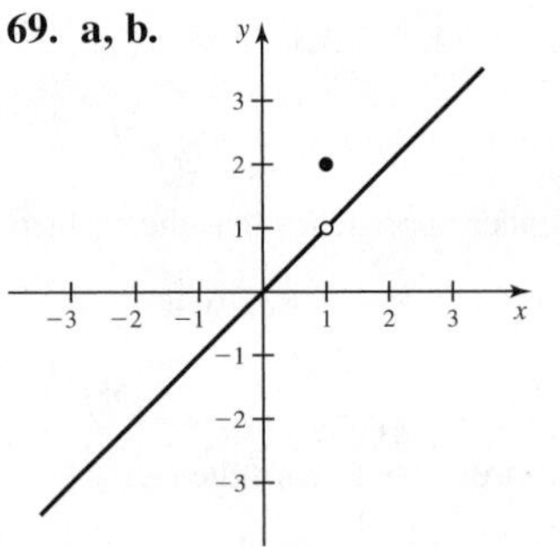

71. a. 2 **b.** 8 **c.** No; $\lim_{x\to 1^-} g(x) = 2$ and $\lim_{x\to 1^+} g(x) = 8$ **73.** $c_1 = \frac{1}{7}; c_2 = \frac{1}{2}; c_3 = \frac{3}{5}$ **75. a.** $A(r)$ is continuous on [0.01, 0.10] and $A(0.01) = 2615.55$, while $A(0.10) = 3984.36$. Thus, $A(0.01) < 3500 < A(0.10)$. So, by the Intermediate Value Theorem, there exists c in (0.01, 0.10) such that $A(c) = 3500$. This is the desired interest rate needed to achieve the goal of \$3500 in 10 years. **b.** $r \approx 7.28\%$ **77.** Yes. Imagine there is a clone of the monk so that he can make the trip up and down on the same day. He must cross paths with his clone at some time between dawn and dusk. **79.** No; f cannot be made continuous at $x = a$ by redefining $f(a)$. **81.** $\lim_{x\to 2} f(x) = -3$; define $f(2)$ to be -3. **83. a.** Yes **b.** No **85.** $a = 0$ removable discontinuity; $a = 1$ infinite discontinuity. **87. a.** $g(x) = x + 1, f(x) = 1/(x - 1)$

Section 2.7 Exercises, pp. 93–96

1. 1 **3.** c **5.** Given any $\varepsilon > 0$, there exists a $\delta > 0$ such that $|f(x) - L| < \varepsilon$ whenever $0 < |x - a| < \delta$. **7.** $0 < \delta < 2$ **9. a.** $\delta = 1$ **b.** $\delta = \frac{1}{2}$ **11. a.** $\delta = 2$ **b.** $\delta = \frac{1}{2}$ **13. a.** $\delta = 1$ **b.** $\delta = 0.79$ **15. a.** $\delta = 1$ **b.** $\delta = \frac{1}{2}$ **c.** $\delta = \varepsilon$ **17. a.** $\delta = 0.23$ **b.** $\delta = 0.12$ **c.** $\delta = \varepsilon/5$ **19.** For any $\varepsilon > 0$, choose $\delta = \varepsilon/8$ **21.** For any $\varepsilon > 0$, choose $\delta = \varepsilon$ **23.** For any $\varepsilon > 0$, choose $\delta = \sqrt{\varepsilon}$ **27. a.** For any $\varepsilon > 0$, choose $\delta > 0$ **b.** For any $\varepsilon > 0$, choose $\delta = \varepsilon$ **29.** For any $N > 0$, choose $\delta = 1/\sqrt{N}$ **31.** For any $N > 0$, choose $\delta = 1/\sqrt{N - 1}$ **33. a.** False **b.** False **c.** True **d.** True **35.** For any $\varepsilon > 0$, choose $\delta = \min\{1, 6\varepsilon\}$ **37.** For any $\varepsilon > 0$, choose $\delta = \min\{1/20, \varepsilon/200\}$ **39.** For $x > a$, $|x - a| = x - a$. **41. a.** For any $\varepsilon > 0$, choose $\delta = \varepsilon/2$ **b.** For any $\varepsilon > 0$, choose $\delta = \varepsilon/3$ **c.** Since $\lim_{x\to 0^+} f(x) = \lim_{x\to 0^-} f(x) = -4$, $\lim_{x\to 0} f(x) = -4$. **43.** For any $\varepsilon > 0$, choose $\delta = \varepsilon^2$

45. a. For each $N > 0$, there is a corresponding $\delta > 0$ such that $f(x) > N$ whenever $a < x < a + \delta$. **b.** For each $N < 0$, there is a corresponding $\delta > 0$ such that $f(x) < N$ whenever $a - \delta < x < a$. **c.** For each $N > 0$, there is a corresponding $\delta > 0$ such that $f(x) > N$ whenever $a - \delta < x < a$. **47.** For any $N > 0$, choose $\delta = 1/N$ **49.** For any $M < 0$, choose $\delta = (-1/M)^{1/4}$ **51.** For any $\varepsilon > 0$, choose $N = 1/\varepsilon$ **53.** $N = M - 1$

Chapter 2 Review Exercises, pp. 96–98

1. a. False **b.** False **c.** False **d.** True **e.** False **f.** False **g.** True **3.** $x = -1$; $\lim_{x\to -1} f(x)$ does not exist; $x = 1$; $\lim_{x\to 1} f(x) \neq f(1)$; $x = 3$; $f(3)$ is undefined. **5. a.** 1.4142 **b.** $\sqrt{2}$ **7.**

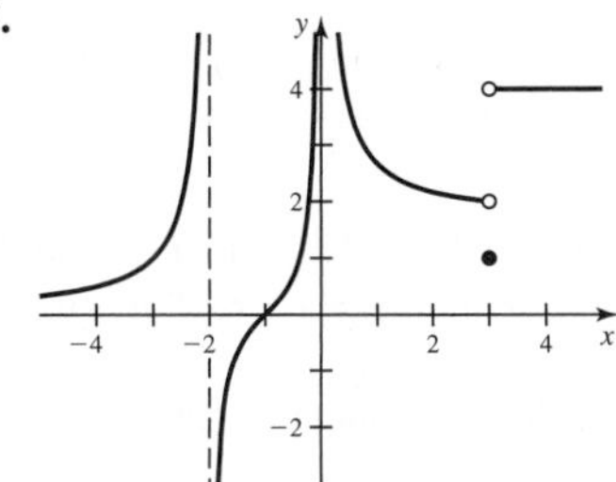

9. $\sqrt{11}$ **11.** 2 **13.** $\frac{1}{3}$ **15.** $-\frac{1}{16}$ **17.** 108 **19.** $\frac{1}{108}$ **21.** 0 **23. a.**

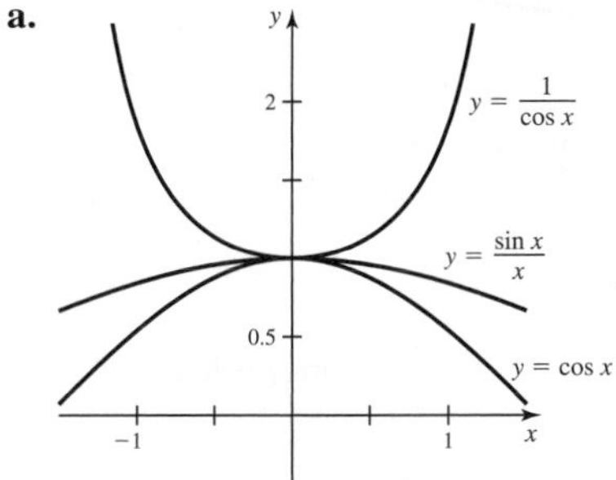

b. $\lim_{x\to 0} \cos x \leq \lim_{x\to 0} \frac{\sin x}{x} \leq \lim_{x\to 0} \frac{1}{\cos x}$;

$$1 \leq \lim_{x\to 0} \frac{\sin x}{x} \leq 1;$$

$$\lim_{x\to 0} \frac{\sin x}{x} = 1$$

25. $-\infty$ **27.** ∞ **29.** $-\infty$ **31.** $\frac{1}{2}$ **33.** ∞ **35.** 5 **37.** $\lim_{x\to\infty} f(x) = -4$; $\lim_{x\to-\infty} f(x) = -4$ **39.** $\lim_{x\to\infty} f(x) = 3$; $\lim_{x\to-\infty} f(x) = 3$ **41.** Horizontal asymptotes at $y = 1$; vertical asymptote at $x = -1$ **43.** No; $f(5)$ does not exist. **45.** Yes; $\lim_{x\to 3^+} h(x) = h(3) = 0$ **47.** $(-\infty, -\sqrt{5}]$ and $[\sqrt{5}, \infty)$; left-continuous at $-\sqrt{5}$ and right-continuous at $\sqrt{5}$ **49.** $(-\infty, -5)$, $(-5, 0)$, $(0, 5)$, and $(5, \infty)$ **51.** $a = 3, b = 0$ **53.**

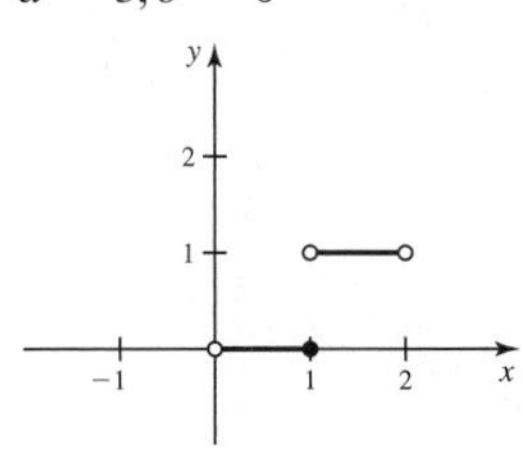

55. b. $P(10) < 50 < P(2)$, $P(10) < 50 < P(30)$ **c.** $x = 5, x = 20$ **d.** No; $P(x) > 30$ for all $x > 0$. **e.** $x = y = 10$ **57.** For any $\varepsilon > 0$, choose $\delta = \varepsilon$ **59.** For any $N > 0$, choose $\delta = 1/\sqrt[4]{N}$.

CHAPTER 3

Section 3.1 Exercises, pp. 109–113

1. Given the point $(a, f(a))$ and any point $(x, f(x))$ near $(a, f(a))$, the slope of the secant line joining these points is $\frac{f(x) - f(a)}{x - a}$. The limit of this quotient as x approaches a is the slope of the tangent line at the point. **3.** The average rate of change over the interval $[a, x]$ is $\frac{f(x) - f(a)}{x - a}$. The limit $\lim_{x\to a} \frac{f(x) - f(a)}{x - a}$ is the slope of the tangent line; it is also the limit of average rates of change, which is the instantaneous rate of change at $x = a$. **5.** $f'(a)$ is the slope of the tangent line at $(a, f(a))$ or the instantaneous rate of change of f at a. **7.** $\frac{dy}{dx}$ is the limit of $\frac{\Delta y}{\Delta x}$ and is the rate of change of y with respect to x. **9.** No.

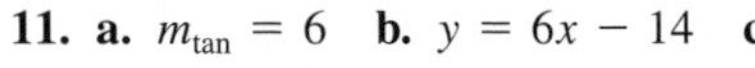
11. a. $m_{\tan} = 6$ **b.** $y = 6x - 14$ **c.**

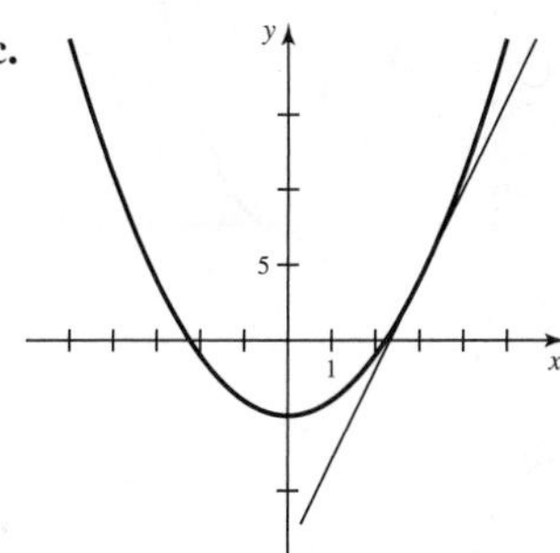

13. a. $m_{\tan} = -5$ **b.** $y = -5x + 1$ **c.**

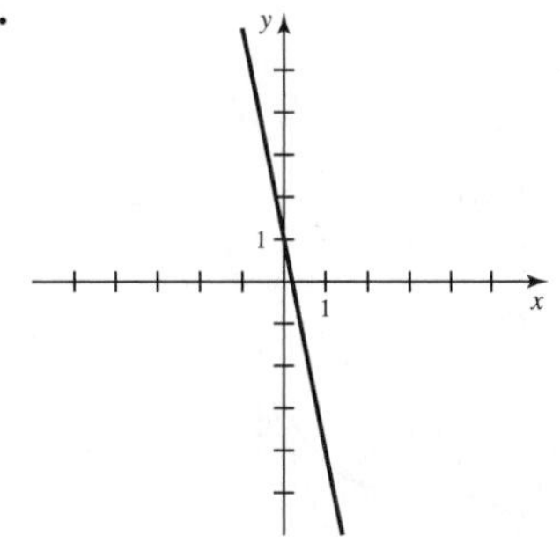

15. a. $m_{\tan} = -1$ **b.** $y = -x - 2$ **c.**

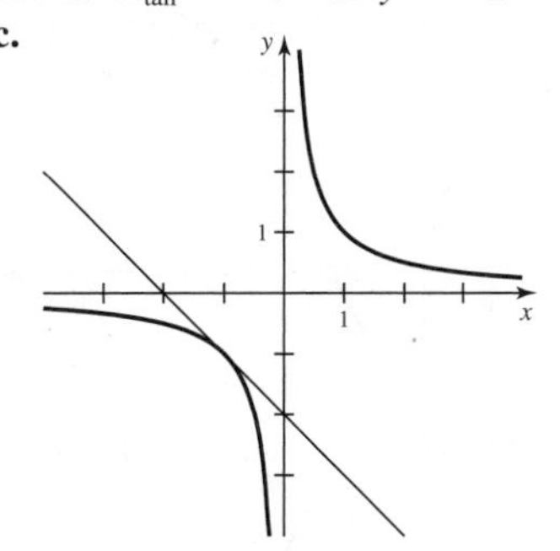

17. a. $m_{\tan} = 2$ **b.** $y = 2x + 1$ **19. a.** $m_{\tan} = -4$ **b.** $y = -4x - 3$ **21. a.** $m_{\tan} = \frac{2}{25}$ **b.** $y = \frac{2}{25}x + \frac{7}{25}$ **23. a.** $f'(-3) = 8$ **b.** $y = 8x$ **25. a.** $f'(-2) = -14$ **b.** $y = -14x - 16$ **27. a.** $f'\left(\frac{1}{4}\right) = -4$ **b.** $y = -4x + 3$ **29. a.** $f'(x) = 6x + 2$ **b.** $y = 8x - 13$

c.

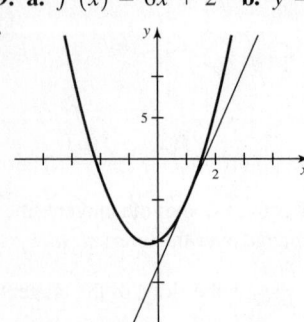

31. a. $f'(x) = 10x - 6$ **b.** $y = 14x - 19$

c.

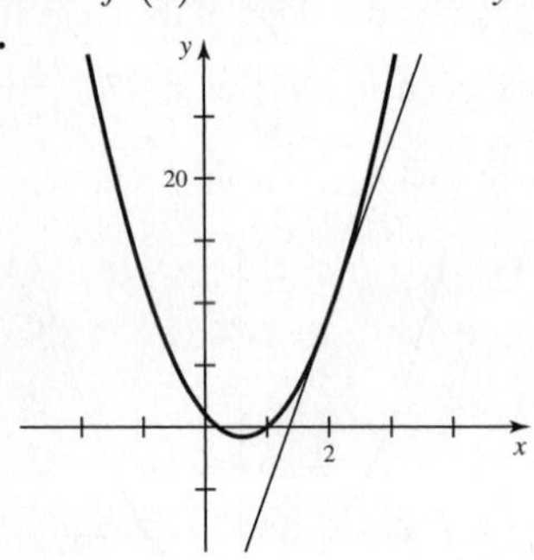

33. a. $2ax + b$ **b.** $8x - 3$ **35.** $-\frac{1}{4}$ **37.** $\frac{1}{5}$

39.

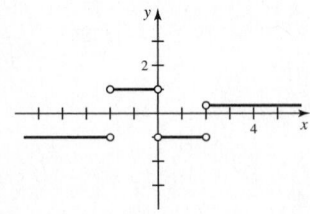

41. a–D; b–C; c–B; d–A **43.**

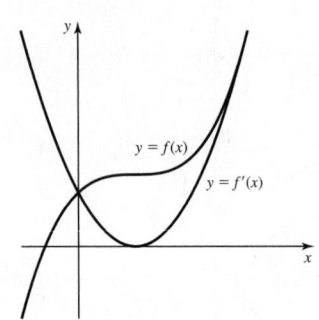

45. a. $x = 1$ **b.** $x = 1, x = 2$ **c.**

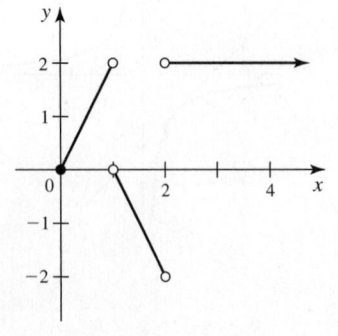

47. a. True **b.** False **c.** True **d.** True

49. a. $f'(x) = \dfrac{3}{2\sqrt{3x + 1}}$ **b.** $y = 3x/10 + 13/5$

51. a. $f'(x) = \dfrac{-6}{(3x + 1)^2}$ **b.** $y = -3x/2 - 5/2$

53. a. C, D **b.** A, B, E **c.** A, B, E, D, C

55. Yes.

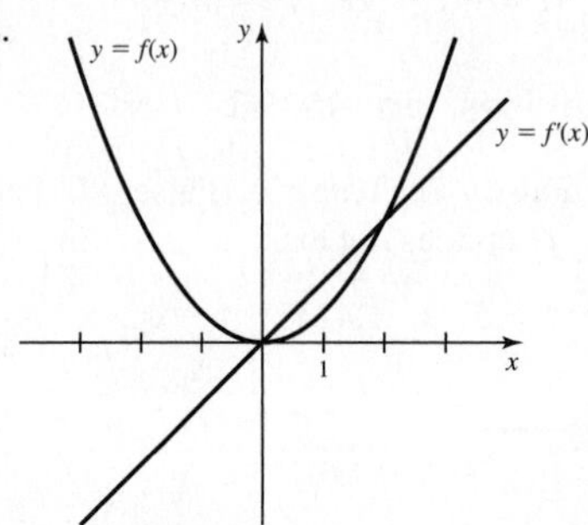

57. a. Approximately 10 kW; approximately −5 kW **b.** $t = 6$ and $t = 18$ **c.** $t = 12$ **59. b.** $f'_+(2) = 1, f'_-(2) = -1$ **c.** f is continuous but not differentiable.

61. a. Vertical tangent line $x = 2$

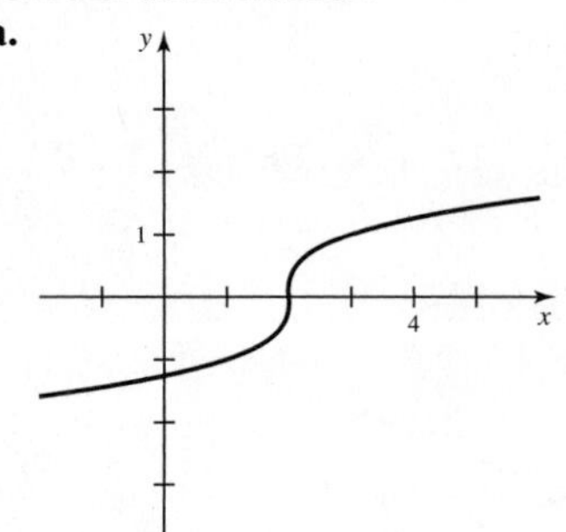

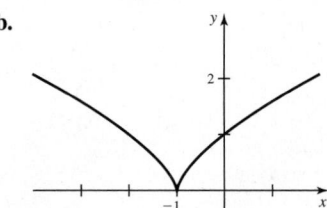

b. Vertical tangent line $x = -1$.

c. Vertical tangent line $x = 4$.

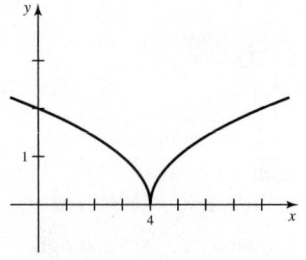

d. Vertical tangent line $x = 0$

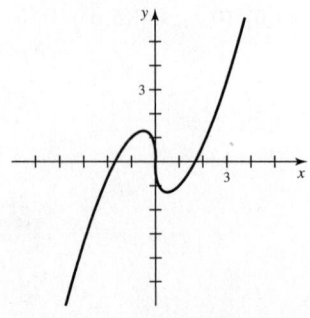

63. $f'(x) = \frac{1}{3}x^{-2/3}$ and $\lim_{x \to 0^-} |f'(0)| = \lim_{x \to 0^+} |f'(0)| = \infty$
65. $f(x) = \frac{1}{x+1}$; $a = 2; -\frac{1}{9}$ **67.** $f(x) = x^4$; $a = 2; 32$
69. No; f is not continuous at $x = 2$. **71.** $a = 4$.

Section 3.2 Exercises, pp. 118–120

1. Using the definition can be tedious. **3.** Take the product of the constant and the derivative of the function. **5.** $f'(x) = 3x^5 - 12x^3 + 101$ **7.** $5x^4$ **9.** 0 **11.** 1 **13.** $15x^2$ **15.** 8 **17.** $200t$ **19.** $12x^3 + 7$ **21.** $40x^3 - 32$ **23.** $6w^2 + 3$ **25.** $18x^2 + 6x + 4$ **27.** $4x^3 + 4x$ **29.** $2w$ for $w \neq 0$ **31.** 1 for $x \neq 1$
33. $\frac{1}{2\sqrt{x}}$ for $x \neq a$ **35. a.** $y = -6x + 5$
b.

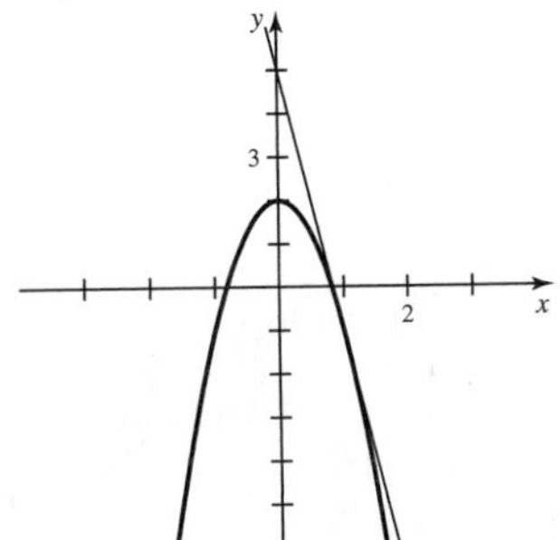

37. a. $y = \frac{x}{4} + 1$ **b.**

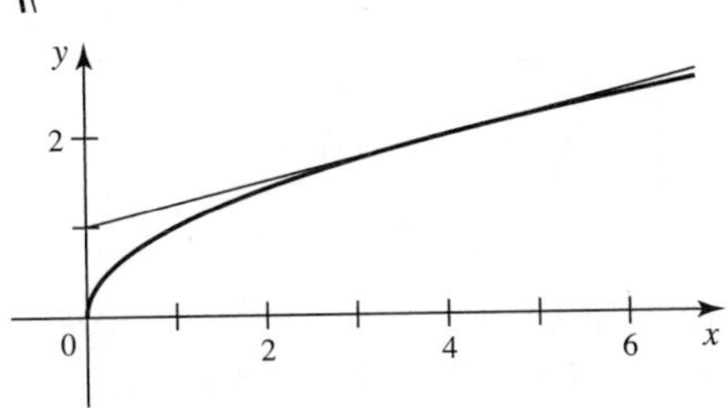

39. a. $x = 3$ **b.** $x = 4$ **41. a.** $(-1, 11), (2, -16)$
b. $(-3, -41), (4, 36)$ **43.** $f'(x) = 20x^3 + 30x^2 + 3$; $f''(x) = 60x^2 + 60x$; $f^{(3)}(x) = 120x + 60$
45. $f'(x) = 1$; $f''(x) = f^{(3)}(x) = 0$ for $x \neq -1$
47. a. False **b.** True **c.** False
49. a. $y = 7x - 1$ **b.** $y = -2x + 5$ **c.** $y = 16x + 4$
51. -10 **53.** 4 **55.** 7.5 **57. a.** $f(x) = \sqrt{x}$; $a = 9$ **b.** $f'(9) = \frac{1}{6}$
59. a. $f(x) = x^{100}$; $a = 1$ **b.** $f'(1) = 100$ **61. a.** $d'(t) = 32t$; ft/s; the velocity of the stone. **b.** 576 ft; ≈ 131 mi/hr
63. a. $\frac{dD}{dg} = 0.10g + 35$; mi/gal; the rate of change of mi driven per gal of gas consumed **b.** 35 mi/gal, 35.5 mi/gal, 36 mi/gal; the gas mileage improves when driving longer distances. **c.** ≈ 427 mi

Section 3.3 Exercises, pp. 126–129

1. $\frac{d}{dx}[f(x) \cdot g(x)] = f'(x)\,g(x) + f(x)\,g'(x)$ **3.** $\frac{d}{dx}(x^n) = nx^{n-1}$ for any integer n **5.** $\frac{d}{dx}(x^n \cdot x^{-n}) = nx^{n-1} \cdot x^{-n} + x^n(-nx^{-n-1}) = nx^{-1} - nx^{-1} = 0$ **7.** $36x^5 - 12x^3$
9. $300x^9 + 135x^8 + 105x^6 + 120x^3 + 45x^2 + 15$

11. $3w^2(2w^3 + 3)$ **13. a.** $6x + 1$ **15. a.** $18y^5 - 52y^3 + 8y$
17. $\frac{1}{(x+1)^2}$ **19.** $\frac{-1}{(t-1)^2}$ **21.** $\frac{2x(x^4 - 2x^2 - 1)}{(x^2 - 1)^2}$
23. a. $2w$ for $w \neq 0$ **25. a.** $\frac{1}{2\sqrt{x}}$
27. a. $y = -3x/2 + 17/2$ **b.**

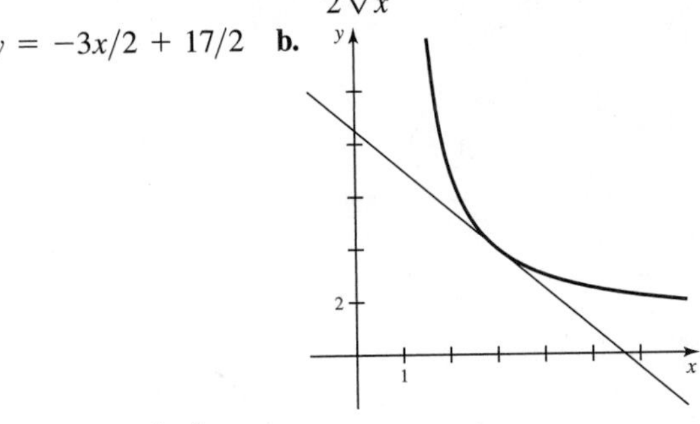

29. a. $y = -x - 4$ **b.**

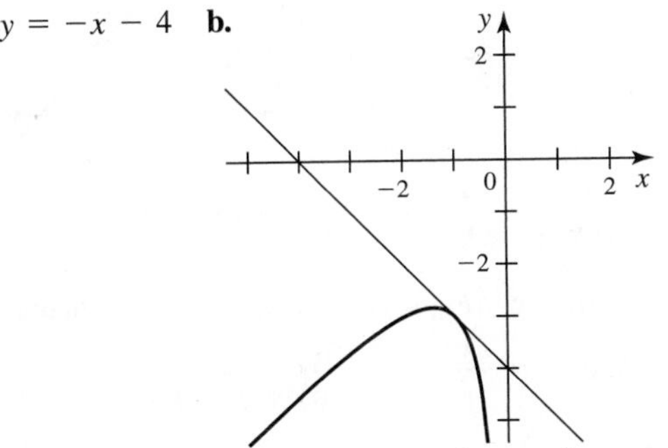

31. $-27x^{-10}$ **33.** $6t - 42/t^8$ **35.** $-3/t^2 - 2/t^3$
37. a. $p'(t) = \left(\frac{20}{t+2}\right)^2$ **b.** $p'(5) \approx 8.16$ **c.** $t = 0$
d. $\lim_{t \to \infty} p'(t) = 0$; the population reaches a steady state.
e.

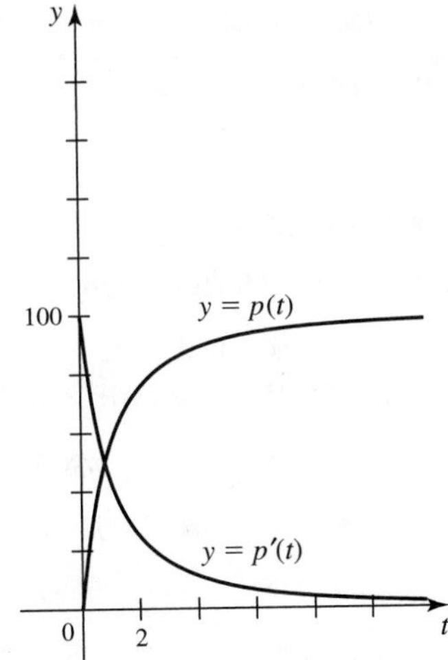

39. a. $x = (-1 \pm \sqrt{3})/2$ **b.** The lines tangent to the graph of $f(x)$ at $x = (-1 \pm \sqrt{3})/2$ are horizontal. **41.** $g'(x) = -3/(2x^2)$
43. $g'(x) = \frac{8x}{(1 - x^2)^2}$ **45. a.** True **b.** False **c.** False
47. $f'(x) = 4x - x^{-2}$
$f''(x) = 4 + 2x^{-3}$
$f^{(3)}(x) = -6x^{-4}$

49. $f'(x) = \dfrac{x^2 + 2x - 7}{(x + 1)^2}$

$f''(x) = \dfrac{16}{(x + 1)^3}$

$f^{(3)}(x) = \dfrac{-48}{(x + 1)^4}$

51. $8x - \dfrac{2}{(5x + 1)^2}$ **53.** $\dfrac{r - 6\sqrt{r} - 1}{2\sqrt{r}(r + 1)^2}$

55. a. $y = -\dfrac{108}{169}x + \dfrac{567}{169}$ **b.**

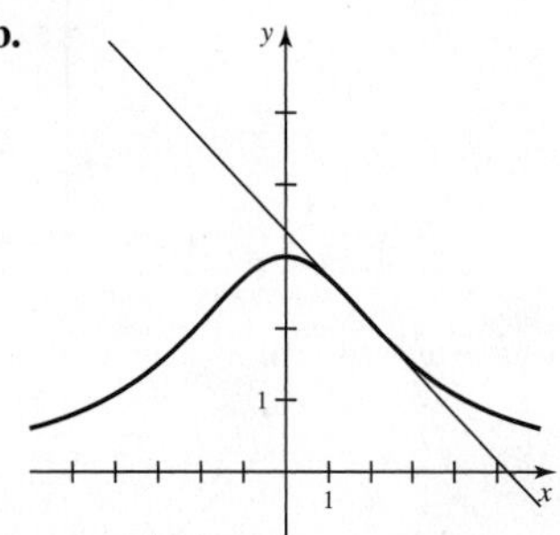

57. $-\frac{3}{2}$ **59.** $\frac{1}{9}$ **61.** $\frac{7}{8}$ **63. a.** $F'(x) = -\dfrac{1.8 \times 10^{10}\,Qq}{x^3}$ N/m **b.** -1.8×10^{19} N/m **c.** $|F'(x)|$ decreases and $F'(x)$ increases as x increases. **65. d.** $c = \dfrac{f(a)-af'(a)-f(b)+bf'(b)}{-f'(a)+f'(b)}$

67. $f''g + 2f'g' + fg''$

69. a. $f'gh + fg'h + fgh'$ **b.** $3x^2 + 4x - 3$

Section 3.4 Exercises, pp. 135–137

1. $\dfrac{\sin x}{x}$ is undefined at $x = 0$. **3.** The tangent and cotangent functions are defined as ratios of the sine and cosine functions.

5. -1 **7.** 3 **9.** 5 **11.** 7 **13.** $\frac{1}{4}$ **15.** $\cos x - \sin x$

17. $3x^3(4 \sin x + x \cos x)$ **19.** $\cos^2 x - \sin^2 x = \cos 2x$

21. $-2 \sin x \cos x = -\sin 2x$ **27.** $\sec x \tan x - \csc x \cot x$

29. $\dfrac{-\csc x}{1 + \csc x}$ **31.** $\cos^2 z - \sin^2 z = \cos 2z$ **33.** $2\csc^2 x \cot x$

35. $2(\sec^2 x \tan x + \csc^2 x \cot x)$ **37. a.** False **b.** False **c.** True **d.** True **39.** a/b **41.** $\frac{3}{4}$ **43.** 0 **45.** $x \cos 2x + \frac{1}{2}\sin 2x$

47. $\dfrac{-2}{1 + \sin x}$ **49.** $\dfrac{2 \sin x}{(1 + \cos x)^2}$ **51. a.** $y = \sqrt{3}x + 2 - \pi\sqrt{3}/6$

b.

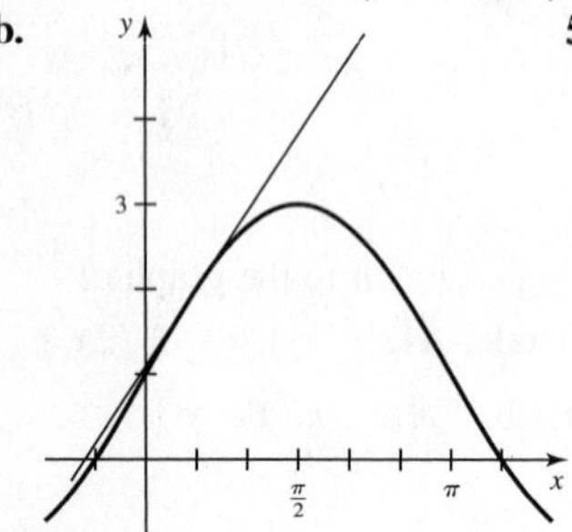

53. a. $y = -2\sqrt{3}x + 2\sqrt{3}\pi/3 + 1$

b.

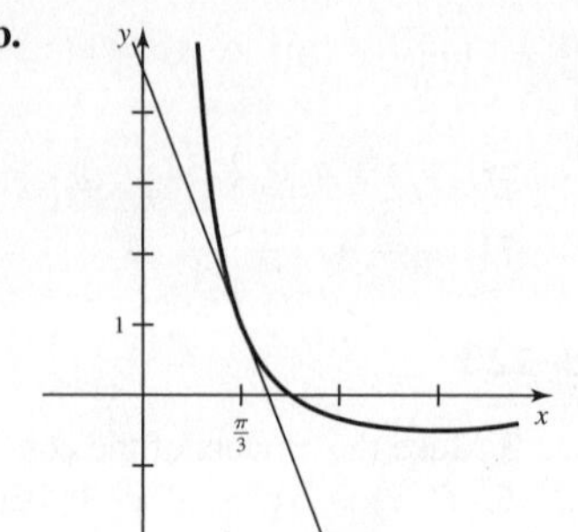

55. $x = 7\pi/6 + 2k\pi$ and $x = 11\pi/6 + 2k\pi$, where k is any integer

57. a.

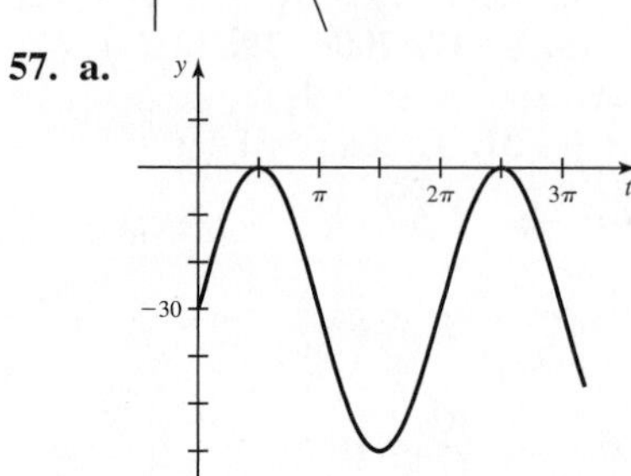

b. $v(t) = 30 \cos t$

c.

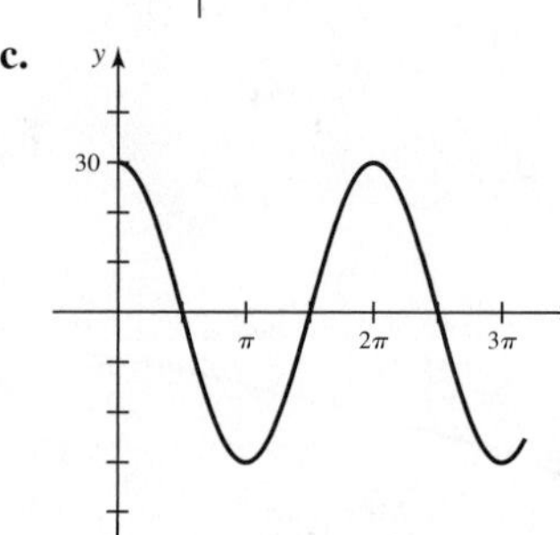

d. $v(t) = 0$ for $t = (2k + 1)\dfrac{\pi}{2}$, where k is any nonnegative integer and the position is $\left((2k + 1)\dfrac{\pi}{2}, 0\right)$ if k is even or $\left((2k + 1)\dfrac{\pi}{2}, -60\right)$ if k is odd.

e. $v(t)$ is at a maximum at $t = 2k\pi$, where k is a nonnegative integer; the position is $(2k\pi, -30)$.

f. $a(t) = -30 \sin t$

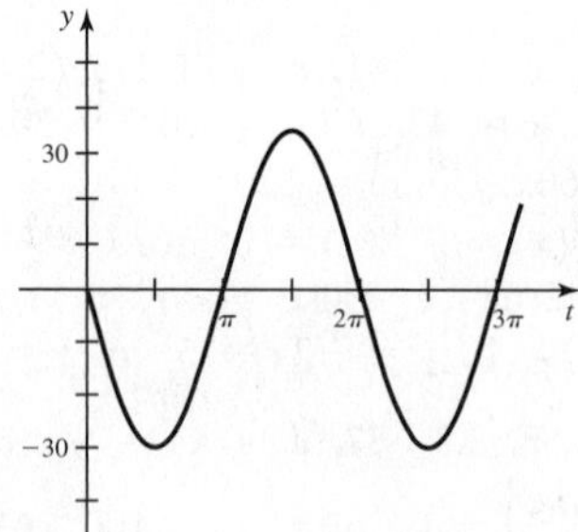

67. a. $2 \sin x \cos x$ **b.** $3 \sin^2 x \cos x$ **c.** $4 \sin^3 x \cos x$ **d.** $n \sin^{n-1} x \cos x$ The conjecture is true for $n = 1$. If it holds for $n = k$, then when $n = k + 1$, we have $\dfrac{d}{dx}(\sin^{k+1} x) = \dfrac{d}{dx}(\sin^k x \cdot \sin x) = \sin^k x \cos x + \sin x \cdot k \sin^{k-1} x \cos x = (k + 1) \sin^k x \cos x$. **69. a.** $f(x) = \sin x$; $a = \pi/6$ **b.** $\sqrt{3}/2$

71. a. $f(x) = \cot x$; $a = \pi/4$ **b.** -2

Section 3.5 Exercises, pp. 145–149

1. The average rate of change is $\dfrac{f(x + \Delta x) - f(x)}{\Delta x}$; whereas the instantaneous rate of change is the limit as Δx goes to zero in

this quotient. **3.** Small **5.** If the position of the object at time t is $s(t)$, then the acceleration at time t is $a(t) = d^2s/dt^2$. **7.** Each of the first 200 stoves costs, on average, \$70 to produce. When 200 stoves have already been produced, the 201st stove costs \$65 to produce.
9. a. 40 mi/hr **b.** 40 mi/hr; yes **c.** -60 mi/hr; -60 mi/hr; south **d.** The police car drives away from the police station going north until about 10:08, when it turns around and heads south, toward the police station. It continues south until it passes the police station at about 11:02 and keeps going south until about 11:40, when it turns around and heads north.
11. a.

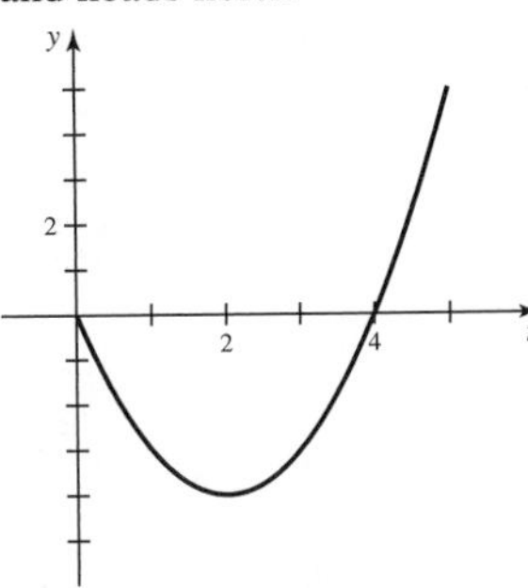

b. $v(t) = 2t - 4$; stationary at $t = 2$, to the right on $(2, 5]$, to the left on $[0, 2)$

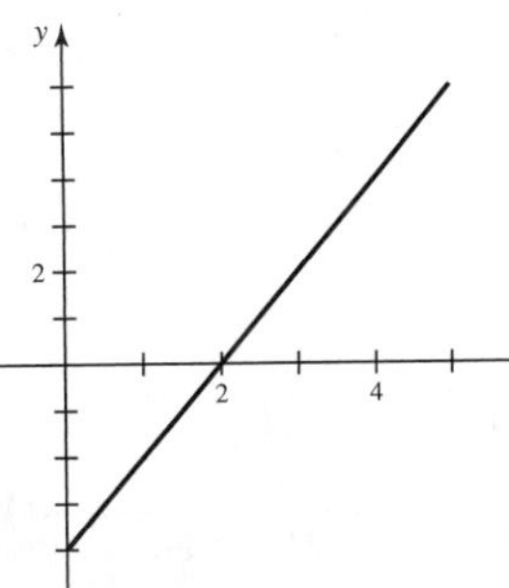

c. $v(1) = -2$ ft/s; $a(1) = 2$ ft/s^2 **d.** $a(2) = 2$ ft/s^2
13. a.

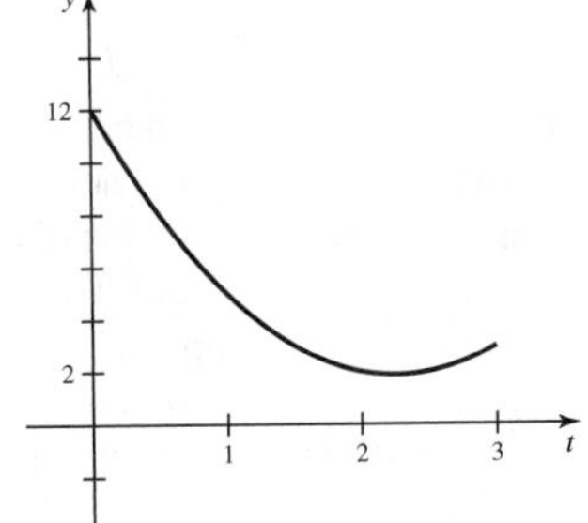

b. $v(t) = 4t - 9$; stationary at $t = \frac{9}{4}$ to the right on $\left(\frac{9}{4}, 3\right]$, to the left on $\left[0, \frac{9}{4}\right)$

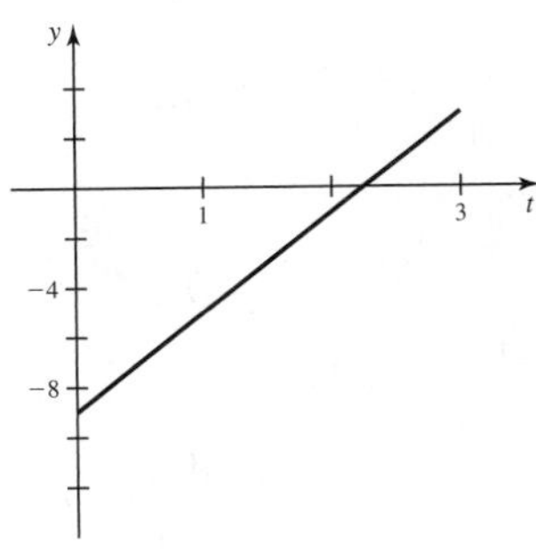

c. $v(1) = -5$ ft/s; $a(1) = 4$ ft/s^2 **d.** $a\left(\frac{9}{4}\right) = 4$ ft/s^2

15. a.

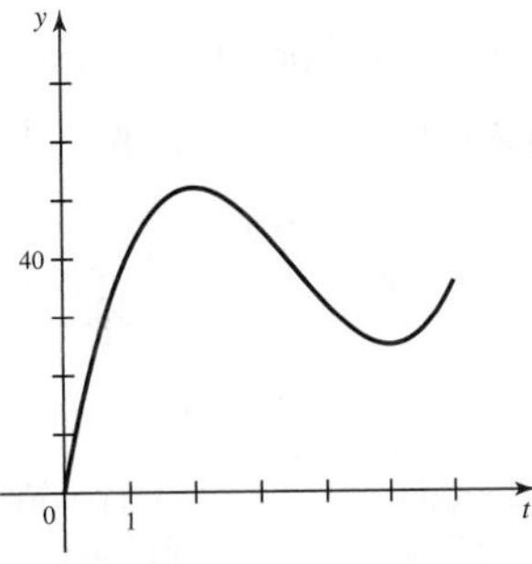

b. $v(t) = 6t^2 - 42t + 60$; stationary at $t = 2$ and $t = 5$, to the right on $[0, 2)$ and $(5, 6]$, to the left on $(2, 5)$

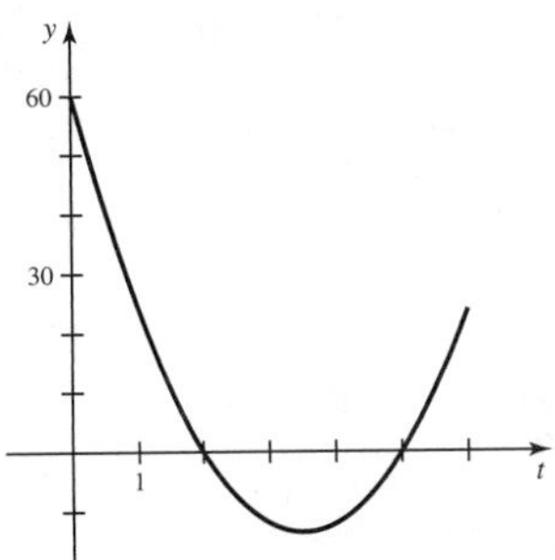

c. $v(1) = 24$ ft/s; $a(1) = -30$ ft/s^2 **d.** $a(2) = -18$ ft/s; $a(5) = 18$ ft/s^2 **17. a.** $v(t) = -32t + 64$ ft/s **b.** At $t = 2$ s **c.** 96 ft **d.** At $2 + \sqrt{6}$ s **e.** $-32\sqrt{6}$ ft/s
19. a. 98,300 people/year **b.** 99,920 people/year in 1997; 95,600 people/year in 2005 **c.** $p'(t) = -0.54t + 101$; population increased, growth rate is positive but decreasing.
21. a. $\overline{C}(x) = \dfrac{1000}{x} + 0.1; C'(x) = 0.1$
b. $\overline{C}(2000) = \$0.60$/item; $C'(2000) = \$0.10$/item
c. The average cost per item when 2000 items are produced is \$0.60/item. The cost of producing the 2001st item is \$0.10.
23. a. $\overline{C}(x) = -0.01x + 40 + 100/x; C'(x) = -0.02x + 40$
b. $\overline{C}(1000) = \$30.10$/item; $C'(1000) = \$20$/item **c.** The average cost per item is about \$30.10 when 1000 items are produced. The cost of producing the 1001st item is \$20.
25. a. False **b.** True **c.** False **d.** True **27.** 37,500 ft
29. a. $t = 1, 2, 3$ **b.** It is moving in the positive direction for t in $(0, 1)$ and $(2, 3)$; it is moving in the negative direction for t in $(1, 2)$ and $t > 3$. **c.**

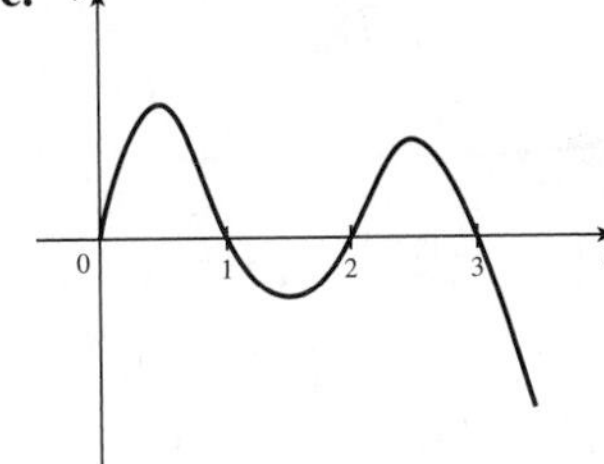

31. a. $P(x) = 0.02x^2 + 50x - 100$
b. $\dfrac{P(x)}{x} = 0.02x + 50 - \dfrac{100}{x}; \dfrac{dP}{dx} = 0.04x + 50$

c. $\dfrac{P(500)}{500} = 59.8$; $\dfrac{dp}{dx}(500) = 70$ **d.** The profit, on average, for each of the first 500 items produced is 59.8; the profit for the 501st item produced is 70. **33. a.** $P(x) = 0.04x^2 + 100x - 800$
b. $\dfrac{P(x)}{x} = 0.04x + 100 - \dfrac{800}{x}$; $\dfrac{dp}{dx} = 0.08x + 100$
c. $\dfrac{P(1000)}{1000} = 139.2$; $\dfrac{dp}{dx}(1000) = 180$ **d.** The average profit per item for each of the first 1000 items produced is \$139.20. The profit for the 1001st item produced is \$180. **35. a.** 1930, 1.1 million people/yr **b.** 1960, 2.9 million people/yr **c.** The population did not decrease. **d.** [1905, 1915], [1930, 1960], [1980, 1990]

37. a.

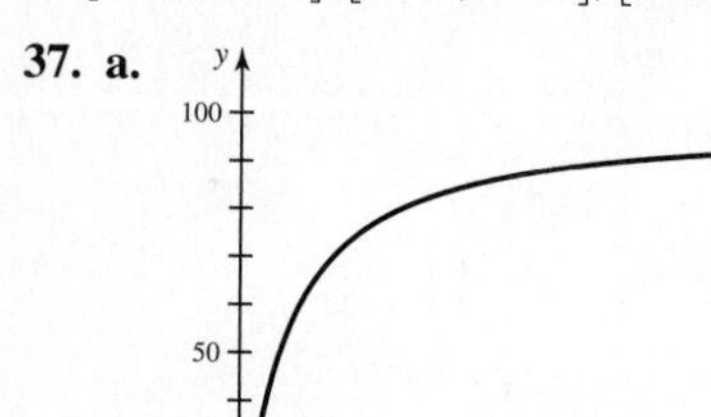

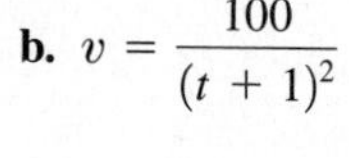
b. $v = \dfrac{100}{(t + 1)^2}$

c.

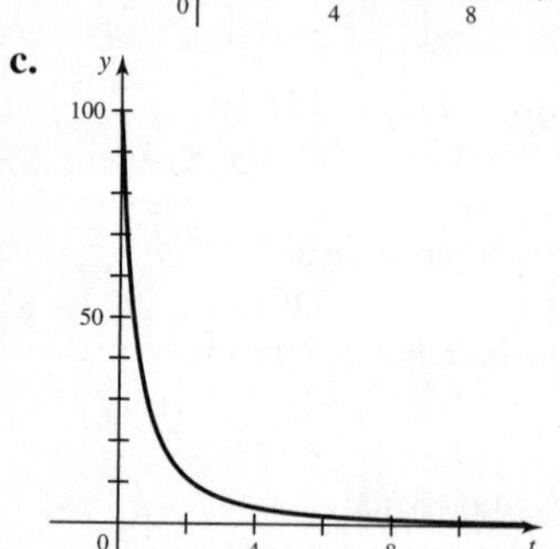

The marble moves fastest at the beginning and slows considerably over the first 5 s. It continues to slow but never actually stops.
d. $t = 4$ s **e.** $t = -1 + \sqrt{2} \approx 0.414$ s

39. a. $C'(x) = \dfrac{-125{,}000{,}000}{x^2} + 1.5$;
$\overline{C}(x) = \dfrac{C(x)}{25{,}000} = 50 + \dfrac{5000}{x} + 0.00006x$

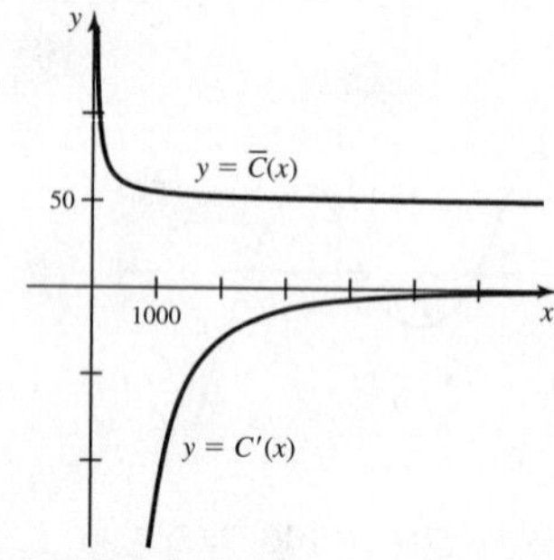

b. $C'(5000) = -3.5$; $\overline{C}(5000) = 51.3$ **c.** Marginal cost: If the batch size is increased from 5000 to 5001, then the cost of producing 25,000 gadgets would *decrease* by about \$3.50. Average cost: When batch size is 5000, it costs \$51.30 *per item* to produce all 25,000 gadgets.

41. a.

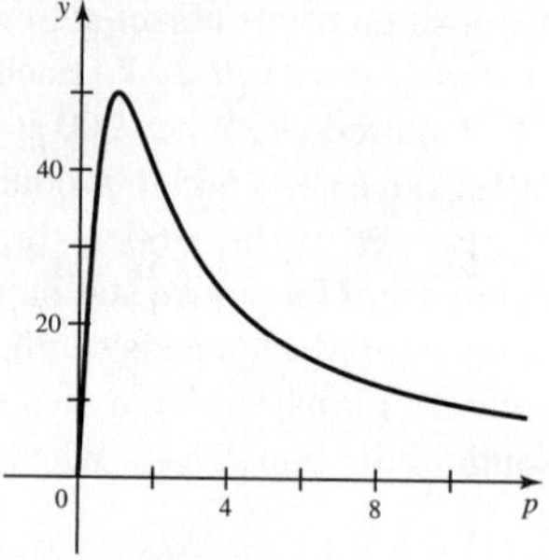

b. $R'(p) = \dfrac{100(1 - p^2)}{(p^2 + 1)^2}$ **c.** $p = 1$

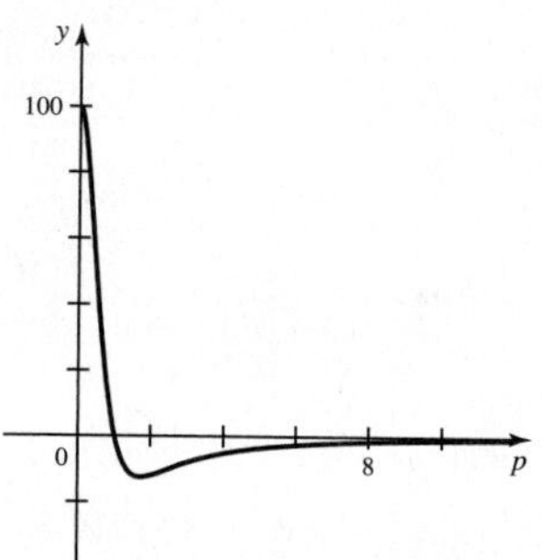

43. a.

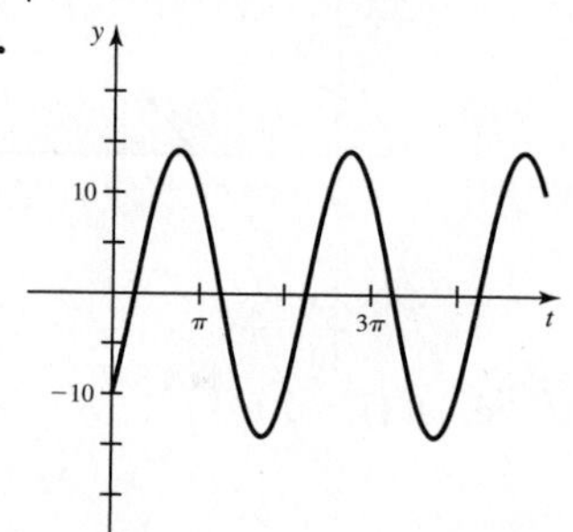

b. $dx/dt = 10\cos t + 10\sin t$ **c.** $t = 3\pi/4 + k\pi$, where k is any positive integer. **d.** The graph implies that the spring never stops oscillating. In reality, the weight would eventually come to rest.
45. a. Juan starts faster than Jean and opens up a big lead. Then, Juan slows down while Jean speeds up. Jean catches up, and the race finishes in a tie. **b.** Same average velocity **c.** Tie **d.** At $t = 2$, $\theta'(2) = \pi/2$ rad/min; $\theta'(4) = \pi =$ Jean's greatest velocity **e.** At $t = 2$, $\varphi'(2) = \pi/2$ rad/min; $\varphi'(0) = \pi =$ Juan's greatest velocity
47. a. $v(0) = 40{,}000\ \text{m}^3$

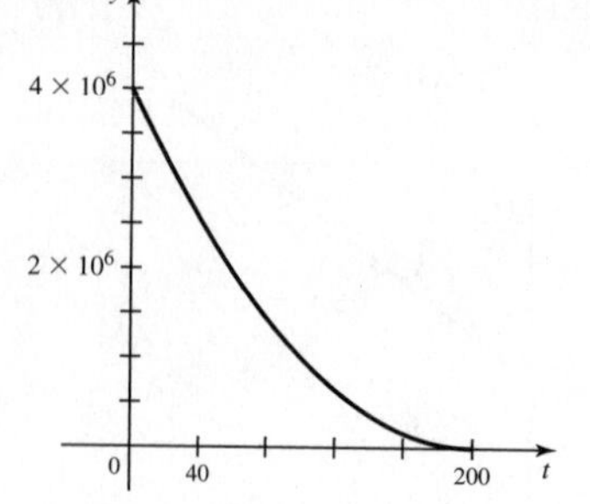

b. 200 hr

c. 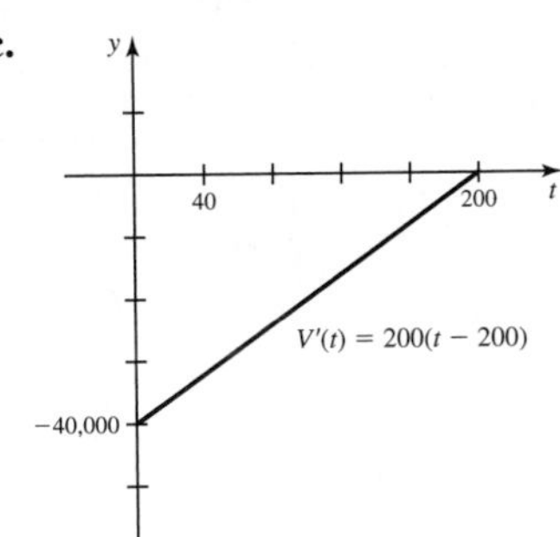

d. The magnitude of the flow rate is greatest (most negative) at $t = 0$ and least (zero) at $t = 200$.

49. a. $-T'(1) = -80, -T'(3) = 80$ **b.** $-T'(x) < 0$ for $0 \le x < 2$; $-T'(x) > 0$ for $2 < x \le 4$ **c.** $-T'(0) = -160 < 0$ and $-T'(4) = 160 > 0$

Section 3.6 Exercises, pp. 154–157

1. $\frac{dy}{dx} = \frac{dy}{du} \cdot \frac{du}{dx}$; $\frac{d}{dx}(f(g(x)) = f'(g(x)) \cdot g'(x)$ **3.** $g(x)$, x **5.** Outer: $f(x) = x^{-5}$; inner: $u = x^2 + 10$ **7.** $30\,(3x + 7)^9$ **9.** $\frac{x}{\sqrt{x^2 + 1}}$ **11.** $10x \sec^2 5x^2$ **13.** $-\frac{\sin x}{2\sqrt{\cos x}}$ **15.** $4x^3 \sec^2 x^4$ **17.** $10\,(6x + 7)(3x^2 + 7x)^9$ **19.** $-\frac{315x^2}{(7x^3 + 1)^4}$ **21.** $3\sec^2(3x + 1)$ **23.** $(12x^2 + 3)\cos(4x^3 + 3x + 1)$ **25.** $5\theta^2 \sec 5\theta \tan 5\theta + 2\theta \sec 5\theta$ **27.** $5 \sec x\,(\sec x + \tan x)^5$ **29. a.** $u = \cos x$, $y = u^3$; $\frac{dy}{dx} = -3\cos^2 x \sin x$ **b.** $u = x^3$, $y = \cos u$; $\frac{dy}{dx} = -3x^2 \sin x^3$ **31. a.** 100 **b.** −100 **c.** −16 **d.** 40 **e.** 40 **33.** $25(12x^5 - 9x^2)(2x^6 - 3x^3 + 3)^{24}$ **35.** $30(1 + 2\tan x)^{14}\sec^2 x$ **37.** $-\frac{\cot x \csc^2 x}{\sqrt{1 + \cot^2 x}}$ **39.** $-15\sin^4(\cos 3x)(\sin 3x)[\cos(\cos 3x)]$ **41.** $\tan x\sqrt{\sec x}\sec^2(\sqrt{\sec x})/2$ **43.** $\frac{1}{2\sqrt{x + \sqrt{x}}}\left(1 + \frac{1}{2\sqrt{x}}\right)$ **45.** $f'(g(x^2))g'(x^2)2x$ **47. a.** True **b.** False **c.** True **d.** False **49.** $\frac{d^2y}{dx^2} = 2\cos x^2 - 4x^2 \sin x^2$ **51.** $\frac{d^2y}{dx^2} = \frac{4(5x^2 - 1)}{(x^2 + 1)^4}$ **53.** $y' = \frac{f'(x)}{2\sqrt{f(x)}}$ **55.** $y = -9x + 35$

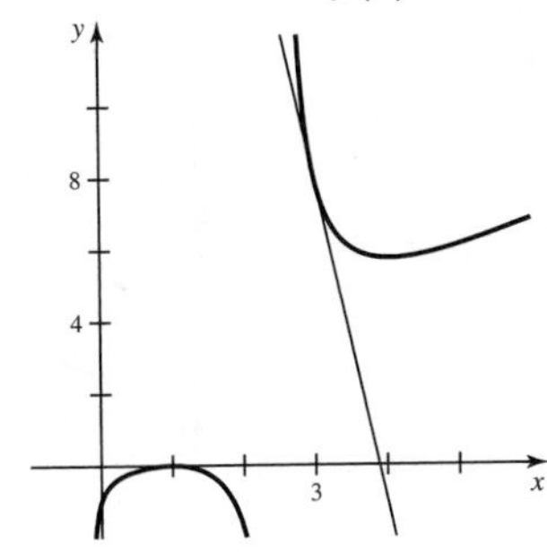

57. a. $h(4) = 9, h'(4) = -6$ **b.** $y = -6x + 33$ **59.** $y = 4\sqrt{3}\,(x - \pi/6) + 2$

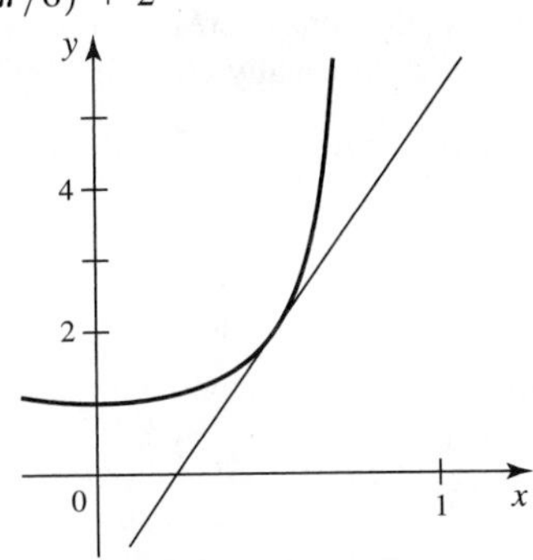

61. a. -3π **b.** -5π **63. a.** $\frac{d^2y}{dt^2} = \frac{-y_0 k}{m}\cos\left(t\sqrt{\frac{k}{m}}\right)$ **65. a.** 10.88 hr **b.** $D'(t) = \frac{6\pi}{365}\sin\left(\frac{2\pi(t + 10)}{365}\right)$ **c.** 2.87 min/day; on March 1, the length of day is increasing at a rate of about 2.87 min/day

d. 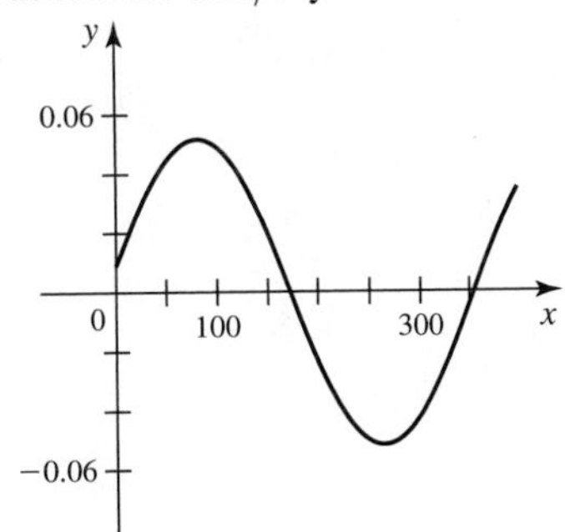

e. Most rapidly: Approximately March 22 and September 22; least rapidly: approximately December 21 and June 21 **67. a.** $E'(t) = 400 + 200\cos\left(\frac{\pi t}{12}\right)$ MW **b.** At noon; $E'(0) = 600$ MW **c.** At midnight; $E'(12) = 200$ MW

d. 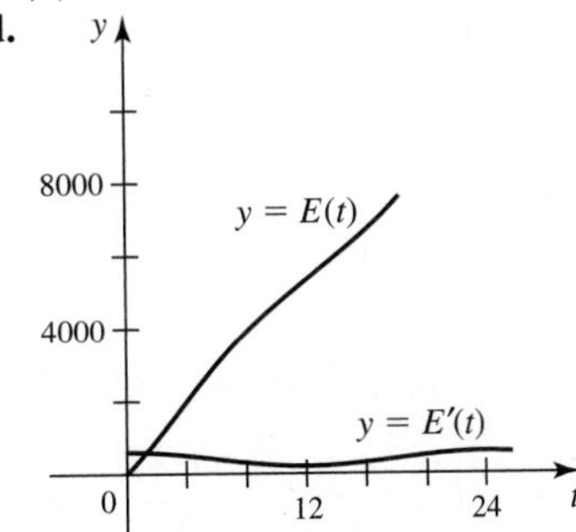

69. a. $f'(x) = -2\cos x \sin x + 2\sin x \cos x = 0$ **b.** $f(0) = \cos^2 0 + \sin^2 0 = 1$; $f(x) = 1$ for all x, by part (b); that is, $\cos^2 x + \sin^2 x = 1$ **73. a.** $h(x) = (x^2 - 3)^5$; $a = 2$ **b.** 20 **75. a.** $h(x) = \sin(x^2)$; $a = \pi/2$ **b.** $\pi\cos(\pi^2/4)$ **77.** $\lim_{x\to 5}\frac{f(x)^2 - f(25)}{x - 5} = 10\,f'(25)$

Section 3.7 Exercises, pp. 162–165

1. There may be more than one expression for y or y'. **3.** When derived implicitly, dy/dx is usually given in terms of both x and y. **5. a.** $\frac{dy}{dx} = \frac{2}{y}$ **b.** 1 **7. a.** $\frac{dy}{dx} = \frac{20x^3}{\cos y}$ **b.** -20

9. a. $\frac{dy}{dx} = -\frac{1}{\sin y}$ **b.** -1 **11.** $\frac{dy}{dx} = \frac{1 - y\cos(xy)}{x\cos(xy) - 1}$

13. $\frac{dy}{dx} = \frac{1}{2y(\sin y^2 + 1)}$ **15.** $\frac{dy}{dx} = \frac{3x^2(x-y)^2 + 2y}{2x}$

17. $\frac{dy}{dx} = \frac{13y - 18x^2}{21y^2 - 13x}$ **19.** $\frac{dy}{dx} = \frac{5\sqrt{x^4 + y^2} - 2x^3}{y - 6y^2\sqrt{x^4 + y^2}}$

21. a. $2^2 + 2 \cdot 1 + 1^2 = 7$ **b.** $y = -5x/4 + 7/2$

23. a. $\sin\pi + 5\left(\frac{\pi^2}{5}\right) = \pi^2$ **b.** $y = \frac{\pi(1+\pi)}{1+2\pi} + \frac{5}{1+2\pi}x$

25. a. $\cos\left(\frac{\pi}{2} - \frac{\pi}{4}\right) + \sin\frac{\pi}{4} = \sqrt{2}$ **b.** $y = \frac{x}{2}$

27. $\frac{d^2y}{dx^2} = \frac{-1}{4y^3}$ **29.** $\frac{d^2y}{dx^2} = \frac{2y^2(5 + 8x\sqrt{y})}{(1 + 2x\sqrt{y})^3}$

31. $\frac{d^2y}{dx^2} = -\frac{\sin y}{(1 - \cos y)^3}$ **33.** $\frac{dy}{dx} = \frac{5}{4}x^{1/4}$ **35.** $\frac{dy}{dx} = \frac{10}{3(5x+1)^{1/3}}$

37. $\frac{dy}{dx} = \frac{-3}{2^{7/4}x^{3/4}(4x-3)^{5/4}}$ **39.** $\frac{dy}{dx} = \frac{5x^2 + 20x + 3}{3(x^2 + 5x + 1)^{2/3}}$

41. $\frac{-1}{4}$ **43.** $\frac{-24}{13}$ **45.** -5 **47. a.** False **b.** True **c.** False **d.** False **49. a.** $y = x - 1$ and $y = -x + 2$

b.

51. a. $y' = \frac{-2xy}{x^2 + 4}$ **b.** $y = \frac{1}{2}x + 2,\ y = -\frac{1}{2}x + 2$

c. $-\frac{16x}{(x^2+4)^2}$ **53. a.** $\left(\frac{5}{4}, \frac{1}{2}\right)$ **b.** No

55. a. $\frac{dy}{dx} = \frac{y - 1}{3y^2 - x} = \frac{1}{2y + 1}$ if $y \neq 1$; $\frac{dy}{dx} = 0$ if $y = 1$

b. $f_1(x) = 1,\ f_2(x) = \frac{-1 + \sqrt{4x - 3}}{2},\ f_3(x) = \frac{-1 - \sqrt{4x - 3}}{2}$

c.

d. $\frac{d}{dx}[f_1(x)] = 0,\ \frac{d}{dx}[f_2(x)] = \frac{1}{\sqrt{4x - 3}},\ \frac{d}{dx}[f_3(x)] = \frac{-1}{\sqrt{4x - 3}}$

57. a. $\frac{dy}{dx} = \frac{x - x^3}{y}$ **b.** $f_1(x) = \sqrt{x^2 - \frac{x^4}{2}};\ f_2(x) = -\sqrt{x^2 - \frac{x^4}{2}}$

c.

d. $\frac{d}{dx}[f_1(x)] = \frac{x - x^3}{\sqrt{x^2 - \frac{x^4}{2}}};\ \frac{d}{dx}[f_2(x)] = \frac{x^3 - x}{\sqrt{x^2 - \frac{x^4}{2}}}$

59. $y = \frac{4x}{5} - \frac{3}{5}$

61. $y = -\frac{1 + 2\pi}{5}x + \pi\left(\frac{25 + \pi + 2\pi^2}{25}\right)$

63. $y = -2x + \frac{5\pi}{4}$

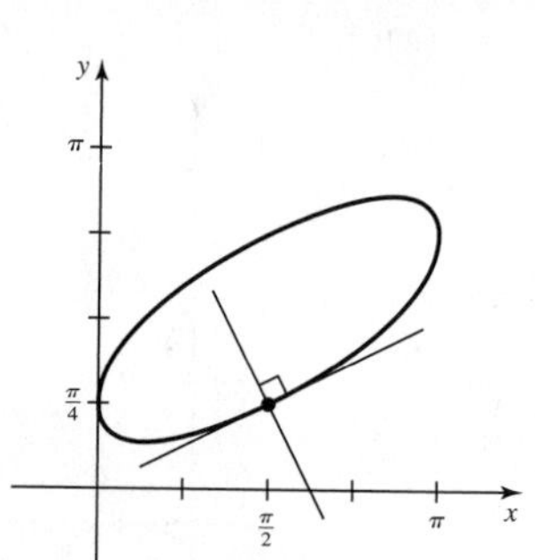

65. a. $y = -\frac{9x}{11} + \frac{20}{11}$ and $y = \frac{11x}{9} - \frac{2}{9}$

b.

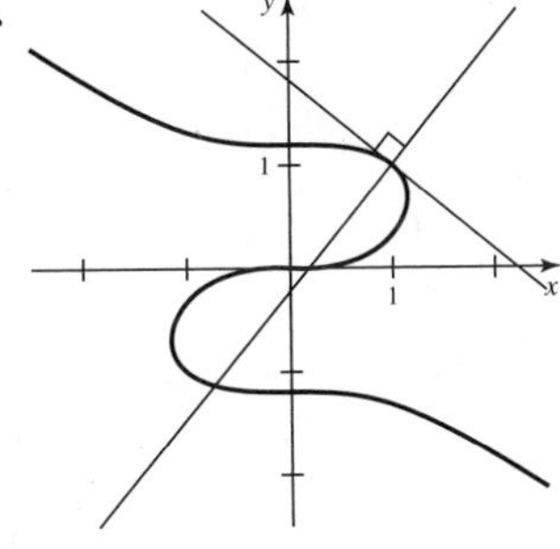

67. a. $y = -\frac{x}{3} + \frac{8}{3}$ and $y = 3x - 4$

b.

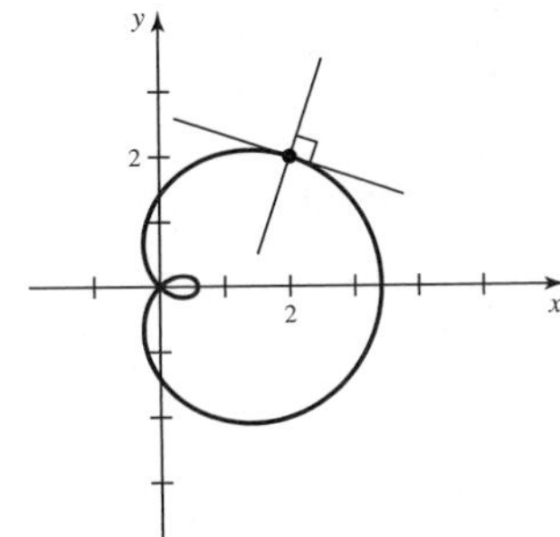

69. a. $\frac{dK}{dL} = \frac{-K}{2L}$ **b.** -4 **71. a.** $\frac{dr}{dh} = \frac{h - 2r}{h}$ **b.** -3

73. Note that for $y = mx$, $dy/dx = m$; for $x^2 + y^2 = a^2$, $dy/dx = -x/y$. **75.** For $xy = a$, $dy/dx = -y/x$. For $x^2 - y^2 = b$, $dy/dx = x/y$. Since $(-y/x) \cdot (x/y) = -1$, the families of curves are orthogonal trajectories.

Section 3.8 Exercises, pp. 169–173

1. As the side length s of a cube changes, the surface area $6s^2$ changes as well. **3.** The other two opposite sides decrease in length. **5. a.** $40 \text{ m}^2/\text{s}$ **b.** $80 \text{ m}^2/\text{s}$

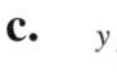
c.

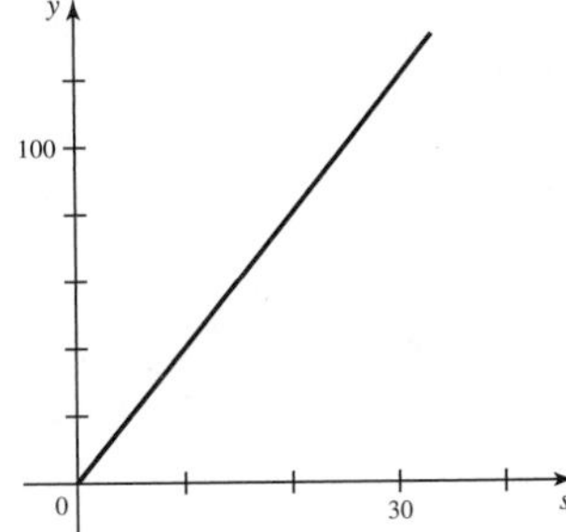

7. $-40\pi \text{ ft}^2/\text{min}$ **9.** $\frac{3}{80\pi}$ in/min **13.** $\frac{1}{500}$ m/min; 2000 min **15.** $10 \tan 20°$ km/hr ≈ 3.6 km/hr **17.** $\frac{5}{24}$ ft/s **19.** $-\frac{8}{3}$ ft/s, $-\frac{32}{3}$ ft/s **21.** $2592\pi \text{ cm}^3/\text{s}$ **23.** $\frac{-8}{9\pi}$ ft/s **25. a.** $\frac{-\sqrt{3}}{10}$ m/hr **b.** $-1 \text{ m}^2/\text{hr}$ **27.** 57.89 ft/s **29.** 4.66 in/s **31.** $\frac{3\sqrt{5}}{2}$ ft/s **33.** ≈ 720.3 mi/hr **35.** 11.06 m/hr **37. a.** 187.5 ft/s **b.** 0.938 rad/s **39.** $\frac{d\theta}{dt} = 0.543$ rad/hr **41.** $\frac{d\theta}{dt} = \frac{1}{5}$ rad/s, $\frac{d\theta}{dt} = \frac{1}{8}$ rad/s **43.** $\frac{d\theta}{dt} = 0$ rad/s for all $t \geq 0$ **45.** -0.0201 rad/s

Review Exercises, pp. 173–176

1. a. False **b.** False **c.** False **d.** False **e.** True
3. a. 16 **b.** $y = 16x - 10$

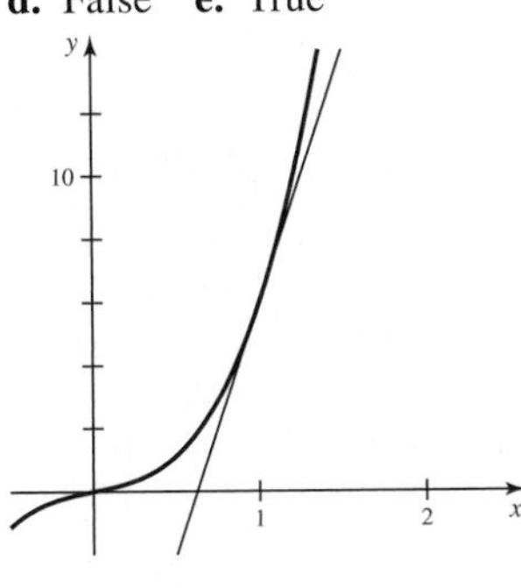

5. a. $\frac{-3}{4}$ **b.** $y = -\frac{3x}{4} + \frac{1}{2}$

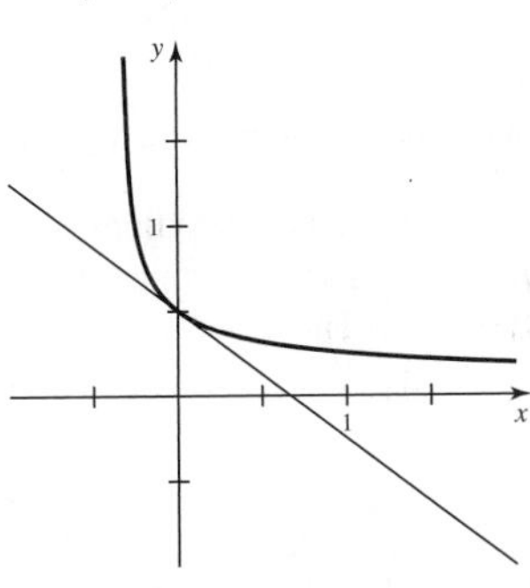

7. a. 2.70 million people/year **b.** The slope of the secant line through the two points is approximately equal to the slope of that tangent line at $t = 55$. **c.** 2.217 million people/year **9. a.** ≈ 40 m/s **b.** ≈ 7 m/s **c.** ≈ 18 m/s

d.

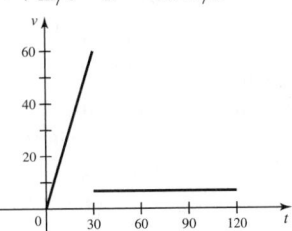

e. The skydiver deployed the parachute.

13.

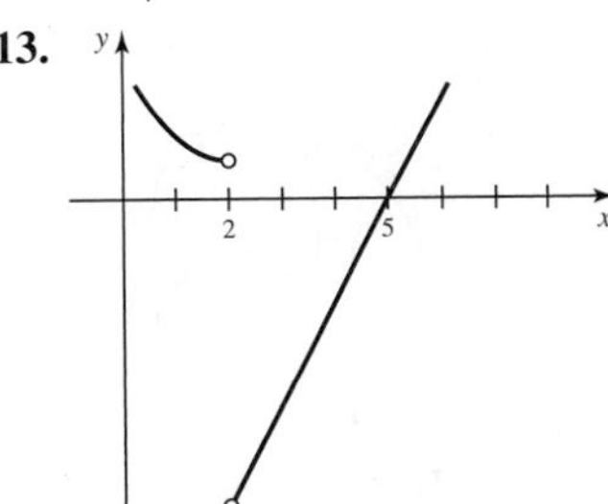

15. $2x^2 + 2\pi x + 7$ **17.** $5t^2 \cos t + 10t \sin t$ **19.** $(8\theta + 12) \sec^2(\theta^2 + 3\theta + 2)$ **21.** $\frac{32u^2 + 8u + 1}{(8u + 1)^2}$ **23.** $\sec^2(\sin\theta) \cdot \cos\theta$ **25.** $\frac{9x \sin x - 2 \sin x + 6x^2 \cos x - 2x \cos x}{\sqrt{3x - 1}}$

27. $\dfrac{dy}{dx} = \dfrac{-y\cos x}{1 + \sin x + \sin y}$

29. $\dfrac{dy}{dx} = -\dfrac{xy}{x^2 + 2y^2}$ **31.** $y = x$ **33.** $y = -\dfrac{4x}{5} + \dfrac{24}{5}$

35. $x = 4$ **37.** $y' = \dfrac{\cos\sqrt{x}}{2\sqrt{x}}, y'' = \dfrac{-(\sqrt{x}\sin\sqrt{x} + \cos\sqrt{x})}{4x^{3/2}}$,

$y''' = \dfrac{3\sqrt{x}\sin\sqrt{x} + (3 - x)\cos\sqrt{x}}{8x^{5/2}}$ **39.** $x^2f'(x) + 2xf(x)$

41. $\dfrac{g(x)[xf'(x) + f(x)] - xf(x)g'(x)}{g^2(x)}$ **43. a.** 27 **b.** $\frac{25}{27}$ **c.** 294

45. $f(x) = \tan(\pi\sqrt{3x - 11})$, $a = 5$; $f'(5) = 3\pi/4$

47. a. $\overline{C}(3000) = \$341.67$; $C'(3000) = \$280$ **b.** The average cost of producing the first 3000 lawnmowers is $341.67 per mower. The cost of producing the 3001st lawnmower is $280.

49. a. 6550 people/year **b.** $p'(40) = 4800$ people/year

51. 50 mi/hr **53.** $-5\sin(65°)$ ft/s or ≈ -4.5 ft/s **55.** 0.166 rad/s

CHAPTER 4

Section 4.1 Exercises, pp. 183–186

1. f has an absolute maximum at c in $[a, b]$ if $f(x) \le f(c)$ for all x in $[a, b]$. f has an absolute minimum at c in $[a, b]$ if $f(x) \ge f(c)$ for all x in $[a, b]$. **3.** The function must be continuous on a closed interval.

5.

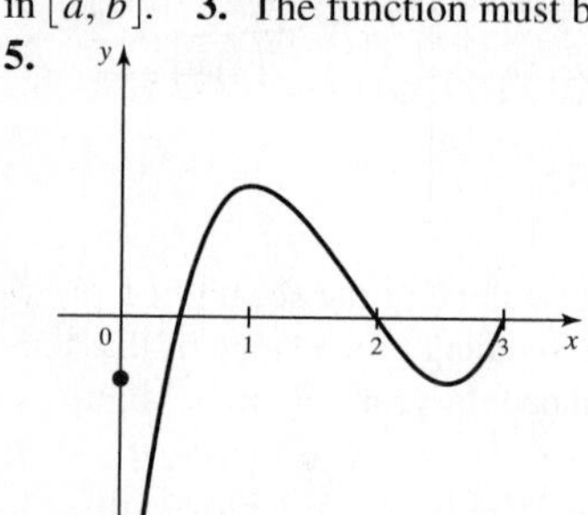

7.

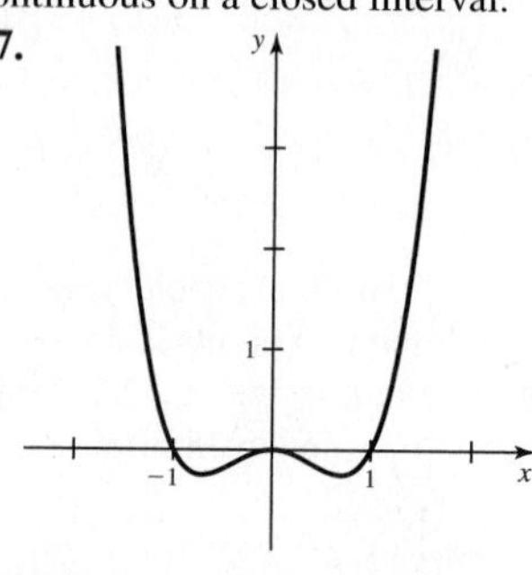

9. Evaluate the function at the critical points and at the endpoints of the interval. **11.** Abs. min at c_2; abs. max at b **13.** Abs. min at a; no abs. max **15.** Local min at q, s; local max at p, r; abs. min at a; abs. max at b **17.** Local max at p and r; local min at q; abs. max at p; abs. min at b

19.

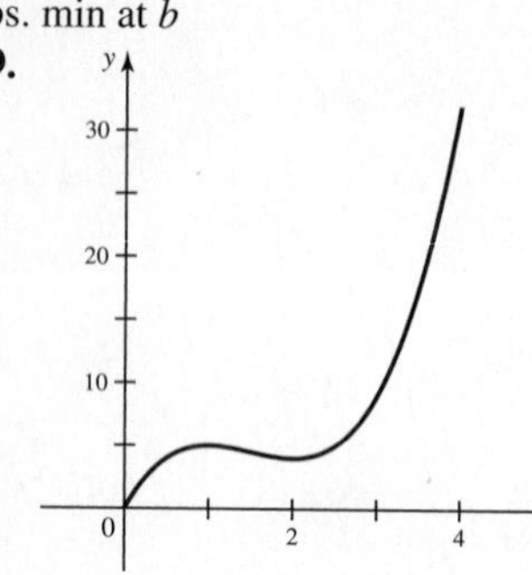

21.

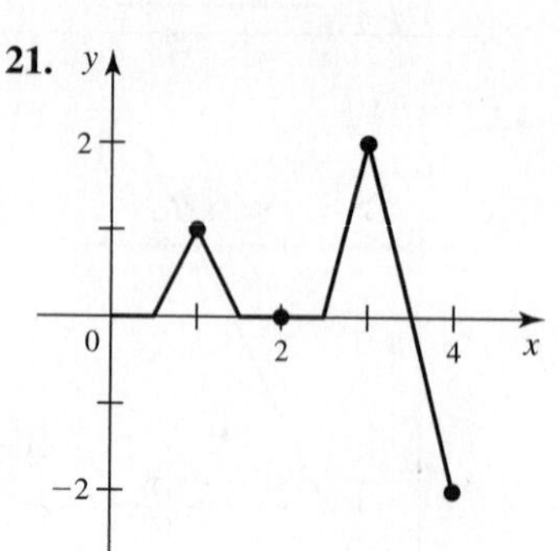

23. a. $x = \frac{2}{3}$ **b.** Local min **25. a.** $x = -\frac{1}{2}, 2$ **b.** $x = -\frac{1}{2}$ local min; $x = 2$ local max **27. a.** $x = \frac{\pi}{6}, \frac{2\pi}{3}$ **b.** $x = \frac{\pi}{6}$ local max, $x = \frac{2\pi}{3}$ local min **29. a.** $x = 2$ **b.** local max

31. a. $x = 0$ **b.** Abs. max: -1 at $x = 3$; abs. min: -10 at $x = 0$ **c.**

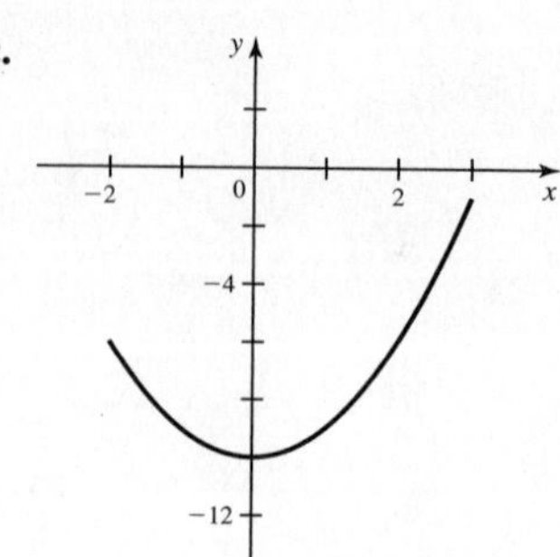

33. a. $x = \pi/2$ **b.** Abs. max: 1 at $x = 0, \pi$; abs. min: 0 at $x = \pi/2$ **c.**

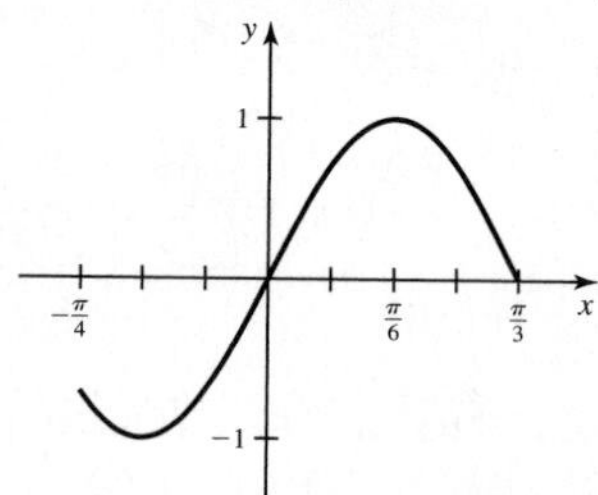

35. a. $x = \pm\pi/6$ **b.** Abs. max: 1 at $x = \pi/6$; abs. min: -1 at $x = -\pi/6$ **c.**

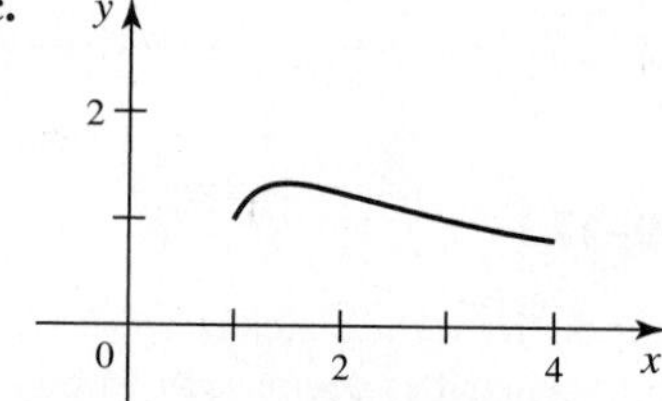

37. a. $x = \frac{3}{2}$ **b.** Abs. max: $\frac{4}{3}$ at $x = \frac{3}{2}$; abs. min: $\frac{13}{16}$ at $x = 4$

c.

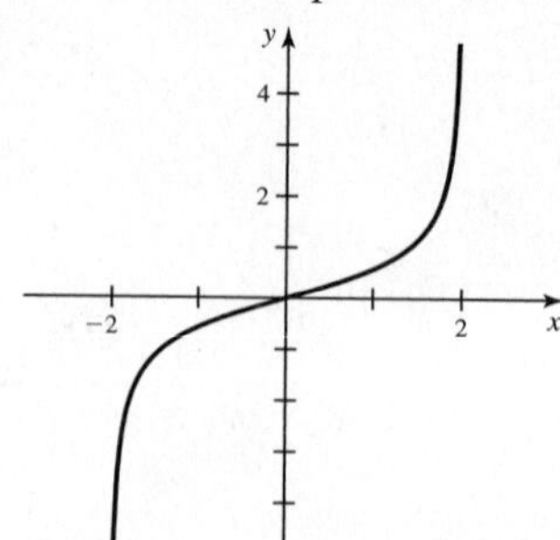

39. a. No critical points **b.** No abs. max or min

c.

41. $t = 2$ s **43. a.** 50 **b.** 45 **45. a.** False **b.** False **c.** False **d.** True **e.** False **47. a.** $x = -4, 0, 1$ **b.** Abs. max: 16 at $x = 2$; abs. min: -128 at $x = -4$

c.

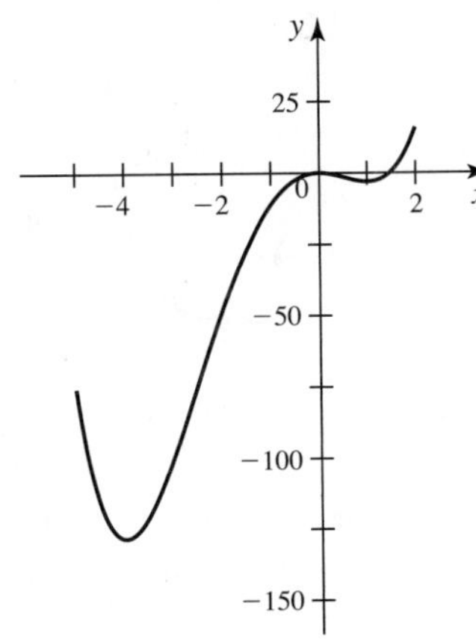

49. a. $x = 0$ **b.** Abs. max: $\sqrt{2}$ at $x = \pm\pi/4$; abs. min: 1 at $x = 0$
c.

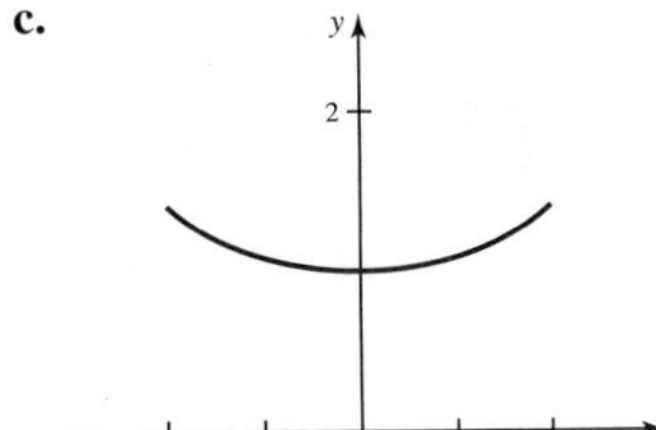

51. a. $x = 8$ **b.** Abs. max: $3\sqrt{2}$ at $x = 6$ and $x = 12$; abs. min: 4 at $x = 8$ **c.**

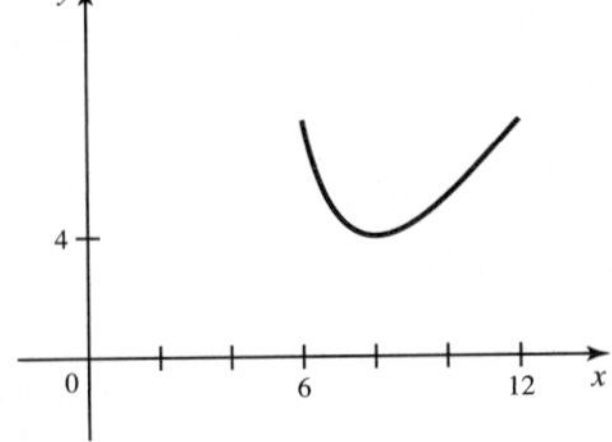

53. If $a \geq 0$, there is no critical point. If $a < 0$, $x = 2a/3$ is the only critical point. **55.** $x = \pm a$ **57. a.** $x = \tan^{-1}2 + k\pi$, for $k = -2, -1, 0, 1$ **b.** $x = \tan^{-1}2 + k\pi$ for $k = -2, 0$ correspond to local max; $x = \tan^{-1}2 + k\pi$, for $k = -1, 1$ correspond to local min. **c.** Abs. max: 2.24; abs. min: -2.24 **59. a.** $x = -\frac{1}{8}$ and $x = 3$ **b.** $x = -\frac{1}{8}$ corresponds to a local min; $x = 3$ is neither **c.** Abs. max: 51.23; abs. min: -12.52 **61. a.** $x = 5 - 4\sqrt{2}$ **b.** $x = 5 - 4\sqrt{2}$ corresponds to a local max. **c.** No abs. max or min **63.** Abs. max: 4 at $x = -1$; abs. min: -8 at $x = 3$

65. a. $T(x) = \dfrac{\sqrt{2500 + x^2}}{2} + \dfrac{50 - x}{4}$ **b.** $x = 50/\sqrt{3}$

c. $T(50/\sqrt{3}) = 34.15$
$T(0) = 37.50$
$T(50) = 35.36$

d.

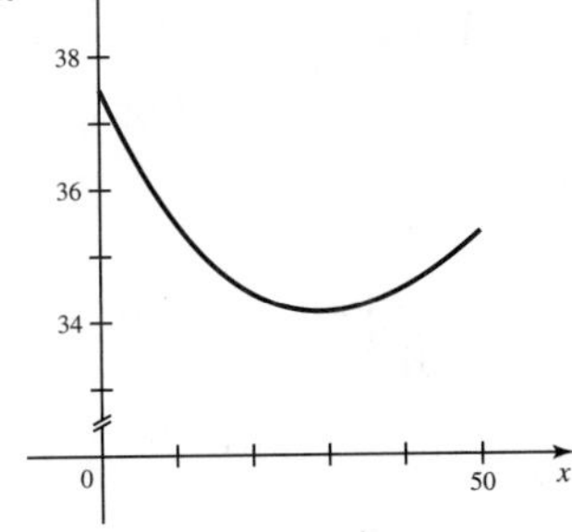

67. a. 1, 3, 0, 1 **b.** Because $g'(2) = 0$, g has a local extreme value of 1 at $x = 2$. Since $h'(2) \neq 0$, h does not have a local extreme value at $x = 2$. **69. a.** A local min at $x = -c$ **b.** A local max at $x = -c$ **71. a.** $f(x) - f(c) \leq 0$ for all x near c
b. $\lim_{x\to c^+} \dfrac{f(x) - f(c)}{x - c} \leq 0$ **c.** $\lim_{x\to c^-} \dfrac{f(x) - f(c)}{x - c} \geq 0$
d. Since $f'(c)$ exists, $\lim_{x\to c^+} \dfrac{f(x) - f(c)}{x - c} = \lim_{x\to c^-} \dfrac{f(x) - f(c)}{x - c}$.
By parts (b) and (c), we must have that $f'(c) = 0$.

Section 4.2 Exercises, pp. 196–199

1. f is increasing on I if $f'(x) > 0$ for all x in I; f decreasing on I if $f'(x) < 0$ for all x in I. **3.**

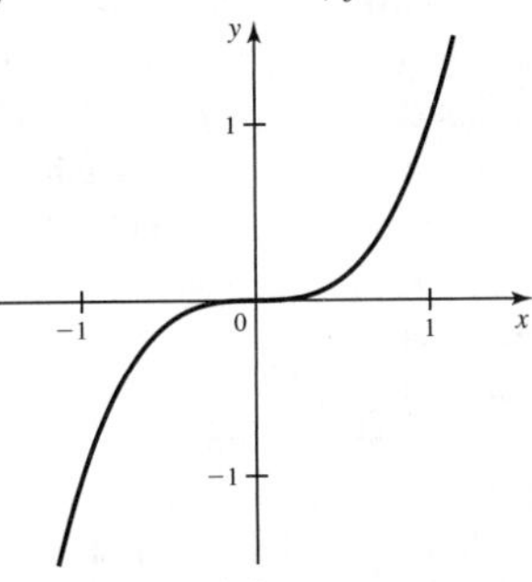

5. Because f has a local maximum at c, $f'(x) > 0$ for $x < c$ and $f'(x) < 0$ for $x > c$. Therefore, f' is decreasing near c and $f''(c) \leq 0$. Equality must be included to account for cases such as $f(x) = -(x - c)^4$.
7. A point in the domain at which f changes concavity. **9.** Yes; consider $f(x) = x^2$ on the interval $[1, 2]$. **11.**

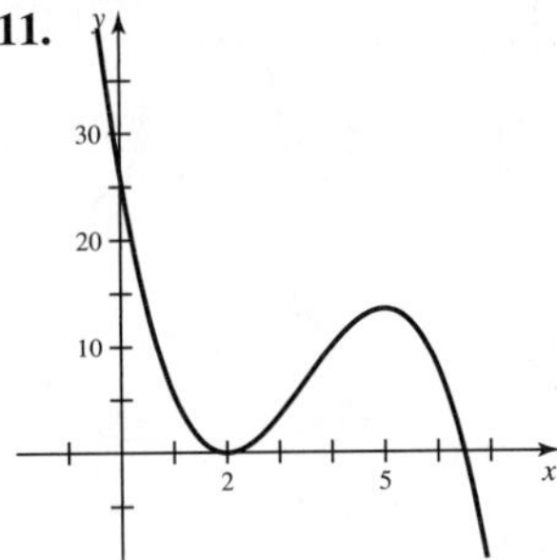

13. **15.**

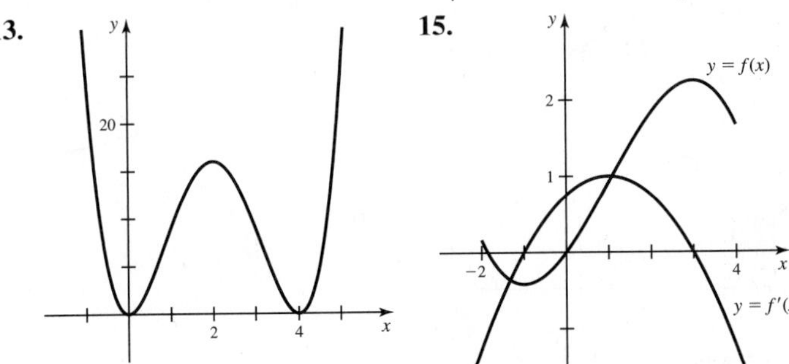

17. Increasing on $(-\infty, 0)$; decreasing on $(0, \infty)$ **19.** Decreasing on $(-\infty, 1)$; increasing on $(1, \infty)$ **21.** Increasing on $(-\infty, 1/2)$; decreasing on $(1/2, \infty)$ **23.** Increasing on the intervals $(-\pi, -2\pi/3)$, $(-\pi/3, 0)$, $(\pi/3, 2\pi/3)$; decreasing on the intervals $(-2\pi/3, -\pi/3)$, $(0, \pi/3)$, $(2\pi/3, \pi)$ **25.** Increasing on $(0, \infty)$; decreasing on $(-\infty, 0)$
27. Decreasing on $(-\infty, 1)$, $(4, \infty)$; increasing on $(1, 4)$
29. a. $x = 0$ **b.** Local min at $x = 0$ **c.** Abs. min: 3 at $x = 0$; abs. max: 12 at $x = -3$ **31. a.** $x = \pm 3/\sqrt{2}$ **b.** Local min at $x = -3/\sqrt{2}$; local max at $x = 3/\sqrt{2}$ **c.** Abs. max: 9/2 at $x = 3/\sqrt{2}$; abs. min: $-9/2$ at $x = -3/\sqrt{2}$

33. a. $x = 8/5$ and $x = 0$ **b.** Local max at $x = 0$; local min at $x = 8/5$ **c.** Abs. min: -26.32 at $x = -5$; abs. max: 2.92 at $x = 5$ **35.** Abs. max $-\frac{14}{3}$ at $x = \frac{1}{3}$ **37.** Abs. min: $36\sqrt[3]{\pi/6}$ at $x = \sqrt[3]{6/\pi}$.

39. **41.**

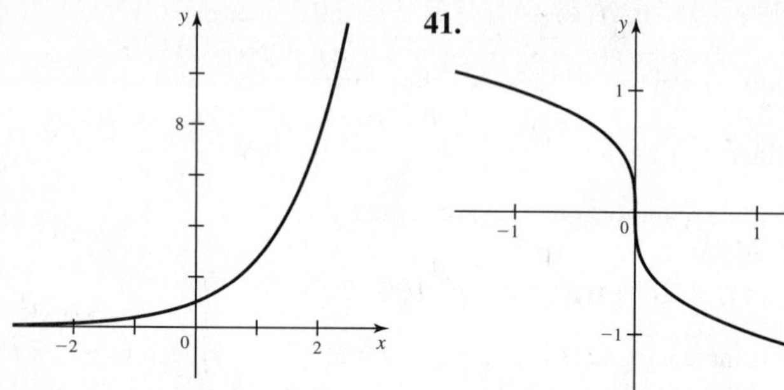

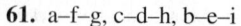

43. Concave up on $(-\infty, 0)$ and $(2, \infty)$; concave down on $(0, 2)$; inflection points at $x = 0$ and $x = 2$ **45.** Concave up on $(-\infty, -3)$; concave down on $(-3, \infty)$; no inflection points **47.** Concave up for $|x| < 1\sqrt{3}$; concave down for $|x| > 1/\sqrt{3}$; inflection points at $x = \pm 1/\sqrt{3}$ **49.** Concave up on $(0, 2)$ and $(4, \infty)$; concave down on $(-\infty, 0)$ and $(2, 4)$; inflection points at $x = 0, 2, 4$ **51.** Critical pt. at $x = 0$; local max at $x = 0$ **53.** Critical pt. at $x = 0$ and $x = 1$; local max at $x = 0$; local min at $x = 1$ **55.** Critical points $x = \pm 3$; local max at $x = 3$; local min at $x = -3$. **57. a.** True **b.** False **c.** True **d.** False **e.** False

59.

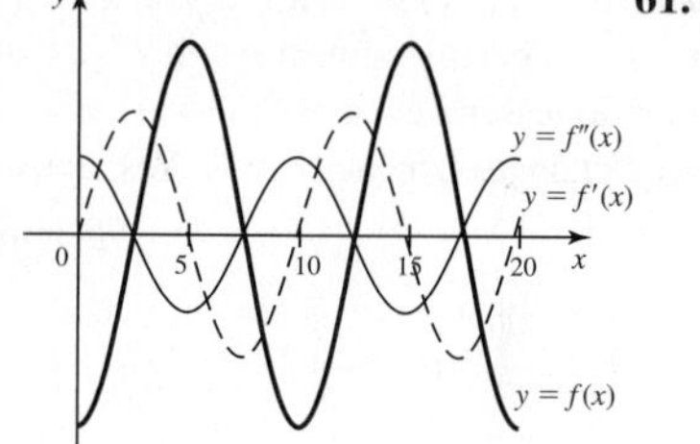

61. a–f–g, c–d–h, b–e–i

63.

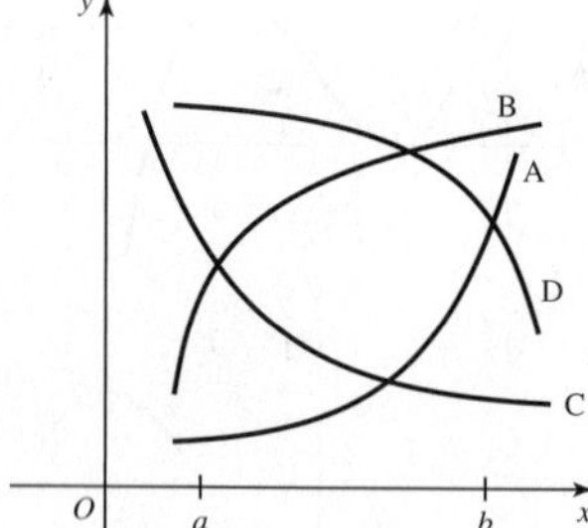

65.

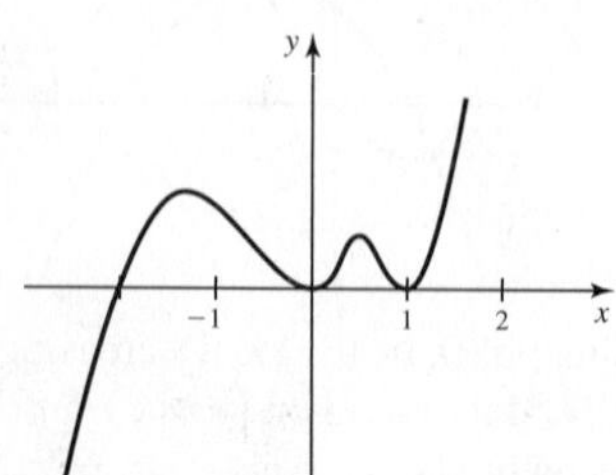

67. a. Increasing on $(-2, 2)$; decreasing on $(-3, -2)$ **b.** Critical pt. at $x = -2$ and $x = 0$; local min at $x = -2$; neither a local min or max at $x = 0$ **c.** Inflection pts. at $x = -1$ and $x = 0$ **d.** Concave up on $(-3, -1)$ and $(0, 2)$; concave down on $(-1, 0)$

e. **f.**

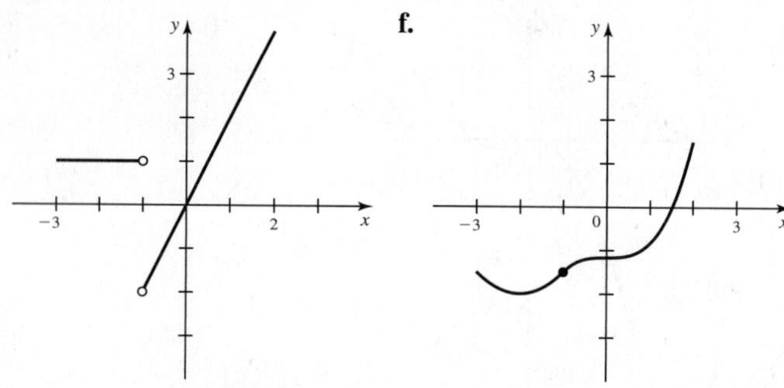

69. Critical pt. at $x = -3$ and $x = 4$; local min at $x = -3$; inconclusive at $x = 4$ **71.** No critical pts. **73. a.** $E = \frac{10p}{10p - 500}$ **b.** -1.4% **c.** $E'(p) = -\frac{ab}{(a - bp)^2} < 0$ for $p \geq 0, p \neq a/b$ **d.** $E(p) = -b$ for $p \geq 0$ **75. a.** 300 **b.** $t = \sqrt{10}$ **c.** $t = \sqrt{b/3}$ **77. a.** $f''(x) = 6x + 2a = 0$ when $x = -a/3$ **b.** $f(-a/3) - f(-a/3 + x) = (a^2/3)x - bx - x^3$; also, $f(-a/3 - x) - f(-a/3) = (a^2/3)x - bx - x^3$

Section 4.3 Exercises, pp. 206–209

1. We need to know over which interval(s) to graph f. **3.** No; polynomials are continuous on $(-\infty, \infty)$; there are no vertical asymptotes. Also, $\lim_{x \to \pm\infty} p(x) = \pm\infty$ where p is any polynomial; there are no horizontal asymptotes. **5.** Evaluate the function at the critical points and at the endpoints. Then find the largest and smallest values among those candidates.

7.

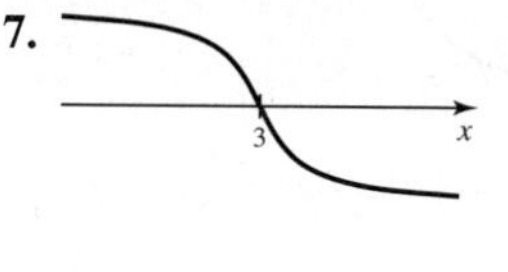

9.

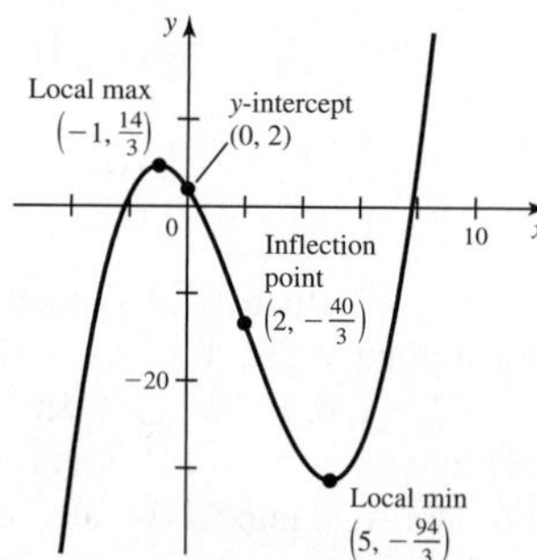

11.

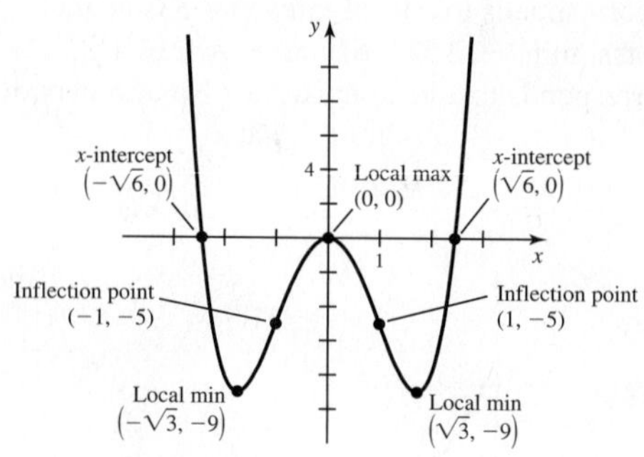

13.

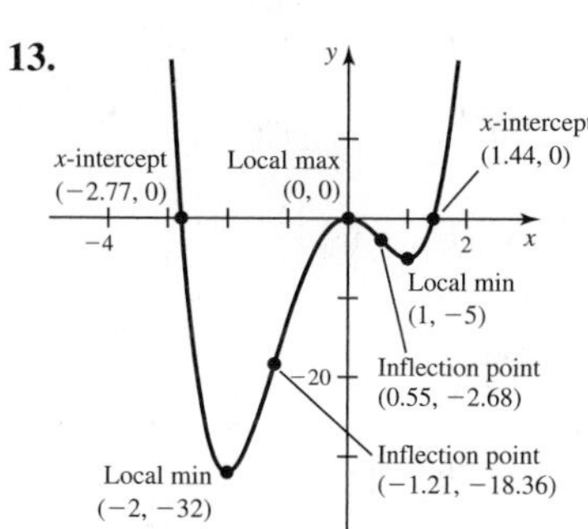

15.

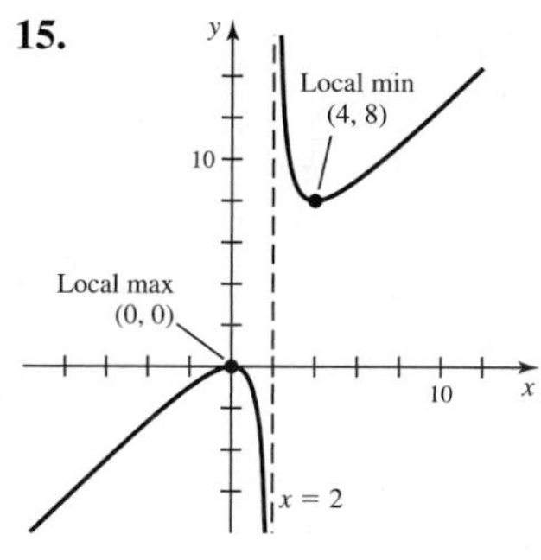

17.

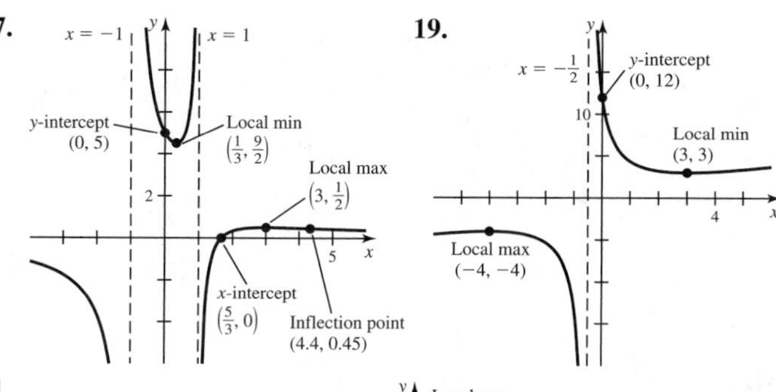

19.

21.

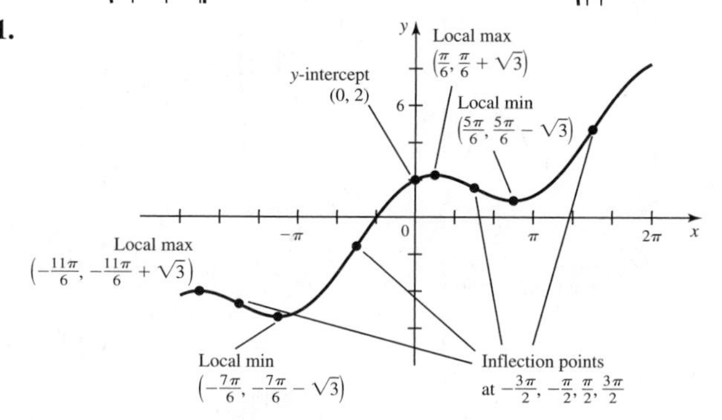

23.

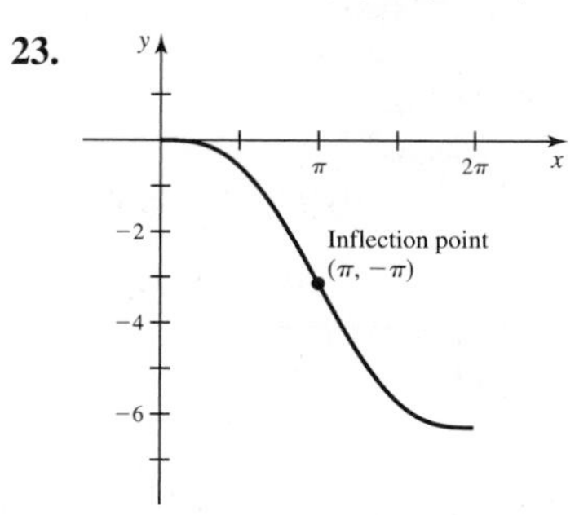

25.

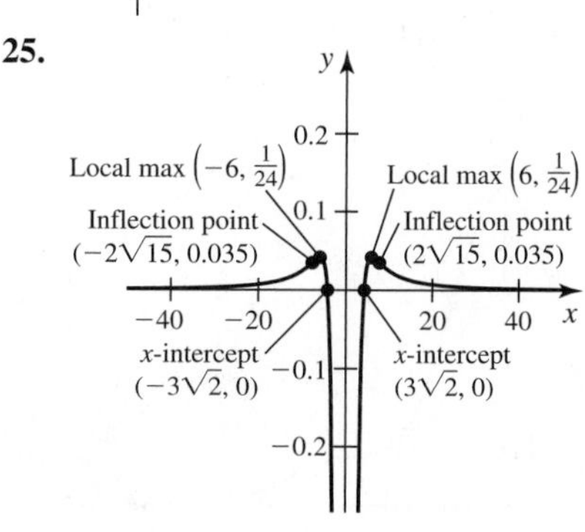

27.

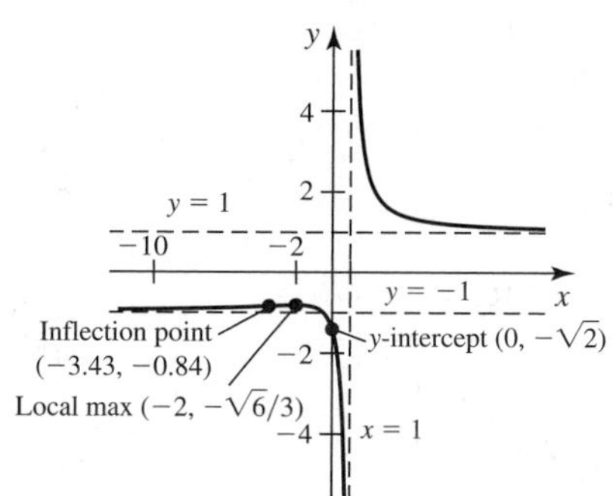

29.

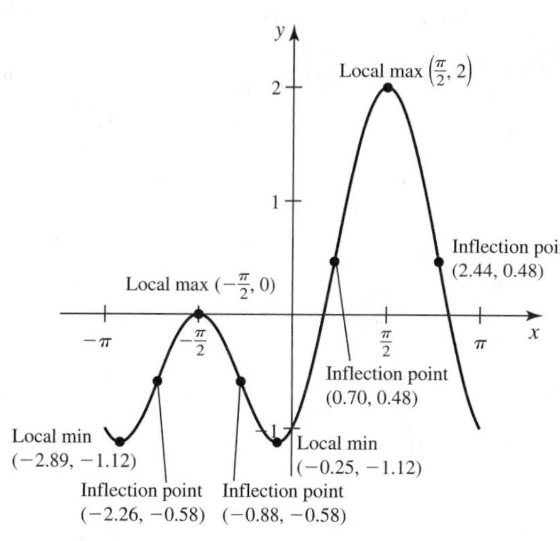

31.

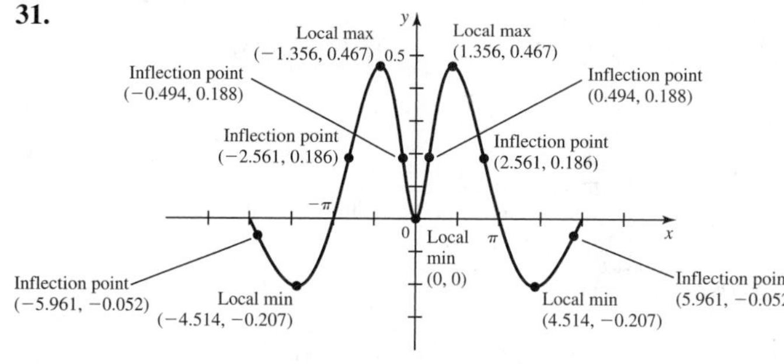

33. a. False **b.** False **c.** False **d.** True

35.

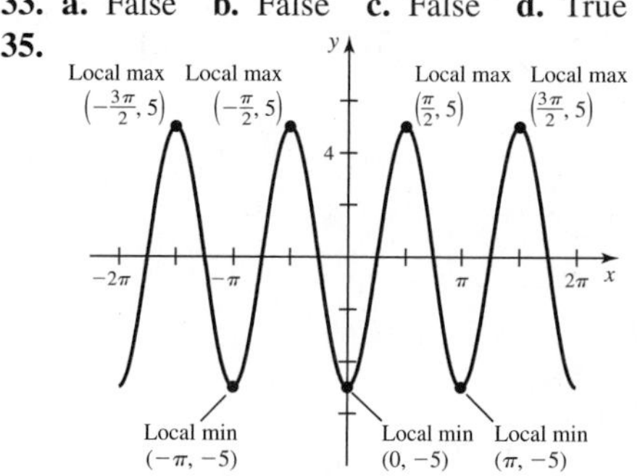

37.

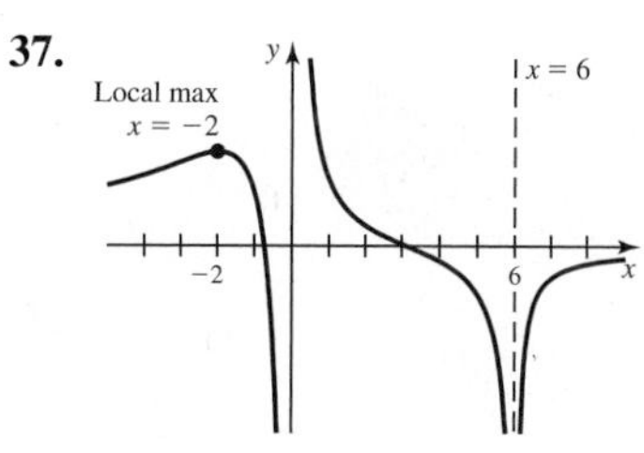

39. Critical pt. at $x = 1, 3$; local max at $x = 1$; local min at $x = 3$; inflection pt. at $x = 2$; increasing on $(0, 1)$, $(3, 4)$; decreasing on $(1, 3)$; concave up on $(2, 4)$; concave down on $(0, 2)$

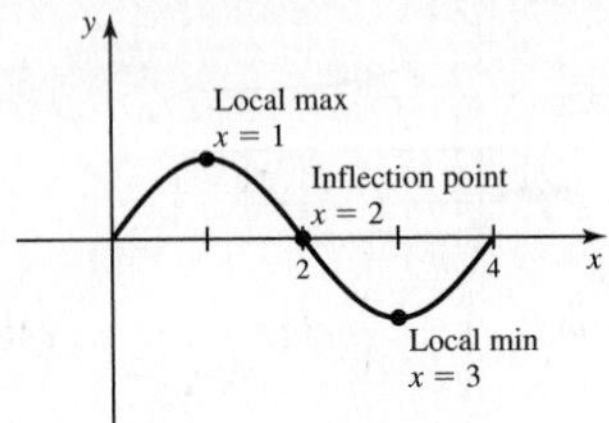

41.

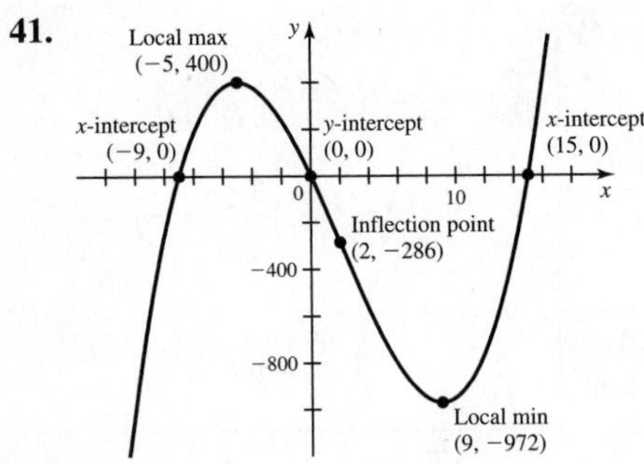

43.

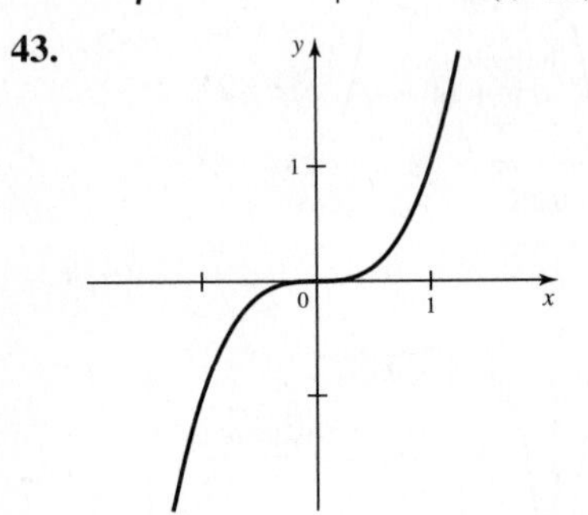

45.

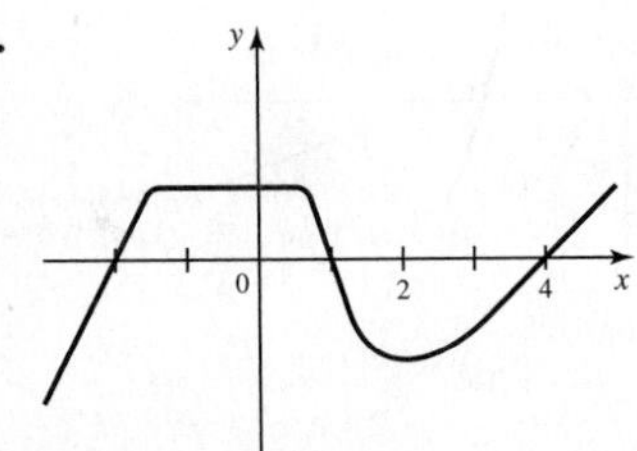

47.

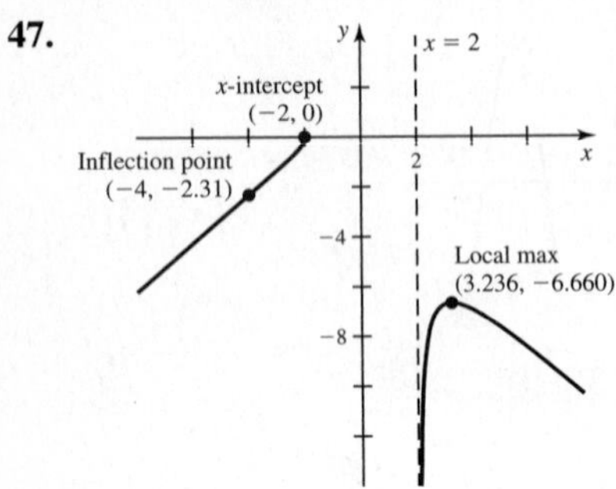

49. a.

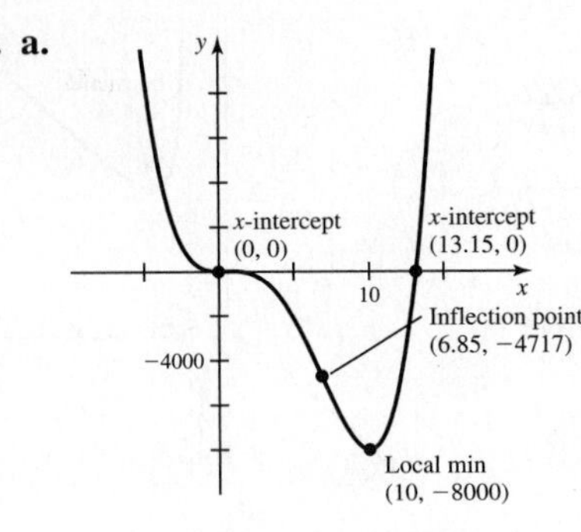

b.

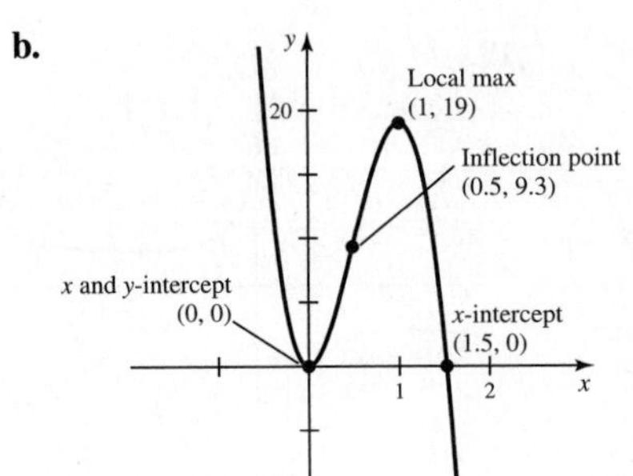

51.

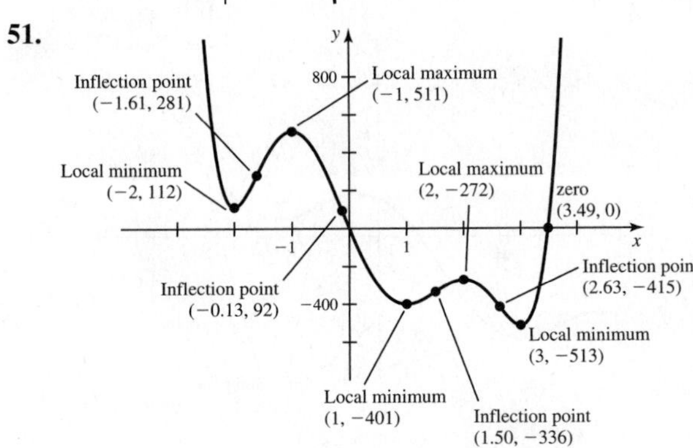

53.

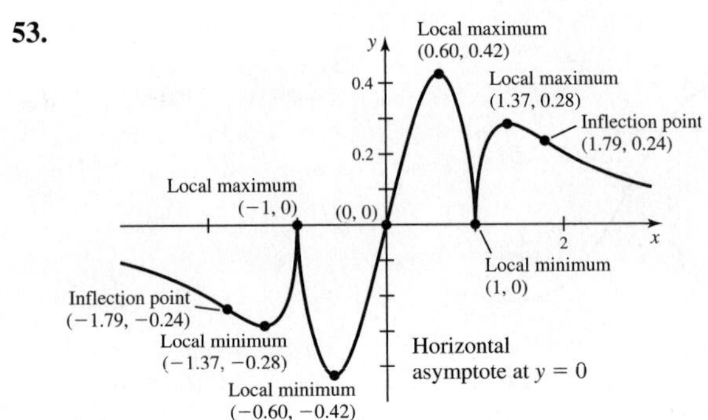

55. a.

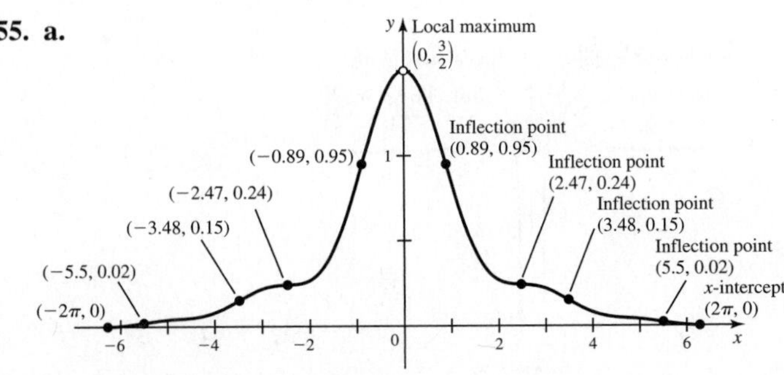

b.

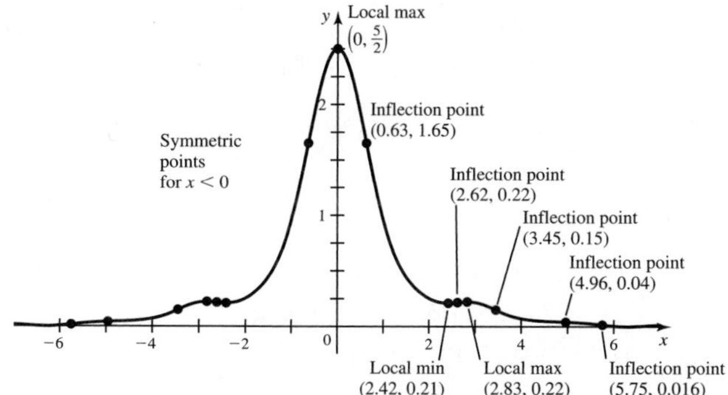

57. (a) a.

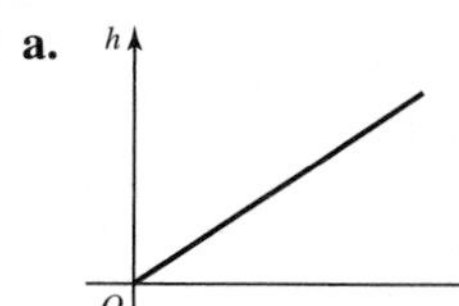

b. Water is being added at all times **c.** No concavity **d.** h' has an abs. max at all points of $[0, 10]$.

(b) a.

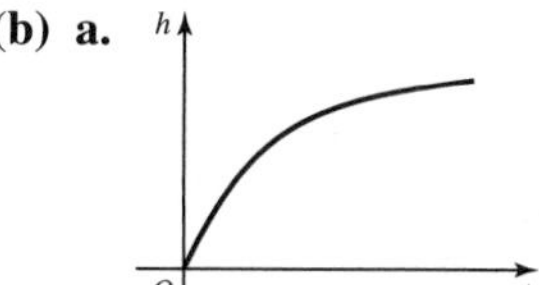

c. Concave down
d. h' has abs. max at $t = 0$.

(c) a.

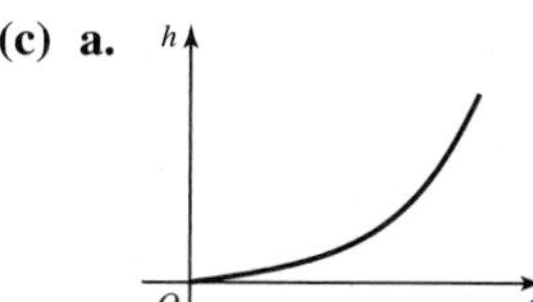

c. Concave up
d. h' has abs. max at $t = 10$.

(d) a.

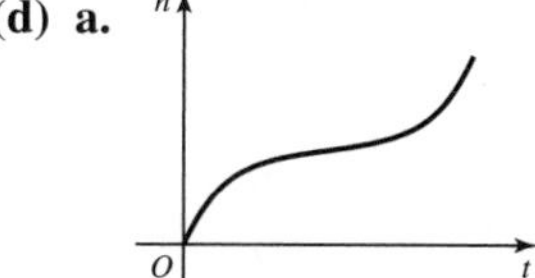

c. Concave up on $(0, 5)$, then concave down on $(5, 10)$; inflection pt. at $t = 5$
d. h' has abs. max at $t = 0$ and $t = 10$.

(e) a.

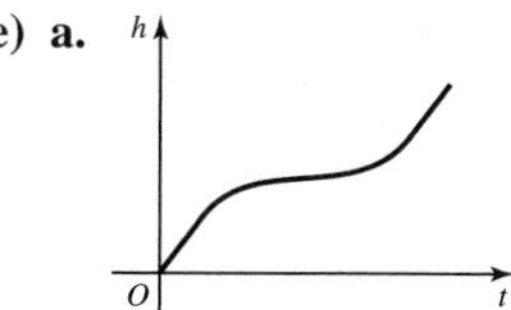

c. First, no concavity; then, concave down, no concavity, concave up, and, finally, no concavity **d.** h' has abs. max at all points of an interval $[0, a]$ and $[b, 10]$.

(f) a.

c. Concave down on $(0, 5)$; concave up on $(5, 10)$; inflection pt. at $t = 5$ **d.** h' has abs. max at $t = 0$ and $t = 10$.

59. $f'(0)$ does not exist.

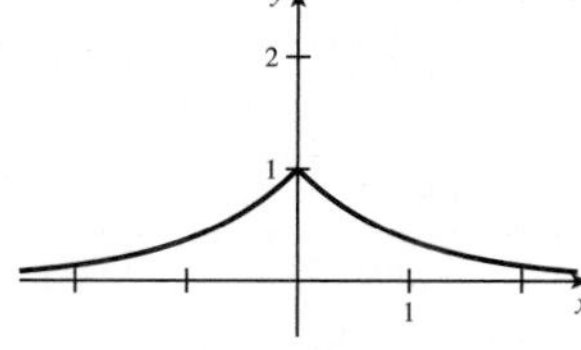

61.

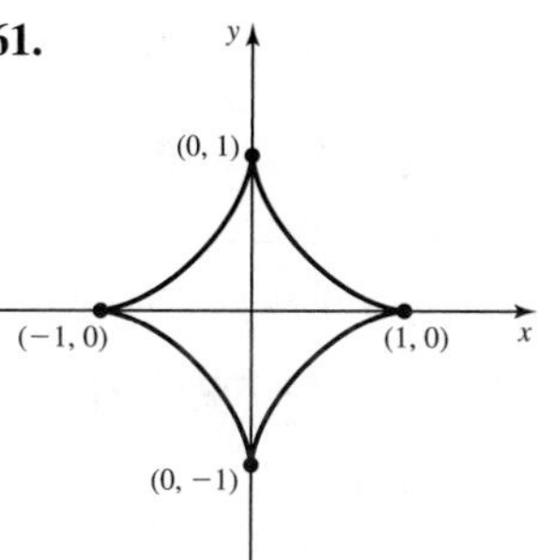

63.

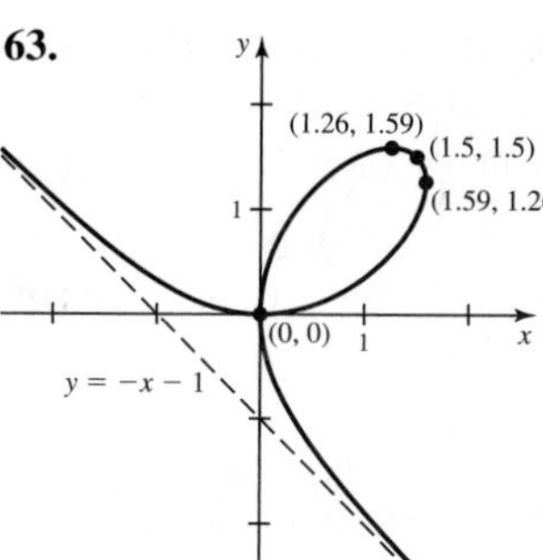

65.

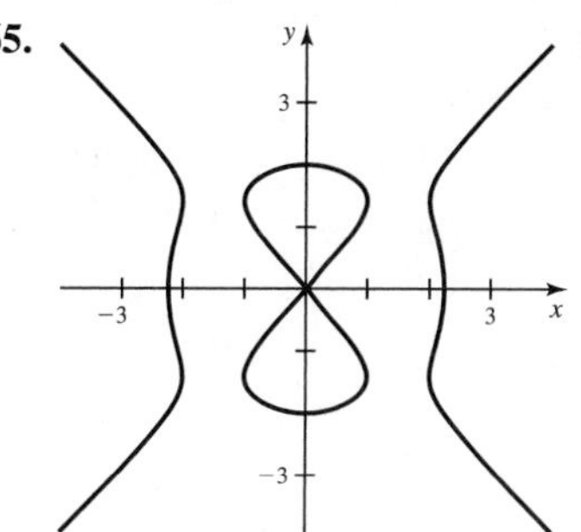

67.

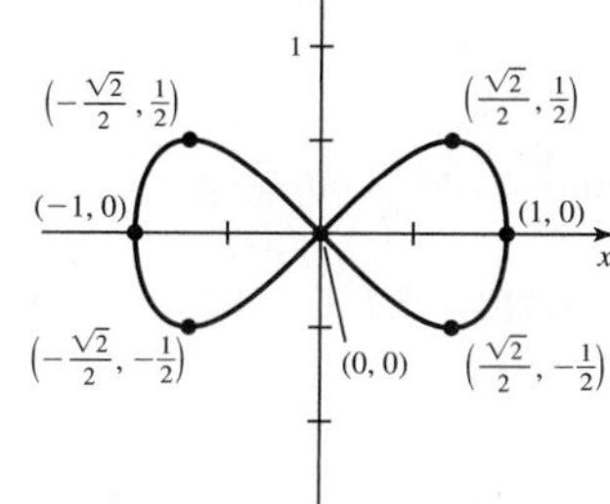

69.

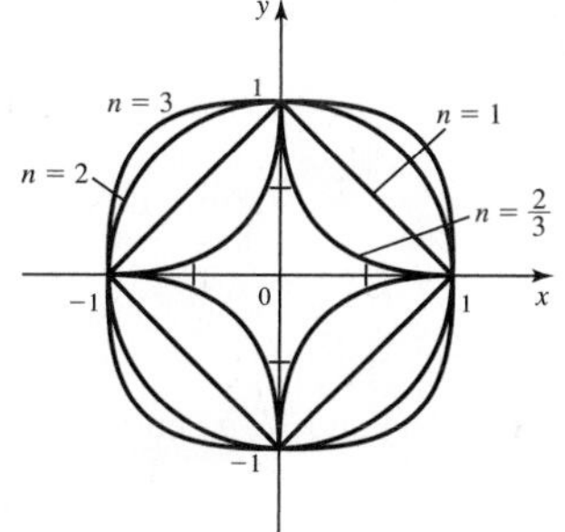

Section 4.4 Exercises, pp. 213–219

1. Objective function, constraints
3. $Q = x^2(10 - x); Q = (10 - y)^2 y$ **5.** Width = length = $\frac{5}{2}$ m
7. $\frac{23}{2}$ and $\frac{23}{2}$ **9.** $5\sqrt{2}$ and $5\sqrt{2}$
11. Length = width = height = $\sqrt[3]{100}$
13. $\dfrac{4}{\sqrt[3]{5}}$ ft by $\dfrac{4}{\sqrt[3]{5}}$ ft by $5^{2/3}$ ft **15. a.** A point $8/\sqrt{5}$ mi from the point on the shore nearest the woman in the direction of the restaurant **b.** $9/\sqrt{13}$ mi/hr **17.** 18.2 ft
19. $\dfrac{10}{\sqrt{2}}$ cm by $\dfrac{5}{\sqrt{2}}$ cm **21.** $\theta = 2\pi\left(1 - \dfrac{\sqrt{6}}{3}\right)$
23. $\sqrt{15}$ m by $2\sqrt{15}$ m **25.** $r/h = \sqrt{2}$ **27.** $r = h = \sqrt[3]{450/\pi}$ m
29. The point $12/\left(\sqrt[3]{2} + 1\right) \approx 5.3$ m from the weaker source
31. A point $7\sqrt{3}/6$ mi from the point on shore nearest the island, in the direction of the power station **33. a.** $P = 2/\sqrt{3}$ units from the midpoint of the base **35.** For $L \le 4r$ max at $\theta = 0$ and $\theta = 2\pi$; min at $\theta = \cos^{-1}(-L/(4r))$ and $\theta = 2\pi - \cos^{-1}(-L/(4r))$. For $L > 4r$, max at $\theta = 0$ and 2π, min at $\theta = \pi$.
37. a. $r = \sqrt[3]{177/\pi} \approx 3.83$ cm; $h = 2\sqrt[3]{177/\pi} \approx 7.67$ cm
b. $r = \sqrt[3]{177/2\pi} \approx 3.04$ cm; $h = 2\sqrt[3]{708/\pi} \approx 12.17$ cm. Part(b) is closer to the real can. **39.** $\sqrt{30} \approx 5.5$ ft **41.** When the seat is at its lowest point **43.** $r = \sqrt{2}\,R/\sqrt{3}; h = 2R/\sqrt{3}$
45. a. $r = 2R/3; h = \frac{1}{3}H$ **b.** $r = R/2; h = H/2$ **47.** 3:1

49. $(1 + \sqrt{3})$ mi ≈ 2.732 mi **51.** You can run 12 mi/hr if you run toward the point 3/16 mi ahead of the locomotive (when it passes the point nearest you). **53. a.** $(-6/5, 2/5)$ **b.** Approx $(0.59, 0.65)$ **c. (i)** $\left(p - \frac{1}{2}, \sqrt{p - \frac{1}{2}}\right)$ **(ii)** $(0, 0)$ **55. a.** 0, 30, 25 **b.** 42.5 mi/hr **c.** The units of $p/g(v)$ are \$/mi and so are the units of W/V. Thus, $L\left(\frac{p}{g(v)} + \frac{w}{v}\right)$ gives the total cost of a trip of L miles. **d.** ≈ 62.9 mi/hr **e.** Neither; the zeros of $C'(v)$ are independent of L. **f.** Decreased slightly, to 62.5 mi/hr **g.** Decreased to 60.8 mi/hr **57. b.** Because the speed of light is constant, travel time is minimized when distance is minimized. **59.** Let the angle of the cuts be φ_1 and φ_2, where $\varphi_1 + \varphi_2 = \theta$. The volume of the notch is proportional to $\tan\varphi_1 + \tan\varphi_2 = \tan\varphi_1 + \tan(\theta - \varphi_1)$, which is minimized when $\varphi_1 = \varphi_2 = \dfrac{\theta}{2}$.

Section 4.5 Exercises, pp. 225–226

1.

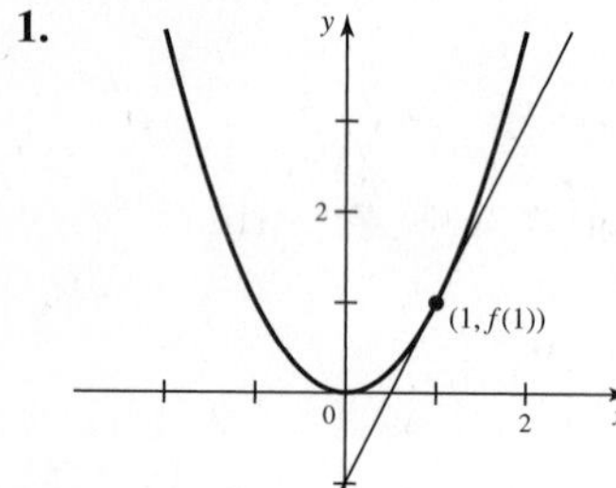

3. $f(x) \approx f(a) + f'(a)(x - a)$, where $f(a)$ and $f'(a)$ are easily evaluated. **5.** $dy = f'(x)\,dx$

7. a. $y = -4x + 16$ **b.**

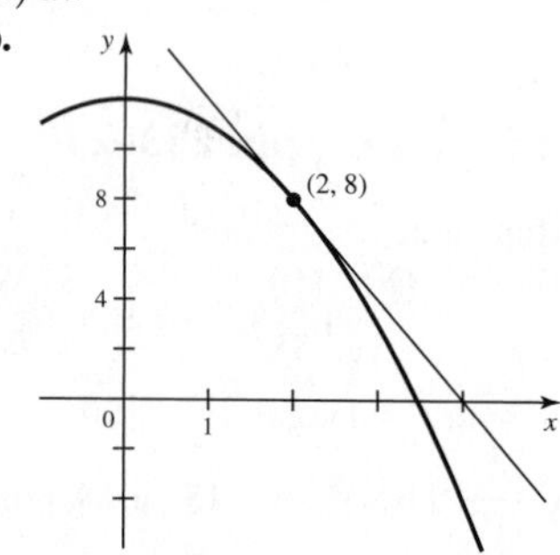

c. 7.6 **d.** 0.13% error **9. a.** $y = 1 - x$ **b.**

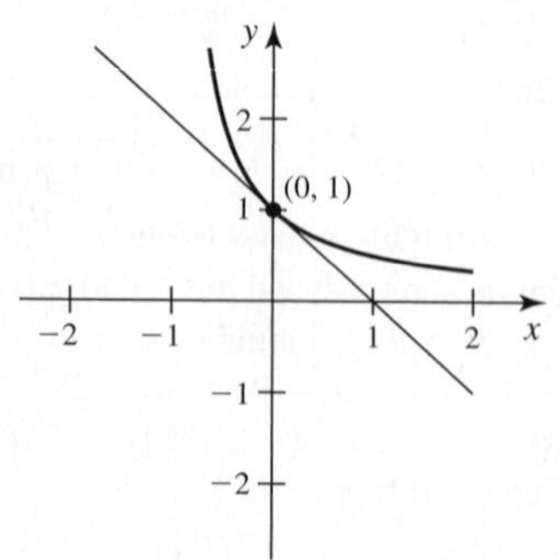

c. 1.1 **d.** 1% error

11. a. $y = 1$ **b.**

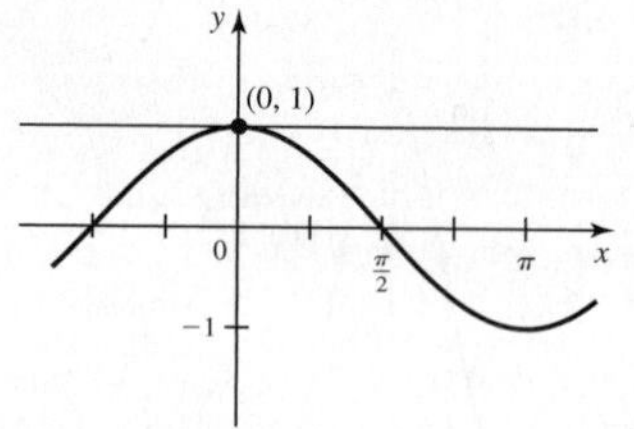

c. 1 **d.** 0.005% error **13.** $y = 1/x$ near $a = 200$; $\frac{1}{203} \approx 0.004925$ **15.** $y = \sqrt{x}$ near $a = 144$; $\sqrt{146} \approx 12\frac{1}{12}$ **17.** $y = 1/x$ near $a = 1$; $1/1.05 \approx 0.95$ **19.** $y = \sin x$ near $a = \frac{\pi}{4}$; $\sin\left(\frac{\pi}{4} + 0.1\right) \approx 11\sqrt{2}/20 \approx 0.778$ **21.** $y = \dfrac{1}{\sqrt[3]{x}}$ near $a = 512$; $\dfrac{1}{\sqrt[3]{510}} \approx \dfrac{769}{6144} \approx 0.125$ **23.** $\Delta V \approx 10\pi$ ft^3 **25.** $\Delta S \approx \dfrac{-59\pi}{5\sqrt{34}}$ m^3 **27.** $dy = 2\,dx$ **29.** $dy = \dfrac{-3}{x^4}\,dx$ **31.** $dy = a \sin x\,dx$ **33.** $dy = (9x^2 - 4)\,dx$ **35. a.** True **b.** False **c.** True **37. a.** $y = 1 - x$; **b.**

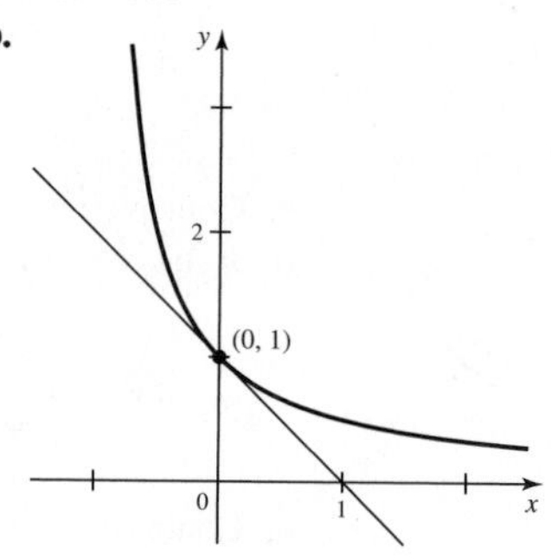

c. $1/1.1 \approx 0.9$ **d.** 1% error **39. a.** $y = 4 + \dfrac{x}{48}$

b.

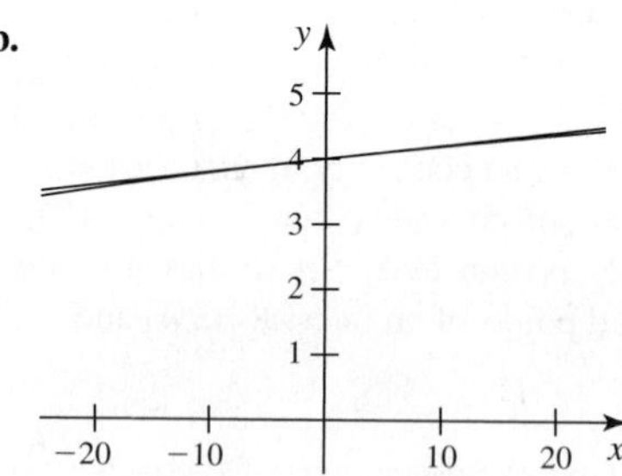

c. $\sqrt[3]{62.5} \approx \dfrac{127}{32} \approx 3.97$ **d.** 0.006% error

41. $L(x) = 2 + (x - 8)/12$

x	Linear Approximation	Exact Value	Percent Error
8.1	$2.008\overline{3}$	2.00829885	1.717×10^{-3}
8.01	$2.0008\overline{3}$	2.000832986	1.734×10^{-5}
8.001	$2.00008\overline{3}$	2.00008333	1.736×10^{-7}
8.0001	$2.000008\overline{3}$	2.000008333	1.735×10^{-9}
7.9	$1.991\overline{6}$	1.991631701	1.736×10^{-3}
7.99	$1.9991\overline{6}$	1.999166319	1.736×10^{-5}
7.999	$1.99991\overline{6}$	1.999916663	1.738×10^{-7}
7.9999	$1.999991\overline{6}$	1.999991667	1.738×10^{-9}

43. a. f; the rate at which f' is changing at 1 is smaller than the rate at which g' is changing at 1. The graph of f bends away from the linear function more slowly than the graph of g. **b.** The larger the value of $|f''(a)|$, the greater the deviation of the curve $y = f(x)$ from the tangent line at points near $x = a$.

Section 4.6 Exercises, pp. 231–232

1. If f is a continuous function on the closed interval $[a, b]$ and is differentiable on (a, b) and the slope of the secant line that joins $(a, f(a))$ to $(b, f(b))$ is zero, then there is at least one value c in (a, b) at which the slope of the line tangent to f at $(c, f(c))$ is also zero.

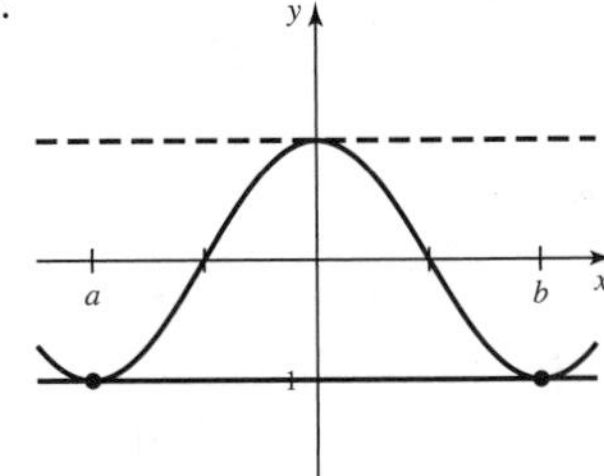

3. $f(x) = |x|$ is not differentiable at 0.

5.

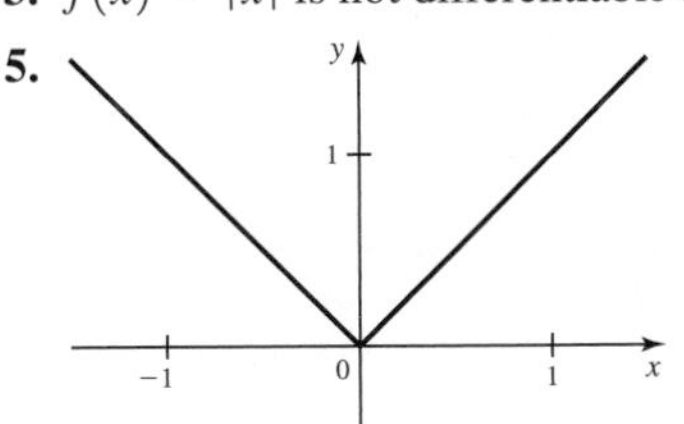

7. $x = \frac{1}{3}$ **9.** $x = \pi/4$

11. Does not apply **13.** Average lapse rate $= 6.3°$/km. You cannot conclude that the lapse rate at a point exceeds the critical value.

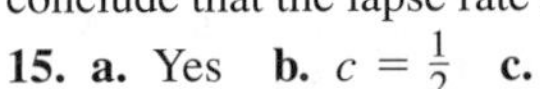

15. a. Yes **b.** $c = \frac{1}{2}$ **c.**

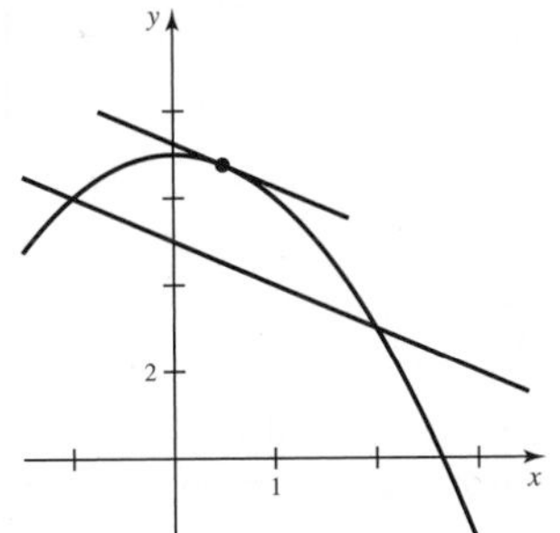

17. a. Yes **b.** $c = \frac{9}{4}$ **c.**

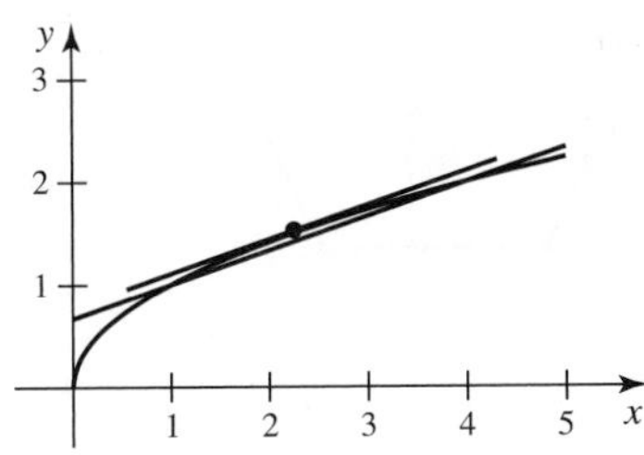

19. a. Yes **b.** $c = \left(\frac{7}{4}\right)^{3/4} \approx 1.52$

c.

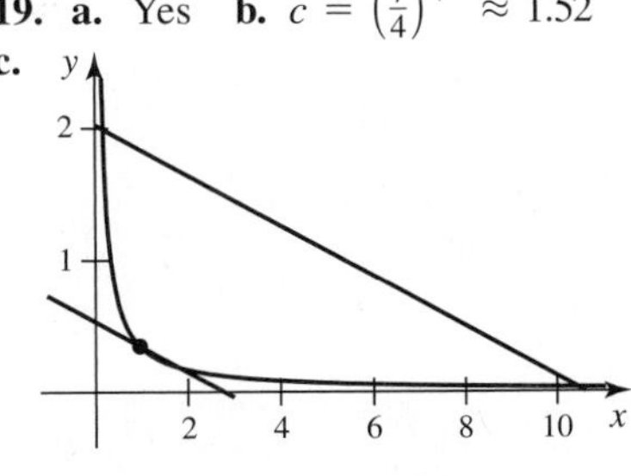

21. a. Does not apply **23. a.** False **b.** True **c.** False **25.** h and p

27.

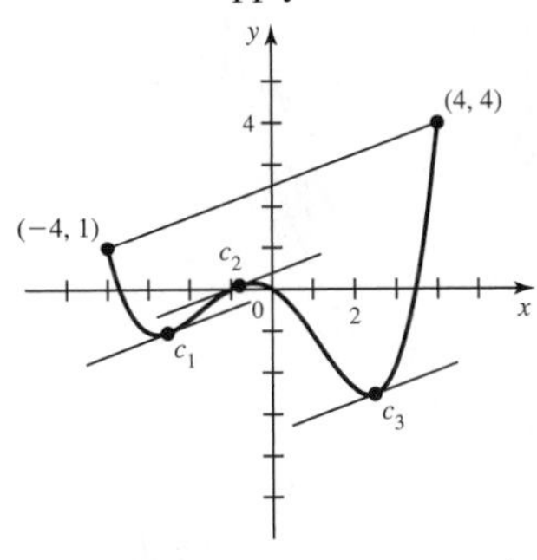

29. The car's average velocity is $(30 - 0)/(28/60) = 64.3$ mi/hr. By the MVT, the car's instantaneous velocity was 64.3 mi/hr at some time. **31.** Average speed $= 11.6$ mi/hr. By MVT, the speed was exactly 11.6 mi/hr at least once. By the Intermediate Value Theorem, all speeds between 0 and 11.6 mi/hr were reached. Because the initial and final speed was 0 mi/hr, the speed of 11 mi/hr was reached at least twice.

33. $\dfrac{f(b) - f(a)}{b - a} = A(a + b) + B$ and $f'(x) = 2Ax + B$; $2Ax + B = A(a + b) + B$ implies that $x = \dfrac{a + b}{2}$, the midpoint of $[a, b]$. **35.** $\tan^2 x$ and $\sec^2 x$ differ by a constant; in fact, $\tan^2 x - \sec^2 x = -1$. **37.** Bolt's average speed was 37.58 km/hr, so he exceeded 37 km/hr during the race. **39. b.** $c = \frac{1}{2}$

Section 4.7 Exercises, pp. 238–239

1. If $\lim_{x\to a} f(x) = 0$ and $\lim_{x\to a} g(x) = 0$, then we say $\lim_{x\to a} f(x)/g(x)$ is of indeterminate form $0/0$. **3.** Take the limit of the quotient of the derivatives of the functions. **5.** If $\lim_{x\to a} f(x)g(x)$ has the indeterminate form $0 \cdot \infty$, then $\lim_{x\to a}\left(\dfrac{f(x)}{1/g(x)}\right)$ has the indeterminate form $0/0$ or ∞/∞. **7.** $0 \cdot \infty$ **9.** -1 **11.** $\frac{12}{5}$ **13.** 4 **15.** $\frac{9}{16}$ **17.** 4 **19.** $-\frac{1}{2}$ **21.** $\cos x$ **23.** $\frac{1}{2}$ **25.** 0 **27.** 1 **29.** 1 **31.** 0 **33.** 0 **35. a.** False **b.** False **c.** False **d.** True **37.** $\frac{2}{5}$ **39.** $-\frac{9}{4}$ **41.** 0 **43.** $\frac{1}{6}$ **45.** ∞ **47.** $-\frac{1}{3}$ **49.** $\sqrt{a/c}$ **51.** 1/3

Section 4.8 Exercises, pp. 247–248

1. Derivative, antiderivative **3.** $x + C$, where C is any real number **5.** $\dfrac{x^{p+1}}{p + 1} + C$, where C is any real number and $p \neq -1$ **7.** 0 **9.** $x^5 + C$ **11.** $-\frac{1}{2}\cos 2x + C$ **13.** $3\tan x + C$ **15.** $y^{-2} + C$ **17.** $\frac{1}{2}x^6 - \frac{1}{2}x^{10} + C$ **19.** $\frac{8}{3}x^{3/2} - 8x^{1/2} + C$ **21.** $(5s + 3)^3/15 + C$ **23.** $\frac{9}{4}x^{4/3} + 6x^{2/3} + 6x + C$ **25.** $-\frac{1}{2}\cos 2y + \frac{1}{3}\sin 3y + C$ **27.** $\tan x - x + C$ **29.** $\tan\theta + \sec\theta + C$ **31.** $F(x) = x^6/6 + 2/x + x - 19/6$ **33.** $F(v) = \sec v + 1$ **35.** $f(x) = x^2 - 3x + 4$ **37.** $g(x) = \dfrac{7}{8}x^8 - \dfrac{x^2}{2} + \dfrac{13}{8}$ **39.** $f(u) = 4\sin u + 2\cos 2u - 3$

41. $f(x) = x^2 - 5x + 4$

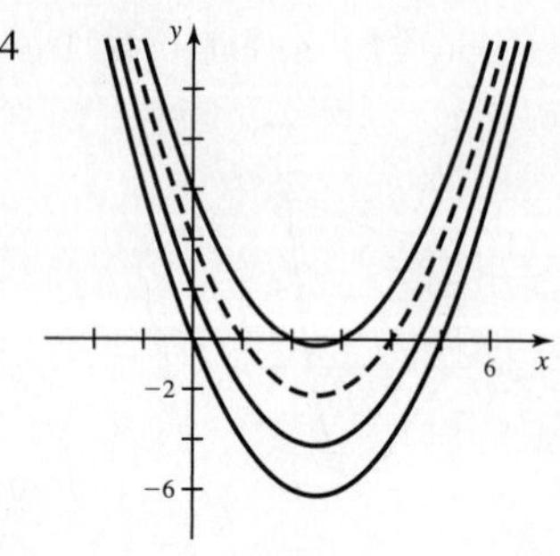

43. $f(x) = \frac{3x^2}{2} - \frac{\cos(\pi x)}{\pi} + \frac{1 - 3\pi}{\pi}$

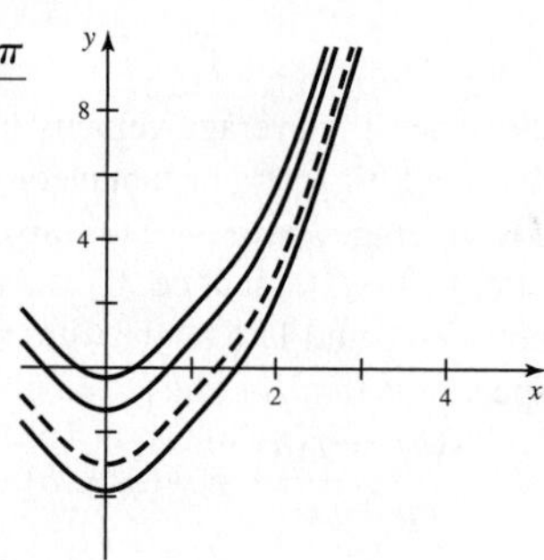

45. $f(t) = 5 - \frac{1}{t}$

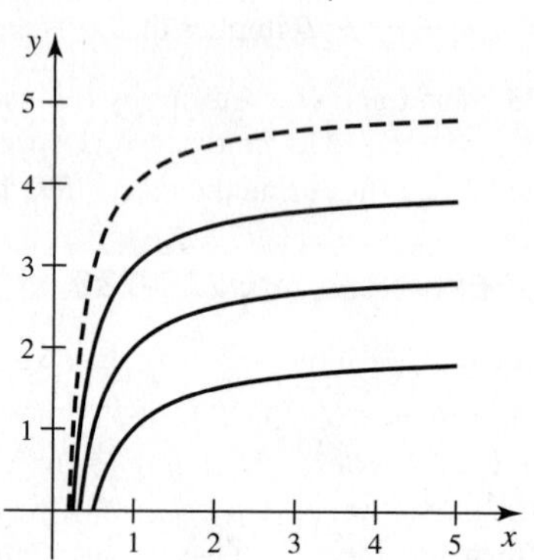

47. $s(t) = t^2 + 4t$

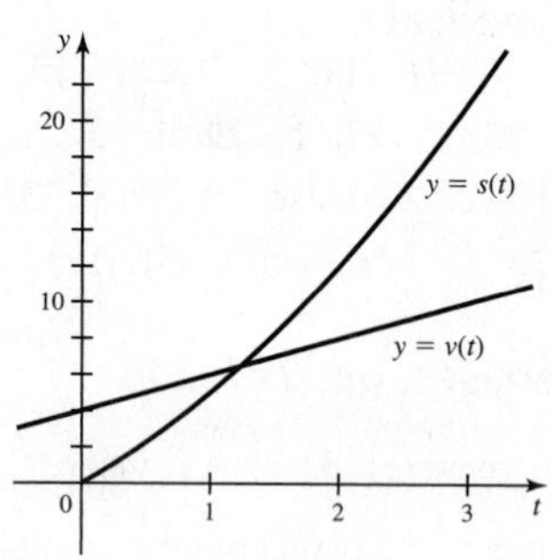

49. $s(t) = \frac{4}{3}t^{3/2} + 1$ **51.** $s(t) = 2t^3 + 2t^2 - 10t$

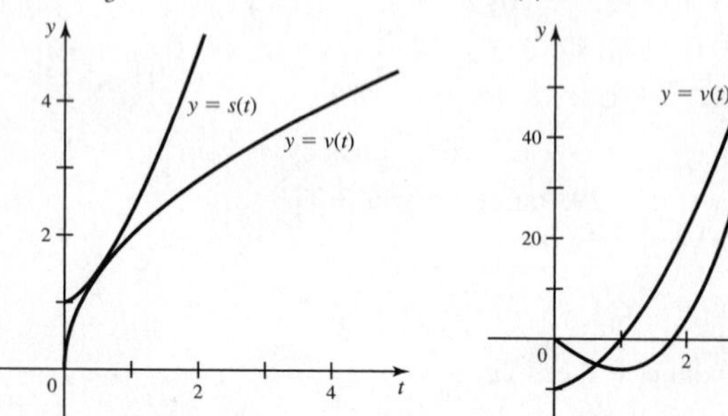

53. Runner A overtakes runner B at $t = \pi/2$ s.
55. a. $v(t) = -9.8t + 30$ **b.** $s(t) = -4.9t^2 + 30t$ **c.** 45.92 m at time $t = 3.06$ **d.** $t = 6.12$ s **57. a.** $v(t) = -9.8t + 10$ **b.** $s(t) = -4.9t^2 + 10t + 400$ **c.** 405.10 m at time $t = 1.02$ **d.** $t = 10.11$ s **59. a.** True **b.** False **c.** True **d.** False **e.** False
61. $2\sqrt{2}\,x^{1/2} + 6x^{1/3} + C$ **63.** $-\cot\theta + 2\theta^3/3 - 3\theta^2/2 + C$
65. $-1/x - 2/\sqrt{x} + C$ **67.** $\frac{4}{15}x^{15/2} - \frac{24}{11}x^{11/6} + C$
69. $F(x) = -\cos x + 3x + 3 - 3\pi$
71. $F(x) = 2x^8 + x^4 + 2x + 1$ **73. a.** $Q(t) = 10t - t^3/30$

b.

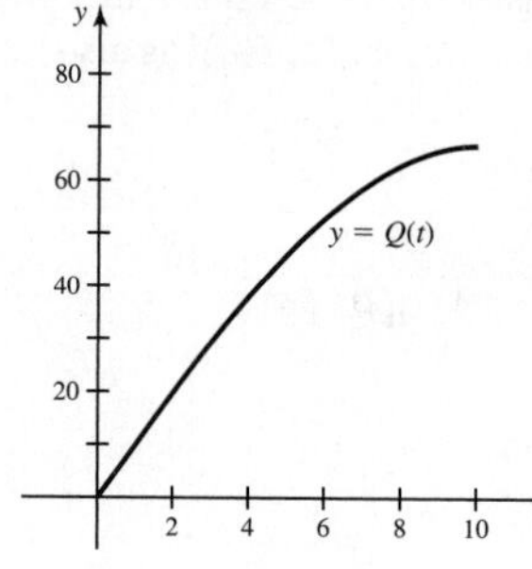

c. $\frac{200}{3}$ gal

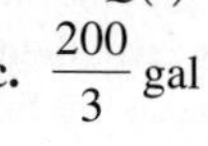

75. $\int \sin^2 x\, dx = x/2 - (\sin 2x)/4 + C$;
$\int \cos^2 x\, dx = x/2 + (\sin 2x)/4 + C$

Review Exercises, pp. 248–250

1. a. False **b.** False **c.** True **d.** True

3. **5.**

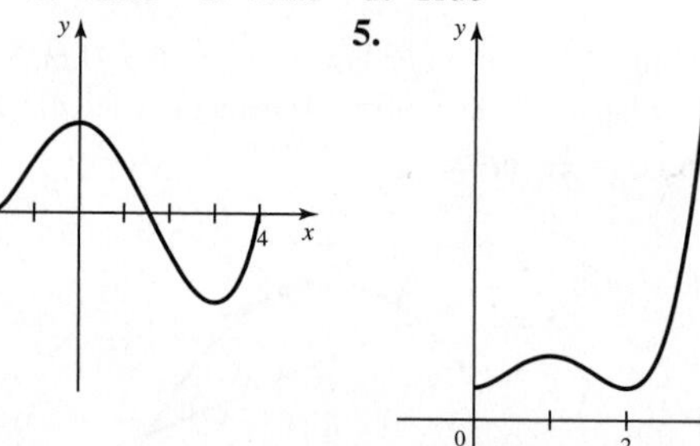

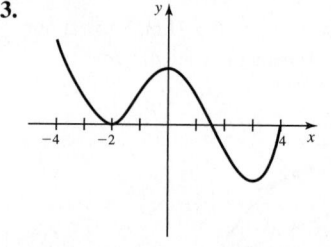

7. $x = 3$ and $x = -2$; no abs. max or min.
9. $x = -4$ and $x = 2$; no abs. max or min
11.

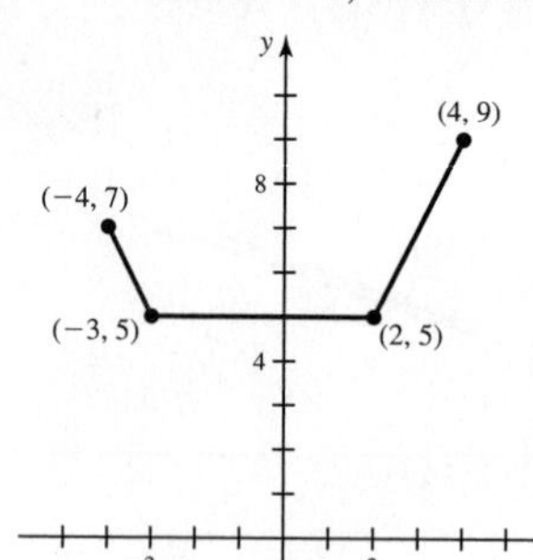

Critical pts.: x in the interval $[-3, 2]$; abs. max: $(4, 9)$; abs. and local min at $(x, 5)$ for all x in $[-3, 2]$; local max at $(x, 5)$ for all x in $(-3, 2)$

13.

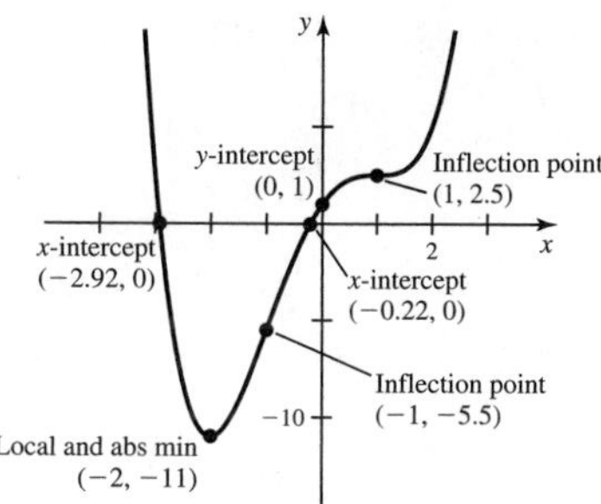

15.

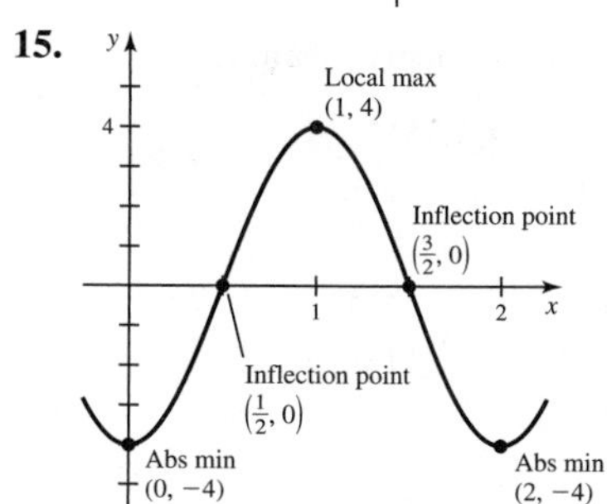

17.

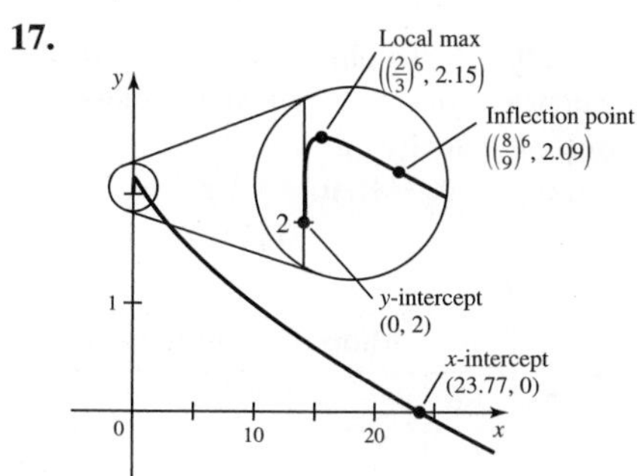

19.

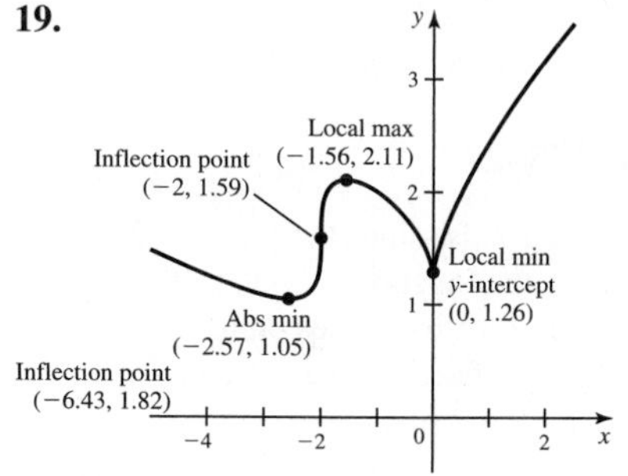

21. $r = 4\sqrt{6}/3$; $h = 4\sqrt{3}/3$

23. a. $a = b = \frac{23}{2}$ **b.** $a = 0, b = 23$ or $a = 23, b = 0$
25. a. $\frac{100}{9}$ cells/week **b.** $t = 2$ weeks **27.** 0 **29.** 12 **31.** 2/3
33. 0 **35.** $-\frac{1}{x} + \frac{4}{3}x^{-3/2} + C$ **37.** $\theta + \frac{1}{3}\sin 3\theta + C$
39. $\frac{1}{2}\sec 2x + C$ **41.** $3x^{4/3} - 5x^{7/5} + 7x^{10/7} + C$
43. $\frac{4}{7}x^{7/4} + \frac{2}{7}x^{7/2} + C$ **45.** $f(t) = -\cos t + t^2 + 6$
47. $h(x) = \frac{x}{2} - \frac{1}{4}\sin 2x + \left(\frac{1}{2} + \frac{\sin 2}{4}\right)$
49. $v(t) = -9.8t + 120$; $s(t) = -4.9t^2 + 120t + 125$
The rocket reaches a height of 859.69 m at time $t = 12.24$ s and then falls to the ground, hitting at time $t = 25.49$ s. **51.** 0

CHAPTER 5

Section 5.1 Exercises, pp. 260–265

1. Displacement = 105 m

3. We can subdivide the interval $[0, \pi/2]$ into several segments, which will be the bases of rectangles that fit under the curve. The heights of the rectangles can be computed by taking the value of $\cos x$ at the right-hand value of each base. We can calculate the area of each rectangle and add them to get a lower bound on the area.
5. $\frac{1}{2}$; 1, 1.5, 2, 2.5, 3; 1, 1.5, 2, 2.5; 1.5, 2, 2.5, 3; 1.25, 1.75, 2.25, 2.75
7. Underestimate; the rectangles all fit under the curve.
9. a. 67 ft **b.** 67.75 ft **11.** Displacement ≈ 2.78 m
13. Displacement ≈ 148.96 mi **15.** 20; 25
17. a. c.

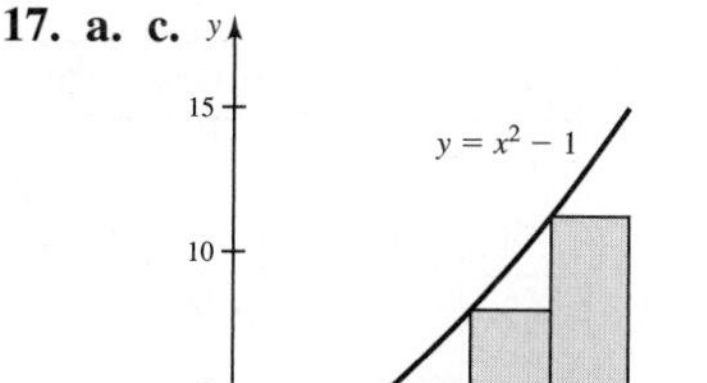

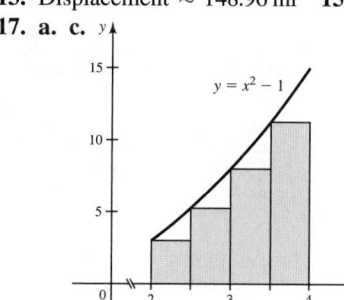

Left Riemann sum underestimates.

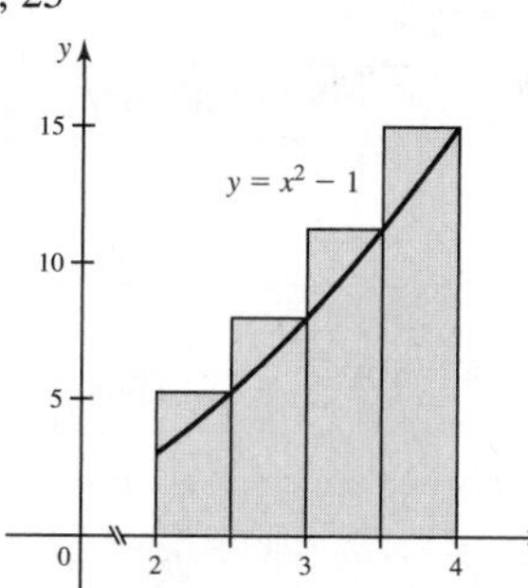

Right Riemann sum overestimates.

b. $\Delta x = \frac{1}{2}$; 2, 2.5, 3, 3.5, 4 **d.** 13.75; 19.75
19. a. c.

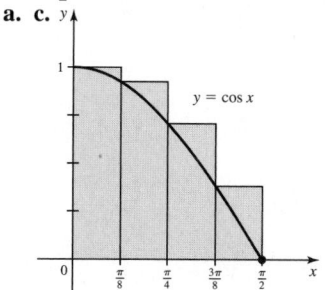

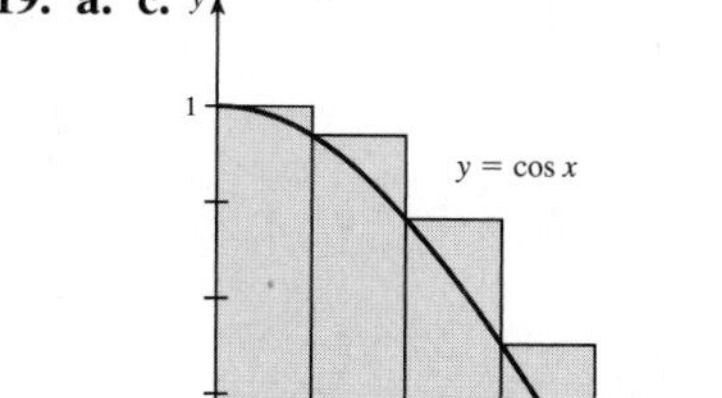

Left Riemann sum overestimates.

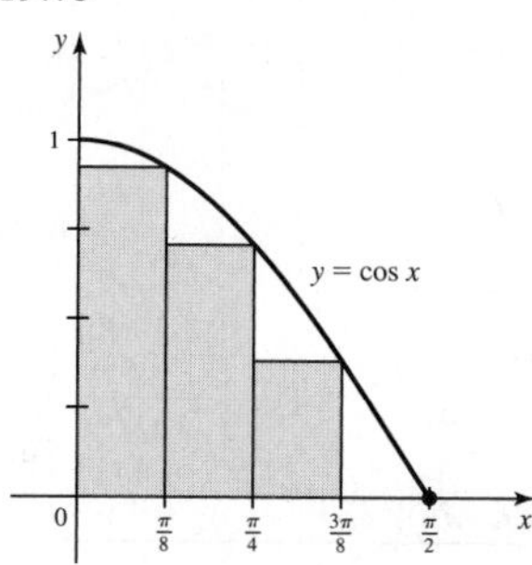

Right Riemann sum underestimates.

b. $\Delta x = \pi/8$; 0, $\pi/8$, $\pi/4$, $3\pi/8$, $\pi/2$ **d.** 1.18; 0.79 **21.** 670
23. a. c.

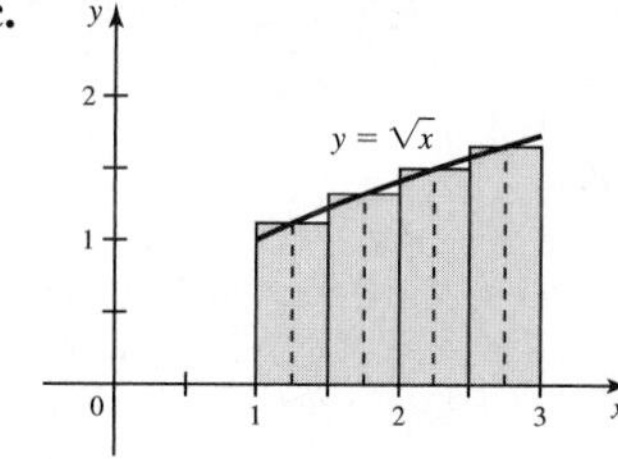

b. $\Delta x = \frac{1}{2}$; 1, $\frac{3}{2}$, 2, $\frac{5}{2}$, 3
d. 2.80

25. a. c.

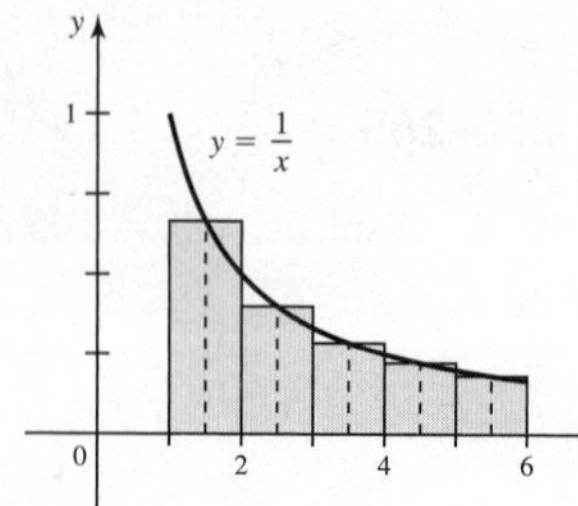

b. $\Delta x = 1$; 1, 2, 3, 4, 5, 6 **d.** 1.76

27. 5.5, 3.5 **29. b.** 110, 117.5 **31. a.** $\sum_{k=1}^{5} k$ **b.** $\sum_{k=1}^{6}(k + 3)$ **c.** $\sum_{k=1}^{4} k^2$ **d.** $\sum_{k=1}^{4} \frac{1}{k}$ **33. a.** 55 **b.** 48 **c.** 30 **d.** 60 **e.** 6 **f.** 6 **g.** 85 **h.** 0 **35. a.** $\frac{1}{10}\sum_{k=1}^{40}\sqrt{\frac{k-1}{10}} \approx 5.227$; $\frac{1}{10}\sum_{k=1}^{40}\sqrt{\frac{k}{10}} \approx 5.427$; $\frac{1}{10}\sum_{k=1}^{40}\sqrt{\frac{2k-1}{20}} \approx 5.3$ **b.** $\frac{16}{3}$ **37. a.** $\frac{1}{15}\sum_{k=1}^{75}\left[\left(\frac{k+29}{15}\right)^2 - 1\right] = \frac{14{,}198}{135} \approx 105.17$; $\frac{1}{15}\sum_{k=1}^{75}\left[\left(\frac{k+30}{15}\right)^2 - 1\right] = \frac{14{,}603}{135} \approx 108.17$; $\frac{1}{15}\sum_{k=1}^{75}\left[\left(\frac{2k+59}{30}\right)^2 - 1\right] = \frac{57{,}599}{540} \approx 106.66$ **b.** 106.7

39.

n	Right Riemann sum
10	10.56
30	10.65
60	10.664
80	10.665

The sums appear to approach $10\frac{2}{3}$.

41.

n	Right Riemann sum
10	5.655
30	6.074
60	6.178
80	6.205

The sums appear to approach 2π.

43. a. True **b.** False **c.** True

45.

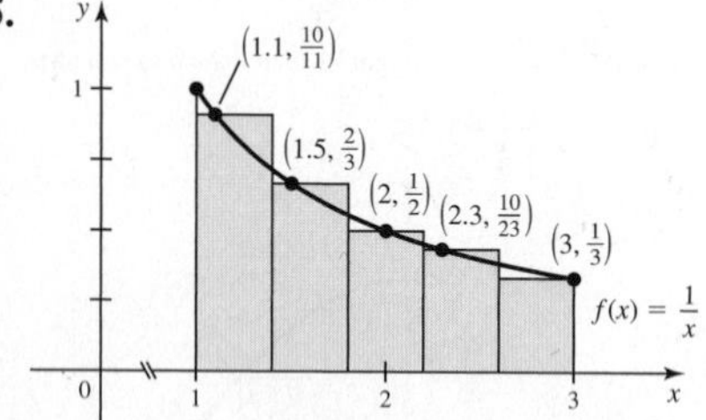

sum ≈ 1.1375

47. $\sum_{k=1}^{50}\left(\frac{4k}{50} + 1\right)\cdot\frac{4}{50} = \frac{304}{25} = 12.16$

49. $\sum_{k=1}^{32}\left(3 + \frac{2k-1}{8}\right)^3 \cdot \frac{1}{4} \approx 3639.1$

51. Left; $[2, 6]$; 4 or Right; $[1, 5]$; 4

53. Midpoint; $[2, 6]$; 4

55. a.

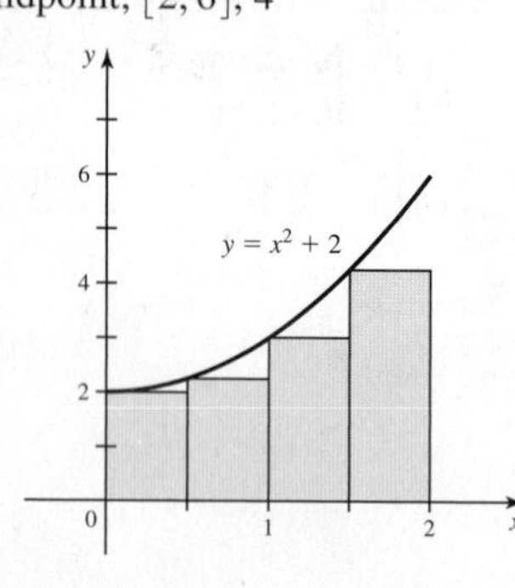

Left Riemann sum is $\frac{23}{4} = 5.75$.

b.

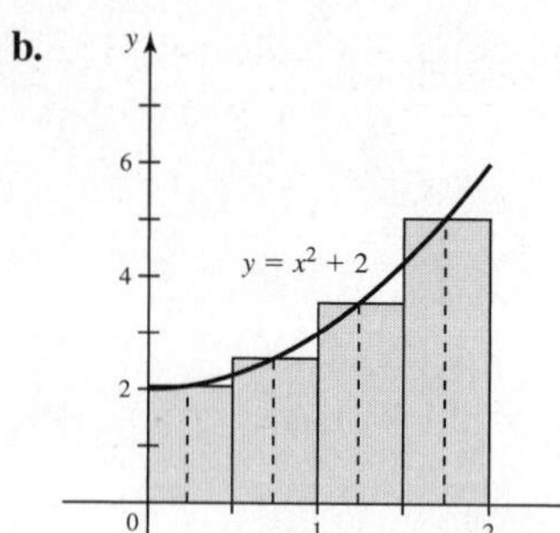

Midpoint Riemann sum is $\frac{53}{8} = 6.625$.

c.

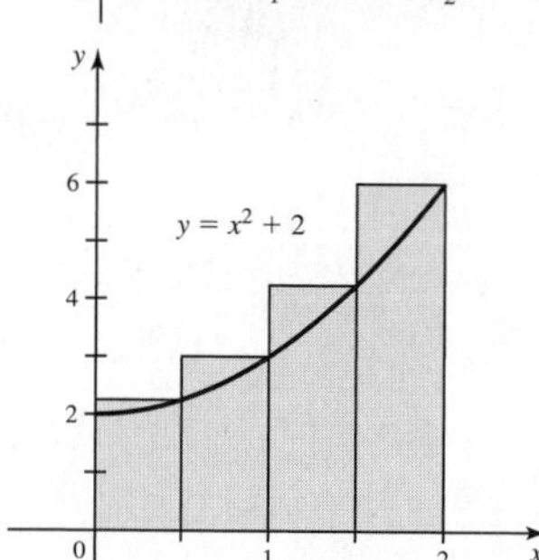

Right Riemann sum is $\frac{31}{4} = 7.75$.

57. Left sum: 34; right sum: 24 **59. a.** The object is speeding up on the interval $[0, 1]$, moving at a constant rate on $[1, 3]$, slowing down on $[3, 5]$, and maintaining a constant velocity on $[5, 6]$. **b.** 30 m **c.** 50 m **d.** $s(t) = 30 + 10t$ **61. a.** 14.5 g **b.** 29.5 g **c.** 44 g **d.** $x = 6\frac{1}{3}$ cm **63.** 107 mi

65.

n	Midpoint Riemann sum
16	0.503906
32	0.500977
64	0.500244

The sums appear to approach 0.5.

67.

n	Midpoint Riemann sum
16	4.7257
32	4.7437
64	4.7485

The sums appear to approach 4.75.

Section 5.2 Exercises, pp. 276–279

1. The area of the regions above the x-axis minus the area of the regions below the x-axis. **3.** When the function is nonnegative on the entire interval; when the function has negative values on the interval **5.** Both integrals = 0. **7.** The length of the interval $[a, a]$ is $a - a = 0$, so the net area is 0. **9.** $\frac{a^2}{2}$

11. a.

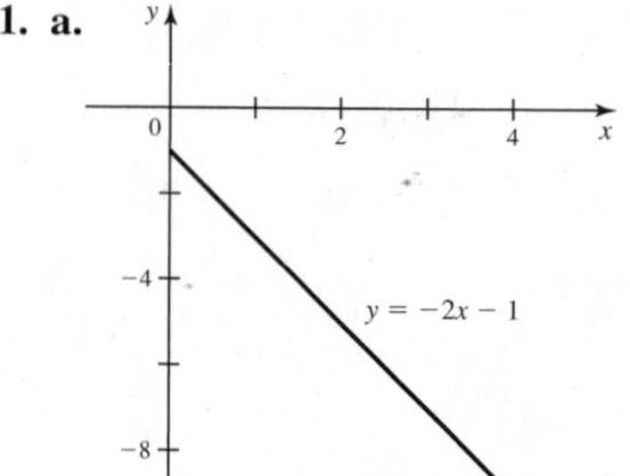

b. −16, −24, −20

13. a.

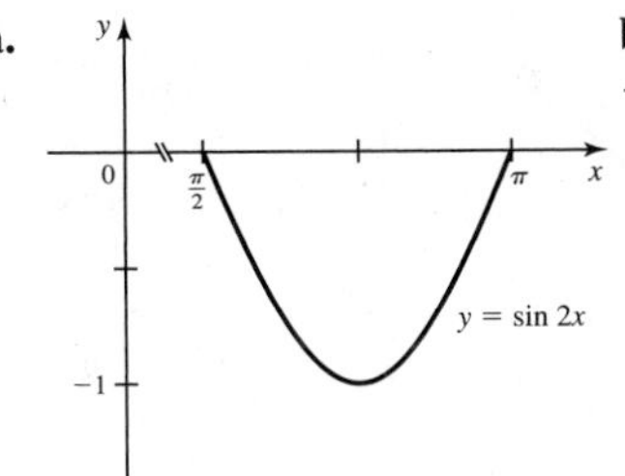

b. $-0.948, -0.948, -1.026$

15. a.

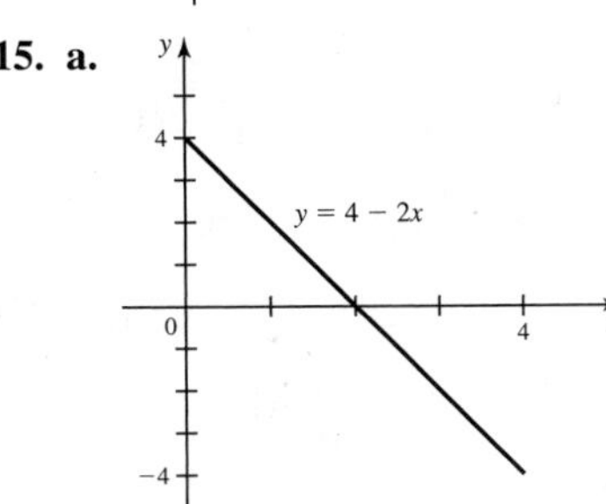

b. $4, -4, 0$ **c.** Positive contributions on $[0, 2]$; negative contributions on $[2, 4]$.

17. a.

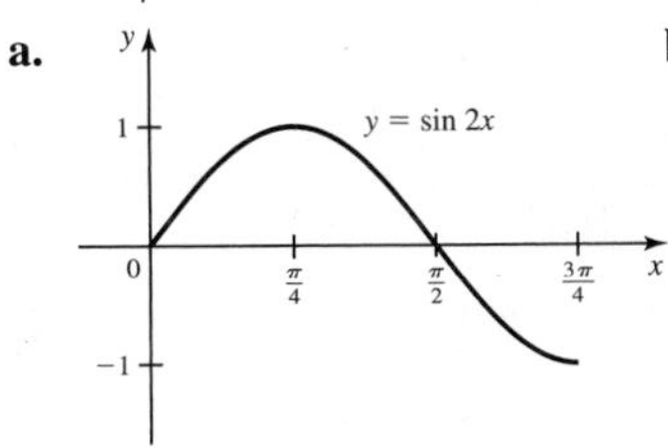

b. $\approx 0.735, \approx 0.146, \approx 0.530$

c. Positive contribution on $[0, \pi/2]$, negative contribution on $[\pi/2, 3\pi/4]$. **19.** $\int_0^2 (x^2 + 1)\,dx$ **21.** $\int_1^2 x \cos x\,dx$

23. 16

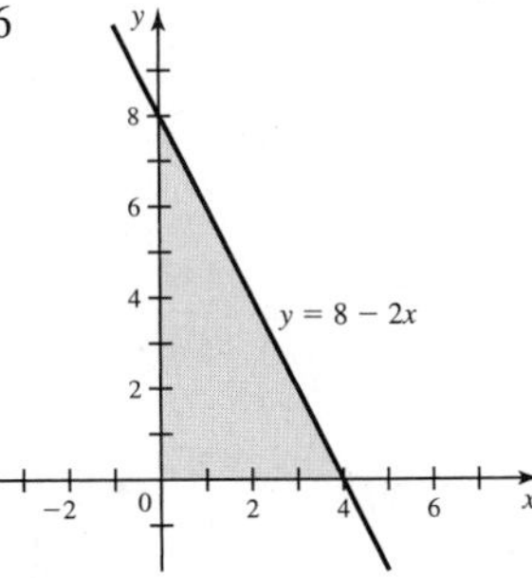

25. $-\frac{5}{2}$

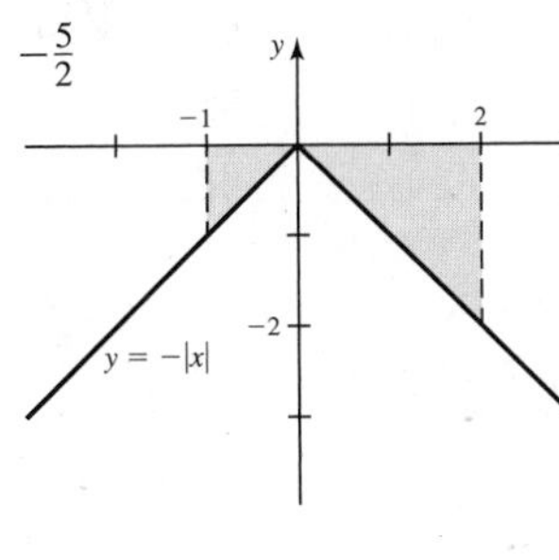

27. 4π

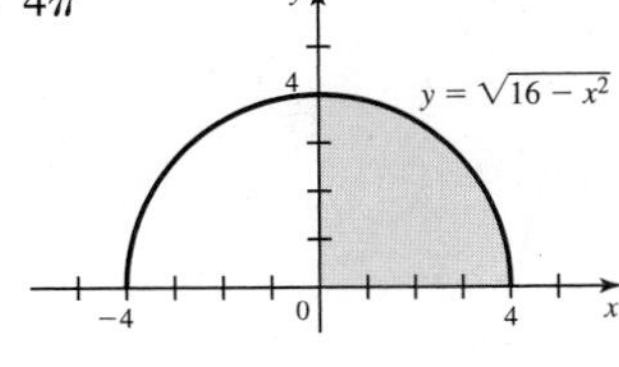

29. 26

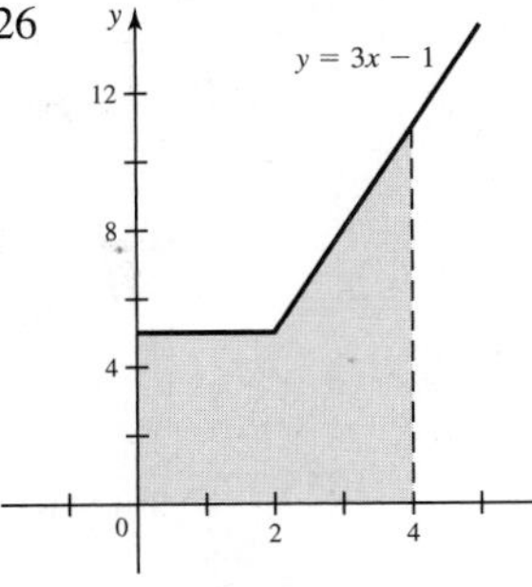

31. 16 **33.** 6 **35.** π **37.** -2π **39. a.** -32 **b.** $\frac{32}{3}$ **c.** -64 **d.** Not possible **41. a.** 10 **b.** -3 **c.** -16 **d.** 3 **43. a.** $\frac{3}{2}$ **b.** $-\frac{3}{4}$ **45.** 6 **47.** 104 **49.** 18 **51. a.** True **b.** True **c.** True **d.** False **e.** False

53. a.

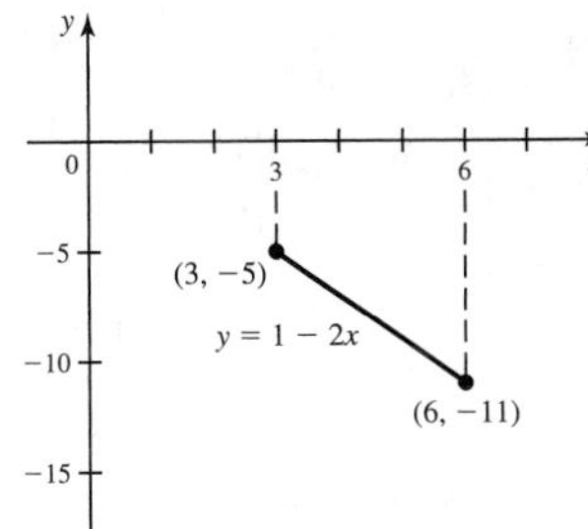

b. $\Delta x = \frac{1}{2}$; 3, 3.5, 4, 4.5, 5, 5.5, 6 **c.** -22.5; -25.5 **d.** The left Riemann sum overestimates; the right Riemann sum underestimates.

55. a.

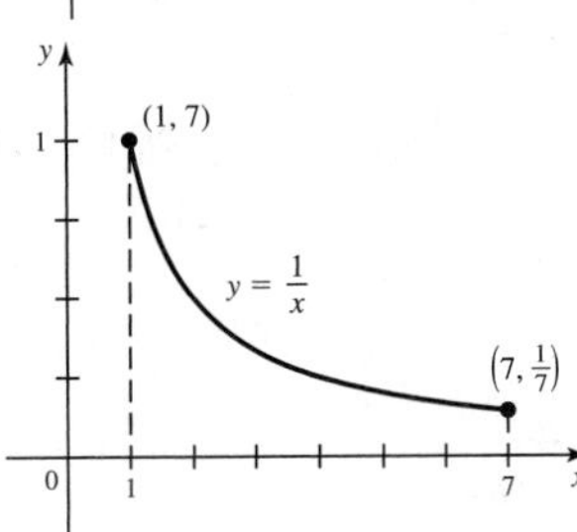

b. $\Delta x = 1$; 1, 2, 3, 4, 5, 6, 7 **c.** $\frac{49}{20}, \frac{223}{140}$ **d.** The left Riemann sum overestimates; The right Riemann sum underestimates.

57. a. $n = 20$

Left: $\sum_{k=1}^{20} \left[\left(\frac{k-1}{20}\right)^2 + 1\right] \cdot \frac{1}{20} = 1.30875$;

right: $\sum_{k=1}^{20} \left[\left(\frac{k}{20}\right)^2 + 1\right] \cdot \frac{1}{20} = 1.35875$

$n = 50$

Left: $\sum_{k=1}^{50} \left[\left(\frac{k-1}{50}\right)^2 + 1\right] \cdot \frac{1}{50} = 1.3234$;

right: $\sum_{k=1}^{50} \left[\left(\frac{k}{50}\right)^2 + 1\right] \cdot \frac{1}{50} = 1.3434$

$n = 100$

Left: $\sum_{k=1}^{100} \left[\left(\frac{k-1}{100}\right)^2 + 1\right] \cdot \frac{1}{100} = 1.32835$;

right: $\sum_{k=1}^{100} \left[\left(\frac{k}{100}\right)^2 + 1\right] \cdot \frac{1}{100} = 1.33835$ **b.** 1.33

59. a. Left: $\frac{3}{n} \sum_{k=1}^{n} \frac{1}{2\left(1 + \frac{3(k-1)}{n}\right)}$; $n = 20, 0.72215$; $n = 50, 0.70454$; $n = 100, 0.69881$.

Right: $\frac{3}{n} \sum_{k=1}^{n} \frac{1}{2\left(1 + \frac{3k}{n}\right)}$; $n = 20, 0.66590$; $n = 50, 0.68204$; $n = 100, 0.68756$.

b. 0.69

61. a. $\sum_{k=1}^{n} \frac{6}{n} \sqrt{\frac{2n + 6k - 3}{2n}}$

b.

n	Midpoint Riemann sum
20	9.33380
50	9.33341
100	9.33335

Estimate: 9.33

63. a. $\sum_{k=1}^{n}(2k-1)(2n+1-2k)\cdot\frac{16}{n^3}$

b.

n	Midpoint Riemann sum
20	10.6800
50	10.6688
100	10.6672

Estimate: 10.67

65. a. 15 **b.** 5 **c.** 3 **d.** −2 **e.** 24 **f.** −10

67. The area is 12; the net area is 0.

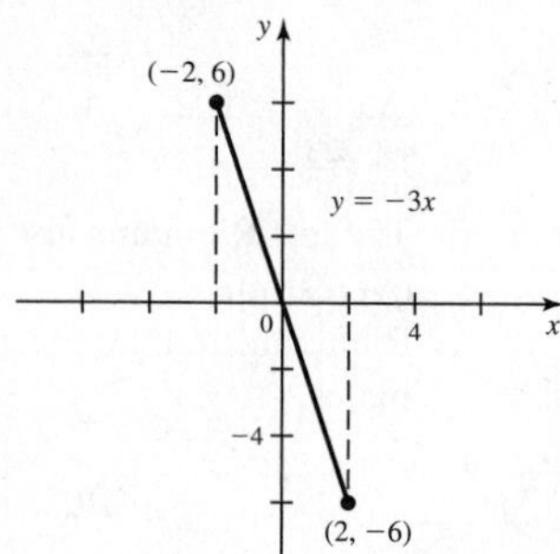
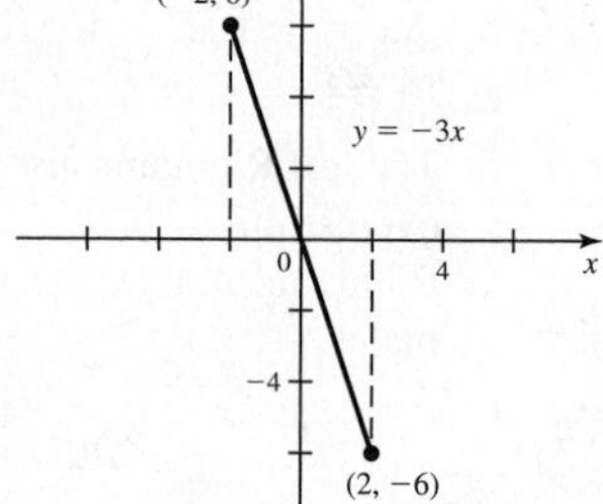

69. The area is 2; the net area is 0.

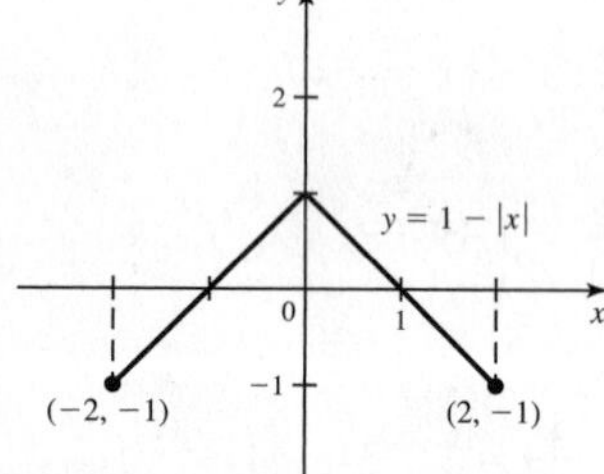

71. 17 **73.** $25\pi/2$ **75.** 25 **79.** For any such partition on the interval $[0,1]$, the grid points are $x_k = k/n$ for $k = 0, 1, \ldots, n$. That is, x_k is rational for each k so that $f(x_k) = 1$ for $k = 0, 1, \ldots, n$. Thus, the left, right, and midpoint Riemann sums are $\sum_{k=1}^{n} 1\cdot(1/n) = 1$.

Section 5.3 Exercises, pp. 290–294

1. A is an antiderivative of f; $A'(x) = f(x)$ **3.** Let f be continuous on $[a,b]$. Then $\int_a^b f(x)\,dx = F(b) - F(a)$, where F is any antiderivative of f. **5.** Increasing **7.** The derivative of the integral of f is f, or $\frac{d}{dx}\left(\int_a^x f(t)\,dt\right) = f(x)$. **9.** $f(x), 0$ **11. a.** 0 **b.** −9 **c.** 25 **d.** 0 **e.** 16

13. a.

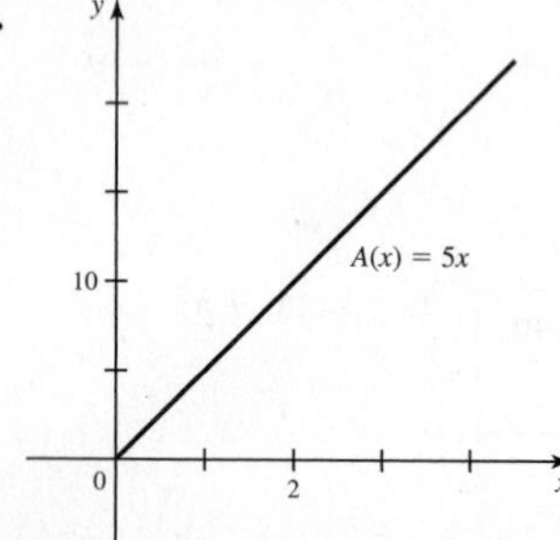

b. $A'(x) = 5$

15. a.

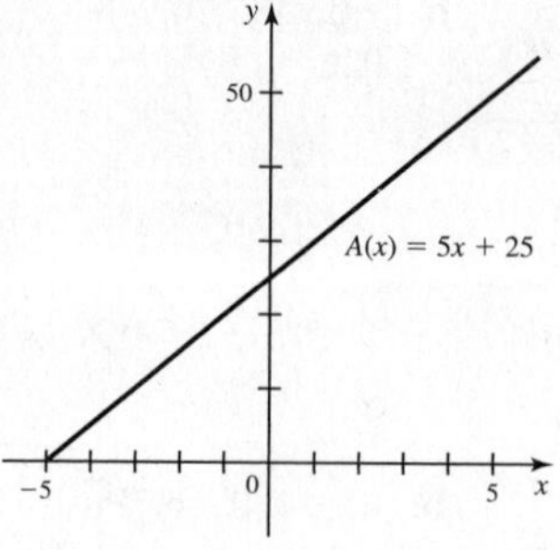

b. $A'(x) = 5$

17. a. $A(2) = 2$, $A(4) = 8$; $A(x) = \frac{1}{2}x^2$ **b.** $F(4) = 6$, $F(6) = 16$; $F(x) = \frac{1}{2}x^2 - 2$ **c.** $A(x) - F(x) = \frac{1}{2}x^2 - \left(\frac{1}{2}x^2 - 2\right) = 2$

19. a.

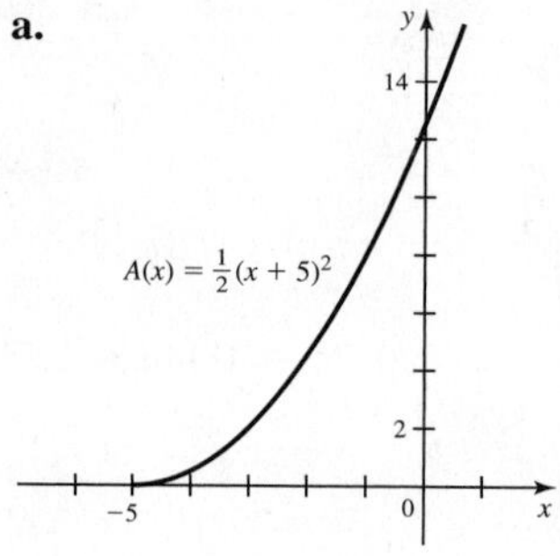

b. $A'(x) = \left[\frac{1}{2}(x+5)^2\right]' = x + 5 = f(x)$

21. a.

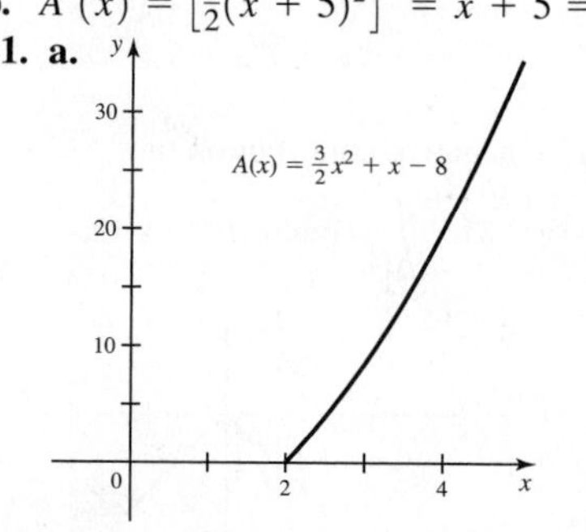

b. $A'(x) = \left(\frac{3}{2}x^2 + x - 8\right)' = 3x + 1 = f(x)$

23. $\frac{7}{3}$ **25.** $\frac{9}{2}$

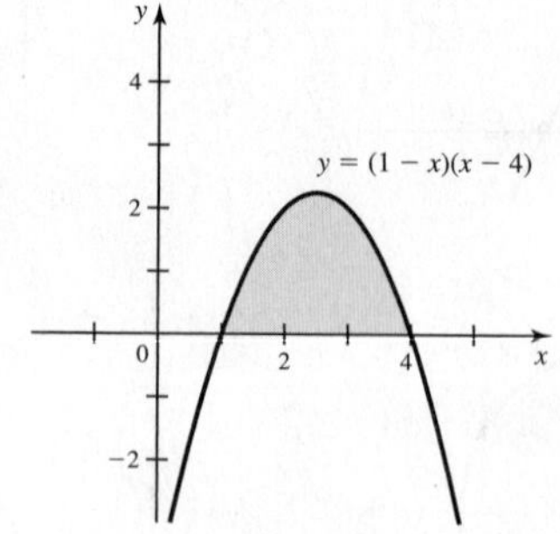

27. $-\frac{125}{6}$

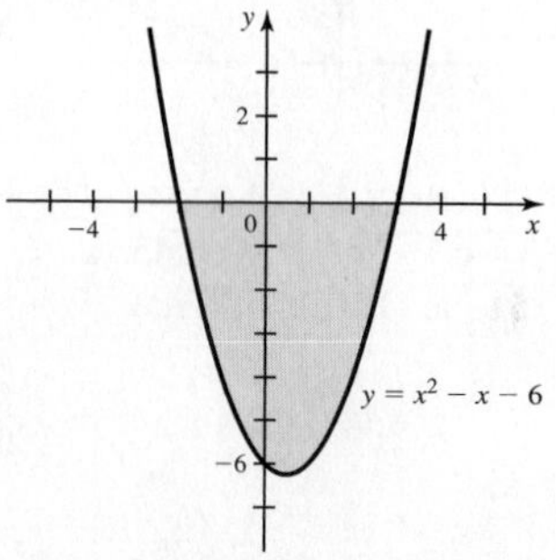

29. $-\frac{10}{3}$

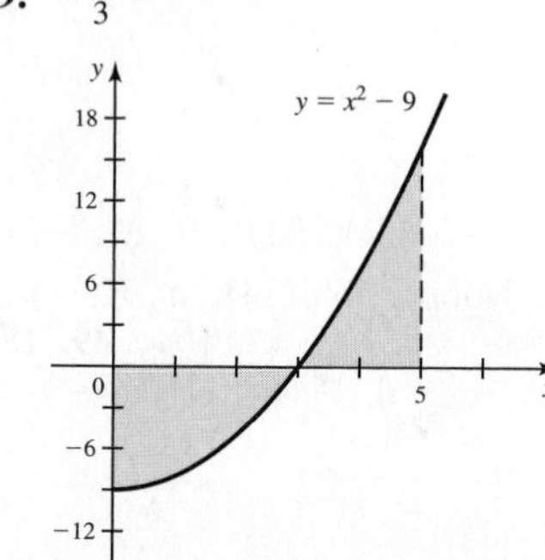

31. $-\frac{32}{3}$ **33.** 0 **35.** $-\frac{3}{8}$ **37.** 1022

39. **(i)** $\frac{14}{3}$ **(ii)** $\frac{14}{3}$

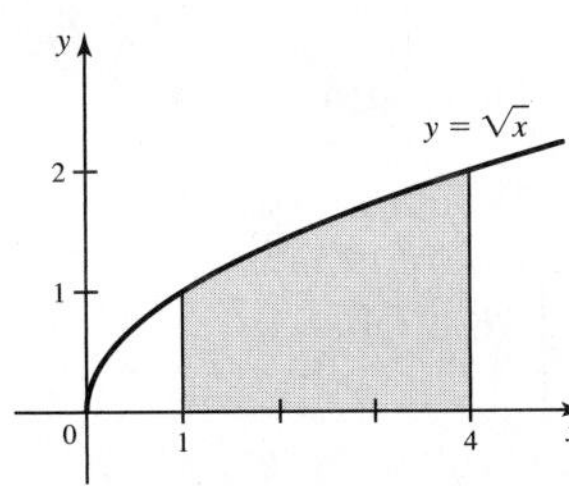

41. **(i)** -51.2 **(ii)** 51.2

43. Area $= \frac{94}{3}$

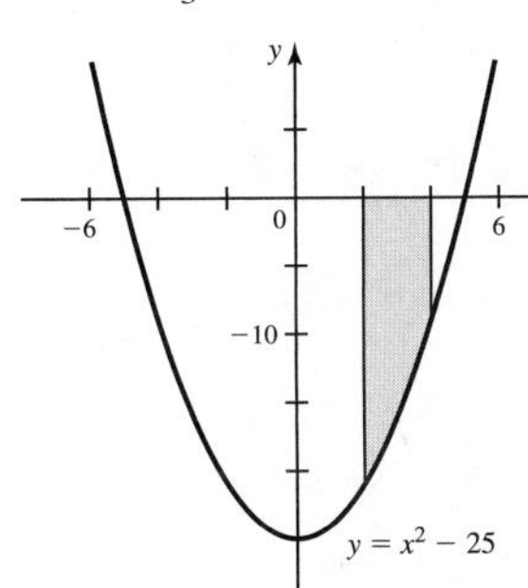

45. Area $= \frac{3}{8}$

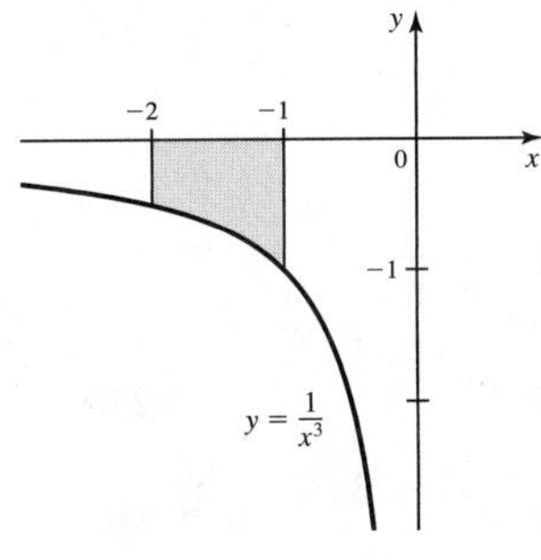

47. Area $= 2$

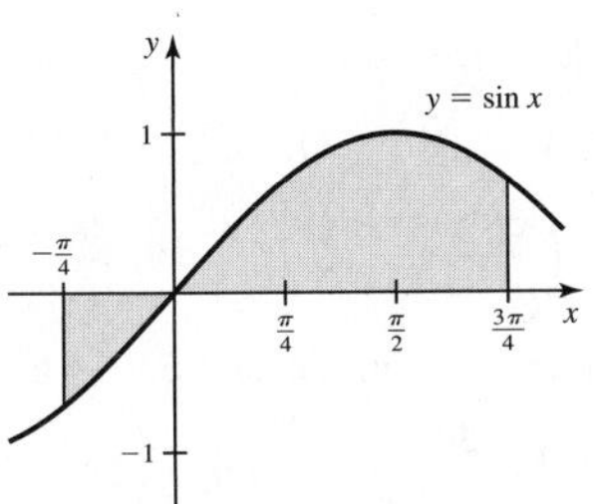

49. $x^2 + x + 1$ **51.** $3/x^4$ **53.** $-\sqrt{x^4 + 1}$ **55.** a–C, b–B, c–D, d–A **57.** **a.** $x \approx 4.5$ **b.** Local min at $x \approx 2$; local max at $x \approx 8$

c.

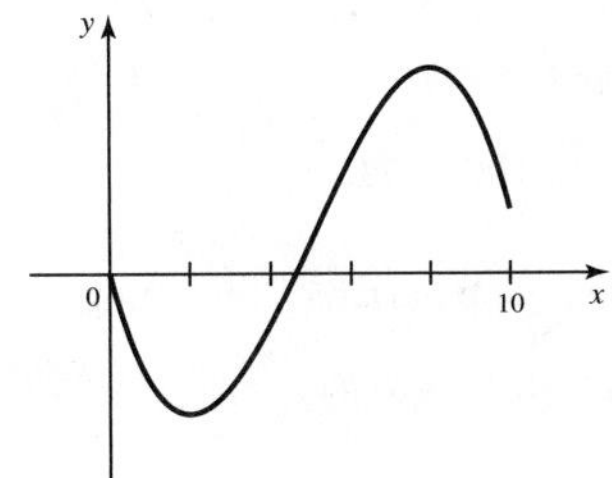

59. **a.** $x = 10$ **b.** Local max at $x = 5$

c.

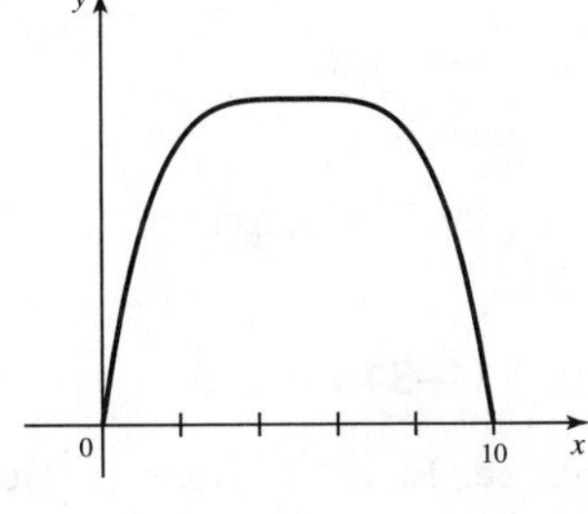

61. $-\pi, -\pi + \frac{9}{2}, -\pi + 9, 5 - \pi$

63. **a.** $A(x) = \sin x$ **b.**

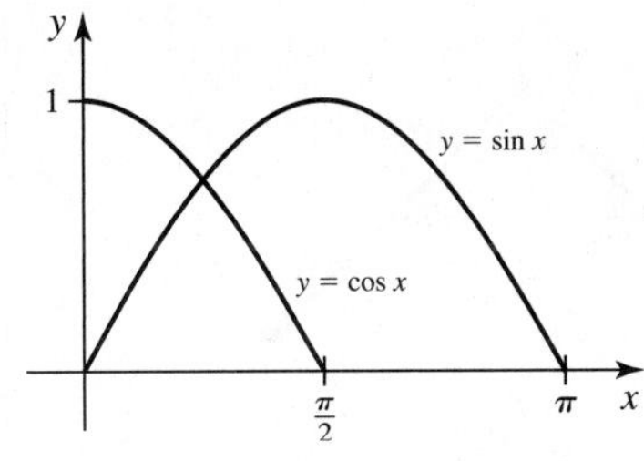

c. $A(b) = 1$; $A(c) = 0$

65. **a.** $A(x) = \frac{2}{3}(x^{3/2} - 1)$ **b.**

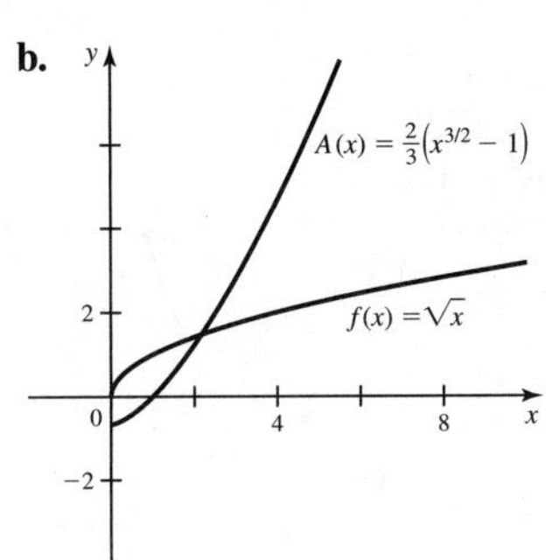

c. $A(b) = \frac{14}{3}$; $A(c) = \frac{52}{3}$

67. **a.**

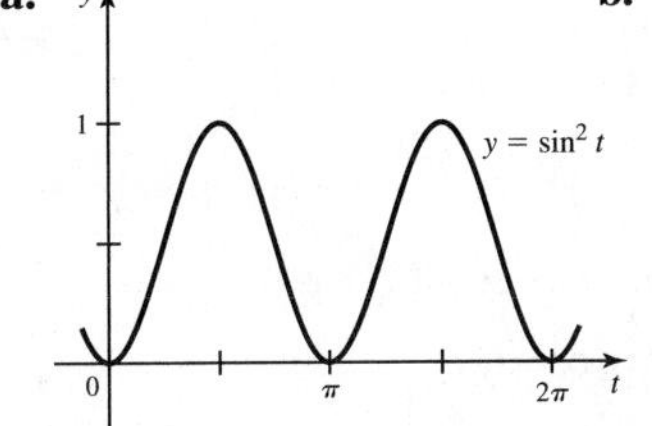

b. $g'(x) = \sin^2(x)$

c.

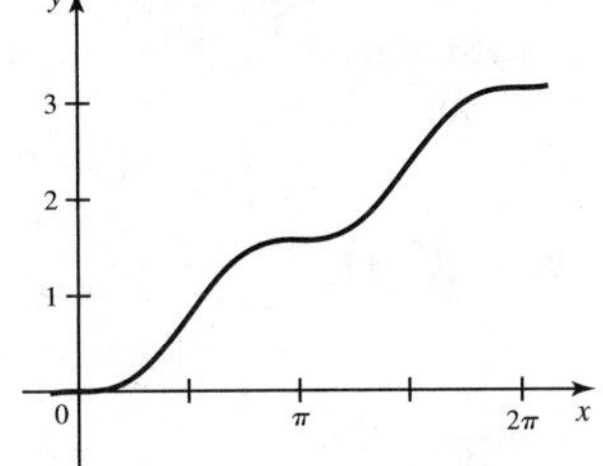

69. **a.**

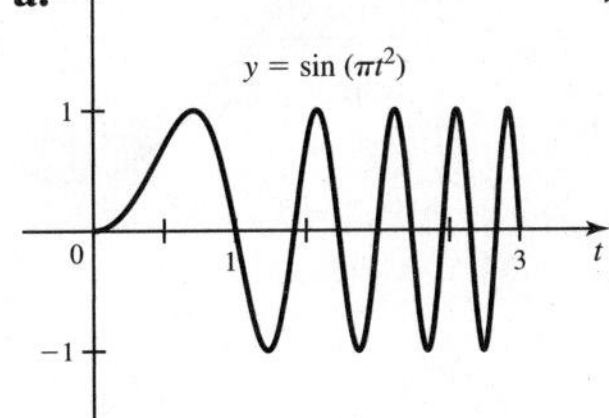

b. $g'(x) = \sin(\pi x^2)$

c.

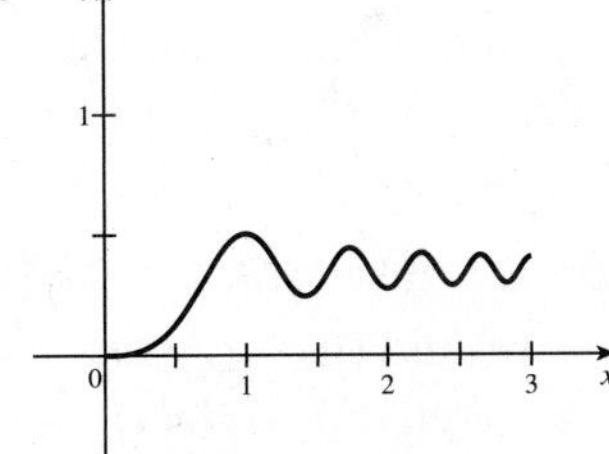

71. **a.** True **b.** True **c.** False **d.** True **73.** $\frac{2}{3}$ **75.** 1 **77.** $\frac{45}{4}$

79.

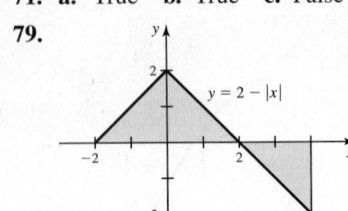

Area $= 6$

81.

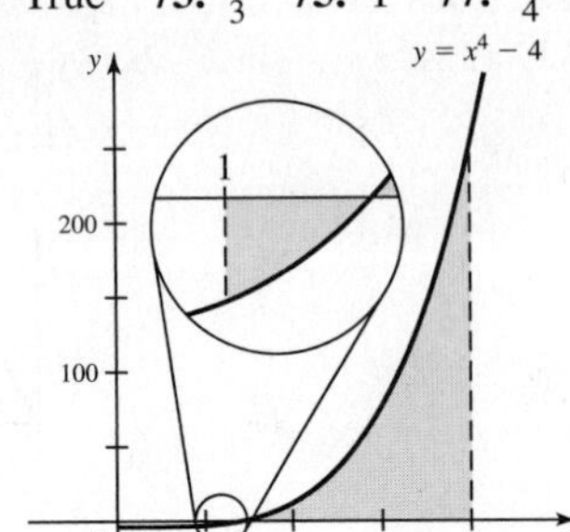

Area ≈ 194.05

83. $f(8) - f(3)$

85. $-(\cos^4 x + 6) \sin x$

87. **a.**

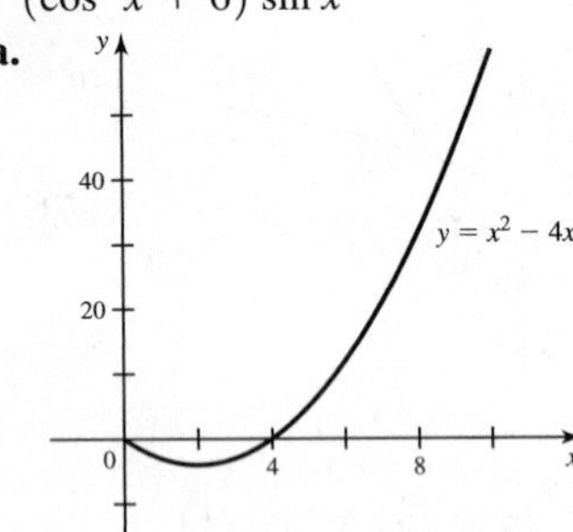

b. $b = 6$

c. $b = \dfrac{3a}{2}$

89. 3 **91.** $f(x) = -2 \sin x + 3$ **93.** $\pi/2 \approx 1.57$

95. $$[s'(x)]^2 + \left[\frac{s''(x)}{2x}\right]^2 = [\sin(x^2)]^2 + \left[\frac{2x\cos(x^2)}{2x}\right]^2 = \sin^2(x^2) + \cos^2(x^2) = 1$$

Section 5.4 Exercises, pp. 299–302

1. If f is odd, the region between f and the positive x-axis and between f and the negative x-axis are reflections of each other through the origin. Thus, on $[-a, a]$, the areas cancel each other out. **3.** Even; even **5.** If f is continuous on $[a, b]$, then there is a c in (a, b) such that $f(c) = \dfrac{1}{b-a}\displaystyle\int_a^b f(x)\,dx.$ **7.** $\frac{1000}{3}$ **9.** $-\frac{88}{3}$ **11.** 0 **13.** 0

15. 0

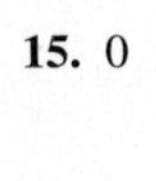

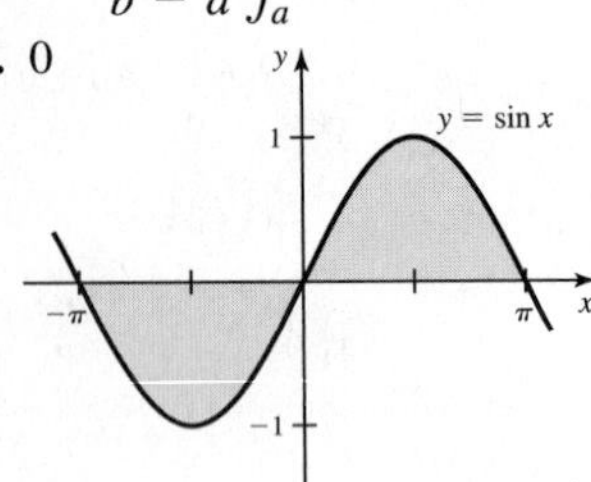

17. 0

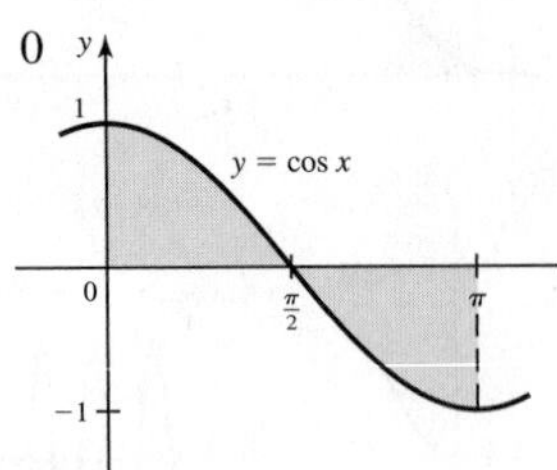

19. $2/\pi$

21. $1/(n+1)$ **23.** $2000/3$ **25.** $20/\pi$ **27.** $\frac{4}{\pi}$ km **29.** $c = 2$ **31.** $c = a/\sqrt{3}$ **33.** $c = \pm\frac{1}{2}$ **35.** **a.** True **b.** True **c.** True **d.** False **37.** 2 **39.** 0 **41.** 420 ft **45.** $f(g(-x)) = f(g(x)) \Rightarrow$ the integrand is even; $\displaystyle\int_{-a}^{a} f(g(x))\,dx = 2\int_0^a f(g(x))\,dx$ **47.** $p(g(-x)) = p(g(x)) \Rightarrow$ the integrand is even; $\displaystyle\int_{-a}^{a} p(g(x))\,dx = 2\int_0^2 p(g(x))\,dx$ **49.** **a.** $a/6$ **b.** $(3 \pm \sqrt{3})/6$, independent of a

53. $c = \sqrt[4]{12}$ **57.**

Even	Even
Even	Odd

Section 5.5 Exercises, pp. 308–311

1. The Chain Rule **3.** $u = g(x)$ **5.** We let a become $g(a)$ and b become $g(b)$. **7.** $\dfrac{x}{2} + \dfrac{\sin 2x}{4} + C$ **9.** $\dfrac{(x+1)^{13}}{13} + C$ **11.** $\dfrac{(2x+1)^{3/2}}{3} + C$ **13.** $\dfrac{(x^2+1)^5}{5} + C$ **15.** $\frac{1}{4}\sin^4 x + C$ **17.** $\dfrac{(x^2-1)^{100}}{100} + C$ **19.** $\dfrac{-(1-4x^3)^{1/2}}{3} + C$ **21.** $\dfrac{(x^2+x)^{11}}{11} + C$ **23.** $\dfrac{(x^4+16)^7}{28} + C$ **25.** $-\dfrac{\sqrt{4-9x^2}}{9} + C$ **27.** $\dfrac{(x^6-3x^2)^5}{30} + C$ **29.** $\frac{2}{3}(x-4)^{1/2}(x+8) + C$ **31.** $\frac{3}{5}(x+4)^{2/3}(x-6) + C$ **33.** $\frac{3}{112}(2x+1)^{4/3}(8x-3) + C$ **35.** $\frac{7}{2}$ **37.** $\frac{1}{3}$ **39.** $(\sqrt{3}+3)/6$ **41.** $\sqrt{2} - 1$ **43.** $22/3$ **45.** π **47.** $\dfrac{\theta}{2} - \dfrac{1}{4}\sin\left(\dfrac{6\theta + \pi}{3}\right) + C$ **49.** $\dfrac{\pi}{4}$ **51.** **a.** True **b.** True **c.** False **d.** False **e.** False **53.** $\frac{1}{10}\tan(10x) + C$ **55.** $\dfrac{1}{2}\tan^2 x + C$ **57.** $\frac{1}{7}\sec^7 x + C$ **59.** $\frac{3}{4}(4 - 3^{2/3})$ **61.** $\frac{32}{3}$ **63.** 1 **65.** $\dfrac{64}{5}$ **67.** $\frac{2}{3}$; constant **69.** **a.** 160 **b.** $\dfrac{4800}{49} \approx 98$ **c.** $\Delta p = \displaystyle\int_0^T \frac{200}{(t+1)^r}\,dt$; decreases as r increases **d.** $r \approx 1.28$ **e.** As $t \to \infty$, the population approaches 100. **71.** $2/\pi$ **73.** One area is $\displaystyle\int_4^9 \frac{(\sqrt{x}-1)^2}{2\sqrt{x}}\,dx$. Changing variables by letting $u = (\sqrt{x} - 1)$ yields $\int_1^2 u^2\,du$, which is the other area. **75.** $7297/12$ **77.** $\dfrac{[f^{(p)}(x)]^{n+1}}{n+1} + C$ **79.** $\frac{2}{15}(3 - 2a)(1+a)^{3/2} + \frac{4}{15}a^{5/2}$ **81.** $\frac{1}{3}\sec^3\theta + C$ **83.** **a.** $I = \int\left(\frac{1}{2}\sin 2x\right)^2 dx = \frac{1}{8}x - \frac{1}{32}\sin 4x + C$ **b.** $I = \int(\sin^2 x - \sin^4 x)\,dx = \frac{1}{8}x - \frac{1}{32}\sin 4x + C$ **87.** $\dfrac{4}{3}(-2 + \sqrt{1+x})\sqrt{1 + \sqrt{1+x}}$ **89.** $-4 + \sqrt{17}$

Chapter 5 Review Exercises, pp. 311–313

1. **a.** True **b.** False **c.** True **d.** True **e.** False **f.** True **g.** True **3.** $\frac{23}{2}$ **5.** 4π **7.** **a.** $1[(3\cdot 2 - 2) + (3\cdot 3 - 2) + (3\cdot 4 - 2)] = 21$

b. $\sum_{k=1}^{n} \frac{3}{n}\left[3\left(1 + \frac{3k}{n}\right) - 2\right]$ **c.** $\frac{33}{2}$ **9.** $\int_0^4 (1 + x^8)\,dx = \frac{36 + 4^9}{9}$
11. $\frac{212}{5}$ **13.** 20 **15.** $x^9 - x^7 + C$ **17.** $\frac{7}{6}$ **19.** $2\sqrt{3} - 3$ **21.** 1
23. $\frac{1}{2}\theta - \frac{1}{20}\sin 10\theta + C$ **25.** $-\frac{1}{3}(x^3 + 3x^2 - 6x)^{-1} + C$
27. a. 20 **b.** 0 **c.** 80 **29.** 18 **31.** 10 **33.** Not enough information **35.** Displacement $= 0$; distance $= 20/\pi$ **37. a.** $\frac{5}{2}$ **b.** 3 **39.** 24 **41.** $f(1) = 0$; $f'(x) > 0$ on $[1, \infty)$; $f''(x) < 0$ on $[1, \infty)$

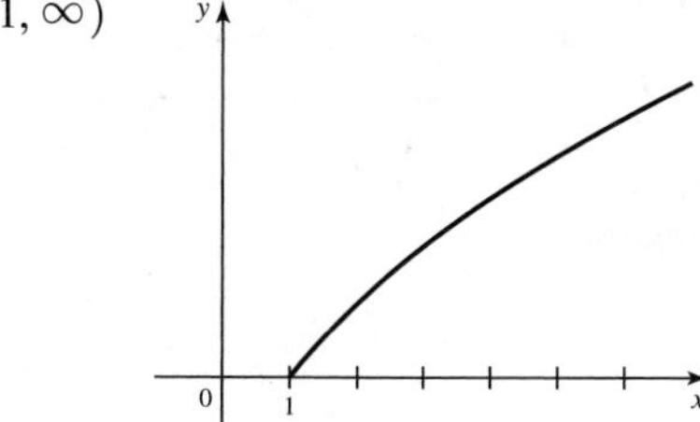

45. $\frac{1}{14}\sec^7(\tan x^2) + C$ **47.** Differentiating the first equation gives the second equation. **49. a.** Increasing on $(-\infty, 1)$ and $(2, \infty)$; decreasing on $(1, 2)$ **b.** Concave up on $\left(\frac{13}{8}, \infty\right)$; concave down on $\left(-\infty, \frac{13}{8}\right)$ **c.** Local max at $x = 1$; local min at $x = 2$ **d.** Inflection point at $x = \frac{13}{8}$

CHAPTER 6

Section 6.1 Exercises, pp. 322–326

1. The position s is the location of the object relative to the origin. The displacement between time $t = a$ and $t = b$ is $s(b) - s(a)$.

The distance traveled between $t = a$ and $t = b$ is $\int_a^b |v(t)|\,dt$,

where $v(t)$ is the velocity at time t. **3.** The displacement between $t = a$ and $t = b$ is $\int_a^b v(t)\,dt$. **5.** $Q(t) = Q(0) + \int_0^t Q'(x)\,dx$

7. a.

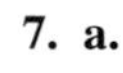

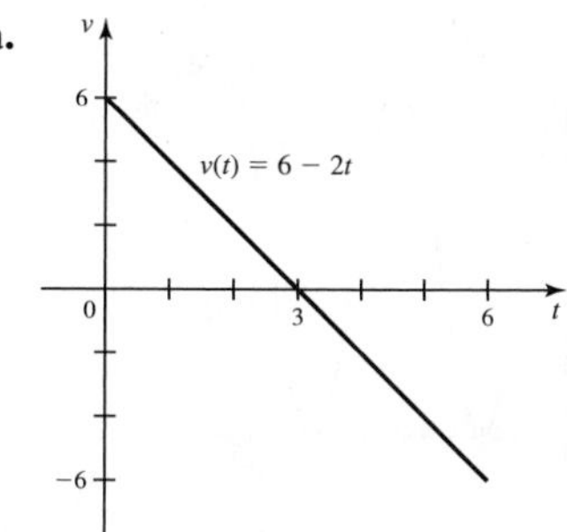

Positive direction for $0 \le t < 3$; negative direction for $3 < t \le 6$
b. 0 **c.** 18 m

9. a.

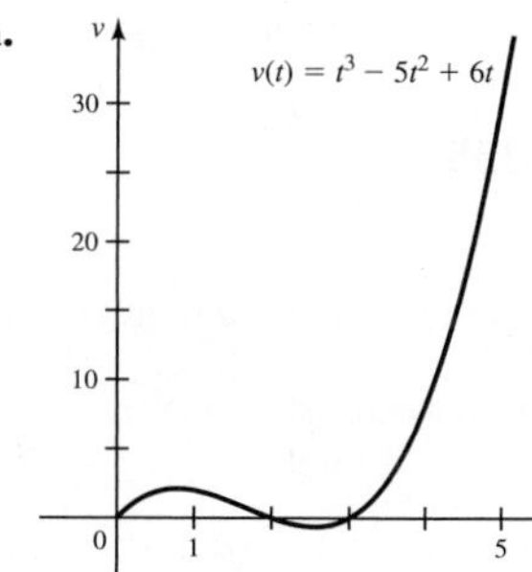

Positive direction for $0 < t < 2, 3 < t < 5$; negative direction for $2 < t < 3$
b. $\frac{275}{12}$ m **c.** 23.75 m

11. a.

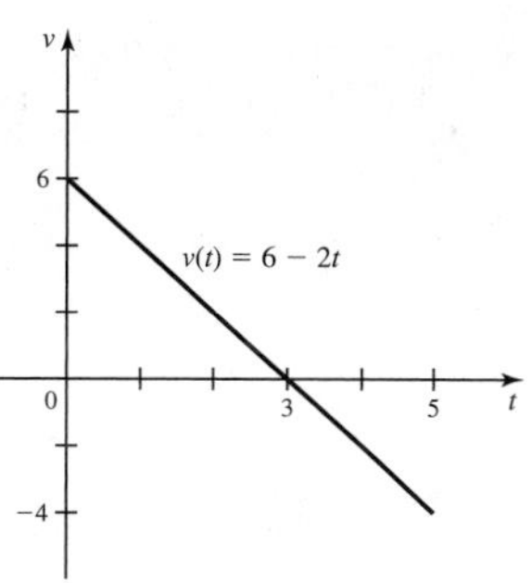

Positive direction for $0 \le t < 3$; negative direction for $3 < t \le 5$

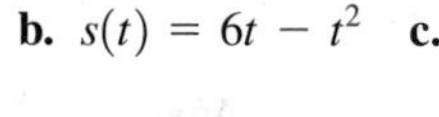

b. $s(t) = 6t - t^2$ **c.**

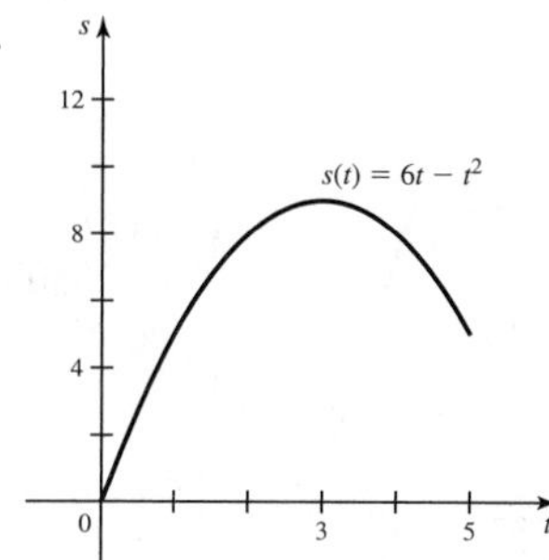

13. a.

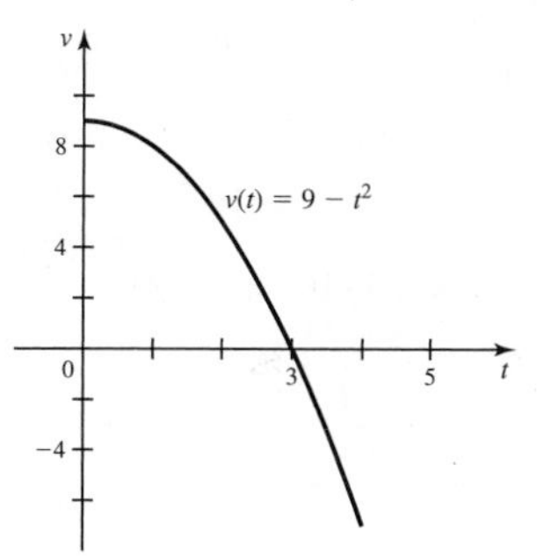

Positive direction for $0 < t < 3$; negative direction for $3 < t < 4$

b. $s(t) = 9t - \frac{t^3}{3} - 2$ **c.**

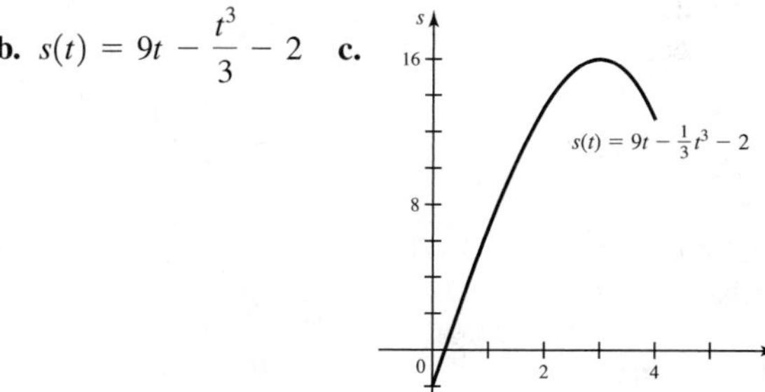

15. a. $s(t) = 2\sin \pi t$ **b.**

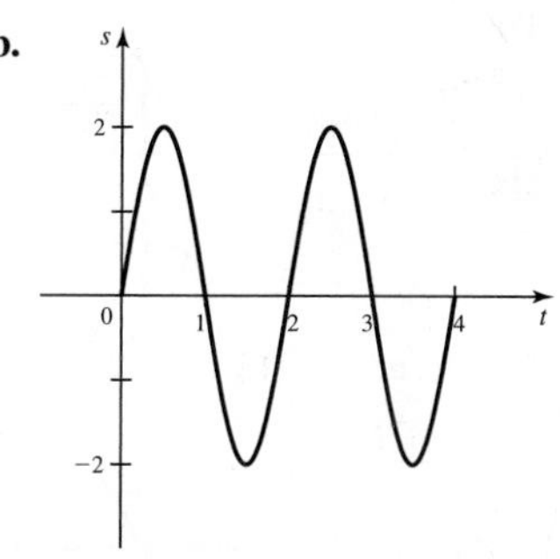

c. $\frac{3}{2}, \frac{7}{2}, \frac{11}{2}$
d. $\frac{1}{2}, \frac{5}{2}, \frac{9}{2}$

17. a. $s(t) = 10t(48 - t^2)$ **b.** 880 mi **c.** $\frac{2720\sqrt{6}}{9} \approx 740.29$ mi

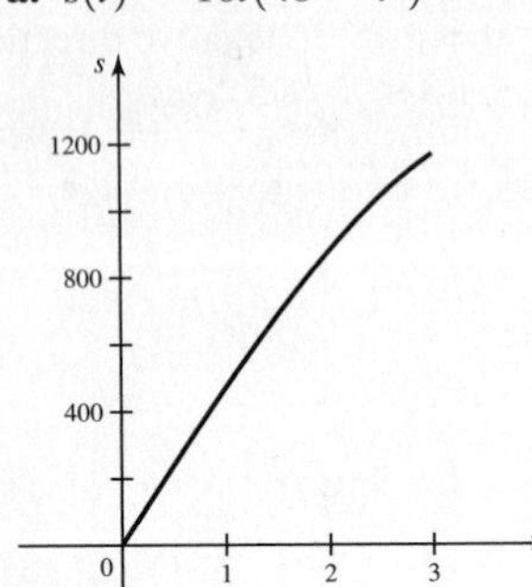

19. a.

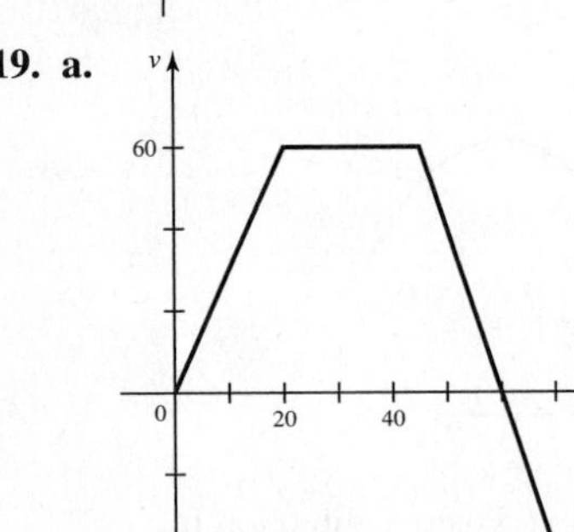

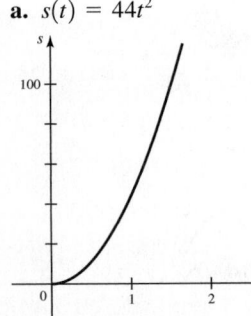

Velocity is a maximum for $20 \le t \le 45$; $v = 0$ at $t = 0$ and $t = 60$ **b.** 1200 m **c.** 2550 m **d.** 2100 m in the positive direction from $s(0)$

21. $s(t) = -4.9t^2 + 20t$; $v(t) = -9.8t + 20$
23. $s(t) = \frac{-0.005}{3}t^3 + 10t$; $v(t) = -0.005t^2 + 10$
25. a. $s(t) = 44t^2$ **b.** 704 ft **c.** $\sqrt{30} \approx 5.477$ s **d.** $\frac{5\sqrt{33}}{11} \approx 2.611$ s **e.** $\frac{89^2}{44} \approx 180.023$ ft

27. 6.154 mi; 1.465 mi **29. a.** 27,250 barrels **b.** 31,000 barrels **c.** 4000 barrels **31. a.** ≈ 2639 people **b.** $P(t) = 250 + 20t^{3/2} + 30t$ **33. a.** 2534 cells; 3334 cells **b.** $N(t) = 1500 - 400\sqrt{2} + 400\sqrt{t+2}$ cells **35. a.** \$96,875 **b.** \$86,875 **37. a.** \$69,583.33 **b.** \$139,583.33 **39. a.** False **b.** True **c.** True **d.** True

41. a. 3 **b.** $\frac{13}{3}$ **c.** 3 **d.** $s(t) = \begin{cases} \frac{-t^2}{2} + 2t, & 0 \le t \le 3 \\ \frac{3t^2}{2} - 10t + 18, & 3 < t \le 4 \\ -t^2 + 10t - 22, & 4 < t \le 5 \end{cases}$

43. $\frac{2}{3}$ **45.** $\frac{25}{3}$ **47. a.**

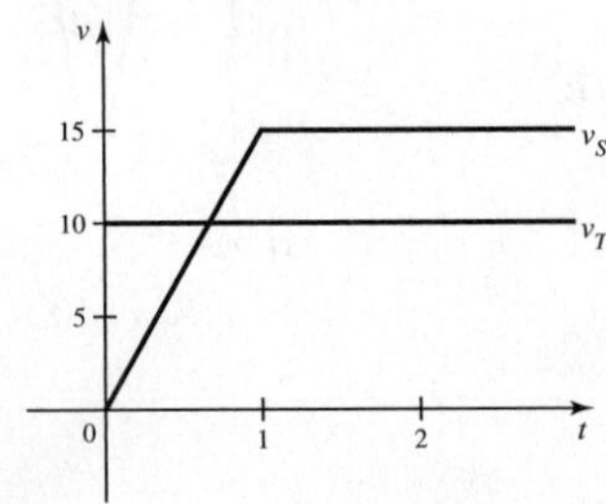

b. Theo **c.** Sasha **d.** Theo hits the 10-mi mark before Sasha; Sasha and Theo hit the 15-mi mark at the same time; Sasha hits the 20-mi mark before Theo. **e.** Sasha **f.** Theo

49. a. Abe initially runs into a headwind; Bess initially runs with a tailwind.

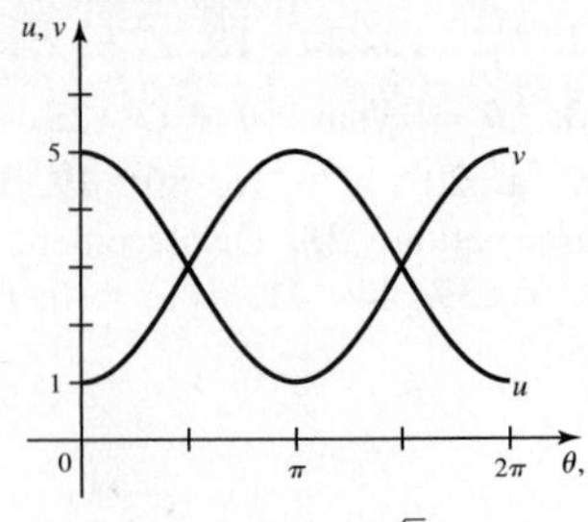

b. Both runners have an average speed of 3 mi/hr. **c.** $\pi\frac{\sqrt{5}}{25}$ hr.

51. a. $\frac{120}{\pi} + 40 \approx 78.20\text{ m}^3$ **b.** $Q(t) = 20\left[t + \frac{12}{\pi}\sin\left(\frac{\pi}{12}t\right)\right]$

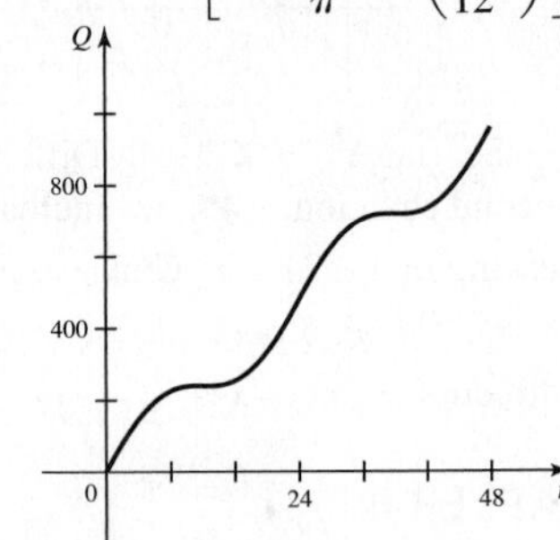

c. After ≈ 122.6 hr **53. a.**

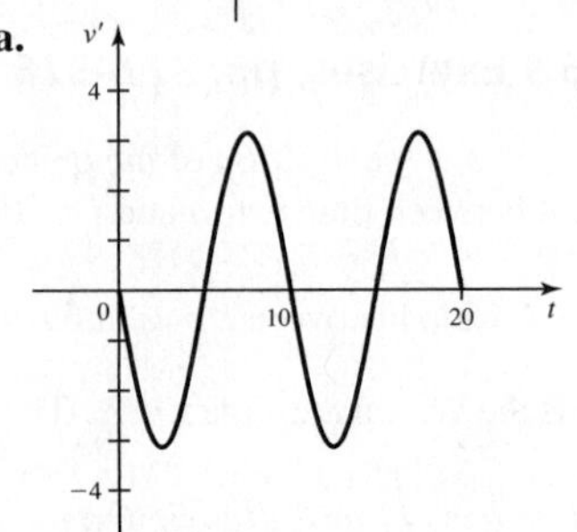

b. $V(t) = 5\cos\left(\frac{\pi t}{5}\right) + 5$

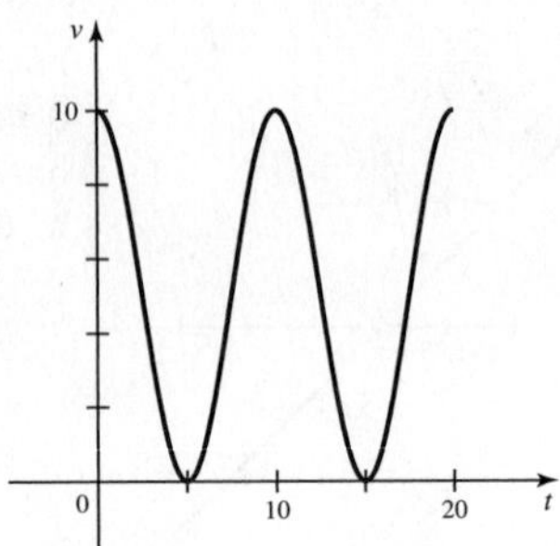

c. 6 breaths/min **55. a.** 7200 MWh or 2.592×10^{13} J **b.** 16,000 kg; 5,840,000 kg **c.** 450 g; 164,250 g **d.** About 1500 turbines

Section 6.2 Exercises, pp. 331–335

1.

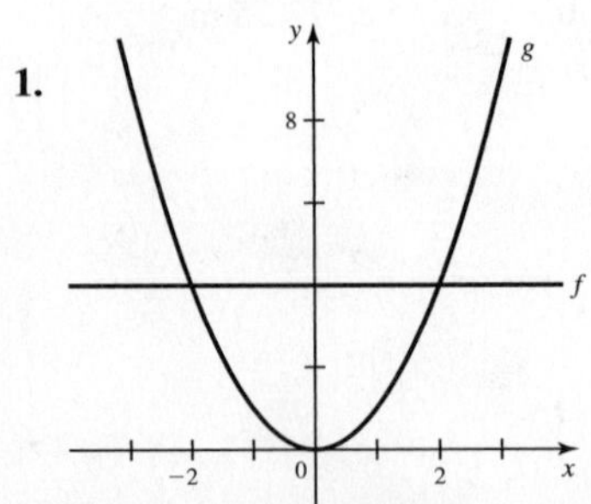

$\int_{-2}^{2}(f(x) - g(x))\,dx$ equals the area between these curves.

3. See solution to Exercise 1. **5.** $\frac{9}{2}$ **7.** $\frac{7}{6}$ **9.** $\frac{25}{2}$ **11.** $\frac{32}{3}$
13. $\frac{256}{5}$ **15.** $2 - \sqrt{2}$ **17.** 1 **19.** 1 **21.** 3

23. 48 **25.** $\frac{9}{2}$ **27. a.** $\int_{-\sqrt{2}}^{-1} (2 - x^2)\,dx + \int_{-1}^{0} (-x)\,dx$

b. $\int_{-1}^{0} \left(y + \sqrt{(y + 2)}\right) dy$

29. a. $2\int_{-3}^{-2} \sqrt{x + 3}\,dx + \int_{-2}^{6} \left(\sqrt{x + 3} - \frac{x}{2}\right) dx$

b. $\int_{-1}^{3} [2y - (y^2 - 3)]\,dy$ **31. a.** $\frac{63}{4}$

b. $\frac{63}{4}$ **33.** $\frac{64}{5}$ **35.** 8 **37.** $\frac{5}{24}$ **39. a.** False **b.** False

c. True **41.** $\frac{1}{6}$ **43.** $\frac{9}{2}$ **45.** $\frac{32}{3}$ **47.** $\frac{63}{4}$ **49.** $2 - \frac{\pi}{2}, \frac{3\pi}{2} + 2$

51. a. Area $(R_1) = \dfrac{p - 1}{2(p + 1)}$ for all positive integers p;

area $(R_2) = \dfrac{q - 1}{2(q + 1)}$ for all positive integers q; they are the same.

b. R_1 has greater area. **c.** R_2 has greater area.

53. $\dfrac{135 + 17\sqrt{17} - 128\sqrt{2}}{96}$ **55.** $\dfrac{81}{2}$ **57.** $\dfrac{n - 1}{2(n + 1)}$

59. $A_n = \dfrac{n - 1}{n + 1}$; $\lim_{n\to\infty} A_n = 1$; the region approximates a square with side length of 1. **61. a.** The lowest $p\%$ of households owns exactly $p\%$ of the wealth for $0 \le p \le 100$. **b.** The function must be increasing because the poorest $p\%$ cannot own more than $p\%$ of the wealth.
c. $p = 1.1$ is most equitable; $p = 4$ is least equitable.

e. $G(p) = 1 - \dfrac{2}{p + 1}$ **f.** $0 \le G < 1$ for $p \ge 1$. **g.** $\dfrac{5}{18}$ **63.** -1

65. $\frac{4}{9}$ **67. a.** $F(a) = a(b^3/6) - b^4/12$; $F(a) = 0$ if $a = b/2$
b. Since $A'(b/2) = 0$ and $A''(b/2) > 0$, A has a minimum at $a = b/2$. The maximum value of $b^4/12$ occurs if $a = 0$ or $a = b$.

69. a.

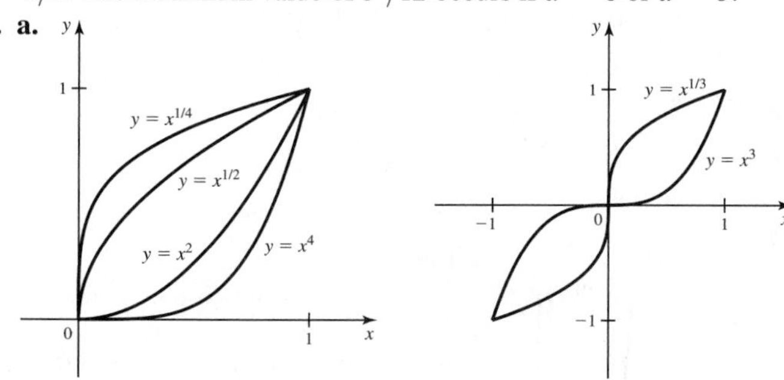

b. $A_n(x)$ is the net area of the region between the graphs of f and g from 0 to x. **c.** $x = n^{n/(n^2-1)}$; the roots decrease with n.

Section 6.3 Exercises, pp. 343–347

1. $A(x)$ is the area of the cross section through the solid at the point x.

3. $V = \int_0^2 \pi(4x^2 - x^4)\,dx$ **5.** The cross sections are disks and $A(x)$ is the area of a disk. **7.** 30 **9.** $\frac{1000}{3}$ **11.** $\frac{\pi}{3}$ **13.** $\dfrac{16\sqrt{2}}{3}$

15. 36π **17.** $\frac{256\pi}{15}$ **19.** $\pi^2/2$ **21.** $\pi(2 - \sqrt{2})$ **23.** $32\pi/3$

25. $\frac{2\pi}{3}(3\sqrt{3} - \pi)$ **27.** $\dfrac{256\pi}{35}$ **29.** $(4\pi - \pi^2)/4$ **31.** 54π
33. $64\pi/5$ **35.** $\frac{256\pi}{3}$ **37.** Volumes are equal. **39.** x-axis
41. a. False **b.** True **c.** True **43.** $\frac{325\pi}{72}$ **45.** $\frac{256\pi}{7}$
47. Volume $S = 8\pi a^{5/2}/15$; volume $T = \pi a^{5/2}/3$
49. a. **b.**

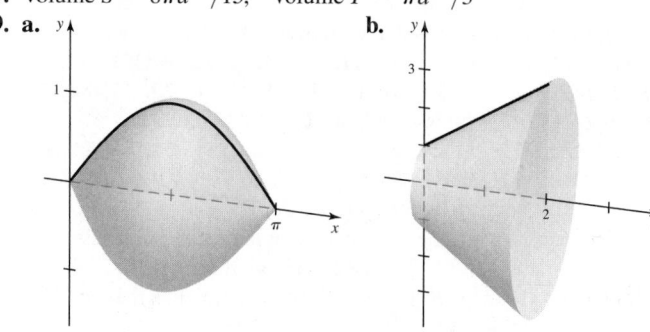

51. a. $\frac{1}{3}V_C$ **b.** $\frac{2}{3}V_C$ **53.** $24\pi^2$ **55.** $\frac{704\pi}{15}$ **57.** $\frac{192\pi}{5}$
61. b. $2/\sqrt{\pi}$ m

Section 6.4 Exercises, pp. 354–357

1. $\int_a^b 2\pi x(f(x) - g(x))\,dx$ **3.** x; y **5.** $\frac{20\pi}{3}$ **7.** π **9.** π

11. 8π **13.** $\dfrac{32\pi}{3}$ **15.** 90π **17.** $11\pi/6$ **19.** $23\pi/15$

21. 24π **23.** 54π **25.** $16\sqrt{2}\,\pi/3$ **27.** $4\pi/15$; shell method
29. $8\pi/27$; shell method **31.** $\dfrac{3456\pi}{5}$; washer method

33. a. True **b.** False **c.** True **35.** $\pi/2$ **37.** $16\pi/3$
39. $608\pi/3$ **41.** $\pi/4$ **43.** $\pi/3$

45. a. $V_1 = \dfrac{\pi}{15}(3a^2 + 10a + 15)$

$V_2 = \dfrac{\pi}{2}(a + 2)$

b. $V(S_1) = V(S_2)$ for $a = 0$ and $a = -\frac{5}{6}$ **49.** $\dfrac{\pi h^2}{3}(24 - h)$

51. $24\pi^2$ **53. a.** $4\pi ab^2/3$ **b.** $4\pi a^2b/3$ **c.** No; they will agree only in the case $a = b$.

Section 6.5 Exercises, pp. 361–363

1. Assuming f' is continuous on $[a, b]$, calculate $f'(x)^2$. Then evaluate the integral $\int_a^b \sqrt{1 + f'(x)^2}\,dx$. **3.** $4\sqrt{5}$ **5.** 168

7. $\frac{4}{3}$ **9.** $\frac{123}{32}$ **11. a.** $\int_{-1}^{1} \sqrt{1 + 4x^2}\,dx$ **b.** 2.96

13. a. $\int_0^{\pi/4} \sqrt{1 + \sec^4 x}\,dx$ **b.** 1.28 **15. a.** $\int_3^4 \sqrt{\dfrac{4x - 7}{4x - 8}}\,dx$

b. 1.08 **17. a.** $\int_0^{\pi} \sqrt{1 + 4\sin^2 2x}\,dx$ **b.** 5.27

19. a. $\int_1^{10} \sqrt{1 + 1/x^4}\,dx$ **b.** 9.15 **21.** $7\sqrt{5}$ **23.** $\frac{123}{32}$

25. a. False **b.** True **c.** False

27. a. $f(x) = \pm 4x^3/3 + C$ **b.** $f(x) = \pm 3\sin 2x + C$
29. $y = 1 - x^2$ **31.** Approximately 1326 m **33. a.** $L/2$ **b.** L/c

Section 6.6 Exercises, pp. 371–374

1. 150 g **3.** Work is the force times the distance moved. **5.** Different volumes of water are moved different distances. **7.** 39, 200 N/m^2 **9.** $\pi + 2$ **11.** 3 **13.** $(2\sqrt{2} - 1)/3$ **15.** 10 **17.** 25 J **19. a.** 112.5 J **b.** 12.5 J **21.** 525 J **23.** 11,484,375 J **25. a.** 66,150π J **b.** No **27. a.** 200,704,000 π/3 J **b.** 120, 422, 400 π J **29. a.** 32,667 J **b.** Yes **31.** 14,700,000 N **33.** 29,400,000 N **35.** 800,000 N **37.** 6737.5 N **39. a.** True **b.** True **c.** True **d.** False **41. a.** Compared to a linear spring $F(x) = 16x$, the restoring force is less for large displacements. **b.** 17.87 J **c.** 31.6 J **43.** 0.28 J **45. a.** 8.87×10^9 J **b.** $500\,GMx/(R(x + R)) = (2 \times 10^{17})x/(R(x + R))$ J **c.** GMm/R **d.** $v = \sqrt{2GM/R}$ **47. a.** 2250g J **b.** 3750g J **51.** The left-hand plate **53. a.** Yes **b.** 4.296 m

Chapter 6 Review Exercises, pp. 374–376

1. a. True **b.** True **c.** True
3. $s(t) = 20t - 5t^2$; displacement $= 20t - 5t^2$;

$$D(t) = \begin{cases} 20t - 5t^2 & 0 \le t < 2 \\ 5t^2 - 20t + 40 & 2 \le t \le 4 \end{cases}$$

5. a. $v(t) = -\dfrac{8}{\pi}\cos\dfrac{\pi t}{4}$

$s(t) = -\dfrac{32}{\pi^2}\sin\dfrac{\pi t}{4}$

b. min value $= -\dfrac{32}{\pi^2}$; max value $= \dfrac{32}{\pi^2}$ **c.** 0; 0 **7. a.** $R(t) = 3t^{4/3}$

b. $R(t) = \begin{cases} 3t^{4/3} & \text{if } 0 \le t \le 8 \\ 2t + 32 & \text{if } t > 8 \end{cases}$ **c.** $t = 59$ min

9. $\dfrac{99}{101}, \dfrac{999}{1001}$ **11.** 8 **13.** 1 **15.** 1/3

17. 16 **19.** $\dfrac{8\pi}{5}$ **21.** $\dfrac{\pi r^2 h}{3}$ **23. a.** V_y **b.** V_y

c. $V_x = \pi\left(\dfrac{a^{1-2p} - 1}{1 - 2p}\right)$ **d.** $V_y = 2\pi\left(\dfrac{a^{2-p} - 1}{2 - p}\right)$

25. $2\sqrt{3} - \frac{4}{3}$ **27.** 63 **29.** 56.25 J **31.** 5.2×10^7 N

CHAPTER 7

Section 7.1 Answers, pp. 384–386

1. $f(x) = x^3$ **3.** The graph of $y = f^{-1}(x)$ is the graph of $y = f(x)$ reflected about the line $y = x$. Therefore, (a, b) is on the graph of f whenever (b, a) is on the graph of f^{-1}. **5.** $y = (x + 4)/3$ **7.** 1/4 **9.** $(-\infty, -1], [-1, 1], [1, \infty)$ **11.** $(-\infty, \infty)$ **13.** $(-\infty, 5) \cup (5, \infty)$ **15. a.** $f^{-1}(x) = (6 - x)/4$ **17. a.** $f^{-1}(x) = (x - 5)/3$ **19. a.** $f^{-1}(x) = x^2 - 2$ for $x \ge 0$

21. a. $f_1(x) = \sqrt{1 - x^2};\ 0 \le x \le 1$
$f_2(x) = \sqrt{1 - x^2};\ -1 \le x \le 0$
$f_3(x) = -\sqrt{1 - x^2};\ -1 \le x \le 0$
$f_4(x) = -\sqrt{1 - x^2};\ 0 \le x \le 1$

b. $f_1^{-1}(x) = \sqrt{1 - x^2};\ 0 \le x \le 1$
$f_2^{-1}(x) = -\sqrt{1 - x^2};\ 0 \le x \le 1$
$f_3^{-1}(x) = -\sqrt{1 - x^2};\ -1 \le x \le 0$
$f_4^{-1}(x) = \sqrt{1 - x^2};\ -1 \le x \le 0$

23. $f^{-1}(x) = \dfrac{8 - x}{4}$

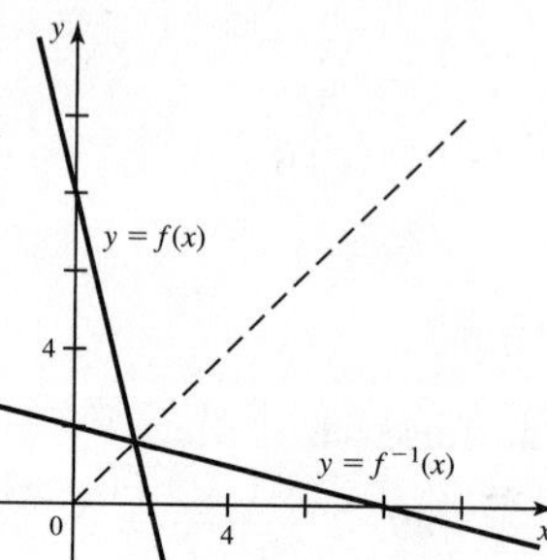

25. $f^{-1}(x) = x^2$ for $x \ge 0$

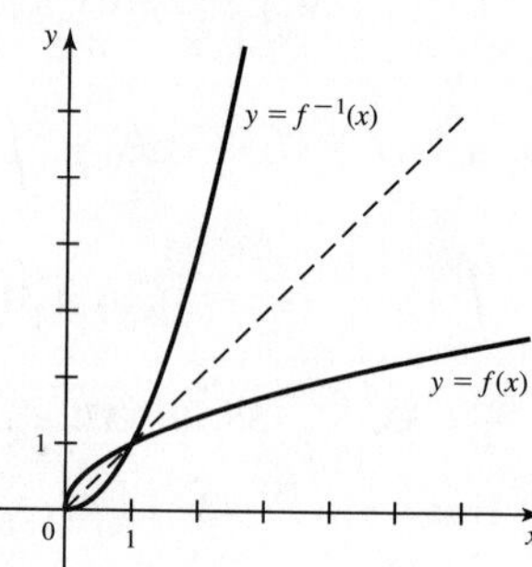

27. $f^{-1}(x) = \sqrt[4]{x - 4}$

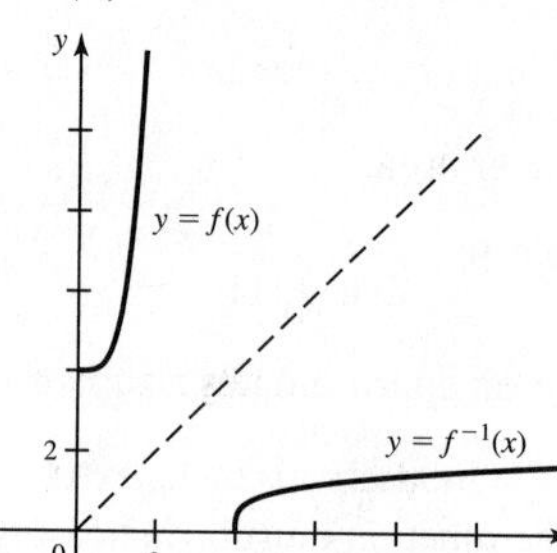

29.

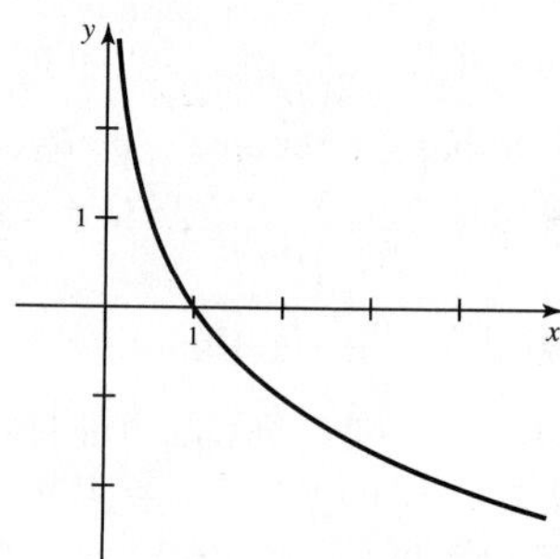

31. $\dfrac{1}{3}$ **33.** $\dfrac{1}{2}$ **35.** 4 **37.** $\dfrac{1}{12}$ **39.** $\dfrac{1}{4}$ **41.** $\dfrac{5}{4}$
43. a. False **b.** True **c.** False **d.** True **e.** True
45. $f^{-1}(x) = \sqrt[3]{x - 1}$, D = **R**
47. $f_1^{-1}(x) = \sqrt{2/x - 2}$, $D_1 = (0, 1]$; $f_2^{-1}(x) = -\sqrt{2/x - 2}$, $D_2 = (0, 1]$ **49.** $f^{-1}(x) = (x + 4)/3$ $(f^{-1})'(x) = \dfrac{1}{3}$
51. $f^{-1}(x) = \sqrt{x + 4}, x \ge -4$ $(f^{-1})'(x) = 1/(2\sqrt{x + 4})$
53. $f^{-1}(x) = x^2 - 2, x \ge 0$ $(f^{-1})'(x) = 2x, x \ge 0$
55. $f^{-1}(x) = \dfrac{1}{x^2}, x \ge 0$ $(f^{-1})'(x) = -2/x^3, x > 0$

57. $r = \sqrt[3]{\dfrac{3V}{4\pi}}$ **59.** $r = \sqrt{\dfrac{V}{10\pi}}$

61. a.

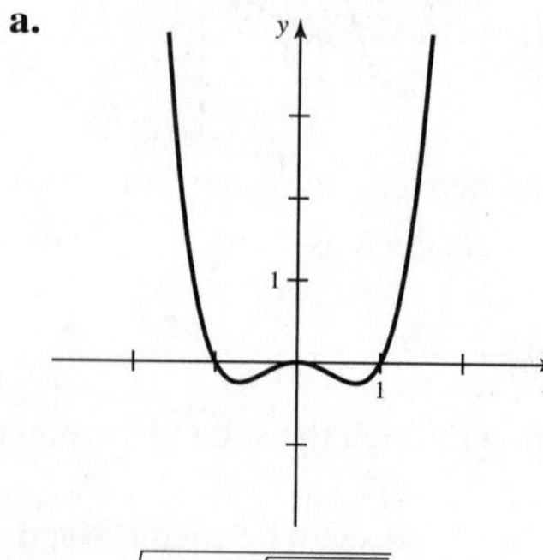

f is one-to-one on the intervals $(-\infty, -1/\sqrt{2}]$, $[-1/\sqrt{2}, 0]$, $[0, 1/\sqrt{2}]$, $[1/\sqrt{2}, \infty]$

b. $x = \pm\sqrt{\dfrac{1 \pm \sqrt{4y + 1}}{2}}$

65. a. $a = f'(x_0); b = y_0 - x_0 f'(x_0)$
b. $c = \dfrac{1}{f'(x_0)};\ d = x_0 - \dfrac{y_0}{f'(x_0)}$
c. $L(x) = f'(x_0)x + y_0 - x_0 f'(x_0)$, so
$L^{-1}(x) = \dfrac{x - y_0 + x_0 f'(x_0)}{f'(x_0)} = M(x).$

Section 7.2 Answers, pp. 396–399

1. $D = \{x: x > 0\};\quad R = \{y: -\infty < y < \infty\}$
3. $x = e^y \Rightarrow 1 = e^y y'(x) \Rightarrow y'(x) = 1/e^y = 1/x$
5. $\dfrac{d}{dx}(\ln kx) = \dfrac{d}{dx}(\ln k + \ln x) = \dfrac{d}{dx}(\ln x)$ **7.** $2/x, x \neq 0$
9. $-2/(x^2 - 1)$ for $|x| > 1$ **11.** $(x^2 + 1)/x + 2x \ln x, x > 0$
13. $1/(x \ln x), x > 1$ **15.** $3 \ln|x - 10| + C$
17. $\ln\left|\dfrac{(x-4)^2}{(2x+1)^{3/2}}\right| + C$ **19.** $6(1 - \ln 2)$
21. $\dfrac{1}{4}\left[\dfrac{1}{\ln^2(\ln 3)} - \dfrac{1}{\ln^2(\ln 4)}\right]$ **23.** $-9e^{-x} - 10e^{2x} - 6e^x$
25. $\dfrac{3e^x + 4e^{2x}}{(e^{-x} + 2)^2}$ **27.** 0 **29.** $y = -\dfrac{3x}{4} + \dfrac{1}{4}$ **31.** $\dfrac{1}{2}e^{2x} + x + C$
33. $\dfrac{98}{3}$ **35.** $\ln|e^x - e^{-x}| + C$ **37.** $2e^{\sqrt{x}} + C$
39. $f'(x) = \dfrac{(x+1)^{10}}{(2x-4)^8}\left[\dfrac{10}{x+1} - \dfrac{8}{x-2}\right]$
41. $f'(x) = 2x^{(\ln x) - 1} \ln x$
43. $f'(x) = \dfrac{(x+1)^{3/2}(x-4)^{5/2}}{(5x+3)^{2/3}} \cdot \left[\dfrac{3}{2(x+1)} + \dfrac{5}{2(x-4)} - \dfrac{10}{3(5x+3)}\right]$
45. $f'(x) = (\sin x)^{\tan x}[1 + \sec^2 x \ln(\sin x)]; 0 < x < \pi, x \neq \pi/2$
47. a. True **b.** False **c.** False **d.** True **e.** False
49.

h	$(1+2h)^{1/h}$	h	$(1+2h)^{1/h}$
10^{-1}	6.1917	-10^{-1}	9.3132
10^{-2}	7.2446	-10^{-2}	7.5404
10^{-3}	7.3743	-10^{-3}	7.4039
10^{-4}	7.3876	-10^{-4}	7.3905
10^{-5}	7.3889	-10^{-5}	7.3892
10^{-6}	7.3890	-10^{-6}	7.3891

$\lim_{h \to 0} (1 + 2h)^{1/h} = e^2$

51.

x	$\dfrac{2^x - 1}{x}$	x	$\dfrac{2^x - 1}{x}$
10^{-1}	0.71773	-10^{-1}	0.66967
10^{-2}	0.69556	-10^{-2}	0.69075
10^{-3}	0.69339	-10^{-3}	0.69291
10^{-4}	0.69317	-10^{-4}	0.69312
10^{-5}	0.69315	-10^{-5}	0.69314
10^{-6}	0.69315	-10^{-6}	0.69315

$\lim_{x \to 0} \dfrac{2^x - 1}{x} = \ln 2$

55. $\dfrac{\ln p}{p - 1}, 0$ **57.** $-20xe^{-10x^2}$ **59.** $\dfrac{1}{2x}$ **61.** $\dfrac{9x^2 - 14x + 11}{(x+2)^4}$
63. $\dfrac{1}{3}e^{x^3} + C$ **65.** $2e - 1$ **67.** $\dfrac{32}{3}$
69. $\dfrac{1}{2}(\ln 2 + 1) \approx 0.85$ **71. a.**

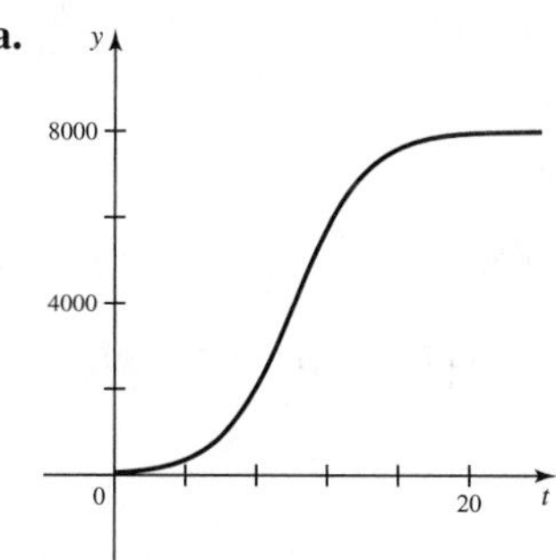

b. $t = 2 \ln(265) \approx 11.2$ years; about 14.5 years
c. $P'(0) \approx 25$ fish/year; $P'(5) \approx 264$ fish/year
d. The population is growing fastest after about 10 years.

73. b. $r(11) \approx 0.0133$; $r(21) \approx 0.0118$; the relative growth rate is decreasing. **c.** $\lim_{t \to \infty} r(t) = 0$; as the population gets close to carrying capacity, the rate of population growth vanishes.
75. a. $\dfrac{1}{200}\,\text{yr}^{-1}$ **b.** $200 \ln 2 \approx 138.63$ yr
79. $\ln 2 = \displaystyle\int_1^2 \frac{dt}{t} < L_2 = \frac{5}{6} < 1$

$$\ln 3 = \int_1^3 \frac{dt}{t} > R_7 = 2\left(\frac{1}{9} + \frac{1}{11} + \frac{1}{13} + \frac{1}{15} + \frac{1}{17} + \frac{1}{19} + \frac{1}{21}\right) \approx 1.00937 > 1$$

Section 7.3 Answers, pp. 406–409

1. $f'(x) = (\ln b)b^x$, which is the result for $f(x) = e^x$ when $b = e$.
3. $b^x = e^{\ln(b^x)} = e^{x \ln b}$ **5.** $\dfrac{4^x}{\ln 4} + C$ **7.** $e^{x \ln 3}, e^{\pi \ln x}, e^{(\sin x)(\ln x)}$
9. 1000 **11.** 2 **13.** ± 2 **15.** ± 4 **17.** $1 + \ln 3/\ln 7$
19. $\ln 5/(3 \ln 3) + 5/3$ **21.** $y' = 5 \ln 4 \cdot 4^x$
23. $y' = 3^x \cdot x^2(x \ln 3 + 3)$ **25.** $A' = 1000(1.045)^{4t} \ln(1.045)$
27. a. About 28.7 s **b.** -46.512 s/1000 ft
c. $dT/da = -2.74 \cdot 2^{-0.274a} \ln 2$
At $t = 8$, $\dfrac{dT}{da} = -0.4150$ min/1000 ft $= -24.938$ s/1000 ft
If a plane is traveling at 30,000 feet and it increases its altitude by 1000 feet, the time of useful consciousness in the event of a sudden loss of pressure would decrease by about 25 seconds.

29. a. About 67.19 hr
b. $Q'(12) = -9.815\ \mu\text{Ci/hr}$
$Q'(24) = -5.201\ \mu\text{Ci/hr}$
$Q'(48) = -1.461\ \mu\text{Ci/hr}$
The rate at which iodine-123 leaves the body decreases with time.
31. $99/(10 \ln 10)$ **33.** 3 **35.** $g'(y) = e^y y^{e-1}(y + e)$
37. $s'(t) = -(\ln 2)2^t \sin 2^t$
39. $f'(x) = \frac{\sqrt{x}}{2}(10x - 9)$ **41.** $4^{2x+1}x^{4x}(1 + \ln 2x)$
43. $(2 \ln 2)x2^{x^2}$ **45.** $2(x + 1)^{2x}\left[\frac{x}{x + 1} + \ln(x + 1)\right]$
47. $y = x \sin 1 + 1 - \sin 1$ **49.** $y = e^{2/e}$ and $y = e^{-2/e}$
51. $y' = \frac{8x}{(x^2 - 1)\ln 3}$ **53.** $y' = -\sin x(\ln(\cos^2 x) + 2)$
55. $y' = -\frac{\ln 4}{x \ln^2 x}$ **57. a.** False **b.** True **c.** False **d.** False
e. True **59.** A is $y = \log_2 x$. B is $y = \log_4 x$. C is $y = \log_{10} x$.
61.

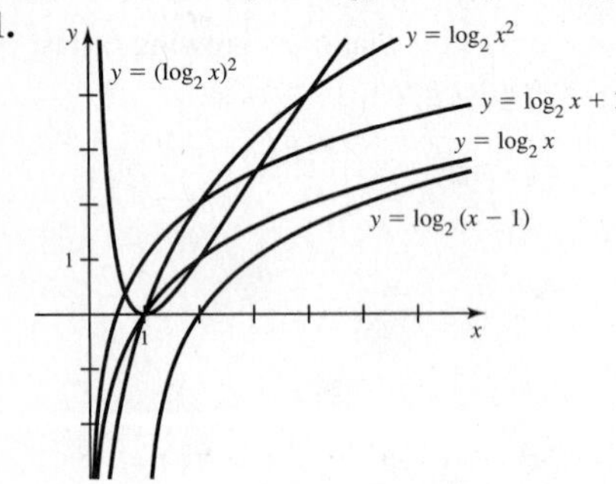

63. $\frac{d^2}{dx^2}[\log x] = \frac{-1}{x^2 \ln 10}$ **65.** $d^3/dx^3 = 2/x$ **67.** $y' = 3^x \ln 3$
69. $f'(x) = 1/(2x \ln 10)$ **71.** $f'(x) = \frac{2}{2x - 1} + \frac{3}{x + 2} + \frac{8}{1 - 4x}$
73. $y = 2$

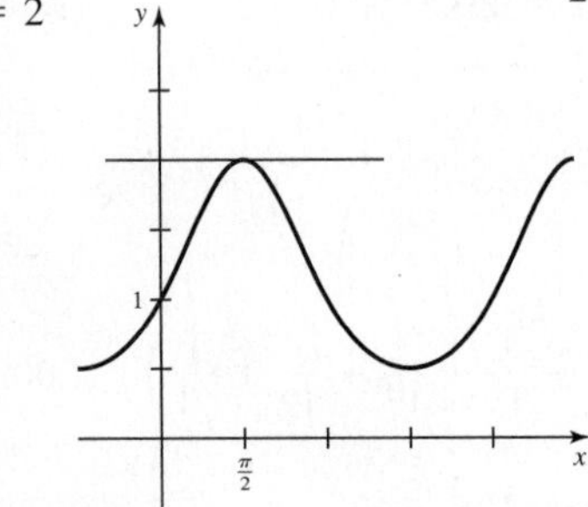

75. $10x^{10x}(1 + \ln x)$ **77.** $x^{\cos x}\left(\frac{\cos x}{x} - (\ln x)\sin x\right)$
79. $\left(1 + \frac{1}{x}\right)^x\left[\ln\left(1 + \frac{1}{x}\right) - \frac{1}{x + 1}\right]$ **81.** $x^{9+x^{10}}(1 + 10 \ln x)$
83. $-\frac{1}{9^x \ln 9} + C$ **85.** $\frac{10^{x^3}}{3 \ln 10} + C$ **87.** $\frac{3 \cdot 3^{\ln 2} - 1}{\ln 3}$ **89.** $1/e$
91. $27(1 + \ln 3)$

Section 7.4 Answers, pp. 416–418

1. The relative growth rate is constant. **3.** The time it takes for a function to double in value **5.** $T_2 = \ln 2/k$ **7.** Compound interest, world population **9.** $\frac{df}{dt} = 10.5; \frac{dg}{dt} \cdot \frac{1}{g} = \frac{10e^{t/10}}{100e^{t/10}} = \frac{1}{10}$
11. $P(t) = 90{,}000e^{0.024t}$ people with $t = 0$ in 2010; in 2039
13. \$134.39 **15. a.** 99.367 yr; $P(100) \approx 564$ million
b. 139 yr and 77 yr; $P(100) \approx 463$ million and $P(100) \approx 688$ million
c. The projections are highly sensitive to the growth rate.
17. $H(t) = 800e^{-0.030t}$ homicides/yr with $t = 0$ in 2010; in 2019
19. 18,928 ft; 125,754 ft **21. a.** 15.87 mg **b.** after 119.59 hr $\approx$ 5 days
23. $\approx$ 1.055 billion yr **25. a.** False **b.** False **c.** True **d.** True
e. True **27.** If $A(t) = A_0e^{kt}$ and $A(T) = 2A_0$, then $e^{kt} = 2$ and $T = (\ln 2)/k$. Thus the doubling time is a constant **29. a.** Bob; Abe
b. $y = 4 \ln(t + 1)$ and $y = 8 - 8e^{-t/2}$; Bob

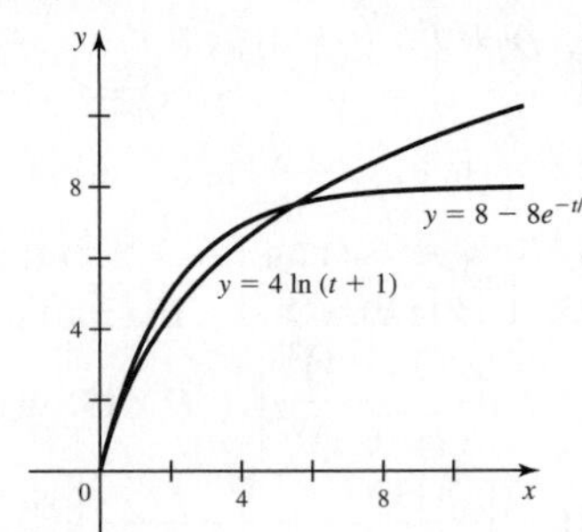

31. $\approx$ 10.034%; no **33.** $\approx$ 1.2643 s **35.** $\approx$ 1044 days
37. \$50 **39.** $k = \ln(1 + r), r = 2^{1/T_2} - 1, T_2 = \frac{\ln 2}{k}$

Section 7.5 Answers, pp. 429–432

1. Sine is not one-to-one on its domain. **3.** Yes; no **5.** Vertical asymptotes at $x = \pi/2$ and $x = -\pi/2$
7. $\frac{d}{dx}(\sin^{-1} x) = \frac{1}{\sqrt{1 - x^2}}; \frac{d}{dx}(\tan^{-1} x) = \frac{1}{1 + x^2};$
$\frac{d}{dx}(\sec^{-1} x) = \frac{1}{|x|\sqrt{x^2 - 1}}$ **9.** $\frac{1}{5}$ **11.** $\pi/3$ **13.** $2\pi/3$ **15.** -1
17. $\sqrt{1 - x^2}$ **19.** $\frac{\sqrt{4 - x^2}}{2}$ **21.** $2x\sqrt{1 - x^2}$
23. $\cos^{-1} x + \cos^{-1}(-x) = \theta + (\pi - \theta) = \pi$

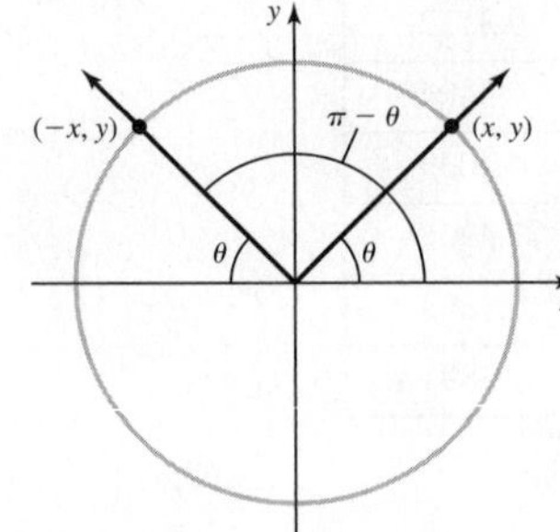

25. $\pi/3$ **27.** $\pi/3$ **29.** $\pi/4$ **31.** $\pi/2 - 2$ **33.** $\frac{1}{\sqrt{x^2 + 1}}$
35. $1/x$ **37.** $x/\sqrt{x^2 + 16}$
39. $\theta = \sin^{-1}\left(\frac{x}{6}\right) = \tan^{-1}\left(\frac{x}{\sqrt{36 - x^2}}\right) = \sec^{-1}\left(\frac{6}{\sqrt{36 - x^2}}\right)$
41. $\frac{2}{\sqrt{1 - 4x^2}}$ **43.** $\frac{-4w}{\sqrt{1 - 4w^2}}$ **45.** $\frac{-2e^{-2x}}{\sqrt{1 - e^{-4x}}}$
47. $\frac{4y}{1 + (2y^2 - 4)^2}$ **49.** $\frac{-1}{2\sqrt{z}(1 + z)}$ **51.** $\frac{1}{|x|\sqrt{x^2 - 1}}$

53. $\dfrac{-1}{|2u+1|\sqrt{u^2+u}}$ **55.** $\dfrac{2y}{(y^2+1)^2+1}$

57. $\dfrac{1}{x|\ln x|\sqrt{(\ln x)^2-1}}$ **59.** $\dfrac{-e^x\sec^2(e^x)}{|\tan e^x|\sqrt{\tan^2 e^x-1}}$

61. $\dfrac{-e^s}{1+e^{2s}}$ **63. a.** ≈ -0.00055 rad/m

b.

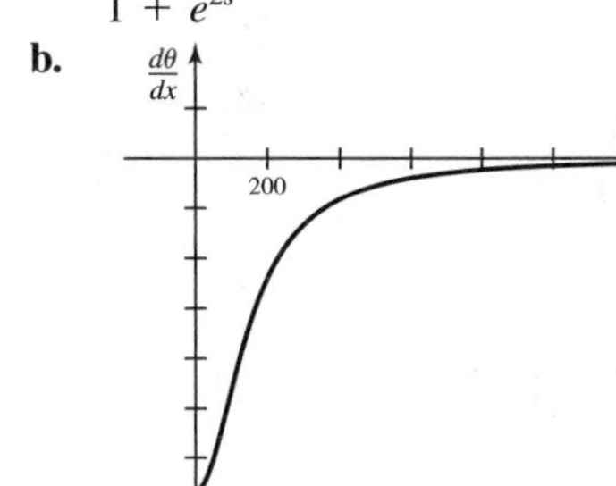

The magnitude of the change in angular size, $|d\theta/dx|$, is greatest when the boat is at the skyscraper (i.e., at $x = 0$)

65. $6\sin^{-1}\left(\dfrac{x}{5}\right)+C$ **67.** $\dfrac{1}{10}\sec^{-1}\left|\dfrac{x}{10}\right|+C$ **69.** $\pi/6$ **71.** $\pi/12$

73. a. False **b.** True **c.** False **d.** True **e.** False **f.** True **g.** True

75. $\sin\theta=\dfrac{12}{13}$; $\tan\theta=\dfrac{12}{5}$; $\sec\theta=\dfrac{13}{5}$; $\csc\theta=\dfrac{13}{12}$; $\cot\theta=\dfrac{5}{12}$

77. $\sin\theta=\dfrac{12}{13}$; $\cos\theta=\dfrac{5}{13}$; $\tan\theta=\dfrac{12}{5}$, $\sec\theta=\dfrac{13}{5}$; $\cot\theta=\dfrac{5}{12}$

79. a.

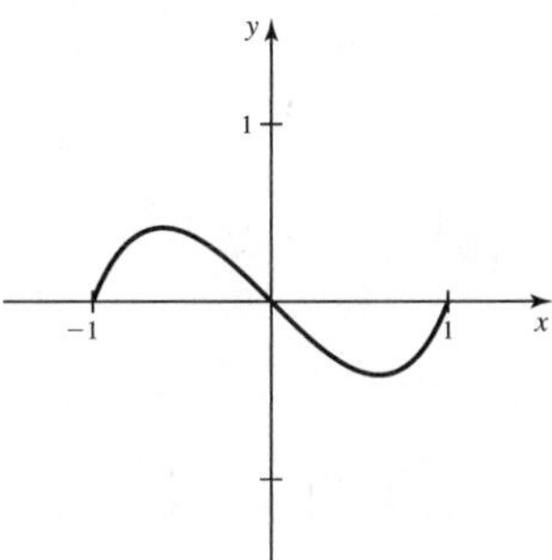

b. $f'(x)=2x\sin^{-1}(x)+\dfrac{x^2-1}{\sqrt{1-x^2}}$

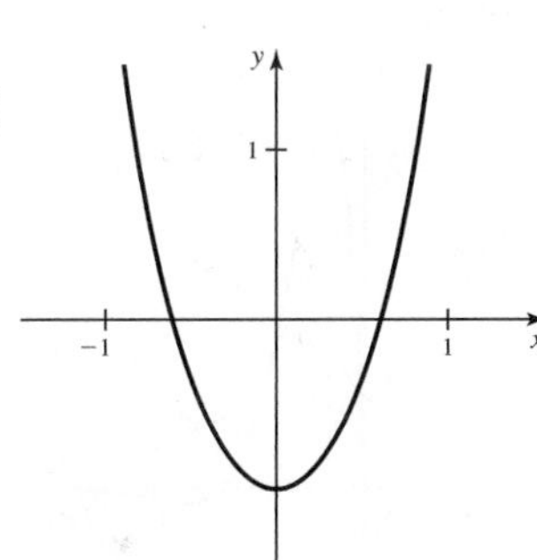

81. a.

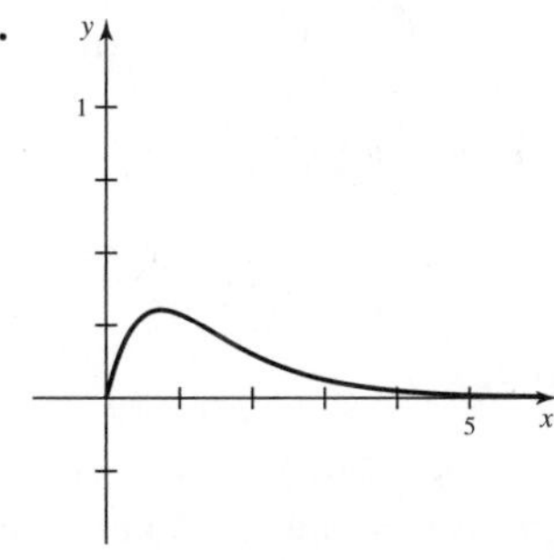

b. $f'(x)=\dfrac{e^{-x}}{1+x^2}-e^{-x}\tan^{-1}x$

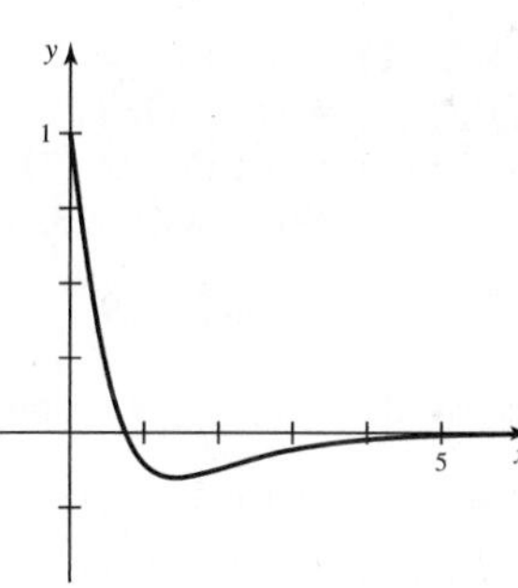

83. $\tan^{-1}(y-2)+C$ **85.** $\dfrac{1}{2}\tan^{-1}(e^x/2)+C$

87. a. $\sin\theta=\dfrac{10}{\ell}$ implies $\theta=\sin^{-1}\left(\dfrac{10}{\ell}\right)$. Thus,

$$\frac{d\theta}{d\ell}=\frac{1}{\sqrt{1-\left(\frac{10}{\ell}\right)^2}}\cdot(-10\ell^{-2})=\frac{-10}{\ell\sqrt{\ell^2-100}}.$$

b. $d\theta/d\ell=-0.0041, -0.0289$, and -0.1984

c. $\lim_{\ell\to10^+} d\theta/d\ell=-\infty$ **d.** The length ℓ is decreasing.

89. a. $d\theta/dc=1/\sqrt{R^2-c^2}$ **b.** $1/R$

93. Use the identity $\cot^{-1}(x)+\tan^{-1}(x)=\pi/2$.

Section 7.6 Answers, pp. 436–438

1. If $\lim_{x\to a} f(x)=1$ and $\lim_{x\to a} g(x)=\infty$, then $f(x)^{g(x)}\to 1^\infty$ as $x\to a$, which is meaningless; so direct substitution does not work.

3. $\lim_{x\to\infty}\dfrac{g(x)}{f(x)}=0$ **5.** $\ln x, x^3, 2^x, x^x$ **7.** 1 **9.** 1 **11.** e **13.** 1

15. e **17.** $e^{0.01x}$ **19.** Comparable growth rates **21.** x^x

23. 1.00001^x **25.** x^x **27.** e^{x^2} **29. a.** False **b.** False **c.** True

d. True **31.** $e^{-1/6}$ **33.** 1 **35.** 1 **37. a.** Approx. 3.44×10^{15}

b. Approx. 3536 **c.** e^{100} **d.** Approx. 163 **39.** 1 **41.** $\ln a-\ln b$

43. b. $\lim_{m\to\infty}(1+r/m)^m=\lim_{m\to\infty}\left(1+\dfrac{1}{(m/r)}\right)^{(m/r)r}=e^r$

45. $\lim_{x\to\infty}\dfrac{x^p}{b^x}=\lim_{t\to\infty}\dfrac{\ln^p t}{t\ln^p b}=0$ (let $t=b^x$, see Example 3).

47. Show $\lim_{x\to\infty}\dfrac{\log_a x}{\log_b x}=\dfrac{\ln b}{\ln a}\neq 0.$ **51. a.** $b>e$

b. e^{ax} grows faster than e^x as $x\to\infty$ for $a>1$; e^{ax} grows slower than e^x as $x\to\infty$ for $0<a<1$.

Review Exercises, pp. 438–440

1. a. True **b.** False **c.** False **d.** True **e.** False **f.** False

g. False **3.** $x=2$; base does not matter

5. $(-\infty,0],[0,2],[2,\infty)$ **7.** $f^{-1}(x)=2+\sqrt{x-1}$

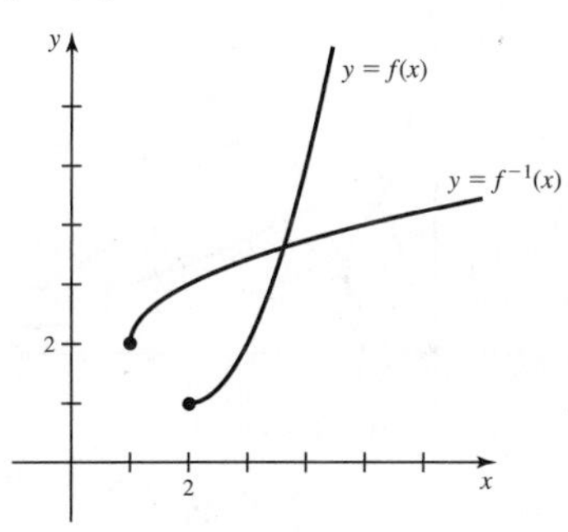

9. $-\sqrt{2}$ **11.** -1 **13.** $(f^{-1})'(x) = -3/x^4$ on $(-\infty, 0)$ and $(0, \infty)$ **15.** $(f^{-1})'(x) = 1/3$ **17.** $(f^{-1})'(x) = 1/(2\sqrt{x+4})$ **19.** $(f^{-1})'(x) = 2x, x \geq 0$ **21.** $(f^{-1})'(x) = -2/x^3, x > 0$ **23.** $(f^{-1})'(1/\sqrt{2}) = \sqrt{2}$ **25.** $(2 + \ln x)\ln x$ **27.** $(2x-1)2^{x^2-x}\ln 2$ **29.** $\dfrac{-1}{|x|\sqrt{x^2-1}}$ **31.** 1 **33.** $\sqrt{3} + \pi/6$ **35.** $\pi/6$ **37.** $-\pi/2$ **39.** x, provided $-1 \leq x \leq 1$ **41.** $\cos\theta = \dfrac{5}{13}$; $\tan\theta = \dfrac{12}{5}$; $\cot\theta = \dfrac{5}{12}$; $\sec\theta = \dfrac{13}{5}$; $\csc\theta = \dfrac{13}{12}$ **43.** $\dfrac{\sqrt{4-x^2}}{2}$ **45.** $\pi/2 - \theta$ **47.** 0 **49.** $1 - 2x^2$ **51.** $\ln 4$ **53.** $\dfrac{1}{2}\ln(x^2 + 8x + 25) + C$ **55.** $\dfrac{3\sqrt{2}}{2}\tan^{-1}(\sqrt{2}x) + C$ **57.** $\pi/6$ **59.** $\pi/6$ **61.** $3\ln 6 + \dfrac{35}{24}$ **63.** $65/32$ **65.** $2\pi\ln 17$

67. a. $s_{\text{Tom}}(t) = -10e^{-2t} + 10$
$s_{\text{Sue}}(t) = -15e^{-t} + 15$

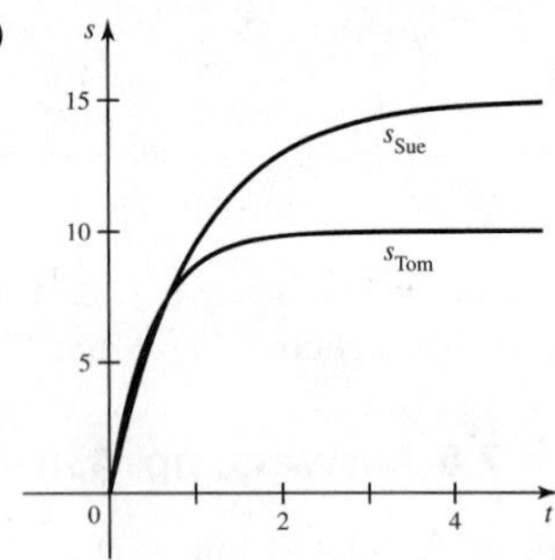

b. $t = 0$ and $t = \ln 2$ **c.** Sue **69.** 48.37 yr **71.** Local max at $x = -\dfrac{1}{2}(\sqrt{5}+1)$; local min at $x = \dfrac{1}{2}(\sqrt{5}-1)$; inflection points at $x = -3$ and $x = 0$; $\lim_{x\to\infty} f(x) = 0$; $\lim_{x\to\infty} f(x) = \infty$.

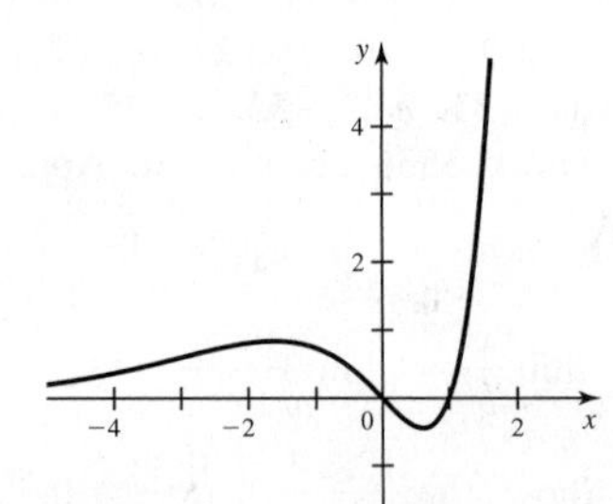

73. $\sqrt{b^2+1} - \sqrt{2} + \ln\left(\dfrac{(\sqrt{b^2+1}-1)(1+\sqrt{2})}{b}\right)$; $b \approx 2.715$ **75.** 1 **77.** 0 **79.** $1/e^3$ **81.** $x^{1/2}$ **83.** $\sqrt{x}$ **85.** 3^x **87.** Comparable growth rates **89.** 1; 1 **91.** $\lim_{x\to 0^+} f(x) = 1$; $\lim_{x\to 0^+} g(x) = 0$

95. a.

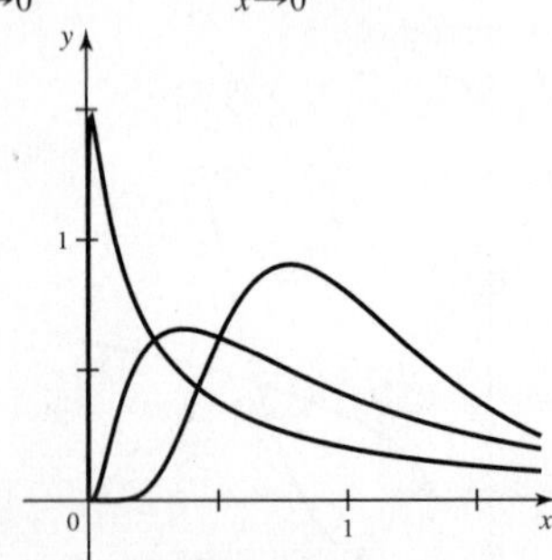

b. $\lim_{x\to 0} f(x) = 0$ **c.** $f'(x^*) = 0$ **d.** $f(x^*) = \dfrac{1}{\sqrt{2\pi}}\dfrac{e^{\sigma^2/2}}{\sigma}$ **e.** $\sigma = 1$ **97.** 5 people per group

CHAPTER 8

Section 8.1 Exercises, pp. 447–449

1. The Product Rule **3.** $u = x^n$ **5.** Those for which the choice for dv is easily integrated and when the resulting new integral is no more difficult than the original **7.** $x\sin x + \cos x + C$ **9.** $te^t - e^t + C$ **11.** $\left(\dfrac{2x^2-1}{4}\right)\cos 2x + \dfrac{x}{2}\sin 2x + C$ **13.** $\dfrac{e^{4x}}{32}(8x^2 - 4x + 1) + C$ **15.** $\dfrac{x^3}{9}(3\ln x - 1) + C$ **17.** $-\dfrac{1}{9x^9}\left(\ln x + \dfrac{1}{9}\right) + C$ **19.** $x\tan^{-1}x - \frac{1}{2}\ln(x^2+1) + C$ **21.** $\dfrac{1}{8}\sin 2x - \dfrac{x}{4}\cos 2x + C$ **23.** $\dfrac{e^x}{2}(\sin x + \cos x) + C$ **25.** $-\dfrac{e^{-x}}{17}(\sin 4x + 4\cos 4x) + C$ **27.** $-e^{-t}(t^3 + 3t^2 + 6t + 6) + C$ **29.** π **31.** $-\frac{1}{2}$ **33.** $\frac{1}{9}(5e^6 + 1)$ **35.** $\left(\dfrac{2\sqrt{3}-1}{12}\right)\pi + \dfrac{1-\sqrt{3}}{2}$ **37.** $\pi(1 - \ln 2)$ **39.** $\dfrac{2\pi}{27}(13e^6 - 1)$ **41. a.** False **b.** True **43.** Let $u = x^n$ and $dv = \cos(ax)\,dx$. **45.** Let $u = \ln^n x$ and $dv = dx$. **47.** $\dfrac{x^2\sin(5x)}{5} + \dfrac{2x\cos(5x)}{25} - \dfrac{2\sin(5x)}{125} + C$ **49.** $x\ln^4 x - 4x\ln^3 x + 12x\ln^2 x - 24x\ln x + 24x + C$ **51.** $(\tan x + 2)\ln(\tan x + 2) - \tan x + C$ **53.** $\displaystyle\int \log_b x\,dx = \int \frac{\ln x}{\ln b}\,dx = \frac{1}{\ln b}(x\ln x - x) + C$ **55.** $2\sqrt{x}\sin\sqrt{x} + 2\cos\sqrt{x} + C$ **57.** $2e^3$ **59.** $\pi(\pi - 2)$ **61.** x-axis $\dfrac{\pi^2}{2}$; y-axis $2\pi^2$ **63. a.** Let $u = x$ and $v = f(x)$. **b.** $\dfrac{e^{3x}}{9}(3x - 1) + C$ **65.** Use $u = \sec x$ and $dv = \sec^2 x\,dx$.

67. a.

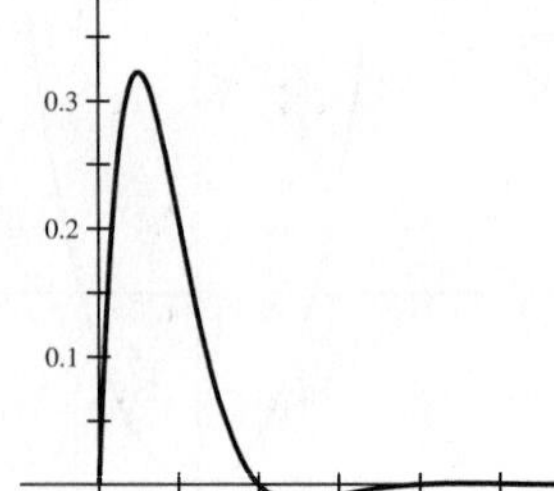

$t = k\pi$ for $k = 0, 1, 2, \ldots$ **b.** $\dfrac{e^{-\pi}+1}{2\pi}$ **c.** $(-1)^n\left(\dfrac{e^{\pi}+1}{2\pi e^{(n+1)\pi}}\right)$ **d.** $a_n = a_{n-1}\cdot\dfrac{1}{e^{\pi}}$

69. $\displaystyle\int_a^b u\,dv + \int_a^b v\,du = A + B = f(b)g(b) - f(a)g(a) = uv\Big]_a^b$ **71. a.** $I_1 = -\frac{1}{2}e^{-x^2} + C$ **b.** $I_3 = -\frac{1}{2}e^{-x^2}(x^2+1) + C$ **c.** $I_5 = -\frac{1}{2}e^{-x^2}(x^4 + 2x^2 + 2) + C$ **d.** $I_{2n+1} = -\frac{1}{2}e^{-x^2}x^{2n} + nI_{2n-1}$

Section 8.2 Exercises, pp. 455–456

1. $\sin^2 x = \frac{1}{2}(1 - \cos 2x)$; $\cos^2 x = \frac{1}{2}(1 + \cos 2x)$ **3.** Rewrite $\sin^3 x$ as $(1 - \cos^2 x)\sin x$. **5.** A reduction formula expresses an integral with a power in the integrand in terms of another integral with a smaller power in the integrand. **7.** Let $u = \tan x$. **9.** $\dfrac{x}{2} - \dfrac{1}{4}\sin 2x + C$ **11.** $-\cos x + \dfrac{2}{3}\cos^3 x - \dfrac{\cos^5 x}{5} + C$

13. $\frac{1}{8}x - \frac{1}{32}\sin 4x + C$ **15.** $\sec x + 2\cos x - \frac{\cos^3 x}{3} + C$
17. $\frac{\sin^3 x \cos^3 x}{6} + \frac{1}{16}x - \frac{1}{64}\sin 4x + C$ **19.** $\tan x - x + C$
21. $\frac{1}{8}\tan^2 4x + \frac{1}{4}\ln|\cos 4x| + C$
23. $4\tan^5 x - \frac{20}{3}\tan^3 x + 20\tan x - 20x + C$
25. $\frac{2}{3}\tan^{3/2} x + C$ **27.** $\tan x - \cot x + C$ **29.** $\frac{4}{3}$ **31.** $\frac{4}{3} - \ln\sqrt{3}$
33. a. True **b.** False **37.** $\frac{1}{a}\ln|\sec ax| + C$, $\frac{1}{a}\ln|\sec ax + \tan ax| + C$ **39.** $\frac{1}{2}\ln\left(\sqrt{2} + \frac{3}{2}\right)$
41. $\frac{1}{3}\tan(\ln\theta)\sec^2(\ln\theta) + \frac{2}{3}\tan(\ln\theta) + C$ **43.** $\ln 4$ **45.** $8\sqrt{2}/3$
47. $\sqrt{2}$ **49.** $2\sqrt{2}/3$ **51.** $\ln(\sqrt{2} + 1)$ **53.** $\frac{1}{2} - \ln\sqrt{2}$
55. $\frac{\cos 4x}{8} - \frac{\cos 10x}{20} + C$ **57.** $\frac{\sin x}{2} - \frac{\sin 5x}{10} + C$
61. $\int_0^{\pi} \sin^2 nx\,dx = \int_0^{\pi}\cos^2 nx\,dx = \pi/2 \quad n = 1, 2, 3, \ldots$. $\int_0^{\pi}\sin^4 nx\,dx = \frac{3\pi}{8}, \quad n = 1, 2, 3, \ldots$

Section 8.3 Exercises, pp. 462–465

1. $x = 3\sec\theta$ **3.** $x = 10\sin\theta$ **5.** $\sqrt{4 - x^2}/x$ **7.** $\pi/6$
9. $25(2\pi/3 - \sqrt{3}/2)$ **11.** $\sin^{-1}(x/4) + C$
13. $3\ln\left(\frac{\sqrt{9 - x^2} - 3}{x}\right) + \sqrt{9 - x^2} + C$
15. $\frac{x}{2}\sqrt{64 - x^2} + 32\sin^{-1}\left(\frac{x}{8}\right) + C$ **17.** $\sin^{-1}(x/6) + C$
19. $\ln\left(\sqrt{x^2 - 81} + x\right) + C$ **21.** $x/\sqrt{1 + 4x^2} + C$
23. $8\sin^{-1}(x/4) - x\sqrt{16 - x^2}/2 + C$
25. $\sqrt{x^2 - 9} - 3\sec^{-1}\left(\frac{x}{3}\right) + C$
27. $\frac{x}{2}\sqrt{4 + x^2} - 2\ln\left(x + \sqrt{4 + x^2}\right) + C$
29. $\sin^{-1}\left(\frac{x + 1}{2}\right) + C$ **31.** $\frac{9}{10}\cos^{-1}\left(\frac{5}{3x}\right) - \frac{45\sqrt{9x^2 - 25}}{90x^2} + C$
33. $\frac{1}{10}\left[\tan^{-1}\left(\frac{x}{5}\right) - \frac{5x}{25 + x^2}\right] + C$
35. $x/\sqrt{100 - x^2} - \sin^{-1}(x/10) + C$
37. $81/(2(81 - x^2)) + \ln\left(\sqrt{81 - x^2}\right) + C$
39. $-1/\sqrt{x^2 - 1} - \sec^{-1}(x) + C$ **41.** $\ln\left(\frac{1 + \sqrt{17}}{4}\right)$
43. $\sqrt{2}/6$ **45.** $\frac{1}{16}[1 - \sqrt{3} - \ln(21 - 12\sqrt{3})]$ **47. a.** False **b.** True **c.** False **d.** False **49.** $\frac{1}{3}\tan^{-1}\left(\frac{x + 3}{3}\right) + C$
51. $\left(\frac{x - 1}{2}\right)\sqrt{x^2 - 2x + 10} - \frac{9}{2}\ln\left(x - 1 + \sqrt{x^2 - 2x + 10}\right) + C$
53. $\frac{x - 4}{\sqrt{9 + 8x - x^2}} - \sin^{-1}\left(\frac{x - 4}{5}\right) + C$ **55.** $\frac{\pi\sqrt{2}}{48}$
57. a. $A_{\text{seg}} = A_{\text{sector}} - A_{\text{triangle}} = \frac{\theta r^2}{2} - \frac{r^2\sin\theta}{2} = \frac{r^2}{2}(\theta - \sin\theta)$

59. a. $\ln 3$ **b.** $\frac{\pi}{3}\tan^{-1}\left(\frac{4}{3}\right)$ **c.** 4π
61. $\frac{1}{4a}\left[20a\sqrt{1 + 400a^2} + \ln\left(20a + \sqrt{1 + 400a^2}\right)\right]$
63. $\frac{1}{81} + \frac{\ln 3}{108}$

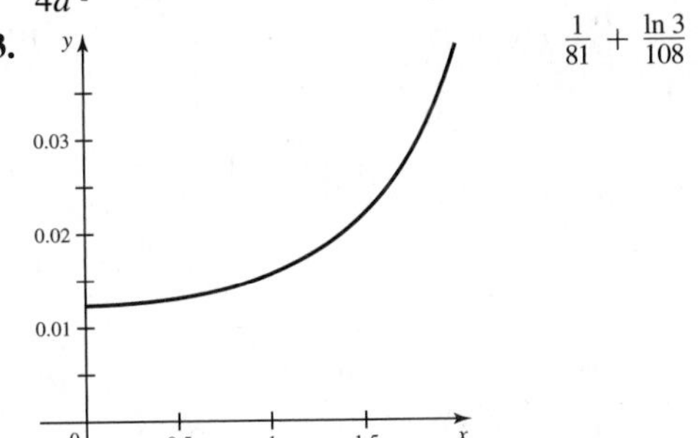

65. $25\left(\sqrt{3} - \ln\sqrt{2 + \sqrt{3}}\right)$

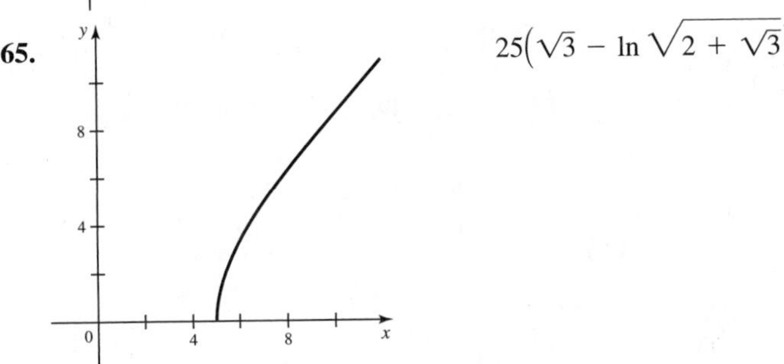

67. $\ln[(2 + \sqrt{3})(\sqrt{2} - 1)]$ **69.** $192\pi^2$
71. b. $\lim_{L\to\infty}\frac{kQ}{a\sqrt{a^2 + L^2}} = \lim_{L\to\infty} 2\rho k\frac{1}{a\sqrt{\left(\frac{a}{L}\right)^2 + 1}} = \frac{2\rho k}{a}$
73. a. $\frac{1}{\sqrt{g}}\left[\frac{\pi}{2} - \sin^{-1}\left(\frac{2\cos b - \cos a + 1}{\cos a + 1}\right)\right]$ **b.** For $b = \pi$, the descent time is $\frac{\pi}{\sqrt{g}}$, a constant.
77. $\pi - 3\sqrt{3}$

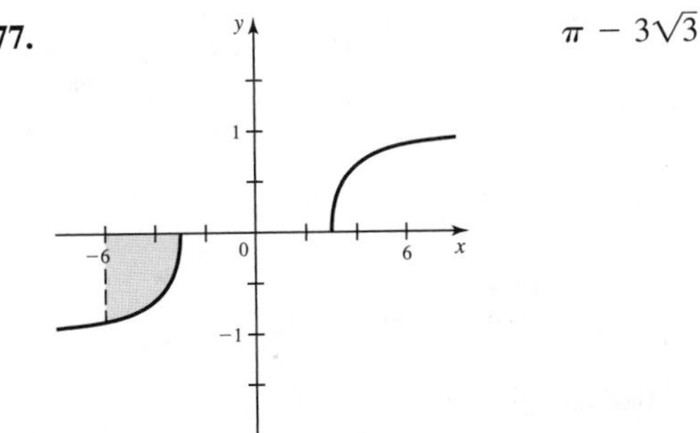

Section 8.4 Exercises, pp. 472–474

1. Rational functions **3. a.** $\frac{A}{x - 3}$ **b.** $\frac{A_1}{(x - 4)}, \frac{A_2}{(x - 4)^2}, \frac{A_3}{(x - 4)^3}$
c. $\frac{Ax + B}{x^2 + 2x + 6}$ **5.** $\frac{\frac{1}{3}}{x - 4} + \frac{-\frac{1}{3}}{x + 2}$ **7.** $\frac{\frac{1}{2}}{x - 4} + \frac{\frac{1}{2}}{x + 4}$
9. $\ln\left|\frac{x - 1}{x + 2}\right|^{1/3} + C$ **11.** $\ln\left|\frac{x - 1}{x + 1}\right|^{3/2} + C$ **13.** $\ln\left|\frac{x - 3}{x + 2}\right|^{2/5} + C$
15. $\ln\left|\frac{x - 6}{x + 4}\right|^{1/10} + C$ **17.** $\ln\left|\frac{(x - 3)^{1/3}(x + 1)}{(x + 3)^{1/3}(x - 1)}\right|^{1/16} + C$
19. $\ln\left|\frac{x - 9}{x}\right|^{1/27} + \frac{1}{3x} + C$ **21.** $\ln|x + 3| + \frac{3}{x + 3} + C$

23. $-\frac{2}{x} + \ln\left|\frac{x+1}{x}\right|^2 + C$ **25.** $\frac{5}{x} + \ln\left|\frac{x}{x+1}\right|^6 + C$

27. $\frac{A}{x-1} + \frac{B}{(x-1)^2} + \frac{Cx+D}{x^2+1}$

29. $\frac{A}{x-4} + \frac{B}{(x-4)^2} + \frac{Cx+D}{x^2+3x+4}$

31. $\ln\left(\frac{|x-4|}{\sqrt{x^2+2x+6}}\right)^{1/15} - \frac{\sqrt{5}}{15}\tan^{-1}\left(\frac{x+1}{\sqrt{5}}\right) + C$

33. $\ln|(x-1)(x^2+4x+5)^{9/2}|^{1/10} - \frac{13}{10}\tan^{-1}(x+2) + C$

35. $\ln|(x-1)^{1/5}(x^2+4)^{2/5}| + \frac{2}{5}\tan^{-1}\left(\frac{x}{2}\right) + C$

37. a. False **b.** False **c.** False **d.** True **39.** ln 6

41. $4\sqrt{2} + \ln(17-12\sqrt{2})^{1/3}$ **43.** $\left(\frac{24}{5} - 2\ln 5\right)\pi$

45. $\frac{2}{3}\pi\ln 2$ **47.** $2\pi\left(3+\ln\frac{2}{5}\right)$ **49.** $x - \ln(1+e^x)+C$

51. $3x + \ln\frac{(x-2)^{14}}{|x-1|} + C$ **53.** $\ln\sqrt{2e^x+1}+C$

55. $\frac{1}{2}\left(\sec x\tan x - \sec^2 x + \ln|\sec x+\tan x|\right)+C$

57. $\ln\left|\frac{e^x-1}{e^x+2}\right|^{1/3}+C$ **59.** $-\frac{1}{2(e^{2x}+1)}+C$

61. $\frac{4}{3}(x+2)^{3/4} - 2(x+2)^{1/2} + 4(x+2)^{1/4} -$ $\ln[(x+2)^{1/4}+1]^4 + C$

63. $2\sqrt{x} - 3\sqrt[3]{x} + 6\sqrt[6]{x} - \ln(\sqrt[6]{x}+1)^6 + C$

65. $\frac{4}{3}\sqrt{1+\sqrt{x}}(\sqrt{x} - 2)+C$ **67.** $\ln\left(\frac{x^2}{x^2+1}\right) + \frac{1}{x^2+1} + C$

69. $\frac{1}{50}\left[\frac{5(3x+4)}{x^2+2x+2} + 11\tan^{-1}(1+x) + \ln\left|\frac{(x-1)^2}{x^2+2x+2}\right|\right]+C$

71. $\ln\sqrt{\left|\frac{x-1}{x+1}\right|}$ **73.** $\tan x - \sec x + C$ **75.** $-\cot x - \csc x + C$

77. $\frac{\sqrt{2}}{2}\ln\left(\frac{\sqrt{2}+1+\tan(\theta/2)}{\sqrt{2}-1-\tan(\theta/2)}\right)+C$ **79. a.** Car A **b.** Car C

c. $S_A(t) = 88t - 88\ln|t+1|$;

$S_B(t) = 88\left[t - \ln(t+1)^2 - \frac{1}{t+1} + 1\right]$;

$S_C(t) = 88(t - \tan^{-1}t)$

d. Car C **81.** Since $\frac{x^4(1-x)^4}{1+x^2} > 0$ on $(0,1)$;

$\int_0^1 \frac{x^4(1-x^4)}{1+x^2}\,dx > 0$; thus, $\frac{22}{7} > \pi$.

Section 8.5 Exercises, pp. 478–480

1. Substitutions, integration by parts, partial fractions **3.** The CAS may not include the constant of integration and it may use a trigonometric identity or other algebraic simplification.

5. $\ln(x+\sqrt{16+x^2})+C$ **7.** $\frac{3}{4}(7+2u-7\ln|7+2u|)+C$

9. $-\frac{1}{4}\cot 2x + C$ **11.** $\frac{\sqrt{4x+1}}{2}+C$

13. $\frac{1}{3}\ln\left|x+\sqrt{x^2-\left(\frac{10}{3}\right)^2}\right|+C$ **15.** $\frac{x}{16\sqrt{16+9x^2}}+C$

17. $-\frac{1}{12}\ln\left|\frac{12+\sqrt{144-x^2}}{x}\right|+C$

19. $\ln x - \frac{1}{10}\ln(x^{10}+1)+C$

21. $\frac{1}{3}\tan^{-1}\left(\frac{x+1}{3}\right)+C$ **23.** $2\ln\left(\sqrt{x-6}+\sqrt{x}\right)+C$

25. $\ln(e^x+\sqrt{4+e^{2x}})+C$ **27.** $-\frac{1}{2}\ln\left|\frac{2+\sin x}{\sin x}\right|+C$

29. $-\frac{\tan^{-1}(x^3)}{3x^3} + \ln\left|\frac{x}{(x^6+1)^{1/6}}\right|+C$

31. $\frac{2(\ln x)^2-1}{4}\sin^{-1}(\ln x) + \frac{\ln x\sqrt{1-(\ln x)^2}}{4}+C$

33. $4\sqrt{17}+\ln(4+\sqrt{17})$ **35.** $\sqrt{5}-\sqrt{2}+\ln\left(\frac{2+2\sqrt{2}}{1+\sqrt{5}}\right)$

37. $\frac{128\pi}{3}$ **39.** $\frac{\pi^2}{4}$ **41.** $\frac{(x-3)\sqrt{3+2x}}{3}+C$

43. $\frac{1}{3}\tan(3x) - x + C$

45. $\frac{(x^2-a^2)^{3/2}}{3} - a^2\sqrt{x^2-a^2} + a^3\cos^{-1}\left(\frac{a}{x}\right)+C$

47. $-\frac{x}{8}(2x^2-5a^2)\sqrt{a^2-x^2} + \frac{3a^4}{8}\sin^{-1}\left(\frac{x}{a}\right)+C$

49. $\frac{\left(\frac{4}{5}\right)^9 - \left(\frac{2}{3}\right)^9}{9}$ **51.** $\frac{1540+243\ln 3}{8}$ **53.** $\frac{\pi}{4}$ **55.** $2 - \frac{\pi^2}{12} - \ln 4$

57. a. True **b.** True **61.** $\frac{1}{8}e^{2x}(4x^3-6x^2+6x-3)+C$

63. $\frac{\tan^3(3y)}{9} - \frac{\tan(3y)}{3} + y + C$

65. $\frac{1}{16}[(8x^2-1)\sin^{-1}(2x) + 2x\sqrt{1-4x^2}]+C$

67. $-\frac{\tan^{-1}x}{x} + \ln\left(\frac{|x|}{\sqrt{x^2+1}}\right)+C$ **69.** $\sin^{-1}\left(\frac{x-a}{a}\right)+C$

71. a.

θ_0	T
0.10	6.27927
0.20	6.26762
0.30	6.24854
0.40	6.22253
0.50	6.19021
0.60	6.15236
0.70	6.10979
0.80	6.06338
0.90	6.01399
1.00	5.96247

b. All are within 10%.

73. $\frac{1}{a^2}[ax - b\ln|b+ax|]+C$

75. $\frac{1}{a^2}\left[\frac{(ax+b)^{n+2}}{n+2} - \frac{b(ax+b)^{n+1}}{n+1}\right]+C$ **77. b.** $\frac{63\pi}{512}$

c. Decrease

Section 8.6 Exercises, pp. 488–490

1. $\frac{1}{2}$ **3.** The Trapezoid Rule approximates areas under curves using trapezoids. **5.** $-1, 1, 3, 5, 7, 9$ **7.** 1.59×10^{-3}; 5.04×10^{-4} **9.** 1.72×10^{-3}; 6.32×10^{-4} **11.** 576; 640; 656 **13.** 0.643950551

15. 704; 672; 664 **17.** 0.622 **19.** $M(25) = 0.63703884$, $T(25) = 0.63578179$; 6.58×10^{-4}, 1.32×10^{-3}

21.

n	$M(n)$	$T(n)$	Abs. Error $M(n)$	Abs. Error $T(n)$
4	99	102	1.00	2.00
8	99.75	100.5	0.250	0.500
16	99.9375	100.125	0.0625	0.125
32	99.984375	100.03125	0.0156	0.0313

23.

n	$M(n)$	$T(n)$	Abs. Error $M(n)$	Abs. Error $T(n)$
4	1.50968181	1.48067370	9.68×10^{-3}	1.93×10^{-2}
8	1.50241228	1.49517776	2.41×10^{-3}	4.82×10^{-3}
16	1.50060256	1.49879502	6.03×10^{-4}	1.20×10^{-3}
32	1.50015061	1.49969879	1.51×10^{-4}	3.01×10^{-4}

25.

n	$M(n)$	$T(n)$	Abs. Error $M(n)$	Abs. Error $T(n)$
4	-1.96×10^{-16}	0	1.96×10^{-16}	0
8	7.63×10^{-17}	-1.41×10^{-16}	7.63×10^{-17}	1.42×10^{-16}
16	1.61×10^{-16}	1.09×10^{-17}	1.61×10^{-16}	1.09×10^{-17}
32	6.27×10^{-17}	-4.77×10^{-17}	6.27×10^{-17}	4.77×10^{-17}

27. $\frac{164}{3} \approx 54.7$ **29.** $\frac{421}{12} \approx 35.1$

31. a. $T(25) = 3.19623162$
$T(50) = 3.19495398$
b. $S(50) = 3.19452809$
c. $e_T(50) = 4.26 \times 10^{-4}$
$e_S(50) = 4.05 \times 10^{-8}$

33. a. $T(50) = 1.00008509$
$T(100) = 1.00002127$
b. $S(100) = 1.00000000$
c. $e_T(100) = 2.13 \times 10^{-5}$
$e_S(100) = 4.57 \times 10^{-9}$

35.

n	$T(n)$	$S(n)$	*Error* $T(n)$	*Error* $S(n)$
4	1820.0000	—	284	—
8	1607.7500	1537.0000	71.8	1
16	1553.9844	1536.0625	18.0	6.25×10^{-2}
32	1540.4990	1536.0039	4.50	3.90×10^{-3}

37.

n	$T(n)$	$S(n)$	*Error* $T(n)$	*Error* $S(n)$
4	0.46911538	—	5.25×10^{-2}	—
8	0.50826998	0.52132152	1.33×10^{-2}	2.85×10^{-4}
16	0.51825968	0.52158957	3.35×10^{-3}	1.74×10^{-5}
32	0.52076933	0.52160588	8.38×10^{-4}	1.08×10^{-6}

39. a. True **b.** False **c.** True

41.

n	$M(n)$	$T(n)$	Abs. Error $M(n)$	Abs. Error $T(n)$
4	0.40635058	0.40634782	1.38×10^{-6}	1.38×10^{-6}
8	0.40634920	0.40634920	7.6×10^{-10}	7.62×10^{-10}
16	0.40634920	0.40634920	6.55×10^{-13}	6.56×10^{-13}
32	0.40634920	0.40634920	8.88×10^{-16}	7.77×10^{-16}

43.

n	$M(n)$	$T(n)$	Abs. Error $M(n)$	Abs. Error $T(n)$
4	4.72531819	4.72507878	0.00012	0.00012
8	4.72519850	4.72519849	9.12×10^{-9}	9.12×10^{-9}
16	4.72519850	4.72519850	0.	8.88×10^{-16}
32	4.72519850	4.72519850	0.	8.88×10^{-16}

49. Approximations will vary; exact value is 38.753792 . . . . **51.** Approximations will vary; exact value is 68.26894921 . . . . **53. a.** Approximately 1.6×10^{11} barrels **b.** Approximately 6.8×10^{10} barrels **55. a.** $T(40) = 0.874799972 \ldots$ **b.** $f''(x) = e^x \cos(e^x) - e^{2x} \sin(e^x)$ **d.** $E_T \leq \frac{1}{3200}$ **59.** Overestimate

Section 8.7 Exercises, pp. 499–502

1. The interval of integration is infinite or the integrand is unbounded on the interval of integration. **3.** $\int_0^1 \frac{1}{\sqrt{x}}\,dx = \lim_{b \to 0^+} \int_b^1 \frac{1}{\sqrt{x}}\,dx$ **5.** 1 **7.** Diverges **9.** $\frac{1}{2}$ **11.** $\frac{1}{(p-1)\,2^{p-1}}$ **13.** $\frac{1}{2}$ **15.** $1/\pi$ **17.** Diverges **19.** Diverges **21.** $\frac{\pi}{3}$ **23.** $3\pi/2$ **25.** $\pi/(\ln 2)$ **27.** 6 **29.** Diverges **31.** $4 \cdot 10^{3/4}/3$ **33.** -2 **35.** π **37.** 2π **39.** $\frac{72 \cdot 2^{1/3}\pi}{5}$ **41.** 48 **43.** 0.76 **45.** 10 mi **47. a.** True **b.** False **c.** False **d.** True **e.** True **49. a.** 2; **b.** 0 **51.** $\int_0^\infty e^{-x^2}\,dx \approx 0.886227$ **53.** $-\frac{1}{4}$ **55.** $\int_0^\infty xe^{-x^2}\,dx = \frac{1}{2}$; $\int_0^\infty x^2 e^{-x^2}\,dx = \sqrt{\pi}/4 \approx 0.443$ **57.** $1/b - 1/a$ **59. a.** $A(a,b) = \frac{e^{-ab}}{a}$ for $a > 0$ **b.** $b = g(a) = \frac{-1}{a}\ln(2a)$ **c.** $b^* = -2/e$ **61. a.** $p < \frac{1}{2}$ **b.** $p < 2$ **67.** \$41,666.67 **71.** 20,000 hr **73. a.** $6.28 \times 10^7 m$ J **b.** 11.2 km/s **c.** ≤ 9 mm **75. a.**

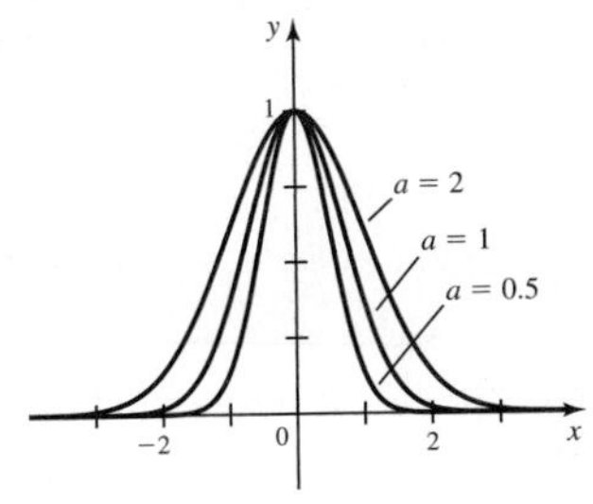

b. $\sqrt{2\pi}, \sqrt{\pi}, \sqrt{\pi/2}$ **c.** $e^{(b^2-4ac)/(4a)}\sqrt{\pi/a}$ **81. a.** π **b.** $\pi/(4e^2)$ **83.** $p > 1$

Section 8.8 Exercises, pp. 509–512

1. Second order **3.** Two constants **5.** A separable equation can be written in the form $g(y)y'(t) = h(t)$. **7.** Integrate both sides with respect to t and convert the integral on the left side to an integral with respect to y. **9.** $y = t^3 - 2t^2 + 10t + 20$ **11.** $y = t^2 + 4\ln t + 1$

13. $y = Ce^{3t} + \frac{4}{3}$ **15.** $y = Ce^{-2x} - 2$ **17.** $y = 7e^{3t} + 2$ **19.** $y = 2e^{-2t} - 2$ **21. a.** $y = 150(1 - e^{-0.02t})$ **b.** 150 mg **c.** $t = \frac{\ln 10}{0.02}$ hr ≈ 115 hr

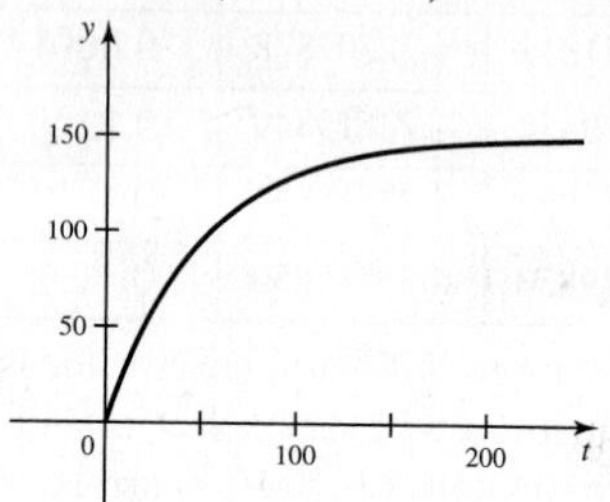

23. $y = \pm\sqrt{2t^3 + C}$ **25.** $y = -2\ln\left(\frac{1}{2}\cos t + C\right)$ **27.** Not separable **29.** $y = \sqrt{e^t - 1}$ **31.** $y = \ln(e^x + 2)$ **33. a.** $P = \frac{200}{3e^{-0.08t} + 1}$

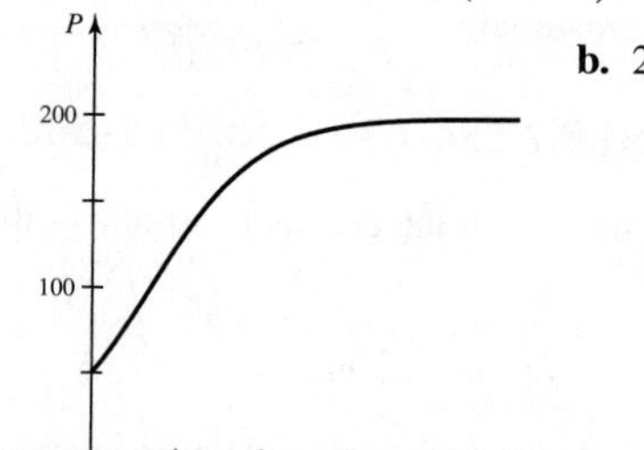

b. 200

35.

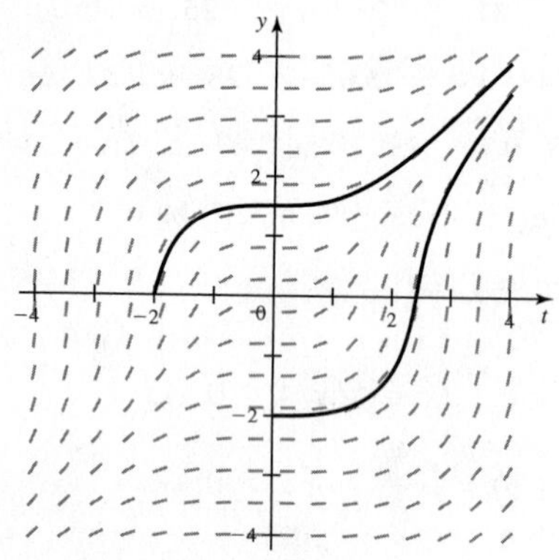

37. A–c, B–b, C–d, D–a **39.**

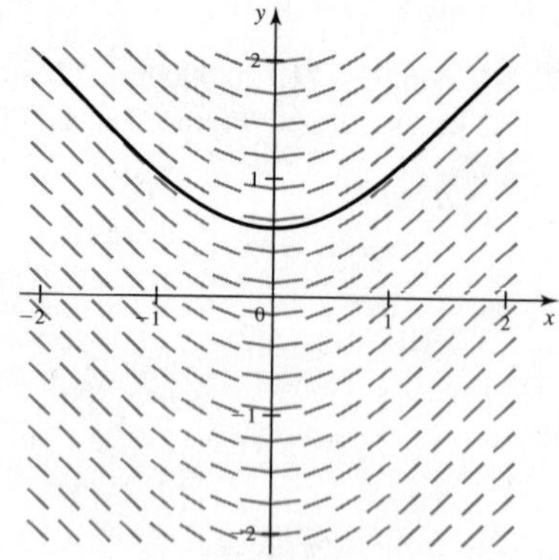

41. a. False **b.** False **c.** False **d.** True **43. a.** $y = 0$

b.

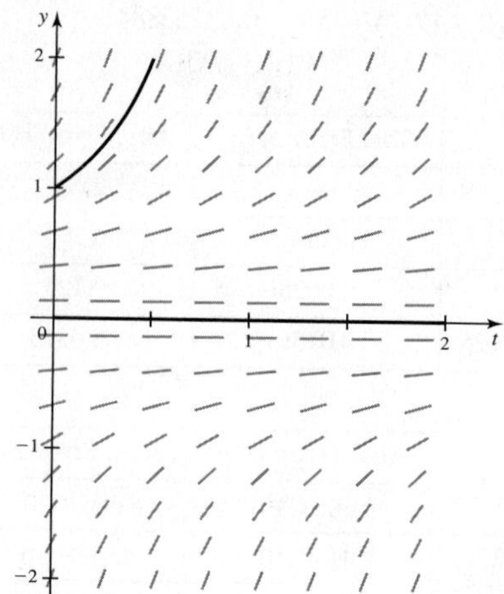

45. a. Equilibrium solutions $y = 0$ and $y = 3$ **b.**

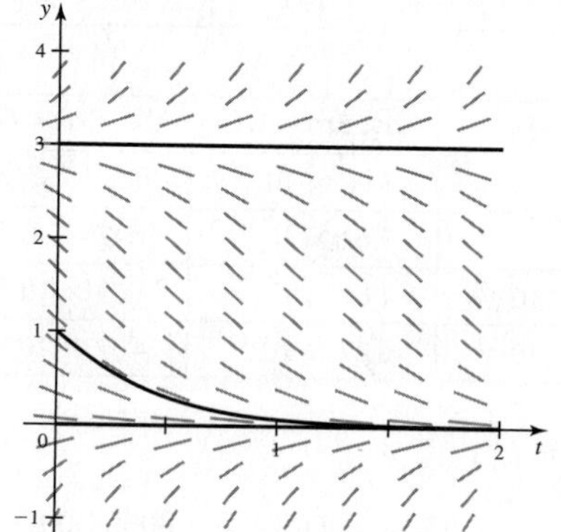

47. a. Equilibrium points $y = 0$, $y = 3$, and $y = -2$ **b.**

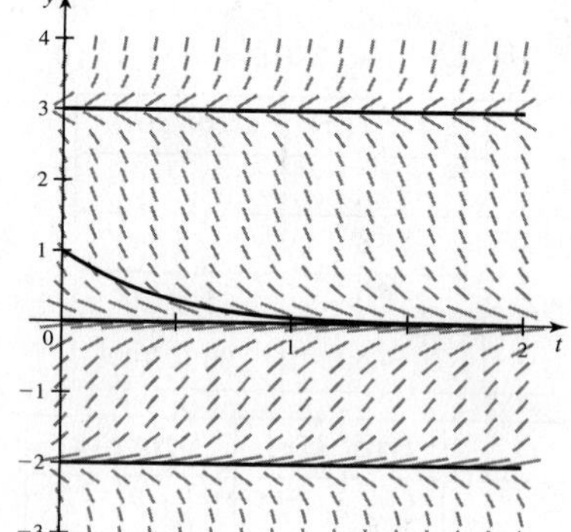

49. $p = 4e^{1-1/t} - 1$ **51.** $w = \tan^{-1}(t^2 + 1)$

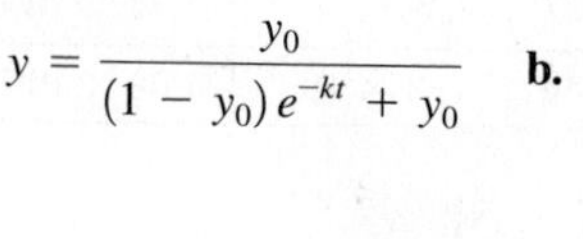

53. a. $y = \frac{y_0}{(1 - y_0)e^{-kt} + y_0}$ **b.**

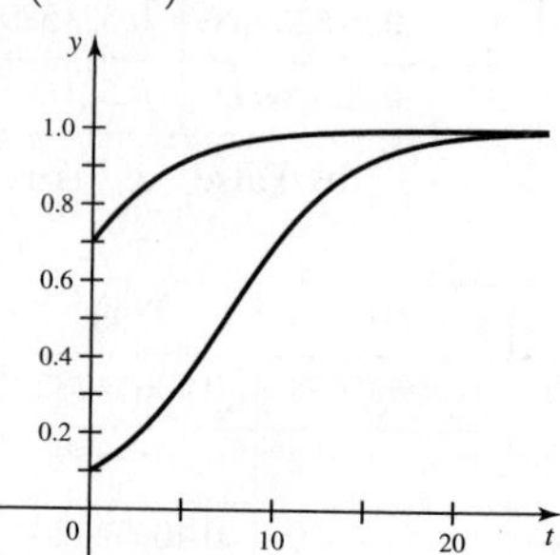

c. For any $0 < y_0 < 1$, $\lim_{t\to\infty} y(t) = 1$. Eventually everyone knows the rumor. **55. b.** $v = \frac{mg}{R}$ **c.** $v = \frac{g}{b}(1 - e^{-bt})$

d.

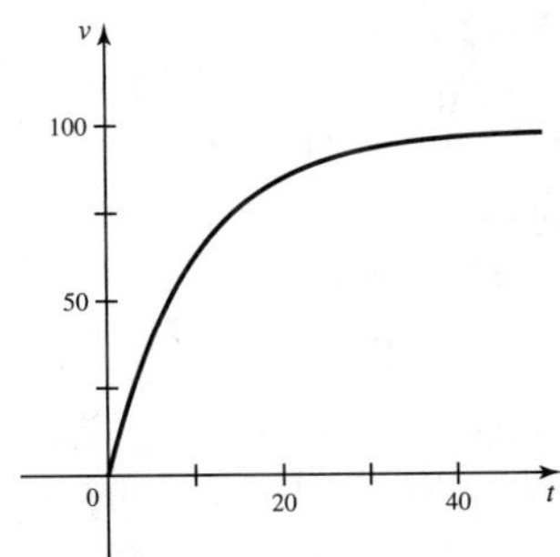

57. a. General solution $y = Ce^{-kt}$ **b.** $y = \frac{1}{kt + 1/y_0}$

c.

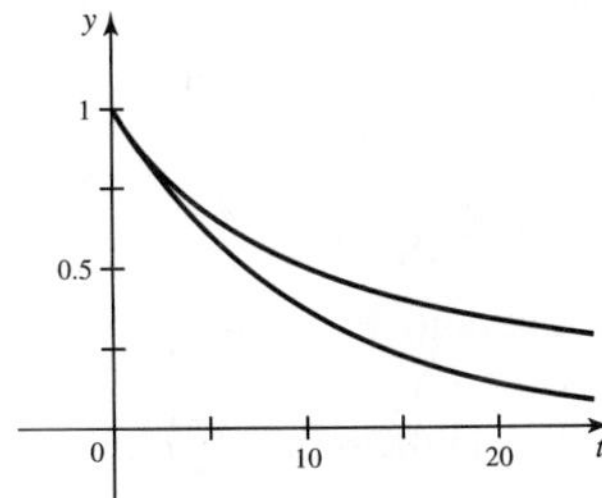

59. a. $B = 20{,}000 - 5000e^{0.05t}$; balance decreases
b. $m = \$2500$; constant balance $= \$50{,}000$

Chapter 8 Review Exercises, pp. 512–514

1. a. True **b.** False **c.** False **3.** $\frac{e^x}{2}(\sin x - \cos x) + C$
5. $\theta/2 + (1/16)\sin(8\theta) + C$ **7.** $(\sec^5 z)/5 + C$
9. $(256 - 147\sqrt{3})/480$ **11.** $\sin^{-1}(x/2) + C$
13. $-\frac{1}{9y}\sqrt{9 - y^2} + C$ **15.** $\pi/9$ **17.** $\frac{1}{8}\ln\left|\frac{x - 5}{x + 3}\right| + C$
19. $(1/4)\ln 2 + \pi/8$ **21.** $\frac{\sqrt{6}}{3}\tan^{-1}\left(\sqrt{\frac{2x - 3}{3}}\right) + C$
23. 1.196288 **25. a.** $T(6) = 9.125$, $M(6) = 8.9375$
b. $T(12) = 9.03125$, $M(12) = 8.984375$ **27.** 0.4054651 **29.** 1
31. $\pi/2$ **33.** $\frac{1}{3}\ln\left|\frac{x - 2}{x + 1}\right| + C$ **35.** $2(x - 2\ln|x + 2|) + C$
37. $e^{2t}/2\sqrt{1 + e^{4t}} + C$ **39.** $\pi(e - 2)$ **41.** $\frac{\pi}{2}(e^2 - 3)$
43. y-axis **45. a.** 1.603 **b.** 1.870 **c.** $b\ln b - b = a\ln a - a$
d. Decreasing **47.** $20/(3\pi)$ **49.** 1901 cars
51. a. $I(p) = \frac{1}{(p - 1)^2}(1 - pe^{1-p})$ if $p \neq 1$, $I(1) = \frac{1}{2}$ **b.** $0, \infty$
c. $I(0) = 1$ **53.** $n = 2$ **55.** $y = 10e^{2t} - 2$
57. $y = \sqrt{t + \ln t + 15}$ **59.** $\pi/2$

61.

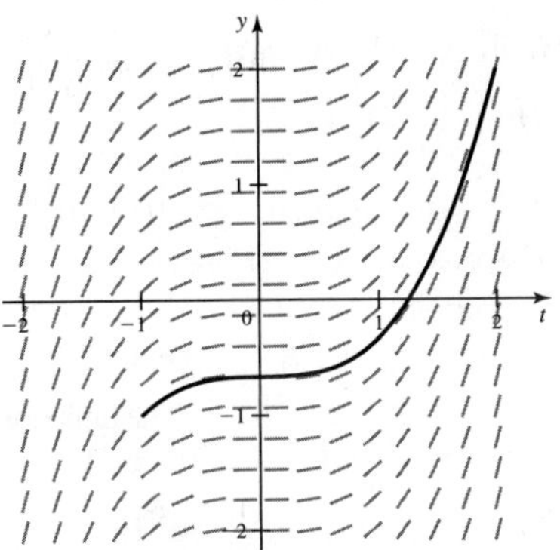

63. $t = \frac{-s - 5\ln s + 50 + 5\ln 50}{10}$
$\lim_{t\to\infty} s(t) = 0$

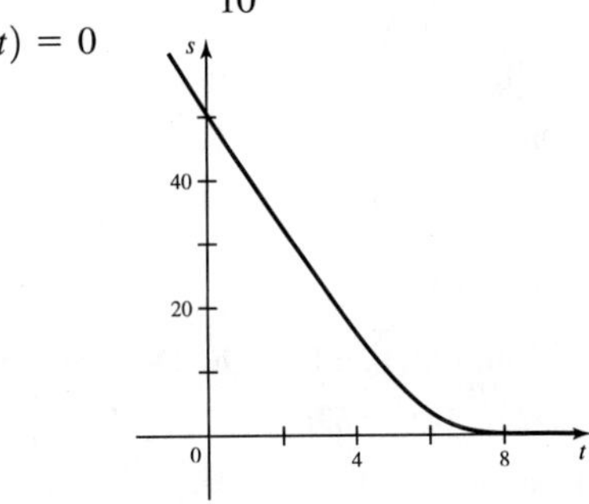

65. a. $V_1(a) = \pi[a\ln^2 a - 2a\ln a + 2(a - 1)]$
b. $V_2(a) = \frac{\pi}{2}(2a^2\ln a - a^2 + 1)$
c. $V_2(a) > V_1(a)$ for all $a > 1$

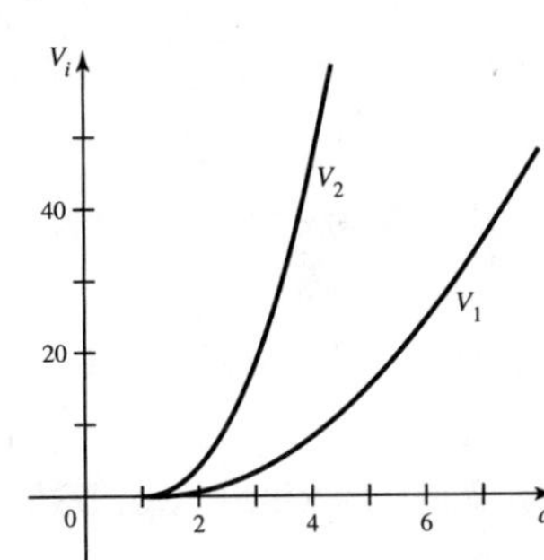

67. $a = \ln 2/(2b)$

CHAPTER 9

Section 9.1 Exercises, pp. 523–526

1. A sequence is an ordered list of numbers. Example: $1, \frac{1}{3}, \frac{1}{9}, \frac{1}{27}, \ldots$
3. 1, 1, 2, 6, 24 **5.** Given a sequence $\{a_1, a_2, \ldots\}$, an infinite series is the sum $a_1 + a_2 + a_3 + \ldots$. Example: $\sum_{k=1}^{\infty}\frac{1}{k^2}$ **7.** 1, 5, 14, 30 **9.** $\frac{1}{10}, \frac{1}{100}, \frac{1}{1000}, \frac{1}{10{,}000}$ **11.** 2, 1, 0, 1 **13.** 10, 18, 42, 114 **15.** 0, 2, 15, 679
17. a. 1/32, 1/64 **b.** $a_1 = 1$, $a_{n+1} = \frac{1}{2}a_n$ for $n \geq 1$

c. $a_n = \frac{1}{2^{n-1}}$ for $n \ge 1$ **19. a.** 32, 64 **b.** $a_1 = 1,\ a_{n+1} = 2a_n$ for $n \ge 1$ **c.** $a_n = 2^{n-1}$ for $n \ge 1$ **21. a.** 243, 729 **b.** $a_1 = 1$, $a_{n+1} = 3a_n$ for $n \ge 1$ **c.** $a_n = 3^{n-1}$ for $n \ge 1$ **23.** 9, 99, 999, 9999; diverges **25.** $-1, \frac{1}{2}, -\frac{1}{3}, \frac{1}{4}$; converges to 0 **27.** $10^{-1}, 10^{-3}, 10^{-7}, 10^{-15}$; converges to 0 **29.** 100, 100, 100, 100; converges to 100 **31. a.** 1, 2, 3, 4 **b.** The limit does not exist. **33. a.** 0, 2, 6, 12 **b.** The limit does not exist. **35. a.** $\frac{1}{3}, \frac{1}{2}, \frac{3}{5}, \frac{2}{3}$ **b.** 1 **37. a.** $\frac{5}{2}, \frac{9}{4}, \frac{17}{8}, \frac{33}{16}$ **b.** 2 **39. a.** 3, 5, 7, 9 **b.** $a_n = 2n + 3,\ n \ge 0$ **c.** The limit does not exist. **41. a.** 0, 1, 3, 7 **b.** $a_n = 2^n - 1,\ n \ge 0$ **c.** The limit does not exist. **43. a.** $1, \frac{3}{2}, \frac{7}{4}, \frac{15}{8}$ **b.** $a_n = 2 - \frac{1}{2^n}$ **c.** Limit is 2. **45. a.** 20, 10, 5, $\frac{5}{2}$ **b.** $h_n = 20\left(\frac{1}{2}\right)^n,\ n \ge 0$ **47. a.** 30, $\frac{15}{2}, \frac{15}{8}, \frac{15}{32}$ **b.** $h_n = 30\left(\frac{1}{4}\right)^n,\ n \ge 0$ **49.** $S_1 = 0.3, S_2 = 0.33, S_3 = 0.333, S_4 = 0.3333$; $\frac{1}{3}$ **51.** $S_1 = 4, S_2 = 4.9, S_3 = 4.99, S_4 = 4.999$; 5 **53. a.** $\frac{2}{3}, \frac{4}{5}, \frac{6}{7}, \frac{8}{9}$ **b.** $S_n = \frac{2n}{2n+1}$ **c.** $\lim_{n\to\infty} S_n = 1$ **55. a.** $\frac{1}{3}, \frac{2}{5}, \frac{3}{7}, \frac{4}{9}$ **b.** $S_n = \frac{n}{2n+1}$ **c.** $\lim_{n\to\infty} S_n = \frac{1}{2}$ **57. a.** True **b.** False **c.** True **59. a.** 40, 70, $\frac{185}{2}, \frac{875}{8}$ **b.** 160 **61. a.** $\frac{1}{2}, \frac{3}{4}, \frac{7}{8}, \frac{15}{16}$ **b.** 1 **63. a.** $\frac{1}{3}, \frac{4}{9}, \frac{13}{27}, \frac{40}{81}$ **b.** $\frac{1}{2}$ **65. a.** $-1, 0, -1, 0$ **b.** Diverges **67. a.** 0.3, 0.33, 0.333, 0.3333 **b.** $\frac{1}{3}$ **69. a.** 20, 10, 5, $\frac{5}{2}, \frac{5}{4}$ **b.** $M_n = 20\left(\frac{1}{2}\right)^n,\ n \ge 0$ **c.** $M_0 = 20, M_{n+1} = \frac{1}{2}M_n$ for $n \ge 0$ **d.** $\lim_{n\to\infty} a_n = 0$ **71. a.** 200, 190, 180.5, 171.475, 162.90125 **b.** $d_n = 200(0.95)^n,\ n \ge 0$ **c.** $d_0 = 200, d_{n+1} = (0.95)d_n$ for $n \ge 0$ **d.** $\lim_{n\to\infty} d_n = 0$. **73. a.** $0.\overline{3} = \sum_{k=1}^{\infty} 3(0.1)^k$ **b.** $\frac{1}{3}$ **75. a.** $0.\overline{1} = \sum_{k=1}^{\infty} (0.1)^k$ **b.** $\frac{1}{9}$ **77. a.** $0.\overline{09} = \sum_{k=1}^{\infty} 9(0.01)^k$ **b.** $\frac{1}{11}$ **79. a.** $0.\overline{037} = \sum_{k=1}^{\infty} 37(0.001)^k$ **b.** $\frac{1}{27}$

Section 9.2 Exercises, pp. 535–538

1. $a_n = \frac{1}{n},\ n \ge 1$ **3.** $a_n = \frac{n}{n+1},\ n \ge 1$ **5.** Converges for $-1 < r \le 1$, diverges otherwise **7.** A sequence $\{a_n\}_{n=1}^{\infty}$ converges to L if, given any $\varepsilon > 0$ there exists a positive integer N such that whenever $n > N$, $|a_n - L| < \varepsilon$

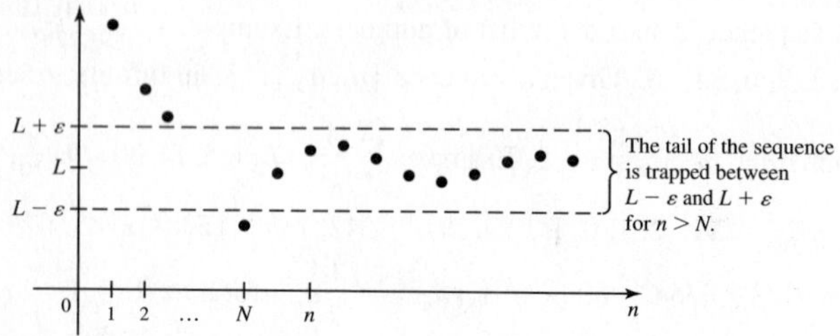

9. 0 **11.** 3/2 **13.** 0 **15.** e^2 **17.** $e^{1/4}$ **19.** 1 **21.** 0 **23.** 0 **25.** 6 **27.** Limit doesn't exist. **29.** 0 **31.** 0 **33.** The limit doesn't exist. **35.** Converges monotonically; 0 **37.** Converges by oscillation; 0 **39.** Diverges monotonically **41.** Diverges by oscillation **43.** 0 **45.** 0 **47. a.** $d_{n+1} = \frac{1}{2}d_n + 80,\ n \ge 1$ **b.** 160 mg **49. a.** \$0, \$100, \$200.75, \$302.26, \$404.53 **b.** $B_{n+1} = 1.0075B_n + 100,\ n \ge 0$ **c.** During the 43rd month **51.** $\{b_n\}$ grows faster than $\{a_n\}$. **53.** $\{a_n\}$ grows faster than $\{b_n\}$. **55.** $\{b_n\}$ grows faster than $\{a_n\}$. **57.** Given a tolerance $\varepsilon > 0$, look beyond a_N where $N > 1/\varepsilon$. **59.** Given a tolerance $\varepsilon > 0$, look beyond a_N where $N > \frac{1}{4}\sqrt{3/\varepsilon}$, provided $\varepsilon < \frac{3}{4}$ **61.** Given a tolerance $\varepsilon > 0$, look beyond a_N where $N > c/(\varepsilon b^2)$. **63. a.** True **b.** False **c.** True **d.** True **e.** False **f.** True **65.** $\{n^2 + 2n - 17\}$ **67.** 0 **69.** 1 **71.** 1/2 **73.** 0 **75.** $n = 4$, $n = 6, n = 25$ **77. a.** $\{h_n\} = \{(200 + 5n)(0.65 - 0.01\,n) - 0.45n\}$ **b.** The profit is maximized after 8 days. **79.** 0.607 **81. b.** $1, \sqrt{2} \approx 1.4142$, 1.5538, 1.5981, 1.6119 **c.** Limit ≈ 1.618 **e.** $\frac{1 + \sqrt{1 + 4p}}{2}$ **83. b.** 1, 2, 1.5, 1.6667, 1.6 **c.** Limit ≈ 1.618 **e.** $\frac{a + \sqrt{a^2 + 4b}}{2}$ **85. a.** 1, 1, 2, 3, 5, 8, 13, 21, 34, 55 **b.** No

Section 9.3 Exercises, pp. 542–545

1. Consecutive terms differ by a constant ratio. Example: $2 + 1 + \frac{1}{2} + \frac{1}{4} + \cdots$ **3.** The constant r in the series $\sum_{k=0}^{\infty} r^k$. **5.** No **7.** 9841 **9.** ≈ 1.1905 **11.** ≈ 0.5392 **13.** $\frac{1 - \pi^7}{1 - \pi}$ **15.** 1 **17.** $\frac{1093}{2916}$ **19.** $\frac{4}{3}$ **21.** 10 **23.** Diverges **25.** $\frac{1}{e^2 - 1}$ **27.** $\frac{1}{7}$ **29.** $\frac{1}{500}$ **31.** $\frac{\pi}{\pi - e}$ **33.** $\frac{312{,}500}{19}$ **35.** $\frac{10}{19}$ **37.** $\frac{3\pi}{\pi + 1}$ **39.** $\frac{9}{460}$ **41.** $0.12 + 0.0012 + \cdots = \frac{4}{33}$ **43.** $0.456 + 0.000456 + \cdots = \frac{152}{333}$ **45.** $0.00952 + 0.00000952 + \cdots = \frac{952}{99{,}900}$ **47.** $S_n = \frac{1}{2} - \frac{1}{n+2}$; $\lim_{n\to\infty} S_n = \frac{1}{2}$ **49.** $S_n = \frac{1}{2} - \frac{1}{n+2}$; $\lim_{n\to\infty} S_n = \frac{1}{2}$ **51.** $S_n = \ln(n + 1)$; $\lim_{n\to\infty} S_n$ diverges **53.** $S_n = \frac{1}{p+1} - \frac{1}{n+p+1}$; $\lim_{n\to\infty} S_n = \frac{1}{p+1}$ **55.** $S_n = \left(\frac{1}{\sqrt{2}} + \frac{1}{\sqrt{3}}\right) - \left(\frac{1}{\sqrt{n+2}} + \frac{1}{\sqrt{n+3}}\right)$; $\lim_{n\to\infty} S_n = \frac{1}{\sqrt{2}} + \frac{1}{\sqrt{3}}$ **57.** $S_n = -\frac{n+1}{4n+3}$; $\lim_{n\to\infty} S_n = -\frac{1}{4}$ **59. a.** True **b.** True **c.** False **61.** $\sum_{k=0}^{\infty}\left(\frac{1}{4}\right)^k A_1 = \frac{A_1}{1 - 1/4} = \frac{4}{3}A_1$ **63.** 462 months **65.** 0 **67.** There will be twice as many children. **69.** $\sqrt{\frac{20}{g}}\frac{1 + \sqrt{p}}{1 - \sqrt{p}}$ s **71. a.** $L_n = 3 \cdot \left(\frac{4}{3}\right)^n$, so $\lim_{n\to\infty} L_n = \infty$ **b.** $\lim_{n\to\infty} A_n = \frac{2\sqrt{3}}{5}$ **73.** $R_n = |S - S_n| = \left|\frac{1}{1 - r} - \left(\frac{1 - r^n}{1 - r}\right)\right| = \left|\frac{r^n}{1 - r}\right|$ **75. a.** 60 **b.** 9 **77. a.** 13 **b.** 15 **79. a.** $1, \frac{5}{6}, \frac{2}{3}$, undefined, undefined **b.** $(-1, 1)$ **81.** Converges for x in $(-\infty, -2)$ or $(0, \infty)$; $f(x) = 3$ for $x = \frac{1}{2}$

Section 9.4 Exercises, pp. 556–558

1. Computation may not show whether the sequence of partial sums converges. **3.** Yes, if the terms are positive and decreasing. **5.** Converges for $p > 1$ and diverges for $p \le 1$. **9.** -2 **11.** $\frac{113}{30}$ **13.** $\frac{17}{10}$ **15.** Diverges **17.** Diverges **19.** Inconclusive **21.** Diverges **23.** Diverges **25.** Converges **27.** Diverges **29.** Converges **31.** Converges **33.** Converges **35. a.** $\frac{1}{5n^5}$ **b.** 3 **c.** $L_n = \sum_{k=1}^{n} \frac{1}{k^6} + \frac{1}{5(n+1)^5}$ $U_n = \sum_{k=1}^{n} \frac{1}{k^6} + \frac{1}{5n^5}$ **d.** (1.017342754, 1.017343512) **37. a.** $\frac{3^{-n}}{\ln 3}$ **b.** 7 **c.** $L_n = \sum_{k=1}^{n} 3^{-k} + \frac{3^{-n-1}}{\ln 3}$ $U_n = \sum_{k=1}^{n} 3^{-k} + \frac{3^{-n}}{\ln 3}$ **d.** (0.499996671, 0.500006947) **39. a.** $\frac{2}{\sqrt{n}}$ **b.** $4 \cdot 10^6$ **c.** $L_n = \sum_{k=1}^{n} \frac{1}{k^{3/2}} + \frac{2}{\sqrt{n+1}}$ $U_n = \sum_{k=1}^{n} \frac{1}{k^{3/2}} + \frac{2}{\sqrt{n}}$ **d.** (2.598359183, 2.627792025) **41. a.** $\frac{1}{2n^2}$ **b.** 23 **c.** $L_n = \sum_{k=1}^{n} \frac{1}{k^3} + \frac{1}{2(n+1)^2}$ $U_n = \sum_{k=1}^{n} \frac{1}{k^3} + \frac{1}{2n^2}$ **d.** (1.201664217, 1.202531986) **43. a.** True **b.** True **c.** False **d.** False **e.** False **f.** False **45.** Converges **47.** Diverges **49.** Converges **51. a.** $p > 1$ **b.** $\sum_{k=2}^{\infty} \frac{1}{k(\ln k)^2}$ converges more quickly. **57.** $\zeta(3) \approx 1.202, \zeta(5) \approx 1.037$ **59.** $\frac{\pi^2}{8}$ **61. a.** $\frac{1}{2}, \frac{7}{12}, \frac{37}{60}$ **63. a.** $\sum_{k=2}^{n} \frac{1}{k}$ **b.** Infinitely many

Section 9.5 Exercises, pp. 564–566

5. Ratio Test **7.** $S_{n+1} - S_n = a_{n+1} > 0$ thus $S_{n+1} > S_n$ **9.** Converges **11.** Converges **13.** Converges **15.** Diverges **17.** Converges **19.** Converges **21.** Converges **23.** Converges **25.** Converges **27.** Converges **29.** Diverges **31.** Converges **33.** Converges **35.** Diverges **37.** Diverges **39. a.** False **b.** True **c.** True **41.** Diverges **43.** Converges **45.** Converges **47.** Converges **49.** Diverges **51.** Converges **53.** Diverges **55.** Converges **57.** Converges **59.** $p > 1$ **61.** $p > 1$ **63.** $p > 2$ **65.** Diverges for all p **67.** Diverges if $|r| \ge 1$ **71.** $x < 1$ **73.** $x \le 1$ **75.** $x < 2$ **77. a.** e^2 **b.** 0

Section 9.6 Exercises, pp. 573–575

1. Because $S_{n+1} - S_n = a_{n+1}$ alternates sign. **3.** Because $\lim_{k\to\infty} a_k = 0$ and the terms $\{a_k\}$ alternate in sign. **5.** $R_n = |S - S_n| \le |S_{n+1} - S_n| = a_{n+1}$ **7.** No; if a series of positive terms converges, if does so absolutely and not conditionally. **9.** Yes, $\sum_{k=1}^{\infty} \frac{(-1)^k}{k^2}$ has this property. **11.** Converges **13.** Converges **15.** Diverges **17.** Diverges **19.** Converges **21.** Diverges **23.** Converges **25.** 10,000 **27.** 5000 **29.** 10 **31.** 3334 **33.** 6 **35.** -0.973 **37.** -0.783 **39.** Converges absolutely **41.** Converges absolutely **43.** Diverges **45.** Converges absolutely **47. a.** False **b.** True **c.** True **d.** True **e.** False **f.** True **g.** True **51.** The conditions of the Alternating Series Test are met; thus $\sum_{k=1}^{\infty} r^k$ converges for $-1 < r < 0$. **55.** x and y are divergent series.

Chapter 9 Review Exercises, pp. 575–577

1. a. False **b.** False **c.** True **d.** False **3.** 0 **5.** 1 **7.** $1/e$ **9.** Diverges **11. a.** $\frac{1}{3}, \frac{11}{24}, \frac{21}{40}, \frac{17}{30}$ **b.** $S_1 = \frac{1}{3}, S_n = \frac{1}{2}\left(\frac{3}{2} - \frac{1}{n+1} - \frac{1}{n+2}\right), n \ge 2$ **c.** 3/4 **13.** Diverges **15.** 1 **17.** 3 **19.** 2/9 **21. a.** Yes; 1.5 **b.** Convergence uncertain. **c.** Appears to diverge **23.** Diverges **25.** Converges **27.** Converges **29.** Converges **31.** Converges **33.** Converges **35.** Converges **37.** Converges absolutely **39.** Converges absolutely **41.** Converges absolutely **43. a.** 0 **b.** $\frac{5}{9}$ **45.** $\lim_{k\to\infty} a_k = 0, \lim_{n\to\infty} S_n = 8$ **47.** $0 < p \le 1$ **49.** 0.25 (to 14 digits); 6.5×10^{-15} **51.** 100 **53. a.** 803 m, 1283 m, $2000(1 - 0.95^N)$ m **b.** 2000 m **55. a.** $\frac{\pi}{2^{n-1}}$ **b.** 2π **57. a.** $B_{n+1} = 1.0025B_n + 100, B_0 = 100$ **b.** $B_n = 40{,}000(1.0025^{n+1} - 1)$ **59. a.** $T_1 = \frac{\sqrt{3}}{16}, T_2 = \frac{7\sqrt{3}}{64}$ **b.** $T_n = \frac{\sqrt{3}}{4}\left(1 - \left(\frac{3}{4}\right)^n\right)$ **c.** $\lim_{n\to\infty} T_n = \frac{\sqrt{3}}{4}$ **d.** 0

CHAPTER 10

Section 10.1 Exercises, pp. 588–590

1. $f(0) = p(0), f'(0) = p'(0)$, and $f''(0) = p''(0)$ **3.** 1, 1.05, 1.04875 **5.** $R_n(x) = f(x) - p_n(x)$ **7. a.** $p_1(x) = 1 - x$ **b.** $p_2(x) = 1 - x + \frac{x^2}{2}$ **c.** 0.8, 0.82 **9. a.** $p_1(x) = 1 - x$ **b.** $p_2(x) = 1 - x + x^2$ **c.** 0.95, 0.9525 **11. a.** $p_1(x) = 2 + \frac{1}{12}(x - 8)$ **b.** $p_2(x) = 2 + \frac{1}{12}(x - 8) - \frac{1}{288}(x - 8)^2$ **c.** $1.958\overline{3}$, 1.95747 **13. a.** $p_0(x) = 1, p_1(x) = 1, p_2(x) = 1 - \frac{x^2}{2}$

b.

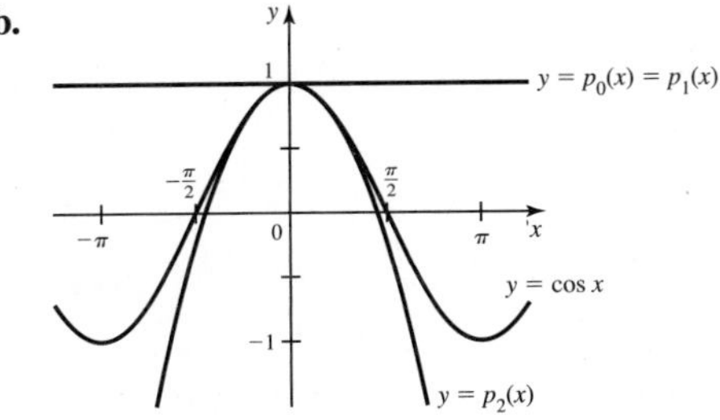

15. a. $p_0(x) = 0,\ p_1(x) = -x,\ p_2(x) = -x - \dfrac{x^2}{2}$

b. 

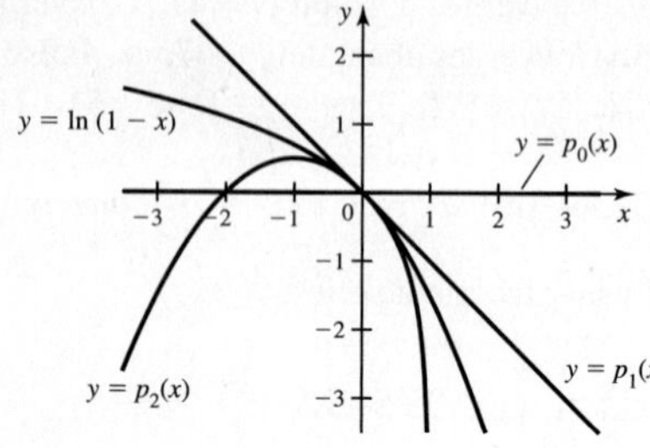

17. a. $p_0(x) = 0,\ p_1(x) = x,\ p_2(x) = x$

b. 

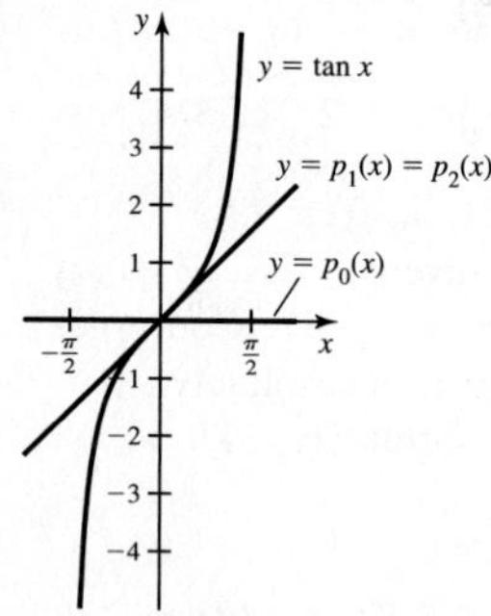

19. a. $p_0(x) = 1,\ p_1(x) = 1 - 3x,\ p_2(x) = 1 - 3x + 6x^2$

b. 

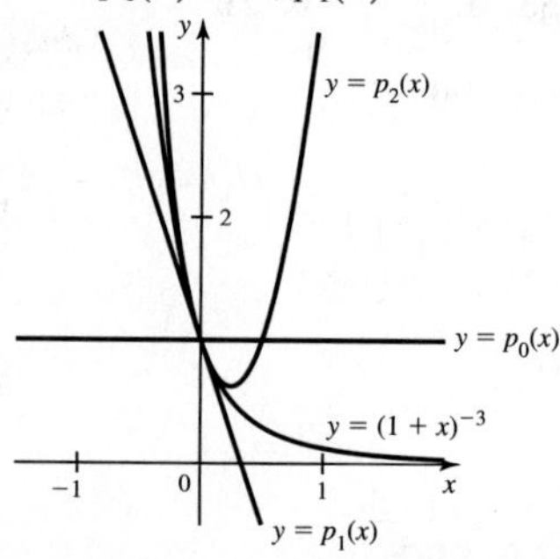

21. a. 1.0247 **b.** 7.58×10^{-6} **23. a.** 0.9624 **b.** 1.50×10^{-4} **25. a.** 0.8613 **b.** 5.42×10^{-4}

27. a. $p_0(x) = \dfrac{\sqrt{2}}{2},\ p_1(x) = p_0(x) + \dfrac{\sqrt{2}}{2}\left(x - \dfrac{\pi}{4}\right),$

$$p_2(x) = p_1(x) - \frac{\sqrt{2}}{4}\left(x - \frac{\pi}{4}\right)^2$$

b.

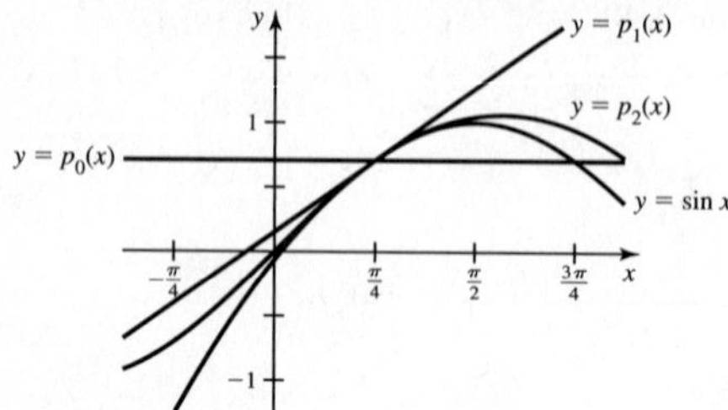

29. a. $p_0(x) = 3,\ p_1(x) = p_0(x) + \dfrac{(x - 9)}{6},$

$$p_2(x) = p_1(x) - \frac{(x - 9)^2}{216}$$

b.

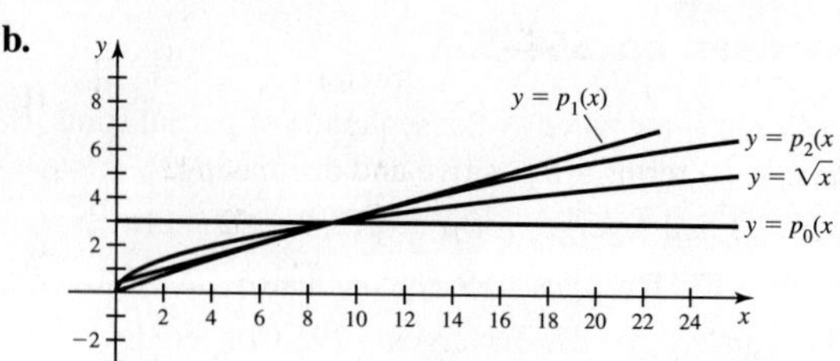

31. a. $p_0(x) = 1,\ p_1(x) = p_0(x) + \dfrac{x - e}{e},$

$$p_2(x) = p_1(x) - \frac{(x - e)^2}{2e^2}$$

b.

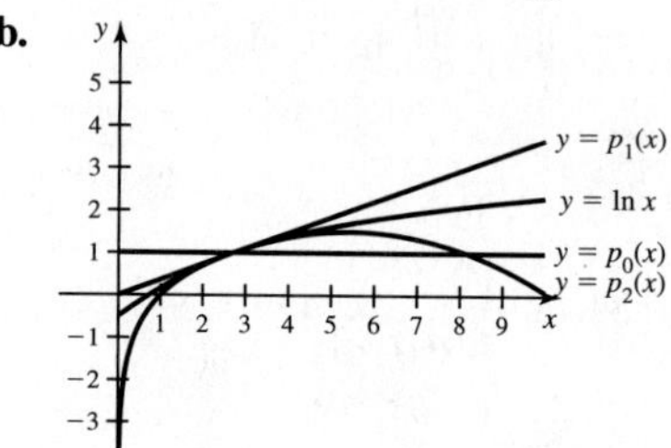

33. a. 1.12749 **b.** 8.85×10^{-6} **35. a.** -0.100333 **b.** 1.34×10^{-6} **37. a.** 1.029564 **b.** 4.86×10^{-7}

39. a. 10.04987563 **b.** 3.88×10^{-9} **41.** $R_n(x) = \dfrac{\sin^{(n+1)}(c)}{(n + 1)!}x^{n+1}$ for some c between x and 0. **43.** $R_n(x) = \dfrac{(-1)^{n+1}e^{-c}}{(n + 1)!}x^{n+1}$ for some c between x and 0. **45.** $R_n(x) = \dfrac{\sin^{(n+1)}(c)}{(n + 1)!}\left(x - \dfrac{\pi}{2}\right)^{n+1}$ for some c between x and $\dfrac{\pi}{2}$. **47.** 2.03×10^{-5} **49.** $1.63 \times 10^{-5}\ (e^{0.25} < 2)$ **51.** 2.60×10^{-4} **53.** With $n = 4$, max error $= 2.49 \times 10^{-3}$ **55.** With $n = 2$, max error $= 4.17 \times 10^{-2}\ (e^{0.5} < 2)$ **57.** With $n = 2$, max error $= 2.67 \times 10^{-3}$ **59.** 4 **61.** 3 **63.** 1 **65. a.** False **b.** True **c.** True **67. a.** C **b.** E **c.** A **d.** D **e.** B **f.** F **69. a.** 0.1; with $n = 2$, 1.67×10^{-4} **b.** 0.2; 1.33×10^{-3} **71. a.** 0.995; with $n = 3$, 4.17×10^{-6} **b.** 0.98; 6.67×10^{-5} **73. a.** 1.05; $\frac{1}{800}$ **b.** 1.1; $\frac{1}{200}$ **75. a.** 1.1; $\frac{1}{100}$ **b.** 1.2; $\frac{1}{25}$

77. a.

x	$\lvert\sin x - p_3(x)\rvert$	$\lvert\sin x - p_5(x)\rvert$
−0.2	2.7×10^{-6}	2.5×10^{-9}
−0.1	8.3×10^{-8}	2.0×10^{-11}
0.0	0	0
0.1	8.3×10^{-8}	2.0×10^{-11}
0.2	2.7×10^{-6}	2.5×10^{-9}

b. The error increases as $|x|$ increases.

79. a.

x	$\lvert e^{-x} - p_1(x)\rvert$	$\lvert e^{-x} - p_2(x)\rvert$
−0.2	2.1×10^{-2}	1.4×10^{-3}
−0.1	5.2×10^{-3}	1.7×10^{-4}
0.0	0	0
0.1	4.8×10^{-3}	1.6×10^{-4}
0.2	1.9×10^{-2}	1.3×10^{-3}

b. The error increases as $|x|$ increases.

81. a.

x	$\|\tan x - p_1(x)\|$	$\|\tan x - p_3(x)\|$
-0.2	2.7×10^{-3}	4.3×10^{-5}
-0.1	3.3×10^{-4}	1.3×10^{-6}
0.0	0	0
0.1	3.3×10^{-4}	1.3×10^{-6}
0.2	2.7×10^{-3}	4.3×10^{-5}

b. The error increases as $|x|$ increases. **83.** Centered at $x = 0$ for all n **85. a.** $y = f(a) + f'(a)(x - a)$

Section 10.2 Exercises, pp. 598–600

1. $c_0 + c_1x + c_2x^2 + c_3x^3$ **3.** Ratio and Root Test **5.** The radius of convergence does not change. The interval of convergence may change. **7.** $|x| < \frac{1}{4}$ **9.** $r = 3; (-3, 3)$ **11.** $R = \infty; (-\infty, \infty)$ **13.** $R = \infty; (-\infty, \infty)$ **15.** $R = \sqrt{3}; (-\sqrt{3}, \sqrt{3})$ **17.** $R = 1; (0, 2)$ **19.** $R = \infty; (-\infty, \infty)$ **21.** $\sum_{k=0}^{\infty}(3x)^k; \left(-\frac{1}{3}, \frac{1}{3}\right)$ **23.** $2\sum_{k=0}^{\infty}x^{k+3}; (-1, 1)$ **25.** $4\sum_{k=0}^{\infty}x^{k+12}; (-1, 1)$ **27.** $-\sum_{k=1}^{\infty}\frac{(3x)^k}{k}$; $\left[-\frac{1}{3}, \frac{1}{3}\right)$ **29.** $-\sum_{k=1}^{\infty}\frac{x^{k+1}}{k}; [-1, 1)$ **31.** $-2\sum_{k=1}^{\infty}\frac{x^{k+6}}{k}; [-1, 1)$ **33.** $g(x) = \sum_{k=1}^{\infty}kx^{k-1}; (-1, 1)$ **35.** $g(x) = \sum_{k=3}^{\infty}\frac{k(k-1)(k-2)}{6}x^{k-3}$; $(-1, 1)$ **37.** $g(x) = -\sum_{k=1}^{\infty}\frac{3^kx^k}{k}; \left[-\frac{1}{3}, \frac{1}{3}\right)$ **39.** $\sum_{k=0}^{\infty}(-x^2)^k; (-1, 1)$ **41.** $\sum_{k=0}^{\infty}\left(-\frac{x}{3}\right)^k; (-3, 3)$ **43.** $\ln 2 - \frac{1}{2}\sum_{k=1}^{\infty}\frac{x^{2k}}{k4^k}; (-2, 2)$ **45. a.** True **b.** True **c.** True **d.** True **47.** $\sum_{k=0}^{\infty}\frac{(-1)^kx^k}{k+1}$ **49.** $\sum_{k=1}^{\infty}\frac{(-x^2)^k}{k!}$ **51.** $|x - a| < R$ **53.** $f(x) = \frac{1}{3 - \sqrt{x}}; 1 < x < 9$ **55.** $f(x) = \frac{e^x}{e^x - 1}; 0 < x < \infty$ **57.** $f(x) = \frac{3}{4 - x^2}; -2 < x < 2$ **59.** $\sum_{k=0}^{\infty}\frac{(-x)^k}{k!}; -\infty < x < \infty$ **61.** $\sum_{k=0}^{\infty}\frac{(-3x)^k}{k!}; -\infty < x < \infty$ **63.** $\lim_{k\to\infty}\left|\frac{c_{k+1}x^{k+1}}{c_kx^k}\right| = \lim_{k\to\infty}\left|\frac{c_{k+1}x^{k+m+1}}{c_kx^{k+m}}\right|$, so by the Ratio Test the two series converge on the same interval. **65. a.** $f(x) \cdot g(x) = c_0d_0 + (c_0d_1 + c_1d_0)x + (c_0d_2 + c_1d_1 + c_2d_0)x^2 + \cdots$. **b.** $\sum_{k=0}^{n}c_kd_{n-k}$ **67. b.** $n = 112$

Section 10.3 Exercises, pp. 610–611

1. The nth Taylor polynomial is the nth partial sum of the corresponding Taylor series. **3.** Calculate $c_k = \frac{f^{(k)}(a)}{k!}$ for $k = 0, 1, 2, \ldots$. **5.** Replace x by x^2 in the Taylor series for $f(x)$; $|x| < 1$. **7.** The Taylor series for a function f converges to f on an interval if, for all x in the interval, $\lim_{n\to\infty} R_n(x) = 0$, where $R_n(x)$ is the remainder at x. **9. a.** $1 - x + \frac{x^2}{2!} - \frac{x^3}{3!}$ **b.** $\sum_{k=0}^{\infty}\frac{(-1)^kx^k}{k!}$ **c.** $(-\infty, \infty)$ **11. a.** $1 - x^2 + x^4 - x^6$ **b.** $\sum_{k=0}^{n}(-1)^kx^{2k}$ **c.** $(-1, 1)$ **13. a.** $1 + 2x + \frac{(2x)^2}{2!} + \frac{(2x)^3}{3!}$ **b.** $\sum_{k=0}^{\infty}\frac{(2x)^k}{k!}$ **c.** $(-\infty, \infty)$ **15. a.** $x - \frac{x^3}{3} + \frac{x^5}{5} - \frac{x^7}{7}$ **b.** $\sum_{k=0}^{\infty}\frac{(-1)^kx^{2k+1}}{2k+1}$ **c.** $[-1, 1]$ **17. a.** $1 - \frac{(x - \pi/2)^2}{2!} + \frac{(x - \pi/2)^4}{4!} - \frac{(x - \pi/2)^6}{6!}$ **b.** $\sum_{k=0}^{\infty}\frac{(-1)^k}{(2k)!}(x - \pi/2)^{2k}$ **19. a.** $1 - (x - 1) + (x - 1)^2 - (x - 1)^3$ **b.** $\sum_{k=0}^{\infty}(-1)^k(x - 1)^k$ **21. a.** $\ln 3 + \frac{(x - 3)}{3} - \frac{(x - 3)^2}{3^2 \cdot 2} + \frac{(x - 3)^3}{3^3 \cdot 3}$ **b.** $\ln 3 + \sum_{k=1}^{\infty}\frac{(-1)^{k+1}(x - 3)^k}{k3^k}$ **23.** $x^2 - \frac{x^4}{2} + \frac{x^6}{3} - \frac{x^8}{4} + \cdots$ **25.** $1 + \frac{x}{2} + \frac{x^2}{6} + \frac{x^3}{24} + \cdots$ **27.** $1 - x^4 + x^8 - x^{12} + \cdots$ **29. a.** $1 - 2x + 3x^2 - 4x^3$ **b.** 0.826 **31. a.** $1 + \frac{1}{4}x - \frac{3}{32}x^2 + \frac{7}{128}x^3$ **b.** 1.029 **33. a.** $1 - \frac{2}{3}x + \frac{5}{9}x^2 - \frac{40}{81}x^3$ **b.** 0.895 **35.** $1 + \frac{x^2}{2} - \frac{x^4}{8} + \frac{x^6}{16} - \cdots$; $[-1, 1]$ **37.** $3 - \frac{3x}{2} - \frac{3x^2}{8} - \frac{3x^3}{16} - \cdots$; $[-1, 1)$ **39.** $a + \frac{x^2}{2a} - \frac{x^4}{8a^3} + \frac{x^6}{16a^5} - \cdots$; $|x| \le a$ **41.** $1 - 8x + 48x^2 - 256x^3 + \cdots$ **43.** $\frac{1}{16} - \frac{x^2}{32} + \frac{3x^4}{256} - \frac{x^6}{256} + \cdots$ **45.** $\frac{1}{9} - \frac{2}{9}\left(\frac{4x}{3}\right) + \frac{3}{9}\left(\frac{4x}{3}\right)^2 - \frac{4}{9}\left(\frac{4x}{3}\right)^3 + \cdots$ **47.** $R_n(x) = \frac{f^{(n+1)}(c)}{(n+1)!}x^{n+1}$, where c is between 0 and x and $f^{(n+1)}(c) = \pm \sin c$ or $\pm \cos c$. Thus, $|R_n(x)| \le \frac{|x|^{n+1}}{(n+1)!} \to 0$ as $n \to \infty$, for $-\infty < x < \infty$. **49.** $R_n(x) = \frac{f^{(n+1)}(c)}{(n+1)!}x^{n+1}$, where c is between 0 and x and $f^{(n+1)}(c) = \begin{cases} e^{-c} & \text{if } n \text{ even} \\ -e^{-c} & \text{if } n \text{ odd} \end{cases}$ Thus, $\lim_{n\to\infty}|R_n(x)| = \lim_{n\to\infty}\left|\frac{x^{n+1}}{e^c(n+1)!}\right| = 0$ and so $\lim_{n\to\infty}R_n(x) = 0$, for $-\infty < x < \infty$. **51. a.** False **b.** True **c.** False **d.** False **e.** True **53. a.** $1 + \frac{x^2}{2!} + \frac{x^4}{4!} + \frac{x^6}{6!} + \cdots$ **b.** $R = \infty$

55. a. $1 - \frac{2}{3}x^2 + \frac{5}{9}x^4 - \frac{40}{81}x^6 + \cdots$ **b.** $R = 1$
57. a. $1 - \frac{1}{2}x^2 - \frac{1}{8}x^4 - \frac{1}{16}x^6 - \cdots$ **b.** $R = 1$
59. a. $1 - 2x^2 + 3x^4 - 4x^6 + \cdots$ **b.** $R = 1$ **61.** $\sqrt[3]{60} \approx 3.9149$ using the first four terms **63.** $\sqrt[4]{13} \approx 1.8989$ using the first four terms
69. $\sum_{k=0}^{\infty}\left(\frac{x-4}{2}\right)^k$ **71.** $\frac{1\cdot3\cdot5\cdot7}{2\cdot4\cdot6\cdot8}x^4, \frac{-1\cdot3\cdot5\cdot7\cdot9}{2\cdot4\cdot6\cdot8\cdot10}x^5$
73. Use three terms of the Taylor series for $\cos x$ centered at $a = \pi/4$; $\cos 40° = \cos(40\pi/180) \approx 0.766$ **75.** Use six terms of the Taylor series for $\sqrt[3]{x}$ centered at $a = 64$; $\sqrt[3]{83} \approx 4.362$ **77. a.** Use three terms of the Taylor series for $\sqrt[3]{125 + x}$ centered at $a = 0$; $\sqrt[3]{128} \approx 5.03968$ **b.** Use three terms of the Taylor series for $\sqrt[3]{x}$ centered at $a = 0$; $\sqrt[3]{128} \approx 5.03968$ **c.** Yes.

Section 10.4 Exercises, pp. 618–620

1. Replace f and g by their Taylor series centered at a and evaluate the limit. **3.** Substitute $x = -0.6$ into the Taylor series for e^x centered at 0. Because the resulting series is an alternating series, the error can be estimated. **5.** $f'(x) = \sum_{k=1}^{\infty} kc_k x^{k-1}$ **7.** 2 **9.** $\frac{2}{3}$ **11.** $\frac{2}{5}$ **13.** $\frac{3}{5}$
15. $-\frac{1}{6}$ **17.** 1 **19.** $\frac{17}{12}$ **21. a.** $1 + x + \frac{x^2}{2!} + \cdots + \frac{x^n}{n!} + \cdots$
b. e^x **c.** $-\infty < x < \infty$
23. a. $1 - x + x^2 - \cdots (-1)^{n-1}x^{n-1} + \cdots$ **b.** $\frac{1}{1+x}$ **c.** $|x| < 1$
25. a. $-2 + 4x - 8\cdot\frac{x^2}{2!} + \cdots + (-2)^n\frac{x^{n-1}}{(n-1)!} + \cdots$ **b.** $-2e^{-2x}$
c. $-\infty < x < \infty$ **27. a.** $2 + 2t + \frac{2t^2}{2!} + \cdots + \frac{2t^n}{n!} + \cdots$
b. $y(t) = 2e^t$
29. a. $2 + 16t + 24t^2 + 24t^3 + \cdots + \frac{3^{n-1}\cdot16}{n!}t^n + \cdots$
b. $y(t) = \frac{16}{3}e^{3t} - \frac{10}{3}$ **31.** 0.2448 **33.** 0.6958 **35.** 0.1498
37. 0.4994 **39.** $e^2 = \sum_{k=0}^{\infty}\frac{2^k}{k!} = 1 + 2 + \frac{2^2}{2!} + \frac{2^3}{3!} + \cdots$
41. $\cos 2 = \sum_{k=0}^{\infty}\frac{(-1)^k 2^{2k}}{(2k)!} = 1 - 2 + \frac{2}{3} - \frac{4}{45} + \cdots$
43. $\ln(3/2) = \sum_{k=1}^{\infty}\frac{(-1)^{k+1}}{k2^k}$
$= \frac{1}{2} - \frac{1}{8} + \frac{1}{24} - \frac{1}{64} + \cdots$
45. $\frac{e^x - 1}{x} = \sum_{k=0}^{\infty}\frac{x^k}{(k+1)!}$. Therefore, $\sum_{k=0}^{\infty}\frac{1}{(k+1)!} = e - 1$.
47. $\sum_{k=1}^{\infty}\frac{(-1)^{k+1}x^k}{k}$ for $-1 < x \le 1$. At $x = 1$, $\sum_{k=1}^{\infty}\frac{(-1)^{k+1}}{k} = \ln 2$.
49. $f(x) = \frac{2}{2-x}$ **51.** $f(x) = \frac{4}{4+x^2}$ **53.** $f(x) = -\ln(1-x)$
55. $f(x) = \frac{-3x^2}{(3+x)^2}$ **57.** $f(x) = \frac{6x^2}{(3-x)^3}$ **59. a.** False
b. False **c.** True **61.** $\frac{a}{b}$ **63.** $e^{-1/6}$ **65.** $f^{(3)}(0) = 0$; $f^{(4)}(0) = 4e$ **67.** $f^{(3)}(0) = 2$; $f^{(4)}(0) = 0$ **69.** 2 **71. a.** 1.5741 using four terms **b.** At least three **c.** More terms would be needed. **73. a.** $S'(x) = \sin(x^2)$; $C'(x) = \cos(x^2)$
b. $\frac{x^3}{3} - \frac{x^7}{7\cdot3!} + \frac{x^{11}}{11\cdot5!} - \frac{x^{15}}{15\cdot7!}$; $x - \frac{x^5}{5\cdot2!} + \frac{x^9}{9\cdot4!} - \frac{x^{13}}{13\cdot6!}$
c. $S(0.05) \approx 0.00004166664807$ $C(-0.25) \approx -0.2499023614$ **d.** 1
e. 2 **75. a.** $1 - \frac{x^2}{4} + \frac{x^4}{64} - \frac{x^6}{2304}$ **b.** $-\infty < x < \infty, R = \infty$
c. $\left(-\frac{x^2}{2} + \frac{3x^4}{16} - \frac{5x^6}{384}\right) + \left(-\frac{x^2}{2} + \frac{x^4}{16} - \frac{x^6}{384}\right) + \left(x^2 - \frac{x^4}{4} + \frac{x^6}{64}\right) = 0.$ **77. a.** The Maclaurin series for $\cos x$ consists of even powers of x, which are even functions. **b.** The Maclaurin series for $\sin x$ consists of odd powers of x, which are odd functions.

Chapter 10 Review Exercises, pp. 621–622

1. a. True **b.** False **c.** True **d.** True **3.** $p_2(x) = 1$
5. $p_3(x) = x - \frac{x^2}{2} + \frac{x^3}{3}$ **7.** $p_2(x) = (x-1) - \frac{(x-1)^2}{2}$
9. a. $p_2(x) = 1 + x + \frac{x^2}{2}$ **b.**

n	$p_n(x)$	error
0	1	7.7×10^{-2}
1	0.92	3.1×10^{-3}
2	0.9232	8.4×10^{-5}

11. a. $p_2(x) = \frac{\sqrt{2}}{2} + \frac{\sqrt{2}}{2}\left(x - \frac{\pi}{4}\right) - \frac{\sqrt{2}}{4}\left(x - \frac{\pi}{4}\right)^2$
b.

n	$p_n(x)$	error
0	0.7071	1.2×10^{-1}
1	0.5960	8.2×10^{-3}
2	0.5873	4.7×10^{-4}

13. $R_3(x) = \frac{\sin c}{4!}x^4, |c| < \pi; |R_3| < \frac{\pi^4}{4!}$ **15.** $(-\infty, \infty), R = \infty$
17. $(-\infty, \infty), R = \infty$ **19.** $(-9, 9), R = 9$ **21.** $\sum_{k=0}^{\infty} x^{2k}; (-1, 1)$
23. $\sum_{k=0}^{\infty} 3^k x^k; \left(-\frac{1}{3}, \frac{1}{3}\right)$ **25.** $\sum_{k=1}^{\infty} kx^{k-1}; (-1, 1)$
27. $1 + 3x + \frac{9x^2}{2!}; \sum_{k=0}^{\infty}\frac{(3x)^k}{k!}$
29. $-(x - \pi/2) + \frac{(x-\pi/2)^3}{3!} - \frac{(x-\pi/2)^5}{5!}$; $\sum_{k=0}^{\infty}(-1)^{k+1}\frac{(x-\pi/2)^{2k+1}}{(2k+1)!}$
31. $x - \frac{x^3}{3} + \frac{x^5}{5}; \sum_{k=0}^{\infty}\frac{(-1)^k x^{2k+1}}{2k+1}$
33. $1 + \frac{x}{3} - \frac{x^2}{9} + \cdots$ **35.** $1 - \frac{3}{2}x + \frac{3}{2}x^2 - \cdots$
37. $R_n(x) = \frac{(-1)^{n+1}e^{-c}}{(n+1)!}x^{n+1}$, where c is between 0 and x.
$\lim_{n\to\infty}|R_n(x)| = \lim_{n\to\infty}\frac{|x^{n+1}|}{e^{|x|}}\cdot\frac{1}{(n+1)!} = 0$ for $-\infty < x < \infty$.

39. $R_n(x) = \dfrac{(-1)^n(1+c)^{-(n+1)}}{n+1}x^{n+1}$ where c is between 0 and x.

$\lim_{n\to\infty} |R_n(x)| = \lim_{n\to\infty}\left(\dfrac{|x|}{1+c}\right)^{n+1} \cdot \dfrac{1}{n+1} < \lim_{n\to\infty} 1^{n+1} \cdot \dfrac{1}{n+1} = 0$

for $|x| \le \frac{1}{2}$. **41.** $\frac{1}{24}$ **43.** $\frac{1}{8}$ **45.** $\frac{1}{6}$

47. $y(x) = 4 + 4x + \dfrac{4^2}{2!}x^2 + \dfrac{4^3}{3!}x^3 + \cdots + \dfrac{4^n}{n!}x^n + \cdots$
$= 3 + e^{4x}$.

49. a. $\sum_{k=1}^{\infty} \dfrac{(-1)^{k+1}}{k}$ **b.** $\sum_{k=1}^{\infty} \dfrac{1}{k2^k}$ **c.** $2\sum_{k=0}^{\infty} \dfrac{x^{2k+1}}{2k+1}$

d. $x = \dfrac{1}{3}$; $2\sum_{k=0}^{\infty} \dfrac{1}{3^{2k+1}(2k+1)}$ **e.** Series in part (d)

CHAPTER 11

Section 11.1 Exercises, pp. 630–633

1. If $x = g(t)$ and $y = h(t)$ for $a \le t \le b$, then plotting the set $\{(g(t), (h(t)) : a \le t \le b\}$ results in a graph in the xy-plane.
3. $x = R\cos(\pi t/5), y = R\sin(\pi t/5)$
5. $x = t; y = t^2, -\infty < t < \infty$

7. a.

t	−10	−8	−6	−4	−2	0	2	4	6	8	10
x	−20	−16	−12	−8	−4	0	4	8	12	16	20
y	−34	−28	−22	−16	−10	−4	2	8	14	20	26

b.

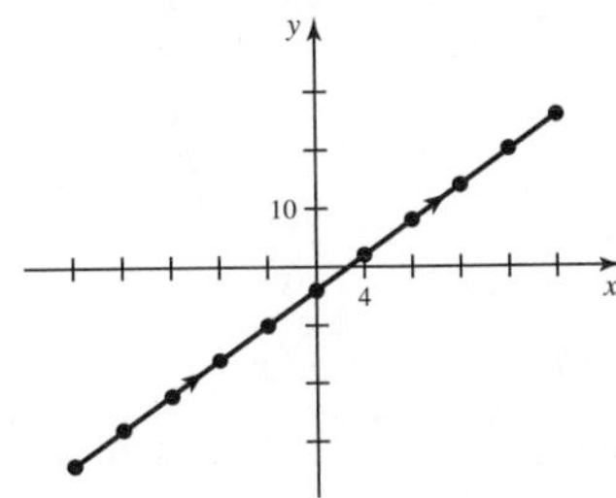

c. $y = \frac{3}{2}x - 4$

d. A line rising up and to the right as t increases

9. a.

t	−5	−4	−3	−2	−1	0	1	2	3	4	5
x	11	10	9	8	7	6	5	4	3	2	1
y	−18	−15	−12	−9	−6	−3	0	3	6	9	12

b.

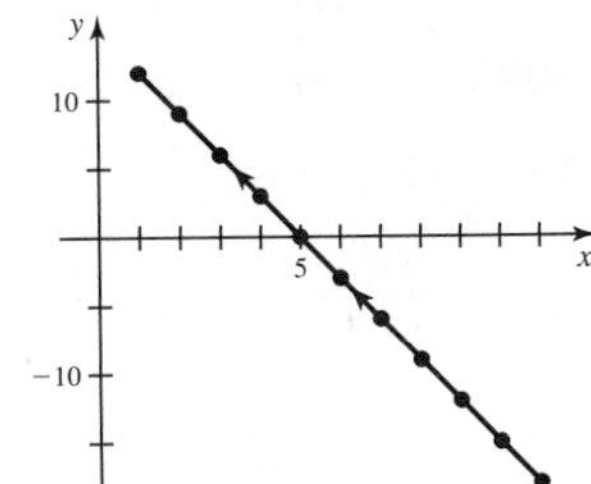

c. $y = -3x + 15$

d. A line rising up and to the left as t increases
11. a. $y = 3x - 12$ **b.** A line rising up and to the right as t increases **13. a.** $y = (x+1)^3$ **b.** A cubic function rising up and to the right as t increases **15.** Center (0, 0); radius 3; lower half of circle generated counterclockwise **17.** Center (0, 0); radius 7; full circle generated counterclockwise

19. $x = 4\cos t$, $y = 4\sin t$, $0 \le t \le 2\pi$: The circle has equation $x^2 + y^2 = 16$.

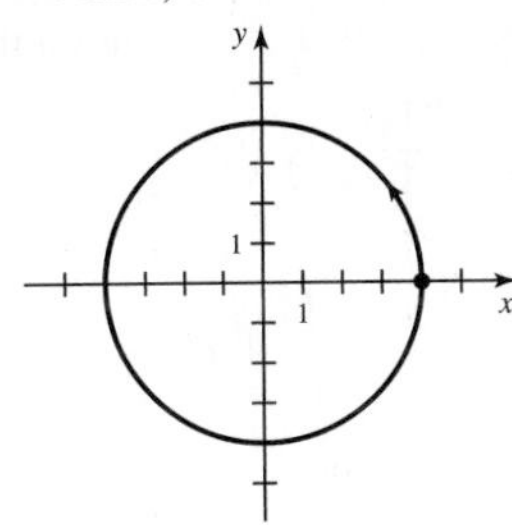

21. $x = 8\sin t - 2$, $y = 8\cos t - 3$, $0 \le t \le 2\pi$: The circle has equation $(x+2)^2 + (y+3)^2 = 64$.

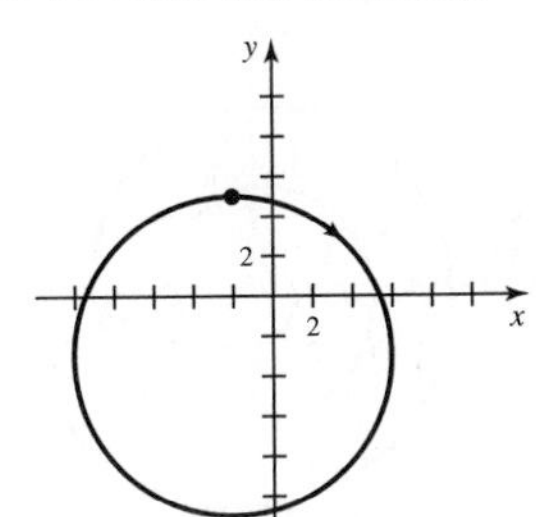

23. $x = 400\cos\left(\dfrac{4\pi t}{3}\right)$, $y = 400\sin\left(\dfrac{4\pi t}{3}\right)$, $0 \le t \le 1.5$ (min) **25.** $x = 50\cos\left(\dfrac{\pi t}{12}\right)$, $y = 50\sin\left(\dfrac{\pi t}{12}\right)$, $0 \le t \le 24$ (s)
27. Slope: −1; point: (3, 1)

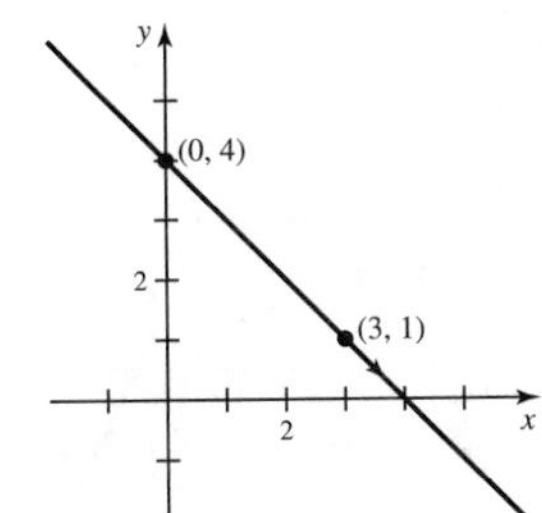

29. Slope: 0; point: (8, 1)

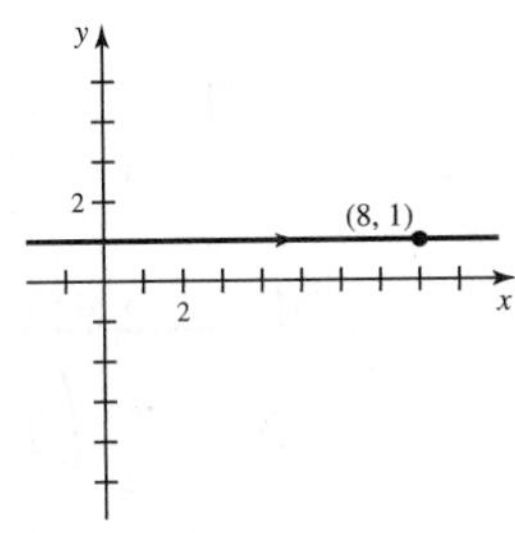

31. $x = 2t, y = 8t, 0 \le t \le 1$
33. $x = -1 + 7t, y = -3 - 13t, 0 \le t \le 1$
35. $x = t, y = 2t^2 - 4, -1 \le t \le 5$ (not unique)

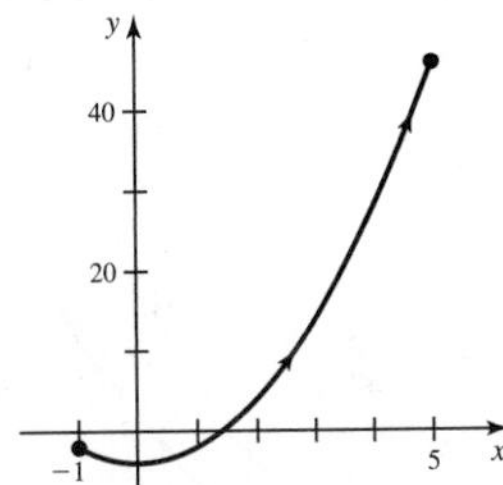

37. $x = 4t - 2, y = -6t + 3, 0 \le t \le 1;$
$x = t + 1, y = 8t - 11, 1 \le t \le 2$ (not unique)

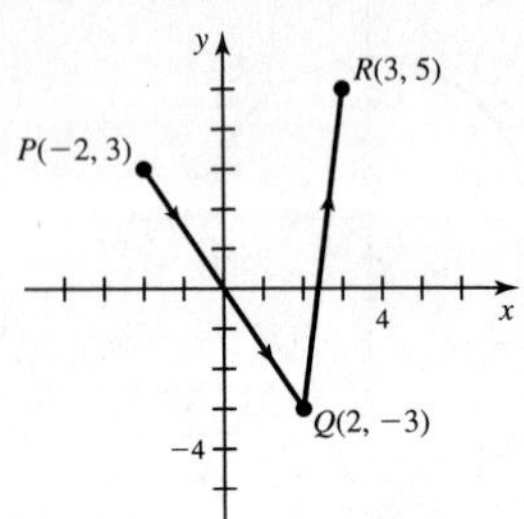

39.

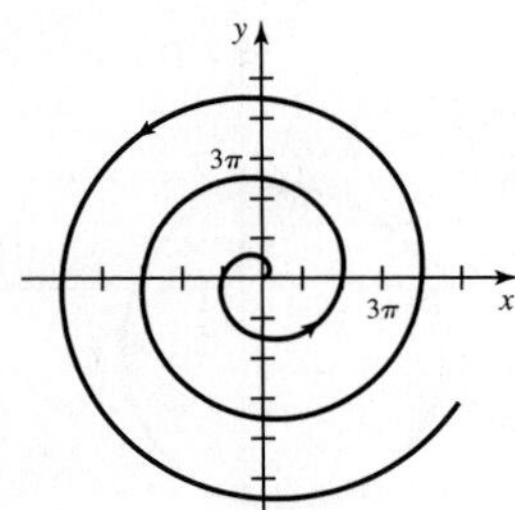

41.

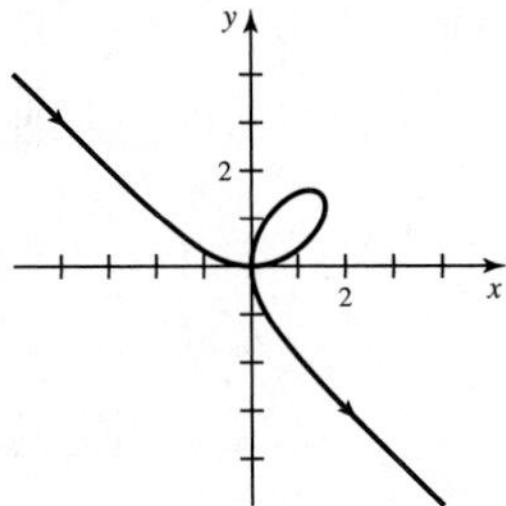

43.

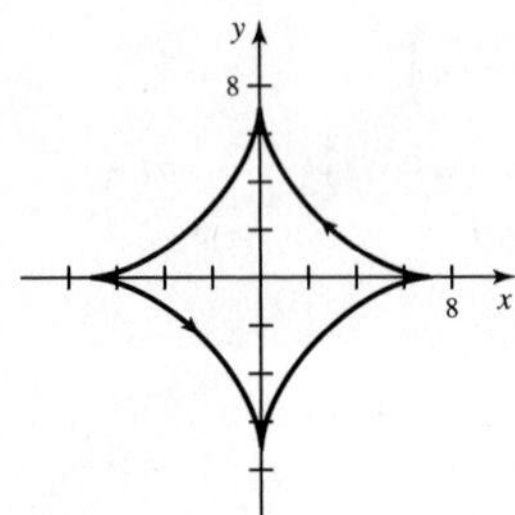

45. a. $\frac{dy}{dx} = -2; -2$ **b.**

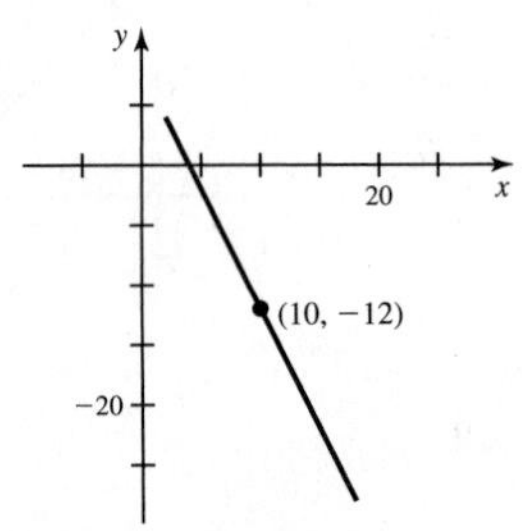

47. a. $\frac{dy}{dx} = -8 \cot t; 0$ **b.**

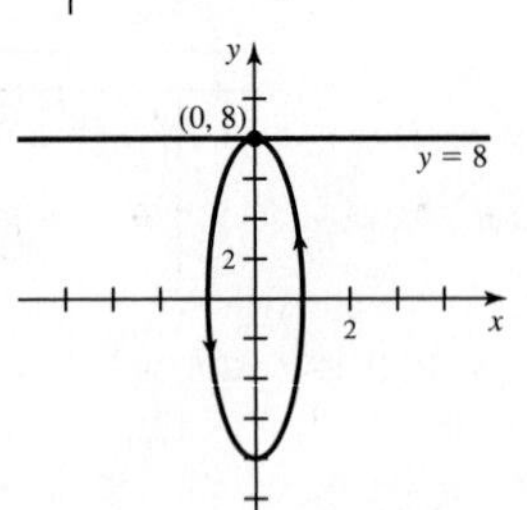

49. a. $\frac{dy}{dx} = \frac{t^2 + 1}{t^2 - 1}, t \ne 0$; undefined **b.**

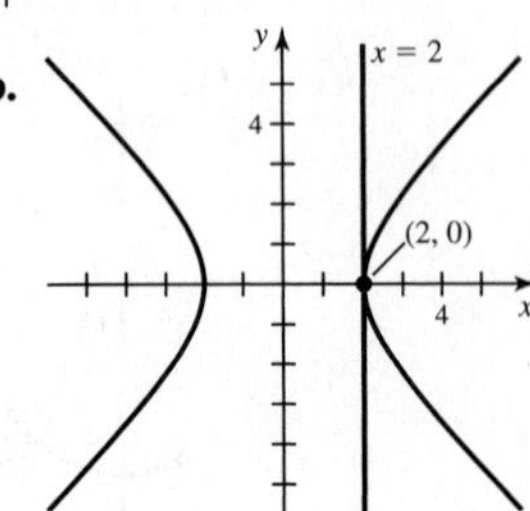

51. a. False **b.** True **c.** False **d.** True
53. $x = 1 + 2t, y = 1 + 4t, -\infty < t < \infty$
55. $x = t^2, y = t, t \ge 0$

57. $0 \le t \le 2\pi$

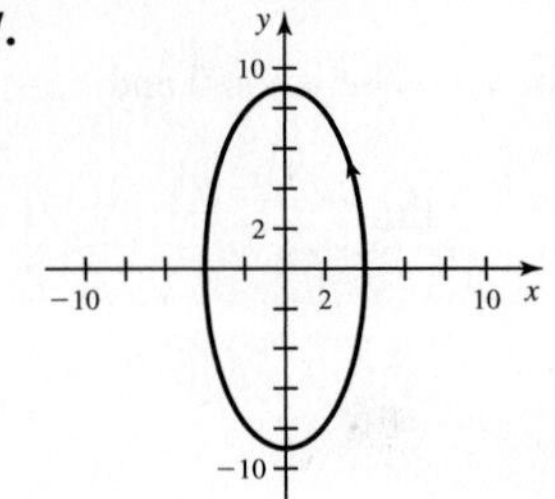

59. $x = 3 \cos t, y = \frac{3}{2} \sin t, 0 \le t \le 2\pi; \left(\frac{x}{3}\right)^2 + \left(\frac{2y}{3}\right)^2 = 1$; in the counterclockwise direction

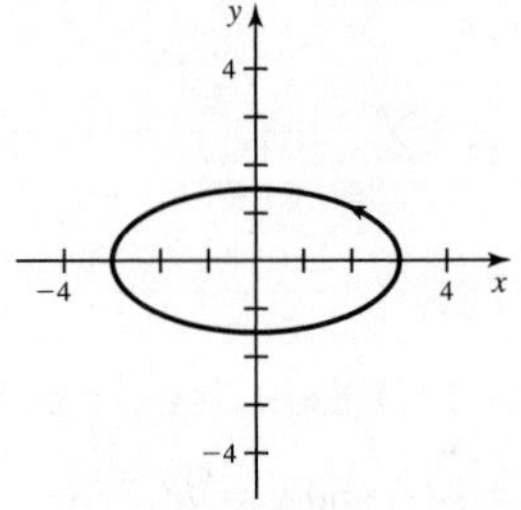

61. $x = 15 \cos t - 2, y = 10 \sin t - 3, 0 \le t \le 2\pi;$
$\left(\frac{x + 2}{15}\right)^2 + \left(\frac{y + 3}{10}\right)^2 = 1$; in the counterclockwise direction

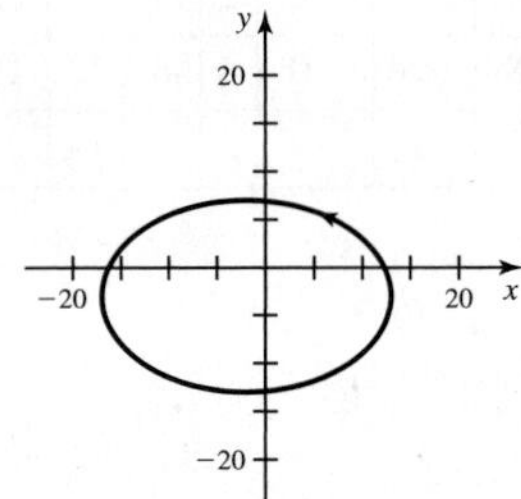

63. a and b **65.** $x^2 + y^2 = 4$ **67.** $y = \sqrt{4 - x^2}$
69. $y = x^2$ **71.** $\left(\frac{-4}{\sqrt{5}}, \frac{8}{\sqrt{5}}\right)$ and $\left(\frac{4}{\sqrt{5}}, \frac{-8}{\sqrt{5}}\right)$ **73.** There are no such points. **75.** $a = p, b = p + \frac{2\pi}{3}$, for all real p **77. a.** $(0, 2)$ and $(0, -2)$ **b.** $(1, \sqrt{2}), (1, -\sqrt{2}), (-1, \sqrt{2}), (-1, -\sqrt{2})$
79. a. $x = \pm a \cos^{2/n}(t), y = \pm b \sin^{2/n}(t)$ **c.** The curves become more square as n increases. **85.** ≈ 2857 m

Section 11.2 Exercises, pp. 642–646

1.

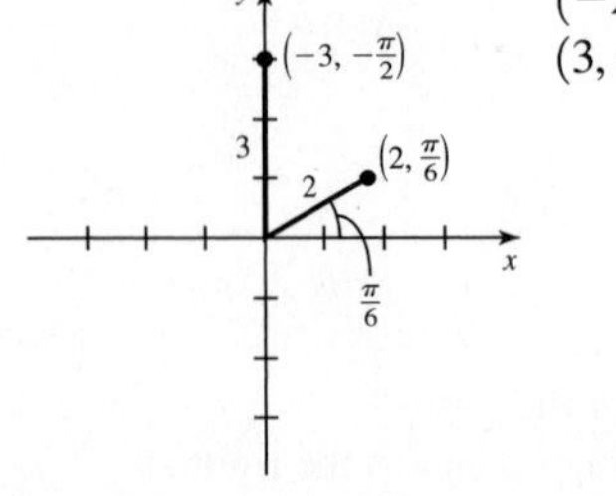

$(-2, -5\pi/6), (2, 13\pi/6);$
$(3, \pi/2), (3, 5\pi/2)$

3. $r^2 = x^2 + y^2, \tan \theta = \frac{y}{x}$ **5.** $r \cos \theta = 5$
7. x-axis symmetry occurs if (r, θ) on the graph implies $(r, -\theta)$ is on the graph. y-axis symmetry occurs if (r, θ) on the graph implies $(r, \pi - \theta) = (-r, -\theta)$ is on the graph. Symmetry about the origin occurs if (r, θ) on the graph implies $(-r, \theta) = (r, \theta + \pi)$ is on the graph.

9.

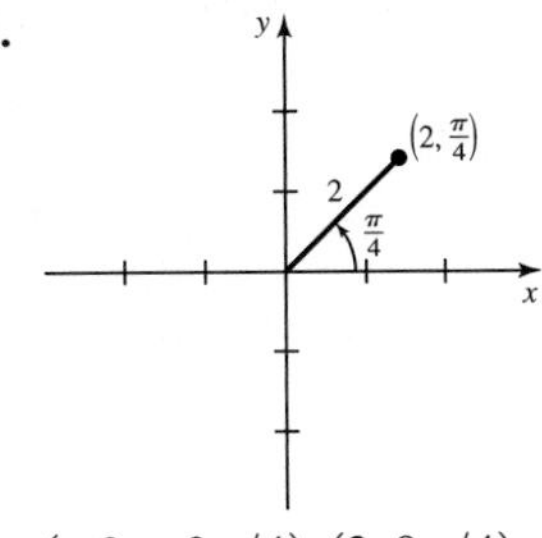

$(-2, -3\pi/4), (2, 9\pi/4)$

11.

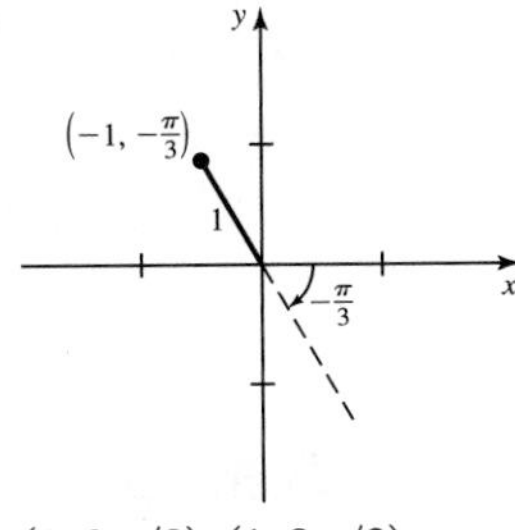

$(1, 2\pi/3), (1, 8\pi/3)$

13.

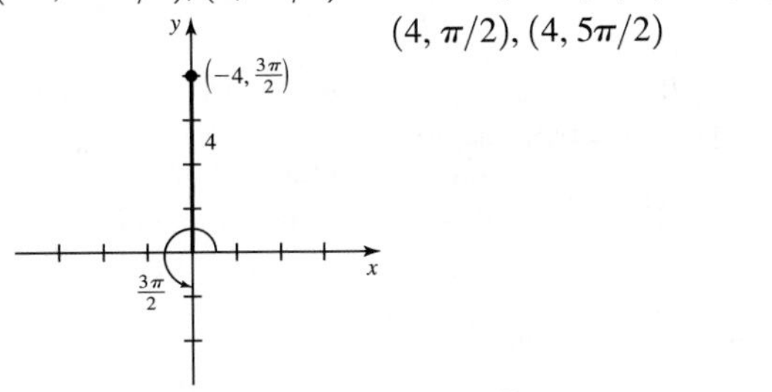

$(4, \pi/2), (4, 5\pi/2)$

15. $(3\sqrt{2}/2, 3\sqrt{2}/2)$ **17.** $(1/2, -\sqrt{3}/2)$
19. $(2\sqrt{2}, -2\sqrt{2})$ **21.** $(2\sqrt{2}, \pi/4), (-2\sqrt{2}, 5\pi/4)$
23. $(2, \pi/3), (-2, 4\pi/3)$ **25.** $(8, 2\pi/3), (-8, -\pi/3)$

27.

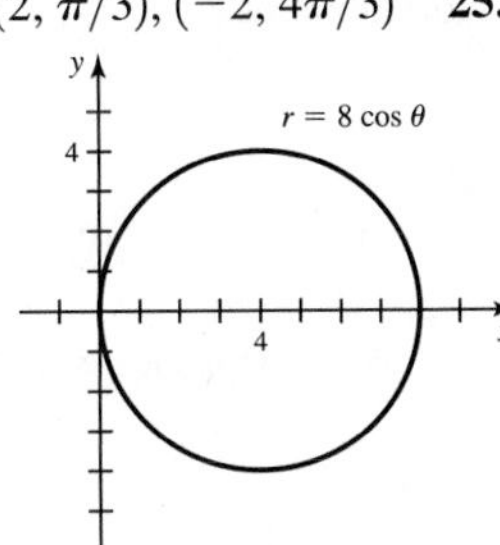

29.

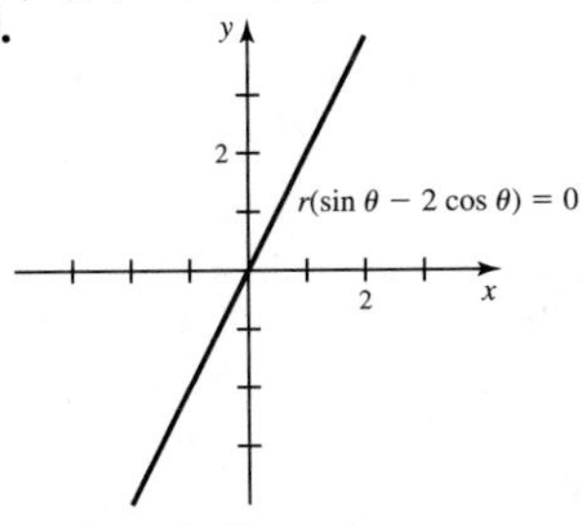

31. $x = -4$; vertical line passing through $(-4, 0)$
33. $x^2 + (y - 1)^2 = 1$; circle of radius 1 centered at $(0, 1)$ and $x = 0$; y-axis **35.** $x^2 + (y - 4)^2 = 16$; circle of radius 4 centered at $(0, 4)$

37.

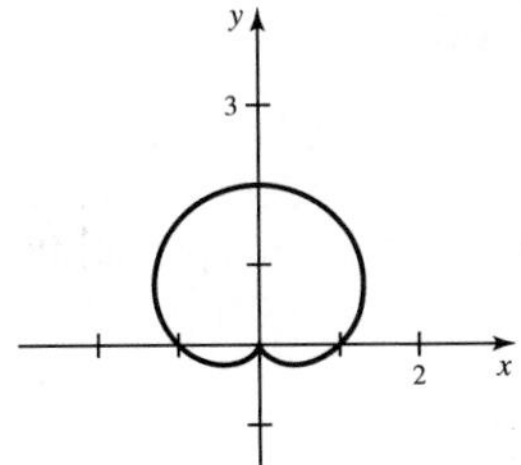

39.

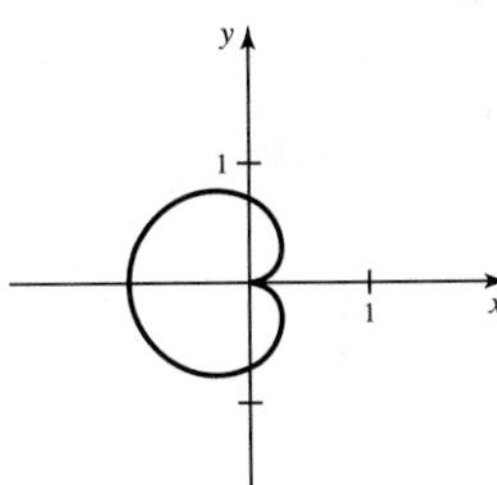

41.

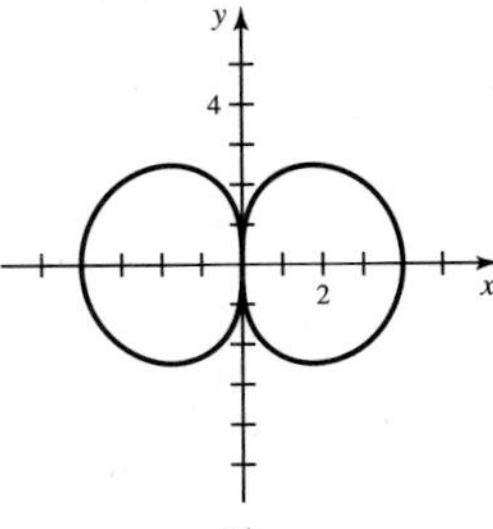

43.

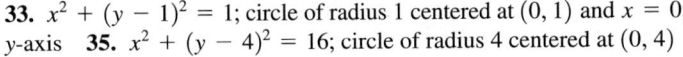

45.

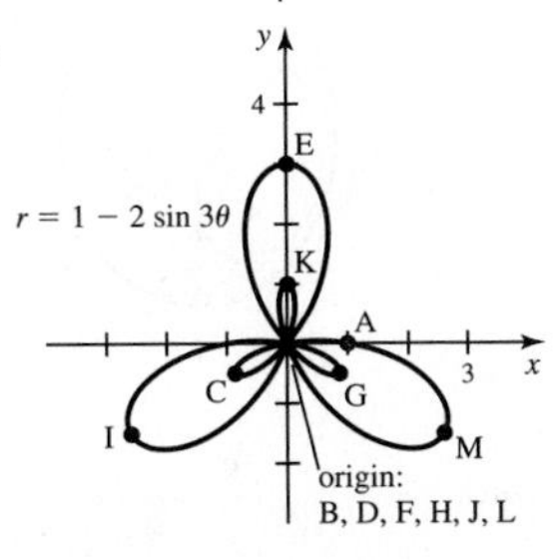

47.

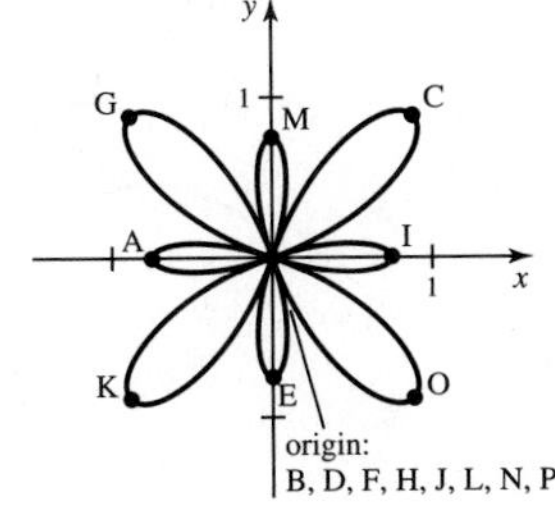

49.

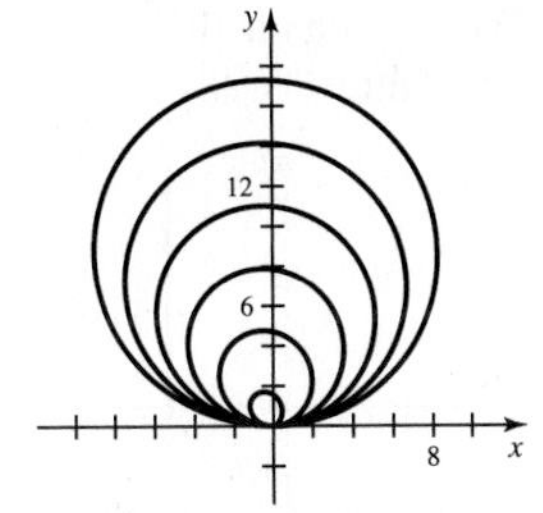

No interval $[0, P]$ generates the entire curve; $-\infty < \theta < \infty$

51.

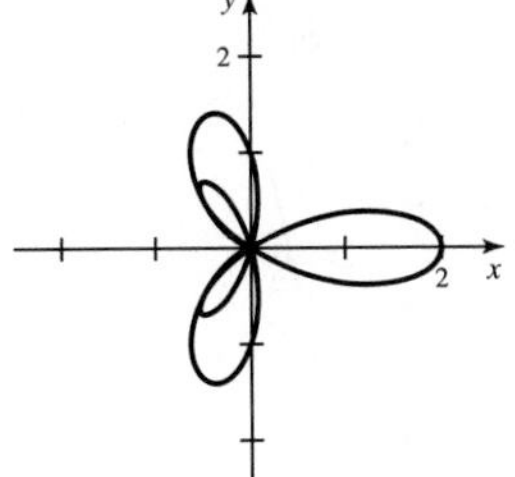

53.

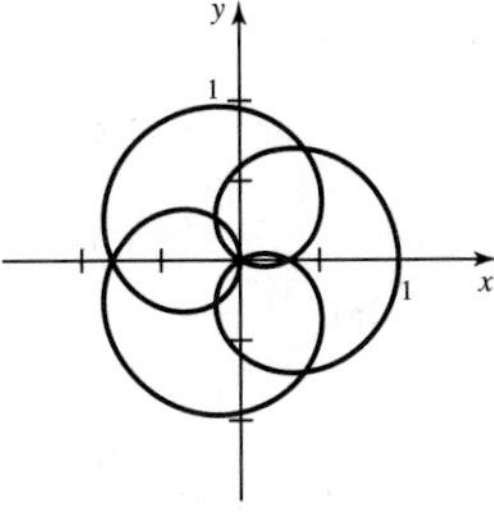

$[0, 2\pi]$ $[0, 5\pi]$
$[0, 2\pi]$

55.

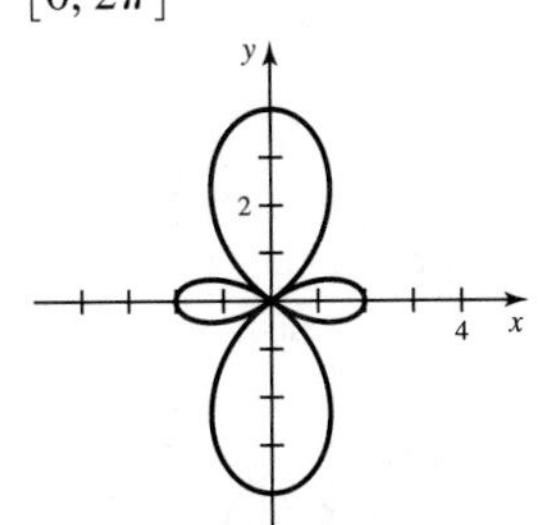

57. a. True **b.** True **c.** False **d.** True

59.

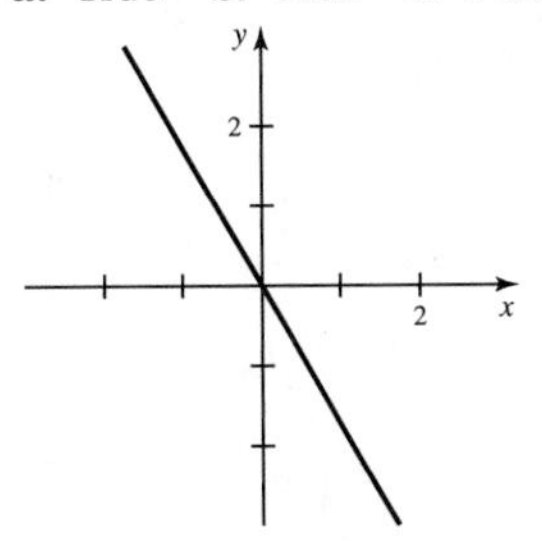

61.

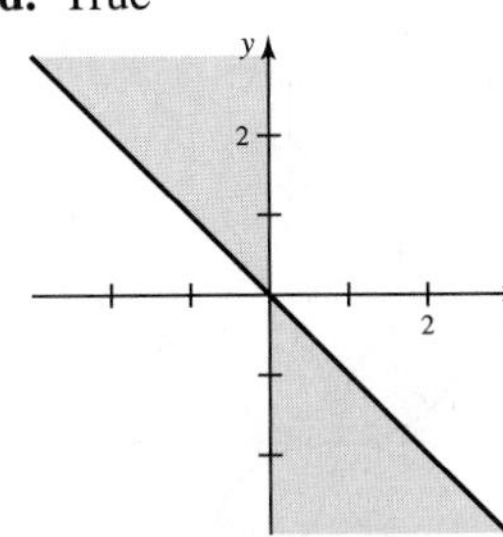

63.

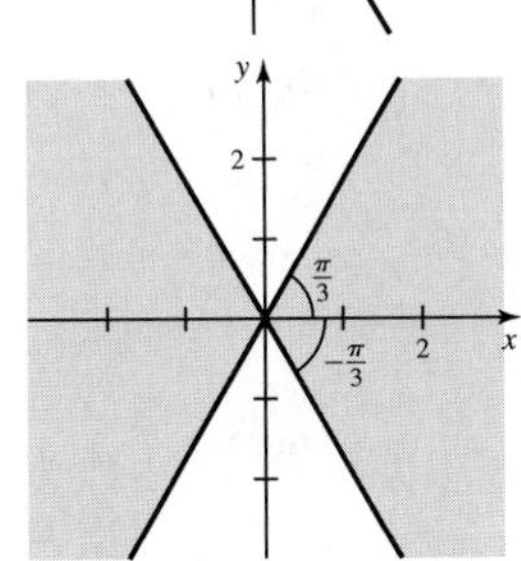

65.

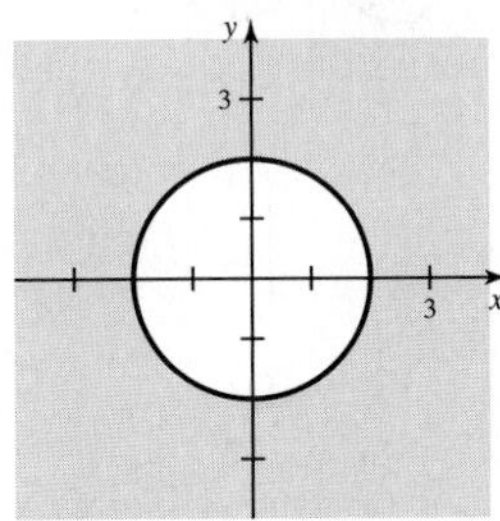

69. A circle of radius 4 and center $(2, \pi/3)$ (polar coordinates)

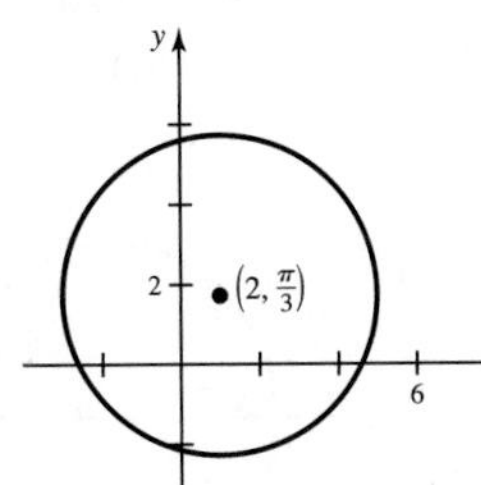

71. A circle of radius 4 centered at $(2, 3)$ (Cartesian coordinates)

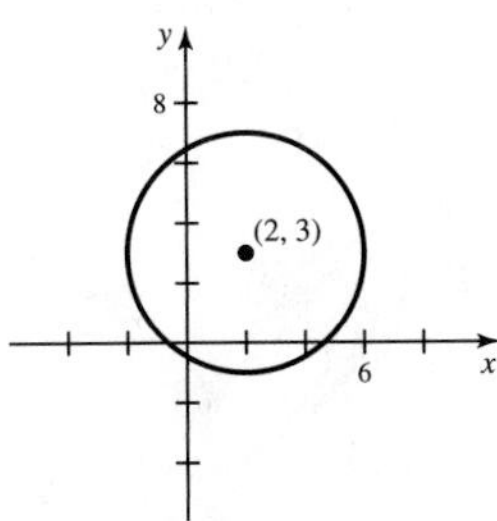

73. A circle of radius 3 centered at $(-1, 2)$ (Cartesian coordinates)

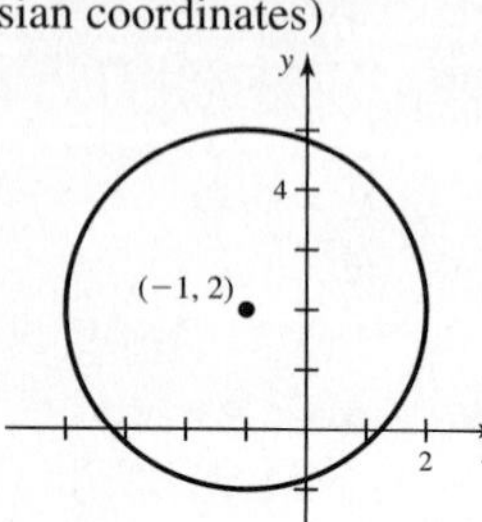

75. Same graph on all three intrevals.

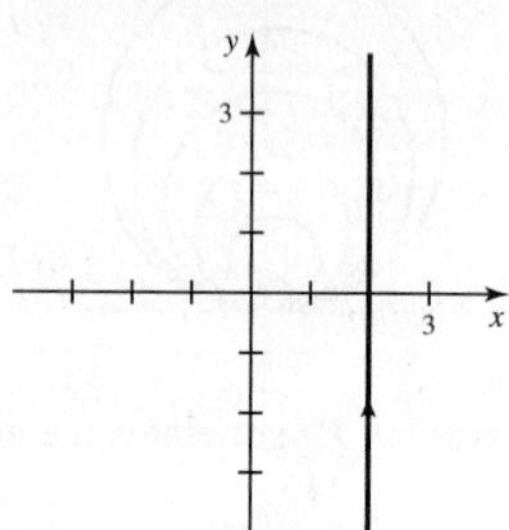

77.

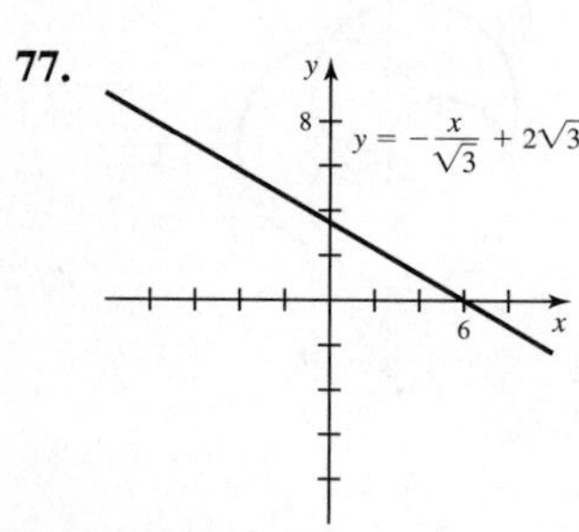

79.

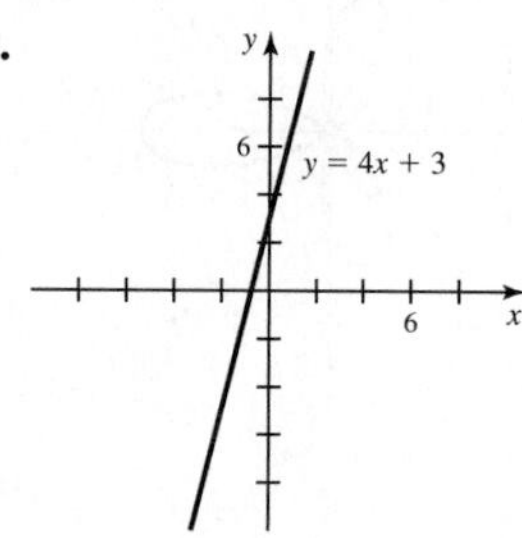

81. a. A **b.** C **c.** B **d.** D **e.** E **f.** F

83.

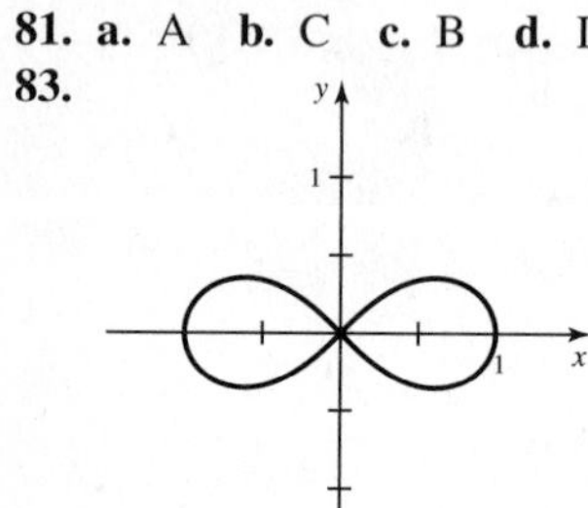

85.

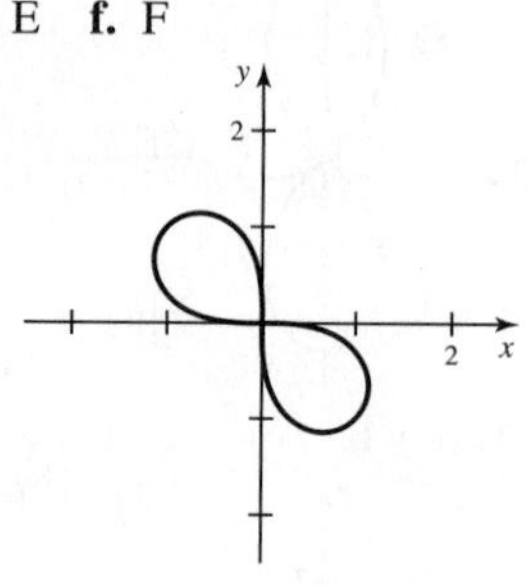

87.

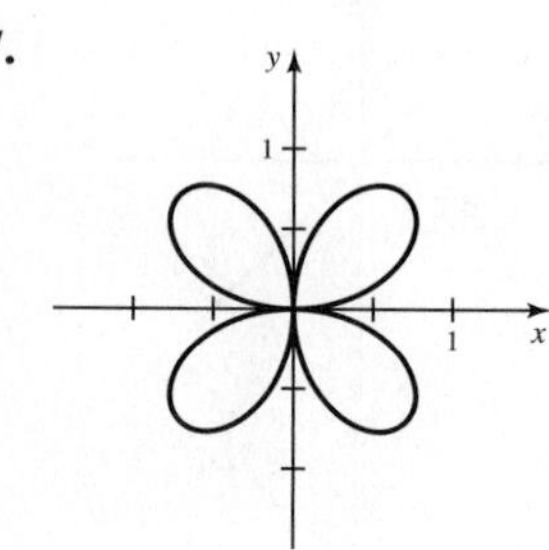

89.

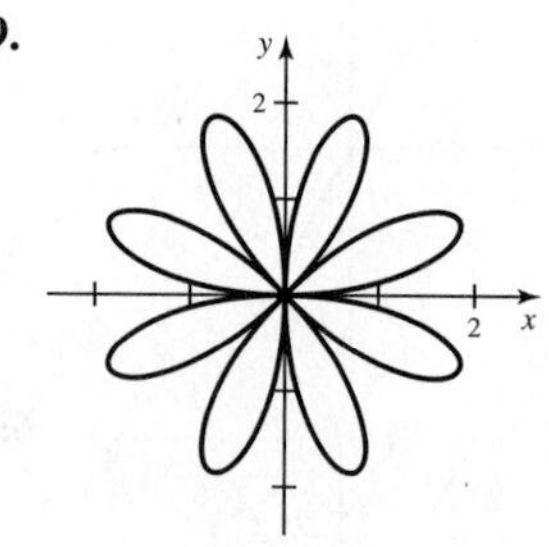

93.

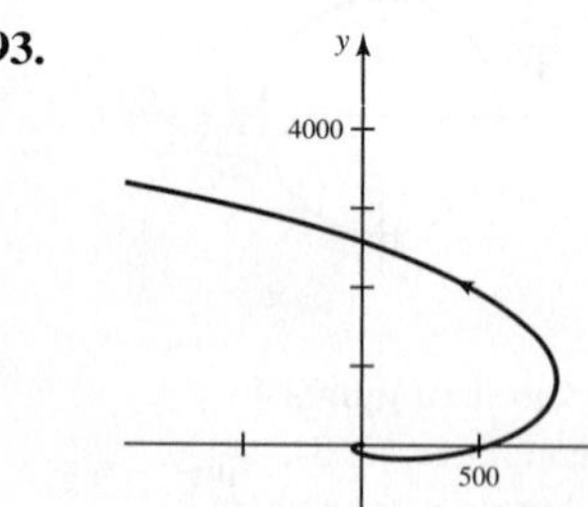

For $a = -1$, the spiral winds inward toward the origin.

95. $(2, 0)$ and $(0, 0)$

97. $(0, 0), \left(\frac{2 - \sqrt{2}}{2}, 3\pi/4\right), \left(\frac{2 + \sqrt{2}}{2}, 7\pi/4\right)$

99. a.

101. a.

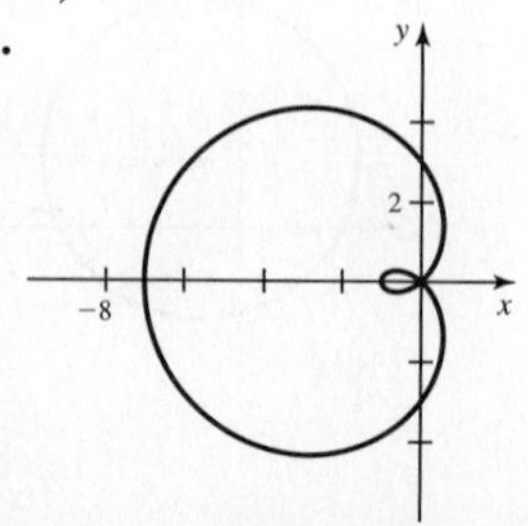

103. $r = a\cos\theta + b\sin\theta = \frac{a}{r}(r\cos\theta) + \frac{b}{r}(r\sin\theta) = \frac{a}{r}x + \frac{b}{r}y$

Thus, $\left(x - \frac{a}{2}\right)^2 + \left(y - \frac{b}{2}\right)^2 = \frac{a^2 + b^2}{4}$.

Center: $\left(\frac{a}{2}, \frac{b}{2}\right)$; radius: $\frac{\sqrt{a^2 + b^2}}{2}$ **105.** Symmetry about the x-axis

Section 11.3 Exercises, pp. 651–653

1. $x = f(\theta)\cos\theta$, $y = f(\theta)\sin\theta$ **3.** The slope of the tangent line is the rate of change of the vertical coordinate with respect to the horizontal coordinate. **5.** 0; $\theta = \pi/2$ **7.** $-\sqrt{3}$; $\theta = 0$ **9.** Vertical, vertical; the curve does not intersect the origin. **11.** 0 at $(-4, \pi/2)$ and $(-4, 3\pi/2)$, undefined at $(4, 0)$ and $(4, \pi)$; $\theta = \pi/4, \theta = 3\pi/4$, $\theta = 5\pi/4, \theta = 7\pi/4$ **13.** ± 1; $\theta = \pm\pi/4$ **15.** Horizontal at $(2\sqrt{2}, \pi/4), (-2\sqrt{2}, 3\pi/4)$; vertical at $(0, \pi/2)$ and $(4, 0)$

17. Horizontal at $(0, 0), (\pm r_1, \theta_1), (\pm r_1, \pi - \theta_1)$, where $r_1 = \frac{2\sqrt{2}}{3}$ and $\cos 2\theta_1 = -\frac{1}{3}$; vertical at $(0, 0), (\pm r_1, \theta_2), (\pm r_1, \pi - \theta_2)$, where $r_1 = \frac{2\sqrt{2}}{3}$ and $\cos 2\theta_2 = \frac{1}{3}$ **19.** Horizontal at $\left(\pm\sqrt{2}, \frac{\pi}{6}\right)$, $\left(\pm\sqrt{2}, -\frac{\pi}{6}\right)$; vertical at $(2, 0)$ and $(2, \pi)$ **21.** 16π **23.** $9\pi/2$ **25.** $\pi/20$ **27.** $2\left(\frac{8\pi}{3} - 2\sqrt{3}\right)$ **29.** $(0, 0), (3/\sqrt{2}, \pi/4)$ **31.** $(2, 0), (0, 0), (r, \theta) \approx (-2 + 2\sqrt{2}, \pm\cos^{-1}(-3 + 2\sqrt{2})) \approx (0.828, \pm 1.74)$ **33. a.** False **b.** False **35.** $2\pi/3 - \sqrt{3}/2$ **37.** $9\pi + 27\sqrt{3}$ **39.** Horizontal: $(0, 0)$, $(4.05, 2.03)$, $(9.83, 4.91)$; vertical: $(1.72, 0.86)$, $(6.85, 3.43)$, $(12.87, 6.44)$

41. a. $A_n = \frac{1}{4e^{(4n+2)\pi}} - \frac{1}{4e^{4n\pi}} - \frac{1}{4e^{(4n-2)\pi}} + \frac{1}{4e^{(4n-4)\pi}}$ **b.** 0 **c.** $e^{-4\pi}$ **43.** 6 **45.** 18π **47.** $(a^2 - 2)\theta^* + \pi - \sin 2\theta^*$, where $\theta^* = \cos^{-1}(a/2)$. **49.** $a^2(\pi/2 + a/3)$

Section 11.4 Exercises, pp. 662–665

1. A parabola is the set of all points in a plane equidistant from a fixed point and a fixed line. **3.** A hyperbola is the set of all points in a plane, the difference of whose distances from two fixed points is constant.

5. Parabola:

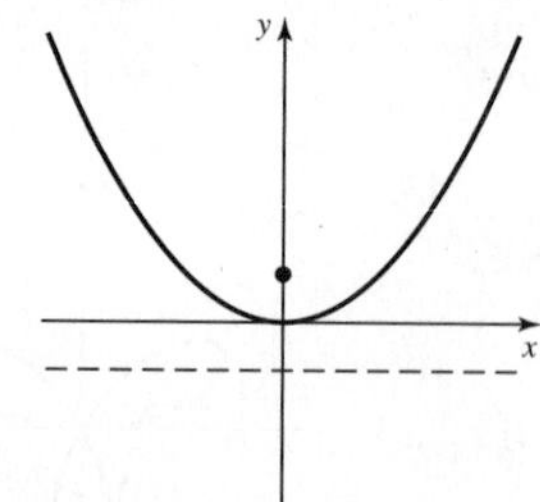

Hyperbola:

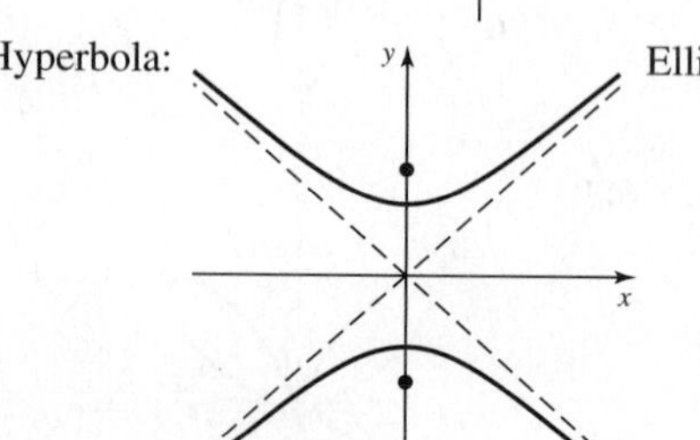

Ellipse:

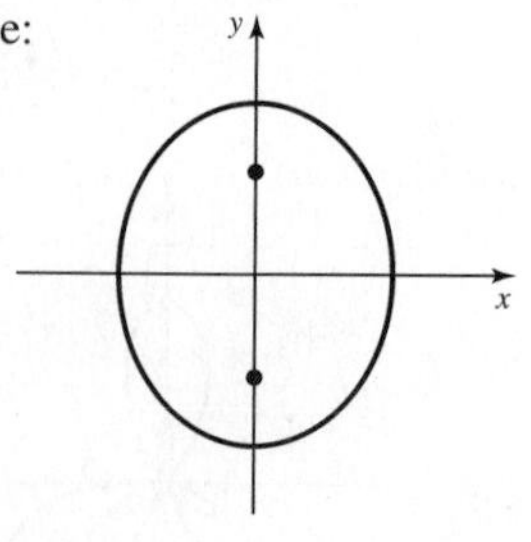

7. $\left(\frac{x}{a}\right)^2 + \frac{y^2}{a^2 - c^2} = 1$ **9.** $(\pm ae, 0)$ **11.** $y = \pm\frac{b}{a}x$

13.

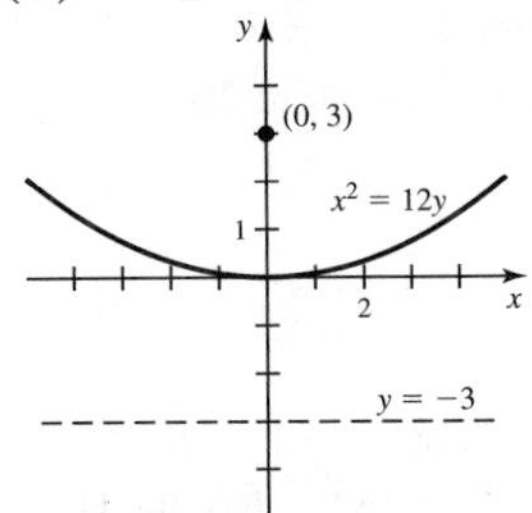

15.

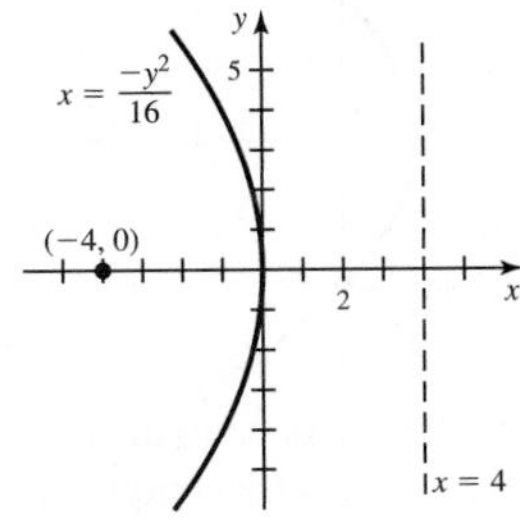

17.

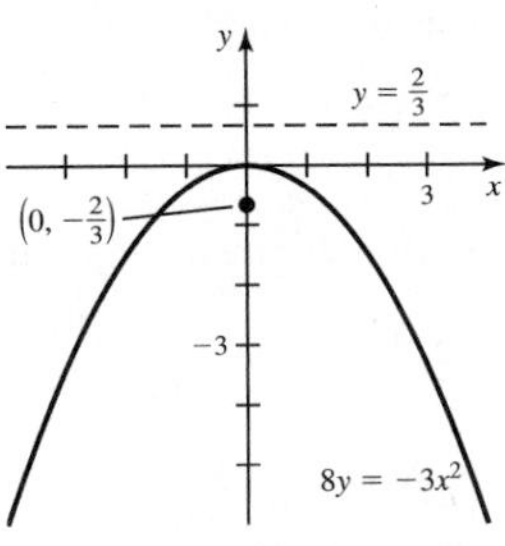

19. $y^2 = 16x$ **21.** $y^2 = 12x$

23. $x^2 = -\frac{2}{3}y$ **25.** $y^2 = 4(x + 1)$

27.

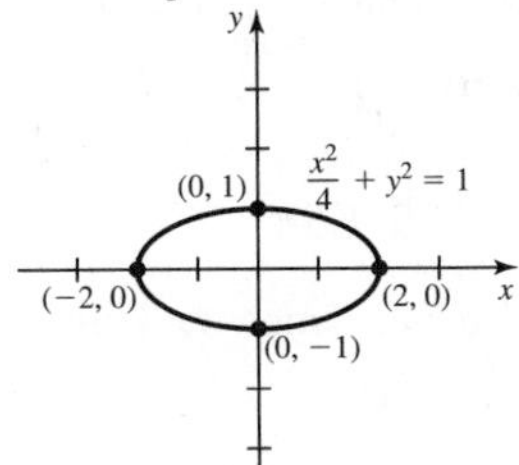

Vertices: $(\pm 2, 0)$; foci: $(\pm\sqrt{3}, 0)$; major axis has length 4; minor axis has length 2.

29.

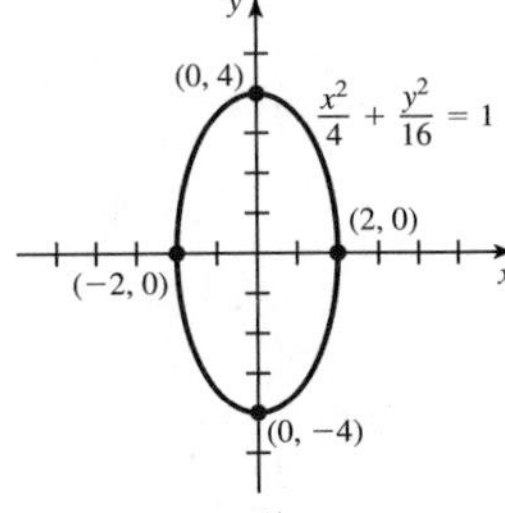

Vertices: $(0, \pm 4)$; foci: $(0, \pm 2\sqrt{3})$; major axis has length 8; minor axis has length 4.

31.

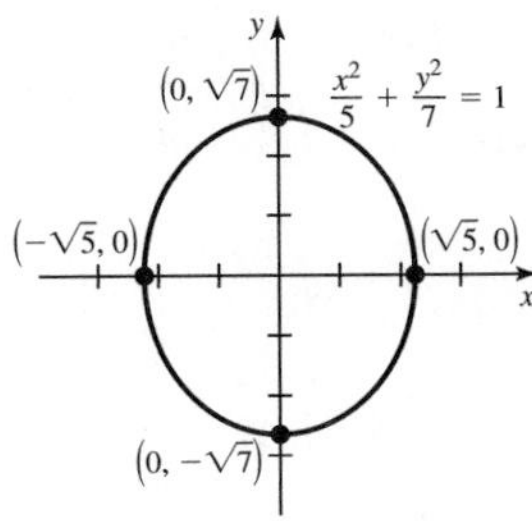

Vertices: $(0, \pm\sqrt{7})$; foci: $(0, \pm\sqrt{2})$; major axis has length $2\sqrt{7}$; minor axis has length $2\sqrt{5}$.

33.

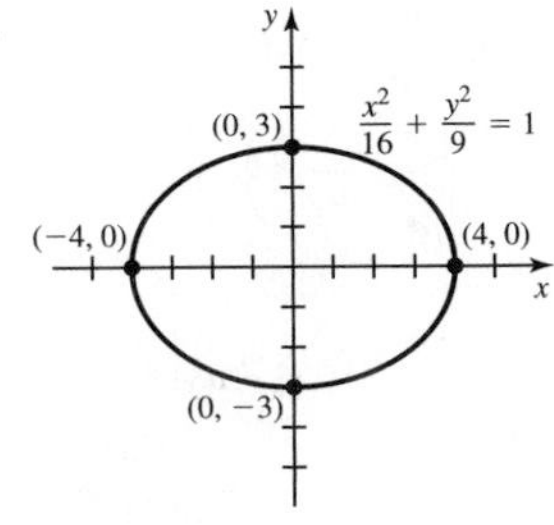

35.

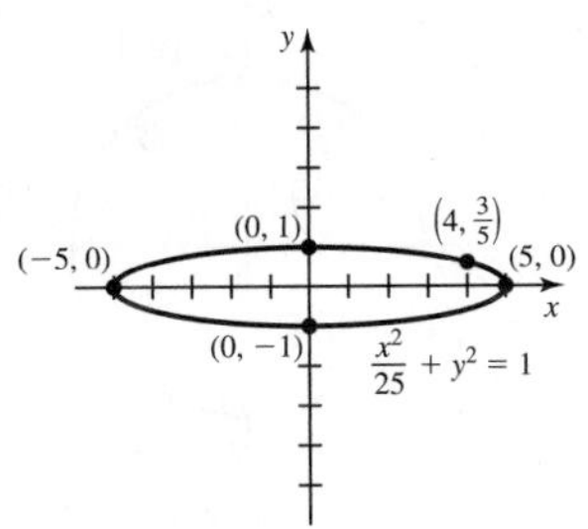

$\frac{x^2}{25} + y^2 = 1$ **37.** $\frac{x^2}{4} + \frac{y^2}{9} = 1$

39.

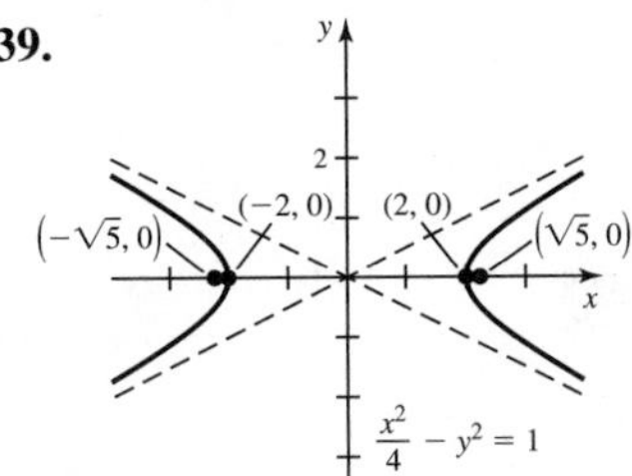

Vertices: $(\pm 2, 0)$; foci: $(\pm\sqrt{5}, 0)$; asymptotes: $y = \pm\frac{1}{2}x$

41.

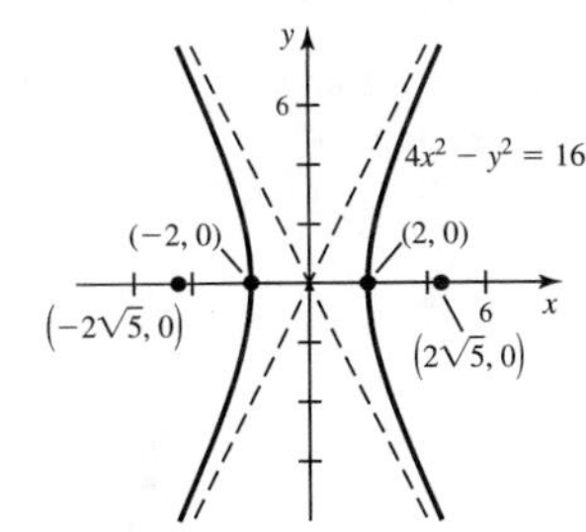

Vertices: $(\pm 2, 0)$; foci: $(\pm 2\sqrt{5}, 0)$; asymptotes: $y = \pm 2x$

43.

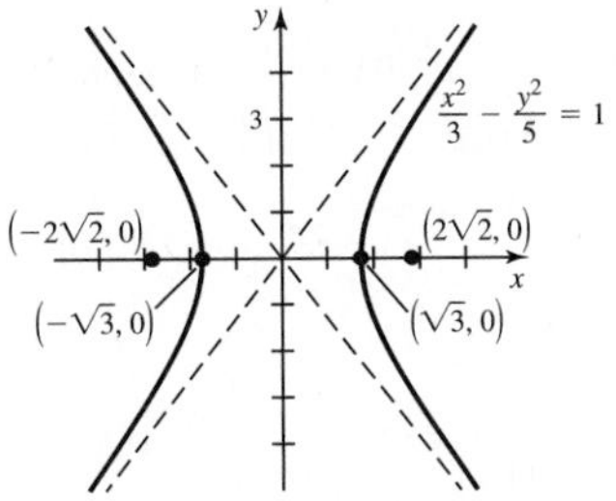

Vertices: $(\pm\sqrt{3}, 0)$; foci: $(\pm 2\sqrt{2}, 0)$; asymptotes: $y = \pm\sqrt{\frac{5}{3}}x$

45.

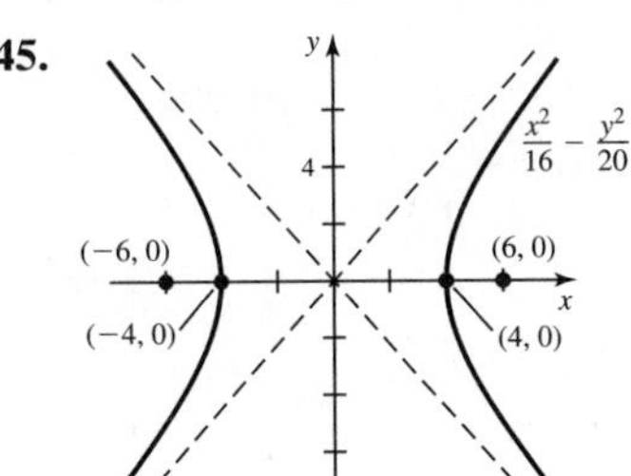

Vertices: $(\pm 4, 0)$; foci: $(\pm 6, 0)$; asymptotes: $y = \pm\frac{\sqrt{5}}{2}x$

47.

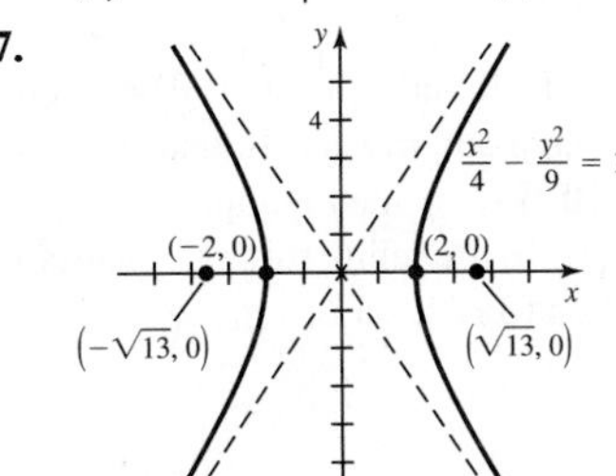

Vertices: $(\pm 2, 0)$; foci: $(\pm\sqrt{13}, 0)$; asymptotes: $y = \pm\frac{3}{2}x$

49. $\dfrac{x^2}{16} - \dfrac{y^2}{9} = 1$ **51.** $\dfrac{x^2}{81} + \dfrac{y^2}{72} = 1$
Directrices:
$x = \pm 27$

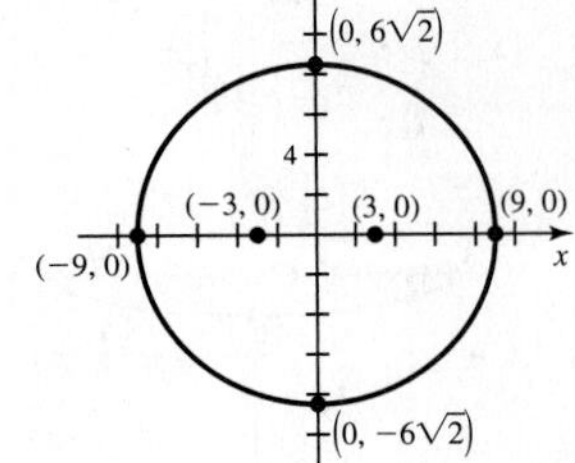

53. $x^2 - \dfrac{y^2}{8} = 1$

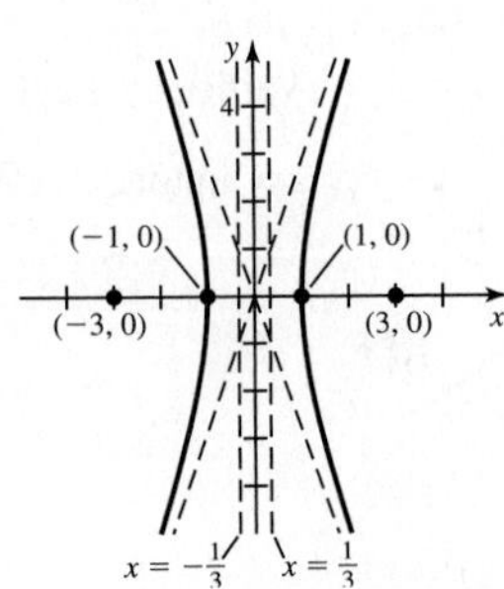

55.

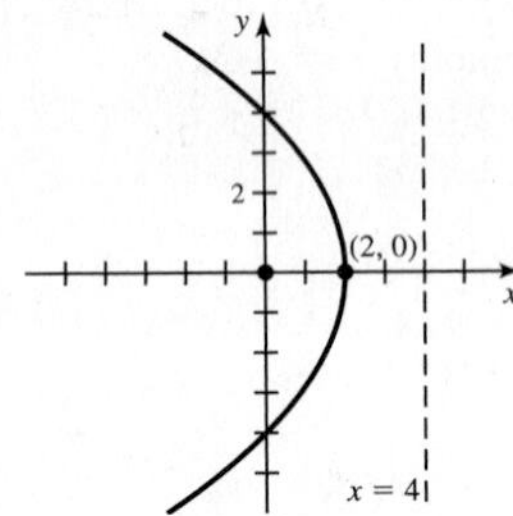

Vertex: (2, 0); focus: (0, 0); directrix: $x = 4$

57.

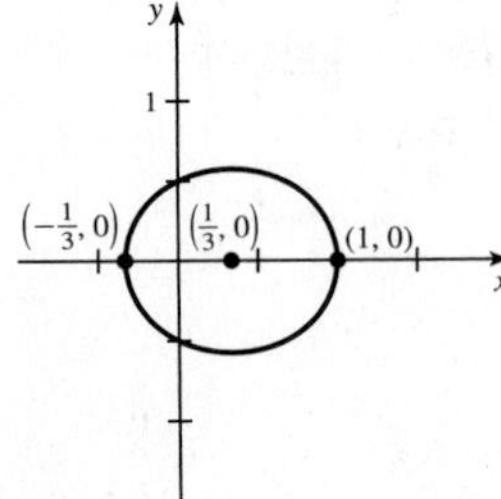

Vertices: $(1, 0), \left(-\frac{1}{3}, 0\right)$; center: $\left(\frac{1}{3}, 0\right)$; foci: $(0, 0), \left(\frac{2}{3}, 0\right)$; directrices: $x = -1, x = \frac{5}{3}$

59.

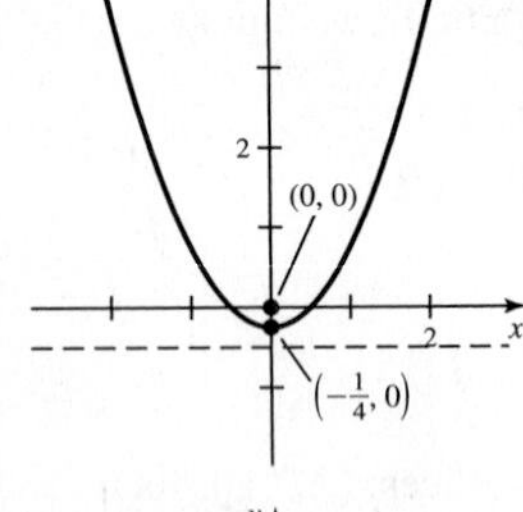

Vertex: $\left(0, -\frac{1}{4}\right)$; focus: (0, 0); directrix: $y = -\frac{1}{2}$

61.

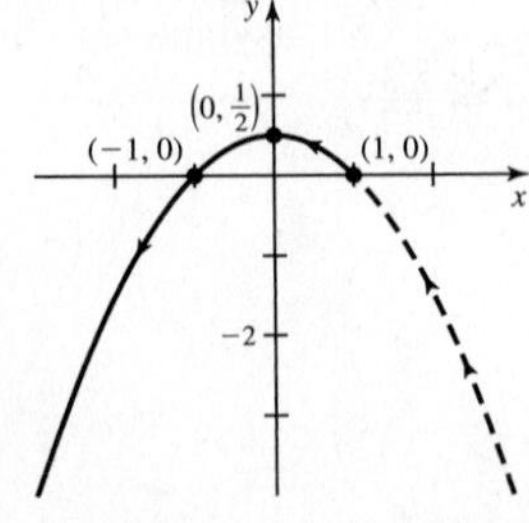

The parabola starts at (1, 0) and goes through quadrants I, II, and III for θ in $[0, 3\pi/2]$; then it approaches (1, 0) by traveling through quadrant IV on $(3\pi/2, 2\pi)$.

63.

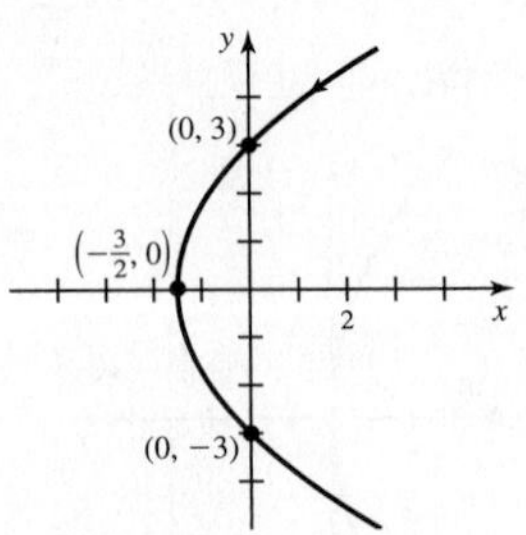

The parabola begins in the first quadrant and passes through the points (0, 3) and then $\left(-\frac{3}{2}, 0\right)$ and $(0, -3)$ as θ ranges from 0 to 2π.

65. The parabolas open to the right if $p > 0$, open to the left if $p < 0$, and are more vertically compressed as $|p|$ decreases. **67. a.** True **b.** True **c.** True **d.** True **69.** $y = 2x + 6$ **71.** $y = \frac{-3}{40}x - \frac{4}{5}$ **73.** $r = \dfrac{-4}{1 + 2\sin\theta}$ **77.** $\dfrac{dy}{dx} = \left(\dfrac{-b^2}{a^2}\right)\left(\dfrac{x}{y}\right)$, so $\dfrac{y - y_0}{x - x_0} = \left(\dfrac{-b^2}{a^2}\right)\left(\dfrac{x_0}{y_0}\right)$, which is equivalent to the given equation. **79.** $\dfrac{4\pi b^2 a}{3}$; $\dfrac{4\pi a^2 b}{3}$; yes, if $a \neq b$ **81. a.** $\dfrac{\pi b^2}{3a^2} \cdot (a - c)^2(2a + c)$ **b.** $\dfrac{4\pi b^4}{3a}$ **91.** $2p$ **97. a.** $u(m) = \dfrac{2m^2 - \sqrt{3m^2 + 1}}{m^2 - 1}$; $v(m) = \dfrac{2m^2 + \sqrt{3m^2 + 1}}{m^2 - 1}$; 2 intersection points for $|m| > 1$ **b.** $\frac{5}{4}, \infty$ **c.** 2, 2 **d.** $2\sqrt{3} - \ln(\sqrt{3} + 2)$

Chapter 11 Review Exercises, pp. 666–668

1. a. False **b.** False **c.** True **d.** False **e.** True **f.** True
3. a.

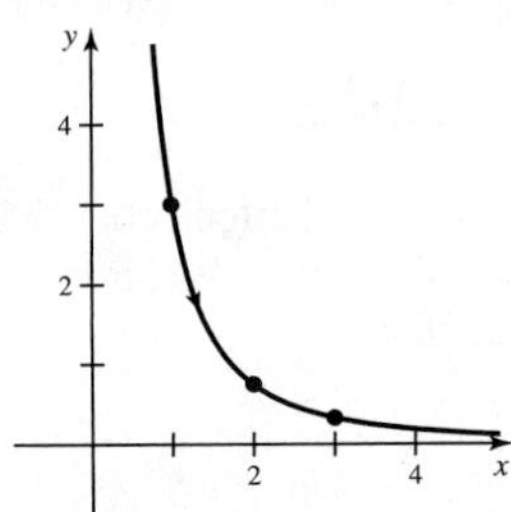

b. $y = 3/x^2$ **c.** The right branch of the function $y = 3/x^2$. **d.** $\dfrac{dy}{dx} = -6$

5. a.

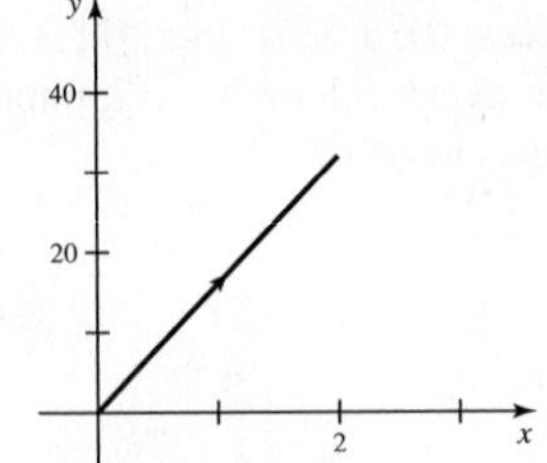

b. $y = 16x$ **c.** A line segment from (0, 0) to (2, 32) **d.** $\dfrac{dy}{dx} = 16$

7. At $t = \pi/6$: $y = (2 + \sqrt{3})x + \left(2 - \dfrac{\pi}{3} - \dfrac{\pi\sqrt{3}}{6}\right)$; at $t = \dfrac{2\pi}{3}$: $y = \dfrac{x}{\sqrt{3}} + 2 - \dfrac{2\pi}{3\sqrt{3}}$

9.

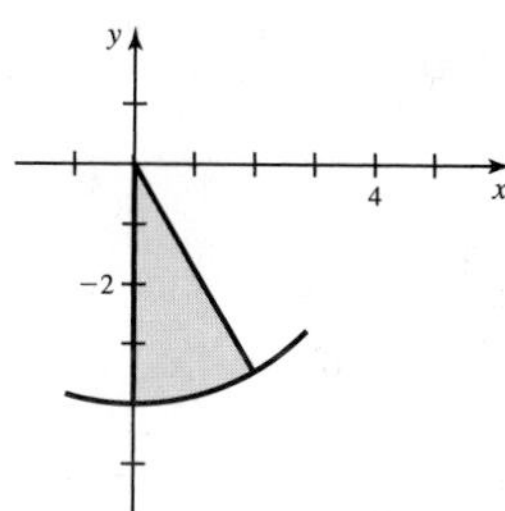

11. $(x-3)^2 + (y+1)^2 = 10$; a circle of radius $\sqrt{10}$ centered at $(3, -1)$

13. a.

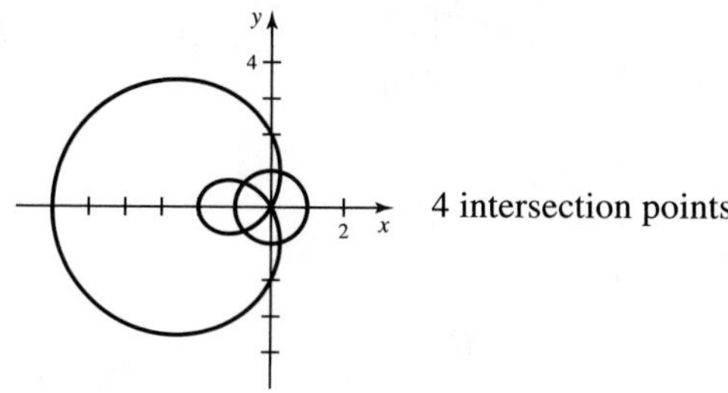

b. (1, 1.32), (1, 4.97), (−1, 0.7), (−1, 5.56)

15. a. (4.73, 2.77), (4.73, 0.38); $(6, \pi/2)$, $(2, 3\pi/2)$ **b.** There is no point at the origin. **c.**

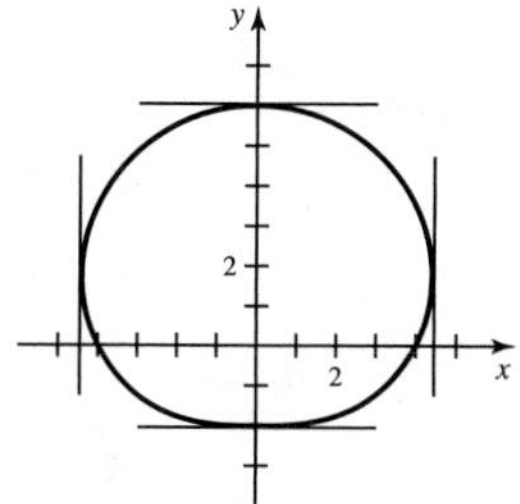

17. a. Horizontal tangent lines at $(1, \pi/6)$ $(1, 5\pi/6)$ $(1, 7\pi/6)$ and $(1, 11\pi/6)$; vertical tangent lines at $(\sqrt{2}, 0)$ and $(\sqrt{2}, \pi)$
b. Tangent lines at the origin have slopes ± 1.
c.

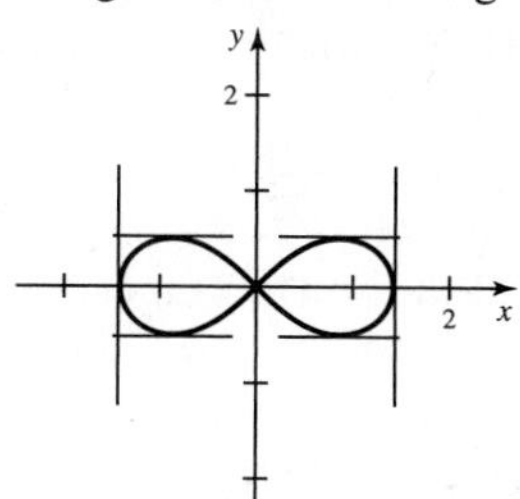

19. $\frac{19\pi}{2}$

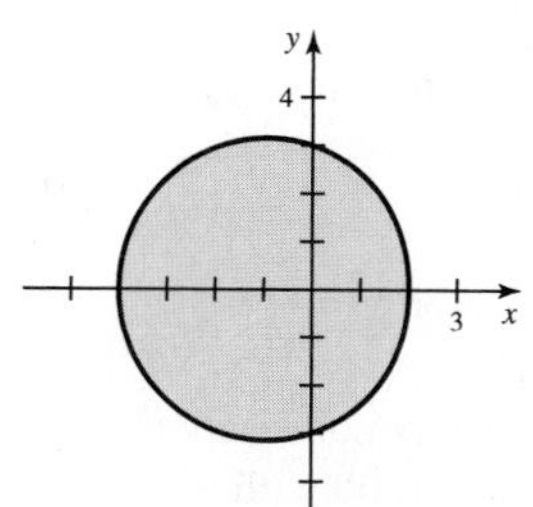

21. $\frac{1}{4}(\sqrt{255} - \cos^{-1}(1/16))$

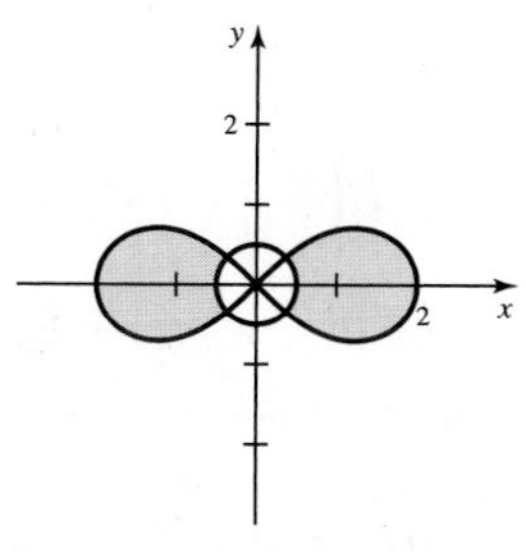

23. a. Hyperbola **b.** Foci $(\pm\sqrt{3}, 0)$, vertices $(\pm 1, 0)$, directrices $x = \pm\frac{1}{\sqrt{3}}$ **c.** $e = \sqrt{3}$ **d.**

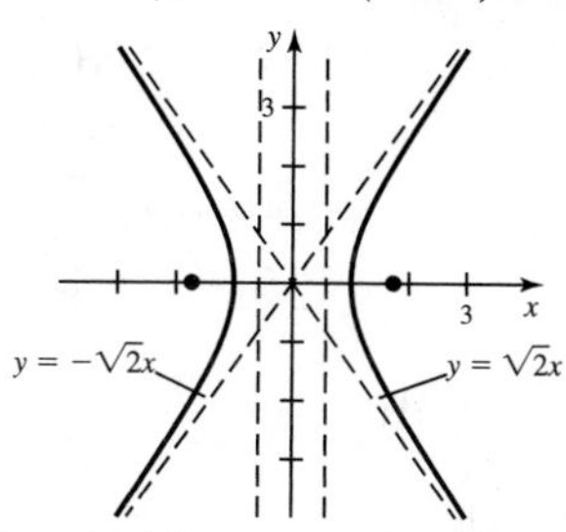

25. a. Hyperbola **b.** Foci $(0, \pm 2\sqrt{5})$, vertices $(0, \pm 4)$, directrices $y = \pm = \frac{8}{\sqrt{5}}$ **c.** $e = \frac{\sqrt{5}}{2}$ **d.**

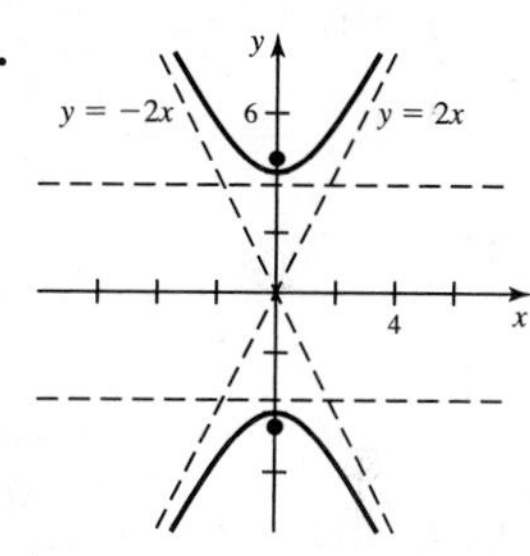

27. a. Ellipse **b.** Foci $(\pm\sqrt{2}, 0)$, vertices $(\pm 2, 0)$, directrices $x = \pm 2\sqrt{2}$ **c.** $e = \frac{\sqrt{2}}{2}$ **d.**

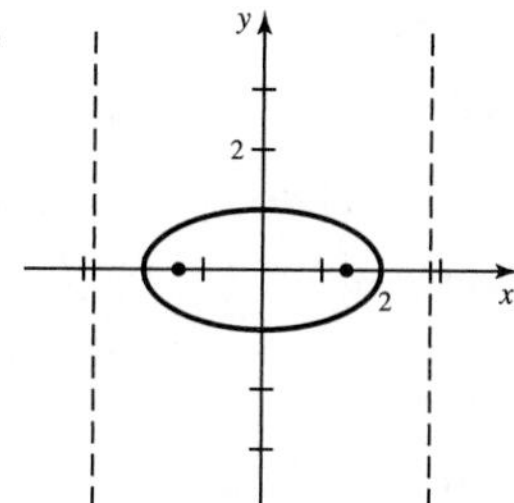

29. $y = \frac{3}{2}x - 2$ **31.** $y = -\frac{3}{5}x - 10$ **33.**

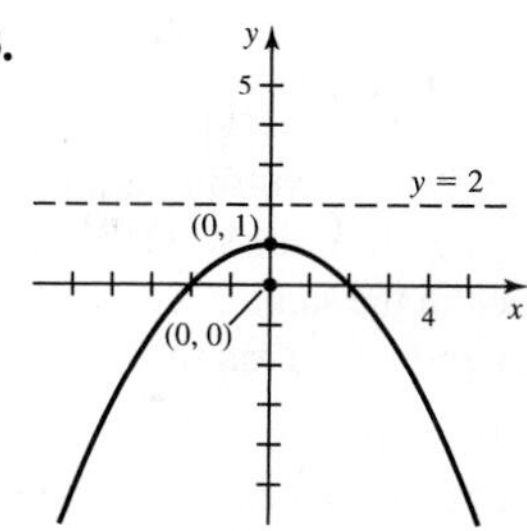

35.

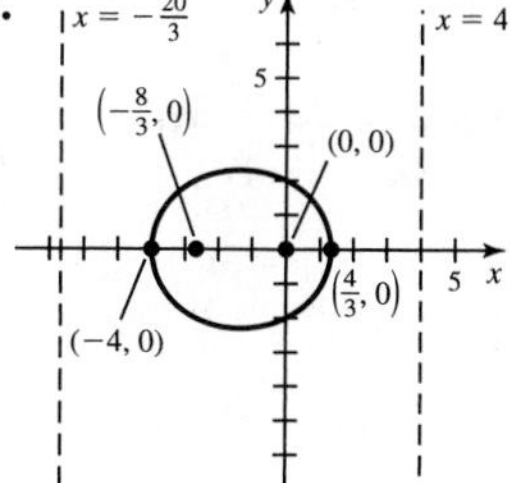

37. a. $x^2 - y^2 = 1$; hyperbola

b. $(\pm 1, 0)$, $(\pm\sqrt{2}, 0)$; $x = \pm\frac{1}{\sqrt{2}}$; $e = \sqrt{2}$

c.

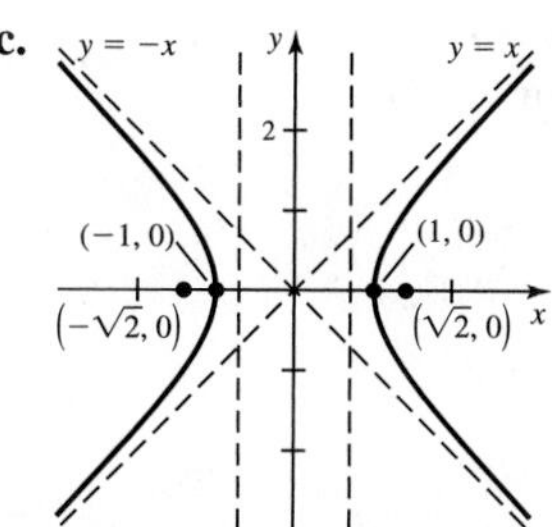

39. $\frac{y^2}{16} + \frac{25x^2}{336} = 1$

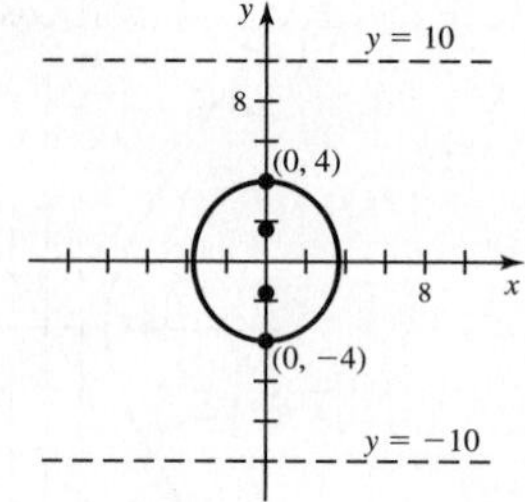

41. $\frac{y^2}{4} - \frac{x^2}{12} = 1;$

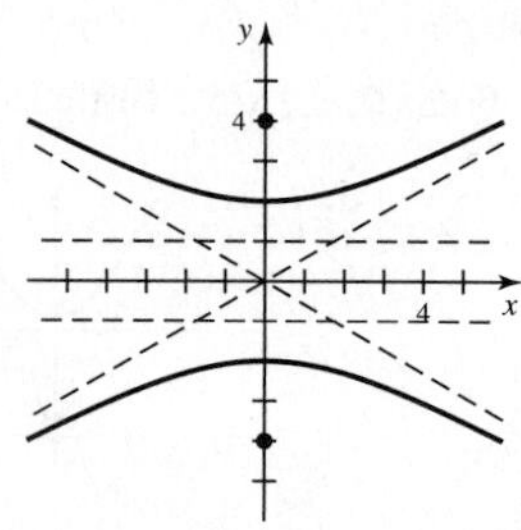

43. $e = 2/3, y = \pm 9, (\pm 2\sqrt{5}, 0)$ **45.** $(0, 0), (0.97, 0.97)$ **47.** $(0, 0)$ and $(r, \theta) = ((2n - 1)\pi, 0), n = 1, 2, 3, \ldots$ **49.** $\frac{2a}{\sqrt{2}} \cdot \frac{2b}{\sqrt{2}}; 2ab$ **51.** $m = \frac{b}{a}$ **55.** $r = \frac{3}{3 - \sin\theta}$

CHAPTER 12

Section 12.1 Exercises, pp. 679–682

3.

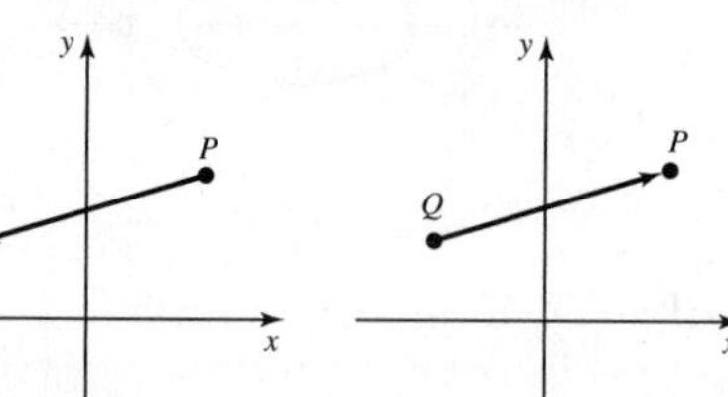

5. There are infinitely many vectors parallel to **v** with the same length as **v**. **7.** If the scalar c is positive, extend the given vector by a multiple of c in the same direction. If $c < 0$, reverse the direction of the vector and extend it by a multiple of $|c|$. **9.** $\mathbf{u} + \mathbf{v} = \langle u_1 + v_1, u_2 + v_2 \rangle$ **11.** $|\langle v_1, v_2 \rangle| = \sqrt{v_1^2 + v_2^2}$ **13.** If P has coordinates (p_1, p_2) and Q has coordinates (q_1, q_2) then the magnitude of $\overrightarrow{PQ}$ is given by $\sqrt{(q_1 - p_1)^2 + (q_2 - p_2)^2}$. **15.** Divide **v** by its length and multiply the result by 10. **17. a.** $3\mathbf{v}$ **b.** $2\mathbf{u}$ **c.** $-3\mathbf{u}$ **d.** $-2\mathbf{u}$ **e.** $\mathbf{v}$ **19. a.** $3\mathbf{u} + 3\mathbf{v}$ **b.** $\mathbf{u} + 2\mathbf{v}$ **c.** $2\mathbf{u} + 5\mathbf{v}$ **d.** $-2\mathbf{u} + 3\mathbf{v}$ **e.** $3\mathbf{u} + 2\mathbf{v}$ **f.** $-3\mathbf{u} - 2\mathbf{v}$ **g.** $-2\mathbf{u} - 4\mathbf{v}$ **h.** $\mathbf{u} - 4\mathbf{v}$ **i.** $-\mathbf{u} - 6\mathbf{v}$ **21. a.**

$\overrightarrow{OP} = \langle 3, 2 \rangle = 3\mathbf{i} + 2\mathbf{j}$
$|\overrightarrow{OP}| = \sqrt{13}$

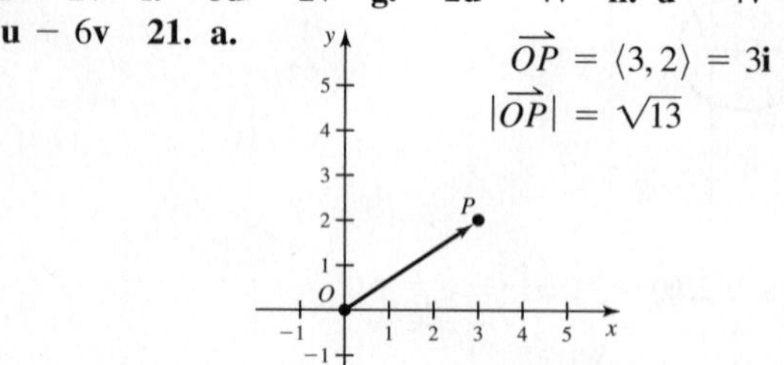

b.

$\overrightarrow{QP} = \langle -1, 0 \rangle = -\mathbf{i}$
$|\overrightarrow{QP}| = 1$

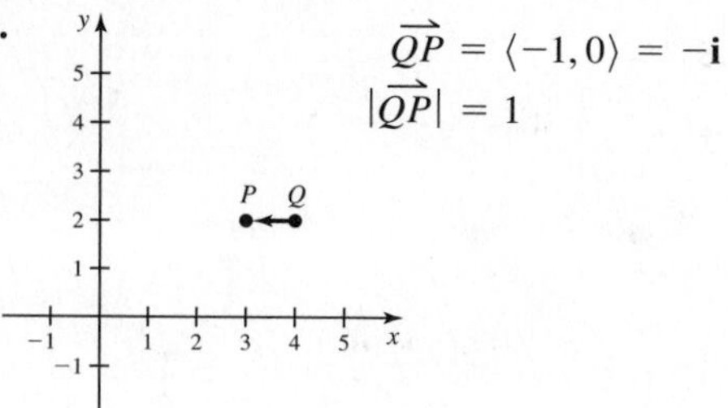

c.

$\overrightarrow{RQ} = \langle 10, 3 \rangle = 10\mathbf{i} + 3\mathbf{j}$
$|\overrightarrow{RQ}| = \sqrt{109}$

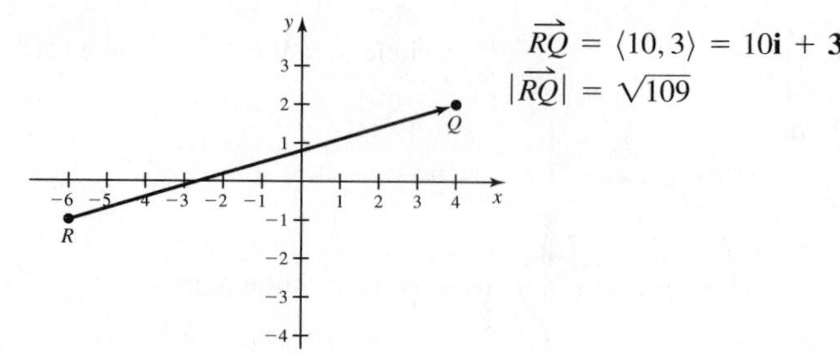

23. $\overrightarrow{QU} = \langle 7, 2 \rangle, \overrightarrow{PT} = \langle 7, 3 \rangle, \overrightarrow{RS} = \langle 2, 3 \rangle$

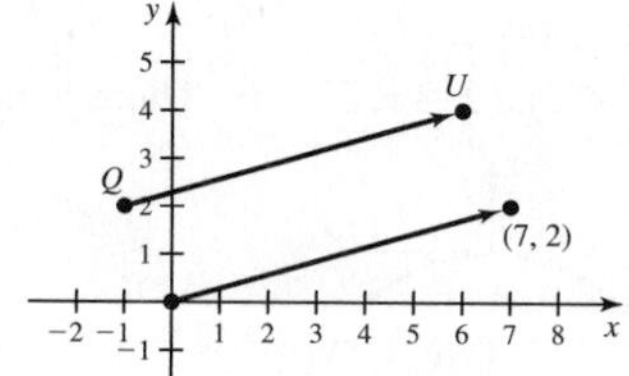

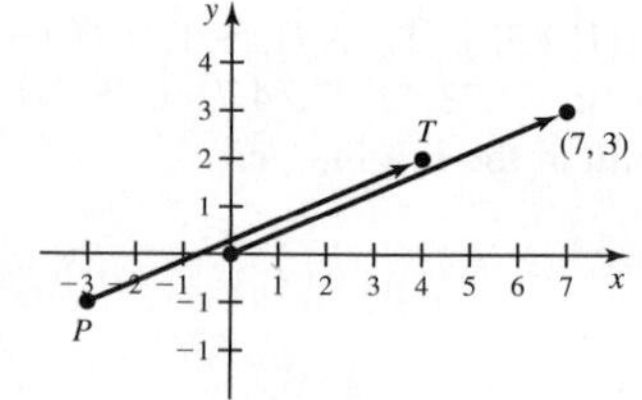

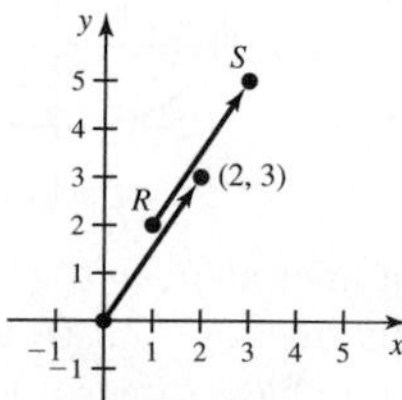

25. $\overrightarrow{QT}$ **27.** $\langle -4, 10 \rangle$ **29.** $\langle 12, -10 \rangle$ **31.** $\langle -28, 82 \rangle$ **33.** $2\sqrt{26}$ **35.** $\langle 6, 18 \rangle, \langle -6, -18 \rangle$ **37.** $\mathbf{u} - \mathbf{v}$ **39.** $-\mathbf{i} + 10\mathbf{j}$ **41.** $\left\langle \frac{6}{\sqrt{61}}, \frac{5}{\sqrt{61}} \right\rangle$ **43.** $\left\langle \frac{-28}{\sqrt{74}}, \frac{20}{\sqrt{74}} \right\rangle, \left\langle \frac{28}{\sqrt{74}}, \frac{-20}{\sqrt{74}} \right\rangle$ **45.** 349.43 mi/hr at a direction 4.64° south of west **47.** 4 m/s at a direction 30° east of north **49. a.** $\langle 20, 20\sqrt{3} \rangle$ **b.** Yes **c.** No **51.** $250\sqrt{2}$ lb **53. a.** True **b.** True **c.** False **d.** False **e.** False **f.** False **g.** False **h.** True **55. a.** $\left\langle \frac{3}{5}, \frac{-4}{5} \right\rangle$ and $\left\langle -\frac{3}{5}, \frac{4}{5} \right\rangle$ **b.** $b = \pm\frac{2\sqrt{2}}{3}$ **c.** $a = \frac{\pm 3}{\sqrt{10}}$ **57.** $\mathbf{x} = \left\langle \frac{1}{5}, -\frac{3}{10} \right\rangle$ **59.** $\mathbf{x} = \left\langle \frac{4}{3}, -\frac{11}{3} \right\rangle$ **61.** $4\mathbf{i} - 8\mathbf{j}$ **63.** $\langle a, b \rangle = \left(\frac{a + b}{2}\right)\mathbf{u} + \left(\frac{b - a}{2}\right)\mathbf{v}$ **65.** $\mathbf{u} = \frac{1}{5}\mathbf{i} + \frac{3}{5}\mathbf{j}, \mathbf{v} = \frac{1}{5}\mathbf{i} - \frac{2}{5}\mathbf{j}$ **67.** $\left\langle \frac{15}{13}, -\frac{36}{13} \right\rangle$ **69.** $\langle 9, 3 \rangle$ **71. a.** $\mathbf{0}$ **b.** The 6:00 vector **c.** Sum any six consecutive vectors. **d.** A vector pointing from 12:00 to 6:00 with a length 12 times the radius of the clock **73.** 50 lb in the direction 36.87° north of east

75. $\mathbf{u} + \mathbf{v} = \langle u_1, u_2 \rangle + \langle v_1, v_2 \rangle = \langle u_1 + v_1, u_2 + v_2 \rangle$
$= \langle v_1 + u_1, v_2 + u_2 \rangle = \langle v_1, v_2 \rangle + \langle u_1, u_2 \rangle$
$= \mathbf{v} + \mathbf{u}$
77. $a(c\mathbf{v}) = a(c\langle v_1, v_2 \rangle) = a(\langle cv_1, cv_2 \rangle)$
$= \langle acv_1, acv_2 \rangle = \langle (ac)v_1, (ac)v_2 \rangle$
$= ac\langle v_1, v_2 \rangle = (ac)\mathbf{v}$
83. a. $\{\mathbf{u}, \mathbf{v}\}$ are linearly dependent; $\{\mathbf{u}, \mathbf{w}\}$ and $\{\mathbf{v}, \mathbf{w}\}$ are linearly independent. **b.** Two linearly dependent vectors are parallel. Two linearly independent vectors are not parallel. **85. a.** $\frac{5}{3}$ **b.** -15

Section 12.2 Exercises, pp. 689–692

1. Move 3 units from the origin in the direction of the positive x-axis, then 2 units in the direction of the negative y-axis, and then 1 unit in the direction of the positive z-axis.
3. It is parallel to the yz-plane and contains the point $(4, 0, 0)$.
5. $\mathbf{u} + \mathbf{v} = \langle 9, 0, -6 \rangle$; $3\mathbf{u} - \mathbf{v} = \langle 3, 20, -22 \rangle$ **7.** $(0, 0, -4)$
9. $A(3, 0, 5), B(3, 4, 0), C(0, 4, 5)$
11. $A(3, -4, 5), B(0, -4, 0), C(0, -4, 5)$
13. a.

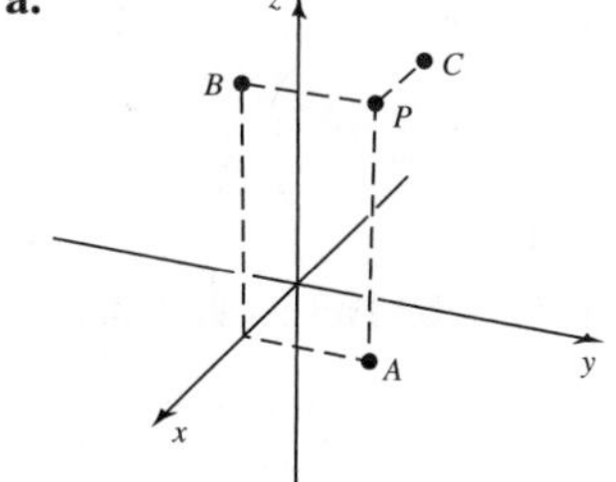

b.

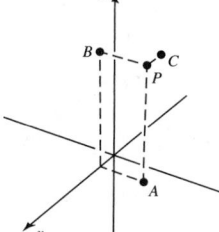

c.

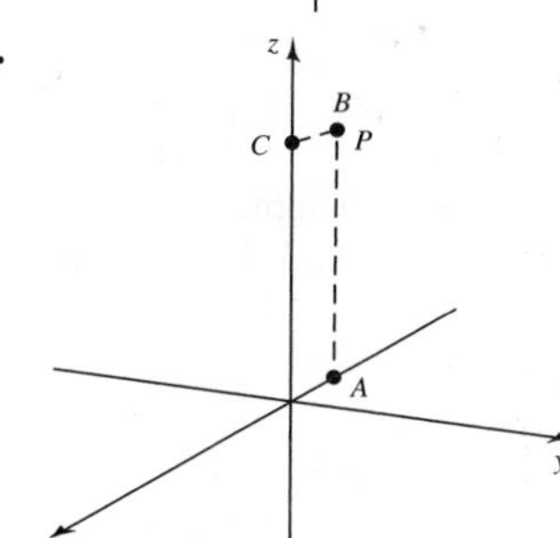

15.

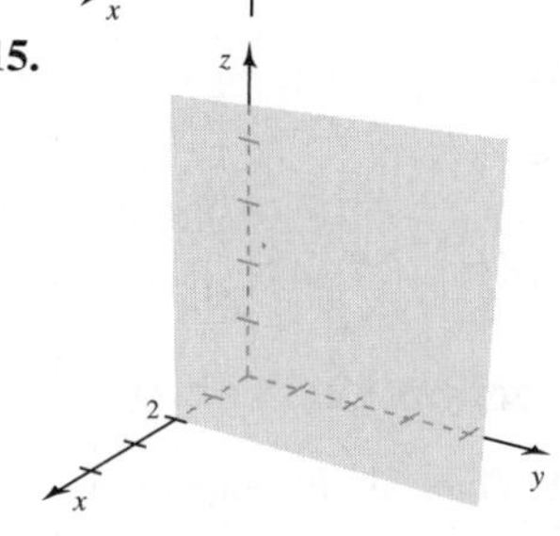

17.

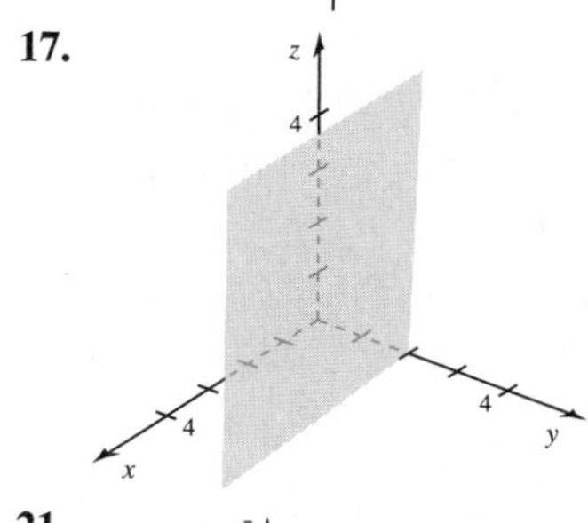

19.

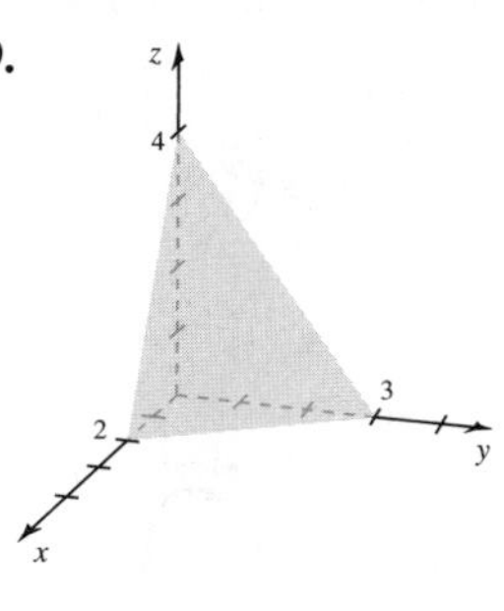

21.

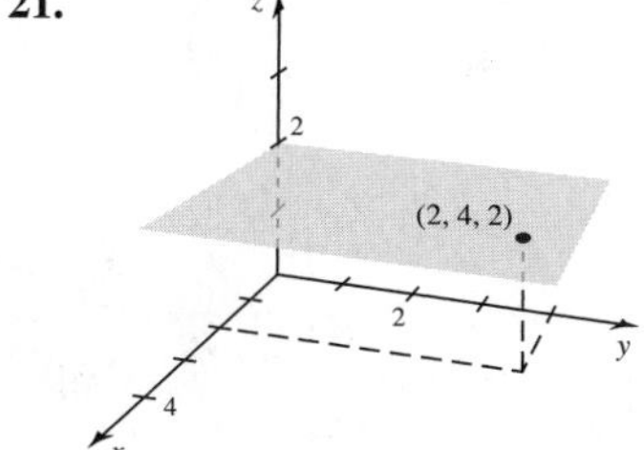

23. $(x - 1)^2 + (y - 2)^2 + (z - 3)^2 = 16$
25. $(x + 2)^2 + y^2 + (z - 4)^2 \leq 1$

27. $\left(x - \frac{3}{2}\right)^2 + \left(y - \frac{3}{2}\right)^2 + (z - 7)^2 = \frac{13}{2}$ **29.** A sphere centered at $(0, 1, 2)$ with radius 3 **31.** The exterior of the ball of center $(0, 7, 0)$ with radius 6 **33.** The ball centered at $(4, 7, 9)$ of radius $\sqrt{211}$ **35. a.** $3\mathbf{u} + 2\mathbf{v} = \langle 9, 9, 4 \rangle$ **b.** $4\mathbf{u} - \mathbf{v} = \langle 1, 12, -2 \rangle$ **c.** $|\mathbf{u} + 3\mathbf{v}| = \sqrt{145}$ **37. a.** $3\mathbf{u} + 2\mathbf{v} = \langle -25, 23, 3 \rangle$ **b.** $4\mathbf{u} - \mathbf{v} = \langle -26, 16, 4 \rangle$ **c.** $|\mathbf{u} + 3\mathbf{v}| = 3\sqrt{51}$
39. a. $\overrightarrow{PQ} = \langle 2, 6, 2 \rangle = 2\mathbf{i} + 6\mathbf{j} + 2\mathbf{k}$ **b.** $|\overrightarrow{PQ}| = 2\sqrt{11}$ **c.** $\left\langle \frac{1}{\sqrt{11}}, \frac{3}{\sqrt{11}}, \frac{1}{\sqrt{11}} \right\rangle$ and $\left\langle -\frac{1}{\sqrt{11}}, -\frac{3}{\sqrt{11}}, -\frac{1}{\sqrt{11}} \right\rangle$
41. a. $\overrightarrow{PQ} = \langle 0, -5, 1 \rangle$ **b.** $|\overrightarrow{PQ}| = \sqrt{26}$ **c.** $\left\langle 0, -\frac{5}{\sqrt{26}}, \frac{1}{\sqrt{26}} \right\rangle$ and $\left\langle 0, \frac{5}{\sqrt{26}}, -\frac{1}{\sqrt{26}} \right\rangle$ **43. a.** $\overrightarrow{PQ} = \langle -2, 4, -2 \rangle$
b. $|\overrightarrow{PQ}| = 2\sqrt{6}$ **c.** $\left\langle -\frac{1}{\sqrt{6}}, \frac{2}{\sqrt{6}}, -\frac{1}{\sqrt{6}} \right\rangle$ and $\left\langle \frac{1}{\sqrt{6}}, -\frac{2}{\sqrt{6}}, \frac{1}{\sqrt{6}} \right\rangle$
45. The speed of the plane is approximately 220 mi/hr; the direction is slightly south of east and upward.

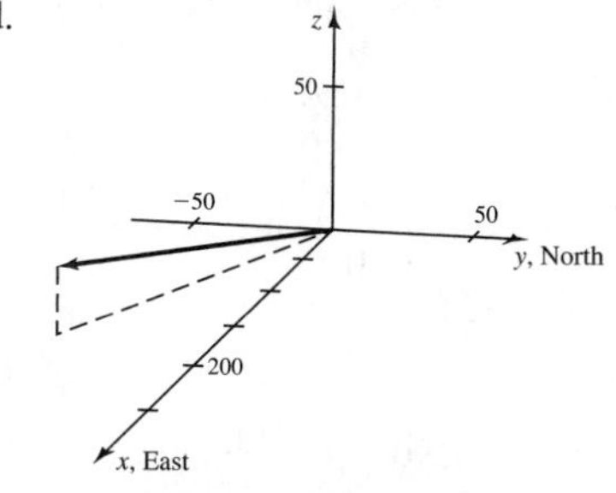

47. $5\sqrt{6}$ knots to the east, $5\sqrt{6}$ knots to the north, 10 knots upward
49. a. False **b.** False **c.** False **d.** True **51.** All points in $\mathbf{R}^3$ except those on the coordinate axes. **53.** $\langle 12, -16, 0 \rangle, \langle -12, 16, 0 \rangle$
55. $\langle -\sqrt{3}, -\sqrt{3}, \sqrt{3} \rangle, \langle \sqrt{3}, \sqrt{3}, -\sqrt{3} \rangle$ **57. a.** Collinear; Q is between P and R. **b.** Collinear; P is between Q and R. **c.** Noncollinear **d.** Noncollinear **59.** $\sqrt{29}$ ft for each piece
61. $\frac{250}{3}\left\langle -\frac{1}{\sqrt{3}}, 1, 2 \right\rangle, \frac{250}{3}\left\langle -\frac{1}{\sqrt{3}}, -1, -2 \right\rangle, \frac{500}{3}\left\langle \frac{1}{\sqrt{3}}, 0, -1 \right\rangle$
63. $(3, 8, 9), (-1, 0, 3)$, or $(1, 0, -3)$

Section 12.3 Exercises, pp. 699–702

1. $\mathbf{u} \cdot \mathbf{v} = |\mathbf{u}||\mathbf{v}| \cos \theta$ **3.** -40
5. $\cos \theta = \frac{\mathbf{u} \cdot \mathbf{v}}{|\mathbf{u}||\mathbf{v}|}$, so $\theta = \cos^{-1}\left(\frac{\mathbf{u} \cdot \mathbf{v}}{|\mathbf{u}||\mathbf{v}|}\right)$
7. Scalar, $\mathbf{u} = |\mathbf{u}| \cos \theta$ is the signed length of the projection of $\mathbf{u}$ in the direction of $\mathbf{v}$. **9.** $0, 90°$ **11.** $100, 45°$ **13.** $-2, 93.2°$ **15.** $2, 87.2°$
17. $-4, 104°$ **19.** $\langle 3, 0 \rangle, 3$ **21.** $\langle 0, 3 \rangle, 3$ **23.** $\frac{6}{5}\langle -2, 1 \rangle, \frac{6}{\sqrt{5}}$
25. $\frac{14}{19}\langle -1, -3, 3 \rangle, -\frac{14}{\sqrt{19}}$ **27.** $\frac{1}{17}\langle 18, 0, 4 \rangle, \frac{10}{\sqrt{85}}$ **29.** $750\sqrt{3}$ ft-lb
31. 400 J **33.** $\langle -5, -5 \rangle, \langle 5, -5 \rangle$ **35.** $\langle -5\sqrt{3}, -5 \rangle, \langle 5\sqrt{3}, -5 \rangle$
37. a. False **b.** True **c.** True **d.** False **e.** False **f.** True
39. $\{\langle 1, a, 4a - 2 \rangle : a \in \mathbf{R}\}$ **41.** $\left\langle \frac{1}{\sqrt{2}}, \frac{1}{\sqrt{2}}, 0 \right\rangle, \left\langle -\frac{1}{\sqrt{2}}, \frac{1}{\sqrt{2}}, 0 \right\rangle$, $\langle 0, 0, 1 \rangle$ (one possibility) **43. a.** $\text{proj}_{\mathbf{k}}\mathbf{u} = |\mathbf{u}| \cos 60° \left(\frac{\mathbf{k}}{|\mathbf{k}|}\right) = \frac{1}{2}\mathbf{k}$ for all such $\mathbf{u}$ **b.** yes **45.** The heads of the vectors lie on the line $y = 3 - x$ **47.** The heads of the vectors lie on the plane $z = 3$.

49. $\mathbf{u} = \left\langle -\frac{4}{5}, \frac{-2}{5} \right\rangle + \left\langle -\frac{6}{5}, \frac{12}{5} \right\rangle$

51. $\mathbf{u} = \left\langle 1, \frac{1}{2}, \frac{1}{2} \right\rangle + \left\langle -2, \frac{3}{2}, \frac{5}{2} \right\rangle$ **53.** $|\mathbf{w}| = \frac{28\sqrt{5}}{5}$

55. $|\mathbf{w}| = \sqrt{\frac{326}{109}}$

57. $\mathbf{I} = \frac{1}{\sqrt{2}}\mathbf{i} + \frac{1}{\sqrt{2}}\mathbf{j}, \mathbf{J} = -\frac{1}{\sqrt{2}}\mathbf{i} + \frac{1}{\sqrt{2}}\mathbf{j};$

$\mathbf{i} = \frac{1}{\sqrt{2}}(\mathbf{I} - \mathbf{J}), \mathbf{j} = \frac{1}{\sqrt{2}}(\mathbf{I} + \mathbf{J})$

59. a. $|\mathbf{I}| = |\mathbf{J}| = |\mathbf{K}| = 1$ **b.** $\mathbf{I}\cdot\mathbf{J} = 0, \mathbf{I}\cdot\mathbf{K} = 0, \mathbf{J}\cdot\mathbf{K} = 0$ **c.** $\langle 1, 0, 0\rangle = \frac{1}{2}\mathbf{I} - (1/\sqrt{2})\mathbf{J} + \frac{1}{2}\mathbf{K}$

61. $\angle P = 78.8°, \angle Q = 47.2°, \angle R = 54.0°$ **63. a.** The faces on $y = 0$ and $z = 0$ **b.** The faces on $y = 1$ and $z = 1$ **c.** The faces on $x = 0$ and $x = 1$ **d.** 0 **e.** 1 **f.** 2 **65. a.** $\left(\frac{2}{\sqrt{3}}, 0, \frac{2\sqrt{2}}{3}\right)$ **b.** $\mathbf{r}_{OP} = \langle\sqrt{3}, -1, 0\rangle, \mathbf{r}_{OQ} = \langle\sqrt{3}, 1, 0\rangle, \mathbf{r}_{PQ} = \langle 0, 2, 0\rangle,$

$\mathbf{r}_{OR} = \left\langle\frac{2}{\sqrt{3}}, 0, \frac{2\sqrt{2}}{3}\right\rangle, r_{PR} = \left\langle -\frac{\sqrt{3}}{3}, 1, \frac{2\sqrt{2}}{3}\right\rangle$

73. a. $\cos^2\alpha + \cos^2\beta + \cos^2\gamma$

$= \left(\frac{\mathbf{v}\cdot\mathbf{i}}{|\mathbf{v}||\mathbf{i}|}\right)^2 + \left(\frac{\mathbf{v}\cdot\mathbf{j}}{|\mathbf{v}||\mathbf{j}|}\right)^2 + \left(\frac{\mathbf{v}\cdot\mathbf{k}}{|\mathbf{v}||\mathbf{k}|}\right)^2$

$= \frac{a^2}{a^2 + b^2 + c^2} + \frac{b^2}{a^2 + b^2 + c^2} + \frac{c^2}{a^2 + b^2 + c^2} = 1$

b. $\langle 1, 1, 0\rangle, 90°$ **c.** $\left\langle\frac{1}{\sqrt{2}}, \frac{1}{\sqrt{2}}, 1\right\rangle, 45°$

d. No. If so, $\left(\frac{\sqrt{3}}{2}\right)^2 + \left(\frac{\sqrt{3}}{2}\right)^2 + \cos^2\gamma = 1,$ which has no solution. **e.** $54.7°$

75. $|\mathbf{u}\cdot\mathbf{v}| = 33 = \sqrt{33}\cdot\sqrt{33} < \sqrt{70}\cdot\sqrt{74} = |\mathbf{u}||\mathbf{v}|$

Section 12.4 Exercises, pp. 707–709

1. $|\mathbf{u}\times\mathbf{v}| = |\mathbf{u}||\mathbf{v}|\sin\theta$ where $0 \le \theta \le \pi$ is the angle between **u** and **v** **3.** 0 **5.** $\mathbf{u}\times\mathbf{v} = \begin{vmatrix} \mathbf{i} & \mathbf{j} & \mathbf{k} \\ u_1 & u_2 & u_3 \\ v_1 & v_2 & v_3 \end{vmatrix}$ **7.** 15

9. 0

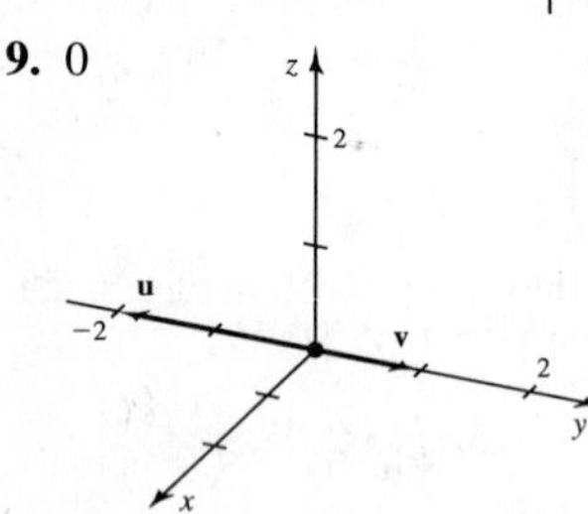

11. 18

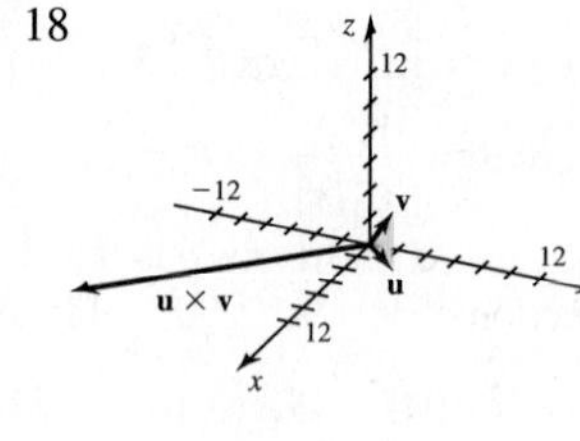

13. i

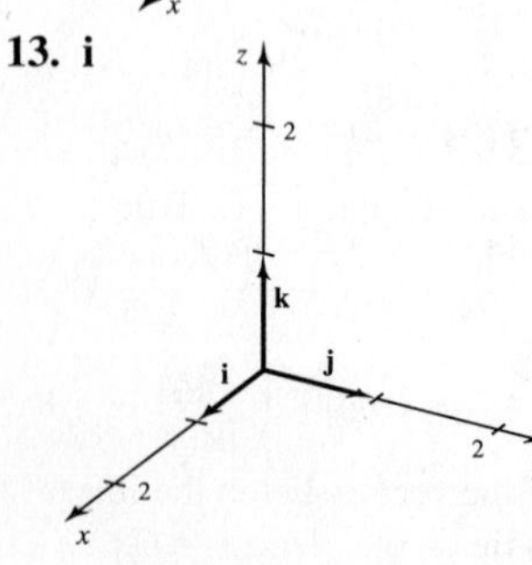

15. −i

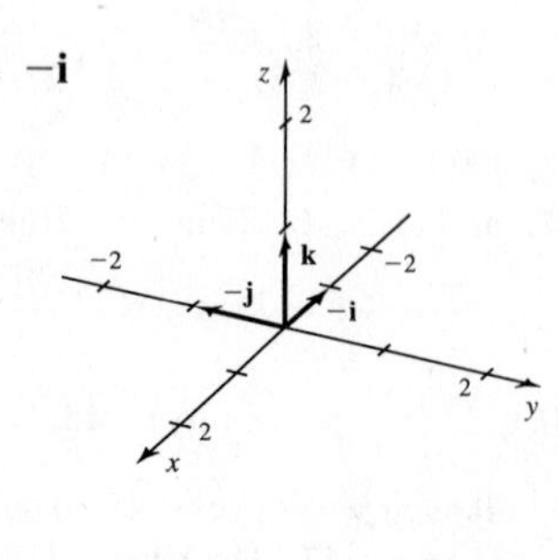

17. 6j

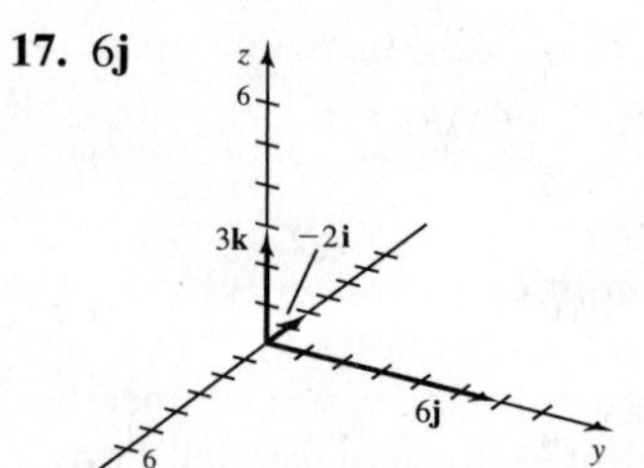

19. 11 **21.** $3\sqrt{10}$

23. $\mathbf{u}\times\mathbf{v} = \langle -30, 18, 9\rangle, \mathbf{v}\times\mathbf{u} = \langle 30, -18, -9\rangle$

25. $\mathbf{u}\times\mathbf{v} = \langle 6, 11, 5\rangle, \mathbf{v}\times\mathbf{u} = \langle -6, -11, -5\rangle$

27. $\mathbf{u}\times\mathbf{v} = \langle 8, 4, 10\rangle, \mathbf{v}\times\mathbf{u} = \langle -8, -4, -10\rangle$

29. $\langle 3, -4, 2\rangle$ **31.** $\langle -8, -40, 16\rangle$ **33.** $\langle 0, 20, -20\rangle$

35. The force $\mathbf{F} = 5\mathbf{i} - 5\mathbf{k}$ produces the greater torque.

37. The magnitude is $20\sqrt{2}$ at a 135° angle with the positive x-axis in the xy-plane.

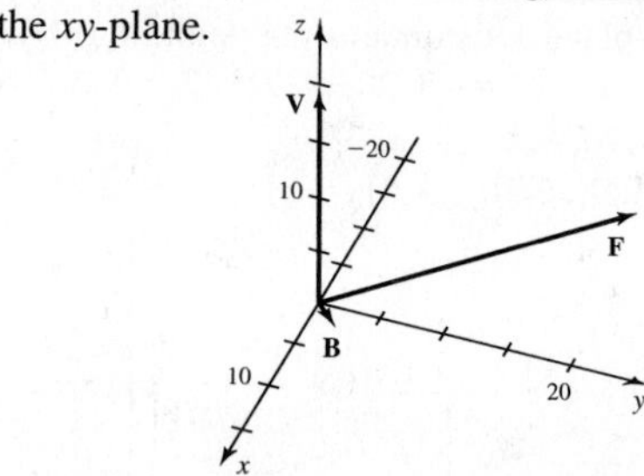

39. $4.53 \times 10^{-14}\,\text{kg}\cdot\text{m/s}^2$ **41. a.** False **b.** False **c.** False **d.** True **e.** False **43.** $\sqrt{6}$ **45.** $4\sqrt{14}$ **47.** $9\sqrt{2}$ **49.** $\frac{7\sqrt{6}}{2}$

51. $\{\langle u_3 - 1, u_3 + 1, u_3\rangle : u_3 \in \mathbf{R}\}$ **53.** $\frac{\sqrt{(ab)^2 + (ac)^2 + (bc)^2}}{2}$

55. $|\mathbf{u}\cdot(\mathbf{v}\times\mathbf{w})| = |\mathbf{u}||\mathbf{v}\times\mathbf{w}||\cos\theta|$ where $|\mathbf{v}\times\mathbf{w}|$ is the area of the base of the parallelepiped and $|\mathbf{u}||\cos\theta|$ is its height.

57. $|\tau| = 26.4\,\text{N}\cdot\text{m}$, Direction: into the page. **59.** $1.76 \times 10^7\,\text{m/s}$

Section 12.5 Exercises, pp. 715–717

1. One **3.** Its output is a vector.

5. $\langle x, y, z\rangle = \langle x_0, y_0, z_0\rangle + t\langle x_1 - x_0, y_1 - y_0, z_1 - z_0\rangle$

7. $\lim_{t\to a}\mathbf{r}(t) = \lim_{t\to a} f(t)\mathbf{i} + \lim_{t\to a} g(t)\mathbf{j} + \lim_{t\to a} h(t)\mathbf{k}$

9. $\langle x, y, z\rangle = \langle 0, 0, 1\rangle + t\langle 0, 1, 0\rangle$

11. $\langle x, y, z\rangle = \langle 0, 1, 1\rangle + t\langle 2, -2, 2\rangle$ **13.** $\langle x, y, z\rangle = t\langle 1, 2, 3\rangle$

15. $\langle x, y, z\rangle = \langle -3, 4, 6\rangle + t\langle 8, -5, -6\rangle$ **17.** $\langle x, y, z\rangle = t\langle 1, 2, 3\rangle$, $0 \le t \le 1$ **19.** $\langle x, y, z\rangle = \langle 2, 4, 8\rangle + t\langle 5, 1, -5\rangle$, $0 \le t \le 1$

21.

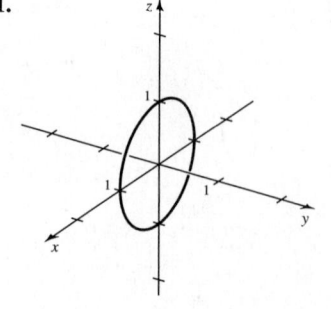

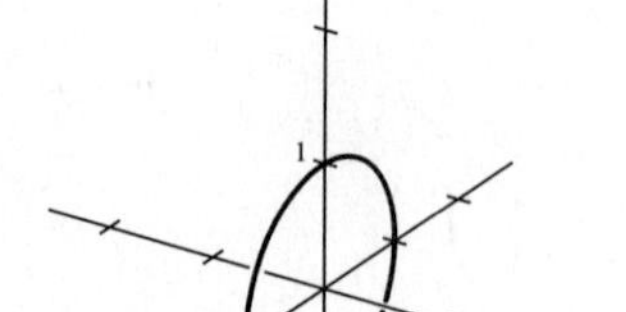

23.

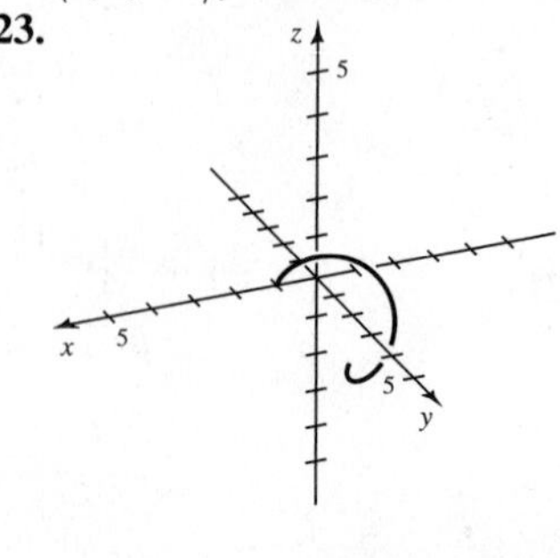

25.

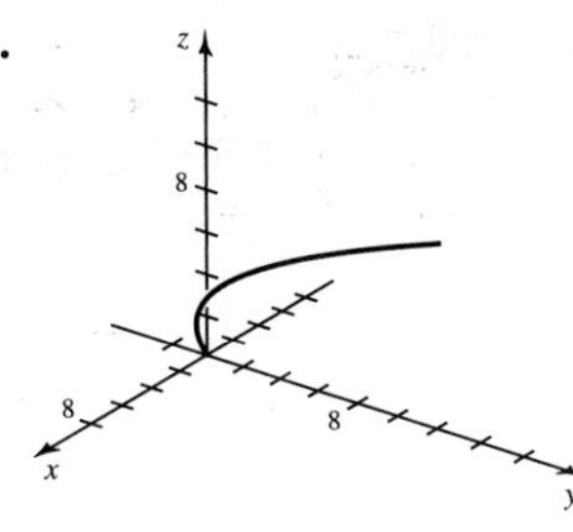

27.

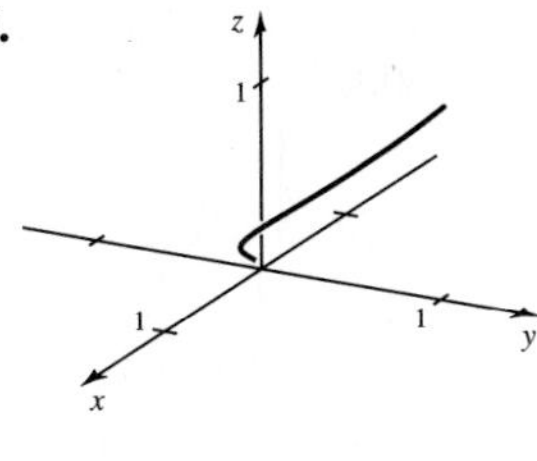

29.

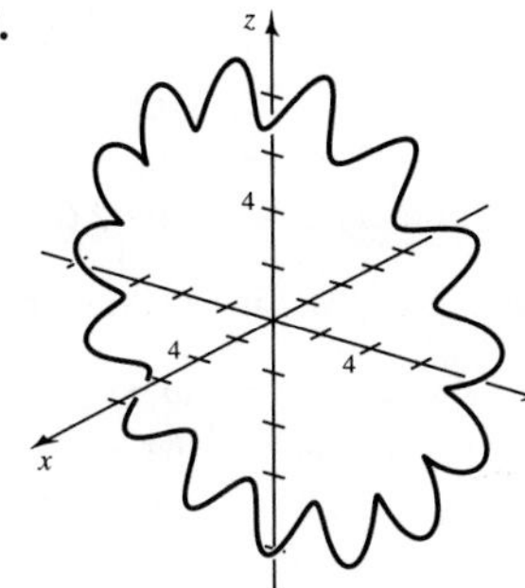

31.

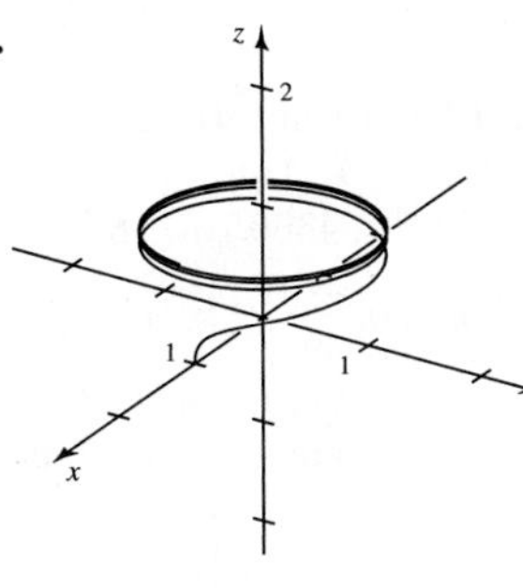

33. $-\mathbf{i} - 4\mathbf{j} + \mathbf{k}$ **35.** $-2\mathbf{j} + \frac{\pi}{2}\mathbf{k}$ **37. a.** True **b.** False **c.** True **d.** True **39.** $\{t : |t| \leq 2\}$ **41.** $\{t : 0 \leq t \leq 2\}$ **43.** $(21, -6, 4)$ **45.** $(16, 0, -8)$ **47.** $(4, 8, 16)$ **49. a.** E **b.** D **c.** F **d.** C **e.** A **f.** B **51. a.** $(50, 0, 0)$ **b.** $5\mathbf{k}$

c.

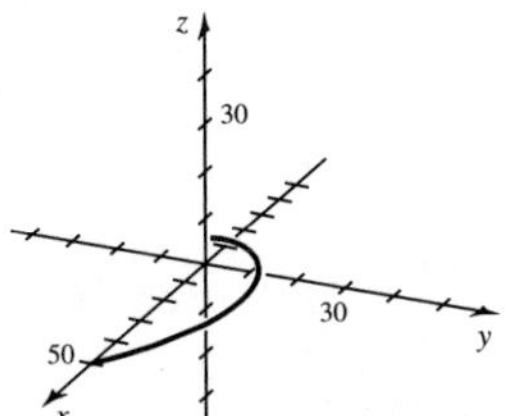

d. $x^2 + y^2 = (50e^{-t})^2$ so $r = 50e^{-t}$. Hence $z = 5 - 5e^{-t} = 5 - \frac{r}{10}$.

53. a.

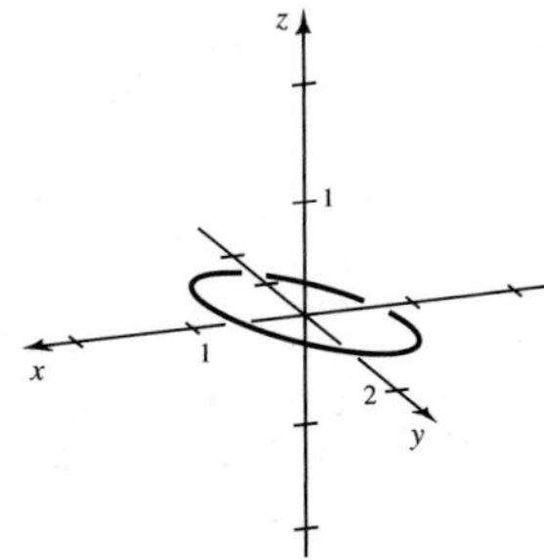

Curve is a tilted circle of radius 1 centered at the origin.

55. $\langle cf - ed, be - af, ad - bc \rangle$ or any scalar multiple

57.

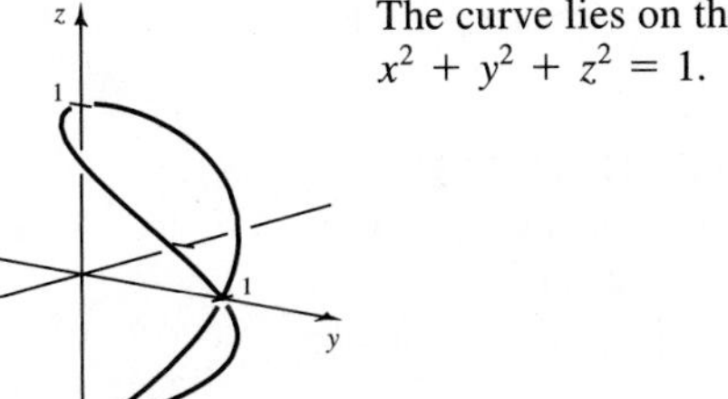

The curve lies on the sphere $x^2 + y^2 + z^2 = 1$.

59. $\frac{2\pi}{(m, n)}$, where (m, n) = greatest common factor of m and n.

Section 12.6 Exercises, pp. 724–726

1. $\mathbf{r}(t) = \langle f'(t), g'(t), h'(t) \rangle$ **3.** $\mathbf{T}(t) = \frac{r'(t)}{|r'(t)|}$

5. $\int \mathbf{r}(t)\,dt = \left(\int f(t)\,dt\right)\mathbf{i} + \left(\int g(t)\,dt\right)\mathbf{j} + \left(\int h(t)\,dt\right)\mathbf{k}$

7. $\left\langle 6t^2, \frac{3}{\sqrt{t}}, -\frac{3}{t^2} \right\rangle$ **9.** $\langle e^t, -2e^{-t}, -8e^{2t} \rangle$

11. $\langle e^{-t}(1 - t), 1 + \ln t, \cos t - t \sin t \rangle$ **13.** $\langle 1, 0, 0 \rangle$

15. $\langle 8, 9, -10 \rangle$ **17.** $\frac{\langle 0, -\sin 2t, 2\cos 2t \rangle}{\sqrt{1 + 3\cos^2 2t}}$

19. $\frac{t^2}{\sqrt{t^4 + 4}}\left\langle 1, 0, -\frac{2}{t^2} \right\rangle$ **21.** $\langle 0, 0, -1 \rangle$ **23.** $\left\langle \frac{2}{\sqrt{5}}, 0, -\frac{1}{\sqrt{5}} \right\rangle$

25. $\langle 30t^{14} + 24t^3, 14t^{13} - 12t^{11} + 9t^2 - 3, -96t^{11} - 24 \rangle$

27. $4t(2t^3 - 1)(t^3 - 2)\langle 3t(t^3 - 2), 1, 0 \rangle$

29. $e^t(2t^3 + 6t^2) - 2e^{-t}(t^2 - 2t - 1) - 16e^{-2t}$

31. $5te^t(t + 2) - 6t^2e^{-t}(t - 3)$

33. $-3t^2 \sin t + 6t \cos t + 2\sqrt{t} \cos 2t + \frac{1}{2\sqrt{t}} \sin 2t$

35. $\langle 2, 0, 0 \rangle, \langle 0, 0, 0 \rangle$ **37.** $\langle -9\cos 3t, -16 \sin 4t, -36 \cos 6t \rangle$, $\langle 27 \sin 3t, -64 \cos 4t, 216 \sin 6t \rangle$

39. $\left\langle -\frac{1}{4}(t + 4)^{-3/2}, -2(t + 1)^{-3}, 2e^{-t^2}(1 - 2t^2) \right\rangle$, $\left\langle \frac{3}{8}(t + 4)^{-5/2}, 6(t + 1)^{-4}, -4te^{-t^2}(3 - 2t^2) \right\rangle$

41. $\left\langle \frac{t^5}{5} - \frac{3t^2}{2}, t^2 - t, 10t \right\rangle + \mathbf{C}$

43. $\left\langle 2 \sin t, -\frac{2}{3} \cos 3t, \frac{1}{2} \sin 8t \right\rangle + \mathbf{C}$

45. $\mathbf{r}(t) = \langle t + 3, t^2 + 2, t^3 - 6 \rangle$

47. $\mathbf{r}(t) = \langle \frac{1}{2}e^{2t} + \frac{1}{2}, 2e^{-t} + t - 1, t - 2e^t + 3 \rangle$ **49.** $\langle 2, 0, 2 \rangle$

51. $\langle 0, 0, 0 \rangle$ **53.** $(e^2 + 1)\langle 1, 2, -1 \rangle$ **55. a.** False **b.** False **c.** True **57.** $\langle 2e^{2t}, -2e^t, 0 \rangle$ **59.** $\left\langle 4, -\frac{2}{\sqrt{t}}, 0 \right\rangle$

61. $\langle 1 + 6t^2, 4t^3, -2 - 3t^2 \rangle$ **63.** $\langle 1, 0 \rangle$ **65.** $\langle 1, 0, 0 \rangle$

67. $\mathbf{r}(t) = \langle a_1t, a_2t, a_3t \rangle$ or $\mathbf{r}(t) = \langle a_1e^{kt}, a_2e^{kt}, a_3e^{kt} \rangle$, where a_i and k are real numbers, for $i = 1, 2, 3$

Section 12.7 Exercises, pp. 735–739

1. $\mathbf{v}(t) = \mathbf{r}'(t)$, speed $= |\mathbf{r}'(t)|$, $\mathbf{a}(t) = \mathbf{r}''(t)$

3. $m\mathbf{a}(t) = \mathbf{F}$ **5.** $\mathbf{v}(t) = \int \mathbf{a}(t)\,dt = \langle v_1(t), v_2(t) \rangle + \mathbf{C}$. Use initial conditions to find **C**. **7. a.** $\mathbf{v}(t) = \langle 2, -4 \rangle$, $|\mathbf{v}(t)| = 2\sqrt{5}$ **b.** $\mathbf{a}(t) = \langle 0, 0 \rangle$ **9. a.** $\mathbf{v}(t) = \langle 8 \cos t, -8 \sin t \rangle$, $|\mathbf{v}(t)| = 8$ **b.** $\mathbf{a}(t) = \langle -8 \sin t, -8 \cos t \rangle$ **11. a.** $\mathbf{v}(t) = \langle 1, -4, 6 \rangle$, $|\mathbf{v}(t)| = \sqrt{53}$ **b.** $\mathbf{a}(t) = \langle 0, 0, 0 \rangle$ **13. a.** $\mathbf{v}(t) = \langle 0, 2t, -e^{-t} \rangle$, $|\mathbf{v}(t)| = \sqrt{4t^2 + e^{-2t}}$ **b.** $\mathbf{a}(t) = \langle 0, 2, e^{-t} \rangle$ **15. a.** $\left[0, \frac{2\pi}{3}\right]$ **b.** $\mathbf{V_r}(t) = \langle -\sin t, 4 \cos t \rangle$, $\mathbf{V_R}(t) = \langle -3 \sin 3t, 12 \cos 3t \rangle$

c.

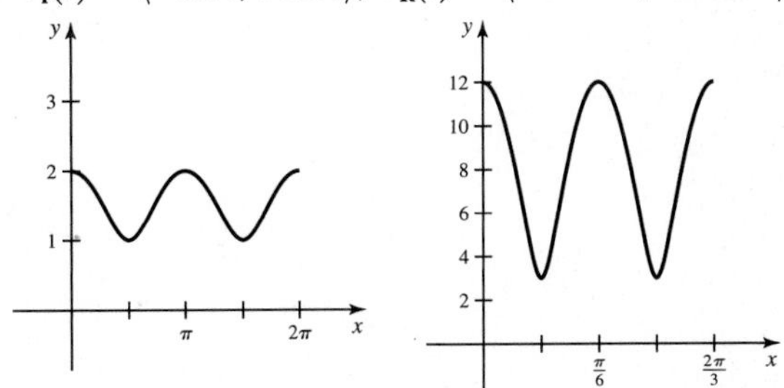

17. a. $[1, e^{36}]$

b. $\mathbf{V_r}(t) = \langle 2t, -8t^3, 18t^5\rangle, \mathbf{V_R}(t) = \left\langle \frac{1}{t}, -\frac{4}{t}\ln t, \frac{9}{t}\ln^2 t\right\rangle$

c.

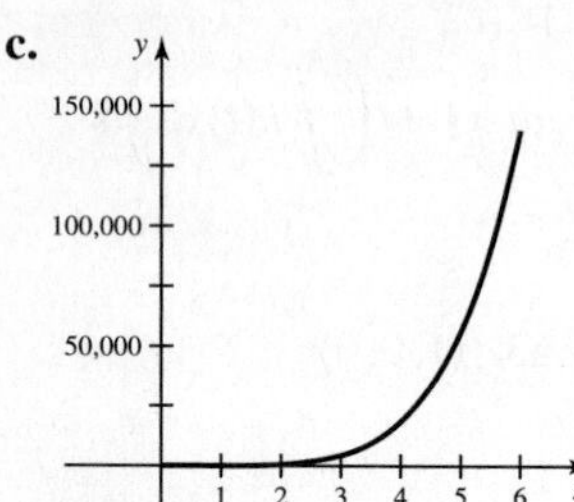

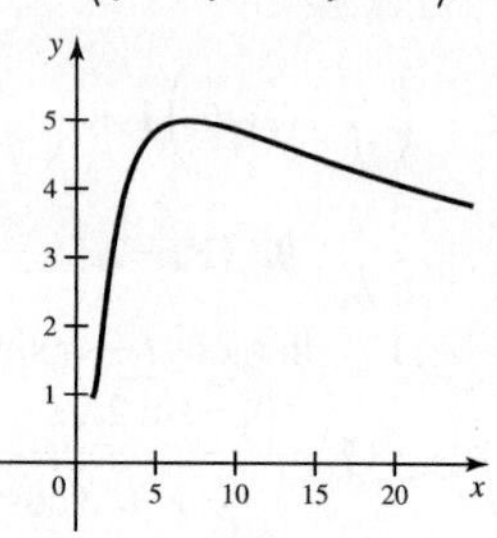

19. $\mathbf{r}(t)$ lies on a circle of radius 8; $\langle -16\sin 2t, 16\cos 2t\rangle \cdot \langle 8\cos 2t, 8\sin 2t\rangle = 0.$

21. $\mathbf{r}(t)$ lies on a sphere of radius 2; $\langle \cos t - \sqrt{3}\sin t, \sqrt{3}\cos t + \sin t\rangle \cdot \langle \sin t + \sqrt{3}\cos t, \sqrt{3}\sin t - \cos t\rangle = 0.$

23. $\mathbf{r}(t)$ does not lie on a sphere.

25. $\mathbf{v}(t) = \langle 0, 10t + 5\rangle, \mathbf{r}(t) = \langle 1, 5t^2 + 5t - 1\rangle$

27. $\mathbf{v}(t) = \langle \sin t, -2\cos t + 3\rangle, \mathbf{r}(t) = \langle -\cos t + 2, -2\sin t + 3t\rangle$

29. a. $\mathbf{v}(t) = \langle 30, -9.8t + 6\rangle, \mathbf{r}(t) = \langle 30t, -4.9t^2 + 6t\rangle$

b.

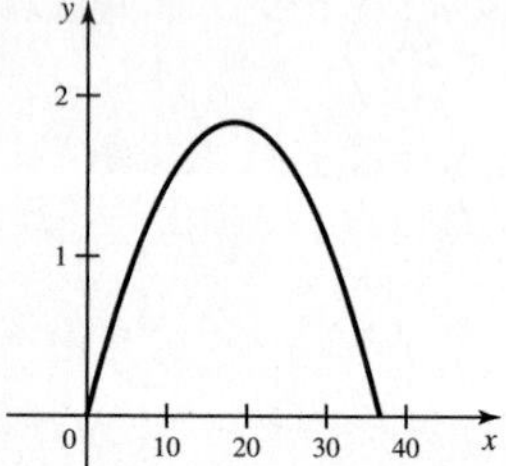

c. $T \approx 1.22$ s, range ≈ 36.7 m **d.** 1.84 m

31. a. $\mathbf{v}(t) = \langle 125, -32t + 125\sqrt{3}\rangle$
$\mathbf{r}(t) = \langle 125t, -16t^2 + 125\sqrt{3}t + 20\rangle$

b. **c.** 13.6 s; 1702.5 ft **d.** 752.4 ft

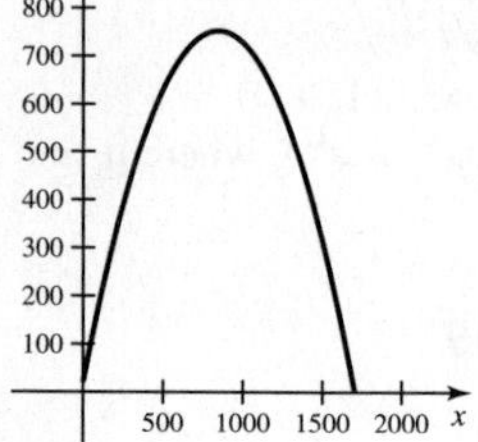

33. $\mathbf{v}(t) = \langle 1, 5, 10t\rangle, \mathbf{r}(t) = \langle t, 5t + 5, 5t^2\rangle$

35. $\mathbf{v}(t) = \langle -\cos t + 1, \sin t + 2, t\rangle$

$\mathbf{r}(t) = \left\langle -\sin t + t, -\cos t + 2t + 1, \frac{t^2}{2}\right\rangle$

37. a. $\mathbf{v}(t) = \langle 200, 200, -9.8t\rangle, \mathbf{r}(t) = \langle 200t, 200t, -4.9t^2 + 1\rangle$

b. **c.** 0.452 s, 127.8 m **d.** 1 m

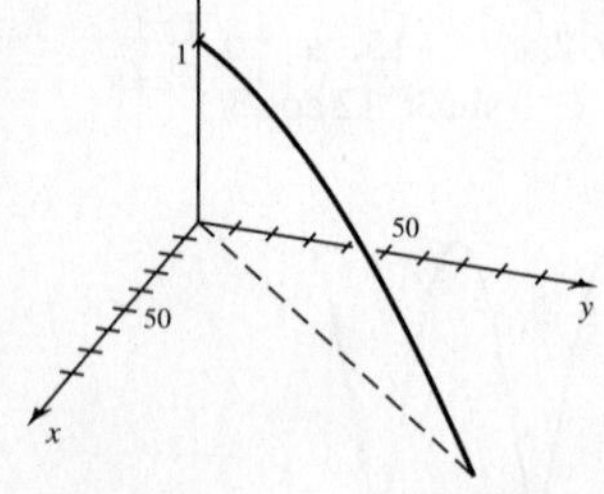

39. a. $\mathbf{v}(t) = \langle 300, 2.5t + 400, -9.8t + 500\rangle$,
$\mathbf{r}(t) = \langle 300t, 1.25t^2 + 400t, -4.9t^2 + 500t + 10\rangle$

b. **c.** 102.1 s, 61,941.5 m

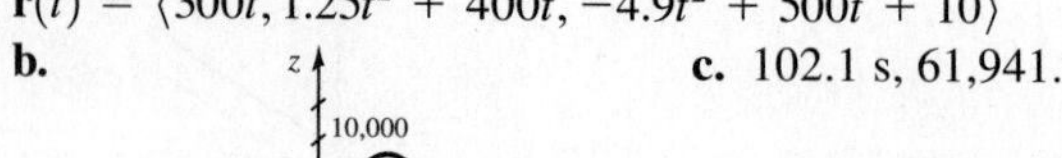

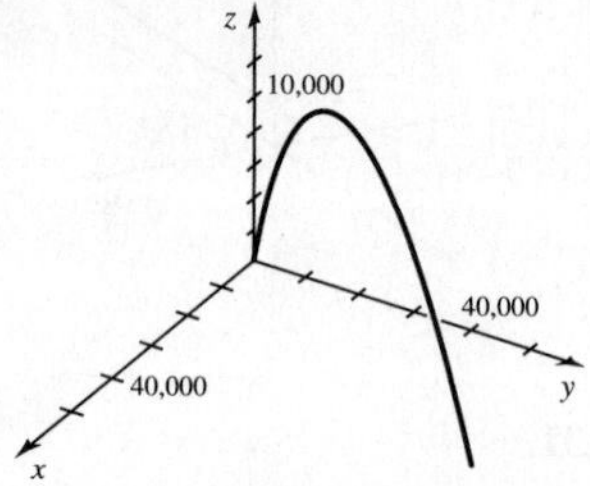

d. 12,765.1 m **41. a.** False **b.** True **c.** False **d.** True **e.** False **f.** True **g.** True **43.** 15.3 s, 1988.3 m, 287.0 m **45.** 21.7 s, 4330.1 ft, 1875 ft **47.** Approximately 27.4° and 62.6°

51. a. $\left[0, \frac{2\pi}{\omega}\right]$ **b.** $\mathbf{v}(t) = \langle -A\omega\sin\omega t, A\omega\cos\omega t\rangle$ is not constant, $|\mathbf{v}(t)| = |A\omega|$ is constant. **c.** $\mathbf{a}(t) = \langle -A\omega^2\cos\omega t, -A\omega^2\sin\omega t\rangle$ **d.** $\mathbf{r}$ and $\mathbf{v}$ are orthogonal, $\mathbf{r}$ and $\mathbf{a}$ are in opposite directions.

e.

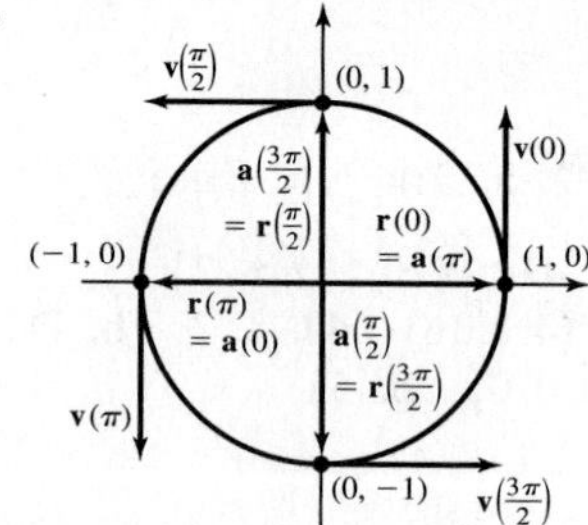

53. a. $\mathbf{r}(t) = \langle 5\sin(\pi t/6), 5\cos(\pi t/6)\rangle$
b. $\mathbf{r}(t) = \left\langle 5\sin\left(\frac{1 - e^{-t}}{5}\right), 5\cos\left(\frac{1 - e^{-t}}{5}\right)\right\rangle$

55. a. $\mathbf{v}(t) = \langle -a\sin t, b\cos t\rangle; |\mathbf{v}(t)| = \sqrt{a^2\sin^2 t + b^2\cos^2 t}$

b.

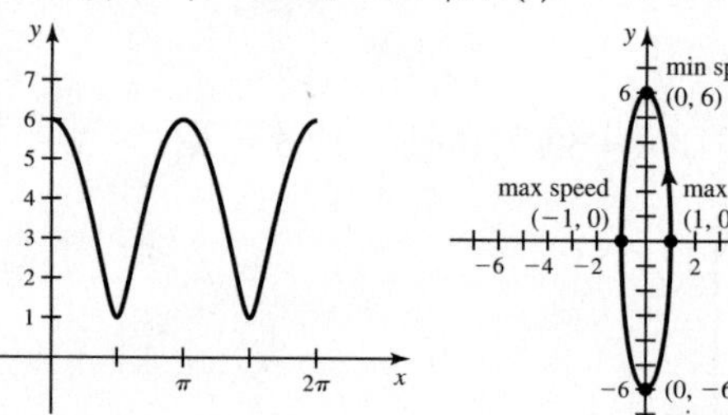

c. Yes **d.** max $\left\{\frac{a}{b}, \frac{b}{a}\right\}$

57. a. $\mathbf{r}(0) = \langle 50, 0, 0\rangle, \lim_{t\to\infty}\mathbf{r}(t) = \langle 0, 0, 5\rangle$ **b.** At $t = 0$

c.

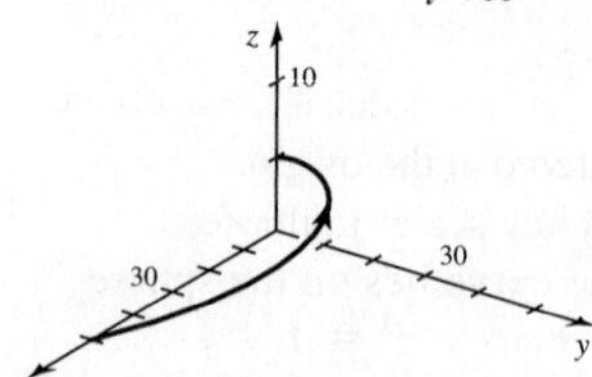

59. Approximately 0.41 rad (23.5°) or 1.04 rad (59.6°)

61. a. 1.2 ft, 0.46 s **b.** 0.88 ft/s **c.** 0.85 ft **d.** Move curve in the second half. **e.** $c = 28.17\ \text{ft/s}^2$

63. $T = \frac{|\mathbf{v}_0|\sin\alpha + \sqrt{|\mathbf{v}_0|^2\sin^2\alpha + 2gy_0}}{g}$, Range $= |\mathbf{v}_0|(\cos\alpha)T$,

Max. ht. $= y_0 + \frac{|\mathbf{v}_0|^2\sin^2\alpha}{2g}$

65. $\{(\cos t, \sin t, c \sin t): t \in \mathbf{R}\}$ satisfies the equations $x^2 + y^2 = 1$ and $z - cy = 0$ so that $\langle \cos t, \sin t, c \sin t\rangle$ lies on the intersection of a right circular cylinder and a plane, which is an ellipse.
69. a. $a^2 + c^2 + e^2 = b^2 + d^2 + f^2$ and $ab + cd + ef = 0$
b. $a^2 + c^2 = b^2 + d^2, ab + cd = 0$, and $a + c = -e$ and $b + d = -f$

Section 12.8 Exercises, pp. 745–747

1. $\sqrt{5}(b - a)$ **3.** $\int_a^b |\mathbf{v}(t)|\, dt$ **5.** 20π **7.** 3π **9.** $\frac{\pi^2}{8}$ **11.** $5\sqrt{34}$

13. $4\pi\sqrt{65}$ **15.** $(10\sqrt{13} - 16) - 24 \ln\left(\frac{5 + \sqrt{13}}{6}\right)$ **17.** $\frac{3}{2}$

19. $3t^2\sqrt{30}; 64\sqrt{30}$ **21.** 26; 26π **23.** 19.38 **25.** 32.50 **27.** πa

29. 32 **31.** $63\sqrt{5}$ **33.** $\frac{2\pi - 3\sqrt{3}}{8}$ **35. a.** True **b.** True **c.** True

37. a. If $a^2 = b^2 + c^2$ then $|\mathbf{r}(t)|^2 = (a \cos t)^2 + (b \sin t)^2 + (c \sin t)^2 = a^2$ so that $\mathbf{r}(t)$ is a circle centered at the origin of radius $|a|$.
b. $2\pi a$. **c.** If $a^2 + c^2 + e^2 = b^2 + d^2 + f^2$ and $ab + cd + ef = 0$, then $\mathbf{r}(t)$ is a circle of radius $\sqrt{a^2 + c^2 + e^2}$ and its arc length is $2\pi\sqrt{a^2 + c^2 + e^2}$.

39. a. $\int_a^b \sqrt{[Ah'(t)]^2 + [Bh'(t)]^2}\, dt$

$= \int_a^b \sqrt{(A^2 + B^2)(h'(t))^2}\, dt = \sqrt{A^2 + B^2} \int_a^b |h'(t)|\, dt$

b. $64\sqrt{29}$ **c.** $\frac{7\sqrt{29}}{4}$ **41.** $\frac{\sqrt{1 + a^2}}{a}$ (where $a > 0$) **43.** 12.85

45. 26.73 **47. a.** 5.102 s **b.** $\int_0^{5.102} \sqrt{400 + (25 - 9.8t)^2}\, dt$

c. 124.43 m **d.** 102.04 m

49. $\int_a^b |\mathbf{r}'(t)|\, dt = \int_a^b \sqrt{[cf'(t)]^2 + [cg'(t)]^2}\, dt$

$= |c| \int_a^b \sqrt{(f'(t))^2 + (g'(t))^2}\, dt = |c|L.$

51. If $\mathbf{r}(t) = \langle t, f(t)\rangle$, then by definition the arc length is

$\int_a^b \sqrt{(t')^2 + [f'(t)]^2}\, dt = \int_a^b \sqrt{1 + (f'(t))^2}\, dt$

$= \int_a^b \sqrt{1 + (f'(x))^2}\, dx.$

Section 12.9 Exercises, pp. 757–760

1. If the parameter t used to describe a trajectory also measures the arc length s of the curve that is generated, we say the curve has been parameterized by its arc length. **3.** No; $|\mathbf{v}(t)| = \sqrt{3} \neq 1$.

5. $\kappa = \frac{1}{|\mathbf{v}|}\left|\frac{d\mathbf{T}}{dt}\right|$ or $\kappa = \frac{|\mathbf{a} \times \mathbf{v}|}{|\mathbf{v}|^3}$ **7.** $\mathbf{N} = \frac{d\mathbf{T}/dt}{|d\mathbf{T}/dt|}$

9. No; $\mathbf{r}(s) = \left\langle \frac{s}{\sqrt{5}}, \frac{2s}{\sqrt{5}}\right\rangle, 0 \le s \le 3\sqrt{5}$

11. No; $\mathbf{r}(s) = \left\langle 2 \cos \frac{s}{2}, 2 \sin \frac{s}{2}\right\rangle$

13. No; $\mathbf{r}(s) = \langle \cos s, \sin s\rangle, 0 \le s \le \pi$ **15.** $\mathbf{T} = \frac{\langle 1, 2, 3\rangle}{\sqrt{14}}, \kappa = 0$

17. $\mathbf{T} = \frac{\langle 1, 2 \cos t, -2 \sin t\rangle}{\sqrt{5}}, \kappa = \frac{1}{5}$

19. $\mathbf{T} = \frac{\langle \sqrt{3} \cos t, \cos t, -2 \sin t\rangle}{2}, \kappa = \frac{1}{2}$

21. $\mathbf{T} = \frac{\langle 1, 4t\rangle}{\sqrt{1 + 16t^2}}, \kappa = \frac{4}{(1 + 16t^2)^{3/2}}$ **23.** $\frac{1}{3}$ **25.** $\frac{2}{(4t^2 + 1)^{3/2}}$

27. $\frac{\sqrt{159}}{(50 \sin^2 t + 3)^{3/2}}$ **29.** $\mathbf{T} = \langle \cos t, -\sin t\rangle, \mathbf{N} = \langle -\sin t, -\cos t\rangle$

31. $\mathbf{T} = \frac{\langle t, -3, 0\rangle}{\sqrt{t^2 + 9}}, \mathbf{N} = \frac{\langle 3, t, 0\rangle}{\sqrt{t^2 + 9}}$ **33.** $\mathbf{T} = \langle -\sin t^2, \cos t^2\rangle$, $\mathbf{N} = \langle -\cos t^2, -\sin t^2\rangle$ **35.** $\mathbf{T} = \frac{\langle 2t, 1\rangle}{\sqrt{4t^2 + 1}}, \mathbf{N} = \frac{\langle 1, -2t\rangle}{\sqrt{4t^2 + 1}}$

37. $a_N = a_T = 0$

39. $\mathbf{a} = \frac{6}{(1 + 5 \cos^2 t)^{1/2}}\mathbf{N} + \left(-\frac{5\sqrt{6} \sin t \cos t}{(1 + 5 \cos^2 t)^{1/2}}\right)\mathbf{T}$

41. $\mathbf{a} = \frac{6t}{\sqrt{9t^2 + 4}}\mathbf{N} + \frac{18t^2 + 4}{\sqrt{9t^2 + 4}}\mathbf{T}$ **43. a.** False **b.** False **c.** False **d.** True **e.** False **45.** $\kappa = \frac{2}{(1 + 4x^2)^{3/2}}$

47. $\kappa = \frac{x}{(x^2 + 1)^{3/2}}$ **51.** $\kappa = \frac{|ab|}{(a^2 \cos^2 t + b^2 \sin^2 t)^{3/2}}$

53. $\kappa = \frac{|2a|}{(1 + 4a^2 t^2)^{3/2}}$

55. b. $\mathbf{v}_A(t) = \langle 1, 2, 3\rangle, \mathbf{a}_A(t) = \langle 0, 0, 0\rangle$ and $\mathbf{v}_B(t) = \langle 2t, 4t, 6t\rangle$, $\mathbf{a}_B(t) = \langle 2, 4, 6\rangle$; A has constant velocity and zero acceleration while B has increasing speed and constant acceleration.
c. $\mathbf{a}_A(t) = 0\mathbf{N} + 0\mathbf{T}, \mathbf{a}_B(t) = 0\mathbf{N} + 2\sqrt{14}\mathbf{T}$; Both normal components are zero since the path is a straight line ($\kappa = 0$).
57. b. $\mathbf{v}_A(t) = \langle -\sin t, \cos t\rangle, \mathbf{a}_A(t) = \langle -\cos t, -\sin t\rangle$
$\mathbf{v}_B(t) = \langle -2t \sin (t^2), 2t \cos (t^2)\rangle$
$\mathbf{a}_B(t) = \langle -4t^2 \cos (t^2) - 2 \sin (t^2), -4t^2 \sin (t^2) + 2 \cos (t^2)\rangle$
c. $\mathbf{a}_A(t) = \mathbf{N} + 0\mathbf{T}, \mathbf{a}_B(t) = 4t^2\mathbf{N} + 2\mathbf{T}$; For A, the acceleration is always normal to the curve, but this is not true for B.

59. b. $\kappa = \frac{1}{2\sqrt{2(1 - \cos t)}}$ **c.**

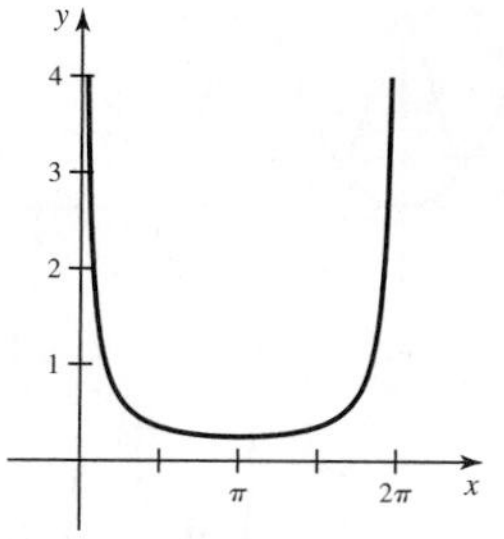

d. Minimum curvature at $\left(\pi, \frac{1}{4}\right)$ **61.** **b.** $\kappa = \frac{1}{t(1 + t^2)^{3/2}}$

c.

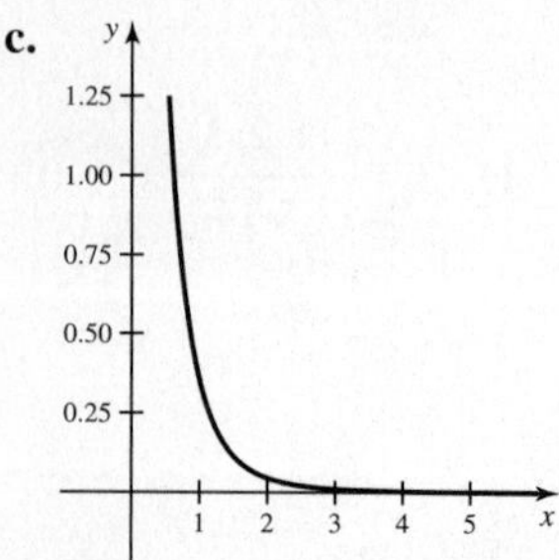

d. No maximum or minimum curvature

63. $\kappa = \dfrac{e^x}{(1 + e^{2x})^{3/2}}, \left(-\dfrac{\ln 2}{2}, \dfrac{1}{\sqrt{2}}\right), \dfrac{2\sqrt{3}}{9}$

65. $\dfrac{1}{\kappa} = \dfrac{1}{2}; x^2 + \left(y - \dfrac{1}{2}\right)^2 = \dfrac{1}{4}$

67. $\dfrac{1}{\kappa} = 4; (x - \pi)^2 + (y + 2)^2 = 16$

69. $\kappa\left(\dfrac{\pi}{2n}\right) = n^2$; κ increases as n increases.

71. a. speed $= \sqrt{V_0^2 - 2V_0 gt \sin\alpha + g^2t^2}$.
b. $\kappa(t) = \dfrac{gV_0 \cos\alpha}{(V_0^2 - 2V_0 gt \sin\alpha + g^2t^2)^{3/2}}$. **c.** Speed has a minimum at $t = \dfrac{V_0 \sin\alpha}{g}$ and $\kappa(t)$ has a maximum at $t = \dfrac{V_0 \sin\alpha}{g}$.

73. $|\mathbf{v}(t)| = \sqrt{a^2 + b^2 + c^2} = 1$ if $a^2 + b^2 + c^2 = 1$.

75. $\kappa = \dfrac{1}{|\mathbf{v}|} \cdot \left|\dfrac{d\mathbf{T}}{dt}\right|$, where $\mathbf{T} = \dfrac{\langle b, d, f\rangle}{\sqrt{b^2 + d^2 + f^2}}$ for b, d, f all constant. Thus, $\dfrac{d\mathbf{T}}{dt} = \mathbf{0}$ so $\kappa = 0$.

77. a. $\kappa_1(x) = \dfrac{2}{(1 + 4x^2)^{3/2}}$

$\kappa_2(x) = \dfrac{12x^2}{(1 + 16x^6)^{3/2}}$

$\kappa_3(x) = \dfrac{30x^4}{(1 + 36x^{10})^{3/2}}$

b.

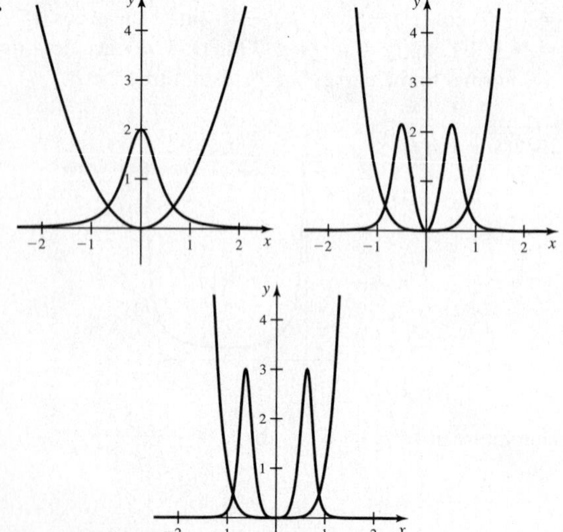

c. κ_1 has its maximum at $x = 0$, κ_2 has its maxima at $x = \pm\sqrt[6]{\frac{1}{56}}$, κ_3 has its maxima at $x = \pm\sqrt[10]{\frac{1}{99}}$. **d.** $\lim\limits_{n\to\infty} z_n = 1$; the maximum curvature of $y = f_n(x)$ occurs closer and closer to the point (1, 1) as $n \to \infty$.

Chapter 12 Review Exercises, pp. 760–762

1. a. True **b.** False **c.** True **d.** True **e.** False **f.** False

3.

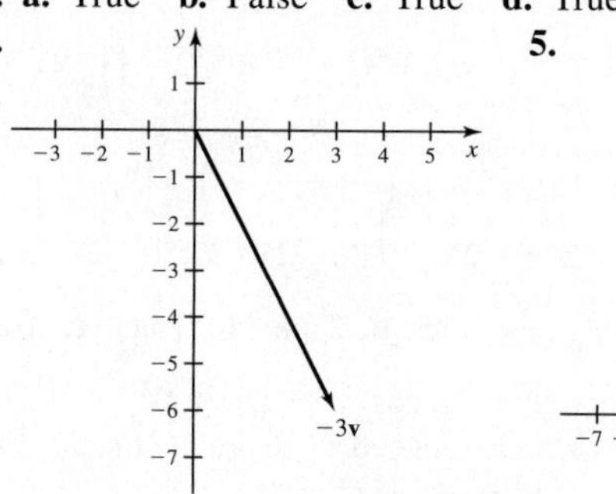

5.

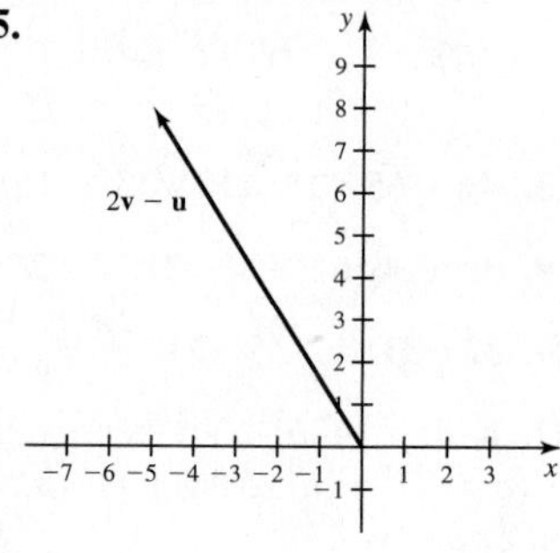

7. $\sqrt{221}$ **9.** $\pm\left\langle -\dfrac{60}{\sqrt{35}}, \dfrac{100}{\sqrt{35}}, \dfrac{20}{\sqrt{35}}\right\rangle$

11. a. $\mathbf{v} = -275\sqrt{2}\mathbf{i} + 275\sqrt{2}\mathbf{j}$ **b.** $-275\sqrt{2}\mathbf{i} + (275\sqrt{2} + 40)\mathbf{j}$

13. $\{(x, y, z): (x - 1)^2 + y^2 + (z + 1)^2 = 16\}$

15. $\{(x, y, z): x^2 + (y - 1)^2 + z^2 > 4\}$ **17.** 50.16 m/s; 4.57° above the horizontal in the northerly horizontal direction.

19. a. 0.3 rad $\approx$ 17°

b. $\text{Scal}_{\mathbf{v}}\mathbf{u} = \dfrac{51}{\sqrt{77}}$, $\text{proj}_{\mathbf{v}}\mathbf{u} = \dfrac{1}{77}\langle 408, 102, -153\rangle$

c. $\text{Scal}_{\mathbf{u}}\mathbf{v} = \dfrac{51}{\sqrt{37}}$, $\text{proj}_{\mathbf{u}}\mathbf{v} = \dfrac{1}{37}\langle 306, 0, -51\rangle$

21. $\pm\left\langle \dfrac{12}{\sqrt{197}}, \dfrac{7}{\sqrt{197}}, \dfrac{2}{\sqrt{197}}\right\rangle$ **23.** $T(\theta) = 39.2 \sin\theta$ has a maximum value of 39.2 N·m $\left(\text{when } \theta = \dfrac{\pi}{2}\right)$ and a minimum value of 0 N·m when $\theta = 0$. Direction does *not* change.

25. $\langle x, y, z\rangle = \langle 0, -3, 9\rangle + t\langle 2, -5, -8\rangle, 0 \le t \le 1$

27. **29.**

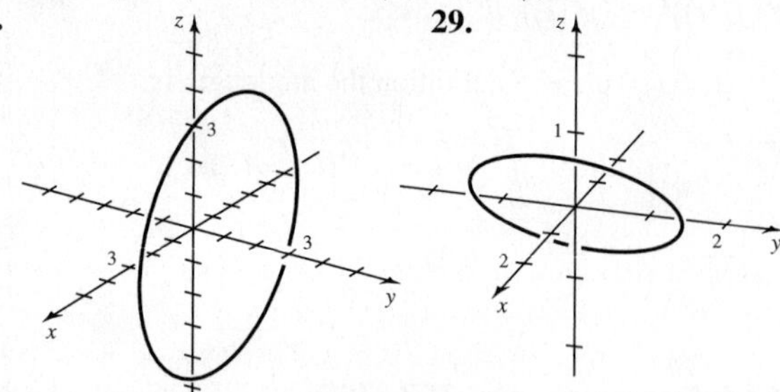

31. a. (116, 30) **b.** 39.1 ft **c.** 2.315 s

d. $\displaystyle\int_0^{2.315} \sqrt{50^2 + (-32t + 50)^2}\, dt$ **e.** 129 ft **f.** 41.4° to 79.6°

33. 40.09 **35. a.** $\mathbf{v} = \langle -6\sin t, 3\cos t\rangle$, $\mathbf{T} = \dfrac{\langle -2\sin t, \cos t\rangle}{\sqrt{1 + 3\sin^2 t}}$

b. $\kappa(t) = \dfrac{2}{3(1 + 3\sin^2 t)^{3/2}}$

c. $\mathbf{N} = \left\langle \dfrac{-\cos t}{\sqrt{1 + 3\sin^2 t}}, -\dfrac{2\sin t}{\sqrt{1 + 3\sin^2 t}} \right\rangle$

d. $|\mathbf{N}| = \sqrt{\dfrac{\cos^2 t + 4\sin^2 t}{1 + 3\sin^2 t}} = \sqrt{\dfrac{(\cos^2 t + \sin^2 t) + 3\sin^2 t}{1 + 3\sin^2 t}}$

$= 1$

$\mathbf{T} \cdot \mathbf{N} = \dfrac{2\sin t\cos t - 2\sin t\cos t}{1 + 3\sin^2 t} = 0$

e.

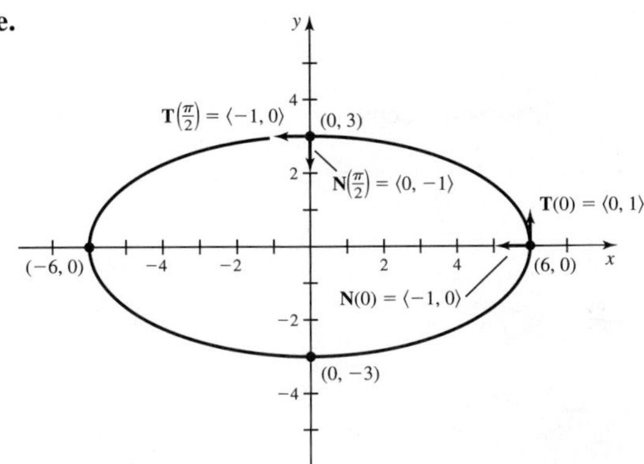

37. a. $\mathbf{v}(t) = \langle -\sin t, -2\sin t, \sqrt{5}\cos t\rangle$

$\mathbf{T}(t) = \left\langle -\dfrac{1}{\sqrt{5}}\sin t, -\dfrac{2}{\sqrt{5}}\sin t, \cos t \right\rangle$

b. $\kappa(t) = \dfrac{1}{\sqrt{5}}$ **c.** $\mathbf{N}(t) = \left\langle -\dfrac{1}{\sqrt{5}}\cos t, -\dfrac{2}{\sqrt{5}}\cos t, -\sin t \right\rangle$

d. $|\mathbf{N}(t)| = \sqrt{\dfrac{1}{5}\cos^2 t + \dfrac{4}{5}\cos^2 t + \sin^2 t} = 1;$

$\mathbf{T} \cdot \mathbf{N} = \left(\dfrac{1}{5}\cos t\sin t + \dfrac{4}{5}\cos t\sin t\right) - \sin t\cos t$

$= 0$

e.

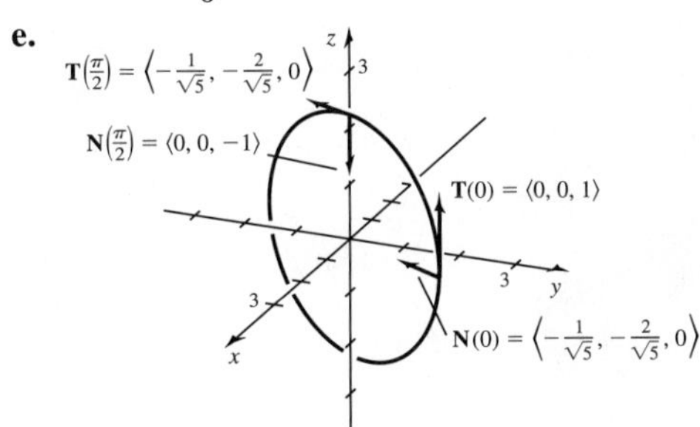

39. a. $\mathbf{a}(t) = 2\mathbf{N} + 0\mathbf{T} = 2\langle -\cos t, -\sin t\rangle$

b.

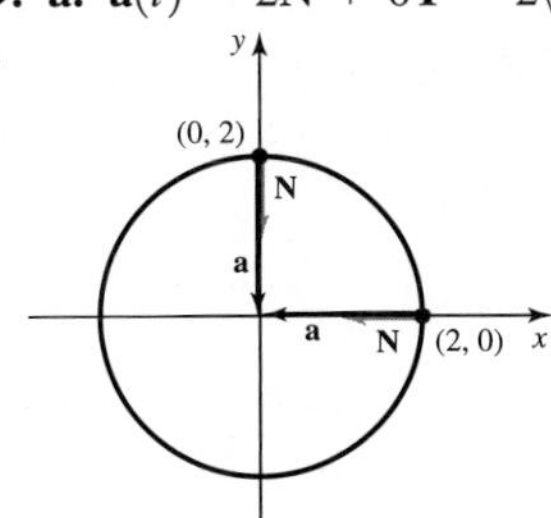

41. a. $a_T = \dfrac{2t}{\sqrt{t^2 + 1}}$ and $a_N = \dfrac{2}{\sqrt{t^2 + 1}}$

b.

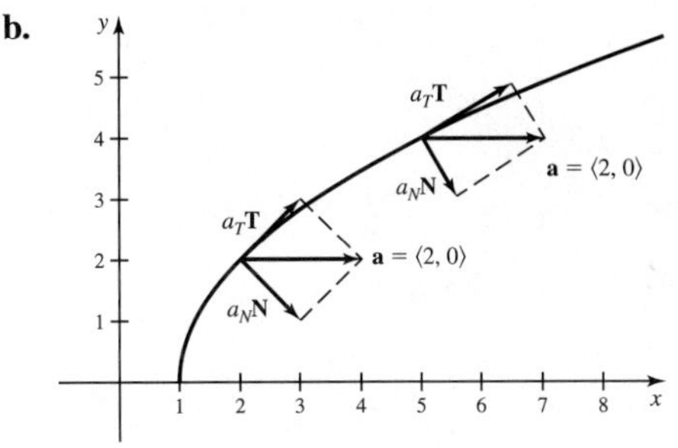

CHAPTER 13

Section 13.1 Exercises, pp. 775–777

1. One point and a normal vector **3.** $x = -6, y = -4, z = 3$ **5.** z-axis; x-axis; y-axis **7.** Intersection of the surface with a plane parallel to one of the coordinate planes **9.** Ellipsoid **11.** $x + y - z = 4$ **13.** $-x + 2y - 3z = 4$ **15.** $7x + 2y + z = 10$ **17.** $4x + 27y + 10z = 21$ **19.** Intercepts $x = 2, y = -3, z = 6$. Traces $3x - 2y = 6, z = 0$; $-2y + z = 6, x = 0$; and $3x + z = 6, y = 0$

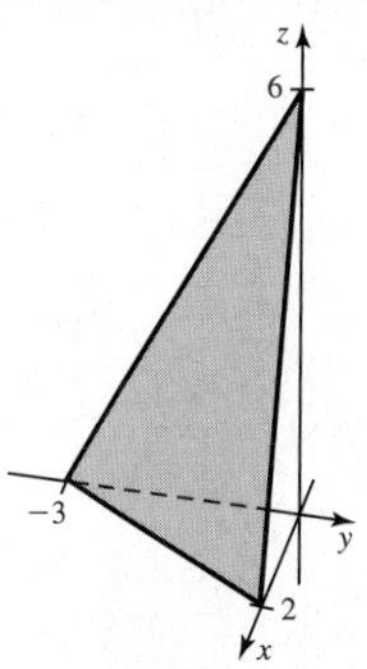

21. Intercepts $x = 30, y = 10, z = -6$. Traces $x + 3y - 30 = 0$, $z = 0$; $x - 5z - 30 = 0, y = 0$; and $3y - 5z - 30 = 0, x = 0$

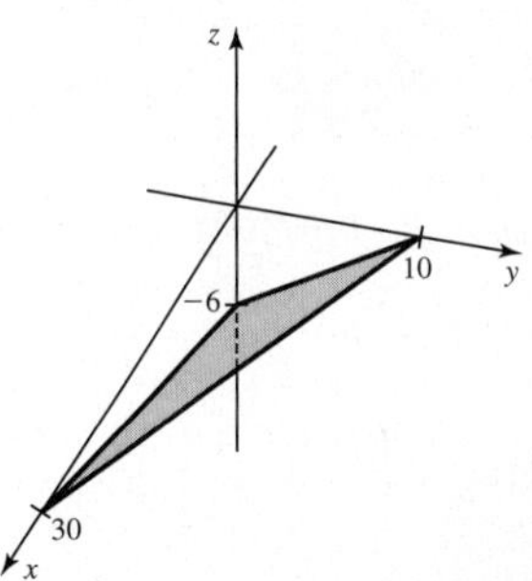

23. Q and T are identical; Q, R, and T are parallel; S is orthogonal to Q, R, and T. **25.** $-x + 2y - 4z = -17$ **27.** $4x + 3y - 2z = -5$ **29.** $x = t, y = 1 + 2t, z = -1 - 3t$ **31.** $x = \frac{7}{5} + 2t, y = \frac{9}{5} + t$, $z = -t$ **33. a.** z-axis **b.**

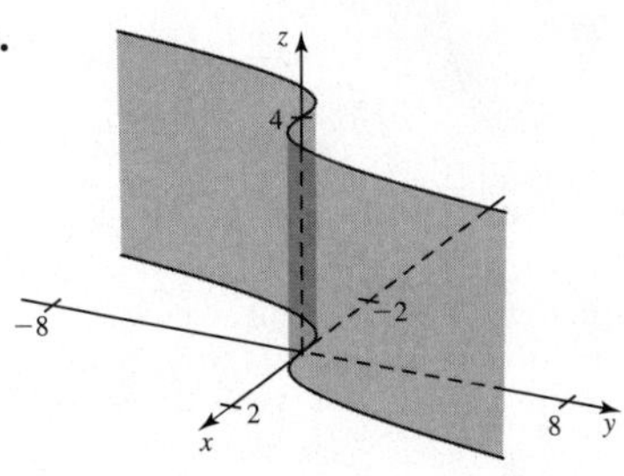

35. a. x-axis **b.**

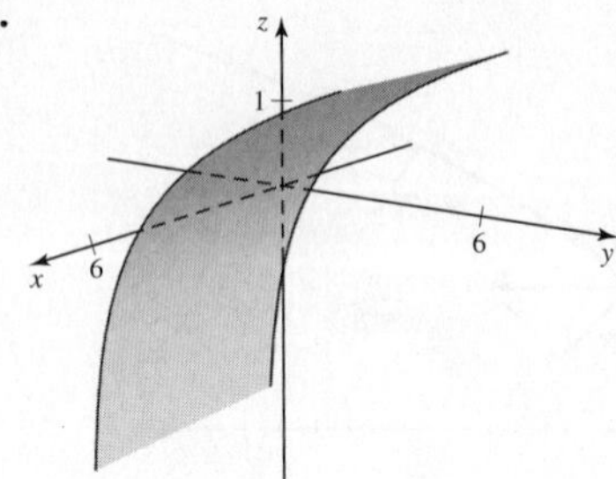

37. a. $x = \pm 1, y = \pm 2, z = \pm 3$ **b.** $x^2 + \dfrac{y^2}{4} = 1, x^2 + \dfrac{z^2}{9} = 1,$
$\dfrac{y^2}{4} + \dfrac{z^2}{9} = 1$ **c.**

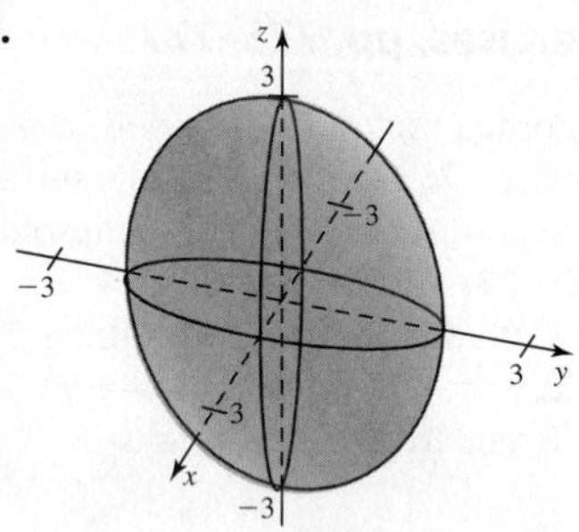

39. a. $x = \pm 3, y = \pm 1, z = \pm 6$ **b.** $\dfrac{x^2}{3} + 3y^2 = 3, \dfrac{x^2}{3} + \dfrac{z^2}{12} = 3,$
$3y^2 + \dfrac{z^2}{12} = 3$ **c.**

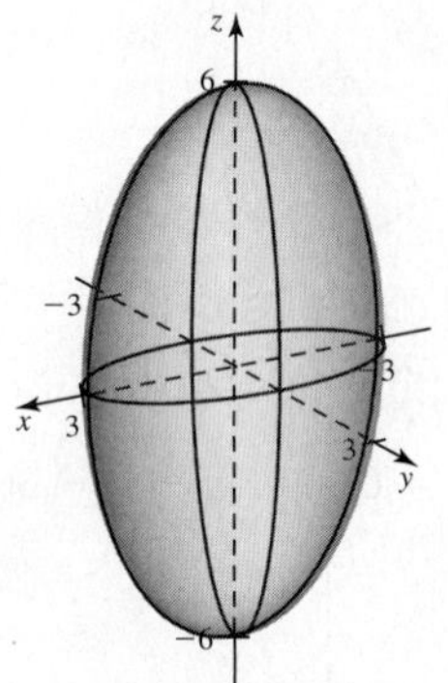

41. a. $x = y = z = 0$ **b.** $x = y^2, x = z^2$, origin
c.

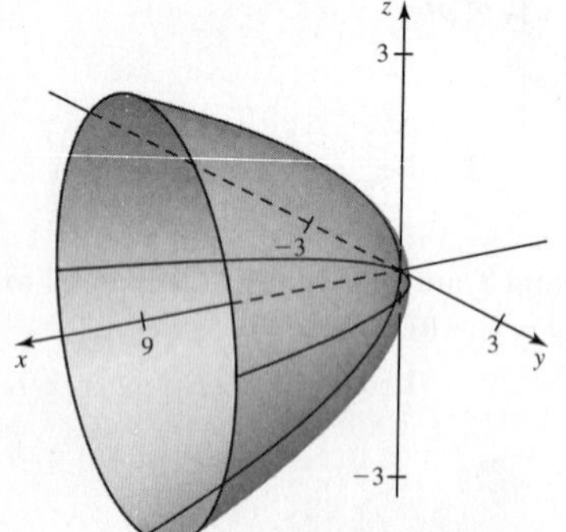

43. a. $x = y = z = 0$ **b.** Origin, $9x - \dfrac{z^2}{4} = 0, x - 9y^2 = 0$

c.

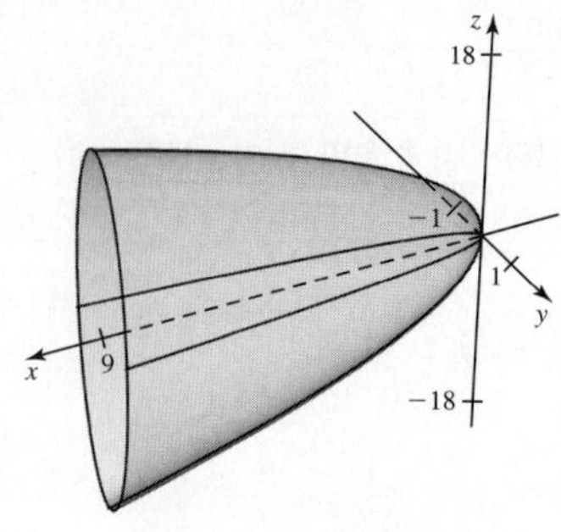

45. a. $x = \pm 5, y = \pm 3$, no z-intercepts
b. $\dfrac{x^2}{25} + \dfrac{y^2}{9} = 1, \dfrac{x^2}{25} - z^2 = 1, \dfrac{y^2}{9} - z^2 = 1$

c.

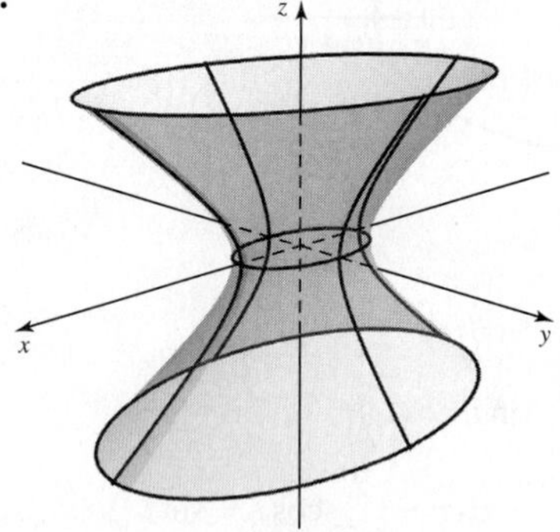

47. a. No x-intercepts, $y = \pm 12, z = \pm\dfrac{1}{2}$ **b.** $-\dfrac{x^2}{4} + \dfrac{y^2}{16} = 9,$
$-\dfrac{x^2}{4} + 36z^2 = 9, \dfrac{y^2}{16} + 36z^2 = 9$
c.

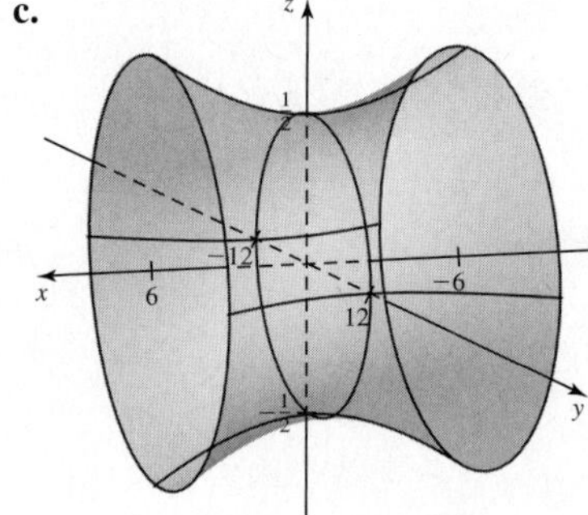

49. a. Origin **b.** $\dfrac{x^2}{9} - y^2 = 0, z = \dfrac{x^2}{9}, z = -y^2$

c.

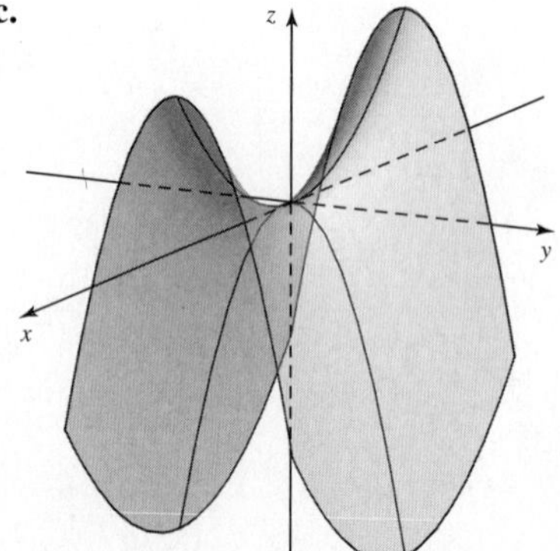

51. a. Origin **b.** $5x - \frac{y^2}{5} = 0, 5x + \frac{z^2}{20} = 0, -\frac{y^2}{5} + \frac{z^2}{20} = 0$

c.

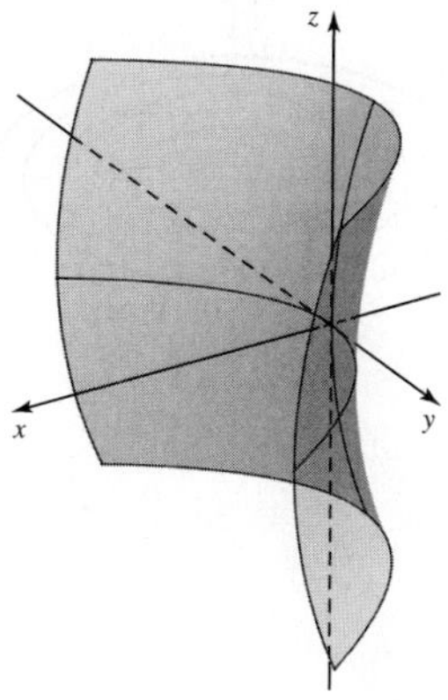

53. a. Origin **b.** $x^2 = z^2, \frac{y^2}{4} = z^2$, xy-trace is the origin

c.

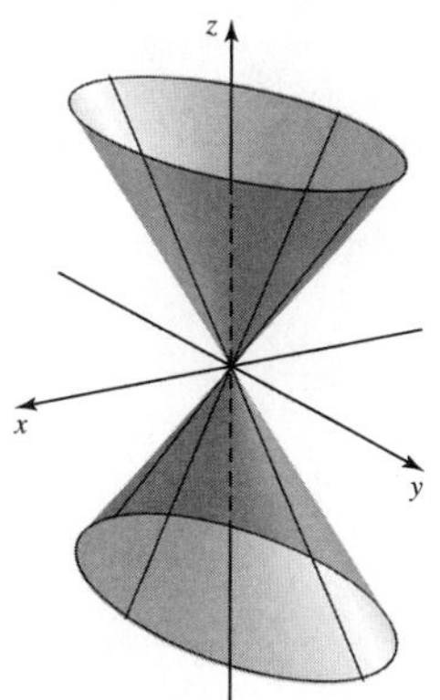

55. a. Origin **b.** $\frac{y^2}{18} = 2x^2, \frac{z^2}{32} = 2x^2$, yz-trace is the origin

c.

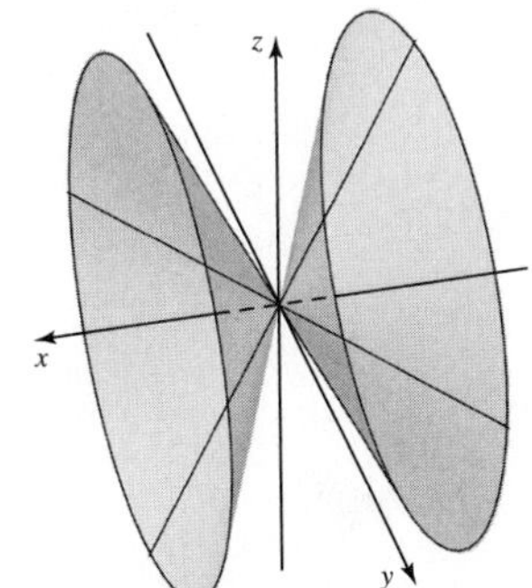

57. a. No x-intercepts, $y = \pm 2$, no z-intercepts **b.** $-x^2 + \frac{y^2}{4} = 1$, no xz-trace, $\frac{y^2}{4} - \frac{z^2}{9} = 1$ **c.**

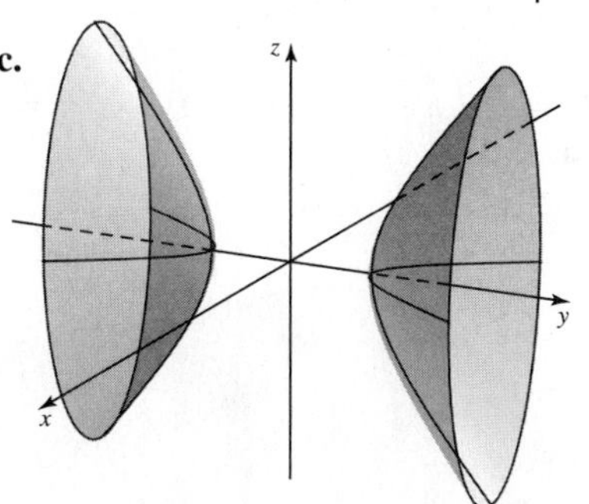

59. a. No x-intercepts, $y = \pm\frac{\sqrt{3}}{3}$, no z-intercepts

b. $-\frac{x^2}{3} + 3y^2 = 1$, no xz-trace, $3y^2 - \frac{z^2}{12} = 1$

c.

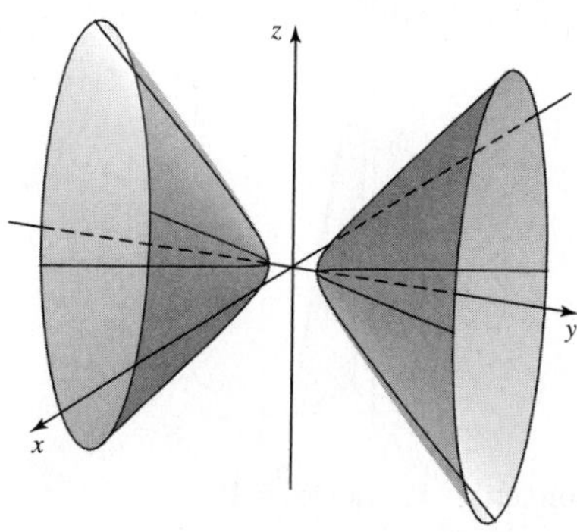

61. a. True **b.** False **c.** False **d.** True **e.** False **f.** False **g.** False **63. a.** D **b.** A **c.** E **d.** F **e.** B **f.** C **65.** Hyperbolic paraboloid **67.** Elliptic paraboloid **69.** Hyperboloid of one sheet **71.** Hyperbolic cylinder **73.** Elliptic hyperboloid **75.** $P(3, 9, 27)$ and $Q(-5, 25, 75)$ **77.** $P\left(\frac{6\sqrt{10}}{5}, \frac{2\sqrt{10}}{5}, \frac{3\sqrt{10}}{10}\right)$ and $Q\left(-\frac{6\sqrt{10}}{5}, -\frac{2\sqrt{10}}{5}, -\frac{3\sqrt{10}}{10}\right)$ **79.** $\theta = \cos^{-1}\left(-\frac{\sqrt{105}}{14}\right) \approx 2.392$ rad; 137° **81.** All except the hyperbolic paraboloid **83. a.**

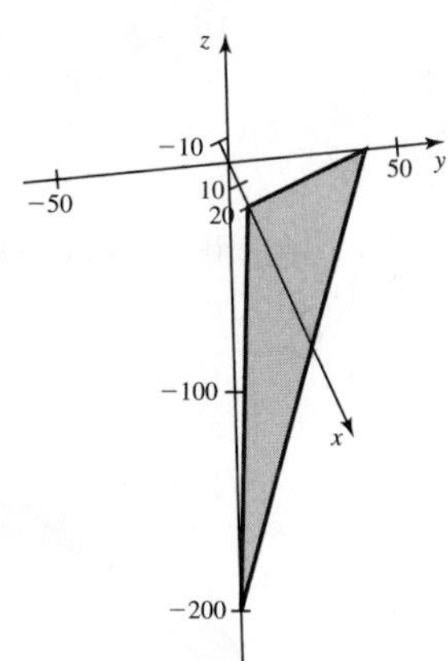

b. Positive **c.** $2x + y = 40$, line in the xy-plane **85. a.** $z = cy$ **b.** $\theta = \tan^{-1} c$ **87.** $\frac{1}{7}\langle -10, 5, -20 \rangle$

Section 13.2 Exercises, pp. 786–789

1. Independent: x and y; dependent: z **3.** $D = \{(x, y): x \neq 0 \text{ or } y \neq 0\}$ **5.** Three **7.** Circles **9.** $n = 6$ **11.** $\mathbf{R}^2$ **13.** $D = \{(x, y): y \neq 0\}$ (xy-plane without the x-axis) **15.** $D = \{(x, y): y < x^2\}$ **17.** $D = \{(x, y): xy \geq 0, (x, y) \neq (0, 0)\}$; first and third quadrant, origin excluded

19. Plane; domain $= \mathbf{R}^2$, range $= \mathbf{R}$

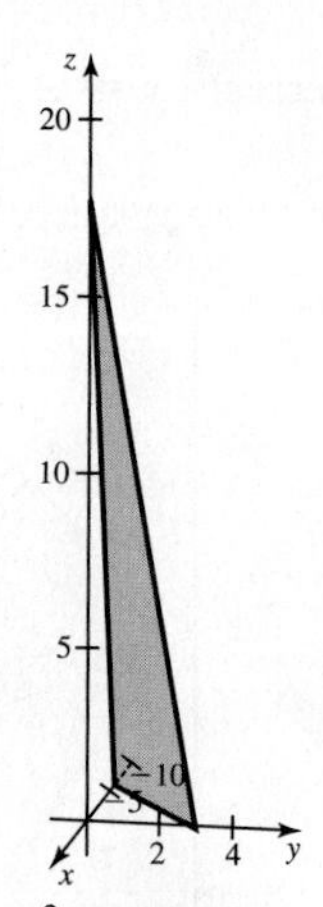

21. Hyperbolic paraboloid; domain $= \mathbf{R}^2$, range $= \mathbf{R}$

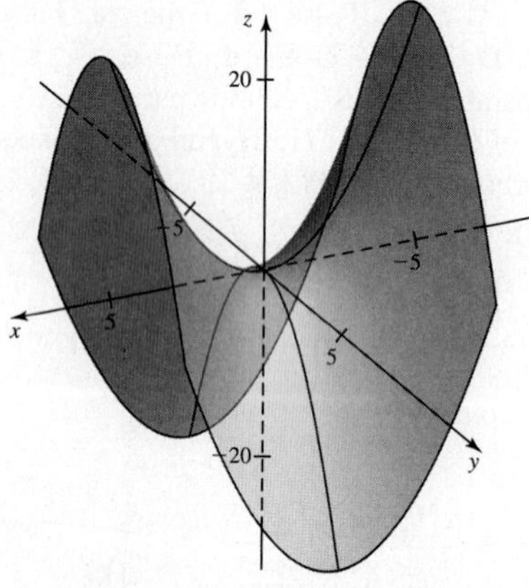

23. Lower part of a hyperboloid of two sheets; domain $= \mathbf{R}^2$, range $= (-\infty, -1]$

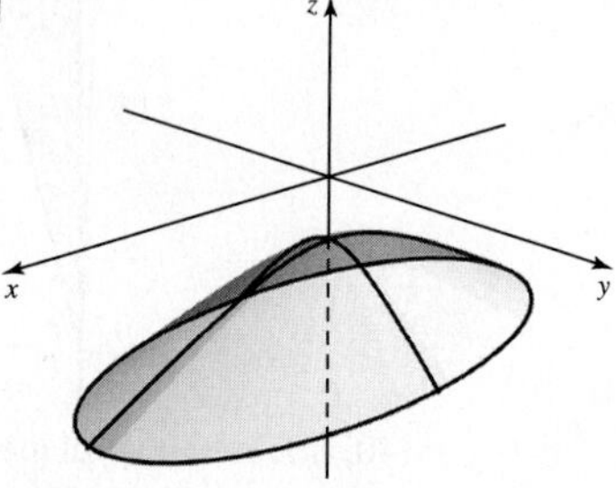

25. Upper half of a hyperboloid of one sheet; domain $= \{(x, y): x^2 + y^2 \geq 1\}$, range $= [0, \infty)$

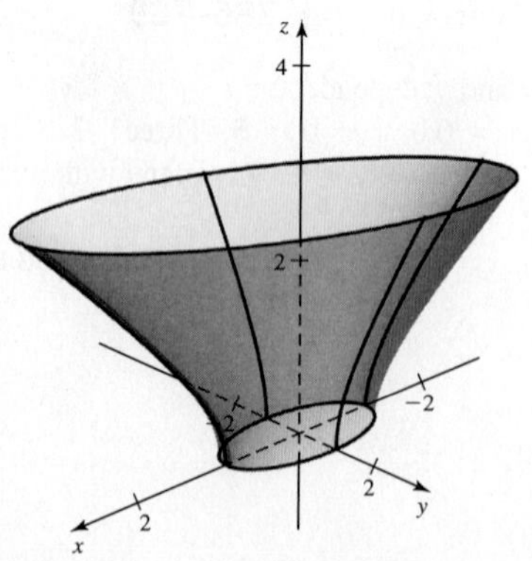

27. a. A **b.** D **c.** B **d.** C **29.**

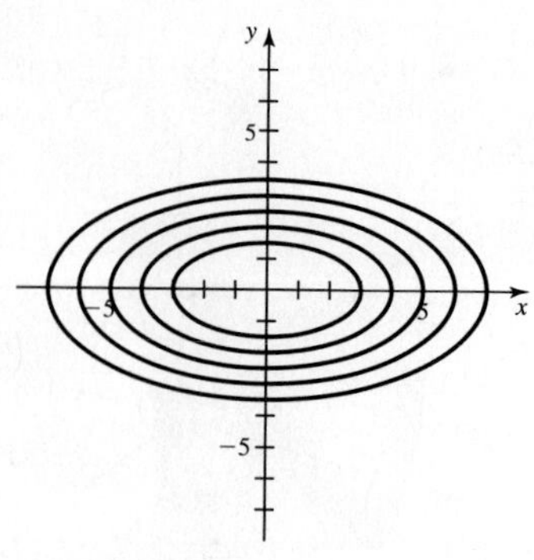

31.

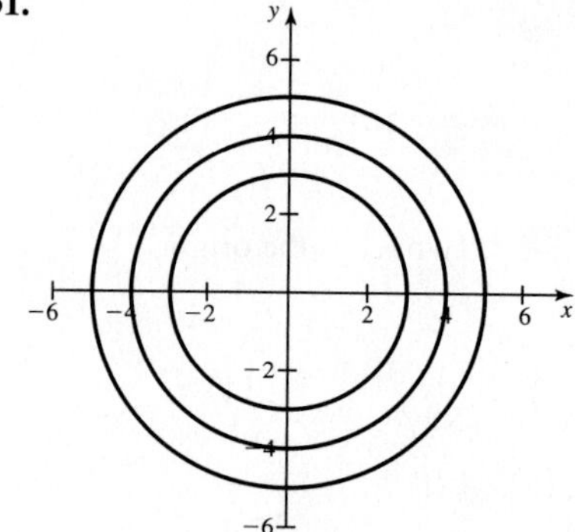

33.

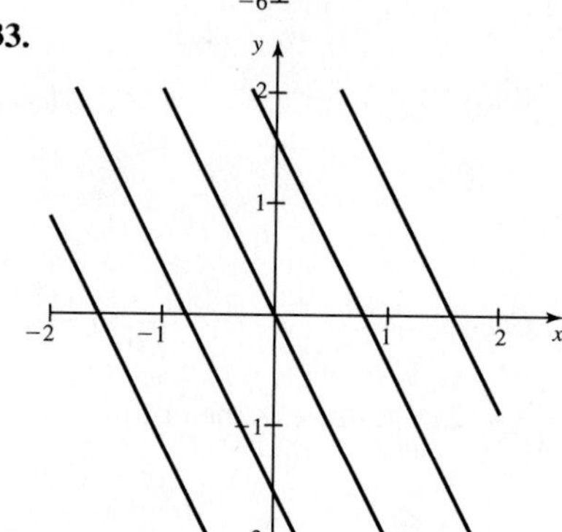

35. a.

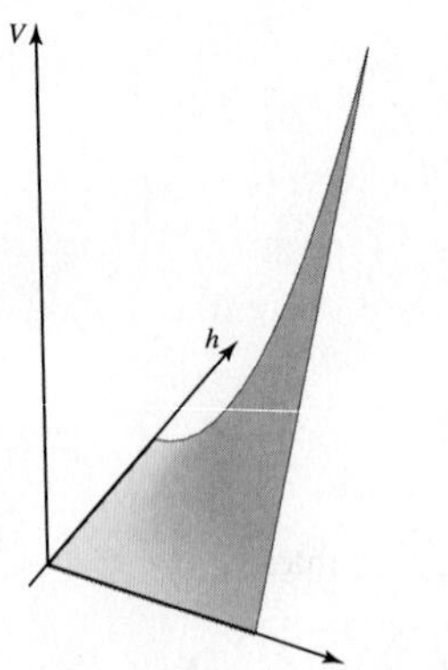

b. $D = \{(r, h): r > 0, h > 0\}$ **c.** $h = 300/(\pi r^2)$

37. a.

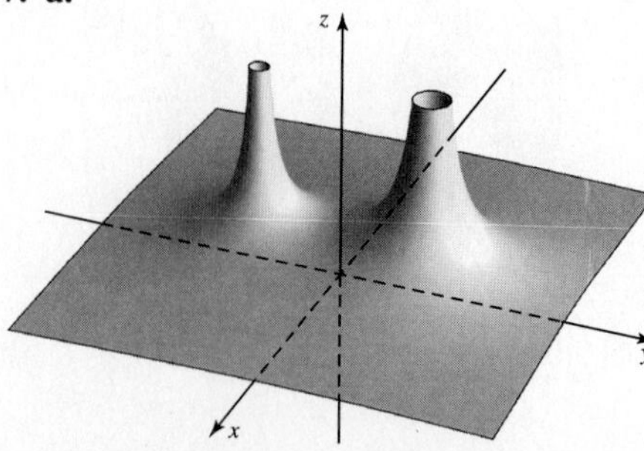

b. $\mathbf{R}^2$ without the points $(0, 1)$ and $(0, -1)$

c. $\varphi(2, 3)$ is greater.

d.

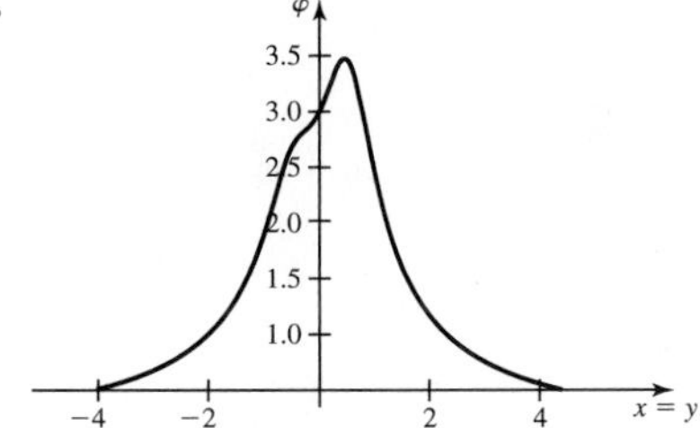

39. a.

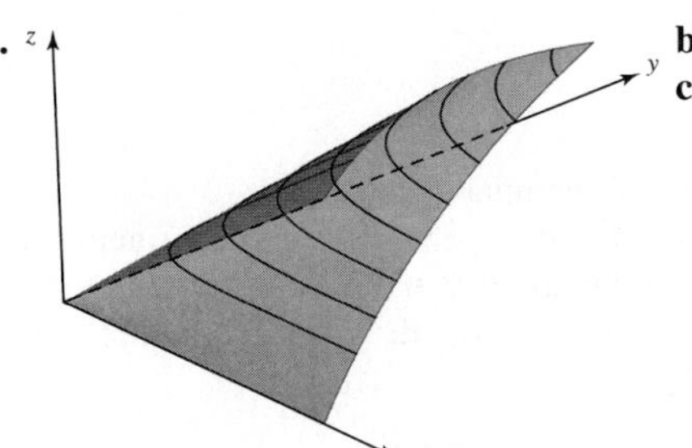

b. $R(10, 10) = 5$ **c.** $R(x, y) = R(y, x)$

41. a.

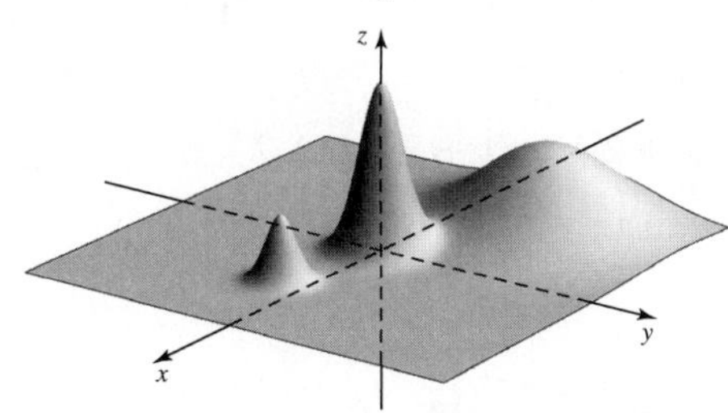

b. $(0, 0), (-5, 3), (4, -1)$
c. $f(0, 0) = 10.17, f(-5, 3) = 5.00, f(4, -1) = 4.00$
43. $D = \{(x, y, z): x \neq z\}$; all points not on the plane $x = z$
45. $D = \{(x, y, z): y \geq z\}$; all points on or below the plane $y = z$
47. $D = \{(x, y, z): x^2 \leq y\}$; all points on the side of the vertical cylinder $y = x^2$ that contains the positive y-axis **49. a.** False **b.** False **c.** True **51. a.** $D = \mathbf{R}^2$, range $= [0, \infty)$
b.

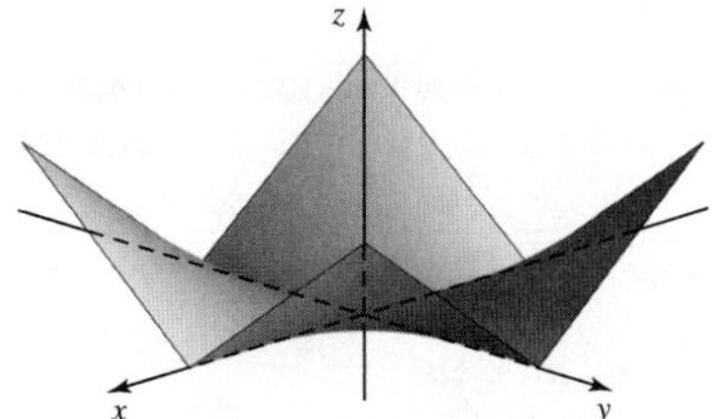

53. a. $D = \{(x, y): x \neq y\}$, range $= \mathbf{R}$
b.

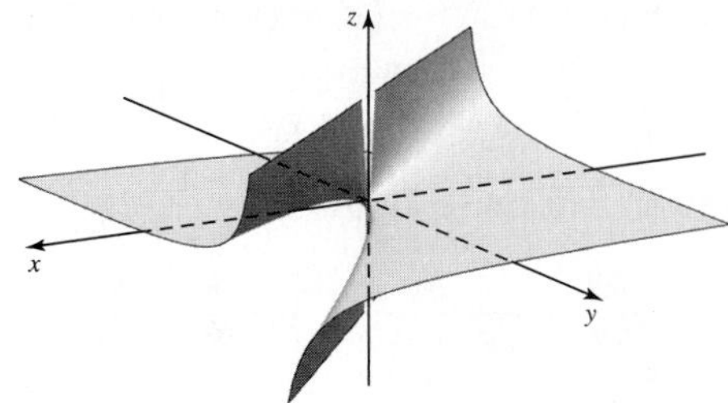

55. a. $D = \{(x, y): y \neq x + \pi/2 + n\pi$ for any integer $n\}$, range $= [0, \infty)$ **b.**

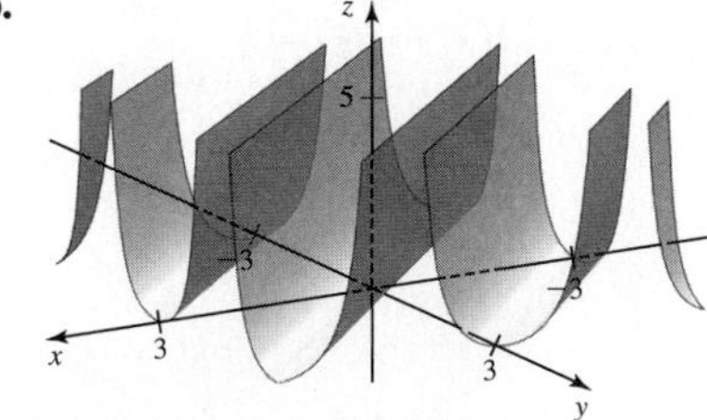

57. Peak at the origin **59.** Depression at $(1, 0)$ **61.** The level curves are $ax + by = d - cz_0$, where c is a constant, which are parallel lines with slope $-a/b$. **63. a.** $P = \dfrac{20{,}000r}{(1 + r)^{240} - 1}$

b. $P = \dfrac{Br}{(1 + r)^{240} - 1}$, with $B = 5000, 10{,}000, 15{,}000, 25{,}000$

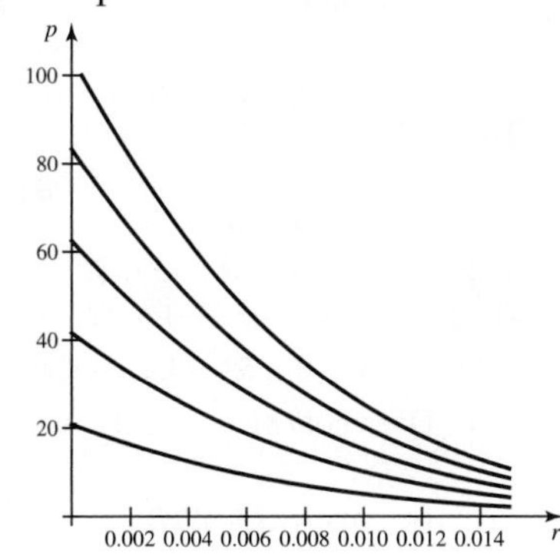

65. a.

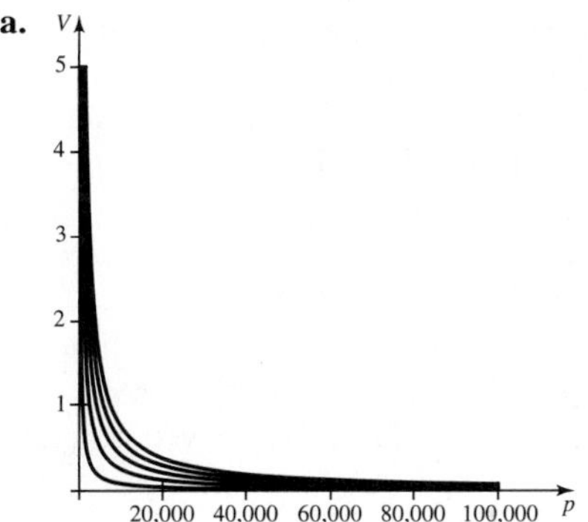

b.

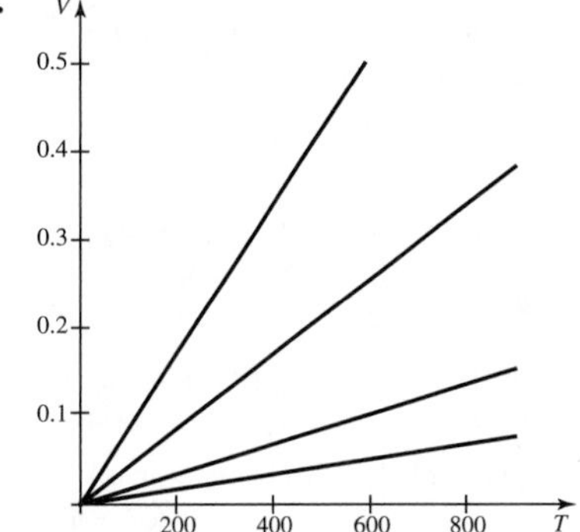

c.

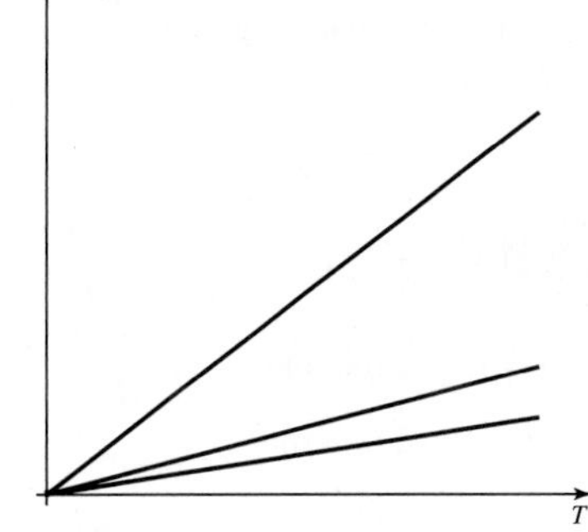

67. $D = \{(x, y): x - 1 \leq y \leq x + 1\}$
69. $D = \{(x, y, z): (x \leq z \text{ and } y \geq -z) \text{ or } (x \geq z \text{ and } y \leq -z)\}$

Section 13.3 Exercises, pp. 797–798

1. The values of $f(x, y)$ are arbitrarily close to L for all (x, y) in a sufficiently small disk centered at (a, b). **3.** Limits are obtained by evaluating the function at a point. **5.** If the function approaches different values along different paths, the limit does not exist. **7.** f must be defined, the limit must exist, and the limit must equal the function value. **9.** At any point where the denominator is nonzero **11.** 101 **13.** 27 **15.** $1/(2\pi)$ **17.** 2 **19.** 6 **21.** 2 **23.** $1/(2\sqrt{2}) = \sqrt{2}/4$ **25.** $L = 1$ along $y = 0$, and $L = -1$ along $x = 0$ **27.** $L = 1$ along $x = 0$, and $L = -2$ along $y = 0$ **29.** $L = 2$ along $y = x$, and $L = 0$ along $y = -x$ **31.** $\mathbf{R}^2$ **33.** All points except the origin **35.** $\mathbf{R}^2$ **37.** $\mathbf{R}^2$ **39.** All points except the origin **41.** $\mathbf{R}^2$ **43.** 6 **45.** -1 **47. a.** False **b.** False **c.** True **d.** False **49.** $\frac{1}{2}$ **51.** 0 **53.** Does not exist **55.** $\frac{1}{4}$ **57.** Does not exist **59.** Does not exist **63.** 1 **65.** 1 **67.** 0

Section 13.4 Exercises, pp. 807–810

1. $f_x(a, b)$ is the slope of the surface in the direction parallel to the x-axis, $f_y(a, b)$ is the slope of the surface in the direction parallel to the y-axis, both taken at (a, b). **3.** $f_x(x, y) = \cos(xy) - xy\sin(xy)$, $f_y(x, y) = -x^2\sin(xy)$ **5.** Think of x and y as being fixed, and take the derivative with respect to the variable z.
7. $f_x(x, y) = 6xy$, $f_y(x, y) = 3x^2$
9. $g_x(x, y) = -2y\sin(2xy)$, $g_y(x, y) = -2x\sin(2xy)$
11. $f_w(w, z) = \dfrac{z^2 - w^2}{(w^2 + z^2)^2}$, $f_z(w, z) = \dfrac{-2wz}{(w^2 + z^2)^2}$
13. $s_y(y, z) = z^3\sec^2(yz)$, $s_z(y, z) = 2z\tan(yz) + yz^2\sec^2(yz)$
15. $G_s(s, t) = \dfrac{\sqrt{st}(t - s)}{2s(s + t)^2}$, $G_t(s, t) = \dfrac{\sqrt{st}(s - t)}{2t(s + t)^2}$
17. $h_{xx}(x, y) = 6x$, $h_{xy}(x, y) = 2y$, $h_{yx}(x, y) = 2y$, $h_{yy}(x, y) = 2x$
19. $f_{xx}(x, y) = -16y^3\sin 4x$, $f_{xy}(x, y) = 12y^2\cos 4x$, $f_{yx}(x, y) = 12y^2\cos 4x$, $f_{yy}(x, y) = 6y\sin 4x$
21. $p_{uu}(u, v) = \dfrac{-2u^2 + 2v^2 + 8}{(u^2 + v^2 + 4)^2}$, $p_{uv}(u, v) = \dfrac{-4uv}{(u^2 + v^2 + 4)^2}$, $p_{vu}(u, v) = \dfrac{-4uv}{(u^2 + v^2 + 4)^2}$, $p_{vv}(u, v) = \dfrac{2u^2 - 2v^2 + 8}{(u^2 + v^2 + 4)^2}$
23. $F_{rr}(r, s) = 0$, $F_{rs}(r, s) = e^s$, $F_{sr}(r, s) = e^s$, $F_{ss}(r, s) = re^s$
31. $f_x(x, y, z) = y + z$, $f_y(x, y, z) = x + z$, $f_z(x, y, z) = x + y$
33. $h_x(x, y, z) = h_y(x, y, z) = h_z(x, y, z) = -\sin(x + y + z)$
35. $F_u(u, v, w) = \dfrac{1}{v + w}$, $F_v(u, v, w) = F_w(u, v, w) = \dfrac{-u}{(v + w)^2}$
37. $f_w(w, x, y, z) = 2wxy^2$, $f_x(w, x, y, z) = w^2y^2 + y^3z^2$, $f_y(w, x, y, z) = 2w^2xy + 3xy^2z^2$, $f_z(w, x, y, z) = 2xy^3z$
39. $h_w(w, x, y, z) = \dfrac{z}{xy}$, $h_x(w, x, y, z) = -\dfrac{wz}{x^2y}$, $h_y(w, x, y, z) = -\dfrac{wz}{xy^2}$, $h_z(w, x, y, z) = \dfrac{w}{xy}$ **41. a.** $\dfrac{\partial V}{\partial P} = -\dfrac{kT}{P^2}$, volume decreases with pressure at fixed temperature **b.** $\dfrac{\partial V}{\partial T} = \dfrac{k}{P}$, volume increases with temperature at fixed pressure

c.

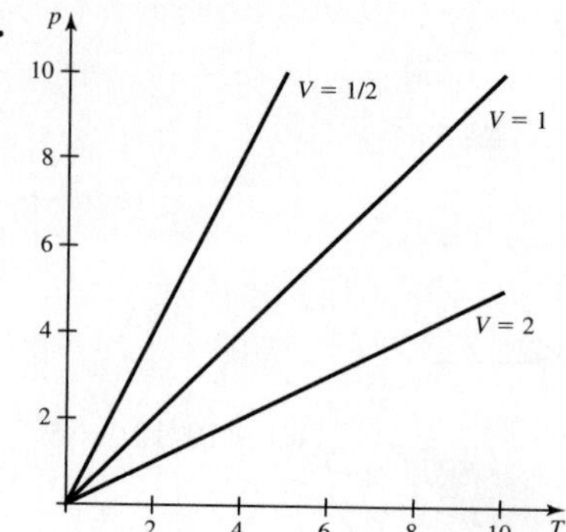

43. a. No **b.** f is not differentiable at $(0, 0)$. **c.** $f_x(0, 0) = f_y(0, 0) = 0$ **d.** f_x and f_y are not continuous at $(0, 0)$. **45. a.** f is continuous at $(0, 0)$. **b.** f is differentiable at $(0, 0)$. **c.** $f_x(0, 0) = f_y(0, 0) = 0$ **d.** f_x and f_y are not continuous at $(0, 0)$. **47. a.** False **b.** False **c.** True
49. $f_x(x, y) = -\dfrac{2x}{1 + (x^2 + y^2)^2}$ $f_y(x, y) = -\dfrac{2y}{1 + (x^2 + y^2)^2}$
51. $h_x(x, y, z) = z(1 + x + 2y)^{z-1}$, $h_y(x, y, z) = 2z(1 + x + 2y)^{z-1}$, $h_z(x, y, z) = (1 + x + 2y)^z\ln(1 + x + 2y)$
53. a. $z_x(x, y) = \dfrac{1}{y^2}$, $z_y(x, y) = \dfrac{-2x}{y^3}$

b.

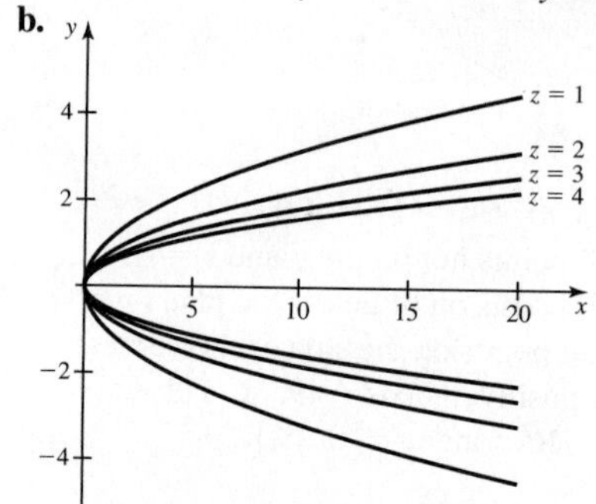

c. z increases as x increases. **d.** z increases as y increases when $y < 0$, z is undefined for $y = 0$, and z decreases as y increases for $y > 0$. **55. a.** $\dfrac{\partial c}{\partial a} = \dfrac{2a - b}{2\sqrt{a^2 + b^2 - ab}}$, $\dfrac{\partial c}{\partial b} = \dfrac{2b - a}{2\sqrt{a^2 + b^2 - ab}}$
b. $\dfrac{\partial c}{\partial a} = \dfrac{2a - b}{2c}$, $\dfrac{\partial c}{\partial b} = \dfrac{2b - a}{2c}$ **c.** $a > \frac{1}{2}b$
57. a. $\varphi_x(x, y) = -\dfrac{2x}{(x^2 + (y - 1)^2)^{3/2}} - \dfrac{x}{(x^2 + (y + 1)^2)^{3/2}}$, $\varphi_y(x, y) = -\dfrac{2(y - 1)}{(x^2 + (y - 1)^2)^{3/2}} - \dfrac{y + 1}{(x^2 + (y + 1)^2)^{3/2}}$ **b.** They both approach zero. **c.** $\varphi_x(0, y) = 0$ **d.** $\varphi_y(x, 0) = \dfrac{1}{(x^2 + 1)^{3/2}}$
59. a. $\dfrac{\partial R}{\partial R_1} = \dfrac{R_2^2}{(R_1 + R_2)^2}$, $\dfrac{\partial R}{\partial R_2} = \dfrac{R_1^2}{(R_1 + R_2)^2}$ **b.** $\dfrac{\partial R}{\partial R_1} = \dfrac{R^2}{R_1^2}$, $\dfrac{\partial R}{\partial R_2} = \dfrac{R^2}{R_2^2}$ **c.** Increase **d.** Decrease
61. $\dfrac{\partial^2 u}{\partial t^2} = -4c^2\cos[2(x + ct)] = c^2\dfrac{\partial^2 u}{\partial x^2}$
63. $\dfrac{\partial^2 u}{\partial t^2} = c^2Af''(x + ct) + c^2Bg''(x - ct) = c^2\dfrac{\partial^2 u}{\partial x^2}$

65. $u_{xx} = 6x \quad u_{yy} = -6x$

67. $u_{xx} = \dfrac{2(x-1)y}{[(x-1)^2 + y^2]^2} - \dfrac{2(x+1)y}{[(x+1)^2 + y^2]^2}$, $u_{yy} = -\dfrac{2(x-1)y}{[(x-1)^2 + y^2]^2} + \dfrac{2(x+1)y}{[(x+1)^2 + y^2]^2}$

69. $u_t = -16e^{-4t} \cos 2x = u_{xx}$ **71.** $u_t = -a^2 Ae^{-a^2 t} \cos ax = u_{xx}$
73. $\varepsilon_1 = \Delta y, \varepsilon_2 = 0$ or $\varepsilon_1 = 0, \varepsilon_2 = \Delta x$ **75. a.** $f_x(x, y) = -h(x)$, $f_y(x, y) = h(y)$ **b.** $f_x(x, y) = yh(xy), f_y(x, y) = xh(xy)$

Section 13.5 Exercises, pp. 816–819

1. One dependent, two intermediate, and one independent variable
3. Multiply each of the partial derivatives of w by the t-derivative of the corresponding function, and add all these expressions.
5.

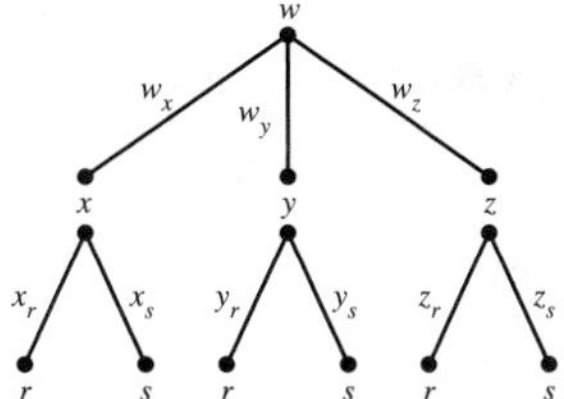

7. $z'(t) = 2t \sin 4t^3 + 12t^4 \cos 4t^3$
9. $w'(t) = -\sin t \sin 3t^4 + 12t^3 \cos t \cos 3t^4$
11. $w'(t) = 20t^4 \sin (t + 1) + 4t^5 \cos (t + 1)$
13. $U'(t) = \dfrac{1 + 2t + 3t^2}{t + t^2 + t^3}$
15. a. $V'(t) = 2\pi r(t)h(t)r'(t) + \pi r(t)^2 h'(t)$ **b.** $V'(t) = 0$ **c.** The volume remains constant. **17.** $z_s = 2s - 3s^2 - 2st + t^2$, $z_t = -s^2 - 2t + 2st + 3t^2$ **19.** $z_s = (t + 1)e^{st+s+t}$, $z_t = (s + 1)e^{st+s+t}$ **21.** $w_s = \dfrac{-2t(t+1)}{(st + s - t)^2}, w_t = \dfrac{2s}{(st + s - t)^2}$
23.

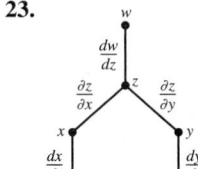

$$\frac{dw}{dt} = \frac{dw}{dz}\left(\frac{\partial z}{\partial x}\frac{dx}{dt} + \frac{\partial z}{\partial y}\frac{dy}{dt}\right)$$

25.

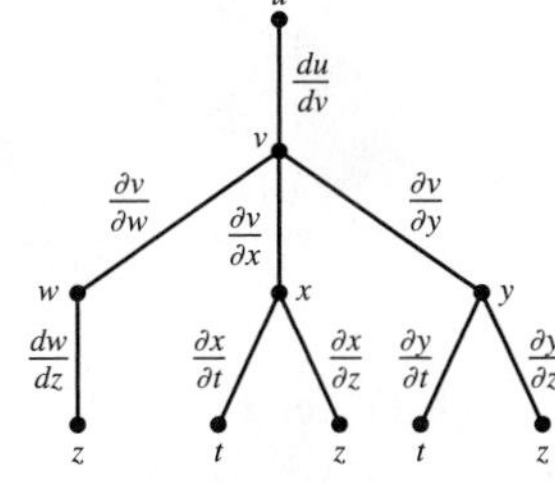

$$\frac{\partial u}{\partial z} = \frac{du}{dv}\left(\frac{\partial v}{\partial w}\frac{dw}{dz} + \frac{\partial v}{\partial x}\frac{\partial x}{\partial z} + \frac{\partial v}{\partial y}\frac{\partial y}{\partial z}\right)$$

27. $\dfrac{dy}{dx} = \dfrac{x}{2y}$
29. $\dfrac{dy}{dx} = -\dfrac{y}{x}$ **31.** $\dfrac{dy}{dx} = -\dfrac{x + y}{2y^3 + x}$ **33.** $\dfrac{\partial s}{\partial x} = \dfrac{2x}{\sqrt{x^2 + y^2}}$, $\dfrac{\partial s}{\partial y} = \dfrac{2y}{\sqrt{x^2 + y^2}}$ **35. a.** False **b.** False

37. $z'(t) = -\dfrac{2t + 2}{x^2} - \dfrac{3t^2}{y^2}$ **39.** $w'(t) = 0$ **41.** $\dfrac{\partial z}{\partial x} = -\dfrac{z^2}{x^2}$
43. a. $w'(t) = af_x + bf_y + cf_z$
b. $w'(t) = ayz + bxz + cxy = 3abct^2$
c. $w'(t) = \sqrt{a^2 + b^2 + c^2}\dfrac{t}{|t|}$
d. $w''(t) = a^2 f_{xx} + b^2 f_{yy} + c^2 f_{zz} + 2abf_{xy} + 2acf_{xz} + 2bcf_{yz}$
45. $\dfrac{\partial z}{\partial x} = -\dfrac{y + z}{x + y}, \dfrac{\partial z}{\partial y} = -\dfrac{x + z}{x + y}$
47. $\dfrac{\partial z}{\partial x} = -\dfrac{yz + 1}{xy - 1}, \dfrac{\partial z}{\partial y} = -\dfrac{xz + 1}{xy - 1}$
49. a. $z'(t) = -2x \sin t + 8y \cos t = 3 \sin 2t$ **b.** $0 < t < \pi/2$ and $\pi < t < 3\pi/2$ **51. a.** $z'(t) = \dfrac{(x + y)e^{-t}}{\sqrt{1 - x^2 - y^2}} = \dfrac{2e^{-2t}}{\sqrt{1 - 2e^{-2t}}}$
b. All $t \geq \frac{1}{2} \ln 2$ **53.** $E'(t) = mx'x'' + my'y'' + mgy' = 0$
55. a. The volume increases. **b.** The volume decreases.
57. a. $\dfrac{\partial P}{\partial V} = -\dfrac{P}{V}, \dfrac{\partial T}{\partial P} = \dfrac{V}{k}, \dfrac{\partial V}{\partial T} = \dfrac{k}{P}$
b. Follows directly from part (a)
59. a. $w'(t) = \dfrac{2t(t^2 + 1)\cos 2t - (t^2 - 1)\sin 2t}{2(t^2 + 1)^2}$
b. Max. value at $t \approx 0.838$, $(x, y, z) \approx (0.669, 0.743, 0.838)$
61. a. $z_x = \dfrac{x}{r}z_r - \dfrac{y}{r^2}z_\theta, z_y = \dfrac{y}{r}z_r + \dfrac{x}{r^2}z_\theta$
b. $z_{xx} = \dfrac{x^2}{r^2}z_{rr} + \dfrac{y^2}{r^4}z_{\theta\theta} - \dfrac{2xy}{r^3}z_{r\theta} + \dfrac{y^2}{r^3}z_r + \dfrac{2xy}{r^4}z_\theta$
c. $z_{yy} = \dfrac{y^2}{r^2}z_{rr} + \dfrac{x^2}{r^4}z_{\theta\theta} + \dfrac{2xy}{r^3}z_{r\theta} + \dfrac{x^2}{r^3}z_r - \dfrac{2xy}{r^4}z_\theta$
d. Add the results from (b) and (c). **63. a.** $\left(\dfrac{\partial z}{\partial x}\right)_y = -\dfrac{F_x}{F_z}$
b. $\left(\dfrac{\partial y}{\partial z}\right)_x = -\dfrac{F_z}{F_y}, \left(\dfrac{\partial x}{\partial y}\right)_z = -\dfrac{F_y}{F_x}$ **c.** Follows from (a) and (b) by multiplication **d.** $\left(\dfrac{\partial w}{\partial x}\right)_{y,z}\left(\dfrac{\partial x}{\partial w}\right)_{x,y}\left(\dfrac{\partial y}{\partial z}\right)_{x,w}\left(\dfrac{\partial x}{\partial y}\right)_{z,w} = 1$
65. a. $\left(\dfrac{\partial w}{\partial x}\right)_y = f_x + f_z\dfrac{dz}{dx} = 18$ **b.** $\left(\dfrac{\partial w}{\partial x}\right)_z = f_x + f_y\dfrac{dy}{dx} = 8$
d. $\left(\dfrac{\partial w}{\partial y}\right)_x = -5, \left(\dfrac{\partial w}{\partial y}\right)_z = 4, \left(\dfrac{\partial w}{\partial z}\right)_x = \dfrac{5}{2}, \left(\dfrac{\partial w}{\partial z}\right)_y = \dfrac{9}{2}$

Section 13.6 Exercises, pp. 828–831

1. Form the dot product between the unit direction vector **u** and the gradient of the function. **3.** Direction of steepest ascent
5. The gradient is orthogonal to the level curves of f.
7. a.

	$(a, b) = (2, 0)$	$(a, b) = (0, 2)$	$(a, b) = (1, 1)$
$\theta = \pi/4$	$-\sqrt{2}$	$-2\sqrt{2}$	$-3\sqrt{2}/2$
$\theta = 3\pi/4$	$\sqrt{2}$	$-2\sqrt{2}$	$-\sqrt{2}/2$
$\theta = 5\pi/4$	$\sqrt{2}$	$2\sqrt{2}$	$3\sqrt{2}/2$

b.

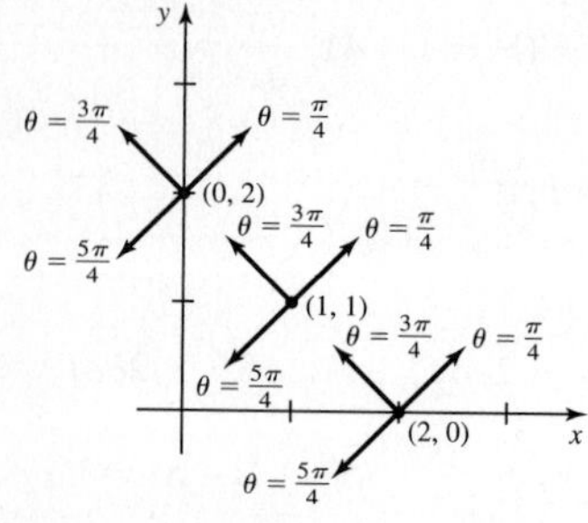

9. $\nabla f(x, y) = \langle 6x, -10y \rangle$, $\nabla f(2, -1) = \langle 12, 10 \rangle$ **11.** $\nabla g(x, y) = \langle 2(x - 4xy - 4y^2), -4x(x + 4y) \rangle$, $\nabla g(-1, 2) = \langle -18, 28 \rangle$ **13.** $\nabla F(x, y) = -2e^{-x^2-2y^2} \langle x, 2y \rangle$, $\nabla F(-1, 2) = 2e^{-9} \langle 1, -4 \rangle$ **15.** $\frac{27}{2} - 6\sqrt{3}$ **17.** $-\frac{2}{\sqrt{5}}$ **19.** 0

21. a. Steepest ascent: $\frac{1}{\sqrt{65}} \langle 1, 8 \rangle$; steepest descent: $-\frac{1}{\sqrt{65}} \langle 1, 8 \rangle$ **b.** $\langle -8, 1 \rangle$ **23. a.** Steepest ascent: $\frac{1}{\sqrt{5}} \langle -2, 1 \rangle$; steepest descent: $\frac{1}{\sqrt{5}} \langle 2, -1 \rangle$ **b.** $\langle 1, 2 \rangle$ **25. a.** Steepest ascent: $\frac{1}{\sqrt{2}} \langle 1, -1 \rangle$; steepest descent: $\frac{1}{\sqrt{2}} \langle -1, 1 \rangle$ **b.** $\langle 1, 1 \rangle$

27. a. $\nabla f(3, 2) = -12\mathbf{i} - 12\mathbf{j}$ **b.** Max increase, $\theta = \frac{5\pi}{4}$; max decrease, $\theta = \frac{\pi}{4}$; no change, $\theta = \frac{3\pi}{4}, \frac{7\pi}{4}$ **c.** $g(\theta) = -12\cos\theta - 12\sin\theta$ **d.** $\theta = \frac{5}{4}\pi, g\left(\frac{5}{4}\pi\right) = 12\sqrt{2}$ **e.** $\nabla f(3, 2) = 12\sqrt{2} \langle \cos\frac{5}{4}\pi, \sin\frac{5}{4}\pi \rangle, |\nabla f(3, 2)| = 12\sqrt{2}$

29. a. $\nabla f(\sqrt{3}, 1) = \frac{\sqrt{6}}{6} \langle \sqrt{3}, 1 \rangle$ **b.** Max increase, $\theta = \frac{\pi}{6}$; max decrease, $\theta = \frac{7\pi}{6}$; no change, $\theta = \frac{2\pi}{3}, \frac{5\pi}{3}$ **c.** $g(\theta) = \frac{\sqrt{2}}{2}\cos\theta + \frac{\sqrt{6}}{6}\sin\theta$ **d.** $\theta = \frac{\pi}{6}, g\left(\frac{\pi}{6}\right) = \frac{\sqrt{6}}{3}$ **e.** $\nabla f(\sqrt{3}, 1) = \frac{\sqrt{6}}{3} \langle \cos\frac{\pi}{6}, \sin\frac{\pi}{6} \rangle, |\nabla f(\sqrt{3}, 1)| = \frac{\sqrt{6}}{3}$

31. a. $\nabla F(-1, 0) = \frac{2}{e}\mathbf{i}$ **b.** Max increase, $\theta = 0$; max decrease, $\theta = \pi$; no change, $\theta = \pm\frac{\pi}{2}$ **c.** $g(\theta) = \frac{2}{e}\cos\theta$ **d.** $\theta = 0, g(0) = \frac{2}{e}$ **e.** $\nabla F(-1, 0) = \frac{2}{e} \langle \cos 0, \sin 0 \rangle, |\nabla F(-1, 0)| = \frac{2}{e}$

33.

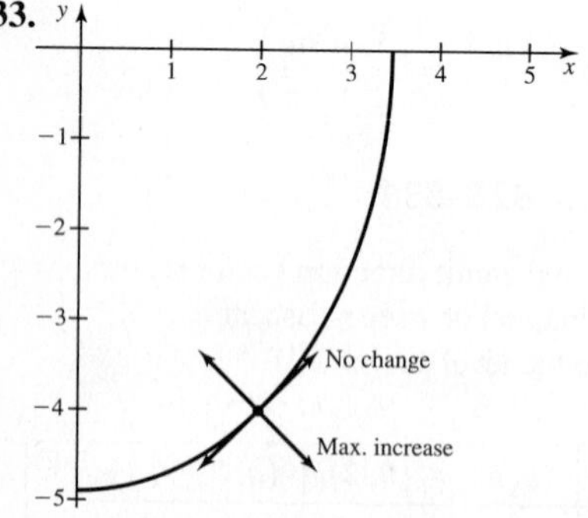

35.

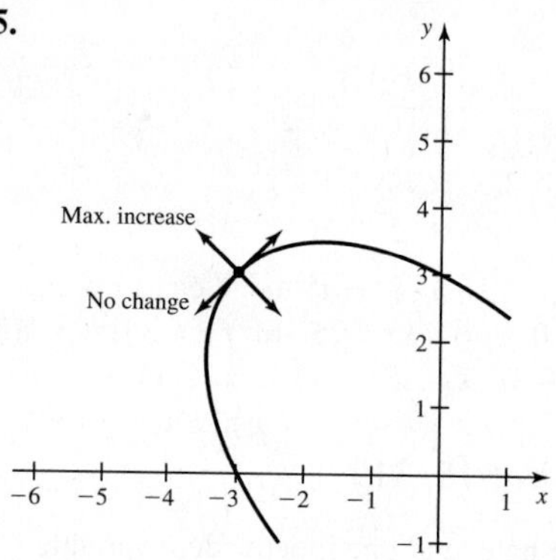

37. $y' = 0$ **39.** Vertical tangent **41.** $y' = -2/\sqrt{3}$ **43.** Vertical tangent **45. a.** $\nabla f = \langle 1, 0 \rangle$ **b.** $x = 4 - t, y = 4, t \geq 0$ **47. a.** $\nabla f = \langle -2x, -4y \rangle$ **b.** $y = x^2, x \geq 1$ **49. a.** $\nabla f(x, y, z) = 2x\mathbf{i} + 4y\mathbf{j} + 8z\mathbf{k}, \nabla f(1, 0, 4) = 2\mathbf{i} + 32\mathbf{k}$ **b.** $\frac{1}{\sqrt{257}}(\mathbf{i} + 16\mathbf{k})$ **c.** $2\sqrt{257}$ **d.** $17\sqrt{2}$ **51. a.** $\nabla f(x, y, z) = 4yz\mathbf{i} + 4xz\mathbf{j} + 4xy\mathbf{k}, \nabla f(1,-1,-1) = 4\mathbf{i} - 4\mathbf{j} - 4\mathbf{k}$ **b.** $\frac{1}{\sqrt{3}}(\mathbf{i} - \mathbf{j} - \mathbf{k})$ **c.** $4\sqrt{3}$ **d.** $\frac{4}{\sqrt{3}}$

53. a. $\nabla f(x, y, z) = \cos(x + 2y - z)(\mathbf{i} + 2\mathbf{j} - \mathbf{k})$ $\nabla f\left(\frac{\pi}{6}, \frac{\pi}{6}, -\frac{\pi}{6}\right) = -\frac{1}{2}\mathbf{i} - \mathbf{j} + \frac{1}{2}\mathbf{k}$ **b.** $\frac{1}{\sqrt{6}}(-\mathbf{i} - 2\mathbf{j} + \mathbf{k})$ **c.** $\sqrt{6}/2$ **d.** $-\frac{1}{2}$

55. a. $\nabla f(x, y, z) = \frac{2}{1 + x^2 + y^2 + z^2}(x\mathbf{i} + y\mathbf{j} + z\mathbf{k})$, $\nabla f(1, 1, -1) = \frac{1}{2}\mathbf{i} + \frac{1}{2}\mathbf{j} - \frac{1}{2}\mathbf{k}$ **b.** $\frac{1}{\sqrt{3}}(\mathbf{i} + \mathbf{j} - \mathbf{k})$ **c.** $\frac{\sqrt{3}}{2}$ **d.** $\frac{5}{6}$

57. a. False **b.** False **c.** False **d.** True **59.** $\pm\frac{1}{\sqrt{5}}(\mathbf{i} - 2\mathbf{j})$

61. $\pm\frac{1}{\sqrt{2}}(\mathbf{i} + \mathbf{j})$ **63.** $x = x_0 + at, y = y_0 + bt$

65. a. $\nabla f(x, y, z) = \langle 2x, 2y, 2z \rangle, \nabla f(1, 1, 1) = \langle 2, 2, 2 \rangle$ **b.** $x + y + z = 3$ **67. a.** $\nabla f(x, y, z) = e^{x+y-z} \langle 1, 1, -1 \rangle$, $\nabla f(1, 1, 2) = \langle 1, 1, -1 \rangle$ **b.** $x + y - z = 0$

69. a.

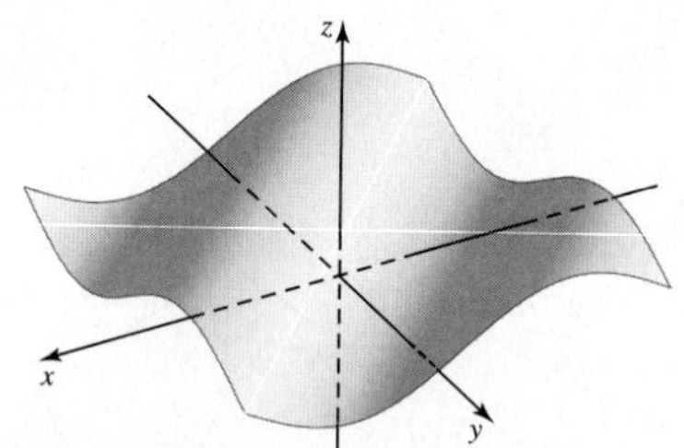

b. $\mathbf{v} = \pm\langle 1, 1 \rangle$ **c.** $\mathbf{v} = \pm\langle 1, -1 \rangle$

73. $\langle u, v \rangle = \langle \pi \cos \pi x \sin 2\pi y, 2\pi \sin \pi x \cos 2\pi y \rangle$

77. $\nabla f(x, y) = \frac{1}{(x^2 + y^2)^2} \langle y^2 - x^2 - 2xy, x^2 - y^2 - 2xy \rangle$

79. $\nabla f(x, y, z) = -\frac{1}{\sqrt{25 - x^2 - y^2 - z^2}} \langle x, y, z \rangle$

81. $\nabla f(x, y, z) = \dfrac{(y + xz)\langle 1, z, y\rangle - (x + yz)\langle z, 1, x\rangle}{(y + xz)^2}$

$= \dfrac{1}{(y + xz)^2}\langle y(1 - z^2), x(z^2 - 1), y^2 - x^2\rangle$

Section 13.7 Exercises, pp. 838–842

1. The gradient of f is a multiple of $\mathbf{n}$. **3.** $F_x(a, b, c)(x - a) + F_y(a, b, c)(y - b) + F_z(a, b, c)(z - c) = 0$ **5.** Multiply the change in x by $f_x(a, b)$ and the change in y by $f_y(a, b)$, and add both terms to f. **7.** $dz = f_x(a, b)dx + f_y(a, b)dy$ **9.** $x + y + z = 6$ and $16x + 13y + 9z + 72 = 0$ **11.** $x + \frac{1}{2}y + \sqrt{3}z = 2 + \frac{\sqrt{3}\pi}{6}$ and $-\frac{1}{2}x + y + \sqrt{3}z = \frac{5\sqrt{3}\pi}{6} - 2$ **13.** $\frac{1}{2}x + \frac{2}{3}y + 2\sqrt{3}z = -2$ and $x - 2y + 2\sqrt{14}z = 2$ **15.** $z = -8x - 4y + 16$ and $z = 4x + 2y + 7$ **17.** $z = 8x - 4y - 4$ and $z = -x - y - 1$ **19.** $z = \frac{7}{25}x - \frac{1}{25}y - \frac{2}{5}$ and $z = -\frac{7}{25}x + \frac{1}{25}y + \frac{6}{5}$ **21. a.** $L(x, y) = 4x + y - 6$ **b.** $L(2.1, 2.99) = 5.39$ **23. a.** $L(x, y) = -6x - 4y + 7$ **b.** $L(3.1, -1.04) = -7.44$ **25. a.** $L(x, y) = x + y$ **b.** $L(0.1, -0.2) = -0.1$ **27.** $dz = -6dx - 5dy = -0.1$ **29.** $dz = dx + dy = 0.05$ **31. a.** The surface area decreases. **b.** Impossible to tell **c.** $dS \approx 5.3$ **d.** $dS \approx 33.95$ **e.** $RdR = rdr$ **33.** $\frac{dA}{A} = 3.5\%$ **35.** $dw = (y^2 + 2xz)dx + (2xy + z^2)dy + (x^2 + 2yz)dz$ **37.** $dw = \frac{dx}{y + z} - \frac{u + x}{(y + z)^2}dy - \frac{u + x}{(y + z)^2}dz + \frac{du}{y + z}$ **39. a.** $dc = 0.035$ **b.** When $\theta = \frac{\pi}{20}$ **41. a.** True **b.** True **c.** False **43.** $z = \frac{1}{2}x + \frac{1}{2}y + \frac{\pi}{4} - 1$ **45.** $\frac{1}{6}(x - \pi) + \frac{\pi}{6}(y - 1) + \pi\left(z - \frac{1}{6}\right) = 0$ **47.** $(1, -1, 1)$ and $(1, -1, -1)$ **49.** Points with $x = 0, \pm\frac{\pi}{2}, \pm\pi$ and $y = \pm\frac{\pi}{2}$, or points with $x = \pm\frac{\pi}{4}, \pm\frac{3\pi}{4}$ and $y = 0, \pm\pi$ **51. a.** $dS = 0.749$ **b.** More sensitive to changes of r **53. a.** $dA = \frac{2}{1225} = 0.00163$ **b.** No. The batting average increases more if he gets a hit than it would decrease if he fails to get a hit. **c.** Yes. The answer depends on whether A is less than 0.500 or greater than 0.500. **55. a.** $dV = \frac{21}{5000} = 0.0042$ **b.** $\frac{dV}{V} = -4\%$ **c.** $2p\%$ **57. a.** $f_r = n(1 - r)^{n-1}, f_n = -(1 - r)^n \ln(1 - r)$ **b.** $\Delta P \approx 0.027$, **c.** $\Delta P \approx 2 \times 10^{-20}$ **59.** $dR = 7/540 \approx 0.0130$ **61. a.** Apply the Chain Rule. **b.** Follows directly from (a) **c.** $d(\ln(xy)) = \frac{dx}{x} + \frac{dy}{y}$ **d.** $d(\ln(x/y)) = \frac{dx}{x} - \frac{dy}{y}$ **e.** $\frac{df}{f} = \frac{dx_1}{x_1} + \frac{dx_2}{x_2} + \cdots + \frac{dx_n}{x_n}$

Section 13.8 Exercises, pp. 849–852

1. It is locally the highest point on the surface, cannot get to a higher point in any direction. **3.** The partial derivatives are both zero, or do not exist. **5.** The discriminant is a determinant; it is defined as $D(a, b) = f_{xx}(a, b)f_{yy}(a, b) - f_{xy}^2(a, b)$. **7.** f has an absolute minimum value at (a, b) if $f(x, y) \geq f(a, b)$ for all (x, y) in the domain of f. **9.** $(0, 0)$ **11.** $\left(\frac{2}{3}, 4\right)$ **13.** $(0, 0), (2, 2)$, and $(-2, -2)$ **15.** Local min at $(0, 0)$ **17.** Saddle point at $(0, 0)$ **19.** Saddle point at $(0, 0)$, local min at $(1, 1)$ and at $(-1, -1)$ **21.** Local min at $(2, 0)$ **23.** Saddle point at $(0, 0)$, local max at $\left(\frac{1}{\sqrt{2}}, \frac{1}{\sqrt{2}}\right)$ and $\left(-\frac{1}{\sqrt{2}}, -\frac{1}{\sqrt{2}}\right)$, local min at $\left(\frac{1}{\sqrt{2}}, -\frac{1}{\sqrt{2}}\right)$ and $\left(-\frac{1}{\sqrt{2}}, \frac{1}{\sqrt{2}}\right)$ **25.** Local max at $\left(\frac{1}{\sqrt{2}}, -\frac{1}{\sqrt{2}}\right)$, local min at $\left(-\frac{1}{\sqrt{2}}, \frac{1}{\sqrt{2}}\right)$ **27.** Saddle point at $(0, 0)$ **29.** Height = 32 in, base is 16 in × 16 in; volume is 8192 in^3 **31.** 2 m × 2 m × 1 m **33.** Critical point at $(0, 0)$, $D(0, 0) = 0$, absolute min **35.** Critical points along the x- and y-axes, all absolute min **37.** Absolute min: $0 = f(0, 1)$; absolute max: $9 = f(0, -2)$ **39.** Absolute min: $4 = f(0, 0)$; absolute max: $7 = f(\pm 1, \pm 1)$ **41.** Absolute min: $-5 = f(-2, 1)$; absolute max: $16 + 8\sqrt{5} = f\left(\frac{8}{\sqrt{5}}, -\frac{4}{\sqrt{5}}\right)$ **43.** Absolute min: $-2 = f\left(-1, -\frac{1}{2}\right)$; absolute max: $24.25 = f(3.969, 0.125)$ **45.** Absolute min: $-4 = f(0, 0)$; no absolute max on R **47.** Absolute max: $2 = f(0, 0)$; no absolute min on R **49.** $P\left(-\frac{5}{3}, \frac{4}{3}, \frac{13}{3}\right)$ **51.** $P\left(\frac{47}{24}, \frac{47}{12}, \frac{235}{24}\right)$ **53. a.** True **b.** False **c.** True **d.** True **55.** Local minimum at $(0.3, -0.3)$, saddle point at $(0, 0)$ **57.** $P\left(\frac{4}{3}, \frac{2}{3}, \frac{4}{3}\right)$ **59.** $x = y = z = \frac{200}{3}$ in all four parts **61. a.** $P\left(1, \frac{1}{3}\right)$ **b.** $P\left(\frac{1}{3}(x_1 + x_2 + x_3), \frac{1}{3}(y_1 + y_2 + y_3)\right)$ **c.** $P(\bar{x}, \bar{y})$, where $\bar{x} = \frac{1}{n}\sum_{k=1}^{n} x_k$ and $\bar{y} = \frac{1}{n}\sum_{k=1}^{n} y_k$ **d.** $d(x, y) = \sqrt{x^2 + y^2} + \sqrt{(x - 2)^2 + y^2} + \sqrt{(x - 1)^2 + (y - 1)^2}$. The absolute min of this function is $1 + \sqrt{3} = f\left(1, \frac{1}{\sqrt{3}}\right)$. **65.** $y = \frac{22}{13}x + \frac{46}{13}$ **67.** $a = b = c = 3$ **69. a.** $\nabla d_1(x, y) = \frac{x - x_1}{d_1(x, y)}\mathbf{i} + \frac{y - y_1}{d_1(x, y)}\mathbf{j}$ **b.** $\nabla d_2(x, y) = \frac{x - x_2}{d_2(x, y)}\mathbf{i} + \frac{y - y_2}{d_2(x, y)}\mathbf{j}$, $\nabla d_3(x, y) = \frac{x - x_3}{d_3(x, y)}\mathbf{i} + \frac{y - y_3}{d_3(x, y)}\mathbf{j}$ **c.** Follows from $\nabla f = \nabla d_1 + \nabla d_2 + \nabla d_3$ **d.** Three unit vectors add to zero. **e.** P is the vertex at the large angle. **f.** $P(0.255457, 0.304504)$ **71. a.** Local max at $(1, 0), (-1, 0)$ **b.** $(1, 0)$ and $(-1, 0)$

Section 13.9 Exercises, pp. 858–860

1. The level curve of f must be tangential to the curve $g = 0$ at the optimal point; thus, the gradients are parallel. **3.** $2x = 2\lambda, 2y = 3\lambda, 2z = -5\lambda, 2x + 3y - 5z + 4 = 0$

5. Max value: $2\sqrt{5} = f\left(\frac{2}{\sqrt{5}}, \frac{4}{\sqrt{5}}\right)$; min value: $-2\sqrt{5} = f\left(-\frac{2}{\sqrt{5}}, -\frac{4}{\sqrt{5}}\right)$ **7.** Max value: $e^8 = f(2, 2)$ **9.** Min value: $-16 = f(\pm 2, 0)$; max value: $2 = f(0, \pm\sqrt{2})$ **11.** Max value: $2\sqrt{11} = f\left(\frac{2}{\sqrt{11}}, \frac{6}{\sqrt{11}}, -\frac{2}{\sqrt{11}}\right)$; min value: $-2\sqrt{11} = f\left(-\frac{2}{\sqrt{11}}, -\frac{6}{\sqrt{11}}, \frac{2}{\sqrt{11}}\right)$ **13.** Max value: $\frac{15{,}625\sqrt{6}}{144} = 265.8 = f\left(\frac{5}{\sqrt{6}}, \frac{5}{\sqrt{3}}, \frac{5}{2}\right)$; Min value: $-\frac{15{,}625\sqrt{6}}{144} = -265.8 = f\left(-\frac{5}{\sqrt{6}}, \frac{5}{\sqrt{3}}, \frac{5}{2}\right)$ **15.** Min value: $6\sqrt[3]{2} = f(\pm\sqrt[3]{4}, \pm\sqrt[3]{4}, \pm\sqrt[3]{4})$; no upper bound **17.** 18 in × 18 in × 36 in **19.** Min distance: 0.6731; max distance: 1.1230 **21.** Dimension: $18/\sqrt{13} \times 8/\sqrt{13}$; vertices at $\left(\pm\frac{9}{\sqrt{13}}, \pm\frac{4}{\sqrt{13}}\right)$ **23.** $P\left(1, \frac{1}{2}, -3\right)$ **25.** Min distance: $\sqrt{38 - 6\sqrt{29}}$, max distance: $\sqrt{38 + 6\sqrt{29}}$ **27.** $\ell = 3$ and $g = \frac{3}{2}$; $U = 15\sqrt{2}$ **29.** $\ell = \frac{16}{5}$ and $g = 1$; $U = 20.287$ **31. a.** True **b.** False **33.** $\frac{\sqrt{6}}{3}\text{ m} \times \frac{\sqrt{6}}{3}\text{ m} \times \frac{\sqrt{6}}{6}\text{ m}$ **35.** $2 \times 1 \times \frac{2}{3}$ **37.** $P\left(\frac{4}{3}, \frac{2}{3}, \frac{4}{3}\right)$ **39.** Min value: $-\frac{7 + \sqrt{661}}{2}$; max value: $\frac{\sqrt{661} - 7}{2}$ **41.** Min value: 0; max value: $6 + 4\sqrt{2}$ **43.** Min value: 1; max value: 8 **45.** $K = 7.5$ and $L = 5$ **47.** $K = aB/P$ and $L = (1 - a)B/q$ **49.** Max: 8 **51.** Max: $\sqrt{a_1^2 + a_2^2 + a_3^2 + \cdots + a_n^2}$ **53. a.** Gradients are perpendicular to level surfaces. **b.** If the gradient was not in the plane spanned by ∇g and ∇h, f could be increased (decreased) by moving the point slightly. **c.** ∇f is a linear combination of ∇g and ∇h, since it belongs to the plane spanned by these two vectors. **d.** The gradient condition from part (c), as well as the constraints, must be satisfied. **55.** Min: $2 - 4\sqrt{2}$; max: $2 + 4\sqrt{2}$ **57.** Min: $\frac{5}{4} = f\left(\frac{1}{2}, 0, 1\right)$; max: $\frac{125}{36} = f\left(-\frac{5}{6}, 0, \frac{5}{3}\right)$

Chapter 13 Review Exercises, pp. 861–864

1. a. False **b.** False **c.** False **d.** False **e.** True **3. a.** $18x - 9y + 2z = 6$ **b.** $x = \frac{1}{3}, y = -\frac{2}{3}, z = 3$ **c.**

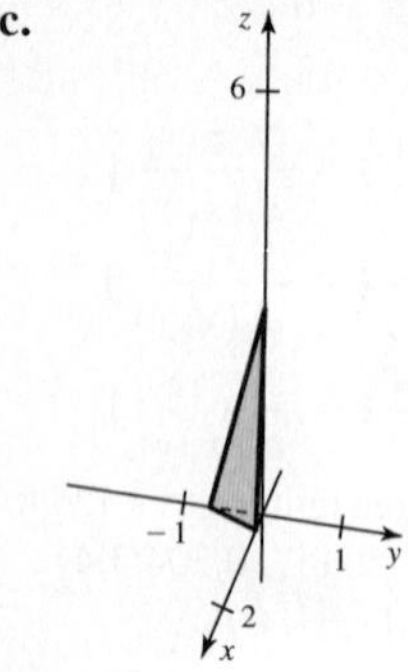

5. $x = t, y = 12 - 9t, z = -6 + 6t$ **7.** $3x + y + 7z = 4$ **9. a.** Hyperbolic paraboloid **b.** $y^2 = 4x^2, z = \frac{x^2}{36}, z = -\frac{y^2}{144}$ **c.** $x = y = z = 0$ **d.**

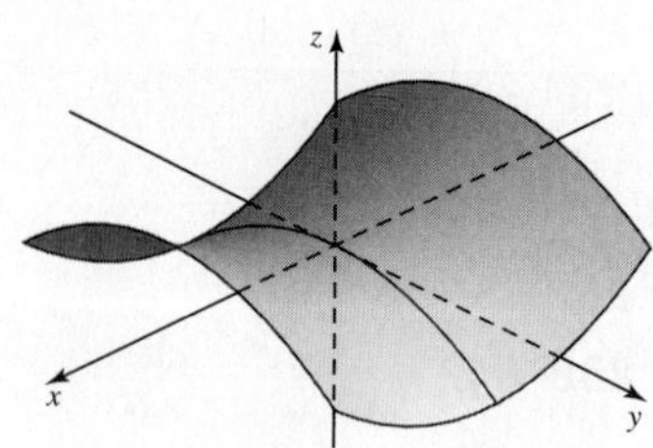

11. a. Elliptic cone **b.** $y^2 = 4x^2$, the xz-trace reduces to the origin, $y^2 = \frac{z^2}{25}$. **c.** Origin **d.**

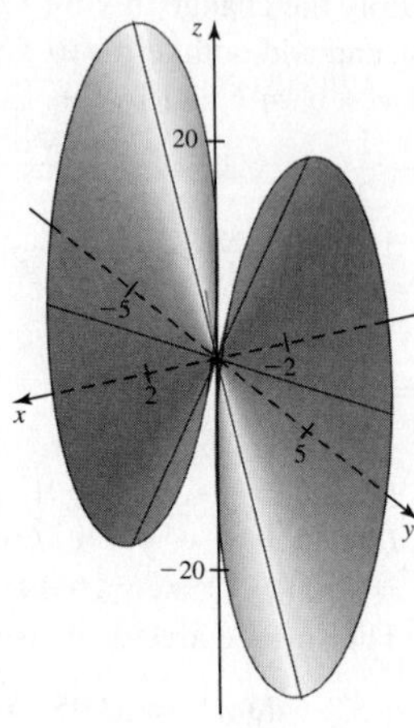

13. a. Elliptic paraboloid **b.** Origin, $z = \frac{x^2}{16}, z = \frac{y^2}{36}$ **c.** Origin **d.**

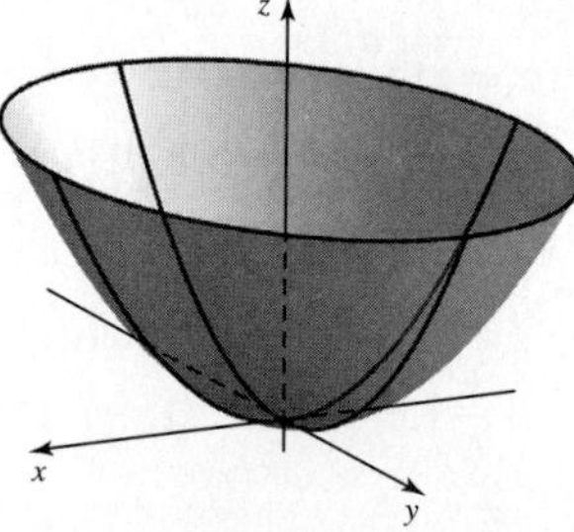

15. a. Hyperboloid of one sheet **b.** $y^2 - 2x^2 = 1, 4z^2 - 2x^2 = 1, y^2 + 4z^2 = 1$ **c.** No x- intercept, $y = \pm 1, z = \pm\frac{1}{2}$ **d.**

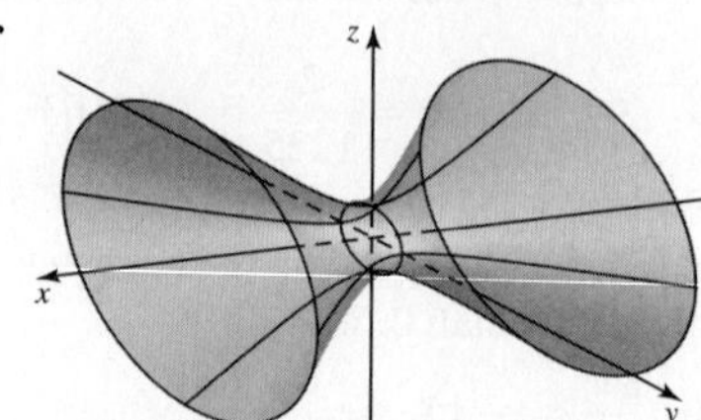

17. a. Hyperboloid of one sheet **b.** $\frac{x^2}{4} + \frac{y^2}{16} = 4, \frac{x^2}{4} - z^2 = 4, \frac{y^2}{16} - z^2 = 4$ **c.** $x = \pm 4, y = \pm 8$, no z-intercept

d.

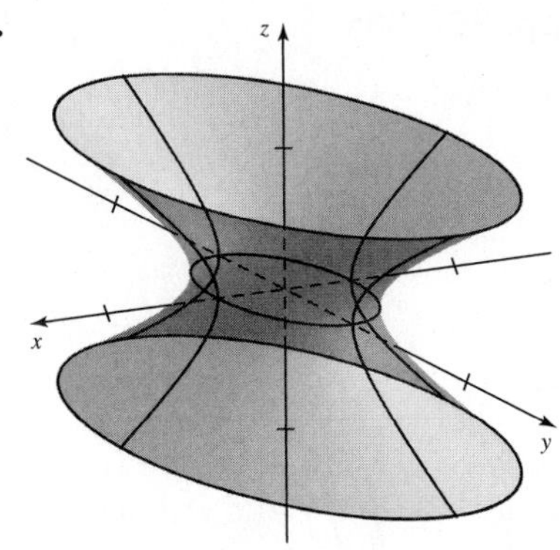

19. a. Ellipsoid **b.** $\dfrac{x^2}{4} + \dfrac{y^2}{16} = 4, \dfrac{x^2}{4} + z^2 = 4, \dfrac{y^2}{16} + z^2 = 4$
c. $x = \pm 4, y = \pm 8, z = \pm 2$ **d.**

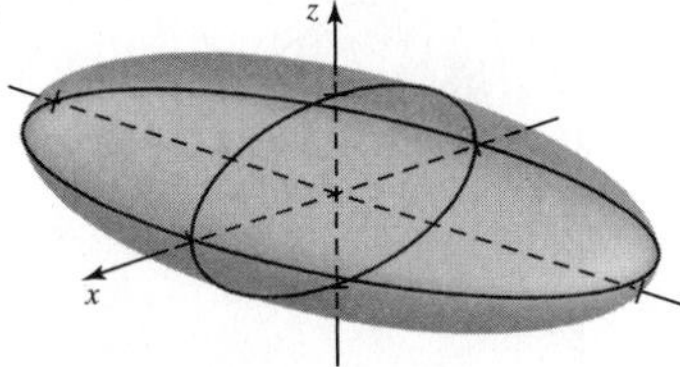

21. a. Elliptic cone **b.** The xy-trace reduces to the origin, $\dfrac{x^2}{9} = \dfrac{z^2}{64}, \dfrac{y^2}{49} = \dfrac{z^2}{64}$. **c.** Origin **d.**

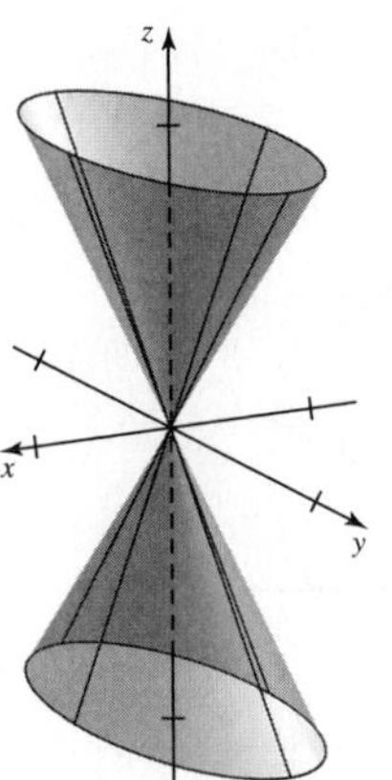

23. $D = \{(x, y): (x, y) \neq (0, 0)\}$

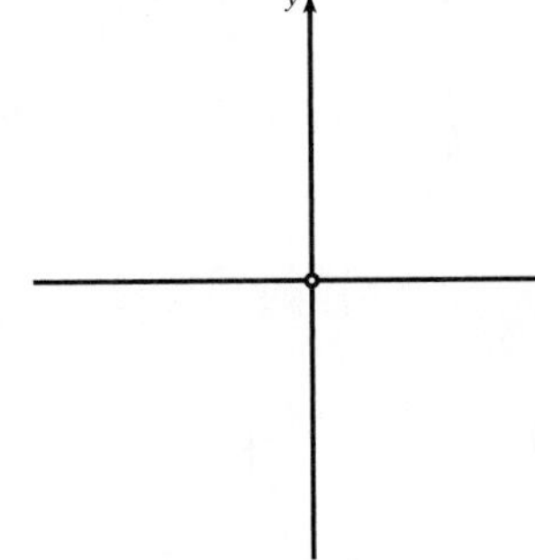

25. $D = \{(x, y): x \geq y^2\}$

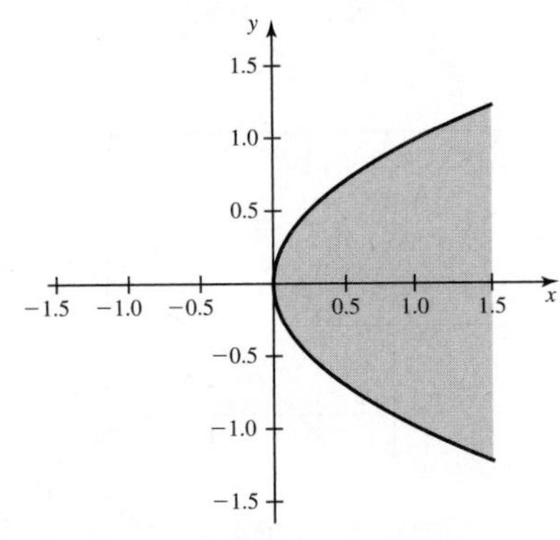

27. a. A **b.** D **c.** C **d.** B **29.**

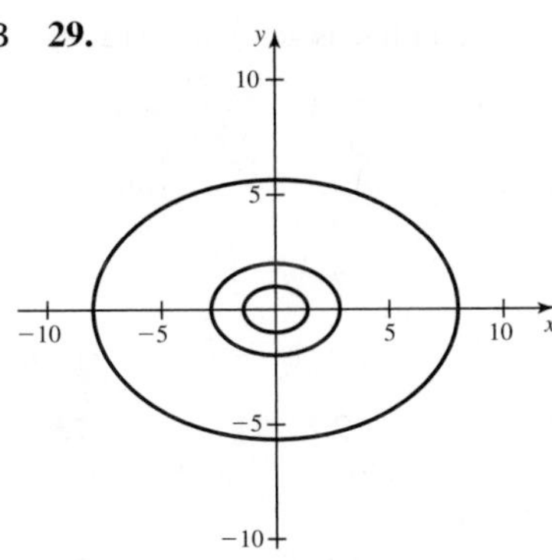

31. 2 **33.** $\frac{2}{3}$ **35.** 4 **37.** $\dfrac{\partial}{\partial x}[xye^{xy}] = y(1 + xy)e^{xy}$, $\dfrac{\partial}{\partial y}[xye^{xy}] = x(1 + xy)e^{xy}$ **39.** $f_x(x, y, z) = e^{x+2y+3z}$, $f_y(x, y, z) = 2e^{x+2y+3z}, f_z(x, y, z) = 3e^{x+2y+3z}$

41. $\dfrac{\partial^2 u}{\partial x^2} = 6y = -\dfrac{\partial^2 u}{\partial y^2}$ **43. a.** V increases with R if r is fixed, $V_R > 0$; V decreases if r increases and R is fixed, $V_r < 0$.
b. $V_r = -4\pi r^2, V_R = 4\pi R^2$ **c.** The volume increases more if R is increased. **45.** $w'(t) = -\dfrac{\cos t \sin t}{\sqrt{1 + \cos^2 t}}$

47. $w_r = \dfrac{2xst + 2y}{x^2 + y^2 + 1} = \dfrac{2rs^2t^2 + 2(r + s + t)}{(rst)^2 + (r + s + t)^2 + 1}$;
$w_s = \dfrac{2xrt + 2y}{x^2 + y^2 + 1} = \dfrac{2r^2st^2 + 2(r + s + t)}{(rst)^2 + (r + s + t)^2 + 1}$;
$w_t = \dfrac{2xrs + 2y}{x^2 + y^2 + 1} = \dfrac{2r^2s^2t + 2(r + s + t)}{(rst)^2 + (r + s + t)^2 + 1}$

49. $\dfrac{dy}{dx} = -\dfrac{2xy}{2y^2 + (x^2 + y^2)\ln(x^2 + y^2)}$

51. a. $z'(t) = -24 \sin t \cos t = -12 \sin(2t)$ **b.** $z'(t) > 0$ for $\dfrac{\pi}{2} < t < \pi$ and $\dfrac{3\pi}{2} < t < 2\pi$

53.

	$(a, b) = (0, 0)$	$(a, b) = (2, 0)$	$(a, b) = (1, 1)$
$\theta = \pi/4$	0	$4\sqrt{2}$	$-2\sqrt{2}$
$\theta = 3\pi/4$	0	$-4\sqrt{2}$	$-6\sqrt{2}$
$\theta = 5\pi/4$	0	$-4\sqrt{2}$	$2\sqrt{2}$

55. $\nabla h(x, y) = \dfrac{x}{\sqrt{2 + x^2 + 2y^2}}\mathbf{i} + \dfrac{2y}{\sqrt{2 + x^2 + 2y^2}}\mathbf{j}$, $\nabla h(2, 1) = \dfrac{\sqrt{2}}{2}\mathbf{i} + \dfrac{\sqrt{2}}{2}\mathbf{j}, D_u(f)(2, 1) = \dfrac{7\sqrt{2}}{10}$

57. $\nabla f(x, y, z) = \cos(x + 2y - z)\,\mathbf{i} + 2\cos(x + 2y - z)\,\mathbf{j} - \cos(x + 2y - z)\,\mathbf{k}, \nabla f\left(\dfrac{\pi}{6}, \dfrac{\pi}{6}, -\dfrac{\pi}{6}\right) = -\dfrac{1}{2}\mathbf{i} - \mathbf{j} + \dfrac{1}{2}\mathbf{k}$, $D_u(f)\left(\dfrac{\pi}{6}, \dfrac{\pi}{6}, -\dfrac{\pi}{6}\right) = -\dfrac{1}{2}$

59. a. Steepest ascent: $\mathbf{u} = \dfrac{\sqrt{2}}{2}\mathbf{i} - \dfrac{\sqrt{2}}{2}\mathbf{j}$;
steepest descent: $\mathbf{u} = -\dfrac{\sqrt{2}}{2}\mathbf{i} + \dfrac{\sqrt{2}}{2}\mathbf{j}$
b. No change: $\mathbf{u} = \pm\left(\dfrac{\sqrt{2}}{2}\mathbf{i} + \dfrac{\sqrt{2}}{2}\mathbf{j}\right)$

61. Tangent line is vertical, $\nabla f(2, 0) = -8\mathbf{i}$ **63.** $E = \dfrac{kx}{x^2 + y^2}\mathbf{i} + \dfrac{ky}{x^2 + y^2}\mathbf{j}$
65. $16x + 2y + z - 8 = 0$ and $8x + y + 8z + 16 = 0$
67. $z = \ln 3 + \dfrac{2}{3}(x - 1) + \dfrac{1}{3}(y - 2);$
$z = \ln 3 - \dfrac{1}{3}(x + 2) - \dfrac{2}{3}(y + 1)$ **69.** $L(x, y) = x + 5y,$
$L(1.95, 0.05) = 2.2$ **71.** -4% **73. a.** $dV = -0.1\pi \text{ m}^3$
b. $dS = -0.05\pi \text{ m}^2$ **75.** Saddle point: $(0, 0)$; local min: $(2, -2)$
77. Saddle points: $(0, 0)$ and $(-2, 2)$; local max: $(0, 2)$; local min: $(-2, 0)$ **79.** Absolute min: $-1 = f(1, 1) = f(-1, -1)$; absolute max: $49 = f(2, -2) = f(-2, 2)$
81. Max: $(1 + 2\sqrt[3]{2})^{3/4}$; min: $-(1 + 2\sqrt[3]{2})^{3/4}$.
83. Max: $f\left(\dfrac{\sqrt{6}}{6}, \dfrac{\sqrt{6}}{3}, -\dfrac{\sqrt{6}}{6}\right) = \sqrt{6}$
min: $f\left(-\dfrac{\sqrt{6}}{6}, -\dfrac{\sqrt{6}}{3}, \dfrac{\sqrt{6}}{6}\right) = -\sqrt{6}$
85. $\dfrac{2a^2}{\sqrt{a^2 + b^2}}$ by $\dfrac{2b^2}{\sqrt{a^2 + b^2}}$
87. $x = \dfrac{1}{2} + \dfrac{\sqrt{10}}{20}, y = \dfrac{3}{2} + \dfrac{3\sqrt{10}}{20} = 3x, z = \dfrac{1}{2} + \dfrac{\sqrt{10}}{2} = \sqrt{10}x$

CHAPTER 14

Section 14.1 Exercises, pp. 872–875

1. $\int_0^2 \int_1^3 xy\, dy\, dx$ or $\int_1^3 \int_0^2 xy\, dx\, dy$ **3.** $\int_{-2}^4 \int_1^5 f(x, y)\, dy\, dx$ or $\int_1^5 \int_{-2}^4 f(x, y)\, dx\, dy$ **5.** $\frac{32}{3}$ **7.** 4 **9.** $\frac{224}{9}$ **11.** $10 - 2e$
13. $\frac{117}{2} = 58.5$ **15.** $\frac{4}{3}$ **17.** $\dfrac{9 - e^2}{2}$ **19.** $\frac{4}{11}$ **21.** $\dfrac{e^{(\ln 2)^3} - (\ln 2)^3 - 1}{3}$
23. $\ln \frac{5}{3}$ **25.** $1/(2 \ln 2)$ **27.** $8/3$ **29. a.** True **b.** False **c.** True
31. a. 1475 **b.** The sum of products of population densities and areas is a Riemann sum. **33.** 60

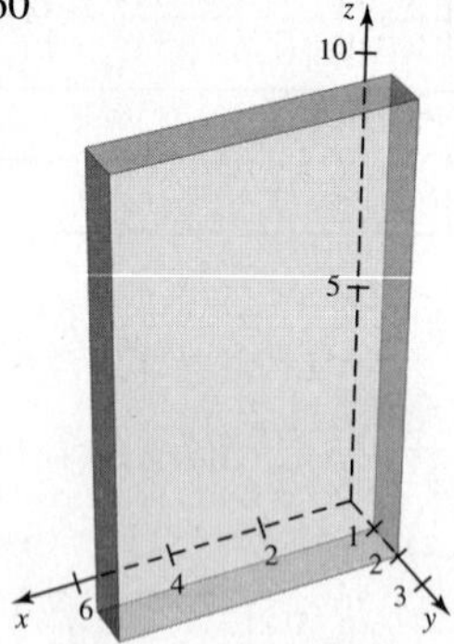

35. $\dfrac{e^2 - 1}{2}\ln(e + 1) - \dfrac{1}{2}(e^2 - e + 1)$ **37.** $10\sqrt{5} - 4\sqrt{2} - 14$
39. 3 **41.** 136 **43.** $a = \pi/6, 5\pi/6$ **45.** $a = \sqrt{6}$
47. a. $\frac{1}{2}\pi^2 + \pi$ **b.** $\frac{1}{2}\pi^2 + \pi$ **c.** $\frac{1}{2}\pi^2 + 2$
49. $\int_c^d \int_a^b f(x)\, dy\, dx = (c - d)\int_a^b f(x)\, dx$. The integral is the area of the cross section of S. **51.** $f(a, b) - f(a, 0) - f(0, b) + f(0, 0)$
53. Use substitution ($u = x^r y^s$ and then $v = x^r$).

Section 14.2 Exercises, pp. 882–885

1.

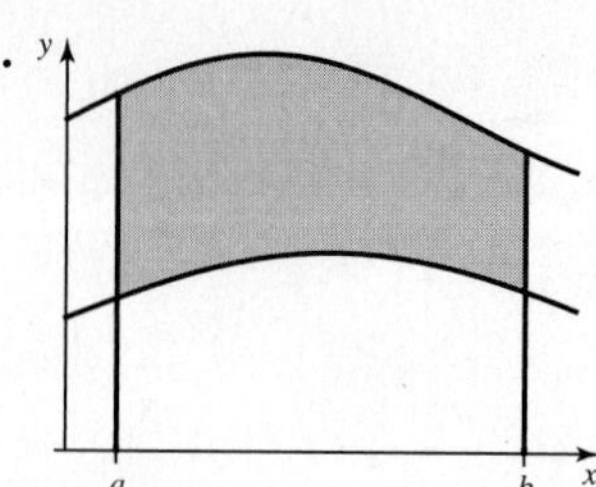

3. $dx\, dy$ **5.** $\int_0^1 \int_{x^2}^{\sqrt{x}} f(x, y)\, dy\, dx$ **7.** $\int_0^2 \int_{x^3}^{4x} f(x, y)\, dy\, dx$

9.

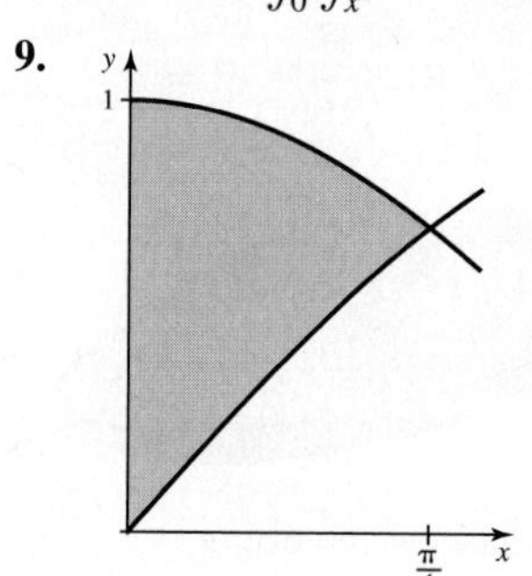

$\int_0^{\pi/4} \int_{\sin x}^{\cos x} f(x, y)\, dy\, dx$

11.

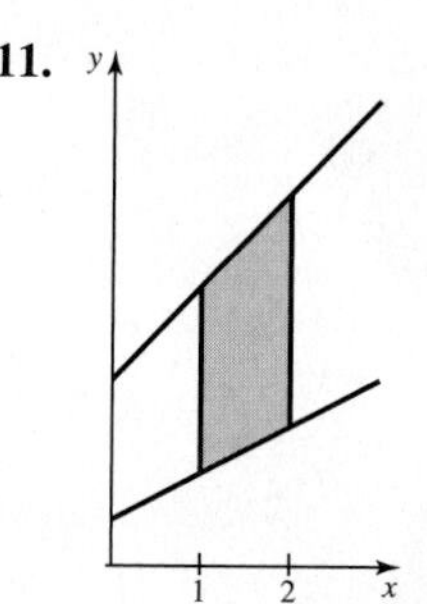

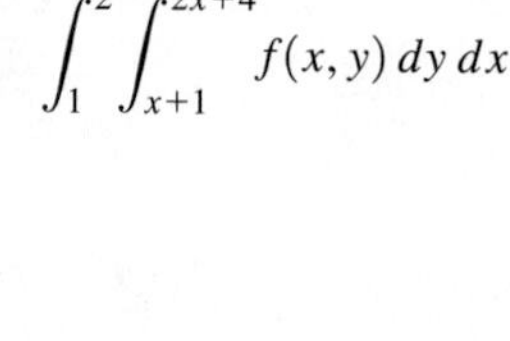

$\int_1^2 \int_{x+1}^{2x+4} f(x, y)\, dy\, dx$

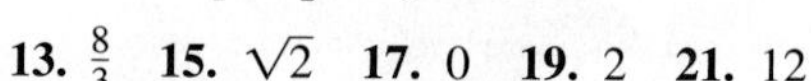

13. $\frac{8}{3}$ **15.** $\sqrt{2}$ **17.** 0 **19.** 2 **21.** 12
23. $\int_0^{18} \int_{y/2}^{(y+9)/3} f(x, y)\, dx\, dy$ **25.** $\int_0^{23} \int_{(y-3)/2}^{(y+7)/3} f(x, y)\, dx\, dy$
27. $\int_1^4 \int_0^{4-y} f(x, y)\, dx\, dy$ **29.** 9

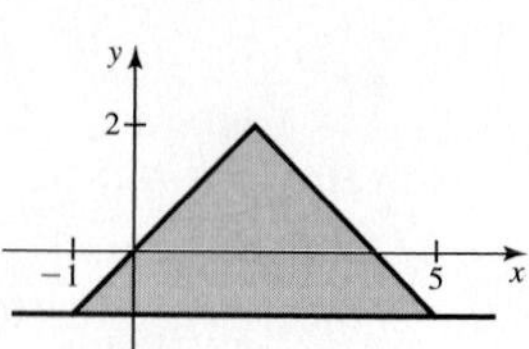

31. 0

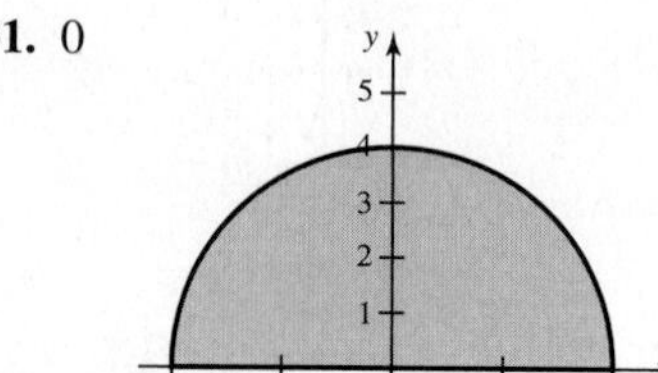

33. $\dfrac{\ln^3 2}{6}$

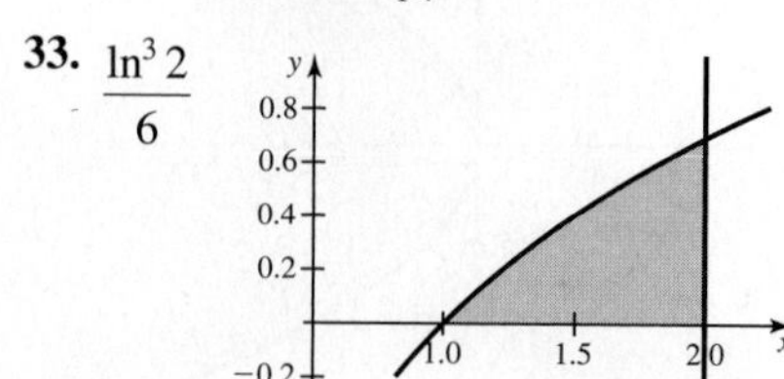

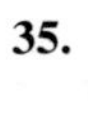

35. $\dfrac{243}{4}$

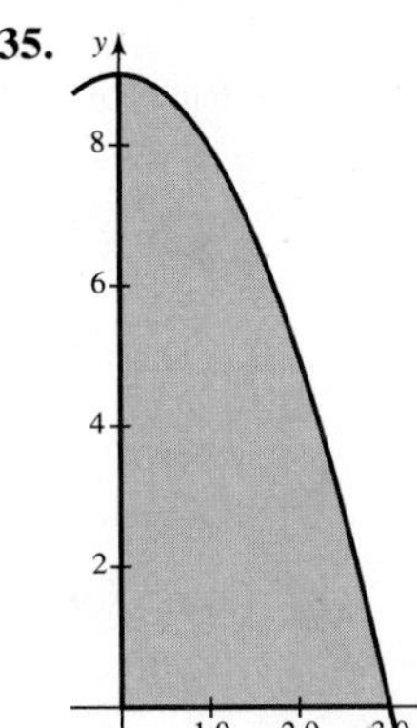

37. $\dfrac{2048}{15}$

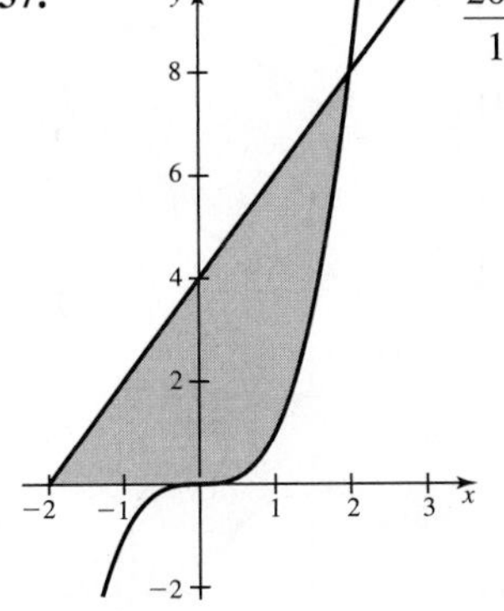

39. $\dfrac{32}{3}$ **41.** 12π **43.** $\displaystyle\int_0^4 \int_{y/2}^{\sqrt{y}} f(x, y)\, dx\, dy$

45. $\displaystyle\int_0^{\ln 2} \int_{1/2}^{e^{-x}} f(x, y)\, dy\, dx$ **47.** $\displaystyle\int_0^{\pi/2} \int_0^{\cos x} f(x, y)\, dy\, dx$

49. $\frac{1}{2}(e - 1)$

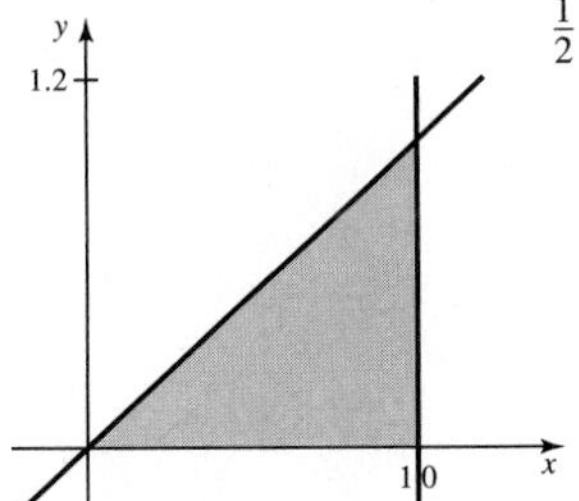

51. 0

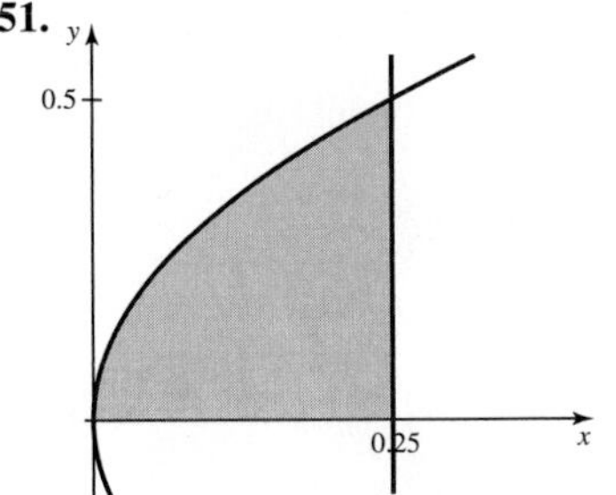

53. $\frac{2}{3}$ **55.** $81\pi/2$ **57.** $\frac{43}{6}$

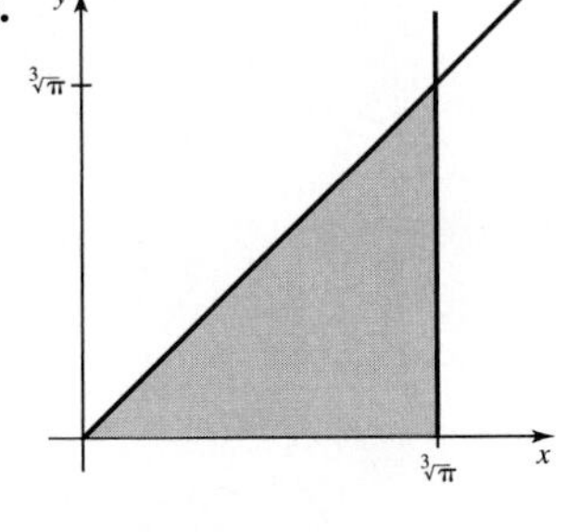

59. $\frac{32}{3}$

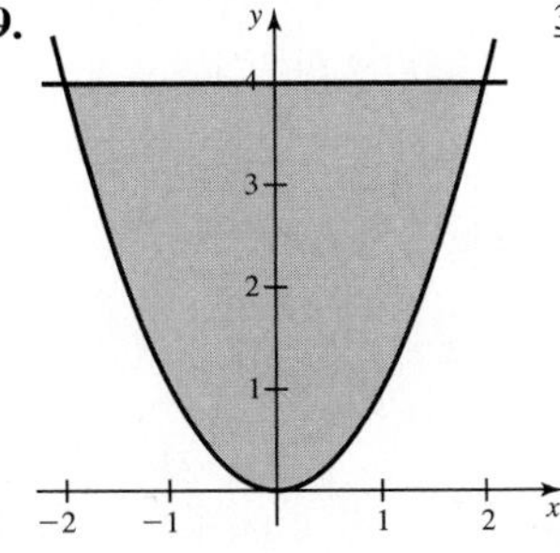

61. 1

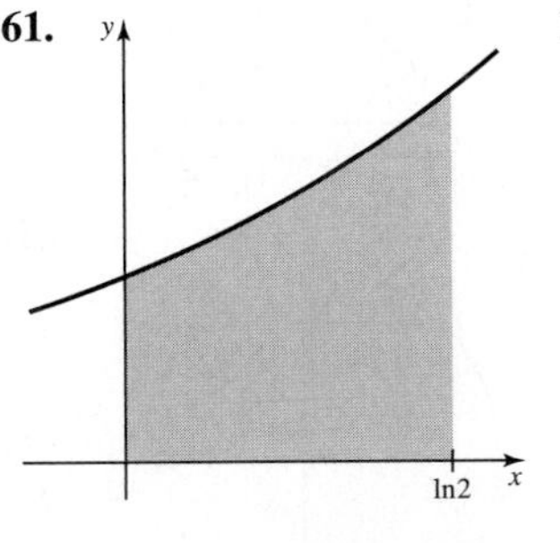

63. $\frac{140}{3}$

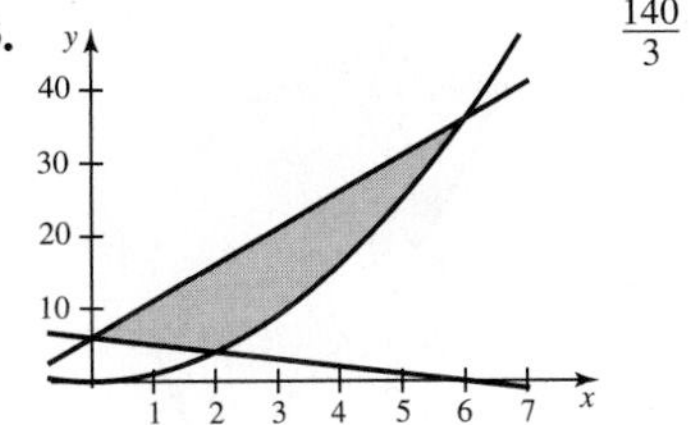

65. **a.** False **b.** False **c.** False **67.** $\frac{9}{8}$ **69.** $\frac{1}{4}\ln 2$

71. $\displaystyle\int_1^e \int_{-\ln x}^{\ln x} f(x, y)\, dy\, dx$

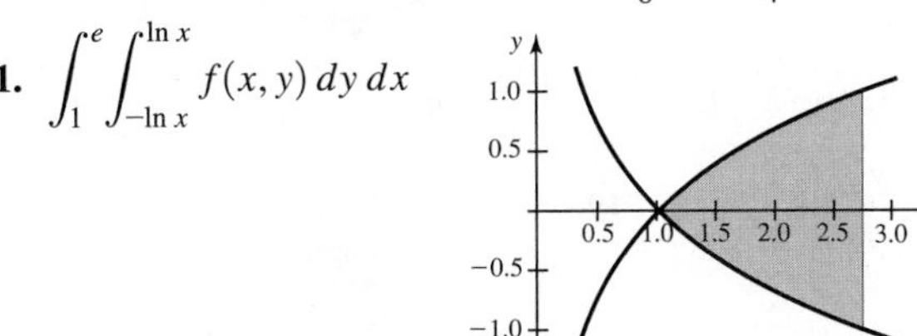

73. $a/3$ **75.** **a.**

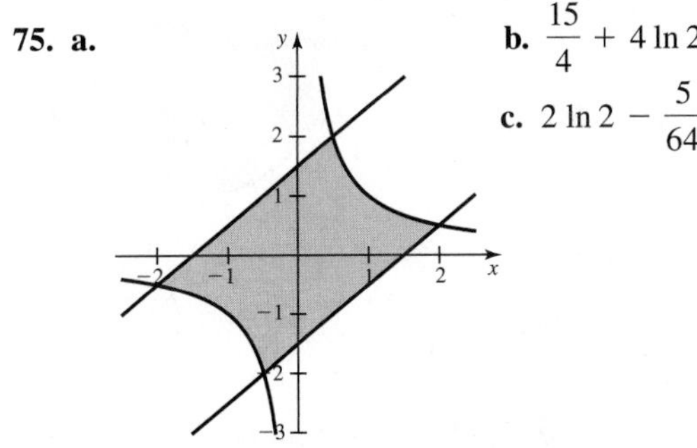

b. $\dfrac{15}{4} + 4\ln 2$

c. $2\ln 2 - \dfrac{5}{64}$

77. $\dfrac{3}{8e^2}$ **79.** 1 **81.** 30 **83.** 16 **85.** $4a\pi$ **87.** The integral over R_1

Section 14.3 Exercises, pp. 892–895

1. It is a polar rectangle because r and θ vary between constants.

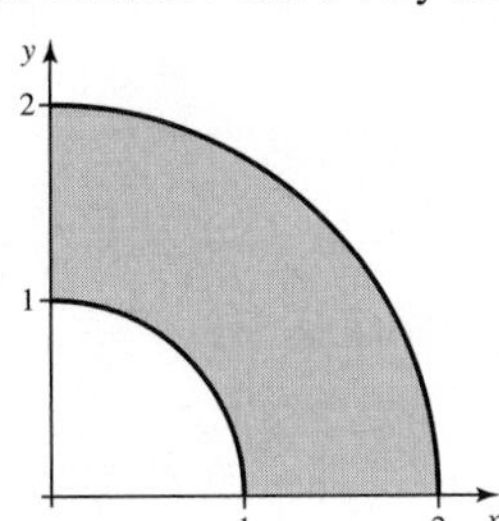

3.

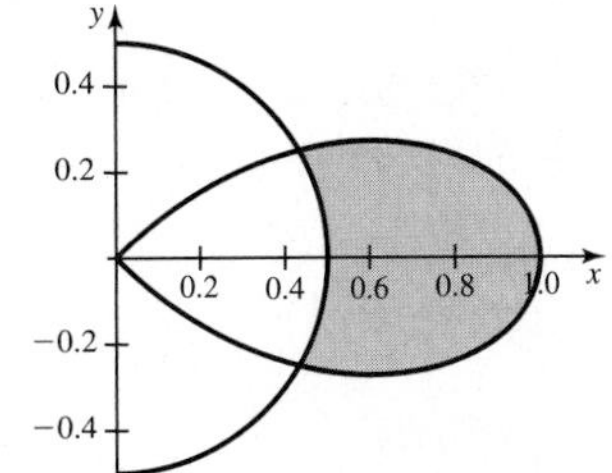

5. $A = \displaystyle\int_\alpha^\beta \int_{g(\theta)}^{h(\theta)} r\, dr\, d\theta$

7.

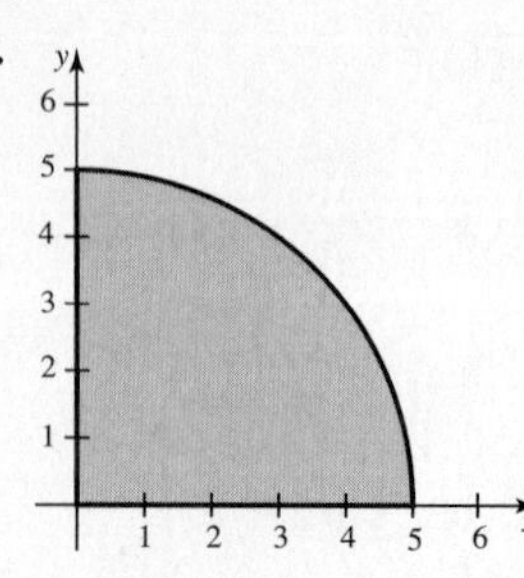

9.

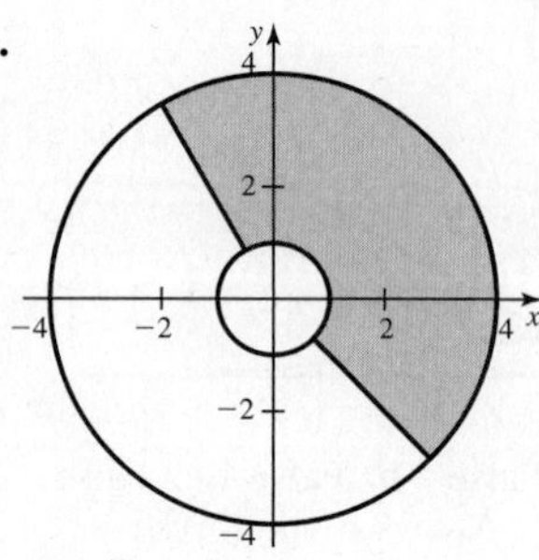

11. $7\pi/2$ **13.** $9\pi/2$ **15.** $\dfrac{62 - 10\sqrt{5}}{3}\pi$

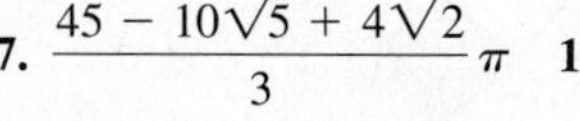

17. $\dfrac{45 - 10\sqrt{5} + 4\sqrt{2}}{3}\pi$ **19.**

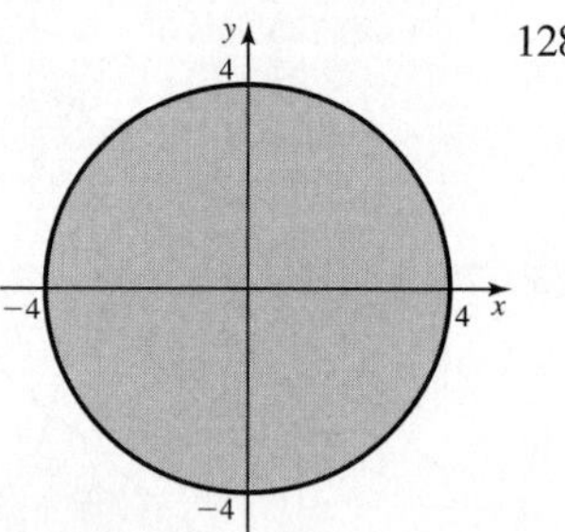

128π

21.

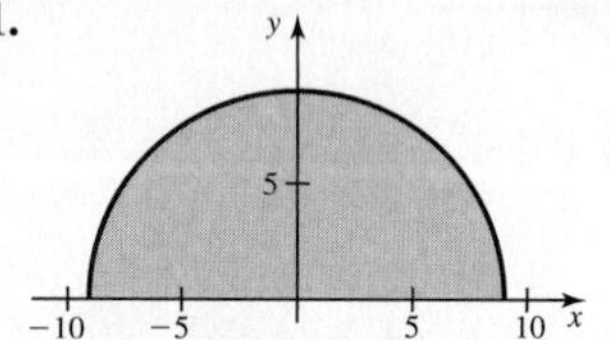

0

23.

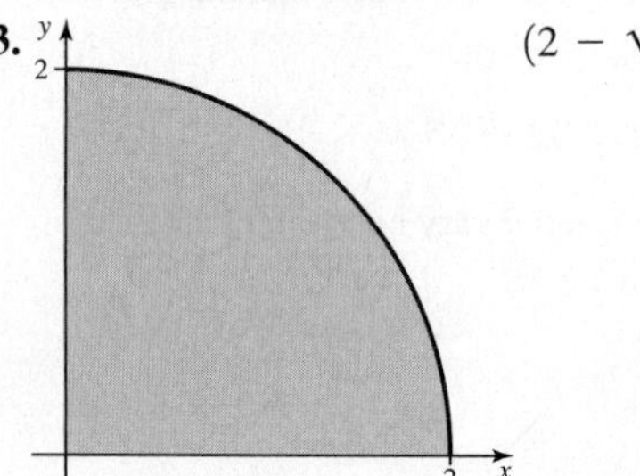

$(2 - \sqrt{3})\pi$

25. $(8 - 24e^{-2})\pi$ **27.** $\dfrac{15625\pi}{3}$

29. $\displaystyle\int_0^{2\pi}\int_0^{1+\frac{1}{2}\cos\theta} f(r,\theta)r\,dr\,d\theta$

31.

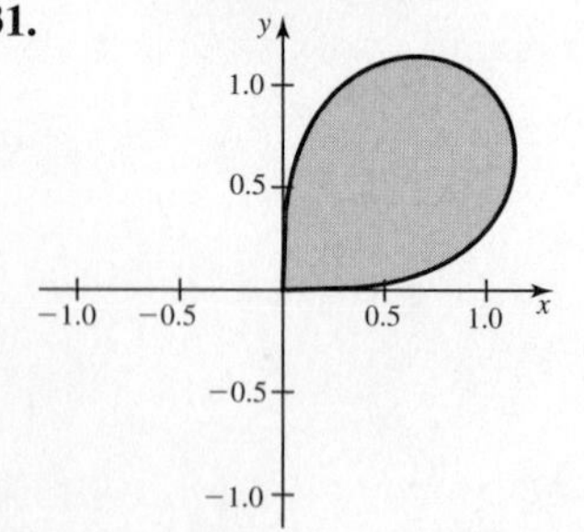

$\displaystyle\int_0^{\pi/2}\int_0^{\sqrt{2\sin 2\theta}} f(r,\theta)r\,dr\,d\theta$

33.

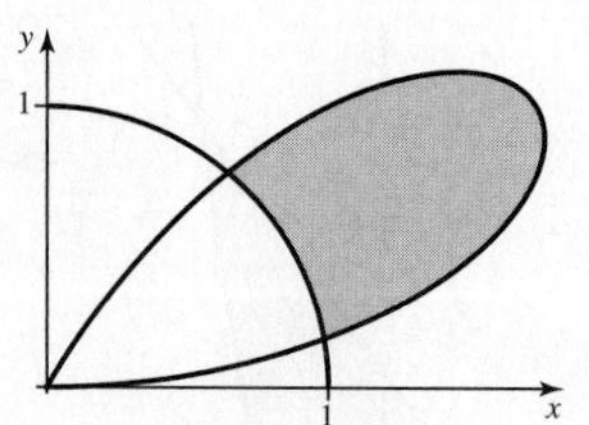

$\displaystyle\int_{\pi/18}^{5\pi/18}\int_1^{2\sin 3\theta} f(r,\theta)r\,dr\,d\theta$

35.

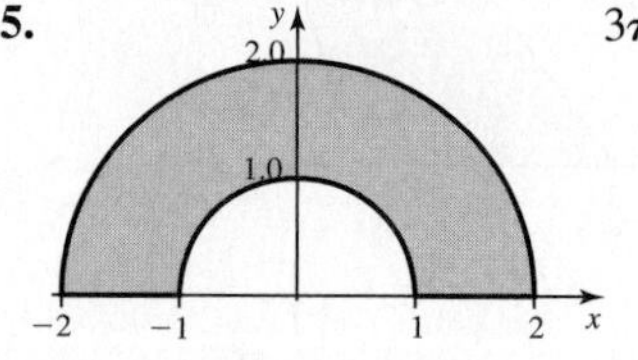

$3\pi/2$

37.

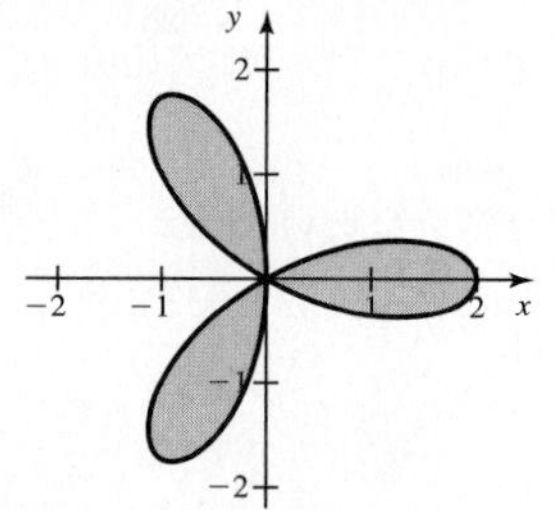

π

39.

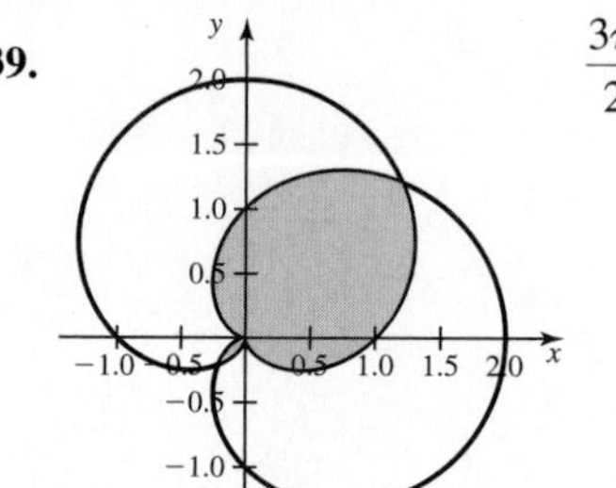

$\dfrac{3\pi}{2} - 2\sqrt{2}$

41. $2a/3$ **43.** $\frac{5}{2}$ **45. a.** False **b.** True **c.** True

47.

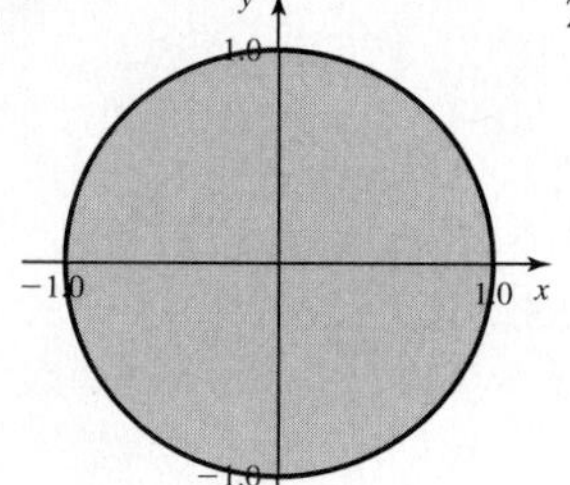

$2\pi/5$

49.

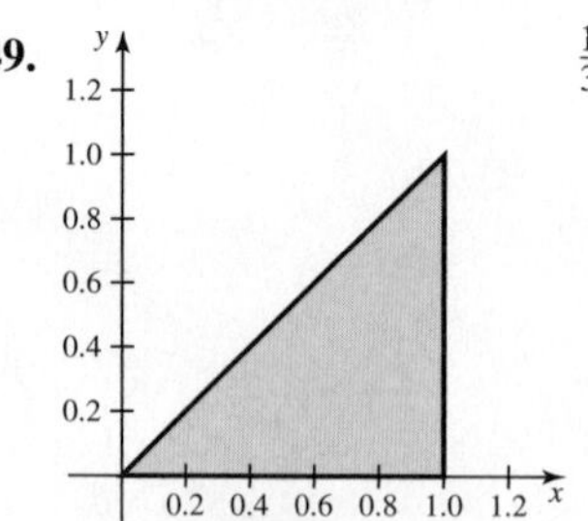

$\frac{1}{3}$

51.

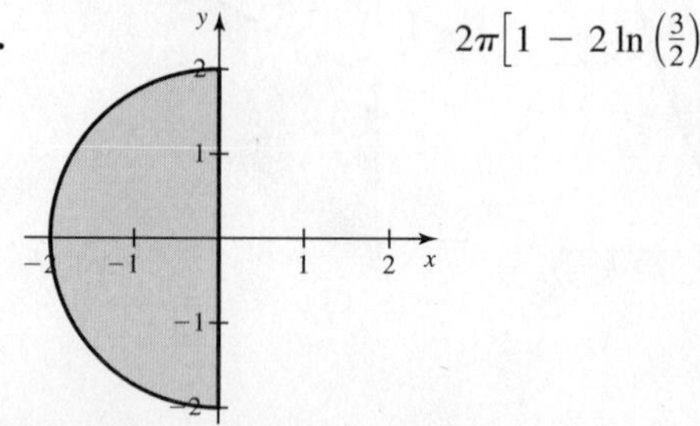

$2\pi\left[1 - 2\ln\left(\frac{3}{2}\right)\right]$

53. The hyperboloid $\left(V = \frac{112}{3}\pi\right)$
55. a. $R = \{(r, \theta): -\pi/4 \le \theta \le \pi/4 \text{ or } 3\pi/4 \le \theta \le 5\pi/4\}$
b. $\frac{a^4}{4}$ **57.** 1 **59.** $\pi/4$ **61. a.** $9\pi/2$ **b.** $\pi + 3\sqrt{3}$
c. $\pi - 3\sqrt{3}/2$ **63.** $30\pi + 42$ **65. b.** $\sqrt{\pi}/2, \frac{1}{2}$, and $\sqrt{\pi}/4$
67. a. $I = \frac{\sqrt{2}}{2}\arctan\left(\frac{\sqrt{2}}{2}\right)$
b. $I = \frac{\sqrt{2}}{4}\arctan\left(\frac{\sqrt{2}}{2}a\right) + \frac{a}{2\sqrt{a^2+1}}\arctan\frac{1}{\sqrt{a^2+1}}$ **c.** $\frac{\sqrt{2}\pi}{8}$

Section 14.4 Exercises, pp. 903–907

1.

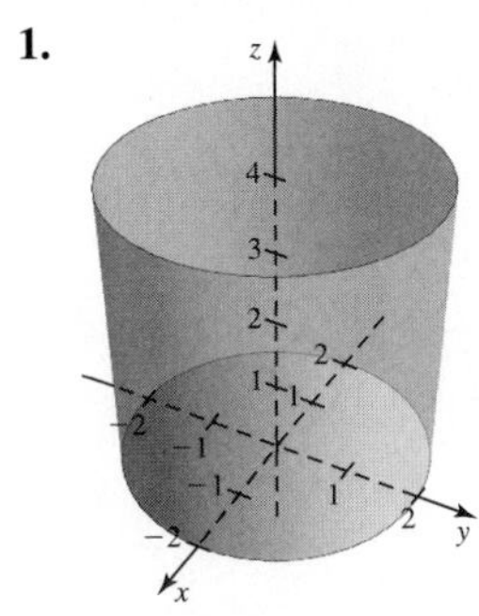

3. $\int_{-9}^{9}\int_{-\sqrt{81-x^2}}^{\sqrt{81-x^2}}\int_{-\sqrt{81-x^2-y^2}}^{\sqrt{81-x^2-y^2}} f(x, y, z)\,dz\,dy\,dx$

5. $\int_0^1\int_0^{\sqrt{1-z^2}}\int_0^{\sqrt{1-z^2-x^2}} f(x, y, z)\,dy\,dx\,dz$ **7.** 24 **9.** 8

11. $2/\pi$ **13.** 0 **15.** 8 **17.** $\frac{32(\sqrt{2}-1)}{3}\pi$ **19.** $\frac{16}{3}$

21. $\frac{2\pi(1 + 19\sqrt{19} - 20\sqrt{10})}{3}$ **23.** 12π **25.** $\frac{2}{3}$ **27.** 128π

29. $(10\sqrt{10} - 1)\frac{\pi}{6}$ **31.** $\frac{3\ln 2}{2} + \frac{e}{16} - 1$ **33.** $\frac{256}{9}$

35. $\int_0^4\int_{y/4-1}^{0}\int_0^5 dz\,dx\,dy = 10$

37. $\int_0^1\int_0^{\sqrt{1-x^2}}\int_0^{\sqrt{1-x^2}} dz\,dy\,dx = \frac{2}{3}$ **39.** $\frac{175}{32(\ln 2)^3}$ **41.** $\frac{10}{3}$

43. $\frac{3}{2}$ **45. a.** False **b.** False **c.** False **47.** 1 **49.** $\frac{16}{3}$ **51.** 2

53. $\frac{224}{3}$ and $\frac{160}{3}$ **55.** $V = \pi r^2 h/3$

57. $V = \frac{\pi h^2}{3}(3R - h)$ **59.** $V = 4\pi abc/3$ **61.** $\frac{1}{24}$

Section 14.5 Exercises, pp. 919–923

1. r measures the distance from the point to the z axis, θ is the angle that the segment from the point to the z-axis makes with the positive xz-plane, and z is the directed distance from the point to the xy-plane. **3.** A cone **5.** It approximates the volume of the cylindrical wedge formed by the changes Δr, $\Delta\theta$, and Δz.

7. $\int_\alpha^\beta\int_{g(\theta)}^{h(\theta)}\int_{G(r,\theta)}^{H(r,\theta)} f(r, \theta, z) r\,dz\,dr\,d\theta$ **9.** Cylindrical coordinates

11. Wedge

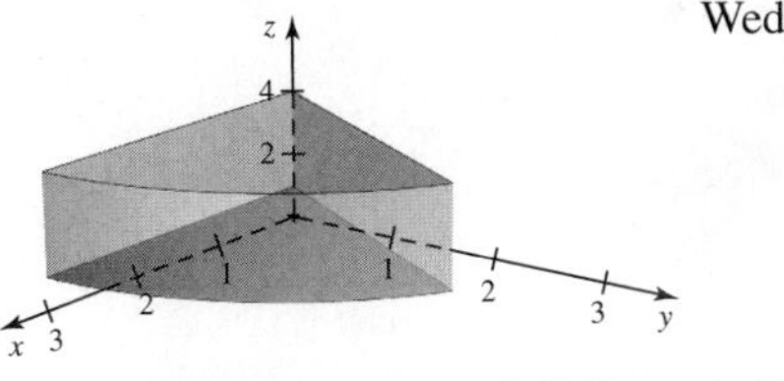

13. Solid bounded by cone and plane $z = 4$

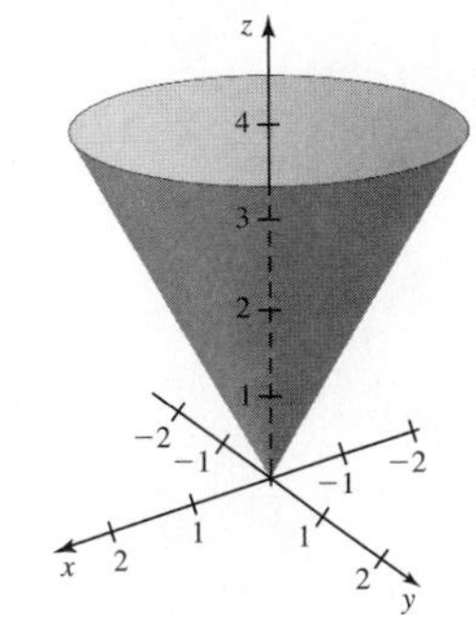

15. 2π **17.** $4\pi/5$ **19.** $\pi(1 - e^{-1})/2$ **21.** $9\pi/4$
23. 560π **25.** 396π **27.** The paraboloid ($V = 44\pi/3$)
29. $\frac{2\pi + 14\pi\sqrt{17}}{3}$ **31.** $\frac{(16 + 17\sqrt{29})\pi}{3}$ **33.** $\frac{1}{3}$

35. Hollow ball

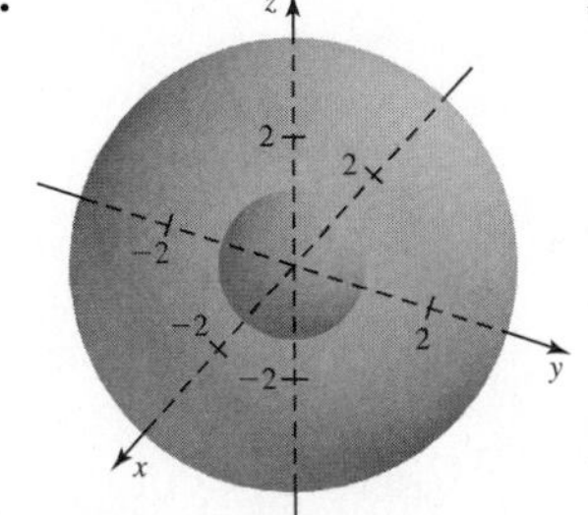

37. Sphere of radius $r = 2$, centered at (0, 0, 2)

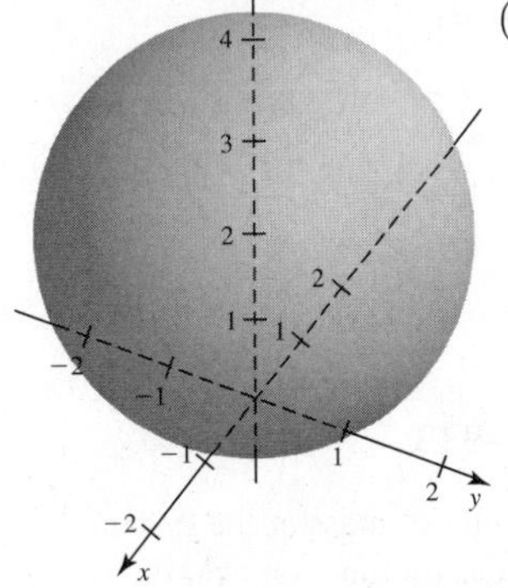

39. $\pi/2$ **41.** $4\pi\ln 2$ **43.** $\pi\left(\frac{188}{9} - \frac{32\sqrt{3}}{3}\right)$ **45.** $32\pi\sqrt{3}/9$

47. $5\pi/12$ **49.** $\frac{8\pi}{3}$ **51.** $\frac{8\pi}{3}(9\sqrt{3} - 11)$ **53. a.** True **b.** True

55. $z = \sqrt{x^2 + y^2 - 1}$; upper half of a hyperboloid of one sheet

57. $\frac{8\pi}{3}(1 - e^{-512}) \approx \frac{8\pi}{3}$ **59.** 32π

61.

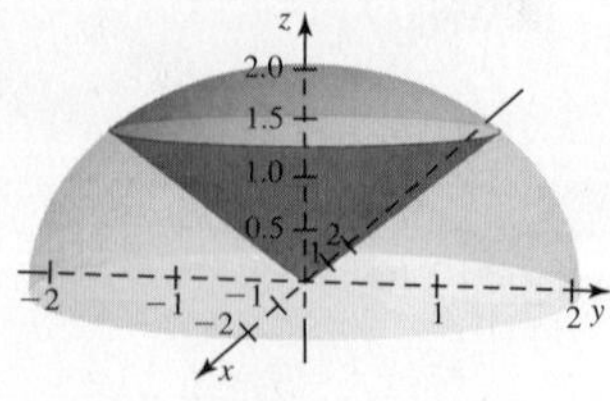

$$\int_0^{2\pi}\int_0^{\sqrt{2}}\int_r^{\sqrt{4-r^2}} f(r,\theta,z)\, r\, dz\, dr\, d\theta$$

$$\int_0^{2\pi}\int_0^{\sqrt{2}}\int_0^{z} f(r,\theta,z)\, r\, dr\, dz\, d\theta + \int_0^{2\pi}\int_{\sqrt{2}}^{2}\int_0^{\sqrt{4-z^2}} f(r,\theta,z)\, r\, dr\, dz\, d\theta$$

$$\int_0^{\sqrt{2}}\int_r^{\sqrt{4-r^2}}\int_0^{2\pi} f(r,\theta,z)\, r\, d\theta\, dz\, dr$$

63.

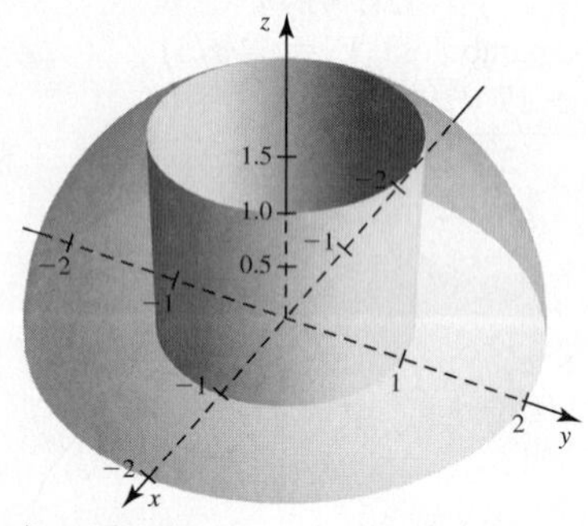

$$\int_{\pi/6}^{\pi/2}\int_0^{2\pi}\int_{\csc\varphi}^{2} f(\rho,\varphi,\theta)\,\rho^2\sin\varphi\, d\rho\, d\theta\, d\varphi$$

$$\int_{\pi/6}^{\pi/2}\int_{\csc\varphi}^{2}\int_0^{2\pi} f(\rho,\varphi,\theta)\,\rho^2\sin\varphi\, d\theta\, d\rho\, d\varphi$$

65. $32\sqrt{3}\pi/9$ **67.** $2\sqrt{2}/3$ **69.** $7\pi/2$ **71.** $\frac{16}{3}$ **73.** 95.6036

77. $V = \dfrac{\pi r^2 h}{3}$ **79.** $V = \dfrac{\pi}{3}(R^2 + rR + r^2)h$

81. $V = \dfrac{\pi R^3(8r - 3R)}{12r}$

Section 14.6 Exercises, pp. 931–933

1. The pivot should be located at the center of mass of the system. **3.** Use a double integral. Integrate the density function over the region occupied by the plate. **5.** Use a triple integral to find the mass of the object and the three moments.

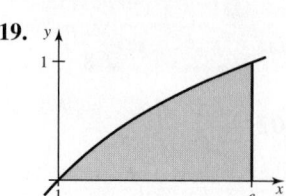

7. $\frac{27}{13}$

9. mass is $2 + \pi$; $\bar{x} = \frac{\pi}{2}$ **11.** mass is $\frac{20}{3}$; $\bar{x} = \frac{9}{5}$

13. mass is 10; $\bar{x} = \frac{8}{3}$ **15.** $\left(\frac{\pi}{2}, \frac{1}{2}\right)$

17. $\left(0, \frac{1}{3}\right)$

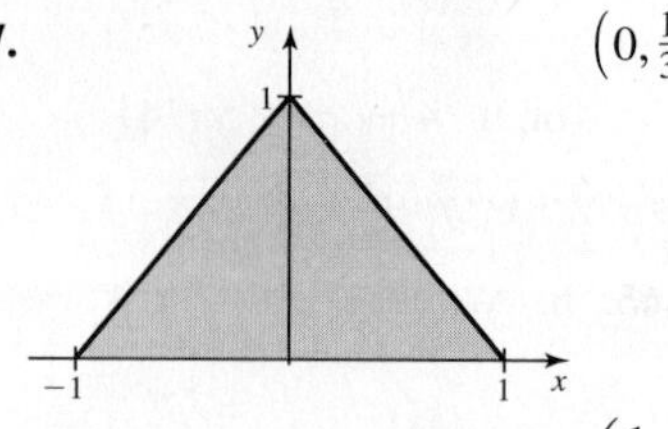

19. $\left(\frac{1}{4}(e^2 + 1), \frac{e}{2} - 1\right) = (2.10, 0.36)$

21. $\left(\frac{7}{3}, 1\right)$, density increases to the right. **23.** $\left(\frac{16}{11}, \frac{16}{11}\right)$; density increases toward the hypotenuse of the triangle.

25. $\left(0, \dfrac{16 + 3\pi}{16 + 12\pi}\right) = (0, 0.4735)$; density increases away from the x-axis.

27. $\left(0, 0, \frac{3}{2}\right)$

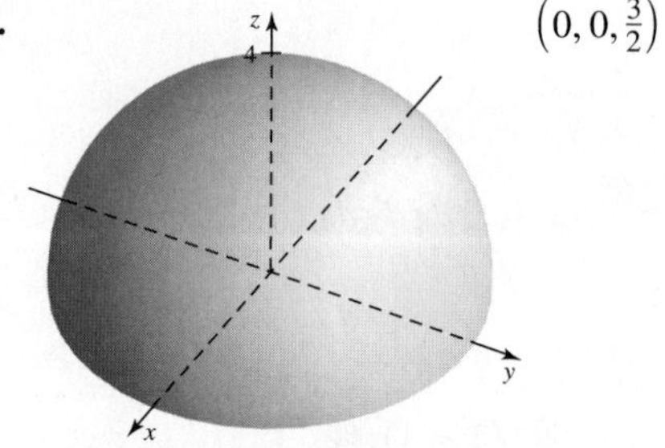

29. $\left(\frac{1}{4}, \frac{1}{4}, \frac{1}{4}\right)$

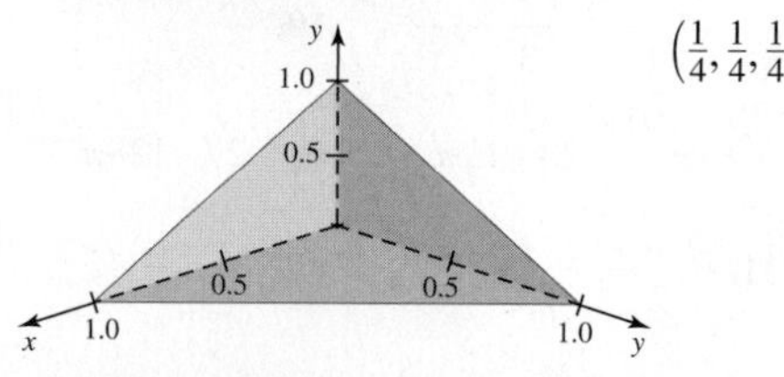

31. $\left(0, -\frac{1}{4}, \frac{5}{8}\right)$

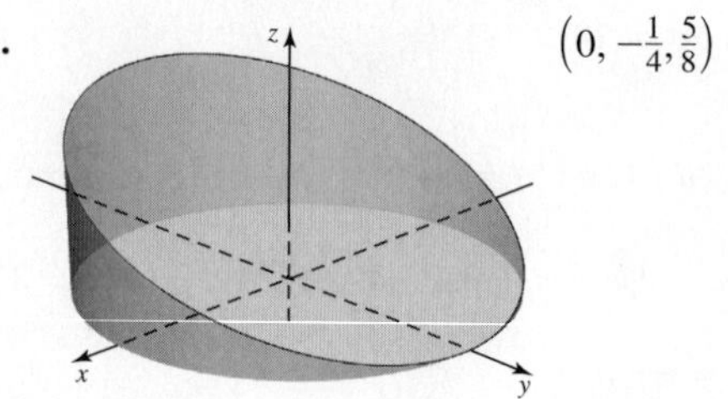

33. $\left(\frac{7}{3}, \frac{1}{2}, \frac{1}{2}\right)$ **35.** $\left(0, 0, \frac{63}{10}\right)$ **37.** $\left(\frac{2}{3}, \frac{7}{3}, \frac{1}{3}\right)$ **39. a.** False **b.** True **c.** False **d.** False **41.** $\bar{x} = \dfrac{\ln(1 + L^2)}{2\tan^{-1} L}$, $\lim_{L\to\infty} \bar{x} = \infty$

43. $\left(0, \frac{8}{9}\right)$ **45.** $\left(0, \dfrac{8}{3\pi}\right)$ **47.** $\left(\frac{5}{6}, 0\right)$ **49.** $\left(\dfrac{128}{105\pi}, \dfrac{128}{105\pi}\right)$

51. On the line of symmetry, $2r/\pi$ units from the diameter.

53. $\left(\dfrac{2a}{3(4 - \pi)}, \dfrac{2a}{3(4 - \pi)}\right)$ **55.** $h/4$ units **57.** $h/3$ units, where h is the height of the triangle **59.** $3a/8$ units

61. a. $\left(0, \frac{4(1 + a + a^2)}{3(1 + a)\pi}\right)$

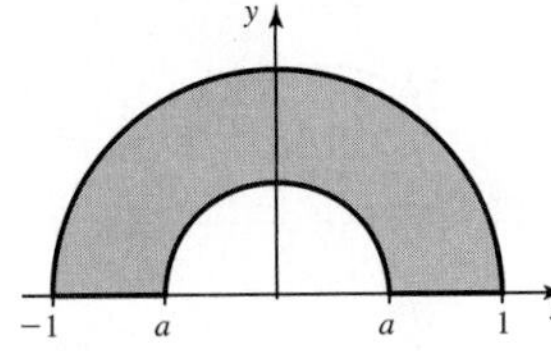

b. $a = \frac{1}{2}\left(-1 + \sqrt{1 + \frac{16}{3\pi - 4}}\right) = 0.4937$

63. Depth $= \frac{40\sqrt{10} - 4}{333}$ cm $= 0.3678$ cm

65. a. $(\bar{x}, \bar{y}) = \left(\frac{-r^2}{R + r}, 0\right)$ (origin at center of large circle);
$(\bar{x}, \bar{y}) = \left(\frac{R^2 + Rr + r^2}{R + r}, 0\right)$ (origin at common point of the circles)
b. *Hint:* Solve $\bar{x} = R - 2r$.

Section 14.7 Exercises, pp. 943–945

1. The image of S is the 2×2 square with vertices at $(0, 0)$, $(2, 0)$, $(2, 2)$ and $(0, 2)$. **3.** $\int_0^1 \int_0^1 f(u + v, u - v)\, 2\, du\, dv$

5. The rectangle with vertices at $(0, 0)$, $(2, 0)$, $\left(2, \frac{1}{2}\right)$ and $\left(0, \frac{1}{2}\right)$

7. The diamond with vertices at $(0, 0)$, $\left(\frac{1}{2}, \frac{1}{2}\right)$, $(1, 0)$ and $\left(\frac{1}{2}, -\frac{1}{2}\right)$

9. The region above the x-axis and bounded by the curves $y^2 = 4 \pm 4x$ **11.** The upper half of the unit circle.

13.

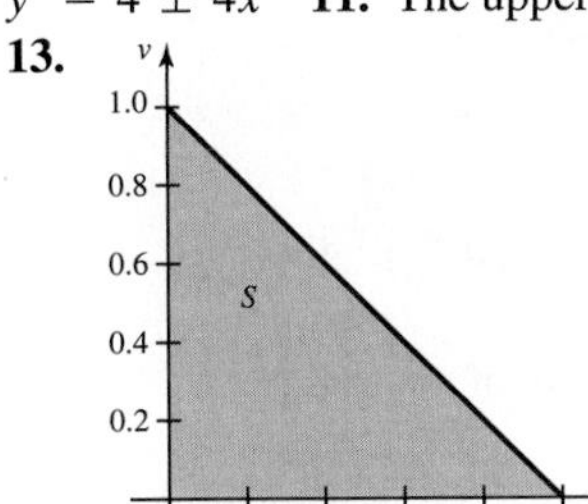

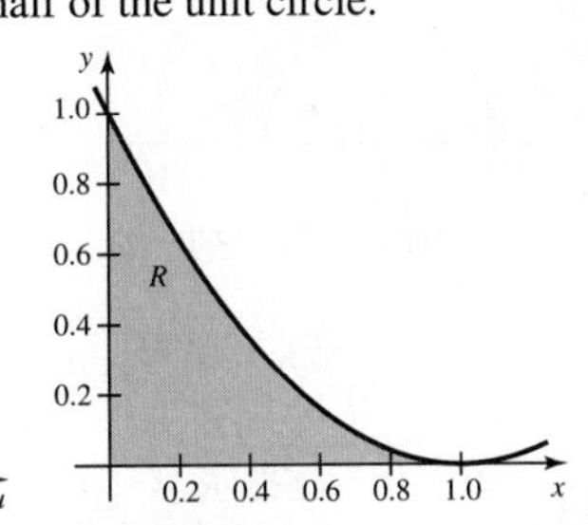

15.

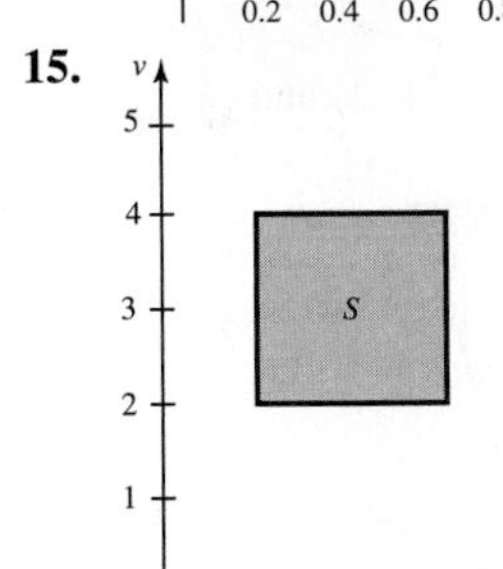

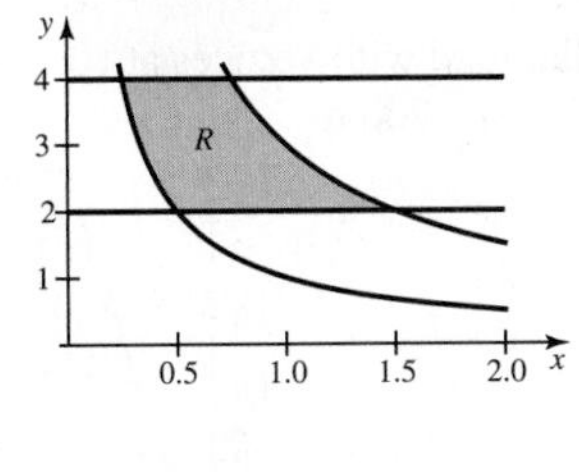

17. -9 **19.** $-4(u^2 + v^2)$ **21.** -1

23. $x = (u + v)/3$, $y = (2u - v)/3$; $-\frac{1}{3}$

25. $x = -(u + 3v)$, $y = -(u + 2v)$; -1

27. a.

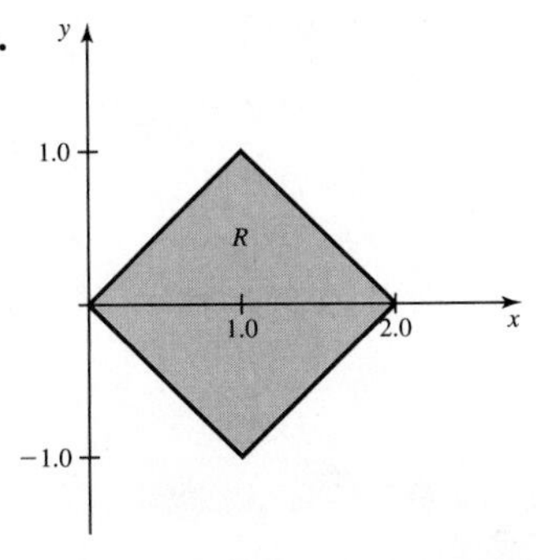

b. $0 \le u \le 1, 0 \le v \le 1$ **c.** $J(u, v) = -2$ **d.** 0

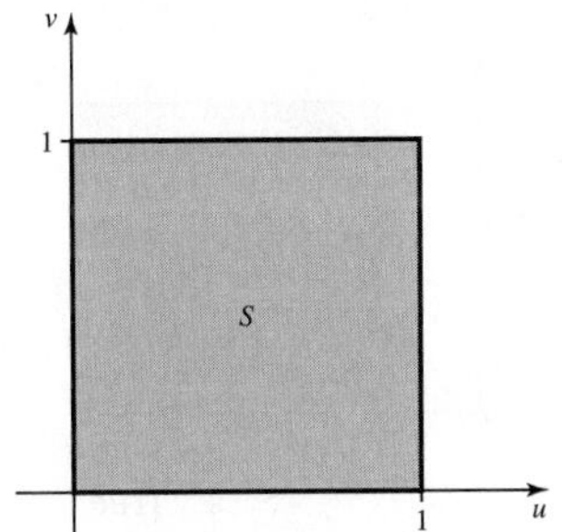

29. a.

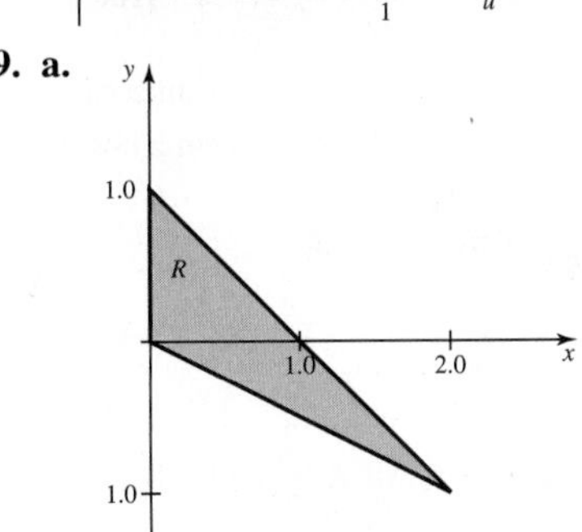

b. $0 \le u \le 1, 0 \le v \le 1 - u$ **c.** $J(u, v) = 2$ **d.** $256\sqrt{2}/945$

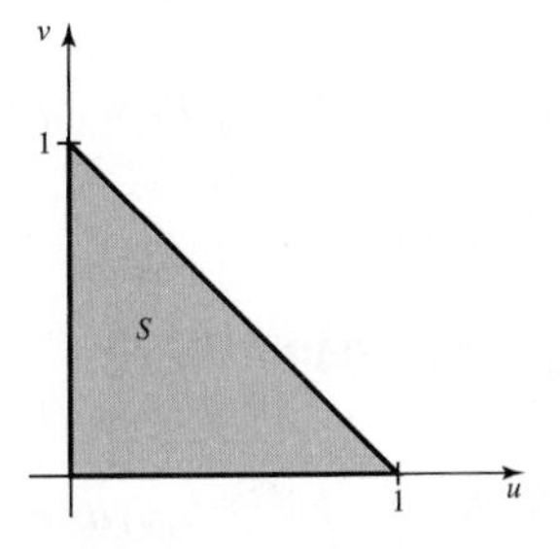

31. $4\sqrt{2}/3$

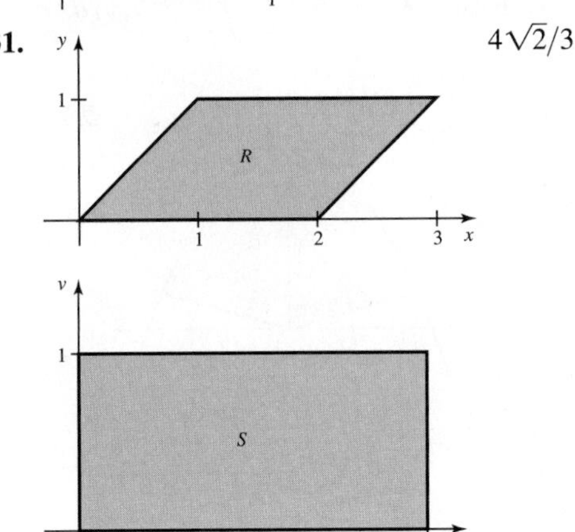

33. $3844/5625$

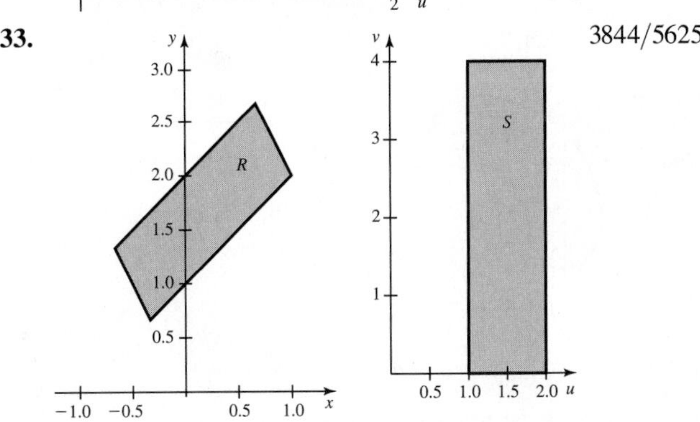

35. $\frac{15 \ln 3}{2}$

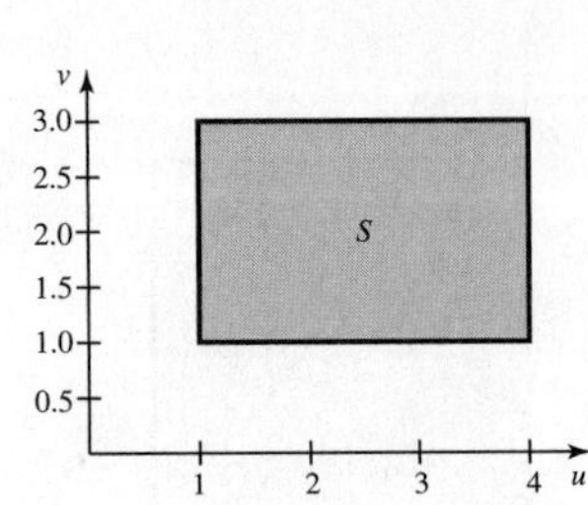

37. 2 **39.** $2w(u^2 - v^2)$ **41.** 5 **43.** $1024\pi/3$ **45. a.** True **b.** True **c.** True

47. *Hint:* $J(\rho, \varphi, \theta) = \begin{vmatrix} \sin\varphi\cos\theta & \rho\cos\varphi\cos\theta & -\rho\sin\varphi\sin\theta \\ \sin\varphi\sin\theta & \rho\cos\varphi\sin\theta & \rho\sin\varphi\cos\theta \\ \cos\varphi & -\rho\sin\varphi & 0 \end{vmatrix}$

49. $a^2b^2/2$ **51.** $(a^2 + b^2)/4$ **53.** $\frac{4\pi abc}{3}$

55. $(\bar{x}, \bar{y}, \bar{z}) = \left(0, 0, \frac{3c}{8}\right)$ **57. a.** $x = a^2 - \frac{y^2}{4a^2}$

b. $x = \frac{y^2}{4b^2} - b^2$ **c.** $J(u, v) = 4(u^2 + v^2)$ **d.** $\frac{80}{3}$ **e.** 160

f. Vertical lines become parabolas opening downward with vertices on the positive y-axis, horizontal lines become parabolas opening upward with vertices on the negative y-axis. **59. a.** S is stretched in the positive u- and v-directions but not in the w-direction. The amount of stretching increases with u and v. **b.** $J(u, v, w) = ad$

c. Volume $= ad$ **d.** $\left(\frac{a + b + c}{2}, \frac{d + e}{2}, \frac{1}{2}\right)$

Chapter 14 Review Exercises, pp. 946–949

1. a. False **b.** True **c.** False **3.** $\frac{26}{3}$ **5.** $\int_0^1 \int_{-\sqrt{y}}^{\sqrt{y}} f(x, y)\, dx\, dy$

7. $\int_0^1 \int_0^{\sqrt{1-x^2}} f(x, y)\, dy\, dx$ **9.** $\frac{304}{3}$

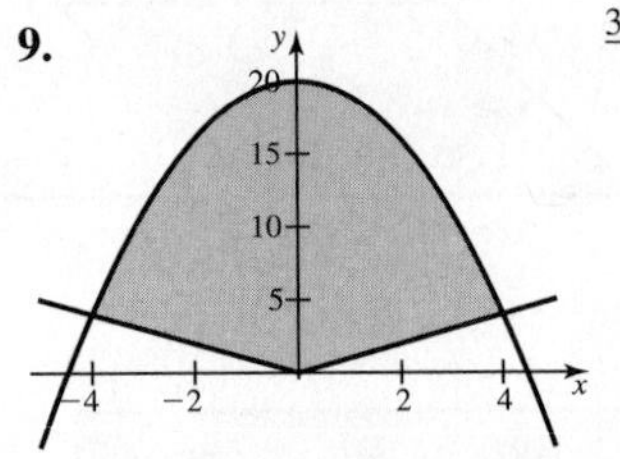

11. $\frac{\sqrt{17} - \sqrt{2}}{2}$ **13.** 8π **15.** $\frac{2}{7\pi^2}$ **17.** $\frac{1}{5}$

19. $\frac{9\pi}{2}$

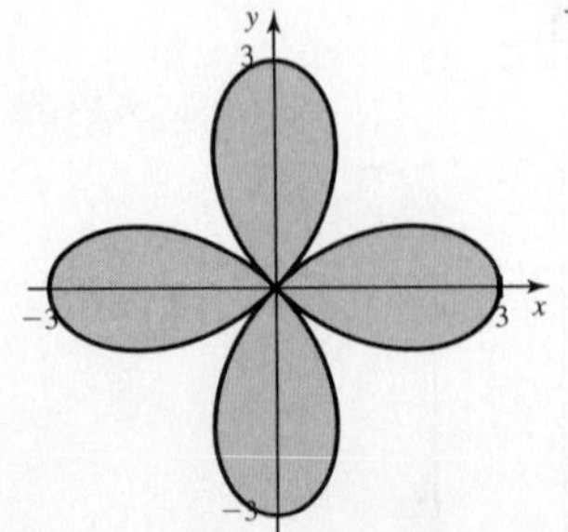

21. $6\pi - 16$

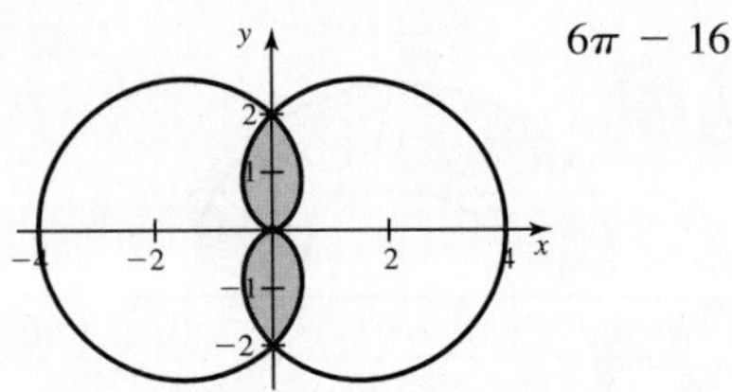

23. 2 **25.** $\int_0^4 \int_0^{\sqrt{16-z^2}} \int_0^{\sqrt{16-y^2-z^2}} dx\, dy\, dz$ **27.** $\pi - \frac{4}{3}$

29. $6(1 - \cos 4)$ **31.** $\frac{848}{9}$ **33.** $\frac{16}{3}$ **35.** $\frac{128}{3}$ **37.** $\frac{\pi}{6} - \frac{\sqrt{3}}{2} + \frac{1}{2}$

39. a. $\frac{512}{15}$ **b.** Five **c.** $\frac{2^{pq+q+1}}{q(p + 1)^2 + p + 1}$ **41.** $\frac{1}{3}$ **43.** π

45. 4π **47.** $\frac{28\pi}{3}$ **49.** $\frac{2048\pi}{105}$

51. $(\bar{x}, \bar{y}) = \left(\frac{\pi}{2}, \frac{\pi}{8}\right)$

53. $(\bar{x}, \bar{y}) = \left(0, \frac{56}{9\pi}\right)$

55. $(\bar{x}, \bar{y}, \bar{z}) = (0, 0, 24)$ **57.** $(\bar{x}, \bar{y}, \bar{z}) = \left(0, 0, \frac{63}{10}\right)$ **59.** $\frac{h}{3}$

61. $\frac{1}{6}\sqrt{4s^2 - b^2} = \frac{h}{3}$, where h is the height of the triangle.

63. a. $\frac{4\pi}{3}$ **b.** $\frac{16Q}{3}$ **65.** $R = \{0 \le x \le 1, 0 \le y \le 1\}$

67. The diamond with vertices at $(0, 0)$, $\left(\frac{1}{2}, -\frac{1}{2}\right)$, $(1, 0)$ and $\left(\frac{1}{2}, \frac{1}{2}\right)$.

69. 14 **71.** 6 **73. a.**

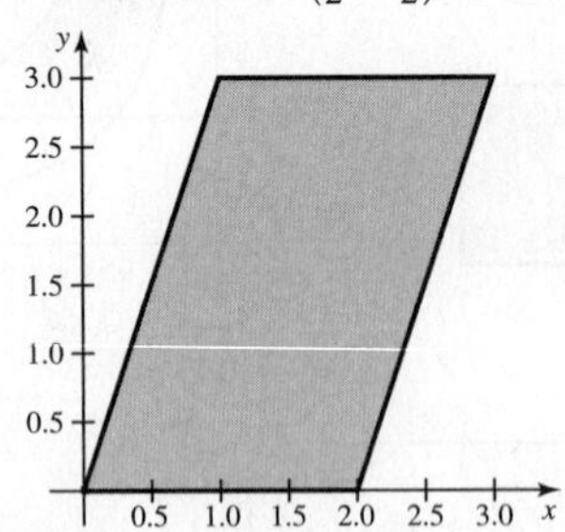

b. $0 \le u \le 2, 0 \le v \le 3$ **c.** $J(u, v) = 1$ **d.** $\frac{63}{2}$

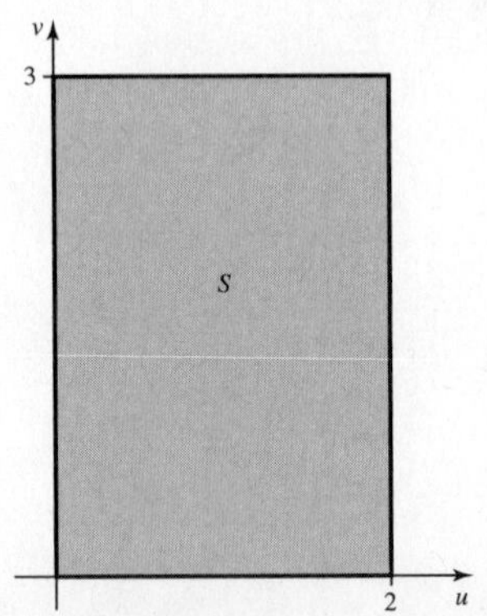

75. a.

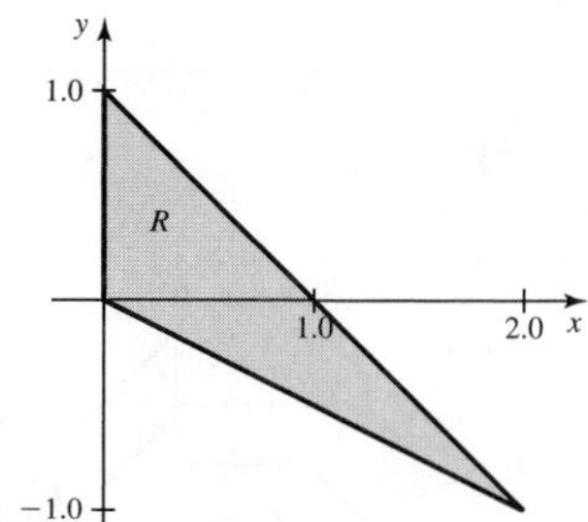

b. $0 \le u \le 1, 0 \le v \le 1 - u$ **c.** $J(u, v) = 2$ **d.** $\dfrac{256\sqrt{2}}{945}$

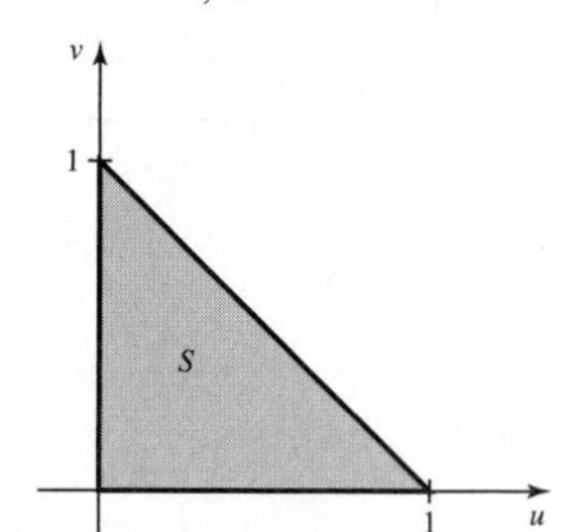

77. 42

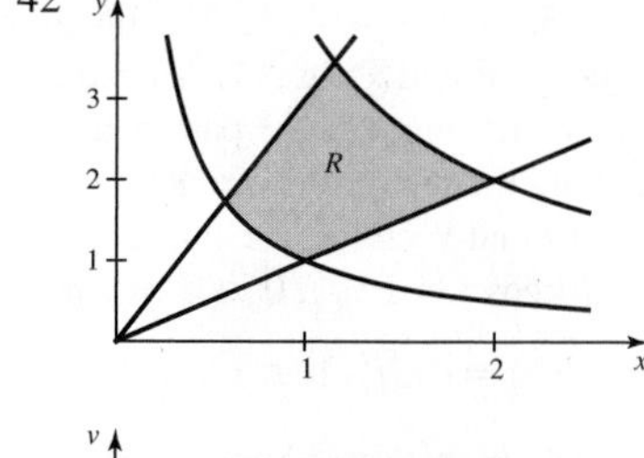

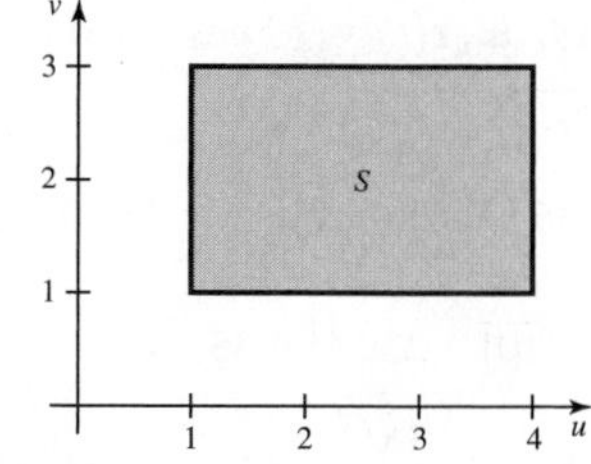

79. $\dfrac{-7}{16}$

CHAPTER 15

Section 15.1 Exercises, pp. 957–959

1. $\mathbf{F} = \langle f, g, h \rangle$ evaluated at (x, y, z) is the velocity vector of an air particle at (x, y, z) at a fixed point in time. **3.** At selected points (a, b), plot the vector $\langle f(a, b), g(a, b) \rangle$. **5.** It shows the direction in which the temperature increases the fastest and the amount of increase.

7.

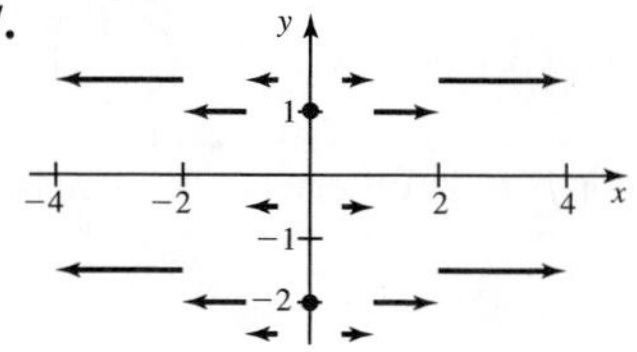

9.

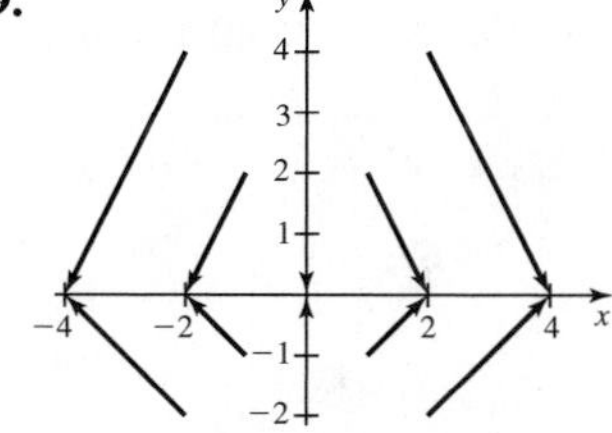

11.

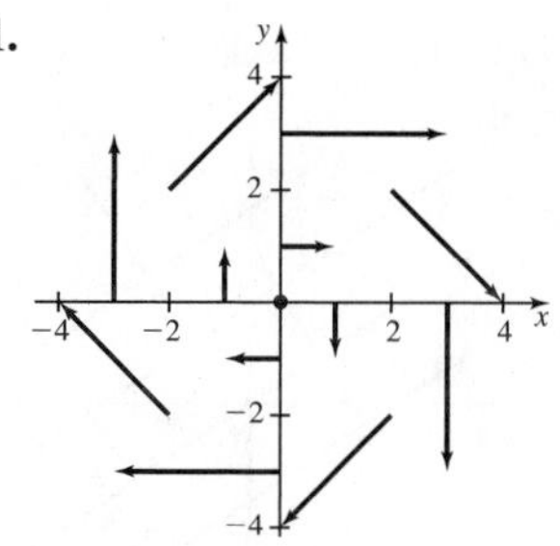

13.

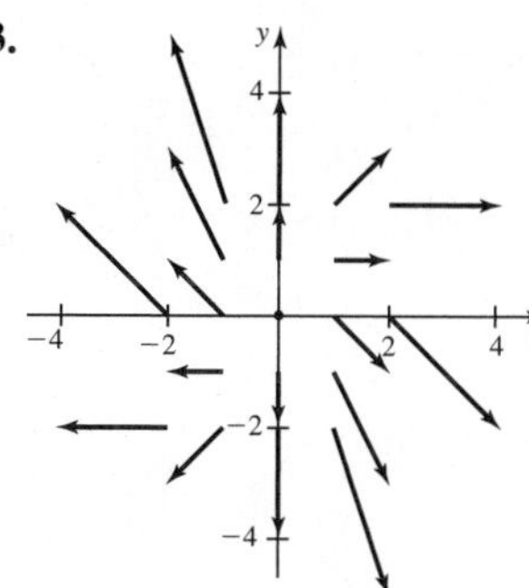

15.

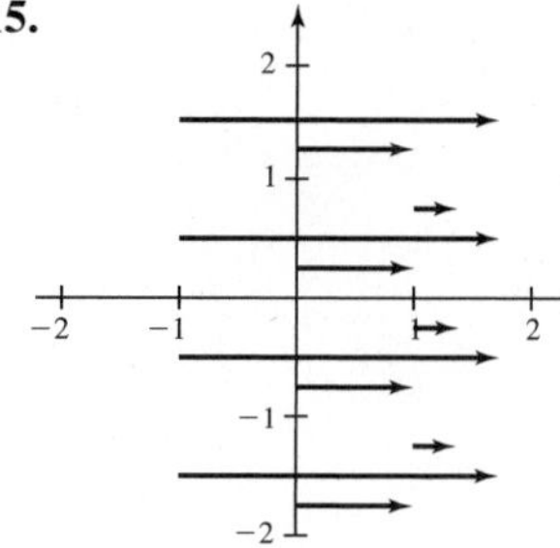

17.

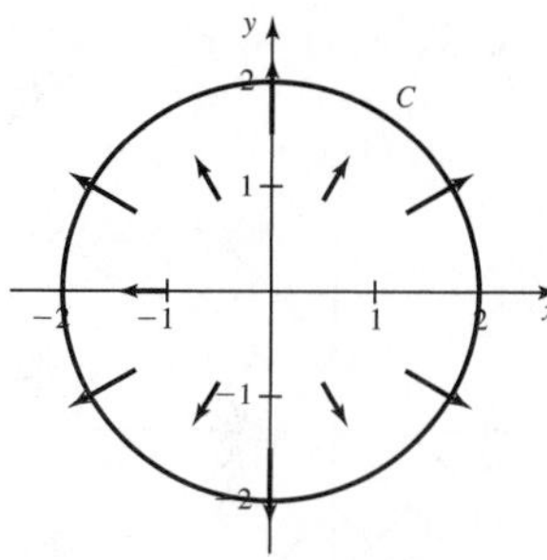

Normal at all points of C

19.

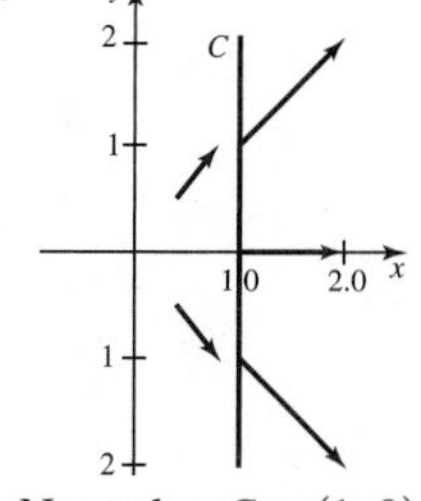

Normal to C at $(1, 0)$

21.

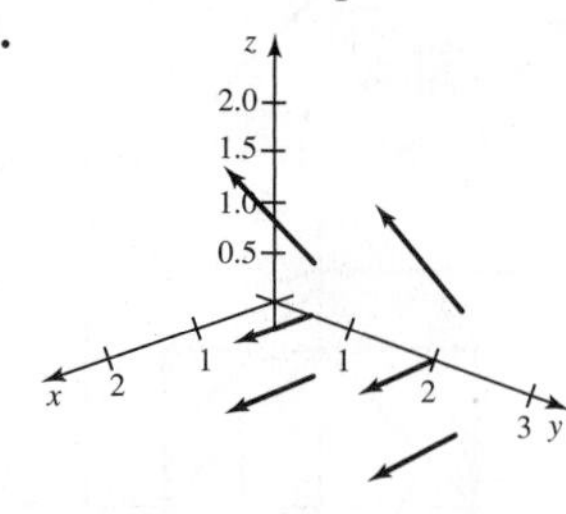

23.

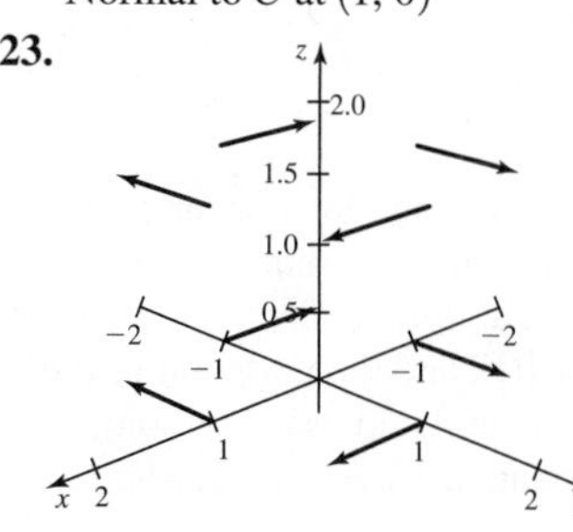

25.

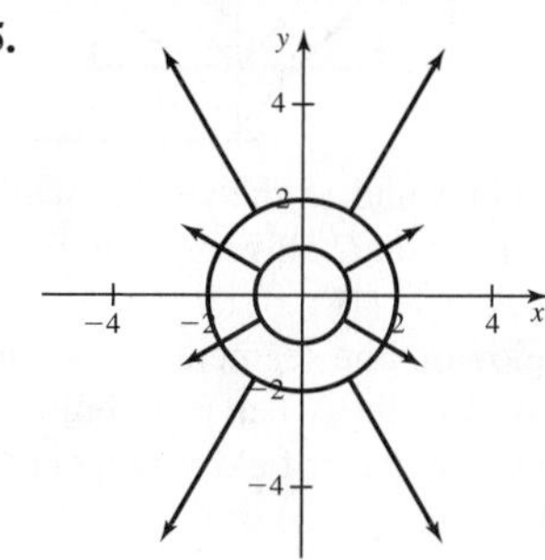

$\nabla\varphi(x, y) = 2\langle x, y \rangle$

27.

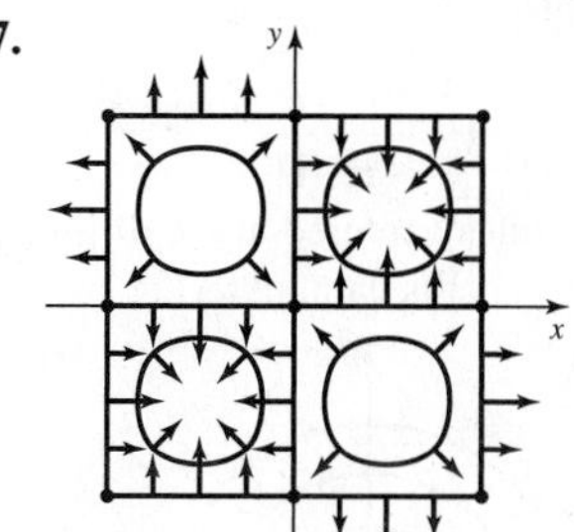

$\nabla\varphi(x, y) = \langle \cos x \sin y, \sin x \cos y \rangle$

29. $\nabla\varphi(x, y, z) = \langle x, y, z \rangle = \mathbf{r}$

31. $\nabla\varphi(x, y, z) = -(x^2 + y^2 + z^2)^{-3/2} \langle x, y, z \rangle = -\dfrac{\mathbf{r}}{|\mathbf{r}|^3}$

33. a. $\nabla\varphi(x, y) = \langle 2, 3\rangle$ **b.** $y' = -2/3$, $\left\langle 1, -\frac{2}{3}\right\rangle \cdot \nabla\varphi(1, 1) = 0$ **c.** $y' = -2/3$, $\left\langle 1, -\frac{2}{3}\right\rangle \cdot \nabla\varphi(x, y) = 0$ **d.**

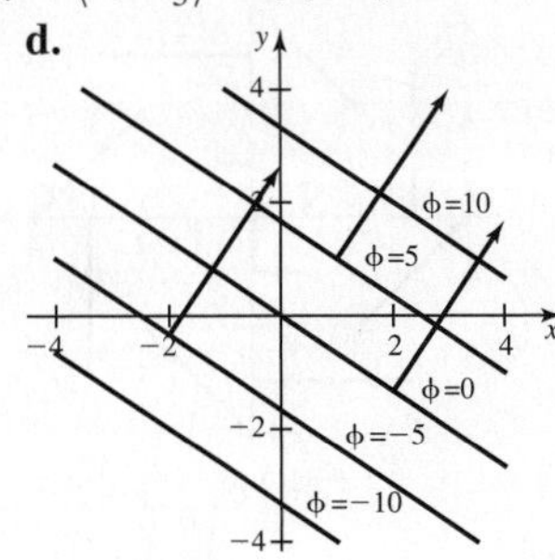

35. a. $\nabla\varphi(x, y) = \langle e^{x-y}, -e^{x-y}\rangle = e^{x-y}\langle 1, -1\rangle$
b. $y' = 1$, $\langle 1, 1\rangle \cdot \nabla\varphi(1, 1) = 0$
c. $y' = 1$, $\langle 1, 1\rangle \cdot \nabla\varphi(x, y) = 0$
d.

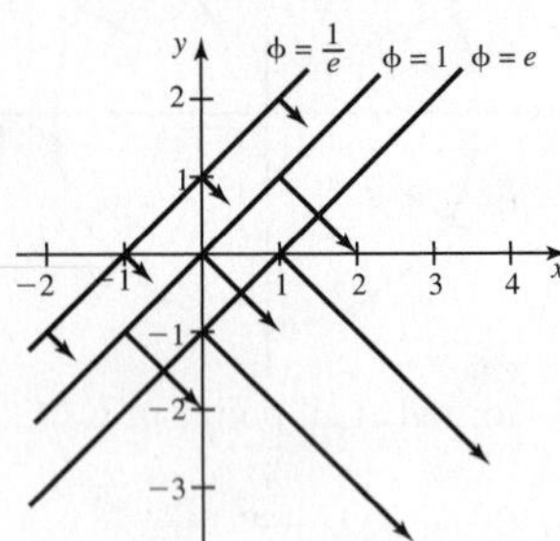

37. a. True **b.** False **c.** True

39.

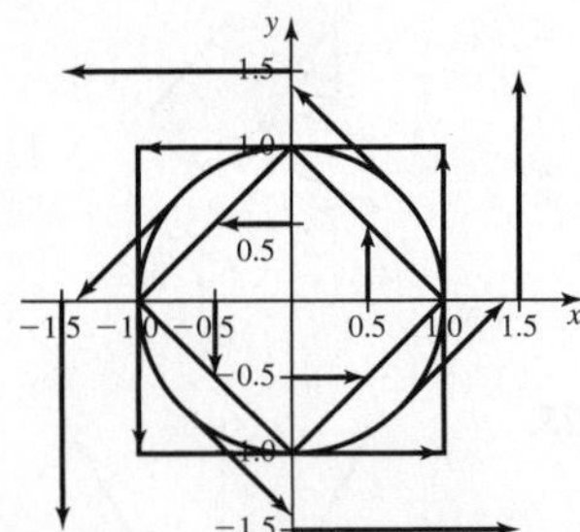

a. For S and D, the vectors with maximum magnitude occur at the vertices; on C all vectors on the boundary have the same maximum magnitude ($|\mathbf{F}| = 1$). **b.** For S and D the field is directed out of the region on line segments between any vertex and the midpoint of the boundary line when proceeding in a counterclockwise direction; on C the vector field is tangent to the boundary curve everywhere.

41. $\mathbf{F} = \langle -y, x\rangle$ or $\mathbf{F} = \langle -1, 1\rangle$

43. $\mathbf{F}(x, y) = \dfrac{\langle x, y\rangle}{\sqrt{x^2 + y^2}} = \dfrac{\mathbf{r}}{|\mathbf{r}|}$, $\mathbf{F}(0, 0) = \mathbf{0}$

45. a. $E = \dfrac{c}{x^2 + y^2}\langle x, y\rangle$ **b.** $E = \dfrac{c}{|\mathbf{r}|^2}\mathbf{r} = \dfrac{c}{|\mathbf{r}|}\dfrac{\mathbf{r}}{|\mathbf{r}|}$
c. *Hint:* The equipotential curves are circles centered at the origin.

47. The tangent vector $\mathbf{v} = \langle 1, y'(x)\rangle$ to $y(x)$ is parallel to $\mathbf{F}$.

49.

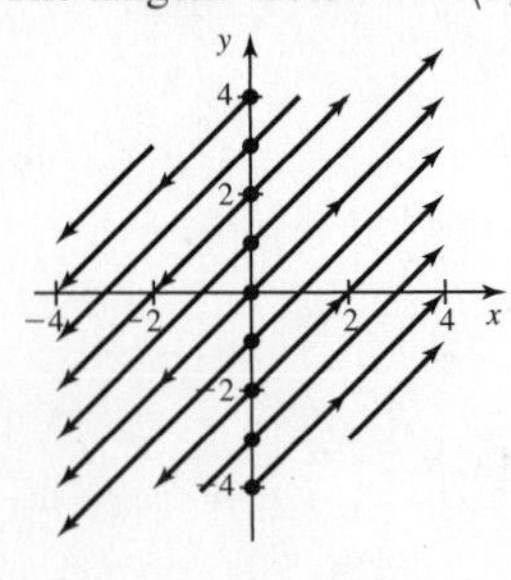

$y = x + C$

51.

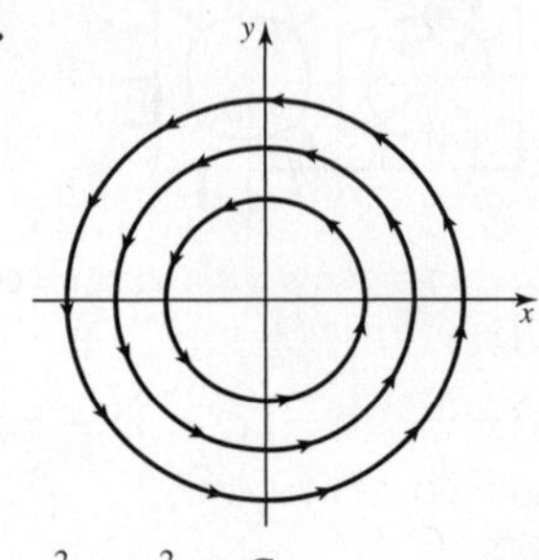

$x^2 + y^2 = C$

53. For $\theta = 0$: $\mathbf{u}_r = \mathbf{i}$ and $\mathbf{u}_\theta = \mathbf{j}$
for $\theta = \frac{\pi}{2}$: $\mathbf{u}_r = \mathbf{j}$ and $\mathbf{u}_\theta = -\mathbf{i}$
for $\theta = \pi$: $\mathbf{u}_r = -\mathbf{i}$ and $\mathbf{u}_\theta = -\mathbf{j}$
for $\theta = \frac{3\pi}{2}$: $\mathbf{u}_r = -\mathbf{j}$ and $\mathbf{u}_\theta = \mathbf{i}$

55.

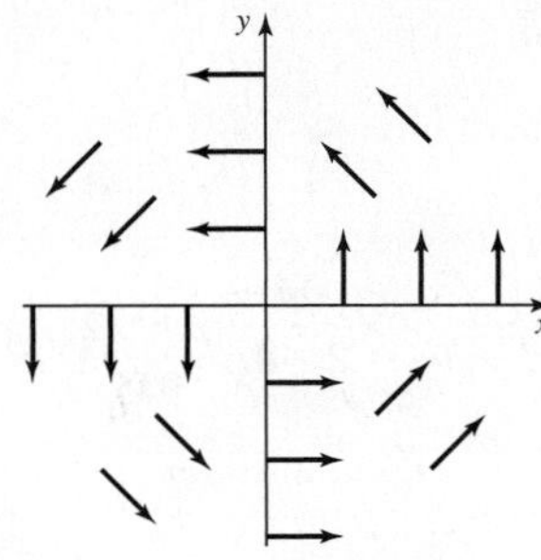

$\mathbf{F} = \dfrac{1}{\sqrt{x^2 + y^2}}\langle -y, x\rangle$

57.

$\mathbf{F} = r\,\mathbf{u}_\theta$

Section 15.2 Exercises, pp. 973–977

1. A line integral is taken along a curve, an ordinary single-variable integral is taken along an interval. **3.** $\sqrt{1 + 4t^2}$ **5.** The integrand of the alternate form is a dot product of $\mathbf{F}$ and $\mathbf{T}\,ds$. **7.** Take the line integral of $\mathbf{F}\cdot\mathbf{T}$ along the curve with arc length as the parameter. **9.** Take the line integral of $\mathbf{F}\cdot\mathbf{n}$ along the curve with arc length as the parameter, where $\mathbf{n}$ is the outward normal vector of the curve. **11.** 0 **13.** $-\frac{32}{3}$ **15. a.** $\mathbf{r}(t) = \langle 4\cos t, 4\sin t\rangle, 0 \le t \le 2\pi$ **b.** $|\mathbf{r}'(t)| = 4$ **c.** 128π **17. a.** $\mathbf{r}(t) = \langle t, t\rangle, 1 \le t \le 10$ **b.** $|\mathbf{r}'(t)| = \sqrt{2}$ **c.** $\dfrac{\sqrt{2}}{2}\ln 10$ **19. a.** $\mathbf{r}(t) = \langle 2\cos t, 4\sin t\rangle$, $0 \le t \le \pi$ **b.** $|\mathbf{r}'(t)| = 2\sqrt{\sin^2 t + 4\cos^2 t}$ **c.** $-8\left[2 + \dfrac{1}{\sqrt{3}}\ln(2 + \sqrt{3})\right] = -22.0828$ **21.** $\dfrac{15}{2}$ **23.** 0 **25.** 0 **27.** $\dfrac{3\sqrt{14}}{2}$ **29.** $-2\pi^2\sqrt{10}$ **31.** $\sqrt{101}$ **33.** $\frac{17}{2}$ **35.** 49 **37.** $\dfrac{3}{4\sqrt{10}}$ **39.** 0 **41.** 16 **43.** 0 **45.** $\dfrac{3\sqrt{3}}{10}$ **47.** 0 **49. a.** Negative **b.** -4π **51. a.** True **b.** True **c.** True **d.** True **53. a.** Both paths require the same work: $W = 28{,}200$. **b.** Both curves require the same work: $W = 28{,}200$. **55. a.** $\dfrac{5\sqrt{5} - 1}{12}$ **b.** $\dfrac{5\sqrt{5} - 1}{12}$ **c.** The results are identical. **57.** *Hint:* $\displaystyle\int_C \mathbf{F}\cdot\mathbf{T}\,ds = \pi r^2(c - b)$ **59.** *Hint:* $\displaystyle\int_C \mathbf{F}\cdot\mathbf{n}\,ds = \pi r^2(a + d)$ **61.** The work equals zero for all three paths. **63.** 409.5 **65. a.** $\ln a$ **b.** No **c.** $\dfrac{1}{6}\left(1 - \dfrac{1}{a^2}\right)$ **d.** Yes **e.** $W = \dfrac{3^{1-p/2}}{2 - p}(a^{2-p} - 1)$ for $p \ne 2$; otherwise $W = \ln a$. **f.** $p > 2$ **67.** ab

Section 15.3 Exercises, pp. 984–986

1. A simple curve has no self-intersections; the initial and terminal points of a closed curve are identical. **3.** Test for equality of partial derivatives as given in Theorem 14.3. **5.** Integrate f with respect to x and make the constant of integration a function of y to obtain $\varphi = \int f\,dx + h(y)$; finally set $\frac{\partial \varphi}{\partial y} = g$ in order to determine h. **7.** The integral must be zero. **9.** Conservative **11.** Conservative **13.** Conservative **15.** $\varphi(x, y) = \frac{1}{2}(x^2 + y^2)$ **17.** Not conservative **19.** $\varphi(x, y) = \sqrt{x^2 + y^2}$ **21.** $\varphi(x, y, z) = xz + y$ **23.** $\varphi(x, y, z) = xy + yz + zx$ **25.** $\varphi(x, y) = \sqrt{x^2 + y^2 + z^2}$ **27.** 0 **29.** 4 **31.** 2 **33.** 0 **35.** 0 **37.** 0 **39. a.** False **b.** True **c.** True **d.** True **41.** $-\frac{1}{2}$ **43.** 0 **45.** 10 **47.** 25 **49.** C_1 negative, C_2 positive **53. a.** Compare partial derivatives. **b.** $\varphi(x, y, z) = \dfrac{GMm}{\sqrt{x^2 + y^2 + z^2}} = \dfrac{GMm}{|\mathbf{r}|}$ **c.** $\varphi(B) - \varphi(A) = GMm\left(\dfrac{1}{r_2} - \dfrac{1}{r_1}\right)$. **d.** No **55. a.** $\dfrac{\partial}{\partial y}\left[\dfrac{-y}{(x^2 + y^2)^{p/2}}\right] = \dfrac{-x^2 + (p - 1)y^2}{(x^2 + y^2)^{1+p/2}}$ and $\dfrac{\partial}{\partial x}\left[\dfrac{x}{(x^2 + y^2)^{p/2}}\right] = \dfrac{-(p - 1)x^2 + y^2}{(x^2 + y^2)^{1+p/2}}$ **b.** The two partial derivatives in (a) are equal if $p = 2$. **c.** $\varphi(x, y) = \tan^{-1}(y/x)$ **59.** $\varphi(x, y) = \frac{1}{2}(x^2 + y^2)$, **61.** $\varphi(x, y) = \frac{1}{2}(x^4 + x^2y^2 + y^4)$

Section 15.4 Exercises, pp. 996–998

1. In both forms the integral of a *derivative* is computed from boundary data. **3.** y^2 **5.** Area $= \frac{1}{2}\oint_C (x\,dy - y\,dx)$, where C encloses the region **7.** The integral in the flux form of Green's Theorem vanishes. **9.** $\mathbf{F} = \langle y, x \rangle$

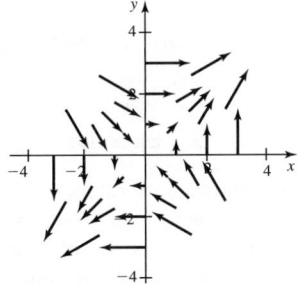

11. a. 0 **b.** Both integrals are zero. **c.** Yes **13. a.** -4 **b.** Both integrals equal -8. **c.** No **15. a.** 0 **b.** Both integrals are zero. **c.** Yes **17.** 25π **19.** 16π **21.** 32 **23. a.** 2 **b.** Both integrals equal 8π **c.** No **25. a.** 0 **b.** Both integrals equal zero. **c.** Yes **27. a.** 0 **b.** Both integrals equal zero. **c.** Yes **29.** 6; not source free **31.** $\frac{8}{3}$; not source free **33.** $\dfrac{23\pi^2}{2} - 48$; not conservative **35. a.** The circulation is zero. **b.** the outward flux equals 3π. **37. a.** The circulation is zero. **b.** The outward flux equals $-\dfrac{15\pi}{2}$. **39. a.** True **b.** False **c.** True **41.** The circulation is zero; the outward flux equals 2π. **43.** The circulation is 5702.4; the outward flux equals zero.

45. Note: $\dfrac{\partial f}{\partial y} = 0 = \dfrac{\partial g}{\partial x}$ **47.** The integral becomes $\iint_R 2\,dA$. **49. a.** $f_x = g_y = 0$ **b.** $\psi(x, y) = -2x + 4y$ **51. a.** $f_x = e^{-x}\sin y = -g_y$ **b.** $\psi(x, y) = e^{-x}\cos y$ **53. a.** *Hint:* $f_x = e^x\cos y$, $f_y = -e^x\sin y$, $g_x = -e^x\sin y$, $g_y = -e^x\cos y$ **b.** $\varphi(x, y) = e^x\cos y$, $\psi(x, y) = e^x\sin y$ **55. a.** *Hint:* $f_x = \dfrac{-y}{x^2 + y^2}$, $f_y = \dfrac{x}{x^2 + y^2}$, $g_x = \dfrac{x}{x^2 + y^2}$, $g_y = \dfrac{y}{x^2 + y^2}$. **b.** $\varphi(x, y) = x\arctan\left(\dfrac{y}{x}\right) + \dfrac{y}{2}\ln(x^2 + y^2) - y$, $\psi(x, y) = y\arctan\left(\dfrac{y}{x}\right) - \dfrac{x}{2}\ln(x^2 + y^2) + x$ **57. a.**

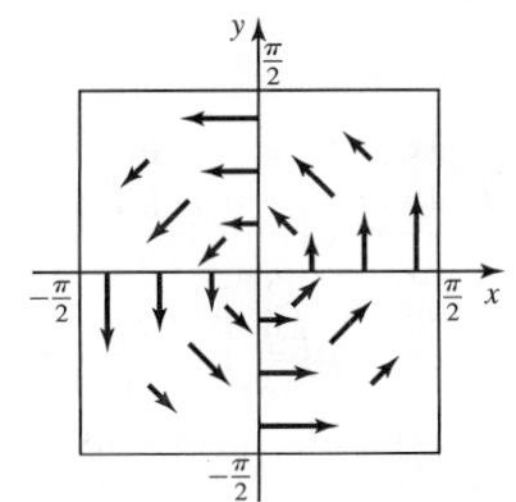

$\mathbf{F} = \langle -4\cos x\sin y, 4\sin x\cos y \rangle$ **b.** Yes, the divergence equals zero. **c.** No, the two-dimensional curl equals $8\cos x\cos y$. **d.** The total flux across the boundary is zero. **e.** The total circulation along C is 32. **59.** $\mathbf{F} = \left\langle \dfrac{f(x)}{d - c}, 0 \right\rangle$ for the rectangle $[a, b] \times [c, d]$. **61. c.** The vector field is undefined at the origin. **63.**

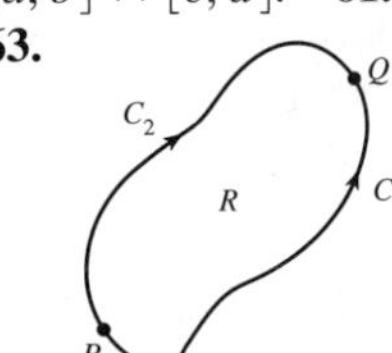

Basic ideas: Let C_1 and C_2 be two smooth simple curves from A to B.

$$\int_{C_1} \mathbf{F}\cdot\mathbf{n}\,ds - \int_{C_2} \mathbf{F}\cdot\mathbf{n}\,ds = \oint_C \mathbf{F}\cdot\mathbf{n}\,ds = \iint_R \operatorname{div}\mathbf{F}\,dA = 0$$

and $\displaystyle\int_{C_1} \mathbf{F}\cdot\mathbf{n}\,ds = \int_{C_1} \psi_x\,dx + \psi_y\,dy = \int_{C_1} d\psi = \psi(B) - \psi(A)$

65. Use $\nabla\varphi \cdot \nabla\psi = \langle f, g \rangle \cdot \langle -g, f \rangle = 0$

Section 15.5 Exercises, pp. 1006–1009

1. Compute $f_x + g_y + h_z$. **3.** There are no sources or sinks. **5.** It indicates the axis and the angular speed of the circulation at a point. **7.** Zero **9.** 3 **11.** 0 **13.** $2(x + y + z)$ **15.** $\dfrac{x^2 + y^2 + 3}{(1 + x^2 + y^2)^2}$ **17.** $\dfrac{1}{|\mathbf{r}|^2}$ **19.** $\dfrac{-1}{|\mathbf{r}|^4}$ **21. a.** Positive for both points **b.** $\operatorname{div}\mathbf{F} = 2$ **c.** Outward everywhere **d.** Positive **23. a.** $\operatorname{curl}\mathbf{F} = 2\mathbf{i}$ **b.** $|\operatorname{curl}\mathbf{F}| = 2$ **25. a.** $\operatorname{curl}\mathbf{F} = 2\mathbf{i} - 2\mathbf{j} + 2\mathbf{k}$ **b.** $|\operatorname{curl}\mathbf{F}| = 2\sqrt{3}$ **27.** $3y\mathbf{k}$ **29.** $-4z\mathbf{j}$ **31.** $\mathbf{0}$ **33.** $\mathbf{0}$ **35.** Follows from partial differentiation of $\dfrac{1}{(x^2 + y^2 + z^2)^{3/2}}$

37. Combine Exercise 36 with Theorem 14.8. **39. a.** False **b.** False **c.** False **d.** False **e.** False **41. a.** No **b.** No **c.** Yes, scalar function **d.** No **e.** No **f.** No **g.** Yes, vector field **h.** No **i.** Yes, vector field **43.** Compute an explicit expression for $\mathbf{a} \times \mathbf{r}$ and then take the required partial derivatives. **45.** $\operatorname{div} \mathbf{F} = 6$ at $(1, 1, 1)$, $(1, -1, -1)$, $(-1, 1, 1)$, and $(-1, -1, -1)$. **47.** $\mathbf{n} = \langle a, b, 2a + b\rangle$, where a and b are real numbers **49.** $\mathbf{F} = \frac{1}{2}(y^2 + z^2)\mathbf{i}$ **51. a.** The wheel does not spin. **b.** Clockwise, looking in the positive y-direction **c.** The wheel does not spin. **53.** $\omega = \dfrac{10}{\sqrt{3}}$, or $\dfrac{5}{\sqrt{3}\pi} = 0.9189$ revolutions per unit time.
55. $\mathbf{F} = -200ke^{-x^2+y^2+z^2}(-x\mathbf{i} + y\mathbf{j} + z\mathbf{k})$
$\nabla \cdot \mathbf{F} = -200k(1 + 2(x^2 + y^2 + z^2))e^{-x^2+y^2+z^2}$
57. a. $\mathbf{F} = \dfrac{GMm\mathbf{r}}{|\mathbf{r}|^3}$ **b.** See Theorem 14.9.

59.
$$\rho\left(\frac{\partial u}{\partial t} + u\frac{\partial u}{\partial x} + v\frac{\partial u}{\partial y} + w\frac{\partial u}{\partial z}\right) = -\frac{\partial p}{\partial x} + \mu\left(\frac{\partial^2 u}{\partial x^2} + \frac{\partial^2 u}{\partial y^2} + \frac{\partial^2 u}{\partial z^2}\right)$$
$$\rho\left(\frac{\partial v}{\partial t} + u\frac{\partial v}{\partial x} + v\frac{\partial v}{\partial y} + w\frac{\partial v}{\partial z}\right) = -\frac{\partial p}{\partial y} + \mu\left(\frac{\partial^2 v}{\partial x^2} + \frac{\partial^2 v}{\partial y^2} + \frac{\partial^2 v}{\partial z^2}\right)$$
$$\rho\left(\frac{\partial w}{\partial t} + u\frac{\partial w}{\partial x} + v\frac{\partial w}{\partial y} + w\frac{\partial w}{\partial z}\right) = -\frac{\partial p}{\partial z} + \mu\left(\frac{\partial^2 w}{\partial x^2} + \frac{\partial^2 w}{\partial y^2} + \frac{\partial^2 w}{\partial z^2}\right)$$

61. a. Use $\nabla \times \mathbf{B} = -Ak\cos(kz - \omega t)\mathbf{i}$ and $\dfrac{\partial \mathbf{E}}{\partial t} = -A\omega\cos(kz - \omega t)\mathbf{i}$. **b.**

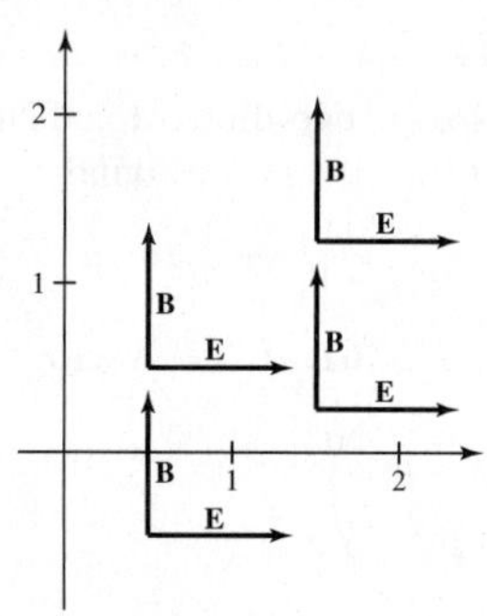

Section 15.6 Exercises, pp. 1022–1025

1. $\mathbf{r}(u, v) = \langle a\cos u, a\sin u, v\rangle$, $0 \le u \le 2\pi$, $0 \le v \le h$
3. $\mathbf{r}(u, v) = \langle a\sin u\cos v, a\sin u\sin v, a\cos u\rangle$, $0 \le u \le \pi$, $0 \le v \le 2\pi$ **5.** Use the parameterization from Problem 3 and compute

$$\int_0^{\pi}\int_0^{2\pi} f(a\sin u\cos v, a\sin u\sin v, a\cos u)\, a^2\sin u\, du\, dv.$$

7. Use the parametrization from Problem 3 and compute

$$\int_0^{\pi}\int_0^{2\pi} a^2\sin u\,(f\sin u\cos v + g\sin u\sin v + h\cos u)\, dv\, du.$$

9. The normal vectors point outward. **11.** $\langle u, v, \frac{1}{3}(16 - 2u + 4v)\rangle$, $|u| < \infty$, $|v| < \infty$ **13.** $\langle v\cos u, v\sin u, v\rangle$, $0 \le u \le 2\pi$, $2 \le v \le 8$ **15.** $\langle 3\cos u, 3\sin u, v\rangle$, $0 \le u \le \dfrac{\pi}{2}$, $0 \le v \le 3$
17. A plane above the square $[1, 3] \times [2, 4]$ **19.** Part of the upper half of the cone $z^2 = 16x^2 + 16y^2$ of height 12 and radius 3 (with $y \ge 0$) **21.** 28π **23.** $16\sqrt{3}$ **25.** $\pi r\sqrt{r^2 + h^2}$ **27.** 1728π

29. 0 **31.** $4\pi\sqrt{5}$ **33.** $8\sqrt{17} + 2\ln(\sqrt{17} + 4) = 37.1743$ **35.** $\dfrac{2\sqrt{3}}{3}$ **37.** $\dfrac{1250\pi}{3}$ **39.** $\dfrac{1}{48}(e - e^{-5} - e^{-7} + e^{-13})$ **41.** $\dfrac{1}{4\pi}$
43. -8 **45.** 0 **47.** $4\pi a$ **49. a.** True **b.** False **c.** True **d.** True
51. $8\pi(4\sqrt{17} + \ln(\sqrt{17} + 4))$ **53.** $8\pi a$ **55. a.** 8 **b.** $4\pi - 8$
57. a. 0 **b.** 0 The flow is always tangential to the surface (radial flow). **59.** $2\pi ah$ **61.** $-400\left(e - \dfrac{1}{e}\right)^2$ **63.** $8\pi a$
65. a. $4\pi(b^3 - a^3)$ **b.** The net flux is zero. **67.** $\left(0, 0, \frac{2}{3}h\right)$
69. $\left(0, 0, \frac{7}{6}\right)$ **73.** Flux $= \displaystyle\iint_S \mathbf{F}\cdot\mathbf{n}\, dS = \iint_A dx\, dy$

Section 15.7 Exercises, pp. 1032–1034

1. The integral measures the circulation along the closed curve C.
3. The circulation along a closed curve can be calculated by integrating the dot product of the curl and the normal vector on an enclosed surface. **5.** -2π for both integrals. **7.** Both integrals are zero.
9. -18π for both integrals. **11.** -24π **13.** $-\frac{128}{3}$ **15.** 15π
17. 0 **19.** -32π **21.** $\nabla \times \mathbf{v} = \langle 1, 0, 0\rangle$; a paddle wheel with its axis aligned with the x-axis will spin with maximum angular speed counterclockwise (looking in the negative x-direction) at all points.
23. $\nabla \times \mathbf{v} = \langle 0, -2, 0\rangle$; a paddle wheel with its axis aligned with the y-axis will spin with maximum angular speed clockwise (looking in the negative y-direction) at all points. **25. a.** False **b.** False **c.** True **d.** True **27.** The circulation is zero. **29.** The circulation is zero.
31. 2π **33.** $\pi(\cos\varphi - \sin\varphi)$, maximum for $\varphi = 0$ **35.** The circulation is 48π; it depends on the radius of the circle but not on the center.
37. a. The normal vectors point toward the z-axis on the curved surface of S and in the direction of $\langle 0, 1, 0\rangle$ on the flat surface of S.
b. 2π **c.** 2π **39.** The integral is π for all a. **41.** The integral is zero for (a) and (b). **43. b.** 2π for any circle of radius r centered at the origin. **c.** $\mathbf{F}$ is not differentiable along the z-axis. **45.** Apply the Chain Rule. **47.** $\displaystyle\int_C \mathbf{F}\cdot d\mathbf{r} = \iint_R \frac{\partial h}{\partial y} - \frac{\partial g}{\partial z}\, dA$

Section 15.8 Exercises, pp. 1043–1046

1. The surface integral measures the flow across the boundary.
3. The flux across the boundary equals the cumulative expansion or contraction of the vector field inside the region. **5.** 32π
7. The outward fluxes are equal to each other. **9.** Both integrals equal 96π. **11.** Both integrals are zero. **13.** The net flux is zero.
15. The net flux is zero. **17.** $16\sqrt{6}\pi$ **19.** $\frac{2}{3}$ **21.** $-\frac{128}{3}\pi$
23. 24π **25.** -224π **27.** 12π **29.** 20 **31. a.** False **b.** False **c.** True **33.** 0 **35.** $\frac{3}{2}$ **37. b.** The net flux between the two spheres is $4\pi(a^2 - \varepsilon^2)$. **39. b.** Use $\nabla \cdot \mathbf{E} = 0$. **c.** The flux across S is the *sum* of the contributions from the individual charges.
d. For an arbitrary volume, we find

$$\frac{1}{\varepsilon_0}\iiint_D q(x, y, z)\, dV = \iint_S \mathbf{E}\cdot\mathbf{n}\, dS = \iiint_D \nabla\cdot\mathbf{E}\, dV.$$

e. Use $\nabla^2\varphi = \nabla\cdot\nabla\varphi$. **41.** 0 **43.** $-(1 - e^{-1})$ **45.** $800\pi a^3 e^{-a^2}$

Chapter 15 Review Exercises, pp. 1046–1049

1. a. False **b.** True **c.** False **d.** False **e.** True
3.

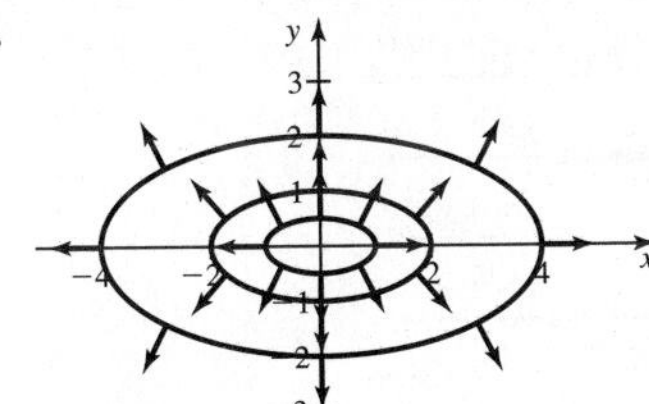

5. $-\frac{\mathbf{r}}{|\mathbf{r}|^3}$ **7. a.** $\mathbf{n} = \frac{1}{2}\langle x, y\rangle$ **b.** 0 **c.** $\frac{1}{2}$ **9.** $\frac{\sqrt{46}}{4}\left(e^{6(\ln 8)^2} - 1\right)$
11. Both integrals are zero. **13.** 0 **15.** The circulation is -4p; the outward flux is zero. **17.** The circulation is zero; the outward flux is 2p. **19.** $\frac{4v_0L^3}{3}$ **21.** $w(x, y, z) = xy + yz^2$ **23.** $w(x, y, z) = xye^z$
25. 0 for both methods **27. a.** $-$p **b.** F is not conservative.
29. 0 **31.** $\frac{20}{3}$ **33.** 8p **35.** The circulation is zero; the outward flux equals 2p. **37. a.** $b = c$ **b.** $a + d = 0$ **c.** $a + d = 0$ and $b = c$
39. $\nabla\cdot\mathbf{F} = 42\ \overline{x^2 + y^2 + z^2} = 4|r|$, $\nabla\times\mathbf{F} = 0$, $\nabla\cdot\mathbf{F} \neq 0$
41. $\nabla\cdot\mathbf{F} = 2y + 12xz^2$, $\nabla\times\mathbf{F} = 0$, $\nabla\cdot\mathbf{F} \neq 0$ **43. a.** -1 and 0
b. $\mathbf{n} = \frac{1}{\sqrt{3}}\langle -1, 1, 1\rangle$ **45.** 18p **47.** $41\overline{3}$ **49.** $\frac{81\overline{3}}{3}$
51. 8p **53.** $4\text{p}a^2$ **55. a.** Use $x = y = 0$ to confirm the highest point; use $z = 0$ to confirm the base. **b.** The hemisphere S has the greater surface area—$2\text{p}a^2$ for S versus $\frac{51\overline{5} - 1}{6}\text{p}a^2$ for T.
57. 0 **59.** 99p **61.** 0 **63.** $\frac{972}{5}$p **65.** $\frac{124}{5}$p **67.** $\frac{32}{3}$

CHAPTER 16

Section 16.1 pp. 1056–1058

1. (d) **3.** (a)
5.

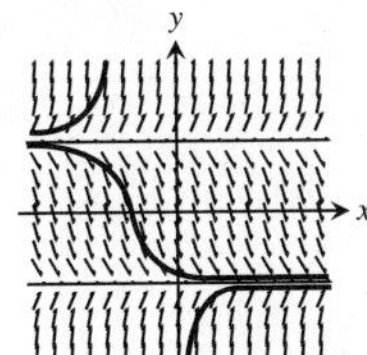

7. $y' = x - y$; $y(1) = -1$ **9.** $y' = -(1 + y)\sin x$; $y(0) = 2$
11. $y(\text{exact}) = \frac{x}{2} - \frac{4}{x}$, $y_1 = -0.25$, $y_2 = 0.3$, $y_3 = 0.75$
13. $y(\text{exact}) = 3e^{x(x+2)}$, $y_1 = 4.2$, $y_2 = 6.216$, $y_3 = 9.697$
15. $y(\text{exact}) = e^{x^2} + 1$, $y_1 = 2.0$, $y_2 = 2.0202$, $y_3 = 2.0618$
17. $y \approx 2.48832$, exact value is e.
19. $y \approx -0.2272$, exact value is $1/\left(1 - 2\sqrt{5}\right) \approx -0.2880$.
23.

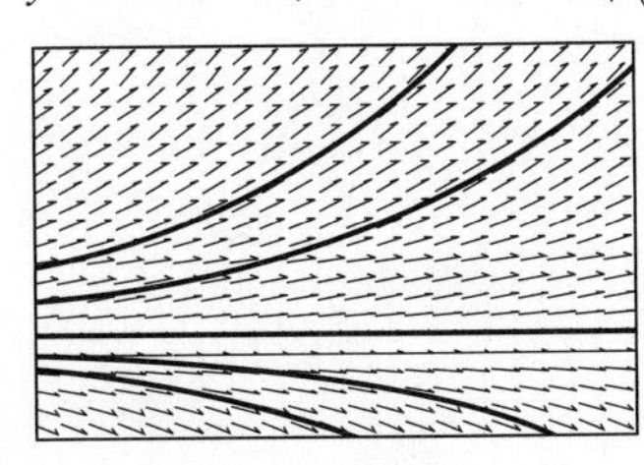

25.

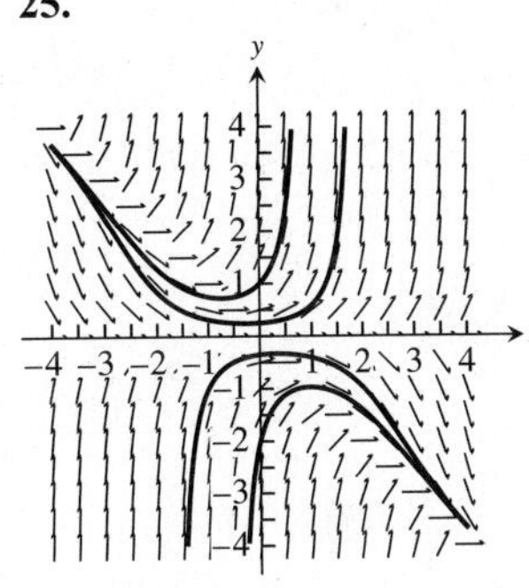

27.

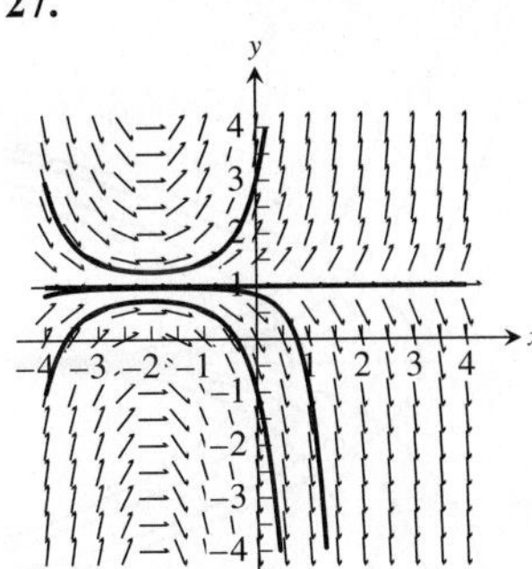

35. Euler's method gives $y \approx 3.45835$; the exact solution is $y = 1 + e \approx 3.71828$.
37. $y \approx 1.5000$; exact value is 1.5275.

Section 16.2, pp. 1063–1064

1. $y = \frac{e^x + C}{x}$, $x > 0$ **3.** $y = \frac{C - \cos x}{x^3}$, $x > 0$

5. $y = \frac{1}{2} - \frac{1}{x} + \frac{C}{x^2}$, $x > 0$ **7.** $y = \frac{1}{2}xe^{x/2} + Ce^{x/2}$

9. $y = x(\ln x)^2 + Cx$

11. $s = \frac{t^3}{3(t-1)^4} - \frac{t}{(t-1)^4} + \frac{C}{(t-1)^4}$
13. $r = (\csc\theta)(\ln|\sec\theta| + C)$, $0 < \theta < \pi/2$
15. $y = \frac{3}{2} - \frac{1}{2}e^{-2t}$ **17.** $y = -\frac{1}{\theta}\cos\theta + \frac{\pi}{2\theta}$

19. $y = 6e^{x^2} - \frac{e^{x^2}}{x + 1}$ **21.** $y = y_0e^{kt}$

23. **(b)** is correct, but **(a)** is not. **25.** $t = \frac{L}{R}\ln 2$ sec

27. **(a)** $i = \frac{V}{R} - \frac{V}{R}e^{-3} = \frac{V}{R}(1 - e^{-3}) \approx 0.95\frac{V}{R}$ amp **(b)** 86%

29. $y = \frac{1}{1 + Ce^{-x}}$ **31.** $y^3 = 1 + Cx^{-3}$

Section 16.3, pp. 1070–1071

1. **(a)** 168.5 m **(b)** 41.13 sec
3. $s(t) = 4.91\left(1 - e^{-(22.36/39.92)t}\right)$

5. $x^2 + y^2 = C$ **7.** $\ln|y| - \frac{1}{2}y^2 = \frac{1}{2}x^2 + C$

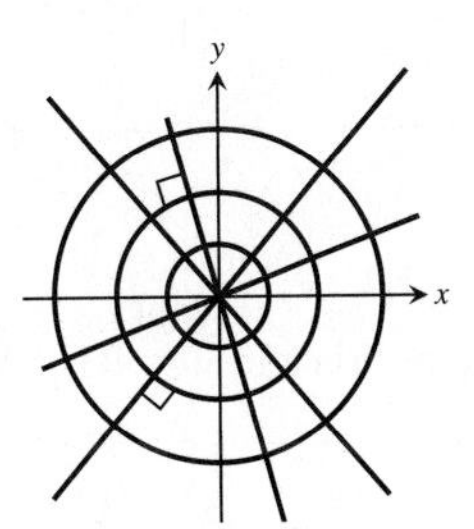

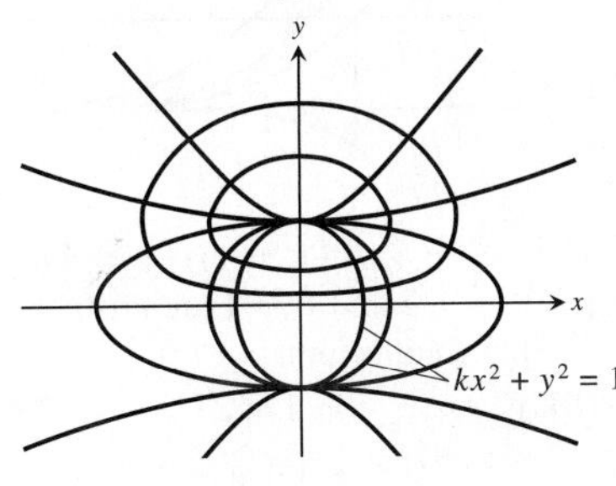

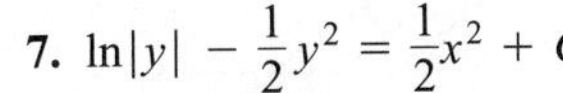

9. $y = \pm\sqrt{2x + C}$

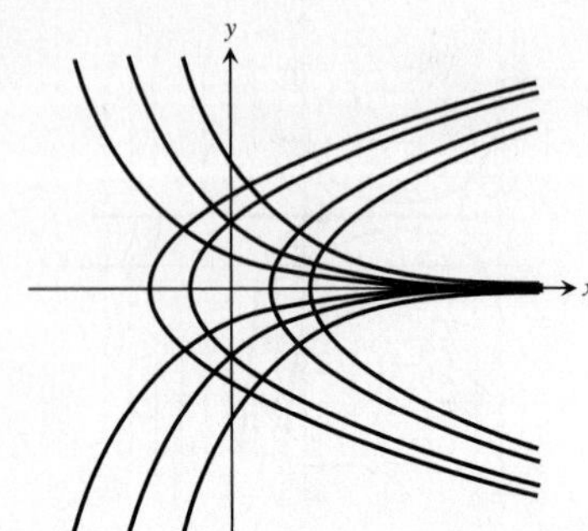

13. **(a)** 10 lb/min **(b)** $(100 + t)$ gal **(c)** $4\left(\frac{y}{100 + t}\right)$ lb/min

(d) $\frac{dy}{dt} = 10 - \frac{4y}{100 + t}$, $y(0) = 50$,

$$y = 2(100 + t) - \frac{150}{\left(1 + \frac{t}{100}\right)^4}$$

(e) Concentration $= \frac{y(25)}{\text{amt. brine in tank}} = \frac{188.6}{125} \approx 1.5$ lb/gal

15. $y(27.8) \approx 14.8$ lb, $t \approx 27.8$ min

Section 16.4, pp. 1076–1078

1. $y' = (y + 2)(y - 3)$

(a) $y = -2$ is a stable equilibrium value and $y = 3$ is an unstable equilibrium.

(b) $y'' = 2(y + 2)\left(y - \frac{1}{2}\right)(y - 3)$

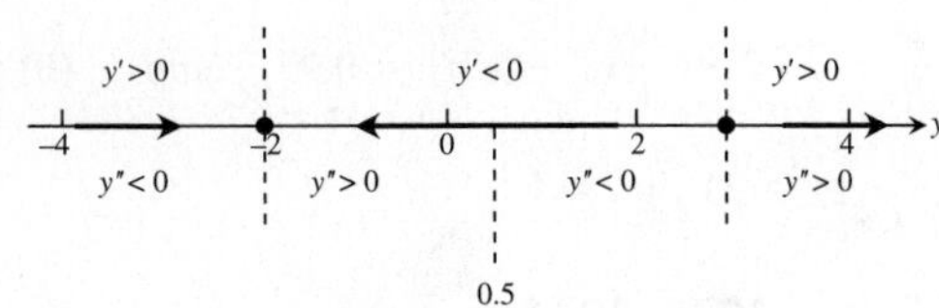

(c)

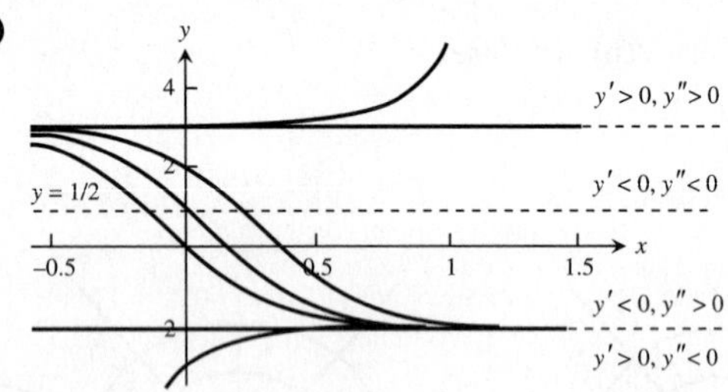

3. $y' = y^3 - y = (y + 1)y(y - 1)$

(a) $y = -1$ and $y = 1$ are unstable equilibria and $y = 0$ is a stable equilibrium.

(b) $y'' = (3y^2 - 1)y'$

$= 3(y + 1)(y + 1/\sqrt{3})y(y - 1/\sqrt{3})(y - 1)$

(c)

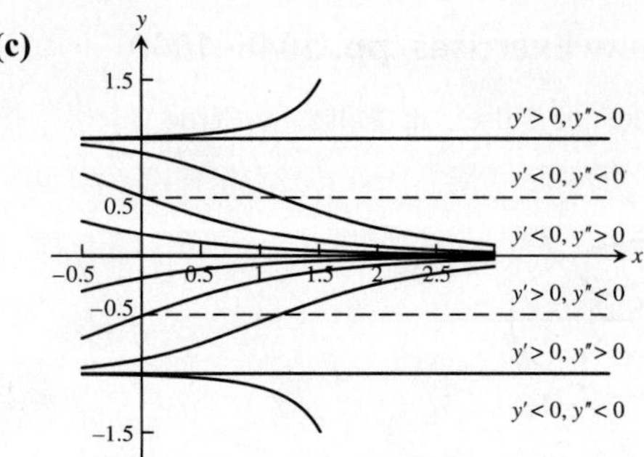

5. $y' = \sqrt{y}, y > 0$

(a) There are no equilibrium values.

(b) $y'' = \frac{1}{2}$

(c)

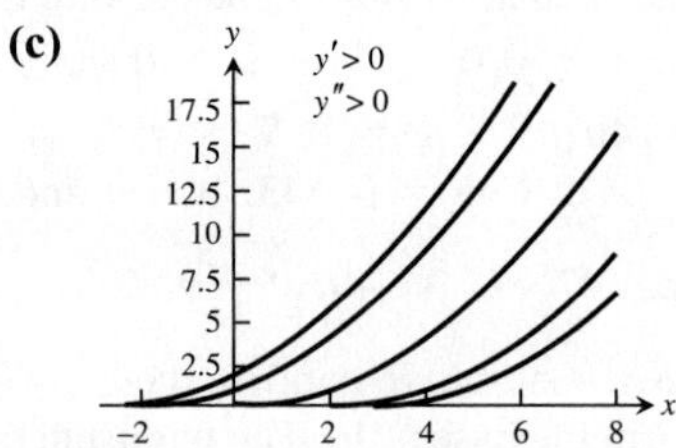

7. $y' = (y - 1)(y - 2)(y - 3)$

(a) $y = 1$ and $y = 3$ are unstable equilibria and $y = 2$ is a stable equilibrium.

(b) $y'' = (3y^2 - 12y + 11)(y - 1)(y - 2)(y - 3) =$

$$3(y - 1)\left(y - \frac{6 - \sqrt{3}}{3}\right)(y - 2)\left(y - \frac{6 + \sqrt{3}}{3}\right)(y - 3)$$

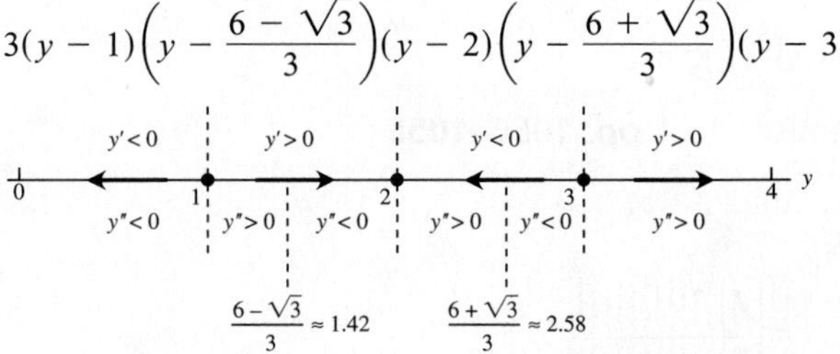

(c)

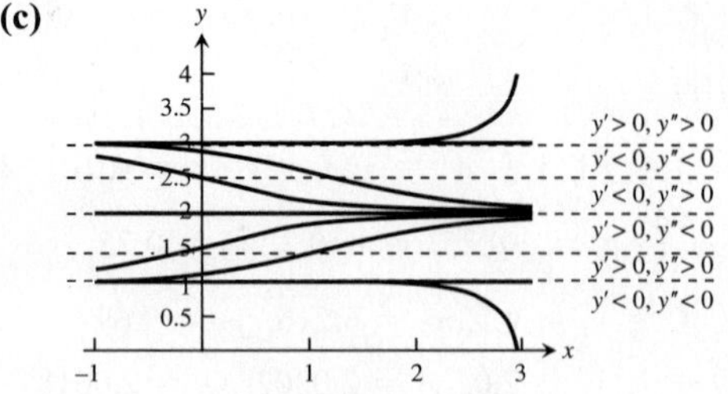

9. $\dfrac{dP}{dt} = 1 - 2P$ has a stable equilibrium at $P = \dfrac{1}{2}$;

$$\frac{d^2P}{dt^2} = -2\frac{dP}{dt} = -2(1 - 2P).$$

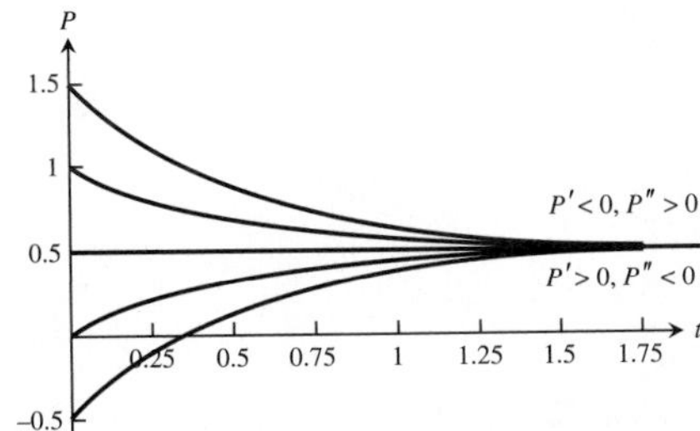

11. $\dfrac{dP}{dt} = 2P(P - 3)$ has a stable equilibrium at $P = 0$ and an unstable equilibrium at $P = 3$; $\dfrac{d^2P}{dt^2} = 2(2P - 3)\dfrac{dP}{dt} = 4P(2P - 3)(P - 3)$.

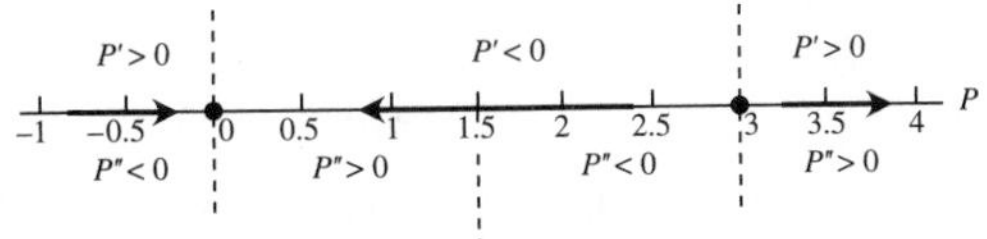

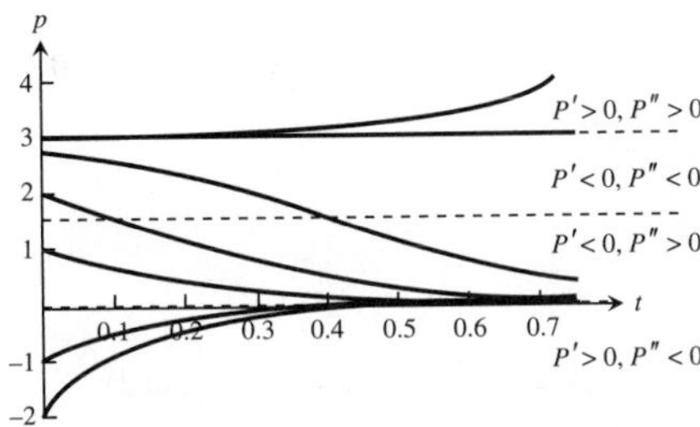

13. Before the catastrophe, the population exhibits logistic growth and $P(t)$ increases toward M_0, the stable equilibrium. After the catastrophe, the population declines logistically and $P(t)$ decreases toward M_1, the new stable equilibrium.

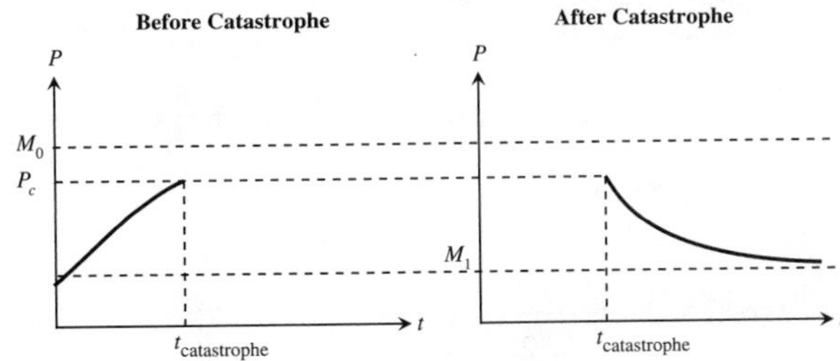

15. $\dfrac{dv}{dt} = g - \dfrac{k}{m}v^2, \quad g, k, m > 0$ and $v(t) \geq 0$

Equilibrium: $\dfrac{dv}{dt} = g - \dfrac{k}{m}v^2 = 0 \Rightarrow v = \sqrt{\dfrac{mg}{k}}$

Concavity: $\dfrac{d^2v}{dt^2} = -2\left(\dfrac{k}{m}v\right)\dfrac{dv}{dt} = -2\left(\dfrac{k}{m}v\right)\left(g - \dfrac{k}{m}v^2\right)$

(a)

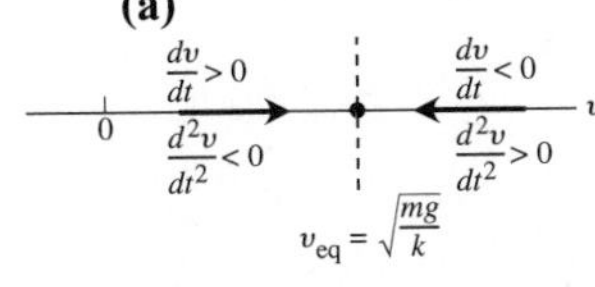

(b)

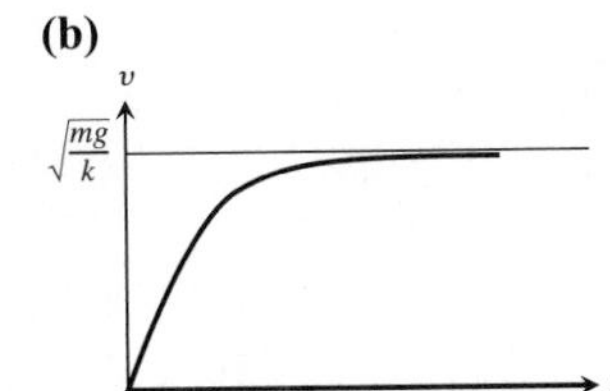

(c) $v_{\text{terminal}} = \sqrt{\dfrac{160}{0.005}} = 178.9 \text{ ft/sec} = 122 \text{ mph}$

17. $F = F_p - F_r$; $ma = 50 - 5|v|$; $\dfrac{dv}{dt} = \dfrac{1}{m}(50 - 5|v|)$. The maximum velocity occurs when $\dfrac{dv}{dt} = 0$ or $v = 10$ ft/sec.

19. Phase line:

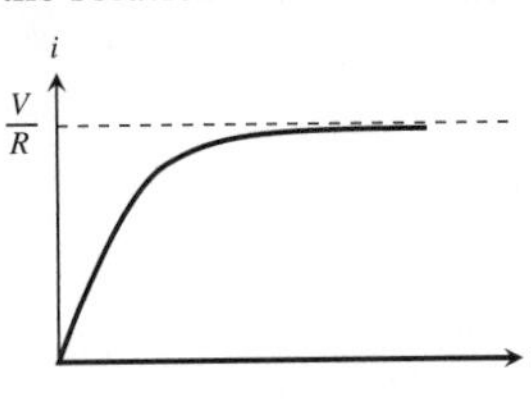

If the switch is closed at $t = 0$, then $i(0) = 0$, and the graph of the solution looks like this:

As $t \rightarrow \infty$, $i(t) \rightarrow i_{\text{steady state}} = \dfrac{V}{R}$.

Section 16.5, pp. 1081–1083

1. Seasonal variations, nonconformity of the environments, effects of other interactions, unexpected disasters, etc.

3. This model assumes that the number of interactions is proportional to the product of x and y:

$$\frac{dx}{dt} = (a - by)x, \quad a < 0,$$

$$\frac{dy}{dt} = m\left(1 - \frac{y}{M}\right)y - nxy = y\left(m - \frac{m}{M}y - nx\right).$$

Rest points are (0, 0), unstable, and (0, M), stable.

5. **(a)** Logistic growth occurs in the absence of the competitor, and involves a simple interaction between the species: growth dominates the competition when either population is small, so it is difficult to drive either species to extinction.

(b) a: per capita growth rate for trout
m: per capita growth rate for bass
b: intensity of competition to the trout
n: intensity of competition to the bass
k_1: environmental carrying capacity for the trout
k_2: environmental carrying capacity for the bass
$\dfrac{a}{b}$: growth versus competition or net growth of trout
$\dfrac{m}{n}$: relative survival of bass

(c) $\dfrac{dx}{dt} = 0$ when $x = 0$ or $y = \dfrac{a}{b} - \dfrac{a}{bk_1}x$,

$\dfrac{dy}{dt} = 0$ when $y = 0$ or $y = k_2 - \dfrac{k_2 n}{m}x$.

By picking $a/b > k_2$ and $m/n > k_1$, we insure that an equilibrium point exists inside the first quadrant.

Practice Exercises, pp. 1084–1085

1. $y = -\ln\left(C - \frac{2}{5}(x-2)^{5/2} - \frac{4}{3}(x-2)^{3/2}\right)$

3. $\tan y = -x \sin x - \cos x + C$ **5.** $(y+1)e^{-y} = -\ln|x| + C$

7. $y = C\frac{x-1}{x}$ **9.** $y = \frac{x^2}{4}e^{x/2} + Ce^{x/2}$

11. $y = \frac{x^2 - 2x + C}{2x^2}$ **13.** $y = \frac{e^{-x} + C}{1 + e^x}$ **15.** $xy + y^3 = C$

17. $y = \frac{2x^3 + 3x^2 + 6}{6(x+1)^2}$ **19.** $y = \frac{1}{3}(1 - 4e^{-x^3})$

21. $y = e^{-x}(3x^3 - 3x^2)$

23.

x	y
0	0
0.1	0.1000
0.2	0.2095
0.3	0.3285
0.4	0.4568
0.5	0.5946
0.6	0.7418
0.7	0.8986
0.8	1.0649
0.9	1.2411
1.0	1.4273

x	y
1.1	1.6241
1.2	1.8319
1.3	2.0513
1.4	2.2832
1.5	2.5285
1.6	2.7884
1.7	3.0643
1.8	3.3579
1.9	3.6709
2.0	4.0057

25. $y(3) \approx 0.8981$

27. **(a)**

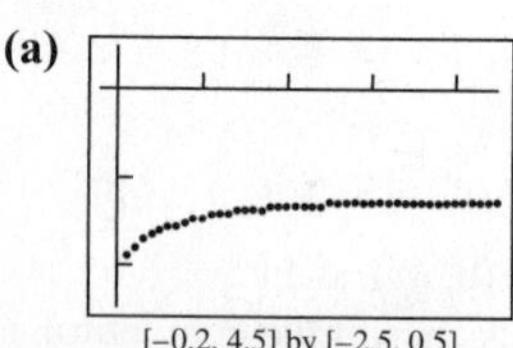

[−0.2, 4.5] by [−2.5, 0.5]

(b) Note that we choose a small interval of x-values because the y-values decrease very rapidly and our calculator cannot handle the calculations for $x \le -1$. (This occurs because the analytic solution is $y = -2 + \ln(2 - e^{-x})$, which has an asymptote at $x = -\ln 2 \approx -0.69$. Obviously, the Euler approximations are misleading for $x \le -0.7$.)

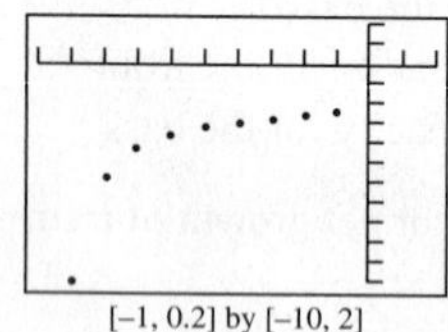

[−1, 0.2] by [−10, 2]

29. $y(\text{exact}) = \frac{1}{2}x^2 - \frac{3}{2}$; $y(2) \approx 0.4$; exact value is $\frac{1}{2}$.

31. $y(\text{exact}) = -e^{(x^2-1)/2}$; $y(2) \approx -3.4192$; exact value is $-e^{3/2} \approx -4.4817$.

33. **(a)** $y = -1$ is stable and $y = 1$ is unstable.

(b) $\frac{d^2y}{dx^2} = 2y\frac{dy}{dx} = 2y(y^2 - 1)$

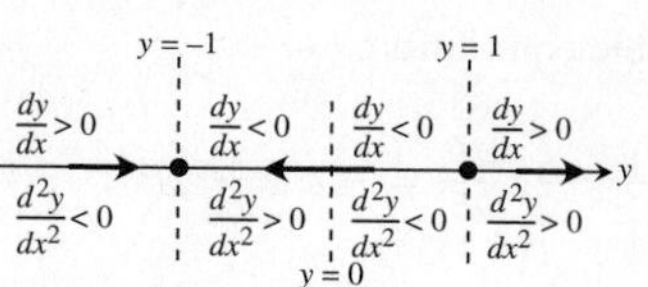

(c)

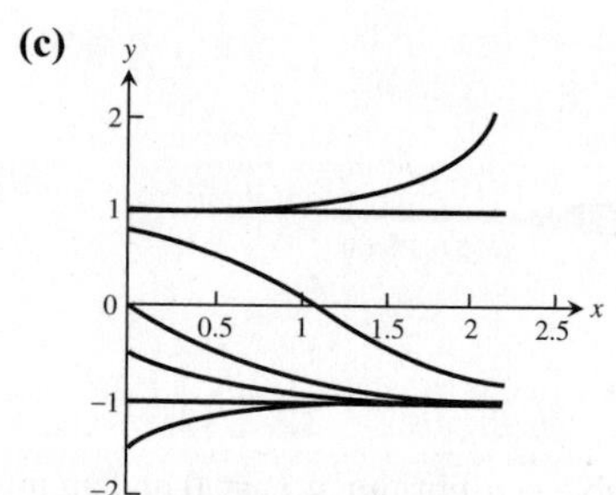

Additional and Advanced Exercises, pp. 1085–1086

1. **(a)** $y = c + (y_0 - c)e^{-k(A/V)t}$

(b) Steady-state solution: $y_\infty = c$

5. $x^2(x^2 + 2y^2) = C$

7. $\ln|x| + e^{-y/x} = C$

9. $\ln|x| - \ln|\sec(y/x - 1) + \tan(y/x - 1)| = C$

CHAPTER 17

Section 17.1 pp. 1093

1. $y = c_1e^{-3x} + c_2e^{4x}$ **3.** $y = c_1e^{-4x} + c_2e^{x}$

5. $y = c_1e^{-2x} + c_2e^{2x}$ **7.** $y = c_1e^{-x} + c_2e^{3x/2}$

9. $y = c_1e^{-x/4} + c_2e^{3x/2}$ **11.** $y = c_1\cos 3x + c_2\sin 3x$

13. $y = c_1\cos 5x + c_2\sin 5x$ **15.** $y = e^x(c_1\cos 2x + c_2\sin 2x)$

17. $y = e^{-x}\left(c_1\cos\sqrt{3}x + c_2\sin\sqrt{3}x\right)$

19. $y = e^{-2x}\left(c_1\cos\sqrt{5}x + c_2\sin\sqrt{5}x\right)$

21. $y = c_1 + c_2x$ **23.** $y = c_1e^{-2x} + c_2xe^{-2x}$

25. $y = c_1e^{-3x} + c_2xe^{-3x}$ **27.** $y = c_1e^{-x/2} + c_2xe^{-x/2}$

29. $y = c_1e^{-x/3} + c_2xe^{-x/3}$ **31.** $y = -\frac{3}{4}e^{-5x} + \frac{3}{4}e^{-x}$

33. $y = \frac{1}{2\sqrt{3}}\sin 2\sqrt{3}x$

35. $y = -\cos 2\sqrt{2}x + \frac{1}{\sqrt{2}}\sin 2\sqrt{2}x$

37. $y = (1 - 2x)e^{2x}$ **39.** $y = 2(1 + 2x)e^{-3x/2}$

41. $y = c_1e^{-x} + c_2e^{3x}$ **43.** $y = c_1e^{-x/2} + c_2xe^{-x/2}$

45. $y = c_1\cos\sqrt{5}x + c_2\sin\sqrt{5}x$ **47.** $y = c_1e^{-x/5} + c_2xe^{-x/5}$

49. $y = e^{-x/2}(c_1\cos x + c_2\sin x)$ **51.** $y = c_1e^{3x/4} + c_2xe^{3x/4}$

53. $y = c_1e^{-4x/3} + c_2xe^{-4x/3}$ **55.** $y = c_1e^{-x/2} + c_2e^{4x/3}$

57. $y = (1 + 2x)e^{-x}$ **59.** $y = \frac{15}{13}e^{-7x/3} + \frac{11}{13}e^{2x}$

Section 17.2, p. 1102

1. $y = c_1 e^{5x} + c_2 e^{-2x} + \frac{3}{10}$

3. $y = c_1 + c_2 e^{x} + \frac{1}{2}\cos x - \frac{1}{2}\sin x$

5. $y = c_1 \cos x + c_2 \sin x - \frac{1}{8}\cos 3x$

7. $y = c_1 e^{2x} + c_2 e^{-x} - 6\cos x - 2\sin x$

9. $y = c_1 e^{x} + c_2 e^{-x} - x^2 - 2 + \frac{1}{2}xe^{x}$

11. $y = c_1 e^{3x} + c_2 e^{-2x} - \frac{1}{4}e^{-x} + \frac{49}{50}\cos x + \frac{7}{50}\sin x$

13. $y = c_1 + c_2 e^{-5x} + x^3 + \frac{3}{5}x^2 - \frac{6}{25}x$

15. $y = c_1 + c_2 e^{3x} + 2x^2 + \frac{4}{3}x + \frac{1}{3}xe^{3x}$

17. $y = c_1 + c_2 e^{-x} + \frac{1}{2}x^2 - x$

19. $y = c_1 \cos x + c_2 \sin x - \frac{1}{2}x\cos x$

21. $y = (c_1 + c_2 x)e^{-x} + \frac{1}{2}x^2 e^{-x}$

23. $y = c_1 e^{x} + c_2 e^{-x} + \frac{1}{2}xe^{x}$

25. $y = e^{-2x}(c_1 \cos x + c_2 \sin x) + 2$

27. $y = A\cos x + B\sin x + x\sin x + \cos x \ln(\cos x)$

29. $y = c_1 + c_2 e^{5x} + \frac{1}{10}x^2 e^{5x} - \frac{1}{25}xe^{5x}$

31. $y = c_1 \cos x + c_2 \sin x - \frac{1}{2}x\cos x + x\sin x$

33. $y = c_1 + c_2 e^{x} + \frac{1}{2}e^{-x} + xe^{x}$

35. $y = c_1 e^{5x} + c_2 e^{-x} - \frac{1}{8}e^{x} - \frac{4}{5}$

37. $y = c_1 \cos x + c_2 \sin x - (\sin x)[\ln(\csc x + \cot x)]$

39. $y = c_1 + c_2 e^{8x} + \frac{1}{8}xe^{8x}$

41. $y = c_1 + c_2 e^{x} - x^4/4 - x^3 - 3x^2 - 6x$

43. $y = c_1 + c_2 e^{-2x} - \frac{1}{3}e^{x} + x^3/6 - x^2/4 + x/4$

45. $y = c_1 \cos x + c_2 \sin x + (x - \tan x)\cos x - \sin x \ln(\cos x)$
$= c_1 \cos x + c_2' \sin x + x\cos x - (\sin x)\ln(\cos x)$

47. $y = ce^{3x} - \frac{1}{2}e^{x}$

49. $y = ce^{3x} + 5xe^{3x}$

51. $y = 2\cos x + \sin x - 1 + \sin x \ln(\sec x + \tan x)$

53. $y = -e^{-x} + 1 + \frac{1}{2}x^2 - x$

55. $y = 2(e^{x} - e^{-x})\cos x - 3e^{-x}\sin x$

57. $y = (1 - x + x^2)e^{x}$

59. $y_p = \frac{1}{4}x^2$

Section 17.3, pp. 1107–1108

1. $my'' + y' + y = 0, \quad y(0) = 2, \ y'(0) = 2$

3. $\frac{25}{32}y'' + 40y = 0, \quad y(0) = \frac{5}{12}, \ y'(0) = \frac{v_0}{12}$

5. $2q'' + 4q' + 10q = 20\cos t, \quad q(0) = 2, \ q'(0) = 3$

7. 0.0864 ft (above equilibrium)

9. $y(t) = 0.2917\cos(7.1552t) + \frac{v_0}{85.8623}\sin(7.1552t)$ (in feet), or $y = 3.5\cos(7.1552t) + \frac{v_0}{0.1398}\sin(7.1552t)$ (in inches).

11. 0.308 sec **13.** 8.334 lb **15.** 24.4949 ft/sec

17. -1.56 ft/sec² (acceleration upward)

19. $q(t) = -8e^{-3t} + 10e^{-2t}, \quad \lim_{t\to\infty} q(t) = 0$

21. $y(t) = 1 + 2e^{-t} - \frac{1}{3}e^{-2t} - \frac{2}{3}e^{-8t}$

23. $y(\pi) = -2$ m (above equilibrium)

25. $q(t) = \frac{1}{5} + \left(\frac{49\sqrt{199}}{995}\sin\frac{\sqrt{199}}{2}t + \frac{49}{5}\cos\frac{\sqrt{199}}{2}t\right)e^{-t/2}$

Section 17.4, p. 1111

1. $y = \frac{c_1}{x^2} + c_2 x$ **3.** $y = \frac{c_1}{x^2} + c_2 x^3$

5. $y = c_1 x^2 + c_2 x^4$ **7.** $y = c_1 x^{-1/3} + c_2$

9. $y = x(c_1 + c_2 \ln x)$

11. $y = x[c_1 \cos(2\ln x) + c_2 \sin(2\ln x)]$

13. $y = \frac{1}{x}[c_1 \cos(3\ln x) + c_2 \sin(3\ln x)]$

15. $y = \frac{1}{\sqrt{x}}[c_1 \cos(\ln x) + c_2 \sin(\ln x)]$

17. $y = \frac{1}{x}(c_1 + c_2 \ln x)$ **19.** $y = c_1 + c_2 \ln x$

21. $y = \frac{1}{\sqrt[3]{x}}(c_1 + c_2 \ln x)$ **23.** $y = x^{-5/4}(c_1 + c_2 \ln x)$

25. $y = \frac{1}{2x^3} + \frac{x}{2}$ **27.** $y = x$

29. $y = x[-\cos(\ln x) + 2\sin(\ln x)]$

Section 17.5, p. 1116

1. $y = c_0 + c_1\left(x - x^2 + \frac{2}{3}x^3 - \cdots\right)$
$= c_0 - \frac{c_1}{2}e^{-2x}$

3. $y = c_0(1 - 2x^2 + \cdots) + c_1\left(x - \frac{2}{3}x^3 + \cdots\right)$
$= c_0 \cos 2x + c_1 \sin 2x$

5. $y = c_1 x + c_2 x^2$

7. $y = c_0\left(1 + \frac{1}{2}x^2 - \frac{1}{6}x^3 + \cdots\right) + c_1\left(x + \frac{1}{6}x^3 + \cdots\right)$

9. $y = c_0\left(1 - x^2 + \frac{5}{12}x^4 - \cdots\right) + c_1x$

11. $y = c_0(1 - 3x^2 + \cdots) + c_1(x - x^3)$

13. $y = c_0\left(1 + x^2 + \frac{2}{3}x^4 + \cdots\right) + c_1\left(x + x^3 + \frac{3}{5}x^5 + \cdots\right)$

15. $y = c_0\left(1 - \frac{3}{2}x^2 + \cdots\right) + c_1\left(x - \frac{1}{2}x^3 + \cdots\right)$

17. $y = c_0\left(1 - \frac{3}{2}x^2 + \frac{1}{8}x^4 + \cdots\right) + c_1\left(x - \frac{1}{3}x^3\right)$

CHAPTER 18

Section 18.1, p. 1121

1. $f(x) = 1$

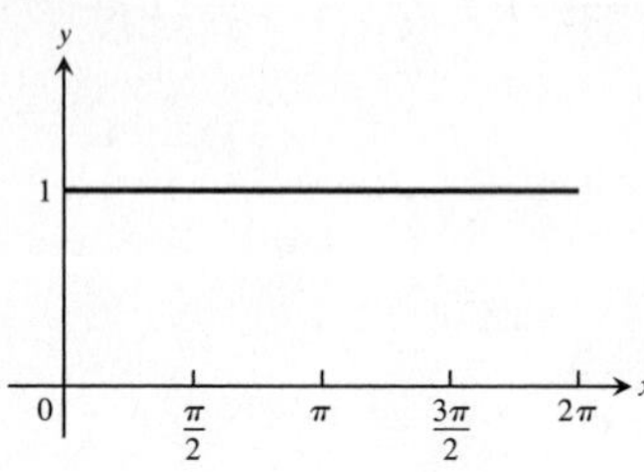

3. $f(x) = \sum_{n=1}^{\infty} \frac{2(-1)^{n+1}\sin(nx)}{n}$

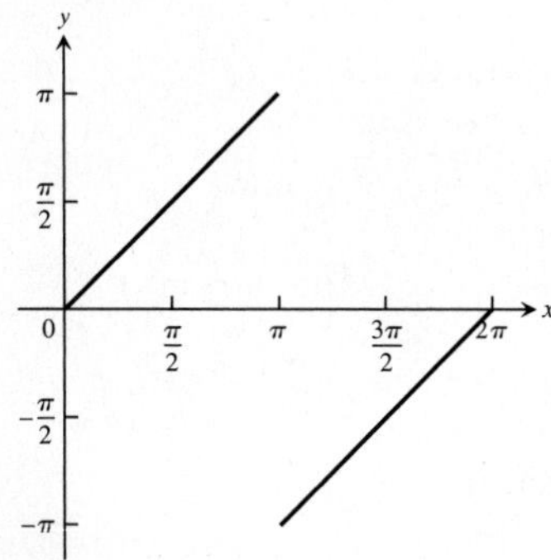

5. $\frac{e^{2\pi} - 1}{\pi}\left(\frac{1}{2} + \sum_{n=1}^{\infty} \frac{\cos(nx)}{n^2 + 1} - \sum_{n=1}^{\infty} \frac{n\sin(nx)}{n^2 + 1}\right)$

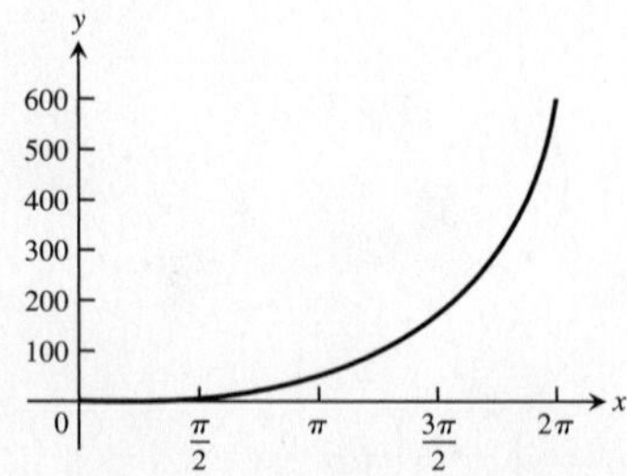

7. $f(x) = \frac{1}{2}\cos x + \frac{1}{\pi}\sum_{n=2}^{\infty} \frac{n(1 + (-1)^n)}{n^2 - 1}\sin nx$

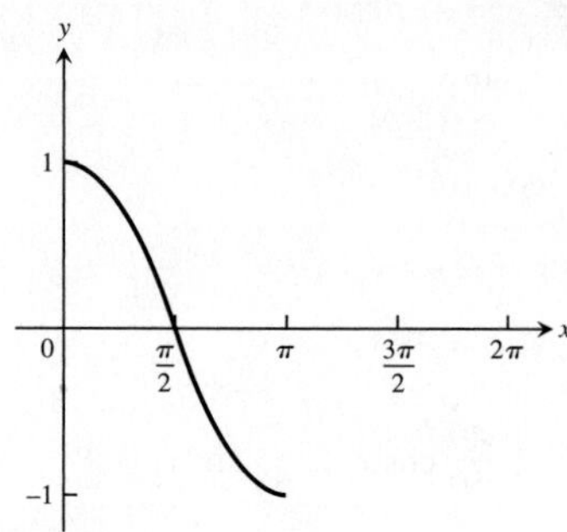

CHAPTER 19

Exercises 19.1, Pages 1123–1130

1. $\frac{1}{3}$ 3. $\frac{1}{2}$ 5. $\frac{9}{2}$ 7. $\frac{32}{3}$ 9. $\frac{1}{6}$ 11. $\frac{9}{2}$ 13. $\frac{1}{2}$ 15. $\frac{9}{2}$

17. 4 19. $\frac{44}{15}$ 21. $\frac{343}{6}$ 23. $\frac{22}{5}$ 25. $\frac{37}{12}$

Exercises 19.2, Pages 1130–1137

1. $\frac{26\pi}{3}$ 3. $\frac{178\pi}{15}$ 5. $\frac{8\pi}{3}$ 7. 2π 9. $\frac{\pi}{3}$ 11. $\frac{\pi}{3}$

13. 2π 15. 8π 17. $\frac{4\pi}{15}$ 19. $\frac{5\pi}{6}$ 21. $\frac{8\pi}{3}$ 23. $\frac{32\pi}{3}$

25. 60π 27. $\frac{100\pi\sqrt{5}}{9}$

Exercises 19.3, Page 1137–1141

1. 2π 3. 2π 5. 4π 7. $\frac{128\pi}{7}$ 9. $\frac{8\pi}{3}$ 11. $\frac{\pi}{3}$

13. $\frac{5\pi}{6}$ 15. $\frac{4\pi}{21}$ 17. $\frac{\pi}{2}$ 19. $\frac{16\pi}{5}$

Exercises 19.4, Pages 1142–1145

1. 15/7 3. −6.75 5. −6 7. $-\frac{11}{3}$ 9. 15 11. 40

13. 11 mi north of Flatville 15. (20/7, 22/7) 17. (−3.8, −7.2)

19. (2.1, −8.4) 21. 100 23. 1.50 mi east and 2.56 mi south of A

Exercises 19.5, Pages 1146–1157

1. 10 cm 3. $\frac{20}{3}$ cm 5. 8.77 cm 7. 4 cm from given end

9. $(4\frac{2}{3}, 4\frac{2}{3})$ 11. (8, 2) 13. (0, 2.95) 15. $(\frac{27}{5}, \frac{9}{8})$

17. (1, −0.4) 19. (0, 1.6) 21. $(\frac{8}{15}, \frac{8}{21})$ 23. $\left(0, \frac{4}{3\pi}\right)$

25. $(\frac{7}{8}, 0)$ 27. $(\frac{3}{4}, 0)$ 29. $(0, \frac{2}{3})$

Exercises 19.6, Pages 1157–1164

1. 516; 3.79 **3.** 1965; 5.98 **5.** 963; 5.17 **7.** 759; 4.87 **9.** $\frac{64}{3}$; 0.894 **11.** $\frac{1}{7}$; 0.463 **13.** $\frac{64}{5}$; 0.894 **15.** 2; 1.41 **17.** 576π; 1.55 **19.** 2.29×10^4; 8.43 **21.** 1458π; 1.73 **23.** 4096π; 2.53

Exercises 19.7, Pages 1164–1174

1. $\frac{63}{4}$ **3.** 25 in.-lb **5.** 675 N cm or 6.75 J **7.** 2.896×10^{-14} J **9. (a)** 900 ft-lb **(b)** 1875 ft-lb **(c)** 2500 ft-lb **11.** 225,800 ft-lb **13.** 602,200 ft-lb **15.** 58,810 ft-lb **17.** 25,000 lb **19.** 352,800 N **21.** 710,500 N **23.** 166.4 lb **25.** 54,660 lb **27.** 21,902 lb **29.** $\frac{13}{3}$ **31.** $\frac{2}{5}$ **33.** 1.70 A

Chapter 19 Review, Pages 1178–1179

1. $\frac{16}{3}$ **2.** $\frac{2}{3}$ **3.** $\frac{1}{12}$ **4.** 8 **5.** $\frac{128}{15}$ **6.** 36 **7.** 8π **8.** 8π **9.** $\frac{\pi}{30}$ **10.** $\frac{8\pi}{3}$ **11.** $\frac{243\pi}{10}$ **12.** $\frac{99\pi}{2}$ **13.** $\frac{256\pi}{5}$ **14.** $\frac{63\pi}{2}$ **15.** 7.5 **16.** $(-1, -6.8)$ **17.** (9.6, 5.3) **18.** $(2\frac{2}{3}, 6\frac{2}{3})$ **19.** $(\frac{3}{2}, \frac{27}{5})$ **20.** $(3, -3.6)$ **21.** $(0, \frac{3}{2})$ **22.** $(\frac{5}{6}, 0)$ **23.** (0, 2) **24.** 462; 4.39 **25.** 192; 2.83 **26.** 576; 4.90 **27.** $\frac{8}{15}$; 0.447 **28.** $\frac{2\pi}{13}$; 0.519 **29.** $\frac{8\pi}{7}$; 0.845 **30.** 126π; 2.65 **31.** 200 in.-lb **32.** 2.62×10^{-16} J **33.** 130,000 ft-lb **34.** 49,920 lb **35.** 816,700 N **36.** 9.5 V **37.** 67.52 A **38.** 20 W

CHAPTER 19

Solutions to Odd-Numbered Exercises

Taken from Chapter 6 of *Student Solutions Manual to Accompany Technical Calculus,* Fifth Edition

Section 19.1 Exercises

1.

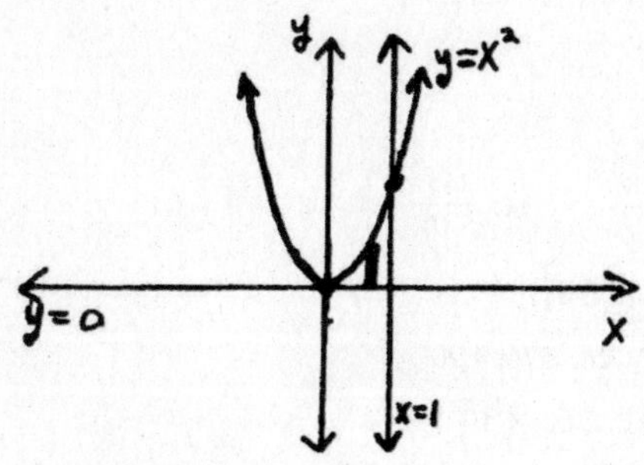

$$A = \int_0^1 x^2\,dx = x^3/3\Big|_0^1 = 1/3$$

3.

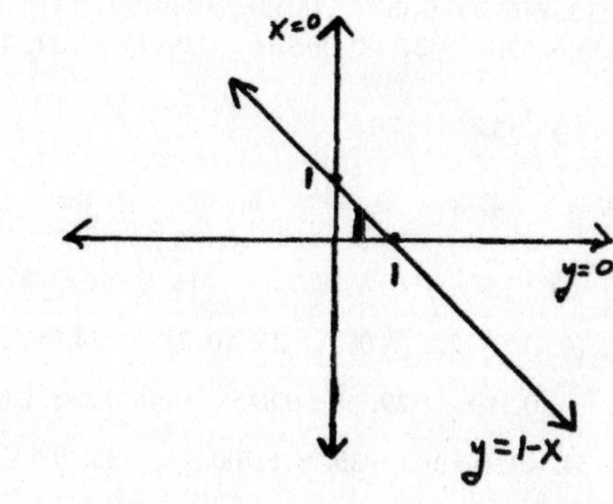

$$A = \int_0^1 (1-x)\,dx = x - x^2/2\Big|_0^1 = 1/2$$

5.

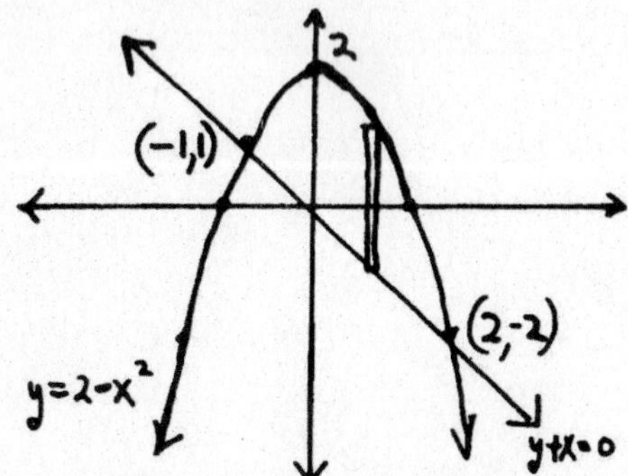

$$A = \int_{-1}^{2} [(2-x^2) - x(-x)]\,dx$$

$$= 2x - x^3/3 = x^2/2\Big|_{-1}^{2} = \frac{9}{2}$$

7.

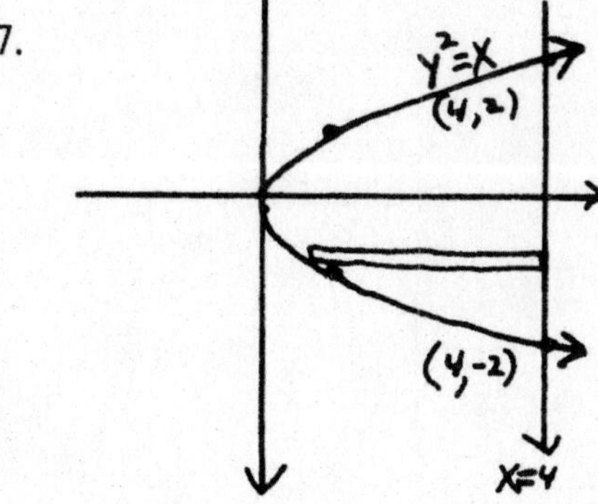

$$A = \int_{-2}^{2} (4-y^2)\,dy = 4y - \frac{y^3}{3}\Big|_{-2}^{2} = \frac{32}{3}$$

9.

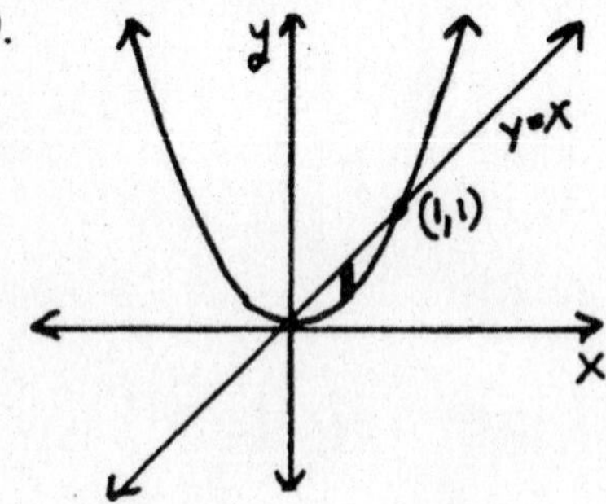

$$A = \int_0^1 (x - x^2)\,dx = x^2/2 - x^3/3\Big|_0^1 = 1/6$$

11.

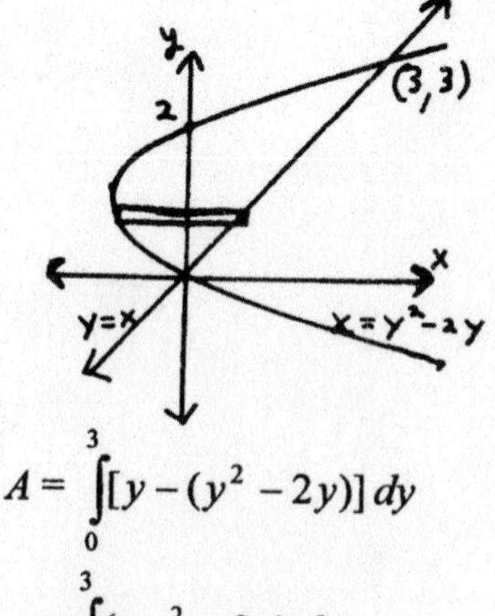

$$A = \int_0^3 [y - (y^2 - 2y)]\,dy$$

$$= \int_0^3 (-y^2 + 3y)\,dy$$

$$= (-y^3/3 + 3y^2/2)\Big|_0^3 = 9/2$$

13. $A = \int_{-1}^{0}(x^3 - x)\,dx + \int_{0}^{1}[0-(x^3 - x)]\,dx$

$= x^4/4 - x^2/2 \Big|_{-1}^{0} + (-x^4/4 + x^2/2)\Big|_{0}^{1} = 1/2$

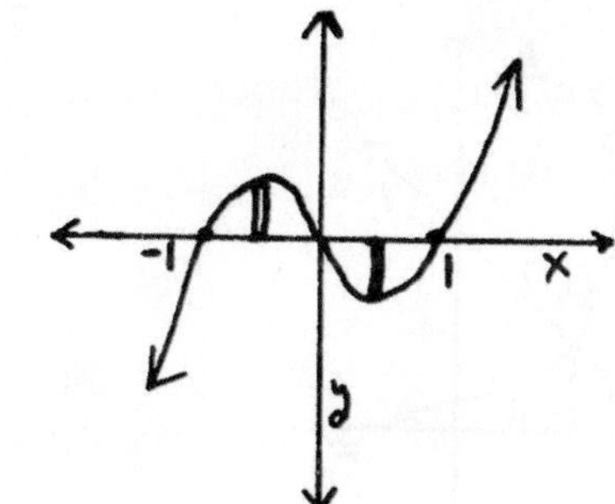

15.

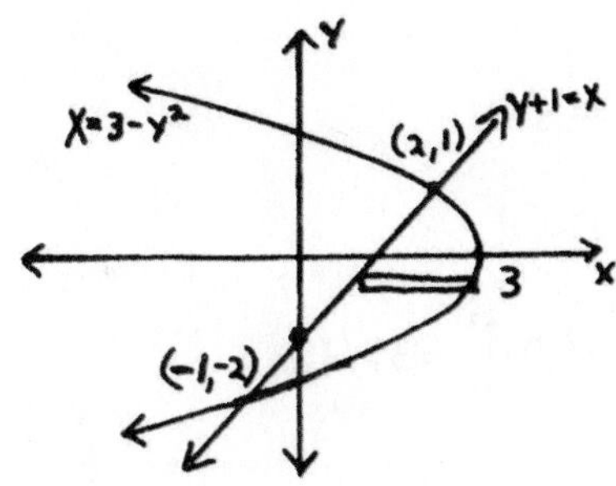

$A = \int_{-2}^{1}[(3-y^2)-(y+1)]\,dy$

$= \int_{-2}^{1}(-y^2 - y + 2)\,dy$

$= (-y^3/3 - y^2/2 + 2y)\Big|_{-2}^{1} = 9/2$

17.

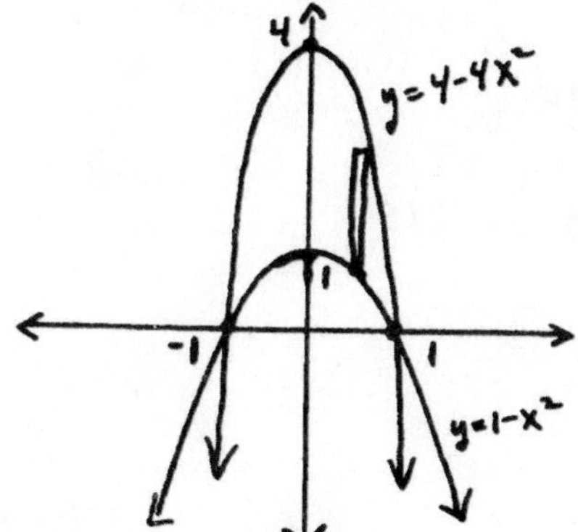

$A = \int_{-1}^{1}[(4-4x^2)-(1-x^2)]\,dx$

$= \int_{-1}^{1}(3-3x^2)\,dx$

$= (3x - x^3)\Big|_{-1}^{1} = 4$

19.

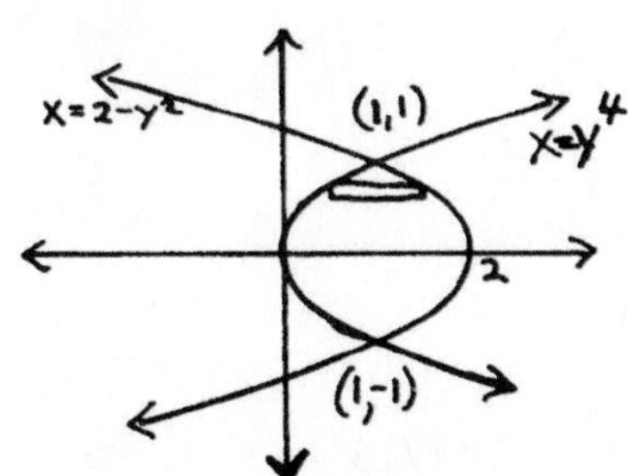

$A = \int_{-1}^{1}[(2-y^2)-y^4]\,dy$

$= (2y - y^3/3 - y^5/5)\Big|_{-1}^{1} = 44/15$

21.

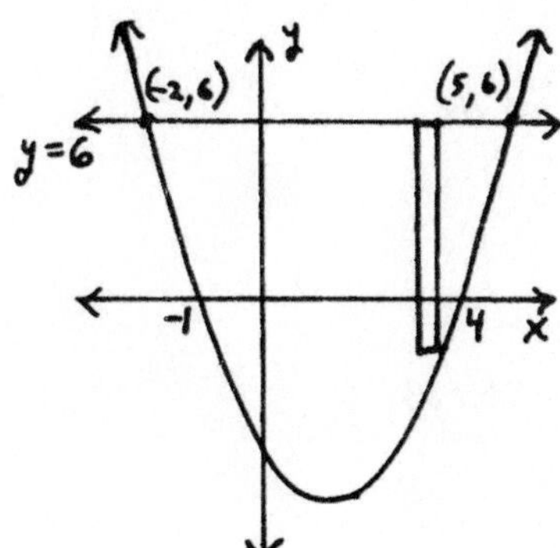

$A = \int_{-2}^{5}[6-(x^2 - 3x - 4)]\,dx$

$= (-x^3/3 + 3x^2/2 + 10x)\Big|_{-2}^{5} = 343/6$

23.

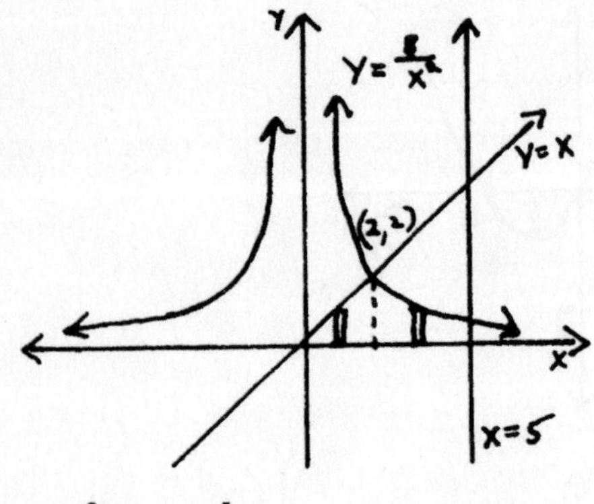

$$A = \int_0^2 x\,dx + \int_2^5 (8/x^2)\,dx$$

$$= x^2/2\Big|_0^2 + (-8/x)\Big|_2^5 = 22/5$$

25.

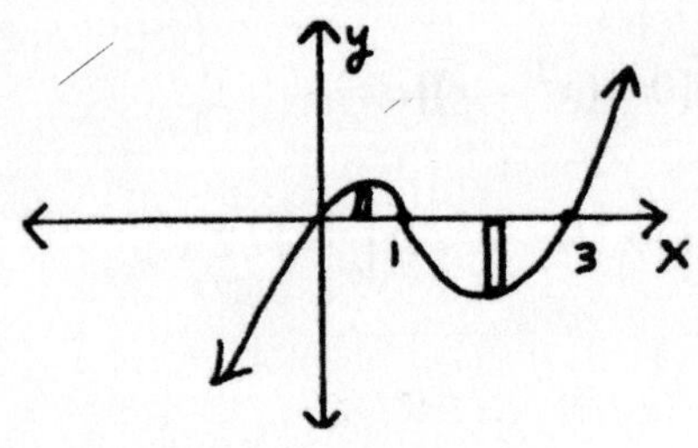

$$A = \int_0^1 [(x^3 - 4x^2 + 3x)]\,dx +$$

$$\int_1^3 [0 - (x^3 - 4x^2 + 3x)]\,dx$$

$$= (x^4/4 - 4x^3/3 + 3x^2/2)\Big|_0^1 +$$

$$(-x^4/4 + 4x^3/3 + 3x^2/2)\Big|_1^3 = 37/12$$

Section 19.2 Exercises

1.

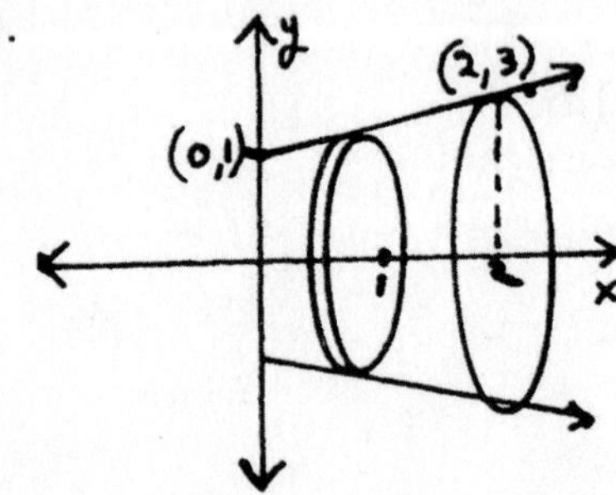

$$V = \pi\int_0^2 y^2\,dx = \pi\int_0^2 (x+1)^2\,dx$$

$$= \pi\int_0^2 (x^2 + 2x + 1)\,dx$$

$$= \pi(x^3/3 + x^2 + 1)\Big|_0^2 = 26\pi/3$$

3.

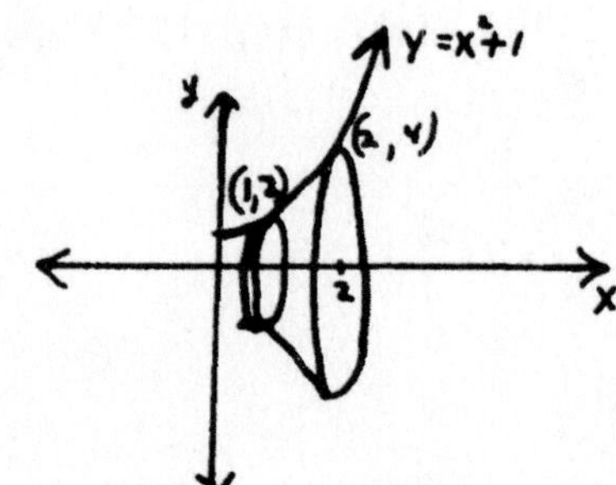

$$V = \pi\int_1^2 y^2\,dx = \pi\int_1^2 (x^2+1)^2\,dx$$

$$= \pi\int_1^2 (x^4 + 2x^2 + 1)\,dx$$

$$= \pi(x^5/5 + 2x^3/3 + x)\Big|_1^2 = 178\pi/15$$

5.

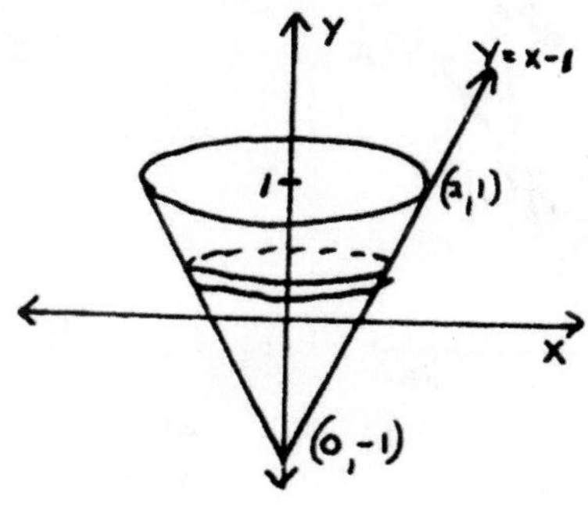

$$V = \pi \int_{-1}^{1} x^2\, dy = \pi \int_{-1}^{1} (y+1)^2\, dy$$

$$= \pi \int_{-1}^{1} (y^2 + 2y + 1)\, dy$$

$$= \pi(y^3/3 + y^2 + y)\Big|_{-1}^{1} = 8\pi/3$$

7.

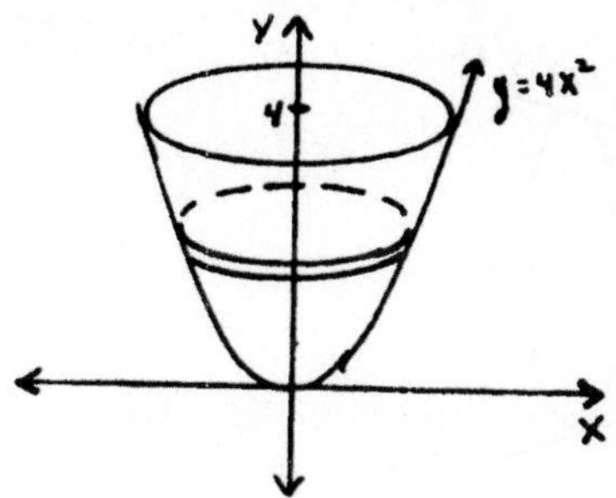

$$V = \pi \int_{0}^{4} x^2\, dy = \pi \int_{0}^{4} (y/4)\, dy$$

$$= \pi(y^2/8)\Big|_{0}^{4} = 2\pi$$

9.

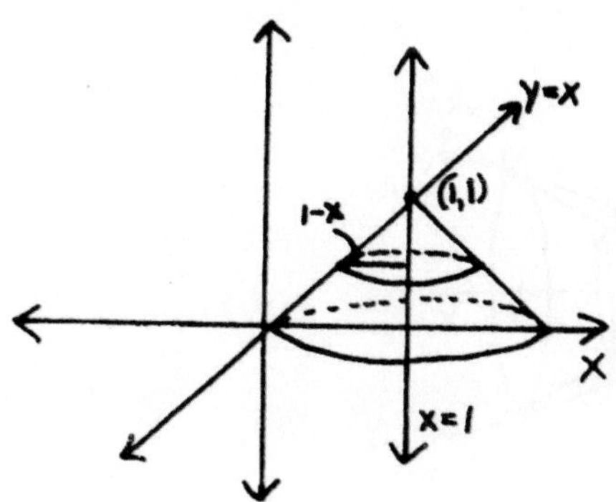

$$V = \pi \int_{0}^{1} (1-x)^2\, dy = \pi \int_{0}^{1} (1-y)^2\, dy$$

$$= \pi \int_{0}^{1} (1 - 2y + y^2)\, dy$$

$$= \pi(y - y^2 + y^3/3)\Big|_{0}^{1} = \frac{\pi}{3}$$

11.

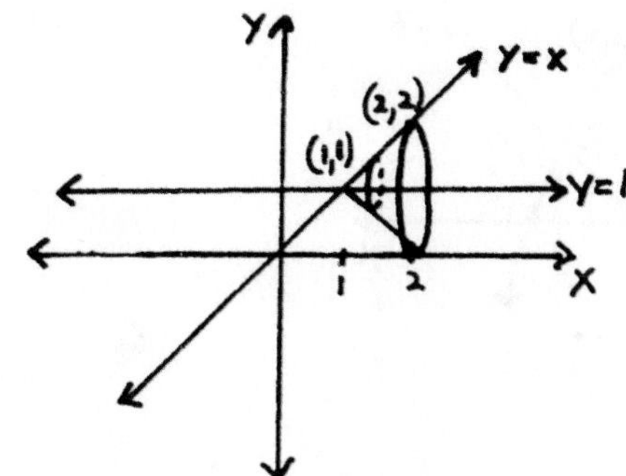

$$V = \pi \int_{1}^{2} (1-y^2)\, dx = \pi \int_{1}^{2} (1-x)^2\, dx$$

$$= \pi \int_{1}^{2} (1 - 2x + x^2)\, dx$$

$$= \pi(x - x^2 + x^3/3)\Big|_{1}^{2} = \pi/3$$

13.

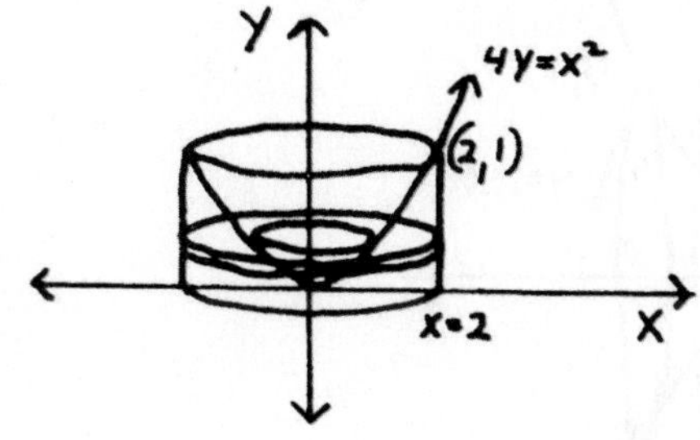

$$V = \pi \int_{0}^{1} (2^2 - x^2)\, dy = \pi \int_{0}^{1} (4 - 4y)\, dy$$

$$= 4\pi(y - y^2/2)\Big|_{0}^{1} = 2\pi$$

15.

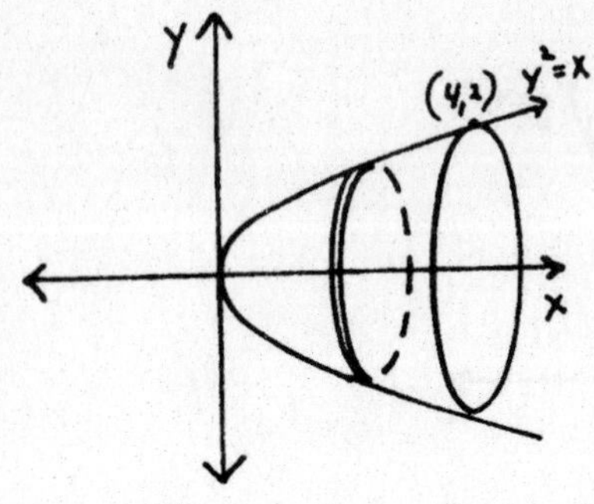

$$V = \pi \int_0^4 y^2\, dx = \pi \int_0^4 x\, dx$$
$$= \pi(x^2/2)\Big|_0^4 = 8\pi$$

17.

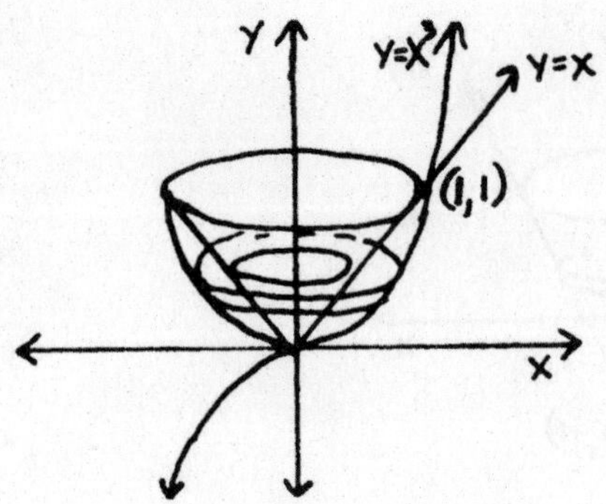

$$V = \pi \int_0^1 [(y^{1/3})^2 - y^2]\, dy$$
$$= \pi \int_0^1 (y^{2/3} - y^2)\, dy$$
$$= \pi(3y^{5/3}/5 - y^3/3)\Big|_0^1 = 4\pi/15$$

19.

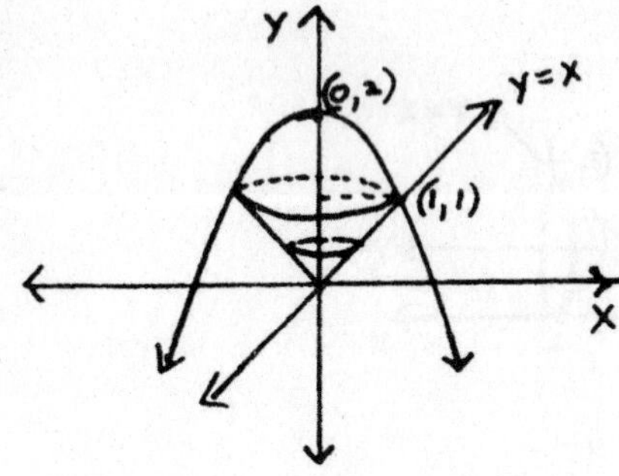

$$V = \pi \int_0^1 y^2\, dy + \pi \int_1^2 (\sqrt{2-y})^2\, dy$$
$$= \pi(y^3/3)\Big|_0^1 + \pi(2y - y^2/2)\Big|_1^2$$
$$= \pi/3 + \pi/2 = 5\pi/6$$

21.

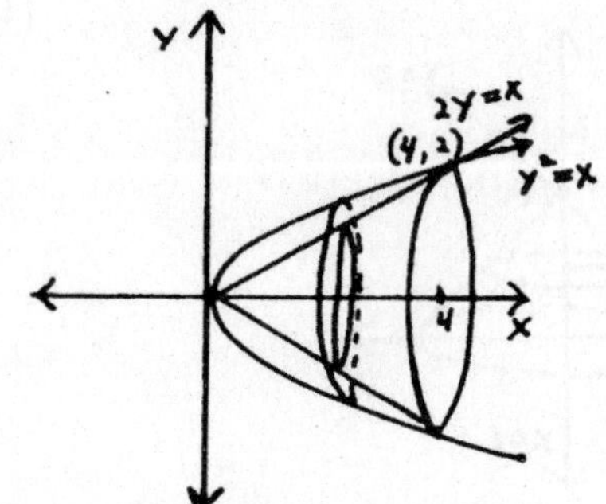

$$V = \pi \int_0^4 [(\sqrt{x})^2 - (x/2)^2]\, dx$$
$$= \pi \int_0^4 (x - x^2/4)\, dx$$
$$= \pi(x^2/2 - x^3/12)\Big|_0^4 = 8\pi/3$$

23. $V = 2\pi \int_0^1 [(3-x^2)^2 - (x^2+1)^2]\, dx$

$$= 2\pi \int_0^1 [(9 - 6x^2 + x^4) - (x^4 + 2x^2 + 1)]\, dx$$
$$= 2\pi \int_0^1 (8 - 8x^2)\, dx = 2\pi(8x - 8x^3/3)\Big|_0^1 = 32\pi/3$$

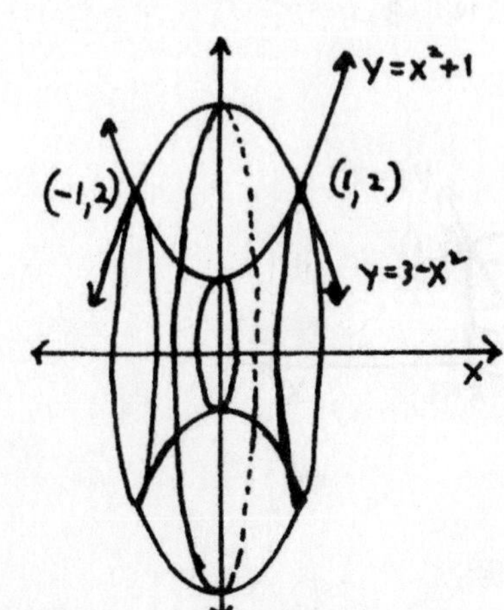

25. $V = 2\pi \int_0^5 y^2\, dx = 2\pi \int_0^5 \frac{225 - 9x^2}{25}\, dx$

$= 2\pi \int_0^5 (9 - 9x^2/25)\, dx$

$= 2\pi(9x - 3x^3/25)\Big|_0^5 = 60\pi$

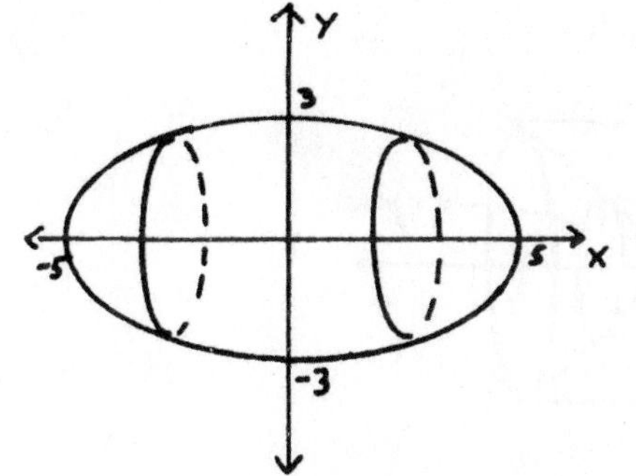

27. intersection of $y = 2$ and

$9x^2 + 25y^2 = 225$
$9x^2 + 25(2)^2 = 225$
$9x^2 = 125$
$x = \pm 5\sqrt{5}/3$

$V = 2\pi \int_0^{5\sqrt{5}/3} (y^2 - 2^2)\, dx$

$= 2\pi \int_0^{5\sqrt{5}/3} \left\{ \frac{225 - 9x^2}{25} - 2^2 \right\} \cdot dx = 2\pi \int_0^{5\sqrt{5}/3} (9 - 9x^2/25 - 4)\, dx$

$= 2\pi \int_0^{5\sqrt{5}/3} (5 - 9x^2/25)\, dx = 2\pi(5x - 3x^3/25)\Big|_0^{5\sqrt{5}/3} = \frac{100\pi\sqrt{5}}{9}$ in^3

29. $V = 2\pi \int_0^r x^2\, dy = 2\pi \int_0^r (r^2 - y^2)\, dy$

$= 2\pi(r^2 y - y^3/3)\Big|_0^r = 2\pi(r^3 - r^3/3) = \frac{4}{3}\pi r^3$

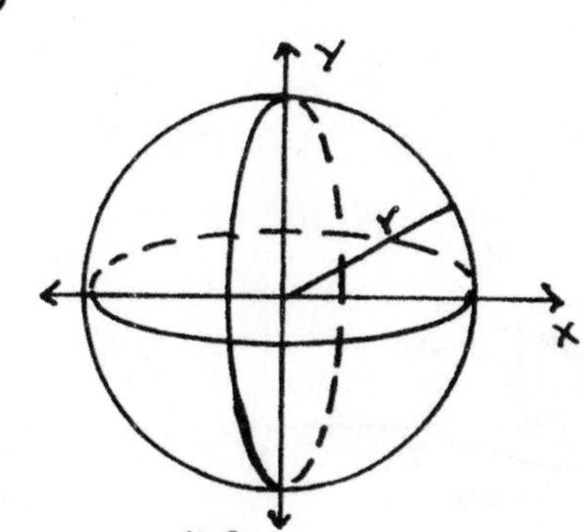

Section 19.3 Exercises

1.

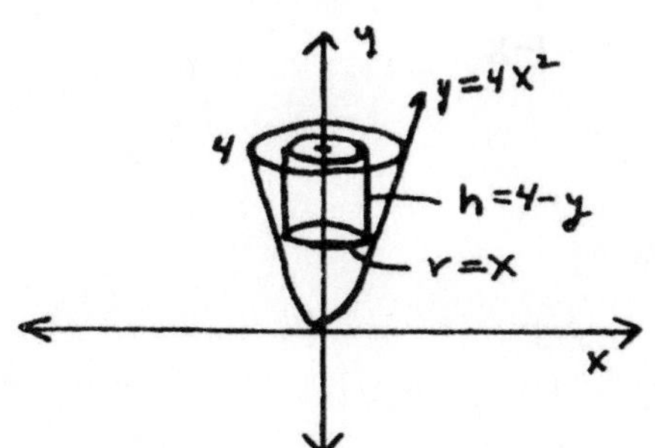

$V = 2\pi \int_0^1 x(4 - 4x^2)\, dx$

$= 2\pi \int_0^4 (4x - 4x^3)\, dx$

$= 2\pi(2x^2 - x^4)\Big|_0^1 = 2\pi$

3.

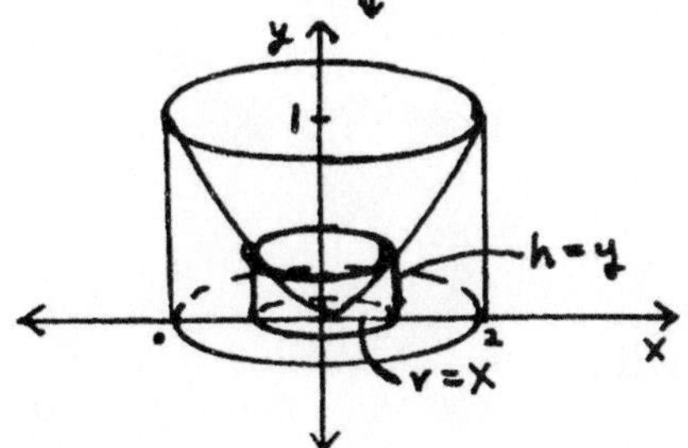

$V = 2\pi \int_0^2 xy\, dx = 2\pi \int_0^2 x(x^2/4)\, dx$

$= 2\pi \int_0^2 (x^3/4)\, dx = 2\pi(x^4/16)\Big|_0^2 = 2\pi$

5.

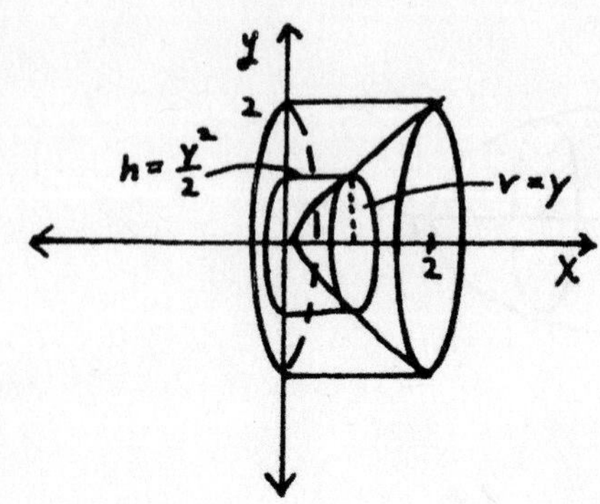

$$V = 2\pi \int_0^2 xy\,dy$$

$$= 2\pi \int_0^2 y(y^2/2)\,dy$$

$$= 2\pi \int_0^2 (y^3/2)\,dy$$

$$= 2\pi (y^4/8)\Big|_0^2 = 4\pi$$

7.

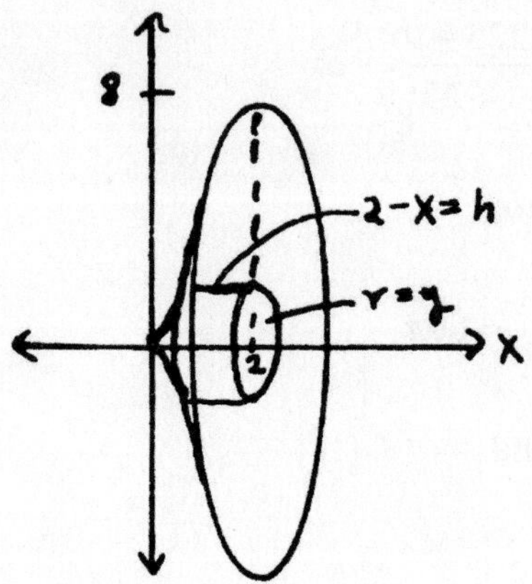

$$V = 2\pi \int_0^8 y(2-x)\,dy$$

$$= 2\pi \int_0^8 y(2-y^{1/3})\,dy$$

$$= 2\pi \int_0^8 (2y - y^{4/3})\,dy$$

$$= 2\pi(y^2 - 3/7)y^{7/3}\Big|_0^8 = 128\pi/7$$

9.

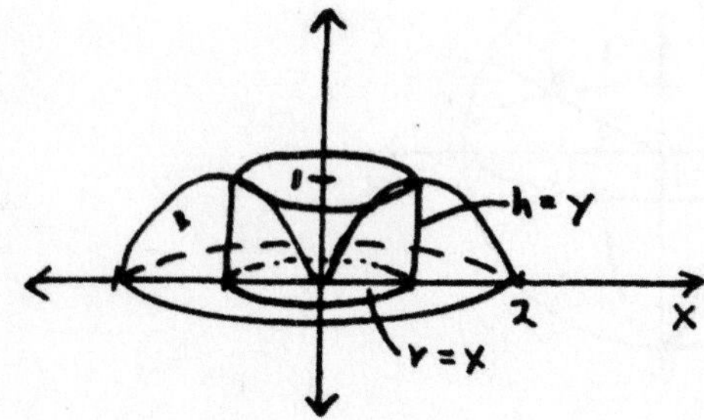

$$V = 2\pi \int_0^2 xy\,dy$$

$$= 2\pi \int_0^2 x(2x - x^2)\,dx$$

$$= 2\pi \int_0^2 (2x^2 - x^3)\,dx$$

$$= 2\pi(2x^3/3 - x^4/4)\Big|_0^2 = 8\pi/3$$

11.

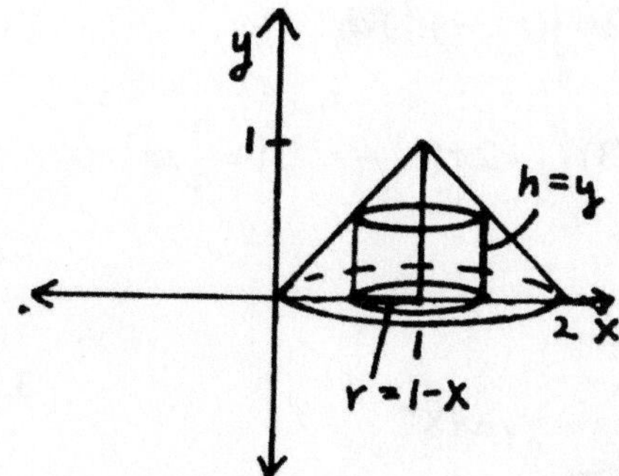

$$V = 2\pi \int_0^1 (1-x)y\,dx$$

$$= 2\pi \int_0^1 (1-x)x\,dx$$

$$= 2\pi \int_0^1 (x - x^2)\,dx$$

$$= 2\pi(x^2/2 - x^3/3)\Big|_0^1 = \pi/3$$

13.

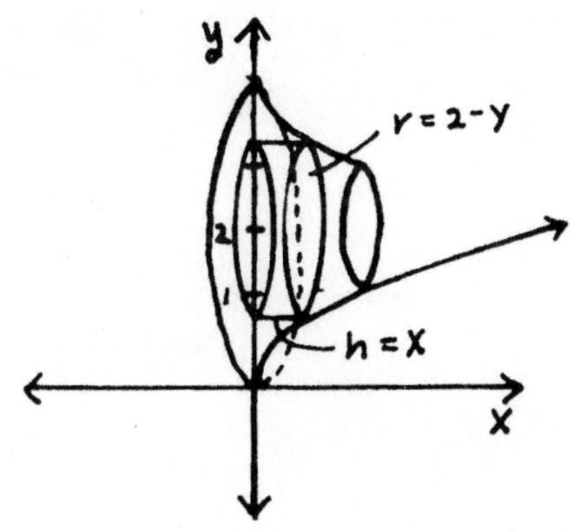

$$V = 2\pi \int_0^1 x(2-y)\,dy$$
$$= 2\pi \int_0^1 y^2(2-y)\,dy$$
$$= 2\pi \int_0^1 (2y^2 - y^3)\,dy$$
$$= 2\pi(2y^3/3 - y^4/4)\Big|_0^1 = 5\pi/6$$

15.

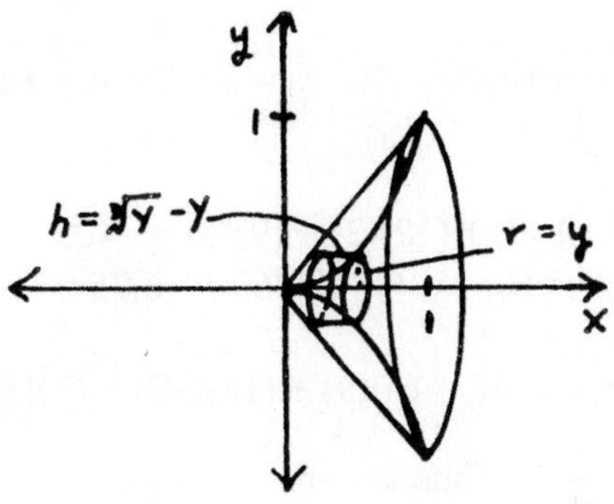

$$V = 2\pi \int_0^1 y(y^{1/3} - y)\,dy$$
$$= 2\pi \int_0^1 (y^{4/3} - y^2)\,dy$$
$$= 2\pi(3y^{7/3}/7 - y^3/3)\Big|_0^1 = 4\pi/21$$

17.

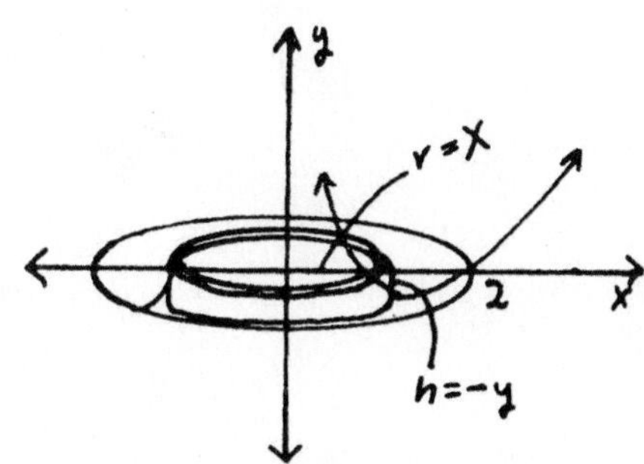

$$V = 2\pi \int_1^2 x(-y)\,dx$$
$$= -2\pi \int_1^2 x(x^2 - 3x + 2)\,dx$$
$$= -2\pi \int_1^2 (x^3 - 3x^2 + 2x)\,dx$$
$$= -2\pi(x^4/4 - x^3 + x^2)\Big|_1^2 = \pi/2$$

19.

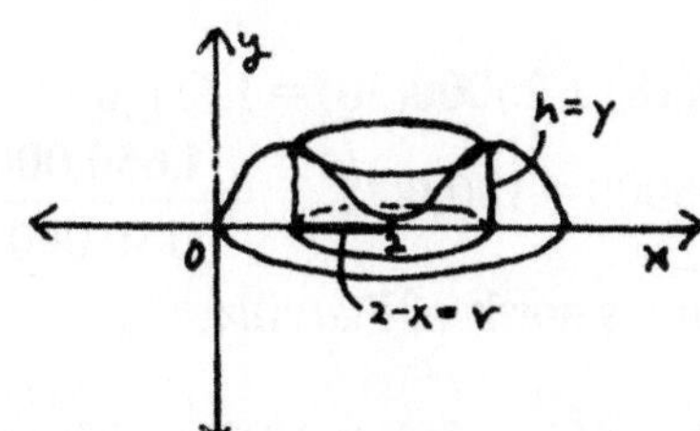

$$V = 2\pi \int_0^2 y(2-x)\,dx$$
$$= 2\pi \int_0^2 x(x-2)^2(2-x)\,dx$$
$$= 2\pi \int_0^2 (-x^4 + 6x^3 - 12x^2 + 8x)\,dx$$
$$= 2\pi(-x^5/5 + 3x^4/2 - 4x^3 + 4x^2)\Big|_0^2$$
$$= 16\pi/5$$

Section 19.4 Exercises

1. $M_o = (3)(-5) + (7)(3) + (4)(6) = 30;\ m = 3 + 7 + 4 = 14$
   $\bar{x} = 30/14 = 15/7$

3. $M_o = (24)(-15) + (15)(-9) + (12)(3) + (9)(6) = -405$
   $m = 24 + 15 + 12 + 9 = 60;\ \bar{x} = -405/60 = -6.75$

5. Given $\bar{x} = 0$, find $(x, 0)$. $M_y = (6)(9) + (18)(-2) + (3)(x);\ m = 3$
   $\bar{x} = \dfrac{M_y}{m}$ so $0 = \dfrac{3x + 18}{3}$ Thus $x = -6$.

7. Given $\bar{x} = 3$, find $(x, 0)$. $M_y = (24)(-8) + (36)(12) + (9)(x) = 240 + 9x$
   $m = 24 + 36 + 9 = 69;\ \bar{x} = M_y/m;\ 3 = \dfrac{240 + 9x}{69};\ x = -11/3$

9. Given $\bar{x} = 0$, find m. $M_y = (6)(-3) + (9)(12) + m(-6) = 90 - 6m$
   $\bar{x} = M_y/m;\ 0 = \dfrac{90 - 6m}{m};\ m = 15$

11. Given $\bar{x} = 3$, find m. $M_y = (25)(-6) + (45)(8) + (40)(10) + m(-4) = 610 - 4m$
    $m = 25 + 45 + 40 + m = 110 + m;\ \bar{x} = M_y/m;\ 3 = \dfrac{610 - 4m}{110 + m};\ m = 40$

13. $M_y = 75000(0) + 50000(18) + 25000(30) = 1{,}650{,}000$
    $m = 75000 + 50000 + 25000 = 150{,}000;\ \bar{x} = \dfrac{1{,}650{,}000}{150{,}000} = 11$
    Thus locate airport 11 miles north of Flatville.

15. $m = 6 + 3 + 12 = 21;\ M_x = 6(4) + 3(2) + 12(3) = 66;$
    $M_y = 6(1) + 3(6) + 12(3) = 60;\ \bar{x} = M_y/m = 60/21 = 20/7$
    $\bar{y} = M_x/m = 66/21 = 22/7$ Thus center of mass is $(20/7, 22/7)$.

17. $m = 8 + 16 + 20 + 36 = 80;\ M_x = 8(12) + 16(8) + 20(-4) + 36(-20) = -576$
    $M_y = 8(8) + 16(-12) + 20(-16) + 36(4) = -304$
    $\bar{x} = M_y/m -304/80 = -3.8;\ \bar{y} = M_x/m = -576/80 = -7.2$
    Thus center of mass is $(-3.8, -7.2)$.

19. Given $\bar{x} = 0$ and $\bar{y} = 0$, find $(x, y);\ m = 6 + 9 + 10 = 25$
    $M_x = 6(2) + 9(8) + 10y = 84 + 10y;\ M_y = 6(4) + 9(-5) + 10x = -21 + 10x$
    $\bar{x} = M_y/m;\ 0 = \dfrac{-21 + 10x}{25};\ x = 2.1;\ \bar{y} = M_x/m = \dfrac{84 + 10y}{25};\ y = -8.4$
    Thus the point is $(2.1, -8.4)$.

21. Given $\bar{x} = -1$ and $\bar{y} = -2$, find m'. $m = 15 + 25 + 40 + m' = 80 + m'$

$$M_y = 15(10) + 25(-6) + 40(8) + m'(-5) = 320 - 5m'$$
$$M_x = 15(3) + 25(-1) + 40(-2) + m'(-3) = -60 - 3m'$$
$$\bar{x} = M_y/m;\ -1 = \frac{320 - 5m'}{80 + m'};\ m' = 100$$

23. Place $A(1250)$ at $(0, 0)$, $B(820)$ at $(6, -3)$, and $C\,(520)$ at $(-2, -8)$; find $(\bar{x}, \bar{y})$, $m = 820 + 520 + 1250 = 2590$;

$$M_x = 820(-3) + 520(-8) + 1250(0) = -6620$$
$$M_y = 820(6) + 520(-2) + 1250(0) = 3880$$
$$\bar{x} = M_y/m = 3880/2590 = 1.50;\ \ \bar{y} = M_x/m = -6620/2590 = -2.56$$

Thus best location: 1.50 mi east and 2.56 mi. south of A.

Section 19.5 Exercises

1. $$\frac{\int_0^{20} x\,dx}{\int_0^{20} dx} = \frac{\left.\frac{x^2}{2}\right|_0^{20}}{\left.x\right|_0^{20}} = \frac{200}{20} = 10$$ Thus center is 10 cm from either end.

3. $$\bar{x} = \frac{M_o}{m} = \frac{\int_0^{10} (0.1x)x\,dx}{\int_0^{10} 0.1x\,dx} = \frac{\int_0^{10} x^2\,dx}{\int_0^{10} x\,dx} = \frac{\left.\frac{x^3}{3}\right|_0^{10}}{\left.\frac{x^2}{2}\right|_0^{10}} = \frac{\frac{1000}{3}}{50} = \frac{20}{3}\text{ cm from lighter end}$$

5. $$\bar{x} = \frac{M_o}{m} = \frac{\int_0^{12} (4 + x^2)\,dx}{\int_0^{12} (4 + x^2)\,dx} = \frac{\left.\frac{1}{4}(x^2 + 4)^2\right|_0^{12}}{\left.(4x + x^3/3)\right|_0^{12}} = \frac{5472}{624} = 8.77\text{ cm from lighter end}$$

7. $$\bar{x} = \frac{M_o}{m} = \frac{\int_0^{6} (kx)x\,dx}{\int_0^{6} kx\,dx} = \frac{\int_0^{6} x^2\,dx}{\int_0^{6} x\,dx} = \frac{\left.\frac{x^3}{3}\right|_0^{6}}{\left.\frac{x^2}{2}\right|_0^{6}} = \frac{72}{18} = 4\text{ cm from given end}$$

9. center of rectangle is $(4, 6)$; $A = 32$
center of square is $(6, 2)$; $A = 16$

$$m = 32 + 16 = 48$$
$$M_y = 32(4) + 16(6) = 224$$
$$M_x = 32(6) + 16(2) = 224$$
$$\bar{x} = \frac{M_y}{m} = \frac{224}{48} = 4\frac{2}{3};\ \bar{y} = \frac{M_x}{m} = \frac{224}{48} = 4\frac{2}{3}$$

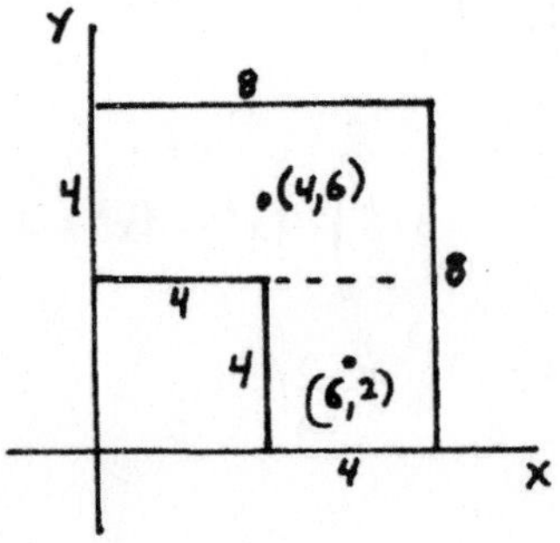

11. center of rectangle 1 is (2, 8); $A = 32$
center of rectangle 2 is (8, 2); $A = 56$
center of rectangle 3 is (14, –4); $A = 32$
$m = 32 + 56 + 32 = 120$
$M_y = 32(2) + 56(8) + 32(14) = 960$
$M_x = 32(8) + 56(2) + 32(-4) = 240$
$\bar{x} = \frac{M_y}{m} = \frac{960}{120} = 8;\ \bar{y} = \frac{M_x}{120} = 2$

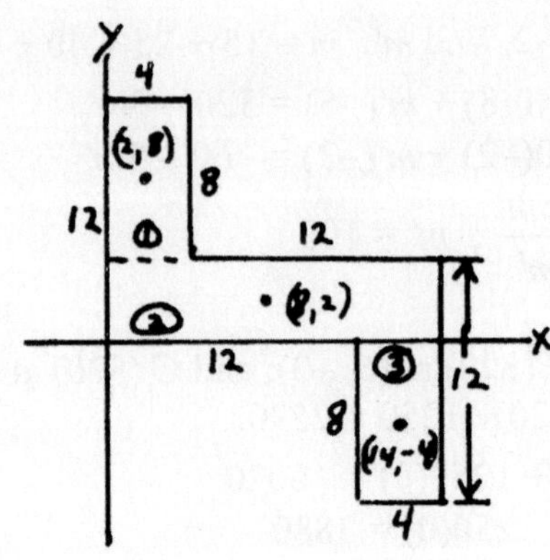

13. center of triangle is $(0, 4 + 2\sqrt{3}/3)$; $A = 4\sqrt{3}$
center of square is (0, 2); $A = 16$
$m = 4\sqrt{3} + 16 = 22.93$
$M_y = 4\sqrt{3}(0) + 16(0) = 0$
$M_x = 4\sqrt{3}(4 + 2\sqrt{3}/3) + 16(2) = 67.71$

$\bar{x} = \frac{M_y}{m} = 0;\ \bar{y} = \frac{M_x}{m} = \frac{67.71}{22.93} = 2.95$

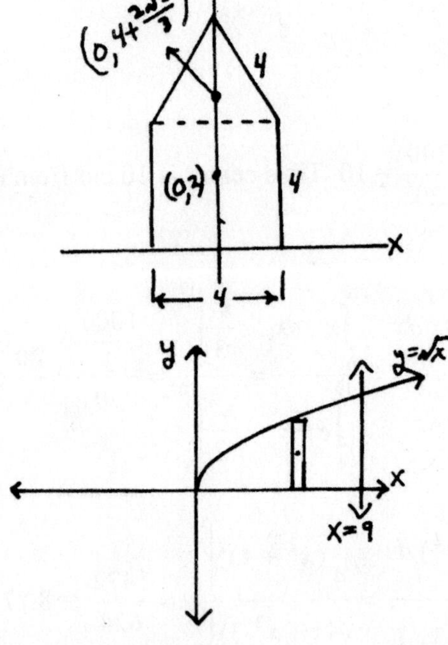

15. $A = \int_0^9 \sqrt{x}\,dx = \frac{2}{3}x^{3/2}\Big|_0^9 = 18$

$\bar{x} = \frac{\int_0^9 x\sqrt{x}\,dx}{18} = \frac{\frac{2}{5}\cdot x^{5/2}\Big|_0^9}{18} = \frac{97.2}{18} = 5.4$

$\bar{y} = \frac{\frac{1}{2}\int_0^9 (\sqrt{x})^2\,dx}{18} = \frac{\frac{1}{2}\cdot\frac{x^2}{2}\Big|_0^9}{18} = \frac{20.25}{18} = \frac{9}{8}$

17. $A = \int_0^2 -(x^2 - 2x)\,dx = -(x^3/3 - x^2)\Big|_0^2 = \frac{4}{3}$

$\bar{x} = \frac{\int_0^2 x[0 - (x^2 - 2x)]\,dx}{4/3} = \frac{\int_0^2 (-x^3 + 2x^2)\,dx}{4/3}$

$= (3/4)(-x^4 + 2x^3/3)\Big|_0^2 = 1$

$\bar{y} = \frac{\frac{1}{2}\int_0^2 [0^2 - (x^2 - 2x)^2]dx}{4/3} = 3/8\int_0^2 -(x^4 - 4x^3 + 4x^2)dx$

$= (-3/8)(x^5/5 - x^4 + 4x^3/3\Big|_0^2 = -2/5$

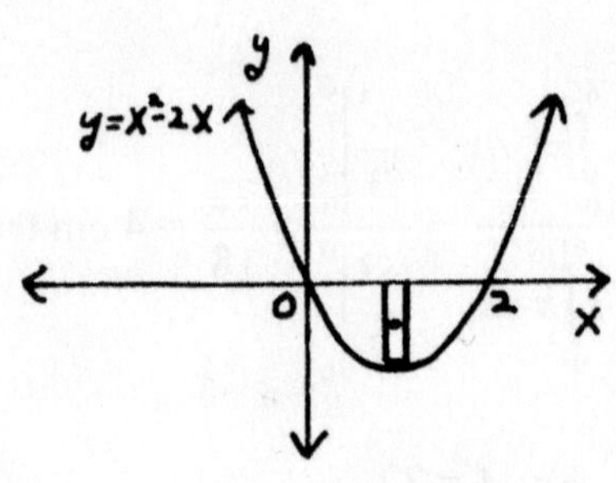

19. $A = \int_{-2}^{2} (4 - x^2)\, dx = (4x - x^3/3)\Big|_{-2}^{2} = 32/3$

$\bar{x} = 0$ from sketch

$$\bar{y} = \frac{\frac{1}{2}\int_{-2}^{2} (4 - x^2)^2\, dx}{32/3} = \frac{3}{64}\int_{-2}^{2} (16 - 8x^2 + x^4)\, dx$$

$$= (3/64)(16x - 8x^3/3 + x^5/5)\Big|_{-2}^{2} = 8/5$$

Thus (0, 8/5).

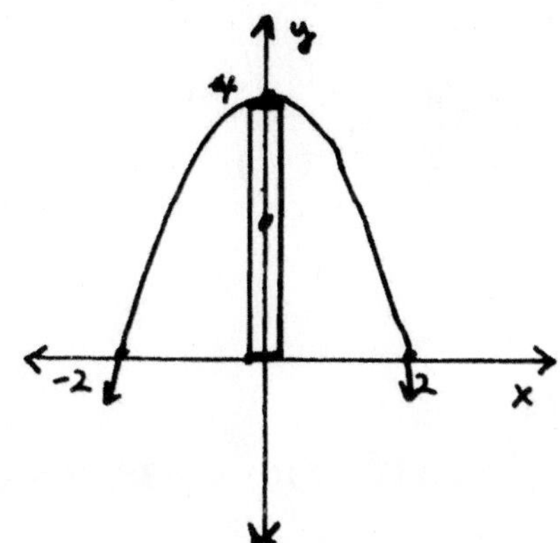

21. $A = \int_{0}^{1} (x - x^3)\, dx = (x^2/2 - x^4/4)\Big|_{0}^{1} = 1/4$

$$\bar{x} = \frac{\int_{0}^{1} x(x - x^3)\, dx}{1/4} = 4(x^3/3 - x^5/5)\Big|_{0}^{1} = 8/15$$

$$\bar{y} = \frac{\frac{1}{2}\int_{0}^{1} (x^2 - x^6)\, dx}{1/4} = 2(x^3/3 - x^7/7)\Big|_{0}^{1} = 8/21$$

Thus (8/15, 8/21).

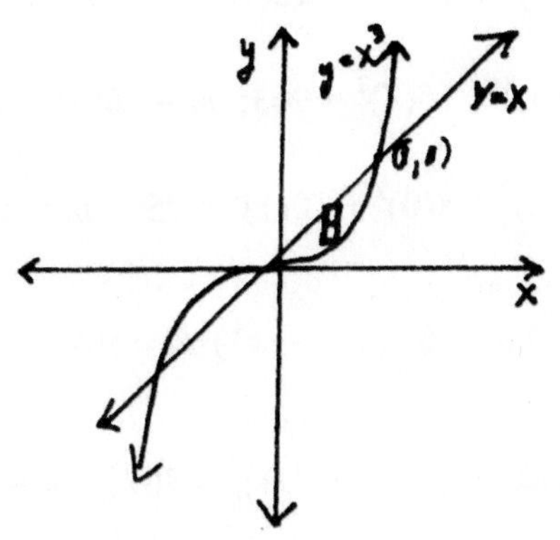

23. $\bar{x} = 0$; $A = (1/2)\pi r^2 = \pi/2$

$$\bar{y} = \frac{\frac{1}{2}\int_{-1}^{1} (\sqrt{1 - x^2})^2\, dx}{\pi/2} = \frac{1}{\pi}\int_{-1}^{1} (1 - x^2)\, dx$$

$$= (1/\pi)(x - x^3/3)\Big|_{-1}^{1} = \frac{4}{3\pi}$$

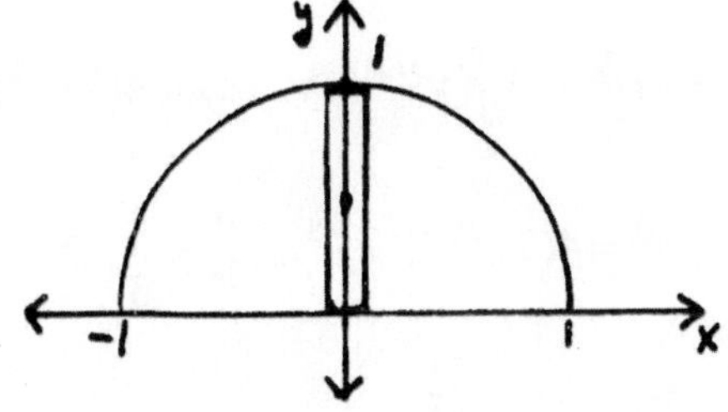

25. $$\bar{x} = \frac{\int_{0}^{1} x(x^3)^2\, dx}{\int_{0}^{1} (x^3)^2\, dx} = \frac{x^8/8\Big|_{0}^{1}}{x^7/7\Big|_{0}^{1}} = \frac{1/8}{1/7} = \frac{7}{8}$$

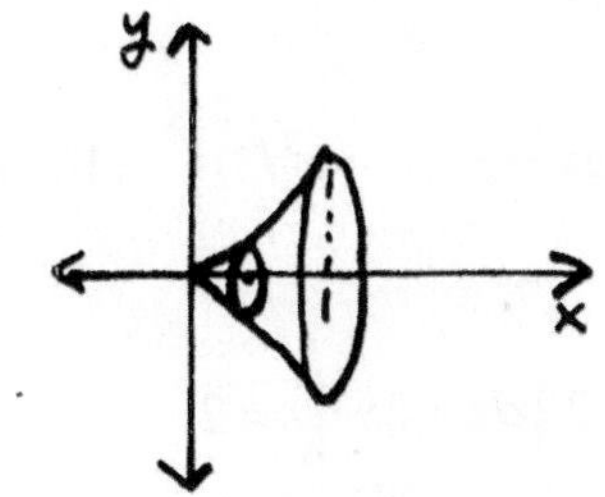

27. $$\bar{x} = \frac{\int_{0}^{3} x(3 - x)^2\, dx}{\int_{0}^{3} (3 - x)^2\, dx} = \frac{(9x^2/2 - 2x^3 + x^4/4)\Big|_{0}^{3}}{(9x - 3x^2 + x^3/3)\Big|_{0}^{3}} = \frac{27/4}{9} = \frac{3}{4};\ \bar{y} = 0$$

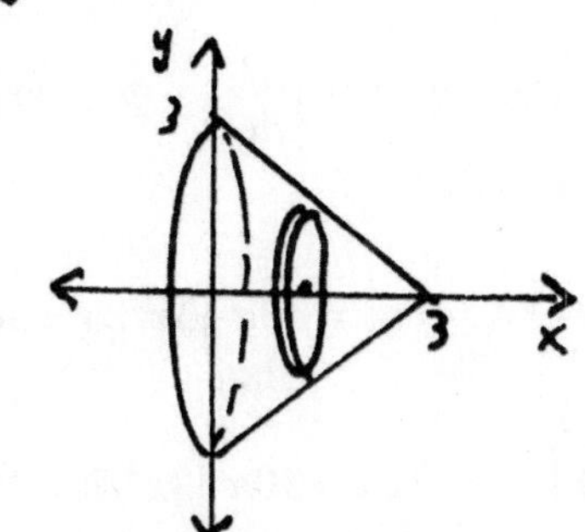

29. $\bar{y} = \dfrac{\int_0^1 y(y)\,dy}{\int_0^1 y\,dy} = \dfrac{y^3/3\,\big|_0^1}{y^2/2\,\big|_0^1} = \dfrac{2}{3}; \bar{x} = 0$

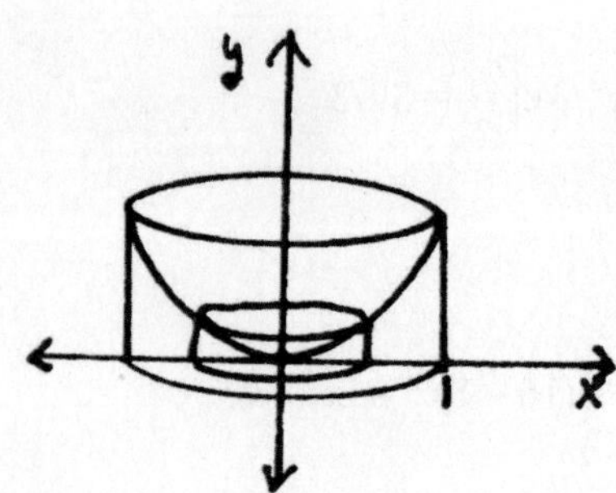

Section 19.6 Exercises

1. $I_y = 9(3)^2 + 12(5)^2 + 15(3)^2 = 516;\ m = 36;\ R = \sqrt{516/36} = 3.79$

3. $I_y = 15(3)^2 + 10(6)^2 + 18(9)^2 + 12(1)^2 = 1965;\ m = 55;\ R = \sqrt{1965/55} = 5.98$

5. $I_x = 9(-2)^2 + 12(4)^2 + 15(7)^2 = 963;\ m = 36;\ R = \sqrt{963/36} = 5.17$

7. $I_x = 9(-9)^2 + 5(-2)^2 + 8(0)^2 + 10(1)^2 = 759;\ m = 32;\ R = \sqrt{759/32} = 4.87$

9. $I_y = 5\int_0^2 x^2(4 - x^2)\,dx = 5\int_0^2 (4x^2 - x^4)\,dx = 5(4x^3/3 - x^5/5)\,\big|_0^2 = 64/3$

$m = 5\int_0^2 (4 - x^2)\,dx = 5(4x - x^3/3)\,\big|_0^2 = 80/3;\ R = \sqrt{(64/3)/(80/3)} = 0.894$

11. $I_x = 4\int_0^1 y^2(\sqrt{y} - y)\,dy = 4\int_0^1 (y^{5/2} - y^3)\,dy = 4(2y^{7/2}/7 - y^4/4)\,\big|_0^1 = 1/7$

$m = 4\int_0^1 (\sqrt{y} - y)\,dy = 4(2y^{3/2}/3 - y^2/2)\,\big|_0^1 = \dfrac{2}{3};\ R = \sqrt{(1/7)/(2/3)} = 0.463$

13. $I_y = 3\int_0^2 x^2[(5 - x^2) - 1]\,dx = 3\int_0^2 (4x^2 - x^4)\,dx = 3(4x^3/3 - x^5/5)\,\big|_0^2 = 64/5$

$m = 3\int_0^2 [(5 - x^2) - 1]\,dx = 3(4x - x^3/3)\,\big|_0^2 = 16\quad R = \sqrt{(64/5)/16} = 0.894$

15. $I_y = 2\int_1^2 x^2(1/x^2)\,dx = 2\int_1^2 dx = 2x\,\big|_1^2 = 2;$

$m = 2\int_1^2 x^{-2}\,dx = 2(-1/x)\,\big|_1^2 = 1;\ R = \sqrt{2/1} = 1.41$

17. $m = 2\pi(15)\int_0^2 x(3x)\,dx = 30\pi\int_0^2 3x^2\,dx = 30\pi x^3\big|_0^2 = 240\pi$

$I_y = 2\pi(15)\int_0^2 x^3(3x)\,dx = 30\pi\int_0^2 3x^4\,dx = 18\pi x^5\,\big|_0^2 = 576\pi;\ R = \sqrt{576\pi/240\pi} = 1.55$

19. $I_x = 2\pi \int_0^{16} y^3(2 - y^{1/2}/2)\,dy = 2\pi \int_0^{16} (2y^3 - y^{7/2})\,dy = 2\pi(y^4/2 - y^{9/2}/9)\Big|_0^{16} = 7282\pi = 2.29 \times 10^4$

$m = 2\pi \int_0^{16} y(2 - y^{1/2}/2)\,dy = 2\pi \int_0^{16} (2y - y^{3/2}/2)\,dy = 2\pi(y^2 - y^{5/2}/5)\Big|_0^{16} = 102.4\pi = 322$;

$R = \sqrt{7282\pi / 102.4\pi} = 8.43$

21. $I_y = 2\pi(12) \int_0^{3} x^3(9 - x^2)\,dx = 24\pi \int_0^{3} (9x^3 - x^5)\,dx = 24\pi(9x^4/4 - x^6/6)\Big|_0^{3} = 1458\pi$;

$m = 2\pi(12) \int_0^{3} x(9 - x^2)\,dx = 24\pi \int_0^{3} (9x - x^3)\,dx = 24\pi(9x^2/2 - x^4/4)\Big|_0^{3} = 486\pi$;

$R = \sqrt{1458\pi / 486\pi} = 1.73$

23. $I_y = 2\pi(15) \int_0^{4} x^3(4x - x^2)\,dx = 30\pi \int_0^{4} (4x^4 - x^5)\,dx = 30\pi(4x^5/5 - x^6/6)\Big|_0^{4} = 4096\pi$;

$m = 2\pi(15) \int_0^{4} x(4x - x^2)\,dx = 30\pi \int_0^{4} (4x^2 - x^3)\,dx = 30\pi(4x^3/3 - x^4/4)\Big|_0^{4} = 640\pi$;

$R = \sqrt{4096\pi / 640\pi} = 2.53$

Section 19.7 Exercises

1. $W = \int_0^{3} (x^3 - x)\,dx = (x^4/4 - x^2/2)\Big|_0^{3} = 63/4$

3. $20 = k(10);\ k = 2;\ W = \int_0^{5} 2x\,dx = x^2\Big|_0^{5} = 25$ in.-lb

5. $150 = 4k;\ k = 75/2;\ W = \int_0^{6} (75x/2)\,dx = (75x^2/4)\Big|_0^{6} = 657\ \text{N} \cdot \text{cm}$ or 6.75 J

7. $W = \int_{0.01}^{0.05} 3.62 \times 10^{-16} x^{-2}\,dx = 3.62 \times 10^{-16}(-1/x)\Big|_{0.01}^{0.05} = 2.896 \times 10^{-14}$ J

9. a) $W = \int_{40}^{50} 2x\,dx = x^2\Big|_{40}^{50} = 900$ ft-lb

b) $W = \int_{25}^{50} 2x\,dx = x^2\Big|_{40}^{50} = 1875$ ft-lb

c) $W = \int_{0}^{50} 2x\,dx = x^2\Big|_{0}^{50} = 2500$ ft-lb

11. $W = \int_0^{12} 62.4\pi(4)^2\, x\, dx = 998.4\pi(x^2/2)\Big|_0^{12} = 225{,}800$ ft-lb

13. $W = \int_{10}^{22} 62.4\pi(4)^2\, x\, dx = 998.4\pi(x^2/2)\Big|_{10}^{22} = 602{,}200$ ft-lb

15. $\dfrac{5}{12} = \dfrac{r}{12-x}$ thus $r = \dfrac{5(12-x)}{12}$

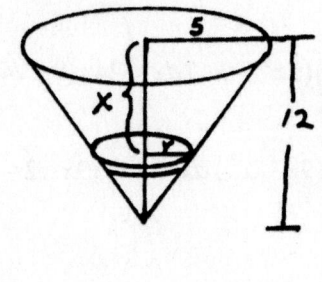

$F = 62.4\pi \dfrac{25(12-x)^2}{144} \Delta x$

$W = \int_0^{12} 10.83\pi x(12-x)^2\, dx$

$= 10.83\pi \int_0^{12} (x^3 - 24x^2 + 144x)\, dx = 10.83\pi(x^4/4 - 8x^3 + 72x^2)\Big|_0^{12}$

$= 58{,}810$ ft-lb

17. $F = 62.4 \int_0^{10} (10-y)(8)\, dy$

$= (62.4)(8)(10y - y^2/2)\Big|_0^{10}$

$= 25{,}000$ lb

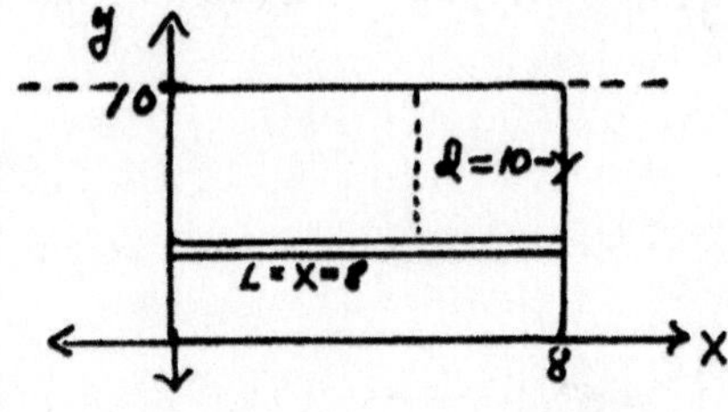

19. $F = 9800 \int_0^{3} (3-y)(8)\, dy$

$= 9800(8)(3y - y^2/2)\Big|_0^{3}$

$= 352{,}800$ N

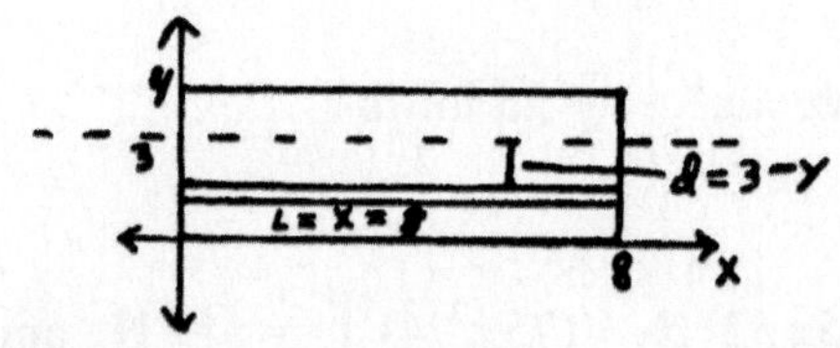

Note: $\rho g = 9800$ kg/(m² s²)
3/4 full; $A = 24$ m²;
depth = 3 m

21. $F = 870(9.80) \int_{-5}^{0} (-y)(2)\sqrt{25-y^2}\, dy$

$= 8526 \int_{-5}^{0} (25-y^2)^{1/2}(-2y)\, dy$

$= 8526(2/3)(25-y^2)^{3/2}\Big|_{-5}^{0} = 710{,}500$ N

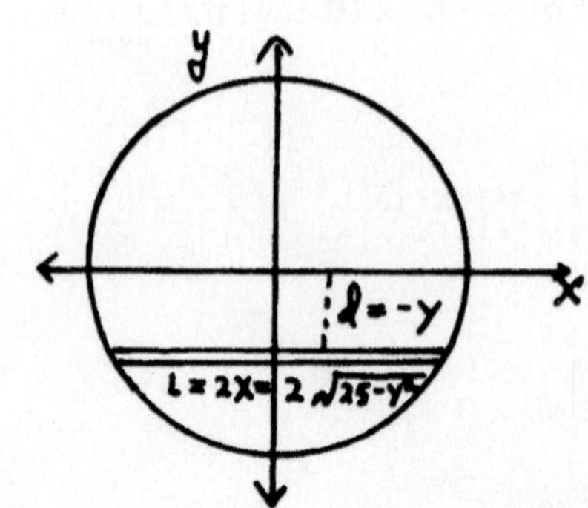

23. $F = 62.4\int_0^2 (2-y)(2y)\,dy$

$= 62.4\int_0^2 (4y-2y^2)\,dy$

$= 62.4(2y^2 - 2y^3/3)\Big|_0^2 = 166.4$ lb

$\dfrac{4}{2} = \dfrac{L}{Y}$ Thus $L = 2y$.

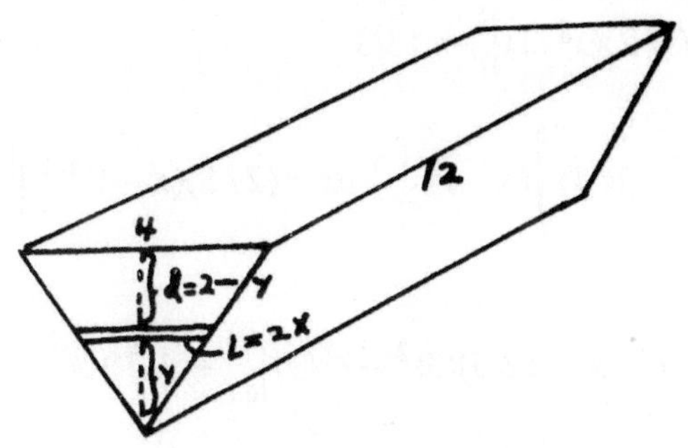

25. $F = 62.4\int_0^6 (14-y)(16-y)\,dy$

$= 62.4\int_0^6 (224 - 30y + y^2)\,dy$

$= 62.4(224y - 15y^2 - y^3/3)\Big|_0^6 = 54{,}660$ lb

Note: equation of line through (5, 6) and (8, 0) is $y = -2(x-8)$

Thus $L = 2x = 16 - y$.

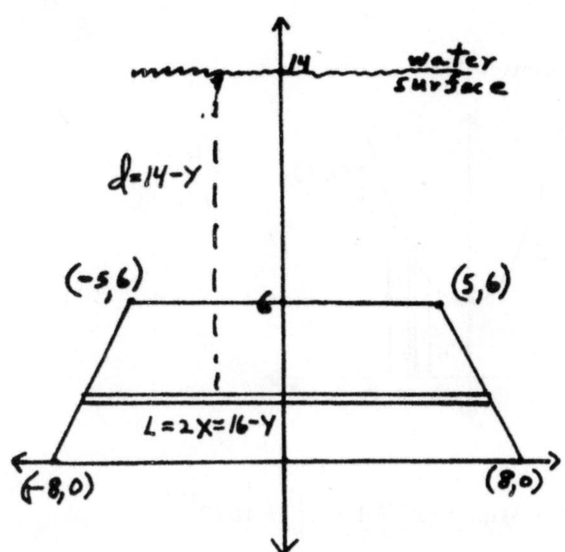

27. $F = 62.4\int_6^9 (9-y)(18)\,dy + 62.4\int_0^6 (9-y)(3y)\,dy$

$= 1123.2\int_6^9 (9-y)\,dy + 187.2\int_0^6 (9y - y^2)\,dy$

$= 1123.2(9y - y^2/2)\Big|_6^9 + 187.2(9y^2/2 - y^3/3)\Big|_0^6 = 5054 + 16{,}848 = 21{,}902$ lb

Note: equation of line through (0, 0) and (18, 6) is $y = x/3$.

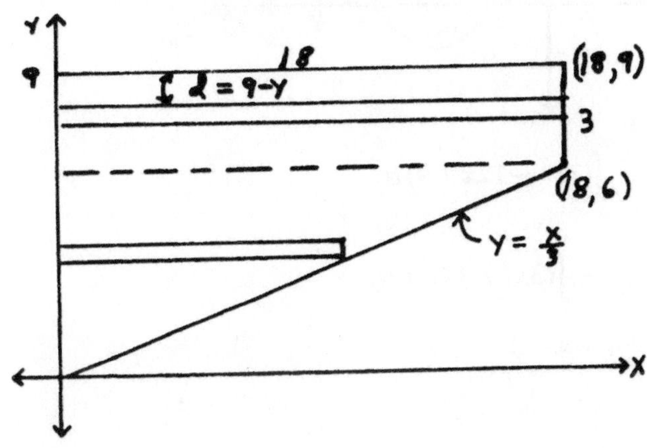

29. $y_{av} = \dfrac{1}{3-1}\displaystyle\int_1^3 x^2\,dx = (1/2)(x^3/3)\Big|_1^3 = 13/3$

31. $y_{av} = \dfrac{1}{10-5}\displaystyle\int_5^{10} \dfrac{dx}{\sqrt{x-1}} = (1/5)\int_5^{10}(x-1)^{-1/2}\,dx = (2/5)(x-1)^{1/2}\Big|_5^{10} = 2/5$

33. $I_{av} = \dfrac{1}{0.5-0.1}\displaystyle\int_{0.1}^{0.5}(6t-t^2)\,dt = (2.5)(3t^2 - t^3/3)\Big|_{0.1}^{0.5} = 1.70\ A$

Section 19 Review

1.

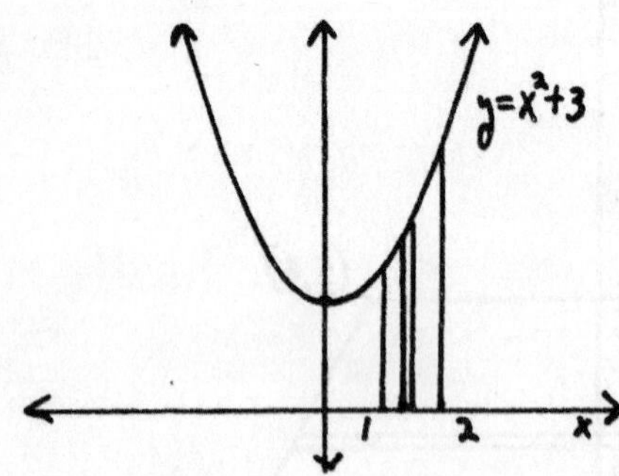

$$A = \int_1^2 (x^2+3)\,dx = (x^3/3+3x)\Big|_1^2 = 16/3$$

2.

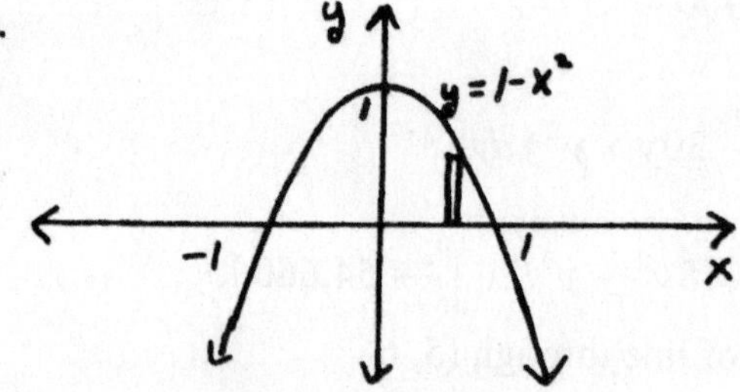

$$A = \int_0^1 (1-x^2)\,dx = (x - x^3/3)\Big|_0^1 = \frac{2}{3}$$

3.

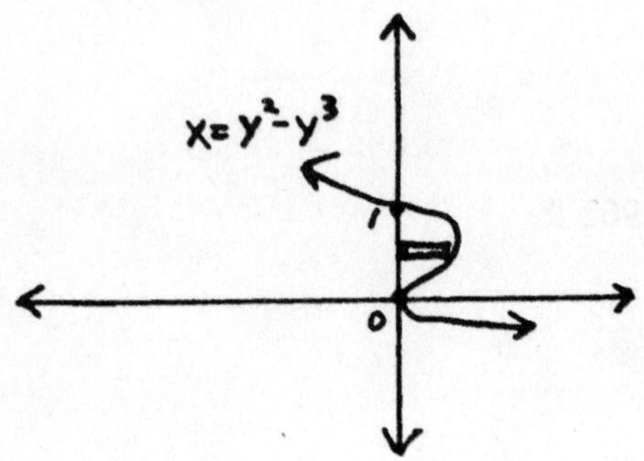

$$A = \int_0^1 (y^2 - y^3)\,dy$$

$$= (y^3/3 - y^4/4)\Big|_0^1 = 1/12$$

4.

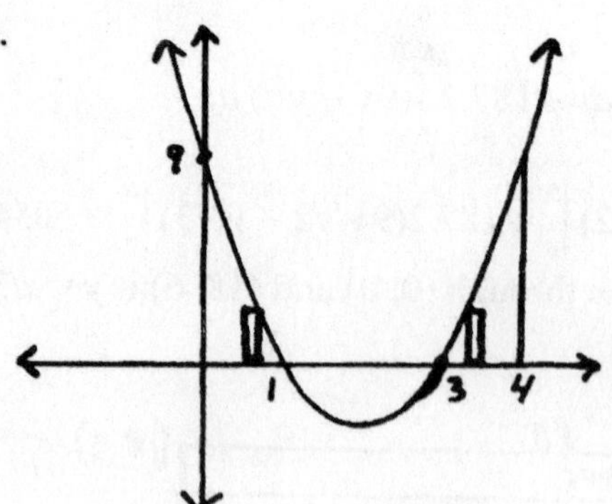

$$A = \int_0^1 (3x^2 - 12x + 9)\,dx$$

$$+ \int_3^4 (3x^2 - 12x + 9)\,dx$$

$$= 4 + 4 = 8$$

5.

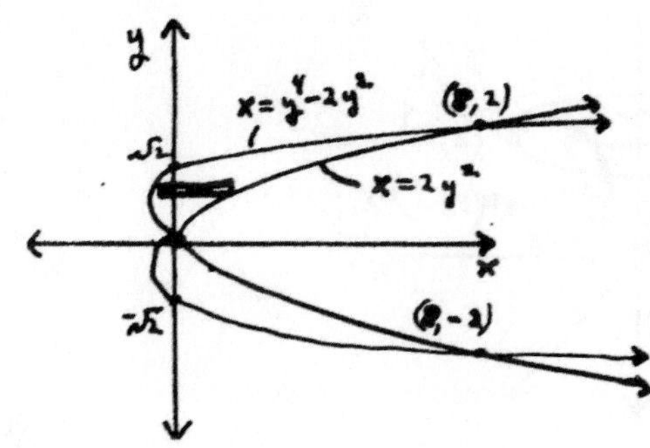

$$A = 2\int_0^2 [2y^2 - (y^4 - 2y^2)]\,dy$$

Note: S: x-axis

$$= 2\int_0^2 (4y^2 - y^4)\,dy$$

$$= 2(4y^3/3 - y^5/5)\Big|_0^2 = 128/15$$

6.

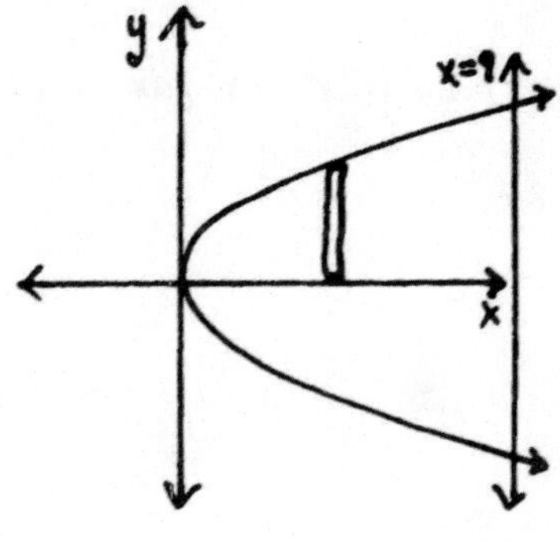

$$A = 2\int_0^9 \sqrt{x}\,dx = 2(2x^{3/2}/3)\Big|_0^9 = 36$$

7. $V = 2\pi \int_0^2 y(4 - y^2)\,dy = 2\pi \int_0^2 (4y - y^3)\,dy$

$$= 2\pi(2y^2 - y^4/4)\Big|_0^2 = 8\pi$$

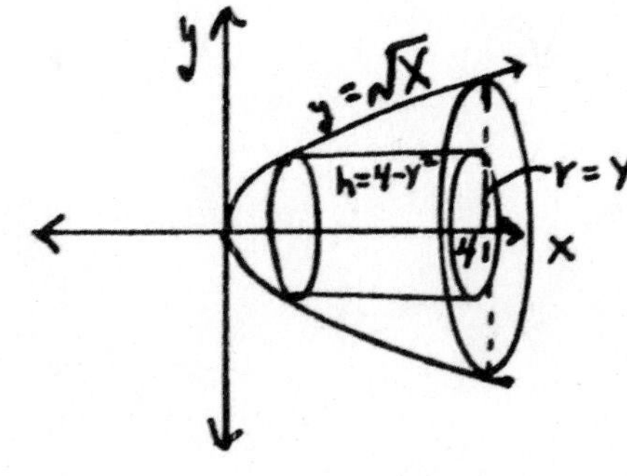

8. (See # 7 diagram)

$$V = \pi \int_0^4 (\sqrt{x})^2\,dx = \pi(x^2/2)\Big|_0^4 = 8\pi$$

9.

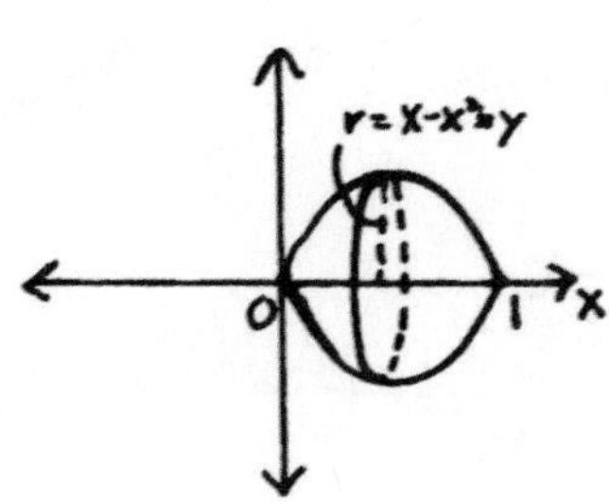

$$V = \pi \int_0^1 (x - x^2)^2\,dx = \pi \int_0^1 (x^2 - 2x^3 + x^4)\,dx$$

$$= \pi(x^3/3 - x^4/2 + x^5/5)\Big|_0^1 = \pi/30$$

10. $V = 2\pi \int_0^2 x[(3x - x^2) - x]\, dx = 2\pi \int_0^2 (2x^2 - x^3)\, dx$

$= 2\pi(2x^3/3 - x^4/4)\Big|_0^2 = \dfrac{8\pi}{3}$

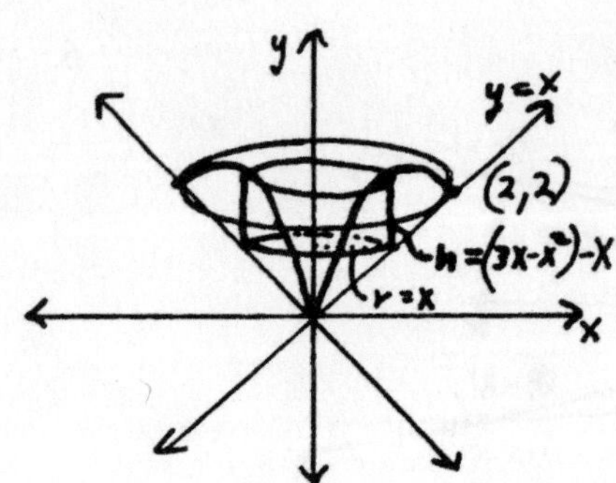

11.

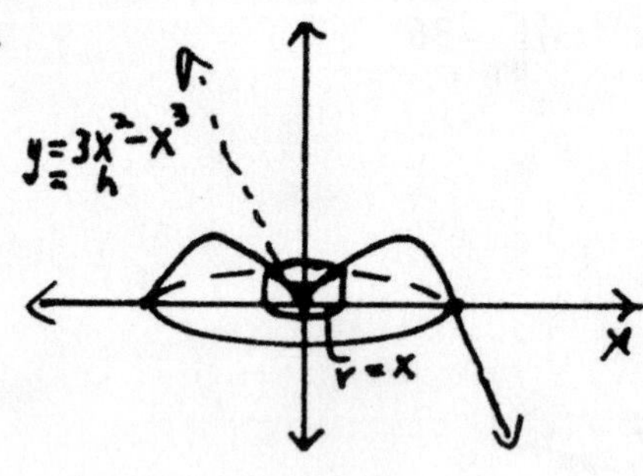

$V = 2\pi \int_0^3 x(3x^2 - x^3)\, dx$

$= 2\pi \int_0^3 (3x^3 - x^4)\, dx$

$= 2\pi(3x^4/4 - x^5/5)\Big|_0^3 = 243\pi/10$

12.

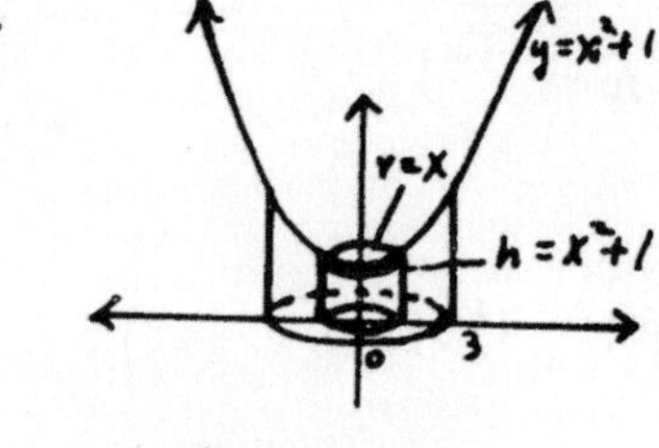

$V = 2\pi \int_0^3 x(x^2 + 1)\, dx$

$= 2\pi \int_0^3 (x^3 + x)\, dx$

$= 2\pi(x^4/4 - x^2/2)\Big|_0^3 = \dfrac{99\pi}{2}$

13.

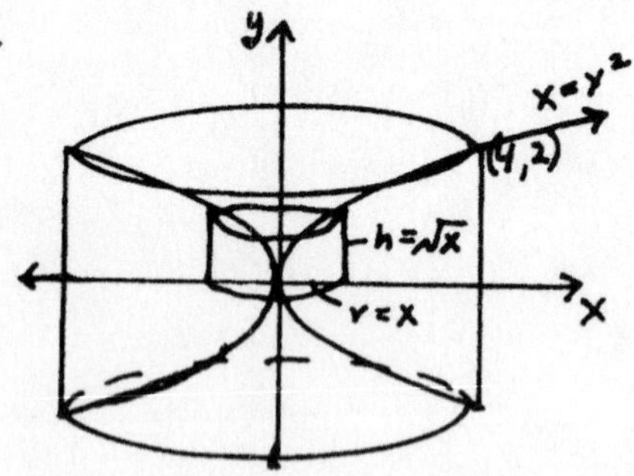

$V = (2)2\pi \int_0^4 x\sqrt{x}\, dx$

$= 4\pi \int_0^4 x^{3/2}\, dx$

$= 4\pi(2x^{5/2}/5)\Big|_0^4 = 256\pi/5$

14.

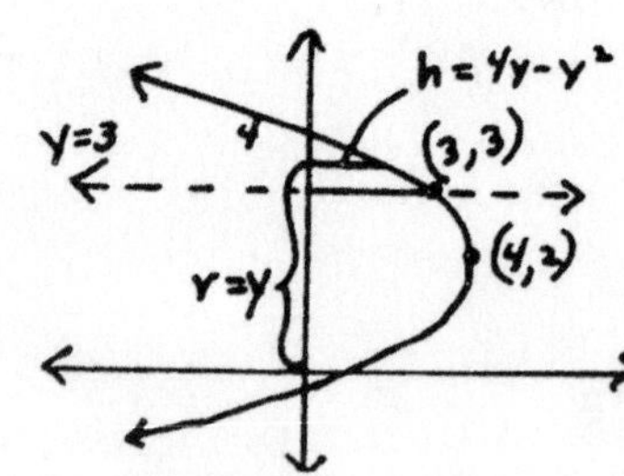

$V = 2\pi \int_0^3 y(4y - y^2)\, dy$

$= 2\pi \int_0^3 (4y^2 - y^3)\, dy$

$= 2\pi(4y^3/3 - y^4/4)\Big|_0^3 = \dfrac{63\pi}{2}$

15. $M_o = 12(-4) + 20(9) + 24(12) = 420;\ m = 12 + 20 + 24 = 56$
$\bar{x} = M_o/m = 420/56 = 7.5$

16. $m = 24 + 36 + 30 = 90;\ M_x = 24(-3) + 36(-15) + 30(0) = -612$
$M_y = 24(11) + 36(-4) + 30(-7) = -90;\ \bar{x} = -90/90 = -1;\ \bar{y} = -612/90 = -6.8$

17. center of top rectangle is (8, 10.5); $A = 40$
center of bottom rectangle is (10, 4); $A = 160$
$M_y = 40(8) + 160(10) = 1920$
$M_x = 40(10.5) + 160(4) = 1060$
$m = 40 + 160 = 200;\ \bar{x} = 1920/200 = 9.6;\ \bar{y} = 1060/200 = 5.3$

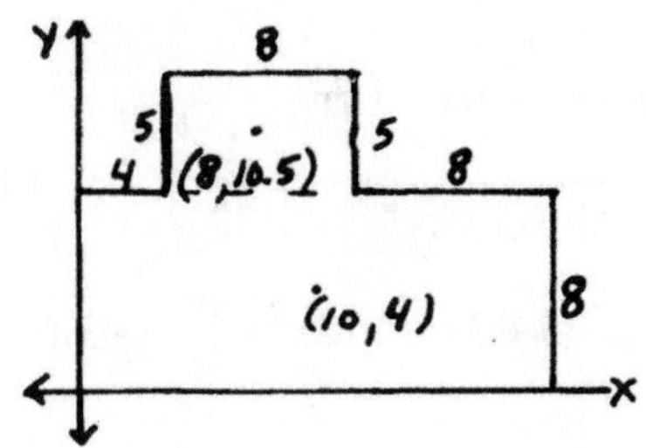

18. $$\bar{x} = \frac{\int_0^4 x(5x)\,dx}{40} = \frac{(5x^3/3)\Big|_0^4}{40} = 2\frac{2}{3}$$
$$\bar{y} = \frac{\frac{1}{2}\int_0^4 (5x)^2\,dx}{40} = \frac{(25x^3/3)\Big|_0^4}{80} = 6\frac{2}{3}$$
$$A = \frac{1}{2}(4)(20) = 40$$

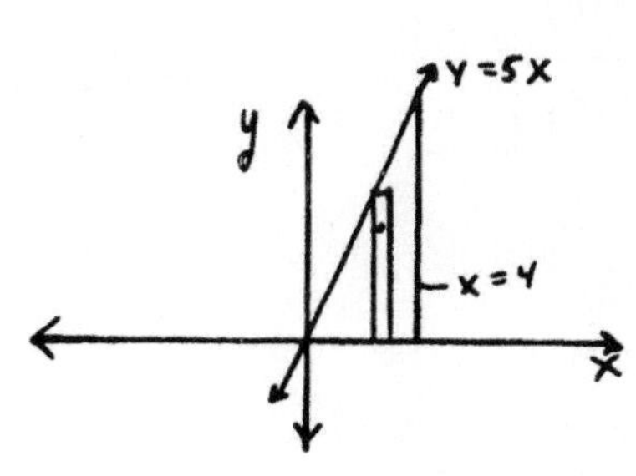

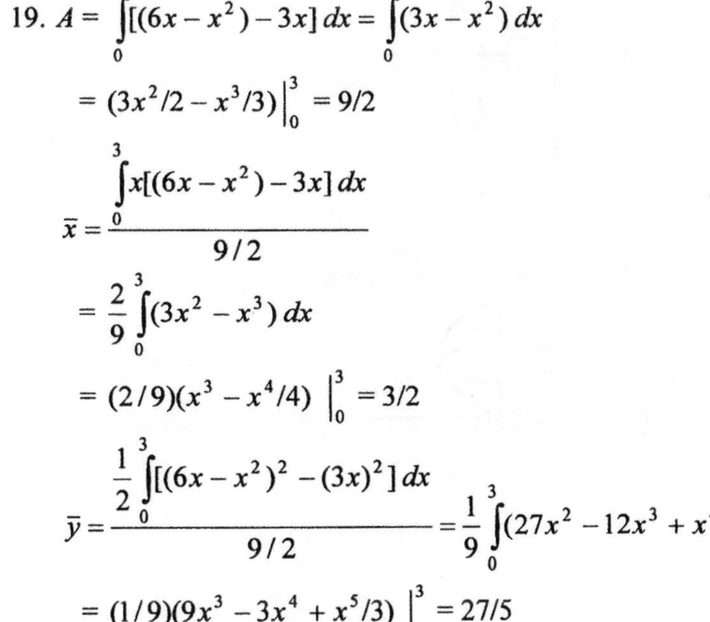

19. $$A = \int_0^3 [(6x - x^2) - 3x]\,dx = \int_0^3 (3x - x^2)\,dx$$
$$= (3x^2/2 - x^3/3)\Big|_0^3 = 9/2$$
$$\bar{x} = \frac{\int_0^3 x[(6x - x^2) - 3x]\,dx}{9/2}$$
$$= \frac{2}{9}\int_0^3 (3x^2 - x^3)\,dx$$
$$= (2/9)(x^3 - x^4/4)\Big|_0^3 = 3/2$$
$$\bar{y} = \frac{\frac{1}{2}\int_0^3 [(6x - x^2)^2 - (3x)^2]\,dx}{9/2} = \frac{1}{9}\int_0^3 (27x^2 - 12x^3 + x^4)\,dx$$
$$= (1/9)(9x^3 - 3x^4 + x^5/3)\Big|_0^3 = 27/5$$

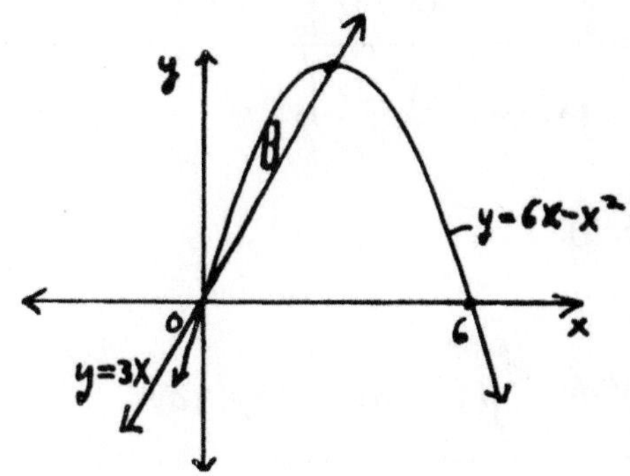

20. $A = \int_0^6 -(x^2 - 6x)\,dx$

$= -(x^3/3 - 3x^2)\Big|_0^6 = 36$

Note: $\bar{x} = 3$

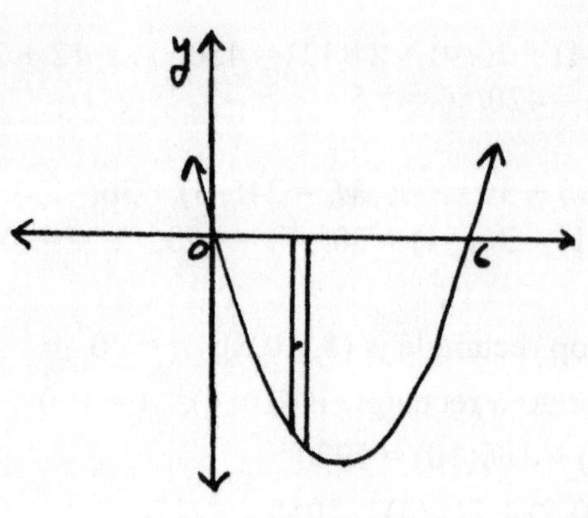

$$\bar{y} = \frac{\frac{1}{2}\int_0^6 [0^2 - (x^2 - 6x)^2]\,dx}{36} = \frac{1}{72}\int_0^6 (-x^4 + 12x^3 - 36x^2)\,dx$$

$= (1/72)(-x^5/5 + 3x^4 - 12x^3)\Big|_0^6 = -3.6$ Thus (3, –3.6).

21. $$\bar{y} = \frac{\int_0^2 y(y/2)^2\,dy}{\int_0^2 (y/2)^2\,dy} = \frac{(y^4/16)\Big|_0^2}{(y^3/12)\Big|_0^2}$$

$= \frac{1}{\frac{8}{12}} = \frac{3}{2}$ Thus (0, 3/2).

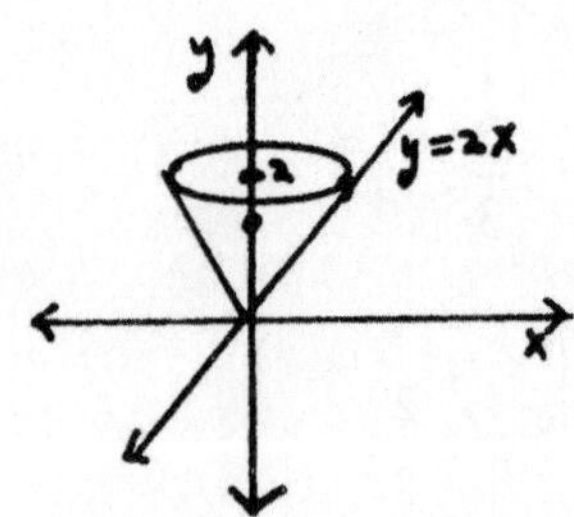

22. $$\bar{x} = \frac{\int_0^1 x(x^2)^2\,dx}{\int_0^1 (x^2)^2\,dx} = \frac{\int_0^1 x^5\,dx}{\int_0^1 x^4\,dx} = \frac{(x^6/6)\Big|_0^1}{(x^5/5)\Big|_0^1}$$

$= \frac{5}{6}$ Thus (5/6, 0).

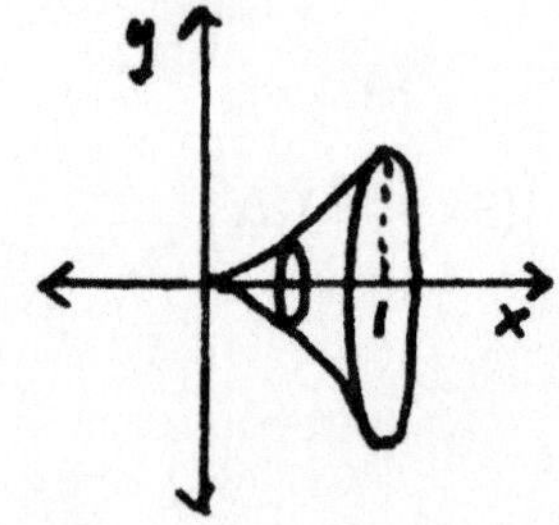

23. $$\bar{y} = \frac{\int_0^4 y(y^2 - 4y)^2\,dy}{\int_0^4 (y^2 - 4y)^2\,dy} = \frac{\int_0^4 (y^5 - 8y^4 + 16y^3)\,dy}{\int_0^4 (y^4 - 8y^3 + 16y^2)\,dy}$$

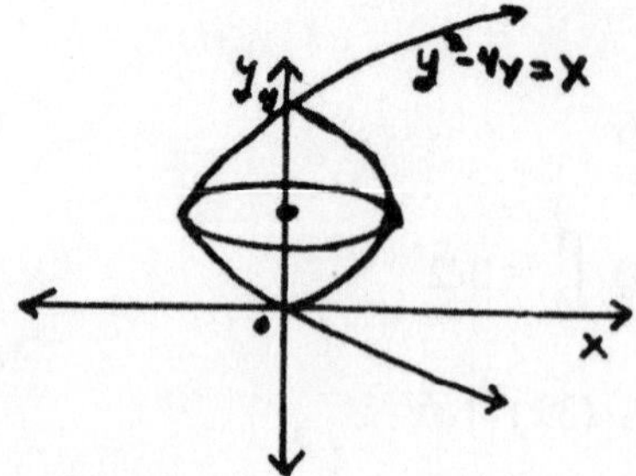

$$= \frac{(y^6/6 - 8y^5/5 + 4y^4)\Big|_0^4}{(y^5/5 - 2y^4 + 16y^3/3)\Big|_0^4} = \frac{68.2\overline{6}}{34.1\overline{3}} = 2;\ \bar{x} = 0$$

24. $I_x = 10(2)^2 + 6(7)^2 + 8(-4)^2 = 462$; $m = 24$; $R = \sqrt{462/24} = 4.39$

25. $I_y = 1\int_0^4 x^2(3x)\,dx = (3/4)x^4\Big|_0^4 = 192;\ m = 1\int_0^4 3x\,dx = (3x^2/2)\Big|_0^4 = 24$

$R = \sqrt{192/24} = 2.83$

26. $I_x = 1\int_0^{12} y^2(4 - y/3)\,dy = (4y^3/3 - y^4/12)\Big|_0^{12} = 576;\ m = 24$ from #25

$R = \sqrt{576/24} = 4.90$

27. $I_x = 4\int_0^1 y^2(1-y^2)\,dy = 4(y^3/3 - y^5/5)\Big|_0^1 = 8/15$

$m = 4\int_0^1 (1-y^2)\,dy = 4(y - y^3/3)\Big|_0^1 = 8/3;$

$\sqrt{(8/15)/(8/3)}$; $R = 0.447$

28. $I_x = 2\pi(4)\int_0^1 y^3(1-y^{1/3})\,dy = 8\pi\int_0^1 (y^3 - y^{10/3})\,dy = 8\pi(y^4/4 - 3y^{13/3}/13)\Big|_0^1 = 2\pi/13$

$m = 2\pi(4)\int_0^1 y(1-y^{1/3})\,dy = 8\pi\int_0^1 (y - y^{4/3})\,dy = 8\pi(y^2/2 - 3y^{7/3}/7)\Big|_0^1 = 4\pi/7$

$R = \sqrt{2\pi/13/4\pi/7} = 0.519$

29. $I_y = 2\pi(4)\int_0^1 x^3(x^3)\,dx = 8\pi\int_0^1 x^6\,dx = 8\pi(x^7/7)\Big|_0^1 = 8\pi/7$

$m = 8\pi\int_0^1 x^3 \cdot x\,dx = 8\pi\int_0^1 x^4\,dx = 8\pi(x^5/5)\Big|_0^1 = 8\pi/5$

$R = \sqrt{(8\pi/7)/(8\pi/5)} = 0.845$

30. $I_y = 2\pi(3)\int_1^4 x^3(1/x)\,dx = 6\pi(x^3/3)\Big|_1^4 = 126\pi;$

$m = 6\pi\int_1^4 x(1/x)\,dx = 6\pi x\Big|_1^4 = 18\pi;\ \ R = \sqrt{126\pi/18\pi} = 2.65$

31. $16 = 4k;\ k = 4;\ W = \int_0^{10} 4x\,dx = 2x^2\Big|_0^{10} = 200$ in.-lb

32. $W = \int_{0.01}^{0.02} 5.24\times10^{-18}x^{-2}\,dx = 5.24\times10^{-18}(x^{-1}/-1)\Big|_{0.01}^{0.02} = 2.62\times10^{-16}$ J

33. $W = \int_0^{200} 4x\,dx + 250(200) = 2x^2\Big|_0^{200} + 50{,}000 = 130{,}000$ ft-lb

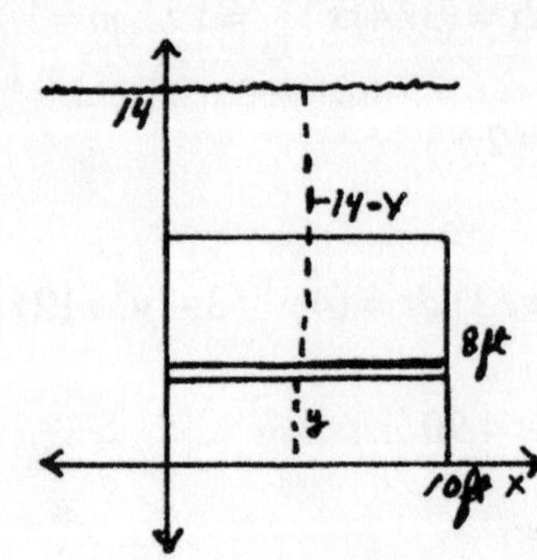

34. $F = 62.4\int_0^8 (14 - y)(10)\,dy$

$= 624(14y - y^2/2)\Big|_0^8 = 49{,}920$ lb

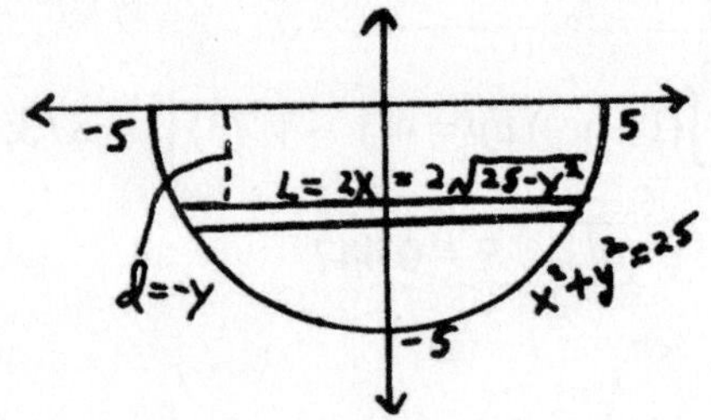

35. $F = 9800\int_{-5}^{0} (-y)(2\sqrt{25 - y^2})\,dy$

$= 9800(2/3)(25 - y^2)^{3/2}\Big|_{-5}^{0}$

816,700 N

36. $V_{av} = \dfrac{1}{3-0}\int_0^3 (t^2 + 3t + 2)\,dt = (1/3)(t^3/3 + 3t^2/2 + 2t)\Big|_0^3 = 9.5$ V

37. $I_{av} = \dfrac{1}{9-4}\int_4^9 4t^{3/2}\,dt = (1/5)(8t^{5/2}/5)\Big|_4^9 = 67.52$ A

38. $P_{av} = \dfrac{1}{3-1}\int_1^3 2t^3\,dt = (1/2)(t^4/2)\Big|_1^3 = 20$ W

APPENDIX A

Exercises, pp. 1128–1129

1. The set of real numbers greater than -4 and less than or equal to 10; $(-4, 10]$;

3. $|x| = \begin{cases} x & \text{if } x \geq 0 \\ -x & \text{if } x < 0 \end{cases}$ **5.** $2x - 4 \geq 3$ or $2x - 4 \leq -3$

7. Take the square root of the sum of the squares of the differences of the x- and y-coordinates. **9.** $y = \sqrt{36 - x^2}$

11. $m = \dfrac{y + 2}{x - 4}$ or $y = m(x - 4) - 2$ **13.** They are equal.

15. 4 **17.** $4uv$ **19.** $\dfrac{-h}{x(x + h)}$ **21.** $(y - y^{-1})(y + y^{-1})$

23. $u = \pm\sqrt{2}, \pm 3$ **25.** $3x^2 + 3xh + h^2$

27. $(1, 5)$

29. $(-\infty, 4] \cup [5, 6)$

31. $\{x: x < -4/3$ or $x > 4\}$; $\left(-\infty, -\frac{4}{3}\right) \cup (4, \infty)$

33. $\{x: -2 < x < -1$ or $2 < x < 3\}$; $(-2, -1) \cup (2, 3)$

35. $y = 2 - \sqrt{9 - (x + 1)^2}$ **37.** $y = \dfrac{5}{3}x + 4$

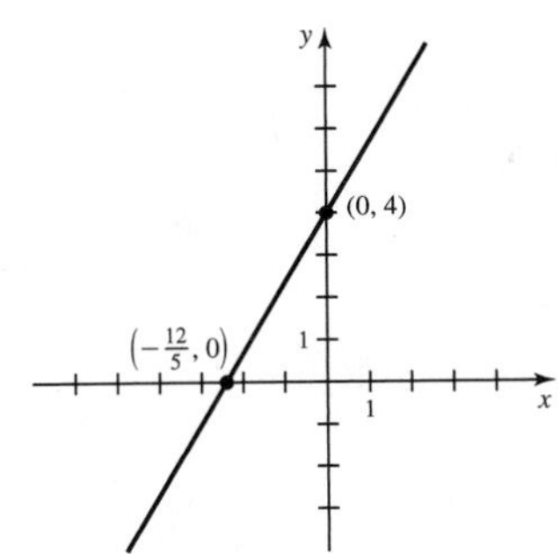

39. $y = \dfrac{4}{5}x - 4$

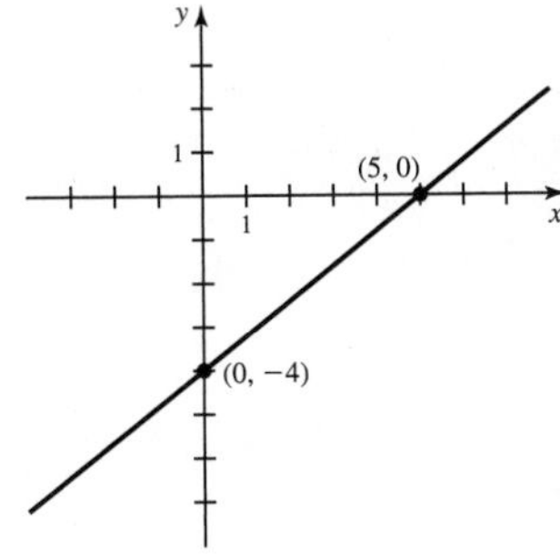

41. $x + 2y = 24$

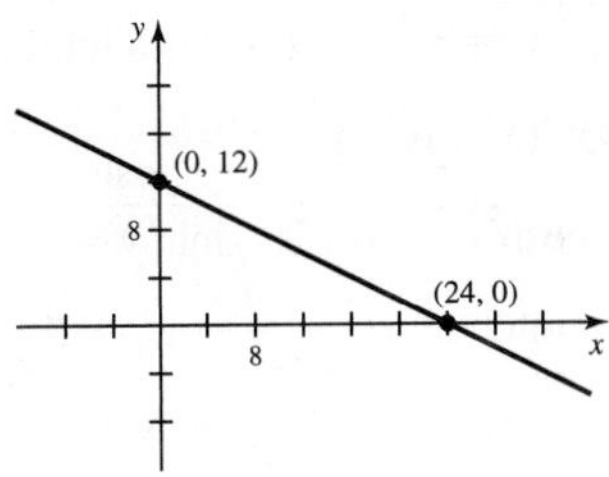

43. $y = \dfrac{1}{3}x - 7$ **45. a.** False **b.** True **c.** False **d.** False **e.** False **f.** True **g.** False **47.** $\{x: |x - 1| \geq 3\}$

49.

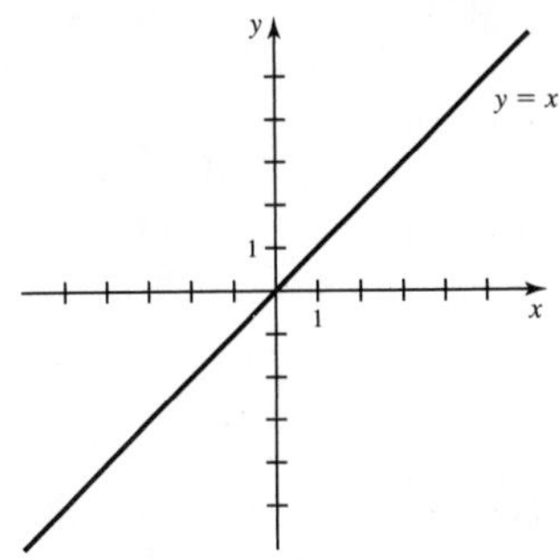

APPENDIX C

Exercises, pp. 1141–1142

1. $\boldsymbol{R}$, $\{x: x \neq 0\}$, $\boldsymbol{R}$, $\{x: x \neq 0\}$ **3.** $\dfrac{3x \sinh 3x - 2\cosh 3x}{x^3}$

5. $y'(x) = \dfrac{\operatorname{sech}(xy) - y}{x}$ **7.** $64/81$

9. Sample proofs: $\dfrac{d}{dx}(\coth x) = \dfrac{d}{dx}\left(\dfrac{\cosh x}{\sinh x}\right)$

$$= \frac{\sinh^2 x - \cosh^2 x}{\sinh^2 x} = -\frac{1}{\sinh^2 x} = -\operatorname{csch}^2 x$$

$$\frac{d}{dx}(\operatorname{sech} x) = \frac{d}{dx}(\cosh x)^{-1} = -(\cosh x)^{-2}\sinh x$$

$$= -\frac{1}{\cosh x}\frac{\sinh x}{\cosh x} = -\operatorname{sech} x \tanh x$$

11. $\dfrac{3\operatorname{sech}^2 3x}{2\sqrt{\tanh 3x}}$ **13.** $-\coth x + C$ **15.** $\dfrac{1}{5}\ln|\sinh 5x| + C$

17. $2\ln\left(\dfrac{\cosh 2}{\cosh 1}\right) \approx 1.78$ **19.** π

21. $L = \int_0^a \sqrt{1 + \sinh^2 x}\, dx = \int_0^a \cosh x\, dx = \sinh a$

23. b. Domain $= \boldsymbol{R}$; range $= \boldsymbol{R}$

c.

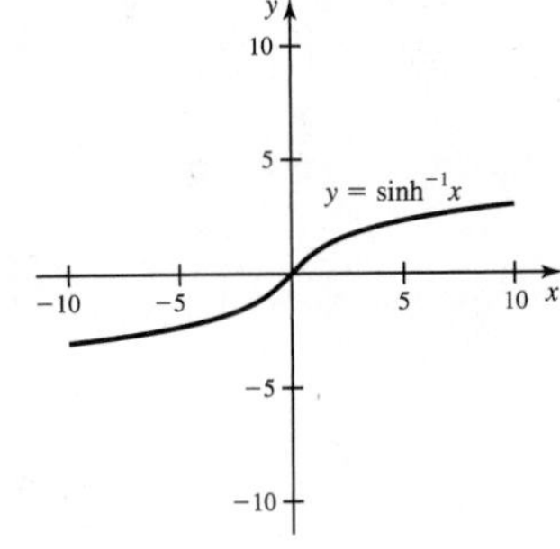

d. $y = \sinh^{-1} x \Rightarrow x = \sinh y$. Differentiating with respect to x gives $1 = (\cosh y)y'(x)$ or $y'(x) = \dfrac{1}{\cosh y}$. Now $\cosh^2 y - \sinh^2 y = 1$ implies that $\cosh y = \sqrt{1 + \sinh^2 y} = \sqrt{1 + x^2}$. Therefore, $y'(x) = \dfrac{d}{dx}(\sinh^{-1} x) = \dfrac{1}{\sqrt{1 + x^2}}$. **25.** $\ln\left(\sqrt{x^2 + 9} + x\right) + C$

27. a. $a = 2$ **b.** $L = 2\ln(2 + \sqrt{3}) \approx 2.63$

c.

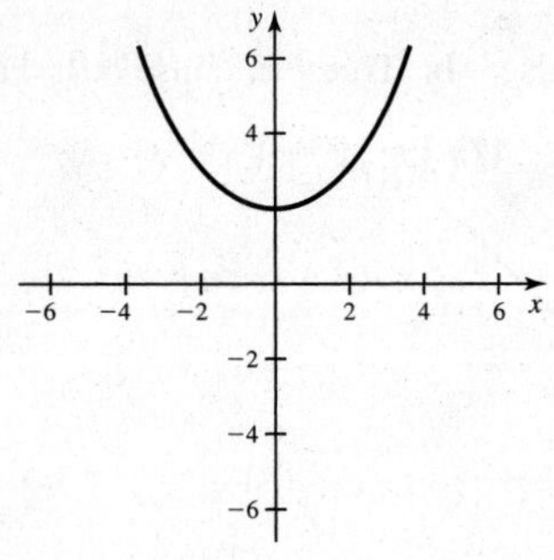

Index

Note: Page numbers in *italics* indicate figures; "t" indicates a table; "e" indicates an exercise.

D

E

F

G

H

I

Q

R

S

T

W

X

Y

Z

TABLE OF INTEGRALS

Substitution Rule	Integration by Parts
$\int f(g(x))g'(x)\,dx = \int f(u)\,du \quad (u = g(x))$	$\int u\,dv = uv - \int v\,du$
$\int_a^b f(g(x))g'(x)\,dx = \int_{g(a)}^{g(b)} f(u)\,du$	$\int_a^b uv'\,dx = uv\Big\vert_a^b - \int_a^b vu'\,dx$

Basic Integrals

1. $\int x^n\,dx = \frac{1}{n+1}x^{n+1} + C;\ n \neq -1$

2. $\int \frac{dx}{x} = \ln|x| + C$

3. $\int \cos ax\,dx = \frac{1}{a}\sin ax + C$

4. $\int \sin ax\,dx = -\frac{1}{a}\cos ax + C$

5. $\int \tan x\,dx = \ln|\sec x| + C$

6. $\int \cot x\,dx = \ln|\sin x| + C$

7. $\int \sec x\,dx = \ln|\sec x + \tan x| + C$

8. $\int \csc x\,dx = -\ln|\csc x + \cot x| + C$

9. $\int e^{ax}\,dx = \frac{1}{a}e^{ax} + C$

10. $\int b^{ax}\,dx = \frac{1}{a\ln b}b^{ax} + C;\ b > 0, b \neq 1$

11. $\int \ln x\,dx = x\ln x - x + C$

12. $\int \log_b x\,dx = \frac{1}{\ln b}(x\ln x - x) + C$

13. $\int \frac{dx}{\sqrt{a^2 - x^2}} = \sin^{-1}\frac{x}{a} + C$

14. $\int \frac{dx}{x^2 + a^2} = \frac{1}{a}\tan^{-1}\frac{x}{a} + C$

15. $\int \frac{dx}{x\sqrt{x^2 - a^2}} = \frac{1}{a}\sec^{-1}\left|\frac{x}{a}\right| + C$

16. $\int \sin^{-1} x\,dx = x\sin^{-1} x + \sqrt{1 - x^2} + C$

17. $\int \cos^{-1} x\,dx = x\cos^{-1} x - \sqrt{1 - x^2} + C$

18. $\int \tan^{-1} x\,dx = x\tan^{-1} x - \frac{1}{2}\ln(1 + x^2) + C$

19. $\int \sec^{-1} x\,dx = x\sec^{-1} x - \ln\left(x + \sqrt{x^2 - 1}\right) + C;\ x \geq 1$

Trigonometric Integrals

20. $\int \cos^2 x\,dx = \frac{x}{2} + \frac{\sin 2x}{4} + C$

21. $\int \sin^2 x\,dx = \frac{x}{2} - \frac{\sin 2x}{4} + C$

22. $\int \sec^2 ax\,dx = \frac{1}{a}\tan ax + C$

23. $\int \csc^2 ax\,dx = -\frac{1}{a}\cot ax + C$

24. $\int \tan^2 x\,dx = \tan x - x + C$

25. $\int \cot^2 x\,dx = -\cot x - x + C$

26. $\int \cos^3 x\,dx = -\frac{1}{3}\sin^3 x + \sin x + C$

27. $\int \sin^3 x\,dx = \frac{1}{3}\cos^3 x - \cos x + C$

28. $\int \sec^3 x\,dx = \frac{1}{2}\sec x\tan x + \frac{1}{2}\ln|\sec x + \tan x| + C$

29. $\int \csc^3 x\,dx = -\frac{1}{2}\csc x\cot x - \frac{1}{2}\ln|\csc x + \cot x| + C$

30. $\int \tan^3 x\,dx = \frac{1}{2}\tan^2 x - \ln|\sec x| + C$

31. $\int \cot^3 x\,dx = -\frac{1}{2}\cot^2 x - \ln|\sin x| + C$

32. $\int \sec^n ax\,\tan ax\,dx = \frac{1}{na}\sec^n ax + C;\ n \neq 0$

33. $\int \csc^n ax\cot ax\,dx = -\frac{1}{na}\csc^n ax + C;\ n \neq 0$

34. $\int \frac{dx}{1 + \sin ax} = -\frac{1}{a}\tan\left(\frac{\pi}{4} - \frac{ax}{2}\right) + C$

35. $\int \frac{dx}{1 - \sin ax} = \frac{1}{a}\tan\left(\frac{\pi}{4} + \frac{ax}{2}\right) + C$

36. $\int \frac{dx}{1 + \cos ax} = \frac{1}{a}\tan\frac{ax}{2} + C$

37. $\int \frac{dx}{1 - \cos ax} = -\frac{1}{a}\cot\frac{ax}{2} + C$

38. $\int \sin mx \cos nx\, dx = -\frac{\cos(m+n)x}{2(m+n)} - \frac{\cos(m-n)x}{2(m-n)} + C;\ m^2 \neq n^2$

39. $\int \sin mx \sin nx\, dx = \frac{\sin(m-n)x}{2(m-n)} - \frac{\sin(m+n)x}{2(m+n)} + C;\ m^2 \neq n^2$

40. $\int \cos mx \cos nx\, dx = \frac{\sin(m-n)x}{2(m-n)} + \frac{\sin(m+n)x}{2(m+n)} + C;\ m^2 \neq n^2$

Reduction Formulas for Trigonometric Functions

41. $\int \cos^n x\, dx = \frac{1}{n}\cos^{n-1} x \sin x + \frac{n-1}{n}\int \cos^{n-2} x\, dx$

42. $\int \sin^n x\, dx = -\frac{1}{n}\sin^{n-1} x \cos x + \frac{n-1}{n}\int \sin^{n-2} x\, dx$

43. $\int \tan^n x\, dx = \frac{\tan^{n-1} x}{n-1} - \int \tan^{n-2} x\, dx;\ n \neq 1$

44. $\int \cot^n x\, dx = -\frac{\cot^{n-1} x}{n-1} - \int \cot^{n-2} x\, dx;\ n \neq 1$

45. $\int \sec^n x\, dx = \frac{\sec^{n-2} x \tan x}{n-1} + \frac{n-2}{n-1}\int \sec^{n-2} x\, dx;\ n \neq 1$

46. $\int \csc^n x\, dx = -\frac{\csc^{n-2} x \cot x}{n-1} + \frac{n-2}{n-1}\int \csc^{n-2} x\, dx;\ n \neq 1$

47. $\int \sin^m x \cos^n x\, dx = -\frac{\sin^{m-1} x \cos^{n+1} x}{m+n} + \frac{m-1}{m+n}\int \sin^{m-2} x \cos^n x\, dx;\ m \neq -n$

48. $\int \sin^m x \cos^n x\, dx = \frac{\sin^{m+1} x \cos^{n-1} x}{m+n} + \frac{n-1}{m+n}\int \sin^m x \cos^{n-2} x\, dx;\ m \neq -n$

49. $\int x^n \sin ax\, dx = -\frac{x^n \cos ax}{a} + \frac{n}{a}\int x^{n-1} \cos ax\, dx;\ a \neq 0$

50. $\int x^n \cos ax\, dx = \frac{x^n \sin ax}{a} - \frac{n}{a}\int x^{n-1} \sin ax\, dx;\ a \neq 0$

Integrals Involving $a^2 - x^2$; $a > 0$

51. $\int \sqrt{a^2 - x^2}\, dx = \frac{x}{2}\sqrt{a^2 - x^2} + \frac{a^2}{2}\sin^{-1}\frac{x}{a} + C$

52. $\int \frac{dx}{x\sqrt{a^2 - x^2}} = -\frac{1}{a}\ln\left|\frac{a + \sqrt{a^2 - x^2}}{x}\right| + C$

53. $\int \frac{dx}{x^2\sqrt{a^2 - x^2}} = -\frac{\sqrt{a^2 - x^2}}{a^2 x} + C$

54. $\int x^2\sqrt{a^2 - x^2}\, dx = \frac{x}{8}(2x^2 - a^2)\sqrt{a^2 - x^2} + \frac{a^4}{8}\sin^{-1}\frac{x}{a} + C$

55. $\int \frac{\sqrt{a^2 - x^2}}{x^2}\, dx = -\frac{1}{x}\sqrt{a^2 - x^2} - \sin^{-1}\frac{x}{a} + C$

56. $\int \frac{x^2}{\sqrt{a^2 - x^2}}\, dx = -\frac{x}{2}\sqrt{a^2 - x^2} + \frac{a^2}{2}\sin^{-1}\frac{x}{a} + C$

57. $\int \frac{dx}{a^2 - x^2} = \frac{1}{2a}\ln\left|\frac{x + a}{x - a}\right| + C$

Integrals Involving $x^2 - a^2$; $a > 0$

58. $\int \sqrt{x^2 - a^2}\, dx = \frac{x}{2}\sqrt{x^2 - a^2} - \frac{a^2}{2}\ln\left|x + \sqrt{x^2 - a^2}\right| + C$

59. $\int \frac{dx}{\sqrt{x^2 - a^2}} = \ln\left|x + \sqrt{x^2 - a^2}\right| + C$

60. $\int \frac{dx}{x^2\sqrt{x^2 - a^2}} = \frac{\sqrt{x^2 - a^2}}{a^2 x} + C$

61. $\int x^2\sqrt{x^2 - a^2}\, dx = \frac{x}{8}(2x^2 - a^2)\sqrt{x^2 - a^2} - \frac{a^4}{8}\ln\left|x + \sqrt{x^2 - a^2}\right| + C$

62. $\int \frac{\sqrt{x^2 - a^2}}{x^2}\, dx = \ln\left|x + \sqrt{x^2 - a^2}\right| - \frac{\sqrt{x^2 - a^2}}{x} + C$

63. $\int \frac{x^2}{\sqrt{x^2 - a^2}}\, dx = \frac{a^2}{2}\ln\left|x + \sqrt{x^2 - a^2}\right| + \frac{x}{2}\sqrt{x^2 - a^2} + C$

64. $\int \frac{dx}{x^2 - a^2} = \frac{1}{2a}\ln\left|\frac{x - a}{x + a}\right| + C$

65. $\int \frac{dx}{x(x^2 - a^2)} = \frac{1}{2a^2}\ln\left|\frac{x^2 - a^2}{x^2}\right| + C$

Integrals Involving $a^2 + x^2$; $a > 0$

66. $\int \sqrt{a^2 + x^2}\, dx = \frac{x}{2}\sqrt{a^2 + x^2} + \frac{a^2}{2}\ln\left(x + \sqrt{a^2 + x^2}\right) + C$

67. $\int \frac{dx}{\sqrt{a^2 + x^2}} = \ln\left(x + \sqrt{a^2 + x^2}\right) + C$

68. $\int \frac{dx}{x^2\sqrt{a^2 + x^2}} = -\frac{\sqrt{a^2 + x^2}}{a^2 x} + C$

69. $\int x^2\sqrt{a^2 + x^2}\, dx = \frac{x}{8}(a^2 + 2x^2)\sqrt{a^2 + x^2} - \frac{a^4}{8}\ln\left(x + \sqrt{a^2 + x^2}\right) + C$

70. $\displaystyle\int \frac{\sqrt{a^2 + x^2}}{x^2}\,dx = \ln\left|x + \sqrt{a^2 + x^2}\right| - \frac{\sqrt{a^2 + x^2}}{x} + C$

71. $\displaystyle\int \frac{x^2}{\sqrt{a^2 + x^2}}\,dx = -\frac{a^2}{2}\ln\left(x + \sqrt{a^2 + x^2}\right) + \frac{x\sqrt{a^2 + x^2}}{2} + C$

72. $\displaystyle\int \frac{\sqrt{a^2 + x^2}}{x}\,dx = \sqrt{a^2 + x^2} - a\ln\left|\frac{a + \sqrt{a^2 + x^2}}{x}\right| + C$

73. $\displaystyle\int \frac{dx}{(a^2 + x^2)^{3/2}} = \frac{x}{a^2\sqrt{a^2 + x^2}} + C$

74. $\displaystyle\int \frac{dx}{x(a^2 + x^2)} = \frac{1}{2a^2}\ln\left(\frac{x^2}{a^2 + x^2}\right) + C$

Integrals Involving $ax \pm b$; $a \neq 0, b > 0$

75. $\displaystyle\int (ax + b)^n\,dx = \frac{(ax + b)^{n+1}}{a(n + 1)} + C;\ n \neq -1$

76. $\displaystyle\int \left(\sqrt{ax + b}\right)^n dx = \frac{2}{a}\frac{\left(\sqrt{ax + b}\right)^{n+2}}{n + 2} + C;\ n \neq -2$

77. $\displaystyle\int \frac{dx}{x\sqrt{ax - b}} = \frac{2}{\sqrt{b}}\tan^{-1}\sqrt{\frac{ax - b}{b}} + C;\ b > 0$

78. $\displaystyle\int \frac{dx}{x\sqrt{ax + b}} = \frac{1}{\sqrt{b}}\ln\left|\frac{\sqrt{ax + b} - \sqrt{b}}{\sqrt{ax + b} + \sqrt{b}}\right| + C;\ b > 0$

79. $\displaystyle\int \frac{x}{ax + b}\,dx = \frac{x}{a} - \frac{b}{a^2}\ln|ax + b| + C$

80. $\displaystyle\int \frac{x^2}{ax + b}\,dx = \frac{1}{2a^3}\left((ax + b)^2 - 4b(ax + b) + 2b^2\ln|ax + b|\right) + C$

81. $\displaystyle\int \frac{dx}{x^2(ax + b)} = -\frac{1}{bx} + \frac{a}{b^2}\ln\left|\frac{ax + b}{x}\right| + C$

82. $\displaystyle\int x\sqrt{ax + b}\,dx = \frac{2}{15a^2}(3ax - 2b)(ax + b)^{3/2} + C$

83. $\displaystyle\int \frac{x}{\sqrt{ax + b}}\,dx = \frac{2}{3a^2}(ax - 2b)\sqrt{ax + b} + C$

84. $\displaystyle\int x(ax + b)^n\,dx = \frac{(ax + b)^{n+1}}{a^2}\left(\frac{ax + b}{n + 2} - \frac{b}{n + 1}\right) + C;\ n \neq -1, -2$

85. $\displaystyle\int \frac{dx}{x(ax + b)} = \frac{1}{b}\ln\left|\frac{x}{ax + b}\right| + C$

Integrals with Exponential and Trigonometric Functions

86. $\displaystyle\int e^{ax}\sin bx\,dx = \frac{e^{ax}(a\sin bx - b\cos bx)}{a^2 + b^2} + C$

87. $\displaystyle\int e^{ax}\cos bx\,dx = \frac{e^{ax}(a\cos bx + b\sin bx)}{a^2 + b^2} + C$

Integrals with Exponential and Logarithmic Functions

88. $\displaystyle\int \frac{dx}{x\ln x} = \ln|\ln x| + C$

89. $\displaystyle\int x^n\ln x\,dx = \frac{x^{n+1}}{n + 1}\left(\ln x - \frac{1}{n + 1}\right) + C;\ n \neq -1$

90. $\displaystyle\int xe^x\,dx = xe^x - e^x + C$

91. $\displaystyle\int x^n e^{ax}\,dx = \frac{1}{a}x^n e^{ax} - \frac{n}{a}\int x^{n-1}e^{ax}\,dx;\ a \neq 0$

92. $\displaystyle\int \ln^n x\,dx = x\ln^n x - n\int \ln^{n-1} x\,dx$

Miscellaneous Formulas

93. $\displaystyle\int x^n\cos^{-1}x\,dx = \frac{1}{n + 1}\left(x^{n+1}\cos^{-1}x + \int \frac{x^{n+1}dx}{\sqrt{1 - x^2}}\right);\ n \neq -1$

94. $\displaystyle\int x^n\sin^{-1}x\,dx = \frac{1}{n + 1}\left(x^{n+1}\sin^{-1}x - \int \frac{x^{n+1}\,dx}{\sqrt{1 - x^2}}\right);\ n \neq -1$

95. $\displaystyle\int x^n\tan^{-1}x\,dx = \frac{1}{n + 1}\left(x^{n+1}\tan^{-1}x - \int \frac{x^{n+1}\,dx}{x^2 + 1}\right);\ n \neq -1$

96. $\displaystyle\int \sqrt{2ax - x^2}\,dx = \frac{x - a}{2}\sqrt{2ax - x^2} + \frac{a^2}{2}\sin^{-1}\left(\frac{x - a}{a}\right) + C;\ a > 0$

97. $\displaystyle\int \frac{dx}{\sqrt{2ax - x^2}} = \sin^{-1}\left(\frac{x - a}{a}\right) + C;\ a > 0$

GRAPHS OF ELEMENTARY FUNCTIONS

Linear functions

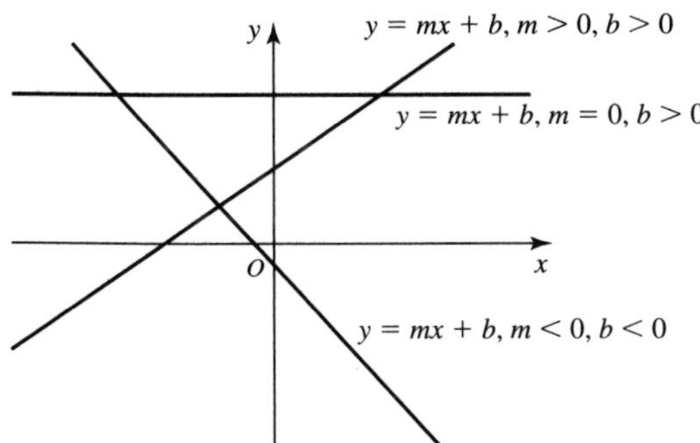

Quadratic functions

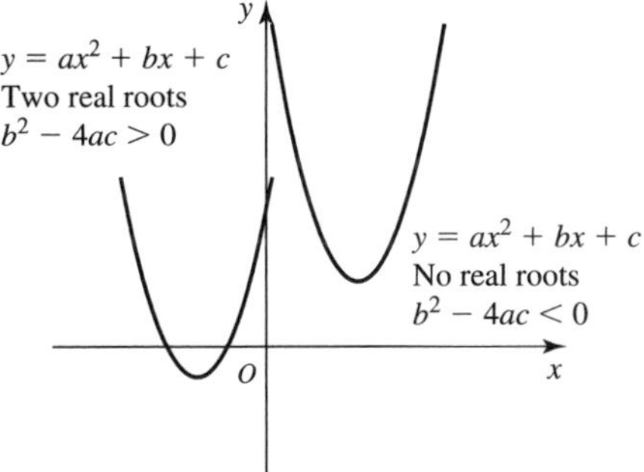

Positive even powers

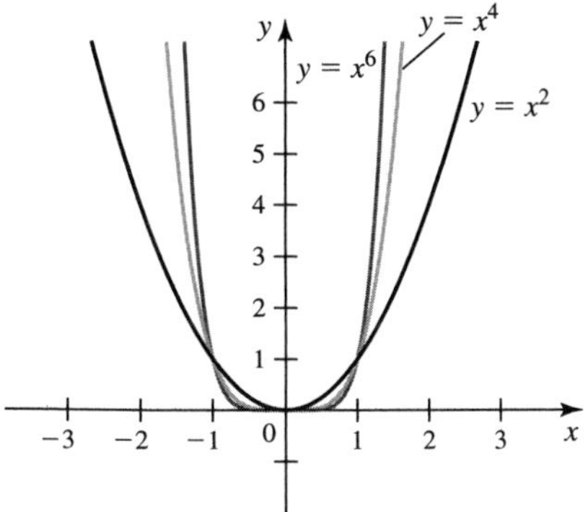

Positive odd powers

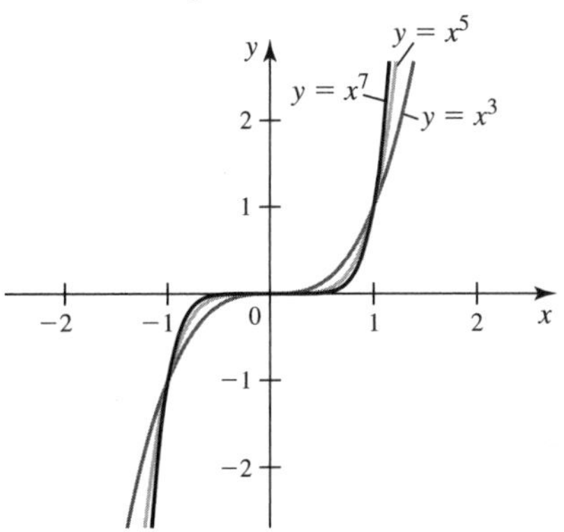

Negative even powers

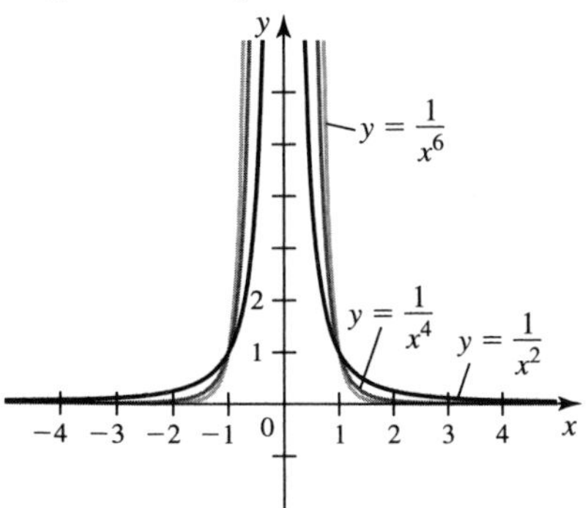

Negative odd powers

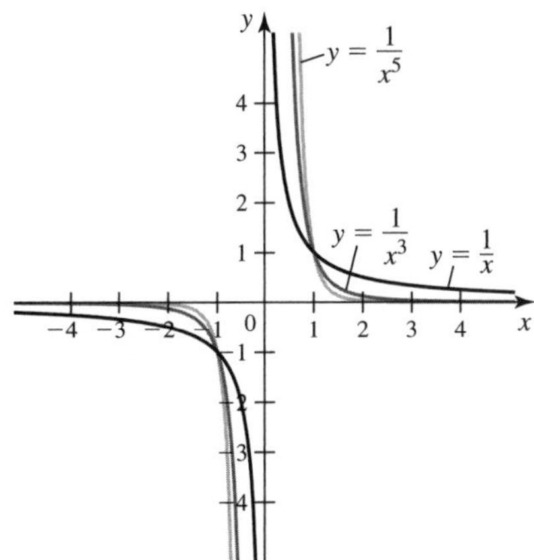

Exponential functions

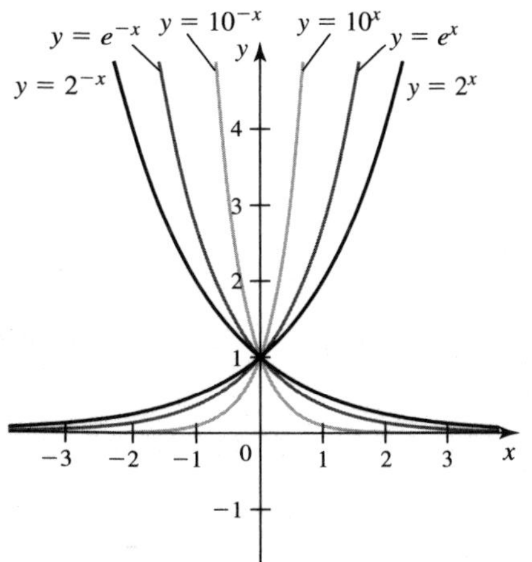

Natural logarithmic and exponential functions

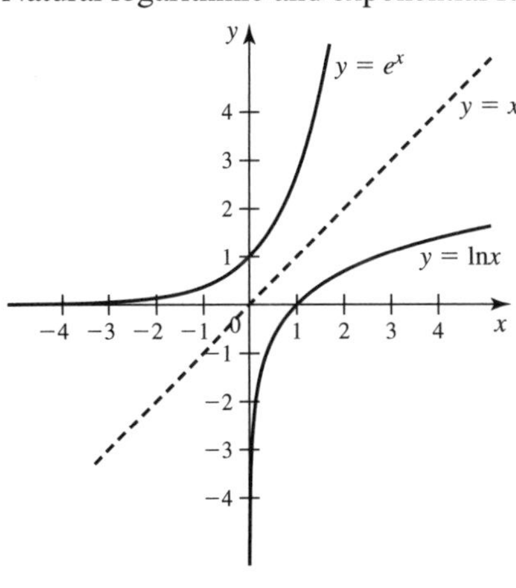

DERIVATIVES

General Formulas

$\frac{d}{dx}(c) = 0$

$\frac{d}{dx}(cf(x)) = cf'(x)$

$\frac{d}{dx}(f(x) + g(x)) = f'(x) + g'(x)$

$\frac{d}{dx}(f(x) - g(x)) = f'(x) - g'(x)$

$\frac{d}{dx}(f(x)g(x)) = f'(x)g(x) + f(x)g'(x)$

$\frac{d}{dx}\left(\frac{f(x)}{g(x)}\right) = \frac{g(x)f'(x) - f(x)g'(x)}{(g(x))^2}$

$\frac{d}{dx}(x^n) = nx^{n-1}$, for real numbers n

$\frac{d}{dx}[f(g(x))] = f'(g(x)) \cdot g'(x)$ (Chain Rule)

Trigonometric Functions

$\frac{d}{dx}(\sin x) = \cos x$

$\frac{d}{dx}(\cos x) = -\sin x$

$\frac{d}{dx}(\tan x) = \sec^2 x$

$\frac{d}{dx}(\cot x) = -\csc^2 x$

$\frac{d}{dx}(\sec x) = \sec x \tan x$

$\frac{d}{dx}(\csc x) = -\csc x \cot x$

Inverse Trigonometric Functions

$\frac{d}{dx}(\sin^{-1} x) = \frac{1}{\sqrt{1 - x^2}}$

$\frac{d}{dx}(\cos^{-1} x) = -\frac{1}{\sqrt{1 - x^2}}$

$\frac{d}{dx}(\tan^{-1} x) = \frac{1}{1 + x^2}$

$\frac{d}{dx}(\cot^{-1} x) = -\frac{1}{1 + x^2}$

$\frac{d}{dx}(\sec^{-1} x) = \frac{1}{|x|\sqrt{x^2 - 1}}$

$\frac{d}{dx}(\csc^{-1} x) = -\frac{1}{|x|\sqrt{x^2 - 1}}$

Exponential and Logarithmic Functions

$\frac{d}{dx}(e^x) = e^x$

$\frac{d}{dx}(b^x) = b^x \ln b$

$\frac{d}{dx}(\ln |x|) = \frac{1}{x}$

$\frac{d}{dx}(\log_b x) = \frac{1}{x \ln b}$

Hyperbolic Functions

$\frac{d}{dx}(\sinh x) = \cosh x$

$\frac{d}{dx}(\cosh x) = \sinh x$

$\frac{d}{dx}(\tanh x) = \text{sech}^2 x$

$\frac{d}{dx}(\coth x) = -\text{csch}^2 x$

$\frac{d}{dx}(\text{sech } x) = -\text{sech } x \tanh x$

$\frac{d}{dx}(\text{csch } x) = -\text{csch } x \coth x$